PETERSON'S

MBA PROGRAMS

U.S., Canadian, and International Business Schools

Peterson's
Thomson Learning™

Australia • Canada • Denmark • Japan • Mexico • New Zealand • Philippines
Puerto Rico • Singapore • South Africa • Spain • United Kingdom • United States

PETERSON'S
™
THOMSON LEARNING

About Peterson's

Founded in 1966, Peterson's, a division of Thomson Learning, is the nation's largest and most respected provider of lifelong learning online resources, software, reference guides, and books. The Education Supersite^{SM} at petersons.com—the Web's most heavily traveled education resource—has searchable databases and interactive tools for contacting U.S.-accredited institutions and programs. CollegeQuest^{SM} (CollegeQuest.com) offers a complete solution for every step of the college decision-making process. GradAdvantage^{TM} (GradAdvantage.org), developed with Educational Testing Service, is the only electronic admissions service capable of sending official graduate test score reports with a candidate's online application. Peterson's serves more than 55 million education consumers annually.

Thomson Learning is among the world's leading providers of lifelong learning, serving the needs of individuals, learning institutions, and corporations with products and services for both traditional classrooms and for online learning. For more information about the products and services offered by Thomson Learning, please visit www.thomsonlearning.com. Headquartered in Stamford, Connecticut, with offices worldwide, Thomson Learning is part of The Thomson Corporation (www.thomson.com), a leading e-information and solutions company in the business, professional, and education marketplaces. The Corporation's common shares are listed on the Toronto and London stock exchanges.

For more information, contact Peterson's, 2000 Lenox Drive, Lawrenceville, NJ 08648; 800-338-3282; or find us on the World Wide Web at: www.petersons.com/about

ISSN 1080-2533
ISBN 0-7689-0441-2

Printed in the United States of America

10 9 8 7 6 5 4 3 2 1   02 01 00

Contents

How to Use This Book

Peterson's Guide to MBA Programs 2001 provides detailed information on nearly 1,000 schools offering more than 2,900 programs of study leading to a Master of Business Administration (MBA) degree or an equivalent graduate-level degree. These programs are offered by accredited colleges and universities in the United States and its territories and by institutions in Canada, Europe, Mexico, Asia, and Africa that offer equivalent or comparable programs of study.

MBA Programs At-A-Glance

This quick reference chart provides an overview of the programs offered at all the colleges and universities included in this guide. Entries in the chart are arranged geographically under the state, territory, province, or country in which they are located. Use this section to compare key facts about schools as you begin your search for the right MBA program. For additional details on particular programs, refer to the Program Profiles section and the In-Depth Descriptions that many schools have chosen to provide.

Entries in the chart include the following information:
Name of institution
Page reference to Program Profile
AACSB–The International Association for Management Education or Association of Collegiate Business Schools and Programs (ACBSP) accreditation
Matriculation calendar (fall, winter, spring, summer, deferred)
Admission requirements (minimum GMAT score, minimum undergraduate GPA, minimum TOEFL score)
Full-time tuition
Part-time tuition
Financial aid availability
Distance learning option availability
Executive MBA program availability

Program Profiles

Profiles begin with the official school name, the name of the business unit (if applicable), and location of the school. If the GradAdvantage logo appears next to the school's name, you may apply to that school on line at http://www.GradAdvantage.org.

Program Overview

This portion of each profile features the following key information for quick reference and comparison: Graduate Business Faculty—the number of full- and part-time faculty members in the graduate business unit. Student Body—the graduate business unit enrollment figures for the most recent academic year, including average age of students enrolled and the percentage of women and minority students enrolled. Admissions—how many applications were received, how many students were admitted, how many students actually enrolled in the graduate business unit in fall 1999, and the percentage of applicants who were accepted; average GMAT score of entering students; and average GPA of entering students. Costs—minimum tuition and fees for full- and part-time study, for both resident and nonresident students. After graduation—the percentage of 1998–99 graduates who were employed within three months of graduation and their average starting salary. Accreditation—whether the institution is accredited by the AACSB–The International Association for Management Education or by the Association of Collegiate Business Schools and Programs (ACBSP). If the MBA or equivalent graduate-level program is offered in conjunction with any other institutions, those institutions will be listed on the last line.

Degrees

This section provides information pertaining to the basic MBA programs offered by the institution and business school described. Information on other graduate management and master's-level degrees that are considered comparable or equivalent to an MBA, such as a Master of Science (MS), is also provided here.

Keep in mind that basic programs at different schools may vary considerably in academic focus, philosophy, and degree requirements, although each is offering an MBA degree or equivalent graduate-level program. Always contact schools directly for details on their programs, curricula, and individual approaches.

Also note that for consistency and data-management purposes, the names of degree concentrations reported by institutions were sometimes translated to fit under a more generalized name. For example, concentrations such as internal communications, management communication, survey of professional communication, business communication, and business writing would all be placed under the general category of business communications.

Details in this section include whether the program is offered full-time, part-time, or both; whether a distance learning option is available; the number of credits required, including elective credits; the minimum and maximum length of the program in months or years; special application requirements, if applicable; and areas of concentration or specialization offered (accounting/finance, economics, marketing, operations, etc.).

Costs

Information on tuition, fees, room and board, and financial aid is provided in this section. Tuition expenses may be indicated separately for full-time or part-time study. Tuition and fees are expressed as dollar amounts per course, credit hour, hour, quarter hour, semester hour, unit, quarter, semester, trimester, term, academic year, or degree program, as specified by the institution. Fees include only charges that apply to all students—not charges for optional services or specific courses. Figures for tuition and fees are designated as official for 1999–2000. For public institutions in which tuition differs according to residence, separate figures are given for area or state residents and for nonresidents. Some non-U.S. institutions have chosen to report figures in currencies other than U.S. dollars. In these instances, readers should refer to current exchange rates in determining equivalents in U.S. dollars.

Average room and board expenses are indicated in either U.S. dollars or non-U.S. currencies. Both on-campus and off-campus costs may be indicated, depending upon the types of housing provided and whether or not institutions provided this data.

Financial Aid

Financial aid information includes the percentage of MBA students who received college-administered financial aid in 1999–2000; what types of aid were granted (grants, scholarships, work-study, loans, etc.); whether or not aid is awarded to part-time students; deadlines for submission of financial aid applications; and contact information, including name, address, phone, fax, and e-mail address.

Resources and Services

Information about online services, personal computer policies, library resources, international exchange programs, internship programs, and placement services can be found at http://www.petersons.com/mba.

International Students

An international student is defined, in this guide, as a person who is not a citizen of the country in which a particular college, university, or other institution is located but is in that country on a visa or temporary basis and does not have the right to remain indefinitely.

This section provides information regarding entrance and application requirements for international students, international student enrollment as a percentage of the total number of students enrolled in the business school, special services or facilities available to international students, availability of student housing, ESL classes, and the availability of financial aid.

Application requirements for international students may include minimum acceptable TOEFL (Test of English as a Foreign Language) score, minimum acceptable IELT (International English Language Test) score, proof of adequate funds, and proof of health immunizations.

Where applicable, the name, address, phone, fax, and e-mail address of the on-campus adviser or other person responsible for working with international students or exchange students are provided.

Application

Specific application requirements and what is recommended, application deadlines and fees, and the name, title, mailing address, telephone number, fax number, and e-mail address of the person who should receive applications for admission are described here.

Application requirements may include letters of recommendation, a written essay, an interview, copies of transcripts of previous college study, a resume/curriculum vitae, a personal statement, computer experience, work experience, or other specific requirements. Application deadlines for spring, fall, or other admission are provided by most schools. Some may process applications on a continuous or rolling basis or offer a deferred entrance plan.

Recommended items to accompany or enhance the application may include a specific bachelor's degree, submission of GMAT (Graduate Management Admission Test) scores, minimum GPA (grade point average), minimum acceptable TOEFL (Test of English as a Foreign Language) score, minimum acceptable IELT (International English Language Test) score, proof of adequate funds, proof of health immunizations (for non-U.S. applicants), and previous work experience.

Additional Information

A special announcement may be included for schools that wish to place additional emphasis on some aspect of their MBA program offerings. In addition, other schools have provided narratives that appear in the In-Depth Descriptions of MBA Programs section immediately following the Program Profiles. These In-Depth Descriptions provide additional information about institutions and their programs.

Data Collection Procedures

Information contained in the Program Profiles, At-A-Glance Chart, and Index sections of this book was collected in the spring of 2000 through Peterson's Survey of MBA and Other Master's-Level Business Degree Programs. Questionnaires were sent to nearly 1,000 U.S. and international institutions offering MBA and equivalent programs. Information was requested from program department contacts, admissions officers, or other appropriate personnel within these institutions in order to ensure accuracy. In some cases, this information was supplemented with data available from school catalogs and brochures and in some instances directly from the institution's Web site on the Internet in order to provide as much detail as possible on a particular school's MBA and/or master's-level degree offerings.

The omission of any particular item from a profile, chart, or index entry indicates that the item was either not applicable, not available at the time of publication, or not provided by the institution. Students should check with specific colleges and universities at the time of application to verify figures such as tuition and fees that may have changed since the publication of this guide.

Why an MBA? Future Trends and Opportunities in the Twenty-first Century

by John C. Hallenborg

MBA degrees are traditionally pursued in two-year, full-time programs; in more than two years in part-time evening and weekend programs; or in one-year intensive MBA programs, usually for executives or others with substantial work experience or those with undergraduate degrees in business.

Master's degrees of all types are on the rise. The plentiful supply of MBAs has allowed employers to be quite discriminating in hiring in recent years, requiring many MBAs to arrive equipped with specialized training and hands-on experience suited to their particular business niche.

Year	Master's Graduates in all Disciplines	Master's Graduates in Business and Management		
		Male	Female	Total
1990–91	337,168	50,883	27,372	78,255
1991–92	352,838	54,705	29,937	84,642
1992–93	369,585	57,651	31,964	89,615
1993–94	387,070	59,335	34,102	93,437
1994–95	397,629	59,109	34,700	93,809
1995–96	405,301	58,685	35,297	93,982

Source: National Center for Education Statistics, U.S. Department of Education. Figures were unavailable beyond 1996.

In comparing the programs profiled in this volume, careful consideration should be given to the time required for studying, as every school varies in its expectations of students. At first, rather than merely communicating with targeted schools via letter, speak with someone in the admissions office who is familiar with your prospective course of study. Such a conversation will more than likely draw you closer to, or deter you from, participating in their program. Especially if you're holding down a job, it is always prudent to map out your time wisely.

Certainly, there are variations on this theme as the working MBA candidate may, for example, distribute a course load to accommodate a work schedule. There is also the related issue of employer assistance. The candidate's choice of school or program might be determined solely by which programs are endorsed and subsidized by the candidate's employer.

The one-year program has been around long enough for employers to gauge many of its attributes as compared to the two-year counterpart. One consensus is that there are many other issues that are more likely to clearly differentiate one candidate from another. An MBA degree can improve a candidate's chances to approximately the same level as a non-MBA candidate with more years of successful work experience.

Of course, the weight assigned to the MBA degree by prospective employers varies considerably, depending on the industry, company, and job assignment. For the savvy salesperson of copiers at a large firm such as Xerox, for example, the company's in-house training would provide more valuable background than an MBA degree, at least until a promotion incorporated management skills into the position. Conversely, someone applying for a middle-management job in the finance department at a midsize company may find an MBA degree indispensable. The point is, the two jobs might be represented on the same salary tier, so it is still a maxim in the transitional process from MBA school to the workplace that the degree's importance is job-specific.

There are other key intangibles that have significance. Acquiring an advanced degree may imbue certain candidates with a feeling of confidence that may signal the difference between a lackluster career wandering the halls of a nondescript organization and a robust, life-affirming career full of welcome challenges and even more welcome rewards.

The knowledge gained in acquiring the MBA degree is not to be taken for granted at any point in the hiring process, as MBA holders can expect dedicated human resource executives to grill potential new hires in detail as to their educational experiences. What can the MBA grad do to improve this process? Graduates can apply their newly acquired knowledge to specific corporate examples to show why they should be hired.

Closing the Loop: Business Schools and Corporations

Ambitious MBA candidates at the turn of the century, looking forward to their careers or perhaps to the exciting prospect of entrepreneurship, cannot afford to presume that every MBA program will meet the educational requirements specific to an industry or profession. In today's job market and that of the near future, the MBA graduate will be expected to deliver both technical and nontechnical skills in every business and industrial sector. As in other areas of graduate study and related employment, the focus is, and will continue to be, on specialized expertise in business management. For business, opportunities abound to work with universities to create new MBA programs that will prepare candidates to fulfill an array of specialized leadership roles. For schools, this phenomenon continues to spur revamping of curricula almost annually to keep pace with the real-world demands that will be placed upon future MBA graduates.

Is it safe to presume that the recruitment managers at most major companies are aware of the changing makeup of the leading business school programs? The answer is most definitely yes and apparent in the variety of degree options, concentrations, and alternative courses of study available to today's MBA student.

How the degree can be obtained today also closely mirrors current business trends—the expectation of an early return on investment, preferably within one to two years. Future MBA programs will likely continue to reflect the choices seen today: the one-year degree, which often dispenses with core programs in favor of specialized courses tailored to specific career paths, and the more traditional two-year and extended MBA programs, which have been the basis of graduate business degrees for decades.

Certainly for the last twenty years or so, benchmark companies and top graduate schools have worked intensively to match academic programs to corporate needs. These relationships are likely to strengthen as more corporations and prospective students, hesitant to invest in two-year programs, are more willing to commit to emerging one-year programs.

Two-Year MBA Versus One-Year MBA

By all accounts, the composition of the MBA degree and how it is acquired will change significantly over the next five to ten years. The perceived value of the MBA degree has changed considerably in the student community and within the corporations that hire MBA graduates by the thousands every year. After a period of flat growth several years ago, the degree now appears dynamic and evolving. Affordable, highly focused, and time-efficient versions of the degree have replaced some multiyear courses of study.

The upsurge seen recently in one-year degrees has been driven, for the most part, by corporate demand, serving mostly experienced professionals and recent undergraduates with some work experience. Although two-year programs are still the norm in most business schools, accelerated and specialized one-year programs are seeing slight increases in enrollment. Business schools have been adversely affected by this trend and are offering degree options that combine an undergraduate business degree with an MBA in a five-year program.

The primary difference between one-year and traditional two-year programs is that with the shorter version, there is little if any overlap with undergraduate business curricula. Thus, it is highly recommended that students who decide on a one-year program enroll soon after receiving their undergraduate degrees and be able to satisfy all core business course requirements. However, some one-year programs require from two to five years' work experience in lieu of the traditional first-year MBA core study courses. In most cases, one-year elective courses are all but tailored to the applicant's career, so that the gradu-

Steven Lavender, President, Morgan/Webber: retained search firm

In answering the one-year versus two-year MBA program question, I have high regard for both programs at top schools such as Harvard, Wharton, Boston University, MIT's Sloan, Stanford, and the University of Chicago.

In the intensive one-year program, the student really lives the program in that time frame. I see it as a firm plus on a resume. A two-year program offers an assignment-oriented course of study, as the student has more time to assert his or her ideas as an individual versus the largely company-oriented slant of one-year programs.

Both of these programs add an attractive package of improved skills to the corporate world, reflecting course study in planning; distribution; the modern structure of marketing; assessments of MIS requirements; and the practical implementation of useful business models.

If you are considering an MBA, gear the course work toward a specialization and limit your choice of schools to those that include the targeted curriculum. This way, you will bring a continued focus on a specialty that today's employers find attractive.

You may wonder when, in a career, it's a good time to acquire an MBA. In today's job market, it's best if you work for six or seven years and then go get yourself an MBA. By the time someone has six years' work experience, he or she knows enough to properly shape a course of MBA study that will be beneficial to the employer.

ate can reenter the workforce as quickly as possible. Classic two-year programs most often focus on elective and specialized course work in the second year after completion of core requirements in the first year.

A number of emerging realities will highlight the one-year MBA degree: technology-based information media will replace class time in many cases as students gain access to CD-ROM and online services; fewer faculty members may be required as schools combine resources to teach fewer classes to more students; and distance learning will replace some on-campus classes. For most schools and students of the future, technology will certainly dictate the learning medium.

In the relatively brief period that one-year MBA graduates have been working, corporations have been neutral about recruiting one-year program versus two-year program graduates, as there is no published evidence that graduates of two-year programs outperform their one-year counterparts.

Albert W. Niemi Jr., Dean of Southern Methodist University's Edwin L. Cox School of Business, explains that "I don't see, in the data that we have collected—in terms of starting salaries—that there is any difference in the way one-year people are treated by industry. One-year grads do as well as two-year grads in terms of earning power in the marketplace."

Despite Niemi's findings, to date there has not been significant movement toward the one-year degree, as at present there are relatively few such programs compared to the total number of MBA programs offered nationwide.

Traditional Course Work Versus In-house Training

Rather than sending employees off company premises for continuing education, many companies choose to hire competent teachers as staff members to provide in-house training. This trend is not yet fully under way, but it is seen as a cost-effective alternative to traditional MBA programs. The one-year MBA and in-house training represent new models for graduate education. "Our dynamic economy is forcing change on all of us, if we are to be competitive and meet new challenges," offers William K. Laidlaw Jr., former Executive Vice President of AACSB–The International Association for Management Education.

Among the programs on the horizon are those directed at problem solving within a limited number of companies or even a single company. These programs are tailored to specific company issues. Typically, collaborative tutoring teams are composed of university professors and corporate upper management.

Changes in the Financial Sector

In the top tiers of the financial markets, there have been many changes following the scandals and management excesses of the 1980s. By close association with these events, the reputation of the MBA degree was somewhat tainted, directly or by implication. Today's graduates are under scrutiny to improve the standing of the degree in the academic and corporate worlds. Clearly, teamwork has superseded personal glory in most corporate environments, and the financial community is no exception.

There has been a considerable shakeout in the better sectors of the financial job market, and many large financial organizations are as vigilant in maintaining a positive public image as they are about profit levels. Any MBA candidate seeking a spot at one of the top investment banks, for example, will have to be aware of issues of public relations in addition to more predictable questions about money markets. Expect this sensitivity to public opinion to remain high for many years. In fact, a reputation for aboveboard dealings is nearly as important as bottom-line performance in today's financial sphere.

At present, the MBA degree is still key in the world of investment banking, as recruitment specialists at banks large and small report that about 90 percent of new hires have the degree.

The New MBA Attitude

How does this job market realignment affect the MBA holder's chances for a lucrative career in finance? The answer is often more in the attitude of the prospect than in the present and future states of the job market. These behavioral issues resound throughout not only the financial sector but also the finance departments of major corporations. The message is: bring us good grades from a good school but also bring along maturity and a problem-solving attitude.

L. Nicholas Deane, former Senior Vice President, Faulkner & Gray, subsidiary of Thomson Financial Services

Faulkner & Gray is a departmentalized organization, and as head of a division that publishes content for professionals in the tax field, I tend to value work experience in that particular area more than a general MBA degree. However, I do recognize the usefulness of MBAs that target disciplines more specifically than, for example, an MBA in marketing, which I do not value very highly. However, in considering my department's needs, I'll flag a resume with an MBA with taxation as a specialty.

My sense is that work experience has more value than an MBA in general business environments, but that as one swings toward the more technical domains, a technically based MBA will look more attractive to an employer. The likelihood is that such a candidate will get up to speed more quickly on what is happening, both good and bad, within a company. And then, there is a greater chance that background in the specific area will serve to provide a base for successful decision making.

The in-depth study of sophisticated financial concepts is the key attribute that sets the MBA degree apart. I like to see well-placed employees armed with this advanced knowledge of finance. All sharp-minded candidates deserve a fair shot. There are experienced people who perform well without an MBA degree. Faulkner & Gray is typical of the high end of the publishing sector that is using technology to migrate from paper-based products to online and other electronically based formats.

As to the one-year degree versus the two-year degree, I have not seen evidence that causes me to prefer a two-year degree over the one-year alternative, but I should stress again that pertinent work background has been a better indicator of good hires than degrees of any sort. It comes down to the individual, the candidate's unique mix of experiences and qualifications. One area that I have seen strength in as the MBA relates to job specs is in financial analysis. I have come to expect the MBA holder to be sophisticated in crunching numbers.

Despite the fact that compensation at the higher levels in banking is very bonus-oriented, the fresh MBA graduate should avoid being a self-serving maverick. The MBA of tomorrow, more than ever before, will have to display strengths in leadership, teamwork, problem solving, and dealing with people. Upper management will be looking for well-rounded individuals who offer a balanced perspective and are ready and able to apply their education in a real-life setting.

Working for Smaller Companies

And what about the option of employment by the thousands of small and midsize firms that populate the American business landscape? The ideal of a "secure job forever" has been replaced by the reality that most Americans will have two or three careers in their lifetimes and may even change jobs every five years or so. Small and middle-market corporations have become the most fertile ground for MBA recruitment and will likely continue to hire more MBAs in the future. In many instances, it is easier for a talented MBA holder to make a significant contribution to a midsize firm in a high-growth mode. The key, of course, may be to identify likely high-growth companies that have the potential for continued growth over a three- to five-year period.

Once again, preparation for a specific industry niche, or better yet a specific company or companies, is key to landing those choice spots that feature a daunting 50:1, or 500:1, applicant/position ratio. Most competing MBAs are aware that the key to landing the desired job is to positively differentiate oneself from other equally qualified candidates. Some MBA students have gone so far as to research potential employers at the beginning of their course work, studying the details of annual reports, product brochures, etc., for the duration of the typical two-year MBA program.

Skills learned in MBA core and specialized courses can be especially valuable in helping to transform technical ideas and concepts into tangible, marketable products. In both large and small businesses in the future, managers will certainly be expected to bring not only technical expertise to the table but also the ability to translate new ideas into profit-sustaining products and services.

The small and midsize firm is often the perfect venue for such creative expression coupled with pragmatic implementation. Smaller firms are already actively recruiting from the ranks of new MBA degree holders to discover the talented individuals whose skills and judgment will drive future growth and product improvement.

MBA candidates should be very selective in targeting small and midsize companies, however, as many smaller firms are adopting a lean corporate structure by not instituting a middle layer of management until they reach the 1,000-employee mark. For the MBA holder this may mean more responsibility within a flat organizational structure and the need to "wear many hats."

Richard Helfrich, former Vice President at California Micro, a semiconductor maker, considers the MBA to be "a strong plus in our hiring considerations. I weigh the degree as the equivalent of three years of solid work experience. But because our products are so technology-based, the master's degree is still our primary qualifier."

Tomorrow's MBA Entrepreneur

There will also be a place for the ambitious MBA holder who cannot wait for others to bring his or her ideas to the marketplace. For many fearless graduates, starting or buying a business may be a quicker and more lucrative route to success. Those with the best chance of making it this way will most likely combine prior technical training with the marketing and financial knowledge acquired with an MBA degree—for example, the electrical engineering whiz who starts a small, niche-focused circuit design firm.

Still, the appeal of running a small business does not get as much media coverage as it should, if the Harvard MBA Class

Bril Flint, former Vice President, Strategic Planning, EMI-Capitol Music

When recruiting management talent for my team, I evaluate candidates across four dimensions: the candidate's long-term career plan and objectives; relevant real-world experience; technical capabilities for the job at hand; and interpersonal skills.

With these parameters in mind, how can a prospective business school student make the best use of an MBA education within the context of overall career advancement?

First, make sure graduate management education really does fit in with your long-term career plan. This may sound like a trivial step, but I have met more people that have not explicitly delineated their objectives than those that have. You can change them as you go along, but make sure the time and money you will spend on business school are really worthwhile.

I also like to see candidates who factor their long-term strategy into their choice of business school. For example, if they want to pursue a career in engineering management, did they pick a school that has a good program in that field, or did they opt for a "name school to get their ticket punched?" I prefer to see the former.

While an MBA from a top school can be a leg up on the competing candidates, I have seen enough successful executives with degrees from middle or lower tier graduate management programs (and many without an MBA degree at all) to know that a degree from a top ten institution is not required to prove and validate the individual's capability. Neither is it a guarantee of success, as I have seen plenty of graduates from top tier schools fail miserably in the working world.

Relevant work experience is really the most important area for me when I look at recruits. Most executives would rather have someone who understands their industry and how it works. I usually prefer the candidate with two years of relevant industry experience over one with two years of business school, no matter how "applied" a business school curriculum claims to be. It simply cannot duplicate the real day-to-day business activity in a particular industry or company.

The bottom line here is: It is better to work several years before you go to business school. (*Editor's Note:* Flint has a master's degree in management from MIT's Sloan School of Management.) If you have identified an industry in which you really want to work long term, go all out to find a job in that line of business before you go to business school. This may mean sacrificing short-term earnings.

I look for candidates who can bring the right "tool box" to the job for which I am recruiting. The appropriate technical skills for the position under consideration can be developed and demonstrated through prior experience, whether in the same industry or in the same functional area in a different line of business.

(continued)

To a lesser, but still important, extent, specific technical skills can be learned in school. To reiterate, if your long-term career strategy should help drive your choice of business school, then developing the appropriate technical capabilities should be the tactical driver in your selection of specific courses to take. In the typical two-year business school program, you have a limited number of elective courses. Make each one count to your advantage; try to leave business school with the appropriate tools at your disposal.

Interpersonal skills have a profound impact on a manager's long-term career path. In every meeting or transaction, others are making assessments of your poise, level of confidence, ability to communicate clearly, your business ethics, competency, and about one hundred other interpersonal traits. As in the other areas, prior work experience is most valuable in developing this skill set. Watch how successful executives interact in a variety of business settings.

Business school is also a good setting to enhance your interpersonal abilities. Working and socializing with classmates from varied backgrounds is good experience and is essential to get the most out of the business school experience.

of 1970 is any indication. In a recent survey of the 723 alumni who are now as a group generally in the peak phases of their careers, only 13 percent worked for *BusinessWeek* 1000 companies. By contrast, 36 percent were self-employed and the majority worked in small businesses (fewer than 500 employees) in one capacity or another.

Opportunities for MBAs in the Twenty-first Century

Because management and finance are functions common to every conceivable type of business or industry, it is difficult to make predictions about job growth for MBAs in particular markets. However, although it may sound simplistic, it is still true that career opportunities will most likely continue to exist for talented MBAs in nearly all areas of the marketplace. Although manufacturing and investment firms have experienced somewhat of a downswing in top management positions in the last few years, a tremendous variety of positions still attract MBAs to accounting, commercial banking, management consulting, consumer products, health care, insurance, services, and chemical companies in functions that include marketing, finance, operations, information systems, and long-term planning. Even many nonprofits are recruiting MBAs to help them redefine and reshape their organizations both economically and socially.

So, what are some of the growth areas for MBA graduates to consider? As in the 1980s and 1990s, there appears to be no limit to the growth potential in the software and telecommunications industries, particularly in the convergence of data and voice technologies. The number of professional jobs in computer software and hardware development and marketing

will also likely only increase over the next ten years, although many companies may start up and then fold or be bought out in these volatile fields.

Telecommunications giants such as AT&T, MCI, and the Regional Bell Companies are already driving much of the development in this sector and will certainly require MBA graduates with a broad range of business and technical skills. MBAs with well-honed analytical and marketing skills will certainly be needed as telecommunications companies continue making forays into the information and entertainment services markets.

Another area for consideration by the eager MBA is publishing and information services. Innumerable products in CD-ROM, CD-I, and online formats are displacing paper equivalents most notably in the professional and academic domains. Books, newspapers, and other information products are certain to follow this trend toward electronic versus paper distribution. Publishing professionals armed with MBA degrees will certainly supply much of the marketing, financial, and strategic expertise needed to help such companies enter these new markets.

Still another high-growth area that may lure many MBAs is the world of entertainment. The creative entrepreneur seeking entry into the television, film, or music industry could be well positioned with an MBA, since bottom-line business issues usually determine if projects are produced. Consulting opportunities for the freelance MBA holder are already numerous in the entertainment industry. This should continue as a promising area of activity for the creative MBA.

For U.S.-based firms in other industry sectors, a significant amount of future growth may come from overseas operations. In the chemicals and polymers sector, for example, many of the management jobs will be in maintaining investments on the Pacific Rim and Eastern Europe, where most of the largest petrochemical conglomerates have joint ventures in place. MBA graduates should be willing to travel abroad to land these types of positions.

Most sources indicate that U.S. industries overall will experience moderate, 3 to 7 percent annual growth in the next ten years. Hiring of MBAs in industries such as construction and real estate, general manufacturing, and foods and beverages is predicted to be moderate by comparison.

Which sectors will be the toughest to enter, based on a flat industry growth forecast for the next ten years? Aerospace, oil and gas, retail, and apparel are some of the major industries that are likely to experience fluctuating growth at best.

Go Global

With the continued advance of telecommunications as the primary medium for data transfer, banks and corporations have permanently erased many commercial barriers between nations. This borderless, global market should be an exciting prospect for the ambitious MBA.

An in-depth review of international trade regulations will serve tomorrow's MBA well since American firms already derive some 50 percent of gross revenues from overseas operations. Given the prodigious growth rate of economies in

Willard Anderson, former Director, Management Development and Diversity, ITT Corporation

At ITT, the MBA degree is very important as part of an overall package of attributes a candidate may have to offer. When we hire an MBA, we expect that new hire to hit the ground running, as there is less time in today's competitive marketplace for in-house training.

We presume that an MBA holder emerging from our group of recruitment schools (Harvard, Columbia, Duke, Northwestern, Wharton, and Stanford) will have considerable business acumen. This is part of the skill set we are seeking. Another key element is an undergraduate course of study that integrates well with the curriculum that was chosen in acquiring an MBA.

Also important in terms of middle-management jobs and marketing leadership positions is that the candidate have three to five years' solid work experience. So, we look for people who have a synergistic mix of MBA and relevant undergraduate training, along with some real time spent solving real business problems.

As to the question of one-year versus two-year MBA programs, we are decidedly in favor of two-year programs. In fact, exceptions are very few. Perhaps 1 in 100 MBA holders will come on board with a one-year degree. This conservative approach has paid off in that we have reaped significant rewards from this hiring system.

We also view the MBA degree as more important today than it was five or ten years ago. In order to move easily within the extensive ITT corporate system, a new management employee needs to be familiar with sophisticated business models and other more advanced business concepts that reflect exposure to the rigors of acquiring an MBA degree. Our undergraduate employees are more deterministic in how they go about their jobs. MBA holders are much more likely to get into developmental work right away.

Overall, ITT is a company that all but requires management candidates to have a two-year MBA and three to five years of work experience. In terms of specialties within the MBA degree, we have had notable success with candidates who stressed finance and marketing in their courses of study.

the developing nations, particularly in Asia and South America, virtually any MBA with skills to lend to those markets should find much success.

There will be more exciting opportunities in the former Eastern Bloc nations as these countries struggle to establish free-market economies. But the challenges are as enormous as the potential rewards. Still, the fearless MBA, armed with street smarts, a good command of the host country's language, and a firm grasp of the cultural keys to market entry, will find plenty of qualified European partners ready to forge ahead.

Similarly, at home, most large companies will be importing and exporting huge quantities of commodities, consumer goods, and financial services. For American MBAs seeking careers at home, the importance of global awareness cannot be overstated. Ten years from now, there will be impressive opportunities for international licensing of technologies, trademarks, and copyrighted products and processes that most Americans take for granted. Clearly, the cosmopolitan MBA will be the first to reap the rewards from emerging international markets in the twenty-first century.

Postgrad Tips

A candidate should zero in on three to five companies that are very attractive, firms wherein one could happily spend the next three to ten years working hard to establish oneself in the business community. If writing is a strong skill, parlay the skill by writing a detailed letter expressing your knowledge of the industry and the company and why you would be an asset to that company.

In the case of public companies, get their latest annual report, analyze it, and have your own views on the company's future ready to share with your interviewer. Do not make the mistake of blindly agreeing with everything the interviewer offers about the firm. If you disagree on a point, assert yourself with an explanation of your perspective on the issue. Never shy away from creating polarized discussion during an interview if you truly believe your position to be correct. Hopefully, your interviewer will recognize your willingness to defend your viewpoint as a trait of a successful executive.

John C. Hallenborg is a writer and business consultant based in Los Angeles, California.

The New MBA: What to Look for in Today's Reinvented Programs

by Carter A. Prescott

Your team's assignment: Climb through different size openings in a massive rope web without touching anything—and do it faster than competing teams. Another assignment: Tell a fellow student about an experience in which you felt odd or left out. Sound like typical MBA fare? If you answered yes, you pass.

Today's graduate business programs are undergoing what some experts tout as nothing less than revolutionary change. In response to new competitive demands on corporations and increasing globalization—both of which require tomorrow's business leaders to be flexible and manage workforces and internal structures that cross cultural and political lines—MBA programs are diversifying and redefining themselves. You'll still graduate with a firm grounding in the staples of business education—finance, strategy, operations management, marketing, and the like—but you'll also learn how to work in teams, how to motivate others, and how to see the "big picture" when solving problems. Strong communication and interpersonal skills are just as important in today's new MBA programs as technical knowledge and the ability to "crunch numbers."

"There's more churning going on right now in management education than at any time in thirty-five years," says Charles W. Hickman, former Director of Projects and Services at AACSB–The International Association for Management Education, which accredits MBA programs in the United States. "The emphasis today is changing from teaching to learning," Hickman notes. "The front-end-load module, where you dump two years of education into a student's head and then sew it up, is over. The world is moving too fast. Companies want MBA graduates to know how to learn, because lifelong learning is the key to success for practicing managers and executives. The MBA is not an end in itself. It positions the degree-holder for a variety of general management positions."

What, you may ask, can you expect to learn from the rope exercise? How to plan, pay attention to detail, and how to work in teams. And the lesson behind baring your soul to a colleague? How to become sensitive to gender and ethnic diversity in order to manage it effectively.

The days when MBA graduates could dazzle their bosses with only a few mentions of decision trees, regression analysis, net present value, and gap planning are gone. You'll still learn these concepts, but you'll be synthesizing them into a broader skill set. Dennis J. Weidenaar, Professor of Economics at the Krannert Graduate School of Management at Purdue University,

calls it the "new management environment." He says it is characterized by "teamwork and alliances, continuous changes in technologies, globalization, and networks that are in instantaneous communication with each other."

How specifically do today's MBA programs prepare you to succeed in this environment? Here are ten primary ways.

1. Cross-Functional, Interdisciplinary Curricula

You'll hear these phrases so often they'll sound like a mantra. Even the venerable Harvard Business School voted to overhaul its MBA curriculum in 1996 to offer students more interdisciplinary courses and more freedom in choosing electives. Across the country, MBA schools are reshaping curricula to teach students the importance of solving problems by synthesizing a variety of subjects. Faculty members from different disciplines coordinate their syllabi and teach in teams to students who work in teams. When Stanford added a new course in human resource management, for example, it was designed by professors of organizational behavior and economics. A cross-functional approach also has proved resoundingly popular with students. After Wharton tested a dramatically revised curriculum, surveys showed that 94 percent of its 1993 graduates who participated in the pilot would do so again, while 60 percent of those who studied under the traditional program would have preferred the new one.

2. New Programs

Whether they are specific sequences or subjects woven into the fabric of an MBA curriculum, you'll find strong mentions of entrepreneurship, ethics, Total Quality Management (TQM), information technology management, and leadership development in nearly all basic MBA programs. Purdue's PL+S Program (Preparing Leaders and Stewards) provides additional course work, community service opportunities, self-assessment, and self-directed team consulting projects with companies, all as avenues for developing leadership skills. Harvard's new "foundations" program places heavy emphasis on career planning, self-assessment, working in groups, and business ethics. Ethical challenges are constantly reinforced in the Pepperdine University curriculum, says Stanley K. Mann, a professor in the Graduate School of Business. "We are training managers to take on responsibilities and obligations, not to put the dollar ahead of everything else."

A new emphasis on entrepreneurship reflects the reality that "the majority of MBA graduates will not work in Fortune 500 companies, because they have been downsizing the most," notes Charles Hickman. Accordingly, many universities help students develop better job-hunting and career development skills.

3. Global Perspectives

Because U.S. corporations increasingly compete around the world, globalization is serious business in the nation's MBA programs. Stanford offers four times as many internationally focused electives as it did ten years ago. Even though Pace University has featured an international business major for twenty years, "we now view it as a jumping-off point to integrate international issues throughout the curriculum," says Dean Arthur L. Centonze. Pepperdine University in Malibu, California, designed a specific Master of International Business program that features eight months of study and internships in France or Germany. Students are required to find their own internships and to be proficient in French or German. Although 6 percent routinely drop out, another third stay abroad for at least a year, postponing their graduation to gain valuable work experience.

4. Increased Student and Faculty Diversity

Business schools have realized that the best way to teach tomorrow's managers to tap the talents of an increasingly diverse workforce is to surround students with a widely diverse student body. They're also recruiting more faculty members who reflect diverse viewpoints and philosophies as well as national origin. While more and more schools are quick to point to their rising numbers of international students, they also refer to the diverse backgrounds and experiences among their MBA students. Students from diverse countries and backgrounds are viewed as a resource that complements what faculty members know and what other students bring to the program. Women students are swelling the ranks of MBA graduates as well.

5. Teamwork, Teamwork, and More Teamwork

Schools are working hard to encourage the same environment of teamwork that graduates will experience in the working world. "Cohort structures," for example, have gained in popularity. In a cohort structure, you are placed with a specified number of fellow students—deliberately chosen for their diversity—either for the first few weeks of class or for the entire first year. Together with other members of your cohort, you'll solve problems as a team, resolve conflicts, sustain morale, achieve accountability, and, it is hoped, learn to reach your goals by becoming interdependent, just as you would in a corporate setting.

Reinvented MBA programs are learning to "pit students against the curriculum and not against one another," says Sam Lundquist, Chief of Staff in the Dean's Office at Wharton. Stanford says its cooperative learning environment is a significant factor in the program's "joy coefficient," as George Parker, Associate Dean for Academic Affairs, describes it.

6. Richer Learning Environment

Hand in hand with curriculum improvements, business schools are finding new ways to strengthen teaching and foster improved student-faculty relationships. Indeed, the "most exciting part" of Wharton's cross-functional curriculum, Lundquist says, is that teams of faculty teach the same students for the entire first year, which "drastically improves the quality of relationships between students and faculty members."

As MBA programs bolster the quality of the learning experience, they are focusing a laser beam on how well professors help students learn. Pace University views faculty members as "the managers of the student learning process," says Centonze. As a result, all programs and courses have objectives that are measured by student exit surveys, faculty questionnaires, and yearly performance evaluations for faculty members. Any underperforming teachers are coached at the school's Center for Faculty Development and Teaching Effectiveness, where their syllabi are reviewed and their classes videotaped.

Increasingly, a variety of teaching methods are employed, including lectures, case studies, computer simulations, and consulting projects. Harvard's curriculum reform was notable for adopting alternative teaching methods in addition to its reliance on the traditional case-study approach and for developing ways to have faculty members spend less time teaching basics.

7. Greater Use of Learning Technologies

MBA programs are making increasing use of distance learning, which uses interactive cable television and computers to take courses directly to students' homes. The University of Maryland, for instance, uses distance learning and team teaching to bundle its assets and hire big-name teachers. Distance learning also is "favored heavily" in Europe, where virtually all programs are part-time, according to Roger McCormick, former Director General of the Association of MBAs in the United Kingdom. Distance learning allows students to learn at their own pace, which is especially helpful for remedial courses and quantitative work, he says.

Business schools are avidly employing other technologies as well, such as interactive cases on CD and real-time data feeds from Wall Street. In fall 1996, the University of Texas at Austin completed a $1.5-million trading room so that its students could experience trading in real time with real dollars from a $2-million investment fund. Videoconferencing is often used for classroom presentations or off-site interviews with corporations.

8. More Applied Learning

At the University of Illinois at Chicago, student and faculty teams tackle corporate projects by interviewing corporate executives, writing reports, and presenting recommendations to the company and to their fellow students. They're not alone. Students at the University of Texas at Austin helped Ford Motor Company better segment its Hispanic marketing efforts. The University of Michigan adopted a medical school model, requiring students to get considerable practical experience working at corporations. At Stanford, corporate leaders such as Andrew

S. Grove, Chairman of the Board of Intel, team with professors to teach classes on strategy in the high-technology industry.

9. Strategic Alliances

To better leverage their resources, schools are joining forces to teach students and to conduct postgraduate training for corporate executives. The Thunderbird School reserves seats at its learning centers around the world for its partner schools in the United States. Business schools at the University of Florida and Fordham University in New York team up with AT&T and MCI, respectively, to offer customized programs for their executives. Corporate advisory boards, long a staple of most MBA programs, are increasingly relied on to provide advice on curricula as well as hiring opportunities. Corporate partners also contribute other sorely needed resources. Purdue has one of the most extensive computing labs of any business school, thanks to the generosity of such high-tech partners as AT&T, Hewlett Packard, IBM, Microsoft, and PictureTel. "The business environment is moving fast, and even elite schools don't have all the money they need to access new markets, technology, and faculty expertise," says Charles Hickman.

10. Customer Focus

It's not uncommon to hear business school professors routinely refer to students and companies as customers—and to treat their needs with the same respect. Many schools are applying Total Quality Management (TQM) principles to operating the business schools themselves. They're becoming more customer-focused, reducing the cycle time for admissions processing and curriculum development, and becoming more efficient to lower tuition or keep it from rising quickly. Seattle University takes classes to the customers, dispatching faculty members to teach evening and breakfast courses near Seattle's biggest employers.

With such evolution occurring day by day at business schools, more than ever before, today's reinvented MBA programs aim to prepare you for the real world of work, where you will work in teams, take a global view, and analyze problems from a multitude of perspectives. To accomplish these goals, MBA programs intend to equip you with the ability to embrace change, accept ambiguity, and lead others with the vision and confidence gained from continuous learning.

With a newly minted MBA degree, you are better qualified to enter new fields, better able to leverage your prior work experience, and more likely to sustain higher earnings over the course of your career. Equally important, you'll have the opportunity to make a significant difference on as broad a scale as you wish. With finely honed analytical skills, the ability to work well with people, and the desire to keep learning, today's MBA graduates can succeed in a broad range of general management positions and add more value than ever before.

Carter A. Prescott is a management communications consultant in New York City.

Choosing the Right Program for Your Career Needs

by Richard L. White, Director of Career Development and Placement Services, Rutgers University

In recent senior surveys, more than 80 percent of Rutgers University students have indicated that they intend to pursue graduate study at some point in the future. Many are thinking about an MBA. The intentions of Rutgers students reflect a national trend: More and more students want additional education, and, in fact, many feel they will need it to achieve their fullest career potential.

From your first thoughts about graduate school to your actual admission and decision to attend a school, you are engaged in an extensive, complex, competitive process. The emphasis of the program you select will greatly influence the direction of your career. In selecting an MBA program, it is critical to match your strengths, interests, and goals with the specific offerings of the school and program.

To organize and manage the process, develop a strategy for evaluating your choices and developing an action plan. At the heart of your action plan are four basic questions that are simple to ask but require self-exploration and research:

- Why do I want to pursue an MBA?
- When and how do I want to pursue an MBA?
- Where do I want to pursue an MBA?
- What schools and programs are right for me?

1. Why Pursue an MBA?

Typically, you are probably thinking about pursuing an MBA for four basic reasons:

- Your chosen profession demands further study
- You want to enhance your marketability and salary
- You want to change careers
- You are committed to further study in your current discipline or a new discipline

Most applicants fit one of these profiles:

- You're currently working with an employer that you would like to stay with long term. You've talked to your boss and colleagues, and they feel that getting an MBA will improve your business and technical knowledge and thus increase your performance and promotional opportunities with the employer. You understand that there probably won't be a big jump in salary when you complete your degree, but in the long term it will pay off. In addition, your employer will pick up the tab through its tuition reimbursement program.
- You're currently working with an employer who doesn't fit into your long-term plans. You're planning to leave in the near future. You see your MBA as the key to opening new opportunities in the same field or a new field and to increasing your salary prospects. You realize that you're on your own with regard to costs (no employer assistance), but you see the short-term investment paying off in the long run.
- You're a senior in college. You've looked at the job market, but you're really leaning toward an MBA program. You're very interested in pursuing your business education, especially because your bachelor's degree is not in business. You understand that the best business schools accept only a small percentage of applicants directly from undergraduate programs, but you have a strong academic record and some good internship and part-time work experience.

Whatever your profile may be, make sure you can articulate your reasons for pursuing an MBA clearly, succinctly, and persuasively both orally and in writing. Review the evolution of your thinking from first thoughts about an MBA to major influences such as people, courses, positions, and research.

To understand your motivation for pursuing an MBA, follow these action steps:

1. Take notes on yourself.
2. Write or revise your resume.
3. Develop a generic personal statement (two or three typed pages), indicating what makes you special and why you want an MBA degree.
4. Request a sampling of MBA applications and begin crafting sample answers to the questions, using parts of your generic personal statement.
5. Read *How to Write a Winning Personal Statement for Graduate and Professional School* by Richard Stelzer (Peterson's, 1997). Check your college's career services library, your campus bookstore, or a local bookstore in the education/reference section.
6. Determine job prospects for MBAs in your intended field—both short-term and long-term. The best resources for short-term job prospects are individual placement reports from business schools, which you can request from the schools of your choice. For long-term prospects, talk to relatives, family friends, or professors. Another great source is alumni, if your school has an alumni career network.

2. When and How Do You Want to Pursue Your MBA?

There are four fairly clear-cut options about when and how to pursue your MBA:

• *Full-time beginning in the fall after your graduation from college.* Keep in mind that MBA programs typically look for candidates with at least one to two years of full-time work experience. If you are a student early in your undergraduate career, one option to explore is a five-year dual-degree (BS/MBA) program.

• *Full-time after a year or more of work.* MBA programs value the diversity and quality of candidates' work experiences, which bring "real-world" perspectives and new ideas into the classroom. Moreover, many MBA students indicate that their MBA course work has even more significance after they continue their professional and career development.

• *Part-time beginning anytime while working.* In most cases, you will take evening classes. As part of your preliminary research, find out if your employer provides full or partial tuition remission. Also explore whether or not your employer values an MBA and whether it will really contribute to your long-term promotability. Finally, try to determine how flexible your employer may be if, for example, you need to take a 4:30 class or need one or two days off to complete a school project.

• *Part-time beginning anytime while not working.* If you're not working, you can take either day or evening classes. But if you're looking for a daytime job, bear in mind that you might want to remain flexible during the day and therefore take your classes at night. The reverse is true if you have a part-time evening job.

To sort out the different possibilities, take these action steps:

1. Research the schools of your choice, using this guide. Compare these five key elements: percentage of full-time versus part-time enrollees; percentage of incoming MBAs who came directly from undergraduate programs; average age; average work experience; and costs.
2. Research the profession and prospective employers, utilizing corporate recruiters, friends in the corporate world, career services and admissions professionals, professional associations, alumni networks, professors, and publications. Consider these elements: availability of tuition remission programs; value of the MBA within the profession or company; balance between a company's BA/BS hiring and MBA hiring.
3. Balance all of the above elements with your personal life and lifestyle and those of the people closest to you.

3. Where Do You Want to Pursue Your MBA?

This is the most complex step in the process, because there are many variables. However, by taking these action steps, you can gain firm control of the process and manage it to your advantage.

Note that these steps are in no order of preference. It would be helpful to put them in rank order in terms of importance for you—or at least group them by "very important," "important," and "less important."

1. Determine the availability of degree programs in your specific field. For example, if you are thinking about an MBA in international business, this guide will tell you which schools offer that program.
2. Determine the quality and reputation of the programs of your choice. This is a crucial element. Employers often base their recruiting decisions on quality and reputation, and you will be associated with the name of your MBA school for the remainder of your career. Three key factors in assessing quality and reputation are faculty, facilities, and student body. In addition to utilizing this guide and perhaps other resources, talk to professors and professionals and "read between the lines" of the admissions literature and placement reports. Feel free to consult various national rankings, but don't take them too seriously. These are often based on journalistic endeavors rather than hard research and often overlook the special offerings of individual programs.
3. Determine the costs of graduate programs—the simple part—and your ability to pay through loans, income, savings, financial aid, and parental support—the not-so-simple part. Pursue those programs that are affordable. Consult the "Paying for Your MBA" section in this guide for an overview of the financing process.
4. Determine the locations of your preferred graduate programs. Do you prefer urban, suburban, or rural locations? Do you have any personal geographical restrictions or preferences? Think about the time and cost of commuting and travel.
5. Determine the size of the programs and the institutions. Most MBA programs are relatively small but the size of institutions varies considerably. Size is critical to the overall environment, character, academic resources, and student-faculty ratios and relationships.

4. What Schools and Programs Are Right for You?

Here, you are putting it all together and generating a list of five to ten schools where you intend to apply. Typically, you will want one or two "stretch" schools, a handful of "good bets," and one or two "safety" schools. Feel free to rank your preferences at the outset of the admissions process, but remain flexible. As you receive admissions decisions, your preferences will probably change and need to change.

Once your admissions acceptances are in hand, how do you make the final important decision? Consider the following steps.

Rank the five most important features of the MBA experience for you. You might also want a second-tier group of five additional features. Focus on these ten features (feel free to add others to the list):

1. Career and placement services (placement report, number of employers recruiting on campus, quality of operation)
2. Class offerings (day, evening, summer, weekend)
3. Cost (tuition, room, board, travel, living expenses)
4. Curricular focus (ethics, diversity, international, etc.)
5. Facilities (dorms, classrooms, libraries)

6. Faculty (general quality, individual faculty members)
7. Location (geographic, urban, rural)
8. Personal considerations (spouse, family, friends)
9. Quality and reputation (general comments)
10. Teaching methodology (lectures, case studies, team projects)

Systematically compare each school with regard to each feature. Rank schools within each feature, assigning a score if you wish.

Once you have done all of the analysis, make sure your heart agrees with your head. If it's a toss-up, go with your instincts. They're probably right.

Using This Guide to Compare Programs

This guide provides answers to many of the key questions you will have about the numerous MBA programs that are available. Consult the individual program profiles as you research and gather information about schools and their specific MBA offerings. You will find the following topics addressed in each profile.

Program Overview

1. How large is both the full-time and part-time faculty?
2. What is the student body profile (full-time and part-time students; average age; percentages of women and members of minority groups?
3. What are the acceptance rates (number of applications versus number accepted)?
4. What is the average GMAT score and GPA?
5. What are the costs (full-time and part-time)?
6. How many graduates were employed three months after graduation, and what is the average starting salary?
7. Is the school accredited?

Degrees

8. What range of graduate business programs is offered (e.g., traditional MBA, full-time, part-time, distance learning, executive MBA, MBA/JD option, MS programs)?

Costs

9. What are the full-time, part-time, day, and evening tuition costs? What are the costs of fees, room, and board?

Financial Aid

10. What percentage of students receive financial aid? When is the application deadline?
11. What is the name, title, address, and telephone number for the financial aid contact?

International Students

12. What is the percentage of international students?
13. What services and facilities are available (international student office, visa services, ESL courses, counseling/support services)?
14. What special application procedures are required (TOEFL test, financial support, immunizations, etc.)?
15. What is the name, title, address, and telephone number of the international student contact?

Application

16. What are the application requirements (forms, fees, degrees, transcripts, recommendations, personal statement, GMAT scores, work experience, etc.)?
17. What else is recommended for admission (resume, essay, spreadsheet, computer experience, etc.)?
18. What is the name, address, telephone number, and e-mail address for the admissions contact?

Once you have completed your preliminary research and request applications from the schools of your choice, you are ready for the next step: completing your application and getting into the school of your choice.

Getting Admitted to MBA Programs

by Samuel T. Lundquist, Chief of Staff, Dean's Office, the Wharton School, University of Pennsylvania

Applicants to MBA programs often spend more time trying to figure out how to get into business school than researching the program itself. Hence, the prospective student has made the first critical error of the admissions process—seeking the elusive "admissions formula" versus making a quality presentation that demonstrates knowledge of self and graduate business education.

There really is not any formula that can predict admission to an MBA program. Business school applicants must enter the selection process understanding the difference between being admissible and being admitted. The distinction between the two varies considerably among business schools, depending on the level of selectivity in the admissions process. While some MBA programs admit all qualified students, others may deny admission to 4 of every 5 applicants who are qualified to be admitted. Understanding this difference is the first step to a successful application.

The Evaluative Process

Applicants to MBA programs should understand how they will be evaluated during the admissions process. In general, presentation, academic profile, professional work experience, and personal qualities will be the four areas in which each applicant will be evaluated. Admissions officers generally evaluate the factors influencing applicants' educational and professional decisions and the corresponding outcomes. Admissions committees do not spend a lot of time evaluating the labels that tend to categorize applicants into special groups. For instance, candidates for admission often assume that the quality of the undergraduate institution that they attended will affect the outcome of their application. A common misconception is that applicants with undergraduate degrees from Ivy League schools are always more desirable candidates for business schools. In fact, the undergraduate institution one attended may not be a significant variable in the admissions process at some business schools.

Applicants are evaluated as individuals. The environment in which they have studied or worked is relevant only when it is given meaning in the context of their life experiences. How the culture of a campus or workplace has influenced one's success is interesting and important to the admissions committee's ability to fully evaluate an application. Therefore, applicants who provide only factual information about their academic and professional profile miss the opportunity to present the most compelling and distinguishing characteristics of their candidacy.

The MBA degree is not a professional license that is required to practice management. Therefore, people of all ages are known to pursue the degree. Older applicants (32 years old and up) often fear that because they are atypical to the traditional graduate school student profile they will be less desirable to business schools. On the contrary, older students offer professional experience, maturity, and perspective that are highly valued in the classroom. The admissions committee does expect older applicants to have highly developed reasons for pursuing the MBA at this stage of their lives. Post-MBA goals are expected to be clearer and more defined than those of their younger counterparts.

Applicants have much more control of the admissions process than they realize. Prospective students determine all of the information that is presented in the application forms, essays, and interviews. They even get to select the people who will serve as references to support their candidacy. The only aspect of the process that an applicant does not control is the competition; that is, who else applies for admission. It is the competition that will determine the threshold between admissibility and acceptance.

Presentation is obviously one of the most important factors in admission. Four other areas are evaluated during the evaluative process. They include academic profile, GMAT score, professional work experience, and personal qualities.

Academic Profile

Business schools seek students who can survive the demands of a rigorous program, and the best way to show your intellectual strength is to demonstrate strong classroom achievement and high aptitude. Your ability to excel as an undergraduate student is directly related to your ability to succeed in a graduate program.

Your undergraduate specialization will have little effect on admission to business school. It is not necessary to take undergraduate courses in business administration because most MBA programs offer or require a core curriculum of basic business courses as part of the graduate degree. However, it is advisable to have basic skills in economics, calculus, and statistics in preparation for graduate study in business.

The Graduate Management Admission Test (GMAT)

Most business schools require applicants to submit the results of their Graduate Management Admission Test (GMAT). The importance of the GMAT in admissions will vary depending on the school. Minimum score requirements do not exist at some business schools. Test scores are certainly not the sole criterion for admission to an MBA program, but to one degree or another, most business schools use them as part of the admissions process.

The GMAT uses a standardized set of criteria to evaluate the basic skills of college graduates, which allows graduate schools to compare and judge applicants. The test measures general verbal and math skills so that schools can assess an applicant's ability to succeed in a graduate-level environment.

- Quantitative section—this section measures mathematical skills and the ability to solve quantitative problems.
- Qualitative section—this section focuses on verbal skills, the ability to understand and interpret written materials, and basic English writing skills.
- Scoring—total scores range from 200 to 800, but scores lower than 300 and higher than 700 are unusual.
- Analytical Writing Assessment—this section requires test-takers to write two essays that measure the ability to think critically and communicate complex ideas through writing in English. This section is scored on a scale of 0 to 6, but scores lower than 2 and higher than 5 are unusual.
- Taking the test—until recently, the GMAT was available throughout the world as a paper-and-pencil test. Since October 1997, however, the GMAT has been available in North America and many other parts of the world only as a computer-adaptive test. (Research has shown that scores from the paper-based test are comparable to those from the computer-based test.) The GMAT is offered by appointment many times each month at hundreds of locations worldwide. It is possible to schedule a test within a few days of taking it, but popular dates, such as weekends, fill up quickly. You should call the test center as early as possible to increase your chances of getting your preferred date. For more information, contact GMAT, Educational Testing Service, P.O. Box 6103, Princeton, NJ 08541-6103 (telephone: 609-771-7330; fax: 609-883-4349; Web site: http://www.gmat.org).

Professional Work Experience

Admission to selective, international business programs usually requires full-time, professional work experience prior to enrollment. While professional work experience is needed to provide a context for the interpretation and use of classroom material, students must also be able to contribute to class discussions and group projects in meaningful ways. Career success is the most effective way to prove your potential for leadership in a managerial capacity.

Personal Qualities

MBA programs want to enroll students who can lead people. The admissions committee seeks men and women who will eventually be responsible for the management of entire organizations. Leadership is one of the basic ingredients for success. Communication skills, initiative, and motivation can become the most important aspects of the admissions process. Personal qualities set the tone for the entire review of an application. It is the one part of an application that is most likely to distinguish a candidate in a compelling way.

The Interview

The interview is the one aspect of the admissions process that varies the most among schools. Some schools, like the Kellogg School at Northwestern, require all applicants to interview prior to admission. Others, such as Stanford's Graduate School of Business, do not interview any of their applicants. Most schools, like Wharton at the University of Pennsylvania, leave the decision to interview up to the applicant. It is one more part of the admissions process that the applicant can control. For those prospective students who do have the interview available to them, it is a highly recommended experience. It is also a great opportunity to take initiative in the admissions process.

If an interview is part of the admissions process, it can be an invaluable opportunity for the applicant to show the strengths and leadership qualities that most business schools are seeking in MBA candidates. The most effective and interesting interviews are those discussions that go beyond the information provided in the written application. Too often interviews remain focused solely on the candidate's resume. The meeting becomes nothing more than a redundancy in the evaluation of a candidacy. It is up to both the interviewer and the applicant to create an exchange of information that solicits useful information that will help the admissions committee understand the context of the choices that the applicant has made throughout life.

In Summary

Categories and labels do not play as significant a role in the process as most applicants assume. Prospective MBA students should take a high level of initiative during the admissions process, while exercising discretion when determining what information is most important for a school to properly evaluate their candidacy.

These guidelines are the first step in understanding the nature of the admissions process from the perspective of an admissions officer. It is vital to recognize that each school has its own policies and procedures in admissions. Careful research and communication will, fundamentally, have the greatest impact on the success of an MBA application.

GradAdvantage: Applying to Business School Just Got a Whole Lot Easier!

Thanks to a cutting-edge service developed by Educational Testing Service, Peterson's, and leading business schools, you can apply to business schools on line. This service, GradAdvantage, allows you to apply to as many schools as you wish, enter most of your personal data only once, and have your application arrive at the admission office with your official Graduate Management Admission Test (GMAT) score attached. To help you identify schools that accept online GradAdvantage applications, the GradAdvantage logo has been placed next to the school's name.

The GradAdvantage Alliance

GradAdvantage brings together the major players in the business school admission arena to develop an online service to make applying to schools easier for you.

Educational Testing Service (ETS), a private, nonprofit corporation headquartered in Princeton, New Jersey, develops, delivers, scores, and manages score reports for "high-stakes" tests. These tests include the SAT, GRE, GMAT, and TOEFL, to name only a few. For millions of American and international students, the results of these tests have helped determine which institution they attend. ETS is moving to simplify the admission process for students and institutions alike and to promote its mission of education access for all.

Peterson's, America's largest education information/communications company, is a leading educational database publisher, the valued publishing partner of admission officers and academic deans at every level, a publisher of books and CDs, and a developer of online services designed to facilitate access to education and career guidance. Peterson's is known globally for the accuracy and breadth of its data first in print, then in software, and now on line with Peterson's Web site, petersons.com. The company is a division of Thomson Learning, Inc. (the education arm of TTC), a multibillion-dollar publishing and information company. At the foundation of most of Peterson's activities is the country's largest education data collection, covering kindergarten through executive training and adult education, which is revised and expanded annually.

The GradAdvantage Web Site: GradAdvantage.org

At GradAdvantage.org, you will find a wealth of information about business schools, financing options, and GMAT registration, as well as a variety of ways to prepare for taking the GMAT and applying to business schools. Click on "New and Registered User Login" to begin applying to business schools on line.

When you click on "Program Search & Financial Aid," you'll find yourself with two choices: links to mba.petersons.com and to MBAExplorer, the Graduate Management Admission Council (GMAC) Web site.

Click on mba.petersons.com and search for the right business school for you by name, concentration, location, average GMAT score, and enrollment size, or do keyword searches to look for particular MBA programs in Peterson's searchable database. Numerous In-Depth Descriptions include detailed program and faculty information. You can join Peterson's MBA discussion board, purchase books and CDs, and find information about distance-learning MBA programs, GMAT test preparation, and financing your education. You can even buy GMAT test-prep products at Peterson's online store.

The Benefits to You

With GradAdvantage, you can complete your applications on line, save your work, and return to it later. You no longer have to find a typewriter or try to match application spacing with your computer printer. It's easy to revise answers or essays as you rethink the questions during the application process before you submit your application.

GradAdvantage will save you lots of time. You can enter most information into multiple applications at the same time. If, for example, you are applying to four schools, as you fill in information for one school, the information automatically cross-fills into the data fields in the other three applications.

You no longer have to worry about express mail or courier services to have your application arrive at the admission offices on time. On average, most MBA applicants have jobs and work on their applications late at night the week or two before applications are due. Now all you have to do is click on "Submit" and your application is on its way to the institutions you designate.

You can pay by credit card to further save you time. Just enter your American Express, MasterCard, or Visa credit card number, and your application will arrive with its electronic payment attached.

Your official GMAT scores will arrive already integrated into your application. ETS has worked closely with Peterson's to guarantee the security of score data. All you have to do is provide information used to ensure that score matching is accurate.

You can work on your application anywhere as long as you can access the Web. All you have to do is remember the URL for the GradAdvantage service: GradAdvantage.org. The platform- and browser-independent service works with both PCs and Macs and with both Microsoft and Netscape Web browsers.

You can also track the progress of each of your applications using GradAdvantage's "Application Manager" interface.

The Future of GradAdvantage

In the future, you will be able to find a host of new functionalities on GradAdvantage to further streamline the application process. To make your life even easier, on GradAdvantage.org you will be able to:

- Have your college transcripts and letters of recommendation electronically authenticated and sent to designated institutions
- Access international transcript-evaluation services
- Learn more about financing your MBA through a variety of financial aid services
- Discover more in-depth information about business schools you should consider in online MBA events

Welcome to the new world of electronic applications! ETS, Peterson's, and GradAdvantage's participating institutions encourage you to save time and money and apply on line using GradAdvantage (http://www.GradAdvantage.org).

Paying for Your MBA

by Bart Astor

Now that you've made a commitment to getting your MBA, the next question is likely to be "How will I pay for it?"

The first thing you will have to decide is whether you will go to school part-time and continue working full-time or go to school full-time while working part-time. About two thirds of MBA students get their degree while they continue working at a full-time job. And though it will take you longer to get your

Types of Financial Aid

Gift Aid (money you do not have to pay back)
Individual grants, scholarships, and fellowships (may be merit-based or need-based)
Sources: business schools, foundations, private companies, community groups

Tuition waivers (awarded by individual business schools)

Company employee educational benefits (a personnel benefit for employees of many large and some small companies. Generally covers only a portion of tuition)

Federal grants (very limited and based on need)

State grants (also very limited)

Self-Help Aid (money you must earn or pay back later)
Work Programs
Federal Work-Study (need-based and awarded by business school)—Source: federal government

Teaching Assistantships—Source: business school

Resident Assistantships—Source: business school

Research Assistantships—Source: business school

Loans
Federal Perkins Loan (need-based, lender is business school)

Federal Subsidized Stafford Loan (need-based, lender is a bank, savings & loan, etc.)

Federal Unsubsidized Stafford Loan (non-need-based)

Federal Direct Loan (similar to Stafford Loans; lender is the federal government)

Private loan programs (e.g., MBA Loans; Business Access Loans, etc.)

Tuition payment plans (private or school-based)

MBA this way, the costs are more manageable and the amount of money you'll need to borrow is kept to a minimum. Furthermore, if you work for one of the many companies that offers either full or partial tuition reimbursement to their employees, this will further reduce your expenses.

Some MBA programs, on the other hand, are only available to full-time students. If you go to one of these schools, it will be impossible for you to work full-time. Therefore, you will have to make some other arrangement to pay the expenses of your schooling and to find the necessary resources for your living expenses.

But it is not only possible to find the resources you will need, it is also quite likely. Unfortunately, though, for most full-time MBA students, most of the money is available through student loans. And the amount of debt an MBA student takes on can be quite sizable.

Most MBA students feel it is worthwhile to take on some debt to pay for a degree that they believe will offer them considerable career advancement. In that sense, then, they view these costs as an investment in their earnings potential. And the numbers have consistently supported this claim. According to a 1998 salary survey conducted by the National Association of Colleges and Employers, average starting salary offers for holders of an MBA is 25 to 40 percent higher than for non-MBA graduates. Looking only at earnings potential, getting an MBA has certainly proved to be an excellent financial investment. And, of course, this does not even consider career opportunities or quality-of-life issues.

The Costs

Now let's look at the cost of getting your MBA degree. All students are required to pay some sort of tuition or fee to go to school (in some state-supported business schools, this may be called a "fee"). This can be a total amount for the year, regardless of the number of credits you take, or a per-credit amount. The annual tuition for a full-time student can range from $2000 or $4000 at some of the state-supported schools to well over $20,000 at some of the higher-priced business schools. In addition, some business schools require all students to pay fees for such things as student activities, health services, etc., much like you may have paid as an undergraduate.

Most business school students pay a little more for books and supplies than they did as an undergraduate. While the amount will differ at each school, the annual amount for a full-time student ranges from $500 to $800. If you will need a computer, that will naturally add a considerable amount to the total cost. Many business schools make computers available to their students, so be sure to check with the school before you purchase a computer. These are the two obvious additional expense categories you will face when you go to business school, and they are generally referred to as "direct costs."

In addition, however, there are other "indirect costs" you face that you may not think of as business school expenses. Rent and living expenses are certainly the largest two. But indirect costs also include transportation to and from school, travel from your home town to the city in which the school is located, personal expenses, and other expenses if appropriate (such as car loan payments and insurance, child care, summer tuition, medical expenses, etc.). If you are going to business school straight out of college, you may not have had to personally pay for these expenses before (although your parents certainly did). If you have been paying them already, then you know you may need to cut back on the amount you spend on some discretionary items, such as clothing and entertainment. As a student, you will have to budget your expenses as carefully as you budget your time. Most business schools can tell you what the average cost of living will be in the area and may offer subsidized housing or, at the very least, a housing office to help you find a place to live.

Financial Aid

Once you've calculated the total amount it will cost you to go to business school, you may find that the amount of income you receive won't be enough. That's where financial aid comes in. If you received financial aid as an undergraduate, then you have a head start: at least you understand some of the basics.

But financial aid is quite different for graduate students. For one, all graduate students are considered independent for federal financial aid. That means your parents are not required to assist you financially (although if they are willing and able, that would certainly help). Secondly, there is very little grant and scholarship money available to graduate students. The bulk of your expenses will be paid either from money you've already saved, money you will earn while you are attending school, or money you will borrow and pay back out of future earnings.

Most business school students take on considerable debt to pay their expenses since there are very few alternatives. If you're going to school part-time and working full-time, your salary in combination with your savings may be enough to avoid having to borrow very much. However, you may still decide it is better to borrow through a government-subsidized loan program than take the necessary funds out of your savings or current income.

If you've decided to go to school full-time, you will probably need to borrow, although many business schools offer fellowships and teaching and research assistantships to some students. Some of these positions and awards may be awarded based on your previous academic and employment record (merit-based) and some based on how much you need it. While everyone will say they need assistance, the definition of need for financial aid is up to the school, not you.

Applying for Financial Aid

When you apply for financial aid, you are generally applying for both merit-based and need-based aid. The application process has changed significantly in the past year or two, so even if you applied for financial aid as an undergraduate, you should pay close attention to the process described here

To qualify for federal aid, most of which will be in the form of loans, every student is required to complete the Free Application for Federal Student Aid (FAFSA), either in paper or electronic form (FAFSA on the Web). The paper form is available in both business school and undergraduate school financial aid offices (your local community college or even your local high school guidance office will have them available as well). You can access FAFSA on the Web at http://www.fafsa.ed.gov.

Soon after January 1, 2001 (for students entering in fall 2001 or spring 2002), you should complete the FAFSA, which asks about your 2000 income and current assets. The application cannot be completed until after January 1, 2001.

Many business schools require that you complete a different application, the Financial Aid PROFILE, to begin the financial aid process and require the form to be completed much earlier, in October or November of 2000. The paper version of the PROFILE information is available from the same places as the FAFSA. It is also available on the Internet at http://www.collegeboard.org.

You can also call a toll-free number (800-778-6888) and "register" your information, including which business schools you are applying to. You must also pay a registration fee of $6 plus $16 per school. A few weeks later you will receive your customized application form containing all the questions the particular schools you are applying to require answers to.

You may have to complete both the FAFSA and the PROFILE. The way to find out is check the PROFILE registration packet for the list of schools that require the PROFILE. You should also read the business school literature or ask someone in the business school financial aid office to be certain.

A few business schools will have their own aid application or use yet a third form, called Need Access. This information will be noted in the brochures they send to you, so be sure to check the literature. Make certain you know if there are deadlines when applying for financial aid. Applying after a deadline can hurt your chances of qualifying for aid.

Once you have submitted an application, the business schools you have designated will receive an output showing an amount you can afford to contribute to your education, calculated based on your income and assets. This number is called the "Expected Family Contribution" (EFC). The EFC from the federal form is the official amount that determines whether you will qualify for federal aid. If this amount is less than the total cost of attendance of the MBA program, you have demonstrated need and will qualify for aid, again, usually low-cost, government-subsidized loans. The output from the PROFILE will give the school an estimate of your federal eligibility and will also give an expected contribution based on additional criteria you provided. This contribution will be used by those schools using the PROFILE to award their own funds. And, like the federal EFC, if your contribution is less than the total cost of the school, you qualify for need-based aid.

But even if your family contribution is higher than the cost of the school, you may still qualify for aid. For one, this EFC is based on your previous year's income, which will likely change significantly when you go to school full-time. You can appeal to the business school financial aid office and ask them to recalculate your need based on the amount you will have when you go to school, rather than on your previous year's income. Secondly, there are government, institutional, and private loans available to students regardless of whether they have demonstrated need (such as the Federal Unsubsidized Stafford Loan, MBA Loans, and Business Access Loans). Although these loans ultimately cost borrowers more since they are not subsidized, they are still sources of income for you to pay your business school costs.

Your Credit History

Since most MBA students have to borrow to pay for their education, making sure you qualify for a loan is critical. For the most part that means your credit record must be free of default or delinquency. You can check your credit history with one or more of the following three major credit bureaus and clean up any adverse credit that appears. You can look up the local numbers in your phone book or call the numbers below:

Equifax
P.O. Box 10596
Atlanta, GA 30348-5496
800-997-2493
Web site: http://www.equifax.com

Trans Union Corporation
P.O. Box 2000
Chester, PA 19022
800-888-4213
Web site: http://www.transunion.com

Experian
P.O. Box 2104
Allen, TX 75013-2104
888-397-3742
Web site: http://www.experian.com/consumer/

Debt Management

Although the limits on borrowing from federal and private programs are quite high, you will want to make sure you are not borrowing more than you will later be able to repay. Use Table 2 below to estimate your MBA school loan monthly payments. Then by estimating your income and the total amount you'll need to borrow for your MBA education, you can use Table 3 to determine whether your loan payments will be affordable.

TABLE 2: ESTIMATED LOAN REPAYMENT SCHEDULE
Monthly Payments for Every $1000 Borrowed

Rate	5 years	10 years	15 years	20 years	25 years
5%	$18.87	$10.61	$ 7.91	$ 6.60	$ 5.85
8%	20.28	12.13	9.56	8.36	7.72
9%	20.76	12.67	10.14	9.00	8.39
10%	21.74	13.77	10.75	9.65	9.09
12%	22.24	14.35	12.00	11.01	10.53
14%	23.27	15.53	13.32	12.44	12.04

You can use this table to estimate your monthly payments on a loan for any of the five repayment periods (5, 10, 15, 20, and 25 years). The amounts listed are the monthly payments for a $1000 loan for each of the interest rates. To estimate your monthly payment, choose the closest interest rate and multiply the amount of the payment listed by the total amount of your loan and then divide by 1,000. For example, for a total loan of $15,000 at 9% to be paid back over 10 years, multiply $12.67 times 15,000 (190,050) divided by 1,000. This yields $190.05 per month.

TABLE 3: DEBT MANAGEMENT GUIDE

Total Outstanding Loan	Years in Repayment	Monthly Payment	Suggested Minimum Monthly Income
$10,000	10	$126	$ 840
20,000	10	253	1,687
30,000	10	380	2,533
40,000	10	506	3,373
50,000	10	633	4,220
20,000	20	179	1,193
30,000	20	270	1,800
40,000	20	360	2,400
50,000	20	450	3,000

International Students

Costs of U.S. business schools for international students are the same as or slightly higher than for U.S. residents. Your Certificate of Eligibility for a student visa will require that you prove that you have sufficient funds for the entire MBA program. United States government aid for international students is virtually nonexistent, and very few business schools make any resources available. You should make sure you have obtained the necessary funds from your own resources, including from your own government.

Additional Information

For more information about financing your education, refer to the personnel office at the company for whom you work and the business school financial aid office. You can also obtain additional information on possible sources of aid from the following Peterson's publications.

• *Grants for Graduate and Postdoctoral Study*
• *Financing Graduate School*

For information about loan options, you can contact the following organizations:

The Access Group
P.O. Box 7430
Wilmington, DE 19803-0430
800-282-1550

ConSern Loans for Education
205 Van Buren Street, Suite 200
Herndon, VA 22070
800-SOS-LOAN

The Education Resources Institute (TERI)
330 Stuart Street, Suite 500
Boston, MA 02116
800-255-TERI

MBA Loans
P.O. Box 59030
Panama City, FL 32412-9030
888-440-4MBA

New England Education Loan Marketing Corporation (Nellie Mae)
50 Braintree Hill Park, Suite 300
Braintree, MA 02184
800-367-8848

USA Group
P.O. Box 7039
Indianapolis, IN 46207-7039
877-USA-GROU

Sallie Mae College Answer Service
11600 Sallie Mae Drive
Reston, VA 20193
800-239-4269

U.S. Department of Education
Office of Student Financial Assistance
Regional Office Building 3
7th and D Streets, SW
Washington, DC 20202
800-433-3243 (Federal Student Aid Information Center)

Going Abroad for Your MBA

by Richard Edelstein

Students are increasingly going abroad to obtain their MBA education. Why? Individuals seeking a management career must prepare themselves to function in international contexts on a global scale. Studying abroad is one of the most effective ways of obtaining knowledge and developing skills that respond to these new demands. In large measure, this reflects the changing nature of business where the globalization of markets and companies is forcing a rethinking of the types of education and experience necessary to pursue a successful career as a manager.

International mobility, cross-cultural skills, and foreign language proficiency have all increased in value to employers. Technical skills remain critical, but international experience and knowledge are increasingly appreciated by companies. Choosing to pursue your MBA education abroad is an excellent way to acquire knowledge and skills that are necessary for the global economy.

This trend of attaching increased value to international experience is most noteworthy in transnational companies that have operations and management responsibility distributed in numerous countries. Hewlett Packard, for example, reorganized its personal computer division and made Grenoble, France, the location of its top management team. This reflects the reality that most of HP's personal computer sales are outside the U.S. It also may be related to the rapid growth of communications technologies that allow companies to communicate easily with management teams irrespective of geographic location.

Another indication of increased demand for managers with specialized international experience and skills is the growth in importance of the so-called "transitional economies" like China, India, Russia, Brazil, and Indonesia. Many firms want to develop joint ventures or start-up operations in these countries but are constrained by lack of personnel who can manage in such different cultural and linguistic contexts. Demand for MBAs who have experience in these countries and have language skills is very high.

Career Paths in Different Countries

The MBA degree is not recognized as the ideal qualification for a business career in all countries. Its acceptance in the U.S. and by many multinational firms as a primary qualification for future managers sometimes leaves the impression of a universal acceptance worldwide. In fact, the majority of countries outside the U.S. have significantly different educational and career paths for their managers. For example, the most common educational qualification for future managers in many countries is an engineering degree. This is the case in Germany, Switzerland, the Scandinavian countries, and many countries in the developing world, such as India and China. Even in France, Belgium, Italy, and Spain, engineering training is a major source of recruitment of managers. Another educational qualification for a business career quite common in other nations is a law degree.

The lack of universal acceptance of the MBA does not imply that it may not be an excellent way to launch your own career. In a world full of different educational philosophies, cultural values, and economic systems, there cannot be a single form of preparation for becoming a manager. The MBA is still the most common qualification for business managers. Nevertheless, it is important to keep in mind that it may not be met with the same degree of acceptance in all countries. This is important to consider if you have particular aspirations to work in countries where it may not have the same recognition that it does in the U.S. It also is useful information for anyone who plans to work in a multinational enterprise where professional colleagues may come from any country. The MBA is only one way to acquire the knowledge and skills necessary to manage a company.

Markets, Hierarchies, and Prestige

Not all MBAs are created equal! Given the choice between going to Harvard or a correspondence course from an unknown institution for your MBA, the answer is obvious. In reality the choice is never that clear, and many individuals must make compromises between where they would like to pursue their degree and where they have a serious chance of being accepted. This is true whether you are applying to institutions in your home country or abroad.

If you want to pursue an MBA abroad, it is important to do some research about the schools you are considering. Learn about their status in the prestige hierarchy and the types of companies that are likely to employ their graduates. Going to a school of high prestige is not always the best choice, depending upon your own abilities and professional goals. Students applying to American schools from abroad frequently assume that the only schools worth attending are the most elite and prestigious schools with international reputations. In fact, the range of schools offering high-quality MBA programs is much larger in number than the top twenty institutions that make it on the *BusinessWeek* survey. Reputation and prestige are important factors to consider in planning your MBA education, but keep in mind that prestige alone does not assure you of an education that is best suited to your individual needs. This is true abroad as well as at home.

Making the Decision to Study Abroad

Why go abroad for your MBA when you can just as easily enter an American program that has an international dimension built into the program? The answer for many people is that they want and need a more intensive experience abroad that allows them to acquire foreign language and cultural skills and to build professional networks that cannot be obtained through an American program. Traveling and becoming a "citizen of the world" are also appealing, although more romantic, reasons for some students. Before you decide to pursue your MBA in another country, however, it is important to consider a few key points.

Personal Goals and Foreign Language Ability

Personal attributes will define whether or not study abroad for an MBA is the right choice for you. Have you already had extensive experiences abroad? Previous experience may make the added value of doing your graduate business studies abroad less significant. But, what about building on the skills you acquired in your previous experience and developing high levels of language competence and specialized knowledge in the country or region where you would like to study?

Studying abroad is clearly a more intensive international experience than anything you could pursue in the U.S. In the end, it is this intensity that distinguishes getting the MBA abroad from getting it at home. If you are doubtful about the need for this intensity of international experience, then you may want to consider staying in the U.S. and entering a program that includes an international emphasis of less intensive character.

Foreign language proficiency can be a defining criterion in deciding whether or not to consider studying abroad. Although there are an increasing number of MBA programs abroad that are taught in English, many of them require some level of proficiency in foreign languages. The United Kingdom, Australia, New Zealand, Hong Kong, and Singapore have MBA programs in English, but most of them are oriented toward a national employment market. Many of the European English-language MBA programs outside these countries are targeted to foreign nationals and actually include few students from the home country where the school is located. The "flagship" management studies program of the school is often taught in the local language and limits admission to students who can demonstrate language proficiency.

A distinction should be made between international MBA programs taught in English and national MBA programs taught in the local language. Each has its market niche and serves different needs. A good example of an institution offering both types of programs is SDA Bocconi in Italy. Bocconi created an English-language international MBA that responds to the needs of students who seek to develop an international career. However, the traditional Bocconi degree program is taught in Italian, is more prestigious, and has an international reputation for training managers, especially for the Italian market. In considering which program to apply to, an American needs to consider both foreign language proficiency and personal needs and goals.

Structure and Cost of MBA Programs Abroad

MBA programs outside the U.S. are frequently structured differently. In Europe, for example, some MBAs are only one year long. Typically this involves 12 months of intensive study with no summer break. In the U.K., the MBA is most often two years in length, following a more American model. Whatever the length of the program, it may have somewhat different course requirements and curricula. Frequently, teaching approaches are also different. Sometimes they are closely tied to the patterns of university education in the host country. Increasing attention is being paid to teaching skills related to teamwork and working in cross-national groups.

Another point to consider is the tendency of off-shore MBA programs to be more application-oriented and less tied to the research faculty. MBA programs in other countries vary significantly in the emphasis placed on teaching versus research as a major focus of faculty reward systems.

The cost of MBA programs outside the U.S. is generally quite competitive, even when you consider the added cost of airfare. Tuition costs for graduate education in the U.S., especially at elite private universities, are among the highest in the world. All in all, you may find the cost of an MBA abroad surprisingly reasonable by comparison. Keep in mind that there is significant variation among schools, so the generalization that programs are less costly has its exceptions.

Cultural Adjustment

Cultural adjustment is a factor that should be considered in applying to an overseas program. Unless you have spent an extended period of time in the country you plan to study in, you are likely to be affected by this change. Reactions to living in another culture vary considerably depending on the person and on the culture. There is always a greater difference in lifestyle, values, and professional life than expected, no matter which country you go to. As noted earlier, acquiring the skill to work and learn in more than one culture is a primary reason for wanting to study abroad in the first place. Still, do not assume this is an easy adjustment or task. It takes a serious commitment to self-improvement and a willingness to be open to entirely new situations to succeed in cross-cultural settings.

Building Professional Networks

One of the keys to a career as a successful manager is the capacity to develop networks of individuals whom you can work with and learn from. These professional networks may be within your present employer, with colleagues in other firms, and, increasingly, in other nations. By choosing to pursue an MBA abroad, you should recognize that you will build different professional networks than you would in the U.S. Alumni associations that are a fixture in American universities and business schools tend to be less well developed in other countries, but where you went to school is often a critical factor in what job opportunities you may have in the future.

In some cases, Americans have some advantages when it comes to applying to MBA programs abroad. Since the MBA is essentially an American invention, one of the most significant ways of gaining credibility for an MBA program outside the

U.S. is to begin attracting American students who might otherwise attend an American institution. Although poorly qualified candidates will not be admitted no matter what their national origin, all things being equal, Americans sometimes have an advantage in the selection process at some schools. This may not continue to be true for very long as more Americans begin enrolling in foreign programs. But for the time being, many MBA programs abroad are interested in recruiting Americans.

Finding the Right Program

Where Do You Want to Work?

One obvious reason for choosing to study for an MBA abroad is to increase your chances of obtaining employment outside the U.S. If you have your heart set on living and working in France or Indonesia, then it makes sense to seriously consider attending an institution in that country. This is especially true if you select a school and program linked to the national employment market. While global markets are certainly a long-term trend, national employment markets are still the norm for most firms, and doing your studies in a particular country will generally enhance your chances of obtaining employment in that country.

This is accomplished in two ways. First, your degree and school/university will be more easily recognized in that national employment market. Second, the school may have placement services, alumni relations, and other ways of connecting graduates into the labor market for management positions. Even if you elect to work for a transnational firm, there are significant benefits to being able to access this national network of business professionals.

Which Country and What Language?

MBA-type degrees are more prevalent in countries like England, France, Belgium, and the Netherlands than in other European countries. In these countries there may be numerous institutions from which to choose. In the remaining European countries, choices are much more limited and may require significant foreign language skill. One way to increase your options is to consider enrolling in a university program in business and economics. In France, for example, there are many degree programs in universities that offer business degrees that are targeted to the national and European job market, often based in an Institut d'Administration des Enterprises or IAE. University-based options are also available in other European countries but in virtually all cases require host country language fluency and a willingness to be one of few foreigners in a program.

In Latin America, the options are numerous if one includes university-based programs in business and economics. Pure MBA-type options are much more limited and often involve only one or two institutions in the country. Still, Latin American countries have created a number of good business schools that offer MBA programs that have international standing. Gatulio Vargas in São Paulo, ESAN in Peru, IESE in Venezuela, and INCAE in Costa Rica/Nicaragua are examples of institutions that offer programs that may interest prospective American students.

In Asia and the Pacific Rim, options are more limited. This is partly due to distinctly different educational systems that reflect different recruitment practices for managers. Japan is well known for a manager recruitment structure that relies on in-company training rather than professional education in the university. This pattern can also be found in other Asian countries, though to a somewhat lesser degree. In Japan, the language barrier can be significant since very few Japanese universities have programs targeted to foreigners taught in English. Combined with the cultural tendency toward in-company education, this makes Japan especially difficult for foreigners to penetrate. One noteworthy exception is the IUJ, the International University of Japan, which does offer an MBA program in English.

Hong Kong, Australia, and New Zealand have MBA programs that are open to Americans and are taught in English. Most are university-based business schools that follow either the American or British models of university education. The Hong Kong programs tend to be focused on special needs of Hong Kong and China. The Australian programs are frequently oriented toward doing business in Asia, especially Southeast Asia. Schools in the Philippines, Indonesia, Malaysia, Singapore, and Thailand may also be of interest to those interested in working in one of the countries that are developing dynamic economies in the midst of transition and rapid growth. The English-based MBA courses are very limited, however, and careful research needs to be done to ensure that the program is up to international standards. The Asian Institute of Management in Manila and Singapore National University are two programs that have gained international credibility in the last decade.

Foreign language requirements are often significant, even at schools that teach in English. Since the study of foreign languages is more commonplace outside the U.S., you should be prepared to study a foreign language even if you are entering an English language–based program. Be sure to inform yourself about foreign language requirements prior to entering a program as this may be an important consideration in preparing for your experience.

Evaluating Quality

In evaluating the quality of a school you need to go deeper than the promotional piece typically sent to prospective students. Are the school and degree accredited by the Ministry of Education in the country where the degree is offered? Too often the school may be licensed by the department of commerce or industry as a business, but its degrees are not recognized by the country's university-level education authorities, usually in the Ministry of Education. If a program is not recognized as academically legitimate in the country where it operates, it is doubtful that its graduates have credibility in the international employment market. The embassy or consulate of the country in which an institution is located can also provide useful information.

A close, common-sense look at faculty qualifications is also important. Are faculty members qualified to teach at the advanced level of an MBA-type program by virtue of their education and experience? How many are full-time permanent faculty? How many are part-time or "contact only" faculty? How many faculty members hold a doctoral degree in the field in which they teach? Be cautious of schools that say they have no full-time faculty because they prefer part-time instructors. This can be a ploy to avoid paying qualified people who require higher levels of salary. Have faculty members done any research or published any articles? Do they have corporate or professional experience related to the course work?

It is always useful to speak with some graduates of the school prior to making a commitment to enroll. Schools will usually provide you with the names of several graduates whom you can contact about their experiences with the school. You can usually get a sense of the quality of the experience they had by asking questions about what the classes were like, how good were the faculty, and what kind of placement services the school provided. If it is possible to make a visit to the school and meet with current students, this is even better.

Financing Your International MBA

As noted earlier, tuition costs abroad are rarely more than those found among leading MBA programs in the U.S. That is not saying much since costs in the U.S. can be as high as $25,000 annually for tuition alone! Still, you are likely to find that MBA programs abroad compare favorably to most cost/benefit analyses. This is especially true for some of the less well known programs that may be outside major capital cities. In instances where the program is less than two years in length, this may also be a factor in considering costs.

Where you may run into problems is in obtaining federally subsidized loans such as are commonly available through many American university financial aid offices. Most of these loans have some restrictions regarding the status of institutions and programs that you can attend and still be eligible for the loan program. Although some loan programs have been more flexible than others in allowing foreign study, you should check with your bank or lender regarding the regulations that apply.

Some institutions have their own loan programs and scholarships to help defray the costs of tuition. Less common are work opportunities, since MBA programs generally require a full-time commitment. Still, it is worth asking the school about the potential for working on campus or assisting in research or consulting activity.

Other major costs to consider are round-trip air travel and the costs of living abroad. In some countries, especially in Europe and Asia, the cost of housing and food will be significantly higher than in the U.S., depending on the specific location.

Studying and Living Abroad

Living abroad requires adaptability, an adventurous spirit, and a willingness to adjust to living in another culture. You will acquire a set of skills and experiences that will contribute to your preparation as a manager and a deeper understanding of your strengths, weaknesses, and values, even if you already have some cross-cultural experience.

Cross-cultural experience is always a challenge and an opportunity. It is always useful to do a lot of reading on the country and region you will live in prior to your departure. Knowing something about the history, geography, and culture is critical to learning how to adapt in your new culture. There are many good reference books available at bookstores and libraries that can help prepare you for your experience abroad. You might also explore the Internet for "chat" groups sharing information on studying and working abroad.

There are often support networks that you can take advantage of when you are abroad. Although you may have a desire to "go native" and avoid anything that is American while abroad, you may want to consider joining groups such as churches, university clubs, and alumni groups abroad as a means to enlarge your support system while living abroad.

The important thing to remember is that not only are you adapting to the rigors of pursuing an MBA program, but also that you will need energy and effort to deal with the adaptation required of the foreign visitor. But, again, this is precisely the reason for pursuing this path in the first place.

International Programs at U.S. Schools

If you are still having doubts as to whether or not studying for an MBA abroad is the right choice for you, you can consider attending one of many MBA programs in the U.S. that incorporate some international experience into the curriculum. This is clearly a less intensive option and cannot compare with living abroad but may be preferable depending upon your needs and goals.

This guide includes information on a range of MBA programs that have international dimensions built into their programs. Several schools that offer a master's degree in international business (requiring significant language and cultural knowledge) rather than a classic MBA are the Lauder Program at the University of Pennsylvania (a joint program of the Wharton School and the College of Arts and Science) and the MIBS programs at the University of South Carolina, Columbia University, and Thunderbird, The American Graduate School of International Management, in Glendale, Arizona.

An increasing number of MBA programs include an international track or international fellows program that requires advanced foreign language competence and an internship abroad. Institutions offering programs with this type of option include UCLA, University of Washington, University of Michigan, University of Chicago, University of Pittsburgh, University of Memphis, Indiana University, San Diego State University, University of Hawaii, and the University of Southern California.

A few MBA programs include joint-degree or double-degree options in conjunction with a business school in another country. The University of Texas at Austin has several double-degree programs that allow a student to pursue a Texas MBA and with a year abroad also acquire a French, German, or Mexican degree at the same time. NYU's Stern School has one of the most extensive exchange programs with foreign business schools of any U.S. university, and a significant percentage of MBA students take advantage of this option. Also available are joint-degree programs that combine an MBA with a master's or doctoral degree in an area specialty such as Asian studies or Eastern European studies. The University of Pittsburgh, the

University of Michigan, and the University of California at Berkeley are among the business schools offering this type of option.

Many other MBA programs are including international internships and group projects outside the U.S. as a major component of their programs. The University of Pennsylvania's Wharton School has integrated a project abroad into the MBA program for a portion of its students. The same is true for the University of California at Berkeley and the University of Michigan.

Does the trend in American MBA programs to integrate international experience for some students make the case for going abroad for the MBA any less compelling? Probably not. An MBA program in the U.S. can never match the intense learning experience of spending a year or two in another country studying business. Moreover, the personal and professional contacts you make while abroad allow you to create an international network that cannot be easily duplicated when studying in most American MBA programs. In the end, you need to weigh the benefits of gaining an intense international experience along with other factors, such as the quality and prestige of the institutions you are considering.

International Students Considering U.S. Programs

Recent years have seen significant increases in the percentages of foreign student enrollments in MBA programs. It is estimated that 20 percent of all business students studying in American colleges and universities are from countries other than the U.S. It is clear that obtaining an MBA in the U.S. is very attractive for many students. Why?

American higher education continues to have a level of quality that places it among the best in the world. It is also attractive because the MBA was invented in the U.S., and obtaining the "original and genuine article" still has some prestige, especially as viewed from abroad. Perhaps an even more important, but less recognized, factor is that studying in the U.S. gives foreign students many of the same international skills and networks that are described above. This can be a tremendous advantage for students who aspire to work for companies with global markets and international management teams.

Will MBA study in the U.S. continue to be as attractive in the future and will it be for the same reasons? The answer to these questions is less clear for several reasons. As business education becomes more of a global commodity and schools outside the U.S. improve the quality of their programs, it may be less appealing to pay the high cost of studying in the U.S. Second, distance learning capabilities may result in greater possibilities for undertaking MBA education without coming to the U.S. Questions of quality and intensity of interaction with other students and faculty make this option less attractive for now, but this is already changing at some U.S. institutions. Finally, MBA education may increasingly be offered by joint ventures or partnerships among and between institutions in several countries, using faculty and facilities in numerous locations. This internationalization of the postgraduate education market will, if it actually happens, alter many of the structures and processes that are currently considered "normal" for most universities and management education centers.

Returning to School for Your MBA

by Barbara B. Reinhold, Ed.D., Director, Career Development, Smith College

Some decisions can be made and implemented quickly—you can often choose a new car, a new place to live, or even a new relationship rather impetuously and have it work out just fine. For the returning student, however, the process of deciding, applying to school, and then earning an MBA is seldom simple. It has to be done with a great deal of forethought and awareness of the considerable sacrifice required.

The good news about being a more mature student is that you'll probably get much more out of it, because there is more of you to take to the classroom—more experience, better judgment, clearer goals, and more appreciation for learning. The bad news is that your life will be more "squeezed" than it would have been before you took on all of life's responsibilities, particularly balancing work and family. In general, however, later is often better than sooner when it comes to getting an MBA.

For mature women and men alike, there are many things to consider before upending your life to pursue an MBA. First, be sure you really need one. It is silly to waste your time and resources being "retooled" in an MBA program if your career goals could be accomplished just as easily by taking targeted courses, getting more training and supervision through your employer, or using your connections to enter a different field or organization and move up. If you are trying to determine if an MBA is really the key to where you want to go, find ways to network with people whose lives and career goals are similar to yours. You might discover that a variety of routes could lead you to your desired goal.

It's essential that you make your own decision about whether and where to apply, using a blend of logic and intuition. Though an MBA requires strong quantitative skills, you'll also need good organizational, decision-making, and communication skills. For returning students, success in an MBA program is often due more to life and work experience than technical knowledge alone. You have more information, more common sense, and more self-awareness at your disposal than you did as an undergraduate student. Use these assets along with your intuition in deciding whether this is really right for you now.

TEN TIPS FOR RETURNING STUDENTS

DECIDING

1. Be sure an MBA is the best route to where you're going—don't embark on a trip until your destination is clear.
2. Make your own decision, using a blend of logic and intuition.
3. Be a discerning customer; ask hard questions about which programs best meet your specific needs.

ARRIVING

4. Learn to market yourself; don't launch the campaign until you're ready.
5. Be sure your support system is in order—at home and at work.
6. Review your skills—technical, quantitative, written, and oral. If you're not really ready, take an extra year to polish those skills.
7. Measure your confidence level—if it's weak, consider counseling to learn how to manage your anxieties and self-doubts.
8. Get your life in good shape before you begin—paying attention to nutrition, exercise, relationships, and all the other things you'll need to sustain you.

THRIVING

9. Ascertain your most effective learning style (from your own self-assessment or more formalized measurements, such as the Learning Styles Inventory or the Myers-Briggs Type Inventory) and design routines and study regimens that best fit your style.
10. Find a group of friends/colleagues right away; collaboration is the key to succeeding and staying healthy through one of the most demanding experiences you'll ever have.

It's important also to be an informed and demanding customer on the front end of the process. Be sure to ask hard questions about how well a school is prepared to respond to the particular concerns you might have, such as being a minority candidate, having children, needing special accommodations of some type, or being in your forties or fifties. The ball will be in their court later; in the first half of the game, however, be aggressive about getting the information you need. For more mature students, the philosophy, resources, and services of the school can be much more important than ranking or reputation.

The application stage is also a great time to practice your marketing skills. This may be the first of many times when you'll have to convince someone of your worth. For returning students this is often frightening. Some have been out of the job market for awhile, while others either want to change careers or are feeling stuck at a career plateau. Any of these situations is likely to leave you feeling less than competitive. This is a good time to figure out what you really have to offer to a particular school and to adjust to the notion of lifelong self-advocacy.

As you begin the difficult task of self-assessment, be honest about your strengths and weaknesses. If your technical, quantitative, or communication competencies are not what they should be in order for you to begin course work in a confident frame of mind, spend a year or so coming up to speed in these areas. Although you'll be taking accounting, statistics, and computer courses as part of the core requirements, it's best to be comfortable with these basic disciplines before you enroll.

Once enrolled, you can do two things to make your life easier. First, take an honest look at your own learning style. Try to determine which methods work best for you; use methods that fit your personality—outlines, memorizing, listening to tapes, discussing concepts with other people, etc. Be proactive and establish a routine. As a returning student with many other life responsibilities, you'll need to take a different approach to studying than you did in undergraduate school.

You'll also find that connecting with classmates is a critical part of doing well. You may be assigned to project teams, but it's a good idea to seek out your own support group as well. Join study groups and relevant student organizations, even though it may seem you can't spare the time. In business school, as in business itself, collaboration and networking are everything!

Becoming a student again is a great adventure—earning an MBA will tax you, test you, stretch you, and reward you. But only you can know if it's right for you. When you applied to college as a high school student, you thought you had all the answers. What's different now is that, although you still don't have all the answers, you probably know much more than you think.

This table includes the names and locations of colleges, universities, and other institutions offering MBA and other master s-level business programs. Schools appear in geographical sequence by U.S. state or territory or by country and then alphabetically by school name. Specific degree information is detailed within the profile for each school. Refer to the page number in the table for the school s profile. If a school submitted incomplete data, one or more columns opposite the school name may be blank.

	Page Number	Accreditation (AA=AACSB, AC=ACBSP)	Minimum GMAT Score	Minimum Undergraduate GPA	Minimum TOEFL Score	TUITION (R) State Resident (NR) Non-Resident	Financial Aid	Distance Learning
ALABAMA								
Alabama Agricultural and Mechanical University, School of Business	83		425	2.8	550	$150 per credit hour (R); $415 per credit hour (NR)		
Auburn University, College of Business	83	AA	578	3.2	550, 213 (CAT)	$3050 per year (R); $9150 per year (NR); $126 per credit (R); $378 per credit (NR)	•	•
Auburn University Montgomery, School of Business	84	AA	500	3	500	$120 per credit hour (R); $360 per credit hour (NR)	•	
Birmingham-Southern College, Program in Public and Private Management	84	AC		3		$9240 per year; $1320 per course	•	
Jacksonville State University, College of Commerce and Business Administration	84	AA	450	3.17	550	$112 per credit hour (R); $224 per credit hour (NR)		
Samford University, School of Business	85	AA	562	3	550	$365 per credit	•	
Spring Hill College, Division of Business and Management	85				550, 213 (CAT)	$255 per credit		
Troy State University, Sorrell College of Business and Commerce	86	AC						•
Troy State University Dothan, School of Business	86	AC	500	3	550	$120 per credit hour (R); $240 per credit hour (NR)		
Troy State University Montgomery, Division of Business	86					$350 per course (R); $350 per course (NR)	•	•
The University of Alabama, The Manderson Graduate School of Business	87	AA	606	3.4	575	$2872 per year (R); $7722 per year (NR)	•	
The University of Alabama at Birmingham, Graduate School of Management	88	AA	530	3	550	$104 per credit (R); $208 per credit (NR)		
The University of Alabama in Huntsville, College of Administrative Science	88	AA	496	3	550	$3880 per year (R); $7956 per year (NR); $182 per credit hour (R); $371 per credit hour (NR)	•	
University of Mobile, School of Business	89		445	3.08	550	$172 per credit hour		
University of North Alabama, College of Business	89	AC	475	3	550	$107 per hour (R); $107 per hour (NR)		•
University of South Alabama, College of Business	89	AA	501	3.06	525	$116 per credit (R); $232 per credit (NR)		•
ALASKA								
Alaska Pacific University, Business Administration Department	90							
University of Alaska Anchorage, College of Business and Public Policy	90	AA	545	3	550	$3335 per year (R); $6197 per year (NR); $167 per credit (R); $326 per credit (NR)	•	
University of Alaska Fairbanks, School of Management	91	AA	550	3.32	550	$3006 per year (R); $5868 per year (NR); $167 per credit hour (R); $326 per credit hour (NR)	•	

	Page Number	Accreditation (AA=AACSB, AC=ACBSP)	Minimum GMAT Score	Minimum Undergraduate GPA	Minimum TOEFL Score	TUITION (R) State Resident (NR) Non-Resident	Financial Aid	Distance Learning
ARIZONA								
Arizona State University, College of Business	91	AA	606	3.3	580, 237 (CAT)	$7344 per year (R); $15,800 per year (NR)	•	
Arizona State University West, School of Management	92	AA	580	3.2	600, 250 (CAT)	$119 per credit hour (R); $405 per credit hour (NR)	•	•
Grand Canyon University, College of Business	92	AC		3.04	550	$320 per credit hour	•	
Northern Arizona University, College of Business Administration	93	AA	535	3.23	550	$5103 per year (R); $12,065 per year (NR)	•	
Thunderbird, The American Graduate School of International Management, Graduate Programs	93	AA	608	3.4	600	$25,300 per year	•	•
The University of Arizona, Karl Eller Graduate School of Management	94	AA						
University of Phoenix, Business Administration and Management Programs	94							•
Western International University, Graduate Programs in Business	95			3	550	$7200 per year; $240 per credit	•	
ARKANSAS								
Arkansas State University, College of Business	95	AA	510		550, 213 (CAT)	$2976 per year (R); $7488 per year (NR); $124 per credit hour (R); $312 per credit hour (NR)		
Henderson State University, School of Business Administration	96	AA						
University of Arkansas, College of Business Administration	96	AA	575	3.4	550, 213 (CAT)	$8829 per year (R); $18,063 per year (NR); $201 per credit hour (R); $444 per credit hour (NR)	•	•
University of Arkansas at Little Rock, College of Business Administration	97	AA	525	3.2	550, 213 (CAT)	$3804 per year (R); $8088 per year (NR); $159 per credit (R); $337 per credit (NR)		•
University of Central Arkansas, College of Business Administration	97	AA	476	3.13	550	$145 per credit hour (R); $298 per credit hour (NR)		
CALIFORNIA								
American InterContinental University, Program in International Business	98				550	$28,240 per year		
Antioch Southern California/Los Angeles, Program in Organizational Management	98				600, 250 (CAT)	$10,800 per year; $355 per unit	•	
Antioch Southern California/Santa Barbara, Program in Organizational Management	98							•
Armstrong University, Graduate School of Business Administration	99							
Azusa Pacific University, School of Business and Management	99		450	3	550	$415 per unit	•	•

	Page Number	Accreditation (AA=AACSB, AC=ACBSP)	Minimum GMAT Score	Minimum Undergraduate GPA	Minimum TOEFL Score	TUITION (R) State Resident (NR) Non-Resident	Financial Aid	Distance Learning
California Baptist University, Graduate Program in Business Administration	99	AC						
California Lutheran University, School of Business	100		525		570, 230 (CAT)	$7290 per year; $405 per credit	•	
California National University for Advanced Studies, College of Business Administration	100			3.3	550	$255 per unit (R)		•
California Polytechnic State University, San Luis Obispo, College of Business	101	AA	551	3.11	550	$2145 per year (R); $10,017 per year (NR)	•	
California State Polytechnic University, Pomona, College of Business Administration	101	AA	537	3.19	580	$184 per unit (NR)		
California State University, Bakersfield, School of Business and Public Administration	102	AA	525	3	550	$1887 per year (R); $9233 per year (NR)		
California State University, Chico, College of Business	102	AA	530	3.3	550	$2140 per year (R); $6000 per year (NR)		
California State University, Dominguez Hills, School of Management	103	AC	510	3.2	550	$1821 per year (R); $4773 per year (NR); $95 per unit (R); $246 per unit (NR)		•
California State University, Fresno, Sid Craig School of Business	103	AA	580	3.4	550	$1834 per year (R); $7738 per year (NR); $246 per unit (NR)	•	
California State University, Fullerton, College of Business and Economics	104	AA	538	3.22	500	$246 per unit (NR)	•	
California State University, Hayward, School of Business and Economics	104	AA	534	3.14	550, 217 (CAT)	$2400 per year (R); $7596 per year (NR); $377 per course (R); $1033 per course (NR)	•	
California State University, Long Beach, College of Business Administration	105	AA	540	3.2	550	$246 per unit (NR)		
California State University, Los Angeles, School of Business and Economics	105	AA	580	3.3	550	$2400 per year (R); $10,000 per year (NR); $363 per quarter (R); $585 per quarter (NR)	•	
California State University, Northridge, College of Business Administration and Economics	106	AA	540	3.2	550	$1970 per year (R); $6398 per year (NR); $652 per semester (R); $246 per unit (NR)	•	
California State University, Sacramento, School of Business Administration	106	AA	530	3.2	550	$7000 per year (NR); $246 per unit (NR)		
California State University, San Bernardino, College of Business and Public Administration	107	AA	502	3.2	550, 213 (CAT)	$1923 per year (R); $7933 per year (NR); $164 per unit (NR)	•	•
California State University, San Marcos, Program in Business Administration	107		540	3.2	550, 213 (CAT)	$8500 per year (R); $14,500 per year (NR)	•	•
California State University, Stanislaus, School of Business Administration	108		500	2.87	550	$1738 per year (R); $8049 per year (NR); $246 per credit (NR)		•
Chapman University, School of Business and Economics	108	AA	524	3.14	550	$14,520 per year; $605 per credit	•	
Claremont Graduate University, Peter F. Drucker Graduate School of Management	109	AA	610	3.2	600, 250 (CAT)	$25,194 per year; $940 per credit	•	
Coleman College, Graduate Program in Information Systems	110							

The table includes the names and locations of colleges, universities, and other institutions offering MBA and other master s-level business programs. Schools appear in geographical sequence by U.S. state or territory or by country and then alphabetically by school name. Specific degree information is detailed within the profile for each school. Refer to the page number in the table for the school s profile. If a school submitted incomplete data, one or more columns opposite the school name may be blank.

	Page Number	Accreditation (AA=AACSB, AC=ACBSP)	Minimum GMAT Score	Minimum Undergraduate GPA	Minimum TOEFL Score	TUITION (R) State Resident (NR) Non-Resident	Financial Aid	Distance Learning
		ADMISSION REQUIREMENTS					OPTION	
College of Notre Dame, Department of Business Administration	110							
Concordia University, Programs in Business Administration	110			3.1	525, 195 (CAT)	$9000 per year; $450 per semester hour		
Dominican University of California, School of Business and International Studies	110				550, 213 (CAT)	$13,676 per year; $556 per unit	•	
Fielding Institute, Program in Organizational Design and Effectiveness	111					$12,750 per year	•	•
Fresno Pacific University, Graduate School	111							
Golden Gate University, School of Business	111				550	$1500 per course		•
Holy Names College, Department of Business	112			3	550, 213 (CAT)	$425 per unit		
Hope International University, Program in Business Administration	112			3.4	550	$375 per credit	•	•
Humboldt State University, School of Business and Economics	113		521	3.2	550	$1996 per year (R); $1996 per year (NR); $1330 per year (R); $1330 per year (NR)		
John F. Kennedy University, School of Management	113				550	$317 per unit		
La Sierra University, School of Business and Management	114		500	3.2		$384 per unit		
Lincoln University, Business Administration Program	114			3.1		$5534 per year; $265 per semester hour	•	
Loyola Marymount University, College of Business Administration	114	AA	570	3.2	600	$17,795 per year; $650 per unit	•	
Monterey Institute of International Studies, Fisher Graduate School of International Business	115		530	3.31	550	$18,750 per year; $785 per credit		
National University, School of Business and Technology	115				550	$8385 per year; $925 per course	•	•
Naval Postgraduate School, Department of Systems Management	116	AA			540	$10,100 per year (R); $10,100 per year (NR)		•
Pacific States University, College of Business	117			2.5	450	$210 per credit	•	
Pepperdine University, The Graziado School of Business and Management	117	AA	605	3.2	550	$23,980 per year; $795 per credit	•	
Saint Mary's College of California, Graduate Business Programs	118		559	3.13	550	$387 per unit	•	
San Diego State University, Graduate School of Business	118	AA	600	3.16	570	$2046 per year (R); $8192 per year (NR)	•	
San Francisco State University, College of Business	119	AA	551	3.2	550, 213 (CAT)	$661 per semester (R); $2137 per semester (NR)		

This table includes the names and locations of colleges, universities, and other institutions offering MBA and other master s-level business programs. Schools appear in geographical sequence by U.S. state or territory or by country and then alphabetically by school name. Specific degree information is detailed within the profile for each school. Refer to the page number in the table for the school s profile. If a school submitted incomplete data, one or more columns opposite the school name may be blank.

	Page Number	Accreditation (AA=AACSB, AC=ACBSP)	Minimum GMAT Score	Minimum Undergraduate GPA	Minimum TOEFL Score	TUITION (R) State Resident (NR) Non-Resident	Financial Aid	Distance Learning
			ADMISSION REQUIREMENTS				OPTION	

This table includes the names and locations of colleges, universities, and other institutions offering MBA and other master s-level business programs. Schools appear in geographical sequence by U.S. state or territory or by country and then alphabetically by school name. Specific degree information is detailed within the profile for each school. Refer to the page number in the table for the school s profile. If a school submitted incomplete data, one or more columns opposite the school name may be blank.

School	Page Number	Accreditation	Min GMAT	Min GPA	Min TOEFL	Tuition	Financial Aid	Distance Learning
San Jose State University, College of Business	119	AA	560	3.25	550, 213 (CAT)	$2017 per year (R); $8377 per year (NR); $330 per unit (R); $330 per unit (NR)	•	•
Santa Clara University, Leavey School of Business	120	AA	650	3.22	600, 250 (CAT)	$499 per unit	•	
Sonoma State University, School of Business and Economics	121		514	3.34	550	$9382 per year (NR); $246 per unit (NR)	•	
Stanford University, Graduate School of Business	121	AA	725	3.56		$27,243 per year		
United States International University, College of Business Administration	121		463	2.97	550	$1480 per course	•	•
University of California, Berkeley, Haas School of Business	122	AA	674	3.5	570, 230 (CAT)	$10,459 per year (R); $20,263 per year (NR); $10,014 per semester (R); $10,014 per semester (NR)	•	
University of California, Davis, Graduate School of Management	123	AA	675	3.2	600, 250 (CAT)	$10,483 per year (R); $19,867 per year (NR)	•	
University of California, Irvine, Graduate School of Management	123	AA	664	3.37	600, 250 (CAT)	$9384 per year (NR)	•	
University of California, Los Angeles, John E. Anderson Graduate School of Management	124	AA	690	3.5		$11,580 per year (R); $20,964 per year (NR)	•	
University of California, Riverside, A. Gary Anderson Graduate School of Management	125		585	3.3	550, 213 (CAT)	$9957 per year (R); $19,761 per year (NR); $3605 per quarter (NR)	•	
University of Judaism, David Lieber School of Graduate Studies	125			3.5	560, 213 (CAT)	$15,505 per year; $625 per credit	•	
University of La Verne, School of Business and Economics	126		520		550	$360 per credit	•	
University of Redlands, Alfred North Whitehead College for Lifelong Learning	126							
University of San Diego, School of Business Administration	127	AA	580	3.23	580, 237 (CAT)	$12,150 per year; $675 per credit	•	
University of San Francisco, McLaren School of Business	127	AA	555	3.15	600	$17,004 per year; $701 per unit		•
University of Southern California, Marshall School of Business	128	AA	650	3.3	600	$23,958 per year		•
University of the Pacific, Eberhardt School of Business	129	AA	530	3.2	550	$20,860 per year; $1836 per course	•	
Woodbury University, School of Business and Management	129		527	3.4	550	$595 per credit		
COLORADO								
College for Financial Planning, Program in Financial Planning	130			2.85		$600 per course		•
Colorado State University, College of Business	130	AA	599	3.2	565			•

	Page Number	Accreditation (AA=AACSB, AC=ACBSP)	Minimum GMAT Score	Minimum Undergraduate GPA	Minimum TOEFL Score	TUITION (R) State Resident (NR) Non-Resident	Financial Aid	Distance Learning
		ADMISSION REQUIREMENTS					**OPTION**	
Colorado Technical University, Program in Management	131			3.5	550	$6528 per year; $265 per credit hour		•
ISIM University, Program in Business Administration	131			3.2		$1245 per course		•
Jones International University, Program in Business Communication	132			3.25	550			•
Regis University, School for Professional Studies	132		500		550, 213 (CAT)	$366 per credit hour		•
University of Colorado at Boulder, Graduate School of Business Administration	132	AA	640	3.23	580	$4502 per year (R); $16,170 per year (NR); $215 per credit hour (R); $862 per credit hour (NR)	•	•
University of Colorado at Colorado Springs, Graduate School of Business Administration	133	AA	545	3.08	550	$2904 per year (R); $10,104 per year (NR); $121 per credit (R); $421 per credit (NR)	•	•
University of Colorado at Denver, Graduate School of Business Administration	134	AA	560	3.04	525	$3844 per year (R); $13,286 per year (NR); $230 per credit (R); $796 per credit (NR)	•	
University of Denver, Daniels College of Business	134	AA	565	3.22	550	$20,606 per year; $557 per quarter hour	•	•
University of Southern Colorado, School of Business	135		500	3	550	$2057 per year (R); $8697 per year (NR); $113 per semester hour (R); $445 per semester hour (NR)	•	
CONNECTICUT								
Albertus Magnus College, Program in Management	136			3	550	$9450 per year; $1050 per course		
Central Connecticut State University, School of Business	136		517	3.23	213 (CAT)	$195 per credit hour (R); $195 per credit hour (NR)		
Eastern Connecticut State University, School of Education and Professional Studies/Graduate Division	137			3.07	550	$2370 per year (R); $5112 per year (NR); $165 per credit hour (R); $165 per credit hour (NR)	•	
Fairfield University, School of Business	137	AA	530	3.2	550	$480 per credit hour		
Quinnipiac University, School of Business	137	AA	460	3.04	575, 233 (CAT)	$430 per credit		
Rensselaer at Hartford, Lally School of Management and Technology	138			3	570	$585 per credit hour	•	•
Sacred Heart University, College of Business	138		507	3.02	525	$415 per credit		•
Southern Connecticut State University, School of Business	139		495	2.8	550	$6370 per year (R); $10,513 per year (NR); $239 per credit (R)		
University of Bridgeport, School of Business	139	AC	545	3.06	575	$380 per credit	•	
University of Connecticut, School of Business Administration	140	AA	631	3.43	575	$6140 per year (R); $14,320 per year (NR); $405 per credit (R); $405 per credit (NR)	•	
University of Hartford, Barney School of Business and Public Administration	141		480	2.5	550	$380 per credit hour		

This table includes the names and locations of colleges, universities, and other institutions offering MBA and other master s-level business programs. Schools appear in geographical sequence by U.S. state or territory or by country and then alphabetically by school name. Specific degree information is detailed within the profile for each school. Refer to the page number in the table for the school s profile. If a school submitted incomplete data, one or more columns opposite the school name may be blank.

This table includes the names and locations of colleges, universities, and other institutions offering MBA and other master s-level business programs. Schools appear in geographical sequence by U.S. state or territory or by country and then alphabetically by school name. Specific degree information is detailed within the profile for each school. Refer to the page number in the table for the school s profile. If a school submitted incomplete data, one or more columns opposite the school name may be blank.

School	Page Number	Accreditation (AA=AACSB, AC=ACBSP)	Minimum GMAT Score	Minimum Undergraduate GPA	Minimum TOEFL Score	TUITION (R) State Resident (NR) Non-Resident	Financial Aid	Distance Learning
University of New Haven, School of Business	141							
Western Connecticut State University, Ancell School of Business and Public Administration	141		520	3.1	550	$178 per credit (R); $178 per credit (NR)		
Yale University, Yale School of Management	142	AA	689	3.47	600, 250 (CAT)	$26,505 per year	•	
DELAWARE								
Delaware State University, Program in Business Administration	143			3	550	$156 per credit (R); $365 per credit (NR)		
Goldey-Beacom College, MBA Program	143		450		525	$371 per credit		
University of Delaware, College of Business and Economics	144	AA	610	3.1	585	$5771 per year (R); $12,991 per year (NR); $307 per credit hour (R); $708 per credit hour (NR)		
Wilmington College, Division of Business	144			3	500	$249 per credit		
DISTRICT OF COLUMBIA								
American University, Kogod School of Business	145	AA	580	3.3	600, 250 (CAT)	$19,407 per year; $721 per credit		
The Catholic University of America, Department of Economics and Business	145		500	3	580	$19,900 per year; $682 per credit hour	•	
Georgetown University, Georgetown MBA, McDonough School of Business	146	AA	641	3.32	600	$25,880 per year	•	
The George Washington University, School of Business and Public Management	146	AA	599	3.21	550	$702 per credit		•
Howard University, School of Business	147	AA	445	3.02	500	$11,370 per year	•	
Southeastern University, College of Graduate Studies	148				550	$250 per credit		
Strayer University, Graduate School	148							•
University of the District of Columbia, School of Business and Public Administration	148		450	2.7	550	$3874 per year (R); $6232 per year (NR); $198 per credit hour (R); $329 per credit hour (NR)		
FLORIDA								
American InterContinental University, Program in International Business	149					$3690 per term		
Barry University, School of Business	149		455	3.42	550, 213 (CAT)	$11,040 per year; $460 per credit	•	
Embry-Riddle Aeronautical University, Department of Business Administration	150	AC	517	3.03	550, 213 (CAT)	$8430 per year; $455 per credit hour	•	

			ADMISSION REQUIREMENTS			OPTION	
This table includes the names and locations of colleges, universities, and other institutions offering MBA and other master s-level business programs. Schools appear in geographical sequence by U.S. state or territory or by country and then alphabetically by school name. Specific degree information is detailed within the profile for each school. Refer to the page number in the table for the school s profile. If a school submitted incomplete data, one or more columns opposite the school name may be blank.	Page Number	Accreditation (AA=AACSB, AC=ACBSP)	Minimum GMAT Score	Minimum Undergraduate GPA	Minimum TOEFL Score	TUITION (R) State Resident (NR) Non-Resident	Financial Aid	Distance Learning
Embry-Riddle Aeronautical University, Extended Campus, Department of Business Administration	150	AC			550, 213 (CAT)	$5712 per year; $238 per credit hour		•
Florida Atlantic University, College of Business	151	AA	536	3.28	600, 250 (CAT)	$148 per credit (R); $509 per credit (NR)		
Florida Institute of Technology, School of Business	151		477	3.34	550, 213 (CAT)	$575 per credit hour		
Florida International University, College of Business Administration	152	AA	530	3.4	500, 173 (CAT)		•	
Florida Metropolitan University–Orlando College, North, Division of Business Administration	152							•
Florida Metropolitan University–Tampa College, Division of Business and Computer Information Sciences	152			2.8	550	$10,000 per year; $292 per credit hour		•
Florida Southern College, Department of Business and Economics	153		590	3.2	550	$290 per credit hour		
Florida State University, College of Business	153	AA	570	3.36	600, 250 (CAT)	$6278 per year (R); $21,790 per year (NR); $146 per credit hour (R); $507 per credit hour (NR)	•	
Jacksonville University, Davis College of Business	154							
Lynn University, School of Business	154							
Nova Southeastern University, Wayne Huizenga Graduate School of Business and Entrepreneurship	154		480	3	550	$10,416 per year; $434 per credit		•
Palm Beach Atlantic College, Rinker School of Business	155		474	3	550	$280 per credit hour		
Rollins College, Crummer Graduate School of Business	155	AA	590	3.2	580	$680 per credit		
Saint Leo University, Graduate Business Studies	156		475	3.25	600	$4050 per year; $225 per credit		
St. Thomas University, Department of Business Administration	156		500	3.2	550, 213 (CAT)	$8190 per year; $455 per credit	•	
Schiller International University, MBA Programs	157				550	$16,270 per year; $1050 per course	•	•
Stetson University, School of Business Administration	157	AC	540	2.9	550	$390 per credit hour		
University of Central Florida, College of Business Administration	158	AA	548	3.3	575, 233 (CAT)	$146 per hour (R); $507 per hour (NR)		
University of Florida, College of Business Administration	158	AA	616	3.14	600, 250 (CAT)	$3750 per year (R); $13,130 per year (NR)	•	•
University of Miami, School of Business Administration	159	AA	620	3.1	550, 213 (CAT)	$899 per credit		
University of North Florida, College of Business Administration	160	AA	522	3.13	550	$2675 per year (R); $9169 per year (NR); $149 per credit hour (R); $509 per credit hour (NR)	•	

This table includes the names and locations of colleges, universities, and other institutions offering MBA and other master s-level business programs. Schools appear in geographical sequence by U.S. state or territory or by country and then alphabetically by school name. Specific degree information is detailed within the profile for each school. Refer to the page number in the table for the school s profile. If a school submitted incomplete data, one or more columns opposite the school name may be blank.

School	Page Number	Accreditation (AA=AACSB, AC=ACBSP)	Minimum GMAT Score	Minimum Undergraduate GPA	Minimum TOEFL Score	TUITION (R) State Resident (NR) Non-Resident	Financial Aid	Distance Learning
University of Sarasota, College of Business	160			3.6	500	$361 per credit hour		•
University of South Florida, College of Business Administration	161	AA	554	3.3	550, 213 (CAT)	$2665 per year (R); $9158 per year (NR); $148 per credit hour (R); $509 per credit hour (NR)	•	
The University of Tampa, College of Business	161	AA	520	3.3	550		•	
University of West Florida, College of Business	162	AA	513	3.35	500, 173 (CAT)	$3582 per year (R); $11,828 per year (NR); $149 per credit (R); $493 per credit (NR)	•	
Webber College, Webber College Graduate School	162		507	3.37	500	$5130 per year; $285 per credit		
GEORGIA								
Albany State University, School of Business	163	AC	450	2.5	550	$94 per credit hour (R); $282 per credit hour (NR)	•	•
American InterContinental University, Program in International Business	163							
Augusta State University, College of Business Administration	163	AA	520	2.94	500, 173 (CAT)	$282 per course (R); $1128 per course (NR)	•	
Berry College, Campbell School of Business	164		494	3.25	550	$385 per credit hour	•	
Brenau University, School of Business and Mass Communication	164				500	$228 per credit hour	•	•
Clark Atlanta University, School of Business Administration	165	AA	415	2.89	500	$13,437 per year; $25,000 per degree program	•	
Columbus State University, College of Business	165				550			
Emory University, Roberto C. Goizueta Business School	166	AA	645	3.4	600	$24,000 per year; $15,999 per year	•	
Georgia College and State University, School of Business	166	AC	521	3.21	500	$2450 per year (R); $7346 per year (NR); $380 per course (R); $1196 per course (NR)	•	
Georgia Institute of Technology, Dupree College of Management	167	AA	635	3.2	600, 250 (CAT)	$4902 per year (R); $17,202 per year (NR)		
Georgia Southern University, College of Business Administration	167	AA	486	3.05	500	$289 per course (R); $1039 per course (NR)		•
Georgia Southwestern State University, School of Business	168			3	550	$1808 per year (R); $7232 per year (NR); $91 per credit hour (R); $363 per credit hour (NR)		•
Georgia State University, J. Mack Robinson College of Business	168	AA	580	3.1	580, 240 (CAT)	$390 per course (R); $1554 per course (NR)		
Kennesaw State University, Michael J. Coles College of Business	169	AA	522	3	550	$91 per credit hour (R); $272 per credit hour (NR)		•
LaGrange College, Division of Business Administration and Economics	169	AC		3.5		$8820 per year; $245 per quarter hour		

	Page Number	Accreditation (AA=AACSB, AC=ACBSP)	Minimum GMAT Score	Minimum Undergraduate GPA	Minimum TOEFL Score	TUITION (R) State Resident (NR) Non-Resident	Financial Aid	Distance Learning
This table includes the names and locations of colleges, universities, and other institutions offering MBA and other master s-level business programs. Schools appear in geographical sequence by U.S. state or territory or by country and then alphabetically by school name. Specific degree information is detailed within the profile for each school. Refer to the page number in the table for the school s profile. If a school submitted incomplete data, one or more columns opposite the school name may be blank.								
Mercer University, Stetson School of Business and Economics	170		471	3.1	550	$1059 per course		
Oglethorpe University, Division of Business Administration	170				500	$1380 per course		
Southern Polytechnic State University, School of Management	171	AC			550	$2496 per year (R); $6836 per year (NR); $91 per credit hour (R); $272 per credit hour (NR)	•	
State University of West Georgia, General MBA	171	AA	520	3.21	550, 213 (CAT)	$2428 per year (R); $8428 per year (NR); $105 per hour (R); $377 per hour (NR)	•	
University of Georgia, Terry College of Business	172	AA	644	3.2	600, 250 (CAT)	$3916 per year (R); $12,604 per year (NR)	•	
Valdosta State University, College of Business Administration	172	AA	530	3.15	550, 213 (CAT)	$2652 per year (R); $9162 per year (NR); $273 semester (R); $1089 per semester (NR)	•	
HAWAII								
Chaminade University of Honolulu, Program in Business Administration	173							
Hawaii Pacific University, Division of Business Administration	173		475	3.1	550	$8920 per year; $372 per credit	•	
University of Hawaii at Manoa, College of Business Administration	174	AA	570	3.52	500	$4091 per year (R); $9979 per year (NR); $168 per credit (R); $415 per credit (NR)	•	•
IDAHO								
Boise State University, College of Business and Economics	174	AA	556	3.18	587, 240 (CAT)	$3500 per year (R); $9100 per year (NR); $157 per credit (R); $157 per credit (NR)	•	
Idaho State University, College of Business	175	AA	520	3.17	550, 213 (CAT)	$3384 per year (R); $9624 per year (NR); $147 per credit hour (R); $237 per credit hour (NR)	•	
University of Idaho, College of Business and Economics	175	AA	540	3.5	550	$2676 per year (R); $8676 per year (NR); $107 per credit (R); $206 per credit (NR)	•	
ILLINOIS								
Aurora University, Dunham School of Business and Professional Studies	176			3	550	$427 per semester hour		•
Benedictine University, Graduate Programs	176		500	2.75	600	$350 per credit		
Bradley University, Foster College of Business Administration	177	AA	607	3.41	500	$13,895 per year; $377 per semester hour	•	
Columbia College Chicago, Department of Management	177				550	$392 per credit hour	•	
DePaul University, Charles H. Kellstadt Graduate School of Business	177	AA	570	3.2	550	$2148 per course	•	
Dominican University, Graduate School of Business	178	AC	550	3.2	550	$14,250 per year; $1435 per course	•	

	Page Number	Accreditation (AA=AACSB, AC=ACBSP)	Minimum GMAT Score	Minimum Undergraduate GPA	Minimum TOEFL Score	TUITION (R) State Resident (NR) Non-Resident	Financial Aid	Distance Learning
Eastern Illinois University, Lumpkin College of Business and Applied Sciences	179	AA						
Governors State University, College of Business and Public Administration	179	AC	450	3.2	550	$98 per credit (R); $294 per credit (NR)	•	
Illinois Institute of Technology, Stuart Graduate School of Business	179	AA	547	3	550	$21,600 per year; $1800 per course	•	
Illinois State University, College of Business	180	AA	549	3.34	600	$2707 per year (R); $6495 per year (NR); $150 per credit hour (R); $361 per credit hour (NR)		
Keller Graduate School of Management, Graduate Program	181			2.9	550	$1300 per course		•
The Lake Forest Graduate School of Management, Graduate Programs	181					$1850 per course	•	
Lewis University, College of Business	181		510	3	550	$470 per credit hour		
Loyola University Chicago, Graduate School of Business	182	AA	540	3.2	550	$26,349 per year; $2186 per course		
National-Louis University, College of Management and Business	183							•
North Central College, Department of Business	183		470	2.85	600, 250 (CAT)	$1464 per course	•	
Northeastern Illinois University, College of Business and Management	183		556	3.27	550	$2700 per year (R); $7480 per year (NR); $100 per credit (R); $299 per credit (NR)	•	•
Northern Illinois University, College of Business	184	AA	539	3.12	550, 213 (CAT)	$305 per credit hour (R); $305 per credit hour (NR)		
North Park University, Center for Management Education	184		540	3.2	600	$1100 per course	•	
Northwestern University, Kellogg Graduate School of Management	185	AA	700	3.45	600	$28,677 per year; $2692 per unit	•	
Olivet Nazarene University, Department of Business	185			3	550	$414 per credit		
Quincy University, Division of Business	186		535		600	$1170 per course		
Rockford College, Program in Business Administration	186		500	3.2	550	$7235 per year; $400 per credit hour	•	
Roosevelt University, Walter E. Heller College of Business Administration	187		470	3	550	$8714 per year; $473 per credit hour	•	
Saint Xavier University, Graham School of Management	187					$8660 per year; $475 per credit		
Southern Illinois University Carbondale, College of Business and Administration	188	AA						
Southern Illinois University Edwardsville, School of Business	188	AA	512	3.5	550	$1448 per year (R); $2658 per year (NR)	•	

This table includes the names and locations of colleges, universities, and other institutions offering MBA and other master s-level business programs. Schools appear in geographical sequence by U.S. state or territory or by country and then alphabetically by school name. Specific degree information is detailed within the profile for each school. Refer to the page number in the table for the school s profile. If a school submitted incomplete data, one or more columns opposite the school name may be blank.

		ADMISSION REQUIREMENTS				OPTION	
This table includes the names and locations of colleges, universities, and other institutions offering MBA and other master s-level business programs. Schools appear in geographical sequence by U.S. state or territory or by country and then alphabetically by school name. Specific degree information is detailed within the profile for each school. Refer to the page number in the table for the school s profile. If a school submitted incomplete data, one or more columns opposite the school name may be blank.	Page Number	Accreditation (AA=AACSB, AC=ACBSP)	Minimum GMAT Score	Minimum Undergraduate GPA	Minimum TOEFL Score	TUITION (R) State Resident (NR) Non-Resident	Financial Aid	Distance Learning
University of Chicago, Graduate School of Business	189	AA	690	3.43	600	$28,555 per year; $2802 per course	•	
University of Illinois at Chicago, College of Business Administration/MBA Programs	189	AA	570	3.3	570	$10,416 per year (R); $17,460 per year (NR); $1818 per course (R); $2992 per course (NR)		
University of Illinois at Springfield, College of Business and Management	190		400	3.13	550	$105 per credit hour (R); $314 per credit hour (NR)	•	•
University of Illinois at Urbana–Champaign, College of Commerce and Business Administration	191	AA	619	3.4	550	$11,846 per year (R); $19,204 per year (NR)		
University of St. Francis, College of Graduate Studies	191			3	550	$400 per credit hour		•
Western Illinois University, College of Business and Technology	192	AA	530	3.35	550	$96 per credit (R); $288 per credit (NR)	•	•
INDIANA								
Ball State University, College of Business	193	AA	540	3.17	550, 213 (CAT)	$4300 per semester (R); $11,000 per semester (NR)	•	•
Bethel College, Program in Business Administration	193		496	3.29	560, 220 (CAT)	$300 per credit hour		
Butler University, College of Business Administration	193	AA						
Indiana Institute of Technology, Program in Business Administration	194							
Indiana State University, School of Business	194	AA	530	3.1	550	$1713 per year (R); $4277 per year (NR); $123 per credit hour (R); $300 per credit hour (NR)		
Indiana University Bloomington, Kelley School of Business	194	AA	634	3.3	580	$9339 per year (R); $18,117 per year (NR)	•	
Indiana University Kokomo, Division of Business and Economics	195							
Indiana University Northwest, Division of Business and Economics	195	AA	500	3.1		$147 per credit hour (R); $344 per credit hour (NR)	•	
Indiana University–Purdue University Fort Wayne, School of Business and Management Sciences	196	AA						
Indiana University–Purdue University Indianapolis, School of Business	196		600	3.3	550	$250 per credit hour (R); $500 per credit hour (NR)		•
Indiana University South Bend, Division of Business and Economics	196	AA	507	2.83	550	$159 per credit hour (R); $378 per credit hour (NR)	•	
Indiana Wesleyan University, Division of Adult and Professional Studies	197					$250 per credit hour		•
Manchester College, Department of Accounting and Business	197							
Oakland City University, School of Adult Programs and Professional Studies	197			3.2	500	$285 per credit hour	•	•

	Page Number	Accreditation (AA=AACSB, AC=ACBSP)	Minimum GMAT Score	Minimum Undergraduate GPA	Minimum TOEFL Score	TUITION (R) State Resident (NR) Non-Resident	Financial Aid	Distance Learning
		ADMISSION REQUIREMENTS					OPTION	
Purdue University, Krannert Graduate School of Management	198	AA	628	3.27	575, 230 (CAT)	$9110 per year (R); $17,670 per year (NR)		•
Purdue University Calumet, School of Management	198		550	2.75	550	$128 per credit hour (R); $280 per credit hour (NR)	•	
University of Indianapolis, Graduate Business Programs	199	AC	436	2.9	550	$280 per credit hour		
University of Notre Dame, Mendoza College of Business	199	AA						•
University of Saint Francis, Department of Business Administration	200		511	2.96	550	$367 per credit hour	•	
University of Southern Indiana, School of Business	200	AA						
IOWA								
Clarke College, Program in Management	200		555	3.2	550	$366 per credit		
Drake University, College of Business and Public Administration	201	AA	537	3.26	550, 213 (CAT)	$340 per credit hour		•
Iowa State University of Science and Technology, College of Business	201	AA	588	3.28	570, 230 (CAT)	$3526 per year (R); $9962 per year (NR); $240 per credit (R); $598 per credit (NR)	•	
Maharishi University of Management, School of Business and Public Administration	202				575	$16,320 per year	•	•
St. Ambrose University, Program in Business Administration	202	AC	540	2.5	550	$1296 per course		•
University of Dubuque, School of Business	203		475		550	$340 per credit		•
The University of Iowa, Henry B. Tippie College of Business	203	AA	623	3.3	600	$4528 per year (R); $11,962 per year (NR)	•	
University of Northern Iowa, School of Business Administration	204	AA	580	3	500	$3510 per year (R); $8358 per year (NR); $184 per credit hour (R); $454 per credit hour (NR)	•	
Upper Iowa University, Program in Business Leadership	204							•
KANSAS								
Baker University, School of Professional and Graduate Studies	205	AC		3.1	600	$325 per credit		
Benedictine College, Executive Master of Business Administration	205				570	$12,500 per year		
Emporia State University, School of Business	205		455	3.1		$115 per credit hour (R); $282 per credit hour (NR)		
Fort Hays State University, College of Business and Leadership	206		500	3.19	550	$96 per credit (R); $254 per credit (NR)	•	

This table includes the names and locations of colleges, universities, and other institutions offering MBA and other master s-level business programs. Schools appear in geographical sequence by U.S. state or territory or by country and then alphabetically by school name. Specific degree information is detailed within the profile for each school. Refer to the page number in the table for the school s profile. If a school submitted incomplete data, one or more columns opposite the school name may be blank.

	Page Number	Accreditation (AA=AACSB, AC=ACBSP)	Minimum GMAT Score	Minimum Undergraduate GPA	Minimum TOEFL Score	TUITION (R) State Resident (NR) Non-Resident	Financial Aid	Distance Learning
		ADMISSION REQUIREMENTS					OPTION	
Friends University, Graduate Programs	206				550	$490 per credit hour		
Kansas State University, College of Business Administration	207	AA	540	3.57	550, 213 (CAT)	$167 per credit hour (R); $395 per credit hour (NR)	•	
Kansas Wesleyan University, Program in Business Administration	207							
MidAmerica Nazarene University, Graduate Studies in Management	207			3.36	600	$6700 per year		
Newman University, Program in Organizational Leadership	208							
Ottawa University, Graduate Studies-Kansas City	208					$215 per credit hour		•
Pittsburg State University, Kelce College of Business	208	AA	516	3.3	550	$2604 per year (R); $6620 per year (NR); $111 per credit hour (R); $278 per credit hour (NR)	•	•
Saint Mary College, Department of Business, Economics and Accounting	209			3.5	550	$270 per credit hour		
University of Kansas, School of Business	209	AA	606	3.26	600, 250 (CAT)	$5844 per year (R); $13,808 per year (NR); $201 per credit hour (R)	•	
Washburn University of Topeka, School of Business	210		513	3.2	550, 213 (CAT)	$139 per credit hour (R); $286 per credit hour (NR)	•	
Wichita State University, W. Frank Barton School of Business	210	AA	514	3.29	550	$117 per credit (R); $346 per credit (NR)	•	
KENTUCKY								
Bellarmine College, W. Fielding Rubel School of Business	211		505	3.15				
Brescia University, Program in Management	211		468	3.17	550, 213 (CAT)	$200 per credit hour		
Eastern Kentucky University, College of Business and Technology	212		460	3.06	550	$145 per credit hour (R); $391 per credit hour (NR)		
Morehead State University, College of Business	212	AC	489	3.2	525	$2640 per year (R); $2640 per year (NR); $177 per credit hour (R); $177 per credit hour (NR)	•	•
Murray State University, College of Business and Public Affairs	213	AA	493	3.15	525	$2674 per year (R); $7446 per year (NR); $156 per hour (R); $418 per hour (NR)	•	•
Northern Kentucky University, College of Business	213	AA	518	3.11	550, 213 (CAT)	$2858 per year (R); $7298 per year (NR); $159 per semester hour (R); $405 per semester hour (NR)	•	
Thomas More College, Program in Business Administration	214							
University of Kentucky, Carol Martin Gatton College of Business and Economics	214	AA	600	3.3	550	$3596 per year (R); $10,116 per year (NR); $188 per credit hour (R); $550 per credit hour (NR)	•	
University of Louisville, College of Business and Public Administration	214	AA	555	3.27	550	$3546 per year (R); $10,066 per year (NR); $207 per semester hour (R); $592 per semester hour (NR)	•	

This table includes the names and locations of colleges, universities, and other institutions offering MBA and other master s-level business programs. Schools appear in geographical sequence by U.S. state or territory or by country and then alphabetically by school name. Specific degree information is detailed within the profile for each school. Refer to the page number in the table for the school s profile. If a school submitted incomplete data, one or more columns opposite the school name may be blank.

	Page Number	Accreditation (AA=AACSB, AC=ACBSP)	Minimum GMAT Score	Minimum Undergraduate GPA	Minimum TOEFL Score	TUITION (R) State Resident (NR) Non-Resident	Financial Aid	Distance Learning
			ADMISSION REQUIREMENTS				OPTION	

This table includes the names and locations of colleges, universities, and other institutions offering MBA and other master s-level business programs. Schools appear in geographical sequence by U.S. state or territory or by country and then alphabetically by school name. Specific degree information is detailed within the profile for each school. Refer to the page number in the table for the school s profile. If a school submitted incomplete data, one or more columns opposite the school name may be blank.

School	Page Number	Accreditation	Min GMAT	Min GPA	Min TOEFL	Tuition	Financial Aid	Distance Learning
Western Kentucky University, College of Business Administration	215	AA						•
LOUISIANA								
Louisiana State University and Agricultural and Mechanical College, E.J. Ourso College of Business Administration	215	AA	584	3.3	550, 213 (CAT)	$2876 per year (R); $8176 per year (NR)	•	
Louisiana Tech University, College of Administration and Business	216	AA	514	3.28	550, 213 (CAT)	$2744 per year (R); $6024 per year (NR)	•	
Loyola University New Orleans, Joseph A. Butt, S.J., College of Business Administration	216	AA	575	3.08	580, 237 (CAT)	$501 per credit hour		
McNeese State University, College of Business	217	AA	505	3.11	525	$1987 per year (R); $3530 per year (NR); $540 per semester (R); $882 per semester (NR)		
Nicholls State University, College of Business Administration	217	AA	470	3.1	550, 213 (CAT)	$2411 per year (R); $6675 per year (NR); $273 per credit hour (R); $273 per credit hour (NR)		
Southeastern Louisiana University, College of Business	218	AA	485	3.1	525	$2100 per year (R); $6096 per year (NR); $117 per credit hour (R); $339 per credit hour (NR)	•	
Southern University and Agricultural and Mechanical College, College of Business	218	AA	456	3.1		$2500 per year (R); $6500 per year (NR)		
Tulane University, A. B. Freeman School of Business	219	AA	644	3.4	624, 263 (CAT)	$25,390 per year; $783 per credit hour	•	•
University of Louisiana at Lafayette, Graduate School	219		500	3	550	$2024 per year (R); $7620 per year (NR)		
University of Louisiana at Monroe, College of Business Administration	220		510	3.28	550, 213 (CAT)	$1016 per year (R); $2979 per year (NR); $110 per credit (R); $110 per credit (NR)		
MAINE								
Maine Maritime Academy, Department of Graduate Studies	221			3.2		$365 per credit (R); $365 per credit (NR)		
Thomas College, Programs in Business	221		514	3.2		$470 per course	•	
University of Maine, The Maine Business School	221	AA	528	3.26	550, 213 (CAT)	$198 per credit (R); $562 per credit (NR)	•	
University of Southern Maine, School of Business	222	AA	558	3.33	550, 213 (CAT)	$182 per credit hour (R); $505 per credit hour (NR)	•	
MARYLAND								
Bowie State University, Business Programs	222				550	$195 per credit (R); $368 per credit (NR)	•	•
College of Notre Dame of Maryland, Graduate Studies	223							
Frostburg State University, College of Business	223				550	$3060 per year (R); $3546 per year (NR); $180 per credit hour (R); $208 per credit hour (NR)		•

	Page Number	Accreditation (AA=AACSB, AC=ACBSP)	Minimum GMAT Score	Minimum Undergraduate GPA	Minimum TOEFL Score	TUITION (R) State Resident (NR) Non-Resident	Financial Aid	Distance Learning
This table includes the names and locations of colleges, universities, and other institutions offering MBA and other master s-level business programs. Schools appear in geographical sequence by U.S. state or territory or by country and then alphabetically by school name. Specific degree information is detailed within the profile for each school. Refer to the page number in the table for the school s profile. If a school submitted incomplete data, one or more columns opposite the school name may be blank.								
Hood College, Department of Economics and Management (Interim)	223				575	$295 per credit hour		
Johns Hopkins University, School of Professional Studies in Business and Education	224			3.25	650, 220 (CAT)	$430 per credit hour	•	
Loyola College in Maryland, Sellinger School of Business and Management	224	AA	531	3.05	550, 213 (CAT)	$6930 per year; $385 per credit	•	
Morgan State University, Earl G. Graves School of Business and Management	225	AA	468	3.06	600	$226 per credit hour (R); $390 per credit hour (NR)		•
Mount Saint Mary's College and Seminary, Program in Business	225		500	3	550	$275 per credit		
Salisbury State University, Franklin P. Perdue School of Business	226	AA	472	3.3	550	$172 per credit hour (R); $340 per credit hour (NR)		
Towson University, College of Graduate Education and Research	226	AA			550	$3510 per year (R); $6948 per year (NR); $195 per credit hour (R); $386 per credit hour (NR)	•	
University of Baltimore, School of Business	227	AA	518	3.2	550, 213 (CAT)	$264 per credit (R); $393 per credit (NR)	•	•
University of Maryland, College Park, Robert H. Smith School of Business	227	AA	647	3.34	600, 250 (CAT)	$11,967 per year (R); $17,025 per year (NR); $582 per credit hour (R); $582 per credit hour (NR)	•	
University of Maryland University College, Graduate School of Management and Technology	228				580	$281 per credit (R); $382 per credit (NR)	•	•
MASSACHUSETTS								
American International College, School of Business Administration	229			3.3	550	$10,160 per year; $405 per hour	•	
Anna Maria College, Program in Business Administration	229		550	2.6	500	$775 per course		•
Arthur D. Little School of Management, Graduate Program	230		550	3	550	$32,000 per year	•	
Assumption College, Department of Business Studies	230		475		500	$322 per credit		
Babson College, F. W. Olin Graduate School of Business	231	AA	637	3.1	600, 250 (CAT)	$23,662 per year; $2208 per course	•	
Bentley College, The Elkin B. McCallum Graduate School of Business	231	AA	539	3.2	580	$17,145 per year; $2135 per course	•	•
Boston College, The Graduate School of the Wallace E. Carroll School of Management	232	AA	645	3.3	600, 250 (CAT)	$23,268 per year; $748 per credit hour	•	
Boston University, School of Management	233	AA	630	3.15	600, 250 (CAT)	$24,496 per year; $743 per credit	•	
Brandeis University, Graduate School of International Economics and Finance	234		600	3.5	600	$25,392 per year; $2280 per course	•	
Brandeis University, Heller Graduate School	234		575	3.4	600	$26,253 per year; $1400 per course	•	

	Page Number	Accreditation (AA=AACSB, AC=ACBSP)	Minimum GMAT Score	Minimum Undergraduate GPA	Minimum TOEFL Score	TUITION (R) State Resident (NR) Non-Resident	Financial Aid	Distance Learning
		ADMISSION REQUIREMENTS					OPTION	
Cambridge College, Program in Management	235					$315 per credit		
Clark University, Graduate School of Management	235	AA	565	3.2	550, 213 (CAT)	$19,990 per year; $1990 per course	•	
Emerson College, School of Communication, Management, and Public Policy	236			3.1	550	$14,112 per year; $588 per credit		
Emmanuel College, Center for Adult Studies	236			3.4	550	$1290 per course		
Fitchburg State College, Division of Graduate and Continuing Education	237				500	$140 per credit hour (R); $140 per credit hour (NR)	•	
Framingham State College, Program in Business Administration	237							
Harvard University, Business School	237	AA	680	3.5		$28,500 per year		
Lesley College, School of Management	238				550, 213 (CAT)	$475 per credit	•	
Massachusetts Institute of Technology, Sloan School of Management	238	AA	690	3.5	600	$28,200 per year	•	•
Nichols College, Graduate Program in Business Administration	239			3.2	550	$1082 per course		
Northeastern University, Graduate School of Business Administration	239	AA	580	3.2	600, 250 (CAT)	$22,150 per year; $550 per credit		•
Salem State College, Program in Business Administration	240		465	2.78	550, 213 (CAT)	$170 per credit hour (R); $260 per credit hour (NR)		
Simmons College, Graduate School of Management	240		560	3.2	550	$620 per credit hour	•	
Suffolk University, Frank Sawyer School of Management	240	AA		3.11	550, 213 (CAT)	$19,590 per year; $1947 per course	•	•
University of Massachusetts Amherst, Isenberg School of Management	241	AA	635	3.3	600, 250 (CAT)	$5642 per year (R); $12,758 per year (NR); $400 per credit (R); $400 per credit (NR)	•	•
University of Massachusetts Boston, College of Management	242		560	3.22	600	$110 per credit (R); $369 per credit (NR)		
University of Massachusetts Dartmouth, Charlton College of Business	242	AA	481		500, 173 (CAT)	$4959 per year (R); $10,733 per year (NR); $86 per credit (R); $327 per credit (NR)		
University of Massachusetts Lowell, College of Management	243	AA	520	3	550, 213 (CAT)	$89 per credit hour (R); $312 per credit hour (NR)		
Western New England College, School of Business	243			2.9		$379 per semester hour		
Worcester Polytechnic Institute, Department of Management	244		575	3.1	550, 213 (CAT)	$703 per credit		•

This table includes the names and locations of colleges, universities, and other institutions offering MBA and other master s-level business programs. Schools appear in geographical sequence by U.S. state or territory or by country and then alphabetically by school name. Specific degree information is detailed within the profile for each school. Refer to the page number in the table for the school s profile. If a school submitted incomplete data, one or more columns opposite the school name may be blank.

	Page Number	Accreditation (AA=AACSB, AC=ACBSP)	ADMISSION REQUIREMENTS			TUITION (R) State Resident (NR) Non-Resident	OPTION	
			Minimum GMAT Score	Minimum Undergraduate GPA	Minimum TOEFL Score		Financial Aid	Distance Learning

This table includes the names and locations of colleges, universities, and other institutions offering MBA and other master s-level business programs. Schools appear in geographical sequence by U.S. state or territory or by country and then alphabetically by school name. Specific degree information is detailed within the profile for each school. Refer to the page number in the table for the school s profile. If a school submitted incomplete data, one or more columns opposite the school name may be blank.

MICHIGAN

School	Page Number	Accreditation	Minimum GMAT Score	Minimum Undergraduate GPA	Minimum TOEFL Score	TUITION	Financial Aid	Distance Learning
Andrews University, School of Business	244			3.12	550, 213 (CAT)	$300 per quarter hour	•	
Aquinas College, Graduate School of Management	245		484	3.63	550, 213 (CAT)	$320 per credit hour	•	
Baker College Center for Graduate Studies, Programs in Business	245		520	3.06	550, 213 (CAT)	$6600 per year; $220 per quarter hour	•	•
Central Michigan University, College of Business Administration	246	AA						
Eastern Michigan University, College of Business	246	AA	500	3.08	500, 213 (CAT)	$5200 per year (R); $11,250 per year (NR); $157 per credit hour (R); $350 per credit hour (NR)		
Ferris State University, College of Business	246		540	3.1	550	$230 per credit hour (R); $470 per credit hour (NR)	•	•
Grand Valley State University, Seidman School of Business	247	AA	573	3.3	550	$187 per credit (R); $394 per credit (NR)	•	
Kettering University, Graduate School	247	AC			580	$1230 per course		•
Lawrence Technological University, College of Management	248	AC						•
Madonna University, Program in Business Administration	248		400	3.1	530	$288 per credit hour	•	•
Michigan State University, Eli Broad Graduate School of Management	249	AA	638	3.35	600	$9800 per year (R); $13,800 per year (NR)	•	
Michigan Technological University, School of Business and Economics	249				520	$182 per credit hour (R); $417 per credit hour (NR)		
Northwood University, Richard DeVos Graduate School of Management	250			3	610	$18,000 per year; $20,000 per degree program	•	
Oakland University, School of Business Administration	250	AA	560	3.2	550	$227 per credit (R); $489 per credit (NR)		
Saginaw Valley State University, College of Business and Management	251		480	3	525	$167 per credit hour (R); $327 per credit hour (NR)		
Siena Heights University, Graduate Studies	251							
Spring Arbor College, School of Business and Management	252			2.99	550	$265 per credit hour	•	
University of Detroit Mercy, College of Business Administration	252	AA	520	3.1		$545 per credit hour		
University of Michigan, School of Business Administration	252	AA	675	3.3	600	$21,684 per year (R); $26,684 per year (NR); $700 per credit hour (R); $700 per credit hour (NR)	•	
University of Michigan–Dearborn, School of Management	253	AA	554	3.27	560, 222 (CAT)	$259 per credit (R); $748 per credit (NR)	•	

This table includes the names and locations of colleges, universities, and other institutions offering MBA and other master s-level business programs. Schools appear in geographical sequence by U.S. state or territory or by country and then alphabetically by school name. Specific degree information is detailed within the profile for each school. Refer to the page number in the table for the school s profile. If a school submitted incomplete data, one or more columns opposite the school name may be blank.

| | | ADMISSION REQUIREMENTS | | | | OPTION | |
	Page Number	Accreditation (AA=AACSB, AC=ACBSP)	Minimum GMAT Score	Minimum Undergraduate GPA	Minimum TOEFL Score	TUITION (R) State Resident (NR) Non-Resident	Financial Aid	Distance Learning
University of Michigan–Flint, School of Management	254	AA	530	3.1	550, 213 (CAT)	$2126 per semester (R); $2126 per semester (NR)	•	
Walsh College of Accountancy and Business Administration, Graduate Programs	254			3	550, 213 (CAT)	$5394 per year; $283 per credit hour	•	•
Wayne State University, School of Business Administration	255	AA	535	3.2	550	$4718 per year (R); $9802 per year (NR); $175 per credit (R); $387 per credit (NR)	•	
Western Michigan University, Haworth College of Business	255	AA						•
MINNESOTA								
Capella University, School of Business	256			3	550, 213 (CAT)	$925 per course		•
College of St. Catherine, Program in Organizational Leadership	256				500	$456 per credit	•	
The College of St. Scholastica, Program in Management	256				575	$536 per credit		
Concordia University at St. Paul, Program in Organizational Management	257							
Metropolitan State University, College of Management	257		510	3.15	550, 213 (CAT)	$145 per credit (R); $226 per credit (NR)		
St. Cloud State University, G.R. Herberger College of Business	257	AA	534	3.26	550	$3564 per year (R); $5411 per year (NR)		
Saint Mary's University of Minnesota, Graduate School	258			3	550	$225 per credit		
Southwest State University, Department of Business Administration	258			3		$135 per credit (R); $214 per credit (NR)		•
University of Minnesota, Duluth, School of Business and Economics	259	AA	550	3.25	550	$7100 per year (R); $7100 per year (NR); $429 per credit (R); $429 per credit (NR)		
University of Minnesota, Twin Cities Campus, Carlson School of Management	259	AA	643	3.3	580, 240 (CAT)	$12,407 per year (R); $17,423 per year (NR); $474 per credit (R); $692 per credit (NR)	•	
University of St. Thomas, Graduate School of Business	260		517	3	550	$437 per credit hour	•	•
MISSISSIPPI								
Delta State University, College of Business	261	AC	500	3.2	550		•	
Jackson State University, School of Business	261	AA	450	3	525	$2688 per year (R); $5546 per year (NR); $150 per hour (R); $150 per hour (NR)	•	•
Millsaps College, School of Management	262	AA	560	3.15	550	$570 per semester hour	•	
Mississippi College, School of Business Administration	262	AC	451	3.28	550	$290 per hour	•	

This table includes the names and locations of colleges, universities, and other institutions offering MBA and other master s-level business programs. Schools appear in geographical sequence by U.S. state or territory or by country and then alphabetically by school name. Specific degree information is detailed within the profile for each school. Refer to the page number in the table for the school s profile. If a school submitted incomplete data, one or more columns opposite the school name may be blank.

	Page Number	Accreditation (AA=AACSB, AC=ACBSP)	Minimum GMAT Score	Minimum Undergraduate GPA	Minimum TOEFL Score	TUITION (R) State Resident (NR) Non-Resident	Financial Aid	Distance Learning
Mississippi State University, College of Business and Industry	263	AA	526	3.29	575, 233 (CAT)	$3017 per year (R); $6119 per year (NR); $168 per credit (R); $340 per credit (NR)	•	
University of Mississippi, School of Business Administration	263	AA	560	3.4	600	$3052 per year (R); $6154 per year (NR); $509 per course (R); $1026 per course (NR)		
University of Southern Mississippi, College of Business Administration	264	AA	524	3.35	525, 250 (CAT)	$3868 per year (R); $7220 per year (NR); $137 per semester hour (R); $172 per semester hour (NR)	•	
MISSOURI								
Avila College, Department of Business and Economics	265		495	3.3	550	$313 per credit hour		
Central Missouri State University, Harmon College of Business Administration	265	AA	500	3	550	$164 per credit hour (R); $328 per credit hour (NR)	•	
Columbia College, Program in Business Administration	265				550	$5400 per year; $180 per credit hour		
Drury University, Breech School of Business Administration	266	AC	530	3.4	550	$8420 per year; $270 per credit hour	•	
Fontbonne College, Department of Business Administration	266				600	$360 per credit hour		
Lincoln University, College of Business and Professional Studies	267		390	3	500	$2948 per year (R); $5756 per year (NR); $117 per credit hour (R); $234 per credit hour (NR)		
Lindenwood University, Department of Business Administration	267				550	$260 per credit	•	
Maryville University of Saint Louis, The John E. Simon School of Business	268		488	3.15	550, 213 (CAT)	$13,000 per year; $386 per credit hour	•	
Northwest Missouri State University, College of Professional and Applied Studies	268	AC	481	3.2	550	$108 per credit (R); $190 per credit (NR)	•	
Rockhurst University, School of Management	269				550	$350 per credit hour		•
Saint Louis University, School of Business and Administration	269	AA	601	3.15	550, 213 (CAT)	$22,038 per year; $630 per credit	•	
Southeast Missouri State University, College of Business	270		525	3.3	550, 213 (CAT)	$120 per credit hour (R); $205 per credit hour (NR)	•	
Southwest Baptist University, College of Business and Computer Science	270	AC						
Southwest Missouri State University, College of Business Administration	270	AA	520	3.33	550, 213 (CAT)	$3070 per year (R); $5970 per year (NR); $115 per credit (R); $230 per credit (NR)	•	
Stephens College, Department of Business Administration	271							•
Truman State University, Division of Business and Accountancy	271	AA	580	3.4	560	$4000 per year (R); $7000 per year (NR); $165 per hour (R); $300 per hour (NR)		
University of Missouri–Columbia, College of Business	272	AA	610	3.35	550	$168 per credit hour (R); $505 per credit hour (NR)	•	

	Page Number	Accreditation (AA=AACSB, AC=ACBSP)	Minimum GMAT Score	Minimum Undergraduate GPA	Minimum TOEFL Score	TUITION (R) State Resident (NR) Non-Resident	Financial Aid	Distance Learning
			ADMISSION REQUIREMENTS				OPTION	

This table includes the names and locations of colleges, universities, and other institutions offering MBA and other master s-level business programs. Schools appear in geographical sequence by U.S. state or territory or by country and then alphabetically by school name. Specific degree information is detailed within the profile for each school. Refer to the page number in the table for the school s profile. If a school submitted incomplete data, one or more columns opposite the school name may be blank.

	Page Number	Accreditation	Min GMAT	Min GPA	Min TOEFL	TUITION	Financial Aid	Distance Learning
University of Missouri–Kansas City, School of Business and Public Administration	272	AA	555	3.3	550, 213 (CAT)	$188 per credit hour (R); $525 per credit hour (NR)	•	
University of Missouri–St. Louis, College of Business Administration	273	AA	565	3.04	550, 213 (CAT)	$5994 per year (R); $16,104 per year (NR); $168 per credit hour (R); $505 per credit hour (NR)		•
Washington University in St. Louis, John M. Olin School of Business	274	AA	624	3.2	590	$25,990 per year; $715 per credit hour	•	
Webster University, School of Business and Technology	274					$368 per credit hour	•	•
William Woods University, College of Graduate and Adult Studies	275							
MONTANA								
Montana State University–Bozeman, College of Business	275	AA	488	3.53	550, 213 (CAT)	$4249 per year (R); $9998 per year (NR); $185 per credit (R); $424 per credit (NR)	•	
The University of Montana–Missoula, School of Business Administration	276	AA	560	3.27	580, 237 (CAT)	$4151 per year (R); $9694 per year (NR); $150 per credit (R); $370 per credit (NR)	•	•
NEBRASKA								
Bellevue University, College of Business	276				460	$9000 per year; $250 per credit	•	•
Chadron State College, Department of Business and Economics	276			3.27	550	$2212 per year (R); $4090 per year (NR); $104 per credit hour (R); $183 per credit hour (NR)	•	•
Creighton University, Eugene C. Eppley College of Business Administration	277	AA	530	3.2	550	$8644 per year; $447 per credit	•	
University of Nebraska at Kearney, College of Business and Technology	278							
University of Nebraska at Omaha, College of Business Administration	278	AA	535	3.36	550, 213 (CAT)	$112 per credit (R); $252 per credit (NR)	•	•
University of Nebraska–Lincoln, College of Business Administration	278	AA	580	3.4	550, 213 (CAT)	$3282 per year (R); $7350 per year (NR); $116 per credit hour (R); $285 per credit hour (NR)	•	•
Wayne State College, Division of Business	279		500	3	550	$282 per course (R); $517 per course (NR)		•
NEVADA								
University of Nevada, Las Vegas, College of Business	279	AA	582	3.15	550, 213 (CAT)	$100 per credit hour (R); $205 per credit hour (NR)	•	
University of Nevada, Reno, College of Business Administration	280	AA						
NEW HAMPSHIRE								
Antioch New England Graduate School, Department of Organization and Management	280			3	550, 213 (CAT)	$12,865 per year; $410 per credit	•	

This table includes the names and locations of colleges, universities, and other institutions offering MBA and other master's-level business programs. Schools appear in geographical sequence by U.S. state or territory or by country and then alphabetically by school name. Specific degree information is detailed within the profile for each school. Refer to the page number in the table for the school's profile. If a school submitted incomplete data, one or more columns opposite the school name may be blank.	Page Number	ADMISSION REQUIREMENTS				TUITION (R) State Resident (NR) Non-Resident	OPTION	
		Accreditation (AA=AACSB, AC=ACBSP)	Minimum GMAT Score	Minimum Undergraduate GPA	Minimum TOEFL Score		Financial Aid	Distance Learning
Dartmouth College, The Tuck School of Business at Dartmouth	281	AA	682	3.4		$27,150 per year	•	
New England College, Program in Organizational Management	281					$195 per credit		
New Hampshire College, Graduate School of Business	281	AC			550	$999 per course		•
Plymouth State College, Department of Graduate Studies in Business	282		469	2.99	500	$273 per credit (R); $299 per credit (NR)	•	
Rivier College, Department of Business Administration	282			2.8	600	$972 per course		
University of New Hampshire, Whittemore School of Business and Economics	283	AA	568	3	550, 213 (CAT)	$6947 per year (R); $15,837 per year (NR); $1150 per course (R); $1350 per course (NR)	•	
NEW JERSEY								
College of Saint Elizabeth, Department of Business Administration/Economics	283			3.5	550, 210 (CAT)			
Fairleigh Dickinson University, Teaneck–Hackensack Campus, Samuel J. Silberman College of Business Administration	284							
Georgian Court College, Program in Business Administration	284	AC			550	$375 per credit	•	
Kean University, School of Business, Government, and Technology	284		500	3.25		$268 per credit (R); $329 per credit (NR)		
Monmouth University, School of Business Administration	285	AA			525	$8754 per year; $456 per credit		
Montclair State University, School of Business	285	AA	509	3.1	550, 213 (CAT)	$5834 per year (R); $7634 per year (NR); $220 per credit (R); $295 per credit (NR)	•	
New Jersey Institute of Technology, School of Management	286	AA	500	3.2	550, 213 (CAT)	$505 per credit (R); $651 per credit (NR)		
The Richard Stockton College of New Jersey, Program in Business Studies	286		450	3	550	$260 per credit (R); $349 per credit (NR)		
Rider University, College of Business Administration	287	AA	533	3.18	585, 240 (CAT)	$8460 per year; $480 per credit hour		
Rowan University, College of Business	287		535	3.42	550, 213 (CAT)	$6686 per year (R); $10,238 per year (NR); $281 per credit (R); $429 per credit (NR)		
Rutgers, The State University of New Jersey, Camden, School of Business	288	AA	563	3.2	550	$9000 per year (R); $13,420 per year (NR); $372 per credit (R); $556 per credit (NR)		
Rutgers, The State University of New Jersey, Newark, Graduate School of Management	288	AA	587	3.17	600, 250 (CAT)	$10,382 per year (R); $14,996 per year (NR); $388 per credit (R); $581 per credit (NR)	•	
Rutgers, The State University of New Jersey, New Brunswick, School of Management and Labor Relations	289		422	3.27	575	$7543 per year (R); $10,703 per year (NR); $279 per credit (R); $412 per credit (NR)		•
Saint Peter's College, MBA Programs	290				550	$9558 per year; $531 per credit		

This table includes the names and locations of colleges, universities, and other institutions offering MBA and other master's-level business programs. Schools appear in geographical sequence by U.S. state or territory or by country and then alphabetically by school name. Specific degree information is detailed within the profile for each school. Refer to the page number in the table for the school's profile. If a school submitted incomplete data, one or more columns opposite the school name may be blank.

	Page Number	Accreditation (AA=AACSB, AC=ACBSP)	Minimum GMAT Score	Minimum Undergraduate GPA	Minimum TOEFL Score	TUITION (R) State Resident (NR) Non-Resident	Financial Aid	Distance Learning
			ADMISSION REQUIREMENTS				OPTION	
Seton Hall University, W. Paul Stillman School of Business	290	AA	560	3.2	550	$15,233 per year; $622 per credit		•
Stevens Institute of Technology, Wesley J. Howe School of Technology Management	291				550	$14,520 per year; $605 per credit hour		•
Thomas Edison State College, Graduate Studies	291				500	$298 per credit (R); $298 per credit (NR)		•
William Paterson University of New Jersey, College of Business	292		485	2.86	550	$230 per credit (R); $327 per credit (NR)		
NEW MEXICO								
College of Santa Fe, Department of Business Administration	292			3.2		$251 per credit	•	
Eastern New Mexico University, College of Business	292	AC	530	3.29	550	$1761 per year (R); $6639 per year (NR); $108 per credit hour (R); $311 per credit hour (NR)		•
New Mexico Highlands University, School of Business	293		450	3.3	525	$72 per credit hour (R); $72 per credit hour (NR)	•	•
New Mexico State University, College of Business Administration and Economics	293	AA	492	3.25	530, 197 (CAT)	$2682 per year (R); $8376 per year (NR); $112 per credit (R); $112 per credit (NR)	•	
University of New Mexico, Robert O. Anderson Graduate School of Management	294	AA	560	3.3	550, 220 (CAT)	$129 per credit hour (R); $129 per credit hour (NR)	•	
Western New Mexico University, Department of Business Administration and Economics	294		500	3.42	550	$60 per credit hour (R); $60 per credit hour (NR)		
NEW YORK								
Adelphi University, School of Business	295		450	2.8	550	$17,000 per year; $650 per credit		•
Alfred University, College of Business	295		505	3.09	590, 243 (CAT)	$23,020 per year; $446 per credit hour		
Audrey Cohen College, School for Business	296		580	3.2	660	$22,314 per year	•	
Bernard M. Baruch College of the City University of New York, Zicklin School of Business	296	AA	580	3.2	570	$4350 per year (R); $7600 per year (NR); $185 per credit (R); $320 per credit (NR)	•	
Canisius College, Wehle School of Business	297	AA	510	3	500, 200 (CAT)	$555 per credit hour	•	
Clarkson University, School of Business	297	AA	560	3.3	600	$21,984 per year; $687 per credit hour		
College of Insurance, Program in Business Administration	298		500	3	550	$624 per credit	•	
The College of Saint Rose, School of Business	298	AC	497	3.1	550	$351 per credit	•	
Columbia University, Graduate School of Business	299	AA	700	3.45	610, 253 (CAT)	$29,174 per year	•	

	Page Number	Accreditation (AA=AACSB, AC=ACBSP)	ADMISSION REQUIREMENTS			TUITION (R) State Resident (NR) Non-Resident	OPTION	
This table includes the names and locations of colleges, universities, and other institutions offering MBA and other master's-level business programs. Schools appear in geographical sequence by U.S. state or territory or by country and then alphabetically by school name. Specific degree information is detailed within the profile for each school. Refer to the page number in the table for the school's profile. If a school submitted incomplete data, one or more columns opposite the school name may be blank.			Minimum GMAT Score	Minimum Undergraduate GPA	Minimum TOEFL Score		Financial Aid	Distance Learning
Cornell University, Professional Field of the Johnson Graduate School of Management	300	AA	675	3.45	600	$25,648 per year	•	
Dowling College, School of Business	300				550	$495 per credit	•	
D'Youville College, Department of Business	301				550	$405 per credit	•	•
Fordham University, College of Business Administration	301	AA	600	3.1	600, 250 (CAT)	$620 per credit	•	
Hofstra University, Frank G. Zarb School of Business	302	AA	570	3.2	580	$474 per credit	•	
Iona College, Hagan School of Business	302	AA	487	3.2	550	$515 per credit	•	•
Lehman College of the City University of New York, Department of Economics and Accounting	303							
Le Moyne College, Department of Business	303		500	3	550	$399 per credit hour		
Long Island University, Brooklyn Campus, School of Business and Public Administration	304		480	3	600	$505 per credit	•	
Long Island University, C.W. Post Campus, College of Management	304		500	2.8	550, 173 (CAT)	$525 per credit	•	
Manhattan College, School of Business	305							
Manhattanville College, School of Graduate and Professional Studies	305			3.1	600	$420 per credit		
Marist College, School of Management	305		522	3.2	550	$462 per credit hour	•	•
Medaille College, Program in Business Administration	306			3.15		$10,740 per year; $448 per credit		
Mercy College, Program in Human Resource Management	306							•
Mount Saint Mary College, Division of Business	306		480	3.21		$389 per credit		•
Nazareth College of Rochester, Program in Management	307			3	550	$456 per credit hour		
New School University, Robert J. Milano Graduate School of Management and Urban Policy	307			3.2	600	$690 per credit	•	•
New York Institute of Technology, School of Management	308		450	3.05	575	$8100 per year; $450 per credit	•	•
New York University, Leonard N. Stern School of Business	308	AA	686	3.4	600, 250 (CAT)	$29,000 per year; $1050 per credit	•	
Pace University, New York City Campus, Lubin School of Business	309	AA	518	3.15	550	$575 per credit	•	•

		ADMISSION REQUIREMENTS				OPTION	
This table includes the names and locations of colleges, universities, and other institutions offering MBA and other master's-level business programs. Schools appear in geographical sequence by U.S. state or territory or by country and then alphabetically by school name. Specific degree information is detailed within the profile for each school. Refer to the page number in the table for the school's profile. If a school submitted incomplete data, one or more columns opposite the school name may be blank.	Page Number	Accreditation (AA=AACSB, AC=ACBSP)	Minimum GMAT Score	Minimum Undergraduate GPA	Minimum TOEFL Score	TUITION (R) State Resident (NR) Non-Resident	Financial Aid	Distance Learning
Polytechnic University-55 Broad Street Manhattan Graduate Center, Department of Management	309						
Polytechnic University, Brooklyn Campus, Department of Management	310					$725 per credit hour	
Polytechnic University, Brooklyn Campus, MSM Extension Israel	310					40,000 Israeli New shekels per year	
Polytechnic University, Farmingdale Campus, Department of Management	311					$725 per credit hour	
Polytechnic University, Westchester Graduate Center, Division of Management	311					$725 per credit hour	
Pratt Institute, Program in Facilities Management	311						
Rensselaer Polytechnic Institute, Lally School of Management and Technology	311	AA	632	3.2	600	$22,205 per year; $700 per credit hour	•
Roberts Wesleyan College, Division of Business and Management	312			3.25	550	$493 per credit hour	
Rochester Institute of Technology, College of Business	313	AA	572	3.1	570, 230 (CAT)	$19,605 per year; $546 per credit hour	•
Sage Graduate School, Division of Management, Communications and Legal Studies	313			2.75	550	$388 per credit hour	
St. Bonaventure University, School of Business	314		480	3.2	600, 250 (CAT)	$8460 per year; $470 per credit hour	
St. John Fisher College, School of Adult and Graduate Education	314		469	3.18	575	$15,600 per year; $550 per credit hour	
St. John's University, Peter J. Tobin College of Business Administration	315	AA	490	3.1	500	$15,270 per year; $630 per credit	•
St. Thomas Aquinas College, Division of Business Administration	315		500	3.2	500	$9900 per year; $405 per credit	
Siena College, School of Business	316		558	3.1	550	$350 per credit hour	
State University of New York at Albany, School of Business	316	AA	591	3.3	580	$5100 per year (R); $8416 per year (NR); $213 per credit hour (R); $351 per credit hour (NR)	•
State University of New York at Binghamton, School of Management	317	AA	551	3.3	570, 230 (CAT)	$6115 per year (R); $9431 per year (NR); $213 per credit hour (R); $351 per credit hour (NR)	•
State University of New York at Buffalo, School of Management	318	AA	600	3.2	550, 213 (CAT)	$5950 per year (R); $9266 per year (NR); $425 per credit (R); $425 per credit (NR)	•
State University of New York at New Paltz, School of Business	318		478	3.3	550	$213 per credit (R); $351 per credit (NR)	
State University of New York at Oswego, School of Business	319		510	3.1	550	$5100 per year (R); $8416 per year (NR); $213 per credit (R); $351 per credit (NR)	
State University of New York at Stony Brook, W. Averell Harriman School for Management and Policy	319		550	3.3	550, 213 (CAT)	$5712 per year (R); $9028 per year (NR); $213 per credit hour (R); $351 per credit hour (NR)	

	Page Number	Accreditation (AA=AACSB, AC=ACBSP)	Minimum GMAT Score	Minimum Undergraduate GPA	Minimum TOEFL Score	TUITION (R) State Resident (NR) Non-Resident	Financial Aid	Distance Learning
		ADMISSION REQUIREMENTS					OPTION	
State University of New York College at Oneonta, Department of Economics and Business	320		616	2.36	500	$213 per credit (R); $351 per credit (NR)	•	
State University of New York Empire State College, Graduate Studies	320				600, 250 (CAT)	$213 per credit (R); $351 per credit (NR)		•
State University of New York Institute of Technology at Utica/Rome, School of Management	321		490	3.3	550, 213 (CAT)	$5701 per year (R); $9017 per year (NR); $230 per credit hour (R); $368 per credit hour (NR)	•	•
State University of New York Maritime College, Program in Transportation Management	321							
Syracuse University, School of Management	321	AA	602	3.2	580, 237 (CAT)	$19,412 per year; $613 per credit	•	•
Union College, Graduate Management Institute	322		570	3.2	550	$14,190 per year; $1560 per course	•	
University of Rochester, William E. Simon Graduate School of Business Administration	322	AA	647	3.2	600, 250 (CAT)	$27,024 per year; $882 per credit hour	•	
Wagner College, Department of Business Administration	323							
NORTH CAROLINA								
Appalachian State University, John A. Walker College of Business	324	AA	505	3.2	550	$230 per course (R); $1920 per course (NR)		
Campbell University, Lundy-Fetterman School of Business	324		490	3.1	550	$190 per semester hour		
Duke University, Fuqua School of Business	324	AA	676	3.33	660, 250 (CAT)	$27,671 per year	•	•
East Carolina University, School of Business	325	AA	508	3.12	550, 213 (CAT)	$2018 per year (R); $4223 per year (NR); $757 per semester (R); $3594 per semester (NR)	•	
Elon College, Martha and Spencer Love School of Business	326		525	3.2	550, 213 (CAT)	$291 per credit hour		
Fayetteville State University, Program in Business Administration	326		490	3.3	550	$1334 per year (R); $8176 per year (NR); $90 per credit (R); $478 per credit (NR)		
Gardner-Webb University, School of Business	326		450	3.15	500	$230 per credit hour		
High Point University, Graduate Studies	327			3	550	$5824 per year; $318 per credit		
Lenoir-Rhyne College, Department of Business	327		513		550	$225 per credit hour		
Meredith College, John E. Weems Graduate School	328		500	3	500, 173 (CAT)	$4950 per year; $275 per credit hour	•	
Montreat College, Business Division	328							
North Carolina Central University, School of Business	328	AC	481	3.01	500	$2151 per year (R); $9421 per year (NR)	•	

This table includes the names and locations of colleges, universities, and other institutions offering MBA and other master's-level business programs. Schools appear in geographical sequence by U.S. state or territory or by country and then alphabetically by school name. Specific degree information is detailed within the profile for each school. Refer to the page number in the table for the school's profile. If a school submitted incomplete data, one or more columns opposite the school name may be blank.

			ADMISSION REQUIREMENTS				OPTION	

This table includes the names and locations of colleges, universities, and other institutions offering MBA and other master's-level business programs. Schools appear in geographical sequence by U.S. state or territory or by country and then alphabetically by school name. Specific degree information is detailed within the profile for each school. Refer to the page number in the table for the school's profile. If a school submitted incomplete data, one or more columns opposite the school name may be blank.	Page Number	Accreditation (AA=AACSB, AC=ACBSP)	Minimum GMAT Score	Minimum Undergraduate GPA	Minimum TOEFL Score	TUITION (R) State Resident (NR) Non-Resident	Financial Aid	Distance Learning
North Carolina State University, College of Management	329	AA	615	3.16	600, 250 (CAT)	$2470 per year (R); $11,636 per year (NR); $886 per semester (R); $4323 per semester (NR)		
Pfeiffer University, Program in Business Administration	329				500	$265 per credit hour		•
Queens College, McColl School of Business	330	AC	560	2.9	550	$18,500 per year; $310 per credit hour		
The University of North Carolina at Chapel Hill, Kenan-Flagler Business School	330	AA	640	3.3	600	$8403 per year (R); $20,353 per year (NR)		•
The University of North Carolina at Charlotte, College of Business Administration	331	AA	549	3.2	550	$1940 per year (R); $9210 per year (NR); $372 per course (R); $2189 per course (NR)	•	
The University of North Carolina at Greensboro, Joseph M. Bryan School of Business and Economics	331	AA	570	3.3	550, 213 (CAT)	$2778 per year (R); $13,666 per year (NR); $1139 per semester (R); $6833 per semester (NR)	•	
The University of North Carolina at Pembroke, Graduate Studies	332		350	3		$1317 per year (R); $4461 per year (NR); $246 per course (R); $2063 per course (NR)		
Wake Forest University, Babcock Graduate School of Management	332	AA	633	3.2	600	$21,300 per year; $2050 per course	•	
Western Carolina University, College of Business	333	AA	505	3.4	550	$1957 per year (R); $9227 per year (NR)	•	•
Wingate University, School of Business and Economics	333	AC	425	3.25	550	$750 per course		
NORTH DAKOTA								
Minot State University, College of Business	334		495	3.62	550	$5380 per year (R); $14,364 per year (NR); $112 per credit (R); $299 per credit (NR)	•	•
North Dakota State University, College of Business Administration	334		550	3.28	550	$116 per credit (R); $286 per credit (NR)	•	
OHIO								
Ashland University, College of Business Administration and Economics	335	AC		3.21	550	$385 per credit hour		
Baldwin-Wallace College, Division of Business Administration	335		485	3	500	$10,600 per year; $1590 per course	•	
Bowling Green State University, College of Business Administration	336	AA	550	3.2	550	$6362 per year (R); $11,910 per year (NR); $298 per credit hour (R); $562 per credit hour (NR)		
Case Western Reserve University, Weatherhead School of Management	336	AA	620	3.2	590, 243 (CAT)	$22,900 per year; $955 per credit hour	•	
Cleveland State University, James J. Nance College of Business Administration	338	AA	513	3.12	525, 195 (CAT)	$5590 per year (R); $11,050 per year (NR); $215 per credit hour (R); $425 per credit hour (NR)		
Franciscan University of Steubenville, Department of Business	338		473	3	550	$280 per credit	•	
Franklin University, Graduate School of Business	339				550	$6165 per year; $290 per credit	•	•

	Page Number	Accreditation (AA=AACSB, AC=ACBSP)	ADMISSION REQUIREMENTS			TUITION (R) State Resident (NR) Non-Resident	OPTION	
This table includes the names and locations of colleges, universities, and other institutions offering MBA and other master's-level business programs. Schools appear in geographical sequence by U.S. state or territory or by country and then alphabetically by school name. Specific degree information is detailed within the profile for each school. Refer to the page number in the table for the school's profile. If a school submitted incomplete data, one or more columns opposite the school name may be blank.			Minimum GMAT Score	Minimum Undergraduate GPA	Minimum TOEFL Score		Financial Aid	Distance Learning
Heidelberg College, Department of Business Administration	339							
John Carroll University, John M. and Mary Jo Boler School of Business	339	AA						
Kent State University, Graduate School of Management	340	AA	540	3.25	550, 213 (CAT)	$5334 per year (R); $10,238 per year (NR); $243 per credit (R); $466 per credit (NR)		
Lake Erie College, Division of Management Studies	340				590	$16,102 per year; $445 per credit hour		
Malone College, Graduate School	341					$350 per credit		
The McGregor School of Antioch University, Department of Management	341			3.1		$9344 per year		
Miami University, Richard T. Farmer School of Business Administration	341	AA	560	3.12	550, 220 (CAT)	$7316 per year (R); $13,970 per year (NR); $278 per credit (R); $555 per credit (NR)		
The Ohio State University, Max M. Fisher College of Business	342	AA	638	3.26	600, 240 (CAT)	$6744 per year (R); $15,879 per year (NR)	•	
Ohio University, College of Business	342	AA	536	3.38	600	$7672 per year (R); $13,236 per year (NR); $238 per credit hour (R); $457 per credit hour (NR)	•	•
Otterbein College, Department of Business, Accounting and Economics	343		530	3.14	550	$210 per credit		
Tiffin University, Program in Business Administration	343	AC		3.4	550	$6600 per year		
The University of Akron, College of Business Administration	344	AA	570	3.2	550, 213 (CAT)	$186 per credit (R); $353 per credit (NR)	•	
University of Cincinnati, College of Business Administration	344	AA						
University of Dayton, School of Business Administration	344	AA	549	3.07	550, 213 (CAT)	$7920 per year; $440 per credit	•	
The University of Findlay, MBA Program	345		350	3.1	525	$313 per credit hour		•
University of Toledo, College of Business Administration	345	AA	511	2.97	550	$6462 per year (R); $12,832 per year (NR); $229 per credit hour (R); $594 per credit hour (NR)	•	
Walsh University, Program in Management	346							
Wright State University, College of Business and Administration	346	AA	538	3.18	550	$5568 per year (R); $9696 per year (NR); $175 per credit (R); $302 per credit (NR)		
Xavier University, College of Business Administration	347	AA	540	3.2	550, 213 (CAT)	$420 per credit	•	
Youngstown State University, Warren P. Williamson Jr. College of Business Administration	347	AC	510	3.15	550	$550 per course (R); $750 per course (NR)	•	

	Page Number	Accreditation (AA=AACSB, AC=ACBSP)	Minimum GMAT Score	Minimum Undergraduate GPA	Minimum TOEFL Score	TUITION (R) State Resident (NR) Non-Resident	Financial Aid	Distance Learning
			ADMISSION REQUIREMENTS				OPTION	

This table includes the names and locations of colleges, universities, and other institutions offering MBA and other master's-level business programs. Schools appear in geographical sequence by U.S. state or territory or by country and then alphabetically by school name. Specific degree information is detailed within the profile for each school. Refer to the page number in the table for the school's profile. If a school submitted incomplete data, one or more columns opposite the school name may be blank.

	Page Number	Accred.	Min GMAT	Min GPA	Min TOEFL	TUITION	Fin. Aid	Dist. Learn.
OKLAHOMA								
Cameron University, School of Graduate and Professional Studies	348		493	3	550, 213 (CAT)	$1494 per year (R); $3456 per year (NR); $83 per credit (R); $192 per credit (NR)	•	•
Northeastern State University, College of Business and Industry	348	AC	450		550	$80 per credit hour (R); $188 per credit hour (NR)		
Oklahoma City University, School of Management and Business Sciences	349			3.25	550	$390 per credit hour	•	
Oklahoma State University, College of Business Administration	349	AA	600		575	$1896 per year (R); $6421 per year (NR); $86 per credit (R); $275 per credit (NR)	•	•
Oral Roberts University, School of Business	350		500	3.2	550, 213 (CAT)	$5216 per year; $272 per credit	•	•
Southeastern Oklahoma State University, School of Business	350							
Southern Nazarene University, School of Business	350		492	3.1	550	$1300 per year		
Southwestern Oklahoma State University, School of Business	351		480		550	$74 per credit (R); $188 per credit (NR)		
University of Central Oklahoma, College of Business Administration	351	AC	440	2.8	550	$1485 per year (R); $2259 per year (NR); $82.50 per credit (R); $126 per credit (NR)	•	
University of Oklahoma, Michael F. Price College of Business	352	AA	600		550	$92 per credit hour (R); $266 per credit hour (NR)	•	
University of Tulsa, College of Business Administration	352	AA						
OREGON								
George Fox University, Department of Business and Economics	352			3.57	550	$22,530 per degree program		
Marylhurst University, Graduate Program in Management	353							•
Oregon Graduate Institute of Science and Technology, Department of Management in Science and Technology	353			3	625	$520 per credit		•
Oregon State University, College of Business	353	AA	565	3.26	575, 233 (CAT)	$6489 per year (R); $11,061 per year (NR)	•	
Portland State University, School of Business Administration	354	AA	602	3.2	550, 213 (CAT)	$6291 per year (R); $10,766 per year (NR); $200 per credit hour (R); $200 per credit hour (NR)		•
University of Oregon, Charles H. Lundquist College of Business	354	AA	619	3.36	575	$8350 per year (R); $13,009 per year (NR)	•	
University of Portland, Dr. Robert B. Pamplin, Jr. School of Business	355	AA	525	3.2	570	$563 per credit hour	•	
Willamette University, Geo. H. Atkinson Graduate School of Management	355	AA	550	3.2	550, 213 (CAT)	$16,010 per year; $532 per credit	•	

		ADMISSION REQUIREMENTS				OPTION	
This table includes the names and locations of colleges, universities, and other institutions offering MBA and other master's-level business programs. Schools appear in geographical sequence by U.S. state or territory or by country and then alphabetically by school name. Specific degree information is detailed within the profile for each school. Refer to the page number in the table for the school's profile. If a school submitted incomplete data, one or more columns opposite the school name may be blank.	Page Number	Accreditation (AA=AACSB, AC=ACBSP)	Minimum GMAT Score	Minimum Undergraduate GPA	Minimum TOEFL Score	TUITION (R) State Resident (NR) Non-Resident	Financial Aid	Distance Learning
PENNSYLVANIA							
Allentown College of St. Francis de Sales, Department of Business	356		530	3.2		$415 per credit	•
The American College, Richard D. Irwin Graduate School	356					$525 per course	• •
Bloomsburg University of Pennsylvania, College of Business	357		510	3.04	550	$3780 per year (R); $6614 per year (NR); $210 per credit hour (R); $367 per credit hour (NR)	
California University of Pennsylvania, School of Graduate Studies	357		470	3.25	550	$4794 per year (R); $7624 per year (NR); $210 per credit (R); $367 per credit (NR)	
Carnegie Mellon University, Graduate School of Industrial Administration	358	AA	653	3.2	600	$25,130 per year; $250 per unit	•
Chatham College, Program in Management	358						
Clarion University of Pennsylvania, College of Business Administration	.359	AA	520	3.29	550	$3780 per year (R); $6610 per year (NR); $210 per credit (R); $367 per credit (NR)	
College Misericordia, Division of Behavioral Science, Education, and Business	359			3		$430 per credit	
Drexel University, College of Business and Administration	359	AA	563	3.23	570	$511 per credit	•
Duquesne University, Graduate School of Business Administration	360	AA	520	3.1	550	$588 per credit	
Eastern College, Graduate Business Programs	361						
Gannon University, School of Business	361						
Geneva College, Department of Business, Accounting and Management	361			3.2		$1260 per year; $420 per credit	
Grove City College, Program in Accounting	362			3	550	$296 per credit	•
Indiana University of Pennsylvania, Eberly College of Business and Information Technology	362		525	3.1	530, 200 (CAT)	$4403 per year (R); $7233 per year (NR); $210 per credit (R); $367 per credit (NR)	
King's College, William G. McGowan School of Business	363		450	3.32	600	$480 per credit hour	
Kutztown University of Pennsylvania, College of Business	363						•
La Roche College, Graduate and Continuing Education Office	363	AC			550	$420 per credit	
La Salle University, School of Business Administration	364	AA					
Lebanon Valley College, MBA Program	364		495			$299 per credit	

		ADMISSION REQUIREMENTS				OPTION	
This table includes the names and locations of colleges, universities, and other institutions offering MBA and other master's-level business programs. Schools appear in geographical sequence by U.S. state or territory or by country and then alphabetically by school name. Specific degree information is detailed within the profile for each school. Refer to the page number in the table for the school's profile. If a school submitted incomplete data, one or more columns opposite the school name may be blank.	Page Number	Accreditation (AA=AACSB, AC=ACBSP)	Minimum GMAT Score	Minimum Undergraduate GPA	Minimum TOEFL Score	TUITION (R) State Resident (NR) Non-Resident	Financial Aid	Distance Learning
Lehigh University, College of Business and Economics	364	AA	601	3.2	570	$21,984 per year; $610 per credit hour	•	•
Marywood University, Department of Business and Managerial Science	365		495	2.9	550	$9162 per year; $499 per credit	•	
Moravian College, Department of Economics and Business	365		500	3	550	$1380 per course		
The Pennsylvania State University at Erie, The Behrend College, Program in Business Administration	366		520	3.2	550, 213 (CAT)	$8225 per year (R); $15,521 per year (NR); $337 per credit (R); $641 per credit (NR)	•	•
The Pennsylvania State University Great Valley Campus, Graduate Studies and Continuing Education	366		540	3.11		$362 per credit (R); $641 per credit (NR)	•	
The Pennsylvania State University Harrisburg Campus of the Capital College, School of Business Administration	367	AA	550	3.18	550	$3143 per year (R); $5769 per year (NR); $337 per credit (R); $641 per credit (NR)	•	
The Pennsylvania State University University Park Campus, The Mary Jean and Frank P. Smeal College of Business Administration	367	AA	608	3.27	600	$8558 per year (R); $15,788 per year (NR)	•	
Philadelphia College of Bible, Organizational Leadership Program	368				550	$5140 per year; $285 per credit	•	
Philadelphia University, School of Business	368		470	3.2	550	$497 per credit	•	
Point Park College, Department of Business	369		482	3.29	500	$6624 per year; $378 per credit		
Robert Morris College, Program in Business Administration	369		462	3.09	500	$386 per credit		
Rosemont College, Division of Accelerated Degree Programs	370				500	$1305 per course		
Saint Francis College, Business Administration Program	370		520	3.2	500	$7938 per year; $441 per credit		
Saint Joseph's University, Erivan K. Haub School of Business	370	AA	510	3	550, 213 (CAT)	$16,610 per year; $510 per credit		•
Seton Hill College, Program in Management	371				550	$6500 per year; $360 per credit	•	
Slippery Rock University of Pennsylvania, College of Information Science and Business Administration	371	AC		3	550	$5348 per year (R); $11,776 per year (NR); $210 per credit (R); $367 per credit (NR)	•	
Temple University, Fox School of Business and Management	372	AA	540	3.1	575, 230 (CAT)	$8642 per year (R); $12,002 per year (NR); $348 per credit (R); $488 per credit (NR)	•	•
University of Pennsylvania, Wharton School	373	AA	691	3.5		$28,116 per year	•	
University of Pittsburgh, Joseph M. Katz Graduate School of Business	373	AA	582	3.14	600	$20,627 per year (R); $32,324 per year (NR); $481 per credit (R); $901 per credit (NR)	•	
The University of Scranton, Program in Business Administration	374	AA	510	3.2	500, 173 (CAT)	$515 per credit		
Villanova University, College of Commerce and Finance	374	AA	590	3.2	600	$12,996 per year; $510 per credit		•

| | | | ADMISSION REQUIREMENTS | | | | OPTION | |
This table includes the names and locations of colleges, universities, and other institutions offering MBA and other master's-level business programs. Schools appear in geographical sequence by U.S. state or territory or by country and then alphabetically by school name. Specific degree information is detailed within the profile for each school. Refer to the page number in the table for the school's profile. If a school submitted incomplete data, one or more columns opposite the school name may be blank.	Page Number	Accreditation (AA=AACSB, AC=ACBSP)	Minimum GMAT Score	Minimum Undergraduate GPA	Minimum TOEFL Score	TUITION (R) State Resident (NR) Non-Resident	Financial Aid	Distance Learning
Waynesburg College, Program in Business Administration	375							
West Chester University of Pennsylvania, School of Business and Public Affairs	375		500	3	550	$4464 per year (R); $7294 per year (NR); $210 per credit (R); $367 per credit (NR)		
Widener University, School of Business Administration	375	AA	510	3.2	550, 213 (CAT)	$520 per credit		
Wilkes University, College of Arts, Sciences and Professional Studies	376		450	3	550	$490 per credit		
York College of Pennsylvania, Department of Business Administration	377		494	3.27	530	$300 per credit hour	•	
RHODE ISLAND								
Bryant College, Graduate School	377	AA	530	3.21		$1100 per course	•	•
Johnson & Wales University, The Alan Shawn Feinstein Graduate School	378				550	$212 per quarter hour	•	
Providence College, Department of Business Administration	378		500	3	550	$8640 per year; $750 per course		
Salve Regina University, Graduate School	379		555		550	$5720 per year; $300 per credit		•
University of Rhode Island, College of Business Administration	379	AA	549	3.1	575, 231 (CAT)	$8683 per year (R); $22,194 per year (NR); $197 per credit (R); $562 per credit (NR)	•	
SOUTH CAROLINA								
Charleston Southern University, Program in Business	380		450	2.91	550	$192 per credit hour		
The Citadel, The Military College of South Carolina, College of Graduate and Professional Studies	380	AA						
Clemson University, College of Business and Public Affairs	380	AA	591	3.27	550, 213 (CAT)	$3870 per year (R); $9646 per year (NR); $245 per credit hour (R); $490 per credit hour (NR)		
Francis Marion University, School of Business	381	AA	485	3	550	$2715 per year (R); $5430 per year (NR); $181 per hour (R); $362 per hour (NR)	•	•
South Carolina State University, Department of Agribusiness and Economics	381		400	2.8	550	$3654 per year (R); $7192 per year (NR); $203 per credit (R); $400 per credit (NR)	•	
University of Charleston, South Carolina, School of Business and Economics	382		551	3.41	550	$145 per credit hour (R); $298 per credit hour (NR)		
University of South Carolina, The Darla Moore School of Business	382	AA	600	3.3	600	$4014 per year (R); $8528 per year (NR); $202 per credit hour (R); $428 per credit hour (NR)	•	•
Winthrop University, School of Business Administration	383	AA						•

	Page Number	Accreditation (AA=AACSB, AC=ACBSP)	Minimum GMAT Score	Minimum Undergraduate GPA	Minimum TOEFL Score	TUITION (R) State Resident (NR) Non-Resident	Financial Aid	Distance Learning
SOUTH DAKOTA								
Black Hills State University, College of Business and Technology	384				520	$88.6 per credit (R); $261 per credit (NR)	•	•
University of South Dakota, School of Business	384	AA	518	3.2	550	$203 per credit (R); $382 per credit (NR)		
TENNESSEE								
Belmont University, Jack C. Massey Graduate School of Business	385		530	3	550	$1600 per course		
Christian Brothers University, School of Business	385		520	3.01	550	$375 per credit hour		
Cumberland University, Program in Business Administration	385		480			$595 per hour		
David Lipscomb University, Business Administration Program	386	AC	491	3.11	570, 230 (CAT)	$15,720 per year; $435 per semester hour	•	
East Tennessee State University, College of Business	386	AA	538	3.1	550	$129 per credit hour (R); $340 per credit hour (NR)	•	•
Lincoln Memorial University, Program in Business Administration	387			3	500	$7746 per year; $215 per semester hour	•	
Middle Tennessee State University, College of Business	387	AA	496	2.6	525	$129 per credit hour (R); $340 per credit hour (NR)		•
Rhodes College, Department of Economics/Business Administration	388				550	$18,561 per year	•	
Southern Adventist University, School of Business and Management	388		550	3.35	600	$280 per hour		•
Tennessee State University, College of Business	389	AA	520	2.8	500	$155 per credit (R); $379 per credit (NR)		
Tennessee Technological University, College of Business Administration	389	AA	523	3.2	550	$3082 per year (R); $5116 per year (NR); $154 per hour (R); $224 per hour (NR)	•	
Trevecca Nazarene University, Major in Organizational Management	389		450	2.98	500, 173 (CAT)	$6763 per year	•	
Tusculum College, Program in Organizational Management	390							
Union University, School of Business Administration	390		512		560	$6600 per year		
The University of Memphis, Fogelman College of Business and Economics	390	AA	530	3.3	550	$3436 per year (R); $8600 per year (NR); $176 per credit hour (R); $402 per credit hour (NR)	•	
The University of Tennessee, College of Business Administration	391	AA	625	3.34	550	$3806 per year (R); $9874 per year (NR)		
The University of Tennessee at Chattanooga, Department of Computer Science	392	AA	500	3.2	500	$2478 per year (R); $6078 per year (NR); $480 per course (R); $1137 per course (NR)	•	•

This table includes the names and locations of colleges, universities, and other institutions offering MBA and other master's-level business programs. Schools appear in geographical sequence by U.S. state or territory or by country and then alphabetically by school name. Specific degree information is detailed within the profile for each school. Refer to the page number in the table for the school's profile. If a school submitted incomplete data, one or more columns opposite the school name may be blank.

ADMISSION REQUIREMENTS

OPTION

		ADMISSION REQUIREMENTS				OPTION	
This table includes the names and locations of colleges, universities, and other institutions offering MBA and other master's-level business programs. Schools appear in geographical sequence by U.S. state or territory or by country and then alphabetically by school name. Specific degree information is detailed within the profile for each school. Refer to the page number in the table for the school's profile. If a school submitted incomplete data, one or more columns opposite the school name may be blank.	Page Number	Accreditation (AA=AACSB, AC=ACBSP)	Minimum GMAT Score	Minimum Undergraduate GPA	Minimum TOEFL Score	TUITION (R) State Resident (NR) Non-Resident	Financial Aid	Distance Learning
The University of Tennessee at Martin, School of Business Administration	392	AA	496	3.19	525, 197 (CAT)	$3332 per year (R); $5260 per year (NR); $187 per credit (R); $293 per credit (NR)		•
Vanderbilt University, Owen Graduate School of Management	393	AA	630	3.1		$25,350 per year	•	
TEXAS								
Abilene Christian University, College of Business Administration	394	AC	515	3	500	$8216 per year; $327 per credit hour	•	
Amber University, Department of Business Administration	394			3		$3960 per year; $495 per course		•
Angelo State University, Department of Business Administration	394	AC	503		550	$36 per credit (R); $249 per credit (NR)	•	
Baylor University, Hankamer School of Business	395	AA	605	3.13	600, 250 (CAT)	$18,490 per year; $355 per course	•	
Dallas Baptist University, Graduate School of Business	395	AC		3	550, 213 (CAT)	$5364 per year; $298 per credit	•	•
Hardin-Simmons University, School of Business and Finance	396	AC	615	2.78	550	$5715 per year; $300 per credit	•	
Houston Baptist University, College of Business and Economics	396		530	2.5	550, 213 (CAT)	$1110 per course	•	
Lamar University, College of Business	397	AA	530	3.2	525	$1294 per year (R); $5128 per year (NR); $186 per course (R); $813 per course (NR)	•	
LeTourneau University, Program in Business Administration	397			3	500	$7329 per year		
Midwestern State University, College of Business Administration	398	AC	450	3	550	$42 per hour (R); $222 per hour (NR)	•	•
Our Lady of the Lake University of San Antonio, School of Business and Public Administration	398	AC	440	3.1	550	$448 per credit hour		
Prairie View A&M University, College of Business	399		430	2.86	550, 220 (CAT)	$1844 per year (R); $5660 per year (NR); $120 per credit (R); $254 per credit (NR)	•	
Rice University, Jesse H. Jones Graduate School of Management	399	AA	640	3.2	600, 250 (CAT)	$18,050 per year	•	
St. Edward's University, The College of Professional and Graduate Studies	400		503	3	550	$7236 per year; $402 per credit hour	•	
St. Mary's University of San Antonio, School of Business Administration	400	AA	487	3.12	550, 133 (CAT)	$404 per credit hour	•	
Sam Houston State University, College of Business Administration	401	AA	493	3.09	550, 213 (CAT)	$795 per year (R); $2739 per year (NR); $94 per credit (R); $308 per credit (NR)		•
Southern Methodist University, Edwin L. Cox School of Business	401	AA	640	3.2	600, 250 (CAT)	$22,994 per year; $803 per credit hour	•	
Southwestern Adventist University, Program in Business Administration	402		450	3.25	520	$285 per credit	•	

		ADMISSION REQUIREMENTS				OPTION	
This table includes the names and locations of colleges, universities, and other institutions offering MBA and other master's-level business programs. Schools appear in geographical sequence by U.S. state or territory or by country and then alphabetically by school name. Specific degree information is detailed within the profile for each school. Refer to the page number in the table for the school's profile. If a school submitted incomplete data, one or more columns opposite the school name may be blank.	Page Number	Accreditation (AA=AACSB, AC=ACBSP)	Minimum GMAT Score	Minimum Undergraduate GPA	Minimum TOEFL Score	TUITION (R) State Resident (NR) Non-Resident	Financial Aid	Distance Learning
Southwest Texas State University, School of Business	402	AA	560	3	550	$2564 per year (R); $7652 per year (NR)	•	
Stephen F. Austin State University, College of Business	403	AA	495	3	550	$120 per course (R); $744 per course (NR)	•	
Tarleton State University, College of Business Administration	403	AC	451			$70 per credit hour (R); $272 per credit hour (NR)	•	
Texas A&M International University, Graduate School of International Trade and Business Administration	404		480	3.24	550	$3344 per year (R); $9825 per year (NR)	•	
Texas A&M University, Lowry Mays Graduate School of Business	404	AA	619	3.3	600, 250 (CAT)	$2595 per year (R); $8319 per year (NR)	•	•
Texas A&M University–Commerce, College of Business and Technology	405	AA	505	3.2	500	$2381 per year (R); $8801 per year (NR)	•	•
Texas A&M University–Corpus Christi, College of Business Administration	405	AA	526	3.2	550, 213 (CAT)	$340 per course (R); $985 per course (NR)	•	
Texas A&M University–Kingsville, College of Business Administration	406	AC						
Texas A&M University–Texarkana, Division of Behavioral Sciences and Business Administration	406		520		550	$2196 per year (R); $7368 per year (NR)	•	
Texas Christian University, M. J. Neeley School of Business	407	AA	580	3.1	550, 213 (CAT)	$12,025 per year; $390 per credit	•	
Texas Southern University, Jesse H. Jones School of Business	407		416	3.07	550	$452 per course (R); $1028 per course (NR)		
Texas Tech University, College of Business Administration	407	AA	550	3.31	550, 213 (CAT)	$1968 per year (R); $7032 per year (NR); $72 per credit (R); $285 per credit (NR)	•	
Texas Wesleyan University, School of Business	408							
Texas Woman's University, Department of Business and Economics	409							
University of Dallas, Graduate School of Management	409		550	3.1	520	$10,629 per year; $399 per credit hour		
University of Houston, College of Business Administration	409	AA						
University of Houston–Clear Lake, School of Business and Public Administration	410	AA	550	3.1	550	$167 per credit hour (R); $301 per credit hour (NR)	•	
University of Houston–Victoria, School of Business Administration	410							•
University of Mary Hardin-Baylor, School of Business	410							
University of North Texas, College of Business Administration	411	AA	540	2.95	550	$151 per credit hour (R); $285 per credit hour (NR)	•	
University of St. Thomas, Cameron School of Business	411	AC						

	Page Number	Accreditation (AA=AACSB, AC=ACBSP)	ADMISSION REQUIREMENTS			TUITION (R) State Resident (NR) Non-Resident	OPTION	
This table includes the names and locations of colleges, universities, and other institutions offering MBA and other master's-level business programs. Schools appear in geographical sequence by U.S. state or territory or by country and then alphabetically by school name. Specific degree information is detailed within the profile for each school. Refer to the page number in the table for the school's profile. If a school submitted incomplete data, one or more columns opposite the school name may be blank.			Minimum GMAT Score	Minimum Undergraduate GPA	Minimum TOEFL Score		Financial Aid	Distance Learning
The University of Texas at Arlington, College of Business Administration	411	AA	556	3.25	550, 213 (CAT)	$4521 per year (R); $11,331 per year (NR); $1001 per semester (R); $2357 per semester (NR)		•
The University of Texas at Austin, Graduate School of Business	412	AA	675	3.4	600	$7568 per year (R); $18,788 per year (NR)	•	
The University of Texas at Brownsville, School of Business	413	AC	450	3.2	550	$1540 per year (R); $4464 per year (NR); $229 per course (R); $892 per course (NR)	•	•
The University of Texas at Dallas, School of Management	414		523	3.2	550	$4393 per year (R); $10,225 per year (NR); $169 per semester hour (R); $385 per semester hour (NR)		•
The University of Texas at El Paso, College of Business Administration	414	AA			600	$2350 per year (R); $7294 per year (NR); $409 per course (R); $1033 per course (NR)		•
The University of Texas at San Antonio, College of Business	415	AA	540	3	500	$110 per credit hour (R); $326 per credit hour (NR)	•	
The University of Texas at Tyler, School of Business Administration	415	AA	507	3.2	550	$337 per course (R); $967 per course (NR)		
The University of Texas–Pan American, College of Business Administration	416	AA	470	3.04	500	$1570 per year (R); $6658 per year (NR); $54 per credit hour (R); $248 per credit hour (NR)		
University of the Incarnate Word, College of Professional Studies	416	AC	428	3.09	560	$395 per credit hour		
Wayland Baptist University, Graduate Programs	417		425	3.32	500	$245 per credit hour	•	
West Texas A&M University, T. Boone Pickens College of Business	417	AC	510	2.5	550	$2160 per year (R); $7992 per year (NR); $60 per credit hour (R); $222 per credit hour (NR)	•	•
UTAH								
Brigham Young University, Marriott School of Management	418	AA	642	3.53	570, 230 (CAT)	$5390 per year; $296 per credit hour	•	
Southern Utah University, School of Business	419	AC	500	3.2	500	$2066 per year (R); $6438 per year (NR); $100 per credit (R); $300 per credit (NR)	•	
University of Utah, Graduate School of Business	419	AA	601	3.4	600, 250 (CAT)	$3752 per year (R); $10,954 per year (NR)	•	
Utah State University, College of Business	420	AA						•
Weber State University, John B. Goddard School of Business and Economics	420	AA	590	3.45	550	$2202 per year (R); $6620 per year (NR)	•	•
Westminster College, The Bill and Vieve Gore School of Business	421	AC	520	3.21	550, 213 (CAT)	$492 per credit		
VERMONT								
Saint Michael's College, Program in Administration and Management	421			3.02	550	$305 per credit hour	•	
School for International Training, Master's Programs in Intercultural Management, Leadership, and Service	421				550, 213 (CAT)	$20,805 per year	•	

		ADMISSION REQUIREMENTS				OPTION	
This table includes the names and locations of colleges, universities, and other institutions offering MBA and other master's-level business programs. Schools appear in geographical sequence by U.S. state or territory or by country and then alphabetically by school name. Specific degree information is detailed within the profile for each school. Refer to the page number in the table for the school's profile. If a school submitted incomplete data, one or more columns opposite the school name may be blank.	Page Number	Accreditation (AA=AACSB, AC=ACBSP)	Minimum GMAT Score	Minimum Undergraduate GPA	Minimum TOEFL Score	TUITION (R) State Resident (NR) Non-Resident	Financial Aid	Distance Learning
University of Vermont, School of Business Administration	422	AA	568	3.2	550	$7032 per year (R); $17,580 per year (NR); $293 per credit (R); $733 per credit (NR)		
VIRGINIA								
Averett College, Program in Business Administration	423				500	$6932 per year; $320 per credit hour		•
The College of William and Mary, School of Business	423	AA	630	3.2	600	$6820 per year (R); $16,500 per year (NR); $240 per credit hour (R); $525 per credit hour (NR)	•	
George Mason University, School of Management	423	AA	620	3.25	600	$258 per credit hour (R); $522 per credit hour (NR)		
Hampton University, School of Business	424		410	2.9		$4075 per year; $225 per credit hour	•	
James Madison University, College of Business	424	AA						•
Lynchburg College, School of Business and Economics	425		520	3.06	550	$280 per credit	•	
Marymount University, School of Business Administration	425	AC	500	3	600	$480 per credit	•	
Old Dominion University, College of Business and Public Administration	426	AA			550	$196 per credit hour (R); $520 per credit hour (NR)		•
Radford University, College of Business and Economics	426	AA	500	3.15	550	$3810 per year (R); $7451 per year (NR); $159 per credit hour (R); $310 per credit hour (NR)	•	
Regent University, School of Business	427			3	550	$13,446 per year; $8964 per degree program	•	
Shenandoah University, Byrd School of Business	427		500	3.1	550	$8820 per year; $490 per credit	•	
University of Richmond, Richard S. Reynolds Graduate School	428	AA	598	3.02	600, 250 (CAT)	$20,240 per year; $1125 per course		
University of Virginia, Colgate Darden Graduate School of Business Administration	428	AA	676	3.3		$16,945 per year (R); $22,671 per year (NR)	•	
Virginia Commonwealth University, School of Business	429	AA	560	3	600	$5112 per year (R); $13,027 per year (NR); $264 per credit (R); $704 per credit (NR)		
Virginia Polytechnic Institute and State University, Pamplin College of Business	429	AA	582	3.19	550, 213 (CAT)	$4950 per year (R); $7758 per year (NR); $229 per credit hour (R); $374 per credit hour (NR)	•	•
Virginia State University, School of Business	430				500	$3804 per year (R); $9322 per year (NR); $135 per credit hour (R); $375 per credit hour (NR)		
WASHINGTON								
Antioch University Seattle, Program in Management	430				600	$13,500 per year; $410 per credit	•	
City University, School of Business and Management Professions	431				540	$7056 per year; $294 per credit hour	•	•

	Page Number	Accreditation (AA=AACSB, AC=ACBSP)	Minimum GMAT Score	Minimum Undergraduate GPA	Minimum TOEFL Score	TUITION (R) State Resident (NR) Non-Resident	Financial Aid	Distance Learning
		ADMISSION REQUIREMENTS					OPTION	

This table includes the names and locations of colleges, universities, and other institutions offering MBA and other master's-level business programs. Schools appear in geographical sequence by U.S. state or territory or by country and then alphabetically by school name. Specific degree information is detailed within the profile for each school. Refer to the page number in the table for the school's profile. If a school submitted incomplete data, one or more columns opposite the school name may be blank.

School	Page Number	Accreditation	Min GMAT	Min GPA	Min TOEFL	Tuition	Financial Aid	Distance Learning
Eastern Washington University, College of Business Administration	431	AA	500	3.56	580	$4626 per year (R); $13,464 per year (NR); $144 per credit (R); $428 per credit (NR)		
Gonzaga University, School of Business Administration	432	AA	531	3.15	550	$425 per credit hour	•	
Pacific Lutheran University, School of Business Administration and Management	432	AA	561	3.1	550, 213 (CAT)	$12,168 per year; $507 per credit	•	
Saint Martin's College, Department of Economics and Business Administration	433							
Seattle Pacific University, School of Business and Economics	433	AA	530	3.2	565, 225 (CAT)	$11,394 per year; $422 per credit hour		
Seattle University, Albers School of Business and Economics	433	AA	576	3.1	580, 237 (CAT)	$465 per quarter hour	•	
University of Washington, School of Business Administration	434	AA	628	3.2	600	$5745 per year (R); $14,283 per year (NR); $1642 per quarter (R); $4081 per quarter (NR)	•	
Washington State University, College of Business and Economics	435	AA	560	3.4	580	$5660 per year (R); $13,872 per year (NR); $268 per credit (R); $678 per credit (NR)	•	
Western Washington University, College of Business and Economics	435	AA	573	3.29	565, 227 (CAT)	$4647 per year (R); $13,623 per year (NR); $140 per credit (R); $426 per credit (NR)	•	
Whitworth College, Graduate School of International Management	436		550	3.2	550	$7300 per year; $365 per credit	•	
WEST VIRGINIA								
Marshall University, Lewis College of Business	436	AC	530	3	525	$121 per credit hour (R); $361 per credit hour (NR)		
University of Charleston, Jones-Benedum Division of Business	437							
West Virginia University, College of Business and Economics	437	AA	562		550	$173 per credit hour (R); $479 per credit hour (NR)		•
West Virginia Wesleyan College, Faculty of Business	437				500	$360 per credit hour		
Wheeling Jesuit University, Department of Business	438		456	3.02	550	$7100 per year; $390 per credit hour		
WISCONSIN								
Cardinal Stritch University, College of Business and Management	438				600	$385 per credit		•
Concordia University Wisconsin, Division of Graduate Studies	438	AC		3.23	550	$325 per credit		•
Edgewood College, Program in Business	439			2.75	550	$360 per credit		
Lakeland College, Graduate Studies Division	439							•

	Page Number	Accreditation (AA=AACSB, AC=ACBSP)	Minimum GMAT Score	Minimum Undergraduate GPA	Minimum TOEFL Score	TUITION (R) State Resident (NR) Non-Resident	Financial Aid	Distance Learning
This table includes the names and locations of colleges, universities, and other institutions offering MBA and other master's-level business programs. Schools appear in geographical sequence by U.S. state or territory or by country and then alphabetically by school name. Specific degree information is detailed within the profile for each school. Refer to the page number in the table for the school's profile. If a school submitted incomplete data, one or more columns opposite the school name may be blank.								
Marian College of Fond du Lac, Business Division	440					$285 per credit		
Marquette University, College of Business Administration	440	AA						
Milwaukee School of Engineering, Engineering Management Program	440							•
Silver Lake College, Program in Management and Organizational Behavior	440			3		$275 per credit	•	
University of Wisconsin–Eau Claire, College of Business	441	AA	530	3.2	550	$2 per year (R); $243 per credit (R); $708 per credit (NR)	•	•
University of Wisconsin–Green Bay, Program in Administrative Science	441					$3787 per year (R); $12,145 per year (NR); $225 per credit (R); $690 per credit (NR)		
University of Wisconsin–La Crosse, College of Business Administration	442	AA	500	3.45	550	$4474 per year (R); $12,832 per year (NR); $253 per credit (R); $718 per credit (NR)		•
University of Wisconsin–Madison, School of Business	442	AA	616	3.26	600, 250 (CAT)	$6524 per year (R); $18,282 per year (NR)	•	
University of Wisconsin–Milwaukee, School of Business Administration	443	AA						
University of Wisconsin–Oshkosh, College of Business Administration	443	AA	540	3.1	550, 213 (CAT)	$245 per credit (R); $710 per credit (NR)		
University of Wisconsin–Parkside, School of Business and Technology	444	AA	543	3.32	550	$248 per credit (R); $713 per credit (NR)		
University of Wisconsin–Stout, Program in Training and Development	444				500, 213 (CAT)	$4194 per year (R); $12,552 per year (NR); $233 per credit (R); $697 per credit (NR)	•	
University of Wisconsin–Whitewater, College of Business and Economics	445	AA						•
WYOMING								
University of Wyoming, College of Business	445	AA	538	3.2	540, 207 (CAT)	$2430 per year (R); $7520 per year (NR); $135 per credit hour (R); $418 per credit hour (NR)	•	•
Inter American University of Puerto Rico, San Germán Campus, Department of Business Administration	446			2.5		$3156 per year; $155 per credit	•	
Pontifical Catholic University of Puerto Rico, College of Business Administration	446			3		$3287 per year		
University of Puerto Rico, Mayagüez Campus, College of Business Administration	446							
University of Puerto Rico, Rio Piedras, Graduate School of Business Administration	447		460	3.4		$75 per credit (R)		
University of the Sacred Heart, Department of Business Administration	447		500	2.75		$3070 per year; $300 per credit	•	
University of the Virgin Islands, Division of Business Administration	448			2.1		$228 per credit (R); $456 per credit (NR)		

This table includes the names and locations of colleges, universities, and other institutions offering MBA and other master's-level business programs. Schools appear in geographical sequence by U.S. state or territory or by country and then alphabetically by school name. Specific degree information is detailed within the profile for each school. Refer to the page number in the table for the school's profile. If a school submitted incomplete data, one or more columns opposite the school name may be blank.

School	Accreditation (AA=AACSB, AC=ACBSP)	Page Number	ADMISSION REQUIREMENTS			TUITION (R) State Resident (NR) Non-Resident	OPTION	
			Minimum GMAT Score	Minimum Undergraduate GPA	Minimum TOEFL Score		Financial Aid	Distance Learning
AUSTRALIA								
Australian National University, Australia Asia Management Centre		448			570		•	
Bond University, School of Business		448						
Curtin University of Technology, Graduate School of Business		449						•
Deakin University, Faculty of Business and Law		449			580	10,400 Australian $ per year; 1300 Australian $ per unit		•
Edith Cowan University, Faculty of Business and Public Management		450			600	13,600 Australian $ per year (NR)	•	•
La Trobe University, Graduate School of Management		450			575	9000 Australian $ per year (R); 1000 Australian $ per course (R)		
Macquarie University, Macquarie Graduate School of Management		451			600	1995 Australian $ per unit (R); 1995 Australian $ per unit (NR)		
Monash University, Monash Mt. Eliza Business School MBA Programme		451			580, 237 (CAT)	25,280 Australian $ per degree program		
Murdoch University, School of Business		452	525		550	14,100 Australian $ per year (R); 4700 Australian $ per trimester (R)		•
Queensland University of Technology, Brisbane Graduate School of Business		452	593		575		•	•
Royal Melbourne Institute of Technology, Graduate School of Business		453			580	12,000 Australian $ per year; 6000 Australian $ per year	•	•
Swinburne University of Technology, Swinburne Graduate School of Management		453			580		•	
The University of Adelaide, Graduate School of Management		454	600		575		•	
University of Melbourne, Melbourne Business School		454	640		610, 253 (CAT)		•	
University of Newcastle, Graduate School of Business		455	550		550	12,311 Australian $ per year (R); 1000 Australian $ per course (R)	•	•
University of New South Wales, Australian Graduate School of Management		455	641			21,000 Australian $ per year (R); 1750 Australian $ per course (R)	•	•
University of South Australia, International Graduate School of Management		456			550	10,218 Australian $ per year	•	•
University of Southern Queensland, Faculty of Business		456						•
The University of Sydney, Australian Graduate School of Management		456						
University of Technology, Sydney, Graduate School of Business		457			575	11,520 Australian $ per year (R); 5920 Australian $ per year (R)		

	Page Number	Accreditation (AA=AACSB, AC=ACBSP)	Minimum GMAT Score	Minimum Undergraduate GPA	Minimum TOEFL Score	TUITION (R) State Resident (NR) Non-Resident	Financial Aid	Distance Learning
The University of Western Australia, Graduate School of Management	457		605		550	1300 Australian $ per unit (R); 2000 Australian $ per unit (NR)		
University of Western Sydney, Macarthur, Faculty of Business and Technology	458							
AUSTRIA								
Vienna University of Economics and Business Administration, WU Wien MBA	458		593	3.3	600	$25,000 per year (R); $25,000 per year (NR)	•	
BANGLADESH								
International University of Business Agriculture and Technology (IUBAT), College of Business Administration	459							
BELGIUM								
The International Management Institute, International Business School	459		500	2	450	$9000 per year		•
Katholieke Universiteit Leuven, Department of Applied Economic Sciences	459							
St. Ignatius University Faculty of Antwerp (UFSIA), Center for Business Administration	460							
CANADA								
Athabasca University, Centre for Innovative Management	460					$25,000 Canadian per degree program (R); $25,000 Canadian per degree program (NR)		•
Carleton University, School of Business	460		550	9/12 scale	550		•	
Concordia University, Faculty of Commerce and Administration	461	AA	610	3.3/4.3 scale	600	$1176 Canadian per year (R); $2195 Canadian per year (NR); $56 Canadian per credit (R); $124 Canadian per credit (NR)	•	
Dalhousie University, Faculty of Management	461		560	3.6/4.3 scale	580, 237 (CAT)	$5900 Canadian per year (R); $5900 Canadian per year (NR); $590 Canadian per course (R); $590 Canadian per course (NR)	•	•
École des Hautes Études Commerciales, Program in Business Administration and Management	462					$3328 Canadian per year (R); $6278 Canadian per year (NR); $87 Canadian per credit (R); $146 Canadian per credit (NR)		
Laurentian University, School of Commerce and Administration	463		574		550	$5640 Canadian per year (R); $11,280 Canadian per year (NR); $564 Canadian per course (R); $1128 Canadian per course (NR)		•
McGill University, Faculty of Management	463		637	3.34	600, 250 (CAT)		•	
McMaster University, Michael G. DeGroote School of Business	464		620	3.5	580, 230 (CAT)	$4856 Canadian per year (R); $4856 Canadian per year (NR); $570 Canadian per course (R); $570 Canadian per course (NR)	•	
Memorial University of Newfoundland, Faculty of Business Administration	464		580	2.5/3 scale	580, 237 (CAT)	$2900 Canadian per year (R); $2900 Canadian per year (NR); $5800 Canadian per degree program (R); $5800 Canadian per degree program (NR)	•	
Queen's University at Kingston, School of Business	465	AA	672	3.2	600, 250 (CAT)	$35,365 Canadian per year (R); $35,365 Canadian per year (NR)		•

	Page Number	Accreditation (AA=AACSB, AC=ACBSP)	Minimum GMAT Score	Minimum Undergraduate GPA	Minimum TOEFL Score	TUITION (R) State Resident (NR) Non-Resident	Financial Aid	Distance Learning
		ADMISSION REQUIREMENTS					**OPTION**	
Saint Mary's University, Faculty of Commerce	465		570	3.3	550	$827 Canadian per credit (R); $1555 Canadian per credit (NR)	•	
Simon Fraser University, Faculty of Business Administration	465		620	3.3	570, 230 (CAT)	$2729 Canadian per year (R); $2729 Canadian per year (NR)	•	
Université de Moncton, Faculty of Administration	466			3		$132 Canadian per credit (R); $176 Canadian per credit (NR)	•	•
Université de Sherbrooke, Faculty of Administration	466							
Université du Québec à Montréal, Ecole des Sciences de la Gestion	467			3.2/ 4.3 scale		$4200 Canadian per year (R); $8000 Canadian per year (NR); $4200 Canadian per year (R); $8000 Canadian per year (NR)		
Université Laval, Faculty of Administrative Sciences	467	AA				$775 Canadian per semester (R); $3728 Canadian per semester (NR)		
University of Alberta, Faculty of Business	467	AA						
University of British Columbia, Faculty of Commerce and Business Administration	468		620	3.3	600, 250 (CAT)	$7235 Canadian per year (R); $7235 Canadian per year (NR)	•	
University of Calgary, Faculty of Management	468	AA	610	3.27	600	$510 Canadian per credit (R); $1020 Canadian per credit (NR)	•	
University of Guelph, Department of Agricultural Economics and Business	469			3	550, 213 (CAT)	$7500 Canadian per year (R); $7500 Canadian per year (NR)	•	
University of Manitoba, Faculty of Management	469	AA	576	3.3	550, 213 (CAT)	$25,600 Canadian per year (R); $9500 Canadian per degree program (R)	•	
University of New Brunswick, Faculty of Administration	470		550	3.3	550	$4350 Canadian per year (R); $435 Canadian per course (R)	•	
University of New Brunswick, Faculty of Business	470		570	3.3/ 4.3 scale	550, 213 (CAT)	$21,050 Canadian per year (R); $21,050 Canadian per year (NR); $435 Canadian per course (R)	•	
University of Ottawa, Faculty of Administration	471		580	3	580	$2550 Canadian per year (R); $7000 Canadian per year (NR); $270 Canadian per credit (R); $750 Canadian per credit (NR)	•	
University of Regina, Faculty of Administration	471		560	3.2	580	$188 Canadian per credit hour (R); $188 Canadian per credit hour (NR)	•	
University of Saskatchewan, College of Commerce	472		538		550, 213 (CAT)	$382 Canadian per course (R); $382 Canadian per course (NR)	•	
University of Toronto, Joseph L. Rotman School of Management	472	AA	672	3.3	600, 250 (CAT)	$16,400 Canadian per year (R); $20,500 Canadian per year (NR)	•	
University of Victoria, Faculty of Business	473		585	3.2	575, 230 (CAT)	$4267 Canadian per year (R); $4267 Canadian per year (NR); $7330 Canadian per degree program (R); $7330 Canadian per degree program (NR)	•	
University of Waterloo, Graduate Studies Office	473				550, 213 (CAT)	$4848 Canadian per year (R)	•	
The University of Western Ontario, Ivey Business School	474		657	3	600	$16,000 Canadian per year (R); $16,000 Canadian per year (NR)	•	
University of Windsor, Faculty of Business Administration	474		575	3.5	600	$4368 Canadian per year (R); $6195 Canadian per year (NR); $837 Canadian per semester (R); $1008 Canadian per semester (NR)	•	

This table includes the names and locations of colleges, universities, and other institutions offering MBA and other master's-level business programs. Schools appear in geographical sequence by U.S. state or territory or by country and then alphabetically by school name. Specific degree information is detailed within the profile for each school. Refer to the page number in the table for the school's profile. If a school submitted incomplete data, one or more columns opposite the school name may be blank.

		ADMISSION REQUIREMENTS				OPTION	
This table includes the names and locations of colleges, universities, and other institutions offering MBA and other master's-level business programs. Schools appear in geographical sequence by U.S. state or territory or by country and then alphabetically by school name. Specific degree information is detailed within the profile for each school. Refer to the page number in the table for the school's profile. If a school submitted incomplete data, one or more columns opposite the school name may be blank.	Page Number	Accreditation (AA=AACSB, AC=ACBSP)	Minimum GMAT Score	Minimum Undergraduate GPA	Minimum TOEFL Score	TUITION (R) State Resident (NR) Non-Resident	Financial Aid	Distance Learning
Wilfrid Laurier University, School of Business and Economics	475		590	9/12 scale	550	$9118 Canadian per year (R); $14,272 Canadian per year (NR); $1102 Canadian per term (R)	•	
York University, Schulich School of Business	475		640	3.3	600	$5000 Canadian per year (R); $2000 Canadian per term (R); $4300 Canadian per term (NR)	•	
CAYMAN ISLANDS								
International College of the Cayman Islands, Graduate Program in Management	476				550	$3000 per year; $100 per credit		
CHINA								
The Chinese University of Hong Kong, Faculty of Business Administration	477	AA						
City University of Hong Kong, Faculty of Business	477		570		550	42,500 Hong Kong dollars per year; 9900 Hong Kong dollars per course		•
Fudan University, School of Management	477							
Hong Kong Baptist University, School of Business	477		500			54,000 Hong Kong dollars per year (R); 54,000 Hong Kong dollars per year (NR)	•	
The Hong Kong University of Science and Technology, School of Business and Management	478							
University of Hong Kong, University of Hong Kong School of Business	478				550	78,600 Hong Kong dollars per year (R); 78,600 Hong Kong dollars per year (NR)		
COSTA RICA								
Instituto Centroamericano de Administración de Empresas, MBA Program	479		580			$14,000 per year	•	
CZECH REPUBLIC								
CMC Graduate School of Business, Business Programs	479		544		550	$500 per course (R)	•	
DENMARK								
Copenhagen Business School, Faculty of Economics and Business Administration	480				575, 230 (CAT)			
EGYPT								
American University in Cairo, School of Business, Economics and Communication	480							
FINLAND								
Helsinki School of Economics and Business Administration, International Center	481							

	Page Number	Accreditation (AA=AACSB, AC=ACBSP)	ADMISSION REQUIREMENTS			TUITION (R) State Resident (NR) Non-Resident	OPTION	
This table includes the names and locations of colleges, universities, and other institutions offering MBA and other master's-level business programs. Schools appear in geographical sequence by U.S. state or territory or by country and then alphabetically by school name. Specific degree information is detailed within the profile for each school. Refer to the page number in the table for the school's profile. If a school submitted incomplete data, one or more columns opposite the school name may be blank.			Minimum GMAT Score	Minimum Undergraduate GPA	Minimum TOEFL Score		Financial Aid	Distance Learning
FRANCE								
Ècole de Management, Cesma MBA	481		600		600, 250 (CAT)	18,000 euros per year	•	
École Supérieure des Sciences Économiques et Commerciales, ESSEC Business School	481		620		500	158,000 French francs per degree program		
ESCP-EAP European School of Management, School of Management	482		574		600	125,000 French francs per year (R); 125,000 French francs per year (NR)		
Groupe CERAM, Ceram ESC Nice School of Management	483							
Groupe ESC Clermont, Clermont Graduate School of Management	483							
Groupe ESC Nantes Atlantique, Groupe ESC Nantes Atlantique Business Programs	483							•
Groupe ESC Toulouse, ESC Toulouse Graduate School of Management	483					40,000 French francs per year		
HEC School of Management, HEC MBA Program	484							
INSEAD (The European Institute of Business Administration), MBA Department	484		685		620, 260 (CAT)	27,900 euros per year	•	
Institut Superieur de Gestion, ISG International School of Business	485		570	3.4	550	85,000 French francs per year; 3000 French francs per course		
L'École Nationale des Ponts et Chaussées, ENPC MBA School of International Management	485		600		550	110,000 French francs per year; 145,000 French francs per degree program	•	
Schiller International University, MBA Program	485				550	106,300 French francs per year; 6900 French francs per course	•	
Schiller International University, MBA Program, Strasbourg, France Campus	486				550	3900 French francs per course	•	
Theseus Institute, International Management Institute	486		600			18,500 euros per year	•	
GERMANY								
ESCP-EAP European School of Management, Business Programs	487							
European Business School, European Business School Germany	487				570, 230 (CAT)	9500 euros per year		
Schiller International University, MBA Program, Heildleberg, Germany	487				550	27,740 German marks per year; 1800 German marks per course	•	
University of Applied Sciences Esslingen, Graduate School	488		620		550		•	
WHU Koblenz, Otto-Beisheim Graduate School of Management	488		649		220 (CAT)	59,000 German marks per degree program	•	

	Page Number	Accreditation (AA=AACSB, AC=ACBSP)	Minimum GMAT Score	Minimum Undergraduate GPA	Minimum TOEFL Score	TUITION (R) State Resident (NR) Non-Resident	Financial Aid	Distance Learning
INDONESIA								
Institut Pengembangan Manajemen Indonesia, Business Programs	489		518					•
IRELAND								
National University of Ireland, Cork, Faculty of Commerce	489		475			5250 Irish punt per year (R); 5250 Irish punt per year (NR)		
National University of Ireland, Dublin, The Michael Smurfit Graduate School of Business	490		585			10,500 Irish punt per year (R); 11,000 Irish punt per year (NR); 5125 Irish punt per semester (R); 5125 Irish punt per semester (NR)		
National University of Ireland, Galway, Faculty of Commerce	490							
University of Limerick, College of Business	490		560		550		•	•
ISRAEL								
Bar-Ilan University, S. Daniel Abraham Center of Economics and Business, The Graduate School of Business	491					$18,000 per year		
Tel Aviv University, Leon Recanati Graduate School of Business Administration	491		600			$2700 per year	•	
ITALY								
Bocconi University, SDA Bocconi	492		630			21,500 euros per year	•	
JAPAN								
International University of Japan, Graduate School of International Management	492		580		550	1,900,000 Japanese yen per year	•	
Waseda University, Graduate School of Asia-Pacific Studies	493					1,706,000 Japanese yen per year; 65,000 Japanese yen per unit	•	
MEXICO								
Duxx Graduate School of Business Leadership, Business Programs	493		550		610, 253 (CAT)	$9500 per year		
Instituto Tecnológico y de Estudios Superiores de Monterrey, Campus Monterrey, Graduate School of Management and Leadership	494			84/ 100 scale		$11,355 per year; $1300 per course		•
Instituto Tecnológico y de Estudios Superiores de Monterrey, Campus Querétaro, Posgrados, MBA Program	494				570	$1280 per course		
Universidad de las Américas–Puebla, School of Business Administration	495				500			

This table includes the names and locations of colleges, universities, and other institutions offering MBA and other master's-level business programs. Schools appear in geographical sequence by U.S. state or territory or by country and then alphabetically by school name. Specific degree information is detailed within the profile for each school. Refer to the page number in the table for the school's profile. If a school submitted incomplete data, one or more columns opposite the school name may be blank.

	Page Number	Accreditation (AA=AACSB, AC=ACBSP)	ADMISSION REQUIREMENTS			TUITION (R) State Resident (NR) Non-Resident	OPTION	
			Minimum GMAT Score	Minimum Undergraduate GPA	Minimum TOEFL Score		Financial Aid	Distance Learning

This table includes the names and locations of colleges, universities, and other institutions offering MBA and other master's-level business programs. Schools appear in geographical sequence by U.S. state or territory or by country and then alphabetically by school name. Specific degree information is detailed within the profile for each school. Refer to the page number in the table for the school's profile. If a school submitted incomplete data, one or more columns opposite the school name may be blank.

	Page Number	Accreditation	Min GMAT	Min GPA	Min TOEFL	TUITION	Financial Aid	Distance Learning
MONACO								
University of Southern Europe, Monaco Graduate Business School	495		510				•	
NETHERLANDS								
Erasmus University Rotterdam, Rotterdam School of Management	495	AA	620			27,500 euros per year	•	
Haagse Hogeschool University, Faculty of Economics and Management	496							
Maastricht School of Management, Business Programs	496				350			
Open University of the Netherlands, Business Programs	497							•
Univeroiteit Nyenrode, Netherlands Business School	497		600	3.5	600, 250 (CAT)	102,500 Dutch guilders per degree program		•
University of Twente, TSM Business School	497		550				•	
NEW ZEALAND								
University of Canterbury, Department of Management	498							
University of Otago, Graduate School of Business	498		600		650	25,000 New Zealand dollars per degree program (R)		
University of Waikato, Waikato Management School	498						•	
Victoria University of Wellington, Graduate School of Business and Government Management	499							
NORWAY								
Norwegian School of Management, Graduate School	499							
PAKISTAN								
Lahore University of Management Sciences, Graduate School of Business Administration	499		560			174,000 Pakistani rupees per year	•	
PERU								
Escuela de Administracion de Negocios para Graduados, Programa Magister	500					$18,500 per year	•	

	Page Number	Accreditation (AA=AACSB, AC=ACBSP)	ADMISSION REQUIREMENTS			TUITION (R) State Resident (NR) Non-Resident	OPTION	
This table includes the names and locations of colleges, universities, and other institutions offering MBA and other master's-level business programs. Schools appear in geographical sequence by U.S. state or territory or by country and then alphabetically by school name. Specific degree information is detailed within the profile for each school. Refer to the page number in the table for the school's profile. If a school submitted incomplete data, one or more columns opposite the school name may be blank.			Minimum GMAT Score	Minimum Undergraduate GPA	Minimum TOEFL Score		Financial Aid	Distance Learning
PORTUGAL								
Universidade Nova de Lisboa, Faculdade de Economia-Gestao	500							
RUSSIAN FEDERATION								
The International Management Institute of St. Petersburg, International Management Institute of St. Petersburg	501		610		500	$6000 per degree program		
SINGAPORE								
Nanyang Technological University, Nanyang Business School	501		610	3.2	600	3500 Singapore dollars per year (R); 2500 Singapore dollars per trimester (R)	•	
National University of Singapore, Graduate School of Business	501							
SLOVENIA								
IEDC-Bled School of Management, School of Business Administration	502		540			15,500 euros per year	•	
SOUTH AFRICA								
Rhodes University, Management Department	503							
University of Cape Town, Graduate School of Business	503		580		600	40,000 South African rand per year (R); 24,000 South African rand per year (R)	•	
University of the Witwatersrand, Graduate School of Business Administration	503		580				•	
SPAIN								
Escola d'Alta Direcció i Administració (EADA), Business Programs	504							
ESCP-EAP European School of Management, Business School	504				600			
Escuela Superior de Administracion y Direccion de Empresas, Business School	504		620		600, 250 (CAT)	14,875 euros per year; 12,770 euros per year	•	
IADE, Instituto Universitario de Administracion de Empresas	505							
Instituto de Empresa, Business School	505		630		620, 260 (CAT)	21,035 ECU per year (R)	•	
Schiller International University, MBA Program, Madrid, Spain Campus	505				550	1,931,000 Spanish pesetas per year; 125,000 Spanish pesetas per course	•	
University of Navarra, IESE	506		640		600	$17,925 per year	•	

	Page Number	Accreditation (AA=AACSB, AC=ACBSP)	Minimum GMAT Score	Minimum Undergraduate GPA	Minimum TOEFL Score	TUITION (R) State Resident (NR) Non-Resident	Financial Aid	Distance Learning
ADMISSION REQUIREMENTS							**OPTION**	

This table includes the names and locations of colleges, universities, and other institutions offering MBA and other master's-level business programs. Schools appear in geographical sequence by U.S. state or territory or by country and then alphabetically by school name. Specific degree information is detailed within the profile for each school. Refer to the page number in the table for the school's profile. If a school submitted incomplete data, one or more columns opposite the school name may be blank.

School	Page Number	Accreditation	Min GMAT	Min GPA	Min TOEFL	Tuition	Financial Aid	Distance Learning
SWEDEN								
Stockholm School of Economics, Department of Business Administration	506							
SWITZERLAND								
American Graduate School of Business, Master of International Business Administration Program	507		520		550	26,000 Swiss francs per year; 2700 Swiss francs per course	•	
Graduate School of Business Administration Zurich, Business Programs	507		560		500	15,000 Swiss francs per year; 30,000 Swiss francs per degree program		•
IMD International Institute for Management Development, Business Programs	508		650			45,000 Swiss francs per year	•	
Schiller International University, American College of Switzerland, MBA Program	508				550	32,200 Swiss francs per year	•	
Université de Lausanne, Ecole des Hautes Etudes Commerciales	508							
University of St. Gallen, Business School	509							
THAILAND								
Bangkok University, Graduate School	509							
Chulalongkorn University, Sasin Graduate Institute of Business Administration	509							
TURKEY								
Bilkent University, School of Business Administration	509		550	2.93	550	$6500 per year	•	
UNITED ARAB EMIRATES								
The American University in Dubai, MBA Program	510			2.9	550, 213 (CAT)	$13,625 per year; $1365 per quarter		
UNITED KINGDOM								
American InterContinental University, Program in Business Administration	510			3.1	550	$5407 per year	•	
Ashridge, Ashridge Executive MBA Program	511							
Aston University, Aston Business School	511		620		600	10,250 British pounds per course (R); 12,750 British pounds per course (NR)		•
City University, Business School	512		620		650	16,000 British pounds per year (R); 16,000 British pounds per year (NR); 20,000 British pounds per degree program (R); 20,000 British pounds per degree program (NR)	•	

This table includes the names and locations of colleges, universities, and other institutions offering MBA and other master's-level business programs. Schools appear in geographical sequence by U.S. state or territory or by country and then alphabetically by school name. Specific degree information is detailed within the profile for each school. Refer to the page number in the table for the school's profile. If a school submitted incomplete data, one or more columns opposite the school name may be blank.

	Page Number	Accreditation (AA=AACSB, AC=ACBSP)	Minimum GMAT Score	Minimum Undergraduate GPA	Minimum TOEFL Score	TUITION (R) State Resident (NR) Non-Resident	Financial Aid	Distance Learning
		ADMISSION REQUIREMENTS					OPTION	
Cranfield University, Cranfield School of Management	512		640		600, 250 (CAT)	18,500 British pounds per year (R); 18,500 British pounds per year (NR); 12,000 British pounds per year (R); 12,000 British pounds per year (NR)	•	
De Montfort University, De Montfort University School of Business	513							•
ESCP-EAP European School of Management, Business Programs	513		570		600, 230 (CAT)		•	
Henley Management College, Business Programs	513					17,000 British pounds per degree program		•
Heriot-Watt University, Edinburgh Business School	514							•
Huron University USA in London, MBA Program	514		550	3	550, 213 (CAT)	9840 British pounds per year; 795 British pounds per course	•	
Imperial College, Management School	515							
Kingston University, Kingston Business School	515				600	5250 British pounds per year		
Lancaster University, Management School	515		613		600, 250 (CAT)	15,000 British pounds per year (R); 15,000 British pounds per year (NR); 15,000 British pounds per degree program (R); 15,000 British pounds per degree program (NR)		•
London School of Economics and Political Science, The Graduate School	516				600	9360 British pounds per year (R); 9360 British pounds per year (NR); 4680 British pounds per year (R); 4680 British pounds per year (NR)	•	
Loughborough University, The Business School—Postgraduate Office	516				550	2700 British pounds per year (R); 2700 British pounds per year (NR)	•	
Manchester Metropolitan University, Faculty of Management and Business, Department of Management	517					9000 British pounds per degree program (R)	•	
Middlesex University, Business School	517				580	9900 British pounds per year (R); 9900 British pounds per year (NR)	•	
Napier University, Napier Business School	518					4995 British pounds per year (R); 7200 British pounds per year (NR); 5775 British pounds per degree program		•
Open University, Business School	518					1520 British pounds per course (R); 1520 British pounds per course (NR)		•
Oxford Brookes University, School of Business	518		520		550, 213 (CAT)	8700 British pounds per year (R)	•	•
Richmond, The American International University in London, School of Business	519		540	3.3	600, 240 (CAT)	14,960 British pounds per year	•	
Schiller International University, Graduate Programs, London Campus	519				550	9600 British pounds per year; 620 British pounds per course	•	•
Sheffield Hallam University, Business School	520		550		500	1300 British pounds per semester (R); 1300 British pounds per semester (NR)		•
South Bank University, Business School	521				600	6250 British pounds per semester (R)	•	
University of Bath, School of Management	521		580		600, 250 (CAT)	15,750 British pounds per year (R); 15,750 British pounds per year (NR); 14,000 British pounds per course (R); 14,000 British pounds per course (NR)	•	

	Page Number	ADMISSION REQUIREMENTS			TUITION (R) State Resident (NR) Non-Resident	OPTION	
This table includes the names and locations of colleges, universities, and other institutions offering MBA and other master's-level business programs. Schools appear in geographical sequence by U.S. state or territory or by country and then alphabetically by school name. Specific degree information is detailed within the profile for each school. Refer to the page number in the table for the school's profile. If a school submitted incomplete data, one or more columns opposite the school name may be blank.		Accreditation (AA=AACSB, AC=ACBSP)	Minimum GMAT Score	Minimum Undergraduate GPA	Minimum TOEFL Score	Financial Aid	Distance Learning
University of Birmingham, Birmingham Business School	522		590		550	8750 British pounds per year (R); 9750 British pounds per year (NR)	•	
University of Brighton, Brighton Business School	522		550		590	7000 British pounds per year (R); 8000 British pounds per year (NR)	•	
University of Cambridge, The Judge Institute Of Management	523				600, 250 (CAT)	$30,400 per year (R); $30,400 per year (NR)	•	•
University of Durham, Business School	523				550	12,000 British pounds per year (R); 9750 British pounds per degree program (R)		•
University of Edinburgh, Edinburgh University Management School	524		600		580		•	
University of Glasgow, University of Glasgow Business School	525		600		570	8000 British pounds per year (R); 11,000 British pounds per year (NR); 4000 British pounds per year (R)		
University of Hull, School of Management	525							
University of London, London Business School	525		680		630, 267 (CAT)		•	
The University of Manchester, Manchester Business School	526		603		580	22,000 British pounds per year (R); 22,000 British pounds per year (NR)		•
University of Newcastle upon Tyne, School of Management	526		530		580	7500 British pounds per year (R); 9500 British pounds per year (NR); 7950 British pounds per degree program (R)		•
University of Northumbria at Newcastle, Newcastle Business School	527				550			•
University of Nottingham, Business School	527							
University of Oxford, Saïd Business School	528		664		600, 250 (CAT)	16,000 British pounds per year (R); 16,000 British pounds per year (NR)	•	
University of Plymouth, Graduate Business School	528				570	2700 British pounds per year (R); 2700 British pounds per year (NR)	•	
University of Reading, ISMA Centre	529		615	3.3	590	9500 British pounds per year	•	
University of Salford, Graduate School of Management	529							
University of Sheffield, Management School	529		575		600, 250 (CAT)	7750 British pounds per year (R)		
University of Stirling, Faculty of Management	530				550, 213 (CAT)		•	
University of Strathclyde, Graduate School of Business	530		590		600, 250 (CAT)	9750 British pounds per degree program (R); 9750 British pounds per degree program (NR)	•	•
University of the West of England, Bristol, Bristol Business School	531				570	9487 British pounds per year (R); 9487 British pounds per year (NR); 8384 British pounds per degree program (R); 8384 British pounds per degree program (NR)		
University of Ulster at Jordanstown, Faculty of Business and Management	531							

| | | ADMISSION REQUIREMENTS | | | | | OPTION | |
	Page Number	Accreditation (AA=AACSB, AC=ACBSP)	Minimum GMAT Score	Minimum Undergraduate GPA	Minimum TOEFL Score	TUITION (R) State Resident (NR) Non-Resident	Financial Aid	Distance Learning
This table includes the names and locations of colleges, universities, and other institutions offering MBA and other master's-level business programs. Schools appear in geographical sequence by U.S. state or territory or by country and then alphabetically by school name. Specific degree information is detailed within the profile for each school. Refer to the page number in the table for the school's profile. If a school submitted incomplete data, one or more columns opposite the school name may be blank.								
University of Wales, Cardiff Business School	531							
University of Warwick, Warwick Business School	532	AA	610		600	19,000 British pounds per year (R); 19,000 British pounds per year (NR); 9075 British pounds per degree program (R)	•	•
University of Westminster, Harrow Business School	532				600	7735 British pounds per year	•	•

Profiles of Business Schools and MBA Programs

This section contains factual profiles of colleges, with a focus on their MBA programs. Each profile covers such items as enrollment, tuition, entrance and admission requirements, financial aid, programs of study, placement, and whom to contact for program information.

The information in each profile was collected via Peterson's MBA and Master's-Level Business Programs Survey, which was sent to the dean or director of the business school or MBA program at each institution.

The profiles are arranged geographically, then alphabetically within the state or country.

ALABAMA

Alabama Agricultural and Mechanical University

Normal, Alabama

SCHOOL OF BUSINESS

Graduate Business Faculty
Full-time: 15

Student Body
Total: 152   Average Age: 28

Admissions
Applications: 25   Average GMAT: 425
Admitted: 17   Average GPA: 2.8
Enrolled: 17

Costs (1999–2000)
Full-time tuition: N/R
Part-time tuition: $150 per credit hour (resident), $415 per credit hour (nonresident)

After Graduation (Class of 1998–99)
Employed within 3 months of graduation: 92%
Average starting salary: $62,000

DEGREES MBA • MS

MBA—Master of Business Administration Full-time and part-time. 36 to 66 total credits required. 24 to 72 months to complete program. *Concentrations:* accounting, economics, finance, human resources, logistics, management, marketing.

MS—Master of Science in Economics Full-time and part-time. GRE is required. At least 36 total credits required. 24 to 72 months to complete program. *Concentrations:* economics.

COSTS

Tuition, state resident: *Part-time* $150 per credit hour. **Tuition, nonresident:** *Part-time* $415 per credit hour. Tuition varies by number of courses or credits taken and local reciprocity agreements. **Required fees:** *Part-time* $120 per semester.

FINANCIAL AID (1999–2000)

7 students received aid, including fellowships, loans, research assistantships, teaching assistantships, and work study. Financial aid application deadline: 4/1. **Financial Aid Contact** Mr. Carlos Clark, Director of Financial Aid, PO Box 1357, Normal, AL 35762-1357. **Phone:** 256-851-5056. **Fax:** 256-851-5407. **E-mail:** financialaid@aamu.edu.

RESOURCES AND SERVICES

Information about online services, personal computer policies, library resources, international exchange programs, internship programs, and placement services at this institution and others can be found at **www.petersons.com/mba**

International Students

Services and Facilities Counseling/support services. Financial aid is available to international students.
Applying *Required:* TOEFL with recommended score of 550 (paper), proof of adequate funds.

International Student Contact Dr. Exir Brennan, Dean of Graduate Studies, PO Box 998, Normal, AL 35762. **Phone:** 256-851-5266. **Fax:** 256-859-3641. **E-mail:** ebrennan@aamu.edu.

■ APPLICATION

Required GMAT, application form, baccalaureate/first degree, essay, 3 letters of recommendation, resume/curriculum vitae, transcripts of college work. **Recommended** Work experience.
Deadlines and Fees *Deadlines:* 7/1 for fall, 10/1 for spring, 3/1 for summer. *Application fee:* $15, $25 (international).
Application Contact Dr. Uchenna Elike, Director, MBA Program, PO Box 429, Normal, AL 35762. **Phone:** 256-858-8487. **Fax:** 256-851-5310. **E-mail:** uelike@aamu.edu.

Auburn University

Auburn University, Alabama

COLLEGE OF BUSINESS

Graduate Business Faculty
Full-time: 85   Part-time: 6

Student Body
Total: 450   Average Age: 27
Full-time: 251   Women: 31%
Part-time: 199

Admissions
Applications: 450   Average GMAT: 578
Admitted: 235   Average GPA: 3.2
Enrolled: 206

Costs (1999–2000)
Full-time tuition: $3050 per academic year (resident), $9150 per academic year (nonresident)
Part-time tuition: $126 per credit (resident), $378 per credit (nonresident)

After Graduation (Class of 1998–99)
Employed within 3 months of graduation: 98%
Average starting salary: $47,350

Accreditation
AACSB—The International Association for Management Education

DEGREES MBA

MBA—Executive Master of Business Administration Full-time. *Distance learning option.* At least 36 total credits required. Minimum of 22 months to complete program. *Concentrations:* executive programs, general MBA.

MBA—Physician's Executive Masters of Business Administration Full-time. *Distance learning option.* At least 36 total credits required. Minimum of 22 months to complete program. *Concentrations:* health care, general MBA.

MBA—Techno-Executive Masters of Business Administration Full-time. *Distance learning option.* At least 36 total credits required. Minimum of 21 months to complete program. *Concentrations:* executive programs, general MBA.

MBA—Video-based Outreach MBA Full-time and part-time. *Distance learning option.* 39 to 42 total credits required. 18 to 60 months to complete program. *Concentrations:* finance, health care, human resources, management information systems, marketing, operations management, production management, technology management.

MBA—Master of Business Administration Full-time and part-time. 36 to 42 total credits required. 18 to 60 months to complete program. *Concentrations:* agribusiness, economics, finance, health care, human resources, management information systems, marketing, operations management, production management, sports/entertainment management, technology management, aviation management.

COSTS

Tuition, state resident: *Full-time* $3050. *Part-time* $126 per credit. **Tuition, nonresident:** *Full-time* $9150. *Part-time* $378 per credit. Tuition varies by number of courses or credits taken. **Graduate housing:** Room and board costs vary by number of occupants, type of accommodation, and type of board plan. *Typical cost:* $5300 (including board).

FINANCIAL AID (1999–2000)

135 students received aid, including fellowships, research assistantships, scholarships, teaching assistantships, and work study. Aid is available to part-time students. Financial aid application deadline: 3/15. **Financial Aid Contact** Mr. Mike Reynolds, Director—Student Financial Aid, 203 Mary Martin Hall, Auburn University, AL 36849. **Phone:** 334-844-4723. **E-mail:** reyom2@auburn.edu.

RESOURCES AND SERVICES

Information about online services, personal computer policies, library resources, international exchange programs, internship programs, and placement services at this institution and others can be found at **www.petersons.com/mba**

International Students

6% of students enrolled are international students.

Services and Facilities Counseling/support services, ESL/language courses, international student housing, international student organization, orientation, visa services. Financial aid is available to international students.
Applying *Required:* TOEFL with recommended score of 213 (computer) or 550 (paper), proof of adequate funds, proof of health/immunizations.

International Student Contact Ms. Mary Jo Wear, Assistant Director, International Programs, 201 Hargis Hall, Auburn University, AL 36849. **Phone:** 334-844-4505. **Fax:** 334-844-5074. **E-mail:** wearmar@auburn.edu.

■ **APPLICATION**

Required GMAT, application form, baccalaureate/first degree, essay, 3 letters of recommendation, personal statement, resume/curriculum vitae, transcripts of college work. **Recommended** Interview, 2 years of work experience.

Deadlines and Fees *Deadlines:* 5/1 for fall, 5/1 for fall (international). *Application fee:* $25, $50 (international).

Application Contact Dr. Daniel M. Gropper, Assistant Dean and Executive Director, MBA Programs, Suite 503, Lowder Building, Auburn University, AL 36849. **Phone:** 334-844-4060. **Fax:** 344-844-2964. **E-mail:** groppdm@auburn.edu.

See full description on page 552.

Auburn University Montgomery

Montgomery, Alabama

SCHOOL OF BUSINESS

Graduate Business Faculty
Full-time: 37   Part-time: 1

Student Body
Total: 227   Women: 37%
Average Age: 33

Admissions
Applications: 75   Average GMAT: 500
Admitted: 68   Average GPA: 3
Enrolled: 63

Costs (1999–2000)
Full-time tuition: N/R
Part-time tuition: $120 per credit hour (resident), $360 per credit hour
(nonresident)

After Graduation (Class of 1998–99)
Employed within 3 months of graduation: 99%
Average starting salary: $36,000

Accreditation
AACSB—The International Association for Management Education

DEGREE MBA

MBA—Master of Business Administration Full-time and part-time. 30 to 47 total credits required. 12 to 50 months to complete program. *Concentrations:* accounting, finance, human resources, management information systems.

COSTS

Tuition, state resident: *Part-time* $120 per credit hour. **Tuition, nonresident:** *Part-time* $360 per credit hour. Tuition varies by number of courses or credits taken. **Graduate housing:** *Typical cost:* $2400 (room only).

FINANCIAL AID (1999–2000)

Loans, scholarships, and teaching assistantships. Aid is available to part-time students. **Financial Aid Contact** Jim Bradsher, Director, Financial Aid, PO Box 244023, Montgomery, AL 36124. **Phone:** 334-244-3571.

RESOURCES AND SERVICES

Information about online services, personal computer policies, library resources, international exchange programs, internship programs, and placement services at this institution and others can be found at **www.petersons.com/mba**

International Students

5% of students enrolled are international students.

Services and Facilities Counseling/support services, ESL/language courses. Financial aid is not available to international students.

Applying *Required:* TOEFL with recommended score of 500 (paper), proof of adequate funds, proof of health/immunizations.

International Student Contact Dr. Jane R. Goodson, MBA Director, School of Business, PO Box 244023, Montgomery, AL 36124. **Phone:** 334-244-3565. **Fax:** 334-244-3792.

■ **APPLICATION**

Required GMAT, application form, baccalaureate/first degree, transcripts of college work.

Deadlines and Fees Applications for domestic and international students are processed on a rolling basis. *Application fee:* $25, $25 (international).

Application Contact Dr. Jane R. Goodson, MBA Director, School of Business, PO Box 244023, Montgomery, AL 36124. **Phone:** 334-244-3565. **Fax:** 334-244-3792.

Birmingham-Southern College

Birmingham, Alabama

PROGRAM IN PUBLIC AND PRIVATE MANAGEMENT

Graduate Business Faculty
Full-time: 19   Part-time: 6

Student Body
Total: 103   Average Age: 37
Full-time: 74   Women: 40%
Part-time: 29

Admissions
Applications: 33   Enrolled: 27
Admitted: 27   Average GPA: 3

Costs (1999–2000)
Full-time tuition: $9240 per academic year
Part-time tuition: $1320 per course

After Graduation (Class of 1998–99)
Employed within 3 months of graduation: 99%
Average starting salary: $65,000

Accreditation
ACBSP—The American Council of Business Schools and Programs

DEGREE MA

MA—Master of Arts in Public and Private Management Full-time and part-time. At least 16 total credits required. 24 to 60 months to complete program. *Concentrations:* public and private management.

COSTS

Tuition *Full-time:* $9240. *Part-time:* $1320 per course.

FINANCIAL AID (1999–2000)

Grants, loans, and scholarships. Aid is available to part-time students. **Financial Aid Contact** Mr. Forrest Stuart, Director of Financial Aid, Box 549016, Birmingham, AL 35254. **Phone:** 205-226-4670. **Fax:** 205-226-3082. **E-mail:** fstuart@bsc.edu.

RESOURCES AND SERVICES

Information about online services, personal computer policies, library resources, international exchange programs, internship programs, and placement services at this institution and others can be found at **www.petersons.com/mba**

International Students

Services and Facilities Counseling/support services. Financial aid is available to international students.

Applying *Required:* Proof of adequate funds, proof of health/immunizations.

International Student Contact Ms. Pat Kidd, Administrative Secretary to Director of Admissions, Box 549018, Birmingham, AL 35214. **Phone:** 205-226-4681. **Fax:** 205-226-3064. **E-mail:** pkidd@bsc.edu.

■ **APPLICATION**

Required Application form, baccalaureate/first degree, essay, interview, 2 letters of recommendation, personal statement, resume/curriculum vitae, transcripts of college work, 3 years of work experience. School will accept GMAT, GRE, and MAT.

Deadlines and Fees *Deadlines:* 8/7 for fall, 12/15 for spring, 4/30 for summer. *Application fee:* $25, $25 (international).

Application Contact Ms. Michele Picard, Coordinator of Marketing, Box 54902, Birmingham, AL 35254. **Phone:** 205-226-4803. **Toll-free Phone:** 800-523-5293. **Fax:** 205-226-4843. **E-mail:** mpicard@bsc.edu.

Jacksonville State University

Jacksonville, Alabama

COLLEGE OF COMMERCE AND BUSINESS ADMINISTRATION

Graduate Business Faculty

Full-time: 17

Student Body
Total: 100
Full-time: 20
Part-time: 80

Average Age: 31
Women: 44%

Admissions
Applications: 15
Admitted: 13
Enrolled: 10

Average GMAT: 450
Average GPA: 3.17

Costs (1999–2000)
Full-time tuition: N/R
Part-time tuition: $112 per credit hour (resident), $224 per credit hour (nonresident)

Accreditation
AACSB—The International Association for Management Education

DEGREE MBA

MBA—Master of Business Administration Full-time and part-time. 30 to 36 total credits required. 18 to 72 months to complete program. *Concentrations:* accounting.

COSTS
Tuition, state resident: *Part-time* $112 per credit hour. **Tuition, nonresident:** *Part-time* $224 per credit hour. Tuition varies by number of courses or credits taken and local reciprocity agreements. **Graduate housing:** Room and board costs vary by campus location, number of occupants, type of accommodation, and type of board plan. *Typical cost:* $1300 (room only).

FINANCIAL AID (1999–2000)
1 student received aid, including research assistantships. Financial aid application deadline: 3/15. **Financial Aid Contact** Mr. Larry Smith, Director of Financial Aid, 700 Pelham Road North, Jacksonville, AL 36265-9982. **Phone:** 256-782-5006.

RESOURCES AND SERVICES
Information about online services, personal computer policies, library resources, international exchange programs, internship programs, and placement services at this institution and others can be found at **www.petersons.com/mba**

International Students
Services and Facilities Counseling/support services, international student housing, visa services. Financial aid is not available to international students.
Applying *Required:* TOEFL with recommended score of 550 (paper), proof of adequate funds, proof of health/immunizations.
International Student Contact Dr. Adrian Aveni, Director of the Office of International Programs and Studies, 700 Pelham Road North, Jacksonville, AL 36265-1602. **Phone:** 256-782-5674. **E-mail:** aaveni@jsucc.jsu.edu.

■ APPLICATION
Required GMAT, application form, baccalaureate/first degree, 3 letters of recommendation, personal statement, resume/curriculum vitae, transcripts of college work.
Deadlines and Fees Applications for domestic and international students are processed on a rolling basis. *Application fee:* $20, $20 (international).
Application Contact Dr. Louise Clark, Associate Dean/MBA Director, 700 Pelham Road North, Jacksonville, AL 36265-9982. **Phone:** 256-782-5780. **Fax:** 256-782-5312. **E-mail:** lclark@jsucc.jsu.edu.

Samford University
Birmingham, Alabama

SCHOOL OF BUSINESS

Graduate Business Faculty
Full-time: 20

Student Body
Total: 128
Full-time: 13
Part-time: 115

Average Age: 31
Women: 45%

Admissions
Applications: 103
Admitted: 87
Enrolled: 60

Average GMAT: 562
Average GPA: 3

Costs (1999–2000)
Full-time tuition: N/R
Part-time tuition: $365 per credit

After Graduation (Class of 1998–99)
Employed within 3 months of graduation: 100%

Accreditation
AACSB—The International Association for Management Education

DEGREES JD/M Acc • JD/MBA • M Acc • MBA • MBA/MS

JD/M Acc—Juris Doctor/Master of Accountancy Full-time. At least 99 total credits required. 36 to 48 months to complete program.
JD/MBA—Juris Doctor/Master of Business Administration Full-time. 99 to 114 total credits required. 36 to 84 months to complete program.
M Acc—Master of Accountancy Full-time and part-time. At least 30 total credits required. 12 to 72 months to complete program. *Concentrations:* accounting.
MBA—Master of Business Administration Full-time and part-time. 33 to 48 total credits required. 12 to 84 months to complete program. *Concentrations:* management.
MBA/MS—Master of Business Administration/Master of Science in Nursing Part-time. 106 to 118 total credits required. 24 to 84 months to complete program.

COSTS
Tuition *Part-time:* $365 per credit. Tuition varies by number of courses or credits taken.

FINANCIAL AID (1999–2000)
6 students received aid, including loans, research assistantships, scholarships, and work study. Aid is available to part-time students.
Financial Aid Contact Ms. Ann Peeples, Director of Financial Aid, 800 Lakeshore Drive, Birmingham, AL 35229-0002. **Phone:** 205-726-2857. **Fax:** 205-726-2738. **E-mail:** appeeple@samford.edu.

RESOURCES AND SERVICES
Information about online services, personal computer policies, library resources, international exchange programs, internship programs, and placement services at this institution and others can be found at **www.petersons.com/mba**

International Students
2% of students enrolled are international students.
Services and Facilities Visa services. Financial aid is not available to international students.
Applying *Required:* TOEFL with recommended score of 550 (paper), proof of adequate funds, proof of health/immunizations.
International Student Contact Mr. Phil Kimrey, International Counselor, Admissions Office, 800 Lakeshore Drive, Birmingham, AL 35229-0002. **Phone:** 205-726-2871. **Fax:** 205-726-2171. **E-mail:** ppkimrey@samford.edu.

■ APPLICATION
Required GMAT, application form, baccalaureate/first degree, essay, 2 letters of recommendation, personal statement, resume/curriculum vitae, transcripts of college work, 3 years of work experience. School will accept GRE.
Deadlines and Fees Applications for domestic and international students are processed on a rolling basis. *Application fee:* $25, $25 (international).
Application Contact Ms. Francoise Horn, Director of Graduate Programs, School of Business, 800 Lakeshore Drive, Birmingham, AL 35229-2306. **Phone:** 205-726-2931. **Fax:** 205-726-2540. **E-mail:** fhhorn@samford.edu.

Spring Hill College
Mobile, Alabama

DIVISION OF BUSINESS AND MANAGEMENT

Graduate Business Faculty
Full-time: 4

Student Body
Total: 59
Full-time: 6
Part-time: 53

Average Age: 31
Women: 36%

Costs (1999–2000)
Full-time tuition: N/R
Part-time tuition: $255 per credit

After Graduation (Class of 1998–99)
Employed within 3 months of graduation: 100%

Spring Hill College (continued)

DEGREE MBA

MBA—MBA program Full-time and part-time. At least 36 total credits required. 24 to 72 months to complete program. *Concentrations:* general MBA.

COSTS

Tuition *Part-time:* $255 per credit. **Required fees:** *Part-time* $10 per semester.

FINANCIAL AID (1999–2000)

15 students received aid, including loans. Aid is available to part-time students. **Financial Aid Contact** Mrs. Betty Harlan, Director of Financial Aid, 4000 Dauphin Street, Mobile, AL 36608-1791. **Phone:** 334-380-3460. **Fax:** 334-460-2176. **E-mail:** bharlan@shc.edu.

RESOURCES AND SERVICES

Information about online services, personal computer policies, library resources, international exchange programs, internship programs, and placement services at this institution and others can be found at www.petersons.com/mba

International Students

3% of students enrolled are international students.

Services and Facilities Counseling/support services, ESL/language courses, visa services. Financial aid is not available to international students.
Applying *Required:* TOEFL with recommended score of 213 (computer) or 550 (paper), proof of adequate funds. *Recommended:* Proof of health/immunizations.
International Student Contact Mrs. Joyce Genz, Associate Dean of Lifelong Learning and Graduate Programs, 4000 Dauphin Street, Mobile, AL 36608-1791. **Phone:** 334-380-3094. **Fax:** 334-460-2190. **E-mail:** jgenz@shc.edu.

■ APPLICATION

Required GMAT, application form, baccalaureate/first degree, transcripts of college work. **Recommended** Interview, work experience.
Deadlines and Fees *Deadlines:* 8/1 for fall, 12/1 for spring, 5/1 for summer, 8/1 for fall (international), 12/1 for spring (international), 5/1 for summer (international). *Application fee:* $25, $25 (international).
Application Contact Dr. Gary Norsworthy, Dean of Lifelong Learning and Graduate Programs, 4000 Dauphin Street, Mobile, AL 36608-1791. **Phone:** 334-380-3094. **Fax:** 334-460-2190. **E-mail:** grad@shc.edu.

Troy State University

Troy, Alabama

SORRELL COLLEGE OF BUSINESS AND COMMERCE

Accreditation
ACBSP—The American Council of Business Schools and Programs

DEGREES MBA

MBA—Executive MBA Part-time. *Distance learning option.* At least 36 total credits required. 24 to 96 months to complete program. *Concentrations:* accounting, management.
MBA—Master of Business Administration Full-time and part-time. At least 30 total credits required. 12 to 96 months to complete program. *Concentrations:* accounting, management.

RESOURCES AND SERVICES

Information about online services, personal computer policies, library resources, international exchange programs, internship programs, and placement services at this institution and others can be found at www.petersons.com/mba

International Students

Services and Facilities Counseling/support services, ESL/language courses, international student housing. Financial aid is available to international students.
International Student Contact Dr. Curtis Porter, Dean, International Programs, 131 Pace Hall, Troy, AL 36082. **Phone:** 334-670-3335. **Fax:** 334-670-3735. **E-mail:** cporter@trojan.troyst.edu.

■ APPLICATION

Application Contact Mrs. Theresa Rodgers, Graduate Admission Counselor, 142 Adams Administration Building, Troy, AL 36082. **Phone:** 334-670-3188. **Fax:** 334-670-3774.

Troy State University Dothan

Dothan, Alabama

SCHOOL OF BUSINESS

Graduate Business Faculty
Full-time: 18 | Part-time: 18

Student Body
Total: 96
Full-time: 34 | Part-time: 62
| Women: 52%

Admissions
Applications: 35 | Average GMAT: 500
Enrolled: 22 | Average GPA: 3

Costs (1999–2000)
Full-time tuition: N/R
Part-time tuition: $120 per credit hour (resident), $240 per credit hour (nonresident)

Accreditation
ACBSP—The American Council of Business Schools and Programs

DEGREES MBA • MS

MBA—Master of Business Administration Full-time and part-time. 60 to 85 total credits required. 15 to 24 months to complete program. *Concentrations:* accounting, human resources, management, management information systems.
MS—Master of Science in Human Resources Management Full-time and part-time. At least 50 total credits required. 12 to 15 months to complete program. *Concentrations:* human resources.

COSTS

Tuition, state resident: *Part-time* $120 per credit hour. **Tuition, nonresident:** *Part-time* $240 per credit hour.

FINANCIAL AID (1999–2000)

Aid is available to part-time students. **Financial Aid Contact** Ms. Jonua Byrd, Director of Financial Aid, PO Box 8368, Dothan, AL 36304-0368. **Phone:** 334-983-6556 Ext. 255. **Fax:** 334-983-6322. **E-mail:** jbyrd@tsud.edu.

RESOURCES AND SERVICES

Information about online services, personal computer policies, library resources, international exchange programs, internship programs, and placement services at this institution and others can be found at www.petersons.com/mba

International Students

Services and Facilities Counseling/support services, tutoring. Financial aid is not available to international students.
Applying *Required:* TOEFL with recommended score of 550 (paper), proof of adequate funds, proof of health/immunizations.
International Student Contact Mrs. Pamela Williamson, Director of Counseling Services, PO Box 8368, Dothan, AL 36304. **Phone:** 334-983-6556 Ext. 221. **Fax:** 334-983-6322. **E-mail:** pwilliamson@tsud.edu.

■ APPLICATION

Required Application form, baccalaureate/first degree, transcripts of college work. School will accept GMAT.
Deadlines and Fees Applications for domestic and international students are processed on a rolling basis. *Application fee:* $20, $20 (international).
Application Contact Ms. Reta Cordell, Director of Graduate Admissions and Records, PO Box 8368, Dothan, AL 36304. **Phone:** 334-983-6556 Ext. 230. **Fax:** 334-983-6322. **E-mail:** rcordell@tsud.edu.

Troy State University Montgomery

Montgomery, Alabama

DIVISION OF BUSINESS

Graduate Business Faculty
Full-time: 10 | Part-time: 7

Student Body
Total: 224
Full-time: 94 | Average Age: 36
Part-time: 130 | Women: 40%

Admissions
Applications: 201

Costs (1999–2000)
Full-time tuition: N/R
Part-time tuition: $350 per course (resident), $350 per course (nonresident)

DEGREES MBA • MS • MSM

MBA—Master of Business Administration Full-time and part-time. At least 55 total credits required. 18 to 96 months to complete program. *Concentrations:* accounting, human resources, industrial administration/management, management, management information systems.

MS—Master of Science in Human Resources Management Full-time and part-time. At least 50 total credits required. 18 to 96 months to complete program. *Concentrations:* human resources.

MSM—Master of Science in Management *Distance learning option.* At least 30 total credits required. 12 months to complete program.

COSTS

Tuition, state resident: *Part-time* $350 per course. **Tuition, nonresident:** *Part-time* $350 per course.

FINANCIAL AID (1999–2000)
10 students received aid, including scholarships. Aid is available to part-time students. **Financial Aid Contact** Ms. Evelyn McKeithen, Director of Financial Aid, PO Drawer 4419, Montgomery, AL 36103-4419. **Phone:** 334-241-9520. **Fax:** 334-241-5427. **E-mail:** emckeithen@tsum.edu.

RESOURCES AND SERVICES
Information about online services, personal computer policies, library resources, international exchange programs, internship programs, and placement services at this institution and others can be found at **www.petersons.com/mba**

International Students
Applying *Required:* TOEFL.

■ APPLICATION

Required Application form, baccalaureate/first degree, interview, resume/curriculum vitae, transcripts of college work. School will accept GMAT, GRE, and MAT. **Recommended** Personal statement.

Deadlines and Fees *Application fee:* $15, $15 (international).

Application Contact Dr. Charles Durham, Dean, PO Drawer 4419, Montgomery, AL 36103-4419. **Phone:** 334-241-9703. **Toll-free Phone:** 800-335-TSUM. **Fax:** 334-241-9734. **E-mail:** cdurham@tsum.edu.

The University of Alabama

Tuscaloosa, Alabama

THE MANDERSON GRADUATE SCHOOL OF BUSINESS

Graduate Business Faculty
Full-time: 88   Part-time: 3

Student Body
Total: 358
Full-time: 330   Average Age: 25
Part-time: 28   Women: 35%

Admissions
Applications: 415   Average GMAT: 606
Admitted: 340   Average GPA: 3.4
Enrolled: 327

Costs (1999–2000)
Full-time tuition: $2872 per academic year (resident), $7722 per academic year (nonresident)
Part-time tuition: N/R

After Graduation (Class of 1998–99)
Employed within 3 months of graduation: 99%
Average starting salary: $47,000

Accreditation
AACSB—The International Association for Management Education

DEGREES JD/MBA • M Ac • MA • MBA • MSC • MTA

JD/MBA—Juris Doctor/Master of Business Administration Full-time. At least 108 total credits required. 48 months to complete program.

M Ac—Master of Accountancy Full-time. At least 30 total credits required. Minimum of 12 months to complete program. *Concentrations:* accounting.

MA—Master of Arts in Banking and Finance Full-time and part-time. At least 30 total credits required. 12 to 24 months to complete program. *Concentrations:* banking, finance.

MA—Master of Arts in Economics Full-time and part-time. At least 30 total credits required. 12 to 24 months to complete program. *Concentrations:* economics, financial economics, international economics.

MA—Master of Arts in Human Resources Management Part-time. At least 30 total credits required. 24 to 60 months to complete program. *Concentrations:* management.

MA—Master of Arts in Management Science Full-time and part-time. At least 30 total credits required. 24 to 36 months to complete program. *Concentrations:* management science, manufacturing management, production management.

MA—Master of Arts in Marketing Full-time. At least 30 total credits required. 10 to 60 months to complete program. *Concentrations:* international business, marketing, marketing research.

MBA—Executive MBA Part-time. At least 49 total credits required. Minimum of 17 months to complete program.

MBA—Master of Business Administration Full-time. At least 49 total credits required. 24 months to complete program. *Concentrations:* accounting, entrepreneurship, finance, human resources, international business, management information systems, marketing, operations management, production management, strategic management.

MSC—Master of Science in Commerce Full-time and part-time. At least 30 total credits required. 24 to 36 months to complete program. *Concentrations:* management science, manufacturing management, production management.

MSC—Master of Science in Commerce in Banking and Finance Full-time. At least 30 total credits required. 12 to 24 months to complete program. *Concentrations:* banking, finance.

MSC—Master of Science in Commerce in Economics Full-time. At least 30 total credits required. 12 to 24 months to complete program. *Concentrations:* economics, financial economics, international economics.

MSC—Master of Science in Commerce in Marketing Full-time. At least 30 total credits required. 10 to 60 months to complete program. *Concentrations:* marketing.

MTA—Master of Tax Accounting Full-time. At least 31 total credits required. Minimum of 12 months to complete program. *Concentrations:* accounting.

COSTS

Tuition, state resident: *Full-time* $2872. **Tuition, nonresident:** *Full-time* $7722. **Required fees:** Fees vary by academic program. **Graduate housing:** Room and board costs vary by number of occupants, type of accommodation, and type of board plan. *Typical cost:* $4000 (including board).

FINANCIAL AID (1999–2000)
136 students received aid, including fellowships, grants, loans, research assistantships, scholarships, and teaching assistantships. Aid is available to part-time students. Financial aid application deadline: 5/15. **Financial Aid Contact** Ms. Jeanetta Allen, Director, Student Financial Aid, Box 870162, 100 East Annex, Tuscaloosa, AL 35487. **Phone:** 205-348-2976.

RESOURCES AND SERVICES
Information about online services, personal computer policies, library resources, international exchange programs, internship programs, and placement services at this institution and others can be found at **www.petersons.com/mba**

International Students
14% of students enrolled are international students.

Services and Facilities Counseling/support services, ESL/language courses, international student housing, visa services. Financial aid is available to international students.

Applying *Required:* TOEFL with recommended score of 575 (paper), proof of adequate funds, proof of health/immunizations.

International Student Contact Ms. Mary S. Williams, Graduate International Admissions Officer, Box 870118, Tuscaloosa, AL 35487. **Phone:** 205-348-5923. **Fax:** 205-348-0400.

■ APPLICATION

Required Application form, baccalaureate/first degree, essay, interview, 3 letters of recommendation, personal statement, resume/curriculum vitae, transcripts of college work. School will accept GMAT.

Deadlines and Fees *Deadlines:* 5/15 for fall, 5/15 for fall (international). *Application fee:* $25, $25 (international).

The University of Alabama (continued)

Application Contact Mrs. Missy Strickland Brazil, Coordinator of Recruiting/Admissions, MBA Program, Box 870223, Tuscaloosa, AL 35487. **Phone:** 205-348-6517. **Fax:** 205-348-4504. **E-mail:** mstrick@cba.ua.edu.

See full description on page 862.

The University of Alabama at Birmingham

Birmingham, Alabama

GRADUATE SCHOOL OF MANAGEMENT

Graduate Business Faculty
Full-time: 50   Part-time: 3

Student Body
Total: 334
Part-time: 334   Average Age: 27
Women: 37%

Admissions
Applications: 240   Average GMAT: 530
Admitted: 190   Average GPA: 3
Enrolled: 140

Costs (1999–2000)
Full-time tuition: N/R
Part-time tuition: $104 per credit (resident), $208 per credit (nonresident)

After Graduation (Class of 1998–99)
Employed within 3 months of graduation: 92%

Accreditation
AACSB—The International Association for Management Education

DEGREES MAC • MBA • MBA/MPH • MBA/MS

MAC—Master of Accountancy Full-time and part-time. At least 30 total credits required. 12 to 84 months to complete program. *Concentrations:* accounting.

MBA—Master of Business Administration Full-time and part-time. 36 to 54 total credits required. 12 to 84 months to complete program.

MBA/MPH—Master of Business Administration/Master of Public Health Full-time and part-time. At least 72 total credits required. 24 to 84 months to complete program.

MBA/MS—Master of Business Administration/Master of Science in Health Administration Full-time. At least 72 total credits required. 33 months to complete program.

COSTS

Tuition, state resident: *Part-time* $104 per credit. **Tuition, nonresident:** *Part-time* $208 per credit. **Required fees:** Tuition and fees vary by number of courses or credits taken and academic program. **Graduate housing:** Room and board costs vary by number of occupants and type of accommodation. *Typical cost:* $1948 (room only).

FINANCIAL AID (1999–2000)

Fellowships. Aid is available to part-time students. Financial aid application deadline: 8/1. **Financial Aid Contact** Ms. Janet May, Director of Financial Aid, Financial Aid Office, 1400 University Boulevard, HUC 317, Birmingham, AL 35294-1150. **Phone:** 205-934-8223. **Fax:** 205-934-8941.

RESOURCES AND SERVICES

Information about online services, personal computer policies, library resources, international exchange programs, internship programs, and placement services at this institution and others can be found at **www.petersons.com/mba**

International Students

8% of students enrolled are international students.

Services and Facilities Counseling/support services, ESL/language courses, visa services. Financial aid is not available to international students.

Applying *Required:* TOEFL with recommended score of 550 (paper), proof of adequate funds, proof of health/immunizations.

International Student Contact Ms. Barbara Whitt, Foreign Student Advisor, Center for International Programs, 1400 University Boulevard, Birmingham, AL 35294-1150. **Phone:** 205-934-3328. **Fax:** 205-934-8664. **E-mail:** ucip003@larry.huc.uab.edu.

■ APPLICATION

Required GMAT, application form, baccalaureate/first degree, personal statement, transcripts of college work.

Deadlines and Fees *Deadlines:* 8/1 for fall, 11/1 for winter, 2/1 for spring, 4/1 for summer, 8/1 for fall (international), 11/1 for winter (international), 2/1 for spring (international), 4/1 for summer (international). *Application fee:* $50, $75 (international).

Application Contact Ms. Pamela Blaylock, Admissions Coordinator, UAB Graduate School, 1400 University Boulevard, HUC 511, Birmingham, AL 35294-1150. **Phone:** 205-934-8227. **Toll-free Phone:** 800-975-GRAD. **Fax:** 205-934-8413. **E-mail:** inquire@gradschool.huc.uab.edu.

The University of Alabama in Huntsville

Huntsville, Alabama

COLLEGE OF ADMINISTRATIVE SCIENCE

Graduate Business Faculty
Full-time: 25   Part-time: 4

Student Body
Total: 153
Full-time: 27   Average Age: 32
Part-time: 126   Women: 41%

Admissions
Applications: 70   Average GMAT: 496
Admitted: 58   Average GPA: 3
Enrolled: 49

Costs (1999–2000)
Full-time tuition: $3880 per academic year (resident), $7956 per academic year (nonresident)
Part-time tuition: $182 per credit hour (resident), $371 per credit hour (nonresident)

Accreditation
AACSB—The International Association for Management Education

DEGREES M Acc • MSM

M Acc—Master of Accountancy Full-time and part-time. 33 to 51 total credits required. 12 to 72 months to complete program. *Concentrations:* accounting.

MSM—Master of Science in Management in Management of Technology Full-time and part-time. 33 to 48 total credits required. 12 to 72 months to complete program. *Concentrations:* technology management.

COSTS

Tuition, state resident: *Full-time* $3880. *Part-time* $182 per credit hour. **Tuition, nonresident:** *Full-time* $7956. *Part-time* $371 per credit hour. **Required fees:** Tuition and fees vary by number of courses or credits taken. **Graduate housing:** Room and board costs vary by number of occupants, type of accommodation, and type of board plan. *Typical cost:* $5500 (including board).

FINANCIAL AID (1999–2000)

20 students received aid, including fellowships, grants, loans, research assistantships, scholarships, teaching assistantships, and work study. Aid is available to part-time students. Financial aid application deadline: 4/1. **Financial Aid Contact** Mr. Andy Weaver, Director of Financial Aid, 301 Sparkman Drive, Huntsville, AL 35899. **Phone:** 256-890-6241. **Fax:** 256-890-6073. **E-mail:** weavera@email.uah.edu.

RESOURCES AND SERVICES

Information about online services, personal computer policies, library resources, international exchange programs, internship programs, and placement services at this institution and others can be found at **www.petersons.com/mba**

International Students

7% of students enrolled are international students.

Services and Facilities Counseling/support services, ESL/language courses, international student organization, visa services. Financial aid is available to international students.

Applying *Required:* TOEFL with recommended score of 550 (paper), proof of adequate funds, proof of health/immunizations.

International Student Contact Mrs. Reva Bailey, Registrar, Office of Admissions, Huntsville, AL 35899. **Phone:** 256-890-6440. **Fax:** 256-890-6073. **E-mail:** baileyr@email.uah.edu.

■ APPLICATION

Required GMAT, application form, baccalaureate/first degree, personal statement, transcripts of college work.

Deadlines and Fees *Deadlines:* 8/10 for fall, 12/10 for spring, 5/10 for summer, 3/16 for fall (international), 7/6 for spring (international), 12/12 for summer (international). *Application fee:* $35, $35 (international).

Application Contact Dr. John Burnett, Assistant Dean, ASB 102, Huntsville, AL 35899. **Phone:** 256-890-6024. **Toll-free Phone:** 800-UAH-CALL. **Fax:** 256-890-7571. **E-mail:** msmprog@email.uah.edu.

University of Mobile

Mobile, Alabama

SCHOOL OF BUSINESS

Graduate Business Faculty
Full-time: 10   Part-time: 3

Student Body
Total: 54   Average Age: 32
Full-time: 3   Women: 70%
Part-time: 51

Admissions
Applications: 27   Average GMAT: 445
Admitted: 20   Average GPA: 3.08
Enrolled: 15

Costs (1999–2000)
Full-time tuition: N/R
Part-time tuition: $172 per credit hour

After Graduation (Class of 1998–99)
Employed within 3 months of graduation: 100%
Average starting salary: $37,000

DEGREE MBA

MBA—Master of Business Administration Full-time and part-time. At least 40 total credits required. 12 to 60 months to complete program.

COSTS

Tuition *Part-time:* $172 per credit hour. Tuition varies by number of courses or credits taken. **Graduate housing:** *Typical cost:* $4280 (including board).

FINANCIAL AID (1999–2000)

Loans and work study. Aid is available to part-time students. Financial aid application deadline: 8/1. **Financial Aid Contact** Mrs. Lydia Houck, Director of Financial Aid, PO Box 12330, Mobile, AL 36663-0220. **Phone:** 334-442-2252.

RESOURCES AND SERVICES

Information about online services, personal computer policies, library resources, international exchange programs, internship programs, and placement services at this institution and others can be found at **www. petersons.com/mba**

International Students

6% of students enrolled are international students.

Services and Facilities Counseling/support services, ESL/language courses. Financial aid is not available to international students.

Applying *Required:* TOEFL with recommended score of 550 (paper), proof of adequate funds, proof of health/immunizations.

International Student Contact Mrs. Kim Leousis, Vice President—Student Services, PO Box 13220, Mobile, AL 36663-0220. **Phone:** 334-442-2290. **Fax:** 334-442-2498. **E-mail:** adminfo@umobile.edu.

■ APPLICATION

Required GMAT, application form, baccalaureate/first degree, transcripts of college work. **Recommended** Work experience.

Deadlines and Fees Applications for domestic and international students are processed on a rolling basis. *Application fee:* $30, $50 (international).

Application Contact Dr. Anne B. Lowery, Dean and MBA Director, School of Business, PO Box 13220, Mobile, AL 36663-0220. **Phone:** 334-442-2332. **Fax:** 334-442-2523. **E-mail:** lowerys@gulftel.com.

University of North Alabama

Florence, Alabama

COLLEGE OF BUSINESS

Graduate Business Faculty
Full-time: 20

Student Body
Total: 110   Average Age: 30
Full-time: 25   Women: 50%
Part-time: 85

Admissions
Average GMAT: 475   Average GPA: 3

Costs (1999–2000)
Full-time tuition: N/R
Part-time tuition: $107 per hour (resident), $107 per hour (nonresident)

Accreditation
ACBSP—The American Council of Business Schools and Programs

DEGREES MBA

MBA—Executive MBA Full-time. *Distance learning option.* At least 33 total credits required. Minimum of 24 months to complete program.

MBA—Master of Business Administration Full-time and part-time. *Distance learning option.* At least 33 total credits required. 12 to 96 months to complete program. *Concentrations:* accounting.

COSTS

Tuition, state resident: *Part-time* $107 per hour. **Tuition, nonresident:** *Part-time* $107 per hour. Tuition varies by number of courses or credits taken. **Graduate housing:** Room and board costs vary by campus location, number of occupants, type of accommodation, and type of board plan. *Typical cost:* $1836 (including board), $780 (room only).

FINANCIAL AID (1999–2000)

Work study. Aid is available to part-time students. Financial aid application deadline: 4/1. **Financial Aid Contact** Dr. Jo Ann Weaver, Director of Student Financial Services, University Station, Florence, AL 35632-0001. **Phone:** 256-760-4278.

RESOURCES AND SERVICES

Information about online services, personal computer policies, library resources, international exchange programs, internship programs, and placement services at this institution and others can be found at **www. petersons.com/mba**

International Students

18% of students enrolled are international students.

Services and Facilities ESL/language courses.
Applying *Required:* TOEFL with recommended score of 550 (paper), proof of health/immunizations.
International Student Contact Mrs. Joan Smith, Records Coordinator, Registrar's Office, Box 5044, Florence, AL 35632-0001. **Phone:** 256-765-4450.

■ APPLICATION

Required GMAT, application form, baccalaureate/first degree, transcripts of college work.

Deadlines and Fees *Application fee:* $25, $25 (international).

Application Contact Mrs. Carolyn Austin, Graduate Admissions Record Specialist, Box 5011, Florence, AL 35632. **Phone:** 256-760-4447. **Fax:** 256-760-4349.

University of South Alabama

Mobile, Alabama

COLLEGE OF BUSINESS

Graduate Business Faculty
Full-time: 45   Part-time: 6

Student Body
Total: 134   Part-time: 84
Full-time: 50   Women: 37%

Admissions
Applications: 55   Average GMAT: 501
Admitted: 52   Average GPA: 3.06
Enrolled: 28

University of South Alabama (continued)

ALASKA

Costs (1999–2000)
Full-time tuition: N/R
Part-time tuition: $116 per credit (resident), $232 per credit (nonresident)

After Graduation (Class of 1998–99)
Employed within 3 months of graduation: 93%

Accreditation
AACSB—The International Association for Management Education

DEGREES M Acc • MBA

M Acc—Master of Accounting Full-time and part-time. At least 33 total credits required. 12 to 60 months to complete program. *Concentrations:* accounting.
MBA—Master of Business Administration Full-time and part-time. *Distance learning option.* At least 30 total credits required. 12 to 60 months to complete program. *Concentrations:* management.

COSTS

Tuition, state resident: *Part-time* $116 per credit. **Tuition, nonresident:** *Part-time* $232 per credit. Tuition varies by number of courses or credits taken and local reciprocity agreements. **Graduate housing:** Room and board costs vary by campus location, number of occupants, type of accommodation, and type of board plan. *Typical cost:* $3296 (including board).

FINANCIAL AID (1999–2000)

9 students received aid, including research assistantships. Financial aid application deadline: 4/1. **Financial Aid Contact** Mr. Grady Collins, Director, AD 260, 307 University Boulevard, Mobile, AL 36688. **Phone:** 334-460-6231.

RESOURCES AND SERVICES

Information about online services, personal computer policies, library resources, international exchange programs, internship programs, and placement services at this institution and others can be found at **www. petersons.com/mba**

International Students

23% of students enrolled are international students.
Services and Facilities Counseling/support services, ESL/language courses, international student organization, language tutoring, orientation, visa services. Financial aid is not available to international students.
Applying *Required:* TOEFL with recommended score of 525 (paper), proof of adequate funds, proof of health/immunizations.
International Student Contact Ms. Brenda Henson, Director—International Admissions, 307 University Boulevard, Mobile, AL 36688. **Phone:** 334-460-6050.

■ APPLICATION

Required GMAT, application form, baccalaureate/first degree, essay, transcripts of college work.
Deadlines and Fees *Deadlines:* 8/1 for fall, 12/1 for spring, 5/1 for summer, 8/1 for fall (international), 12/1 for spring (international), 5/1 for summer (international). *Application fee:* $25, $25 (international).
Application Contact Dr. Randolph Flynn, Associate Dean, College of Business, 307 University Boulevard, Mobile, AL 36688. **Phone:** 334-460-6418. **Fax:** 334-460-6529. **E-mail:** rflynn@usamail.usouthal.edu.

Alaska Pacific University

Anchorage, Alaska

BUSINESS ADMINISTRATION DEPARTMENT

DEGREES MBA

MBA—Master of Business Administration in Telecommunications Management Full-time and part-time. At least 36 total credits required. 12 to 84 months to complete program.
MBA—Master of Business Administration Full-time and part-time. At least 36 total credits required. 12 to 84 months to complete program. *Concentrations:* management.

RESOURCES AND SERVICES

Information about online services, personal computer policies, library resources, international exchange programs, internship programs, and placement services at this institution and others can be found at **www. petersons.com/mba**

International Students

Services and Facilities Counseling/support services, international student organization. Financial aid is available to international students.
International Student Contact Kirsty Gladkoff, Assistant Director of Admissions, 4101 University Drive, Anchorage, AK 99508-4672. **Phone:** 907-564-8248. **Fax:** 907-564-8317. **E-mail:** apu@corecom.net.

■ APPLICATION

Application Contact Kirsty Gladkoff, Assistant Director of Admissions, 4101 University Drive, Anchorage, AK 99508-4672. **Phone:** 907-564-8248. **Fax:** 907-564-8317. **E-mail:** apu@corecom.net.

University of Alaska Anchorage

Anchorage, Alaska

COLLEGE OF BUSINESS AND PUBLIC POLICY

Graduate Business Faculty
Full-time: 19

Student Body
Total: 94
Full-time: 35
Part-time: 59

Average Age: 35
Women: 48%

Admissions
Applications: 31
Admitted: 20
Enrolled: 19

Average GMAT: 545
Average GPA: 3

Costs (1999–2000)
Full-time tuition: $3335 per academic year (resident), $6197 per academic year (nonresident)
Part-time tuition: $167 per credit (resident), $326 per credit (nonresident)

After Graduation (Class of 1998–99)
Employed within 3 months of graduation: 100%

Accreditation
AACSB—The International Association for Management Education

DEGREE MBA

MBA—Master of Business Administration Full-time and part-time. 36 to 54 total credits required. 12 to 84 months to complete program. *Concentrations:* management.

COSTS

Tuition, state resident: *Full-time* $3006. *Part-time* $167 per credit. **Tuition, nonresident:** *Full-time* $5868. *Part-time* $326 per credit. **Required fees:** *Full-time* $329. *Part-time* $229 per year. Fees vary by number of courses or credits taken. **Graduate housing:** Room and board costs vary by number of occupants, type of accommodation, and type of board plan. *Typical cost:* $6380 (including board), $3680 (room only).

FINANCIAL AID (1999–2000)
26 students received aid, including loans, research assistantships, scholarships, teaching assistantships, and work study. Aid is available to part-time students. **Financial Aid Contact** Mr. Rick Weems, Student Financial Aid Director, 3211 Providence Drive, Anchorage, AK 99508-8060. **Phone:** 907-786-1586. **Fax:** 907-786-6122. **E-mail:** anrdw1@acad2.alaska.edu.

RESOURCES AND SERVICES
Information about online services, personal computer policies, library resources, international exchange programs, internship programs, and placement services at this institution and others can be found at www.petersons.com/mba

International Students
30% of students enrolled are international students.

Services and Facilities Counseling/support services, ESL/language courses, international student housing, visa services. Financial aid is available to international students.

Applying *Required:* TOEFL with recommended score of 550 (paper), proof of adequate funds, proof of health/immunizations.

International Student Contact Ms. Leslie Tuovinen, International Student Advisor, 3211 Providence Drive, Anchorage, AK 99508-8060. **Phone:** 907-786-1573. **Fax:** 907-786-4888. **E-mail:** anlat@acad2.alaska.edu.

■ APPLICATION
Required GMAT, application form, baccalaureate/first degree, transcripts of college work. **Recommended** Interview, resume/curriculum vitae, work experience.

Deadlines and Fees Applications for domestic and international students are processed on a rolling basis. *Application fee:* $45, $45 (international).

Application Contact Mr. Michael Smith, MBA Program Assistant, 3211 Providence Drive, Anchorage, AK 99508-8060. **Phone:** 907-786-4129. **Fax:** 907-786-4119. **E-mail:** anmbs1@uaa.alaska.edu.

University of Alaska Fairbanks

Fairbanks, Alaska

SCHOOL OF MANAGEMENT

Graduate Business Faculty
Full-time: 19   Part-time: 5

Student Body
Total: 51
Full-time: 21   Average Age: 32
Part-time: 30   Women: 59%

Admissions
Applications: 35   Average GMAT: 550
Admitted: 25   Average GPA: 3.32
Enrolled: 15

Costs (1999–2000)
Full-time tuition: $3006 per academic year (resident), $5868 per academic year (nonresident)
Part-time tuition: $167 per credit hour (resident), $326 per credit hour (nonresident)

After Graduation (Class of 1998–99)
Employed within 3 months of graduation: 80%

Accreditation
AACSB—The International Association for Management Education

DEGREES MBA • MS

MBA—Master of Business Administration in Capital Markets Full-time. 31 to 54 total credits required. 12 to 84 months to complete program.

MBA—Master of Business Administration in General Management Full-time and part-time. 30 to 54 total credits required. 12 to 84 months to complete program. *Concentrations:* accounting, resources management.

MS—Master of Science in Resource Economics Full-time and part-time. At least 30 total credits required. 12 to 84 months to complete program.

COSTS
Tuition, state resident: *Full-time* $3006. *Part-time* $167 per credit hour. **Tuition, nonresident:** *Full-time* $5868. *Part-time* $326 per credit hour. Tuition varies by class time, number of courses or credits taken, and local reciprocity agreements. **Required fees:** Tuition and fees vary by class time and number of courses or credits taken. **Graduate housing:** Room and board costs vary by number of

occupants, type of accommodation, and type of board plan. *Typical cost:* $4600 (including board), $2800 (room only).

FINANCIAL AID (1999–2000)
7 students received aid, including fellowships, grants, loans, research assistantships, scholarships, and teaching assistantships. Financial aid application deadline: 3/15. **Financial Aid Contact** Mr. Donald Scheaffer, Director of Financial Aid, PO Box 756360, Fairbanks, AK 99775-6360. **Phone:** 907-474-7256. **Fax:** 907-474-7065. **E-mail:** fndes@aurora.alaska.edu.

RESOURCES AND SERVICES
Information about online services, personal computer policies, library resources, international exchange programs, internship programs, and placement services at this institution and others can be found at www.petersons.com/mba

International Students
8% of students enrolled are international students.

Services and Facilities Counseling/support services, visa services. Financial aid is available to international students.

Applying *Required:* TOEFL with recommended score of 550 (paper), proof of adequate funds, proof of health/immunizations.

International Student Contact Mr. John Lehman, Director of International Programs, PO Box 757760 International Programs, Fairbanks, AK 99775-6340. **Phone:** 907-474-7317. **Fax:** 907-474-7900. **E-mail:** fnnkk@aurora.alaska.edu.

■ APPLICATION
Required GMAT, application form, baccalaureate/first degree, essay, interview, 3 letters of recommendation, personal statement, resume/curriculum vitae, transcripts of college work.

Deadlines and Fees Applications for domestic and international students are processed on a rolling basis. *Application fee:* $35, $35 (international).

Application Contact Dr. Jacob Joseph, Director, MBA Program, PO Box 756080, Fairbanks, AK 99775-6080. **Phone:** 907-474-6532. **Fax:** 907-474-5219. **E-mail:** famba@som.uaf.edu.

ARIZONA

Arizona State University

Tempe, Arizona

COLLEGE OF BUSINESS

Graduate Business Faculty
Full-time: 165

Student Body
Total: 1,026
Full-time: 370   Average Age: 32
Part-time: 656   Women: 28%

Admissions
Applications: 1,544   Average GMAT: 606
Admitted: 843   Average GPA: 3.3
Enrolled: 569

Costs (1999–2000)
Full-time tuition: $7344 per academic year (resident), $15,800 per academic year (nonresident)
Part-time tuition: N/R

After Graduation (Class of 1998–99)
Employed within 3 months of graduation: 96%
Average starting salary: $85,000

Accreditation
AACSB—The International Association for Management Education

DEGREES JD/MBA • MBA • MBA/M Acc • MBA/MHSA • MBA/MIM • MBA/MS • MBA/MTAX

JD/MBA—Juris Doctor/Master of Business Administration Full-time. At least 117 total credits required. 48 to 60 months to complete program.

MBA—Day MBA Full-time. At least 60 total credits required. 22 to 24 months to complete program. *Concentrations:* finance, information management, inter-

Arizona State University (continued)

national business, logistics, management information systems, marketing, production management, sports/entertainment management.

MBA—Evening MBA Full-time and part-time. At least 48 total credits required. 24 to 36 months to complete program.

MBA—Executive MBA Full-time and part-time. At least 48 total credits required. 22 to 24 months to complete program.

MBA—High Technology MBA Full-time and part-time. At least 48 total credits required. 24 to 36 months to complete program.

MBA/M Acc—Master of Business Administration/Master of Accountancy and Information Systems Full-time and part-time. At least 63 total credits required. Maximum of 24 months to complete program.

MBA/MHSA—Master of Business Administration/Master of Health Services Administration Full-time. At least 72 total credits required. 22 to 24 months to complete program.

MBA/MIM—Master of Business Administration/Master of International Management Full-time. At least 66 total credits required. Minimum of 22 months to complete program.

MBA/MS—Master of Business Administration/Master of Science in Economics Full-time and part-time. At least 66 total credits required. 22 to 24 months to complete program.

MBA/MS—Master of Business Administration/Master of Science Full-time and part-time. At least 60 total credits required. 22 to 24 months to complete program.

MBA/MTAX—Master of Business Administration/Master of Science in Taxation Full-time and part-time. At least 63 total credits required. 22 to 24 months to complete program.

COSTS

Tuition, state resident: *Full-time* $7344. **Tuition, nonresident:** *Full-time* $15,800. Tuition varies by class time, number of courses or credits taken, and academic program. **Required fees:** Tuition and fees vary by class time and academic program.

FINANCIAL AID (1999–2000)

Fellowships, loans, research assistantships, scholarships, and teaching assistantships. Financial aid application deadline: 3/1. **Financial Aid Contact** Ms. Marilynn Singleton, Financial Aid Counselor, Graduate College, PO Box 871003, Tempe, AZ 85287-1003. **Phone:** 480-965-3521. **Fax:** 480-965-5151. **E-mail:** marilynn.singleton@asu.edu.

RESOURCES AND SERVICES

Information about online services, personal computer policies, library resources, international exchange programs, internship programs, and placement services at this institution and others can be found at **www.petersons.com/mba**

International Students

12% of students enrolled are international students.

Services and Facilities Counseling/support services, ESL/language courses, international student housing, international student organization, orientation, visa services. Financial aid is available to international students.
Applying *Required:* TOEFL with recommended score of 237 (computer) or 580 (paper), proof of adequate funds, proof of health/immunizations. *Recommended:* TWE.
International Student Contact Ms. Suzanne Steadman, Director of International Student Program, Student Services Building, B265, Tempe, AZ 85287-0512. **Phone:** 480-965-7451. **Fax:** 480-965-9608. **E-mail:** ssteadman@asu.edu.

■ APPLICATION

Required GMAT, application form, baccalaureate/first degree, essay, 2 letters of recommendation, personal statement, resume/curriculum vitae, transcripts of college work, 2 years of work experience. **Recommended** Interview.
Deadlines and Fees *Deadlines:* 5/1 for fall, 3/1 for fall (international). *Application fee:* $45, $45 (international).
Application Contact Ms. Judith Heilala, Director, Recruiting and Admissions, MBA Program, PO Box 874906, College of Business, Tempe, AZ 85287-4906. **Phone:** 480-965-3332. **Fax:** 480-965-8569. **E-mail:** asu.mba@asu.edu.

See full description on page 546.

Arizona State University West

Phoenix, Arizona

SCHOOL OF MANAGEMENT

Graduate Business Faculty
Full-time: 36 | Part-time: 3

Student Body
Total: 450 | Average Age: 33
Part-time: 450 | Women: 29%

Admissions
Average GMAT: 580 | Average GPA: 3.2

Costs (1999–2000)
Full-time tuition: N/R
Part-time tuition: $119 per credit hour (resident), $405 per credit hour (nonresident)

Accreditation
AACSB—The International Association for Management Education

DEGREES MBA • MBA/MIM

MBA—On Campus Evening Program Full-time and part-time. At least 45 total credits required. 18 to 72 months to complete program.
MBA—The Connect MBA *Distance learning option.* 25 months to complete program.
MBA—The Scottsdale MBA Part-time. At least 45 total credits required. 32 months to complete program.
MBA/MIM—ASU West/Thunderbird Dual Degree Full-time. At least 72 total credits required. 20 to 45 months to complete program. *Concentrations:* international management.

COSTS

Tuition, state resident: *Part-time* $119 per credit hour. **Tuition, nonresident:** *Part-time* $405 per credit hour. **Required fees:** *Part-time* $200 per course. Tuition and fees vary by class time, number of courses or credits taken, campus location, and academic program.

FINANCIAL AID (1999–2000)

Loans, research assistantships, scholarships, and work study. Aid is available to part-time students. **Financial Aid Contact** Financial Aid Services, PO Box 37100, Phoenix, AZ 85069-7100. **Phone:** 602-543-8178.

RESOURCES AND SERVICES

Information about online services, personal computer policies, library resources, international exchange programs, internship programs, and placement services at this institution and others can be found at **www.petersons.com/mba**

International Students

Services and Facilities Counseling/support services, visa services. Financial aid is not available to international students.
Applying *Required:* TOEFL with recommended score of 250 (computer) or 600 (paper), proof of adequate funds, proof of health/immunizations.
International Student Contact Ms. Marge Runyan, Graduate Studies Coordinator, PO Box 37100, Phoenix, AZ 85069-7100. **Phone:** 602-543-4567. **Fax:** 602-543-4561. **E-mail:** mrunyon@asu.edu.

■ APPLICATION

Required GMAT, application form, baccalaureate/first degree, essay, 2 letters of recommendation, personal statement, resume/curriculum vitae, transcripts of college work. **Recommended** Work experience.
Deadlines and Fees *Deadlines:* 6/1 for fall, 11/1 for spring, 4/1 for summer, 4/1 for fall (international), 8/1 for spring (international), 1/1 for summer (international). *Application fee:* $45, $45 (international).
Application Contact Mr. Jon Delany, MBA Program Coordinator, PO Box 37100, Phoenix, AZ 85069-7100. **Phone:** 602-543-6201 Ext. 6123. **Fax:** 602-543-6221. **E-mail:** delany@asu.edu.

Grand Canyon University

Phoenix, Arizona

COLLEGE OF BUSINESS

Graduate Business Faculty
Full-time: 10

Student Body
Total: 69
Full-time: 19

Part-time: 50
Women: 33%

Admissions
Applications: 63
Admitted: 55

Enrolled: 29
Average GPA: 3.04

Costs (1999–2000)
Full-time tuition: N/R
Part-time tuition: $320 per credit hour

Accreditation
ACBSP—The American Council of Business Schools and Programs

DEGREE MBA

MBA—Master of Business Administration Full-time and part-time. At least 36 total credits required. 18 to 60 months to complete program. *Concentrations:* accounting, health care, international business.

COSTS

Tuition *Part-time:* $320 per credit hour. **Required fees:** Fees vary by number of courses or credits taken. **Graduate housing:** Room and board costs vary by number of occupants, type of accommodation, and type of board plan. *Typical cost:* $4246 (including board).

FINANCIAL AID (1999–2000)

16 students received aid, including loans, scholarships, and work study. Aid is available to part-time students. Financial aid application deadline: 3/15. **Financial Aid Contact** Ms. Rosanna Short, Financial Aid Director, 3300 West Camelback Road, Phoenix, AZ 85017-3030. **Phone:** 602-589-2885. **Fax:** 602-589-2044. **E-mail:** rshort@grand-canyon.edu.

RESOURCES AND SERVICES

Information about online services, personal computer policies, library resources, international exchange programs, internship programs, and placement services at this institution and others can be found at **www.petersons.com/mba**

International Students
17% of students enrolled are international students.

Services and Facilities Counseling/support services, ESL/language courses, international student housing. Financial aid is available to international students.
Applying *Required:* TOEFL with recommended score of 550 (paper), proof of adequate funds, proof of health/immunizations. *Recommended:* TWE.

International Student Contact Dr. Treva Gibson, Director of International Education and E.A.S.E. Program, 3300 West Camelback Road, Phoenix, AZ 85017-3030. **Phone:** 602-589-2808. **Fax:** 602-841-8771.

■ APPLICATION

Required GMAT, application form, baccalaureate/first degree, interview, transcripts of college work. **Recommended** Work experience.

Deadlines and Fees *Application fee:* $25, $25 (international).

Application Contact Dr. Rob Jones, Associate Dean, Graduate Studies, 3300 West Camelback Road, PO Box 11097, Phoenix, AZ 85017-3030. **Phone:** 602-589-2867. **Toll-free Phone:** 800-800-9776. **Fax:** 602-589-2532. **E-mail:** robjo24@aol.com.

Northern Arizona University

Flagstaff, Arizona

COLLEGE OF BUSINESS ADMINISTRATION

Graduate Business Faculty
Full-time: 53

Part-time: 1

Student Body
Total: 84
Full-time: 54
Part-time: 30

Average Age: 31
Women: 40%

Admissions
Applications: 105
Admitted: 50
Enrolled: 45

Average GMAT: 535
Average GPA: 3.23

Costs (1999–2000)
Full-time tuition: $5103 per academic year (resident), $12,065 per academic year (nonresident)
Part-time tuition: N/R

After Graduation (Class of 1998–99)
Employed within 3 months of graduation: 92%
Average starting salary: $57,000

Accreditation
AACSB—The International Association for Management Education

DEGREE MBA

MBA—Master of Business Administration Full-time and part-time. At least 31 total credits required. 10 to 72 months to complete program. *Concentrations:* economics, electronic commerce (e-commerce), entrepreneurship, finance, financial management/planning, health care, human resources, information management, international business, international development management, international economics, international finance, international management, international marketing, management, management consulting, management information systems, marketing, organizational behavior/development, organizational management, production management, strategic management, technology management, hospitality management.

COSTS

Tuition, state resident: *Full-time* $5103. **Tuition, nonresident:** *Full-time* $12,065. **Tuition, international:** *Full-time* $12,065. Tuition varies by number of courses or credits taken. **Graduate housing:** Room and board costs vary by number of occupants, type of accommodation, and type of board plan. *Typical cost:* $6970 (including board).

FINANCIAL AID (1999–2000)

33 students received aid, including loans, research assistantships, scholarships, teaching assistantships, and work study. Financial aid application deadline: 3/1. **Financial Aid Contact** Mr. James Pritchard, Director, Financial Aid, PO Box 4108, Flagstaff, AZ 86011-4108. **Phone:** 520-523-4951. **Fax:** 520-523-1551. **E-mail:** finaid@nau.edu.

RESOURCES AND SERVICES

Information about online services, personal computer policies, library resources, international exchange programs, internship programs, and placement services at this institution and others can be found at **www.petersons.com/mba**

International Students
24% of students enrolled are international students.

Services and Facilities Counseling/support services, ESL/language courses, housing location assistance, international student organization, language tutoring, orientation, visa services. Financial aid is available to international students.
Applying *Required:* TOEFL with recommended score of 550 (paper), proof of adequate funds, proof of health/immunizations.

International Student Contact Dr. Joan Fagerburg, Assistant Dean, Student Life, University Union 201, Box 06015, Flagstaff, AZ 86011. **Phone:** 520-523-6772. **E-mail:** joan.fagerburg@nau.edu.

■ APPLICATION

Required GMAT, application form, baccalaureate/first degree, essay, 3 letters of recommendation, personal statement, transcripts of college work. **Recommended** Resume/curriculum vitae, work experience.

Deadlines and Fees Applications for domestic and international students are processed on a rolling basis. *Application fee:* $45, $45 (international).

Application Contact Dr. Mason S. Gerety, Director, MBA Program, Box 15066, Flagstaff, AZ 86011. **Phone:** 520-523-7342. **Fax:** 520-523-7331. **E-mail:** cba-mba@mail.cba.nau.edu.

Thunderbird, The American Graduate School of International Management

Glendale, Arizona

GRADUATE PROGRAMS

Graduate Business Faculty
Full-time: 110

Part-time: 39

Student Body
Total: 1,504
Full-time: 1,504

Average Age: 29
Women: 35%

Admissions
Applications: 1,558
Admitted: 1,231
Enrolled: 462

Average GMAT: 608
Average GPA: 3.4

Thunderbird, The American Graduate School of International Management
(continued)

Costs (1999–2000)
Full-time tuition: $25,300 per academic year
Part-time tuition: N/R

After Graduation (Class of 1998–99)
Employed within 3 months of graduation: 91%
Average starting salary: $62,897

Accreditation
AACSB—The International Association for Management Education

DEGREES EMIM • MBA/MIM • MIM • MIMLA

EMIM—Executive Master of International Management *Distance learning option.* At least 50 total credits required. Minimum of 23 months to complete program. *Concentrations:* international management.

MBA/MIM—Master of Business Administration/Master of International Management Full-time. *Distance learning option.* 66 to 72 total credits required. 20 to 28 months to complete program. *Concentrations:* international management.

MIM—Master of International Management Full-time. *Distance learning option.* 60 total credits required. 16 months to complete program. *Concentrations:* entrepreneurship, international finance, international management, international marketing.

MIMLA—Master of International Management for Latin America Full-time. *Distance learning option.* At least 50 total credits required. Minimum of 22 months to complete program.

COSTS
Tuition *Full-time:* $24,000. Tuition varies by number of courses or credits taken and academic program. **Required fees:** *Full-time* $1300. Fees vary by campus location. **Graduate housing:** Room and board costs vary by campus location and type of accommodation. *Typical cost:* $6100 (including board).

FINANCIAL AID (1999–2000)
1128 students received aid, including fellowships, grants, research assistantships, scholarships, and work study. **Financial Aid Contact** Ms. Catherine King-Todd, Director of Financial Aid, 15249 North 59th Avenue, Glendale, AZ 85306-3236. **Phone:** 602-978-7888. **Fax:** 602-439-5432. **E-mail:** kingtodc@t-bird.edu.

RESOURCES AND SERVICES
Information about online services, personal computer policies, library resources, international exchange programs, internship programs, and placement services at this institution and others can be found at **www. petersons.com/mba**

International Students
48% of students enrolled are international students.
Services and Facilities Counseling/support services, ESL/language courses, housing location assistance, international student housing, international student organization, visa services, newsletter. Financial aid is available to international students.
Applying *Required:* TOEFL with recommended score of 600 (paper), proof of adequate funds.
International Student Contact Ms. Mary Lee Carter, Director, Programs for Foreign Students and Scholars, 15249 North 59th Avenue, Glendale, AZ 85306-3236. **Phone:** 602-978-7599. **Fax:** 602-439-5432. **E-mail:** carterml@t-bird.edu.

■ APPLICATION
Required GMAT, application form, baccalaureate/first degree, essay, 3 letters of recommendation, personal statement, resume/curriculum vitae, transcripts of college work, 2 years of work experience.
Deadlines and Fees *Deadlines:* 1/31 for fall, 7/31 for winter, 7/31 for spring, 1/31 for summer, 1/31 for fall (international), 7/31 for winter (international), 7/31 for spring (international), 1/31 for summer (international). *Application fee:* $125, $125 (international).
Application Contact Ms. Judith Johnson, Dean of Admissions/Financial Aid, 15249 North 59th Avenue, Glendale, AZ 85306-3236. **Phone:** 602-978-7100. **Fax:** 602-439-5432. **E-mail:** tbird@t-bird.edu.

See full description on page 854.

The University of Arizona
Tucson, Arizona
KARL ELLER GRADUATE SCHOOL OF MANAGEMENT

Accreditation
AACSB—The International Association for Management Education

DEGREES JD/MBA • MBA • MBA/MIM • MBA/MS

JD/MBA—Juris Doctor/Master of Business Administration Full-time. At least 90 total credits required. 45 months to complete program. *Concentrations:* accounting, economics, entrepreneurship, finance, human resources, international business, legal administration, management, management information systems, marketing, marketing research, operations management.

MBA—Master of Business Administration Full-time and part-time. At least 60 total credits required. 21 to 24 months to complete program. *Concentrations:* accounting, economics, entrepreneurship, finance, financial management/planning, human resources, industrial administration/management, information management, international business, management, management consulting, management information systems, management systems analysis, marketing, marketing research, new venture management, operations management, technology management.

MBA/MIM—Master of Business Administration/Master of International Management Full-time. At least 75 total credits required. 38 to 41 months to complete program. *Concentrations:* accounting, banking, decision sciences, economics, entrepreneurship, finance, health care, human resources, international and area business studies, international banking, international business, international development management, international economics, international finance, international logistics, international management, international marketing, international trade, management, management information systems, marketing, marketing research, operations management, production management.

MBA/MS—Master of Business Administration/Master of Science in Management Information Systems Full-time. At least 75 total credits required. 38 to 41 months to complete program. *Concentrations:* accounting, economics, entrepreneurship, finance, human resources, international business, management, management information systems, marketing, marketing research, operations management.

RESOURCES AND SERVICES
Information about online services, personal computer policies, library resources, international exchange programs, internship programs, and placement services at this institution and others can be found at **www. petersons.com/mba**

International Students
Services and Facilities Counseling/support services, ESL/language courses. Financial aid is available to international students.
International Student Contact Mr. David Currey, Global Students Office, 915 North Tyndall Avenue, Tucson, AZ 85721. **Phone:** 520-621-4627. **Fax:** 520-621-4069. **E-mail:** currey@u.arizona.edu.

■ APPLICATION
Application Contact Ms. Susan Salinas Wong, Director of Admissions and Assistant Dean, Eller Graduate School of Management, 210 McClelland Hall, PO Box 210108, Tucson, AZ 85721-0108. **Phone:** 520-621-4008. **Fax:** 520-621-2606. **E-mail:** ellernet@bpa.arizona.edu.

See full description on page 864.

University of Phoenix
Phoenix, Arizona
BUSINESS ADMINISTRATION AND MANAGEMENT PROGRAMS

DEGREES MA • MBA

MA—Master of Arts in Organizational Management Full-time. *Distance learning option.* At least 39 total credits required.

MBA—Master of Business Administration in Global Management Full-time. *Distance learning option.* At least 41 total credits required.

MBA—Master of Business Administration in Health Care Management Full-time. *Distance learning option.* At least 40 total credits required.

MBA—Master of Business Administration in Technology Management Full-time. *Distance learning option.* At least 45 total credits required.

MBA—Master of Business Administration Full-time. *Distance learning option.* At least 45 total credits required.

RESOURCES AND SERVICES
Information about online services, personal computer policies, library resources, international exchange programs, internship programs, and

placement services at this institution and others can be found at **www. petersons.com/mba**

International Students

Services and Facilities Financial aid is not available to international students.

■ APPLICATION

Application Contact Department of Graduate Business, 4615 East Elwood Road, PO Box 52069, Phoenix, AZ 85072-2069.

Western International University

Phoenix, Arizona

GRADUATE PROGRAMS IN BUSINESS

Graduate Business Faculty
Part-time: 200

Student Body
Total: 411   Average Age: 35

Admissions
Applications: 800   Average GPA: 3
Admitted: 782

Costs (1999–2000)
Full-time tuition: $7200 per academic year
Part-time tuition: $240 per credit

DEGREES MBA • MPA • MS

MBA—Master of Business Administration in Finance Full-time and part-time. 36 to 55 total credits required. 15 to 72 months to complete program. *Concentrations:* finance.

MBA—Master of Business Administration in Information Technology Full-time and part-time. 36 to 55 total credits required. 15 to 72 months to complete program. *Concentrations:* management information systems.

MBA—Master of Business Administration in International Business Full-time and part-time. 36 to 55 total credits required. 15 to 72 months to complete program. *Concentrations:* international business.

MBA—Master of Business Administration in Management Full-time and part-time. 36 to 55 total credits required. 15 to 72 months to complete program. *Concentrations:* management.

MBA—Master of Business Administration in Marketing Full-time and part-time. 36 to 55 total credits required. 15 to 72 months to complete program. *Concentrations:* marketing.

MPA—Master of Public Administration Full-time and part-time. 36 to 52 total credits required. 15 to 72 months to complete program.

MS—Master of Science in Information Systems Engineering Full-time and part-time. 36 to 67 total credits required. 15 to 72 months to complete program. *Concentrations:* system management.

MS—Master of Science in Information Technology Full-time and part-time. 36 to 55 total credits required. 15 to 72 months to complete program. *Concentrations:* technology management.

Western International University (WIU) was established on the principle that a global business perspective is vital in the emerging international marketplace. International issues and technology are key themes throughout WIU's programs. Taught by professors with real-world experience, American business techniques are coupled with a comprehensive view of global business. WIU's international emphasis can be found in the faculty, which includes respected industry professionals, and in the students, who come from more than thirty countries, including the United States. WIU's students are primarily working professionals who are serious about assuming leadership roles in the global environment. The diversity of the student body brings a broad range of cultural experiences to the campus and provides future executives with an understanding of cross-cultural communication. WIU recognizes that this high level of diversity necessitates a flexible and practical approach to learning. WIU's flexible schedule enables students to expedite their academic progress. Classes meet once a week over a two-month session. New classes begin every month, which enables students to take one or more classes at a time in order to shorten the length of their degree program. At WIU, the attributes of traditional and nontraditional educational approaches are combined, with an emphasis on practical application.

COSTS

Tuition *Full-time:* $7200. *Part-time:* $240 per credit. **Tuition, international:** *Full-time* $8550. Tuition varies by campus location and academic program.

FINANCIAL AID (1999–2000)

Loans, scholarships, and work study. Aid is available to part-time students. **Financial Aid Contact** Mr. Tim Browning, Director of Finance and Admissions, 9215 North Black Canyon Highway, Phoenix, AZ 85260. **Phone:** 602-943-2311 Ext. 116. **Fax:** 602-371-8637. **E-mail:** tim. browning@apollogrp.edu.

RESOURCES AND SERVICES

Information about online services, personal computer policies, library resources, international exchange programs, internship programs, and placement services at this institution and others can be found at **www. petersons.com/mba**

International Students

Services and Facilities Counseling/support services, ESL/language courses, housing location assistance, international student organization, orientation, visa services. Financial aid is not available to international students.

Applying *Required:* Proof of adequate funds, proof of health/immunizations. *Recommended:* TOEFL with recommended score of 550 (paper), TWE with recommended score of 5.

International Student Contact Ms. Heather Bridges, International Student Advisement, 9215 North Black Canyon Highway, Phoenix, AZ 85021-2718. **Phone:** 602-943-2311 Ext. 171. **Fax:** 602-943-3204. **E-mail:** heather.bridges@ apollogrp.edu.

■ APPLICATION

Required Application form, baccalaureate/first degree, personal statement, transcripts of college work. **Recommended** Interview.

Deadlines and Fees Applications for domestic and international students are processed on a rolling basis. *Application fee:* $85, $125 (international).

Application Contact Mr. Doug Gaer, Director of Enrollment, 9215 North Black Canyon Highway, Phoenix, AZ 85021-2718. **Phone:** 602-943-2311 Ext. 126. **Fax:** 602-371-8637. **E-mail:** doug.gaer@apollogrp.edu.

ARKANSAS

Arkansas State University

Jonesboro, State University, Arkansas

COLLEGE OF BUSINESS

Graduate Business Faculty
Full-time: 52   Part-time: 2

Student Body
Total: 104   Average Age: 29
Full-time: 49   Women: 36%
Part-time: 55

Admissions
Applications: 53   Enrolled: 36
Admitted: 45   Average GMAT: 510

Costs (1999–2000)
Full-time tuition: $2976 per academic year (resident), $7488 per academic year (nonresident)
Part-time tuition: $124 per credit hour (resident), $312 per credit hour (nonresident)

Accreditation
AACSB—The International Association for Management Education

DEGREE MBA

MBA—Master of Business Administration Full-time and part-time. At least 30 total credits required. 12 to 72 months to complete program. *Concentrations:* management.

COSTS

Tuition, state resident: *Full-time* $2976. *Part-time* $124 per credit hour. **Tuition, nonresident:** *Full-time* $7488. *Part-time* $312 per credit hour. Tuition varies by class time. **Required fees:** *Part-time* $19 per hour. Fees vary by academic program.

FINANCIAL AID (1999–2000)

Fellowships, research assistantships, and work study. Aid is available to part-time students.

Arkansas State University (continued)

RESOURCES AND SERVICES
Information about online services, personal computer policies, library resources, international exchange programs, internship programs, and placement services at this institution and others can be found at **www.petersons.com/mba**

International Students
33% of students enrolled are international students.

Services and Facilities Counseling/support services, ESL/language courses, international student organization, language tutoring, orientation, visa services. Financial aid is available to international students.

Applying *Required:* TOEFL with recommended score of 213 (computer) or 550 (paper), proof of adequate funds, proof of health/immunizations.

International Student Contact Assistant Director for International Affairs, PO Box 2220, State University, AR 72467. **Phone:** 870-972-2329. **Fax:** 870-972-3892.

■ APPLICATION
Required GMAT, application form, baccalaureate/first degree, 2 letters of recommendation, transcripts of college work, 1 year of work experience.

Deadlines and Fees Applications for domestic and international students are processed on a rolling basis. *Application fee:* $15, $25 (international).

Application Contact Dr. William Roe, Director of Graduate Business Programs, PO Box 2220, State University, AR 72467-1630. **Phone:** 870-972-3035. **Fax:** 870-972-3744. **E-mail:** wroe@cherokee.astate.edu.

Henderson State University
Arkadelphia, Arkansas

SCHOOL OF BUSINESS ADMINISTRATION

Accreditation
AACSB—The International Association for Management Education

DEGREE MBA

MBA—Master of Business Administration Full-time and part-time. 30 to 36 total credits required. *Concentrations:* accounting, economics, finance, management, marketing.

RESOURCES AND SERVICES
Information about online services, personal computer policies, library resources, international exchange programs, internship programs, and placement services at this institution and others can be found at **www.petersons.com/mba**

International Students
Services and Facilities Orientation, visa services.
International Student Contact Katherine Vlassek, 1100 Henderson Street, Arkadelphia, AR 71999-0001. **Phone:** 870-230-5265.

■ APPLICATION
Application Contact Registrar, PO Box 7534, Arkadelphia, AR 71999-0001. **Phone:** 870-230-5000 Ext. 3293.

University of Arkansas
Fayetteville, Arkansas

COLLEGE OF BUSINESS ADMINISTRATION

Graduate Business Faculty
Full-time: 81   Part-time: 12

Student Body
Total: 149
Full-time: 122   Average Age: 27
Part-time: 27   Women: 46%

Admissions
Applications: 174   Average GMAT: 575
Admitted: 120   Average GPA: 3.4
Enrolled: 91

Costs (1999–2000)
Full-time tuition: $8829 per academic year (resident), $18,063 per academic year (nonresident)

Part-time tuition: $201 per credit hour (resident), $444 per credit hour (nonresident)

After Graduation (Class of 1998–99)
Employed within 3 months of graduation: 82%
Average starting salary: $43,500

Accreditation
AACSB—The International Association for Management Education

DEGREES M Acc • MA • MBA • MIS • MTLM

M Acc—Master of Accountancy Full-time. At least 30 total credits required. Minimum of 9 months to complete program.

MA—Master of Arts in Economics Full-time. GRE score required. 30 to 39 total credits required. 9 to 24 months to complete program. *Concentrations:* international economics.

MBA—Managerial MBA Part-time. *Distance learning option.* At least 38 total credits required. 24 to 48 months to complete program. *Concentrations:* entrepreneurship, finance, international business, marketing.

MBA—Master of Business Administration Full-time. At least 38 total credits required. 12 months to complete program. *Concentrations:* entrepreneurship, finance, international business, marketing.

MIS—Master of Information Systems Full-time and part-time. At least 30 total credits required. Minimum of 12 months to complete program. *Concentrations:* information management, telecommunications management.

MTLM—Master of Transportation and Logistics Management Full-time and part-time. At least 30 total credits required. Minimum of 12 months to complete program.

COSTS

Tuition, state resident: *Full-time* $7638. *Part-time* $201 per credit hour. **Tuition, nonresident:** *Full-time* $16,872. *Part-time* $444 per credit hour. **Tuition, international:** *Full-time* $16,872. Tuition varies by number of courses or credits taken and local reciprocity agreements. **Required fees:** *Full-time* $1191. *Part-time* $189 per semester. Tuition and fees vary by number of courses or credits taken. **Graduate housing:** Room and board costs vary by number of occupants, type of accommodation, and type of board plan. *Typical cost:* $6400 (including board).

FINANCIAL AID (1999–2000)
98 students received aid, including fellowships, research assistantships, scholarships, teaching assistantships, and work study. Aid is available to part-time students. Financial aid application deadline: 2/15. **Financial Aid Contact** Graduate School of Business, Sam M. Walton College of Business Administration, Suite 475, Fayetteville, AR 72701. **Phone:** 501-575-2851. **Fax:** 501-575-8721. **E-mail:** gso@walton.uark.edu.

RESOURCES AND SERVICES
Information about online services, personal computer policies, library resources, international exchange programs, internship programs, and placement services at this institution and others can be found at **www.petersons.com/mba**

International Students
31% of students enrolled are international students.

Services and Facilities Counseling/support services, ESL/language courses, international student housing, international student organization, language tutoring, orientation, visa services. Financial aid is available to international students.

Applying *Required:* TOEFL with recommended score of 213 (computer) or 550 (paper), proof of adequate funds, proof of health/immunizations.

International Student Contact International Admissions, 215 Hunt Hall, Fayetteville, AR 72701. **Phone:** 501-575-6246. **Fax:** 501-575-7515. **E-mail:** intlap@comp.uark.edu.

■ APPLICATION
Required GMAT, application form, baccalaureate/first degree, essay, 3 letters of recommendation, personal statement, resume/curriculum vitae, transcripts of college work. School will accept GRE. **Recommended** Interview, 2 years of work experience.

Deadlines and Fees *Deadlines:* 2/15 for fall, 2/15 for fall (international). *Application fee:* $40, $50 (international).

Application Contact Ms. Michele Halsell, Managing Director, Graduate School of Business, Sam M. Walton College of Business Administration, Suite 475, Fayetteville, AR 72701. **Phone:** 501-575-2851. **Fax:** 501-575-8721. **E-mail:** gsb@walton.uark.edu.

See full description on page 866.

University of Arkansas at Little Rock

Little Rock, Arkansas

COLLEGE OF BUSINESS ADMINISTRATION

Graduate Business Faculty
Full-time: 42   Part-time: 10

Student Body
Total: 205   Average Age: 29
Full-time: 26   Women: 42%
Part-time: 179

Admissions
Applications: 88   Average GMAT: 525
Admitted: 79   Average GPA: 3.2
Enrolled: 55

Costs (1999–2000)
Full-time tuition: $3804 per academic year (resident), $8088 per academic year (nonresident)
Part-time tuition: $159 per credit (resident), $337 per credit (nonresident)

After Graduation (Class of 1998–99)
Employed within 3 months of graduation: 95%
Average starting salary: $40,000

Accreditation
AACSB—The International Association for Management Education

DEGREES MBA

MBA—Executive MBA Part-time. 5 years of work experience required. At least 46 total credits required. 17 months to complete program.

MBA—Master of Business Administration Full-time and part-time. *Distance learning option.* 30 to 48 total credits required. 12 to 60 months to complete program. *Concentrations:* accounting, finance, international business, management, management information systems, marketing.

COSTS

Tuition, state resident: *Full-time* $3408. *Part-time* $142 per credit. **Tuition, nonresident:** *Full-time* $7692. *Part-time* $320 per credit. **Required fees:** *Full-time* $396. *Part-time* $16.50 per credit. Tuition and fees vary by number of courses or credits taken. **Graduate housing:** Room and board costs vary by type of accommodation and type of board plan. *Typical cost:* $2600 (room only).

FINANCIAL AID (1999–2000)

15 students received aid, including loans, research assistantships, and work study. Aid is available to part-time students. Financial aid application deadline: 4/1. **Financial Aid Contact** Ms. Roberta Moore, MBA Advisor, 2801 South University Avenue, Little Rock, AR 72204. **Phone:** 501-569-3048. **Fax:** 501-569-8898. **E-mail:** rmmoore@ualr.edu.

RESOURCES AND SERVICES

Information about online services, personal computer policies, library resources, international exchange programs, internship programs, and placement services at this institution and others can be found at www. petersons.com/mba

International Students

15% of students enrolled are international students.

Services and Facilities Counseling/support services, ESL/language courses, housing location assistance, international student organization, orientation. Financial aid is not available to international students.
Applying *Required:* TOEFL with recommended score of 213 (computer) or 550 (paper), proof of adequate funds, proof of health/immunizations.
International Student Contact Ms. Robbin Fulmore, International English Language Program, 2801 South University Avenue, Little Rock, AR 72204. **Phone:** 501-569-3583. **Fax:** 501-569-3581. **E-mail:** rsfulmore@ualr.edu.

■ APPLICATION

Required Application form, baccalaureate/first degree, transcripts of college work. School will accept GMAT.

Deadlines and Fees Applications for domestic and international students are processed on a rolling basis. *Application fee:* $30 (international).

Application Contact Ms. Roberta Moore, MBA Advisor, 2801 South University Avenue, Little Rock, AR 72204. **Phone:** 501-569-3048. **Fax:** 501-569-8898. **E-mail:** rmmoore@ualr.edu.

University of Central Arkansas

Conway, Arkansas

COLLEGE OF BUSINESS ADMINISTRATION

Graduate Business Faculty
Full-time: 13

Student Body
Total: 47   Part-time: 28
Full-time: 19

Admissions
Applications: 122   Average GMAT: 476
Admitted: 83   Average GPA: 3.13
Enrolled: 31

Costs (1999–2000)
Full-time tuition: N/R
Part-time tuition: $145 per credit hour (resident), $298 per credit hour (nonresident)

After Graduation (Class of 1998–99)
Employed within 3 months of graduation: 85%

Accreditation
AACSB—The International Association for Management Education

DEGREE MBA

MBA—Master of Business Administration Full-time and part-time. At least 30 total credits required. 12 to 72 months to complete program.

COSTS

Tuition, state resident: *Part-time* $145 per credit hour. **Tuition, nonresident:** *Part-time* $298 per credit hour. **Required fees:** Tuition and fees vary by number of courses or credits taken. **Graduate housing:** Room and board costs vary by number of occupants, type of accommodation, and type of board plan. *Typical cost:* $3150 (including board).

FINANCIAL AID (1999–2000)

Work study. Financial aid application deadline: 2/15. **Financial Aid Contact** Mrs. Julia Robison, Director of Financial Aid, 201 Bernard, Conway, AR 72035-0001. **Phone:** 501-450-3140. **E-mail:** juliar@ecom. uca.edu.

RESOURCES AND SERVICES

Information about online services, personal computer policies, library resources, international exchange programs, internship programs, and placement services at this institution and others can be found at **www. petersons.com/mba**

International Students

Services and Facilities Counseling/support services, ESL/language courses, international student housing. Financial aid is not available to international students.
Applying *Required:* TOEFL with recommended score of 550 (paper), proof of adequate funds, proof of health/immunizations.
International Student Contact Ms. Lisa Shoemake, Immigration Advisor, 201 Donaghey Avenue, Torreyson Library 304, Conway, AR 72035. **Phone:** 501-450-3445. **Fax:** 501-450-5095. **E-mail:** lisas@ecom.uca.edu.

■ APPLICATION

Required GMAT, application form, baccalaureate/first degree, transcripts of college work. **Recommended** Interview, letter(s) of recommendation.

Deadlines and Fees Applications for domestic students are processed on a rolling basis. *Deadlines:* 6/15 for fall (international), 11/1 for spring (international), 4/15 for summer (international). *Application fee:* $25, $40 (international).

Application Contact Dr. Rebecca Gatlin-Watts, MBA Director, Burdick 222, 201 Donaghey Avenue, Conway, AR 72035. **Phone:** 501-450-3411. **Fax:** 501-450-5302. **E-mail:** rebeccag@mail.uca.edu.

CALIFORNIA

American InterContinental University

Los Angeles, California

PROGRAM IN INTERNATIONAL BUSINESS

Graduate Business Faculty
Full-time: 5

Student Body
Total: 50   Full-time: 50

Costs (1999–2000)
Full-time tuition: $28,240 per academic year
Part-time tuition: N/R

DEGREES MBA • MIT

MBA—Master of Business Administration Full-time and part-time. 60 total credits required. Minimum of 10 months to complete program.

MIT—Master of Information Technology Full-time and part-time. 60 total credits required. Minimum of 12 months to complete program. *Concentrations:* management information systems.

COSTS

Tuition *Full-time:* $28,240. **Graduate housing:** *Typical cost:* $4500 (room only).

FINANCIAL AID (1999–2000)

Financial Aid Contact Joe Johnson, Director of Financial Aid, 12655 West Jefferson Boulevard, Los Angeles, CA 90066. **Phone:** 310-302-2447. **E-mail:** jjohnson@aiuniv.edu.

RESOURCES AND SERVICES

Information about online services, personal computer policies, library resources, international exchange programs, internship programs, and placement services at this institution and others can be found at **www. petersons.com/mba**

International Students

Services and Facilities Counseling/support services, international student housing, international student organization, orientation, visa services.
Applying *Required:* TOEFL with recommended score of 550 (paper), proof of adequate funds.
International Student Contact Linda Foxman, Senior Admissions Officer, 12655 West Jefferson Boulevard, Los Angeles, CA 90066. **Phone:** 310-302-2414. **E-mail:** lfoxman@aiuniv.edu.

▪ APPLICATION

Required Application form, baccalaureate/first degree, interview, 2 letters of recommendation, personal statement, resume/curriculum vitae, transcripts of college work, work experience.
Deadlines and Fees Applications for domestic and international students are processed on a rolling basis. *Application fee:* $50, $50 (international).
Application Contact Linda Foxman, Senior Admissions Officer, 12655 West Jefferson Boulevard, Los Angeles, CA 90066. **Phone:** 310-302-2414. **E-mail:** lfoxman@aiuniv.edu.

Antioch Southern California/Los Angeles

Marina del Rey, California

PROGRAM IN ORGANIZATIONAL MANAGEMENT

Graduate Business Faculty
Full-time: 2   Part-time: 12

Student Body
Total: 37
Full-time: 7   Average Age: 36
Part-time: 30   Women: 78%

Admissions
Applications: 14   Enrolled: 9
Admitted: 11

Costs (1999–2000)
Full-time tuition: $10,800 per academic year
Part-time tuition: $355 per unit

DEGREE MA

MA—Organizational Management Full-time and part-time. At least 60 total credits required. 15 to 60 months to complete program. *Concentrations:* human resources, leadership, organizational behavior/development, organizational management.

COSTS

Tuition *Full-time:* $10,650. *Part-time:* $355 per unit. **Tuition, international:** *Full-time* $10,650. Tuition varies by number of courses or credits taken and academic program. **Required fees:** *Full-time* $150. *Part-time* $50 per quarter.

FINANCIAL AID (1999–2000)

22 students received aid, including grants, loans, and work study. Aid is available to part-time students. Financial aid application deadline: 3/24. **Financial Aid Contact** Ms. Jodi Valpey, Director of Financial Aid, 13274 Fiji Way, Marina del Rey, CA 90292-7090. **Phone:** 310-578-1080 Ext. 118. **Fax:** 310-822-4824. **E-mail:** jodi_valpey@antiochla.edu.

RESOURCES AND SERVICES

Information about online services, personal computer policies, library resources, international exchange programs, internship programs, and placement services at this institution and others can be found at **www. petersons.com/mba**

International Students

Services and Facilities Counseling/support services, visa services. Financial aid is not available to international students.
Applying *Required:* TOEFL with recommended score of 250 (computer) or 600 (paper), proof of adequate funds.
International Student Contact Mr. Scott Russell, Director of Admissions, 13274 Fiji Way, Marina del Rey, CA 90292-7090. **Phone:** 310-578-1080 Ext. 249. **Fax:** 310-822-4824. **E-mail:** scott_russell@antiochla.edu.

▪ APPLICATION

Required Application form, baccalaureate/first degree, essay, interview, 2 letters of recommendation, personal statement, resume/curriculum vitae, transcripts of college work. School will accept GMAT, GRE, and MAT. **Recommended** Work experience.
Deadlines and Fees *Deadlines:* 8/4 for fall, 11/3 for winter, 2/2 for spring, 5/4 for summer, 8/4 for fall (international), 11/3 for winter (international), 2/2 for spring (international), 5/4 for summer (international). *Application fee:* $60, $60 (international).
Application Contact Mr. Scott Schroeder, Director of Admissions, 13274 Fiji Way, Marina del Rey, CA 90292-7090. **Phone:** 310-578-1080. **Toll-free Phone:** 800-7-ANTIOCH. **Fax:** 310-822-4824. **E-mail:** admissions@antiochla.edu.

Antioch Southern California/ Santa Barbara

Santa Barbara, California

PROGRAM IN ORGANIZATIONAL MANAGEMENT

DEGREE MA

MA—Master of Arts in Organizational Management Full-time and part-time. *Distance learning option.* At least 60 total credits required. Minimum of 15 months to complete program. *Concentrations:* business ethics, human resources, international business, international management, management, managerial economics, nonprofit management, nonprofit organization, public and private management, technology management.

RESOURCES AND SERVICES

Information about online services, personal computer policies, library resources, international exchange programs, internship programs, and placement services at this institution and others can be found at **www. petersons.com/mba**

International Students

Services and Facilities Visa services.
International Student Contact Ms. Carol Flores, Director of Admissions, 801 Garden Street, Santa Barbara, CA 93101-1580. **Phone:** 805-962-8179 Ext. 113. **Fax:** 805-962-4786. **E-mail:** cflores@antiochsb.edu.

■ APPLICATION

Application Contact Ms. Rose Chrynko, Admissions Counselor, 801 Garden Street, Santa Barbara, CA 93101-1580. **Phone:** 805-962-8179 Ext. 112. **Fax:** 805-962-4786. **E-mail:** admissions@antiochsb.edu.

Armstrong University

Oakland, California

GRADUATE SCHOOL OF BUSINESS ADMINISTRATION

DEGREE MBA

MBA—Master of Business Administration Full-time and part-time. At least 36 total credits required. 12 to 24 months to complete program. *Concentrations:* accounting, finance, international business, management, management information systems, marketing.

RESOURCES AND SERVICES

Information about online services, personal computer policies, library resources, international exchange programs, internship programs, and placement services at this institution and others can be found at **www. petersons.com/mba**

International Students

Services and Facilities Counseling/support services, ESL/language courses, housing location assistance, orientation, visa services. Financial aid is not available to international students.
International Student Contact Tiffany Lian, Director of Admissions, 1608 Webster Street, Oakland, CA 94612. **Phone:** 510-835-7900. **Fax:** 510-835-8935. **E-mail:** info@armstrong-u.edu.

■ APPLICATION

Application Contact Tiffany Lian, Director of Admissions, Office of Admissions, 1608 Webster Street, Oakland, CA 94612. **Phone:** 510-835-7900 Ext. 12. **Toll-free Phone:** 800-222-9297. **Fax:** 510-835-8935. **E-mail:** info@armstrong-u.edu.

See full description on page 548.

Azusa Pacific University

Azusa, California

SCHOOL OF BUSINESS AND MANAGEMENT

Graduate Business Faculty

Full-time: 11	Part-time: 6

Student Body

Total: 161	
Full-time: 45	Average Age: 26
Part-time: 116	Women: 39%

Admissions

Applications: 73	
Admitted: 72	Average GMAT: 450
Enrolled: 52	Average GPA: 3

Costs (1999–2000)
Full-time tuition: N/R
Part-time tuition: $415 per unit

After Graduation (Class of 1998–99)
Employed within 3 months of graduation: 90%
Average starting salary: $35,000

DEGREES MA • MBA • MS

MA—Human and Organizational Development Full-time and part-time. 36 total credits required. 12 to 60 months to complete program.
MBA—Weekend MBA Part-time. *Distance learning option.* 36 total credits required. 18 months to complete program.
MBA—Master of Business Administration Full-time and part-time. 36 to 48 total credits required. 12 to 60 months to complete program.
MS—Master of Science in Human Resource Development Full-time and part-time. At least 36 total credits required. 12 to 60 months to complete program.

The School of Business and Management (SBM) at Azusa Pacific University (APU) prepares today's students to be tomorrow's leaders. The Master of Business Administration (M.B.A.) Program equips students to lead organizations with practical and theoretical knowledge. Whether starting or enhancing a career in management, consulting, financing, banking, or strategic or global marketing, APU's M.B.A. provides students with the necessary tools to succeed in today's competitive world. Classes are available on weeknights and weekends.

Students in the M.B.A. Program are taught by professors who are themselves business professionals who span the gamut from accounting to marketing consultants. Dynamic faculty members encourage and challenge students to be entrepreneurial and apply what they learn in the classroom to real-world situations.

The School of Business and Management is located in an ideal environment for M.B.A. students—26 miles northeast of the sprawling Los Angeles metropolis. The proximity of APU to Los Angeles provides students with easy accessibility to internships and employment opportunities.

Azusa Pacific's M.B.A. Program offers small classes that are tailored to students' career interests. The intimate class setting fosters a high level of teacher-student interaction and also enables students to network with one another. The SBM is a member of the AACSB-The International Association for Management Education and the Association of Collegiate Business Schools and Programs (ACBSP).

COSTS

Tuition *Part-time:* $415 per unit. Tuition varies by number of courses or credits taken and academic program. **Graduate housing:** Room and board costs vary by number of occupants, type of accommodation, and type of board plan. *Typical cost:* $2500 (including board), $1650 (room only).

FINANCIAL AID (1999–2000)

20 students received aid, including loans and scholarships. Aid is available to part-time students. **Financial Aid Contact** Ms. Debbie Serrano, Associate Director, 901 East Alosta Avenue, PO Box 7000, Azusa, CA 91702-7000. **Phone:** 626-815-5440. **Fax:** 626-815-5445. **E-mail:** dserrano@apu.edu.

RESOURCES AND SERVICES

Information about online services, personal computer policies, library resources, international exchange programs, internship programs, and placement services at this institution and others can be found at **www. petersons.com/mba**

International Students

17% of students enrolled are international students.
Services and Facilities Counseling/support services, ESL/language courses, visa services. Financial aid is available to international students.
Applying *Required:* TOEFL with recommended score of 550 (paper), proof of adequate funds, proof of health/immunizations.
International Student Contact Ms. Mary Grams, Director, International Student Affairs, 901 East Alosta Avenue, PO Box 7000, Azusa, CA 91702-7000. **Phone:** 626-815-6000 Ext. 3055. **E-mail:** mgrams@apu.edu.

■ APPLICATION

Required Application form, baccalaureate/first degree, 3 letters of recommendation, resume/curriculum vitae, transcripts of college work. School will accept GMAT or GRE or MAT. **Recommended** Personal statement.
Deadlines and Fees Applications for domestic students are processed on a rolling basis. *Deadlines:* 8/1 for fall (international), 12/1 for spring (international), 4/1 for summer (international). *Application fee:* $45, $65 (international).
Application Contact Graduate Admission Office, 901 East Alosta Avenue, PO Box 7000, Azusa, CA 91702-7000. **Phone:** 626-815-5470. **Toll-free Phone:** 800-TALK APU. **Fax:** 626-815-5445. **E-mail:** graduatecenter@apu.edu.

California Baptist University

Riverside, California

GRADUATE PROGRAM IN BUSINESS ADMINISTRATION

Accreditation
ACBSP—The American Council of Business Schools and Programs

DEGREES MBA

MBA—Emphasis in Management Full-time and part-time. At least 48 total credits required. 18 to 60 months to complete program. *Concentrations:* management.
MBA—Emphasis in Management Information Systems Full-time and part-time. At least 48 total credits required. 18 to 60 months to complete program.

RESOURCES AND SERVICES

Information about online services, personal computer policies, library resources, international exchange programs, internship programs, and placement services at this institution and others can be found at **www. petersons.com/mba**

California Baptist University (continued)

International Students

Services and Facilities Counseling/support services, ESL/language courses, international student housing. Financial aid is not available to international students. **International Student Contact** Mrs. Gail Ronveaux, Director of Graduate Services, 8432 Magnolia Avenue, Riverside, CA 92504. **Phone:** 909-343-4249. **Fax:** 909-351-1808. **E-mail:** gradservice@calbaptist.edu.

■ APPLICATION

Application Contact Mrs. Gail Ronveaux, Director of Graduate Services, 8432 Magnolia Avenue, Riverside, CA 92504. **Phone:** 909-343-4249. **Toll-free Phone:** 877-228-8877. **Fax:** 909-351-1808. **E-mail:** gronveau@calbaptist.edu.

California Lutheran University

Thousand Oaks, California

SCHOOL OF BUSINESS

Graduate Business Faculty

Full-time: 11	Part-time: 24

Student Body

Total: 219	Average Age: 30
Full-time: 79	Women: 49%
Part-time: 140	

Admissions

Applications: 67	Enrolled: 47
Admitted: 60	Average GMAT: 525

Costs (1999–2000)
Full-time tuition: $7290 per academic year
Part-time tuition: $405 per credit

After Graduation (Class of 1998–99)
Average starting salary: $50,000

DEGREE MBA

MBA—Master of Business Administration Full-time and part-time. At least 42 total credits required. 15 to 84 months to complete program. *Concentrations:* entrepreneurship, finance, health care, information management, international business, management, marketing, organizational behavior/development.

T*he curriculum at California Lutheran University (CLU) is based on skills relevant to the current business environment—analytical and leadership skills, technological know-how, human resource strategies, and strategic planning techniques.*

Innovation and relevance are the hallmarks of the program, as illustrated by the seven distinctive professional tracks. They combine the value of the general M.B.A. with the opportunity to gain specialized knowledge in a specific area. The University monitors current and emerging trends and builds its curriculum accordingly. Staying current with the changing business environment ensures that CLU's M.B.A. graduates are well prepared not only to be successful in today's business world but are also able to cope and succeed in the future.

The program is designed to develop competencies and skills for innovative and responsible leadership. CLU's M.B.A. program has helped professionals equip themselves to cope with new challenges in a changing world, acquire leadership skills to prepare for promotion into management, make a smooth transition into a new career field, stand out in a job search with enhanced skills and an advanced degree, gain satisfaction from personal and professional growth, make smart financial decisions in personal and professional life, form a strong network with professional peers and faculty experts, and succeed as an entrepreneur.

COSTS

Tuition *Full-time:* $7290. *Part-time:* $405 per credit.

FINANCIAL AID (1999–2000)

70 students received aid, including loans, scholarships, and teaching assistantships. Aid is available to part-time students. **Financial Aid Contact** Ms. Betsy Kocher, Director, Student Financial Planning, 60 West Olsen Road, #1375, Thousand Oaks, CA 91360-2700. **Phone:** 805-493-3115. **Fax:** 805-493-3114. **E-mail:** kocher@robles.callutheran.edu.

RESOURCES AND SERVICES

Information about online services, personal computer policies, library resources, international exchange programs, internship programs, and placement services at this institution and others can be found at **www.petersons.com/mba**

International Students

Services and Facilities Counseling/support services, international student organization, orientation, visa services. Financial aid is not available to international students.
Applying *Required:* TOEFL with recommended score of 230 (computer) or 570 (paper), proof of adequate funds, proof of health/immunizations.
International Student Contact Miss Paula Avery, International Coordinator, 60 West Olsen Road, #6450, Thousand Oaks, CA 91360-2787. **Phone:** 805-493-3967. **Fax:** 805-493-3114. **E-mail:** avery@clunet.edu.

■ APPLICATION

Required GMAT, application form, baccalaureate/first degree, interview, 3 letters of recommendation, personal statement, transcripts of college work. **Recommended** Resume/curriculum vitae, 2 years of work experience.
Deadlines and Fees Applications for domestic and international students are processed on a rolling basis. *Application fee:* $50, $50 (international).
Application Contact Mrs. Anita Hanney, MBA Admission Counselor, Graduate Enrollment Services, 60 West Olsen Road, #2300, Thousand Oaks, CA 91360-2700. **Phone:** 805-493-3127. **Fax:** 805-493-3542. **E-mail:** hanney@clunet.edu.

California National University for Advanced Studies

North Hills, California

COLLEGE OF BUSINESS ADMINISTRATION

Graduate Business Faculty
Part-time: 31

Student Body

Total: 77	Women: 43%
Average Age: 37	

Admissions
Average GPA: 3.3

Costs (1999–2000)
Full-time tuition: N/R
Part-time tuition: $255 per unit (resident)

After Graduation (Class of 1998–99)
Employed within 3 months of graduation: 100%
Average starting salary: $60,000

DEGREES MBA • MHRM

MBA—Master of Business Administration Distance learning option. 36 to 45 total credits required. 18 to 24 months to complete program. *Concentrations:* accounting, finance, health care, human resources, international business, management, management information systems, marketing, quality management.

MHRM—Master of Human Resources Management Distance learning option. At least 36 total credits required. 18 to 24 months to complete program. *Concentrations:* human resources, organizational behavior/development, training and development.

COSTS

Tuition, state resident: *Part-time* $255 per unit. Tuition varies by number of courses or credits taken and academic program.

FINANCIAL AID (1999–2000)

Aid is available to part-time students. **Financial Aid Contact** Ms. Stephanie Smith, Registrar, 16909 Parthenia Street, North Hills, CA 91343. **Phone:** 800-782-2422. **Fax:** 818-830-2418.

RESOURCES AND SERVICES

Information about online services, personal computer policies, library resources, international exchange programs, internship programs, and placement services at this institution and others can be found at **www.petersons.com/mba**

International Students

Services and Facilities Financial aid is not available to international students.
Applying *Recommended:* TOEFL with recommended score of 550 (paper).
International Student Contact Ms. Stephanie Smith, Registrar, 16909 Parthenia Street, North Hills, CA 91343. **Phone:** 800-782-2422. **Fax:** 818-830-2418.

■ APPLICATION

Required Application form, baccalaureate/first degree, essay, interview, personal statement, resume/curriculum vitae, transcripts of college work. **Recommended** Letter(s) of recommendation, work experience.

Deadlines and Fees Applications for domestic and international students are processed on a rolling basis. *Application fee:* $50, $100 (international).

Application Contact Ms. Jeanne Cunneff, Admissions Representative, 16909 Parthenia Street, North Hills, CA 91343. **Phone:** 818-830-2411.

California Polytechnic State University, San Luis Obispo

San Luis Obispo, California

COLLEGE OF BUSINESS

Graduate Business Faculty
Full-time: 53   Part-time: 32

Student Body
Total: 103   Average Age: 27
Full-time: 101   Women: 27%
Part-time: 2

Admissions
Applications: 148   Average GMAT: 551
Admitted: 93   Average GPA: 3.11
Enrolled: 56

Costs (1999–2000)
Full-time tuition: $2145 per academic year (resident), $10,017 per academic year (nonresident)
Part-time tuition: N/R

Accreditation
AACSB—The International Association for Management Education

DEGREES MBA • MBA/MS • MS

MBA—Master of Business Administration Full-time. At least 96 total credits required. 24 to 84 months to complete program. *Concentrations:* agribusiness, management.

MBA/MS—Master of Business Administration/Master of Science in Computer Science Full-time. At least 96 total credits required. 24 to 84 months to complete program. *Concentrations:* agribusiness, manufacturing management.

MBA/MS—Master of Business Administration/Master of Science in Electrical Engineering Full-time. At least 96 total credits required. 24 to 84 months to complete program. *Concentrations:* agribusiness, manufacturing management.

MBA/MS—Master of Business Administration/Master of Science in Engineering Management Full-time. 96 to 99 total credits required. 24 to 84 months to complete program. *Concentrations:* agribusiness, manufacturing management.

MBA/MS—Master of Business Administration/Master of Science in Mechanical Engineering Full-time. At least 96 total credits required. 24 to 84 months to complete program. *Concentrations:* agribusiness, manufacturing management.

MS—Master of Science in Industrial and Technical Studies Full-time and part-time. At least 45 total credits required. 10 to 84 months to complete program.

COSTS

Tuition, state resident: *Full-time* $0. **Tuition, nonresident:** *Full-time* $7872. **Tuition, international:** *Full-time* $7872. **Required fees:** *Full-time* $2145. Tuition and fees vary by number of courses or credits taken. **Graduate housing:** *Typical cost:* $5068 (including board).

FINANCIAL AID (1999–2000)

Grants, loans, research assistantships, scholarships, teaching assistantships, and work study. Aid is available to part-time students.
Financial Aid Contact Mr. John Anderson, Director, Financial Aid Office, San Luis Obispo, CA 93407. **Phone:** 805-756-2927. **Fax:** 805-756-7243. **E-mail:** anderson@calpoly.edu.

RESOURCES AND SERVICES

Information about online services, personal computer policies, library resources, international exchange programs, internship programs, and placement services at this institution and others can be found at **www. petersons.com/mba**

International Students

9% of students enrolled are international students.

Services and Facilities Counseling/support services, ESL/language courses, language tutoring. Financial aid is not available to international students.

Applying *Required:* TOEFL with recommended score of 550 (paper), TWE with recommended score of 4.5, proof of adequate funds, proof of health/immunizations.

International Student Contact Ms. Barbara Andre, International Student Advisor, Global Affairs, San Luis Obispo, CA 93407. **Phone:** 805-756-5837. **Fax:** 805-756-5484. **E-mail:** bandre@calpoly.edu.

■ APPLICATION

Required GMAT, application form, baccalaureate/first degree, essay, 2 letters of recommendation, resume/curriculum vitae, transcripts of college work. **Recommended** Interview, 3 years of work experience.

Deadlines and Fees *Deadlines:* 7/1 for fall, 4/1 for fall (international). *Application fee:* $55, $55 (international).

Application Contact Dr. Earl Keller, Director, Graduate Programs, Graduate Programs, College of Business, San Luis Obispo, CA 93407. **Phone:** 805-756-2588. **Fax:** 805-756-0110. **E-mail:** eckeller@calpoly.edu.

California State Polytechnic University, Pomona

Pomona, California

COLLEGE OF BUSINESS ADMINISTRATION

Student Body
Total: 419   Average Age: 33
Full-time: 293   Women: 41%
Part-time: 126

Admissions
Applications: 97   Average GMAT: 537
Admitted: 66   Average GPA: 3.19
Enrolled: 32

Costs (1999–2000)
Full-time tuition: N/R
Part-time tuition: $184 per unit (nonresident)

After Graduation (Class of 1998–99)
Employed within 3 months of graduation: 80%
Average starting salary: $46,000

Accreditation
AACSB—The International Association for Management Education

DEGREES MBA • MSBA

MBA—Entrepreneurship Full-time and part-time. At least 48 total credits required. Maximum of 84 months to complete program. *Concentrations:* entrepreneurship.

MBA—General Master of Business Administration Full-time and part-time. At least 48 total credits required. Maximum of 84 months to complete program.

MBA—Professional Master of Business Administration Full-time and part-time. At least 48 total credits required. Maximum of 84 months to complete program.

MBA—Master of Business Administration Full-time and part-time. At least 48 total credits required. Maximum of 84 months to complete program. *Concentrations:* accounting, entrepreneurship, finance, human resources, information management, international business, marketing, operations management, production management, real estate.

MSBA—IS Audit Full-time and part-time. At least 48 total credits required. Maximum of 84 months to complete program. *Concentrations:* information management.

COSTS

Tuition, nonresident: *Part-time* $184 per unit. Tuition varies by campus location. **Required fees:** Fees vary by number of courses or credits taken.

FINANCIAL AID (1999–2000)

Loans and teaching assistantships. Aid is available to part-time students.
Financial Aid Contact Ms. Marjorie Melendez, Assistant Director of Financial Aid, 3801 West Temple Avenue, Pomona, CA 91768-2557. **Phone:** 909-869-3702. **E-mail:** mamelendez@csupomona.edu.

RESOURCES AND SERVICES

Information about online services, personal computer policies, library resources, international exchange programs, internship programs, and placement services at this institution and others can be found at **www. petersons.com/mba**

International Students

27% of students enrolled are international students.

California State Polytechnic University, Pomona (continued)

Services and Facilities Counseling/support services, ESL/language courses, international student housing, visa services.
Applying *Required:* TOEFL with recommended score of 580 (paper), proof of adequate funds, proof of health/immunizations.
International Student Contact Mr. John Moutou, International Student Advisor, 3801 West Temple Avenue, Pomona, CA 91768-2557. **Phone:** 909-869-3338. **E-mail:** jnmoutou@csupomona.edu.

■ **APPLICATION**

Required GMAT, application form, baccalaureate/first degree, 2 letters of recommendation, personal statement, resume/curriculum vitae, transcripts of college work, 2 years of work experience.
Deadlines and Fees *Deadlines:* 7/13 for fall, 10/4 for winter, 1/10 for spring, 4/3 for summer, 7/13 for fall (international), 10/4 for winter (international), 1/10 for spring (international), 4/3 for summer (international). *Application fee:* $55, $55 (international).
Application Contact Dr. Eric J. McLaughlin, Director, Graduate Business Programs, 3801 West Temple Avenue, Pomona, CA 91768-2557. **Phone:** 909-869-2363. **Fax:** 909-869-4559. **E-mail:** directorgba@csupomona.edu.

California State University, Bakersfield

Bakersfield, California

SCHOOL OF BUSINESS AND PUBLIC ADMINISTRATION

Graduate Business Faculty
Full-time: 24   Part-time: 17
Student Body
Total: 718   Women: 50%
Average Age: 30
Admissions
Applications: 80   Average GMAT: 525
Admitted: 67   Average GPA: 3
Enrolled: 64

Costs (1999–2000)
Full-time tuition: $1887 per academic year (resident), $9233 per academic year (nonresident)
Part-time tuition: N/R

Accreditation
AACSB—The International Association for Management Education

DEGREES MBA • MPA • MS

MBA—Master of Business Administration Full-time and part-time. At least 48 total credits required. 12 to 84 months to complete program. *Concentrations:* management.

MPA—Master of Public Administration Full-time and part-time. At least 55 total credits required. 24 to 84 months to complete program.

MS—Master of Science in Health Care Management Full-time and part-time. At least 55 total credits required. 24 to 84 months to complete program.

COSTS

Tuition, state resident: *Full-time* $1887. **Tuition, nonresident:** *Full-time* $9233. **Graduate housing:** Room and board costs vary by campus location, type of accommodation, and type of board plan. *Typical cost:* $4603 (including board).

FINANCIAL AID (1999–2000)

Financial Aid Contact Financial Aid Office, 9001 Stockdale Highway, Bakersfield, CA 93311-1022. **Phone:** 661-664-3016. **Fax:** 661-664-6800.

RESOURCES AND SERVICES

Information about online services, personal computer policies, library resources, international exchange programs, internship programs, and placement services at this institution and others can be found at **www.petersons.com/mba**

International Students

6% of students enrolled are international students.
Services and Facilities Counseling/support services, ESL/language courses, international student organization, language tutoring, orientation.
Applying *Required:* TOEFL with recommended score of 550 (paper), proof of adequate funds, proof of health/immunizations.

International Student Contact Ms. Jan Titus, Director, Center for International Education, 9001 Stockdale Highway, Bakersfield, CA 93311-1022. **Phone:** 661-664-2014. **Fax:** 661-664-6914.

■ **APPLICATION**

Required GMAT, application form, baccalaureate/first degree, 2 letters of recommendation, personal statement, resume/curriculum vitae, transcripts of college work. **Recommended** Interview, 3 years of work experience.
Deadlines and Fees *Deadlines:* 7/1 for fall, 11/1 for winter, 3/1 for spring, 7/1 for fall (international), 11/1 for winter (international), 3/1 for spring (international). *Application fee:* $55, $55 (international).
Application Contact Thomas Mishoe, MBA Coordinator, 9001 Stockdale Highway, Bakersfield, CA 93311-1022. **Phone:** 661-664-3099. **Fax:** 661-664-2438. **E-mail:** tmishoe@csubak.edu.

California State University, Chico

Chico, California

COLLEGE OF BUSINESS

Graduate Business Faculty
Full-time: 60   Part-time: 15
Student Body
Total: 80   Average Age: 27
Full-time: 50   Women: 36%
Part-time: 30
Admissions
Applications: 90   Average GMAT: 530
Admitted: 45   Average GPA: 3.3
Enrolled: 27

Costs (1999–2000)
Full-time tuition: $2140 per academic year (resident), $6000 per academic year (nonresident)
Part-time tuition: N/R

After Graduation (Class of 1998–99)
Employed within 3 months of graduation: 95%
Average starting salary: $55,000

Accreditation
AACSB—The International Association for Management Education

DEGREES MBA • MS

MBA—Master of Business Administration Full-time and part-time. At least 30 total credits required. 12 to 60 months to complete program. *Concentrations:* finance, human resources, management, management information systems, marketing, production management.

MS—Master of Science in Accountancy Full-time and part-time. At least 30 total credits required. 12 to 60 months to complete program. *Concentrations:* accounting, management information systems.

COSTS

Tuition, state resident: *Full-time* $2140. **Tuition, nonresident:** *Full-time* $6000. Tuition varies by number of courses or credits taken. **Graduate housing:** Room and board costs vary by number of occupants, type of accommodation, and type of board plan. *Typical cost:* $5600 (including board).

FINANCIAL AID (1999–2000)

25 students received aid, including loans, research assistantships, teaching assistantships, and work study. Aid is available to part-time students. Financial aid application deadline: 3/1. **Financial Aid Contact** Financial Aid, 408 West First Street, Chico, CA 95929. **Phone:** 530-898-6451. **Fax:** 530-898-6824.

RESOURCES AND SERVICES

Information about online services, personal computer policies, library resources, international exchange programs, internship programs, and placement services at this institution and others can be found at **www.petersons.com/mba**

International Students

21% of students enrolled are international students.
Services and Facilities Counseling/support services, ESL/language courses, international student organization, orientation. Financial aid is not available to international students.

Applying *Required:* TOEFL with recommended score of 550 (paper), proof of adequate funds, proof of health/immunizations. *Recommended:* TSE, TWE.
International Student Contact Mr. James Luyirika-Sewagudde, Jr., Advisor, Center for International Studies, 408 West First Street, Chico, CA 95929-0875. **Phone:** 530-898-6880. **Fax:** 530-898-6889.

■ **APPLICATION**

Required GMAT, application form, baccalaureate/first degree, 3 letters of recommendation, personal statement, resume/curriculum vitae, transcripts of college work. **Recommended** 2 years of work experience.
Deadlines and Fees *Deadlines:* 4/15 for fall, 10/15 for spring, 3/1 for fall (international), 10/1 for spring (international). *Application fee:* $55, $55 (international).
Application Contact Ms. Sandy Jensen, Secretary, Business Graduate Programs, 408 West First Street, Chico, CA 95929-0041. **Phone:** 530-898-4425. **Fax:** 530-898-5889. **E-mail:** sjensen@csuchico.edu.

California State University, Dominguez Hills

Carson, California

SCHOOL OF MANAGEMENT

Graduate Business Faculty
Full-time: 45   Part-time: 30

Student Body
Total: 485
Full-time: 73   Average Age: 34
Part-time: 412   Women: 51%

Admissions
Applications: 163   Average GMAT: 510
Admitted: 104   Average GPA: 3.2
Enrolled: 83

Costs (1999–2000)
Full-time tuition: $1821 per academic year (resident), $4773 per academic year (nonresident)
Part-time tuition: $95 per unit (resident), $246 per unit (nonresident)

Accreditation
ACBSP—The American Council of Business Schools and Programs

DEGREE MBA

MBA—Master of Business Administration Full-time and part-time. *Distance learning option.* 30 to 57 total credits required. 12 to 24 months to complete program. *Concentrations:* international business, management.

COSTS

Tuition, state resident: *Full-time* $1821. *Part-time* $95 per unit. **Tuition, nonresident:** *Full-time* $4773. *Part-time* $246 per unit. **Required fees:** Tuition and fees vary by number of courses or credits taken.

FINANCIAL AID (1999–2000)

15 students received aid. Aid is available to part-time students. **Financial Aid Contact** Mr. James Woods, Director, Financial Aid, Office of Financial Aid, Carson, CA 90742. **Phone:** 310-243-3691. **Fax:** 310-516-4498. **E-mail:** jwood@dhvx20.csudh.edu.

RESOURCES AND SERVICES

Information about online services, personal computer policies, library resources, international exchange programs, internship programs, and placement services at this institution and others can be found at **www.petersons.com/mba**

International Students

13% of students enrolled are international students.

Services and Facilities Counseling/support services, ESL/language courses, international student housing, visa services. Financial aid is not available to international students.
Applying *Required:* TOEFL with recommended score of 550 (paper), proof of adequate funds, proof of health/immunizations.
International Student Contact Mr. Dan Joseffini, International Student Officer, School Of Management, Carson, CA 90747-0001. **Phone:** 310-243-2215. **Fax:** 310-217-6976. **E-mail:** djoseffini@research.csudh.edu.

■ **APPLICATION**

Required GMAT, application form, baccalaureate/first degree, personal statement, transcripts of college work. **Recommended** 2 letters of recommendation, resume/curriculum vitae.
Deadlines and Fees *Deadlines:* 6/1 for fall, 12/1 for spring, 5/1 for fall (international), 11/1 for spring (international). *Application fee:* $55, $55 (international).
Application Contact Ms. Eileen Hall, MBA Coordinator, School of Management, 1000 East Victoria Street, Carson, CA 90747-0001. **Phone:** 310-243-3465. **Fax:** 310-516-4178. **E-mail:** ehall@soma.csudh.edu.

California State University, Fresno

Fresno, California

SID CRAIG SCHOOL OF BUSINESS

Graduate Business Faculty
Full-time: 30   Part-time: 4

Student Body
Total: 210   Average Age: 28
Full-time: 42   Women: 38%
Part-time: 168

Admissions
Applications: 115   Average GMAT: 580
Admitted: 64   Average GPA: 3.4
Enrolled: 38

Costs (1999–2000)
Full-time tuition: $1834 per academic year (resident), $7738 per academic year (nonresident)
Part-time tuition: $246 per unit (nonresident)

After Graduation (Class of 1998–99)
Employed within 3 months of graduation: 95%
Average starting salary: $52,000

Accreditation
AACSB—The International Association for Management Education

DEGREE MBA

MBA—Master of Business Administration Full-time and part-time. 36 to 51 total credits required. 18 to 60 months to complete program. *Concentrations:* agribusiness, entrepreneurship, finance, human resources, international business, management, management information systems, marketing.

COSTS

Tuition, state resident: *Full-time* $0. **Tuition, nonresident:** *Full-time* $5904. *Part-time* $246 per unit. **Tuition, international:** *Full-time* $5904. Tuition varies by number of courses or credits taken. **Required fees:** *Full-time* $1834. *Part-time* $620 per semester. **Graduate housing:** Room and board costs vary by number of occupants, type of accommodation, and type of board plan. *Typical cost:* $5500 (including board).

FINANCIAL AID (1999–2000)

Fellowships, grants, research assistantships, scholarships, teaching assistantships, and work study. Financial aid application deadline: 3/1. **Financial Aid Contact** Dr. Joseph Heuston, Director, 5241 North Maple Avenue, Fresno, CA 93740-0064. **Phone:** 559-278-2182. **Fax:** 559-278-4833.

RESOURCES AND SERVICES

Information about online services, personal computer policies, library resources, international exchange programs, internship programs, and placement services at this institution and others can be found at **www.petersons.com/mba**

International Students

13% of students enrolled are international students.

Services and Facilities Counseling/support services, ESL/language courses, housing location assistance, international student organization, language tutoring, orientation, visa services. Financial aid is available to international students.
Applying *Required:* TOEFL with recommended score of 550 (paper), proof of adequate funds, proof of health/immunizations.
International Student Contact Ms. Juliene Landrith, International Admissions, 5241 North Maple Avenue, Fresno, CA 93740-0056. **Phone:** 559-278-3977. **Fax:** 559-278-7879. **E-mail:** julienne@csufresno.edu.

California State University, Fresno (continued)

■ APPLICATION

Required GMAT, application form, baccalaureate/first degree, 2 letters of recommendation, personal statement, transcripts of college work. **Recommended** Resume/curriculum vitae, 2 years of work experience.

Deadlines and Fees *Deadlines:* 6/1 for fall, 10/1 for spring, 4/1 for fall (international), 9/1 for spring (international). *Application fee:* $55, $55 (international).

Application Contact Ms. Nee Goto, Administrative Assistant, 5245 North Backer Avenue, Fresno, CA 93740-0008. **Phone:** 559-278-2107. **Fax:** 559-278-4911. **E-mail:** mkeppler@csufresno.edu.

California State University, Fullerton

Fullerton, California

COLLEGE OF BUSINESS AND ECONOMICS

Graduate Business Faculty
Full-time: 43   Part-time: 5

Student Body
Total: 497   Women: 44%

Admissions
Applications: 643   Average GMAT: 538
Admitted: 275   Average GPA: 3.22
Enrolled: 134

Costs (1999–2000)
Full-time tuition: N/R
Part-time tuition: $246 per unit (nonresident)

Accreditation
AACSB—The International Association for Management Education

DEGREES MBA • MS

MBA—Master of Business Administration, Specialist Part-time. At least 33 total credits required. 12 to 60 months to complete program. *Concentrations:* accounting, finance, management, management information systems, management science, marketing.

MBA—Master of Business Administration Part-time. *Distance learning option.* At least 57 total credits required. 24 to 60 months to complete program.

MS—Master of Science in Accountancy Full-time and part-time. At least 30 total credits required. 12 to 60 months to complete program.

MS—Master of Science in Management Science Full-time and part-time. At least 33 total credits required. 12 to 60 months to complete program. *Concentrations:* management information systems.

MS—Master of Science in Taxation Full-time and part-time. At least 30 total credits required. 12 to 60 months to complete program.

COSTS

Tuition, nonresident: *Part-time* $246 per unit. **Required fees:** *Full-time* $1887. *Part-time* $628 per semester. Fees vary by number of courses or credits taken. **Graduate housing:** Room and board costs vary by type of accommodation. *Typical cost:* $6732 (including board).

FINANCIAL AID (1999–2000)

28 students received aid, including fellowships, grants, loans, scholarships, teaching assistantships, and work study. Aid is available to part-time students. Financial aid application deadline: 3/1. **Financial Aid Contact** Ms. Deborah Gordon, Director of Financial Aid, PO Box 6804, Fullerton, CA 92834-6804. **Phone:** 714-278-3128. **Fax:** 714-278-7090. **E-mail:** fa@fullerton.edu.

RESOURCES AND SERVICES

Information about online services, personal computer policies, library resources, international exchange programs, internship programs, and placement services at this institution and others can be found at **www.petersons.com/mba**

International Students

31% of students enrolled are international students.

Services and Facilities Counseling/support services, ESL/language courses. Financial aid is not available to international students.
Applying *Required:* TOEFL with recommended score of 500 (paper), proof of adequate funds, proof of health/immunizations.

International Student Contact Mr. Robert Ericksen, Director of International Education and Exchange, PO Box 34080, Fullerton, CA 92834-6830. **Phone:** 714-278-2787. **Fax:** 714-278-7292. **E-mail:** bericksen@fullerton.edu.

■ APPLICATION

Required GMAT, application form, baccalaureate/first degree, essay, personal statement, transcripts of college work. **Recommended** Letter(s) of recommendation, resume/curriculum vitae.

Deadlines and Fees Applications for domestic and international students are processed on a rolling basis. *Application fee:* $55, $55 (international).

Application Contact Dr. Thomas Johnson, Associate Dean, PO Box 34080, Fullerton, CA 92834-6848. **Phone:** 714-278-2592. **Fax:** 714-278-7101. **E-mail:** twjohnson@fullerton.edu.

California State University, Hayward

Hayward, California

SCHOOL OF BUSINESS AND ECONOMICS

Graduate Business Faculty
Full-time: 75

Student Body
Total: 638   Average Age: 32
Full-time: 385   Women: 49%
Part-time: 253

Admissions
Applications: 320   Average GMAT: 534
Admitted: 240   Average GPA: 3.14
Enrolled: 168

Costs (1999–2000)
Full-time tuition: $2400 per academic year (resident), $7596 per academic year (nonresident)
Part-time tuition: $377 per course (resident), $1033 per course (nonresident)

After Graduation (Class of 1998–99)
Employed within 3 months of graduation: 99%

Accreditation
AACSB—The International Association for Management Education

DEGREES EMBA • MA • MBA • MS

EMBA—Executive MBA in Vienna/Beijing Part-time. At least 47 total credits required. 12 months to complete program.

MA—Master of Arts in Economics Part-time. At least 45 total credits required. 12 to 60 months to complete program. *Concentrations:* economics.

MBA—Master of Business Administration Part-time. At least 45 total credits required. 12 to 60 months to complete program. *Concentrations:* accounting, economics, entrepreneurship, finance, human resources, international business, management, management information systems, management science, marketing, materials management, new venture management, operations management, strategic management, taxation, telecommunications management.

MS—Master of Science in Business Administration: Computer Information Systems/Quantitative Part-time. At least 45 total credits required. 12 to 60 months to complete program. *Concentrations:* decision sciences, management information systems.

MS—Master of Science in Taxation Part-time. At least 45 total credits required. 12 to 60 months to complete program. *Concentrations:* taxation.

MS—Master of Science in Telecommunications Systems Part-time. At least 45 total credits required. 12 to 60 months to complete program.

COSTS

Tuition, state resident: *Full-time* $2400. *Part-time* $377 per course. **Tuition, nonresident:** *Full-time* $7596. *Part-time* $1033 per course. **Tuition, international:** *Full-time* $7596. Tuition varies by number of courses or credits taken. **Graduate housing:** Room and board costs vary by number of occupants, type of accommodation, and type of board plan. *Typical cost:* $6680 (including board).

FINANCIAL AID (1999–2000)

70 students received aid, including fellowships, grants, loans, scholarships, teaching assistantships, and work study. Aid is available to part-time students. Financial aid application deadline: 3/2. **Financial Aid Contact** Ms. Betty Harris, Director, Financial Aid Office, 25800 Carlos Bee

Boulevard, Hayward, CA 94542-3000. **Phone:** 510-885-3018. **Fax:** 510-885-4627. **E-mail:** bharris@csuhayward.edu.

RESOURCES AND SERVICES
Information about online services, personal computer policies, library resources, international exchange programs, internship programs, and placement services at this institution and others can be found at **www. petersons.com/mba**

International Students
18% of students enrolled are international students.

Services and Facilities Counseling/support services, ESL/language courses, housing location assistance, international student housing, orientation, visa services, on and off-campus employment assistance. Financial aid is not available to international students.
Applying *Required:* TOEFL with recommended score of 217 (computer) or 550 (paper), proof of adequate funds, proof of health/immunizations.
International Student Contact Ms. Kathy Vizcarro, Enrollment Services, 25800 Carlos Bee Boulevard, Hayward, CA 94542-3000. **Phone:** 510-885-3828. **Fax:** 510-885-3816. **E-mail:** kvizcarr@csuhayward.edu.

■ **APPLICATION**

Required Application form, baccalaureate/first degree, personal statement, transcripts of college work. School will accept GMAT. **Recommended** Letter(s) of recommendation, resume/curriculum vitae, 2 years of work experience.
Deadlines and Fees *Deadlines:* 6/1 for fall, 9/1 for winter, 1/1 for spring, 4/1 for summer, 3/1 for fall (international), 11/1 for spring (international). *Application fee:* $55, $55 (international).
Application Contact Dr. Donna Wiley, Director of School of Business and Economics Graduate Programs, School of Business and Economics, Hayward, CA 94542. **Phone:** 510-885-3964. **Fax:** 510-885-2176. **E-mail:** dwiley@csuhayward.edu.

California State University, Long Beach

Long Beach, California

COLLEGE OF BUSINESS ADMINISTRATION

Graduate Business Faculty

Full-time: 32	Part-time: 7

Student Body

Total: 340	Average Age: 28
Full-time: 88	Women: 47%
Part-time: 252	

Admissions

Applications: 260	Average GMAT: 540
Admitted: 120	Average GPA: 3.2
Enrolled: 82	

Costs (1999–2000)
Full-time tuition: N/R
Part-time tuition: $246 per unit (nonresident)

Accreditation
AACSB—The International Association for Management Education

DEGREES MBA

MBA—Fully Employed MBA Part-time. Up to 49 total credits required. Maximum of 24 months to complete program.

MBA—Master of Business Administration Full-time and part-time. 37 to 49 total credits required. 24 to 84 months to complete program. *Concentrations:* finance, human resources, management, management information systems, marketing.

COSTS

Tuition, nonresident: *Part-time* $246 per unit. **Required fees:** *Full-time* $1800. Tuition and fees vary by number of courses or credits taken. **Graduate housing:** Room and board costs vary by number of occupants, type of accommodation, and type of board plan. *Typical cost:* $7800 (including board).

FINANCIAL AID (1999–2000)

Fellowships, loans, and work study. Aid is available to part-time students. **Financial Aid Contact** Gloria Kapp, 1250 Bellflower Boulevard, Long Beach, CA 90840-0119. **Phone:** 562-985-8403. **E-mail:** gkapp@csulb.edu.

RESOURCES AND SERVICES
Information about online services, personal computer policies, library resources, international exchange programs, internship programs, and placement services at this institution and others can be found at **www. petersons.com/mba**

International Students
23% of students enrolled are international students.

Services and Facilities Counseling/support services, ESL/language courses, housing location assistance, international student housing, orientation, visa services. **Applying** *Required:* TOEFL with recommended score of 550 (paper), proof of adequate funds.

International Student Contact Robert Prather, Assistant Director, International Admissions, 1250 Bellflower Boulevard, Long Beach, CA 90840-0119. **Phone:** 562-985-5476. **Fax:** 562-985-1725. **E-mail:** rprather@csulb.edu.

■ **APPLICATION**

Required GMAT, application form, baccalaureate/first degree, essay, 2 letters of recommendation, personal statement, resume/curriculum vitae, transcripts of college work. **Recommended** Work experience.
Deadlines and Fees *Application fee:* $55, $55 (international).
Application Contact Paula Gloeckner, MBA Evaluator, 1250 Bellflower Boulevard, Long Beach, CA 90840-0119. **Phone:** 562-985-1797. **Fax:** 562-985-5590. **E-mail:** paula@csulb.edu.

California State University, Los Angeles

Los Angeles, California

SCHOOL OF BUSINESS AND ECONOMICS

Graduate Business Faculty

Full-time: 80	Part-time: 39

Student Body

Total: 330	Average Age: 31
Part-time: 330	Women: 54%

Admissions

Applications: 388	Average GMAT: 580
Admitted: 166	Average GPA: 3.3
Enrolled: 87	

Costs (1999–2000)
Full-time tuition: $2400 per academic year (resident), $10,000 per academic year (nonresident)
Part-time tuition: $363 per quarter (resident), $585 per quarter (nonresident)

After Graduation (Class of 1998–99)
Employed within 3 months of graduation: 95%

Accreditation
AACSB—The International Association for Management Education

DEGREES MA • MBA • MS

MA—Master of Arts in Economics Full-time and part-time. At least 45 total credits required. 18 to 48 months to complete program. *Concentrations:* financial economics, international economics.

MBA—Master of Business Administration Full-time and part-time. 2 years of work experience required. At least 48 total credits required. 18 to 48 months to complete program. *Concentrations:* accounting, business information science, economics, finance, health care, international business, management, marketing.

MS—Information Systems Full-time and part-time. At least 45 total credits required. 18 to 48 months to complete program. *Concentrations:* management information systems.

MS—Master of Science in Accountancy Full-time and part-time. At least 45 total credits required. 18 to 48 months to complete program. *Concentrations:* accounting.

MS—Master of Science in Business Administration Full-time and part-time. At least 45 total credits required. 18 to 48 months to complete program. *Concentrations:* economics, finance, international business, management, management information systems, marketing.

MS—Master of Science in Health Care Management Full-time and part-time. At least 45 total credits required. 18 to 48 months to complete program. *Concentrations:* health care.

California State University, Los Angeles (continued)

COSTS

Tuition, state resident: *Full-time* $2400. *Part-time* $363 per quarter. **Tuition, nonresident:** *Full-time* $10,000. *Part-time* $585 per quarter. Tuition varies by number of courses or credits taken. **Graduate housing:** Room and board costs vary by campus location, number of occupants, and type of accommodation. *Typical cost:* $4800 (room only).

FINANCIAL AID (1999–2000)

32 students received aid, including fellowships, grants, scholarships, teaching assistantships, and work study. Aid is available to part-time students. Financial aid application deadline: 3/1. **Financial Aid Contact** Mr. Vu Tran, Director of Student Financial Services, 5151 State University Drive, Los Angeles, CA 90032-4221. **Phone:** 323-343-3245. **Fax:** 323-343-3166. **E-mail:** tru@calstatela.edu.

RESOURCES AND SERVICES

Information about online services, personal computer policies, library resources, international exchange programs, internship programs, and placement services at this institution and others can be found at **www. petersons.com/mba**

International Students

27% of students enrolled are international students.

Services and Facilities Counseling/support services, ESL/language courses, international student housing, language tutoring, visa services. Financial aid is not available to international students.

Applying *Required:* TOEFL with recommended score of 550 (paper), proof of adequate funds, proof of health/immunizations.

International Student Contact Mr. Harold Martin, International Student Advisor, 5151 State University Drive, Los Angeles, CA 90032-4221. **Phone:** 323-343-3170. **Fax:** 323-343-6478. **E-mail:** hmartin@calstatela.edu.

■ APPLICATION

Required GMAT, application form, baccalaureate/first degree, essay, 3 letters of recommendation, personal statement, resume/curriculum vitae, transcripts of college work, 2 years of work experience. **Recommended** Interview.

Deadlines and Fees *Deadlines:* 6/15 for fall, 10/1 for winter, 12/1 for spring, 3/1 for summer, 3/1 for fall (international), 9/1 for winter (international), 10/1 for spring (international). *Application fee:* $55, $55 (international).

Application Contact Dr. Ashish Vaidya, Director, MBA Program, 5151 State University Drive, Los Angeles, CA 90032-4221. **Phone:** 323-343-5156. **Fax:** 323-343-5480. **E-mail:** avaidya@calstatela.edu.

California State University, Northridge

Northridge, California

COLLEGE OF BUSINESS ADMINISTRATION AND ECONOMICS

Graduate Business Faculty

Full-time: 28	Part-time: 1

Student Body

Total: 312	Part-time: 300
Full-time: 12	Average Age: 30

Admissions

Applications: 159	Average GMAT: 540
Admitted: 90	Average GPA: 3.2
Enrolled: 46	

Costs (1999–2000)
Full-time tuition: $1970 per academic year (resident), $6398 per academic year (nonresident)
Part-time tuition: $652 per semester (resident), $246 per unit (nonresident)

After Graduation (Class of 1998–99)
Employed within 3 months of graduation: 95%

Accreditation
AACSB—The International Association for Management Education

DEGREE MBA

MBA—Evening MBA Full-time and part-time. At least 33 total credits required. 12 to 60 months to complete program. *Concentrations:* accounting, business

law, economics, finance, international business, management, management information systems, management science, marketing, taxation.

COSTS

Tuition, state resident: *Full-time* $1970. *Part-time* $652 per semester. **Tuition, nonresident:** *Full-time* $6398. *Part-time* $246 per unit. Tuition varies by number of courses or credits taken. **Graduate housing:** Room and board costs vary by number of occupants, type of accommodation, and type of board plan. *Typical cost:* $5763 (including board).

FINANCIAL AID (1999–2000)

Grants, loans, teaching assistantships, and work study. Aid is available to part-time students. Financial aid application deadline: 3/2. **Financial Aid Contact** CSUN Financial Aid Office, 18111 Nordhoff Street, Northridge, CA 91330-8380. **Phone:** 818-885-3000.

RESOURCES AND SERVICES

Information about online services, personal computer policies, library resources, international exchange programs, internship programs, and placement services at this institution and others can be found at **www. petersons.com/mba**

International Students

Services and Facilities Counseling/support services, ESL/language courses, housing location assistance, international student housing, international student organization, visa services. Financial aid is available to international students. **Applying** *Required:* TOEFL with recommended score of 550 (paper), proof of adequate funds, proof of health/immunizations.

International Student Contact Ms. Mary Baxton, Associate Director, International Admissions, 18111 Nordhoff Street, Northridge, CA 91330. **Phone:** 818-677-3778. **E-mail:** mbaxton@csun.edu.

■ APPLICATION

Required Application form, baccalaureate/first degree, resume/curriculum vitae, transcripts of college work. School will accept GMAT. **Recommended** Essay, 3 letters of recommendation, personal statement, 2 years of work experience.

Deadlines and Fees *Deadlines:* 4/1 for fall, 11/1 for spring, 4/30 for fall (international), 11/30 for spring (international). *Application fee:* $55, $55 (international).

Application Contact Ms. Kristen Walker, Assistant Director of Graduate Programs, 18111 Nordhoff Street, Business Building 3105, Northridge, CA 91330-8380. **Phone:** 818-677-2467. **Fax:** 818-677-3188. **E-mail:** kristen.walker@csun.edu.

California State University, Sacramento

Sacramento, California

SCHOOL OF BUSINESS ADMINISTRATION

Admissions

Average GMAT: 530	Average GPA: 3.2

Costs (1999–2000)
Full-time tuition: $7000 per academic year (nonresident)
Part-time tuition: $246 per unit (nonresident)

After Graduation (Class of 1998–99)
Average starting salary: $37,000

Accreditation
AACSB—The International Association for Management Education

DEGREES MBA • MS

MBA—Master of Business Administration Full-time and part-time. 31 to 52 total credits required. Maximum of 84 months to complete program. *Concentrations:* accounting, finance, human resources, management information systems, marketing, real estate.

MS—Master of Science in Accountancy Full-time and part-time. 30 to 49 total credits required. Maximum of 84 months to complete program. *Concentrations:* accounting, taxation.

MS—Master of Science in Business Administration Full-time and part-time. 30 to 49 total credits required. Maximum of 84 months to complete program. *Concentrations:* management information systems, taxation.

COSTS

Tuition, nonresident: *Full-time* $7000. *Part-time* $246 per unit. **Required fees:** Tuition and fees vary by class time and number of courses or credits taken.

Graduate housing: Room and board costs vary by number of occupants and type of board plan. *Typical cost:* $6000 (including board).

FINANCIAL AID (1999–2000)

Financial Aid Contact Ms. Linda Joy Clemons, Director, Financial Aid, Sacramento, CA 95819-6044. **Phone:** 916-278-6554. **Fax:** 916-278-6082. **E-mail:** ljclemons@csus.edu.

RESOURCES AND SERVICES

Information about online services, personal computer policies, library resources, international exchange programs, internship programs, and placement services at this institution and others can be found at **www.petersons.com/mba**

International Students

Services and Facilities Counseling/support services, ESL/language courses, international student housing, visa services.
Applying *Required:* TOEFL with recommended score of 550 (paper), proof of adequate funds, proof of health/immunizations.
International Student Contact Mr. Eric Merchant, Coordinator, International Students/Programs, Office of International Programs, Sacramento, CA 95819-6012. **Phone:** 916-278-6686. **Fax:** 916-278-7471. **E-mail:** ericmer@csus.edu.

■ APPLICATION

Required GMAT, application form, baccalaureate/first degree, transcripts of college work. School will accept GRE. **Recommended** Personal statement, resume/curriculum vitae, work experience.
Deadlines and Fees *Deadlines:* 5/1 for fall, 11/1 for spring, 5/1 for fall (international), 11/1 for spring (international). *Application fee:* $55, $55 (international).
Application Contact Dr. John E. Merchant, Coordinator, Graduate Programs, College of Business Administration, Sacramento, CA 95819-6088. **Phone:** 916-278-6772. **Fax:** 916-278-5767. **E-mail:** sbagrad@csus.edu.

California State University, San Bernardino

San Bernardino, California

COLLEGE OF BUSINESS AND PUBLIC ADMINISTRATION

Graduate Business Faculty
Full-time: 45   Part-time: 3

Student Body
Total: 302
Full-time: 207   Average Age: 27
Part-time: 95   Women: 46%

Admissions
Applications: 217   Average GMAT: 502
Admitted: 148   Average GPA: 3.2
Enrolled: 100

Costs (1999–2000)
Full-time tuition: $1923 per academic year (resident), $7933 per academic year (nonresident)
Part-time tuition: $164 per unit (nonresident)

Accreditation
AACSB—The International Association for Management Education

DEGREE MBA

MBA—Master of Business Administration Full-time and part-time. *Distance learning option.* 48 to 96 total credits required. 15 to 84 months to complete program. *Concentrations:* accounting, entrepreneurship, finance, human resources, information management, management, marketing, operations management.

COSTS

Tuition, state resident: *Full-time* $1923. **Tuition, nonresident:** *Full-time* $7933. *Part-time* $164 per unit. **Tuition, international:** *Full-time* $7933. **Graduate housing:** Room and board costs vary by number of occupants, type of accommodation, and type of board plan. *Typical cost:* $4965 (room only).

FINANCIAL AID (1999–2000)

Grants, loans, research assistantships, scholarships, and work study. Aid is available to part-time students. Financial aid application deadline: 3/1. **Financial Aid Contact** Mr. Ted Krug, Financial Aid Director, 5500 University Parkway, San Bernardino, CA 94207-2392. **Phone:** 909-880-7800. **Fax:** 909-880-7024. **E-mail:** tkrug@csusb.edu.

RESOURCES AND SERVICES

Information about online services, personal computer policies, library resources, international exchange programs, internship programs, and placement services at this institution and others can be found at **www.petersons.com/mba**

International Students

45% of students enrolled are international students.
Services and Facilities Counseling/support services, ESL/language courses, international student organization. Financial aid is available to international students.
Applying *Required:* TOEFL with recommended score of 213 (computer) or 550 (paper), proof of adequate funds.
International Student Contact Mrs. Elsa Ochoa-Fernandez, Director, International Student Services, 5500 University Parkway, San Bernardino, CA 92407-2397. **Phone:** 909-880-5197. **Fax:** 909-880-7020. **E-mail:** elsa@csusb.edu.

■ APPLICATION

Required GMAT, application form, baccalaureate/first degree, essay, personal statement, transcripts of college work. School will accept GRE. **Recommended** Resume/curriculum vitae.
Deadlines and Fees *Deadlines:* 7/1 for fall, 11/1 for winter, 2/1 for spring, 7/1 for fall (international), 10/1 for winter (international), 1/1 for spring (international). *Application fee:* $55, $55 (international).
Application Contact Dr. Sue Greenfeld, MBA Director, College of Business and Public Administration, 5500 University Parkway, San Bernardino, CA 92407-2397. **Phone:** 909-880-5703. **Fax:** 909-880-7026. **E-mail:** sgreenfe@csusb.edu.

California State University, San Marcos

San Marcos, California

PROGRAM IN BUSINESS ADMINISTRATION

Graduate Business Faculty
Full-time: 30   Part-time: 20

Student Body
Total: 150   Average Age: 33
Full-time: 150   Women: 40%

Admissions
Applications: 160   Average GMAT: 540
Admitted: 83   Average GPA: 3.2
Enrolled: 78

Costs (1999–2000)
Full-time tuition: $8500 per academic year (resident), $14,500 per academic year (nonresident)
Part-time tuition: N/R

After Graduation (Class of 1998–99)
Employed within 3 months of graduation: 98%
Average starting salary: $60,000

DEGREE MBA

MBA—Fully-employed MBA Full-time. *Distance learning option.* 3 years of work experience required. 39 to 51 total credits required. 16 to 21 months to complete program. *Concentrations:* management.

COSTS

Tuition, state resident: *Full-time* $6000. **Tuition, nonresident:** *Full-time* $12,000. **Tuition, international:** *Full-time* $12,000. **Required fees:** *Full-time* $2500.

FINANCIAL AID (1999–2000)

25 students received aid, including fellowships, loans, scholarships, teaching assistantships, and work study. Aid is available to part-time students. Financial aid application deadline: 4/1. **Financial Aid Contact** Mr. Paul Phillips, Director of Financial Aid, College of Business Administration, 333 South Twin Oaks Valley Road, San Marcos, CA 92096-0001. **Phone:** 760-750-4850. **Fax:** 760-750-3047. **E-mail:** finaid@csusm.edu.

RESOURCES AND SERVICES

Information about online services, personal computer policies, library resources, international exchange programs, internship programs, and placement services at this institution and others can be found at **www.petersons.com/mba**

California State University, San Marcos (continued)

International Students

7% of students enrolled are international students.

Services and Facilities ESL/language courses, orientation, visa services.
Applying *Required:* TOEFL with recommended score of 213 (computer) or 550 (paper), proof of adequate funds, proof of health/immunizations.
International Student Contact Dr. Jack Leu, Faculty Director of Graduate Programs, College of Business Administration, 333 South Twin Oaks Valley Road, San Marcos, CA 92096-0001. **Phone:** 760-750-4265. **Fax:** 760-750-4263. **E-mail:** mba@csusm.edu.

■ APPLICATION

Required GMAT, application form, baccalaureate/first degree, essay, interview, 3 letters of recommendation, resume/curriculum vitae, transcripts of college work, 3 years of work experience. School will accept GMAT or GRE.
Deadlines and Fees *Deadlines:* 7/1 for fall, 2/1 for spring, 7/1 for fall (international), 2/1 for spring (international). *Application fee:* $55, $55 (international).
Application Contact Dr. Jack Leu, Faculty Director of Graduate Programs, College of Business Administration, 333 South Twin Oaks Valley Road, San Marcos, CA 92096-0001. **Phone:** 760-750-4267. **Fax:** 760-750-4263. **E-mail:** mba@csusm.edu.

California State University, Stanislaus

Turlock, California

SCHOOL OF BUSINESS ADMINISTRATION

Graduate Business Faculty

Full-time: 27	Part-time: 13

Student Body

Total: 130	Women: 38%
Average Age: 31	

Admissions

Applications: 40	Average GMAT: 500
Admitted: 40	Average GPA: 2.87
Enrolled: 36	

Costs (1999–2000)
Full-time tuition: $1738 per academic year (resident), $8049 per academic year (nonresident)
Part-time tuition: $246 per credit (nonresident)

After Graduation (Class of 1998–99)
Employed within 3 months of graduation: 99%
Average starting salary: $52,000

DEGREE MBA

MBA—Master of Business Administration Full-time and part-time. *Distance learning option.* At least 63 total credits required. 12 to 84 months to complete program.

COSTS

Tuition, state resident: *Full-time* $1738. **Tuition, nonresident:** *Full-time* $8049. *Part-time* $246 per credit. **Required fees:** Tuition and fees vary by number of courses or credits taken. **Graduate housing:** Room and board costs vary by campus location, number of occupants, type of accommodation, and type of board plan. *Typical cost:* $5600 (including board).

FINANCIAL AID (1999–2000)

Fellowships, grants, loans, and work study. Financial aid application deadline: 3/2. **Financial Aid Contact** Ms. Joan Hillery, Director, Financial Aid, 801 West Monte Vista Avenue, Turlock, CA 95382. **Phone:** 209-667-3336. **Fax:** 209-667-3080. **E-mail:** jhillery@stan.csustan.edu.

RESOURCES AND SERVICES

Information about online services, personal computer policies, library resources, international exchange programs, internship programs, and placement services at this institution and others can be found at **www.petersons.com/mba**

International Students

10% of students enrolled are international students.

Services and Facilities Counseling/support services, ESL/language courses, international student housing, visa services. Financial aid is not available to inter-

national students.

Applying *Required:* TOEFL with recommended score of 550 (paper), proof of adequate funds, proof of health/immunizations.
International Student Contact Dr. Robert Santos, Coordinator of International Student Programs, 801 West Monte Vista Avenue, Turlock, CA 95382. **Phone:** 209-667-3381. **Fax:** 209-667-3333. **E-mail:** santos_bob@macmail.csustan.edu.

■ APPLICATION

Required Application form, baccalaureate/first degree, 3 letters of recommendation, personal statement, transcripts of college work. School will accept GMAT. **Recommended** Essay, resume/curriculum vitae.
Deadlines and Fees *Deadlines:* 8/15 for fall, 12/15 for winter, 1/15 for spring, 7/30 for fall (international), 12/15 for winter (international), 1/15 for spring (international). *Application fee:* $55, $55 (international).
Application Contact Dr. Randall Brown, Director, MBA Programs, 801 West Monte Vista Avenue, Turlock, CA 95382. **Phone:** 209-667-3280. **Toll-free Phone:** 800-300-7420. **Fax:** 209-667-3080. **E-mail:** kcravinh@toto.csustan.edu.

Chapman University

Orange, California

SCHOOL OF BUSINESS AND ECONOMICS

Graduate Business Faculty

Full-time: 23	Part-time: 8

Student Body

Total: 196	Average Age: 30
Full-time: 49	Women: 40%
Part-time: 147	

Admissions

Applications: 141	Average GMAT: 524
Admitted: 104	Average GPA: 3.14
Enrolled: 79	

Costs (1999–2000)
Full-time tuition: $14,520 per academic year
Part-time tuition: $605 per credit

Accreditation
AACSB—The International Association for Management Education

DEGREES MBA

MBA—Executive MBA Part-time. At least 48 total credits required. Minimum of 21 months to complete program.

MBA—Master of Business Administration Full-time and part-time. At least 49 total credits required. 18 to 84 months to complete program.

COSTS

Tuition *Full-time:* $14,520. *Part-time:* $605 per credit. Tuition varies by academic program. **Graduate housing:** *Typical cost:* $7000 (including board).

FINANCIAL AID (1999–2000)

59 students received aid, including grants, loans, research assistantships, and scholarships. Aid is available to part-time students. Financial aid application deadline: 3/1. **Financial Aid Contact** Greg Ball, Director, Financial Aid, Orange, CA 92866. **Phone:** 714-997-6741. **Fax:** 714-997-6743.

RESOURCES AND SERVICES

Information about online services, personal computer policies, library resources, international exchange programs, internship programs, and placement services at this institution and others can be found at **www.petersons.com/mba**

International Students

17% of students enrolled are international students.

Services and Facilities Counseling/support services, ESL/language courses, visa services.
Applying *Required:* TOEFL with recommended score of 550 (paper), proof of adequate funds. *Recommended:* Proof of health/immunizations.
International Student Contact Mrs. Vicky Koerner, Director, International Student Services and Study Abroad, Argyros Forum, Orange, CA 92866. **Phone:** 714-997-6829. **Fax:** 714-997-6825. **E-mail:** koerner@nexus.chapman.edu.

■ APPLICATION

Required GMAT, application form, baccalaureate/first degree, letter(s) of recommendation, personal statement, transcripts of college work. **Recommended** Interview, resume/curriculum vitae, work experience.

Deadlines and Fees *Deadlines:* 6/15 for fall, 11/15 for spring, 4/15 for summer, 5/15 for fall (international), 10/15 for spring (international), 3/15 for summer (international). *Application fee:* $40, $40 (international).

Application Contact Ms. Debra Gonda, Associate Director, The George L. Argyros School of Business and Economics, Orange, CA 92866. **Phone:** 714-997-6745. **Fax:** 714-532-6081. **E-mail:** gonda@chapman.edu.

See full description on page 588.

Claremont Graduate University

Claremont, California

PETER F. DRUCKER GRADUATE SCHOOL OF MANAGEMENT

Graduate Business Faculty
Full-time: 20   Part-time: 8

Student Body
Total: 316   Part-time: 169
Full-time: 147   Women: 31%

Admissions
Applications: 407   Average GMAT: 610
Admitted: 218   Average GPA: 3.2
Enrolled: 73

Costs (1999–2000)
Full-time tuition: $25,194 per academic year
Part-time tuition: $940 per credit

After Graduation (Class of 1998–99)
Employed within 3 months of graduation: 95%
Average starting salary: $73,200

Accreditation
AACSB—The International Association for Management Education

DEGREES EMBA • MA • MBA • MBA/MA • MBA/MIS • MBA/MS • MS • PhD/MBA

EMBA—Executive Master of Business Administration Part-time. At least 48 total credits required. 24 to 60 months to complete program. *Concentrations:* leadership, strategic management.

MA—Master of Arts in Management Part-time. At least 32 total credits required. 12 to 60 months to complete program. *Concentrations:* leadership, strategic management.

MBA—Drucker MBA Full-time and part-time. At least 60 total credits required. 16 to 60 months to complete program. *Concentrations:* finance, marketing, strategic management.

MBA/MA—Master of Business Administration/Master of Arts in Economics Full-time and part-time. At least 96 total credits required. 36 to 60 months to complete program. *Concentrations:* finance, marketing, strategic management.

MBA/MA—Master of Business Administration/Master of Arts in Politics and Policy Full-time and part-time. At least 96 total credits required. 36 to 60 months to complete program. *Concentrations:* finance, marketing, strategic management.

MBA/MA—Master of Business Administration/Master of Arts in Psychology Full-time and part-time. At least 80 total credits required. 36 to 60 months to complete program. *Concentrations:* finance, marketing, strategic management.

MBA/MIS—Master of Business Administration/Master of Information Systems Full-time and part-time. At least 80 total credits required. 36 to 60 months to complete program. *Concentrations:* finance, marketing, strategic management.

MBA/MS—Master of Business Administration/Master of Science in Human Resources Design Full-time and part-time. At least 84 total credits required. 36 to 60 months to complete program. *Concentrations:* finance, marketing, strategic management.

MBA/MS—Master of Business Administration/Master of Science in Management of Information Science Full-time and part-time. At least 104 total credits required. 36 to 60 months to complete program. *Concentrations:* finance, marketing, strategic management.

MS—Master of Science in Financial Engineering Full-time and part-time. At least 48 total credits required. 24 to 60 months to complete program.

PhD/MBA—Doctor of Philosophy in Economics/Master of Business Administration Full-time and part-time. At least 120 total credits required. 60 to 84 months to complete program. *Concentrations:* finance, marketing, strategic management.

PhD/MBA—Doctor of Philosophy in Management of Information Systems/Master of Business Administration Full-time and part-time. At least 124 total credits required. 60 to 84 months to complete program. *Concentrations:* finance, marketing, strategic management.

PhD/MBA—Doctor of Philosophy in Politics and Policy/Master of Business Administration Full-time and part-time. At least 120 total credits required. 60 to 84 months to complete program. *Concentrations:* finance, marketing, strategic management.

PhD/MBA—Doctor of Philosophy/Master of Business Administration Full-time and part-time. At least 120 total credits required. 60 to 84 months to complete program. *Concentrations:* finance, marketing, strategic management.

PhD/MBA—Doctor of Philosophy/Master of Business Administration Full-time and part-time. At least 120 total credits required. 60 to 84 months to complete program. *Concentrations:* finance, marketing, strategic management.

*T*he Drucker M.B.A. offers students a world-class education that features state-of-the-art facilities, an outstanding faculty, and small class sizes. Students, who are the top priority at Drucker, are offered a program that prepares tomorrow's leaders by providing the elements that allow students not only to learn but also to develop and excel.

The Drucker School is a learning community in which education is a process of exchange that is facilitated by the faculty. Students learn from faculty members and each other. Students are drawn from diverse backgrounds in terms of ethnicity, education, and job history. This diversity enriches the Drucker experience in preparing graduates for positions in the global marketplace. The emphasis is on general management and equipping students with a wide range of cross-functional tools and a sound understanding of management-related topics that is unsurpassed. Concentrations are available in strategy, marketing, information management, and finance.

COSTS

Tuition *Full-time:* $25,044. *Part-time:* $940 per credit. **Tuition, international:** *Full-time* $25,044. Tuition varies by number of courses or credits taken. **Required fees:** *Full-time* $150. *Part-time* $150 per year. **Graduate housing:** Room and board costs vary by number of occupants, type of accommodation, and type of board plan. *Typical cost:* $12,250 (including board).

FINANCIAL AID (1999–2000)

93 students received aid, including fellowships, grants, loans, research assistantships, scholarships, and work study. Aid is available to part-time students. **Financial Aid Contact** Ms. Donna Espinoza, Director of Financial Aid, 170 East 10th Street, Claremont, CA 91711. **Phone:** 909-621-8337. **Fax:** 909-607-7285. **E-mail:** finaid@cgu.edu.

RESOURCES AND SERVICES

Information about online services, personal computer policies, library resources, international exchange programs, internship programs, and placement services at this institution and others can be found at **www.petersons.com/mba**

International Students

20% of students enrolled are international students.

Services and Facilities Counseling/support services, ESL/language courses, housing location assistance, international student housing, international student organization, language tutoring, orientation, visa services. Financial aid is available to international students.

Applying *Required:* TOEFL with recommended score of 250 (computer) or 600 (paper), proof of adequate funds, proof of health/immunizations.

International Student Contact Ms. Julie Mugdaruk, International Student Advisor, McManus 131, 170 East Tenth Street, Claremont, CA 91745-6163. **Phone:** 909-621-8069. **Fax:** 909-607-7285. **E-mail:** admiss@cgu.edu.

■ APPLICATION

Required GMAT, application form, baccalaureate/first degree, essay, 3 letters of recommendation, personal statement, resume/curriculum vitae, transcripts of college work. **Recommended** Interview, 5 years of work experience.

Deadlines and Fees *Deadlines:* 5/1 for fall, 11/1 for spring, 5/1 for fall (international), 11/1 for spring (international). *Application fee:* $40, $40 (international).

Application Contact Mr. Jack H. Day, III, Assistant Director, MBA Admissions, Drucker Graduate School of Management, 1021 North Dartmouth Avenue, Claremont, CA 91711. **Phone:** 909-607-7811. **Toll-free Phone:** 800-944-4312. **Fax:** 909-607-9104. **E-mail:** drucker@cgu.edu.

See full description on page 592.

Coleman College

La Mesa, California

GRADUATE PROGRAM IN INFORMATION SYSTEMS

Costs (1999–2000)
Full-time tuition: N/R   Part-time tuition: N/R

DEGREE MS

MS—Master of Science in Information Systems 54 to 58 total credits required.

FINANCIAL AID (1999–2000)
Financial Aid Contact Financial Aid Office, La Mesa, CA 91942-1500.

RESOURCES AND SERVICES
Information about online services, personal computer policies, library resources, international exchange programs, internship programs, and placement services at this institution and others can be found at **www.petersons.com/mba**

International Students
International Student Contact International Student Advisor, 7380 Parkway Drive, La Mesa, CA 91942-1500. **E-mail:** intladvisor@coleman.edu.

■ APPLICATION

Required Application form, baccalaureate/first degree, essay, 3 letters of recommendation, transcripts of college work, 2 years of work experience.
Application Contact Graduate Admissions Office, 7380 Parkway Drive, La Mesa, CA 91942-1500. **E-mail:** admissions@coleman.edu.

College of Notre Dame

Belmont, California

DEPARTMENT OF BUSINESS ADMINISTRATION

DEGREES MBA • MS

MBA—Master of Business Administration Full-time and part-time. Work experience required. At least 36 total credits required. 12 to 48 months to complete program. *Concentrations:* finance, human resources, international business, management information systems, marketing, organizational management.
MS—Master of Science in Systems Management Full-time and part-time. At least 36 total credits required. 12 to 48 months to complete program.
MS—Master of Science in e-Business Management Full-time. At least 30 total credits required. Minimum of 15 months to complete program.

RESOURCES AND SERVICES
Information about online services, personal computer policies, library resources, international exchange programs, internship programs, and placement services at this institution and others can be found at www.petersons.com/mba

International Students
Services and Facilities Counseling/support services, ESL/language courses, international student housing, international student organization, orientation, visa services. Financial aid is not available to international students.
International Student Contact Ms. Virginia Spinelli, Coordinator, 1500 Ralston Avenue, Belmont, CA 94002. **Phone:** 650-508-3512. **Fax:** 650-508-3736.

■ APPLICATION

Application Contact Ms. Barbara Sterner, Assistant to the Graduate Dean for Admissions, 1500 Ralston Avenue, Belmont, CA 94002-1997. **Phone:** 650-508-3527. **Fax:** 650-508-3662. **E-mail:** barbara@cnd.edu.

Concordia University

Irvine, California

PROGRAMS IN BUSINESS ADMINISTRATION

Graduate Business Faculty
Full-time: 2   Part-time: 2

Student Body
Total: 15
Part-time: 15   Average Age: 30
                       Women: 47%

Admissions
Applications: 25   Enrolled: 17
Admitted: 20   Average GPA: 3.1

Costs (1999–2000)
Full-time tuition: $9000 per academic year
Part-time tuition: $450 per semester hour

DEGREE MBA

MBA—Entrepreneurial MBA Full-time and part-time. At least 40 total credits required. 12 to 48 months to complete program. *Concentrations:* entrepreneurship.

COSTS

Tuition *Full-time:* $9000. *Part-time:* $450 per semester hour. **Tuition, international:** *Full-time* $9000.

FINANCIAL AID (1999–2000)
4 students received aid, including loans. Aid is available to part-time students. Financial aid application deadline: 7/1. **Financial Aid Contact** Dr. Richard Harms, PhD, MBA Chair, 1530 Concordia West, Irvine, CA 92612-3299. **E-mail:** harms@cui.edu.

RESOURCES AND SERVICES
Information about online services, personal computer policies, library resources, international exchange programs, internship programs, and placement services at this institution and others can be found at **www.petersons.com/mba**

International Students

Services and Facilities ESL/language courses, orientation. Financial aid is not available to international students.
Applying *Required:* TOEFL with recommended score of 195 (computer) or 525 (paper).
International Student Contact Dr. Richard Harms, PhD, MBA Chair, 1530 Concordia West, Irvine, CA 92612-3299. **Phone:** 949-854-8002 Ext. 1210. **Fax:** 949-854-6854. **E-mail:** harms@cui.edu.

■ APPLICATION

Required GMAT, application form, baccalaureate/first degree, interview, 2 letters of recommendation, personal statement, transcripts of college work, 2 years of work experience. **Recommended** Essay.
Deadlines and Fees Applications for domestic and international students are processed on a rolling basis. *Application fee:* $25.
Application Contact Dr. Richard Harms, PhD, MBA Chair, 1530 Concordia West, Irvine, CA 92612-3299. **Phone:** 949-854-8002 Ext. 1210. **Toll-free Phone:** 800-229-1200. **Fax:** 949-854-6854. **E-mail:** harms@cui.edu.

Dominican University of California

San Rafael, California

SCHOOL OF BUSINESS AND INTERNATIONAL STUDIES

Graduate Business Faculty
Full-time: 5   Part-time: 15

Student Body
Total: 95   Average Age: 37
Full-time: 14   Women: 54%
Part-time: 81

Admissions
Applications: 74   Enrolled: 29
Admitted: 52

Costs (1999–2000)
Full-time tuition: $13,676 per academic year
Part-time tuition: $556 per unit

DEGREES MA • MBA

MA—Master of Arts in International Economic and Political Assessment in the Pacific Basin Full-time and part-time. At least 42 total credits required. Minimum of 15 months to complete program. *Concentrations:* Asian business studies, international and area business studies, international business.

MBA—Master of Business Administration in International Business, Pacific Basin Full-time and part-time. At least 42 total credits required. Minimum of 15 months to complete program. *Concentrations:* Asian business studies, international and area business studies, international business.

MBA—Master of Business Administration in Strategic Leadership Part-time. At least 36 total credits required. Minimum of 24 months to complete program. *Concentrations:* business policy/strategy, organizational management, strategic management.

COSTS
Tuition *Full-time:* $13,344. *Part-time:* $556 per unit. **Required fees:** *Full-time* $332. *Part-time* $332 per year. Tuition and fees vary by academic program. **Graduate housing:** Room and board costs vary by type of board plan. *Typical cost:* $8036 (including board).

FINANCIAL AID (1999–2000)
7 students received aid, including fellowships, grants, loans, research assistantships, and work study. Aid is available to part-time students. **Financial Aid Contact** Ms. Susan Gutierrez, Director of Financial Aid, 50 Acacia Avenue, San Rafael, CA 94901-2298. **Phone:** 415-257-1321. **Fax:** 415-257-0190. **E-mail:** gutierrez@dominican.edu.

RESOURCES AND SERVICES
Information about online services, personal computer policies, library resources, international exchange programs, internship programs, and placement services at this institution and others can be found at **www.petersons.com/mba**

International Students
17% of students enrolled are international students.
Services and Facilities Counseling/support services, ESL/language courses, housing location assistance, international student housing, visa services. Financial aid is available to international students.
Applying *Required:* TOEFL with recommended score of 213 (computer) or 550 (paper), proof of adequate funds.
International Student Contact Mr. Wesley Young, Director, Division of Graduate Business Studies, 50 Acacia Avenue, San Rafael, CA 94901-2298. **Phone:** 415-257-1359. **Fax:** 415-459-3206. **E-mail:** pbsadm@dominican.edu.

■ APPLICATION
Required GMAT, application form, baccalaureate/first degree, 3 letters of recommendation, resume/curriculum vitae, transcripts of college work. **Recommended** Work experience.
Deadlines and Fees Applications for domestic and international students are processed on a rolling basis. *Application fee:* $40, $40 (international).
Application Contact Mr. Wesley Young, Director, Division of Graduate Business Studies, 50 Acacia Avenue, San Rafael, CA 94901-2298. **Phone:** 415-257-1359. **Fax:** 415-459-3206. **E-mail:** pbsadm@dominican.edu.
See full description on page 624.

Fielding Institute
Santa Barbara, California
PROGRAM IN ORGANIZATIONAL DESIGN AND EFFECTIVENESS

Graduate Business Faculty
Full-time: 3 | Part-time: 8

Student Body
Total: 74 | Women: 66%
Full-time: 74

Admissions
Applications: 28 | Enrolled: 19
Admitted: 22

Costs (1999–2000)
Full-time tuition: $12,750 per academic year
Part-time tuition: N/R

DEGREE MA
MA—MA in Organizational Management Full-time. *Distance learning option.* At least 52 total credits required. 20 months to complete program. *Concentrations:* organizational management.

COSTS
Tuition *Full-time:* $12,750. **Tuition, international:** *Full-time* $12,750.

FINANCIAL AID (1999–2000)
Loans and scholarships. **Financial Aid Contact** Raul Aldama, Financial Aid Officer, Santa Barbara, CA 93105. **Phone:** 805-687-1099 Ext. 4008. **Fax:** 805-687-9793. **E-mail:** rmaldama@fielding.edu.

RESOURCES AND SERVICES
Information about online services, personal computer policies, library resources, international exchange programs, internship programs, and placement services at this institution and others can be found at **www.petersons.com/mba**

International Students
4% of students enrolled are international students.
Services and Facilities Financial aid is not available to international students. **International Student Contact** Kim Ford, Enrollment Officer, 2112 Santa Barbara Street, Santa Barbara, CA 93105. **Phone:** 805-898-4049. **Fax:** 805-898-4149. **E-mail:** kford@fielding.edu.

■ APPLICATION
Required Application form, baccalaureate/first degree, essay, letter(s) of recommendation, personal statement, resume/curriculum vitae, transcripts of college work, work experience. **Recommended** Interview.
Deadlines and Fees *Deadlines:* 8/1 for fall, 1/1 for winter, 8/1 for fall (international), 1/1 for winter (international). *Application fee:* $75.
Application Contact Kim Ford, Enrollment Officer, 2112 Santa Barbara Street, Santa Barbara, CA 93105. **Phone:** 805-898-4049. **Toll-free Phone:** 800-340-1099. **Fax:** 805-898-4149. **E-mail:** kford@fielding.edu.

Fresno Pacific University
Fresno, California
GRADUATE SCHOOL
DEGREE MA
MA—Master of Arts in Administrative Leadership (Management and Leadership Program) Part-time. At least 37 total credits required. 16 to 36 months to complete program. *Concentrations:* entrepreneurship, health care, management, nonprofit management.

RESOURCES AND SERVICES
Information about online services, personal computer policies, library resources, international exchange programs, internship programs, and placement services at this institution and others can be found at **www.petersons.com/mba**

International Students
Services and Facilities Counseling/support services, ESL/language courses. **International Student Contact** Mr. Philip Hofer, Director of International Programs and Services, 1717 South Chestnut Avenue, Fresno, CA 93702. **Phone:** 559-453-2069. **E-mail:** plhofer@fresno.edu.

■ APPLICATION
Application Contact Dr. James N. Holm, Jr., Administrative Leadership Program Director, 1717 South Chestnut Avenue, Fresno, CA 93702. **Phone:** 559-453-3668. **Fax:** 559-453-2001. **E-mail:** jnholm@fresno.edu.

Golden Gate University
San Francisco, California
SCHOOL OF BUSINESS

Graduate Business Faculty
Full-time: 25 | Part-time: 250

Student Body
Total: 1,323 | Average Age: 34
Full-time: 482 | Women: 47%
Part-time: 841

Admissions
Applications: 718 | Enrolled: 301
Admitted: 474

Costs (1999–2000)
Full-time tuition: N/R
Part-time tuition: $1500 per course

After Graduation (Class of 1998–99)
Employed within 3 months of graduation: 90%

DEGREES M Acc • MA • MBA • MS

Golden Gate University (continued)

M Acc—Master of Accountancy Full-time and part-time. *Distance learning option.* 30 to 51 total credits required. Maximum of 72 months to complete program. *Concentrations:* accounting.

MA—Master of Arts in Arts Administration Full-time and part-time. *Distance learning option.* 36 to 42 total credits required. Maximum of 72 months to complete program. *Concentrations:* arts administration/management.

MBA—Executive MBA Full-time and part-time. At least 36 total credits required. Maximum of 72 months to complete program.

MBA—Master of Business Administration Full-time and part-time. *Distance learning option.* 36 to 48 total credits required. Maximum of 72 months to complete program. *Concentrations:* accounting, electronic commerce (e-commerce), finance, human resources, international business, management, marketing, operations management.

MS—Master of Science Full-time and part-time. *Distance learning option.* 30 to 48 total credits required. Maximum of 72 months to complete program. *Concentrations:* finance, human resources, marketing.

COSTS

Tuition *Part-time:* $1500 per course. Tuition varies by academic program.

FINANCIAL AID (1999–2000)

Financial Aid Contact Financial Aid Officer, 536 Mission Street, San Francisco, CA 94105-2968. **Phone:** 415-442-7270. **Fax:** 415-442-7807. **E-mail:** info@ggu.edu.

RESOURCES AND SERVICES

Information about online services, personal computer policies, library resources, international exchange programs, internship programs, and placement services at this institution and others can be found at **www.petersons.com/mba**

International Students

26% of students enrolled are international students.

Services and Facilities Counseling/support services, ESL/language courses, housing location assistance, international student organization, orientation.
Applying *Required:* TOEFL with recommended score of 550 (paper), proof of adequate funds, proof of health/immunizations.

International Student Contact Ms. Rachael Weber, Director, International Student Services, 536 Mission Street, San Francisco, CA 94105-2968. **Phone:** 415-442-7291. **Fax:** 415-442-7284. **E-mail:** rweber@ggu.edu.

■ APPLICATION

Required Application form, baccalaureate/first degree, essay, interview, personal statement, resume/curriculum vitae, transcripts of college work, 5 years of work experience. School will accept GMAT.

Deadlines and Fees Applications for domestic students are processed on a rolling basis. *Deadlines:* 7/1 for fall (international), 11/1 for spring (international), 3/1 for summer (international). *Application fee:* $55, $70 (international).

Application Contact Enrollment Services, 536 Mission Street, San Francisco, CA 94105-2968. **Phone:** 415-442-7800. **Toll-free Phone:** 800-448-4968. **Fax:** 415-442-7807. **E-mail:** info@ggu.edu.

See full description on page 670.

Holy Names College

Oakland, California

DEPARTMENT OF BUSINESS

Graduate Business Faculty
Full-time: 3 | Part-time: 2

Student Body
Total: 28 | Average Age: 37
Part-time: 28 | Women: 57%

Admissions
Applications: 18 | Enrolled: 8
Admitted: 8 | Average GPA: 3

Costs (1999–2000)
Full-time tuition: N/R
Part-time tuition: $425 per unit

DEGREE MBA

MBA—Master of Business Administration Full-time and part-time. At least 33 total credits required. 15 to 84 months to complete program. *Concentrations:* finance, management, marketing.

COSTS

Tuition *Part-time:* $425 per unit. **Graduate housing:** Room and board costs vary by number of occupants. *Typical cost:* $6400 (including board).

FINANCIAL AID (1999–2000)

Loans. Aid is available to part-time students. Financial aid application deadline: 3/1. **Financial Aid Contact** Ms. Jo Ann Berridge, Dean of Admission and Financial Aid, 3500 Mountain Boulevard, Oakland, CA 94619-1699. **Phone:** 510-436-1327. **Fax:** 510-436-1666. **E-mail:** dao@hnc.edu.

RESOURCES AND SERVICES

Information about online services, personal computer policies, library resources, international exchange programs, internship programs, and placement services at this institution and others can be found at **www.petersons.com/mba**

International Students

14% of students enrolled are international students.

Services and Facilities Counseling/support services, ESL/language courses, international student housing, orientation. Financial aid is not available to international students.
Applying *Required:* TOEFL with recommended score of 213 (computer) or 550 (paper), proof of adequate funds.

International Student Contact Ms. Jo Ann Berridge, Dean of Admission and Financial Aid, 3500 Mountain Boulevard, Oakland, CA 94619-1699. **Phone:** 510-436-1351. **Fax:** 510-436-1325.

■ APPLICATION

Required Application form, baccalaureate/first degree, 2 letters of recommendation, personal statement, resume/curriculum vitae, transcripts of college work. **Recommended** Interview, 3 years of work experience.

Deadlines and Fees Applications for domestic students are processed on a rolling basis. *Deadlines:* 7/15 for fall (international), 11/15 for winter (international). *Application fee:* $35, $35 (international).

Application Contact Ms. Jo Ann Berridge, Dean of Admission and Financial Aid, 3500 Mountain Boulevard, Oakland, CA 94619-1699. **Phone:** 510-436-1351. **Fax:** 510-436-1325.

Hope International University

Fullerton, California

PROGRAM IN BUSINESS ADMINISTRATION

Graduate Business Faculty
Full-time: 2 | Part-time: 15

Student Body
Total: 95

Admissions
Applications: 20 | Enrolled: 15
Admitted: 19 | Average GPA: 3.4

Costs (1999–2000)
Full-time tuition: N/R
Part-time tuition: $375 per credit

After Graduation (Class of 1998–99)
Employed within 3 months of graduation: 90%
Average starting salary: $43,000

DEGREES MBA • MS

MBA—Master of Business Administration Full-time and part-time. *Distance learning option.* At least 48 total credits required. Minimum of 24 months to complete program. *Concentrations:* international development management, nonprofit management.

MS—Master of Science in Management Full-time and part-time. *Distance learning option.* At least 36 total credits required. Minimum of 24 months to complete program. *Concentrations:* international development management, nonprofit management.

COSTS

Tuition *Part-time:* $375 per credit.

FINANCIAL AID (1999–2000)
20 students received aid, including grants and scholarships. Aid is available to part-time students. **Financial Aid Contact** Ms. Karen Adams, Financial Aid Office, 2500 East Nutwood Avenue, Fullerton, CA 92631-3138. **Phone:** 800-762-1294 Ext. 230.

RESOURCES AND SERVICES
Information about online services, personal computer policies, library resources, international exchange programs, internship programs, and placement services at this institution and others can be found at **www.petersons.com/mba**

International Students
Services and Facilities Counseling/support services, ESL/language courses, international student housing, international student organization, visa services. Financial aid is available to international students.
Applying *Required:* TOEFL with recommended score of 550 (paper), proof of adequate funds, proof of health/immunizations.
International Student Contact Wendy Harr, Management Program Coordinator, 2500 East Nutwood Avenue, Fullerton, CA 92831. **Phone:** 714-879-3901 Ext. 2641. **Fax:** 714-738-4564. **E-mail:** hiu_graduate@hiu.edu.

■ APPLICATION
Required Application form, baccalaureate/first degree, essay, 2 letters of recommendation, personal statement, transcripts of college work. **Recommended** Work experience.
Deadlines and Fees Applications for domestic and international students are processed on a rolling basis. *Application fee:* $100, $100 (international).
Application Contact Kaylene Carr, Director of Admissions and Marketing, 2500 East Nutwood Avenue, Fullerton, CA 92631-3138. **Phone:** 714-879-3901 Ext. 2626. **Toll-free Phone:** 800-762-1294. **Fax:** 714-738-4564. **E-mail:** kcarr@hiu.edu.

Humboldt State University
Arcata, California

SCHOOL OF BUSINESS AND ECONOMICS

Graduate Business Faculty
Full-time: 10 — Part-time: 1

Student Body
Total: 14 — Average Age: 30
Full-time: 5 — Women: 36%
Part-time: 9

Admissions
Average GMAT: 521 — Average GPA: 3.2

Costs (1999–2000)
Full-time tuition: $1996 per academic year (resident), $1996 per academic year (nonresident)
Part-time tuition: $1330 per year (resident), $1330 per year (nonresident)

After Graduation (Class of 1998–99)
Average starting salary: $24,000

DEGREE MBA
MBA—Master of Business Administration Full-time and part-time. At least 31 total credits required. 24 to 84 months to complete program. *Concentrations:* management.

COSTS
Tuition, state resident: *Full-time* $1996. *Part-time* $1330 per year. **Tuition, nonresident:** *Full-time* $1996. *Part-time* $1330 per year. **Required fees:** Fees vary by number of courses or credits taken. **Graduate housing:** Room and board costs vary by number of occupants, type of accommodation, and type of board plan. *Typical cost:* $5391 (including board).

FINANCIAL AID (1999–2000)
3 students received aid, including fellowships and work study. Aid is available to part-time students. Financial aid application deadline: 3/1. **Financial Aid Contact** Kay Burgess, Director, Financial Aid, Arcata, CA 95521-8299. **Phone:** 707-826-4321. **Fax:** 707-826-5360.

RESOURCES AND SERVICES
Information about online services, personal computer policies, library resources, international exchange programs, internship programs, and placement services at this institution and others can be found at **www.petersons.com/mba**

International Students
7% of students enrolled are international students.
Services and Facilities Counseling/support services, ESL/language courses, visa services. Financial aid is not available to international students.
Applying *Required:* TOEFL with recommended score of 550 (paper), proof of adequate funds, proof of health/immunizations.
International Student Contact Ms. Meryl Jewell, International Student Admissions Officer, Siemens Hall 210, Arcata, CA 95521-8299. **Phone:** 707-826-6199. **Fax:** 707-826-6194. **E-mail:** jewell@laurel.humboldt.edu.

■ APPLICATION
Required Application form, baccalaureate/first degree, personal statement, transcripts of college work. School will accept GMAT.
Deadlines and Fees *Deadlines:* 5/1 for fall, 12/1 for spring, 11/30 for fall (international), 8/31 for spring (international). *Application fee:* $55, $55 (international).
Application Contact Dr. Saeed Mortazavi, Director of MBA Program, School of Business and Economics, Arcata, CA 95521-8299. **Phone:** 707-826-3224. **Fax:** 707-826-6666. **E-mail:** sm5@axe.humboldt.edu.

John F. Kennedy University
Orinda, California

SCHOOL OF MANAGEMENT

Graduate Business Faculty
Full-time: 3 — Part-time: 125

Student Body
Total: 124 — Average Age: 40
Full-time: 45 — Women: 68%
Part-time: 79

Admissions
Applications: 52 — Enrolled: 15
Admitted: 26

Costs (1999–2000)
Full-time tuition: N/R
Part-time tuition: $317 per unit

DEGREES MA • MBA
MA—Master of Arts in Management Full-time. At least 54 total credits required. 24 months to complete program. *Concentrations:* management.
MBA—Master of Business Administration Full-time and part-time. At least 52 total credits required. 21 to 36 months to complete program. *Concentrations:* entrepreneurship, finance, financial management/planning, international business, leadership, management, marketing, organizational management.

COSTS
Tuition *Part-time:* $317 per unit. **Required fees:** *Part-time* $9 per quarter. Tuition and fees vary by academic program.

FINANCIAL AID (1999–2000)
60 students received aid, including fellowships and loans. Aid is available to part-time students. Financial aid application deadline: 3/2. **Financial Aid Contact** Mindy Bergeron, Director of Financial Aid, 12 Altarinda Road, Orinda, CA 94563-2689. **Phone:** 925-258-2385. **Fax:** 925-254-6964.

RESOURCES AND SERVICES
Information about online services, personal computer policies, library resources, international exchange programs, internship programs, and placement services at this institution and others can be found at **www.petersons.com/mba**

International Students
Services and Facilities Counseling/support services. Financial aid is not available to international students.
Applying *Required:* TOEFL with recommended score of 550 (paper), TWE with recommended score of 3, proof of adequate funds, proof of health/immunizations.
International Student Contact Susan Sermeno, International Student Advisor, 12 Altarinda Road, Orinda, CA 94563-2689. **Phone:** 925-258-2339. **Fax:** 925-254-6964.

■ APPLICATION
Required Application form, baccalaureate/first degree, interview, 2 letters of recommendation, personal statement, resume/curriculum vitae, transcripts of college work. **Recommended** 5 years of work experience.

John F. Kennedy University (continued)

Deadlines and Fees Applications for domestic students are processed on a rolling basis. *Deadlines:* 6/30 for fall (international), 9/30 for winter (international), 12/30 for spring (international), 4/30 for summer (international). *Application fee:* $50, $50 (international).

Application Contact Ellena Bloedorn, Director of Admissions and Records, 12 Altarinda Road, Orinda, CA 94563-2689. **Phone:** 925-258-2213. **Fax:** 925-254-6964. **E-mail:** proginfo@jfku.edu.

La Sierra University

Riverside, California

SCHOOL OF BUSINESS AND MANAGEMENT

Admissions
Average GMAT: 500   Average GPA: 3.2

Costs (1999–2000)
Full-time tuition: N/R
Part-time tuition: $384 per unit

DEGREE MBA

MBA—Master of Business Administration Full-time and part-time. At least 48 total credits required. 12 to 60 months to complete program. *Concentrations:* accounting, finance, human resources, management, marketing.

COSTS

Tuition *Part-time:* $384 per unit. **Graduate housing:** Room and board costs vary by number of occupants, type of accommodation, and type of board plan. *Typical cost:* $3882 (including board).

FINANCIAL AID (1999–2000)

Financial Aid Contact Financial Aid Office, 4700 Pierce Street, Riverside, CA 92515. **Phone:** 909-785-2175. **Fax:** 909-785-2911. **E-mail:** mdietel@lasierra.edu.

RESOURCES AND SERVICES

Information about online services, personal computer policies, library resources, international exchange programs, internship programs, and placement services at this institution and others can be found at **www.petersons.com/mba**

International Students

Services and Facilities Counseling/support services, ESL/language courses.
International Student Contact Mrs. Jennifer Tyner, International Student Office, 4700 Pierce Street, Riverside, CA 92515. **Phone:** 909-785-2237. **Fax:** 909-785-2555. **E-mail:** jtyner@lasierra.edu.

■ APPLICATION

Required GMAT, application form, baccalaureate/first degree, 2 letters of recommendation, personal statement, transcripts of college work. **Recommended** Interview, resume/curriculum vitae.

Deadlines and Fees Applications for domestic and international students are processed on a rolling basis. *Application fee:* $30, $30 (international).

Application Contact Dr. Tom Smith, Director of Admissions, 4700 Pierce Street, Riverside, CA 92515. **Phone:** 909-785-2176. **Fax:** 909-785-2447. **E-mail:** tsmith@lasierra.edu.

Lincoln University

Oakland, California

BUSINESS ADMINISTRATION PROGRAM

Graduate Business Faculty
Full-time: 5   Part-time: 8
Student Body
Total: 100   Average Age: 26
Full-time: 100   Women: 43%
Admissions
Applications: 46   Enrolled: 15
Admitted: 37   Average GPA: 3.1
Costs (1999–2000)
Full-time tuition: $5534 per academic year
Part-time tuition: $265 per semester hour

After Graduation (Class of 1998–99)
Employed within 3 months of graduation: 75%

DEGREE MBA

MBA—Master of Business Administration Full-time and part-time. 36 to 60 total credits required. 12 to 24 months to complete program. *Concentrations:* Asian business studies, international business, management, management information systems.

COSTS

Tuition *Full-time:* $4770. *Part-time:* $265 per semester hour. Tuition varies by number of courses or credits taken and academic program. **Required fees:** *Full-time* $764. *Part-time* $180 per semester. Tuition and fees vary by academic program.

FINANCIAL AID (1999–2000)

10 students received aid, including scholarships. Financial aid application deadline: 7/1. **Financial Aid Contact** Dr. Clarence Rippel, President, 401 Fifteenth Street, Oakland, CA 94612. **Phone:** 510-628-8016. **Fax:** 510-628-8015. **E-mail:** luadm@best.com.

RESOURCES AND SERVICES

Information about online services, personal computer policies, library resources, international exchange programs, internship programs, and placement services at this institution and others can be found at **www.petersons.com/mba**

International Students

100% of students enrolled are international students.

Services and Facilities Counseling/support services, ESL/language courses, international student organization, orientation, visa services. Financial aid is available to international students.
Applying *Required:* Proof of adequate funds. *Recommended:* TOEFL, proof of health/immunizations.
International Student Contact Dr. Pete Bogue, Director of Admissions/Registrar, 401 Fifteenth Street, Oakland, CA 94612. **Phone:** 510-628-8010. **Fax:** 510-628-8026. **E-mail:** luadm@best.com.

■ APPLICATION

Required Application form, baccalaureate/first degree, transcripts of college work. School will accept GMAT. **Recommended** Letter(s) of recommendation.

Deadlines and Fees Applications for domestic and international students are processed on a rolling basis. *Application fee:* $50, $50 (international).

Application Contact Ms. Maria Delos Reyes, Admissions Officer, 401 Fifteenth Street, Oakland, CA 94612. **Phone:** 510-628-8010. **Fax:** 510-628-8026. **E-mail:** luadm@best.com.

Loyola Marymount University

Los Angeles, California

COLLEGE OF BUSINESS ADMINISTRATION

Graduate Business Faculty
Full-time: 40   Part-time: 26
Student Body
Total: 419   Average Age: 29
Full-time: 105   Women: 44%
Part-time: 314
Admissions
Applications: 415   Average GMAT: 570
Admitted: 269   Average GPA: 3.2
Enrolled: 139
Costs (1999–2000)
Full-time tuition: $17,795 per academic year
Part-time tuition: $650 per unit

Accreditation
AACSB—The International Association for Management Education

DEGREES EMBA • JD/MBA • MBA

EMBA—Executive MBA Program Part-time. Minimum 6 years work experience, June deadline, GMAT required, no concentrations. 54 total credits required. 21 months to complete program.

JD/MBA—Juris Doctor/Master of Business Administration Full-time. At least 30 total credits required. 12 to 60 months to complete program. *Concentrations:* business law.

MBA—Master of Business Administration for International Managers Full-time. At least 45 total credits required. 12 months to complete program. *Concentrations:* international business.

MBA—Master of Business Administration Full-time and part-time. At least 30 total credits required. 12 to 60 months to complete program. *Concentrations:* accounting, business policy/strategy, entrepreneurship, finance, human resources, international business, international finance, international management, international marketing, management, management information systems, marketing.

The flexibility of Loyola Marymount University's M.B.A. program attracts both fully employed professionals who attend on a part-time basis and full-time students. Classes are offered year-round, with all classes scheduled in the late afternoon and evening. The M.B.A. program is accredited by the American Assembly of Collegiate Schools of Business. More than 90 percent of all classes are taught by faculty members with doctorates from prestigious universities.

Classes are held in a variety of state-of-the-art student-centered classrooms in the magnificent Conrad N. Hilton Center for Business. The facility offers M.B.A. students access to many advanced technological features.

M.B.A. students participate in case competitions during the annual Business Ethics Fortnight. Loyola Marymount's commitment to business ethics is directed by Dr. Thomas White, the Hilton Chair in Business Ethics. Student business plans are often entered in national entrepreneurial competitions. LMU's commitment to the entrepreneurial spirit has been enhanced by the recent appointment of Dr. Fred Kiesner to the Hilton Chair in Entrepreneurship.

The international program has been enhanced by the addition of a semester-long foreign experience available through an exchange program with the EDHEC Graduate School of Business in Lille, France. In addition, students find the comparative-management-systems sequence, featuring visits to a number of foreign companies over a three-week period, to be very valuable.

COSTS

Tuition *Full-time:* $17,550. *Part-time:* $650 per unit. **Required fees:** *Full-time* $245. *Part-time* $188 per semester. Fees vary by number of courses or credits taken.

FINANCIAL AID (1999–2000)

188 students received aid, including grants, loans, research assistantships, scholarships, and work study. Aid is available to part-time students. **Financial Aid Contact** Mr. John Neu, Graduate Financial Aid Counselor, 7900 Loyola Boulevard, Los Angeles, CA 90045-8350. **Phone:** 310-338-2753. **Fax:** 310-338-2793.

RESOURCES AND SERVICES

Information about online services, personal computer policies, library resources, international exchange programs, internship programs, and placement services at this institution and others can be found at **www.petersons.com/mba**

International Students

13% of students enrolled are international students.

Services and Facilities Counseling/support services, ESL/language courses, international student organization, language tutoring, orientation, visa services. Financial aid is available to international students.

Applying *Required:* TOEFL with recommended score of 600 (paper), proof of adequate funds, proof of health/immunizations.

International Student Contact Ms. Sandrell Doerr, International Services Coordinator, 7900 Loyola Boulevard, Los Angeles, CA 90045. **Phone:** 310-338-2937. **Fax:** 310-338-5976. **E-mail:** sdoerr@lmumail.lmu.edu.

■ APPLICATION

Required Application form, baccalaureate/first degree, essay, 2 letters of recommendation, personal statement, resume/curriculum vitae, transcripts of college work. School will accept GMAT. **Recommended** Work experience.

Deadlines and Fees Applications for domestic and international students are processed on a rolling basis. *Application fee:* $35, $35 (international).

Application Contact Ms. Charisse Woods, MBA Program Coordinator, Master of Business Administration Program, 7900 Loyola Boulevard, Los Angeles, CA 90045-8387. **Phone:** 310-338-2848. **Toll-free Phone:** 888-946-5681. **Fax:** 310-338-2899. **E-mail:** cwoods@lmumail.lmu.edu.

See full description on page 714.

Monterey Institute of International Studies

Monterey, California

FISHER GRADUATE SCHOOL OF INTERNATIONAL BUSINESS

Graduate Business Faculty

Full-time: 11	Part-time: 10

Student Body

Total: 119	
Full-time: 115	Average Age: 28
Part-time: 4	Women: 50%

Admissions

Applications: 122	
Admitted: 108	Average GMAT: 530
Enrolled: 46	Average GPA: 3.31

Costs (1999–2000)
Full-time tuition: $18,750 per academic year
Part-time tuition: $785 per credit

After Graduation (Class of 1998–99)
Employed within 3 months of graduation: 67%
Average starting salary: $51,000

DEGREE MBA

MBA—Master of Business Administration Full-time. At least 64 total credits required. 12 to 21 months to complete program. *Concentrations:* Asian business studies, decision sciences, electronic commerce (e-commerce), entrepreneurship, finance, human resources, international and area business studies, international banking, international business, international development management, international economics, international finance, international management, international marketing, international trade, marketing, nonprofit management.

COSTS

Tuition *Full-time:* $18,750. *Part-time:* $785 per credit.

FINANCIAL AID (1999–2000)

Financial Aid Contact Mr. Michael Benson, Director of Financial Aid, 425 Van Buren Street, Monterey, CA 93940. **Phone:** 831-647-4119. **Fax:** 831-647-4199. **E-mail:** mbenson@miis.edu.

RESOURCES AND SERVICES

Information about online services, personal computer policies, library resources, international exchange programs, internship programs, and placement services at this institution and others can be found at **www.petersons.com/mba**

International Students

50% of students enrolled are international students.

Services and Facilities Counseling/support services, ESL/language courses, housing location assistance, international student housing, international student organization, orientation, visa services.

Applying *Required:* TOEFL with recommended score of 550 (paper), proof of adequate funds.

International Student Contact Mrs. Jane Roberts, International Admissions Officer, 425 Van Buren Street, Monterey, CA 93940-2691. **Phone:** 831-647-4124. **Fax:** 831-647-4188. **E-mail:** jroberts@miis.edu.

■ APPLICATION

Required GMAT, application form, baccalaureate/first degree, essay, 2 letters of recommendation, personal statement, resume/curriculum vitae, transcripts of college work. **Recommended** Interview, 3 years of work experience.

Deadlines and Fees Applications for domestic and international students are processed on a rolling basis. *Application fee:* $50, $50 (international).

Application Contact Ms. Christy Herlick Gibson, Academic Programs Associate, 425 Van Buren Street, Monterey, CA 93940-2691. **Phone:** 831-647-6586. **Fax:** 831-647-6506. **E-mail:** christy.gibson@miis.edu.

See full description on page 732.

National University

La Jolla, California

SCHOOL OF BUSINESS AND TECHNOLOGY

Graduate Business Faculty

National University (continued)

Student Body
Total: 1,029
Full-time: 701
Part-time: 328

Full-time: 19
Part-time: 119

Average Age: 34
Women: 41%

Admissions
Enrolled: 246

Costs (1999–2000)
Full-time tuition: $8385 per academic year
Part-time tuition: $925 per course

DEGREES GMBA • MA • MBA • MHA • MS

GMBA—Global Master of Business Administration Full-time and part-time. *Distance learning option.* 45 to 60 total credits required. 9 to 48 months to complete program. *Concentrations:* international business.

MA—Master of Arts in Management Full-time and part-time. *Distance learning option.* 45 to 60 total credits required. 9 to 48 months to complete program. *Concentrations:* management.

MA—Master of Arts Full-time and part-time. 45 to 65 total credits required. 9 to 48 months to complete program. *Concentrations:* human resources.

MBA—Master of Business Administration Full-time and part-time. *Distance learning option.* 55 to 108 total credits required. 10 to 48 months to complete program. *Concentrations:* accounting, commerce, electronic commerce (e-commerce), financial management/planning, health care, human resources, international business, marketing, public policy and administration, technology management, telecommunications management.

MHA—Master of Healthcare Administration Full-time and part-time. 60 to 80 total credits required. 12 to 48 months to complete program. *Concentrations:* health care.

MS—MS Industrial Engineering Management Full-time and part-time. 45 to 75 total credits required. 9 to 48 months to complete program. *Concentrations:* industrial administration/management.

MS—Master of Science in Electronic Commerce Full-time and part-time. *Distance learning option.* 45 to 70 total credits required. 9 to 48 months to complete program. *Concentrations:* electronic commerce (e-commerce).

MS—Master of Science in Engineering Management Full-time and part-time. *Distance learning option.* 45 to 73 total credits required. 9 to 48 months to complete program. *Concentrations:* electronic commerce (e-commerce), system management, engineering.

MS—Master of Science in Environmental Management Full-time and part-time. 45 to 80 total credits required. Minimum of 9 months to complete program.

MS—Master of Science in Technology Management Full-time and part-time. *Distance learning option.* 45 to 65 total credits required. 9 to 48 months to complete program. *Concentrations:* electronic commerce (e-commerce), technology management.

MS—Master of Science in Telecommunications Systems Management Full-time and part-time. *Distance learning option.* 45 to 70 total credits required. 9 to 48 months to complete program. *Concentrations:* telecommunications management.

COSTS

Tuition *Full-time:* $8325. *Part-time:* $925 per course. **Tuition, international:** *Full-time* $8325. Tuition varies by campus location. **Required fees:** *Full-time* $60. *Part-time* $60 per year.

FINANCIAL AID (1999–2000)

Fellowships, grants, loans, and scholarships. Aid is available to part-time students. **Financial Aid Contact** Mr. Matt Levine, Director of Financial Aid, 11255 North Torrey Pines Road, La Jolla, CA 92037-1011. **Phone:** 619-642-8512. **Fax:** 619-642-8720. **E-mail:** mlevine@nu.edu.

RESOURCES AND SERVICES

Information about online services, personal computer policies, library resources, international exchange programs, internship programs, and placement services at this institution and others can be found at **www.petersons.com/mba**

International Students

24% of students enrolled are international students.

Services and Facilities Counseling/support services, ESL/language courses, orientation, visa services. Financial aid is not available to international students.

Applying *Required:* TOEFL with recommended score of 550 (paper), proof of adequate funds.

International Student Contact Ms. Tuey Carte, Director of International Student Services, 4121 Camino Del Rio South, San Diego, CA 92108-4107. **Phone:** 619-563-7206. **Fax:** 619-563-7393. **E-mail:** tcarte@nu.edu.

■ APPLICATION

Required Application form, baccalaureate/first degree, interview, transcripts of college work, 4 years of work experience.

Deadlines and Fees Applications for domestic and international students are processed on a rolling basis. *Application fee:* $60, $100 (international).

Application Contact Ms. Nancy Rohland, Director of Enrollment Management, 11255 North Torrey Pines Road, La Jolla, CA 92037-1011. **Phone:** 858-642-8180. **Toll-free Phone:** 800-628-8648. **Fax:** 858-642-8709. **E-mail:** advisor@nu.edu.

See full description on page 736.

Naval Postgraduate School

Monterey, California

DEPARTMENT OF SYSTEMS MANAGEMENT

Graduate Business Faculty
Full-time: 62

Part-time: 5

Student Body
Total: 384
Full-time: 301
Part-time: 83

Average Age: 28
Women: 15%

Costs (1999–2000)
Full-time tuition: $10,100 per academic year (resident), $10,100 per academic year (nonresident)
Part-time tuition: N/R

After Graduation (Class of 1998–99)
Employed within 3 months of graduation: 100%
Average starting salary: $45,000

Accreditation
AACSB—The International Association for Management Education

DEGREES MBA • MS

MBA—Master of Business Administration Part-time. *Distance learning option.* 48 to 64 total credits required. Minimum of 18 months to complete program.

MS—Master of Science in Contract Management Part-time. *Distance learning option.* Must be military officer on active duty or government employee. At least 50 total credits required. Minimum of 27 months to complete program. *Concentrations:* contract management.

MS—Master of Science in Information Technology Management Full-time and part-time. Must be military officer on active duty or government employee. 48 to 128 total credits required. 21 to 24 months to complete program. *Concentrations:* information management, management information systems, system management, technology management, telecommunications management.

MS—Master of Science in International Resource Planning and Management Full-time and part-time. Must be military officer on active duty or government employee. 48 to 86 total credits required. 18 to 21 months to complete program. *Concentrations:* international development management, international economics, managerial economics, resources management.

MS—Master of Science in Leadership and Human Resource Development Full-time. *Distance learning option.* Must be military officer on active duty or government employee. At least 54 total credits required. Minimum of 12 months to complete program.

MS—Master of Science in Management Full-time and part-time. Must be military officer on active duty or government employee. 48 to 116 total credits required. 18 to 24 months to complete program. *Concentrations:* contract management, financial management/planning, leadership, logistics, management, management science, management systems analysis, manpower administration, materials management, project management, resources management, system management.

MS—Master of Science in Program Management Part-time. *Distance learning option.* Must be military officer on active duty or government employee. At least 48 total credits required. Minimum of 27 months to complete program. *Concentrations:* resources management.

COSTS

Tuition, state resident: *Full-time* $10,100. **Tuition, nonresident:** *Full-time* $10,100. Tuition varies by number of courses or credits taken and academic program.

RESOURCES AND SERVICES

Information about online services, personal computer policies, library resources, international exchange programs, internship programs, and

placement services at this institution and others can be found at **www. petersons.com/mba**

International Students

12% of students enrolled are international students.

Services and Facilities Counseling/support services, ESL/language courses, international student housing, visa services. Financial aid is not available to international students.

Applying *Required:* TOEFL with recommended score of 540 (paper), proof of health/immunizations. *Recommended:* TWE.

International Student Contact Col. Gary Roser, International Programs Officer, 699 Dyer Road, M-5, Monterey, CA 93943. **Phone:** 831-656-2186. **Fax:** 831-656-3064. **E-mail:** groser@nps.navy.mil.

■ APPLICATION

Required Baccalaureate/first degree, transcripts of college work.

Deadlines and Fees *Deadlines:* 7/1 for fall, 10/1 for winter, 1/1 for spring, 5/1 for summer.

Application Contact Ms. Karen Collyer, Director of Admissions, 589 Dyer Road, Room 103C, Monterey, CA 93943. **Phone:** 831-656-3093. **Fax:** 831-656-2891. **E-mail:** kcollyer@nps.navy.mil.

Pacific States University

Los Angeles, California

COLLEGE OF BUSINESS

Graduate Business Faculty
Full-time: 4

Part-time: 18

Student Body
Total: 90
Full-time: 83
Part-time: 7

Average Age: 30
Women: 32%

Admissions
Applications: 100
Admitted: 71

Enrolled: 22
Average GPA: 2.5

Costs (1999–2000)
Full-time tuition: N/R
Part-time tuition: $210 per credit

DEGREES MBA

MBA—Master of Business Administration in Finance Full-time and part-time. 60 to 72 total credits required. 18 to 24 months to complete program. *Concentrations:* finance.

MBA—Master of Business Administration in International Business Full-time and part-time. 60 to 72 total credits required. 18 to 24 months to complete program. *Concentrations:* international business.

MBA—Master of Business Administration in Management of Technology Full-time and part-time. 60 to 72 total credits required. 18 to 24 months to complete program. *Concentrations:* technology management.

MBA—Master of Business Administration in Real Estate Management Full-time and part-time. 60 to 72 total credits required. 18 to 24 months to complete program. *Concentrations:* real estate.

COSTS

Tuition *Part-time:* $210 per credit. **Required fees:** *Part-time* $70 per quarter.

FINANCIAL AID (1999–2000)

10 students received aid, including grants, loans, and scholarships. Aid is available to part-time students. **Financial Aid Contact** Mai Diep, Financial Aid Officer, 1516 South Western Avenue, Los Angeles, CA 90006. **Phone:** 323-731-2383. **Fax:** 323-731-7276. **E-mail:** admission@psuca.edu.

RESOURCES AND SERVICES

Information about online services, personal computer policies, library resources, international exchange programs, internship programs, and placement services at this institution and others can be found at **www. petersons.com/mba**

International Students

94% of students enrolled are international students.

Services and Facilities Counseling/support services, ESL/language courses, international student housing. Financial aid is not available to international students.

Applying *Required:* Proof of adequate funds. *Recommended:* TOEFL with recommended score of 450 (paper), proof of health/immunizations.

International Student Contact Min Sang Kim, Assistant to the Dean, 1516 South Western Avenue, Los Angeles, CA 90006. **Phone:** 323-731-2383. **Fax:** 323-731-7276. **E-mail:** admission@psuca.edu.

■ APPLICATION

Required Application form, baccalaureate/first degree, essay, transcripts of college work. School will accept GMAT. **Recommended** Letter(s) of recommendation, personal statement.

Deadlines and Fees Applications for international students are processed on a rolling basis. *Application fee:* $50, $380 (international).

Application Contact Min Sang Kim, Assistant to the Dean, 1516 South Western Avenue, Los Angeles, CA 90006. **Phone:** 323-731-2383. **Toll-free Phone:** 888-200-0383. **Fax:** 323-731-7276. **E-mail:** admission@psuca.edu.

Pepperdine University

Culver City, California

THE GRAZIADO SCHOOL OF BUSINESS AND MANAGEMENT

Graduate Business Faculty
Full-time: 75

Part-time: 54

Student Body
Total: 2,157
Full-time: 200
Part-time: 1,957

Average Age: 32
Women: 37%

Admissions
Applications: 336
Admitted: 203
Enrolled: 109

Average GMAT: 605
Average GPA: 3.2

Costs (1999–2000)
Full-time tuition: $23,980 per academic year
Part-time tuition: $795 per credit

After Graduation (Class of 1998–99)
Employed within 3 months of graduation: 70%
Average starting salary: $69,000

Accreditation
AACSB—The International Association for Management Education

DEGREES JD/MBA • MBA • MBA/MPP • MIB • MSTM

JD/MBA—Juris Doctor/Master of Business Administration Full-time. Must be admitted to law school. At least 130 total credits required. 45 months to complete program. *Concentrations:* finance, marketing, strategic management.

MBA—Executive MBA Part-time. Minimum of 7 years of work experience (including 2 years of mid-to upper-level management) required. At least 50 total credits required. 20 months to complete program. *Concentrations:* strategic management.

MBA—One-year MBA Full-time. Minimum of 3 years of full-time work experience required plus business undergraduate degree for the 12-month track. 48 to 60 total credits required. 12 to 15 months to complete program. *Concentrations:* finance, international business, management, marketing, public policy and administration, strategic management.

MBA—Presidential/Key Executive MBA Part-time. Minimum of 10 years of work experience (at least 2 years in a senior-level position) required. At least 50 total credits required. 20 months to complete program. *Concentrations:* strategic management.

MBA—Professional MBA Full-time and part-time. May take MAT instead of GMAT. 48 to 60 total credits required. 24 to 84 months to complete program. *Concentrations:* finance, management, marketing, strategic management.

MBA—Two-year MBA Full-time. 60 to 64 total credits required. 20 months to complete program. *Concentrations:* electronic commerce (e-commerce), finance, international business, management, marketing, strategic management, technology management.

MBA/MPP—Master of Business Administration/Master of Public Policy Full-time. Must apply separately to School of Public Policy. At least 96 total credits required. 32 months to complete program. *Concentrations:* finance, Latin American business studies, marketing, public policy and administration.

MIB—Master of International Business Full-time. Beginner level of foreign language proficiency minimum in French, German, or Spanish recommended. 56 to 72 total credits required. 20 months to complete program. *Concentrations:* European business studies, finance, international finance, international marketing, Latin American business studies, marketing, strategic management.

MSTM—Master of Science in Technology Management Part-time. Minimum of 7 years of work experience (at least 2 years at managerial-level) required. At least 40 total credits required. 20 months to complete program. *Concentrations:* strategic management, technology management.

COSTS

Tuition *Full-time:* $23,980. *Part-time:* $795 per credit. **Tuition, international:** *Full-time* $23,980. **Required fees:** Tuition and fees vary by class time, number of courses or credits taken, campus location, and academic program. **Graduate housing:** Room and board costs vary by number of occupants, type of accommodation, and type of board plan. *Typical cost:* $5000 (room only).

FINANCIAL AID (1999–2000)

1300 students received aid, including loans and scholarships. Aid is available to part-time students. Financial aid application deadline: 5/1. **Financial Aid Contact** Ms. Sandi Ford, Director for Financial Aid, 400 Corporate Pointe, Culver City, CA 90230. **Phone:** 310-568-5530. **Fax:** 310-568-5779. **E-mail:** sford@pepperdine.edu.

RESOURCES AND SERVICES

Information about online services, personal computer policies, library resources, international exchange programs, internship programs, and placement services at this institution and others can be found at **www. petersons.com/mba**

International Students

5% of students enrolled are international students.

Services and Facilities Counseling/support services, ESL/language courses, housing location assistance, international student housing, international student organization, orientation, visa services, tax filing seminar, business communication courses. Financial aid is available to international students.
Applying *Required:* TOEFL with recommended score of 550 (paper), proof of adequate funds, proof of health/immunizations.
International Student Contact Mr. Richard Dawson, Director, International Student Services, 24255 Pacific Coast Highway, Malibu, CA 90263-4246. **Phone:** 310-456-4246. **Fax:** 310-317-7403. **E-mail:** rdawson@pepperdine.edu.

▪ APPLICATION

Required GMAT, application form, baccalaureate/first degree, essay, 2 letters of recommendation, personal statement, resume/curriculum vitae, transcripts of college work. **Recommended** Interview, 3 years of work experience.
Deadlines and Fees *Deadlines:* 5/1 for fall, 5/1 for fall (international). *Application fee:* $45, $45 (international).
Application Contact Ms. Stacie Rathel, Associate Director of Marketing and Student Recruitment, 24255 Pacific Coast Highway, Malibu, CA 90263-4100. **Phone:** 310-456-4858. **Fax:** 310-456-4876. **E-mail:** gsbmadm@pepperdine.edu.

See full description on page 764.

Saint Mary's College of California

Moraga, California

GRADUATE BUSINESS PROGRAMS

Graduate Business Faculty
Full-time: 13 — Part-time: 27

Student Body
Total: 307
Full-time: 157 — Average Age: 33
Part-time: 150 — Women: 33%

Admissions
Applications: 102
Admitted: 67 — Average GMAT: 559
Enrolled: 52 — Average GPA: 3.13

Costs (1999–2000)
Full-time tuition: N/R
Part-time tuition: $387 per unit

After Graduation (Class of 1998–99)
Employed within 3 months of graduation: 95%

DEGREES MBA

MBA—Executive MBA Full-time. 5 years of work experience required. At least 56 total credits required. 21 months to complete program. *Concentrations:* management.

MBA—Master of Business Administration Full-time and part-time. At least 72 total credits required. 12 to 72 months to complete program. *Concentrations:* finance, international business, marketing.

COSTS

Tuition *Part-time:* $387 per unit. Tuition varies by class time and academic program.

FINANCIAL AID (1999–2000)

Grants. Aid is available to part-time students. Financial aid application deadline: 3/2. **Financial Aid Contact** Ms. Billie Jones, Director of Financial Aid, PO Box 4530, Moraga, CA 94575. **Phone:** 925-631-4370. **Fax:** 925-376-2965. **E-mail:** bjones@stmarys-ca.edu.

RESOURCES AND SERVICES

Information about online services, personal computer policies, library resources, international exchange programs, internship programs, and placement services at this institution and others can be found at **www. petersons.com/mba**

International Students

2% of students enrolled are international students.

Services and Facilities Counseling/support services, ESL/language courses. Financial aid is not available to international students.
Applying *Required:* TOEFL with recommended score of 550 (paper), proof of adequate funds.
International Student Contact Ms. Maureen Little, Advising Services, PO Box 3091, Moraga, CA 94575. **Phone:** 925-631-4352. **Fax:** 925-631-4651. **E-mail:** mlittle@stmarys-ca.edu.

▪ APPLICATION

Required GMAT, application form, baccalaureate/first degree, interview, 2 letters of recommendation, personal statement, transcripts of college work. **Recommended** Resume/curriculum vitae.
Deadlines and Fees Applications for domestic and international students are processed on a rolling basis. *Application fee:* $50, $50 (international).
Application Contact Ms. Ruth Watson, Director of Admissions and External Relations, 1928 Saint Mary's Road, PO Box 4240, Moraga, CA 94575-4240. **Phone:** 925-631-4500 Ext. 4503. **Fax:** 925-376-6521. **E-mail:** smcmba@st.marys-ca.edu.

See full description on page 806.

San Diego State University

San Diego, California

GRADUATE SCHOOL OF BUSINESS

Graduate Business Faculty
Full-time: 73 — Part-time: 24

Student Body
Total: 721
Full-time: 280 — Average Age: 28
Part-time: 441 — Women: 36%

Admissions
Applications: 888
Admitted: 341 — Average GMAT: 600
Enrolled: 220 — Average GPA: 3.16

Costs (1999–2000)
Full-time tuition: $2046 per academic year (resident), $8192 per academic year (nonresident)
Part-time tuition: N/R

After Graduation (Class of 1998–99)
Average starting salary: $43,101

Accreditation
AACSB—The International Association for Management Education

DEGREES MBA • MBA/MA • MS

MBA—Master of Business Administration Full-time and part-time. At least 49 total credits required. 24 to 48 months to complete program. *Concentrations:* entrepreneurship, finance, health care, international business, management, management information systems, marketing, operations management, real estate.

MBA/MA—Master of Business Administration/Master of Arts in Latin American Studies Full-time. At least 70 total credits required. Minimum of 36 months to complete program.

MS—Master of Science in Accountancy Full-time and part-time. At least 30 total credits required. Minimum of 12 months to complete program. *Concentrations:* accounting.

MS—Master of Science in Business Administration Full-time and part-time. At least 30 total credits required. Minimum of 12 months to complete program. *Concentrations:* entrepreneurship, finance, financial management/planning, human resources, international business, management, management information systems, marketing, production management, real estate, taxation.

COSTS
Tuition, state resident: *Full-time* $1854. **Tuition, nonresident:** *Full-time* $8000. **Tuition, international:** *Full-time* $8000. Tuition varies by class time, number of courses or credits taken, and campus location. **Required fees:** *Full-time* $192. *Part-time* $192 per year. Tuition and fees vary by number of courses or credits taken. **Graduate housing:** Room and board costs vary by number of occupants, type of accommodation, and type of board plan. *Typical cost:* $5935 (including board), $3544 (room only).

FINANCIAL AID (1999–2000)
Fellowships, grants, loans, research assistantships, scholarships, teaching assistantships, and work study. Aid is available to part-time students.
Financial Aid Contact Financial Aid Office, 5500 Campanile Drive, San Diego, CA 92182-7436. **Phone:** 619-594-6323.

RESOURCES AND SERVICES
Information about online services, personal computer policies, library resources, international exchange programs, internship programs, and placement services at this institution and others can be found at **www.petersons.com/mba**

International Students
13% of students enrolled are international students.
Services and Facilities Counseling/support services, ESL/language courses, international student housing, visa services. Financial aid is not available to international students.
Applying *Required:* TOEFL with recommended score of 570 (paper), proof of adequate funds, proof of health/immunizations.
International Student Contact Mr. Ron Moffatt, Director of International Programs, 5500 Campanile Drive, San Diego, CA 92182-5101. **Phone:** 619-594-1982. **Fax:** 619-594-1973. **E-mail:** isc.resources@sdsu.edu.

■ APPLICATION
Required GMAT, application form, baccalaureate/first degree, transcripts of college work. **Recommended** 3 letters of recommendation, personal statement, resume/curriculum vitae, 10 years of work experience.
Deadlines and Fees *Deadlines:* 4/15 for fall, 11/1 for spring, 4/15 for fall (international), 8/31 for spring (international). *Application fee:* $55, $55 (international).
Application Contact Mrs. Shira Scott, Graduate Admissions Coordinator, 5500 Campanile Drive, San Diego, CA 92182-8228. **Phone:** 619-594-8073. **Fax:** 619-594-1863. **E-mail:** sdsumba@mail.sdsu.edu.

San Francisco State University
San Francisco, California

COLLEGE OF BUSINESS

Graduate Business Faculty
Full-time: 102 — Part-time: 40

Student Body
Total: 856
Full-time: 323 — Average Age: 29
Part-time: 533 — Women: 47%

Admissions
Applications: 607 — Average GMAT: 551
Admitted: 373 — Average GPA: 3.2
Enrolled: 191

Costs (1999–2000)
Full-time tuition: N/R
Part-time tuition: $661 per semester (resident), $2137 per semester (nonresident)

After Graduation (Class of 1998–99)
Employed within 3 months of graduation: 95%

Accreditation
AACSB—The International Association for Management Education

DEGREES MBA • MSBA • MST
MBA—Master of Business Administration Full-time and part-time. 30 to 54 total credits required. 12 to 84 months to complete program. *Concentrations:* accounting, business information science, business policy/strategy, entrepreneurship, finance, human resources, information management, international business, international finance, Japanese business studies, leadership, management, management information systems, marketing, marketing research, operations management, organizational behavior/development, port/maritime management, quantitative analysis, strategic management, taxation.
MSBA—Master of Science in Business Administration Full-time and part-time. 30 to 57 total credits required. 12 to 84 months to complete program. *Concentrations:* accounting, business information science, business policy/strategy, entrepreneurship, finance, human resources, information management, international business, international finance, Japanese business studies, leadership, management, management information systems, marketing, new venture management, operations management, organizational behavior/development, port/maritime management, quantitative analysis, strategic management, taxation.
MST—Master of Science in Taxation Full-time and part-time. 30 total credits required. 12 to 60 months to complete program. *Concentrations:* taxation.

COSTS
Tuition, state resident: *Part-time* $661 per semester. **Tuition, nonresident:** *Part-time* $2137 per semester. Tuition varies by number of courses or credits taken. **Graduate housing:** *Typical cost:* $7000 (including board).

FINANCIAL AID (1999–2000)
Fellowships, loans, research assistantships, and work study. **Financial Aid Contact** Ms. Barbara Hubler, Director, Financial Aid, 1600 Holloway Avenue, San Francisco, CA 94132-1722. **Phone:** 415-338-2437. **Fax:** 415-338-0949. **E-mail:** finaid@sfsu.edu.

RESOURCES AND SERVICES
Information about online services, personal computer policies, library resources, international exchange programs, internship programs, and placement services at this institution and others can be found at **www.petersons.com/mba**

International Students
30% of students enrolled are international students.
Services and Facilities Counseling/support services, ESL/language courses, international student housing, international student organization, language tutoring, orientation, visa services, english writing course. Financial aid is not available to international students.
Applying *Required:* TOEFL with recommended score of 213 (computer) or 550 (paper), proof of adequate funds, proof of health/immunizations. *Recommended:* TWE with recommended score of 4.
International Student Contact Ms. Marilyn Cheung, Coordinator, International Outreach Services, Office of International Programs, 1600 Holloway Avenue, San Francisco, CA 94132. **Phone:** 415-338-1362. **E-mail:** mcheung@sfsu.edu.

■ APPLICATION
Required GMAT, application form, baccalaureate/first degree, personal statement, transcripts of college work. **Recommended** Essay, 2 letters of recommendation, resume/curriculum vitae, 2 years of work experience.
Deadlines and Fees *Deadlines:* 5/15 for fall, 11/15 for spring, 4/15 for fall (international), 10/15 for spring (international). *Application fee:* $55, $55 (international).
Application Contact Mr. Albert Koo, Admissions Coordinator, College of Business 325, San Francisco, CA 94132. **Phone:** 415-338-1935. **Fax:** 415-338-6237. **E-mail:** mba@sfsu.edu.

San Jose State University
San Jose, California

COLLEGE OF BUSINESS

Graduate Business Faculty
Full-time: 95 — Part-time: 65

Student Body
Total: 725 — Part-time: 407
Full-time: 318 — Average Age: 32

Admissions
Applications: 670 — Average GMAT: 560
Admitted: 311 — Average GPA: 3.25
Enrolled: 118

Costs (1999–2000)

Full-time tuition: $2017 per academic year (resident), $8377 per academic year (nonresident)
Part-time tuition: $330 per unit (resident), $330 per unit (nonresident)

After Graduation (Class of 1998–99)

Employed within 3 months of graduation: 98%
Average starting salary: $60,000

Accreditation

AACSB—The International Association for Management Education

DEGREES MBA • MS

MBA—Accelerated Off-campus MBA Part-time. 39 to 48 total credits required. 16 to 30 months to complete program.

MBA—MBA-One Full-time. 48 total credits required. 12 months to complete program. *Concentrations:* management.

MBA—Traditional MBA Part-time. 39 to 48 total credits required. 18 to 48 months to complete program.

MS—Master of Science in Accountancy Full-time. At least 45 total credits required. 12 months to complete program.

MS—Master of Science in Taxation Part-time. 39 to 48 total credits required. 9 to 48 months to complete program.

MS—Master of Science in Transportation Management Part-time. *Distance learning option.* At least 30 total credits required. 24 to 36 months to complete program.

COSTS

Tuition, state resident: *Full-time* $2017. *Part-time* $330 per unit. **Tuition, nonresident:** *Full-time* $8377. *Part-time* $330 per unit. **Tuition, international:** *Full-time* $8377. Tuition varies by class time, number of courses or credits taken, campus location, and academic program. **Required fees:** Tuition and fees vary by academic program. **Graduate housing:** Room and board costs vary by number of occupants, type of accommodation, and type of board plan. *Typical cost:* $10,000 (including board).

FINANCIAL AID (1999–2000)

250 students received aid, including fellowships, grants, loans, scholarships, and work study. Aid is available to part-time students. Financial aid application deadline: 3/2. **Financial Aid Contact** Financial Aid Office, One Washington Square, San Jose, CA 95192-0036. **Phone:** 408-924-6100. **Fax:** 408-924-6089.

RESOURCES AND SERVICES

Information about online services, personal computer policies, library resources, international exchange programs, internship programs, and placement services at this institution and others can be found at **www.petersons.com/mba**

International Students

Services and Facilities Counseling/support services, ESL/language courses, housing location assistance, international student housing, international student organization, language tutoring, orientation, visa services. Financial aid is not available to international students.
Applying *Required:* TOEFL with recommended score of 213 (computer) or 550 (paper), proof of adequate funds, proof of health/immunizations.
International Student Contact Helen Stevens, Director, International Student Services, One Washington Square, San Jose, CA 95192-0221. **Phone:** 408-924-5920. **Fax:** 408-924-5978. **E-mail:** sjsuipss@email.sjsu.edu.

■ APPLICATION

Required GMAT, application form, baccalaureate/first degree, personal statement, transcripts of college work.
Deadlines and Fees *Deadlines:* 5/1 for fall, 9/15 for spring, 3/1 for fall (international), 8/31 for spring (international). *Application fee:* $55, $55 (international).
Application Contact Ms. Amy Kassing, Assistant Director, Advising and Admission, One Washington Square, San Jose, CA 95192-0162. **Phone:** 408-924-3420. **Fax:** 408-924-3426. **E-mail:** kassing_a@cob.sjsu.edu.

Santa Clara University

Santa Clara, California

LEAVEY SCHOOL OF BUSINESS

Graduate Business Faculty

Full-time: 78

Part-time: 18

Student Body
Total: 993
Full-time: 149
Part-time: 844

Average Age: 29
Women: 32%

Admissions
Applications: 473
Admitted: 267
Enrolled: 177

Average GMAT: 650
Average GPA: 3.22

Costs (1999–2000)
Full-time tuition: N/R
Part-time tuition: $499 per unit

After Graduation (Class of 1998–99)
Employed within 3 months of graduation: 95%
Average starting salary: $83,500

Accreditation
AACSB—The International Association for Management Education

DEGREES JD/MBA • MBA

JD/MBA—Juris Doctor/Master of Business Administration/Law Program Full-time. 120 to 135 total credits required. 36 to 72 months to complete program. *Concentrations:* accounting, electronic commerce (e-commerce), entrepreneurship, finance, international business, leadership, management information systems, marketing, marketing research, operations management, quantitative analysis, technology management.

MBA—Executive MBA Full-time. 10 years of work experience required. 54 to 58 total credits required. 16 months to complete program.

MBA—Master of Business Administration in Food and Agribusiness Full-time and part-time. 45 to 72 total credits required. 15 to 72 months to complete program. *Concentrations:* accounting, electronic commerce (e-commerce), entrepreneurship, finance, international business, leadership, management information systems, marketing, marketing research, operations management, quantitative analysis, technology management.

MBA—Master of Business Administration Full-time and part-time. 45 to 72 total credits required. 15 to 72 months to complete program. *Concentrations:* accounting, electronic commerce (e-commerce), entrepreneurship, finance, international business, leadership, management information systems, marketing, marketing research, operations management, quantitative analysis, technology management.

COSTS

Tuition *Part-time:* $499 per unit. Tuition varies by number of courses or credits taken and academic program. **Required fees:** *Full-time* $56.

FINANCIAL AID (1999–2000)

60 students received aid, including fellowships, loans, research assistantships, scholarships, and work study. Aid is available to part-time students. Financial aid application deadline: 7/1. **Financial Aid Contact** Ms. Jana Hee, Associate Director, Graduate Business Admissions, MBA Office, Kenna 225, Santa Clara, CA 95053-0001. **Phone:** 408-554-4500. **Fax:** 408-554-2332. **E-mail:** mbaadmissions@scu.edu.

RESOURCES AND SERVICES

Information about online services, personal computer policies, library resources, international exchange programs, internship programs, and placement services at this institution and others can be found at **www.petersons.com/mba**

International Students

5% of students enrolled are international students.

Services and Facilities Counseling/support services, housing location assistance, orientation. Financial aid is not available to international students.
Applying *Required:* TOEFL with recommended score of 250 (computer) or 600 (paper), TWE with recommended score of 4, proof of adequate funds.
International Student Contact International Students Resources, Benson 214, Santa Clara, CA 95053. **Phone:** 408-554-4318. **Fax:** 408-554-2709.

■ APPLICATION

Required GMAT, application form, baccalaureate/first degree, essay, 2 letters of recommendation, transcripts of college work. **Recommended** Resume/curriculum vitae, work experience.
Deadlines and Fees *Deadlines:* 6/1 for fall, 9/1 for winter, 12/1 for spring, 6/1 for fall (international), 9/1 for winter (international), 12/1 for spring (international). *Application fee:* $55, $75 (international).

Application Contact Ms. Jana Hee, Associate Director, Graduate Business Admissions, MBA Office, Kenna Hall #225, Santa Clara, CA 95053-0001. **Phone:** 408-554-4500. **Fax:** 408-554-2332. **E-mail:** mbaadmissions@scu.edu.
See full description on page 814.

Sonoma State University

Rohnert Park, California

SCHOOL OF BUSINESS AND ECONOMICS

Graduate Business Faculty
Full-time: 10

Student Body
Total: 57
Full-time: 16
Part-time: 41

Average Age: 36
Women: 53%

Admissions
Applications: 42
Admitted: 20
Enrolled: 13

Average GMAT: 514
Average GPA: 3.34

Costs (1999–2000)
Full-time tuition: $9382 per academic year (nonresident)
Part-time tuition: $246 per unit (nonresident)

After Graduation (Class of 1998–99)
Employed within 3 months of graduation: 100%

DEGREE MBA

MBA—Master of Business Administration Part-time. 30 to 48 total credits required. 24 to 84 months to complete program.

COSTS

Tuition, nonresident: *Full-time* $7380. *Part-time* $246 per unit. **Required fees:** *Full-time* $2002. Tuition and fees vary by number of courses or credits taken. **Graduate housing:** Room and board costs vary by number of occupants, type of accommodation, and type of board plan. *Typical cost:* $6300 (including board).

FINANCIAL AID (1999–2000)

Grants, loans, scholarships, and work study. Aid is available to part-time students. **Financial Aid Contact** Financial Aid Office, 1801 East Cotati Avenue, Rohnert Park, CA 94928-3609. **Phone:** 707-664-2389.

RESOURCES AND SERVICES

Information about online services, personal computer policies, library resources, international exchange programs, internship programs, and placement services at this institution and others can be found at www. petersons.com/mba

International Students

7% of students enrolled are international students.

Services and Facilities Counseling/support services, ESL/language courses, housing location assistance, international student housing, international student organization, orientation. Financial aid is not available to international students.
Applying *Required:* TOEFL with recommended score of 550 (paper), proof of adequate funds, proof of health/immunizations.
International Student Contact Office of Admissions, 1801 East Cotati Avenue, Rohnert Park, CA 94928-3609. **Phone:** 707-664-2778. **Fax:** 707-664-2060.

■ APPLICATION

Required GMAT, application form, baccalaureate/first degree, personal statement, transcripts of college work. **Recommended** Letter(s) of recommendation, work experience.
Deadlines and Fees *Application fee:* $55, $55 (international).
Application Contact Office of Admissions, 1801 East Cotati Avenue, Rohnert Park, CA 94928-3609. **Phone:** 707-664-2778. **Fax:** 707-664-2060.

Stanford University

Stanford, California

GRADUATE SCHOOL OF BUSINESS

Graduate Business Faculty
Full-time: 84

Part-time: 31

Student Body
Total: 724
Full-time: 724

Average Age: 26
Women: 30%

Admissions
Applications: 6,606
Enrolled: 365

Average GMAT: 725
Average GPA: 3.56

Costs (1999–2000)
Full-time tuition: $27,243 per academic year
Part-time tuition: N/R

After Graduation (Class of 1998–99)
Employed within 3 months of graduation: 100%
Average starting salary: $87,500

Accreditation
AACSB—The International Association for Management Education

DEGREES MBA • MS

MBA—Master of Business Administration Full-time. At least 100 total credits required. 18 months to complete program. *Concentrations:* health care, international management, public management.

MS—Master of Science in Management Full-time. At least 52 total credits required. 10 months to complete program.

COSTS

Tuition *Full-time:* $27,243. **Tuition, international:** *Full-time* $27,243. Tuition varies by academic program. **Graduate housing:** Room and board costs vary by campus location, number of occupants, type of accommodation, and type of board plan. *Typical cost:* $12,006 (including board).

FINANCIAL AID (1999–2000)

Fellowships and loans. **Financial Aid Contact** Financial Aid Office, Graduate School of Business, 518 Memorial Way, Stanford, CA 94305-5015. **Phone:** 650-723-3282. **Fax:** 650-725-3328. **E-mail:** finaid@gsb. stanford.edu.

RESOURCES AND SERVICES

Information about online services, personal computer policies, library resources, international exchange programs, internship programs, and placement services at this institution and others can be found at www. petersons.com/mba

International Students

32% of students enrolled are international students.

Services and Facilities Counseling/support services, housing location assistance, orientation. Financial aid is available to international students.
Applying *Required:* TOEFL, proof of adequate funds. *Recommended:* TWE.
International Student Contact Director of Admissions, Graduate School of Business, 518 Memorial Way, Stanford, CA 94305-5015. **Phone:** 650-723-2766. **Fax:** 650-725-7831. **E-mail:** mba@gsb.stanford.edu.

■ APPLICATION

Required Application form, baccalaureate/first degree, essay, 3 letters of recommendation, personal statement, resume/curriculum vitae, transcripts of college work. School will accept GMAT. **Recommended** 2 years of work experience.
Deadlines and Fees *Deadlines:* 11/3 for fall, 11/3 for fall (international). *Application fee:* $160, $160 (international).
Application Contact MBA Admissions Office, Graduate School of Business, 518 Memorial Way, Stanford, CA 94305-5015. **Phone:** 650-723-2766. **Fax:** 650-725-7831. **E-mail:** mba@gsb.stanford.edu.

United States International University

San Diego, California

COLLEGE OF BUSINESS ADMINISTRATION

Graduate Business Faculty
Full-time: 13

Part-time: 14

Student Body
Total: 168
Full-time: 55
Part-time: 113

Average Age: 28
Women: 39%

Admissions
Applications: 100
Admitted: 90

Average GMAT: 463
Average GPA: 2.97

Costs (1999–2000)
Full-time tuition: N/R
Part-time tuition: $1480 per course

After Graduation (Class of 1998–99)
Employed within 3 months of graduation: 96%
Average starting salary: $42,000

DEGREES MBA • MIBA

MBA—Master of Business Administration Full-time and part-time. *Distance learning option.* 48 to 70 total credits required. 12 to 36 months to complete program. *Concentrations:* finance, information management, management information systems, marketing, strategic management.

MIBA—Master of International Business Administration Full-time and part-time. *Distance learning option.* 48 to 70 total credits required. 12 to 36 months to complete program. *Concentrations:* finance, information management, management information systems, marketing, strategic management.

COSTS
Tuition *Part-time:* $1480 per course. Tuition varies by number of courses or credits taken, campus location, and academic program. **Required fees:** *Full-time* $548. *Part-time* $117 per quarter. **Graduate housing:** Room and board costs vary by campus location, number of occupants, and type of accommodation. *Typical cost:* $5400 (including board).

FINANCIAL AID (1999–2000)
63 students received aid, including loans, research assistantships, scholarships, teaching assistantships, and work study. Aid is available to part-time students. Financial aid application deadline: 4/2. **Financial Aid Contact** Ms. Tina Moncada, Assistant Dean, Admissions and Financial Aid, 10455 Pomerado Road, San Diego, CA 92131-1799. **Phone:** 858-635-4700. **Fax:** 858-635-4848. **E-mail:** tmoncada@usiu.edu.

RESOURCES AND SERVICES
Information about online services, personal computer policies, library resources, international exchange programs, internship programs, and placement services at this institution and others can be found at **www.petersons.com/mba**

International Students
56% of students enrolled are international students.

Services and Facilities Counseling/support services, ESL/language courses, housing location assistance, international student housing, international student organization, language tutoring, orientation, visa services. Financial aid is available to international students.

Applying *Required:* TOEFL with recommended score of 550 (paper), proof of adequate funds.

International Student Contact Dr. Bijan Massrour, Director, International Student Services Office, 10455 Pomerado Road, San Diego, CA 92131-1799. **Phone:** 858-635-4564. **Fax:** 858-635-4728. **E-mail:** bmassrou@usiu.edu.

■ APPLICATION
Required GMAT, application form, baccalaureate/first degree, essay, letter(s) of recommendation, personal statement, transcripts of college work. **Recommended** Resume/curriculum vitae.

Deadlines and Fees Applications for domestic and international students are processed on a rolling basis. *Application fee:* $40, $40 (international).

Application Contact Ms. Susan Topham, Director of Admissions, 10455 Pomerado Road, San Diego, CA 92131-1799. **Phone:** 858-635-4885. **Fax:** 858-635-4739. **E-mail:** stopham@usiu.edu.

University of California, Berkeley

Berkeley, California

HAAS SCHOOL OF BUSINESS

Graduate Business Faculty
Full-time: 68
Part-time: 38

Student Body
Total: 792
Full-time: 467
Part-time: 325
Average Age: 28
Women: 32%

Admissions
Applications: 4,132
Admitted: 576
Enrolled: 359
Average GMAT: 674
Average GPA: 3.5

Costs (1999–2000)
Full-time tuition: $10,459 per academic year (resident), $20,263 per academic year (nonresident)
Part-time tuition: $10,014 per semester (resident), $10,014 per semester (nonresident)

After Graduation (Class of 1998–99)
Employed within 3 months of graduation: 99%
Average starting salary: $81,105

Accreditation
AACSB—The International Association for Management Education

DEGREES JD/MBA • MBA • MBA/MA • MBA/MIAS • MBA/MPH

JD/MBA—Juris Doctor/Master of Business Administration Full-time. At least 125 total credits required. 45 to 54 months to complete program. *Concentrations:* business information science, entrepreneurship, finance, financial economics, information management, international and area business studies, international business, management, management information systems, marketing, nonprofit management, operations management, organizational behavior/development, real estate, strategic management, technology management.

MBA—Evening MBA Program Part-time. At least 36 total credits required. 28 to 45 months to complete program. *Concentrations:* electronic commerce (e-commerce), entrepreneurship, finance, financial economics, information management, management, management information systems, marketing, organizational behavior/development, real estate, strategic management, technology management.

MBA—Master of Business Administration Full-time. At least 56 total credits required. 21 months to complete program. *Concentrations:* accounting, business policy/strategy, electronic commerce (e-commerce), entrepreneurship, finance, financial economics, financial management/planning, health care, human resources, information management, international and area business studies, international business, international finance, international management, management, management information systems, marketing, new venture management, nonprofit management, operations management, organizational behavior/development, real estate, strategic management, technology management.

MBA/MA—Master of Business Administration/Master of Arts in Asian Studies Full-time. At least 76 total credits required. 33 to 54 months to complete program. *Concentrations:* Asian business studies, business information science, entrepreneurship, finance, financial economics, information management, international and area business studies, international business, Japanese business studies, management, management information systems, marketing, nonprofit management, operations management, organizational behavior/development, real estate, strategic management, technology management.

MBA/MIAS—Master of Business Administration/Master of International Area Studies Full-time. At least 80 total credits required. 33 to 54 months to complete program. *Concentrations:* accounting, Asian business studies, entrepreneurship, European business studies, finance, financial economics, information management, international and area business studies, international business, international development management, international finance, international management, Japanese business studies, management, management information systems, marketing, nonprofit management, operations management, organizational behavior/development, real estate, strategic management, technology management.

MBA/MPH—Master of Business Administration/Master of Public Health in Health Services Management Full-time. At least 80 total credits required. 33 to 54 months to complete program. *Concentrations:* health care, management, nonprofit management, nonprofit organization.

COSTS
Tuition, state resident: *Full-time* $10,459. *Part-time* $10,014 per semester. **Tuition, nonresident:** *Full-time* $20,263. *Part-time* $10,014 per semester. **Tuition, international:** *Full-time* $20,263. **Required fees:** Tuition and fees vary by academic program. **Graduate housing:** Room and board costs vary by number of occupants, type of accommodation, and type of board plan. *Typical cost:* $9600 (including board), $6600 (room only).

FINANCIAL AID (1999–2000)
365 students received aid, including fellowships, grants, loans, research assistantships, scholarships, teaching assistantships, and work study. Aid is available to part-time students. Financial aid application deadline: 3/1. **Financial Aid Contact** Ms. Debi Fidler, Financial Aid Coordinator, Walter A. Haas School of Business, Room S472, Berkeley, CA 94720-1900. **Phone:** 510-643-1680. **Fax:** 510-643-6659. **E-mail:** fidler@haas.berkeley.edu.

RESOURCES AND SERVICES
Information about online services, personal computer policies, library resources, international exchange programs, internship programs, and

placement services at this institution and others can be found at **www.petersons.com/mba**

International Students
21% of students enrolled are international students.

Services and Facilities Counseling/support services, ESL/language courses, international student housing, visa services. Financial aid is available to international students.

Applying *Required:* TOEFL with recommended score of 230 (computer) or 570 (paper), proof of adequate funds.

International Student Contact Mr. John Pliska, MBA Admissions Advisor, Walter A. Haas School of Business, 440 Student Services Building, #1902, Berkeley, CA 94720-1902. **Phone:** 510-642-1405. **Fax:** 510-643-6659. **E-mail:** mbaadms@haas.berkeley.edu.

■ APPLICATION
Required GMAT, application form, baccalaureate/first degree, essay, 2 letters of recommendation, personal statement, resume/curriculum vitae, transcripts of college work, 2 years of work experience.

Deadlines and Fees *Application fee:* $125, $125 (international).

Application Contact Ms. Cherie Scricca, Director, MBA Admissions, Walter A. Haas School of Business, 440 Student Services Building, #1902, Berkeley, CA 94720-1902. **Phone:** 510-642-1405. **Fax:** 510-643-6659. **E-mail:** mbaadms@haas.berkeley.edu.

University of California, Davis
Davis, California

GRADUATE SCHOOL OF MANAGEMENT

Graduate Business Faculty
Full-time: 23 — Part-time: 15

Student Body
Total: 129
Full-time: 129 — Average Age: 29, Women: 38%

Admissions
Applications: 401
Admitted: 144 — Average GMAT: 675, Average GPA: 3.2
Enrolled: 66

Costs (1999–2000)
Full-time tuition: $10,483 per academic year (resident), $19,867 per academic year (nonresident)
Part-time tuition: N/R

After Graduation (Class of 1998–99)
Employed within 3 months of graduation: 98%
Average starting salary: $65,000

Accreditation
AACSB—The International Association for Management Education

DEGREES MBA

MBA—Working Professional MBA Program Part-time. At least 72 total credits required. 36 to 48 months to complete program. *Concentrations:* accounting, environmental economics/management, finance, health care, management, management information systems, marketing, technology management.

MBA—Master of Business Administration Full-time. At least 72 total credits required. 24 months to complete program. *Concentrations:* accounting, agribusiness, finance, international management, management, management information systems, management science, marketing, public management, technology management.

COSTS
Tuition, state resident: *Full-time* $10,483. **Tuition, nonresident:** *Full-time* $19,867. **Tuition, international:** *Full-time* $19,867. **Required fees:** *Full-time* $0. Fees vary by number of courses or credits taken and academic program. **Graduate housing:** Room and board costs vary by campus location, number of occupants, type of accommodation, and type of board plan. *Typical cost:* $7256 (including board).

FINANCIAL AID (1999–2000)
81 students received aid, including grants, loans, research assistantships, scholarships, teaching assistantships, and work study. Financial aid application deadline: 3/1. **Financial Aid Contact** Barbara Raney, Graduate Financial Aid Office, One Shields Avenue, Davis, CA 95616. **Phone:** 530-752-5039. **Fax:** 530-752-7337. **E-mail:** gradfinaid@ucdavis.edu.

RESOURCES AND SERVICES
Information about online services, personal computer policies, library resources, international exchange programs, internship programs, and placement services at this institution and others can be found at **www.petersons.com/mba**

International Students
9% of students enrolled are international students.

Services and Facilities Counseling/support services, ESL/language courses, housing location assistance, language tutoring, orientation, visa services. Financial aid is not available to international students.

Applying *Required:* TOEFL with recommended score of 250 (computer) or 600 (paper), proof of adequate funds, proof of health/immunizations.

International Student Contact Elke Breker, International Student Advisor, Services for International Students and Scholars, One Shields Avenue, Davis, CA 95616. **Phone:** 530-752-0864. **Fax:** 530-752-5822. **E-mail:** ecbreker@ucdavis.edu.

■ APPLICATION
Required GMAT, application form, baccalaureate/first degree, essay, 3 letters of recommendation, personal statement, resume/curriculum vitae, transcripts of college work. **Recommended** Interview, work experience.

Deadlines and Fees *Deadlines:* 4/1 for fall, 4/1 for fall (international). *Application fee:* $40, $40 (international).

Application Contact Mr. Donald A. Blodger, Assistant Dean of Admissions and Student Services, 107 AOB IV, Davis, CA 95616. **Phone:** 530-752-7658. **Fax:** 530-752-2924. **E-mail:** gsm@ucdavis.edu.

See full description on page 874.

University of California, Irvine
Irvine, California

GRADUATE SCHOOL OF MANAGEMENT

Graduate Business Faculty
Full-time: 40 — Part-time: 30

Student Body
Total: 796
Full-time: 299 — Average Age: 33, Women: 27%
Part-time: 497

Admissions
Applications: 1,268
Admitted: 588 — Average GMAT: 664, Average GPA: 3.37
Enrolled: 379

Costs (1999–2000)
Full-time tuition: $9384 per academic year (nonresident)
Part-time tuition: N/R

After Graduation (Class of 1998–99)
Employed within 3 months of graduation: 96%
Average starting salary: $73,300

Accreditation
AACSB—The International Association for Management Education

DEGREES MBA

MBA—Executive MBA Part-time. At least 92 total credits required. 24 months to complete program.

MBA—Fully-employed MBA Part-time. At least 92 total credits required. 33 to 36 months to complete program.

MBA—Health Care Executive MBA Part-time. At least 92 total credits required. 24 months to complete program.

MBA—Master of Business Administration Full-time. At least 92 total credits required. 21 to 24 months to complete program. *Concentrations:* accounting.

COSTS
Tuition, nonresident: *Full-time* $9384. Tuition varies by academic program. **Graduate housing:** Room and board costs vary by number of occupants, type of accommodation, and type of board plan. *Typical cost:* $7074 (including board).

FINANCIAL AID (1999–2000)
550 students received aid, including fellowships, grants, loans, research assistantships, scholarships, teaching assistantships, and work study. Financial aid application deadline: 3/2. **Financial Aid Contact** Ms. Alda Ruggiero, Financial Aid Advisor, 250 Graduate School of Management, Irvine, CA 92697-3125. **Phone:** 949-824-5728. **Fax:** 949-824-5087. **E-mail:** aruggier@gsm.uci.edu.

University of California, Irvine (continued)

RESOURCES AND SERVICES
Information about online services, personal computer policies, library resources, international exchange programs, internship programs, and placement services at this institution and others can be found at **www.petersons.com/mba**

International Students
10% of students enrolled are international students.

Services and Facilities Counseling/support services, ESL/language courses, international student housing, orientation, visa services. Financial aid is not available to international students.

Applying *Required:* TOEFL with recommended score of 250 (computer) or 600 (paper), proof of adequate funds, proof of health/immunizations.

International Student Contact Mr. Raphael Randles, Admissions and Marketing Assistant, 202 Graduate School of Management, Irvine, CA 92697-3125. **Phone:** 949-824-4622. **Fax:** 949-824-2944. **E-mail:** gsm-mba@uci.edu.

■ APPLICATION
Required GMAT, application form, baccalaureate/first degree, essay, interview, 2 letters of recommendation, personal statement, resume/curriculum vitae, transcripts of college work. **Recommended** Work experience.

Deadlines and Fees *Deadlines:* 5/1 for fall, 5/1 for fall (international). *Application fee:* $75, $75 (international).

Application Contact Mr. Raphael Randles, Admissions and Marketing Assistant, 202 Graduate School of Management, Irvine, CA 92697-3125. **Phone:** 949-824-4622. **Fax:** 949-824-2944. **E-mail:** gsm-mba@uci.edu.

See full description on page 876.

University of California, Los Angeles

Los Angeles, California

JOHN E. ANDERSON GRADUATE SCHOOL OF MANAGEMENT

Graduate Business Faculty

Full-time: 99	Part-time: 56

Student Body

Total: 1,108	
Full-time: 711	Average Age: 28
Part-time: 397	Women: 29%

Admissions

Applications: 4,926	Average GMAT: 690
Admitted: 635	Average GPA: 3.5
Enrolled: 329	

Costs (1999–2000)
Full-time tuition: $11,580 per academic year (resident), $20,964 per academic year (nonresident)
Part-time tuition: N/R

After Graduation (Class of 1998–99)
Employed within 3 months of graduation: 98.9%
Average starting salary: $78,500

Accreditation
AACSB—The International Association for Management Education

DEGREES JD/MBA • MBA • MBA/MA • MBA/MS • MD/MBA • MN/MBA

JD/MBA—Juris Doctor/Master of Business Administration Full-time. At least 185 total credits required. 45 to 48 months to complete program. *Concentrations:* accounting, entrepreneurship, finance, human resources, industrial/labor relations, international business, international economics, international finance, international management, international marketing, management, management information systems, management science, managerial economics, marketing, nonprofit management, operations management, organizational behavior/development, production management, real estate, strategic management, technology management.

MBA—Executive MBA Part-time. Laptop computer required. At least 66 total credits required. 23 months to complete program.

MBA—Full-time MBA Full-time. At least 96 total credits required. 21 to 24 months to complete program. *Concentrations:* accounting, entrepreneurship, finance, human resources, industrial/labor relations, international business, international economics, international finance, international management, international marketing, management, management information systems, management science, managerial economics, marketing, nonprofit management, operations management, organizational behavior/development, production management, real estate, strategic management, technology management.

MBA—Fully-employed MBA Part-time. Laptop computer required. At least 84 total credits required. 28 to 34 months to complete program.

MBA/MA—Master of Business Administration/Master of Arts in Latin American Studies Full-time. At least 120 total credits required. 30 to 36 months to complete program. *Concentrations:* accounting, entrepreneurship, finance, human resources, industrial/labor relations, international business, international economics, international finance, international management, international marketing, management, management information systems, management science, managerial economics, marketing, nonprofit management, operations management, organizational behavior/development, production management, real estate, strategic management, technology management.

MBA/MA—Master of Business Administration/Master of Arts in Urban Studies Full-time. At least 144 total credits required. 33 to 36 months to complete program. *Concentrations:* accounting, entrepreneurship, finance, human resources, industrial/labor relations, international business, international economics, international finance, international management, international marketing, management, management information systems, management science, managerial economics, marketing, nonprofit management, operations management, organizational behavior/development, production management, real estate, strategic management, technology management.

MBA/MS—Master of Business Administration/Master of Science in Computer Science Full-time. At least 96 total credits required. 33 to 36 months to complete program. *Concentrations:* accounting, entrepreneurship, finance, human resources, industrial/labor relations, international business, international economics, international finance, international management, international marketing, management, management information systems, management science, managerial economics, marketing, nonprofit management, operations management, organizational behavior/development, production management, real estate, strategic management, technology management.

MBA/MS—Master of Business Administration/Master of Science in Library Science Full-time. At least 124 total credits required. 33 to 36 months to complete program. *Concentrations:* accounting, entrepreneurship, finance, human resources, industrial/labor relations, international business, international economics, international finance, international management, international marketing, management, management information systems, management science, managerial economics, marketing, nonprofit management, operations management, organizational behavior/development, production management, real estate, strategic management, technology management.

MBA/MS—Master of Business Administration/Master of Science in Public Health Full-time. At least 132 total credits required. 33 to 36 months to complete program. *Concentrations:* accounting, entrepreneurship, finance, human resources, industrial/labor relations, international business, international economics, international finance, international management, international marketing, management, management information systems, management science, managerial economics, marketing, nonprofit management, operations management, organizational behavior/development, production management, real estate, strategic management, technology management.

MD/MBA—Doctor of Medicine/Master of Business Administration Full-time. At least 96 total credits required. 60 to 63 months to complete program. *Concentrations:* accounting, entrepreneurship, finance, human resources, industrial/labor relations, international business, international economics, international finance, international management, international marketing, management, management information systems, management science, managerial economics, marketing, nonprofit management, operations management, organizational behavior/development, production management, real estate, strategic management, technology management.

MN/MBA—Master of Nursing/Master of Business Administration Full-time. At least 129 total credits required. 33 to 36 months to complete program. *Concentrations:* accounting, entrepreneurship, finance, human resources, industrial/labor relations, international business, international economics, international finance, international management, international marketing, management, management information systems, management science, managerial economics, marketing, nonprofit management, operations management, organizational behavior/development, production management, real estate, strategic management, technology management.

COSTS
Tuition, state resident: *Full-time* $11,580. **Tuition, nonresident:** *Full-time* $20,964. Tuition varies by academic program. **Graduate housing:** Room and board costs vary by number of occupants and type of accommodation. *Typical cost:* $8717 (including board).

FINANCIAL AID (1999–2000)
196 students received aid, including fellowships, grants, loans, research assistantships, scholarships, teaching assistantships, and work study. Aid

is available to part-time students. **Financial Aid Contact** Mrs. Marta Klock, Financial Aid Director, 110 Westwood Plaza, Box 951481, Los Angeles, 90095-1481, United States Minor Outlying Islands. **Phone:** 310-825-6944. **Fax:** 310-825-8582. **E-mail:** mba.admissions@anderson.ucla.edu.

RESOURCES AND SERVICES
Information about online services, personal computer policies, library resources, international exchange programs, internship programs, and placement services at this institution and others can be found at **www.petersons.com/mba**

International Students
18% of students enrolled are international students.

Services and Facilities Counseling/support services, ESL/language courses, international student housing, visa services. Financial aid is available to international students.

Applying *Required:* TOEFL.

International Student Contact Mr. Randy Rutledge, Assistant Director, MBA Admissions, 110 Westwood Plaza, Box 951481, Los Angeles, CA 90095-1481. **Phone:** 310-825-6944. **Fax:** 310-825-8582. **E-mail:** mba.admissions@anderson.ucla.edu.

■ APPLICATION
Required Application form, baccalaureate/first degree, essay, letter(s) of recommendation, personal statement, resume/curriculum vitae, transcripts of college work. School will accept GMAT. **Recommended** Interview, work experience.

Deadlines and Fees *Deadlines:* 11/1 for fall, 12/29 for winter, 3/27 for spring, 1/27 for fall (international). *Application fee:* $125, $125 (international).

Application Contact Mrs. Linda Baldwin, Director of MBA Admissions, 110 Westwood Plaza, Box 951481, Los Angeles, CA 90095-1481. **Phone:** 310-825-6944. **Fax:** 310-825-8582. **E-mail:** mba.admissions@anderson.ucla.edu.

See full description on page 878.

University of California, Riverside
Riverside, California

A. GARY ANDERSON GRADUATE SCHOOL OF MANAGEMENT

Graduate Business Faculty
Full-time: 26 — Part-time: 7

Student Body
Total: 147
Full-time: 134 — Average Age: 27
Part-time: 13 — Women: 46%

Admissions
Applications: 268 — Average GMAT: 585
Admitted: 133 — Average GPA: 3.3
Enrolled: 50

Costs (1999–2000)
Full-time tuition: $9957 per academic year (resident), $19,761 per academic year (nonresident)
Part-time tuition: $3605 per quarter (nonresident)

After Graduation (Class of 1998–99)
Employed within 3 months of graduation: 85%
Average starting salary: $52,000

DEGREE MBA

MBA—Master of Business Administration Full-time and part-time. At least 92 total credits required. 18 to 24 months to complete program. *Concentrations:* accounting, entrepreneurship, environmental economics/management, finance, human resources, international management, management, management information systems, management science, marketing, operations management, organizational behavior/development, production management.

COSTS
Tuition, state resident: *Full-time* $0. **Tuition, nonresident:** *Full-time* $9804. *Part-time* $1634 per quarter. **Tuition, international:** *Full-time* $9804. **Required fees:** *Full-time* $9957. *Part-time* $1971 per quarter. Tuition and fees vary by number of courses or credits taken. **Graduate housing:** Room and board costs vary by number of occupants, type of accommodation, and type of board plan. *Typical cost:* $8245 (including board).

FINANCIAL AID (1999–2000)
60 students received aid, including fellowships, grants, loans, research assistantships, scholarships, teaching assistantships, and work study. Aid is available to part-time students. Financial aid application deadline: 2/1. **Financial Aid Contact** Mr. Gary Kuzas, Director of MBA Admissions, Graduate School of Management, Anderson Hall, Riverside, CA 92521-0203. **Phone:** 909-787-4551 Ext. 2525. **Fax:** 909-787-3970. **E-mail:** gary.kuzas@ucr.edu.

RESOURCES AND SERVICES
Information about online services, personal computer policies, library resources, international exchange programs, internship programs, and placement services at this institution and others can be found at **www.petersons.com/mba**

International Students
56% of students enrolled are international students.

Services and Facilities Counseling/support services, ESL/language courses, housing location assistance, international student organization, language tutoring, visa services. Financial aid is available to international students.

Applying *Required:* TOEFL with recommended score of 213 (computer) or 550 (paper), proof of adequate funds.

International Student Contact Dr. Lana Zhou, Assistant Director for International Student Program, International Student Service Center, Watkins House, Riverside, CA 92521-0307. **Phone:** 909-787-4113. **Fax:** 909-787-3778. **E-mail:** lana.zhou@ucr.edu.

■ APPLICATION
Required GMAT, application form, baccalaureate/first degree, essay, 2 letters of recommendation, transcripts of college work. **Recommended** Interview, personal statement, resume/curriculum vitae.

Deadlines and Fees *Deadlines:* 5/1 for fall, 9/1 for winter, 12/1 for spring, 2/1 for fall (international), 7/1 for winter (international), 10/1 for spring (international). *Application fee:* $40, $40 (international).

Application Contact Mr. Gary Kuzas, Director of MBA Admissions, A. Gary Anderson Graduate School of Management, Anderson Hall, Riverside, CA 92521-0203. **Phone:** 909-787-4551 Ext. 2525. **Fax:** 909-787-3970. **E-mail:** gary.kuzas@ucr.edu.

See full description on page 880.

University of Judaism
Bel Air, California

DAVID LIEBER SCHOOL OF GRADUATE STUDIES

Graduate Business Faculty
Full-time: 3 — Part-time: 13

Student Body
Total: 31
Full-time: 20 — Average Age: 28
Part-time: 11 — Women: 71%

Admissions
Applications: 11 — Enrolled: 9
Admitted: 11 — Average GPA: 3.5

Costs (1999–2000)
Full-time tuition: $15,505 per academic year
Part-time tuition: $625 per credit

After Graduation (Class of 1998–99)
Employed within 3 months of graduation: 95%
Average starting salary: $48,000

DEGREES MA • MBA

MA—Master of Arts in Nonprofit Management Full-time and part-time. At least 32 total credits required. Minimum of 12 months to complete program. *Concentrations:* marketing, nonprofit management, nonprofit organization, resources management.

MBA—Master of Business Administration in Nonprofit Management Full-time and part-time. At least 53 total credits required. Minimum of 24 months to complete program. *Concentrations:* marketing, nonprofit management, nonprofit organization, resources management.

COSTS
Tuition *Full-time:* $15,000. *Part-time:* $625 per credit. **Required fees:** *Full-time* $505. **Graduate housing:** Room and board costs vary by number of occupants, type of accommodation, and type of board plan. *Typical cost:* $8000 (including board).

University of Judaism (continued)

FINANCIAL AID (1999–2000)
16 students received aid, including fellowships, grants, loans, research assistantships, scholarships, and work study. Aid is available to part-time students. Financial aid application deadline: 3/2. **Financial Aid Contact** Ms. Deborah Rhodes, Director of Financial Aid, 15600 Mulholland Drive, Bel Air, CA 90077. **Phone:** 310-476-9777 Ext. 252. **Fax:** 310-471-3657. **E-mail:** finaid@uj.edu.

RESOURCES AND SERVICES
Information about online services, personal computer policies, library resources, international exchange programs, internship programs, and placement services at this institution and others can be found at **www.petersons.com/mba**

International Students
3% of students enrolled are international students.

Services and Facilities Counseling/support services, international student housing. Financial aid is available to international students.
Applying *Required:* TOEFL with recommended score of 213 (computer) or 560 (paper), proof of health/immunizations.
International Student Contact Ms. Cecily Bryan, Director of Graduate Admissions, 15600 Mulholland Drive, Bel Air, CA 90077-1599. **Phone:** 310-476-9777 Ext. 261. **Fax:** 310-471-3657. **E-mail:** admissions@uj.edu.

■ APPLICATION
Required GMAT or GRE, application form, baccalaureate/first degree, essay, 2 letters of recommendation, personal statement, transcripts of college work. School will accept GMAT and GRE. **Recommended** Interview, resume/curriculum vitae, work experience.
Deadlines and Fees *Deadlines:* 3/1 for fall, 11/1 for spring, 3/1 for fall (international), 11/1 for spring (international). *Application fee:* $35, $35 (international).
Application Contact Ms. Cecily Bryan, Director of Graduate Admissions, 15600 Mulholland Drive, Bel Air, CA 90077-1599. **Phone:** 310-476-9777 Ext. 261. **Toll-free Phone:** 888-UJ-FOR-ME. **Fax:** 310-471-3657. **E-mail:** admissions@uj.edu.

University of La Verne
La Verne, California

SCHOOL OF BUSINESS AND ECONOMICS

Graduate Business Faculty

Full-time: 14 — Part-time: 52

Student Body

Total: 943
Full-time: 274 — Average Age: 36
Part-time: 669 — Women: 54%

Admissions
Average GMAT: 520

Costs (1999–2000)
Full-time tuition: N/R
Part-time tuition: $360 per credit

DEGREES JD/MBA • MBA • MS

JD/MBA—Juris Doctor/Master of Business Administration Full-time and part-time. 48 to 96 months to complete program. *Concentrations:* accounting, contract management, finance, health care, information management, international management, leadership, legal administration, management, marketing.

MBA—Career MBA Full-time and part-time. 36 to 54 total credits required. 12 to 60 months to complete program. *Concentrations:* accounting, finance, health care, information management, international management, leadership, management, marketing.

MBA—MBA for Experienced Professionals Full-time and part-time. 33 to 51 total credits required. 12 to 60 months to complete program. *Concentrations:* accounting, finance, health care, information management, international management, leadership, management, marketing.

MS—Master of Science in Business Organizational Management Full-time and part-time. 36 to 45 total credits required. 24 to 60 months to complete program. *Concentrations:* health care, human resources.

COSTS
Tuition *Part-time:* $360 per credit. Tuition varies by number of courses or credits taken, campus location, and academic program. **Required fees:** Tuition and fees vary by academic program. **Graduate housing:** Room and board costs vary by number of occupants. *Typical cost:* $2800 (including board).

FINANCIAL AID (1999–2000)
37 students received aid, including fellowships, loans, scholarships, and work study. Aid is available to part-time students. **Financial Aid Contact** Mr. Edward Mervine, Director of Financial Aid, 1950 Third Street, LaVerne, CA 91750. **Phone:** 909-593-3511 Ext. 4135. **Fax:** 909-392-2703.

RESOURCES AND SERVICES
Information about online services, personal computer policies, library resources, international exchange programs, internship programs, and placement services at this institution and others can be found at **www.petersons.com/mba**

International Students
10% of students enrolled are international students.

Services and Facilities Counseling/support services, ESL/language courses, housing location assistance, international student housing, international student organization, orientation, visa services. Financial aid is not available to international students.
Applying *Required:* TOEFL with recommended score of 550 (paper), proof of adequate funds.
International Student Contact Philip Hofer, International Student Services Director, 1950 Third Street, La Verne, CA 91750-4443. **Phone:** 909-593-3511 Ext. 4330. **Fax:** 909-392-0713. **E-mail:** hoferp@ulv.edu.

■ APPLICATION
Required Application form, baccalaureate/first degree, essay, 3 letters of recommendation, personal statement, transcripts of college work. School will accept GMAT and GRE. **Recommended** Resume/curriculum vitae, 3 years of work experience.
Deadlines and Fees Applications for domestic and international students are processed on a rolling basis. *Application fee:* $35, $35 (international).
Application Contact Dr. Julius Walecki, Director of Program Development, 1950 Third Street, La Verne, CA 91750-4443. **Phone:** 909-593-3511 Ext. 4192. **Toll-free Phone:** 800-955-4858. **Fax:** 909-392-2704. **E-mail:** waleckij@ulv.edu.

University of Redlands
Redlands, California

ALFRED NORTH WHITEHEAD COLLEGE FOR LIFELONG LEARNING

DEGREES MA • MBA • MSIT

MA—Master of Arts in Management Full-time. At least 32 total credits required. 18 months to complete program. *Concentrations:* human resources, industrial/labor relations, management information systems, quality management.

MBA—Master of Business Administration Full-time. 41 to 53 total credits required. 24 to 30 months to complete program. *Concentrations:* information management, international business, management information systems.

MSIT—Master of Science in Interactive Telecommunications At least 39 total credits required. 24 months to complete program. *Concentrations:* electronic commerce (e-commerce), information systems, telecommunications management.

RESOURCES AND SERVICES
Information about online services, personal computer policies, library resources, international exchange programs, internship programs, and placement services at this institution and others can be found at **www.petersons.com/mba**

International Students
Services and Facilities Financial aid is not available to international students.
International Student Contact James E. Niles, Dean of Admissions, 1200 East Colton Avenue, PO Box 3080, Redlands, CA 92373-0999. **Phone:** 909-335-4065. **Fax:** 909-335-5325. **E-mail:** niles@uor.edu.

■ APPLICATION
Application Contact James E. Niles, Dean of Admissions, 1200 East Colton Avenue, PO Box 3080, Redlands, CA 92373-0999. **Phone:** 909-335-4065. **Toll-free Phone:** 888-999-9844. **Fax:** 909-335-5325. **E-mail:** niles@uor.edu.

University of San Diego

San Diego, California

SCHOOL OF BUSINESS ADMINISTRATION

Graduate Business Faculty
Full-time: 62

Part-time: 3

Student Body
Total: 308
Full-time: 116
Part-time: 192

Average Age: 28
Women: 40%

Admissions
Applications: 323
Admitted: 156
Enrolled: 88

Average GMAT: 580
Average GPA: 3.23

Costs (1999–2000)
Full-time tuition: $12,150 per academic year
Part-time tuition: $675 per credit

After Graduation (Class of 1998–99)
Employed within 3 months of graduation: 80%
Average starting salary: $52,000

Accreditation
AACSB—The International Association for Management Education

DEGREES IMBA • IMBA/MBA • IMBA/MSF • IMBA/MSMT • JD/IMBA • JD/MBA • MBA • MBA/MS • MBA/MSF • MBA/MSMT • MS

IMBA—International Master of Business Administration Full-time and part-time. 30 to 48 total credits required. 12 to 36 months to complete program.

IMBA/MBA—Master of International Business at USD/Master of Business Administration at ITESM Full-time and part-time. 20 to 28 months to complete program.

IMBA/MSF—Master of International Business at USD/Master of Science Finance at ITESM Full-time and part-time. 19 to 26 months to complete program.

IMBA/MSMT—International Master of Business Administration at USD/ Master of Science at ITESM Full-time and part-time. 19 to 26 months to complete program.

JD/IMBA—Joint USD Degree Full-time and part-time. 103 to 133 total credits required. 36 to 48 months to complete program.

JD/MBA—Joint USD Degree Full-time and part-time. 103 to 133 total credits required. 36 to 48 months to complete program. *Concentrations:* entrepreneurship, finance, international business, management, marketing, materials management, project management, real estate.

MBA—Joint MBA conferred in conjunction with ITESM Full-time and part-time. 2 years full-time work experience. At least 48 total credits required. 20 to 26 months to complete program. *Concentrations:* electronic commerce (e-commerce), entrepreneurship, finance, international business, management, marketing, materials management, project management, real estate, supply chain management.

MBA—Master of Business Administration Full-time and part-time. 2 years full-time work experience. 30 to 48 total credits required. 12 to 36 months to complete program. *Concentrations:* electronic commerce (e-commerce), entrepreneurship, finance, international business, management, marketing, materials management, project management, real estate, supply chain management.

MBA/MS—Master of Business Administration/Master of Science in Nursing Full-time and part-time. At least 60 total credits required. 12 to 36 months to complete program.

MBA/MSF—Master of Business Administration at USD/Master of Science Finance at ITESM Full-time and part-time. At least 48 total credits required. 19 to 24 months to complete program.

MBA/MSMT—Master of Business Administration at USD/Master of Marketing at ITESM Full-time and part-time. 19 to 24 months to complete program.

MS—Master of Science in Electronic Commerce Full-time and part-time. 2 years full-time work experience. At least 30 total credits required. Minimum of 12 months to complete program. *Concentrations:* electronic commerce (e-commerce).

MS—Master of Science in Executive Leadership Part-time. 5 years work experience. 36 total credits required. 24 months to complete program. *Concentrations:* leadership.

MS—Master of Science in Global Leadership Part-time. 30 total credits required. 12 months to complete program. *Concentrations:* leadership.

COSTS

Tuition *Full-time:* $12,150. *Part-time:* $675 per credit. **Required fees:** Tuition and fees vary by number of courses or credits taken. **Graduate housing:** Room and board costs vary by number of occupants, type of accommodation, and type of board plan. *Typical cost:* $8080 (including board).

FINANCIAL AID (1999–2000)

130 students received aid, including fellowships, grants, loans, research assistantships, and work study. Aid is available to part-time students. Financial aid application deadline: 5/1. **Financial Aid Contact** Ms. Judith Lewis Logue, Director of Financial Aid Services, 5998 Alcala Park, San Diego, CA 92110-2492. **Phone:** 619-260-4720.

RESOURCES AND SERVICES

Information about online services, personal computer policies, library resources, international exchange programs, internship programs, and placement services at this institution and others can be found at **www. petersons.com/mba**

International Students

18% of students enrolled are international students.

Services and Facilities Counseling/support services, international student housing, orientation, visa services, publications, alumni network, campus activities, health insurance information. Financial aid is not available to international students.

Applying *Required:* TOEFL with recommended score of 237 (computer) or 580 (paper), TWE with recommended score of 4.5, proof of adequate funds.

International Student Contact Ms. Yvette Fontaine, Director of International Resources, 5998 Alcala Park, San Diego, CA 92110-2492. **Phone:** 619-260-4678. **Fax:** 619-260-4170. **E-mail:** yvettef@acusd.edu.

■ APPLICATION

Required GMAT, application form, baccalaureate/first degree, essay, 3 letters of recommendation, personal statement, resume/curriculum vitae, transcripts of college work, 2 years of work experience.

Deadlines and Fees *Deadlines:* 5/1 for fall, 11/15 for spring, 3/15 for summer, 5/1 for fall (international), 11/15 for spring (international), 3/15 for summer (international). *Application fee:* $45, $45 (international).

Application Contact Ms. Mary Jane Tiernan, Director of Graduate Admissions, 5998 Alcala Park, San Diego, CA 92110-2492. **Phone:** 619-260-4524. **Toll-free Phone:** 800-248-4873. **Fax:** 619-260-4158. **E-mail:** grads@acusd.edu.

See full description on page 956.

University of San Francisco

San Francisco, California

MCLAREN SCHOOL OF BUSINESS

Graduate Business Faculty
Full-time: 51

Part-time: 38

Student Body
Total: 470
Full-time: 258
Part-time: 212

Average Age: 27
Women: 39%

Admissions
Applications: 588
Admitted: 341
Enrolled: 165

Average GMAT: 555
Average GPA: 3.15

Costs (1999–2000)
Full-time tuition: $17,004 per academic year
Part-time tuition: $701 per unit

After Graduation (Class of 1998–99)
Employed within 3 months of graduation: 80%
Average starting salary: $55,520

Accreditation
AACSB—The International Association for Management Education

DEGREES EMBA • EMMDS • JD/MBA • MBA • MBA/MS

EMBA—Executive MBA Full-time and part-time. At least 48 total credits required. Maximum of 22 months to complete program.

EMMDS—Executive Master of Management and Disability Services Full-time and part-time. At least 48 total credits required. Maximum of 30 months to complete program.

JD/MBA—Juris Doctor/Master of Business Administration Full-time and part-time. LSAT required. At least 48 total credits required. Maximum of 48 months to complete program. *Concentrations:* finance, international business, management, marketing, telecommunications management.

MBA—Master of Business Administration Full-time and part-time. *Distance learning option.* At least 48 total credits required. 18 to 24 months to complete

University of San Francisco (continued)

program. *Concentrations:* electronic commerce (e-commerce), finance, international business, management, marketing, telecommunications management.

MBA/MS—Master of Science in Nursing/Master of Business Administration Full-time and part-time. GRE required. At least 48 total credits required. Maximum of 30 months to complete program. *Concentrations:* finance, international business, management, marketing, telecommunications management.

COSTS

Tuition *Full-time:* $16,824. *Part-time:* $701 per unit. **Tuition, international:** *Full-time* $16,824. Tuition varies by number of courses or credits taken. **Required fees:** *Full-time* $180. *Part-time* $62.50 per semester. Fees vary by academic program and local reciprocity agreements. **Graduate housing:** Room and board costs vary by number of occupants and type of board plan. *Typical cost:* $8448 (including board).

FINANCIAL AID (1999–2000)

211 students received aid, including fellowships, loans, research assistantships, and work study. Aid is available to part-time students. Financial aid application deadline: 3/2. **Financial Aid Contact** Susan Murphy, Financial Aid Director, 2130 Fulton Street, San Francisco, CA 94117. **Phone:** 415-422-6303.

RESOURCES AND SERVICES

Information about online services, personal computer policies, library resources, international exchange programs, internship programs, and placement services at this institution and others can be found at **www.petersons.com/mba**

International Students

37% of students enrolled are international students.

Services and Facilities Counseling/support services, ESL/language courses, housing location assistance, international student organization, language tutoring, orientation. Financial aid is not available to international students.

Applying *Required:* TOEFL with recommended score of 600 (paper), proof of adequate funds, proof of health/immunizations.

International Student Contact Ms. Kuni Hay, International Student Advisor, 2130 Fulton Street, Lower Level, Gillson Hall, San Francisco, CA 94117-1080. **Phone:** 415-422-2654.

■ APPLICATION

Required Application form, baccalaureate/first degree, essay, 2 letters of recommendation, personal statement, transcripts of college work. School will accept GMAT. **Recommended** Work experience.

Deadlines and Fees *Deadlines:* 6/1 for fall, 11/10 for spring, 4/1 for summer, 6/1 for fall (international), 11/10 for spring (international), 4/1 for summer (international). *Application fee:* $55, $65 (international).

Application Contact Ms. Cathleen Fusco, MBA Program Director, 2130 Fulton Street, San Francisco, CA 94117. **Phone:** 415-422-6314. **Fax:** 415-422-2502. **E-mail:** mbausf@usfca.edu.

See full description on page 958.

University of Southern California

Los Angeles, California

MARSHALL SCHOOL OF BUSINESS

Graduate Business Faculty
Full-time: 173   Part-time: 42

Student Body
Total: 1,703   Average Age: 30
Full-time: 540   Women: 30%
Part-time: 1,163

Admissions
Applications: 2,950   Average GMAT: 650
Admitted: 1,200   Average GPA: 3.3
Enrolled: 800

Costs (1999–2000)
Full-time tuition: $23,958 per academic year
Part-time tuition: N/R

After Graduation (Class of 1998–99)
Employed within 3 months of graduation: 98%
Average starting salary: $70,000

Accreditation
AACSB—The International Association for Management Education

DEGREES EMBA • JD/MBA • JD/MBTax • M Acc • MBA • MBA/MA • MBA/MRED • MBA/MS • MBT • MS

EMBA—Executive MBA Part-time. At least 63 total credits required. 22 months to complete program. *Concentrations:* management.

JD/MBA—Juris Doctor/Master of Business Administration Full-time. At least 91 total credits required. 48 to 60 months to complete program.

JD/MBTax—Juris Doctor/Master of Business Taxation Full-time. At least 91 total credits required. 48 to 60 months to complete program. *Concentrations:* taxation.

M Acc—Master of Accounting Full-time and part-time. At least 33 total credits required. 10 to 60 months to complete program. *Concentrations:* accounting.

MBA—Full-time MBA Full-time. At least 61 total credits required. 24 to 60 months to complete program. *Concentrations:* banking, entrepreneurship, finance, financial management/planning, human resources, information management, international and area business studies, management, management information systems, marketing, operations management, real estate, technology management.

MBA—MBA Program for Professionals and Managers Part-time. At least 63 total credits required. 33 to 60 months to complete program. *Concentrations:* banking, entrepreneurship, finance, financial management/planning, human resources, information management, management, management information systems, marketing, operations management, real estate, technology management.

MBA—Master of Business Administration in International Business Education and Research Full-time. At least 56 total credits required. 11 months to complete program. *Concentrations:* international business.

MBA/MA—Master of Business Administration/Master of Arts in East Asian Area Studies Full-time and part-time. *Distance learning option.* At least 72 total credits required. 36 to 60 months to complete program.

MBA/MRED—Master of Business Administration/Master of Real Estate Development Full-time and part-time. At least 80 total credits required. 36 to 60 months to complete program.

MBA/MS—Master of Business Administration/Master of Science of Gerontology Full-time and part-time. At least 66 total credits required. 36 to 60 months to complete program.

MBT—Master of Business Taxation Full-time and part-time. At least 45 total credits required. 10 to 60 months to complete program. *Concentrations:* taxation.

MS—Master of Science in Business Administration Full-time and part-time. At least 26 total credits required. 12 to 60 months to complete program.

MS—Master of Science in Information and Operations Management Full-time and part-time. At least 30 total credits required. 12 to 60 months to complete program. *Concentrations:* information management, operations management.

In addition to its two-year M.B.A. program, the USC Marshall School of Business offers a unique one-year international M.B.A. program for managers who are pursuing international and Pacific Rim-related careers. The Marshall International Business Education and Research (IBEAR) M.B.A. Program begins in mid-August each year and includes a preparatory program and nineteen courses in four 11-week terms. It includes special features such as international consulting projects for major multinational firms, a team-building retreat, optional language courses, attendance at off-campus international business events, and an extensive international guest executive speaker series. Participants have access to the extensive resources of the Marshall School, which has 174 full-time faculty members.

IBEAR M.B.A. participants average 33 years of age and nine years of work experience. They come from fifteen or more countries each year. Enrollment is limited to 56 participants. Graduates join a network of more than 850 well-placed IBEAR alumni and 50,000 USC Marshall School alumni. Scholarships are available to domestic and international applicants. For information, students should contact the IBEAR Program at 213-740-7140, fax: 213-740-7559, or e-mail: ibear@usc.edu, or visit the School's Web site at http://www.ibear.com.

COSTS

Tuition *Full-time:* $23,958. **Required fees:** Tuition and fees vary by number of courses or credits taken and academic program. **Graduate housing:** Room and board costs vary by campus location, number of occupants, type of accommodation, and type of board plan. *Typical cost:* $11,000 (including board).

FINANCIAL AID (1999–2000)

Fellowships, loans, research assistantships, teaching assistantships, and work study. Aid is available to part-time students. **Financial Aid Contact** Ms. Grace Kim, Assistant Director of Admissions, Bridge Hall 101, Los Angeles, CA 90089-1421. **Phone:** 213-740-7846. **Fax:** 213-749-8520.

RESOURCES AND SERVICES

Information about online services, personal computer policies, library resources, international exchange programs, internship programs, and

placement services at this institution and others can be found at **www. petersons.com/mba**

International Students
20% of students enrolled are international students.
Services and Facilities Counseling/support services, ESL/language courses, visa services. Financial aid is not available to international students.
Applying *Required:* TOEFL with recommended score of 600 (paper), proof of adequate funds, proof of health/immunizations.
International Student Contact Ms. Christy Moody, Manager, International Exchange Programs, Hoffman Hall 200, Los Angeles, CA 90089-1421. **Phone:** 213-740-6878. **Fax:** 213-740-1037. **E-mail:** lmiller@marshall.usc.edu.

■ APPLICATION
Required GMAT, application form, baccalaureate/first degree, essay, 2 letters of recommendation, personal statement, resume/curriculum vitae, transcripts of college work. **Recommended** Interview, work experience.
Deadlines and Fees *Deadlines:* 4/1 for fall, 4/1 for fall (international). *Application fee:* $90, $125 (international).
Application Contact Keith Vaughn, Director of Admissions, Bridge Hall 101, USC, Los Angeles, CA 90089-1421. **Phone:** 213-740-7846. **Fax:** 213-749-8520. **E-mail:** uscmba@sba.usc.edu.

See full description on pages 962 and 964.

University of the Pacific
Stockton, California

EBERHARDT SCHOOL OF BUSINESS

Graduate Business Faculty
Full-time: 23

Student Body

Total: 90	Average Age: 28
Full-time: 38	Women: 42%
Part-time: 52	

Admissions

Applications: 71	Average GMAT: 530
Admitted: 54	Average GPA: 3.2
Enrolled: 30	

Costs (1999–2000)
Full-time tuition: $20,860 per academic year
Part-time tuition: $1836 per course

After Graduation (Class of 1998–99)
Employed within 3 months of graduation: 95%
Average starting salary: $50,000

Accreditation
AACSB—The International Association for Management Education

DEGREE MBA

MBA—Master of Business Administration Full-time and part-time. 30 to 54 total credits required. 10 to 18 months to complete program. *Concentrations:* entrepreneurship, management.

Established in 1851 as California's first chartered institution of higher education, the University of the Pacific (UOP) is an independent university known for its diversity of academic programs and outstanding teaching faculty. The University draws its students from more than forty states and fifty other countries.

The UOP M.B.A. is committed to the cultivation of leadership skills and the innovative spirit of its students. The M.B.A. program was designed with the conviction that leadership and innovation are the managerial ingredients necessary to create the products, services, and processes needed to compete effectively in the global economy.

To achieve these objectives, UOP's M.B.A. program designers had to rethink traditional assumptions about business education. The curriculum goes beyond courses in the basic skills of finance, accounting, marketing, and production by incorporating newly designed courses that encourage students to tackle business problems in the context and form in which they actually occur.

Integrative problem-focused courses like global business competition, technology and innovation, strategic management, leadership and change, and managing quality and productivity dominate the M.B.A.'s advanced phase. By emphasizing the focus on leadership and innovation, a unique specialization in entrepreneurship is available to interested students.

COSTS
Tuition *Full-time:* $18,360. *Part-time:* $1836 per course. **Required fees:** *Full-time* $2500. Tuition and fees vary by number of courses or credits taken. **Graduate housing:** Room and board costs vary by number of occupants, type of accommodation, and type of board plan. *Typical cost:* $7000 (including board), $5800 (room only).

FINANCIAL AID (1999–2000)
Fellowships, loans, research assistantships, and scholarships. Aid is available to part-time students. **Financial Aid Contact** Financial Aid Office, 3601 Pacific Avenue, Stockton, CA 95211-0197. **Phone:** 209-946-2421.

RESOURCES AND SERVICES
Information about online services, personal computer policies, library resources, international exchange programs, internship programs, and placement services at this institution and others can be found at **www. petersons.com/mba**

International Students
7% of students enrolled are international students.
Services and Facilities Counseling/support services, ESL/language courses, orientation, visa services. Financial aid is available to international students.
Applying *Required:* TOEFL with recommended score of 550 (paper), proof of adequate funds. *Recommended:* TSE, TWE, proof of health/immunizations.
International Student Contact Mrs. Donna Cheshire, Director, International Services, 3601 Pacific Avenue, Stockton, CA 95211-0197. **Phone:** 209-946-2629. **Fax:** 209-946-2586. **E-mail:** dcheshir@uop.edu.

■ APPLICATION
Required GMAT, application form, baccalaureate/first degree, essay, 3 letters of recommendation, personal statement, transcripts of college work. **Recommended** Interview, resume/curriculum vitae, 1 year of work experience.
Deadlines and Fees *Deadlines:* 5/1 for fall, 11/1 for spring, 3/1 for summer, 5/1 for fall (international), 11/1 for spring (international), 3/1 for summer (international). *Application fee:* $50, $50 (international).
Application Contact Mr. Christopher Lozano, Director, Student Recruitment, 3601 Pacific Avenue, Stockton, CA 95211-0197. **Toll-free Phone:** 800-952-3179. **Fax:** 209-946-2586. **E-mail:** mba@uop.edu.

See full description on page 978.

Woodbury University
Burbank, California

SCHOOL OF BUSINESS AND MANAGEMENT

Graduate Business Faculty

Full-time: 8	Part-time: 24

Student Body

Total: 185	Average Age: 32
Full-time: 52	Women: 47%
Part-time: 133	

Admissions

Applications: 102	Average GMAT: 527
Admitted: 75	Average GPA: 3.4
Enrolled: 60	

Costs (1999–2000)
Full-time tuition: N/R
Part-time tuition: $595 per credit

After Graduation (Class of 1998–99)
Employed within 3 months of graduation: 90%
Average starting salary: $47,000

DEGREES MBA

MBA—Accelerated MBA Full-time and part-time. 36 to 54 total credits required. 12 to 24 months to complete program. *Concentrations:* accounting, Asian business studies, economics, entrepreneurship, finance, international and area business studies, international business, management, marketing, organizational management.

MBA—Master of Business Administration Full-time and part-time. 36 to 54 total credits required. 24 to 72 months to complete program. *Concentrations:* accounting, Asian business studies, economics, entrepreneurship, finance, international and area business studies, international business, management, marketing, organizational management.

COSTS

Tuition *Part-time:* $595 per credit. **Required fees:** Tuition and fees vary by campus location and academic program. **Graduate housing:** Room and board costs vary by number of occupants and type of board plan. *Typical cost:* $6084 (including board).

FINANCIAL AID (1999–2000)

60 students received aid. Aid is available to part-time students. Financial aid application deadline: 6/30. **Financial Aid Contact** Ms. Cleo Williams, Director of Financial Aid, 7500 Glenoaks Boulevard, Burbank, CA 91510-7846. **Phone:** 818-767-0888 Ext. 273. **Fax:** 818-767-4816. **E-mail:** williams@vaxb.woodbury.edu.

RESOURCES AND SERVICES

Information about online services, personal computer policies, library resources, international exchange programs, internship programs, and placement services at this institution and others can be found at **www.petersons.com/mba**

International Students

28% of students enrolled are international students.

Services and Facilities Counseling/support services, ESL/language courses, international student housing, visa services. Financial aid is not available to international students.

Applying *Required:* TOEFL with recommended score of 550 (paper), proof of adequate funds.

International Student Contact Ms. Jocelyn Chong, Director, International Student Services, 7500 Glenoaks Boulevard, Burbank, CA 91510-7846. **Phone:** 818-767-0888 Ext. 261. **Fax:** 818-767-0032. **E-mail:** jchong@vaxb.woodbury.edu.

■ APPLICATION

Required Application form, baccalaureate/first degree, essay, 2 letters of recommendation, transcripts of college work. School will accept GMAT. **Recommended** Interview, resume/curriculum vitae.

Deadlines and Fees Applications for domestic students are processed on a rolling basis. *Application fee:* $35, $50 (international).

Application Contact Ms. Roxanne Rafii, Assistant Dean, 7500 Glenoaks Boulevard, Burbank, CA 91510-7846. **Phone:** 818-767-0888 Ext. 260. **Fax:** 818-767-0032. **E-mail:** wec6@vaxb.woodbury.edu.

See full description on page 1020.

COLORADO

College for Financial Planning

Greenwood Village, Colorado

PROGRAM IN FINANCIAL PLANNING

Graduate Business Faculty
Full-time: 8

Student Body
Total: 751	Average Age: 42
Part-time: 751	Women: 36%

Admissions
Applications: 227	Enrolled: 129
Admitted: 147	Average GPA: 2.85

Costs (1999–2000)
Full-time tuition: N/R
Part-time tuition: $600 per course

DEGREE MS

MS—Master of Science in Financial Planning Part-time. *Distance learning option.* At least 36 total credits required. 18 to 60 months to complete program. *Concentrations:* finance, financial management/planning.

COSTS

Tuition *Part-time:* $600 per course.

RESOURCES AND SERVICES

Information about online services, personal computer policies, library resources, international exchange programs, internship programs, and placement services at this institution and others can be found at **www.petersons.com/mba**

International Students

Services and Facilities Financial aid is not available to international students. **International Student Contact** Mr. Glen Steelman, Registrar, 6161 South Syracuse Way, Greenwood Village, CO 80111. **Phone:** 303-220-1200 Ext. 4861. **Fax:** 303-220-4941. **E-mail:** gss@fp.edu.

■ APPLICATION

Required Application form, baccalaureate/first degree, personal statement, transcripts of college work. **Recommended** Resume/curriculum vitae.

Deadlines and Fees *Application fee:* $225, $275 (international).

Application Contact Mr. Glen Steelman, Registrar, 6161 South Syracuse Way, Greenwood Village, CO 80111. **Phone:** 303-220-1200 Ext. 4861. **Fax:** 303-220-4941. **E-mail:** gss@fp.edu.

Colorado State University

Fort Collins, Colorado

COLLEGE OF BUSINESS

Graduate Business Faculty
Full-time: 52	Part-time: 26

Student Body
Total: 543	Average Age: 36
Full-time: 43	Women: 32%
Part-time: 500	

Admissions
Applications: 472	Average GMAT: 599
Admitted: 262	Average GPA: 3.2
Enrolled: 174	

Costs (1999–2000)
Full-time tuition: N/R
Part-time tuition: N/R

After Graduation (Class of 1998–99)
Employed within 3 months of graduation: 95%
Average starting salary: $58,700

Accreditation
AACSB—The International Association for Management Education

DEGREES MBA • MS

MBA—Accelerated MBA Full-time. At least 36 total credits required. Minimum of 11 months to complete program.

MBA—Evening MBA Part-time. *Distance learning option.* Minimum of 4 years of work experience required. At least 36 total credits required. Minimum of 21 months to complete program.

MBA—Executive MBA Part-time. Minimum of 8 years of work experience required. At least 36 total credits required. Minimum of 21 months to complete program.

MS—Master of Science in Business Administration Full-time. At least 30 total credits required. Minimum of 12 months to complete program. *Concentrations:* management information systems.

MS—Master of Science in Business Administration Full-time and part-time. At least 32 total credits required. Minimum of 12 months to complete program. *Concentrations:* accounting.

COSTS

Required fees: Tuition and fees vary by number of courses or credits taken and academic program. **Graduate housing:** Room and board costs vary by number of occupants, type of accommodation, and type of board plan. *Typical cost:* $5556 (including board).

FINANCIAL AID (1999–2000)

18 students received aid, including fellowships, research assistantships, teaching assistantships, and work study. Financial aid application deadline: 2/1. **Financial Aid Contact** Mr. Bill Haid, Director of Enrollment Services, 103 Administration Annex, Fort Collins, CO 80523-8024. **Phone:** 970-491-6321. **Fax:** 970-491-5010.

RESOURCES AND SERVICES

Information about online services, personal computer policies, library resources, international exchange programs, internship programs, and placement services at this institution and others can be found at **www.petersons.com/mba**

International Students

13% of students enrolled are international students.

Services and Facilities Counseling/support services, ESL/language courses, international student housing, international student organization, orientation. Financial aid is available to international students.
Applying *Required:* TOEFL with recommended score of 565 (paper), proof of adequate funds, proof of health/immunizations.
International Student Contact Mr. Sean McFeely, Foreign Student Advisor, 315 Aylesworth, Fort Collins, CO 80523-8009. **Phone:** 970-491-5917. **Fax:** 970-491-5501.

▪ APPLICATION

Required Application form, baccalaureate/first degree, 3 letters of recommendation, personal statement, transcripts of college work. School will accept GMAT. **Recommended** Resume/curriculum vitae.
Deadlines and Fees *Deadlines:* 4/1 for fall, 10/1 for spring, 2/15 for fall (international). *Application fee:* $30, $30 (international).
Application Contact Ms. Rachel Stoll, Graduate Admissions, College of Business, Fort Collins, CO 80523. **Phone:** 970-491-3704. **Toll-free Phone:** 800-491-4622 Ext. 4. **Fax:** 970-491-2348.

See full description on page 608.

Colorado Technical University

Colorado Springs, Colorado

PROGRAM IN MANAGEMENT

Graduate Business Faculty
Full-time: 13 | Part-time: 21

Student Body
Total: 561
Full-time: 355 — Average Age: 34
Part-time: 206 — Women: 37%

Admissions
Applications: 165 — Enrolled: 147
Admitted: 155 — Average GPA: 3.5

Costs (1999–2000)
Full-time tuition: $6528 per academic year
Part-time tuition: $265 per credit hour

DEGREES MBA • MS

MBA—MBA in Finance and Accounting Full-time and part-time. At least 52 total credits required. 20 to 30 months to complete program. *Concentrations:* accounting, finance.

MBA—MBA in e-Commerce Full-time and part-time. At least 52 total credits required. 20 to 30 months to complete program. *Concentrations:* electronic commerce (e-commerce).

MS—MS in Management Full-time and part-time. 48 to 52 total credits required. 18 to 30 months to complete program. *Concentrations:* health care, human resources, information management, logistics, management, management information systems, organizational behavior/development.

MS—MS in Project Management Full-time and part-time. *Distance learning option.* 48 to 52 total credits required. 18 to 30 months to complete program. *Concentrations:* project management.

COSTS

Tuition *Full-time:* $6360. *Part-time:* $265 per credit hour. **Tuition, international:** *Full-time* $6360. Tuition varies by number of courses or credits taken. **Required fees:** *Full-time* $168. *Part-time* $56 per quarter.

FINANCIAL AID (1999–2000)

158 students received aid, including loans and work study. Aid is available to part-time students. **Financial Aid Contact** Ms. Kathleen Gailor, Director of Financial Aid, Colorado Technical University, 4435 North Chestnut Street, Colorado Springs, CO 80907-3896. **Phone:** 719-598-0200. **Fax:** 719-598-3740. **E-mail:** kgailor@cos.coloradotech.edu.

RESOURCES AND SERVICES

Information about online services, personal computer policies, library resources, international exchange programs, internship programs, and

placement services at this institution and others can be found at **www.petersons.com/mba**

International Students

9% of students enrolled are international students.

Services and Facilities Counseling/support services, housing location assistance. Financial aid is not available to international students.
Applying *Required:* TOEFL with recommended score of 550 (paper), proof of adequate funds.
International Student Contact Mr. Bill Sommers, Admissions Manager, Colorado Technical University, 4435 North Chestnut Street, Colorado Springs, CO 80907-3896. **Phone:** 719-598-0200. **Fax:** 719-598-3740. **E-mail:** bsommers@cos.coloradotech.edu.

▪ APPLICATION

Required Application form, baccalaureate/first degree, essay, personal statement, transcripts of college work. **Recommended** Interview, resume/curriculum vitae.

Deadlines and Fees Applications for domestic and international students are processed on a rolling basis. *Application fee:* $100, $100 (international).

Application Contact Ms. Judy Galante, Graduate Admissions Advisor, Colorado Technical University, 4435 North Chestnut Street, Colorado Springs, CO 80907-3896. **Phone:** 719-598-0200. **Fax:** 719-598-3740. **E-mail:** jgalante@cos.coloradotech.edu.

ISIM University

Denver, Colorado

PROGRAM IN BUSINESS ADMINISTRATION

Graduate Business Faculty
Full-time: 1 | Part-time: 28

Student Body
Total: 124
Part-time: 124 — Average Age: 37
Women: 19%

Admissions
Applications: 59 — Enrolled: 9
Admitted: 24 — Average GPA: 3.2

Costs (1999–2000)
Full-time tuition: N/R
Part-time tuition: $1245 per course

After Graduation (Class of 1998–99)
Employed within 3 months of graduation: 100%

DEGREES MBA • MSIT

MBA—Executive MBA *Distance learning option.* 20 years work experience. At least 36 total credits required. 18 to 30 months to complete program. *Concentrations:* finance, information management, strategic management.

MBA—Master of Business Administration *Distance learning option.* At least 36 total credits required. 18 to 30 months to complete program. *Concentrations:* finance, information management, strategic management.

MSIT—Master of Science in Information Technology *Distance learning option.* At least 36 total credits required. 18 to 30 months to complete program. *Concentrations:* technology management.

COSTS

Tuition *Part-time:* $1245 per course.

RESOURCES AND SERVICES

Information about online services, personal computer policies, library resources, international exchange programs, internship programs, and placement services at this institution and others can be found at **www.petersons.com/mba**

International Students

30% of students enrolled are international students.

Services and Facilities Financial aid is not available to international students.
Applying *Recommended:* Proof of adequate funds.

International Student Contact Robin Thompson, Admissions Mentor, 501 South Cherry Street Suite 350, Denver, CO 80246. **Phone:** 303-333-1144 Ext. 177. **Fax:** 303-336-1144. **E-mail:** admissions@isim.edu.

ISIM University (continued)

■ APPLICATION

Required Application form, baccalaureate/first degree, essay, 3 letters of recommendation, personal statement, resume/curriculum vitae, transcripts of college work. **Recommended** Work experience.

Deadlines and Fees Applications for domestic and international students are processed on a rolling basis. *Application fee:* $75, $75 (international).

Application Contact Ms. Robin Thompson, Admissions Office, 501 South Cherry Street, Suite 350, Denver, CO 80246. **Phone:** 303-333-4224 Ext. 177. **Toll-free Phone:** 800-441-4746. **Fax:** 303-336-1144. **E-mail:** admissions@isim.edu.

Jones International University

Englewood, Colorado

PROGRAM IN BUSINESS COMMUNICATION

Graduate Business Faculty
Full-time: 2   Part-time: 28

Admissions
Applications: 12   Enrolled: 12
Admitted: 12   Average GPA: 3.25

Costs (1999–2000)
Full-time tuition: N/R
Part-time tuition: N/R

DEGREES MA • MBA

MA—Master of Arts in Business Communication Full-time and part-time. *Distance learning option.* At least 35 total credits required. Minimum of 12 months to complete program.

MBA—Online MBA Program *Concentrations:* electronic commerce (e-commerce), entrepreneurship, health care, information management, international management, project management.

RESOURCES AND SERVICES

Information about online services, personal computer policies, library resources, international exchange programs, internship programs, and placement services at this institution and others can be found at **www. petersons.com/mba**

International Students

Applying *Required:* TOEFL with recommended score of 550 (paper).

■ APPLICATION

Required Application form, baccalaureate/first degree, essay, 3 letters of recommendation, resume/curriculum vitae. **Recommended** 2 years of work experience.

Deadlines and Fees Applications for domestic and international students are processed on a rolling basis. *Application fee:* $75, $75 (international).

Application Contact Ms. Gloria Brown, Admissions Coordinator, 9697 East Mineral Avenue, Englewood, CO 80112. **Phone:** 303-784-8048. **Toll-free Phone:** 800-811-5663. **Fax:** 303-784-8547. **E-mail:** admissions@international.edu.

See full description on page 698.

Regis University

Denver, Colorado

SCHOOL FOR PROFESSIONAL STUDIES

Graduate Business Faculty
Full-time: 16   Part-time: 500

Student Body
Total: 2,437   Average Age: 36

Admissions
Admitted: 810   Average GMAT: 500
Enrolled: 686

Costs (1999–2000)
Full-time tuition: N/R
Part-time tuition: $366 per credit hour

After Graduation (Class of 1998–99)
Employed within 3 months of graduation: 90%

DEGREES MBA • MNM • MS

MBA—Master of Business Administration Full-time and part-time. *Distance learning option.* 2 years of full-time business work experience required; GMAT for international students required. 30 to 45 total credits required. 18 to 72 months to complete program. *Concentrations:* accounting, finance, information management, international business, management information systems, marketing, operations management.

MNM—Master of Nonprofit Management Full-time and part-time. *Distance learning option.* Non-profit experience; GMAT for international students required. At least 36 total credits required. 24 to 72 months to complete program. *Concentrations:* nonprofit management, nonprofit organization.

MS—Master of Science in Computer Information Systems Full-time and part-time. *Distance learning option.* GMAT for international students required. At least 36 total credits required. 24 to 72 months to complete program. *Concentrations:* information management, management information systems, system management, technology management.

MS—Master of Science in Management Full-time and part-time. *Distance learning option.* 2 admissions essays and 3 years of supervisory/administrative experience required; GMAT for international students required. At least 36 total credits required. 24 to 72 months to complete program. *Concentrations:* leadership, management, management science.

COSTS

Tuition *Part-time:* $366 per credit hour. Tuition varies by academic program.

FINANCIAL AID (1999–2000)

Fellowships, loans, and work study. Aid is available to part-time students. **Financial Aid Contact** Director of Financial Aid, 3333 Regis Boulevard, Mail Stop A-8, Denver, CO 80221. **Phone:** 303-458-4066. **E-mail:** regisfa@regis.edu.

RESOURCES AND SERVICES

Information about online services, personal computer policies, library resources, international exchange programs, internship programs, and placement services at this institution and others can be found at **www. petersons.com/mba**

International Students

Services and Facilities Visa services, admissions advisor. Financial aid is not available to international students.

Applying *Required:* TOEFL with recommended score of 213 (computer) or 550 (paper), TWE with recommended score of 4.5, proof of adequate funds. *Recommended:* TSE.

International Student Contact Graduate Admissions, 3333 Regis Boulevard Mail Stop L-16, Denver, CO 80221. **Phone:** 800-677-9270. **Fax:** 303-964-5538. **E-mail:** masters@regis.edu.

■ APPLICATION

Required Application form, baccalaureate/first degree, essay, interview, 2 letters of recommendation, resume/curriculum vitae, transcripts of college work, 2 years of work experience. School will accept GMAT.

Deadlines and Fees Applications for domestic students are processed on a rolling basis. *Deadlines:* 7/1 for fall (international), 10/15 for spring (international), 3/1 for summer (international). *Application fee:* $75, $75 (international).

Application Contact Graduate Admissions, 3333 Regis Boulevard, Mail Stop L-16, Denver, CO 80211-1099. **Phone:** 303-458-4080. **Toll-free Phone:** 800-677-9270. **Fax:** 303-964-5538. **E-mail:** masters@regis.edu.

University of Colorado at Boulder

Boulder, Colorado

GRADUATE SCHOOL OF BUSINESS ADMINISTRATION

Graduate Business Faculty
Full-time: 66   Part-time: 33

Student Body
Total: 284   Average Age: 30
Full-time: 177   Women: 30%
Part-time: 107

Admissions
Applications: 434
Admitted: 175
Enrolled: 99

Average GMAT: 640
Average GPA: 3.23

Costs (1999–2000)
Full-time tuition: $4502 per academic year (resident), $16,170 per academic year (nonresident)
Part-time tuition: $215 per credit hour (resident), $862 per credit hour (nonresident)

After Graduation (Class of 1998–99)
Employed within 3 months of graduation: 91%
Average starting salary: $65,568

Accreditation
AACSB—The International Association for Management Education

DEGREES JD/MBA • MBA • MBA/MS • MS

JD/MBA—Juris Doctor/Master of Business Administration Full-time. Must submit separate applications to both MBA and School of Law. At least 141 total credits required. 48 months to complete program. *Concentrations:* accounting, entrepreneurship, finance, management, marketing, operations management, organizational management, real estate, technology management.

MBA—Master of Business Administration Full-time and part-time. At least 51 total credits required. 24 to 60 months to complete program. *Concentrations:* accounting, entrepreneurship, finance, management, marketing, operations management, organizational management, real estate, technology management.

MBA/MS—Master of Business Administration/Master of Science in Telecommunications Full-time and part-time. *Distance learning option.* Must submit separate applications to both MBA and Telecommunications programs. At least 66 total credits required. 24 to 60 months to complete program. *Concentrations:* accounting, entrepreneurship, finance, management, marketing, operations management, organizational management, real estate, technology management, telecommunications management.

MS—Master of Science in Business Administration Full-time and part-time. At least 30 total credits required. 12 to 60 months to complete program. *Concentrations:* accounting, taxation.

COSTS
Tuition, state resident: *Full-time* $3848. *Part-time* $215 per credit hour. **Tuition, nonresident:** *Full-time* $15,516. *Part-time* $862 per credit hour. Tuition varies by class time, number of courses or credits taken, campus location, and academic program. **Required fees:** *Full-time* $654. *Part-time* $654 per year. Tuition and fees vary by campus location. **Graduate housing:** Room and board costs vary by campus location, number of occupants, type of accommodation, and type of board plan. *Typical cost:* $5288 (including board).

FINANCIAL AID (1999–2000)
80 students received aid, including fellowships, grants, loans, research assistantships, scholarships, teaching assistantships, and work study. Aid is available to part-time students. Financial aid application deadline: 3/1. **Financial Aid Contact** Ms. Jan Stump, Financial Aid Counselor, Office of Financial Aid, Campus Box 106, Boulder, CO 80309. **Phone:** 303-492-5091. **Fax:** 303-492-0838. **E-mail:** finaid@colorado.edu.

RESOURCES AND SERVICES
Information about online services, personal computer policies, library resources, international exchange programs, internship programs, and placement services at this institution and others can be found at **www. petersons.com/mba**

International Students
7% of students enrolled are international students.

Services and Facilities Counseling/support services, ESL/language courses, housing location assistance, international student housing, international student organization, language tutoring, orientation, visa services. Financial aid is not available to international students.

Applying *Required:* TOEFL with recommended score of 580 (paper), proof of adequate funds, proof of health/immunizations.

International Student Contact Mr. Tom Naumann, International Admissions, Campus Box 65, Boulder, CO 80309-0065. **Phone:** 303-492-7536. **E-mail:** thomas.naumann@colorado.edu.

■ APPLICATION
Required GMAT, application form, baccalaureate/first degree, essay, 3 letters of recommendation, personal statement, resume/curriculum vitae, transcripts of college work, 2 years of work experience.
Deadlines and Fees *Deadlines:* 2/15 for fall, 12/1 for fall (international). *Application fee:* $40, $60 (international).

Application Contact Mr. Toby Williams, Assistant Director, Admissions Operations, Graduate School of Business Administration, Campus Box 419, Boulder, CO 80309-0419. **Phone:** 303-492-1831. **Fax:** 303-492-1727. **E-mail:** busgrad@colorado.edu.

See full description on page 886.

University of Colorado at Colorado Springs
Colorado Springs, Colorado

GRADUATE SCHOOL OF BUSINESS ADMINISTRATION

Graduate Business Faculty
Full-time: 24

Part-time: 9

Student Body
Total: 292
Full-time: 193
Part-time: 99

Average Age: 32
Women: 43%

Admissions
Applications: 79
Admitted: 67
Enrolled: 49

Average GMAT: 545
Average GPA: 3.08

Costs (1999–2000)
Full-time tuition: $2904 per academic year (resident), $10,104 per academic year (nonresident)
Part-time tuition: $121 per credit (resident), $421 per credit (nonresident)

After Graduation (Class of 1998–99)
Employed within 3 months of graduation: 95%
Average starting salary: $55,000

Accreditation
AACSB—The International Association for Management Education

DEGREE MBA

MBA—Master of Business Administration Full-time and part-time. *Distance learning option.* 36 to 48 total credits required. 12 to 60 months to complete program. *Concentrations:* accounting, finance, health care, human resources, international business, leadership, management information systems, marketing, operations management, production management, technology management.

The M.B.A. program at the University of Colorado at Colorado Springs allows students the opportunity to explore cutting-edge issues that challenge businesses and offers the ultimate in flexible delivery of courses. The Graduate School of Business Administration has earned accreditation by AACSB-The International Association for Management Education, which places this program among the top 30 percent of business programs in the U.S. Full-time, doctorally qualified faculty members enrich students' classroom experience with their own experience in research, academic publishing, community involvement, and industry consulting. Eleven areas of emphasis are offered in the on-campus program, including accounting, finance, health-care administration, information systems, international business, leadership and human resources management, marketing, operations management, services management, and technology management.

The M.B.A. program meets the needs of working professionals by offering opportunities for both part-time and full-time study in either an on-campus or online distance format. Admitted M.B.A. students may take courses in either or both mediums. The M.B.A. degree may be completed entirely online and does not require an on-campus residency. Distance courses are delivered via the Internet and are particularly convenient for students whose schedules prevent them from attending regularly scheduled classes. On-campus classes typically meet one night per week.

COSTS
Tuition, state resident: *Full-time* $2904. *Part-time* $121 per credit. **Tuition, nonresident:** *Full-time* $10,104. *Part-time* $421 per credit. Tuition varies by number of courses or credits taken and academic program. **Required fees:** Tuition and fees vary by number of courses or credits taken. **Graduate housing:** Room and board costs vary by number of occupants, type of accommodation, and type of board plan. *Typical cost:* $7000 (including board).

FINANCIAL AID (1999–2000)
153 students received aid, including grants, loans, research assistantships, and work study. Aid is available to part-time students. Financial aid application deadline: 3/1. **Financial Aid Contact** Mr. Doug

University of Colorado at Colorado Springs (continued)

Nelson, Counseling Coordinator, Financial Aid/Student Employment, PO Box 7150, Colorado Springs, CO 80933-7150. **Phone:** 719-262-3460. **Fax:** 719-262-3650. **E-mail:** finaidse@mail.uccs.edu.

RESOURCES AND SERVICES
Information about online services, personal computer policies, library resources, international exchange programs, internship programs, and placement services at this institution and others can be found at **www. petersons.com/mba**

International Students
4% of students enrolled are international students.
Services and Facilities Counseling/support services, housing location assistance, international student organization, orientation. Financial aid is not available to international students.
Applying *Required:* TOEFL with recommended score of 550 (paper), proof of adequate funds, proof of health/immunizations.
International Student Contact Ms. Irene Martinez, International Student Services Coordinator, PO Box 7150, Colorado Springs, CO 80933-7150. **Phone:** 719-262-3819. **Fax:** 719-262-3362. **E-mail:** imartine@mail.uccs.edu.

■ APPLICATION
Required Application form, baccalaureate/first degree, transcripts of college work. School will accept GMAT and GRE. **Recommended** Letter(s) of recommendation, personal statement, resume/curriculum vitae.
Deadlines and Fees *Deadlines:* 6/1 for fall, 11/1 for spring, 4/1 for summer, 6/1 for fall (international), 11/1 for spring (international), 4/1 for summer (international). *Application fee:* $60, $75 (international).
Application Contact Ms. Barbara Neiberg, MBA Program Director, PO Box 7150, Colorado Springs, CO 80933-7150. **Phone:** 719-262-3408. **Fax:** 719-262-3494. **E-mail:** busadvsr@mail.uccs.edu.

University of Colorado at Denver

Denver, Colorado

GRADUATE SCHOOL OF BUSINESS ADMINISTRATION

Graduate Business Faculty

Full-time: 67	Part-time: 40

Student Body

Total: 1,334	Average Age: 33
Full-time: 383	Women: 42%
Part-time: 951	

Admissions

Applications: 725	Average GMAT: 560
Admitted: 523	Average GPA: 3.04
Enrolled: 303	

Costs (1999–2000)
Full-time tuition: $3844 per academic year (resident), $13,286 per academic year (nonresident)
Part-time tuition: $230 per credit (resident), $796 per credit (nonresident)

After Graduation (Class of 1998–99)
Employed within 3 months of graduation: 90%

Accreditation
AACSB—The International Association for Management Education

DEGREES EMBA • MBA • MBA-H • MBA/MIM • MBA/MS • MS

EMBA—Executive MBA Part-time. 48 total credits required. 22 months to complete program.
MBA—11-Month Accelerated MBA Full-time. 48 total credits required. 11 months to complete program.
MBA—Master of Business Administration in E-Business Part-time. *Distance learning option.* At least 48 total credits required. 22 months to complete program. *Concentrations:* business information science.
MBA—Master of Business Administration Full-time and part-time. *Distance learning option.* At least 48 total credits required. 16 to 60 months to complete program.
MBA-H—Master of Business Administration in Health Administration Full-time and part-time. *Distance learning option.* 2 recommendation letters. At least 48

total credits required. 16 to 60 months to complete program. *Concentrations:* health care.
MBA/MIM—Master of Business Administration/Master of International Management Full-time and part-time. *Distance learning option.* At least 66 total credits required. 24 to 36 months to complete program. *Concentrations:* international business.
MBA/MS—Master of Business Administration/Master of Science Full-time and part-time. *Distance learning option.* At least 66 total credits required. 27 to 86 months to complete program. *Concentrations:* accounting, finance, information management, international business, management, management information systems, marketing.
MS—Master of Science Full-time and part-time. *Distance learning option.* 30 to 48 total credits required. 9 to 60 months to complete program. *Concentrations:* accounting, finance, international business, management, management information systems, marketing.

COSTS
Tuition, state resident: *Full-time* $3844. *Part-time* $230 per credit. **Tuition, nonresident:** *Full-time* $13,286. *Part-time* $796 per credit. **Tuition, international:** *Full-time* $13,286. Tuition varies by number of courses or credits taken, academic program, and local reciprocity agreements. **Required fees:** *Part-time* $210 per semester.

FINANCIAL AID (1999–2000)
462 students received aid, including loans, research assistantships, scholarships, and work study. Aid is available to part-time students.
Financial Aid Contact Ms. Ellie Miller, Director of Financial Aid, Campus Box 125, PO Box 173364, Denver, CO 80217-3364. **Phone:** 303-556-2886. **Fax:** 303-556-2325. **E-mail:** finaid@carbon.cudenver.edu.

RESOURCES AND SERVICES
Information about online services, personal computer policies, library resources, international exchange programs, internship programs, and placement services at this institution and others can be found at **www. petersons.com/mba**

International Students
10% of students enrolled are international students.
Services and Facilities Counseling/support services, ESL/language courses, housing location assistance, international student organization, language tutoring, orientation, visa services. Financial aid is available to international students.
Applying *Required:* TOEFL with recommended score of 525 (paper), proof of adequate funds. *Recommended:* TSE, TWE.
International Student Contact Shelly Townley, Admissions Coordinator, Campus Box 165, PO Box 173364, Denver, CO 80217-3364. **Phone:** 303-556-5900. **Fax:** 303-556-5904. **E-mail:** gbusiness@maroon.cudenver.edu.

■ APPLICATION
Required GMAT, application form, baccalaureate/first degree, essay, interview, personal statement, transcripts of college work. School will accept GRE. **Recommended** Letter(s) of recommendation, resume/curriculum vitae, work experience.
Deadlines and Fees *Deadlines:* 7/1 for fall, 11/1 for spring, 4/1 for summer, 3/1 for fall (international), 7/1 for spring (international), 12/1 for summer (international). *Application fee:* $50, $60 (international).
Application Contact Admissions Coordinator, Campus Box 165, PO Box 173364, Denver, CO 80217-3364. **Phone:** 303-556-5900. **Fax:** 303-556-5904. **E-mail:** gbusiness@maroon.cudenver.edu.

See full description on page 888.

University of Denver

Denver, Colorado

DANIELS COLLEGE OF BUSINESS

Graduate Business Faculty

Full-time: 80	Part-time: 15

Student Body

Total: 819	Average Age: 30
Full-time: 459	Women: 37%
Part-time: 360	

Admissions

Applications: 878	Average GMAT: 565
Admitted: 639	Average GPA: 3.22
Enrolled: 342	

Costs (1999–2000)
Full-time tuition: $20,606 per academic year
Part-time tuition: $557 per quarter hour

After Graduation (Class of 1998–99)
Employed within 3 months of graduation: 77%
Average starting salary: $57,659

Accreditation
AACSB—The International Association for Management Education

DEGREES M Acc • MBA • MIM • MRECM • MS • MSIT

M Acc—Master of Accountancy Full-time and part-time. At least 48 total credits required. 12 to 60 months to complete program.

MBA—Emerging Leaders MBA Part-time. 3 years of managerial experience required. At least 60 total credits required. Maximum of 18 months to complete program.

MBA—Executive MBA Part-time. Seven years managerial experience required. At least 60 total credits required. Maximum of 18 months to complete program.

MBA—Master of Business Administration Full-time and part-time. At least 72 total credits required. 15 to 60 months to complete program. *Concentrations:* accounting, construction management, electronic commerce (e-commerce), entrepreneurship, finance, international business, management information systems, marketing, real estate, travel industry/tourism management.

MIM—Master of International Management Full-time and part-time. At least 79 total credits required. 18 to 60 months to complete program. *Concentrations:* accounting, construction management, electronic commerce (e-commerce), entrepreneurship, finance, management information systems, marketing, real estate, travel industry/tourism management.

MRECM—Master of Real Estate and Construction Management Full-time and part-time. *Distance learning option.* At least 64 total credits required. 15 to 60 months to complete program.

MS—Master of Science in Finance Full-time and part-time. At least 64 total credits required. 18 to 60 months to complete program.

MS—Master of Science in Management Full-time and part-time. 54 to 66 total credits required. 15 to 60 months to complete program. *Concentrations:* health care, legal administration, sports/entertainment management, telecommunications management, training and development.

MSIT—Master of Science in Information Technology Full-time and part-time. At least 64 total credits required. 12 to 60 months to complete program. *Concentrations:* electronic commerce (e-commerce).

Founded in 1908, the University of Denver Daniels College of Business is the nation's eighth-oldest collegiate school of business. It has been accredited by the AACSB-The International Association for Management Education since 1923. Located in the heart of Denver, Colorado, the Daniels College of Business is an integral part of the city that is the business, cultural, and recreational center of the Rocky Mountain West.

The Daniels College of Business M.B.A. Program reflects the real-world decision making that is required of today's managers and prepares men and women for leadership in a vast range of careers and industries. The heart of the M.B.A. program is the integrated core curriculum, where courses mirror the cross-functional involvement found in business decision making. Instead of separate courses for each discipline, the Daniels M.B.A. program uses seven major courses to present business fundamentals, such as accounting, financial management, marketing, statistics, and current business issues, in an inter-related format that provides a comprehensive view of business the way it actually operates.

The program focuses on flexibility. Day and evening courses are available for both full- and part-time schedules, and numerous specialization options are available. The Daniels College of Business M.B.A. Program provides an outstanding learning experience that is the cornerstone of achievement for career success.

COSTS
Tuition *Full-time:* $20,052. *Part-time:* $557 per quarter hour. Tuition varies by number of courses or credits taken and academic program. **Required fees:** *Full-time* $554. *Part-time* $506 per year. **Graduate housing:** Room and board costs vary by number of occupants, type of accommodation, and type of board plan. *Typical cost:* $8100 (including board).

FINANCIAL AID (1999–2000)
Grants, loans, research assistantships, scholarships, teaching assistantships, and work study. Aid is available to part-time students. Financial aid application deadline: 2/15. **Financial Aid Contact** Ms. Laurel Shurtlef, Business Operations Manager, 2101 South University Boulevard, Denver, CO 80208. **Phone:** 303-871-4193. **Fax:** 303-871-4466. **E-mail:** lshurtle@du.edu.

RESOURCES AND SERVICES
Information about online services, personal computer policies, library resources, international exchange programs, internship programs, and placement services at this institution and others can be found at **www. petersons.com/mba**

International Students
25% of students enrolled are international students.
Services and Facilities Counseling/support services, ESL/language courses, international student organization, language tutoring, orientation, visa services. Financial aid is not available to international students.
Applying *Required:* TOEFL with recommended score of 550 (paper), proof of adequate funds.
International Student Contact Ms. Tara Fletcher, International Student Advisor, 2200 South Josephine Street, Denver, CO 80208. **Phone:** 303-871-4911. **Fax:** 303-733-6122. **E-mail:** tfletche@du.edu.

■ **APPLICATION**
Required Application form, baccalaureate/first degree, essay, interview, 2 letters of recommendation, resume/curriculum vitae, transcripts of college work. School will accept GMAT and GRE. **Recommended** Work experience.
Deadlines and Fees *Deadlines:* 5/15 for fall, 12/15 for spring, 5/15 for fall (international), 12/15 for spring (international). *Application fee:* $50, $50 (international).
Application Contact Ms. Jan Johnsen-Brocker, Assistant Dean, 2101 South University Boulevard, Denver, CO 80208. **Phone:** 303-871-2161. **Fax:** 303-871-4466. **E-mail:** jjohnsen@du.edu.

See full description on page 896.

University of Southern Colorado
Pueblo, Colorado

SCHOOL OF BUSINESS

Graduate Business Faculty
Full-time: 10

Student Body
Total: 131
Full-time: 59
Part-time: 72

Average Age: 31
Women: 50%

Admissions
Applications: 80
Admitted: 70
Enrolled: 59

Average GMAT: 500
Average GPA: 3

Costs (1999–2000)
Full-time tuition: $2057 per academic year (resident), $8697 per academic year (nonresident)
Part-time tuition: $113 per semester hour (resident), $445 per semester hour (nonresident)

After Graduation (Class of 1998–99)
Employed within 3 months of graduation: 75%
Average starting salary: $55,000

DEGREE MBA

MBA—Master of Business Administration Full-time and part-time. At least 36 total credits required. 12 to 72 months to complete program. *Concentrations:* management.

COSTS
Tuition, state resident: *Full-time* $1808. *Part-time* $90 per semester hour. **Tuition, nonresident:** *Full-time* $8448. *Part-time* $422 per semester hour. **Tuition, international:** *Full-time* $8448. **Required fees:** *Full-time* $249. *Part-time* $23 per semester hour. Tuition and fees vary by number of courses or credits taken. **Graduate housing:** Room and board costs vary by number of occupants, type of accommodation, and type of board plan. *Typical cost:* $5444 (including board).

FINANCIAL AID (1999–2000)
6 students received aid, including loans, research assistantships, scholarships, and work study. Aid is available to part-time students.
Financial Aid Contact Ms. Linda DiPrince, Associate Director, 2200 Bonforte Boulevard, Pueblo, CO 81001-4901. **Phone:** 719-549-2753. **Fax:** 719-549-2088.

RESOURCES AND SERVICES
Information about online services, personal computer policies, library resources, international exchange programs, internship programs, and placement services at this institution and others can be found at **www. petersons.com/mba**

University of Southern Colorado (continued)

International Students
44% of students enrolled are international students.

Services and Facilities Counseling/support services, ESL/language courses, international student housing, visa services. Financial aid is not available to international students.

Applying *Required:* TOEFL with recommended score of 550 (paper), proof of adequate funds, proof of health/immunizations.

International Student Contact Ms. Annie Williams, Coordinator of the International Student Center, 2200 Bonforte Boulevard, Pueblo, CO 81001-4901. **Phone:** 719-549-2116. **Fax:** 719-549-2938. **E-mail:** annewill@uscolo.edu.

■ APPLICATION
Required GMAT, application form, baccalaureate/first degree, transcripts of college work.

Deadlines and Fees Applications for domestic and international students are processed on a rolling basis. *Application fee:* $35, $35 (international).

Application Contact Mr. Jon Valdez, Admissions Administrative Assistant III, 2200 Bonforte Boulevard, Pueblo, CO 81001-4901. **Phone:** 719-549-2997. **Toll-free Phone:** 800-572-4769 (in-state), 800-872-4769 (out-of-state). **Fax:** 719-549-2419. **E-mail:** jvaldez@uscolo.edu.

CONNECTICUT

Albertus Magnus College
New Haven, Connecticut

PROGRAM IN MANAGEMENT

Graduate Business Faculty
Full-time: 9   Part-time: 15

Student Body
Total: 210
Full-time: 210   Average Age: 35
Women: 51%

Admissions
Applications: 138   Enrolled: 121
Admitted: 122   Average GPA: 3

Costs (1999–2000)
Full-time tuition: $9450 per academic year
Part-time tuition: $1050 per course

After Graduation (Class of 1998–99)
Employed within 3 months of graduation: 100%

DEGREE MSM

MSM—Master of Science in Management Full-time. At least 36 total credits required. 18 to 24 months to complete program.

COSTS
Tuition *Full-time:* $9450. *Part-time:* $1050 per course. **Graduate housing:** *Typical cost:* $6324 (including board).

FINANCIAL AID (1999–2000)
Loans. Aid is available to part-time students. **Financial Aid Contact** Ms. Melanie Reistetter, Office of Financial Aid, New Dimensions Office, One Long Wharf, Room 216, New Haven, CT 06511.

RESOURCES AND SERVICES
Information about online services, personal computer policies, library resources, international exchange programs, internship programs, and placement services at this institution and others can be found at **www.petersons.com/mba**

International Students
Services and Facilities Financial aid is not available to international students.
Applying *Required:* TOEFL with recommended score of 550 (paper).
International Student Contact Ms. Eileen Perillo, Registrar, 700 Prospect Street, New Haven, CT 06511. **Phone:** 203-773-8514. **Fax:** 203-773-3117.

■ APPLICATION
Required Application form, baccalaureate/first degree, essay, letter(s) of recommendation, personal statement, transcripts of college work, 3 years of work experience.

Deadlines and Fees *Application fee:* $35, $35 (international).

Application Contact Admission Office, New Dimensions, One Long Wharf, Room 216, New Haven, CT 06511. **Phone:** 203-773-8501. **Toll-free Phone:** 800-578-9160.

Central Connecticut State University
New Britain, Connecticut

SCHOOL OF BUSINESS

Graduate Business Faculty
Full-time: 11   Part-time: 1

Student Body
Total: 70   Part-time: 40
Full-time: 30   Women: 40%

Admissions
Applications: 85   Average GMAT: 517
Admitted: 65   Average GPA: 3.23
Enrolled: 42

Costs (1999–2000)
Full-time tuition: N/R
Part-time tuition: $195 per credit hour (resident), $195 per credit hour (nonresident)

DEGREE MBA

MBA—Master of Business Administration Full-time and part-time. At least 33 total credits required. 14 to 72 months to complete program. *Concentrations:* accounting, entrepreneurship, international business, international management, international marketing, management, management information systems, manpower administration.

COSTS
Tuition, state resident: *Part-time* $195 per credit hour. **Tuition, nonresident:** *Part-time* $195 per credit hour.

FINANCIAL AID (1999–2000)
Loans and work study. **Financial Aid Contact** Financial Aid Office, 1615 Stanley Street, New Britain, CT 06050. **Phone:** 860-832-2205.

RESOURCES AND SERVICES
Information about online services, personal computer policies, library resources, international exchange programs, internship programs, and placement services at this institution and others can be found at **www.petersons.com/mba**

International Students
50% of students enrolled are international students.

Services and Facilities Counseling/support services, ESL/language courses. Financial aid is available to international students.

Applying *Required:* TOEFL with recommended score of 213 (computer), proof of adequate funds, proof of health/immunizations.

International Student Contact Ms. Bonnie Cofer, Assistant Director of International Affairs Center, New Britain, CT 06040. **Phone:** 860-832-2050. **Fax:** 860-832-2047.

■ APPLICATION
Required GMAT, application form, baccalaureate/first degree, essay, 2 letters of recommendation, personal statement, resume/curriculum vitae, transcripts of college work. **Recommended** Work experience.

Deadlines and Fees *Deadlines:* 5/1 for fall, 10/1 for spring, 5/1 for fall (international), 10/1 for spring (international). *Application fee:* $40, $40 (international).

Application Contact Dr. George Claffey, Director of Graduate Business Programs, School of Business, 1615 Stanley Street, New Britain, CT 06050. **Phone:** 860-832-3210. **Fax:** 860-832-3219. **E-mail:** claffey@ccsu.edu.

Eastern Connecticut State University

Willimantic, Connecticut

SCHOOL OF EDUCATION AND PROFESSIONAL STUDIES/ GRADUATE DIVISION

Graduate Business Faculty
Full-time: 3 | Part-time: 4

Student Body
Total: 66
Full-time: 1
Part-time: 65
Average Age: 39
Women: 56%

Admissions
Applications: 20
Admitted: 20
Enrolled: 20
Average GPA: 3.07

Costs (1999–2000)
Full-time tuition: $2370 per academic year (resident), $5112 per academic year (nonresident)
Part-time tuition: $165 per credit hour (resident), $165 per credit hour (nonresident)

DEGREE MS

MS—Master of Science in Organizational Management Full-time and part-time. At least 36 total credits required. 18 to 72 months to complete program. *Concentrations:* organizational management.

COSTS

Tuition, state resident: *Full-time* $1316. *Part-time* $165 per credit hour. **Tuition, nonresident:** *Full-time* $4058. *Part-time* $165 per credit hour. **Tuition, international:** *Full-time* $4058. **Required fees:** *Full-time* $1054. Tuition and fees vary by number of courses or credits taken and local reciprocity agreements.

FINANCIAL AID (1999–2000)

4 students received aid, including grants, loans, and work study. Aid is available to part-time students. Financial aid application deadline: 3/15. **Financial Aid Contact** Mr. Richard Savage, Director of Financial Aid, 83 Windham Street, Willimantic, CT 06226. **Phone:** 860-465-5205. **Fax:** 860-465-2811. **E-mail:** savager@ecsu.ctstateu.edu.

RESOURCES AND SERVICES

Information about online services, personal computer policies, library resources, international exchange programs, internship programs, and placement services at this institution and others can be found at **www.petersons.com/mba**

International Students

Services and Facilities Counseling/support services. Financial aid is available to international students.
Applying *Required:* TOEFL with recommended score of 550 (paper), proof of adequate funds, proof of health/immunizations.
International Student Contact Director of International Programs, 83 Windham Street, Willimantic, CT 06226. **Phone:** 860-465-4427.

■ APPLICATION

Required Application form, baccalaureate/first degree, essay, 2 letters of recommendation, personal statement, transcripts of college work, work experience. **Recommended** Resume/curriculum vitae.
Deadlines and Fees Applications for domestic and international students are processed on a rolling basis. *Application fee:* $40, $40 (international).
Application Contact Ms. Hazel Gage, Graduate Division Secretary, 83 Windham Street, Willimantic, CT 06226. **Phone:** 860-465-5292. **Fax:** 860-465-4538. **E-mail:** gage@ecsu.ctstateu.edu.

Fairfield University

Fairfield, Connecticut

SCHOOL OF BUSINESS

Graduate Business Faculty
Full-time: 40 | Part-time: 2

Student Body
Total: 257
Full-time: 18
Part-time: 239
Average Age: 27
Women: 42%

Admissions
Applications: 79
Admitted: 71
Enrolled: 48
Average GMAT: 530
Average GPA: 3.2

Costs (1999–2000)
Full-time tuition: N/R
Part-time tuition: $480 per credit hour

Accreditation
AACSB—The International Association for Management Education

DEGREES EMBA • MBA • MS

Master of Science in Management Full-time and part-time. At least 32 total credits required. 12 to 36 months to complete program. *Concentrations:* management information systems.

MBA—Master of Business Administration Full-time and part-time. 36 to 62 total credits required. 18 to 60 months to complete program. *Concentrations:* accounting, finance, health care, human resources, international business, management information systems, marketing, taxation.

MS—Master of Science in Financial Management Full-time and part-time. 36 to 68 total credits required. 24 to 60 months to complete program. *Concentrations:* financial management/planning.

COSTS

Tuition *Part-time:* $480 per credit hour. Tuition varies by number of courses or credits taken. **Graduate housing:** Room and board costs vary by number of occupants and type of board plan. *Typical cost:* $7630 (including board).

FINANCIAL AID (1999–2000)

Loans and research assistantships. **Financial Aid Contact** Susan Kadir, Director of Financial Aid, 1073 North Benson Road, Fairfield, CT 06430. **Phone:** 203-254-4000 Ext. 4125. **E-mail:** skadir@fair1.fairfield.edu.

RESOURCES AND SERVICES

Information about online services, personal computer policies, library resources, international exchange programs, internship programs, and placement services at this institution and others can be found at **www.petersons.com/mba**

International Students

5% of students enrolled are international students.
Services and Facilities Counseling/support services, visa services. Financial aid is not available to international students.
Applying *Required:* TOEFL with recommended score of 550 (paper), proof of adequate funds, proof of health/immunizations.
International Student Contact Alexander Scott, Associate Director of Admissions, 1073 North Benson Road, Fairfield, CT 06430-5195. **Phone:** 203-254-4000 Ext. 2906. **Fax:** 203-254-4199.

■ APPLICATION

Required GMAT, application form, baccalaureate/first degree, 2 letters of recommendation, personal statement, transcripts of college work. **Recommended** 3 years of work experience.
Deadlines and Fees *Deadlines:* 8/15 for fall, 12/15 for spring, 5/15 for summer, 5/15 for fall (international), 10/15 for spring (international). *Application fee:* $50, $50 (international).
Application Contact Pamela Curry, Assistant Director of Graduate Programs, School of Business, Fairfield, CT 06430. **Phone:** 203-254-4000 Ext. 3019. **Fax:** 203-254-4029. **E-mail:** mba@fair1.fairfield.edu.

See full description on page 648.

Quinnipiac University

Hamden, Connecticut

SCHOOL OF BUSINESS

Graduate Business Faculty
Full-time: 18 | Part-time: 5

Student Body
Total: 188
Full-time: 32
Part-time: 156
Average Age: 27
Women: 44%

Admissions
Applications: 87
Admitted: 64
Enrolled: 52
Average GMAT: 460
Average GPA: 3.04

Quinnipiac University (continued)

Costs (1999–2000)
Full-time tuition: N/R
Part-time tuition: $430 per credit

Accreditation
AACSB—The International Association for Management Education

DEGREES JD/MBA • JD/MHA • MBA • MHA

JD/MBA—Juris Doctor/Master of Business Administration Full-time and part-time. Minimum of 48 months to complete program.

JD/MHA—Juris Doctor/Master of Health Administration Full-time and part-time. Minimum of 48 months to complete program.

MBA—Master of Business Administration Full-time and part-time. At least 39 total credits required. 14 to 36 months to complete program. *Concentrations:* accounting, economics, finance, health care, international business, management, management information systems, marketing, taxation.

MHA—Master of Health Administration in General Health Administration Full-time and part-time. At least 39 total credits required. 14 to 36 months to complete program.

MHA—Master of Health Administration in Long-term Care Administration Full-time and part-time. At least 45 total credits required. 20 to 48 months to complete program.

COSTS
Tuition *Part-time:* $430 per credit. **Required fees:** *Full-time* $390. *Part-time* $20 per semester. Tuition and fees vary by number of courses or credits taken.

FINANCIAL AID (1999–2000)
Research assistantships. Aid is available to part-time students. **Financial Aid Contact** Ms. Louise Howe, Associate Director of Graduate Admissions and Financial Aid, 275 Mount Carmel Avenue, Hamden, CT 06518-1904. **Phone:** 800-462-1944. **Fax:** 203-582-5238. **E-mail:** graduate@quinnipiac.edu.

RESOURCES AND SERVICES
Information about online services, personal computer policies, library resources, international exchange programs, internship programs, and placement services at this institution and others can be found at **www.petersons.com/mba**

International Students
3% of students enrolled are international students.

Services and Facilities Counseling/support services, housing location assistance, visa services. Financial aid is not available to international students.
Applying *Required:* TOEFL with recommended score of 233 (computer) or 575 (paper), proof of adequate funds, proof of health/immunizations.
International Student Contact Ms. Leonora Campbell, Associate Dean of Student Affairs, 275 Mount Carmel Avenue, Hamden, CT 06518. **Phone:** 203-582-8723. **Fax:** 203-582-8796. **E-mail:** campbell@quinnipiac.edu.

■ APPLICATION
Required Application form, baccalaureate/first degree, 2 letters of recommendation, resume/curriculum vitae, transcripts of college work. School will accept GMAT. **Recommended** Essay, interview, personal statement, work experience.
Deadlines and Fees Applications for domestic students are processed on a rolling basis. *Deadlines:* 8/1 for fall (international), 12/1 for spring (international), 5/1 for summer (international). *Application fee:* $45, $45 (international).
Application Contact Mr. Scott Farber, Director of Graduate Admissions, 275 Mount Carmel Avenue, Hamden, CT 06518-1904. **Phone:** 203-582-8795. **Toll-free Phone:** 800-462-1944. **Fax:** 203-582-3443. **E-mail:** graduate@quinnipiac.edu.

See full description on page 778.

Rensselaer at Hartford

Hartford, Connecticut

LALLY SCHOOL OF MANAGEMENT AND TECHNOLOGY

Graduate Business Faculty
Full-time: 26	Part-time: 23

Student Body
Total: 1,297	Average Age: 32
Full-time: 61	Women: 32%
Part-time: 1,236	

Admissions
Enrolled: 410	Average GPA: 3

Costs (1999–2000)
Full-time tuition: N/R
Part-time tuition: $585 per credit hour

After Graduation (Class of 1998–99)
Employed within 3 months of graduation: 98%

DEGREES MBA • MS

MBA—Master of Business Administration Full-time and part-time. *Distance learning option.* GMAT required. At least 60 total credits required. 24 to 60 months to complete program. *Concentrations:* entrepreneurship, environmental economics/management, finance, health care, international management, management information systems, manufacturing management, marketing, research and development administration.

MS—Master of Science in Environmental Management and Policy Full-time and part-time. *Distance learning option.* At least 45 total credits required. 24 to 60 months to complete program.

MS—Master of Science in Management Full-time and part-time. *Distance learning option.* At least 30 total credits required. 12 to 60 months to complete program. *Concentrations:* entrepreneurship, environmental economics/management, finance, health care, international management, management information systems, manufacturing management, marketing, research and development administration.

COSTS
Tuition *Part-time:* $585 per credit hour.

FINANCIAL AID (1999–2000)
80 students received aid, including loans and scholarships. Aid is available to part-time students. Financial aid application deadline: 8/8. **Financial Aid Contact** Ms. Gayle Hoffman, Financial Aid Officer, 275 Windsor Street, Hartford, CT 06120. **Phone:** 860-548-2422. **Fax:** 860-548-7823.

RESOURCES AND SERVICES
Information about online services, personal computer policies, library resources, international exchange programs, internship programs, and placement services at this institution and others can be found at **www.petersons.com/mba**

International Students
3% of students enrolled are international students.

Services and Facilities Counseling/support services. Financial aid is not available to international students.
Applying *Required:* TOEFL with recommended score of 570 (paper), proof of adequate funds, proof of health/immunizations.
International Student Contact Mr. John Gonyea, Admissions Specialist and International Student Advisor, 275 Windsor Street, Hartford, CT 06120. **Phone:** 860-548-2406. **Fax:** 860-548-7823.

■ APPLICATION
Required Application form, baccalaureate/first degree, 2 letters of recommendation, resume/curriculum vitae, transcripts of college work. School will accept GMAT.

Deadlines and Fees Applications for domestic and international students are processed on a rolling basis. *Application fee:* $35, $35 (international).

Application Contact Ms. Rebecca Danchak, Director of Admissions, 275 Windsor Street, Hartford, CT 06120. **Phone:** 860-548-2421. **Fax:** 860-548-7823. **E-mail:** rdanchak@rh.edu.

Sacred Heart University

Fairfield, Connecticut

COLLEGE OF BUSINESS

Graduate Business Faculty
Full-time: 29	Part-time: 38

Student Body
Total: 563	Average Age: 32
Full-time: 44	Women: 51%
Part-time: 519	

Admissions
Applications: 132	Average GMAT: 507
Admitted: 64	Average GPA: 3.02
Enrolled: 62	

Costs (1999–2000)
Full-time tuition: N/R
Part-time tuition: $415 per credit

DEGREES MBA • MBA/MS

MBA—Master of Business Administration Full-time and part-time. *Distance learning option.* At least 36 total credits required. 12 to 72 months to complete program. *Concentrations:* accounting, economics, finance, human resources, international business, management, management information systems, marketing.

MBA/MS—Master of Business Administration/Master of Science in Nursing Full-time and part-time. 48 to 75 total credits required. 15 to 72 months to complete program. *Concentrations:* health care.

COSTS

Tuition *Part-time:* $415 per credit. Tuition varies by number of courses or credits taken. **Required fees:** *Full-time* $85. *Part-time* $85 per term. **Graduate housing:** Room and board costs vary by number of occupants, type of accommodation, and type of board plan. *Typical cost:* $6500 (including board).

FINANCIAL AID (1999–2000)

Research assistantships, teaching assistantships, and work study.
Financial Aid Contact Mr. Carl Nykaza, Director of Financial Assistance for Graduate Programs, 5151 Park Avenue, Fairfield, CT 06432-1000. **Phone:** 203-371-7983. **Fax:** 203-365-7608.

RESOURCES AND SERVICES

Information about online services, personal computer policies, library resources, international exchange programs, internship programs, and placement services at this institution and others can be found at **www.petersons.com/mba**

International Students

2% of students enrolled are international students.

Services and Facilities Counseling/support services, ESL/language courses, housing location assistance, visa services. Financial aid is not available to international students.
Applying *Required:* TOEFL with recommended score of 525 (paper), proof of adequate funds, proof of health/immunizations.
International Student Contact Dr. Theresa I. Madonna, Advisor and Academic Director of Graduate Programs, 5151 Park Avenue, Fairfield, CT 06432-1000. **Phone:** 203-371-7850. **Fax:** 203-365-7538. **E-mail:** madonnat@sacredheart.edu

■ APPLICATION

Required GMAT, application form, baccalaureate/first degree, essay, 2 letters of recommendation, resume/curriculum vitae, transcripts of college work. **Recommended** Interview, work experience.

Deadlines and Fees Applications for domestic and international students are processed on a rolling basis. *Application fee:* $40, $100 (international).

Application Contact Dr. Theresa I. Gonzales, Advisor and Academic Director of Graduate Programs, 5151 Park Avenue, Fairfield, CT 06432-1000. **Phone:** 203-371-7850. **Fax:** 203-371-7538. **E-mail:** madonnat@sacredheart.edu.

See full description on page 798.

Southern Connecticut State University

New Haven, Connecticut

SCHOOL OF BUSINESS

Graduate Business Faculty
Full-time: 14   Part-time: 14

Student Body
Total: 106
Full-time: 93   Average Age: 32.6
Part-time: 13   Women: 51%

Admissions
Applications: 126
Admitted: 50   Average GMAT: 495
Enrolled: 46   Average GPA: 2.8

Costs (1999–2000)
Full-time tuition: $6370 per academic year (resident), $10,513 per academic year (nonresident)
Part-time tuition: $239 per credit (resident)

After Graduation (Class of 1998–99)
Employed within 3 months of graduation: 100%
Average starting salary: $65,000

DEGREES MBA

MBA—MBA in Accounting Full-time. Application deadline: 4/15. At least 36 total credits required. 15 to 30 months to complete program.
MBA—Master of Business Administration Full-time and part-time. At least 60 total credits required. 24 months to complete program.

COSTS

Tuition, state resident: *Full-time* $6370. *Part-time* $239 per credit. **Tuition, nonresident:** *Full-time* $10,513. Tuition varies by academic program.

FINANCIAL AID (1999–2000)

38 students received aid, including loans and research assistantships. Aid is available to part-time students. Financial aid application deadline: 4/15. **Financial Aid Contact** Mr. Ken Maginnis, Financial Aid Office, 501 Crescent Street, New Haven, CT 06515-1355. **Phone:** 203-392-5222. **E-mail:** maginnis@scsu.ctstateu.edu.

RESOURCES AND SERVICES

Information about online services, personal computer policies, library resources, international exchange programs, internship programs, and placement services at this institution and others can be found at **www.petersons.com/mba**

International Students

8% of students enrolled are international students.

Services and Facilities Counseling/support services, visa services. Financial aid is not available to international students.
Applying *Required:* TOEFL with recommended score of 550 (paper), proof of adequate funds, proof of health/immunizations.
International Student Contact Aliya Amin, International Student Advisor, 501 Crescent Street, New Haven, CT 06515. **Phone:** 203-392-6821. **E-mail:** amin@scsu.ctstateu.edu.

■ APPLICATION

Required GMAT, application form, baccalaureate/first degree, essay, 3 letters of recommendation, resume/curriculum vitae, transcripts of college work, 3 years of work experience. **Recommended** Interview, personal statement.

Deadlines and Fees Applications for domestic and international students are processed on a rolling basis. *Application fee:* $40, $40 (international).

Application Contact Mr. Dan Mitchell, Director, MBA, New Haven, CT 06515-1355. **Phone:** 203-392-5633. **Fax:** 203-392-5988. **E-mail:** mitchell.d@scsu.ctstateu.edu.

University of Bridgeport

Bridgeport, Connecticut

SCHOOL OF BUSINESS

Graduate Business Faculty
Full-time: 14   Part-time: 21

Student Body
Total: 182   Average Age: 31
Full-time: 85   Women: 48%
Part-time: 97

Admissions
Applications: 264   Average GMAT: 545
Admitted: 213   Average GPA: 3.06
Enrolled: 40

Costs (1999–2000)
Full-time tuition: N/R
Part-time tuition: $380 per credit

Accreditation
ACBSP—The American Council of Business Schools and Programs

DEGREE MBA

MBA—Master of Business Administration Full-time and part-time. At least 54 total credits required. 12 to 60 months to complete program. *Concentrations:* accounting, economics, finance, international business, management, management information systems, marketing.

University of Bridgeport (continued)

COSTS

Tuition *Part-time:* $380 per credit. Tuition varies by class time, number of courses or credits taken, and academic program. **Required fees:** *Full-time* $841. *Part-time* $50 per semester. Tuition and fees vary by class time and number of courses or credits taken. **Graduate housing:** Room and board costs vary by number of occupants and type of board plan. *Typical cost:* $6970 (including board), $3780 (room only).

FINANCIAL AID (1999–2000)

36 students received aid, including fellowships, grants, loans, research assistantships, scholarships, teaching assistantships, and work study. Aid is available to part-time students. Financial aid application deadline: 6/1. **Financial Aid Contact** Ms. Jacklyn C. Stoltz, Director of Financial Aid, 380 University Avenue, Bridgeport, CT 06601. **Phone:** 203-576-4568. **Fax:** 203-576-4941. **E-mail:** finaid@bridgeport.edu.

RESOURCES AND SERVICES

Information about online services, personal computer policies, library resources, international exchange programs, internship programs, and placement services at this institution and others can be found at **www.petersons.com/mba**

International Students

76% of students enrolled are international students.

Services and Facilities Counseling/support services, ESL/language courses, international student organization, orientation. Financial aid is available to international students.

Applying *Required:* TOEFL with recommended score of 575 (paper), proof of adequate funds, proof of health/immunizations.

International Student Contact Ms. Dawn Valenti, Director of International Affairs, 380 University Avenue, Bridgeport, CT 06601. **Phone:** 203-576-4395. **Fax:** 203-576-4941.

■ APPLICATION

Required GMAT, application form, baccalaureate/first degree, essay, 2 letters of recommendation, personal statement, resume/curriculum vitae, transcripts of college work. **Recommended** Interview, work experience.

Deadlines and Fees Applications for domestic students are processed on a rolling basis. *Deadlines:* 8/1 for fall (international), 1/1 for spring (international), 5/1 for summer (international). *Application fee:* $25, $50 (international).

Application Contact Ms. Diane Richardson, Director of the MBA Program, School of Business, 230 Park Avenue, Bridgeport, CT 06601. **Phone:** 203-576-4363. **Fax:** 203-576-4388.

See full description on page 870.

University of Connecticut

Storrs, Connecticut

SCHOOL OF BUSINESS ADMINISTRATION

Graduate Business Faculty
Full-time: 55

Student Body
Total: 937
Full-time: 98
Part-time: 839
Average Age: 28
Women: 39%

Admissions
Applications: 375
Admitted: 133
Enrolled: 59
Average GMAT: 631
Average GPA: 3.43

Costs (1999–2000)
Full-time tuition: $6140 per academic year (resident), $14,320 per academic year (nonresident)
Part-time tuition: $405 per credit (resident), $405 per credit (nonresident)

After Graduation (Class of 1998–99)
Employed within 3 months of graduation: 97%
Average starting salary: $56,000

Accreditation
AACSB—The International Association for Management Education

DEGREES JD/MBA • MBA • MBA/MA • MBA/MPA • MBA/MPH • MBA/MS • MBA/MSW • MD/MBA

JD/MBA—Juris Doctor/Master of Business Administration Full-time and part-time. At least 116 total credits required. 48 to 60 months to complete program.

MBA—Executive MBA Part-time. At least 48 total credits required. 21 months to complete program.

MBA—Master of Business Administration Full-time. At least 57 total credits required. 24 to 60 months to complete program. *Concentrations:* electronic commerce (e-commerce), finance, health care, information management, management consulting.

MBA—Master of Business Administration Part-time. At least 57 total credits required. 24 to 72 months to complete program. *Concentrations:* accounting, finance, health care, international business, management, marketing, real estate, technology management.

MBA/MA—Master of Business Administration/Master of Arts in African Studies Full-time. At least 72 total credits required. Minimum of 30 months to complete program.

MBA/MA—Master of Business Administration/Master of Arts in European Studies Full-time. At least 72 total credits required. Minimum of 30 months to complete program. *Concentrations:* Asian business studies, European business studies.

MBA/MA—Master of Business Administration/Master of Arts in Latin American Full-time. At least 72 total credits required. Minimum of 30 months to complete program.

MBA/MPA—Master of Business Administration/Master of Public Affairs Full-time and part-time. Up to 69 total credits required. Maximum of 33 months to complete program.

MBA/MPH—Master of Business Administration/Master of Public Health Full-time and part-time. Up to 78 total credits required. Maximum of 33 months to complete program.

MBA/MS—Master of Business Administration/Master of Science in Nursing Full-time and part-time. At least 63 total credits required. 18 to 60 months to complete program.

MBA/MSW—Master of Business Administration/Master of Social Work Full-time and part-time. At least 57 total credits required. Minimum of 30 months to complete program.

MD/MBA—Doctor of Medicine/Master of Business Administration Full-time and part-time. Maximum of 60 months to complete program.

COSTS

Tuition, state resident: *Full-time* $5118. *Part-time* $405 per credit. **Tuition, nonresident:** *Full-time* $13,298. *Part-time* $405 per credit. **Required fees:** *Full-time* $1022. Tuition and fees vary by class time, number of courses or credits taken, and campus location. **Graduate housing:** Room and board costs vary by number of occupants, type of accommodation, and type of board plan. *Typical cost:* $5852 (including board), $3210 (room only).

FINANCIAL AID (1999–2000)

45 students received aid, including fellowships, research assistantships, scholarships, and teaching assistantships. Financial aid application deadline: 3/1. **Financial Aid Contact** Ms. Mona Lucas, Director, Student Financial Aid Office, 233 Glenbrook Road, U-116, Wilbur Cross Building, Storrs, CT 06269-4116. **Phone:** 860-486-2819. **Fax:** 860-486-0945. **E-mail:** wwwfaid@uconnvm.uconn.edu.

RESOURCES AND SERVICES

Information about online services, personal computer policies, library resources, international exchange programs, internship programs, and placement services at this institution and others can be found at **www.petersons.com/mba**

International Students

6% of students enrolled are international students.

Services and Facilities Counseling/support services, ESL/language courses, international student housing, international student organization, language tutoring, orientation, visa services. Financial aid is available to international students.

Applying *Required:* TOEFL with recommended score of 575 (paper), proof of adequate funds, proof of health/immunizations.

International Student Contact Ms. Laine Kingo, Program Coordinator, School of Business administration, 368 Fairfield Road, U-41 MBA, Storrs, CT 06269-2041. **Phone:** 860-486-0319. **Fax:** 860-486-5222. **E-mail:** uconnmba@sba.uconn.edu.

■ APPLICATION

Required GMAT, application form, baccalaureate/first degree, essay, 2 letters of recommendation, personal statement, resume/curriculum vitae, transcripts of college work, 2 years of work experience.

Deadlines and Fees *Deadlines:* 4/1 for fall, 1/31 for fall (international). *Application fee:* $40, $45 (international).

Application Contact Ms. Laine Kingo, Program Coordinator, School of Business Administration, 368 Fairfield Road, U-41 MBA, Storrs, CT 06269-2041. **Phone:** 860-486-0319. **Fax:** 860-486-5222. **E-mail:** uconnmba@sba.uconn.edu.

See full description on page 890.

University of Hartford

West Hartford, Connecticut

BARNEY SCHOOL OF BUSINESS AND PUBLIC ADMINISTRATION

Graduate Business Faculty
Full-time: 28   Part-time: 13

Student Body
Total: 451
Full-time: 174   Average Age: 31
Part-time: 277   Women: 44%

Admissions
Applications: 283   Average GMAT: 480
Admitted: 177   Average GPA: 2.5
Enrolled: 122

Costs (1999–2000)
Full-time tuition: N/R
Part-time tuition: $380 per credit hour

After Graduation (Class of 1998–99)
Employed within 3 months of graduation: 91.7%
Average starting salary: $40,000

DEGREES MBA • ME/MBA • MS • MST

MBA—Executive Master of Business Administration for the Health Care Professional Part-time. At least 48 total credits required. Minimum of 21 months to complete program.

MBA—Master of Business Administration Full-time and part-time. At least 51 total credits required. 12 to 60 months to complete program. *Concentrations:* accounting, finance, insurance, international business, management, management information systems, marketing, organizational behavior/development, public management, taxation.

ME/MBA—Master of Engineering/Master of Business Administration Full-time and part-time. At least 60 total credits required. 18 to 60 months to complete program. *Concentrations:* management.

MS—Accelerated Master of Science in Professional Accountancy Full-time. At least 48 total credits required. 15 months to complete program. *Concentrations:* accounting.

MS—Master of Science in Professional Accounting Full-time and part-time. At least 30 total credits required. 12 to 60 months to complete program. *Concentrations:* accounting, taxation.

MST—Master of Science in Taxation Full-time and part-time. At least 30 total credits required. 12 to 60 months to complete program. *Concentrations:* taxation.

COSTS
Tuition *Part-time:* $380 per credit hour. **Required fees:** *Full-time* $220.

FINANCIAL AID (1999–2000)
Loans and research assistantships. Aid is available to part-time students. Financial aid application deadline: 5/1. **Financial Aid Contact** Joseph Martinkovic, Director of Student Financial Assistance, 200 Bloomfield Avenue, West Hartford, CT 06117-1500. **Phone:** 860-768-4904. **Fax:** 860-768-4961.

RESOURCES AND SERVICES
Information about online services, personal computer policies, library resources, international exchange programs, internship programs, and placement services at this institution and others can be found at **www. petersons.com/mba**

International Students
25% of students enrolled are international students.
Services and Facilities ESL/language courses. Financial aid is not available to international students.
Applying *Required:* TOEFL with recommended score of 550 (paper), proof of adequate funds, proof of health/immunizations.
International Student Contact Mr. Richard Lazzerini, Associate Director of International Programs, 200 Bloomfield Avenue, West Hartford, CT 06117-1500. **Phone:** 860-768-4873. **Fax:** 860-768-4726.

■ APPLICATION
Required GMAT, application form, baccalaureate/first degree, 2 letters of recommendation, personal statement, resume/curriculum vitae, transcripts of college work.
Deadlines and Fees *Application fee:* $40, $55 (international).
Application Contact Mr. David Wilcox, Assistant Director of Graduate Programs, 200 Bloomfield Avenue, West Hartford, CT 06117-1500. **Phone:** 860-768-5102. **Fax:** 860-768-5160. **E-mail:** dwilcox@mail.hartford.edu.

University of New Haven

West Haven, Connecticut

SCHOOL OF BUSINESS

DEGREES MBA • MBA/MPA • MBA/MS • MPA • MS

MBA—Executive MBA Part-time. At least 30 total credits required. 22 months to complete program.

MBA—Master of Business Administration Full-time and part-time. GMAT score required. At least 51 total credits required. 12 to 60 months to complete program. *Concentrations:* accounting, business information science, business policy/strategy, finance, health care, human resources, industrial administration/management, international business, logistics, management, management science, marketing, operations management, public relations, sports/entertainment management, technology management.

MBA/MPA—Master of Business Administration/Master of Public Administration Full-time and part-time. At least 72 total credits required. 24 to 60 months to complete program.

MBA/MS—Master of Business Administration/Master of Science in Industrial Engineering Full-time and part-time. At least 72 total credits required. 24 to 60 months to complete program.

MPA—Master of Public Administration Full-time and part-time. At least 42 total credits required. 15 to 60 months to complete program.

MS—Master of Science in Accounting Full-time and part-time. At least 42 total credits required. 15 to 60 months to complete program.

MS—Master of Science in Finance and Financial Services Full-time and part-time. At least 42 total credits required. 15 to 60 months to complete program.

MS—Master of Science in Health Care Administration Full-time and part-time. At least 42 total credits required. 15 to 60 months to complete program.

MS—Master of Science in Industrial Relations Full-time and part-time. At least 39 total credits required. 12 to 60 months to complete program.

MS—Master of Science in Taxation Full-time and part-time. At least 36 total credits required. 15 to 60 months to complete program.

RESOURCES AND SERVICES
Information about online services, personal computer policies, library resources, international exchange programs, internship programs, and placement services at this institution and others can be found at **www. petersons.com/mba**

International Students
Services and Facilities Counseling/support services, ESL/language courses, international student housing. Financial aid is not available to international students.
International Student Contact Ms. Lisa Carraretto, Director, International Services, 300 Orange Avenue, West Haven, CT 06516-1916. **Phone:** 800-DIAL-UNH Ext. 7338. **Fax:** 203-932-7343. **E-mail:** lisacarr@charger.newhaven.edu.

■ APPLICATION
Application Contact Mr. Joseph F. Spellman, Director of Graduate Admissions, 300 Orange Avenue, West Haven, CT 06516-1916. **Phone:** 203-932-7133. **Fax:** 203-932-7137. **E-mail:** gradinfo@charger.newhaven.edu.

See full description on page 936.

Western Connecticut State University

Danbury, Connecticut

ANCELL SCHOOL OF BUSINESS AND PUBLIC ADMINISTRATION

Graduate Business Faculty
Full-time: 8   Part-time: 2

Student Body
Total: 102   Part-time: 100
Full-time: 2   Average Age: 35

Admissions
Enrolled: 14
Average GMAT: 520
Average GPA: 3.1

Costs (1999–2000)
Full-time tuition: N/R
Part-time tuition: $178 per credit (resident), $178 per credit (nonresident)

After Graduation (Class of 1998–99)
Employed within 3 months of graduation: 99%

DEGREES MBA • MHA

MBA—Master of Business Administration Part-time. 30 to 54 total credits required. 24 to 96 months to complete program. *Concentrations:* accounting, management.

MHA—Master of Health Administration Part-time. At least 36 total credits required. 24 to 72 months to complete program. *Concentrations:* health care.

COSTS
Tuition, state resident: *Part-time* $178 per credit. **Tuition, nonresident:** *Part-time* $178 per credit. **Graduate housing:** Room and board costs vary by type of board plan. *Typical cost:* $4758 (including board).

FINANCIAL AID (1999–2000)
Fellowships and work study. Aid is available to part-time students.
Financial Aid Contact Mr. William Hawkins, Director of Financial Aid, 181 White Street, Danbury, CT 06810-6885. **Phone:** 203-837-8586. **Fax:** 203-837-8528. **E-mail:** hawkinsw@wcsu.ctstateu.edu.

RESOURCES AND SERVICES
Information about online services, personal computer policies, library resources, international exchange programs, internship programs, and placement services at this institution and others can be found at **www.petersons.com/mba**

International Students
Applying *Required:* TOEFL with recommended score of 550 (paper), proof of adequate funds, proof of health/immunizations.

■ APPLICATION
Required GMAT, application form, baccalaureate/first degree, 2 letters of recommendation, transcripts of college work. **Recommended** Interview, personal statement, resume/curriculum vitae.

Deadlines and Fees *Application fee:* $40, $40 (international).

Application Contact Mr. Chris Shankle, Assistant Director of University Admissions, 181 White Street, Danbury, CT 06810-6885. **Phone:** 203-837-9005. **Fax:** 203-837-8338. **E-mail:** shanklec@wcsu.ctstateu.edu.

Yale University
New Haven, Connecticut

YALE SCHOOL OF MANAGEMENT

Graduate Business Faculty
Full-time: 47
Part-time: 49

Student Body
Total: 432
Full-time: 432
Average Age: 27
Women: 32%

Admissions
Applications: 1,897
Admitted: 448
Enrolled: 228
Average GMAT: 689
Average GPA: 3.47

Costs (1999–2000)
Full-time tuition: $26,505 per academic year
Part-time tuition: N/R

After Graduation (Class of 1998–99)
Employed within 3 months of graduation: 97%
Average starting salary: $78,734

Accreditation
AACSB—The International Association for Management Education

DEGREES JD/MBA • MBA • MBA/M Arch • MBA/M Div • MBA/MA • MBA/MF • MBA/MPH • MBA/MSN • MD/MBA

JD/MBA—Business and Law Full-time. Students must apply to each school independently. Minimum of 48 months to complete program.

MBA—Master of Business Administration Full-time. At least 72 total credits required. Minimum of 24 months to complete program. *Concentrations:* finance, leadership, marketing, nonprofit management, operations management, public management, strategic management.

MBA/M Arch—Business and Architecture Full-time. Students must apply to each school independently. Minimum of 48 months to complete program.

MBA/M Div—Business and Divinity Full-time. Students must apply to each school independently. At least 75 total credits required. Minimum of 36 months to complete program.

MBA/MA—Business and International Relations Full-time. Students must apply to each school independently. At least 75 total credits required. Minimum of 36 months to complete program.

MBA/MA—East Asian Studies Full-time. Students must apply to each school independently. At least 75 total credits required. Minimum of 36 months to complete program.

MBA/MA—Russian and East European Studies Full-time. Students must apply to each school independently. At least 75 total credits required. Minimum of 36 months to complete program.

MBA/MF—Business and Environment Full-time. Students must apply to each school independently. At least 75 total credits required. Minimum of 36 months to complete program.

MBA/MPH—Business and Public Health Full-time. Students must apply to each school independently. At least 84 total credits required. Minimum of 36 months to complete program.

MBA/MSN—Business and Nursing Full-time. Students must apply to each school independently. Minimum of 36 months to complete program.

MD/MBA—Business and Medicine Full-time. Students must apply to each school independently. Minimum of 60 months to complete program.

COSTS
Tuition *Full-time:* $26,380. **Required fees:** *Full-time* $125.

FINANCIAL AID (1999–2000)
265 students received aid, including grants, loans, and scholarships. Financial aid application deadline: 2/15. **Financial Aid Contact** Karen Wellman, Financial Aid Administrator, Box 208200, New Haven, CT 06520-8200. **Phone:** 203-432-5173. **Fax:** 203-432-9916.

RESOURCES AND SERVICES
Information about online services, personal computer policies, library resources, international exchange programs, internship programs, and placement services at this institution and others can be found at **www.petersons.com/mba**

International Students
26% of students enrolled are international students.

Services and Facilities Counseling/support services, ESL/language courses, housing location assistance, international student housing, orientation, visa services, writing tutor. Financial aid is available to international students.
Applying *Required:* TOEFL with recommended score of 250 (computer) or 600 (paper), proof of adequate funds, proof of health/immunizations.

International Student Contact Dr. Shalini D. Bhutani, Director, Office of International Students and Scholars, 246 Church Street, New Haven, CT 06520. **Phone:** 203-432-2305. **Fax:** 203-432-7166.

■ APPLICATION
Required GMAT, application form, baccalaureate/first degree, essay, 3 letters of recommendation, personal statement, resume/curriculum vitae, transcripts of college work. **Recommended** Interview, 2 years of work experience.

Deadlines and Fees *Deadlines:* 3/15 for fall, 3/15 for fall (international). *Application fee:* $150, $150 (international).

Application Contact Mr. James Stevens, Director, Admissions, 135 Prospect Street, PO Box 208200, New Haven, CT 06520-2800. **Phone:** 203-432-5932. **Fax:** 203-432-7004. **E-mail:** mba.admissions@yale.edu.

DELAWARE

Delaware State University

Dover, Delaware

PROGRAM IN BUSINESS ADMINISTRATION

Graduate Business Faculty
Part-time: 5

Student Body
Total: 29
Full-time: 3
Part-time: 26

Average Age: 30
Women: 66%

Admissions
Applications: 35
Admitted: 28

Enrolled: 26
Average GPA: 3

Costs (1999–2000)
Full-time tuition: N/R
Part-time tuition: $156 per credit (resident), $365 per credit (nonresident)

After Graduation (Class of 1998–99)
Employed within 3 months of graduation: 98%

DEGREE MBA

MBA—Master of Business Administration Full-time and part-time. At least 30 total credits required. 12 to 84 months to complete program.

COSTS

Tuition, state resident: *Part-time* $156 per credit. **Tuition, nonresident:** *Part-time* $365 per credit. Tuition varies by number of courses or credits taken. **Graduate housing:** Room and board costs vary by type of board plan. *Typical cost:* $2345 (including board).

FINANCIAL AID (1999–2000)

Fellowships, loans, and work study. Aid is available to part-time students. **Financial Aid Contact** Dr. John C. Stith, Director of Academics and MBA Program, 1200 North Dupont Highway, Dover, DE 19901. **Phone:** 302-857-6906. **Fax:** 302-857-6908. **E-mail:** jcstith@dsc.edu.

RESOURCES AND SERVICES

Information about online services, personal computer policies, library resources, international exchange programs, internship programs, and placement services at this institution and others can be found at **www.petersons.com/mba**

International Students

17% of students enrolled are international students.

Services and Facilities Counseling/support services.
Applying *Required:* TOEFL with recommended score of 550 (paper), proof of adequate funds.
International Student Contact Dr. Hazell Reed, Dean, Graduate Studies and Research, Dover, DE 19901. **Phone:** 302-857-6800. **Fax:** 302-857-6800. **E-mail:** hreed@dsc.edu.

■ APPLICATION

Required Application form, baccalaureate/first degree, 3 letters of recommendation, transcripts of college work. School will accept GMAT.

Deadlines and Fees Applications for domestic and international students are processed on a rolling basis. *Application fee:* $25, $25 (international).

Application Contact Dr. John C. Stith, Director of Academics and MBA Program, 1200 North DuPont Highway, Dover, DE 19901-2277. **Phone:** 302-857-6906. **Fax:** 302-857-6908. **E-mail:** jcstith@dsc.edu.

Goldey-Beacom College

Wilmington, Delaware

MBA PROGRAM

Graduate Business Faculty
Full-time: 20

Student Body
Total: 143
Full-time: 138

Part-time: 5
Average Age: 30

Women: 50%

Admissions
Applications: 34
Admitted: 33

Enrolled: 31
Average GMAT: 450

Costs (1999–2000)
Full-time tuition: N/R
Part-time tuition: $371 per credit

DEGREES MBA

MBA—Masters of Business Administration Full-time and part-time. At least 36 total credits required. 24 to 84 months to complete program. *Concentrations:* finance, human resources, information management, marketing.

MBA—Master of Business Administration Full-time and part-time. At least 39 total credits required. 24 to 84 months to complete program. *Concentrations:* finance, human resources, information management, marketing.

*L*ocated in the suburbs of Wilmington, Delaware, Goldey-Beacom College is a small, private college with a tradition of excellence, specializing exclusively in business education since 1886. The College is accredited nationally by ACBSP and regionally by the Commission on Higher Education of the Middle States Association of Colleges and Schools.

The M.B.A. Program is specifically aimed at the working professional and manager. It combines a convenient location, convenient course schedule, small class size, friendly atmosphere, teaching-oriented and experienced faculty members, and an open-minded administration.

The M.B.A. Program develops skills needed to successfully manage in tomorrow's global marketplace. The twelve required courses build upon a basic foundation of business knowledge gained through formal education, work experience, or specialized training. With all courses offered in the evening, the M.B.A. can be earned in two years, on a part-time basis, by taking courses in the fall, spring, and summer semesters. Students may pursue the Comprehensive M.B.A. or concentrations in human resource management, financial management, accounting, and marketing management.

The M.B.A. Program features case studies, team projects, small group seminars, research, and practical experience led and taught by an outstanding faculty, the members of which all have both the Ph.D. and significant business experience. Formal instruction is enhanced through interaction with dynamic executives from both large corporations and small businesses, who share their business expertise and acumen.

COSTS

Tuition *Part-time:* $366 per credit. Tuition varies by number of courses or credits taken and academic program. **Required fees:** *Part-time* $5 per credit. **Graduate housing:** *Typical cost:* $3590 (room only).

FINANCIAL AID (1999–2000)

Loans. Aid is available to part-time students. **Financial Aid Contact** Financial Aid, 4701 Limestone Road, Wilmington, DE 19808-1999. **Phone:** 302-998-8814 Ext. 265.

RESOURCES AND SERVICES

Information about online services, personal computer policies, library resources, international exchange programs, internship programs, and placement services at this institution and others can be found at **www.petersons.com/mba**

International Students

10% of students enrolled are international students.

Services and Facilities Counseling/support services, visa services. Financial aid is not available to international students.
Applying *Required:* TOEFL with recommended score of 525 (paper), proof of adequate funds, proof of health/immunizations.
International Student Contact Ms. Alison Boord White, Assistant Director of Admissions, 4701 Limestone Road, Wilmington, DE 19808-1999. **Phone:** 800-833-4877 Ext. 289. **Fax:** 302-996-5408. **E-mail:** whitea@goldey.gbc.edu.

■ APPLICATION

Required GMAT, application form, baccalaureate/first degree, 3 letters of recommendation, personal statement, transcripts of college work.

Deadlines and Fees Applications for domestic students are processed on a rolling basis. *Deadlines:* 7/1 for fall (international), 11/1 for spring (international), 4/1 for summer (international). *Application fee:* $30, $30 (international).

Application Contact Ms. Alison Boord White, Assistant Director of Admissions, 4701 Limestone Road, Wilmington, DE 19808. **Fax:** 302-996-5409. **E-mail:** graduate@goldey.gbc.edu.

University of Delaware

Newark, Delaware

COLLEGE OF BUSINESS AND ECONOMICS

Graduate Business Faculty
Full-time: 90   Part-time: 5

Student Body
Total: 405   Average Age: 26
Full-time: 139   Women: 36%
Part-time: 266

Admissions
Applications: 266   Average GMAT: 610
Admitted: 120   Average GPA: 3.1
Enrolled: 101

Costs (1999–2000)
Full-time tuition: $5771 per academic year (resident), $12,991 per academic year (nonresident)
Part-time tuition: $307 per credit hour (resident), $708 per credit hour (nonresident)

After Graduation (Class of 1998–99)
Employed within 3 months of graduation: 77%
Average starting salary: $53,230

Accreditation
AACSB—The International Association for Management Education

DEGREES MBA • MBA/MA • MSA

MBA—Executive MBA Full-time. At least 48 total credits required. 19 months to complete program.

MBA—Master of Business Administration Full-time and part-time. 36 to 48 total credits required. 11 to 60 months to complete program. *Concentrations:* accounting, arts administration/management, economics, finance, information management, international business, management, marketing, operations management, technology management.

MBA/MA—Master of Arts in Economics/Master of Business Administration Full-time and part-time. 57 total credits required. 20 to 40 months to complete program.

MSA—Master of Science in Accounting Full-time and part-time. 36 to 48 total credits required. 11 to 60 months to complete program. *Concentrations:* accounting.

COSTS

Tuition, state resident: *Full-time* $5530. *Part-time* $307 per credit hour. **Tuition, nonresident:** *Full-time* $12,750. *Part-time* $708 per credit hour. Tuition varies by class time and academic program. **Required fees:** *Full-time* $241. *Part-time* $120 per semester. **Graduate housing:** Room and board costs vary by number of occupants, type of accommodation, and type of board plan. *Typical cost:* $7200 (including board).

FINANCIAL AID (1999–2000)

21 students received aid, including fellowships, research assistantships, teaching assistantships, and work study. Financial aid application deadline: 2/1. **Financial Aid Contact** Mr. Ronald Sibert, Director of MBA Programs, 103 MBNA America Hall, Newark, DE 19716. **Phone:** 302-831-2221. **Fax:** 302-831-3329. **E-mail:** mbaprograms@udel.edu.

RESOURCES AND SERVICES

Information about online services, personal computer policies, library resources, international exchange programs, internship programs, and placement services at this institution and others can be found at **www.petersons.com/mba**

International Students

16% of students enrolled are international students.

Services and Facilities Counseling/support services, ESL/language courses. Financial aid is available to international students.
Applying *Required:* TOEFL with recommended score of 585 (paper), proof of adequate funds, proof of health/immunizations.
International Student Contact Ms. Mary Politakis, Staff Assistant, Foreign Student and Scholar Services, 4 Kent Way, Newark, DE 19716. **Phone:** 302-831-2115. **Fax:** 302-831-2123. **E-mail:** mary.politakis@mvs.udel.edu.

■ APPLICATION

Required GMAT, application form, baccalaureate/first degree, essay, interview, 2 letters of recommendation, personal statement, resume/curriculum vitae, transcripts of college work. **Recommended** 2 years of work experience.

Deadlines and Fees *Deadlines:* 5/1 for fall, 5/1 for fall (international). *Application fee:* $45, $45 (international).
Application Contact Mr. Ronald Sibert, Director of MBA Programs, 103 MBNA America Hall, Newark, DE 19716. **Phone:** 302-831-2221. **Fax:** 302-831-3329. **E-mail:** mbaprograms@udel.edu.

See full description on page 894.

Wilmington College

New Castle, Delaware

DIVISION OF BUSINESS

Graduate Business Faculty
Full-time: 10   Part-time: 65

Student Body
Total: 1,405   Average Age: 33
Full-time: 259   Women: 73%
Part-time: 1,146

Admissions
Applications: 70   Enrolled: 68
Admitted: 70   Average GPA: 3

Costs (1999–2000)
Full-time tuition: N/R
Part-time tuition: $249 per credit

After Graduation (Class of 1998–99)
Employed within 3 months of graduation: 100%
Average starting salary: $35,000

DEGREES MBA • MS

MBA—Master of Business Administration Full-time and part-time. At least 36 total credits required. 12 to 60 months to complete program. *Concentrations:* health care.

MS—Master of Science in Management Full-time and part-time. At least 36 total credits required. 12 to 60 months to complete program. *Concentrations:* health care, human resources, public policy and administration.

COSTS

Tuition *Part-time:* $249 per credit. Tuition varies by campus location. **Required fees:** *Full-time* $50.

FINANCIAL AID (1999–2000)

Financial Aid Contact Lynn Iocono, Director, Financial Aid, 320 DuPont Highway, New Castle, DE 19720. **Phone:** 302-328-9407 Ext. 106. **Fax:** 302-328-5902.

RESOURCES AND SERVICES

Information about online services, personal computer policies, library resources, international exchange programs, internship programs, and placement services at this institution and others can be found at **www.petersons.com/mba**

International Students

0.4% of students enrolled are international students.

Services and Facilities International admission procedures. Financial aid is not available to international students.
Applying *Required:* TOEFL with recommended score of 500 (paper), proof of adequate funds, proof of health/immunizations.
International Student Contact Ms. Barbara Wilson, International Student Advisor, 320 DuPont Highway, New Castle, DE 19720-6491. **Phone:** 302-328-9407 Ext. 151. **Fax:** 302-328-5902.

■ APPLICATION

Required Application form, baccalaureate/first degree, interview, 2 letters of recommendation, personal statement, transcripts of college work, 3 years of work experience.

Deadlines and Fees Applications for domestic and international students are processed on a rolling basis. *Application fee:* $25, $25 (international).
Application Contact Dr. Clinton D. Robertson, Coordinator of MBA Program, 518 North King Street, Wilmington, DE 19801. **Phone:** 302-655-5400. **Fax:** 302-655-7360.

DISTRICT OF COLUMBIA

American University

Washington, District of Columbia

KOGOD SCHOOL OF BUSINESS

Graduate Business Faculty
Full-time: 57

Part-time: 21

Student Body
Total: 549

Full-time: 291

Part-time: 258

Average Age: 26

Women: 43%

Admissions
Applications: 793

Admitted: 516

Enrolled: 192

Average GMAT: 580

Average GPA: 3.3

Costs (1999–2000)
Full-time tuition: $19,407 per academic year

Part-time tuition: $721 per credit

After Graduation (Class of 1998–99)
Employed within 3 months of graduation: 80%

Average starting salary: $56,000

Accreditation
AACSB—The International Association for Management Education

DEGREES MBA • MS

MBA—Master of Business Administration Full-time and part-time. 39 to 51 total credits required. Minimum of 18 months to complete program. *Concentrations:* accounting, developmental economics, electronic commerce (e-commerce), entrepreneurship, finance, human resources, international business, international finance, international management, international marketing, management information systems, marketing, organizational behavior/development, real estate, taxation.

MS—Master of Science in Accounting Full-time and part-time. 30 to 57 total credits required. 12 to 24 months to complete program.

MS—Master of Science in Finance Full-time and part-time. 30 to 42 total credits required. 12 to 24 months to complete program.

MS—Master of Science in Personnel and Human Resource Management Full-time and part-time. 30 to 39 total credits required. 12 to 24 months to complete program.

MS—Master of Science in Taxation Full-time and part-time. 30 to 57 total credits required. 12 to 24 months to complete program.

COSTS

Tuition *Full-time:* $19,292. *Part-time:* $721 per credit. Tuition varies by number of courses or credits taken and academic program. **Required fees:** *Full-time* $115. *Part-time* $80 per year. **Graduate housing:** Room and board costs vary by campus location, number of occupants, type of accommodation, and type of board plan. *Typical cost:* $10,000 (including board).

FINANCIAL AID (1999–2000)

85 students received aid, including fellowships, loans, research assistantships, and work study. Aid is available to part-time students. Financial aid application deadline: 2/1. **Financial Aid Contact** Ms. Sondra Smith, Director of Graduate Admissions and Financial Aid, Kogod School of Business, 4400 Massachusetts Avenue, NW, Washington, DC 20016. **Phone:** 202-885-1913. **Fax:** 202-885-1078. **E-mail:** aumbams@american.edu.

RESOURCES AND SERVICES

Information about online services, personal computer policies, library resources, international exchange programs, internship programs, and placement services at this institution and others can be found at **www.petersons.com/mba**

International Students

Services and Facilities Counseling/support services, ESL/language courses, housing location assistance, international student housing, international student organization, language tutoring, orientation, visa services. Financial aid is available to international students.

Applying *Required:* TOEFL with recommended score of 250 (computer) or 600 (paper), proof of adequate funds, proof of health/immunizations.

International Student Contact Fanta Aw, Director, International Student Services, Butler Pavilion, Room 408, 4400 Massachusetts Avenue, NW, Washington, DC 20016. **Phone:** 202-885-3357. **Fax:** 202-885-3354.

■ APPLICATION

Required GMAT, application form, baccalaureate/first degree, essay, interview, letter(s) of recommendation, personal statement, resume/curriculum vitae, transcripts of college work. **Recommended** 2 years of work experience.

Deadlines and Fees Applications for international students are processed on a rolling basis. *Application fee:* $50, $50 (international).

Application Contact Ms. Sondra Smith, Director of Graduate Admissions and Financial Aid, Kogod School of Business, 4400 Massachusetts Avenue, NW, Washington, DC 20016. **Phone:** 202-885-1913. **Toll-free Phone:** 800-AN-AU-MBA. **Fax:** 202-885-1078. **E-mail:** aumbams@american.edu.

See full description on page 544.

The Catholic University of America

Washington, District of Columbia

DEPARTMENT OF ECONOMICS AND BUSINESS

Graduate Business Faculty
Full-time: 12

Part-time: 8

Student Body
Total: 21

Full-time: 9

Part-time: 12

Average Age: 30

Women: 62%

Admissions
Applications: 40

Admitted: 25

Enrolled: 5

Average GMAT: 500

Average GPA: 3

Costs (1999–2000)
Full-time tuition: $19,900 per academic year

Part-time tuition: $682 per credit hour

DEGREES MA • MS

MA—Master of Arts in Economics Full-time and part-time. At least 30 total credits required. 18 to 24 months to complete program. *Concentrations:* economics.

MA—Master of Arts in Financial Management Full-time and part-time. At least 36 total credits required. 18 to 24 months to complete program. *Concentrations:* finance, management.

MA—Master of Arts in Human Resources Management Full-time and part-time. At least 36 total credits required. 18 to 24 months to complete program. *Concentrations:* human resources, management.

MA—Master of Arts in International Political Economics Full-time and part-time. At least 36 total credits required. 18 to 24 months to complete program. *Concentrations:* international economics.

MS—Master of Science in Accounting Full-time and part-time. At least 30 total credits required. 18 to 24 months to complete program. *Concentrations:* accounting.

COSTS

Tuition *Full-time:* $19,100. *Part-time:* $682 per credit hour. **Required fees:** *Full-time* $800. *Part-time* $800 per year. Tuition and fees vary by number of courses or credits taken and academic program. **Graduate housing:** Room and board costs vary by number of occupants, type of accommodation, and type of board plan. *Typical cost:* $4400 (including board).

FINANCIAL AID (1999–2000)

4 students received aid, including loans, scholarships, teaching assistantships, and work study. Aid is available to part-time students. Financial aid application deadline: 2/1. **Financial Aid Contact** Dr. Kevin Forbes, Chairperson, Department of Business and Economics, Washington, DC 20064. **Phone:** 202-319-4794. **Fax:** 202-319-4426. **E-mail:** forbes@cua.edu.

RESOURCES AND SERVICES

Information about online services, personal computer policies, library resources, international exchange programs, internship programs, and placement services at this institution and others can be found at **www.petersons.com/mba**

The Catholic University of America (continued)

International Students

48% of students enrolled are international students.

Services and Facilities Counseling/support services, ESL/language courses, international student housing, visa services.

Applying *Required:* TOEFL with recommended score of 580 (paper), proof of adequate funds, proof of health/immunizations.

International Student Contact Dr. Jean Claude Leon, Department of Business and Economics, Washington, DC 20064. **Phone:** 202-319-5236. **Fax:** 202-319-4426.

■ APPLICATION

Required Application form, baccalaureate/first degree, 3 letters of recommendation, transcripts of college work. School will accept GMAT and GRE. **Recommended** Essay, personal statement.

Deadlines and Fees Applications for domestic and international students are processed on a rolling basis. *Application fee:* $50, $50 (international).

Application Contact Graduate Admissions, Cardinal Station Post Office, Washington, DC 20064. **Phone:** 202-319-5057.

Georgetown University

Washington, District of Columbia

GEORGETOWN MBA, MCDONOUGH SCHOOL OF BUSINESS

Graduate Business Faculty

Full-time: 64	Part-time: 16

Student Body

Total: 530	Average Age: 28
Full-time: 530	Women: 38%

Admissions

Applications: 1,900	Average GMAT: 641
Admitted: 650	Average GPA: 3.32
Enrolled: 262	

Costs (1999–2000)
Full-time tuition: $25,880 per academic year
Part-time tuition: N/R

After Graduation (Class of 1998–99)
Employed within 3 months of graduation: 95%
Average starting salary: $63,857

Accreditation
AACSB—The International Association for Management Education

DEGREES JD/MBA • MBA • MBA/MPP • MBA/MS • MD/MBA

JD/MBA—Juris Doctor/Master of Business Administration Full-time. At least 122 total credits required. Minimum of 48 months to complete program.

MBA—International Executive MBA Full-time. At least 60 total credits required. Minimum of 18 months to complete program.

MBA—Master of Business Administration Full-time. At least 60 total credits required. Minimum of 21 months to complete program.

MBA/MPP—Master of Business Administration/Master of Public Policy Full-time. At least 87 total credits required. Minimum of 36 months to complete program.

MBA/MS—Master of Business Administration/Master of Science in Foreign Service Full-time. At least 90 total credits required. Minimum of 36 months to complete program.

MD/MBA—Doctor of Medicine/Master of Business Administration Full-time. Minimum of 60 months to complete program.

COSTS

Tuition *Full-time:* $23,880. Tuition varies by number of courses or credits taken and academic program. **Required fees:** *Full-time* $2000. Tuition and fees vary by academic program.

FINANCIAL AID (1999–2000)

142 students received aid, including loans, research assistantships, scholarships, and work study. Financial aid application deadline: 2/1.
Financial Aid Contact Mr. Bill Brosseau, Counselor, Main Campus, Office of Student Financial Services—MBA Contact, G-19 Healy Building, Washington, DC 20057. **Phone:** 202-687-4547. **Fax:** 202-687-6542. **E-mail:** brosseab@gunet.georgetown.edu.

RESOURCES AND SERVICES

Information about online services, personal computer policies, library resources, international exchange programs, internship programs, and placement services at this institution and others can be found at **www.petersons.com/mba**

International Students

38% of students enrolled are international students.

Services and Facilities Counseling/support services, ESL/language courses, housing location assistance, orientation, visa services. Financial aid is available to international students.

Applying *Required:* TOEFL with recommended score of 600 (paper), proof of adequate funds, proof of health/immunizations.

International Student Contact Mr. Robin McWilliams, Coordinator International Programs and Student Services, 3520 Prospect Street Northwest, Suite 211, Washington, DC 20057-1148. **Phone:** 202-687-3938. **Fax:** 202-687-7809. **E-mail:** crm5@msb.edu.

■ APPLICATION

Required GMAT, application form, baccalaureate/first degree, essay, 2 letters of recommendation, resume/curriculum vitae, transcripts of college work, 3 years of work experience. **Recommended** Interview, personal statement.

Deadlines and Fees *Deadlines:* 4/15 for fall, 2/1 for fall (international). *Application fee:* $75, $75 (international).

Application Contact Mr. Robert Wheeler, Director of Admissions, 3520 Prospect Street Northwest, Suite 215, Box 571148, Washington, DC 20057-1148. **Phone:** 202-687-4200. **Fax:** 202-687-7809. **E-mail:** wheelerr@msb.edu.

See full description on page 664.

The George Washington University

Washington, District of Columbia

SCHOOL OF BUSINESS AND PUBLIC MANAGEMENT

Graduate Business Faculty

Full-time: 133	Part-time: 57

Student Body

Total: 2,310	Average Age: 32
Full-time: 968	Women: 41%
Part-time: 1,342	

Admissions

Applications: 2,991	Average GMAT: 599
Admitted: 1,475	Average GPA: 3.21
Enrolled: 719	

Costs (1999–2000)
Full-time tuition: N/R
Part-time tuition: $702 per credit

After Graduation (Class of 1998–99)
Employed within 3 months of graduation: 90%
Average starting salary: $61,000

Accreditation
AACSB—The International Association for Management Education

DEGREES JD/MBA • M Acc • MBA • MBA/MA • MPA • MPP • MSAM • MSF • MSIST • MSPM • MTA

JD/MBA—Juris Doctor/Master of Business Administration Full-time and part-time. GMAT, LSAT, and dual application required. At least 108 total credits required. 45 months to complete program. *Concentrations:* accounting, business policy/strategy, decision sciences, electronic commerce (e-commerce), entrepreneurship, environmental economics/management, finance, health care, human resources, information management, international business, logistics, management, management consulting, management information systems, management science, marketing, marketing research, operations management, organizational behavior/development, public policy and administration, real estate, strategic management, travel industry/tourism management.

M Acc—Master of Accountancy Full-time and part-time. GMAT score required. 35 to 40 total credits required. 12 to 60 months to complete program. *Concentrations:* accounting, taxation.

MBA—Accelerated MBA Part-time. GMAT, interview, and 4 years of work experience typically required. 40 to 48 total credits required. 24 months to complete program. *Concentrations:* accounting, business policy/strategy, decision sciences, electronic commerce (e-commerce), entrepreneurship, environmental economics/management, finance, health care, human resources, information management, international business, logistics, management, management consulting, management information systems, management science, marketing, marketing research, operations management, organizational behavior/development, public policy and administration, real estate, strategic management, travel industry/tourism management.

MBA—Executive MBA Part-time. Interview, GMAT score, and 10 years of work experience typically required (5 years in mid- to upper-level management or senior professional experience). 60 total credits required. 21 months to complete program. *Concentrations:* management.

MBA—Full-time MBA Full-time. GMAT required, minimum of 1-3 years of work experience preferred. 50 to 54 total credits required. 21 to 30 months to complete program. *Concentrations:* accounting, business policy/strategy, decision sciences, electronic commerce (e-commerce), entrepreneurship, environmental economics/management, finance, health care, human resources, information management, international business, logistics, management, management consulting, management information systems, management science, marketing, marketing research, operations management, organizational behavior/development, public policy and administration, real estate, strategic management, travel industry/tourism management.

MBA—Part-Time MBA Part-time. GMAT and 3 years minimum of work experience required; must be fully employed. 40 to 48 total credits required. 36 to 60 months to complete program. *Concentrations:* management.

MBA/MA—Master of Business Administration/Master of Arts in International Affairs Full-time and part-time. GMAT, GRE, and application to joint degree program required. At least 56 total credits required. 20 to 60 months to complete program. *Concentrations:* international business.

MPA—Master of Public Administration Full-time and part-time. GRE score required. Up to 40 total credits required. 18 to 60 months to complete program. *Concentrations:* finance, public management, public policy and administration.

MPP—Master of Public Policy Full-time and part-time. GRE required. At least 40 total credits required. 18 to 60 months to complete program. *Concentrations:* public and private management, public policy and administration.

MSAM—Master of Science in Acquisition Management Full-time and part-time. GRE or GMAT score required. 33 to 36 total credits required. 12 to 60 months to complete program.

MSF—Master of Science in Finance Full-time and part-time. GRE or GMAT score required, interview preferred. 48 to 69 total credits required. 12 to 24 months to complete program.

MSIST—Master of Science in Information Systems Technology Full-time and part-time. GRE required for applicants without related undergraduate degree. 30 to 33 total credits required. 12 to 60 months to complete program. *Concentrations:* management information systems, project management, technology management.

MSPM—Master of Science in Project Management Full-time and part-time. *Distance learning option.* GRE or GMAT scores and an interview are recommended. 27 to 36 total credits required. 12 to 60 months to complete program.

MTA—Master of Tourism Administration Full-time and part-time. GMAT or GRE score required. At least 36 total credits required. Minimum of 12 months to complete program.

COSTS

Tuition *Part-time:* $702 per credit. **Required fees:** Tuition and fees vary by number of courses or credits taken, campus location, and academic program.

FINANCIAL AID (1999–2000)

Fellowships, loans, teaching assistantships, and work study. Aid is available to part-time students. Financial aid application deadline: 2/1. **Financial Aid Contact** Mr. Daniel Small, Director, Student Financial Assistance, 2121 Eye Street, NW, Suite 310, Washington, DC 20052. **Phone:** 202-994-6620.

RESOURCES AND SERVICES

Information about online services, personal computer policies, library resources, international exchange programs, internship programs, and placement services at this institution and others can be found at **www.petersons.com/mba**

International Students

27% of students enrolled are international students.

Services and Facilities Counseling/support services, ESL/language courses, housing location assistance, international student organization, language tutoring, orientation, visa services. Financial aid is available to international students. **Applying** *Required:* TOEFL with recommended score of 550 (paper), proof of adequate funds, proof of health/immunizations. *Recommended:* TSE, TWE. **International Student Contact** Mr. Alan Williams, Assistant Director, Marketing and Recruitment, School of Business and Public Management, 710 21st Street,

NW, Government Hall 209, Washington, DC 20052. **Phone:** 202-994-5536. **Fax:** 202-994-3571. **E-mail:** sbpmapp@gwu.edu.

■ APPLICATION

Required Application form, baccalaureate/first degree, essay, 3 letters of recommendation, personal statement, resume/curriculum vitae, transcripts of college work. School will accept GMAT and GRE. **Recommended** Work experience. **Deadlines and Fees** *Deadlines:* 4/1 for fall, 10/1 for spring, 4/1 for fall (international), 10/1 for spring (international). *Application fee:* $60, $60 (international). **Application Contact** Ms. Dorothy J. Umans, Director, Graduate Admissions, School of Business and Public Management, 710 21st Street, NW, Government Hall 209, Washington, DC 20052. **Phone:** 202-994-6584. **Fax:** 202-994-6382. **E-mail:** sbpmapp@gwis2.circ.gwu.edu.

See full description on page 666.

Howard University

Washington, District of Columbia

SCHOOL OF BUSINESS

Graduate Business Faculty
Full-time: 5

Student Body

Total: 16	Average Age: 22
Full-time: 16	Women: 56%

Admissions

Applications: 291	Average GMAT: 445
Admitted: 40	Average GPA: 3.02
Enrolled: 16	

Costs (1999–2000)
Full-time tuition: $11,370 per academic year
Part-time tuition: N/R

After Graduation (Class of 1998–99)
Average starting salary: $65,000

Accreditation
AACSB—The International Association for Management Education

DEGREES JD/MBA • MBA

JD/MBA—Juris Doctor/Master of Business Administration Full-time. At least 127 total credits required. 48 months to complete program.

MBA—Master of Business Administration in Health Services Administration Full-time. 48 to 54 total credits required. 24 to 72 months to complete program.

MBA—Masters of Business Administration in Finance Full-time and part-time. 48 to 54 total credits required. 24 to 78 months to complete program.

MBA—Master of Business Administration Full-time and part-time. 48 to 54 total credits required. 24 to 72 months to complete program. *Concentrations:* accounting, electronic commerce (e-commerce), entrepreneurship, finance, health care, human resources, information management, international business, marketing, supply chain management.

COSTS

Tuition *Full-time:* $11,370. Tuition varies by number of courses or credits taken. **Graduate housing:** *Typical cost:* $9400 (including board), $6700 (room only).

FINANCIAL AID (1999–2000)

Fellowships, grants, loans, research assistantships, scholarships, teaching assistantships, and work study. Financial aid application deadline: 6/1. **Financial Aid Contact** Director of Financial Aid and Student Employment, Washington, DC 20059. **Phone:** 202-806-2800.

RESOURCES AND SERVICES

Information about online services, personal computer policies, library resources, international exchange programs, internship programs, and placement services at this institution and others can be found at **www.petersons.com/mba**

International Students

Services and Facilities Housing location assistance, international student organization, orientation. Financial aid is available to international students. **Applying** *Required:* TOEFL with recommended score of 500 (paper), proof of adequate funds, proof of health/immunizations.

International Student Contact Director of International Student Services, Office of International Student Services, 2400 6th Street NW, Washington, DC 20059. **Phone:** 202-806-7517.

Howard University (continued)

■ **APPLICATION**

Required GMAT, application form, baccalaureate/first degree, 2 letters of recommendation, personal statement, resume/curriculum vitae, transcripts of college work. **Recommended** 1 year of work experience.

Deadlines and Fees *Deadlines:* 4/1 for fall, 11/1 for spring, 3/15 for summer, 4/1 for fall (international), 11/1 for spring (international), 3/15 for summer (international). *Application fee:* $45, $45 (international).

Application Contact MBA Program Office, 2400 Sixth Street, Washington, DC 20059-0002. **Phone:** 202-806-1514. **Fax:** 202-797-9363.

Southeastern University

Washington, District of Columbia

COLLEGE OF GRADUATE STUDIES

Graduate Business Faculty
Full-time: 7   Part-time: 51

Student Body
Total: 503   Average Age: 33.2
Full-time: 273   Women: 57%
Part-time: 230

Admissions
Applications: 168   Enrolled: 120
Admitted: 168

Costs (1999–2000)
Full-time tuition: N/R
Part-time tuition: $250 per credit

After Graduation (Class of 1998–99)
Employed within 3 months of graduation: 95%

DEGREES MBA • MPA • MS

MBA—Master of Business Administration Full-time and part-time. At least 45 total credits required. 12 to 84 months to complete program. *Concentrations:* accounting, finance, financial management/planning, information management, international management, management, marketing.

MPA—Master of Public Administration Full-time and part-time. At least 45 total credits required. 12 to 84 months to complete program. *Concentrations:* health care.

MS—Master of Science Full-time and part-time. At least 45 total credits required. 12 to 84 months to complete program. *Concentrations:* taxation.

COSTS

Tuition *Part-time:* $250 per credit. Tuition varies by number of courses or credits taken. **Required fees:** *Full-time* $300.

FINANCIAL AID (1999–2000)

72 students received aid, including loans and work study. Aid is available to part-time students. **Financial Aid Contact** Mr. Willis Parker, Director of Financial Aid, 501 Eye Street, Washington, DC 20024. **Phone:** 202-488-8162 Ext. 244. **Fax:** 202-488-8093. **E-mail:** willis@admin.seu. edu.

RESOURCES AND SERVICES

Information about online services, personal computer policies, library resources, international exchange programs, internship programs, and placement services at this institution and others can be found at **www. petersons.com/mba**

International Students

69% of students enrolled are international students.

Services and Facilities Counseling/support services, ESL/language courses, visa services. Financial aid is not available to international students.

Applying *Required:* TOEFL with recommended score of 550 (paper).

International Student Contact Ms. Gayle Damelin, Director of Student Services, 501 Eye Street, Washington, DC 20024. **E-mail:** gayle@admin.seu.edu.

■ **APPLICATION**

Required Application form, baccalaureate/first degree, 2 letters of recommendation, personal statement, resume/curriculum vitae, transcripts of college work. School will accept GRE. **Recommended** Interview, 3 years of work experience.

Deadlines and Fees Applications for domestic students are processed on a rolling basis. *Deadlines:* 7/1 for fall (international), 10/1 for winter (international),

12/1 for spring (international), 4/1 for summer (international). *Application fee:* $45, $45 (international).

Application Contact Mr. Jack Flinter, Jr., Director of Admissions, 501 Eye Street, Washington, DC 20024. **Phone:** 202-488-8162 Ext. 211. **Fax:** 202-488-8093. **E-mail:** jackf@admin.seu.edu.

Strayer University

Washington, District of Columbia

GRADUATE SCHOOL

DEGREES MSA • MSBA • MSIS

MSA—Master of Science in Professional Accounting Full-time and part-time. *Distance learning option.* At least 54 total credits required. 12 to 120 months to complete program. *Concentrations:* accounting.

MSBA—Master of Science in Business Administration Full-time and part-time. *Distance learning option.* At least 54 total credits required. 12 to 120 months to complete program. *Concentrations:* management.

MSIS—Master of Science in Information Systems Full-time and part-time. *Distance learning option.* At least 54 total credits required. 12 to 120 months to complete program. *Concentrations:* management information systems.

RESOURCES AND SERVICES

Information about online services, personal computer policies, library resources, international exchange programs, internship programs, and placement services at this institution and others can be found at **www. petersons.com/mba**

International Students

Services and Facilities Counseling/support services, international student organization, visa services. Financial aid is not available to international students. **International Student Contact** Ms. Cyndi Wastler, Manager of Student Certification, PO Box 1310, Newington, VA 22122. **Phone:** 703-339-2516. **Fax:** 703-339-3961. **E-mail:** clw@strayer.edu.

■ **APPLICATION**

Application Contact Mr. Michael Williams, Campus Coordinator, 1025 15th Street, NW, Washington, DC 20005-2603. **Phone:** 202-408-2400. **Fax:** 202-289-1831. **E-mail:** mw@strayer.edu.

University of the District of Columbia

Washington, District of Columbia

SCHOOL OF BUSINESS AND PUBLIC ADMINISTRATION

Graduate Business Faculty
Full-time: 8   Part-time: 5

Student Body
Total: 140   Average Age: 30
Full-time: 15   Women: 36%
Part-time: 125

Admissions
Applications: 50   Average GMAT: 450
Admitted: 40   Average GPA: 2.7
Enrolled: 32

Costs (1999–2000)
Full-time tuition: $3874 per academic year (resident), $6232 per academic year (nonresident)
Part-time tuition: $198 per credit hour (resident), $329 per credit hour (nonresident)

After Graduation (Class of 1998–99)
Employed within 3 months of graduation: 90%

DEGREES MBA • MPA

MBA—Master of Business Administration Full-time and part-time. At least 36 total credits required. 24 to 60 months to complete program. *Concentrations:* accounting, finance, international business, management, marketing.

MPA—Master of Public Administration Full-time and part-time. At least 36 total credits required. 24 to 60 months to complete program. *Concentrations:* public management, public policy and administration.

COSTS

Tuition, district resident: *Full-time* $3564. *Part-time* $198 per credit hour. **Tuition, nonresident:** *Full-time* $5922. *Part-time* $329 per credit hour. Tuition varies by number of courses or credits taken. **Required fees:** *Full-time* $310. *Part-time* $155 per semester.

FINANCIAL AID (1999–2000)

Loans and work study. **Financial Aid Contact** Allice Dais, Director of Financial Aid, 4200 Connecticut Avenue, NW, Washington, DC 20008-1175. **Phone:** 202-274-5060.

RESOURCES AND SERVICES

Information about online services, personal computer policies, library resources, international exchange programs, internship programs, and placement services at this institution and others can be found at www. petersons.com/mba

International Students

14% of students enrolled are international students.

Services and Facilities Counseling/support services, ESL/language courses, orientation.
Applying *Required:* TOEFL with recommended score of 550 (paper), proof of adequate funds, proof of health/immunizations.
International Student Contact Dr. Hany Makhlouf, Director of MBA and MPA, 4200 Connecticut Avenue, NW, Washington, DC 20008-1175. **Phone:** 202-274-7040. **Fax:** 202-274-7022.

■ APPLICATION

Required Application form, baccalaureate/first degree, essay, 2 letters of recommendation, personal statement, transcripts of college work. School will accept GMAT.
Deadlines and Fees Applications for domestic and international students are processed on a rolling basis. *Application fee:* $20, $20 (international).
Application Contact Dr. Hany Makhlouf, Director of MBA and MPA, 4200 Connecticut Avenue, NW, Washington, DC 20008-1175. **Phone:** 202-274-7040. **Fax:** 202-274-7022.

FLORIDA

American InterContinental University

Plantation, Florida

PROGRAM IN INTERNATIONAL BUSINESS

Graduate Business Faculty
Full-time: 4   Part-time: 20

Student Body
Total: 6   Women: 83%
Part-time: 6

Admissions
Applications: 8   Enrolled: 6
Admitted: 6

Costs (1999–2000)
Full-time tuition: N/R
Part-time tuition: $3690 per term

DEGREE MBA

MBA—Global Technology Management Full-time and part-time. Up to 60 total credits required. 7 to 14 months to complete program. *Concentrations:* information management, international business, management, technology management.

COSTS

Tuition *Part-time:* $3690 per term. Tuition varies by number of courses or credits taken. **Required fees:** *Part-time* $130 per course.

RESOURCES AND SERVICES

Information about online services, personal computer policies, library resources, international exchange programs, internship programs, and placement services at this institution and others can be found at www. petersons.com/mba

International Students

Services and Facilities Counseling/support services, visa services.
International Student Contact John Kramer, Registrar, 8151 West Peters Road, Suite 1000, Plantation, FL 33324. **Phone:** 954-835-0951. **Fax:** 954-835-1024. **E-mail:** jkramer@aiuniv.edu.

■ APPLICATION

Required Application form, baccalaureate/first degree, essay, interview, resume/curriculum vitae, transcripts of college work. **Recommended** 2 letters of recommendation, 3 years of work experience.
Deadlines and Fees Applications for domestic and international students are processed on a rolling basis. *Application fee:* $50, $50 (international).
Application Contact Ms. Kathleen Farrow, Director of Enrollment, 8151 West Peters Road, Suite 1000, Plantation, FL 33324. **Phone:** 954-835-0951. **Fax:** 954-835-1020. **E-mail:** kfarrow@aiuniv.edu.

Barry University

Miami Shores, Florida

SCHOOL OF BUSINESS

Graduate Business Faculty
Full-time: 8   Part-time: 13

Student Body
Total: 98   Part-time: 77
Full-time: 21   Women: 43%

Admissions
Applications: 67   Average GMAT: 455
Admitted: 46   Average GPA: 3.42
Enrolled: 26

Costs (1999–2000)
Full-time tuition: $11,040 per academic year
Part-time tuition: $460 per credit

DEGREES MBA • MBA/MS • MS

MBA—Master of Business Administration Full-time and part-time. At least 36 total credits required. 20 to 60 months to complete program. *Concentrations:* accounting, finance, health care, international business, management, management information systems, marketing.

MBA/MS—MBA-Master of Science in Nursing Part-time. At least 69 total credits required. Maximum of 84 months to complete program.

MBA/MS—MBA-Master of Science in Sport Management Part-time. At least 57 total credits required. 32 to 84 months to complete program. *Concentrations:* international business, management information systems.

MS—Electronic Commerce Full-time and part-time. At least 30 total credits required. 20 to 60 months to complete program.

COSTS

Tuition *Full-time:* $11,040. *Part-time:* $460 per credit.

FINANCIAL AID (1999–2000)

51 students received aid, including loans, research assistantships, and scholarships. Aid is available to part-time students. **Financial Aid Contact** Ms. Celia Melis, Associate Director, Graduate Financial Aid, 11300 Northeast Second Avenue, Miami Shores, FL 33161-6695. **Phone:** 305-899-3670. **Fax:** 305-899-3104. **E-mail:** finaid@mail.barry.edu.

RESOURCES AND SERVICES

Information about online services, personal computer policies, library resources, international exchange programs, internship programs, and placement services at this institution and others can be found at www. petersons.com/mba

International Students

32% of students enrolled are international students.

Services and Facilities Counseling/support services, ESL/language courses, housing location assistance, visa services. Financial aid is not available to international students.
Applying *Required:* TOEFL with recommended score of 213 (computer) or 550 (paper), proof of adequate funds, proof of health/immunizations.

Barry University (continued)

International Student Contact Ms. Joy DeMarchis, Director, International Student Services, 11300 Northeast Second Avenue, Miami Shores, FL 33161-6695. **Phone:** 305-899-3082. **Fax:** 305-899-3083. **E-mail:** jdemarchis@mail.barry.edu.

■ **APPLICATION**

Required Application form, baccalaureate/first degree, essay, 2 letters of recommendation, transcripts of college work. School will accept GMAT.

Deadlines and Fees Applications for domestic and international students are processed on a rolling basis. *Application fee:* 30 Australian dollars, 30 Australian dollars (international).

Application Contact Mr. Jose Poza, Marketing Director, 11300 Northeast Second Avenue, Miami Shores, FL 33161-6695. **Phone:** 305-899-3500. **Toll-free Phone:** 800-269-1111. **Fax:** 305-892-6412. **E-mail:** jpoza@mail.barry.edu.

Embry-Riddle Aeronautical University

Daytona Beach, Florida

DEPARTMENT OF BUSINESS ADMINISTRATION

Graduate Business Faculty
Full-time: 12

Student Body
Total: 81
Full-time: 47
Part-time: 34

Average Age: 28
Women: 19%

Admissions
Applications: 56
Admitted: 46
Enrolled: 36

Average GMAT: 517
Average GPA: 3.03

Costs (1999–2000)
Full-time tuition: $8430 per academic year
Part-time tuition: $455 per credit hour

Accreditation
ACBSP—The American Council of Business Schools and Programs

DEGREE MBA

MBA—MBA in Aviation Business Administration Full-time and part-time. 36 to 39 total credits required. 18 to 84 months to complete program.

COSTS

Tuition *Full-time:* $8190. *Part-time:* $455 per credit hour. **Tuition, international:** *Full-time* $8190. Tuition varies by number of courses or credits taken, campus location, and academic program. **Required fees:** *Full-time* $240. **Graduate housing:** Room and board costs vary by campus location, number of occupants, type of accommodation, and type of board plan. *Typical cost:* $5370 (including board), $2800 (room only).

FINANCIAL AID (1999–2000)

53 students received aid, including fellowships, loans, research assistantships, scholarships, teaching assistantships, and work study. Aid is available to part-time students. Financial aid application deadline: 6/30. **Financial Aid Contact** Richard Ritzman, Director, Financial Aid Office, 600 South Clyde Morris Boulevard, Daytona Beach, FL 32114-3900. **Phone:** 904-226-6300. **Fax:** 904-226-6307. **E-mail:** vanceg@cts.db.erau.edu.

RESOURCES AND SERVICES

Information about online services, personal computer policies, library resources, international exchange programs, internship programs, and placement services at this institution and others can be found at **www.petersons.com/mba**

International Students

48% of students enrolled are international students.

Services and Facilities Counseling/support services, ESL/language courses, housing location assistance, international student organization. Financial aid is not available to international students.

Applying *Required:* TOEFL with recommended score of 213 (computer) or 550 (paper), TSE, proof of adequate funds, proof of health/immunizations.

International Student Contact Judith Assad, Director, International Student Services, 600 South Clyde Morris Boulevard, Daytona Beach, FL 32114-3900. **Phone:** 904-226-6579. **Fax:** 904-226-7920. **E-mail:** assadj@cts.db.erau.edu.

■ **APPLICATION**

Required GMAT, application form, baccalaureate/first degree, 3 letters of recommendation, personal statement, transcripts of college work.

Deadlines and Fees *Deadlines:* 8/6 for fall, 12/8 for spring, 4/7 for summer, 6/6 for fall (international), 10/6 for spring (international), 2/7 for summer (international). *Application fee:* $30, $50 (international).

Application Contact Stacey Wilkins, Graduate Admissions Specialist, 600 South Clyde Morris Boulevard, Daytona Beach, FL 32114-3900. **Phone:** 904-226-6115. **Fax:** 904-226-6299. **E-mail:** wilkinss@cts.db.erau.edu.

See full description on page 636.

Embry-Riddle Aeronautical University, Extended Campus

Daytona Beach, Florida

DEPARTMENT OF BUSINESS ADMINISTRATION

Graduate Business Faculty
Full-time: 96

Student Body
Total: 768
Full-time: 22
Part-time: 746

Average Age: 36
Women: 17%

Admissions
Applications: 227
Admitted: 193

Enrolled: 179

Costs (1999–2000)
Full-time tuition: $5712 per academic year
Part-time tuition: $238 per credit hour

Accreditation
ACBSP—The American Council of Business Schools and Programs

DEGREES MBA • MS

MBA—MBA in Aviation Business Administration Full-time and part-time. *Distance learning option.* 36 to 39 total credits required. Maximum of 84 months to complete program.

MS—Master of Science in Technical Management Full-time and part-time. *Distance learning option.* 39 total credits required. Maximum of 84 months to complete program.

COSTS

Tuition *Full-time:* $5712. *Part-time:* $238 per credit hour. **Tuition, international:** *Full-time* $5712. Tuition varies by campus location.

FINANCIAL AID (1999–2000)

55 students received aid, including loans. Aid is available to part-time students. **Financial Aid Contact** Richard Ritzman, Director of Financial Aid, 600 South Clyde Morris Boulevard, Daytona Beach, FL 32114-3900. **Phone:** 904-226-6300. **Fax:** 904-226-6307. **E-mail:** ritzmanr@cts.db.erau.edu.

RESOURCES AND SERVICES

Information about online services, personal computer policies, library resources, international exchange programs, internship programs, and placement services at this institution and others can be found at **www.petersons.com/mba**

International Students

2% of students enrolled are international students.

Services and Facilities Counseling/support services, ESL/language courses. Financial aid is not available to international students.

Applying *Required:* TOEFL with recommended score of 213 (computer) or 550 (paper), TSE, proof of adequate funds.

International Student Contact Pam Thomas, Director of Admissions and Records, 600 South Clyde Morris Boulevard, Daytona Beach, FL 32114. **Phone:** 904-226-6909. **Fax:** 904-226-6984. **E-mail:** ecinfo@ec.db.erau.edu.

■ **APPLICATION**

Required Application form, baccalaureate/first degree, essay, 3 letters of recommendation, personal statement, transcripts of college work. **Recommended** Interview.

Deadlines and Fees Applications for domestic and international students are processed on a rolling basis. *Application fee:* $30, $50 (international).

Application Contact Pam Thomas, Director of Admissions and Records, 600 South Clyde Morris Boulevard, Daytona Beach, FL 32114-3900. **Phone:** 904-226-6909. **Toll-free Phone:** 800-522-6787. **Fax:** 904-226-6984. **E-mail:** ecinfo@ec.db.erau.edu.

Florida Atlantic University

Boca Raton, Florida

COLLEGE OF BUSINESS

Graduate Business Faculty

Full-time: 104	Part-time: 9

Student Body

Total: 529	Average Age: 30
Full-time: 189	Women: 47%
Part-time: 340	

Admissions

Applications: 429	Average GMAT: 536
Admitted: 270	Average GPA: 3.28
Enrolled: 94	

Costs (1999–2000)
Full-time tuition: N/R
Part-time tuition: $148 per credit (resident), $509 per credit (nonresident)

After Graduation (Class of 1998–99)
Employed within 3 months of graduation: 95%
Average starting salary: $44,000

Accreditation
AACSB—The International Association for Management Education

DEGREES M Acc • M Tax • MBA

M Acc—Master of Accounting Full-time and part-time. At least 33 total credits required. 12 to 60 months to complete program. *Concentrations:* accounting.

M Tax—Master of Taxation Full-time and part-time. At least 33 total credits required. 12 to 60 months to complete program. *Concentrations:* taxation.

MBA—Executive MBA Full-time. At least 48 total credits required. 20 months to complete program. *Concentrations:* entrepreneurship, international business, management.

MBA—Weekend MBA Full-time. At least 39 total credits required. 24 months to complete program. *Concentrations:* entrepreneurship, international business, management.

MBA—Master of Business Administration Full-time and part-time. 39 to 51 total credits required. 12 to 84 months to complete program. *Concentrations:* accounting, arts administration/management, decision sciences, economics, electronic commerce (e-commerce), entrepreneurship, finance, financial management/planning, health care, international business, management, marketing, operations management, real estate, sports/entertainment management, travel industry/tourism management.

COSTS
Tuition, state resident: *Part-time* $148 per credit. **Tuition, nonresident:** *Part-time* $509 per credit. Tuition varies by academic program and local reciprocity agreements. **Required fees:** *Full-time* $50. Fees vary by number of courses or credits taken. **Graduate housing:** Room and board costs vary by campus location, number of occupants, type of accommodation, and type of board plan. *Typical cost:* $6320 (including board), $4330 (room only).

FINANCIAL AID (1999–2000)
32 students received aid, including fellowships, loans, research assistantships, teaching assistantships, and work study. Aid is available to part-time students. Financial aid application deadline: 3/1. **Financial Aid Contact** Ms. Carole Pfeilsticker, Director of Student Financial Aid, 777 Glades Road, PO Box 3091, Boca Raton, FL 33431-0991. **Phone:** 561-297-3530. **Fax:** 561-297-3517. **E-mail:** pfeilsti@fau.edu.

RESOURCES AND SERVICES
Information about online services, personal computer policies, library resources, international exchange programs, internship programs, and placement services at this institution and others can be found at **www.petersons.com/mba**

International Students

Services and Facilities Counseling/support services, ESL/language courses, international student housing, visa services. Financial aid is available to international students.

Applying *Required:* TOEFL with recommended score of 250 (computer) or 600 (paper), proof of adequate funds, proof of health/immunizations. *Recommended:* TSE with recommended score of 250.

International Student Contact Ms. Susan D'Amico, Director, Student Affairs, International Student and Scholars, SO 301, Boca Raton, FL 33431-0991. **Phone:** 561-297-3049. **Fax:** 561-297-2447. **E-mail:** damicos@fau.edu.

■ APPLICATION

Required GMAT, application form, baccalaureate/first degree, transcripts of college work. **Recommended** 2 years of work experience.

Deadlines and Fees *Deadlines:* 6/15 for fall, 10/15 for spring, 3/15 for summer, 5/15 for fall (international), 9/15 for spring (international), 2/15 for summer (international). *Application fee:* $20, $20 (international).

Application Contact Mrs. Ella Smith, Graduate Advisor, College of Business, Bue 126, Boca Raton, FL 33461-0991. **Phone:** 561-297-3650. **Fax:** 561-297-3686. **E-mail:** smith@fau.edu.

Florida Institute of Technology

Melbourne, Florida

SCHOOL OF BUSINESS

Graduate Business Faculty

Full-time: 12	Part-time: 10

Student Body

Total: 46	Average Age: 35
Full-time: 8	Women: 35%
Part-time: 38	

Admissions

Applications: 59	Average GMAT: 477
Admitted: 33	Average GPA: 3.34
Enrolled: 13	

Costs (1999–2000)
Full-time tuition: N/R
Part-time tuition: $575 per credit hour

After Graduation (Class of 1998–99)
Employed within 3 months of graduation: 98%

DEGREE MBA

MBA—Master of Business Administration Full-time and part-time. At least 36 total credits required. Minimum of 12 months to complete program.

COSTS
Tuition *Part-time:* $575 per credit hour. **Graduate housing:** Room and board costs vary by number of occupants, type of accommodation, and type of board plan. *Typical cost:* $5270 (including board), $2270 (room only).

FINANCIAL AID (1999–2000)
5 students received aid, including research assistantships and teaching assistantships. Financial aid application deadline: 3/1. **Financial Aid Contact** Mr. John Lally, Director, Financial Aid, 150 West University Boulevard, Melbourne, FL 32901-6975. **Phone:** 800-666-4348. **Fax:** 321-724-2778. **E-mail:** jlally@fit.edu.

RESOURCES AND SERVICES
Information about online services, personal computer policies, library resources, international exchange programs, internship programs, and placement services at this institution and others can be found at **www.petersons.com/mba**

International Students
4% of students enrolled are international students.

Services and Facilities Counseling/support services, ESL/language courses, international student housing, international student organization, language tutoring, orientation. Financial aid is not available to international students.

Applying *Required:* TOEFL with recommended score of 213 (computer) or 550 (paper), proof of adequate funds, proof of health/immunizations. *Recommended:* TSE with recommended score of 230, TWE.

International Student Contact Ms. Christine Frank, International Student Director and Scholar Services Director, 150 West University Boulevard, Melbourne, FL 32901-6975. **Phone:** 321-674-8053. **Fax:** 321-728-4570. **E-mail:** cfrank@fit.edu.

Florida Institute of Technology (continued)

■ APPLICATION

Required GMAT, application form, baccalaureate/first degree, transcripts of college work.

Deadlines and Fees Applications for domestic and international students are processed on a rolling basis. *Application fee:* $50, $50 (international).

Application Contact Ms. Carolyn Farrior, Associate Dean, Graduate Admission, 150 West University Boulevard, Melbourne, FL 32901-6975. **Phone:** 321-674-7118. **Toll-free Phone:** 800-944-4348. **Fax:** 321-723-9468. **E-mail:** cfarrior@fit.edu.

Florida International University

Miami, Florida

COLLEGE OF BUSINESS ADMINISTRATION

Graduate Business Faculty
Full-time: 82 | Part-time: 13

Student Body
Total: 893
Full-time: 142 | Average Age: 32
Part-time: 751 | Women: 48%

Admissions
Applications: 1,835 | Average GMAT: 530
Admitted: 439 | Average GPA: 3.4
Enrolled: 328

Costs (1999–2000)
Full-time tuition: N/R
Part-time tuition: N/R

After Graduation (Class of 1998–99)
Employed within 3 months of graduation: 95%
Average starting salary: $65,000

Accreditation
AACSB—The International Association for Management Education

DEGREES EMBA • EMST • EVEMBA • IMBA • M Acc • MS • MSMIS • MST

EMBA—Executive MBA Part-time. Eight years management experience, interview required. 46 total credits required. 21 months to complete program.

EMST—Executive Master of Science in Taxation Part-time. 30 total credits required. 12 to 72 months to complete program. *Concentrations:* taxation.

EVEMBA—Evening Master of Business Administration Part-time. 46 to 61 total credits required. 36 to 60 months to complete program. *Concentrations:* accounting, finance, human resources, international business, management information systems, marketing, organizational behavior/development.

IMBA—International Master of Business Administration Full-time. 46 total credits required. 12 to 24 months to complete program.

M Acc—Master of Accountancy Part-time. 30 to 60 total credits required. 36 to 72 months to complete program. *Concentrations:* accounting.

MS—Master of Science in Finance Part-time. 36 to 67 total credits required. 36 to 60 months to complete program. *Concentrations:* finance.

MSMIS—Master of Science in Management Information Systems Part-time. 30 total credits required. 13 months to complete program.

MST—Master of Science in Taxation Part-time. 30 total credits required. 36 to 72 months to complete program. *Concentrations:* taxation.

COSTS

Required fees: Tuition and fees vary by number of courses or credits taken and academic program. **Graduate housing:** Room and board costs vary by campus location, number of occupants, type of accommodation, and type of board plan. *Typical cost:* $10,000 (including board).

FINANCIAL AID (1999–2000)

Fellowships, loans, research assistantships, scholarships, teaching assistantships, and work study. Aid is available to part-time students.
Financial Aid Contact Ms. Ana Sarasti, Director, Financial Aid Office, University Park, Miami, FL 33199. **Phone:** 305-348-2489. **Fax:** 305-348-2346. **E-mail:** sarastia@fiu.edu.

RESOURCES AND SERVICES

Information about online services, personal computer policies, library resources, international exchange programs, internship programs, and placement services at this institution and others can be found at **www.petersons.com/mba**

International Students

7% of students enrolled are international students.

Services and Facilities Counseling/support services, ESL/language courses, housing location assistance, international student organization, language tutoring, orientation. Financial aid is available to international students.

Applying *Required:* TOEFL with recommended score of 173 (computer) or 500 (paper), proof of adequate funds, proof of health/immunizations.

International Student Contact Ms. Ana Sippin, Director, International Student Services, University Park, Miami, FL 33199. **Phone:** 305-348-2421. **Fax:** 305-348-1521. **E-mail:** sippina@fiu.edu.

■ APPLICATION

Required Application form, baccalaureate/first degree, 3 letters of recommendation, personal statement, resume/curriculum vitae, transcripts of college work. School will accept GMAT or GRE. **Recommended** Interview, work experience.

Deadlines and Fees Applications for domestic and international students are processed on a rolling basis. *Application fee:* $20, $20 (international).

Application Contact Ms. Eleanor Polster, Graduate Coordinator, FIU University Park Campus, Miami, FL 33199. **Phone:** 305-348-3256. **Fax:** 305-348-1763. **E-mail:** polstere@fiu.edu.

See full description on page 654.

Florida Metropolitan University– Orlando College, North

Orlando, Florida

DIVISION OF BUSINESS ADMINISTRATION

DEGREE MBA

MBA—Master of Business Administration Full-time. *Distance learning option.* 54 to 56 total credits required. 18 to 24 months to complete program. *Concentrations:* accounting, information management, international business, management, marketing.

RESOURCES AND SERVICES

Information about online services, personal computer policies, library resources, international exchange programs, internship programs, and placement services at this institution and others can be found at **www.petersons.com/mba**

■ APPLICATION

Application Contact Ms. Charlene Donnelly-Meyer, Director of Admissions, 5421 Diplomat Circle, Orlando, FL 32810-5674. **Phone:** 407-628-5870. **Fax:** 407-628-1344.

Florida Metropolitan University– Tampa College

Tampa, Florida

DIVISION OF BUSINESS AND COMPUTER INFORMATION SCIENCES

Graduate Business Faculty
Full-time: 1 | Part-time: 8

Student Body
Total: 80
Full-time: 52 | Average Age: 32
Part-time: 28 | Women: 46%

Admissions
Applications: 12 | Enrolled: 4
Admitted: 11 | Average GPA: 2.8

Costs (1999–2000)
Full-time tuition: $10,000 per academic year
Part-time tuition: $292 per credit hour

After Graduation (Class of 1998–99)
Employed within 3 months of graduation: 100%

DEGREE MBA

MBA—Master of Business Administration Full-time and part-time. *Distance learning option.* At least 54 total credits required. 15 to 60 months to complete program. *Concentrations:* accounting, human resources, international business, management information systems.

COSTS

Tuition *Full-time:* $9900. *Part-time:* $292 per credit hour. **Tuition, international:** *Full-time* $9900. **Required fees:** *Full-time* $100. *Part-time* $25 per quarter.

FINANCIAL AID (1999–2000)

19 students received aid, including work study. Aid is available to part-time students. **Financial Aid Contact** Mr. Rod Kirkwood, Director of Financial Aid, 3319 West Hillsborough Avenue, Tampa, FL 33614-5899. **Phone:** 813-879-6000 Ext. 145. **Fax:** 813-871-2483. **E-mail:** rkirkwood@cci.edu.

RESOURCES AND SERVICES

Information about online services, personal computer policies, library resources, international exchange programs, internship programs, and placement services at this institution and others can be found at **www.petersons.com/mba**

International Students

44% of students enrolled are international students.

Services and Facilities ESL/language courses, international student organization. Financial aid is not available to international students.
Applying *Required:* TOEFL with recommended score of 550 (paper), proof of adequate funds.
International Student Contact Mr. Lee Garner, Director of Admissions, 3319 West Hillsborough Avenue, Tampa, FL 33614. **Phone:** 813-879-6000 Ext. 129. **Fax:** 813-871-2483. **E-mail:** lgarner@cci.edu.

■ APPLICATION

Required Application form, baccalaureate/first degree, interview, personal statement, resume/curriculum vitae, transcripts of college work. School will accept GMAT or GRE.
Deadlines and Fees *Deadlines:* 10/16 for fall, 1/23 for winter, 4/23 for spring, 7/23 for summer, 10/16 for fall (international), 1/23 for winter (international), 4/23 for spring (international), 7/23 for summer (international). *Application fee:* $50, $50 (international).
Application Contact Mr. Lee Garner, Director of Admissions, 3319 West Hillsborough Avenue, Tampa, FL 33614. **Phone:** 813-879-6000 Ext. 129. **Fax:** 813-871-2483. **E-mail:** lgarner@cci.edu.

Florida Southern College

Lakeland, Florida

DEPARTMENT OF BUSINESS AND ECONOMICS

Graduate Business Faculty
Full-time: 14   Part-time: 6

Student Body
Total: 56
Part-time: 56   Average Age: 34
                                       Women: 61%

Admissions
Applications: 63   Average GMAT: 590
Admitted: 45   Average GPA: 3.2
Enrolled: 35

Costs (1999–2000)
Full-time tuition: N/R
Part-time tuition: $290 per credit hour

DEGREE MBA

MBA—Master of Business Administration Full-time and part-time. 36 to 52 total credits required. 18 to 84 months to complete program. *Concentrations:* accounting.

COSTS

Tuition *Part-time:* $290 per credit hour.

FINANCIAL AID (1999–2000)

36 students received aid, including loans. Aid is available to part-time students. Financial aid application deadline: 4/1. **Financial Aid Contact** Mr. David Bodwell, Director of Financial Aid, 111 Lake Hollingsworth Drive, Lakeland, FL 33801-5698. **Phone:** 863-680-4142. **Fax:** 863-680-4567.

RESOURCES AND SERVICES

Information about online services, personal computer policies, library resources, international exchange programs, internship programs, and placement services at this institution and others can be found at **www.petersons.com/mba**

International Students

4% of students enrolled are international students.

Services and Facilities Counseling/support services. Financial aid is not available to international students.
Applying *Required:* TOEFL with recommended score of 550 (paper), proof of adequate funds, proof of health/immunizations.
International Student Contact Mr. Bill Walker, Coordinator of External Programs, 111 Lake Hollingsworth Drive, Lakeland, FL 33801-5698. **Phone:** 863-680-4205. **Fax:** 863-680-4120.

■ APPLICATION

Required Application form, baccalaureate/first degree, 3 letters of recommendation, transcripts of college work. School will accept GMAT and GRE. **Recommended** Work experience.
Deadlines and Fees *Deadlines:* 8/1 for fall, 12/1 for spring, 4/1 for summer, 8/1 for fall (international), 12/1 for spring (international), 4/1 for summer (international). *Application fee:* $30, $30 (international).
Application Contact Mr. Bill Walker, Coordinator of External Programs, 111 Lake Hollingsworth Drive, Lakeland, FL 33801-5698. **Phone:** 863-680-4131. **Fax:** 863-680-4120. **E-mail:** hwalker@flsouthern.edu.

Florida State University

Tallahassee, Florida

COLLEGE OF BUSINESS

Graduate Business Faculty
Full-time: 85

Student Body
Total: 215
Full-time: 105   Average Age: 28
Part-time: 110   Women: 42%

Admissions
Applications: 214   Average GMAT: 570
Admitted: 156   Average GPA: 3.36
Enrolled: 126

Costs (1999–2000)
Full-time tuition: $6278 per academic year (resident), $21,790 per academic year (nonresident)
Part-time tuition: $146 per credit hour (resident), $507 per credit hour (nonresident)

After Graduation (Class of 1998–99)
Employed within 3 months of graduation: 95%
Average starting salary: $50,000

Accreditation
AACSB—The International Association for Management Education

DEGREES JD/MBA • M Acc • MBA • MSM

JD/MBA—Juris Doctor/Master of Business Administration Full-time. At least 113 total credits required. 36 to 48 months to complete program.

M Acc—Master of Accounting Full-time and part-time. At least 33 total credits required. 12 to 36 months to complete program. *Concentrations:* accounting, taxation.

MBA—Master of Business Administration Full-time and part-time. 42 to 43 total credits required. 12 to 30 months to complete program. *Concentrations:* entrepreneurship, finance, marketing, supply chain management.

MSM—Master of Science in Management Full-time and part-time. At least 32 total credits required. 12 to 36 months to complete program. *Concentrations:* management information systems.

COSTS

Tuition, state resident: *Full-time* $6278. *Part-time* $146 per credit hour. **Tuition, nonresident:** *Full-time* $21,790. *Part-time* $507 per credit hour. **Tuition, international:** *Full-time* $21,790. Tuition varies by campus location. **Graduate housing:** Room and board costs vary by campus location, number of occupants, type of accommodation, and type of board plan. *Typical cost:* $6000 (room only).

Florida State University (continued)

FINANCIAL AID (1999–2000)
45 students received aid, including fellowships, grants, loans, research assistantships, scholarships, and teaching assistantships. Financial aid application deadline: 1/15.

RESOURCES AND SERVICES
Information about online services, personal computer policies, library resources, international exchange programs, internship programs, and placement services at this institution and others can be found at **www.petersons.com/mba**

International Students
Services and Facilities Counseling/support services, ESL/language courses, international student housing, international student organization, orientation, visa services. Financial aid is not available to international students.
Applying *Required:* TOEFL with recommended score of 250 (computer) or 600 (paper), proof of adequate funds, proof of health/immunizations.
International Student Contact Ms. Roberta Christie, Director of Student Affairs, International Student Center, Room 107 ISH, Tallahassee, FL 32306-4240. **Phone:** 850-644-3050. **Fax:** 850-644-9951. **E-mail:** rchristie@admin.fsu.edu.

■ APPLICATION
Required GMAT, application form, baccalaureate/first degree, interview, 3 letters of recommendation, personal statement, resume/curriculum vitae, transcripts of college work, 2 years of work experience.
Deadlines and Fees *Deadlines:* 6/1 for fall, 10/1 for spring, 3/1 for summer, 3/3 for fall (international), 9/8 for spring (international), 2/1 for summer (international). *Application fee:* $20, $20 (international).
Application Contact Ms. Scheri Martin, Coordinator of Graduate Programs, Graduate Office, College of Business, Tallahassee, FL 32306-1110. **Phone:** 850-644-6458. **Fax:** 850-644-0915. **E-mail:** smartin@cob.fsu.edu.

See full description on page 656.

Jacksonville University
Jacksonville, Florida

DAVIS COLLEGE OF BUSINESS

DEGREES EMBA • MBA

EMBA—Executive Master of Business Administration Full-time. At least 40 total credits required. 24 months to complete program.
MBA—Master of Business Administration Full-time and part-time. At least 30 total credits required. 12 to 60 months to complete program.

RESOURCES AND SERVICES
Information about online services, personal computer policies, library resources, international exchange programs, internship programs, and placement services at this institution and others can be found at **www.petersons.com/mba**

International Students
Services and Facilities Counseling/support services, ESL/language courses, international student housing, orientation, visa services.
International Student Contact Ms. Sara Jeanne Myers, International Advisor, Assistant Dean of Students, 2800 University Boulevard North, Jacksonville, FL 32211. **Phone:** 904-745-7070. **Fax:** 904-745-7066. **E-mail:** smyers1@ju.edu.

■ APPLICATION
Application Contact Pamela Kirk Prentice, Director of Graduate Business Programs, 2800 University Boulevard North, Jacksonville, FL 32211. **Phone:** 904-745-7433. **Fax:** 904-745-7463. **E-mail:** mba@ju.edu.

Lynn University
Boca Raton, Florida

SCHOOL OF BUSINESS

DEGREE MBA

MBA—Master of Business Administration Full-time and part-time. At least 36 total credits required. 12 to 48 months to complete program. *Concentrations:* health care, international management, sports/entertainment management, travel industry/tourism management, hospitality management.

RESOURCES AND SERVICES
Information about online services, personal computer policies, library resources, international exchange programs, internship programs, and placement services at this institution and others can be found at **www.petersons.com/mba**

International Students
Services and Facilities Counseling/support services, ESL/language courses, visa services. Financial aid is not available to international students.
International Student Contact Ms. Shelia Sheppard-Sciarra, International Student Affairs Coordinator, 3601 North Military Trail, Boca Raton, FL 33431-5598. **Phone:** 561-237-7079.

■ APPLICATION
Application Contact Ms. Pat Sieredzki, Graduate Admission Coordinator, Admissions Office, 3601 North Military Trail, Boca Raton, FL 33431-5598. **Phone:** 561-237-7841. **Fax:** 561-237-7100. **E-mail:** psieredzki@lynn.edu.

Nova Southeastern University
Fort Lauderdale, Florida

WAYNE HUIZENGA GRADUATE SCHOOL OF BUSINESS AND ENTREPRENEURSHIP

Graduate Business Faculty
Full-time: 27 — Part-time: 200

Student Body
Total: 1,576 — Average Age: 35
Full-time: 118 — Women: 47%
Part-time: 1,458

Admissions
Applications: 671 — Average GMAT: 480
Admitted: 570 — Average GPA: 3
Enrolled: 445

Costs (1999–2000)
Full-time tuition: $10,416 per academic year
Part-time tuition: $434 per credit

DEGREES M Acc • MBA • MIBA • MPA • MS • MTX
M Acc—Master of Accounting Part-time. *Distance learning option.* At least 41 total credits required. 18 to 60 months to complete program. *Concentrations:* taxation.
MBA—Master of Business Administration Full-time and part-time. *Distance learning option.* At least 43 total credits required. 12 to 60 months to complete program. *Concentrations:* accounting, entrepreneurship, finance, health care, human resources, international business, management information systems, marketing, system management.
MIBA—Master of International Business Administration Full-time and part-time. *Distance learning option.* At least 41 total credits required. 12 to 60 months to complete program.
MPA—Master of Public Administration Full-time and part-time. *Distance learning option.* At least 48 total credits required. 18 to 60 months to complete program.
MS—Master of Science in Human Resource Management Part-time. *Distance learning option.* At least 43 total credits required. 18 to 60 months to complete program.
MTX—Master of Taxation Part-time. At least 36 total credits required. 18 to 60 months to complete program.

COSTS
Tuition *Full-time:* $10,416. *Part-time:* $434 per credit. Tuition varies by number of courses or credits taken and academic program. **Required fees:** Fees vary by campus location. **Graduate housing:** Room and board costs vary by number of occupants, type of accommodation, and type of board plan. *Typical cost:* $9000 (including board).

FINANCIAL AID (1999–2000)
800 students received aid, including loans, research assistantships, and work study. Aid is available to part-time students. Financial aid application deadline: 4/1. **Financial Aid Contact** Office of Student Financial Aid, 3301 College Avenue, Fort Lauderdale, FL 33314. **Phone:** 800-522-3243. **Fax:** 954-262-3966.

RESOURCES AND SERVICES
Information about online services, personal computer policies, library resources, international exchange programs, internship programs, and

placement services at this institution and others can be found at **www.petersons.com/mba**

International Students
16% of students enrolled are international students.
Services and Facilities Counseling/support services, visa services. Financial aid is not available to international students.
Applying *Required:* TOEFL with recommended score of 550 (paper), proof of adequate funds.
International Student Contact Ms. Debra Puzzo, International Student Advisor, 3301 College Avenue, Fort Lauderdale, FL 33314. **Phone:** 800-541-6682 Ext. 7240. **Fax:** 954-262-7265. **E-mail:** puzzo@nsu.nova.edu.

■ **APPLICATION**
Required Application form, baccalaureate/first degree, transcripts of college work. School will accept GMAT or GRE.
Deadlines and Fees *Deadlines:* 3/1 for fall, 5/31 for winter, 11/30 for spring, 8/30 for summer, 3/1 for fall (international), 5/31 for winter (international), 11/30 for spring (international), 8/30 for summer (international). *Application fee:* $50, $50 (international).
Application Contact Mr. Dan Schuckers, Office of Enrollment Management, 3100 SW 9th Avenue, Fort Lauderdale, FL 33315-3025. **Phone:** 800-672-7223 Ext. 5052. **Fax:** 954-262-3822. **E-mail:** schuckers@huizenga.nova.edu.

See full description on page 754.

Palm Beach Atlantic College
West Palm Beach, Florida

RINKER SCHOOL OF BUSINESS

Graduate Business Faculty
Full-time: 5 | Part-time: 21

Student Body
Total: 110
Full-time: 11 | Average Age: 33
Part-time: 99 | Women: 34%

Admissions
Applications: 107
Admitted: 39 | Average GMAT: 474
Enrolled: 36 | Average GPA: 3

Costs (1999–2000)
Full-time tuition: N/R
Part-time tuition: $280 per credit hour

DEGREE MBA

MBA—Management Full-time and part-time. At least 36 total credits required. 12 to 72 months to complete program. *Concentrations:* finance, management.

COSTS
Tuition *Part-time:* $280 per credit hour. Tuition varies by number of courses or credits taken and academic program. **Graduate housing:** Room and board costs vary by type of board plan. *Typical cost:* $9140 (including board), $6400 (room only).

FINANCIAL AID (1999–2000)
Financial Aid Contact Mrs. Lisa Lofton, Director of Student Financial Planning, PO Box 24708, West Palm Beach, FL 33416-4708. **Phone:** 561-803-2110. **Fax:** 561-803-2115 Ext. 2130. **E-mail:** lofton1@pbac.edu.

RESOURCES AND SERVICES
Information about online services, personal computer policies, library resources, international exchange programs, internship programs, and placement services at this institution and others can be found at **www.petersons.com/mba**

International Students
5% of students enrolled are international students.
Services and Facilities Counseling/support services, ESL/language courses. Financial aid is available to international students.
Applying *Required:* TOEFL with recommended score of 550 (paper), proof of adequate funds, proof of health/immunizations.
International Student Contact Ms. Cybelle Seeds, School of Arts and Sciences, PO Box 24708, West Palm Beach, FL 33416-4708. **Phone:** 561-803-2355. **E-mail:** seedsc@pbac.edu.

■ **APPLICATION**
Required GMAT, application form, baccalaureate/first degree, essay, interview, 3 letters of recommendation, transcripts of college work.
Deadlines and Fees Applications for international students are processed on a rolling basis. *Application fee:* $35, $35 (international).
Application Contact Mrs. Carolanne Brown, Coordinator, Graduate Studies, PO Box 24708, West Palm Beach, FL 33416-4708. **Phone:** 561-803-2121 Ext. 2124. **Toll-free Phone:** 800-281-3466 (in-state), 800-GO-TO-PBA (out-of-state). **Fax:** 561-803-2115. **E-mail:** grad@pbac.edu.

Rollins College
Winter Park, Florida

CRUMMER GRADUATE SCHOOL OF BUSINESS

Graduate Business Faculty
Full-time: 18 | Part-time: 7

Student Body
Total: 380
Full-time: 174 | Average Age: 29
Part-time: 206 | Women: 34%

Admissions
Applications: 525
Admitted: 262 | Average GMAT: 590
Enrolled: 177 | Average GPA: 3.2

Costs (1999–2000)
Full-time tuition: N/R
Part-time tuition: $680 per credit

After Graduation (Class of 1998–99)
Employed within 3 months of graduation: 98%
Average starting salary: $52,000

Accreditation
AACSB—The International Association for Management Education

DEGREES MBA

MBA—Accelerated MBA Full-time. At least 58 total credits required. 11 to 60 months to complete program. *Concentrations:* accounting, electronic commerce (e-commerce), finance, international and area business studies, management, management information systems, marketing, operations management.
MBA—Early Advantage MBA Full-time. Work experience is not required. At least 59 total credits required. 21 to 60 months to complete program. *Concentrations:* accounting, electronic commerce (e-commerce), finance, international and area business studies, management, management information systems, marketing, operations management.
MBA—Executive MBA Full-time. At least 49 total credits required. 21 to 60 months to complete program. *Concentrations:* management.
MBA—Professional MBA Part-time. At least 50 total credits required. 32 to 60 months to complete program. *Concentrations:* accounting, finance, international and area business studies, management, management information systems, marketing, operations management.

COSTS
Tuition *Part-time:* $680 per credit. Tuition varies by number of courses or credits taken and academic program. **Graduate housing:** *Typical cost:* $9000 (including board).

FINANCIAL AID (1999–2000)
140 students received aid, including fellowships, research assistantships, and work study. **Financial Aid Contact** Mr. Phil Asbury, Director of Financial Aid, Winter Park, FL 32789-4499. **Phone:** 407-646-2395. **Fax:** 407-646-2173. **E-mail:** pasbury@rollins.edu.

RESOURCES AND SERVICES
Information about online services, personal computer policies, library resources, international exchange programs, internship programs, and placement services at this institution and others can be found at **www.petersons.com/mba**

International Students
15% of students enrolled are international students.
Services and Facilities Counseling/support services, housing location assistance, orientation, visa services. Financial aid is available to international students.
Applying *Required:* TOEFL with recommended score of 580 (paper), proof of adequate funds.

Rollins College (continued)

International Student Contact Ms. Brenda Corey, International Advisor, 1000 Holt Avenue—2722, Winter Park, FL 32789-4499. **Phone:** 407-646-2415. **Fax:** 407-646-2522. **E-mail:** bcorey@rollins.edu.

■ **APPLICATION**

Required GMAT, application form, baccalaureate/first degree, essay, interview, 2 letters of recommendation, personal statement, resume/curriculum vitae, transcripts of college work, 3 years of work experience.

Deadlines and Fees Applications for domestic and international students are processed on a rolling basis. *Application fee:* $40, $40 (international).

Application Contact Barbara Williams, Assistant Director of Admissions, Crummer Graduate School of Business, 1000 Holt Avenue—2722, Winter Park, FL 32789-4499. **Phone:** 407-628-6374. **Toll-free Phone:** 800-866-2405. **Fax:** 407-646-2522. **E-mail:** bwilliams@rollins.edu.

See full description on page 792.

Saint Leo University

Saint Leo, Florida

GRADUATE BUSINESS STUDIES

Graduate Business Faculty
Full-time: 1   Part-time: 6

Student Body
Total: 128
Full-time: 98   Average Age: 38
Part-time: 30   Women: 57%

Admissions
Applications: 50   Average GMAT: 475
Admitted: 40   Average GPA: 3.25
Enrolled: 30

Costs (1999–2000)
Full-time tuition: $4050 per academic year
Part-time tuition: $225 per credit

After Graduation (Class of 1998–99)
Employed within 3 months of graduation: 100%

DEGREES MBA

MBA—Accelerated 12-months MBA Full-time. At least 36 total credits required. 12 months to complete program.

MBA—Graduate Business Studies Full-time and part-time. At least 36 total credits required. 24 to 60 months to complete program. *Concentrations:* management.

COSTS

Tuition *Full-time:* $4050. *Part-time:* $225 per credit.

FINANCIAL AID (1999–2000)

29 students received aid, including loans. Aid is available to part-time students. Financial aid application deadline: 3/1. **Financial Aid Contact** Dr. Pat Watkins, Director, Financial Aid, PO Box 6665, MC 2228, Saint Leo, FL 33574-6665. **Phone:** 352-588-8270. **Fax:** 352-588-8403. **E-mail:** facampus@saintleo.edu.

RESOURCES AND SERVICES

Information about online services, personal computer policies, library resources, international exchange programs, internship programs, and placement services at this institution and others can be found at **www.petersons.com/mba**

International Students

0.8% of students enrolled are international students.

Services and Facilities Counseling/support services, international student organization, orientation, visa services. Financial aid is not available to international students.

Applying *Required:* TOEFL with recommended score of 600 (paper), proof of adequate funds.

International Student Contact Mr. Martin Smith, Director of Graduate Admission, MC 2008 PO Box 6665, Saint Leo, FL 33574-6665. **Phone:** 352-588-8283. **Fax:** 352-588-8257. **E-mail:** martin.smith@saintleo.edu.

■ **APPLICATION**

Required Application form, baccalaureate/first degree, interview, 2 letters of recommendation, resume/curriculum vitae, transcripts of college work, 5 years of work experience. School will accept GMAT.

Deadlines and Fees Applications for domestic and international students are processed on a rolling basis. *Application fee:* $45, $45 (international).

Application Contact Mr. Martin Smith, Director of Graduate Admission, MC2008, PO Box 6665, Saint Leo, FL 33574-6665. **Phone:** 352-588-8283. **Toll-free Phone:** 800-334-5532. **Fax:** 352-588-8257. **E-mail:** martin.smith@saintleo.edu.

St. Thomas University

Miami, Florida

DEPARTMENT OF BUSINESS ADMINISTRATION

Graduate Business Faculty
Full-time: 25   Part-time: 38

Student Body
Total: 243   Women: 75%
Average Age: 27

Admissions
Applications: 139   Average GMAT: 500
Admitted: 74   Average GPA: 3.2
Enrolled: 48

Costs (1999–2000)
Full-time tuition: $8190 per academic year
Part-time tuition: $455 per credit

DEGREES M Acc • MBA • MS

M Acc—Master of Accounting Full-time and part-time. At least 30 total credits required. 12 to 36 months to complete program.

MBA—Master of Business Administration Full-time and part-time. 42 to 51 total credits required. 18 to 60 months to complete program. *Concentrations:* accounting, international business, management, sports/entertainment management.

MS—Master of Science in Health Management Full-time and part-time. At least 36 total credits required. 12 to 60 months to complete program.

MS—Master of Science in Human Resources Management Full-time and part-time. At least 36 total credits required. 12 to 60 months to complete program.

MS—Master of Science in Management Full-time and part-time. At least 36 total credits required. 12 to 60 months to complete program. *Concentrations:* human resources, international business, management, public management.

MS—Master of Science in Sports Administration Full-time and part-time. At least 36 total credits required. 12 to 60 months to complete program.

COSTS

Tuition *Full-time:* $8190. *Part-time:* $455 per credit. Tuition varies by number of courses or credits taken. **Required fees:** *Part-time* $45 per semester.

FINANCIAL AID (1999–2000)

Loans, scholarships, and work study. Aid is available to part-time students. **Financial Aid Contact** Ms. Anh Do, Director of Financial Aid, 16400 Northeast 32nd Avenue, Miami, FL 33054-6459. **Phone:** 305-628-6725. **Fax:** 305-628-6754. **E-mail:** ado@stu.edu.

RESOURCES AND SERVICES

Information about online services, personal computer policies, library resources, international exchange programs, internship programs, and placement services at this institution and others can be found at **www.petersons.com/mba**

International Students

Services and Facilities Counseling/support services, ESL/language courses, housing location assistance, international student housing, international student organization, visa services. Financial aid is not available to international students.

Applying *Required:* TOEFL with recommended score of 213 (computer) or 550 (paper), proof of adequate funds. *Recommended:* TWE with recommended score of 4, proof of health/immunizations.

International Student Contact Dr. Carlos Rossie, Associate Director of Graduate Admissions, 16400 Northwest 32nd Avenue, Miami, FL 33054-6459. **Phone:** 305-628-6614. **Fax:** 305-628-6591. **E-mail:** crossie@stu.edu.

■ **APPLICATION**

Required Application form, baccalaureate/first degree, essay, interview, 2 letters of recommendation, personal statement, transcripts of college work. School will accept GMAT and GRE. **Recommended** Resume/curriculum vitae, work experience.

Deadlines and Fees Applications for domestic and international students are processed on a rolling basis. *Application fee:* $45, $45 (international).

Application Contact Dr. Carlos Rossie, Associate Director of Graduate Admissions, 16400 Northwest 32nd Avenue, Miami, FL 33054-6459. **Phone:** 305-628-6614. **Toll-free Phone:** 800-367-9006 (in-state), 800-367-9010 (out-of-state). **Fax:** 305-628-6591. **E-mail:** crossie@stu.edu.

See full description on page 810.

Schiller International University

Dunedin, Florida

MBA PROGRAMS

Graduate Business Faculty
Full-time: 5

Part-time: 30

Student Body
Total: 102
Full-time: 61
Part-time: 41

Average Age: 26
Women: 53%

Costs (1999–2000)
Full-time tuition: $16,270 per academic year
Part-time tuition: $1050 per course

After Graduation (Class of 1998–99)
Employed within 3 months of graduation: 92.3%

DEGREES MA • MBA • MIM • MN

MA—Master of Arts in Business Communication Full-time and part-time. At least 36 total credits required. 9 to 24 months to complete program.

MA—Master of Arts in International Hotel and Tourism Management Full-time and part-time. At least 45 total credits required. 12 to 24 months to complete program. *Concentrations:* international management.

MBA—MBA in Information Technology Full-time and part-time. At least 45 total credits required. 12 to 24 months to complete program. *Concentrations:* information management.

MBA—MBA in Public Administration Full-time and part-time. At least 45 total credits required. 12 to 24 months to complete program. *Concentrations:* public policy and administration.

MBA—Master of Business Administration in International Business Full-time and part-time. *Distance learning option.* At least 45 total credits required. 12 to 24 months to complete program. *Concentrations:* international business.

MBA—Master of Business Administration in International Hotel and Tourism Management Full-time and part-time. *Distance learning option.* At least 45 total credits required. 12 to 24 months to complete program. *Concentrations:* travel industry/tourism management.

MIM—Master of International Management in International Business Full-time and part-time. At least 45 total credits required. 12 to 24 months to complete program. *Concentrations:* international management.

MN—Master of Nursing Part-time. At least 36 total credits required. 12 to 24 months to complete program.

COSTS

Tuition *Full-time:* $15,750. *Part-time:* $1050 per course. Tuition varies by number of courses or credits taken and campus location. **Required fees:** *Full-time* $520. Tuition and fees vary by campus location. **Graduate housing:** Room and board costs vary by campus location, number of occupants, type of accommodation, and type of board plan. *Typical cost:* $5200 (including board).

FINANCIAL AID (1999–2000)

Grants, loans, scholarships, and work study. Financial aid application deadline: 4/1. **Financial Aid Contact** Ms. Teri Reeves, Financial Aid Director, 453 Edgewater Drive, Dunedin, FL 34698-7532. **Phone:** 727-736-5082 Ext. 250. **Fax:** 727-738-8405. **E-mail:** teri_reeves@schiller.edu.

RESOURCES AND SERVICES

Information about online services, personal computer policies, library resources, international exchange programs, internship programs, and placement services at this institution and others can be found at www.petersons.com/mba

International Students

83% of students enrolled are international students.

Services and Facilities Counseling/support services, ESL/language courses, housing location assistance, international student housing, orientation, visa services. Financial aid is available to international students.

Applying *Required:* Proof of adequate funds. *Recommended:* TOEFL with recommended score of 550 (paper).

International Student Contact Mr. Markus Leibrecht, Dean of Students, 453 Edgewater Drive, Dunedin, FL 34698-7532. **Phone:** 727-736-5082 Ext. 237. **Fax:** 727-734-0359. **E-mail:** admissions@schiller.edu.

▪ APPLICATION

Required GMAT, application form, baccalaureate/first degree, essay, transcripts of college work. **Recommended** Resume/curriculum vitae, work experience.

Deadlines and Fees Applications for domestic and international students are processed on a rolling basis. *Application fee:* $35, $35 (international).

Application Contact Director of Admissions, 453 Edgewater Drive, Dunedin, FL 34698-7532. **Phone:** 727-736-5082 Ext. 239. **Toll-free Phone:** 800-336-4133. **Fax:** 727-734-0359. **E-mail:** admissions@schiller.edu.

See full description on page 816.

Stetson University

DeLand, Florida

SCHOOL OF BUSINESS ADMINISTRATION

Graduate Business Faculty
Full-time: 36

Student Body
Total: 150
Full-time: 70
Part-time: 80

Average Age: 25
Women: 44%

Admissions
Applications: 400
Admitted: 175
Enrolled: 110

Average GMAT: 540
Average GPA: 2.9

Costs (1999–2000)
Full-time tuition: N/R
Part-time tuition: $390 per credit hour

After Graduation (Class of 1998–99)
Employed within 3 months of graduation: 90%
Average starting salary: $35,000

Accreditation
AACSB—The International Association for Management Education
ACBSP—The American Council of Business Schools and Programs

DEGREES JD/MBA • M Acc • MBA

JD/MBA—Juris Doctor/Master of Business Administration Full-time. At least 96 total credits required. 12 to 96 months to complete program.

M Acc—Master of Accountancy Full-time and part-time. 30 to 60 total credits required. 12 to 96 months to complete program.

MBA—Master of Business Administration Full-time and part-time. 30 to 60 total credits required. 12 to 96 months to complete program. *Concentrations:* finance.

COSTS

Tuition *Part-time:* $390 per credit hour. Tuition varies by campus location and academic program. **Graduate housing:** Room and board costs vary by campus location, number of occupants, and type of board plan. *Typical cost:* $6000 (including board).

FINANCIAL AID (1999–2000)

25 students received aid, including loans, research assistantships, and work study. Aid is available to part-time students. Financial aid application deadline: 3/15. **Financial Aid Contact** Robert Lynn, Director of Student Financial Planning, 421 North Woodland Boulevard, DeLand, FL 32720-3781. **Phone:** 904-822-7120. **Fax:** 904-822-7126.

RESOURCES AND SERVICES

Information about online services, personal computer policies, library resources, international exchange programs, internship programs, and placement services at this institution and others can be found at www.petersons.com/mba

International Students

7% of students enrolled are international students.

Stetson University (continued)

Services and Facilities Counseling/support services, international student organization, language tutoring, orientation, visa services. Financial aid is not available to international students.

Applying *Required:* TOEFL with recommended score of 550 (paper), proof of adequate funds, proof of health/immunizations.

International Student Contact Dr. Frank A. DeZoort, Director, Graduate Business Programs, 421 North Woodland Boulevard, Unit 8398, DeLand, FL 32720-3774. **Phone:** 904-822-7410. **Fax:** 904-822-7413. **E-mail:** f.dezoort@stetson.edu.

■ **APPLICATION**

Required GMAT, application form, baccalaureate/first degree, 3 letters of recommendation, transcripts of college work. **Recommended** Interview, personal statement, resume/curriculum vitae.

Deadlines and Fees *Deadlines:* 7/15 for fall, 12/15 for spring, 4/15 for summer, 6/15 for fall (international), 11/15 for spring (international), 3/15 for summer (international). *Application fee:* $25, $25 (international).

Application Contact Dr. Frank A. DeZoort, Director, Graduate Business Programs, 421 North Woodland Boulevard, Unit 8398, DeLand, FL 32720-3774. **Phone:** 904-822-7410. **Fax:** 904-822-7413. **E-mail:** f.dezoort@stetson.edu.

University of Central Florida

Orlando, Florida

COLLEGE OF BUSINESS ADMINISTRATION

Graduate Business Faculty
Full-time: 75

Student Body
Total: 702
Part-time: 702

Average Age: 30
Women: 51%

Admissions
Applications: 259
Admitted: 182
Enrolled: 140

Average GMAT: 548
Average GPA: 3.3

Costs (1999–2000)
Full-time tuition: N/R
Part-time tuition: $146 per hour (resident), $507 per hour (nonresident)

After Graduation (Class of 1998–99)
Employed within 3 months of graduation: 98%
Average starting salary: $52,000

Accreditation
AACSB—The International Association for Management Education

DEGREES EMBA • MA • MBA • MS • MSM

EMBA—Executive MBA Part-time. At least 33 total credits required. 16 months to complete program.

MA—Master of Arts in Applied Economics Part-time. At least 30 total credits required. 12 to 36 months to complete program.

MBA—Master of Business Administration Part-time. At least 33 total credits required. 12 to 36 months to complete program. *Concentrations:* economics, entrepreneurship, finance, human resources, international and area business studies, management information systems, marketing.

MS—Master of Science in Accounting Part-time. At least 30 total credits required. 12 to 24 months to complete program.

MS—Master of Science in Taxation Part-time. At least 30 total credits required. 12 to 24 months to complete program.

MSM—Human Resource Change Management Part-time. At least 30 total credits required. 12 to 36 months to complete program.

MSM—Management Information Systems Part-time. At least 30 total credits required. 12 to 36 months to complete program.

COSTS

Tuition, state resident: *Part-time* $146 per hour. **Tuition, nonresident:** *Part-time* $507 per hour. **Required fees:** *Part-time* $55 per semester.

FINANCIAL AID (1999–2000)

87 students received aid, including fellowships, loans, research assistantships, teaching assistantships, and work study. Aid is available to part-time students. Financial aid application deadline: 3/15. **Financial Aid Contact** Ms. Mary McKinney, Director, Financial Aid Office, PO Box

25000, AD 120, Orlando, FL 32816. **Phone:** 407-823-2827. **E-mail:** mckinney@ucf1vm.cc.ucf.edu.

RESOURCES AND SERVICES
Information about online services, personal computer policies, library resources, international exchange programs, internship programs, and placement services at this institution and others can be found at **www.petersons.com/mba**

International Students

18% of students enrolled are international students.

Services and Facilities Counseling/support services, ESL/language courses, housing location assistance, international student organization, visa services. Financial aid is available to international students.

Applying *Required:* TOEFL with recommended score of 233 (computer) or 575 (paper), proof of adequate funds, proof of health/immunizations.

International Student Contact Ms. Ragda Kurdy, Coordinator, International Student Services, PO Box 25000, Ying International Center, Orlando, FL 32816. **Phone:** 407-823-2337. **Fax:** 407-823-2526.

■ **APPLICATION**

Required GMAT, application form, baccalaureate/first degree, essay, 3 letters of recommendation, resume/curriculum vitae, transcripts of college work. **Recommended** 2 years of work experience.

Deadlines and Fees *Deadlines:* 7/15 for fall, 12/1 for spring, 4/15 for summer, 3/1 for fall (international), 8/1 for spring (international), 12/1 for summer (international). *Application fee:* $20, $20 (international).

Application Contact Ms. Melanie Key, Graduate Admissions, PO Box 25000, Orlando, FL 32816. **Phone:** 407-823-5693. **Fax:** 407-823-6442. **E-mail:** mkey@mail.ucf.edu.

University of Florida

Gainesville, Florida

COLLEGE OF BUSINESS ADMINISTRATION

Graduate Business Faculty
Full-time: 90

Student Body
Total: 517
Full-time: 395
Part-time: 122

Average Age: 29
Women: 26%

Admissions
Applications: 655
Admitted: 245
Enrolled: 150

Average GMAT: 616
Average GPA: 3.14

Costs (1999–2000)
Full-time tuition: $3750 per academic year (resident), $13,130 per academic year (nonresident)
Part-time tuition: N/R

After Graduation (Class of 1998–99)
Employed within 3 months of graduation: 97%
Average starting salary: $63,000

Accreditation
AACSB—The International Association for Management Education

DEGREES JD/MBA • MBA • MBA/MESS • MBA/MS • Pharm D/MBA

JD/MBA—Juris Doctor/Master of Business Administration Full-time. At least 124 total credits required. 42 to 48 months to complete program.

MBA—Executive MBA Full-time. At least 48 total credits required. 20 months to complete program. *Concentrations:* management.

MBA—Internet MBA Part-time. *Distance learning option.* At least 48 total credits required. 27 months to complete program. *Concentrations:* management.

MBA—MBA for Professionals Part-time. At least 48 total credits required. 27 months to complete program. *Concentrations:* management.

MBA—MBA for Professionals (1 year) Full-time. Undergraduate degree in business completed within 7 years prior to start of program. At least 32 total credits required. 12 months to complete program. *Concentrations:* management.

MBA—Traditional MBA Full-time. At least 48 total credits required. 24 months to complete program. *Concentrations:* arts administration/management, business policy/strategy, decision sciences, electronic commerce (e-commerce), entrepreneurship, finance, human resources, information management, international and area business studies, Latin American business studies, management, marketing, public policy and administration, real estate, sports/entertainment management, supply chain management, technology management.

MBA—Traditional MBA (1 year) Full-time. Undergraduate degree in business completed within 7 years prior to the start of program. At least 32 total credits required. 11 months to complete program. *Concentrations:* arts administration/management, business policy/strategy, decision sciences, electronic commerce (e-commerce), entrepreneurship, finance, human resources, information management, international and area business studies, Latin American business studies, management, marketing, public policy and administration, real estate, sports/entertainment management, supply chain management, technology management.

MBA/MESS—Master of Business Administration/Master of Exercise and Sport Science Full-time. At least 66 total credits required. 24 to 36 months to complete program.

MBA/MS—Master of Business Administration/Master of Science in Business and Biotechnology Full-time. At least 68 total credits required. 24 to 72 months to complete program.

Pharm D/MBA—Doctor of Pharmacy/Master of Business Administration Full-time. At least 164 total credits required. 24 to 72 months to complete program.

For more than fifty years, the University of Florida has developed successful leaders and managers for a challenging business environment. That commitment will be carried into the next century with renewed ambition, focus, and spirit.

The Florida M.B.A. is consistently rated a "best buy" in business education. The combination of a nationally recognized program, high quality of life, and low cost of attendance offers tremendous value. Continuous refinement of the programs strengthens the value of the degree.

Innovative new programs and a modular curriculum provide greater flexibility and accessibility. With nearly fifty degree options, concentrations, and international exchanges, students can customize their learning experience. The Florida M.B.A. degree is available to full-time, in-residence students as well as working professionals. The latest creation, the Internet M.B.A., incorporates leading-edge technology and periodic classroom interaction to deliver a fully accredited, high-caliber degree via distance education.

The Florida M.B.A. programs integrate distinguished faculty members, talented students, a dedicated staff, and successful alumni to form a cooperative, team-oriented, and supportive community. Leading researchers and high-quality teachers provide a solid academic foundation. Small class sizes, a low student-faculty ratio, and an expanded program staff ensure that individual needs are met throughout the M.B.A. experience. Qualified candidates are invited to explore these exciting opportunities with the Florida M.B.A. programs.

COSTS
Tuition, state resident: *Full-time* $3750. **Tuition, nonresident:** *Full-time* $13,130. **Tuition, international:** *Full-time* $13,130. Tuition varies by number of courses or credits taken. **Required fees:** Fees vary by academic program. **Graduate housing:** Room and board costs vary by number of occupants, type of accommodation, and type of board plan. *Typical cost:* $6230 (including board), $3810 (room only).

FINANCIAL AID (1999–2000)
277 students received aid, including fellowships, loans, research assistantships, scholarships, and teaching assistantships. Aid is available to part-time students. Financial aid application deadline: 4/15. **Financial Aid Contact** Mr. Bill Watson, MBA Financial Aid Coordinator, PO Box 114025, S107 Criser Hall, Gainesville, FL 32611-4025. **Phone:** 352-392-1275 Ext. 3386. **Fax:** 352-392-2861. **E-mail:** bill_watson@sfa.ufl.edu.

RESOURCES AND SERVICES
Information about online services, personal computer policies, library resources, international exchange programs, internship programs, and placement services at this institution and others can be found at **www.petersons.com/mba**

International Students
18% of students enrolled are international students.
Services and Facilities Counseling/support services, ESL/language courses, housing location assistance, international student organization, orientation, visa services. Financial aid is not available to international students.
Applying *Required:* TOEFL with recommended score of 250 (computer) or 600 (paper), proof of adequate funds, proof of health/immunizations.
International Student Contact Ms. Lorraine White, Admissions Coordinator, 134 Bryan Hall, PO Box 117152, Gainesville, FL 32611-7152. **Phone:** 352-392-7992 Ext. 2. **Fax:** 352-392-8791. **E-mail:** mbaadmiss@notes.cba.ufl.edu.

■ APPLICATION
Required Application form, baccalaureate/first degree, essay, 2 letters of recommendation, resume/curriculum vitae, transcripts of college work, 2 years of work experience. School will accept GMAT or GRE. **Recommended** Interview.

Deadlines and Fees *Deadlines:* 4/15 for fall, 3/15 for fall (international). *Application fee:* $20, $20 (international).
Application Contact Ms. Laura Parks, Director of Admissions, 134 Bryan Hall, Box 117152, Gainesville, FL 32611-7152. **Phone:** 352-392-7992 Ext. 2. **Toll-free Phone:** 877-4-FLA-MBA. **Fax:** 352-392-8791. **E-mail:** mbaadmiss@notes.cba.ufl.edu.

See full description on page 900.

University of Miami
Coral Gables, Florida
SCHOOL OF BUSINESS ADMINISTRATION

Graduate Business Faculty

Full-time: 117	Part-time: 65

Student Body

Total: 1,253	
Full-time: 1,121	Average Age: 26
Part-time: 132	Women: 36%

Admissions

Applications: 734	Average GMAT: 620
Admitted: 341	Average GPA: 3.1
Enrolled: 210	

Costs (1999–2000)
Full-time tuition: N/R
Part-time tuition: $899 per credit

After Graduation (Class of 1998–99)
Employed within 3 months of graduation: 64%
Average starting salary: $51,925

Accreditation
AACSB—The International Association for Management Education

DEGREES JD/MBA • MA • MBA • MBA/MS • MPA • MS

JD/MBA—Juris Doctor/Master of Business Administration Full-time. At least 142 total credits required. 36 to 72 months to complete program.

MA—Master of Arts in Economics Full-time and part-time. At least 30 total credits required. 12 to 72 months to complete program.

MBA—Executive MBA Full-time. At least 51 total credits required. 23 months to complete program. *Concentrations:* international business, management.

MBA—MBA Track I or II Full-time and part-time. 36 to 58 total credits required. 12 to 72 months to complete program. *Concentrations:* accounting, business law, economics, electronic commerce (e-commerce), finance, financial management/planning, human resources, international business, leadership, logistics, management, management information systems, management science, marketing, public policy and administration, quality management, strategic management, taxation, telecommunications management.

MBA/MS—Master of Business Administration/Master of Science in Industrial Engineering Full-time. At least 63 total credits required. 25 months to complete program.

MPA—Master of Public Administration Full-time and part-time. 36 to 48 total credits required. 12 to 72 months to complete program.

MPA—Master of Professional Accountancy Full-time and part-time. At least 30 total credits required. 12 to 72 months to complete program.

MS—Master of Science in Computer Information Systems Full-time and part-time. At least 30 total credits required. 12 to 72 months to complete program.

MS—Master of Science in Management Science Full-time and part-time. At least 30 total credits required. 12 to 72 months to complete program. *Concentrations:* quality management.

MS—Master of Science in Taxation Full-time and part-time. At least 30 total credits required. 12 to 72 months to complete program.

COSTS
Tuition *Part-time:* $899 per credit. **Required fees:** *Full-time* $199. Fees vary by number of courses or credits taken. **Graduate housing:** Room and board costs vary by number of occupants, type of accommodation, and type of board plan. *Typical cost:* $9614 (including board).

FINANCIAL AID (1999–2000)
550 students received aid, including fellowships, loans, research assistantships, and work study. Financial aid application deadline: 3/1. **Financial Aid Contact** Director, Financial Assistance Services, PO Box 248187, Coral Gables, FL 33124-5240. **Phone:** 305-284-5212. **Fax:** 305-284-4082. **E-mail:** ofas@umiamivm.ir.miami.edu.

University of Miami (continued)

RESOURCES AND SERVICES
Information about online services, personal computer policies, library resources, international exchange programs, internship programs, and placement services at this institution and others can be found at **www. petersons.com/mba**

International Students
37% of students enrolled are international students.

Services and Facilities Counseling/support services, ESL/language courses, international student organization, orientation. Financial aid is available to international students.

Applying *Required:* TOEFL with recommended score of 213 (computer) or 550 (paper), proof of adequate funds, proof of health/immunizations.

International Student Contact Ms. Teresa De la Guardia, Director, International Student Services, Building 21-F, Coral Gables, FL 33124-5550. **Phone:** 305-284-2928. **Fax:** 305-284-3409. **E-mail:** tdelagua@umiamivm.ir.miami.edu.

■ APPLICATION
Required GMAT, application form, baccalaureate/first degree, personal statement, resume/curriculum vitae, transcripts of college work. School will accept GRE. **Recommended** Letter(s) of recommendation.

Deadlines and Fees Applications for domestic and international students are processed on a rolling basis. *Application fee:* $50, $50 (international).

Application Contact Ms. Dierdre Lacativa, Director, Graduate Business Recruiting and Admissions, PO Box 248505, Coral Gables, FL 33124-6524. **Phone:** 305-284-2510. **Toll-free Phone:** 800-531-7137. **Fax:** 305-284-1878. **E-mail:** mba@miami.edu.

See full description on page 922.

University of North Florida
Jacksonville, Florida

COLLEGE OF BUSINESS ADMINISTRATION

Graduate Business Faculty

Full-time: 40	Part-time: 5

Student Body

Total: 466	
Full-time: 105	Average Age: 30
Part-time: 361	Women: 48%

Admissions

Applications: 283	Average GMAT: 522
Admitted: 136	Average GPA: 3.13
Enrolled: 104	

Costs (1999–2000)
Full-time tuition: $2675 per academic year (resident), $9169 per academic year (nonresident)
Part-time tuition: $149 per credit hour (resident), $509 per credit hour (nonresident)

After Graduation (Class of 1998–99)
Employed within 3 months of graduation: 95%
Average starting salary: $49,000

Accreditation
AACSB—The International Association for Management Education

DEGREES M Acc • MBA • MHRM

M Acc—Master of Accountancy Full-time and part-time. 36 to 81 total credits required. 12 to 60 months to complete program. *Concentrations:* accounting, taxation.

MBA—Master of Business Administration Full-time and part-time. 39 to 60 total credits required. 12 to 60 months to complete program. *Concentrations:* accounting, economics, finance, human resources, logistics, management, marketing.

MHRM—Master of Human Resources Management Full-time and part-time. 36 to 63 total credits required. 12 to 60 months to complete program. *Concentrations:* human resources, industrial/labor relations.

COSTS
Tuition, state resident: *Full-time* $2675. *Part-time* $149 per credit hour. **Tuition, nonresident:** *Full-time* $9169. *Part-time* $509 per credit hour. **Graduate housing:** Room and board costs vary by number of occupants, type of accommoda-

tion, and type of board plan. *Typical cost:* $5100 (including board), $2790 (room only).

FINANCIAL AID (1999–2000)
88 students received aid, including fellowships, grants, loans, research assistantships, scholarships, and work study. Aid is available to part-time students. Financial aid application deadline: 3/15. **Financial Aid Contact** Ms. Janice Nowak, Director, Financial Aid, 4567 St. Johns Bluff Road South, Jacksonville, FL 32224-2645. **Phone:** 904-620-2604. **Fax:** 904-620-2400. **E-mail:** jnowak@unf.edu.

RESOURCES AND SERVICES
Information about online services, personal computer policies, library resources, international exchange programs, internship programs, and placement services at this institution and others can be found at **www. petersons.com/mba**

International Students
6% of students enrolled are international students.

Services and Facilities Counseling/support services, ESL/language courses, international student housing, international student organization, orientation, visa services. Financial aid is not available to international students.

Applying *Required:* TOEFL with recommended score of 550 (paper), proof of adequate funds, proof of health/immunizations.

International Student Contact Mr. Christopher Johnson, Coordinator, International Student Affairs, 4567 St. Johns Bluff Road South, Jacksonville, FL 32224-2645. **Phone:** 904-626-2768. **Fax:** 904-620-3925. **E-mail:** cjohnson@unf. edu.

■ APPLICATION
Required GMAT, application form, baccalaureate/first degree, transcripts of college work.

Deadlines and Fees *Deadlines:* 7/5 for fall, 11/1 for spring, 3/9 for summer, 5/1 for fall (international), 10/1 for spring (international), 2/1 for summer (international). *Application fee:* $20, $20 (international).

Application Contact Dr. Jeff Michelman, Associate Dean and Director of Graduate Studies, College of Business Administration, 4567 St. Johns Bluff Road South, Jacksonville, FL 32224-2645. **Phone:** 904-620-2590. **Fax:** 904-620-2594. **E-mail:** jmichelm@unf.edu.

University of Sarasota
Sarasota, Florida

COLLEGE OF BUSINESS

Graduate Business Faculty

Full-time: 7	Part-time: 6

Student Body

Total: 606	
Full-time: 204	Average Age: 35
Part-time: 402	Women: 40%

Admissions
Average GPA: 3.6

Costs (1999–2000)
Full-time tuition: N/R
Part-time tuition: $361 per credit hour

DEGREE MBA

MBA—Master of Business Administration Full-time and part-time. *Distance learning option.* 36 to 42 total credits required. 15 to 36 months to complete program. *Concentrations:* finance, health care, human resources, international trade, marketing.

COSTS
Tuition *Part-time:* $361 per credit hour. Tuition varies by academic program.

FINANCIAL AID (1999–2000)
110 students received aid, including loans. Aid is available to part-time students. **Financial Aid Contact** Ana Mendez, Director, Financial Aid/Argosy Education Group, 20 South Clark Street, Chicago, IL 60603. **E-mail:** 102556.2652@compuserve.com.

RESOURCES AND SERVICES
Information about online services, personal computer policies, library resources, international exchange programs, internship programs, and placement services at this institution and others can be found at **www. petersons.com/mba**

International Students
10% of students enrolled are international students.

Services and Facilities Counseling/support services, orientation, visa services. Financial aid is not available to international students.

Applying *Required:* TOEFL with recommended score of 500 (paper), proof of adequate funds. *Recommended:* Proof of health/immunizations.

International Student Contact Dr. Gordana Pesakovic, International Student Coordinator, 5250 17th Street, Sarasota, FL 34235-8242. **Phone:** 941-379-0404 Ext. 251. **Fax:** 941-379-9464. **E-mail:** 102556.2652@compuserve.com.

■ APPLICATION

Required Application form, baccalaureate/first degree, essay, interview, 3 letters of recommendation, personal statement, resume/curriculum vitae, transcripts of college work. **Recommended** Work experience.

Deadlines and Fees Applications for domestic and international students are processed on a rolling basis. *Application fee:* $50, $50 (international).

Application Contact Ed Jump, Admissions Director, 5250 17th Street, Sarasota, FL 34235-8242. **Phone:** 941-379-0404 Ext. 251. **Toll-free Phone:** 800-331-5995. **Fax:** 941-379-9464. **E-mail:** 102556.2652@compuserve.com.

University of South Florida
Tampa, Florida

COLLEGE OF BUSINESS ADMINISTRATION

Graduate Business Faculty
Full-time: 123 — Part-time: 1

Student Body
Total: 965
Full-time: 377 — Average Age: 28
Part-time: 588 — Women: 41%

Admissions
Applications: 624
Admitted: 454 — Average GMAT: 554
Enrolled: 277 — Average GPA: 3.3

Costs (1999–2000)
Full-time tuition: $2665 per academic year (resident), $9158 per academic year (nonresident)
Part-time tuition: $148 per credit hour (resident), $509 per credit hour (nonresident)

After Graduation (Class of 1998–99)
Average starting salary: $48,800

Accreditation
AACSB—The International Association for Management Education

DEGREES M Acc • MA • MBA • MSM

M Acc—Master of Accountancy Full-time and part-time. At least 30 total credits required. Minimum of 12 months to complete program. *Concentrations:* accounting, taxation.

MA—Master of Arts in Economics Full-time and part-time. At least 30 total credits required. Minimum of 12 months to complete program.

MBA—Executive MBA Full-time. 8 years of work experience required. At least 57 total credits required. 20 months to complete program.

MBA—MBA Program for Physicians Full-time. MD or DO required. At least 57 total credits required. 21 months to complete program.

MBA—Saturday MBA for Professionals Full-time. At least 57 total credits required. 30 months to complete program. *Concentrations:* finance, international business, marketing.

MBA—Master of Business Administration Full-time and part-time. 36 to 57 total credits required. 12 to 60 months to complete program. *Concentrations:* entrepreneurship, finance, health care, international business, management, management information systems, marketing, quality management.

MSM—Master of Science in Management in Information Systems Full-time and part-time. At least 32 total credits required. Minimum of 12 months to complete program.

MSM—Master of Science in Management in Leadership and Organizational Effectiveness Full-time and part-time. At least 32 total credits required. Minimum of 12 months to complete program.

COSTS

Tuition, state resident: *Full-time* $2665. *Part-time* $148 per credit hour. **Tuition, nonresident:** *Full-time* $9158. *Part-time* $509 per credit hour. **Tuition, international:** *Full-time* $9158. Tuition varies by campus location and local reciproc-

ity agreements. **Graduate housing:** Room and board costs vary by number of occupants, type of accommodation, and type of board plan. *Typical cost:* $5250 (including board).

FINANCIAL AID (1999–2000)
70 students received aid, including fellowships, research assistantships, scholarships, and teaching assistantships. Financial aid application deadline: 3/1. **Financial Aid Contact** Wendy Baker, Assistant Director of Graduate Studies, 4202 East Fowler Avenue, Tampa, FL 33620-5500. **Phone:** 813-974-3335. **Fax:** 813-974-4518. **E-mail:** mba2@coba.usf.edu.

RESOURCES AND SERVICES
Information about online services, personal computer policies, library resources, international exchange programs, internship programs, and placement services at this institution and others can be found at **www.petersons.com/mba**

International Students
8% of students enrolled are international students.

Services and Facilities Counseling/support services, ESL/language courses, international student organization, orientation, visa services.

Applying *Required:* TOEFL with recommended score of 213 (computer) or 550 (paper), proof of adequate funds, proof of health/immunizations.

International Student Contact Wendy Baker, Assistant Director of Graduate Studies, 4202 East Fowler Avenue, Tampa, FL 33620-5500. **Phone:** 813-974-3335. **Fax:** 813-974-4518. **E-mail:** mba2@coba.usf.edu.

■ APPLICATION

Required GMAT, application form, baccalaureate/first degree, resume/curriculum vitae, transcripts of college work. School will accept GRE.

Deadlines and Fees *Deadlines:* 5/15 for fall, 10/15 for spring, 3/1 for fall (international), 8/1 for spring (international). *Application fee:* $20, $20 (international).

Application Contact Wendy Baker, Assistant Director of Graduate Studies, 4202 East Fowler Avenue, Tampa, FL 33620-5500. **Phone:** 813-974-3335. **Fax:** 813-974-4518. **E-mail:** mba2@coba.usf.edu.

The University of Tampa
Tampa, Florida

COLLEGE OF BUSINESS

Graduate Business Faculty
Full-time: 28

Student Body
Total: 370
Full-time: 110 — Average Age: 30
Part-time: 260 — Women: 39%

Admissions
Applications: 232
Admitted: 100 — Average GMAT: 520
Enrolled: 88 — Average GPA: 3.3

Costs (1999–2000)
Full-time tuition: N/R
Part-time tuition: N/R

After Graduation (Class of 1998–99)
Employed within 3 months of graduation: 81%
Average starting salary: $55,867

Accreditation
AACSB—The International Association for Management Education

DEGREE MBA

MBA—Master of Business Administration Full-time and part-time. 39 to 60 total credits required. 16 to 84 months to complete program. *Concentrations:* accounting, finance, information management, international business, management, management information systems, marketing.

COSTS

Required fees: *Full-time* $140. **Graduate housing:** Room and board costs vary by number of occupants and type of accommodation. *Typical cost:* $5416 (including board), $2768 (room only).

FINANCIAL AID (1999–2000)
123 students received aid, including grants, loans, research assistantships, and scholarships. Aid is available to part-time students. **Financial Aid Contact** Ms. JoEllen Soucier, Director, Financial Aid, 401

The University of Tampa (continued)

West Kennedy Boulevard, Plant Hall #427, Tampa, FL 33606-1490. **Phone:** 813-253-6219. **Fax:** 813-258-7439. **E-mail:** jsoucier@alpha.utampa.edu.

RESOURCES AND SERVICES
Information about online services, personal computer policies, library resources, international exchange programs, internship programs, and placement services at this institution and others can be found at **www.petersons.com/mba**

International Students
19% of students enrolled are international students.

Services and Facilities Counseling/support services, ESL/language courses, housing location assistance, international student organization, language tutoring, orientation, visa services, career services. Financial aid is not available to international students.

Applying *Required:* TOEFL with recommended score of 550 (paper), proof of adequate funds, proof of health/immunizations.

International Student Contact Mrs. Sally Moorehead, Coordinator, International Student Affairs, Box 70F, 401 West Kennedy Boulevard, Tampa, FL 33606-1490. **Phone:** 813-258-7433 Ext. 3659. **Fax:** 813-258-7404. **E-mail:** smoorehead@alpha.utampa.edu.

■ APPLICATION
Required GMAT, application form, baccalaureate/first degree, 2 letters of recommendation, transcripts of college work. **Recommended** Essay, interview, personal statement, resume/curriculum vitae, work experience.

Deadlines and Fees Applications for domestic and international students are processed on a rolling basis. *Application fee:* $35, $35 (international).

Application Contact Mr. Fernando Nolasco, Associate Director, MBA Program, Box 10, 401 West Kennedy Boulevard, Tampa, FL 33606-1490. **Phone:** 813-258-7409. **Toll-free Phone:** 800-MINARET. **Fax:** 813-259-5403. **E-mail:** fnolasco@alpha.utampa.edu.

See full description on page 966.

University of West Florida

Pensacola, Florida

COLLEGE OF BUSINESS

Graduate Business Faculty
Full-time: 26 | Part-time: 5

Student Body
Total: 224 | Average Age: 32
Full-time: 52 | Women: 50%
Part-time: 172

Admissions
Applications: 91 | Average GMAT: 513
Admitted: 70 | Average GPA: 3.35
Enrolled: 46

Costs (1999–2000)
Full-time tuition: $3582 per academic year (resident), $11,828 per academic year (nonresident)
Part-time tuition: $149 per credit (resident), $493 per credit (nonresident)

Accreditation
AACSB—The International Association for Management Education

DEGREES M Acc • MBA

M Acc—Master of Accounting Full-time and part-time. At least 30 total credits required. Minimum of 12 months to complete program. *Concentrations:* accounting.

MBA—Master of Business Administration Full-time and part-time. At least 36 total credits required. Minimum of 12 months to complete program. *Concentrations:* accounting, finance, leadership, management, marketing.

COSTS
Tuition, state resident: *Full-time* $2848. *Part-time* $119 per credit. **Tuition, nonresident:** *Full-time* $11,094. *Part-time* $462 per credit. **Tuition, international:** *Full-time* $11,094. Tuition varies by campus location. **Required fees:** *Full-time* $734. *Part-time* $31 per credit. **Graduate housing:** Room and board costs vary by number of occupants, type of accommodation, and type of board plan. *Typical cost:* $2200 (room only).

FINANCIAL AID (1999–2000)
Fellowships, grants, research assistantships, scholarships, and work study. Aid is available to part-time students. Financial aid application deadline: 4/1. **Financial Aid Contact** Dr. C. Raymond Bennett, Director, Student Financial Aid, 11000 University Parkway, Pensacola, FL 32514-5750. **Phone:** 850-474-2400. **E-mail:** rbennett@uwf.edu.

RESOURCES AND SERVICES
Information about online services, personal computer policies, library resources, international exchange programs, internship programs, and placement services at this institution and others can be found at **www.petersons.com/mba**

International Students
5% of students enrolled are international students.

Services and Facilities Counseling/support services, ESL/language courses, visa services. Financial aid is available to international students.
Applying *Required:* TOEFL with recommended score of 173 (computer) or 500 (paper), proof of adequate funds, proof of health/immunizations.

International Student Contact Ms. Kay Mackenzie, Assistant Director, Student Affairs, 11000 University Parkway, Pensacola, FL 32514-5750. **Phone:** 850-474-2384. **Fax:** 850-474-3145. **E-mail:** smackenz@uwf.edu.

■ APPLICATION
Required GMAT, application form, baccalaureate/first degree, essay, interview, 2 letters of recommendation, personal statement, resume/curriculum vitae, transcripts of college work. **Recommended** Work experience.

Deadlines and Fees *Deadlines:* 7/1 for fall, 11/1 for spring, 4/1 for summer, 5/15 for fall (international), 10/15 for spring (international), 2/14 for summer (international). *Application fee:* $20, $20 (international).

Application Contact Ms. Francy Dowhal, Admissions/Registrar Officer, 11000 University Parkway, Pensacola, FL 32514-5750. **Phone:** 850-474-2352. **E-mail:** fdowhal@uwf.edu.

Webber College

Babson Park, Florida

WEBBER COLLEGE GRADUATE SCHOOL

Graduate Business Faculty
Full-time: 6

Student Body
Total: 33 | Average Age: 27
Full-time: 26 | Women: 36%
Part-time: 7

Admissions
Applications: 23 | Average GMAT: 507
Admitted: 20 | Average GPA: 3.37
Enrolled: 18

Costs (1999–2000)
Full-time tuition: $5130 per academic year
Part-time tuition: $285 per credit

After Graduation (Class of 1998–99)
Employed within 3 months of graduation: 100%

DEGREES MBA

MBA—Master of Business Administration Full-time and part-time. At least 36 total credits required. 19 to 94 months to complete program. *Concentrations:* accounting.

MBA—Master of Business Administration Part-time. At least 36 total credits required. 19 to 94 months to complete program.

COSTS
Tuition *Full-time:* $5130. *Part-time:* $285 per credit. **Tuition, international:** *Full-time* $5130. **Graduate housing:** Room and board costs vary by number of occupants, type of accommodation, and type of board plan. *Typical cost:* $3600 (including board), $2000 (room only).

FINANCIAL AID (1999–2000)
4 students received aid, including loans and work study. Financial aid application deadline: 5/15. **Financial Aid Contact** Mrs. Kathy Wilson, Financial Aid Director, Box 96, Babson Park, FL 33827. **Phone:** 863-638-2930. **Fax:** 863-638-1317.

RESOURCES AND SERVICES
Information about online services, personal computer policies, library resources, international exchange programs, internship programs, and

placement services at this institution and others can be found at **www. petersons.com/mba**

International Students
33% of students enrolled are international students.

Services and Facilities Counseling/support services, ESL/language courses, housing location assistance, language tutoring, orientation. Financial aid is available to international students.

Applying *Required:* TOEFL with recommended score of 500 (paper), proof of adequate funds.

International Student Contact Mrs. Jeanne Sobieraski, MBA Marketing Coordinator, 1201 North Scenic Highway, Babson Park, FL 33827. **Phone:** 869-638-2927. **Fax:** 863-638-2823.

■ APPLICATION
Required Application form, baccalaureate/first degree, essay, 3 letters of recommendation, resume/curriculum vitae, transcripts of college work. School will accept GMAT. **Recommended** Interview, 1 year of work experience.

Application Contact Mrs. Jeanne Sobierajski, MBA Marketing Coordinator, Box 96, Babson Park, FL 33827. **Phone:** 863-638-2927. **Fax:** 863-638-2823. **E-mail:** mba@webber.edu.

See full description on page 1010.

GEORGIA

Albany State University
Albany, Georgia

SCHOOL OF BUSINESS

Graduate Business Faculty
Full-time: 12

Student Body
Total: 55
Full-time: 4
Part-time: 51

Average Age: 28
Women: 64%

Admissions
Applications: 23
Admitted: 19
Enrolled: 15

Average GMAT: 450
Average GPA: 2.5

Costs (1999–2000)
Full-time tuition: N/R
Part-time tuition: $94 per credit hour (resident), $282 per credit hour (nonresident)

Accreditation
ACBSP—The American Council of Business Schools and Programs

DEGREE MBA

MBA—Master of Business Administration Full-time and part-time. *Distance learning option.* At least 36 total credits required. 18 to 60 months to complete program.

COSTS
Tuition, state resident: *Part-time* $94 per credit hour. **Tuition, nonresident:** *Part-time* $282 per credit hour. **Required fees:** Tuition and fees vary by number of courses or credits taken.

FINANCIAL AID (1999–2000)
Loans, research assistantships, scholarships, and work study. Aid is available to part-time students. Financial aid application deadline: 4/1.
Financial Aid Contact Mrs. Kathleen Caldwell, Financial Aid Office, 504 College Drive, Albany, GA 31705. **Phone:** 912-430-4646. **Fax:** 912-430-3936. **E-mail:** kcaldwell@asurams.edu.

RESOURCES AND SERVICES
Information about online services, personal computer policies, library resources, international exchange programs, internship programs, and placement services at this institution and others can be found at **www. petersons.com/mba**

International Students
4% of students enrolled are international students.

Services and Facilities Counseling/support services, ESL/language courses, housing location assistance, international student organization, orientation, visa services. Financial aid is available to international students.
Applying *Required:* TOEFL with recommended score of 550 (paper), proof of adequate funds, proof of health/immunizations.
International Student Contact Diane Frink, Graduate Admissions Officer, 504 College Drive, Graduate School, Albany, GA 31705-2717. **Phone:** 912-430-5118. **Fax:** 912-430-6398. **E-mail:** dfrink@asurams.edu.

■ APPLICATION
Required GMAT, application form, baccalaureate/first degree, 2 letters of recommendation, transcripts of college work. **Recommended** Resume/curriculum vitae, work experience.

Deadlines and Fees *Deadlines:* 4/15 for fall, 10/15 for spring, 3/1 for summer, 4/15 for fall (international), 10/15 for spring (international), 3/1 for summer (international). *Application fee:* $20, $20 (international).

Application Contact Diane Frink, Graduate Admissions Officer, College of Business, 504 College Avenue, Graduate School, Albany, GA 31705-2717. **Phone:** 912-430-5118. **Fax:** 912-430-6398. **E-mail:** dfrink@asurams.edu.

American InterContinental University
Atlanta, Georgia

PROGRAM IN INTERNATIONAL BUSINESS

DEGREES MBA • MIT

MBA—Master of Business Administration in International Business Full-time and part-time. GMAT or GRE. At least 60 total credits required. Minimum of 10 months to complete program.

MIT—Information Technology Full-time and part-time. CPAB (Computer Programming Aptitude Battery) test. 80 total credits required. 12 to 24 months to complete program.

RESOURCES AND SERVICES
Information about online services, personal computer policies, library resources, international exchange programs, internship programs, and placement services at this institution and others can be found at **www. petersons.com/mba**

International Students

Services and Facilities Financial aid is available to international students.
International Student Contact International Enrollment Coordinator, Center for Global Studies-SIA, 6600 Peachtree-Dunwoody Road, 500 Embassy Row, Dunwoody, GA 30328. **Phone:** 404-965-5000. **Fax:** 404-965-8006. **E-mail:** international@aiuniv.edu.

■ APPLICATION
Application Contact Dunwoody Admissions Office, 6600 Peachtree-Dunwoody Road, 500 Embassy Row, Dunwoody, GA 30328. **Phone:** 404-965-5400. **Toll-free Phone:** 800-353-1744 (in-state), 888-757-4422 (out-of-state). **E-mail:** dunwoody@aiuniv.edu.

Augusta State University
Augusta, Georgia

COLLEGE OF BUSINESS ADMINISTRATION

Graduate Business Faculty
Full-time: 14

Student Body
Total: 111
Full-time: 37
Part-time: 74

Average Age: 29
Women: 56%

Admissions
Applications: 42
Admitted: 41
Enrolled: 37

Average GMAT: 520
Average GPA: 2.94

Costs (1999–2000)
Full-time tuition: N/R
Part-time tuition: $282 per course (resident), $1128 per course (nonresident)

Augusta State University (continued)

After Graduation (Class of 1998–99)
Employed within 3 months of graduation: 90%

Accreditation
AACSB—The International Association for Management Education

DEGREE MBA

MBA—Master of Business Administration Full-time and part-time. At least 36 total credits required. 16 to 72 months to complete program.

COSTS

Tuition, state resident: *Part-time* $282 per course. **Tuition, nonresident:** *Part-time* $1128 per course. Tuition varies by number of courses or credits taken and local reciprocity agreements.

FINANCIAL AID (1999–2000)
Loans, research assistantships, scholarships, and work study. Aid is available to part-time students. Financial aid application deadline: 6/1. **Financial Aid Contact** Kevin Wellwood, Director of Financial Aid, 2500 Walton Way, Augusta, GA 30904-2200. **Phone:** 706-737-1431. **Fax:** 706-737-1767.

RESOURCES AND SERVICES
Information about online services, personal computer policies, library resources, international exchange programs, internship programs, and placement services at this institution and others can be found at **www. petersons.com/mba**

International Students
5% of students enrolled are international students.

Services and Facilities Counseling/support services. Financial aid is not available to international students.
Applying *Required:* TOEFL with recommended score of 173 (computer) or 500 (paper), proof of adequate funds, proof of health/immunizations.
International Student Contact Dr. Frank Chou, Foreign Student Advisor, 2500 Walton Way, Augusta, GA 30904-2200. **Phone:** 706-667-4952.

■ APPLICATION

Required GMAT, application form, baccalaureate/first degree, transcripts of college work. **Recommended** Work experience.
Deadlines and Fees *Deadlines:* 7/15 for fall, 12/1 for spring, 4/10 for summer, 6/15 for fall (international), 11/1 for spring (international), 3/15 for summer (international). *Application fee:* $20, $20 (international).
Application Contact Ms. Miyoko Jackson, Graduate Degree Program Specialist, College of Business Administration, 2500 Walton Way, Augusta, GA 30904-2200. **Phone:** 706-737-1565. **Fax:** 706-667-4064. **E-mail:** mbainfo@aug.edu.

Berry College

Mount Berry, Georgia

CAMPBELL SCHOOL OF BUSINESS

Graduate Business Faculty
Full-time: 7

Student Body
Total: 31	Average Age: 32
Part-time: 31	Women: 45%

Admissions
Applications: 15	Average GMAT: 494
Admitted: 7	Average GPA: 3.25
Enrolled: 5	

Costs (1999–2000)
Full-time tuition: N/R
Part-time tuition: $385 per credit hour

After Graduation (Class of 1998–99)
Employed within 3 months of graduation: 60%

DEGREE MBA

MBA—General Business MBA Part-time. At least 36 total credits required. 12 to 72 months to complete program. *Concentrations:* accounting, management.

COSTS

Tuition *Part-time:* $385 per credit hour. Tuition varies by number of courses or credits taken.

FINANCIAL AID (1999–2000)
4 students received aid, including loans, research assistantships, and scholarships. Aid is available to part-time students. Financial aid application deadline: 4/1. **Financial Aid Contact** Mr. William Fron, Director of Financial Aid, Office of Financial Aid, PO Box 495007, Mount Berry, GA 30149-5007. **Phone:** 706-236-2244. **Fax:** 706-290-2160. **E-mail:** wfron@berry.edu.

RESOURCES AND SERVICES
Information about online services, personal computer policies, library resources, international exchange programs, internship programs, and placement services at this institution and others can be found at **www. petersons.com/mba**

International Students
3% of students enrolled are international students.

Services and Facilities Counseling/support services, visa services. Financial aid is not available to international students.
Applying *Required:* TOEFL with recommended score of 550 (paper), proof of adequate funds, proof of health/immunizations.
International Student Contact Dr. Carol Willis, Associate Dean of Students, PO Box 495009, Mount Berry, GA 30149-5009. **Phone:** 706-236-2207. **Fax:** 706-290-2649. **E-mail:** cwillis@berry.edu.

■ APPLICATION

Required GMAT, application form, baccalaureate/first degree, 2 letters of recommendation, transcripts of college work. **Recommended** Interview, work experience.
Deadlines and Fees *Deadlines:* 7/26 for fall, 12/6 for spring, 4/19 for summer, 2/26 for fall (international), 7/6 for spring (international), 11/19 for summer (international). *Application fee:* $25, $30 (international).
Application Contact Mrs. Barbara Henderson, Secretary for Graduate Studies in Business, Campbell School of Business, PO Box 49, Mount Berry, GA 30149-5024. **Phone:** 706-236-1751. **Toll-free Phone:** 800-BERRYGA. **Fax:** 706-238-7926. **E-mail:** mba@berry.edu.

Brenau University

Gainesville, Georgia

SCHOOL OF BUSINESS AND MASS COMMUNICATION

Graduate Business Faculty
Full-time: 8	Part-time: 18

Student Body
Total: 341	Average Age: 34
Full-time: 90	Women: 44%
Part-time: 251	

Costs (1999–2000)
Full-time tuition: N/R
Part-time tuition: $228 per credit hour

After Graduation (Class of 1998–99)
Employed within 3 months of graduation: 95%
Average starting salary: $50,000

DEGREES MBA

MBA—Leadership Development Full-time and part-time. *Distance learning option.* 30 to 60 total credits required. 18 to 84 months to complete program. *Concentrations:* leadership, management.

MBA—Master of Business Administration in Accounting Full-time and part-time. 36 to 60 total credits required. 24 to 84 months to complete program. *Concentrations:* accounting.

MBA—Master of Business Administration in Healthcare Management Full-time and part-time. 33 to 60 total credits required. 18 to 84 months to complete program. *Concentrations:* health care.

MBA—Master of Business Administration in Management Full-time and part-time. 42 to 60 total credits required. 24 to 84 months to complete program. *Concentrations:* management, organizational management.

COSTS

Tuition *Part-time:* $228 per credit hour. Tuition varies by number of courses or credits taken and campus location.

FINANCIAL AID (1999-2000)

Fellowships, grants, loans, and scholarships. Financial aid application deadline: 6/1. **Financial Aid Contact** Mrs. Pam Barrett, Director of Financial Aid, One Centennial Circle, Gainesville, GA 30501-3697. **Phone:** 770-534-6152. **Fax:** 770-538-4306. **E-mail:** pbarrett@lib.brenau.edu.

RESOURCES AND SERVICES

Information about online services, personal computer policies, library resources, international exchange programs, internship programs, and placement services at this institution and others can be found at **www.petersons.com/mba**

International Students

0.9% of students enrolled are international students.

Services and Facilities Financial aid is available to international students.
Applying *Required:* TOEFL with recommended score of 500 (paper).

■ APPLICATION

Required Application form, baccalaureate/first degree, interview, personal statement, transcripts of college work. School will accept GMAT, GRE, and MAT. **Recommended** Work experience.

Deadlines and Fees Applications for domestic and international students are processed on a rolling basis. *Application fee:* $30, $30 (international).

Application Contact Ms. Kathy Cobb, Director of Admissions, Evening and Weekend College, One Centennial Circle, Gainesville, GA 30501. **Phone:** 770-534-6162. **Fax:** 770-538-4701. **E-mail:** kcobb@lib.brenau.edu.

Clark Atlanta University

Atlanta, Georgia

SCHOOL OF BUSINESS ADMINISTRATION

Graduate Business Faculty
Full-time: 25 | Part-time: 3

Student Body
Total: 180 | Average Age: 28
Full-time: 148 | Women: 60%
Part-time: 32

Admissions
Applications: 300 | Average GMAT: 415
Admitted: 117 | Average GPA: 2.89
Enrolled: 76

Costs (1999-2000)
Full-time tuition: $13,437 per academic year
Part-time tuition: $25,000 per degree program

After Graduation (Class of 1998-99)
Employed within 3 months of graduation: 85%
Average starting salary: $70,000

Accreditation
AACSB—The International Association for Management Education

DEGREES MBA

MBA—Part-time MBA Program Part-time. Minimum of 3 years of work experience required. At least 54 total credits required. 21 to 60 months to complete program. *Concentrations:* finance, marketing.

MBA—Master of Business Administration Full-time and part-time. At least 60 total credits required. 21 to 60 months to complete program. *Concentrations:* decision sciences, finance, health care, marketing.

COSTS

Tuition *Full-time:* $13,237. *Part-time:* $25,000 per degree program. **Tuition, international:** *Full-time* $13,237. Tuition varies by class time. **Required fees:** *Full-time* $200. **Graduate housing:** Room and board costs vary by number of occupants, type of accommodation, and type of board plan. *Typical cost:* $4500 (including board), $2298 (room only).

FINANCIAL AID (1999-2000)

53 students received aid, including scholarships and work study. Financial aid application deadline: 4/1. **Financial Aid Contact** Ms. Cele Echols, Director of Admissions and Financial Aid, James P. Brawley Drive at Fair Street, SW, Atlanta, GA 30314. **Phone:** 404-880-8479. **Fax:** 404-880-6159.

RESOURCES AND SERVICES

Information about online services, personal computer policies, library resources, international exchange programs, internship programs, and placement services at this institution and others can be found at **www.petersons.com/mba**

International Students

10% of students enrolled are international students.

Services and Facilities Counseling/support services, orientation, visa services. Financial aid is available to international students.
Applying *Required:* TOEFL with recommended score of 500 (paper), proof of adequate funds, proof of health/immunizations.

International Student Contact Ms. Yvonne Jackson, Program Coordinator, International Student Services, James P. Brawley Drive at Fair Street, SW, Atlanta, GA 30314. **Phone:** 404-880-8771. **Fax:** 404-880-8625.

■ APPLICATION

Required GMAT, application form, baccalaureate/first degree, essay, 3 letters of recommendation, resume/curriculum vitae, transcripts of college work. **Recommended** Work experience.

Deadlines and Fees *Deadlines:* 4/1 for fall, 4/1 for fall (international). *Application fee:* $40, $55 (international).

Application Contact Ms. Cele Echols, Director of Admissions and Financial Aid, James P. Brawley Drive at Fair Street, SW, Atlanta, GA 30314. **Phone:** 404-880-8479. **Fax:** 404-880-6159.

Columbus State University

Columbus, Georgia

COLLEGE OF BUSINESS

Graduate Business Faculty
Full-time: 13 | Part-time: 1

Student Body
Total: 46 | Part-time: 29
Full-time: 17

Costs (1999-2000)
Full-time tuition: N/R
Part-time tuition: N/R

DEGREE MBA

MBA—Master of Business Administration Full-time and part-time. At least 30 total credits required. 18 to 72 months to complete program.

COSTS

Graduate housing: Room and board costs vary by type of accommodation and type of board plan. *Typical cost:* $4000 (including board).

FINANCIAL AID (1999-2000)

Financial Aid Contact Mr. Al Pinckney, Director, Financial Aid, 4225 University Avenue, Columbus, GA 31907-5645. **Phone:** 706-568-2036. **Fax:** 706-568-2230. **E-mail:** financial_aid@colstate.edu.

RESOURCES AND SERVICES

Information about online services, personal computer policies, library resources, international exchange programs, internship programs, and placement services at this institution and others can be found at **www.petersons.com/mba**

International Students

Services and Facilities Counseling/support services, international student organization.
Applying *Required:* TOEFL with recommended score of 550 (paper), proof of adequate funds, proof of health/immunizations.

International Student Contact Dr. Michael Daniels, Associate Dean, Abbott Turner College of Business, 4225 University Avenue, Columbus, GA 31907. **Phone:** 706-568-2129. **Fax:** 706-568-2184. **E-mail:** grad_studies@colstate.edu.

■ APPLICATION

Required GMAT, application form, baccalaureate/first degree, essay, resume/curriculum vitae, transcripts of college work.

Deadlines and Fees Applications for domestic and international students are processed on a rolling basis. *Application fee:* $20, $20 (international).

Application Contact Dr. Michael Daniels, Associate Dean, Abbott Turner College of Business, 4225 University Avenue, Columbus, GA 31907. **Phone:** 706-568-2129. **Fax:** 706-568-2184. **E-mail:** grad_studies@colstate.edu.

Emory University

Atlanta, Georgia

ROBERTO C. GOIZUETA BUSINESS SCHOOL

Graduate Business Faculty
Full-time: 61   Part-time: 15

Student Body
Total: 530   Average Age: 26
Full-time: 357   Women: 30%
Part-time: 173

Admissions
Applications: 1,099   Average GMAT: 645
Admitted: 387   Average GPA: 3.4
Enrolled: 180

Costs (1999–2000)
Full-time tuition: $24,000 per academic year
Part-time tuition: $15,999 per year

After Graduation (Class of 1998–99)
Employed within 3 months of graduation: 96%
Average starting salary: $72,750

Accreditation
AACSB—The International Association for Management Education

DEGREES JD/MBA • MBA • MBA/MPH • MN/MBA

JD/MBA—Juris Doctor/Master of Business Administration Full-time and part-time. At least 77 total credits required. 48 months to complete program.

MBA—Day MBA Full-time. At least 63 total credits required. 21 months to complete program. *Concentrations:* accounting, entrepreneurship, finance, human resources, international business, management, management information systems, marketing, operations management, organizational behavior/development, quantitative analysis, strategic management.

MBA—Evening MBA Part-time. At least 57 total credits required. 33 months to complete program.

MBA—Executive MBA Part-time. At least 54 total credits required. 16 months to complete program.

MBA—One-year MBA Full-time. At least 43 total credits required. 12 months to complete program.

MBA/MPH—Master of Business Administration/Master of Public Health Full-time and part-time. At least 81 total credits required. Maximum of 28 months to complete program.

MN/MBA—Master of Nursing/Master of Business Administration Full-time and part-time. At least 92 total credits required. Minimum of 23 months to complete program.

COSTS

Tuition *Full-time:* $24,000. *Part-time:* $15,999 per year. Tuition varies by number of courses or credits taken and academic program. **Required fees:** Tuition and fees vary by academic program. **Graduate housing:** Room and board costs vary by campus location, number of occupants, and type of accommodation. *Typical cost:* $8000 (room only).

FINANCIAL AID (1999–2000)

218 students received aid, including fellowships, loans, research assistantships, scholarships, and work study. Aid is available to part-time students. Financial aid application deadline: 3/1. **Financial Aid Contact** Ms. Brenda Hill, Associate Director, Financial Aid, Office of Financial Aid, Atlanta, GA 30322. **Phone:** 404-727-1141. **Fax:** 404-727-6709.

RESOURCES AND SERVICES

Information about online services, personal computer policies, library resources, international exchange programs, internship programs, and placement services at this institution and others can be found at **www. petersons.com/mba**

International Students

23% of students enrolled are international students.

Services and Facilities Counseling/support services, language tutoring, visa services. Financial aid is not available to international students.

Applying *Required:* TOEFL with recommended score of 600 (paper), proof of adequate funds, proof of health/immunizations.

International Student Contact Nancy Roth Remington, Director of International Programs, 1300 Clifton Road, NE, Atlanta, GA 30322-2710. **Phone:** 404-727-2553. **Fax:** 404-727-0868. **E-mail:** nancy_remington@bus.emory.edu.

■ APPLICATION

Required GMAT, application form, baccalaureate/first degree, essay, 3 letters of recommendation, personal statement, resume/curriculum vitae, transcripts of college work. **Recommended** Interview, work experience.

Deadlines and Fees *Deadlines:* 3/31 for fall, 3/31 for fall (international). *Application fee:* $70, $70 (international).

Application Contact Julie Barefoot, Assistant Dean of Admissions and Student Services, 1300 Clifton Road, NE, Atlanta, GA 30322-2710. **Phone:** 404-727-6311. **Fax:** 404-727-4612. **E-mail:** admissions@bus.emory.edu.

See full description on page 642.

Georgia College and State University

Milledgeville, Georgia

SCHOOL OF BUSINESS

Graduate Business Faculty
Full-time: 34   Part-time: 2

Student Body
Total: 157   Average Age: 29
Full-time: 40   Women: 46%
Part-time: 117

Admissions
Applications: 105   Average GPA: 3.21
Average GMAT: 521

Costs (1999–2000)
Full-time tuition: $2450 per academic year (resident), $7346 per academic year (nonresident)
Part-time tuition: $380 per course (resident), $1196 per course (nonresident)

Accreditation
AACSB—The International Association for Management Education
ACBSP—The American Council of Business Schools and Programs

DEGREES MBA • MMIS

MBA—Master of Business Administration Full-time and part-time. 30 to 57 total credits required. 12 to 84 months to complete program.

MMIS—Master of Management Information Systems Full-time and part-time. 36 to 60 total credits required. 12 to 84 months to complete program. *Concentrations:* accounting.

COSTS

Tuition, state resident: *Full-time* $2044. *Part-time* $273 per course. **Tuition, nonresident:** *Full-time* $6940. *Part-time* $1089 per course. **Tuition, international:** *Full-time* $6940. Tuition varies by number of courses or credits taken. **Required fees:** *Full-time* $406. *Part-time* $107 per course. Fees vary by campus location. **Graduate housing:** Room and board costs vary by number of occupants, type of accommodation, and type of board plan. *Typical cost:* $4140 (including board), $2180 (room only).

FINANCIAL AID (1999–2000)

Loans, research assistantships, and scholarships. Aid is available to part-time students. Financial aid application deadline: 3/15. **Financial Aid Contact** Ms. Suzanne Buttram, Director of Financial Aid, CBX 030, Milledgeville, GA 31061. **Phone:** 912-445-5149. **Fax:** 912-445-0729 **E-mail:** sbuttram@mail.gcsu.edu.

RESOURCES AND SERVICES

Information about online services, personal computer policies, library resources, international exchange programs, internship programs, and placement services at this institution and others can be found at **www. petersons.com/mba**

International Students

16% of students enrolled are international students.

Services and Facilities Counseling/support services, ESL/language courses, international student organization, orientation, visa services. Financial aid is available to international students.

Applying *Required:* TOEFL with recommended score of 500 (paper), proof of adequate funds, proof of health/immunizations.

International Student Contact Dr. Dwight Call, Assistant Vice President for International Education, CBX 046, Milledgeville, GA 31061. **Phone:** 912-445-4789. **Fax:** 912-445-2623. **E-mail:** dwither@mail.gcsu.edu.

■ **APPLICATION**

Required GMAT, application form, baccalaureate/first degree, transcripts of college work.

Deadlines and Fees *Deadlines:* 7/15 for fall, 12/1 for spring, 5/1 for summer, 5/1 for fall (international), 10/1 for spring (international). *Application fee:* $25, $25 (international).

Application Contact Ms. Lynn Hanson, Director, Graduate Programs in Business, CBX 019, Milledgeville, GA 31061. **Phone:** 912-445-5115. **Toll-free Phone:** 800-342-0471. **Fax:** 912-445-5249. **E-mail:** lhanson@mail.gcsu.edu.

Georgia Institute of Technology

Atlanta, Georgia

DUPREE COLLEGE OF MANAGEMENT

Graduate Business Faculty
Full-time: 55

Student Body
Total: 230
Full-time: 230

Average Age: 27
Women: 30%

Admissions
Applications: 500
Admitted: 199
Enrolled: 106

Average GMAT: 635
Average GPA: 3.2

Costs (1999–2000)
Full-time tuition: $4902 per academic year (resident), $17,202 per academic year (nonresident)
Part-time tuition: N/R

After Graduation (Class of 1998–99)
Employed within 3 months of graduation: 98%
Average starting salary: $78,000

Accreditation
AACSB—The International Association for Management Education

DEGREES MS • MSM

MS—Master of Science in Management of Technology Part-time. At least 54 total credits required. 18 months to complete program. *Concentrations:* technology management.

MSM—Master of Science in Management Full-time. At least 60 total credits required. 18 to 21 months to complete program. *Concentrations:* accounting, business policy/strategy, electronic commerce (e-commerce), entrepreneurship, finance, information management, international and area business studies, international business, international management, management, management consulting, management information systems, manufacturing management, marketing, marketing research, new venture management, operations management, organizational behavior/development, production management, strategic management, technology management.

COSTS

Tuition, state resident: *Full-time* $4902. **Tuition, nonresident:** *Full-time* $17,202. **Tuition, international:** *Full-time* $17,202. Tuition varies by number of courses or credits taken and academic program. **Graduate housing:** Room and board costs vary by campus location, number of occupants, type of accommodation, and type of board plan. *Typical cost:* $5400 (including board).

FINANCIAL AID (1999–2000)

Fellowships, loans, research assistantships, teaching assistantships, and work study. Financial aid application deadline: 2/15. **Financial Aid Contact** Mr. Jerry McTier, Director of Financial Aid, Student and Financial Planning and Services, 225 North Avenue, NW, Atlanta, GA 30332-0460. **Phone:** 404-894-1938. **Fax:** 404-894-7412. **E-mail:** jerry.mctier@success.gatech.edu.

RESOURCES AND SERVICES

Information about online services, personal computer policies, library resources, international exchange programs, internship programs, and placement services at this institution and others can be found at **www.petersons.com/mba**

International Students

15% of students enrolled are international students.

Services and Facilities Counseling/support services, ESL/language courses, housing location assistance, international student housing, international student organization, orientation, visa services. Financial aid is not available to international students.

Applying *Required:* TOEFL with recommended score of 250 (computer) or 600 (paper), proof of adequate funds, proof of health/immunizations.
International Student Contact Ms. Linda Duckworth, International Student Services, 225 North Avenue, NW, Atlanta, GA 30332-0284. **Phone:** 404-894-7475. **Fax:** 404-894-7682.

■ **APPLICATION**

Required Application form, baccalaureate/first degree, essay, 2 letters of recommendation, resume/curriculum vitae, transcripts of college work. School will accept GMAT. **Recommended** Interview, work experience.

Deadlines and Fees *Deadlines:* 4/15 for fall, 2/15 for fall (international). *Application fee:* $50, $50 (international).

Application Contact Ms. Carita Reynolds, Admissions and Student Services Coordinator, Dupree College of Management, 755 Ferst Avenue, Room 212, Atlanta, GA 30332-0520. **Phone:** 404-894-8722. **Toll-free Phone:** 800-869-1014. **Fax:** 404-894-4199. **E-mail:** msm@mgt.gatech.edu.

Georgia Southern University

Statesboro, Georgia

COLLEGE OF BUSINESS ADMINISTRATION

Graduate Business Faculty
Full-time: 36

Part-time: 19

Student Body
Total: 312
Full-time: 84
Part-time: 228

Average Age: 28
Women: 45%

Admissions
Applications: 112
Admitted: 112
Enrolled: 112

Average GMAT: 486
Average GPA: 3.05

Costs (1999–2000)
Full-time tuition: N/R
Part-time tuition: $289 per course (resident), $1039 per course (nonresident)

Accreditation
AACSB—The International Association for Management Education

DEGREES M Acc • MBA

M Acc—Master of Accountancy Full-time and part-time. *Distance learning option.* At least 33 total credits required. 15 to 84 months to complete program. *Concentrations:* accounting.

MBA—Web MBA Full-time. 54 total credits required. 24 months to complete program.

MBA—Master of Business Administration Full-time and part-time. *Distance learning option.* 33 to 52 total credits required. 15 to 84 months to complete program. *Concentrations:* accounting, international trade, logistics.

COSTS

Tuition, state resident: *Part-time* $289 per course. **Tuition, nonresident:** *Part-time* $1039 per course. Tuition varies by number of courses or credits taken.

FINANCIAL AID (1999–2000)

Research assistantships, teaching assistantships, and work study. Aid is available to part-time students. Financial aid application deadline: 4/15. **Financial Aid Contact** Ms. Pamela Pierce, Director of Financial Aid, PO Box 8065, Statesboro, GA 30460-8065. **Phone:** 912-681-5413. **Fax:** 912-681-0573.

RESOURCES AND SERVICES

Information about online services, personal computer policies, library resources, international exchange programs, internship programs, and placement services at this institution and others can be found at **www.petersons.com/mba**

International Students

12% of students enrolled are international students.

Services and Facilities Counseling/support services, ESL/language courses, housing location assistance, international student housing, international student organization, language tutoring, orientation, visa services.
Applying *Required:* TOEFL with recommended score of 500 (paper), proof of adequate funds, proof of health/immunizations.
International Student Contact Mr. Maher Tubbeh, Director, International Student Program, PO Box 8063, Statesboro, GA 30460-8063. **Phone:** 912-681-0382. **Fax:** 912-681-0694.

■ **APPLICATION**

Required Application form, baccalaureate/first degree, transcripts of college work. School will accept GMAT.

Deadlines and Fees *Deadlines:* 7/1 for fall, 11/15 for spring, 4/1 for summer, 6/1 for fall (international), 10/1 for spring (international), 2/15 for summer (international).

Application Contact Dr. J. Michael McDonald, Director of Graduate Studies, PO Box 8050, Statesboro, GA 30460. **Phone:** 912-681-5767. **Fax:** 912-486-7480. **E-mail:** mmcdonal@gsaix2.cc.gasou.edu.

Georgia Southwestern State University

Americus, Georgia

SCHOOL OF BUSINESS

Graduate Business Faculty
Full-time: 9   Part-time: 3

Student Body
Total: 55   Part-time: 39
Full-time: 16

Admissions
Average GPA: 3

Costs (1999–2000)
Full-time tuition: $1808 per academic year (resident), $7232 per academic year (nonresident)
Part-time tuition: $91 per credit hour (resident), $363 per credit hour (nonresident)

DEGREES MSA

MSA—Master of Science in Administration in Accounting Full-time and part-time. *Distance learning option.* At least 30 total credits required. 12 to 48 months to complete program.

MSA—Master of Science in Administration in Management Full-time and part-time. *Distance learning option.* At least 30 total credits required. 12 to 48 months to complete program.

COSTS

Tuition, state resident: *Full-time* $1808. *Part-time* $91 per credit hour. **Tuition, nonresident:** *Full-time* $7232. *Part-time* $363 per credit hour. **Required fees:** Tuition and fees vary by number of courses or credits taken. **Graduate housing:** Room and board costs vary by number of occupants and type of board plan. *Typical cost:* $3540 (including board).

FINANCIAL AID (1999–2000)

Research assistantships and teaching assistantships. **Financial Aid Contact** Freida Jones, Director of Financial Aid, 800 Wheatley Street, Americus, GA 31709-4693. **Phone:** 912-928-1378. **E-mail:** fjjones@canes.gsw.edu.

RESOURCES AND SERVICES

Information about online services, personal computer policies, library resources, international exchange programs, internship programs, and placement services at this institution and others can be found at **www.petersons.com/mba**

International Students

Services and Facilities Counseling/support services, ESL/language courses, international student housing. Financial aid is available to international students.

Applying *Required:* TOEFL with recommended score of 550 (paper), proof of adequate funds, proof of health/immunizations.

International Student Contact Angela Walker, Director of Multicultural Activities, 800 Wheatley Street, Americus, GA 31709-4693. **Phone:** 912-928-1387. **E-mail:** ayw@canes.gsw.edu.

■ **APPLICATION**

Required GMAT, application form, baccalaureate/first degree, letter(s) of recommendation, transcripts of college work. School will accept GRE. **Recommended** Interview, resume/curriculum vitae.

Deadlines and Fees Applications for domestic and international students are processed on a rolling basis. *Application fee:* $20, $20 (international).

Application Contact John Kooti, Dean, School of Business Administration, 800 Wheatley Street, Americus, GA 31709-4693. **Phone:** 912-931-2090. **Fax:** 918-931-2092. **E-mail:** schobus@canes.gsw.edu.

Georgia State University

Atlanta, Georgia

J. MACK ROBINSON COLLEGE OF BUSINESS

Graduate Business Faculty
Full-time: 177   Part-time: 29

Student Body
Total: 2,689   Average Age: 28
Full-time: 1,045   Women: 36%
Part-time: 1,644

Admissions
Applications: 1,276   Average GMAT: 580
Admitted: 712   Average GPA: 3.1
Enrolled: 532

Costs (1999–2000)
Full-time tuition: N/R
Part-time tuition: $390 per course (resident), $1554 per course (nonresident)

After Graduation (Class of 1998–99)
Employed within 3 months of graduation: 85%
Average starting salary: $56,157

Accreditation
AACSB—The International Association for Management Education

DEGREES JD/MBA • M Tax • MAS • MBA • MBA/MHA • MIB • MPA • MS

JD/MBA—Juris Doctor/Master of Business Administration Full-time and part-time. 39 to 48 total credits required. 12 to 60 months to complete program.

M Tax—Master of Taxation Full-time and part-time. At least 30 total credits required. 12 to 60 months to complete program.

MAS—Master of Actuarial Science Full-time. At least 32 total credits required. 15 to 60 months to complete program. *Concentrations:* actuarial science.

MBA—Executive MBA Full-time. 47 to 48 total credits required. 18 months to complete program.

MBA—Master of Business Administration Full-time and part-time. 39 to 48 total credits required. 12 to 60 months to complete program. *Concentrations:* accounting, decision sciences, economics, electronic commerce (e-commerce), finance, financial management/planning, health care, human resources, information management, international business, management, marketing, real estate, risk management, hospitality management.

MBA/MHA—Master of Business Administration/Master of Health Administration Full-time. 51 to 54 total credits required. 36 to 60 months to complete program.

MIB—Master of International Business Full-time and part-time. At least 33 total credits required. 12 to 60 months to complete program.

MPA—Master of Professional Accountancy Full-time and part-time. At least 30 total credits required. 12 to 60 months to complete program.

MS—Master of Science in Health Administration Full-time and part-time. At least 36 total credits required. 12 to 60 months to complete program. *Concentrations:* health care.

MS—Master of Science in Real Estate Full-time and part-time. At least 36 total credits required. 12 to 60 months to complete program.

MS—Master of Science Full-time and part-time. 30 to 36 total credits required. 12 to 60 months to complete program. *Concentrations:* decision sciences, economics, finance, financial management/planning, human resources, information management, management, marketing, risk management.

COSTS

Tuition, state resident: *Part-time* $390 per course. **Tuition, nonresident:** *Part-time* $1554 per course. Tuition varies by number of courses or credits taken and local reciprocity agreements. **Required fees:** *Part-time* $234 per semester. **Graduate housing:** *Typical cost:* $4190 (room only).

FINANCIAL AID (1999–2000)

Fellowships, research assistantships, and teaching assistantships. Aid is available to part-time students. Financial aid application deadline: 5/1.

RESOURCES AND SERVICES

Information about online services, personal computer policies, library resources, international exchange programs, internship programs, and placement services at this institution and others can be found at **www. petersons.com/mba**

International Students

16% of students enrolled are international students.

Services and Facilities Counseling/support services, ESL/language courses, international student housing, international student organization, orientation, visa services. Financial aid is available to international students.

Applying *Required:* TOEFL with recommended score of 240 (computer) or 580 (paper), proof of adequate funds, proof of health/immunizations. *Recommended:* TWE.

International Student Contact Mr. Douglas Podoll, Director, International Student Services, Office of International Services and Programs, University Plaza, Atlanta, GA 30303. **Phone:** 404-463-9073.

■ APPLICATION

Required GMAT, application form, baccalaureate/first degree, essay, transcripts of college work. **Recommended** Letter(s) of recommendation, work experience.

Deadlines and Fees *Deadlines:* 5/1 for fall, 10/1 for spring, 2/1 for summer, 5/1 for fall (international), 10/1 for spring (international), 2/1 for summer (international). *Application fee:* $25, $25 (international).

Application Contact Office of Academic Assistance and Master's Admissions, J. Mack Robinson College of Business, University Plaza, Atlanta, GA 30303-3087. **Phone:** 404-651-1913. **Fax:** 404-651-0219.

See full description on page 668.

Kennesaw State University

Kennesaw, Georgia

MICHAEL J. COLES COLLEGE OF BUSINESS

Graduate Business Faculty
Full-time: 92   Part-time: 3

Student Body
Total: 944
Full-time: 485   Average Age: 37
Part-time: 459   Women: 44%

Admissions
Applications: 212   Average GMAT: 522
Admitted: 185   Average GPA: 3
Enrolled: 138

Costs (1999–2000)
Full-time tuition: N/R
Part-time tuition: $91 per credit hour (resident), $272 per credit hour (nonresident)

Accreditation
AACSB—The International Association for Management Education

DEGREES M Acc • MBA

M Acc—Master of Accounting Full-time and part-time. *Distance learning option.* At least 36 total credits required. 12 to 72 months to complete program. *Concentrations:* management, taxation.

MBA—Executive MBA Full-time. *Distance learning option.* 5 years of work experience required. At least 36 total credits required. 18 months to complete program.

MBA—Master of Business Administration Full-time and part-time. *Distance learning option.* At least 36 total credits required. 12 to 72 months to complete program. *Concentrations:* accounting, economics, entrepreneurship, finance, human resources, information management, international business, management, marketing, operations management.

During the past year, U.S. News & World Report, Business Week, Entrepreneur Magazine, *and* Success Magazine, *have heralded the leadership in innovation and entrepreneurship programs developed by the Michael J. Coles College of Business. The M.B.A. program now features the opportunity to major in this most important discipline that is the mainstay of private enterprise systems and economic growth and development worldwide. Course-work in entrepreneurship, innovation and creativity, new venture analysis, entrepreneurial finance, the award-winning consulting services class, and family business make this program unique and appealing. This expertise combined with what the* Wall Street Journal *has called one of the finest family enterprise programs in the nation makes the Coles School a true leader in the field of small, family, and emerging enterprises. Entrepreneurship is but one*

of ten formal majors in this program, which is accredited by AACSB-The International Association for Management Education. The Coles School, situated in suburban Atlanta, is committed to supporting the academic and professional needs of the more than 1,000 students enrolled in graduate business programs. The School combines new, state-of-the-art facilities and 85 committed faculty members for a global educational experience.*

COSTS

Tuition, state resident: *Part-time* $91 per credit hour. **Tuition, nonresident:** *Part-time* $272 per credit hour. Tuition varies by number of courses or credits taken.

FINANCIAL AID (1999–2000)

38 students received aid, including work study. Aid is available to part-time students. Financial aid application deadline: 8/1. **Financial Aid Contact** Dr. Terry Faust, Office of Financial Aid, 1000 Chastain Road, Kennesaw, GA 30144-5591. **Phone:** 770-423-6074. **E-mail:** cmatson@ksumail.kennesaw.edu.

RESOURCES AND SERVICES

Information about online services, personal computer policies, library resources, international exchange programs, internship programs, and placement services at this institution and others can be found at **www. petersons.com/mba**

International Students

7% of students enrolled are international students.

Services and Facilities Counseling/support services. Financial aid is not available to international students.

Applying *Required:* TOEFL with recommended score of 550 (paper), proof of adequate funds, proof of health/immunizations.

International Student Contact Mr. Tom Hughes, Sr., Director, Graduate Admissions, Office of Admissions, 1000 Chastain Road, Kennesaw, GA 30144-5591. **Phone:** 770-423-6300. **Fax:** 707-423-6541. **E-mail:** thughes@kennesaw. edu.

■ APPLICATION

Required Application form, baccalaureate/first degree, interview, letter(s) of recommendation, personal statement, resume/curriculum vitae, transcripts of college work. School will accept GMAT. **Recommended** Work experience.

Deadlines and Fees *Deadlines:* 7/21 for fall, 11/17 for spring, 4/13 for summer, 7/21 for fall (international), 11/17 for spring (international), 4/13 for summer (international). *Application fee:* $20, $20 (international).

Application Contact Ms. Susan Cochran, Administrative Coordinator, Michael J. Coles College of Business, 1000 Chastain Road, Kennesaw, GA 30144-5591. **Phone:** 770-423-6472. **Fax:** 770-423-6141. **E-mail:** susan_cochran@coles2.kennesaw.edu.

See full description on page 702.

LaGrange College

LaGrange, Georgia

DIVISION OF BUSINESS ADMINISTRATION AND ECONOMICS

Graduate Business Faculty
Full-time: 5

Student Body
Total: 28
Full-time: 11   Average Age: 34
Part-time: 17   Women: 46%

Admissions
Applications: 14   Enrolled: 10
Admitted: 14   Average GPA: 3.5

Costs (1999–2000)
Full-time tuition: $8820 per academic year
Part-time tuition: $245 per quarter hour

Accreditation
ACBSP—The American Council of Business Schools and Programs

DEGREE MBA

MBA—Master of Business Administration Full-time and part-time. At least 60 total credits required. 18 to 60 months to complete program.

COSTS

Tuition *Full-time:* $8820. *Part-time:* $245 per quarter hour.

LaGrange College (continued)

FINANCIAL AID (1999–2000)
12 students received aid, including loans. Aid is available to part-time students. Financial aid application deadline: 6/1. **Financial Aid Contact** Ms. Sylvia Smith, Director of Financial Aid, 601 Broad Street, LaGrange, GA 30240. **Phone:** 706-812-7249. **Fax:** 718-812-7348. **E-mail:** ssmith@lgc.edu.

RESOURCES AND SERVICES
Information about online services, personal computer policies, library resources, international exchange programs, internship programs, and placement services at this institution and others can be found at **www. petersons.com/mba**

International Students
Services and Facilities Financial aid is not available to international students. **Applying** *Required:* Proof of adequate funds, proof of health/immunizations. *Recommended:* TOEFL.

International Student Contact Mr. Andy Geeter, Director of Admission, 601 Broad Street, LaGrange, GA 30240. **Phone:** 706-812-7253. **Fax:** 706-812-7354. **E-mail:** ageeter@lgc.edu.

■ APPLICATION
Required GMAT, application form, baccalaureate/first degree, interview, personal statement, resume/curriculum vitae, transcripts of college work, 2 years of work experience. **Recommended** Essay, letter(s) of recommendation.

Deadlines and Fees Applications for domestic and international students are processed on a rolling basis. *Application fee:* $25, $25 (international).

Application Contact Mr. Andy Geeter, Director of Admission, 601 Broad Street, La Grange, GA 30240. **Phone:** 706-812-7253. **Toll-free Phone:** 800-593-2885. **Fax:** 706-812-7348. **E-mail:** ageeter@lgc.edu.

Mercer University
Macon, Georgia

STETSON SCHOOL OF BUSINESS AND ECONOMICS

Graduate Business Faculty
Full-time: 36   Part-time: 8

Student Body
Total: 689
Full-time: 315   Average Age: 32
Part-time: 374   Women: 50%

Admissions
Applications: 232   Average GMAT: 471
Admitted: 172   Average GPA: 3.1
Enrolled: 127

Costs (1999–2000)
Full-time tuition: N/R
Part-time tuition: $1059 per course

After Graduation (Class of 1998–99)
Employed within 3 months of graduation: 95%

DEGREES EMBA • MBA • MSHCM • MSTM

EMBA—Executive MBA in International Business Part-time. At least 39 total credits required. Minimum of 21 months to complete program.

MBA—Master of Business Administration Full-time and part-time. 36 to 54 total credits required. 12 to 60 months to complete program. *Concentrations:* finance, international business, management.

MSHCM—Master of Science in Health Care Management Part-time. At least 39 total credits required. 15 to 60 months to complete program.

MSTM—Master of Science in Technology Management Part-time. At least 39 total credits required. 15 to 60 months to complete program.

COSTS
Tuition *Part-time:* $1059 per course. Tuition varies by class time and campus location.

FINANCIAL AID (1999–2000)
417 students received aid, including loans and work study. Aid is available to part-time students. Financial aid application deadline: 5/1. **Financial Aid Contact** Ms. Margaret McGinness, Director of Financial Aid, 3001 Mercer University Drive, Atlanta, GA 30341-4155. **Phone:** 678-547-6134. **Fax:** 678-547-6135. **E-mail:** mcginness_ma@mercer.edu.

RESOURCES AND SERVICES
Information about online services, personal computer policies, library resources, international exchange programs, internship programs, and placement services at this institution and others can be found at **www. petersons.com/mba**

International Students
18% of students enrolled are international students.

Services and Facilities Counseling/support services, ESL/language courses, housing location assistance, international student organization. Financial aid is not available to international students.
Applying *Required:* TOEFL with recommended score of 550 (paper), proof of adequate funds, proof of health/immunizations.

International Student Contact Mrs. Argy Russell, Director of Admissions, Stetson School of Business and Economics, 3001 Mercer University Drive, Atlanta, GA 30341-4155. **Phone:** 678-547-6206. **Fax:** 678-547-6367. **E-mail:** russell_a@mercer.edu.

■ APPLICATION
Required GMAT, application form, baccalaureate/first degree, transcripts of college work.

Deadlines and Fees Applications for domestic and international students are processed on a rolling basis. *Application fee:* $35, $50 (international).

Application Contact Mrs. Argy Russell, Director of Admissions, Stetson School of Business and Economics, 3001 Mercer University Drive, Atlanta, GA 30341-4155. **Phone:** 678-547-6417. **Fax:** 678-547-6367. **E-mail:** russell_a@mercer.edu.

Oglethorpe University
Atlanta, Georgia

DIVISION OF BUSINESS ADMINISTRATION

Graduate Business Faculty
Full-time: 7   Part-time: 1

Student Body
Total: 53   Average Age: 31
Full-time: 8   Women: 57%
Part-time: 45

Admissions
Applications: 22   Enrolled: 13
Admitted: 17

Costs (1999–2000)
Full-time tuition: N/R
Part-time tuition: $1380 per course

DEGREE MBA

MBA—Master of Business Administration Full-time and part-time. At least 40 total credits required. Minimum of 24 months to complete program. *Concentrations:* accounting.

COSTS
Tuition *Part-time:* $1380 per course. Tuition varies by number of courses or credits taken and academic program. **Required fees:** Tuition and fees vary by academic program.

FINANCIAL AID (1999–2000)
11 students received aid. **Financial Aid Contact** Mr. Patrick Bonones, Director of Financial Aid, 4484 Peachtree Road, NE, Atlanta, GA 30319-2797. **Phone:** 404-364-8354. **Fax:** 404-364-8500. **E-mail:** pbonones@facstaff.oglethorpe.edu.

RESOURCES AND SERVICES
Information about online services, personal computer policies, library resources, international exchange programs, internship programs, and placement services at this institution and others can be found at **www. petersons.com/mba**

International Students
6% of students enrolled are international students.

Services and Facilities Counseling/support services, international student housing. **Applying** *Required:* TOEFL with recommended score of 500 (paper).

International Student Contact Mr. Marshall Nason, Associate Dean—Community Life, 4484 Peachtree Road, NE, Atlanta, GA 30319-2797. **Phone:** 404-364-8424. **Fax:** 404-364-8442. **E-mail:** nason@facstaff.oglethorpe.edu.

■ APPLICATION

Required GMAT, application form, baccalaureate/first degree, essay, 2 letters of recommendation, transcripts of college work. **Recommended** Interview, personal statement, resume/curriculum vitae, work experience.

Deadlines and Fees Applications for domestic and international students are processed on a rolling basis. *Application fee:* $30, $30 (international).

Application Contact Mr. Bill Price, Associate Dean for Graduate Enrollment Management, 4484 Peachtree Road, Atlanta, GA 30319-2797. **Phone:** 404-364-8314. **Fax:** 404-364-8500. **E-mail:** bprice@facstaff.oglethorpe.edu.

Southern Polytechnic State University

Marietta, Georgia

SCHOOL OF MANAGEMENT

Graduate Business Faculty
Full-time: 5

Student Body
Total: 68	Average Age: 32
Full-time: 19	Women: 46%
Part-time: 49	

Admissions
Applications: 26	Enrolled: 17
Admitted: 26	

Costs (1999–2000)
Full-time tuition: $2496 per academic year (resident), $6836 per academic year (nonresident)
Part-time tuition: $91 per credit hour (resident), $272 per credit hour (nonresident)

After Graduation (Class of 1998–99)
Employed within 3 months of graduation: 86%
Average starting salary: $50,750

Accreditation
ACBSP—The American Council of Business Schools and Programs

DEGREE MS

MS—Master of Science in Management Full-time and part-time. At least 36 total credits required. 12 to 60 months to complete program. *Concentrations:* management information systems, marketing, operations management, technology management.

COSTS

Tuition, state resident: *Full-time* $2170. *Part-time* $91 per credit hour. **Tuition, nonresident:** *Full-time* $6510. *Part-time* $272 per credit hour. **Tuition, international:** *Full-time* $6510. Tuition varies by number of courses or credits taken and local reciprocity agreements. **Required fees:** *Full-time* $326. *Part-time* $163 per semester. **Graduate housing:** Room and board costs vary by number of occupants, type of accommodation, and type of board plan. *Typical cost:* $4452 (including board), $2142 (room only).

FINANCIAL AID (1999–2000)

Grants, loans, scholarships, teaching assistantships, and work study. Aid is available to part-time students. Financial aid application deadline: 3/15. **Financial Aid Contact** Dr. Emerelle McNair, Director of Financial Aid, 1100 South Marietta Parkway, Marietta, GA 30060-2896. **Phone:** 770-528-7290. **Fax:** 770-528-7301. **E-mail:** emcnair@spsu.edu.

RESOURCES AND SERVICES

Information about online services, personal computer policies, library resources, international exchange programs, internship programs, and placement services at this institution and others can be found at **www.petersons.com/mba**

International Students

28% of students enrolled are international students.

Services and Facilities Counseling/support services, international student organization, visa services. Financial aid is available to international students. **Applying** *Required:* TOEFL with recommended score of 550 (paper), proof of adequate funds, proof of health/immunizations.

International Student Contact Ms. Charlotte Janis, Director of International Services, 1100 South Marietta Parkway, Marietta, GA 30060-2896. **Phone:** 770-528-7903. **Fax:** 770-528-7913. **E-mail:** cjanis@spsu.edu.

■ APPLICATION

Required GMAT, application form, baccalaureate/first degree, 3 letters of recommendation, transcripts of college work. **Recommended** Work experience.

Deadlines and Fees *Deadlines:* 8/1 for fall, 12/1 for spring, 5/1 for summer, 8/1 for fall (international), 12/1 for spring (international), 5/1 for summer (international). *Application fee:* $20, $20 (international).

Application Contact Dr. Robert Yancy, Dean, School of Management, 1100 South Marietta Parkway, Marietta, GA 30060-2896. **Phone:** 770-528-7440. **Toll-free Phone:** 800-635-3204. **Fax:** 770-528-4967. **E-mail:** ryancy@spsu.edu.

State University of West Georgia

Carrollton, Georgia

GENERAL MBA

Graduate Business Faculty
Full-time: 30

Student Body
Total: 79	Average Age: 30
Full-time: 36	Women: 33%
Part-time: 43	

Admissions
Enrolled: 25	Average GPA: 3.21
Average GMAT: 520	

Costs (1999–2000)
Full-time tuition: $2428 per academic year (resident), $8428 per academic year (nonresident)
Part-time tuition: $105 per hour (resident), $377 per hour (nonresident)

After Graduation (Class of 1998–99)
Employed within 3 months of graduation: 98%

Accreditation
AACSB—The International Association for Management Education

DEGREES MBA • MPA

MBA—General MBA Full-time and part-time. 30 to 33 total credits required. Minimum of 12 months to complete program.

MPA—Master of Professional Accountancy Full-time and part-time. At least 30 total credits required. Minimum of 12 months to complete program.

COSTS

Tuition, state resident: *Full-time* $2428. *Part-time* $105 per hour. **Tuition, nonresident:** *Full-time* $8428. *Part-time* $377 per hour. Tuition varies by number of courses or credits taken and local reciprocity agreements. **Required fees:** Tuition and fees vary by number of courses or credits taken. **Graduate housing:** Room and board costs vary by number of occupants, type of accommodation, and type of board plan. *Typical cost:* $3806 (including board), $2026 (room only).

FINANCIAL AID (1999–2000)

12 students received aid, including research assistantships and scholarships. Financial aid application deadline: 3/1. **Financial Aid Contact** Dr. Jack Jenkins, Dean, Graduate School, Carrollton, GA 30118. **Phone:** 770-836-6419. **Fax:** 770-830-2301. **E-mail:** jjenkins@westga.edu.

RESOURCES AND SERVICES

Information about online services, personal computer policies, library resources, international exchange programs, internship programs, and placement services at this institution and others can be found at **www.petersons.com/mba**

International Students

29% of students enrolled are international students.

Services and Facilities Counseling/support services, international student housing, international student organization, orientation. Financial aid is available to international students.

Applying *Required:* TOEFL with recommended score of 213 (computer) or 550 (paper), proof of adequate funds, proof of health/immunizations.

International Student Contact Ms. Sylvia E. Shortt, Assistant Director, Student Development, Student Development Center, 137 Parker Hall, Carrollton, GA 30118. **Phone:** 770-836-6428. **Fax:** 770-836-4502. **E-mail:** sshortt@westga.edu.

State University of West Georgia (continued)

■ APPLICATION

Required GMAT, application form, baccalaureate/first degree, 3 letters of recommendation, transcripts of college work. **Recommended** Personal statement, resume/curriculum vitae, work experience.

Deadlines and Fees *Deadlines:* 8/1 for fall, 12/17 for spring, 4/24 for summer, 7/1 for fall (international), 11/1 for spring (international), 3/1 for summer (international). *Application fee:* $20, $20 (international).

Application Contact Mr. John Wells, Director, MBA Program, Richards College of Business, Back Campus Drive, Carrollton, GA 30118-3000. **Phone:** 770-836-6467. **Fax:** 770-836-6774. **E-mail:** jwells@westga.edu.

University of Georgia

Athens, Georgia

TERRY COLLEGE OF BUSINESS

Graduate Business Faculty

Full-time: 106	Part-time: 8

Student Body

Total: 393	Average Age: 26
Full-time: 389	Women: 35%
Part-time: 4	

Admissions

Applications: 1,225	Average GMAT: 644
Admitted: 369	Average GPA: 3.2
Enrolled: 258	

Costs (1999–2000)
Full-time tuition: $3916 per academic year (resident), $12,604 per academic year (nonresident)
Part-time tuition: N/R

After Graduation (Class of 1998–99)
Employed within 3 months of graduation: 93%
Average starting salary: $57,000

Accreditation
AACSB—The International Association for Management Education

DEGREES JD/MBA • M Acc • MA • MBA • MMR

JD/MBA—Juris Doctor/Master of Business Administration Full-time. At least 126 total credits required. 40 months to complete program. *Concentrations:* accounting, economics, electronic commerce (e-commerce), entrepreneurship, finance, insurance, international business, management information systems, marketing, materials management, operations management, organizational management, production management, real estate, risk management.

M Acc—Master of Accountancy Full-time and part-time. At least 30 total credits required. 9 to 24 months to complete program. *Concentrations:* accounting, taxation.

MA—Master of Arts in Economics Full-time. 30 to 36 total credits required. 9 to 36 months to complete program. *Concentrations:* economics, financial economics, international economics.

MBA—Full-time MBA Full-time. 41 to 66 total credits required. 11 to 22 months to complete program. *Concentrations:* accounting, economics, electronic commerce (e-commerce), entrepreneurship, finance, insurance, international business, management information systems, marketing, materials management, operations management, organizational management, production management, real estate, risk management.

MMR—Master of Marketing Research Full-time. At least 40 total credits required. 18 months to complete program. *Concentrations:* marketing research.

COSTS

Tuition, state resident: *Full-time* $2896. **Tuition, nonresident:** *Full-time* $11,584. **Required fees:** *Full-time* $1020. Tuition and fees vary by number of courses or credits taken. **Graduate housing:** Room and board costs vary by number of occupants, type of accommodation, and type of board plan. *Typical cost:* $4852 (including board).

FINANCIAL AID (1999–2000)

150 students received aid, including research assistantships and scholarships. Financial aid application deadline: 3/1. **Financial Aid Contact** Student Financial Aid, Academic Building, Athens, GA 30602-6114. **Phone:** 706-542-6147. **E-mail:** osfa@arches.uga.edu.

RESOURCES AND SERVICES

Information about online services, personal computer policies, library resources, international exchange programs, internship programs, and placement services at this institution and others can be found at **www.petersons.com/mba**

International Students

19% of students enrolled are international students.

Services and Facilities Counseling/support services, ESL/language courses, international student housing, international student organization, orientation, visa services. Financial aid is available to international students.

Applying *Required:* TOEFL with recommended score of 250 (computer) or 600 (paper), proof of adequate funds, proof of health/immunizations.

International Student Contact Foreign Student Advisors, Office of International Education, 201 Barrow Hall, Athens, GA 30602-2407. **Phone:** 706-542-7903. **Fax:** 706-542-6622. **E-mail:** oie@www.uga.edu.

■ APPLICATION

Required GMAT, application form, baccalaureate/first degree, essay, 3 letters of recommendation, transcripts of college work. **Recommended** Interview, resume/curriculum vitae, 2 years of work experience.

Deadlines and Fees *Deadlines:* 3/1 for fall, 2/1 for summer, 3/1 for fall (international), 2/1 for summer (international). *Application fee:* $30, $30 (international).

Application Contact Mr. Donald Perry, Jr., Director, MBA Admissions, Terry College of Business, 346 Brooks Hall, Athens, GA 30602-6264. **Phone:** 706-542-5671. **Fax:** 706-542-5351. **E-mail:** terrymba@terry.uga.edu.

Valdosta State University

Valdosta, Georgia

COLLEGE OF BUSINESS ADMINISTRATION

Graduate Business Faculty
Full-time: 13

Student Body

Total: 37	Average Age: 32
Part-time: 37	Women: 54%

Admissions

Applications: 45	Average GMAT: 530
Admitted: 28	Average GPA: 3.15
Enrolled: 17	

Costs (1999–2000)
Full-time tuition: $2652 per academic year (resident), $9162 per academic year (nonresident)
Part-time tuition: $273 per semester (resident), $1089 per semester (nonresident)

After Graduation (Class of 1998–99)
Employed within 3 months of graduation: 100%
Average starting salary: $52,000

Accreditation
AACSB—The International Association for Management Education

DEGREES M Acc • MBA

M Acc—Master of Accountancy Full-time and part-time. At least 30 total credits required. 24 to 84 months to complete program. *Concentrations:* accounting.

MBA—Master of Business Administration Part-time. At least 30 total credits required. 24 to 84 months to complete program.

COSTS

Tuition, state resident: *Full-time* $2652. *Part-time* $273 per semester. **Tuition, nonresident:** *Full-time* $9162. *Part-time* $1089 per semester. Tuition varies by number of courses or credits taken, academic program, and local reciprocity agreements. **Required fees:** Tuition and fees vary by number of courses or credits taken and academic program. **Graduate housing:** Room and board costs vary by type of accommodation and type of board plan. *Typical cost:* $4380 (including board).

FINANCIAL AID (1999–2000)

Loans, scholarships, and work study. Financial aid application deadline: 3/1. **Financial Aid Contact** Mr. Tommy Moore, Director of Financial Aid, Office of Financial Aid, Valdosta, GA 31698. **Phone:** 912-333-5935. **Fax:** 912-333-5430. **E-mail:** tmoore@valdosta.edu.

RESOURCES AND SERVICES

Information about online services, personal computer policies, library resources, international exchange programs, internship programs, and

placement services at this institution and others can be found at **www.petersons.com/mba**

International Students

11% of students enrolled are international students.

Services and Facilities Counseling/support services, international student organization, orientation, visa services. Financial aid is not available to international students.

Applying *Required:* TOEFL with recommended score of 213 (computer) or 550 (paper), proof of adequate funds, proof of health/immunizations.

International Student Contact Miss Dawn Clemeshaw, Foreign Student Advisor, Office of International Programs, Valdosta, GA 31698. **Phone:** 912-333-7410. **Fax:** 912-245-3849. **E-mail:** dclemesh@valdosta.edu.

■ APPLICATION

Required Application form, baccalaureate/first degree, essay, resume/curriculum vitae, transcripts of college work. School will accept GMAT. **Recommended** Work experience.

Deadlines and Fees Applications for domestic and international students are processed on a rolling basis. *Application fee:* $20, $20 (international).

Application Contact Dr. Jacqueline Eastman, MBA Director, College of Business Administration, Valdosta, GA 31698. **Phone:** 912-245-3848. **Fax:** 912-245-6498. **E-mail:** jeastman@valdosta.edu.

HAWAII

Chaminade University of Honolulu

Honolulu, Hawaii

PROGRAM IN BUSINESS ADMINISTRATION

DEGREES MBA • MPA

MBA—Master of Business Administration Full-time and part-time. At least 48 total credits required. 12 to 60 months to complete program. *Concentrations:* accounting, Asian business studies, contract management, finance, human resources, international business, international management, Japanese business studies, management, management information systems, marketing, taxation.

MPA—Master of Public Administration Full-time and part-time. At least 36 total credits required. 12 to 60 months to complete program. *Concentrations:* public policy and administration.

RESOURCES AND SERVICES

Information about online services, personal computer policies, library resources, international exchange programs, internship programs, and placement services at this institution and others can be found at **www.petersons.com/mba**

International Students

Services and Facilities Counseling/support services, ESL/language courses, international student organization, visa services. Financial aid is not available to international students.

International Student Contact Ms. Kimberly Day, International Student Advisor, 3140 Waialae Avenue, Honolulu, HI 96816-1578. **Phone:** 808-739-4688.

■ APPLICATION

Application Contact Mr. James Moses, Assistant MBA Program Director, 3140 Waialae Avenue, Honolulu, HI 96816-1578. **Phone:** 808-739-4612. **Fax:** 808-735-4734. **E-mail:** mba@chaminade.edu.

Hawaii Pacific University

Honolulu, Hawaii

DIVISION OF BUSINESS ADMINISTRATION

Graduate Business Faculty
Full-time: 44   Part-time: 30

Student Body
Total: 1,125   Part-time: 485
Full-time: 640   Average Age: 30

Women: 47%

Admissions
Applications: 834   Average GMAT: 475
Admitted: 623   Average GPA: 3.1
Enrolled: 286

Costs (1999–2000)
Full-time tuition: $8920 per academic year
Part-time tuition: $372 per credit

After Graduation (Class of 1998–99)
Employed within 3 months of graduation: 75%
Average starting salary: $40,000

DEGREES MA • MBA • MS

MA—Master of Arts in Human Resource Management Full-time and part-time. At least 42 total credits required. Minimum of 18 months to complete program. *Concentrations:* human resources.

MA—Master of Arts in Management Full-time and part-time. At least 42 total credits required. Minimum of 18 months to complete program. *Concentrations:* management.

MA—Master of Arts in Organizational Change Full-time and part-time. At least 42 total credits required. Minimum of 18 months to complete program. *Concentrations:* organizational behavior/development.

MBA—Executive MBA Full-time. At least two years of experience in a field of business required. At least 45 total credits required. Minimum of 18 months to complete program.

MBA—Master of Business Administration Full-time and part-time. At least 45 total credits required. Minimum of 18 months to complete program. *Concentrations:* accounting, finance, human resources, information management, international business, management, marketing, nonprofit management, travel industry/tourism management.

MS—Master of Science in Information Systems Full-time and part-time. At least 42 total credits required. Minimum of 18 months to complete program. *Concentrations:* information management.

COSTS

Tuition *Full-time:* $8920. *Part-time:* $372 per credit. Tuition varies by number of courses or credits taken. **Graduate housing:** Room and board costs vary by number of occupants and type of accommodation. *Typical cost:* $8120 (including board), $5670 (room only).

FINANCIAL AID (1999–2000)

225 students received aid, including loans, research assistantships, scholarships, and work study. Aid is available to part-time students. Financial aid application deadline: 3/15. **Financial Aid Contact** Ms. Jodi Kuba, Director of Financial Aid, 1164 Bishop Street, Honolulu, HI 96813. **Phone:** 808-544-0253. **Fax:** 808-544-1136.

RESOURCES AND SERVICES

Information about online services, personal computer policies, library resources, international exchange programs, internship programs, and placement services at this institution and others can be found at **www.petersons.com/mba**

International Students

38% of students enrolled are international students.

Services and Facilities Counseling/support services, ESL/language courses, international student organization, visa services. Financial aid is not available to international students.

Applying *Required:* Proof of adequate funds. *Recommended:* TOEFL with recommended score of 550 (paper), TWE, proof of health/immunizations.

International Student Contact Ms. Anne Newton, Director, International Student Office, 1132 Bishop Street, Honolulu, HI 96813. **Phone:** 808-544-0230. **Fax:** 808-544-1136. **E-mail:** anewton@hpu.edu.

■ APPLICATION

Required Application form, baccalaureate/first degree, 2 letters of recommendation, transcripts of college work. School will accept GMAT, GRE, and GMAT or GRE. **Recommended** Essay, personal statement, resume/curriculum vitae, work experience.

Deadlines and Fees Applications for domestic and international students are processed on a rolling basis. *Application fee:* $50, $50 (international).

Application Contact Mr. George Moyer, Associate Dean, Graduate Service Center, 1164 Bishop Street, Suite 1510, Honolulu, HI 96813. **Phone:** 808-544-1120. **Toll-free Phone:** 800-669-4724. **Fax:** 808-544-0280. **E-mail:** gradservctr@hpu.edu.

See full description on page 674.

University of Hawaii at Manoa

Honolulu, Hawaii

COLLEGE OF BUSINESS ADMINISTRATION

Graduate Business Faculty
Full-time: 51   Part-time: 14

Student Body
Total: 335   Average Age: 30
Full-time: 147   Women: 44%
Part-time: 188

Admissions
Applications: 381   Average GMAT: 570
Admitted: 181   Average GPA: 3.52
Enrolled: 110

Costs (1999–2000)
Full-time tuition: $4091 per academic year (resident), $9979 per
  academic year (nonresident)
Part-time tuition: $168 per credit (resident), $415 per credit
  (nonresident)

After Graduation (Class of 1998–99)
Employed within 3 months of graduation: 80%
Average starting salary: $38,000

Accreditation
AACSB—The International Association for Management Education

DEGREES EMBA • JD/MBA • M Acc • MBA • NIMBA

EMBA—Executive MBA Full-time. 5 years of full-time work experience required.
At least 48 total credits required. 22 months to complete program.

JD/MBA—Dual Degree MBA/JD Full-time and part-time. Must submit separate
applications to both programs. 122 to 128 total credits required. 60 to 84
months to complete program.

M Acc—Master of Accounting Full-time and part-time. At least 30 total credits
required. 12 to 84 months to complete program. *Concentrations:* accounting.

MBA—China-focused Executive MBA Full-time. At least 48 total credits required.
15 months to complete program. *Concentrations:* Chinese business studies.

MBA—Japan-focused Executive MBA Full-time. At least 48 total credits required.
15 months to complete program. *Concentrations:* Japanese business studies.

MBA—Master of Business Administration Full-time and part-time. 42 to 48
total credits required. 24 to 84 months to complete program.

NIMBA—Master of Business Administration for the Neighboring Islands Part-
time. *Distance learning option.* 42 to 48 total credits required. 24 to 48 months
to complete program.

COSTS
Tuition, state resident: *Full-time* $4032. *Part-time* $168 per credit. **Tuition,
nonresident:** *Full-time* $9920. *Part-time* $415 per credit. **Tuition, international:**
Full-time $9920. Tuition varies by number of courses or credits taken and local
reciprocity agreements. **Required fees:** *Full-time* $58.7. *Part-time* $53.4 per
semester.

FINANCIAL AID (1999–2000)
72 students received aid, including grants, loans, and scholarships. Aid
is available to part-time students. Financial aid application deadline:
3/1. **Financial Aid Contact** Ms. Gayle Koki, Interim Director of Financial
Aid, 2600 Campus Road, Student Services Center, Room 112, Honolulu,
HI 96822. **Phone:** 808-956-7251. **Fax:** 808-956-3985. **E-mail:** gkoki@
kala.ssc.hawaii.edu.

RESOURCES AND SERVICES
Information about online services, personal computer policies, library
resources, international exchange programs, internship programs, and
placement services at this institution and others can be found at **www.
petersons.com/mba**

International Students
17% of students enrolled are international students.

Services and Facilities Counseling/support services, ESL/language courses, international student organization, visa services. Financial aid is available to international students.
Applying *Required:* TOEFL with recommended score of 500 (paper), proof of
adequate funds, proof of health/immunizations.
International Student Contact Ms. Martha Staff, Foreign Student Advisor, International Student Office, 2600 Campus Road, Student Services Center, Room
414, Honolulu, HI 96822. **Phone:** 808-956-8613. **Fax:** 808-956-5076. **E-mail:**
mstaff@hawaii.edu.

■ APPLICATION
Required GMAT, application form, baccalaureate/first degree, essay, personal
statement, resume/curriculum vitae, transcripts of college work. **Recommended**
Work experience.
Deadlines and Fees *Deadlines:* 5/1 for fall, 11/1 for spring, 5/1 for fall (inter-
national), 11/1 for spring (international). *Application fee:* $25, $50 (international).
Application Contact Merrianne Bieler, Assistant Dean, College of Business
Administration, 2404 Maile Way, Business Administration B201, Honolulu, HI
96822. **Phone:** 808-956-2491. **Fax:** 808-956-9890. **E-mail:** osas@busadm.
cba.hawaii.edu.

See full description on pages 902 and 904.

IDAHO

Boise State University

Boise, Idaho

COLLEGE OF BUSINESS AND ECONOMICS

Graduate Business Faculty
Full-time: 41   Part-time: 3

Student Body
Total: 154   Average Age: 32
Full-time: 36   Women: 42%
Part-time: 118

Admissions
Applications: 89   Average GMAT: 556
Admitted: 68   Average GPA: 3.18
Enrolled: 60

Costs (1999–2000)
Full-time tuition: $3500 per academic year (resident), $9100 per
  academic year (nonresident)
Part-time tuition: $157 per credit (resident), $157 per credit
  (nonresident)

Accreditation
AACSB—The International Association for Management Education

DEGREES MBA • MS

MBA—Master of Business Administration Full-time and part-time. 33 to 54
total credits required. 12 to 84 months to complete program. *Concentrations:*
accounting, entrepreneurship, finance, financial management/planning, management, management information systems, marketing, organizational management, public policy and administration, taxation.

MS—Master of Science in Accountancy Full-time and part-time. At least 30
total credits required. 12 to 84 months to complete program. *Concentrations:*
accounting.

MS—Master of Science in Management Information Systems Full-time and part-
time. GMAT or GRE required. 30 to 45 total credits required. 12 to 84 months
to complete program. *Concentrations:* management information systems.

MS—Master of Science in Taxation Full-time and part-time. 30 to 33 total credits
required. 12 to 84 months to complete program. *Concentrations:* taxation.

COSTS
Tuition, state resident: *Full-time* $3500. *Part-time* $157 per credit. **Tuition,
nonresident:** *Full-time* $9100. *Part-time* $157 per credit. **Required fees:** Tuition
and fees vary by class time and number of courses or credits taken. **Graduate
housing:** Room and board costs vary by number of occupants, type of accommodation, and type of board plan. *Typical cost:* $6200 (including board).

FINANCIAL AID (1999–2000)
15 students received aid, including loans, research assistantships,
scholarships, teaching assistantships, and work study. Financial aid
application deadline: 2/1. **Financial Aid Contact** Mrs. J. Renee
Anchustegui, Program Coordinator, Business Graduate Studies, 1910
University Drive, B117, Boise, ID 83725-1600. **Phone:** 208-426-1126.
Fax: 208-426-4989. **E-mail:** ranchust@boisestate.edu.

RESOURCES AND SERVICES
Information about online services, personal computer policies, library
resources, international exchange programs, internship programs, and

placement services at this institution and others can be found at **www. petersons.com/mba**

International Students
12% of students enrolled are international students.

Services and Facilities Counseling/support services, ESL/language courses, housing location assistance, international student organization, orientation, visa services. Financial aid is available to international students.

Applying *Required:* TOEFL with recommended score of 240 (computer) or 587 (paper), proof of adequate funds. *Recommended:* TSE, TWE, proof of health/immunizations.

International Student Contact Ms. Debbie Lareau, Foreign Student Services Coordinator, Enrollment Services, 1910 University Drive, Boise, ID 83725. **Phone:** 208-426-1757. **Fax:** 208-426-3765. **E-mail:** dlareau@boisestate.edu.

▪ APPLICATION
Required GMAT, application form, baccalaureate/first degree, essay, 2 letters of recommendation, personal statement, resume/curriculum vitae, transcripts of college work. **Recommended** 2 years of work experience.

Deadlines and Fees *Deadlines:* 2/1 for fall, 10/1 for spring, 2/1 for fall (international), 9/1 for spring (international). *Application fee:* $20, $30 (international).

Application Contact Mrs. J. Renee Anchustegui, Program Coordinator, Graduate Business Studies, 1910 University Drive, B117, Boise, ID 83725-1600. **Phone:** 208-426-1126. **Fax:** 208-426-4989. **E-mail:** ranchust@boisestate.edu.

See full description on page 568.

Idaho State University
Pocatello, Idaho

COLLEGE OF BUSINESS

Graduate Business Faculty
Full-time: 41	Part-time: 3

Student Body
Total: 127	
Full-time: 29	Average Age: 34
Part-time: 98	Women: 35%

Admissions
Applications: 170	Average GMAT: 520
Admitted: 140	Average GPA: 3.17
Enrolled: 75	

Costs (1999–2000)
Full-time tuition: $3384 per academic year (resident), $9624 per academic year (nonresident)

Part-time tuition: $147 per credit hour (resident), $237 per credit hour (nonresident)

After Graduation (Class of 1998–99)
Employed within 3 months of graduation: 90%

Accreditation
AACSB—The International Association for Management Education

DEGREES MBA

MBA—Master of Business Administration Full-time and part-time. 30 to 48 total credits required. 12 to 36 months to complete program.

MBA—Master of Business Administration Full-time and part-time. 30 to 48 total credits required. 12 to 36 months to complete program. *Concentrations:* health care, management information systems.

MBA—Master of Business Administration in Accounting Full-time and part-time. 33 to 51 total credits required. 12 to 36 months to complete program. *Concentrations:* accounting.

COSTS
Tuition, state resident: *Full-time* $3384. *Part-time* $147 per credit hour. **Tuition, nonresident:** *Full-time* $9624. *Part-time* $237 per credit hour. Tuition varies by number of courses or credits taken, academic program, and local reciprocity agreements. **Graduate housing:** Room and board costs vary by number of occupants, type of accommodation, and type of board plan. *Typical cost:* $2980 (including board).

FINANCIAL AID (1999–2000)
10 students received aid, including teaching assistantships and work study. Aid is available to part-time students. **Financial Aid Contact** Douglas Severs, Financial Aid Office, Campus Box 8077, Pocatello, ID 83209-8077. **Phone:** 208-282-2756. **Fax:** 208-282-4755. **E-mail:** sevedoug@isu.edu.

RESOURCES AND SERVICES
Information about online services, personal computer policies, library resources, international exchange programs, internship programs, and placement services at this institution and others can be found at **www. petersons.com/mba**

International Students
6% of students enrolled are international students.

Services and Facilities Counseling/support services, international student housing. Financial aid is available to international students.

Applying *Required:* TOEFL with recommended score of 213 (computer) or 550 (paper).

International Student Contact Michelle Lewis, International Student Advisor, Box 8123, Pocatello, ID 83209. **Phone:** 208-282-2941. **Fax:** 208-282-3719. **E-mail:** lewimich@isu.edu.

▪ APPLICATION
Required Application form, baccalaureate/first degree, resume/curriculum vitae, transcripts of college work. School will accept GMAT.

Deadlines and Fees *Deadlines:* 7/1 for fall, 12/1 for spring, 5/1 for summer, 7/1 for fall (international), 12/1 for spring (international), 5/1 for summer (international). *Application fee:* $35, $35 (international).

Application Contact Dr. George Johnson, MBA Director, College of Business, Box 8020, Pocatello, ID 83209. **Phone:** 208-282-2504. **Fax:** 208-282-4367. **E-mail:** johngor@isu.edu.

University of Idaho
Moscow, Idaho

COLLEGE OF BUSINESS AND ECONOMICS

Graduate Business Faculty
Full-time: 7	Part-time: 3

Student Body
Total: 11	
Full-time: 8	Average Age: 27
Part-time: 3	Women: 55%

Admissions
Applications: 7	Average GMAT: 540
Admitted: 5	Average GPA: 3.5
Enrolled: 5	

Costs (1999–2000)
Full-time tuition: $2676 per academic year (resident), $8676 per academic year (nonresident)

Part-time tuition: $107 per credit (resident), $206 per credit (nonresident)

Accreditation
AACSB—The International Association for Management Education

DEGREE M Acct

M Acct—Master of Accounting Full-time and part-time. At least 30 total credits required. *Concentrations:* accounting.

COSTS
Tuition, state resident: *Full-time* $2676. *Part-time* $107 per credit. **Tuition, nonresident:** *Full-time* $8676. *Part-time* $206 per credit. **Required fees:** Fees vary by number of courses or credits taken and local reciprocity agreements. **Graduate housing:** Room and board costs vary by campus location, number of occupants, type of accommodation, and type of board plan. *Typical cost:* $4000 (including board).

FINANCIAL AID (1999–2000)
5 students received aid, including loans, scholarships, teaching assistantships, and work study. Financial aid application deadline: 2/15. **Financial Aid Contact** Student Financial Aid, Moscow, ID 83844-4291. **Phone:** 208-885-6312. **Fax:** 208-885-5592.

RESOURCES AND SERVICES
Information about online services, personal computer policies, library resources, international exchange programs, internship programs, and placement services at this institution and others can be found at **www. petersons.com/mba**

International Students
18% of students enrolled are international students.

Services and Facilities Counseling/support services, ESL/language courses, international student organization, orientation. Financial aid is available to inter-

University of Idaho (continued)

national students.
Applying *Required:* TOEFL with recommended score of 550 (paper), proof of adequate funds.
International Student Contact International Programs Office, 216/219 Merrill Hall, Moscow, ID 83844-3013. **Phone:** 208-885-8984. **Fax:** 208-885-2859.

■ APPLICATION

Required Application form, baccalaureate/first degree, transcripts of college work.
Deadlines and Fees *Deadlines:* 7/1 for fall, 11/1 for spring, 4/1 for summer, 6/1 for fall (international), 10/1 for spring (international), 3/15 for summer (international). *Application fee:* $35, $45 (international).
Application Contact Graduate Admissions Office, Moscow, ID 83844-3019. **Phone:** 208-885-4001. **Toll-free Phone:** 800-422-3019.

ILLINOIS

Aurora University

Aurora, Illinois

DUNHAM SCHOOL OF BUSINESS AND PROFESSIONAL STUDIES

Graduate Business Faculty
Full-time: 9 — Part-time: 4

Student Body
Total: 200 — Average Age: 34
Full-time: 60 — Women: 36%
Part-time: 140

Admissions
Applications: 68 — Enrolled: 35
Admitted: 52 — Average GPA: 3

Costs (1999–2000)
Full-time tuition: N/R
Part-time tuition: $427 per semester hour

After Graduation (Class of 1998–99)
Employed within 3 months of graduation: 98%

DEGREE MBA

MBA—Master of Business Administration Part-time. *Distance learning option.* At least 36 total credits required. Minimum of 33 months to complete program.

COSTS

Tuition *Part-time:* $427 per semester hour. **Graduate housing:** *Typical cost:* $4500 (including board).

FINANCIAL AID (1999–2000)

10 students received aid, including loans. Aid is available to part-time students. **Financial Aid Contact** Ms. Heather Gutierrez, Director of Financial Aid, 347 South Gladstone Avenue, Aurora, IL 60506-4892. **Phone:** 630-844-5448.

RESOURCES AND SERVICES

Information about online services, personal computer policies, library resources, international exchange programs, internship programs, and placement services at this institution and others can be found at **www.petersons.com/mba**

International Students

0.5% of students enrolled are international students.
Services and Facilities Counseling/support services. Financial aid is not available to international students.
Applying *Required:* TOEFL with recommended score of 550 (paper), proof of adequate funds, proof of health/immunizations.
International Student Contact Dr. Leo Loughead, MBA Program Manager, 347 South Gladstone Avenue, Aurora, IL 60506-4892. **Phone:** 630-844-3830. **Fax:** 630-844-7830. **E-mail:** loughead@aurora.edu.

■ APPLICATION

Required Application form, baccalaureate/first degree, interview, 2 letters of recommendation, transcripts of college work, 2 years of work experience.
Deadlines and Fees Applications for domestic and international students are processed on a rolling basis. *Application fee:* $25, $25 (international).
Application Contact Dr. Leo Loughead, MBA Program Manager, 347 South Gladstone Avenue, Aurora, IL 60506-4892. **Phone:** 630-844-3830. **Fax:** 630-844-7830. **E-mail:** loughead@aurora.edu.

Benedictine University

Lisle, Illinois

GRADUATE PROGRAMS

Graduate Business Faculty
Full-time: 10 — Part-time: 86

Student Body
Total: 311 — Average Age: 33
Full-time: 73 — Women: 39%
Part-time: 238

Admissions
Applications: 135 — Average GMAT: 500
Admitted: 107 — Average GPA: 2.75
Enrolled: 100

Costs (1999–2000)
Full-time tuition: N/R
Part-time tuition: $350 per credit

DEGREES MBA • MBA/MPH • MBA/MSMIS • MBA/MSMOB

MBA—Accelerated MBA Part-time. At least 64 total credits required. 22 months to complete program.
MBA—Evening MBA Full-time and part-time. At least 64 total credits required. 12 to 72 months to complete program. *Concentrations:* accounting, finance, human resources, international business, leadership, management, management information systems, marketing, operations management, technology management.
MBA—Executive MBA for Business Leaders and Senior Health Professionals Full-time. At least 64 total credits required. 18 months to complete program. *Concentrations:* health care.
MBA/MPH—Master of Business Administration/Master of Public Health Full-time and part-time. At least 96 total credits required. 24 to 72 months to complete program.
MBA/MSMIS—Master of Business Administration/Master of Science in Management Information Systems Full-time and part-time. At least 96 total credits required. 24 to 72 months to complete program. *Concentrations:* management information systems.
MBA/MSMOB—Master of Business Administration/Master of Science in Management and Organizational Behavior Full-time and part-time. At least 96 total credits required. 24 to 72 months to complete program. *Concentrations:* human resources, organizational behavior/development.

COSTS

Tuition *Part-time:* $350 per credit.

FINANCIAL AID (1999–2000)

154 students received aid, including loans and work study. Aid is available to part-time students. **Financial Aid Contact** Bryant Anderson, Director of Benedictine Central, 5700 College Road, Lisle, IL 60532-0900. **Phone:** 630-829-6500. **Fax:** 630-829-6456.

RESOURCES AND SERVICES

Information about online services, personal computer policies, library resources, international exchange programs, internship programs, and placement services at this institution and others can be found at **www.petersons.com/mba**

International Students

0.3% of students enrolled are international students.
Services and Facilities ESL/language courses. Financial aid is not available to international students.
Applying *Required:* TOEFL with recommended score of 600 (paper).
International Student Contact Dr. John Mickus, Dean, College of Arts and Sciences Director, International Office, 5700 College Road, Lisle, IL 60532-0900. **Phone:** 630-829-6342. **E-mail:** jmickus@ben.edu.

■ APPLICATION

Required Application form, baccalaureate/first degree, essay, 2 letters of recommendation, personal statement, transcripts of college work. School will accept GMAT or GRE or MAT. **Recommended** Interview, work experience.

Deadlines and Fees *Application fee:* $30, $30 (international).

Application Contact Ms. Kristin Lighty, Director, Adult and Graduate Programs, 5700 College Road, Lisle, IL 60532-0900. **Phone:** 630-829-6200. **Fax:** 630-829-6584. **E-mail:** gradadm@ben.edu.

Bradley University

Peoria, Illinois

FOSTER COLLEGE OF BUSINESS ADMINISTRATION

Graduate Business Faculty
Full-time: 34   Part-time: 6

Student Body
Total: 166
Full-time: 13   Average Age: 27
Part-time: 153   Women: 37%

Admissions
Applications: 70
Admitted: 44   Average GMAT: 607
Enrolled: 23   Average GPA: 3.41

Costs (1999–2000)
Full-time tuition: $13,895 per academic year
Part-time tuition: $377 per semester hour

After Graduation (Class of 1998–99)
Employed within 3 months of graduation: 99%

Accreditation
AACSB—The International Association for Management Education

DEGREES MBA • MS

MBA—Master of Business Administration Full-time and part-time. 32 to 57 total credits required. 12 to 60 months to complete program. *Concentrations:* accounting, finance, health care, information management, management, marketing.

MS—Master of Science in Accounting Full-time and part-time. At least 30 total credits required. 12 to 60 months to complete program.

COSTS

Tuition *Full-time:* $13,880. *Part-time:* $377 per semester hour. **Tuition, international:** *Full-time* $13,880. **Required fees:** *Full-time* $15. Tuition and fees vary by number of courses or credits taken. **Graduate housing:** Room and board costs vary by number of occupants, type of accommodation, and type of board plan. *Typical cost:* $6392 (including board).

FINANCIAL AID (1999–2000)

Loans, research assistantships, and scholarships. Aid is available to part-time students. Financial aid application deadline: 3/1. **Financial Aid Contact** Mrs. Sheryl Kristensen, Graduate School Office, 118 Bradley Hall, Peoria, IL 61625. **Phone:** 309-677-3215. **Fax:** 309-677-3343. **E-mail:** sak@bradley.edu.

RESOURCES AND SERVICES

Information about online services, personal computer policies, library resources, international exchange programs, internship programs, and placement services at this institution and others can be found at **www. petersons.com/mba**

International Students

14% of students enrolled are international students.

Services and Facilities Counseling/support services, orientation. Financial aid is available to international students.
Applying *Required:* TOEFL with recommended score of 500 (paper), proof of adequate funds, proof of health/immunizations.
International Student Contact Ms. Flecia Thomas, Director, Multicultural Student Services, 1501 West Bradley Avenue, Peoria, IL 61625-0002. **Phone:** 309-677-2646. **Fax:** 309-677-3739. **E-mail:** frances@bradley.edu.

■ APPLICATION

Required GMAT, application form, baccalaureate/first degree, 2 letters of recommendation, personal statement, resume/curriculum vitae, transcripts of college work.

Deadlines and Fees Applications for domestic students are processed on a rolling basis. *Deadlines:* 3/1 for fall (international), 10/1 for spring (international). *Application fee:* $50, $50 (international).

Application Contact Dr. Rob Baer, Interim Dean, 123 Baker Hall, Peoria, IL 61625. **Phone:** 309-677-2253. **Fax:** 309-677-3374. **E-mail:** rbb@bradley. edu.

Columbia College Chicago

Chicago, Illinois

DEPARTMENT OF MANAGEMENT

Graduate Business Faculty
Full-time: 5   Part-time: 17

Student Body
Total: 56
Full-time: 33   Average Age: 32
Part-time: 23   Women: 75%

Admissions
Applications: 33   Enrolled: 22
Admitted: 27

Costs (1999–2000)
Full-time tuition: N/R
Part-time tuition: $392 per credit hour

DEGREE MA

MA—Arts, Entertainment and Media Management Full-time and part-time. At least 42 total credits required. 24 to 60 months to complete program. *Concentrations:* arts administration/management.

COSTS

Tuition *Part-time:* $392 per credit hour. **Graduate housing:** *Typical cost:* $4988 (room only).

FINANCIAL AID (1999–2000)

Fellowships, loans, scholarships, teaching assistantships, and work study. Aid is available to part-time students. **Financial Aid Contact** Ms. Diane Brazier, Financial Aid Advisor, 600 South Michigan Avenue, Chicago, IL 60605. **Phone:** 312-663-1600 Ext. 7266. **Fax:** 312-344-8045.

RESOURCES AND SERVICES

Information about online services, personal computer policies, library resources, international exchange programs, internship programs, and placement services at this institution and others can be found at **www. petersons.com/mba**

International Students

Services and Facilities Counseling/support services, ESL/language courses, housing location assistance, international student organization, language tutoring, visa services. Financial aid is available to international students.
Applying *Required:* TOEFL with recommended score of 550 (paper).
International Student Contact Admissions—Graduate School, 600 South Michigan Avenue, Chicago, IL 60605. **Phone:** 312-344-7262. **Fax:** 312-344-8047.

■ APPLICATION

Required Application form, baccalaureate/first degree, essay, letter(s) of recommendation, personal statement, transcripts of college work. **Recommended** Interview, work experience.

Deadlines and Fees *Deadlines:* 8/15 for fall, 12/7 for spring, 6/14 for fall (international), 11/15 for spring (international). *Application fee:* $50, $50 (international).

Application Contact Admissions—Graduate School, 600 South Michigan Avenue, Chicago, IL 60605. **Phone:** 312-344-7262. **Fax:** 312-344-8047.

DePaul University

Chicago, Illinois

CHARLES H. KELLSTADT GRADUATE SCHOOL OF BUSINESS

Graduate Business Faculty
Full-time: 119   Part-time: 59

Student Body
Total: 2,518
Full-time: 1,276   Average Age: 29
Part-time: 1,242   Women: 36%

Admissions
Applications: 934
Admitted: 713
Enrolled: 500

Average GMAT: 570
Average GPA: 3.2

Costs (1999–2000)
Full-time tuition: N/R
Part-time tuition: $2148 per course

Accreditation
AACSB—The International Association for Management Education

DEGREES JD/MBA • M Acc • MBA • MS

JD/MBA—Juris Doctor/Master of Business Administration Full-time and part-time. At least 140 total credits required. 34 to 46 months to complete program. *Concentrations:* accounting, economics, entrepreneurship, finance, human resources, international business, management information systems, marketing, operations management.

M Acc—Master of Accountancy Full-time and part-time. 52 to 72 total credits required. 18 to 72 months to complete program. *Concentrations:* accounting.

MBA—Day MBA Full-time. At least 88 total credits required. 18 months to complete program. *Concentrations:* international finance, international marketing.

MBA—Evening MBA Full-time and part-time. 60 to 84 total credits required. 18 to 72 months to complete program. *Concentrations:* accounting, economics, entrepreneurship, finance, human resources, international business, management information systems, marketing, operations management.

MBA—Weekend MBA Full-time and part-time. 60 to 80 total credits required. 18 to 34 months to complete program. *Concentrations:* strategic management.

MS—Marketing Analysis Full-time and part-time. 60 to 92 total credits required. 18 to 72 months to complete program.

MS—Master of Science in Accountancy Full-time and part-time. 60 to 64 total credits required. 15 to 72 months to complete program. *Concentrations:* accounting.

MS—Master of Science in Finance Full-time and part-time. At least 52 total credits required. 18 to 72 months to complete program. *Concentrations:* finance.

MS—Master of Science in Management Information Systems Full-time and part-time. At least 116 total credits required. 24 to 72 months to complete program. *Concentrations:* management information systems.

MS—Master of Science in Taxation Full-time and part-time. 52 to 64 total credits required. 18 to 72 months to complete program. *Concentrations:* taxation.

COSTS

Tuition *Part-time:* $2148 per course. Tuition varies by academic program. **Required fees:** *Full-time* $10. *Part-time* $10 per quarter.

FINANCIAL AID (1999–2000)
Research assistantships, scholarships, and work study. Aid is available to part-time students. Financial aid application deadline: 4/30. **Financial Aid Contact** Ms. Christine Munoz, Director of Admissions, 1 East Jackson Boulevard, Chicago, IL 60604-2287. **Phone:** 312-362-8810. **Fax:** 312-362-6677. **E-mail:** mbainfo@wppost.depaul.edu.

RESOURCES AND SERVICES
Information about online services, personal computer policies, library resources, international exchange programs, internship programs, and placement services at this institution and others can be found at **www.petersons.com/mba**

International Students
5% of students enrolled are international students.
Services and Facilities Counseling/support services, ESL/language courses, orientation, visa services. Financial aid is available to international students. **Applying** *Required:* TOEFL with recommended score of 550 (paper), proof of adequate funds. *Recommended:* TSE, TWE.
International Student Contact Ms. Christine Munoz, Director of Admissions, 1 East Jackson Boulevard, Chicago, IL 60604-2287. **Phone:** 312-362-8810. **Fax:** 312-362-6677. **E-mail:** mbainfo@wppost.depaul.edu.

■ APPLICATION
Required GMAT, application form, baccalaureate/first degree, personal statement, transcripts of college work. **Recommended** Interview, 2 letters of recommendation, resume/curriculum vitae, work experience.
Deadlines and Fees *Deadlines:* 7/1 for fall, 10/1 for winter, 2/1 for spring, 4/1 for summer, 6/1 for fall (international), 9/1 for winter (international), 1/1 for spring (international), 3/1 for summer (international). *Application fee:* $40, $40 (international).

Application Contact Ms. Christine Munoz, Director of Admissions, 1 East Jackson Boulevard, Chicago, IL 60604-2287. **Phone:** 312-362-8810. **Fax:** 312-362-6677. **E-mail:** mbainfo@wppost.depaul.edu.

Dominican University

River Forest, Illinois

GRADUATE SCHOOL OF BUSINESS

Graduate Business Faculty
Full-time: 17

Part-time: 37

Student Body
Total: 292
Average Age: 29

Women: 52%

Admissions
Applications: 145
Admitted: 76
Enrolled: 59

Average GMAT: 550
Average GPA: 3.2

Costs (1999–2000)
Full-time tuition: $14,250 per academic year
Part-time tuition: $1435 per course

Accreditation
ACBSP—The American Council of Business Schools and Programs

DEGREES JD/MBA • MBA • MBA/MSLIS • MS

JD/MBA—Juris Doctor/Master of Business Administration Full-time and part-time. 77 to 98 total credits required. Minimum of 36 months to complete program. *Concentrations:* accounting, entrepreneurship, finance, health care, human resources, international business, management, management information systems, marketing.

MBA—Master of Business Administration Full-time and part-time. 30 to 51 total credits required. Minimum of 12 months to complete program. *Concentrations:* accounting, entrepreneurship, finance, health care, human resources, international business, management, management information systems, marketing.

MBA/MSLIS—Master of Business Administration/Master of Science in Library and Information Science Full-time and part-time. 54 to 75 total credits required. 24 to 72 months to complete program. *Concentrations:* accounting, entrepreneurship, finance, health care, human resources, international business, management, management information systems, marketing.

MS—Master of Science in Accounting Full-time and part-time. 30 to 51 total credits required. Minimum of 12 months to complete program. *Concentrations:* accounting.

MS—Master of Science in Computer Information Systems Full-time and part-time. 36 to 45 total credits required. Minimum of 12 months to complete program.

MS—Master of Science in Management Information Systems Full-time and part-time. 36 to 51 total credits required. Minimum of 12 months to complete program.

MS—Master of Science in Organization Management Full-time and part-time. 30 to 45 total credits required. Minimum of 12 months to complete program. *Concentrations:* health care, human resources.

COSTS
Tuition *Full-time:* $14,250. *Part-time:* $1425 per course. Tuition varies by number of courses or credits taken. **Required fees:** *Part-time* $10 per course. Fees vary by number of courses or credits taken and academic program. **Graduate housing:** Room and board costs vary by number of occupants and type of board plan. *Typical cost:* $5000 (including board).

FINANCIAL AID (1999–2000)
Grants. Aid is available to part-time students. **Financial Aid Contact** Mr. Howard Florine, Director of Financial Aid, 7900 West Division Street, River Forest, IL 60305. **Phone:** 708-524-6809. **Fax:** 708-366-5360. **E-mail:** florineh@email.dom.edu.

RESOURCES AND SERVICES
Information about online services, personal computer policies, library resources, international exchange programs, internship programs, and placement services at this institution and others can be found at **www.petersons.com/mba**

International Students
17% of students enrolled are international students.
Services and Facilities Counseling/support services, ESL/language courses, housing location assistance, international student housing, language tutoring, orientation, visa services. Financial aid is available to international students.

Applying *Required:* TOEFL with recommended score of 550 (paper), proof of adequate funds, proof of health/immunizations.

International Student Contact Dr. Sue Ponremy, International Student Advisor, 7900 West Division Street, River Forest, IL 60305. **Phone:** 708-524-6965. **Fax:** 708-366-5360. **E-mail:** sponremy@email.dom.edu.

■ **APPLICATION**

Required GMAT, application form, baccalaureate/first degree, essay, 3 letters of recommendation, personal statement, transcripts of college work. **Recommended** Resume/curriculum vitae.

Deadlines and Fees Applications for domestic and international students are processed on a rolling basis. *Application fee:* $25, $25 (international).

Application Contact Ms. Roberta McMahon, Assistant Dean for Graduate Business Programs, 7900 West Division Street, River Forest, IL 60305. **Phone:** 708-524-6507. **Fax:** 708-524-6939. **E-mail:** rmcmahon@email.dom.edu.

See full description on page 622.

Eastern Illinois University

Charleston, Illinois

LUMPKIN COLLEGE OF BUSINESS AND APPLIED SCIENCES

Accreditation
AACSB—The International Association for Management Education

DEGREE MBA

MBA—Master of Business Administration Full-time and part-time. At least 33 total credits required. 12 to 72 months to complete program. *Concentrations:* management.

RESOURCES AND SERVICES
Information about online services, personal computer policies, library resources, international exchange programs, internship programs, and placement services at this institution and others can be found at **www.petersons.com/mba**

International Students

Services and Facilities Counseling/support services, ESL/language courses, international student housing, language tutoring. Financial aid is available to international students.

International Student Contact International Student Advisor, International Programs, 600 Lincoln Avenue, Charleston, IL 61920-3099. **Phone:** 217-581-2321. **Fax:** 217-581-7207. **E-mail:** csmst@eiu.edu.

■ **APPLICATION**

Application Contact Coordinator of Graduate Business Studies, 600 Lincoln Avenue, Charleston, IL 61920-3099. **Phone:** 217-581-3028. **Fax:** 217-581-6029. **E-mail:** cfjpw@eiu.edu.

Governors State University

University Park, Illinois

COLLEGE OF BUSINESS AND PUBLIC ADMINISTRATION

Graduate Business Faculty

Full-time: 32	Part-time: 20

Student Body

Total: 244	
Full-time: 18	Average Age: 36.4
Part-time: 226	Women: 48%

Admissions

Applications: 132	Average GMAT: 450
Admitted: 75	Average GPA: 3.2
Enrolled: 55	

Costs (1999–2000)
Full-time tuition: N/R
Part-time tuition: $98 per credit (resident), $294 per credit (nonresident)

After Graduation (Class of 1998–99)
Employed within 3 months of graduation: 75%

Accreditation
ACBSP—The American Council of Business Schools and Programs

DEGREE MBA

MBA—Master of Business Administration Full-time and part-time. 33 to 45 total credits required. 12 to 60 months to complete program. *Concentrations:* accounting, health care, human resources, international business, management, management information systems, marketing, public management.

COSTS

Tuition, state resident: *Part-time* $98 per credit. **Tuition, nonresident:** *Part-time* $294 per credit. Tuition varies by number of courses or credits taken. **Required fees:** Fees vary by campus location.

FINANCIAL AID (1999–2000)
50 students received aid, including research assistantships, scholarships, and work study. Aid is available to part-time students. Financial aid application deadline: 5/1. **Financial Aid Contact** Ms. Judith Wood, Academic Advisor, College of Business and Public Administration, University Park, IL 60466-0975. **Phone:** 708-534-4391. **Fax:** 708-534-6981. **E-mail:** j-wood@govst.edu.

RESOURCES AND SERVICES
Information about online services, personal computer policies, library resources, international exchange programs, internship programs, and placement services at this institution and others can be found at **www.petersons.com/mba**

International Students

2% of students enrolled are international students.

Services and Facilities Counseling/support services, ESL/language courses, housing location assistance, visa services. Financial aid is available to international students.

Applying *Required:* TOEFL with recommended score of 550 (paper), proof of adequate funds.

International Student Contact Ms. Vreni Mendoza, Coordinator of Office of International Services, Office of International Services, University Park, IL 60466-0975. **Phone:** 708-534-3087. **Fax:** 708-534-8951. **E-mail:** v-mendoz@govst.edu.

■ **APPLICATION**

Required GMAT, application form, baccalaureate/first degree, transcripts of college work.

Deadlines and Fees *Deadlines:* 7/15 for fall, 11/15 for winter, 3/31 for spring, 3/31 for summer, 7/1 for fall (international), 11/1 for winter (international), 3/15 for spring (international), 3/15 for summer (international).

Application Contact Ms. Judith Wood, Academic Advisor, College of Business and Public Administration, University Park, IL 60466-0975. **Phone:** 708-534-4391. **Fax:** 708-534-6981. **E-mail:** j-wood@govst.edu.

Illinois Institute of Technology

Chicago, Illinois

STUART GRADUATE SCHOOL OF BUSINESS

Graduate Business Faculty

Full-time: 19	Part-time: 30

Student Body

Total: 493	Average Age: 30
Full-time: 144	Women: 31%
Part-time: 349	

Admissions

Applications: 414	Average GMAT: 547
Admitted: 240	Average GPA: 3
Enrolled: 136	

Costs (1999–2000)
Full-time tuition: $21,600 per academic year
Part-time tuition: $1800 per course

After Graduation (Class of 1998–99)
Employed within 3 months of graduation: 93%
Average starting salary: $50,000

Accreditation
AACSB—The International Association for Management Education

DEGREES JD/MBA • MBA • MBA/MPA • MBA/MS • MS

JD/MBA—Juris Doctor/Master of Business Administration Full-time and part-time. 48 to 72 months to complete program.

MBA—Master of Business Administration Full-time and part-time. At least 72 total credits required. 12 to 72 months to complete program. *Concentrations:* finance, information management, international business, management science,

Illinois Institute of Technology (continued)

marketing, operations management, organizational management, quality management, strategic management.

MBA/MPA—Master of Business Administration/Master of Public Administration Full-time and part-time. At least 105 total credits required. 24 to 72 months to complete program.

MBA/MS—MBA/MS in Environmental Management Full-time and part-time. At least 105 total credits required. 24 to 72 months to complete program.

MBA/MS—MBA/MS in Marketing Communication Full-time and part-time. At least 105 total credits required. 24 to 72 months to complete program.

MS—Master of Science in E-Commerce Full-time and part-time. At least 50 total credits required. 12 to 72 months to complete program. *Concentrations:* electronic commerce (e-commerce).

MS—Master of Science in Environmental Management Full-time and part-time. At least 50 total credits required. 12 to 72 months to complete program.

MS—Master of Science in Finance Full-time and part-time. At least 50 total credits required. 12 to 72 months to complete program.

MS—Master of Science in Marketing Communication Part-time. At least 50 total credits required. 12 to 72 months to complete program.

MS—Master of Science in Operations and Technology Management Part-time. At least 48 total credits required. 18 months to complete program.

COSTS

Tuition *Full-time:* $21,600. *Part-time:* $1800 per course. Tuition varies by number of courses or credits taken and academic program. **Graduate housing:** Room and board costs vary by campus location, number of occupants, type of accommodation, and type of board plan. *Typical cost:* $9350 (including board).

FINANCIAL AID (1999–2000)

243 students received aid, including fellowships, loans, scholarships, and work study. **Financial Aid Contact** Dr. Lynn Miller, Assistant Dean, Admission and MBA Program, 565 West Adams Street, Chicago, IL 60661-3691. **Phone:** 312-906-6544. **Fax:** 312-906-6549. **E-mail:** lmiller@stuart.iit.edu.

RESOURCES AND SERVICES

Information about online services, personal computer policies, library resources, international exchange programs, internship programs, and placement services at this institution and others can be found at **www.petersons.com/mba**

International Students

41% of students enrolled are international students.

Services and Facilities Counseling/support services, ESL/language courses, international student housing, international student organization, orientation, visa services. Financial aid is available to international students.

Applying *Required:* TOEFL with recommended score of 550 (paper), proof of adequate funds, proof of health/immunizations.

International Student Contact Dr. Lynn Miller, Assistant Dean, Admission and MBA Program, 565 West Adams Street, Chicago, IL 60661-3691. **Phone:** 312-906-6544. **Fax:** 312-906-6549. **E-mail:** lmiller@stuart.iit.edu.

■ APPLICATION

Required GMAT or GRE, application form, baccalaureate/first degree, essay, 2 letters of recommendation, personal statement, transcripts of college work. **Recommended** Interview, resume/curriculum vitae, work experience.

Deadlines and Fees *Deadlines:* 8/15 for fall, 10/15 for winter, 2/1 for spring, 4/15 for summer, 7/1 for fall (international), 9/1 for winter (international), 1/1 for spring (international), 3/1 for summer (international). *Application fee:* $50, $50 (international).

Application Contact Dr. Lynn Miller, Assistant Dean, Admission and MBA Program, 565 West Adams Street, Chicago, IL 60661-3691. **Phone:** 312-906-6544. **Toll-free Phone:** 800-MBA NEXT. **Fax:** 312-906-6549. **E-mail:** lmiller@stuart.iit.edu.

See full description on page 678.

Illinois State University

Normal, Illinois

COLLEGE OF BUSINESS

Graduate Business Faculty
Full-time: 62   Part-time: 2

Student Body
Total: 239	Average Age: 31
Full-time: 69	Women: 40%
Part-time: 170	

Admissions
Applications: 100	Average GMAT: 549
Admitted: 79	Average GPA: 3.34
Enrolled: 52	

Costs (1999–2000)
Full-time tuition: $2707 per academic year (resident), $6495 per academic year (nonresident)
Part-time tuition: $150 per credit hour (resident), $361 per credit hour (nonresident)

After Graduation (Class of 1998–99)
Employed within 3 months of graduation: 95%
Average starting salary: $41,000

Accreditation
AACSB—The International Association for Management Education

DEGREES MBA • MPA • MS

MBA—Master of Business Administration Full-time and part-time. 36 to 53 total credits required. 12 to 72 months to complete program. *Concentrations:* accounting, agribusiness, business education, business law, entrepreneurship, finance, human resources, insurance, international business, management, management information systems, marketing, organizational behavior/development.

MPA—Master of Professional Accounting Full-time and part-time. 150 total credits required. 60 to 84 months to complete program. *Concentrations:* accounting.

MS—Master of Science in Accounting Full-time and part-time. 33 to 71 total credits required. 12 to 72 months to complete program.

COSTS

Tuition, state resident: *Full-time* $1895. *Part-time* $105 per credit hour. **Tuition, nonresident:** *Full-time* $5683. *Part-time* $316 per credit hour. **Required fees:** *Full-time* $812. *Part-time* $45.1 per credit hour. **Graduate housing:** Room and board costs vary by number of occupants, type of accommodation, and type of board plan. *Typical cost:* $4248 (including board), $2252 (room only).

FINANCIAL AID (1999–2000)

110 students received aid, including loans, research assistantships, teaching assistantships, and work study. Aid is available to part-time students. Financial aid application deadline: 4/1. **Financial Aid Contact** Ms. Jennifer Fissel, Financial Aid Advisor, Campus Box 2320, Normal, IL 61790-2320. **Phone:** 309-438-2231. **Fax:** 309-438-3755. **E-mail:** jmfisse@ilstu.edu.

RESOURCES AND SERVICES

Information about online services, personal computer policies, library resources, international exchange programs, internship programs, and placement services at this institution and others can be found at **www.petersons.com/mba**

International Students

18% of students enrolled are international students.

Services and Facilities Counseling/support services, ESL/language courses, international student housing, international student organization, orientation, visa services. Financial aid is available to international students.

Applying *Required:* TOEFL with recommended score of 600 (paper), proof of adequate funds, proof of health/immunizations.

International Student Contact Ms. Sara Jome, Coordinator, Foreign Student and Scholar Services, International Studies, Campus Box 6120, Normal, IL 61790-6120. **Phone:** 309-438-5365. **Fax:** 309-438-3987. **E-mail:** sjjome@ilstu.edu.

■ APPLICATION

Required GMAT, application form, baccalaureate/first degree, essay, 2 letters of recommendation, personal statement, resume/curriculum vitae, transcripts of college work.

Deadlines and Fees *Deadlines:* 8/7 for fall, 1/2 for spring, 5/7 for summer, 3/1 for fall (international), 10/1 for spring (international), 3/15 for summer (international). *Application fee:* $30, $30 (international).

Application Contact Dr. Lee Graf, Director of MBA Program, Campus Box 5500, Normal, IL 61790-5500. **Phone:** 309-438-8388. **Fax:** 309-438-7255. **E-mail:** isumba@exchange.cob.ilstu.edu.

See full description on page 680.

Keller Graduate School of Management

Oakbrook Terrace, Illinois

GRADUATE PROGRAM

Graduate Business Faculty
Full-time: 36   Part-time: 765

Student Body
Total: 4,783
Full-time: 871   Average Age: 34
Part-time: 3,912   Women: 44%

Admissions
Average GPA: 2.9

Costs (1999–2000)
Full-time tuition: N/R
Part-time tuition: $1300 per course

After Graduation (Class of 1998–99)
Employed within 3 months of graduation: 95%

DEGREES MAFM • MBA • MHRM • MISM • MPM • MTM

MAFM—Master of Accounting and Financial Management Full-time and part-time. *Distance learning option.* At least 60 total credits required. 18 to 60 months to complete program.

MBA—Master of Business Administration Full-time and part-time. *Distance learning option.* At least 64 total credits required. 18 to 60 months to complete program. *Concentrations:* accounting, finance, human resources, information management, management, marketing, project management.

MHRM—Master of Human Resources Management Full-time and part-time. *Distance learning option.* At least 60 total credits required. 18 to 60 months to complete program.

MISM—Master of Information Systems Management Full-time and part-time. *Distance learning option.* At least 60 total credits required. 18 to 60 months to complete program.

MPM—Master of Project Management Full-time and part-time. *Distance learning option.* At least 52 total credits required. 18 to 60 months to complete program. *Concentrations:* project management.

MTM—Master of Telecommunications Management Full-time and part-time. *Distance learning option.* At least 60 total credits required. 18 to 60 months to complete program.

COSTS

Tuition *Part-time:* $1300 per course. Tuition varies by number of courses or credits taken and campus location.

FINANCIAL AID (1999–2000)

Loans. Aid is available to part-time students. **Financial Aid Contact** Mr. Michael Alexander, Financial Aid Office, 1 Tower Lane, Oakbrook Terrace, IL 60181. **Phone:** 630-574-1957. **Fax:** 630-574-1969.

RESOURCES AND SERVICES

Information about online services, personal computer policies, library resources, international exchange programs, internship programs, and placement services at this institution and others can be found at **www.petersons.com/mba**

International Students

Services and Facilities Financial aid is not available to international students.
Applying *Required:* TOEFL with recommended score of 550 (paper), proof of adequate funds, proof of health/immunizations.
International Student Contact Mr. Michael Alexander, Director, Central Services, 1 Tower Lane, Oakbrook Terrace, IL 60181. **Phone:** 630-574-1957. **Fax:** 630-574-1969. **E-mail:** malexander@keller.edu.

■ APPLICATION

Required Application form, baccalaureate/first degree, interview, transcripts of college work, 5 years of work experience. School will accept GMAT and GRE.
Deadlines and Fees Applications for domestic and international students are processed on a rolling basis.
Application Contact Mr. Michael Alexander, Director, Central Services, 1 Tower Lane, Oakbrook Terrace, IL 60181. **Phone:** 630-574-1957. **Fax:** 630-574-1969. **E-mail:** malexander@keller.edu.

See full description on page 700.

The Lake Forest Graduate School of Management

Lake Forest, Illinois

GRADUATE PROGRAMS

Graduate Business Faculty
Part-time: 147

Student Body
Total: 703   Average Age: 32
Part-time: 703   Women: 35%

Costs (1999–2000)
Full-time tuition: N/R
Part-time tuition: $1850 per course

DEGREE MBA

MBA—Evening/Weekend MBA Part-time. 4 years of work experience required. At least 64 total credits required. 20 to 72 months to complete program.

COSTS

Tuition *Part-time:* $1850 per course. Tuition varies by number of courses or credits taken.

FINANCIAL AID (1999–2000)

Loans and scholarships. Aid is available to part-time students. **Financial Aid Contact** Ms. Terry Hamlin, Financial Aid Coordinator, 280 North Sheridan Road, Lake Forest, IL 60045. **Phone:** 847-234-5005 Ext. 241. **Fax:** 847-295-3666. **E-mail:** thamlin@lfgsm.edu.

RESOURCES AND SERVICES

Information about online services, personal computer policies, library resources, international exchange programs, internship programs, and placement services at this institution and others can be found at **www.petersons.com/mba**

International Students

Services and Facilities Financial aid is not available to international students.

■ APPLICATION

Required GMAT or GRE, application form, baccalaureate/first degree, essay, interview, 2 letters of recommendation, transcripts of college work, 4 years of work experience. **Recommended** Resume/curriculum vitae.
Deadlines and Fees *Deadlines:* 7/13 for fall, 12/21 for winter.
Application Contact Ms. Tracey Macklin, Director of Admissions, Lake Forest Campus, 280 North Sheridan Road, Lake Forest, IL 60045. **E-mail:** admiss@lfgsm.edu.

See full description on page 704.

Lewis University

Romeoville, Illinois

COLLEGE OF BUSINESS

Graduate Business Faculty
Full-time: 18   Part-time: 46

Student Body
Total: 350   Average Age: 37
Full-time: 8   Women: 45%
Part-time: 342

Admissions
Applications: 158   Average GMAT: 510
Admitted: 156   Average GPA: 3
Enrolled: 142

Costs (1999–2000)
Full-time tuition: N/R
Part-time tuition: $470 per credit hour

After Graduation (Class of 1998–99)
Employed within 3 months of graduation: 90%
Average starting salary: $58,000

DEGREES MBA • MBA/MS

MBA—Master of Business Administration Full-time and part-time. 36 to 54 total credits required. 12 to 60 months to complete program. *Concentrations:*

Lewis University (continued)

accounting, finance, health care, human resources, international business, management information systems, marketing, operations management.

MBA/MS—Master of Business Administration/Master of Science in Nursing Full-time and part-time. At least 72 total credits required. 30 to 84 months to complete program.

COSTS

Tuition *Part-time:* $470 per credit hour. **Graduate housing:** Room and board costs vary by number of occupants and type of board plan. *Typical cost:* $2300 (room only).

FINANCIAL AID (1999–2000)

4 students received aid. Aid is available to part-time students. Financial aid application deadline: 5/1. **Financial Aid Contact** Ms. Janeen Decharinte, Director of Financial Aid, 500 South Independence Boulevard, Romeoville, IL 60446. **Phone:** 815-838-0500 Ext. 5263. **Fax:** 815-838-9456. **E-mail:** decharja@lewisu.edu.

RESOURCES AND SERVICES

Information about online services, personal computer policies, library resources, international exchange programs, internship programs, and placement services at this institution and others can be found at **www.petersons.com/mba**

International Students

2% of students enrolled are international students.

Services and Facilities Counseling/support services, ESL/language courses, international student organization, visa services. Financial aid is not available to international students.

Applying *Required:* TOEFL with recommended score of 550 (paper), proof of adequate funds, proof of health/immunizations.

International Student Contact Mr. Robert Tucker, Executive Director, Graduate School of Management, 500 South Independence Boulevard, Romeoville, IL 60446. **Phone:** 815-836-5339. **Fax:** 815-838-3330. **E-mail:** tuckerro@lewisu.edu.

■ APPLICATION

Required GMAT, application form, baccalaureate/first degree, personal statement, transcripts of college work, 3 years of work experience. **Recommended** Interview, letter(s) of recommendation, resume/curriculum vitae.

Deadlines and Fees Applications for domestic and international students are processed on a rolling basis. *Application fee:* $35, $35 (international).

Application Contact Mr. Robert Tucker, Executive Director, Graduate School of Management, 500 South Independence Boulevard, Romeoville, IL 60446. **Phone:** 815-836-5339. **Toll-free Phone:** 800-897-9000. **Fax:** 815-838-3330. **E-mail:** tuckerro@lewisu.edu.

Loyola University Chicago

Chicago, Illinois

GRADUATE SCHOOL OF BUSINESS

Graduate Business Faculty
Full-time: 72   Part-time: 15

Student Body
Total: 935
Full-time: 221   Average Age: 27
Part-time: 714   Women: 45%

Admissions
Applications: 720
Admitted: 486   Average GMAT: 540
Enrolled: 244   Average GPA: 3.2

Costs (1999–2000)
Full-time tuition: $26,349 per academic year
Part-time tuition: $2186 per course

After Graduation (Class of 1998–99)
Employed within 3 months of graduation: 92%
Average starting salary: $54,518

Accreditation
AACSB—The International Association for Management Education

DEGREES JD/MBA • MBA • MBA/MSIMC • MBA/MSISM • MBA/MSN • MBA/MSPH • MSA • MSIMC • MSISM

JD/MBA—Juris Doctor/Master of Business Administration Full-time and part-time. 128 to 140 total credits required. 48 to 96 months to complete program. *Concentrations:* accounting, business law, electronic commerce (e-commerce), environmental economics/management, finance, health care, international business, management, management information systems, managerial economics, marketing, operations management, strategic management.

MBA—Master of Business Administration Full-time and part-time. 42 to 54 total credits required. 12 to 60 months to complete program. *Concentrations:* accounting, electronic commerce (e-commerce), environmental economics/management, finance, health care, international business, management, management information systems, managerial economics, marketing, operations management, strategic management.

MBA/MSIMC—Master of Business Administration/Master of Science in Integrated Marketing Communication Full-time and part-time. 66 to 78 total credits required. 18 to 60 months to complete program. *Concentrations:* accounting, business law, electronic commerce (e-commerce), environmental economics/management, finance, health care, international business, management, management information systems, managerial economics, marketing, operations management, strategic management.

MBA/MSISM—Master of Business Administration/Master of Science in Information Systems Management Full-time and part-time. 69 to 81 total credits required. 18 to 60 months to complete program. *Concentrations:* accounting, business law, electronic commerce (e-commerce), environmental economics/management, finance, health care, international business, management, management information systems, managerial economics, marketing, operations management, strategic management.

MBA/MSN—Master of Business Administration/Master of Science in Nursing Full-time and part-time. 69 to 81 total credits required. 36 to 84 months to complete program. *Concentrations:* accounting, business law, electronic commerce (e-commerce), environmental economics/management, finance, health care, international business, management, management information systems, managerial economics, marketing, operations management, strategic management.

MBA/MSPH—Master of Business Administration/Master of Pharmacology Full-time and part-time. 63 to 78 total credits required. 24 to 60 months to complete program. *Concentrations:* accounting, electronic commerce (e-commerce), environmental economics/management, finance, health care, international business, management, management information systems, managerial economics, marketing, operations management, strategic management.

MSA—Master of Science in Accounting Full-time and part-time. At least 36 total credits required. 12 to 60 months to complete program.

MSIMC—Master of Science in Integrated Marketing Communications Full-time and part-time. 42 to 54 total credits required. 12 to 60 months to complete program.

MSISM—Master of Science in Information Systems Management Full-time and part-time. 36 to 48 total credits required. 12 to 60 months to complete program.

COSTS

Tuition *Full-time:* $26,232. *Part-time:* $2186 per course. Tuition varies by academic program. **Required fees:** *Full-time* $117.

FINANCIAL AID (1999–2000)

300 students received aid, including loans, research assistantships, and work study. Aid is available to part-time students. Financial aid application deadline: 4/15. **Financial Aid Contact** Mr. Terry Richards, Student Financial Assistance, 6525 North Sheridan Road, Chicago, IL 60626-5208. **Phone:** 773-508-3155. **Fax:** 773-508-3397. **E-mail:** lufinaid@luc.edu.

RESOURCES AND SERVICES

Information about online services, personal computer policies, library resources, international exchange programs, internship programs, and placement services at this institution and others can be found at **www.petersons.com/mba**

International Students

15% of students enrolled are international students.

Services and Facilities Counseling/support services, ESL/language courses, international student housing, visa services. Financial aid is available to international students.

Applying *Required:* TOEFL with recommended score of 550 (paper), proof of adequate funds, proof of health/immunizations.

International Student Contact Mr. John Heise, Director, International Services, 6525 North Sheridan Road, Chicago, IL 60626-5208. **Phone:** 773-508-3899. **Fax:** 773-508-3895. **E-mail:** jheise@luc.edu.

■ APPLICATION

Required GMAT, application form, baccalaureate/first degree, 3 letters of recommendation, transcripts of college work. **Recommended** Essay, interview, personal statement, resume/curriculum vitae, 3 years of work experience.

Deadlines and Fees *Deadlines:* 7/1 for fall, 10/1 for winter, 1/1 for spring, 5/1 for summer, 6/1 for fall (international), 8/1 for winter (international), 11/1 for spring (international), 2/1 for summer (international). *Application fee:* $50, $50 (international).

Application Contact Ms. Dana Sendziol, Director of Admissions, Graduate School of Business, 820 North Michigan Avenue, Chicago, IL 60611-2196. **Phone:** 312-915-6120. **Fax:** 312-915-7207. **E-mail:** mba-loyola@luc.edu.

See full description on page 716.

National-Louis University

Evanston, Illinois

COLLEGE OF MANAGEMENT AND BUSINESS

DEGREES MBA • MS

MBA—Master of Business Administration Full-time and part-time. *Distance learning option.* At least 37 total credits required. 22 months to complete program.
MS—Master of Science in Human Resource Management and Development Full-time and part-time. *Distance learning option.* At least 33 total credits required. 18 months to complete program.
MS—Master of Science in Managerial Leadership Full-time and part-time. *Distance learning option.* At least 33 total credits required. 18 months to complete program.

RESOURCES AND SERVICES
Information about online services, personal computer policies, library resources, international exchange programs, internship programs, and placement services at this institution and others can be found at **www.petersons.com/mba**

International Students

Services and Facilities ESL/language courses. Financial aid is not available to international students.
International Student Contact Ms. Ewa Ludwiczuk, 2840 Sheridan Road, Evanston, IL 60201-1730. **Phone:** 800-443-5522 Ext. 3417. **Fax:** 312-621-1205. **E-mail:** elud@chicago1.nl.edu.

■ APPLICATION

Application Contact Office of Graduate Admissions, 2840 Sheridan Road, Evanston, IL 60201-1730. **Phone:** 847-475-1100 Ext. 5111. **Toll-free Phone:** 888-NLU TODAY. **E-mail:** nluinfo@wheeling1.nl.edu.

North Central College

Naperville, Illinois

DEPARTMENT OF BUSINESS

Graduate Business Faculty
Full-time: 14

Student Body
Total: 190
Full-time: 15
Part-time: 175

Average Age: 33
Women: 47%

Admissions
Applications: 56
Admitted: 49
Enrolled: 34

Average GMAT: 470
Average GPA: 2.85

Costs (1999–2000)
Full-time tuition: N/R
Part-time tuition: $1464 per course

DEGREES MBA • MS

MBA—Master of Business Administration Full-time and part-time. 36 to 48 total credits required. 24 to 75 months to complete program. *Concentrations:* business ethics, business information science, financial management/planning, human resources, information management, leadership, management, marketing.
MS—Master of Science in Management Information Systems Full-time and part-time. 42 to 51 total credits required. 12 to 75 months to complete program. *Concentrations:* management information systems.

N orth Central College in Naperville, Illinois, provides an education that exceeds the high standards of today's business world. The Master of Business Administration (M.B.A.) program is designed with today's complex business environment in mind and allows students to develop an individualized program of study targeted to their personal career goals. With eleven specialized areas of concentration, North Central's M.B.A. combines traditional knowledge with skills deemed important for effective management within the work environment.

Distinguished professors teach commonly used and accepted business solutions, emphasizing an interdisciplinary, cutting-edge approach to understanding the intricacies of today's organizations. They enjoy teaching and are deeply committed to providing students with the tools they need to excel. Students come away from this program knowing they have received a tremendous education that immediately applies to real-world situations.

North Central students enjoy the strengths of a small college that is centered in a high-tech corridor and offers unlimited internship and employment opportunities. An average class size of 17 students provides scholars with personal attention and guidance and simultaneously challenges them academically.

The M.B.A. program at North Central College is characterized by a high level of excellence and integrity, one-on-one teaching, and a classroom atmosphere where learning is interactive.

COSTS
Tuition *Part-time:* $1464 per course. Tuition varies by academic program.

FINANCIAL AID (1999–2000)
15 students received aid, including loans and scholarships. Aid is available to part-time students. **Financial Aid Contact** Ms. Katherine Edmunds, Director of Financial Aid, 30 North Brainard Street, PO Box 3063, Naperville, IL 60566-7063. **Phone:** 630-637-5600. **Fax:** 630-637-5608. **E-mail:** finaid@noctrl.edu.

RESOURCES AND SERVICES
Information about online services, personal computer policies, library resources, international exchange programs, internship programs, and placement services at this institution and others can be found at **www.petersons.com/mba**

International Students

3% of students enrolled are international students.

Services and Facilities Counseling/support services, ESL/language courses, housing location assistance, international student organization, language tutoring, orientation, visa services. Financial aid is available to international students.
Applying *Required:* TOEFL with recommended score of 250 (computer) or 600 (paper), proof of adequate funds, proof of health/immunizations. *Recommended:* TWE.
International Student Contact Dr. John Shindler, Coordinator of International Programs, 30 North Brainard Street, Naperville, IL 60566-7063. **Phone:** 630-637-5287. **Fax:** 630-637-5134. **E-mail:** jsh@noctrl.edu.

■ APPLICATION

Required GMAT, application form, baccalaureate/first degree, interview, personal statement, transcripts of college work. **Recommended** Resume/curriculum vitae, work experience.
Deadlines and Fees Applications for domestic students are processed on a rolling basis. *Deadlines:* 7/15 for fall (international), 11/1 for winter (international), 1/15 for spring (international), 4/15 for summer (international). *Application fee:* $25, $25 (international).
Application Contact Ms. Martha Stolze, Coordinator of Graduate Admission, 30 North Brainard Street, PO Box 3063, Naperville, IL 60566-7063. **Phone:** 630-637-5814. **Toll-free Phone:** 888-595-4723. **Fax:** 630-637-5819.

Northeastern Illinois University

Chicago, Illinois

COLLEGE OF BUSINESS AND MANAGEMENT

Graduate Business Faculty
Full-time: 28

Student Body
Total: 73
Full-time: 19
Part-time: 54

Average Age: 33
Women: 40%

Admissions
Applications: 71
Admitted: 33
Enrolled: 31

Average GMAT: 556
Average GPA: 3.27

Costs (1999–2000)
Full-time tuition: $2700 per academic year (resident), $7480 per academic year (nonresident)

Northeastern Illinois University (continued)

Part-time tuition: $100 per credit (resident), $299 per credit (nonresident)

DEGREE MBA

MBA—Master of Business Administration Full-time and part-time. *Distance learning option.* 33 to 51 total credits required. 15 to 60 months to complete program. *Concentrations:* accounting, finance, international business, management, marketing.

COSTS

Tuition, state resident: *Full-time* $2700. *Part-time* $100 per credit. **Tuition, nonresident:** *Full-time* $7480. *Part-time* $299 per credit. **Required fees:** Tuition and fees vary by number of courses or credits taken.

FINANCIAL AID (1999–2000)

38 students received aid, including grants, loans, research assistantships, scholarships, teaching assistantships, and work study. Aid is available to part-time students. **Financial Aid Contact** Dr. Peter Stonebraker, Coordinator of Graduate Programs, 5500 North St. Louis Avenue, Chicago, IL 60625-4699. **Phone:** 773-794-2642. **Fax:** 773-794-6288. **E-mail:** p-stonebraker@neiu.edu.

RESOURCES AND SERVICES

Information about online services, personal computer policies, library resources, international exchange programs, internship programs, and placement services at this institution and others can be found at **www.petersons.com/mba**

International Students

21% of students enrolled are international students.

Services and Facilities ESL/language courses, visa services. Financial aid is available to international students.

Applying *Required:* TOEFL with recommended score of 550 (paper), proof of adequate funds.

International Student Contact Dr. Peter Stonebraker, Coordinator of Graduate Programs, 5500 North St. Louis Avenue, Chicago, IL 60625-4699. **Phone:** 773-794-2642. **Fax:** 773-794-6288. **E-mail:** p-stonebraker@neiu.edu.

■ APPLICATION

Required GMAT, application form, baccalaureate/first degree, essay, 2 letters of recommendation, personal statement, transcripts of college work. **Recommended** Resume/curriculum vitae, work experience.

Deadlines and Fees *Deadlines:* 7/15 for fall, 12/10 for spring, 5/1 for summer, 5/15 for fall (international), 9/15 for spring (international), 3/15 for summer (international).

Application Contact Dr. Peter Stonebraker, Coordinator of Graduate Programs, 5500 North St. Louis Avenue, Chicago, IL 60625-4699. **Phone:** 773-794-2642. **Fax:** 773-794-6288. **E-mail:** p-stonebraker@neiu.edu.

Northern Illinois University

De Kalb, Illinois

COLLEGE OF BUSINESS

Graduate Business Faculty
Full-time: 73   Part-time: 5

Student Body
Total: 743	
Full-time: 180	Average Age: 32
Part-time: 563	Women: 42%

Admissions
Applications: 493	Average GMAT: 539
Admitted: 425	Average GPA: 3.12
Enrolled: 291	

Costs (1999–2000)
Full-time tuition: N/R
Part-time tuition: $305 per credit hour (resident), $305 per credit hour (nonresident)

After Graduation (Class of 1998–99)
Employed within 3 months of graduation: 95%
Average starting salary: $63,000

Accreditation
AACSB—The International Association for Management Education

DEGREES MAS • MBA • MS • MST

MAS—Master of Accounting Science Full-time and part-time. GMAT score (minimum 475) required. 30 to 66 total credits required. 12 to 72 months to complete program.
MBA—Evening MBA Part-time. 2 years of work experience and GMAT score (minimum 450) required. 31 to 49 total credits required. 12 to 72 months to complete program.
MBA—Executive MBA Full-time. 5 years of work experience and GMAT score (minimum 450) required. At least 49 total credits required. 24 months to complete program.
MS—Master of Science in Management Information Systems Full-time and part-time. GMAT score (minimum 500) required. 30 to 51 total credits required. 12 to 72 months to complete program.
MST—Master of Science in Taxation At least 30 total credits required. 12 to 72 months to complete program.

COSTS

Tuition, state resident: *Part-time* $130 per credit hour. **Tuition, nonresident:** *Part-time* $130 per credit hour. **Required fees:** *Part-time* $175 per credit hour. Fees vary by class time, number of courses or credits taken, campus location, and academic program. **Graduate housing:** Room and board costs vary by campus location, number of occupants, type of accommodation, and type of board plan. *Typical cost:* $4396 (including board).

FINANCIAL AID (1999–2000)

Fellowships, research assistantships, teaching assistantships, and work study. Aid is available to part-time students. **Financial Aid Contact** Kathleen Brunson, Director, Student Financial Aid Office, Swen Parsons 245, DeKalb, IL 60115-2872. **Phone:** 815-753-1395. **Fax:** 815-753-9475.

RESOURCES AND SERVICES

Information about online services, personal computer policies, library resources, international exchange programs, internship programs, and placement services at this institution and others can be found at **www.petersons.com/mba**

International Students

12% of students enrolled are international students.

Services and Facilities Counseling/support services, ESL/language courses, housing location assistance, international student organization, orientation, visa services. Financial aid is available to international students.

Applying *Required:* TOEFL with recommended score of 213 (computer) or 550 (paper), proof of adequate funds, proof of health/immunizations.

International Student Contact Mark D. Thackaberry, Director, International Student and Faculty Office, Homes Student Center, Room 023, DeKalb, IL 60115. **Phone:** 815-753-1346. **Fax:** 815-753-8279. **E-mail:** ca0mtd1@niu.edu.

■ APPLICATION

Required GMAT, application form, baccalaureate/first degree, 2 letters of recommendation, personal statement, resume/curriculum vitae, transcripts of college work, 2 years of work experience.

Deadlines and Fees *Deadlines:* 6/1 for fall, 11/1 for spring, 4/1 for summer, 5/1 for fall (international), 10/1 for spring (international). *Application fee:* $30, $30 (international).

Application Contact Larry Jacobs, Director, Graduate Studies in Business and Research, NIU College of Business, Wirtz Hall 140, DeKalb, IL 60115-2897. **Phone:** 815-753-1245. **Fax:** 815-753-3300. **E-mail:** cobgrads@niu.edu.

See full description on page 748.

North Park University

Chicago, Illinois

CENTER FOR MANAGEMENT EDUCATION

Graduate Business Faculty
Full-time: 7   Part-time: 15

Student Body
Total: 235	
Full-time: 5	Average Age: 33
Part-time: 230	Women: 54%

Admissions
Applications: 109	Average GMAT: 540
Admitted: 80	Average GPA: 3.2
Enrolled: 56	

Costs (1999–2000)
Full-time tuition: N/R
Part-time tuition: $1100 per course

DEGREES M Mgt • MBA • MBA/MA • MBA/MS

M Mgt—Master of Management Full-time and part-time. At least 36 total credits required. 12 to 72 months to complete program. *Concentrations:* entrepreneurship, finance, human resources, international business, management, marketing, nonprofit management, nonprofit organization, organizational behavior/development.

MBA—Master of Business Administration Full-time and part-time. 32 to 40 total credits required. 12 to 72 months to complete program. *Concentrations:* entrepreneurship, finance, human resources, international business, management, marketing, nonprofit management, nonprofit organization, organizational behavior/development.

MBA/MA—Master of Business Administration/Master of Arts in Theological Studies Full-time and part-time. At least 114 total credits required. 36 to 72 months to complete program.

MBA/MS—Master of Business Administration/Master of Science in Nursing Full-time and part-time. At least 62 total credits required. 24 to 72 months to complete program.

COSTS
Tuition *Part-time:* $1100 per course. **Required fees:** Tuition and fees vary by academic program.

FINANCIAL AID (1999–2000)
150 students received aid, including grants, loans, and scholarships. Aid is available to part-time students. **Financial Aid Contact** Mr. Christopher Nicholson, Director of Admissions, Graduate and Continuing Education, 3225 West Foster Avenue, Chicago, IL 60625-4895. **Phone:** 773-244-5518. **Fax:** 773-244-4953. **E-mail:** cln@northpark.edu.

RESOURCES AND SERVICES
Information about online services, personal computer policies, library resources, international exchange programs, internship programs, and placement services at this institution and others can be found at **www.petersons.com/mba**

International Students
9% of students enrolled are international students.

Services and Facilities Counseling/support services, ESL/language courses, international student housing, orientation, visa services. Financial aid is available to international students.

Applying *Required:* TOEFL with recommended score of 600 (paper), proof of adequate funds, proof of health/immunizations.

International Student Contact Dr. Sally Ivaska, Director, Office of International Studies, 3225 West Foster Avenue, Chicago, IL 60625-4895. **Phone:** 773-244-5571. **E-mail:** sivaska@northpark.edu.

▪ APPLICATION
Required Application form, baccalaureate/first degree, 2 letters of recommendation, resume/curriculum vitae, transcripts of college work. School will accept GMAT or GRE or MAT. **Recommended** Interview, work experience.

Deadlines and Fees Applications for domestic students are processed on a rolling basis. *Application fee:* $20, $20 (international).

Application Contact Mr. Christopher Nicholson, Director of Admissions, Graduate and Continuing Education, 3225 West Foster Avenue, Chicago, IL 60625-4895. **Phone:** 773-244-5518. **Toll-free Phone:** 800-888-6728. **Fax:** 773-244-4953. **E-mail:** cln@northpark.edu.

See full description on page 750.

Northwestern University
Evanston, Illinois

KELLOGG GRADUATE SCHOOL OF MANAGEMENT

Graduate Business Faculty
Full-time: 150 • Part-time: 103

Student Body
Total: 2,504
Full-time: 1,200 — Average Age: 29
Part-time: 1,304 — Women: 33%

Admissions
Applications: 6,200
Admitted: 950 — Average GMAT: 700
Enrolled: 624 — Average GPA: 3.45

Costs (1999–2000)
Full-time tuition: $28,677 per academic year
Part-time tuition: $2692 per unit

After Graduation (Class of 1998–99)
Employed within 3 months of graduation: 100%
Average starting salary: $90,000

Accreditation
AACSB—The International Association for Management Education

DEGREES JD/MMgt • M Mgt • MD/MMgt • MMgt/MS

JD/MMgt—Juris Doctor/Master of Management Full-time. Maximum of 48 months to complete program.

M Mgt—Master of Management in Manufacturing Full-time. At least 23 total credits required. 22 to 24 months to complete program.

M Mgt—Master of Management Full-time and part-time. At least 23 total credits required. 21 to 24 months to complete program. *Concentrations:* accounting, business law, decision sciences, electronic commerce (e-commerce), entrepreneurship, finance, health care, human resources, industrial/labor relations, information management, international business, management, managerial economics, marketing, nonprofit organization, operations management, organizational behavior/development, real estate, technology management, training and development.

MD/MMgt—Doctor of Medicine/Master of Management Full-time. At least 66 total credits required. Maximum of 60 months to complete program.

MMgt/MS—Master of Management/Master of Science in Nursing Full-time. At least 30 total credits required. Maximum of 24 months to complete program.

COSTS
Tuition *Full-time:* $28,677. *Part-time:* $2692 per unit. Tuition varies by class time. **Graduate housing:** Room and board costs vary by number of occupants, type of accommodation, and type of board plan. *Typical cost:* $10,755 (including board).

FINANCIAL AID (1999–2000)
800 students received aid, including grants, loans, and scholarships. Financial aid application deadline: 4/15. **Financial Aid Contact** Ms. Michele Rogers, Associate Director of Financial Aid, 2001 North Sheridan Road, Evanston, IL 60208. **Phone:** 847-491-3308. **Fax:** 847-491-4960. **E-mail:** myrogers@nwu.edu.

RESOURCES AND SERVICES
Information about online services, personal computer policies, library resources, international exchange programs, internship programs, and placement services at this institution and others can be found at **www.petersons.com/mba**

International Students
24% of students enrolled are international students.

Services and Facilities Counseling/support services, housing location assistance, international student organization, visa services. Financial aid is not available to international students.

Applying *Required:* TOEFL with recommended score of 600 (paper), proof of adequate funds.

International Student Contact Office of Admissions, Kellogg Graduate School of Management, 2001 North Sheridan Road, Evanston, IL 60208. **Phone:** 847-491-3308. **Fax:** 847-491-4960. **E-mail:** kellogg-admissions@nwu.edu.

▪ APPLICATION
Required Application form, baccalaureate/first degree, essay, interview, 1 letter of recommendation, personal statement, resume/curriculum vitae, transcripts of college work, 4 years of work experience. School will accept GMAT.

Deadlines and Fees *Deadlines:* 11/14 for fall, 1/15 for winter, 3/16 for spring, 11/14 for fall (international), 1/15 for winter (international). *Application fee:* $160, $160 (international).

Application Contact Office of Admissions, Kellogg Graduate School of Business, 2001 North Sheridan Road, Evanston, IL 60208. **Phone:** 847-491-3308. **Fax:** 847-491-4960. **E-mail:** kellogg-admissions@nwu.edu.

Olivet Nazarene University
Bourbonnais, Illinois

DEPARTMENT OF BUSINESS

Graduate Business Faculty
Full-time: 5 • Part-time: 8

Olivet Nazarene University (continued)

Admissions
Average GPA: 3

Costs (1999–2000)
Full-time tuition: N/R
Part-time tuition: $414 per credit

After Graduation (Class of 1998–99)
Employed within 3 months of graduation: 100%

DEGREE MBA

MBA—Master of Business Administration Full-time. At least 35 total credits required. 24 to 28 months to complete program. *Concentrations:* management.

COSTS
Tuition *Part-time:* $414 per credit.

FINANCIAL AID (1999–2000)
Loans. **Financial Aid Contact** Ms. Pat Forquer, Adult Studies Counselor, PO Box 592, Kankakee, IL 60901-0592. **Phone:** 815-939-5075.

RESOURCES AND SERVICES
Information about online services, personal computer policies, library resources, international exchange programs, internship programs, and placement services at this institution and others can be found at **www. petersons.com/mba**

International Students
Services and Facilities Counseling/support services. Financial aid is not available to international students.
Applying *Required:* TOEFL with recommended score of 550 (paper), proof of adequate funds.
International Student Contact Mrs. Joan W. Dean, Director of Student Services, PO Box 592, Kankakee, IL 60901-0592. **Phone:** 815-939-5017. **Fax:** 815-939-5028.

■ APPLICATION
Required Application form, baccalaureate/first degree, interview, 2 letters of recommendation, personal statement, resume/curriculum vitae, transcripts of college work, 3 years of work experience.
Deadlines and Fees Applications for domestic students are processed on a rolling basis. *Deadlines:* 4/1 for fall (international), 9/30 for spring (international). *Application fee:* $20, $20 (international).
Application Contact School of Graduate Adult Studies, PO Box 592, Kankakee, IL 60901-0592. **Phone:** 815-939-5186. **Fax:** 815-939-5028. **E-mail:** admissions@ olivet.edu.

Quincy University

Quincy, Illinois

DIVISION OF BUSINESS

Graduate Business Faculty
Full-time: 9

Student Body

Total: 105	Average Age: 27
Full-time: 20	Women: 51%
Part-time: 85	

Admissions

Applications: 30	Enrolled: 28
Admitted: 28	Average GMAT: 535

Costs (1999–2000)
Full-time tuition: N/R
Part-time tuition: $1170 per course

After Graduation (Class of 1998–99)
Employed within 3 months of graduation: 100%

DEGREE MBA

MBA—Master of Business Administration Full-time and part-time. 30 to 36 total credits required. 12 to 60 months to complete program.

COSTS
Tuition *Part-time:* $1170 per course. Tuition varies by class time and number of courses or credits taken.

FINANCIAL AID (1999–2000)
Aid is available to part-time students. **Financial Aid Contact** James Reed, Financial Aid Officer, 1800 College Avenue, Quincy, IL 62301-2699. **Phone:** 217-228-5260.

RESOURCES AND SERVICES
Information about online services, personal computer policies, library resources, international exchange programs, internship programs, and placement services at this institution and others can be found at **www. petersons.com/mba**

International Students
Services and Facilities ESL/language courses, housing location assistance, international student housing, language tutoring, orientation. Financial aid is not available to international students.
Applying *Required:* TOEFL with recommended score of 600 (paper), proof of adequate funds, proof of health/immunizations.
International Student Contact Dr. Richard Magliari, MBA Director, 1800 College Avenue, Quincy, IL 62301-2699. **Phone:** 217-228-5391. **E-mail:** mba_director@quincy.edu.

■ APPLICATION
Required GMAT, application form, baccalaureate/first degree, 2 letters of recommendation, transcripts of college work. **Recommended** Work experience.
Deadlines and Fees Applications for domestic and international students are processed on a rolling basis. *Application fee:* $25, $25 (international).
Application Contact Dr. Richard Magliari, MBA Director, 1800 College Avenue, Quincy, IL 62301-2699. **Toll-free Phone:** 800-688-4295. **Fax:** 217-228-5651. **E-mail:** mba_director@quincy.edu.

Rockford College

Rockford, Illinois

PROGRAM IN BUSINESS ADMINISTRATION

Graduate Business Faculty

Full-time: 12	Part-time: 2

Student Body

Total: 100	Average Age: 32
Full-time: 5	Women: 50%
Part-time: 95	

Admissions

Applications: 30	Average GMAT: 500
Admitted: 26	Average GPA: 3.2
Enrolled: 25	

Costs (1999–2000)
Full-time tuition: $7235 per academic year
Part-time tuition: $400 per credit hour

After Graduation (Class of 1998–99)
Employed within 3 months of graduation: 98%

DEGREE MBA

MBA—Master of Business Administration Full-time and part-time. 36 to 50 total credits required. 20 to 60 months to complete program. *Concentrations:* accounting, finance, management, marketing, nonprofit organization, public management.

COSTS
Tuition *Full-time:* $7200. *Part-time:* $400 per credit hour. Tuition varies by number of courses or credits taken. **Required fees:** *Full-time* $35. *Part-time* $35 per semester hour. **Graduate housing:** Room and board costs vary by campus location, number of occupants, type of accommodation, and type of board plan. *Typical cost:* $4800 (including board).

FINANCIAL AID (1999–2000)
10 students received aid, including grants, loans, and research assistantships. Aid is available to part-time students. Financial aid application deadline: 4/1. **Financial Aid Contact** Mrs. Judy Seebach, Director of Financial Aid, 5050 East State Street, Rockford, IL 61108-2393. **Phone:** 815-226-3385. **Fax:** 815-226-4119.

RESOURCES AND SERVICES
Information about online services, personal computer policies, library resources, international exchange programs, internship programs, and placement services at this institution and others can be found at **www. petersons.com/mba**

International Students
10% of students enrolled are international students.

Services and Facilities Counseling/support services, ESL/language courses, housing location assistance, international student housing, international student organization, visa services. Financial aid is not available to international students.
Applying *Required:* TOEFL with recommended score of 550 (paper), proof of adequate funds, proof of health/immunizations.
International Student Contact Ms. Stacy Peterson, International Student Coordinator, 5050 East State Street, Rockford, IL 61108-2393. **Phone:** 815-226-3336. **Fax:** 815-226-4119.

■ APPLICATION
Required GMAT, application form, baccalaureate/first degree, essay, 3 letters of recommendation, personal statement, transcripts of college work. **Recommended** Interview, resume/curriculum vitae, 5 years of work experience.
Deadlines and Fees Applications for domestic and international students are processed on a rolling basis. *Application fee:* $35, $35 (international).
Application Contact Mr. Jeffrey Fahrenwald, Director, MBA Program, 5050 East State Street, Rockford, IL 61108-2393. **Phone:** 815-226-4178. **Fax:** 815-226-4119. **E-mail:** jfahrenwald@rockford.edu.

Roosevelt University
Chicago, Illinois

WALTER E. HELLER COLLEGE OF BUSINESS ADMINISTRATION

Graduate Business Faculty
Full-time: 26 — Part-time: 42

Student Body
Total: 705 — Average Age: 32
Full-time: 86 — Women: 53%
Part-time: 619

Admissions
Applications: 244 — Average GMAT: 470
Admitted: 221 — Average GPA: 3
Enrolled: 152

Costs (1999–2000)
Full-time tuition: $8714 per academic year
Part-time tuition: $473 per credit hour

DEGREES MBA • MS

MBA—Master of Business Administration Full-time and part-time. At least 36 total credits required. 12 to 72 months to complete program. *Concentrations:* accounting, arts administration/management, economics, finance, health care, human resources, international business, management, management information systems, marketing, nonprofit management, organizational behavior/development, quantitative analysis, real estate, risk management, telecommunications management, hospitality management.

MS—Master of Science in Accounting Full-time and part-time. At least 30 total credits required. 12 to 72 months to complete program.

MS—Master of Science in Human Resources Management Full-time and part-time. At least 30 total credits required. 12 to 72 months to complete program. *Concentrations:* human resources.

MS—Master of Science in Information Systems Full-time and part-time. At least 30 total credits required. 12 to 72 months to complete program. *Concentrations:* accounting, finance, financial management/planning, management, marketing.

MS—Master of Science in International Business Full-time and part-time. At least 30 total credits required. 12 to 72 months to complete program. *Concentrations:* accounting, economics, finance, management, management information systems, marketing.

COSTS
Tuition *Full-time:* $8514. *Part-time:* $473 per credit hour. Tuition varies by number of courses or credits taken. **Required fees:** *Full-time* $200. **Graduate housing:** Room and board costs vary by number of occupants and type of board plan. *Typical cost:* $6000 (including board).

FINANCIAL AID (1999–2000)
4 students received aid, including scholarships and work study. Aid is available to part-time students. **Financial Aid Contact** Mr. Walter O'Neill, Director of Financial Aid, 430 South Michigan Avenue, Chicago, IL 60605-1394. **Phone:** 312-341-3612.

RESOURCES AND SERVICES
Information about online services, personal computer policies, library resources, international exchange programs, internship programs, and placement services at this institution and others can be found at **www.petersons.com/mba**

International Students
17% of students enrolled are international students.

Services and Facilities Counseling/support services, ESL/language courses, international student housing, international student organization, language tutoring, visa services. Financial aid is available to international students.
Applying *Required:* TOEFL with recommended score of 550 (paper), TWE with recommended score of 3.5, proof of adequate funds.
International Student Contact Ms. Colleen Earley, International Admissions Coordinator, 430 South Michigan Avenue, Chicago, IL 60605-1394. **Phone:** 312-341-3531. **Fax:** 312-341-6377.

■ APPLICATION
Required GMAT, application form, baccalaureate/first degree, transcripts of college work. **Recommended** Letter(s) of recommendation, personal statement, resume/curriculum vitae.
Deadlines and Fees Applications for domestic students are processed on a rolling basis. *Deadlines:* 6/1 for fall (international), 10/1 for spring (international), 3/1 for summer (international). *Application fee:* $25, $35 (international).
Application Contact Ms. Marilyn Nance, Director, MBA Program, Walter E. Heller College of Business Administration, 430 South Michigan Avenue, Chicago, IL 60605-1394. **Phone:** 312-341-3820. **Fax:** 312-341-3827. **E-mail:** mnance@roosevelt.edu.

See full description on page 794.

Saint Xavier University
Chicago, Illinois

GRAHAM SCHOOL OF MANAGEMENT

Graduate Business Faculty
Full-time: 15 — Part-time: 6

Student Body
Total: 210 — Average Age: 37
Full-time: 19 — Women: 53%
Part-time: 191

Costs (1999–2000)
Full-time tuition: $8660 per academic year
Part-time tuition: $475 per credit

DEGREES MBA • MBA/MS • MPH • MS

MBA—Master of Business Administration Full-time and part-time. At least 39 total credits required. 12 to 60 months to complete program. *Concentrations:* finance, financial management/planning, health care, management, marketing.

MBA/MS—Master of Business Administration/Master of Science in Nursing Full-time and part-time. At least 39 total credits required. 12 to 60 months to complete program. *Concentrations:* finance, health care, management, marketing.

MPH—Master of Public Health Full-time and part-time. At least 36 total credits required. 18 to 60 months to complete program.

MS—Master of Science Full-time and part-time. *Concentrations:* finance, health care, management.

COSTS
Tuition *Full-time:* $8550. *Part-time:* $475 per credit. **Tuition, international:** *Full-time* $8550. **Required fees:** *Full-time* $110. *Part-time* $45 per semester. **Graduate housing:** Room and board costs vary by number of occupants and type of board plan. *Typical cost:* $6088 (including board), $3276 (room only).

FINANCIAL AID (1999–2000)
20 students received aid, including loans, research assistantships, and work study. Aid is available to part-time students. **Financial Aid Contact** Financial Aid Office, 3700 West 103rd Street, Chicago, IL 60655-3105. **Phone:** 773-298-3070.

RESOURCES AND SERVICES
Information about online services, personal computer policies, library resources, international exchange programs, internship programs, and placement services at this institution and others can be found at **www.petersons.com/mba**

International Students
1.0% of students enrolled are international students.

Saint Xavier University (continued)

Services and Facilities Counseling/support services, housing location assistance, international student housing. Financial aid is available to international students.
Applying *Required:* TOEFL, proof of adequate funds.
International Student Contact Coordinator of International Students and Studies, 3700 West 103rd Street, Chicago, IL 60655-3105. **Phone:** 773-298-3061.

■ APPLICATION

Required GMAT, application form, baccalaureate/first degree, 2 letters of recommendation, transcripts of college work. School will accept GRE and MAT. **Recommended** Personal statement, work experience.
Deadlines and Fees Applications for domestic and international students are processed on a rolling basis. *Application fee:* $35, $35 (international).
Application Contact Anne Hurley, Admissions, 3700 West 103rd Street, Chicago, IL 60655-3105. **Phone:** 773-298-3050. **Toll-free Phone:** 800-462-9288. **Fax:** 773-298-3070. **E-mail:** admissions@sxu.edu.

Southern Illinois University Carbondale

Carbondale, Illinois

COLLEGE OF BUSINESS AND ADMINISTRATION

Accreditation
AACSB—The International Association for Management Education

DEGREES EMBA • JD/MBA • MBA • MBA/MA • MBA/MS

EMBA—Executive Master of Business Administration Part-time. Minimum of 5 years of managerial experience required. At least 33 total credits required. 18 months to complete program.
JD/MBA—Juris Doctor/Master of Business Administration Full-time. At least 105 total credits required. 36 to 48 months to complete program.
MBA—Master of Business Administration Full-time and part-time. At least 33 total credits required. 12 to 24 months to complete program. *Concentrations:* accounting, finance, international business, management, management information systems, marketing, organizational behavior/development, production management.
MBA/MA—Master of Business Administration/Master of Arts in Mass Communication Full-time and part-time. At least 51 total credits required. 12 to 30 months to complete program.
MBA/MS—Master of Business Administration/Master of Science in Agribusiness Economics Full-time and part-time. At least 51 total credits required. 12 to 30 months to complete program.

RESOURCES AND SERVICES
Information about online services, personal computer policies, library resources, international exchange programs, internship programs, and placement services at this institution and others can be found at **www.petersons.com/mba**

International Students
Services and Facilities Counseling/support services, ESL/language courses, international student housing, international student organization, visa services. Financial aid is available to international students.
International Student Contact Graduate Programs Office, College of Business and Administration, Carbondale, IL 62901-4625.

■ APPLICATION
Application Contact Graduate Programs Office, College of Business and Administration, Carbondale, IL 62901-4625.

See full description on page 826.

Southern Illinois University Edwardsville

Edwardsville, Illinois

SCHOOL OF BUSINESS

Graduate Business Faculty
Full-time: 50   Part-time: 13
Student Body

Total: 288   Average Age: 31
Full-time: 87   Women: 42%
Part-time: 201
Admissions
Average GMAT: 512   Average GPA: 3.5
Costs (1999–2000)
Full-time tuition: $1448 per academic year (resident), $2658 per academic year (nonresident)
Part-time tuition: N/R

After Graduation (Class of 1998–99)
Employed within 3 months of graduation: 94%

Accreditation
AACSB—The International Association for Management Education

DEGREES MA • MBA • MS

MA—Master of Arts in Economics and Finance Full-time and part-time. 30 to 40 total credits required. 12 to 72 months to complete program. *Concentrations:* economics, finance, financial economics.
MBA—Master of Business Administration Full-time and part-time. 30 to 58 total credits required. 12 to 72 months to complete program. *Concentrations:* business information science, decision sciences, economics, electronic commerce (e-commerce), finance, human resources, information management, international business, management, manpower administration, marketing, organizational management.
MS—Master of Science in Accountancy Full-time and part-time. 30 to 48 total credits required. 12 to 72 months to complete program. *Concentrations:* accounting.
MS—Master of Science in Computing and Information Systems Full-time and part-time. 33 to 54 total credits required. 12 to 72 months to complete program. *Concentrations:* business information science, management information systems, management systems analysis, system management.
MS—Master of Science in Economics and Finance Full-time and part-time. 30 to 48 total credits required. 12 to 72 months to complete program. *Concentrations:* economics, finance, financial economics.
MS—Master of Science in Marketing Research Full-time and part-time. 36 to 54 total credits required. 12 to 72 months to complete program. *Concentrations:* marketing, marketing research.

The School of Business at Southern Illinois University Edwardsville prepares students to be leaders in today's global economy. Faculty members provide the benefit of their real-world experience and impressive academic credentials through a curriculum that is focused on knowledge-based leadership. The M.B.A. degree requires 30 hours for those with appropriate undergraduate foundation courses in business. The program consists of four required and six elective courses. Up to 24 hours of foundation courses may be required. Program courses include External Environment of Business; International Business Environment: Leadership, Influence, and Managerial Effectiveness; and Strategic Management. Electives are in finance, management information systems, and marketing, with additional electives also available in accounting, economics, and management. Specializations in MIS and e-business are also available. Learning formats are flexible, with courses meeting one night a week for ten weeks or courses available concentrated into two weekends. These formats allow rapid completion of the degree. The School also offers master's degrees in accounting, computing and information science, economics and finance, and marketing research.

COSTS
Tuition, state resident: *Full-time* $1448. **Tuition, nonresident:** *Full-time* $2658. Tuition varies by local reciprocity agreements. **Graduate housing:** Room and board costs vary by number of occupants, type of accommodation, and type of board plan. *Typical cost:* $1650 (room only).

FINANCIAL AID (1999–2000)
61 students received aid, including fellowships, loans, research assistantships, scholarships, teaching assistantships, and work study. Aid is available to part-time students. **Financial Aid Contact** Ms. Marion Smithson, Director of Student Work and Financial Aid, Box 1060, Edwardsville, IL 62026. **Phone:** 618-650-3880. **Fax:** 618-650-3885. **E-mail:** msmiths@siue.edu.

RESOURCES AND SERVICES
Information about online services, personal computer policies, library resources, international exchange programs, internship programs, and placement services at this institution and others can be found at **www.petersons.com/mba**

International Students

19% of students enrolled are international students.

Services and Facilities Counseling/support services, ESL/language courses, international student housing. Financial aid is not available to international students.

Applying *Required:* TOEFL with recommended score of 550 (paper), proof of adequate funds, proof of health/immunizations.

International Student Contact Ms. Antoinette Liston, Advisor, Box 1616, Edwardsville, IL 62026. **Phone:** 618-650-3785. **E-mail:** aliston@siue.edu.

■ APPLICATION

Required Application form, baccalaureate/first degree, transcripts of college work. School will accept GMAT.

Deadlines and Fees *Deadlines:* 7/23 for fall, 12/10 for spring, 4/21 for summer, 7/23 for fall (international), 12/10 for spring (international), 4/21 for summer (international). *Application fee:* $25, $25 (international).

Application Contact Dr. Kathryn Martell, Associate Dean for Academic Affairs, Box 1051, Edwardsville, IL 62026-1051. **Phone:** 618-650-3412. **Fax:** 618-650-3979. **E-mail:** kmartel@siue.edu.

See full description on page 828.

University of Chicago

Chicago, Illinois

GRADUATE SCHOOL OF BUSINESS

Graduate Business Faculty

Full-time: 107	Part-time: 64

Student Body

Total: 2,843	
Full-time: 1,124	Average Age: 28
Part-time: 1,719	Women: 22%

Admissions

Applications: 5,750	Average GMAT: 690
Admitted: 1,697	Average GPA: 3.43
Enrolled: 1,130	

Costs (1999–2000)

Full-time tuition: $28,555 per academic year
Part-time tuition: $2802 per course

After Graduation (Class of 1998–99)

Employed within 3 months of graduation: 98%
Average starting salary: $82,372

Accreditation

AACSB—The International Association for Management Education

DEGREES IMBA • MBA

IMBA—International MBA Full-time. Fluency in second language. At least 76 total credits required. 15 to 60 months to complete program. *Concentrations:* accounting, business policy/strategy, economics, entrepreneurship, finance, financial management/planning, human resources, international business, management, management science, managerial economics, marketing, operations management, organizational behavior/development, production management, statistics.

MBA—Evening MBA Part-time. At least 66 total credits required. 30 to 60 months to complete program. *Concentrations:* accounting, business policy/strategy, economics, entrepreneurship, finance, financial management/planning, human resources, international business, management, management science, managerial economics, marketing, operations management, organizational behavior/development, production management, statistics.

MBA—Executive MBA, Asia Part-time. 10 years of work experience. 66 total credits required. 20 months to complete program.

MBA—Executive MBA, Europe Part-time. Average of 10 years work experience. 66 total credits required. 20 months to complete program.

MBA—Executive MBA, North America Part-time. 10 years of work experience. 66 total credits required. 20 months to complete program.

MBA—Full-time MBA Full-time. At least 66 total credits required. 12 to 60 months to complete program. *Concentrations:* accounting, economics, entrepreneurship, finance, human resources, industrial/labor relations, international business, management, marketing, operations management, organizational behavior/development, production management, statistics.

MBA—Weekend MBA Part-time. At least 66 total credits required. 30 to 60 months to complete program. *Concentrations:* accounting, business policy/strategy, economics, entrepreneurship, finance, financial management/planning, human resources, international business, management, management science,

managerial economics, marketing, operations management, organizational behavior/development, production management, statistics.

COSTS

Tuition *Full-time:* $28,020. *Part-time:* $2802 per course. **Required fees:** *Full-time* $535. *Part-time* $125 per term. Tuition and fees vary by academic program. **Graduate housing:** Room and board costs vary by campus location, number of occupants, and type of accommodation. *Typical cost:* $10,500 (including board).

FINANCIAL AID (1999–2000)

1200 students received aid, including grants, loans, scholarships, and work study. Aid is available to part-time students. Financial aid application deadline: 6/30. **Financial Aid Contact** Ms. Priscilla Parker, Associate Director, Financial Aid, 1101 East 58th Street, Chicago, IL 60637-1513. **Phone:** 773-702-3076. **Fax:** 773-834-1355. **E-mail:** priscilla.parker@gsb.uchicago.edu.

RESOURCES AND SERVICES

Information about online services, personal computer policies, library resources, international exchange programs, internship programs, and placement services at this institution and others can be found at **www.petersons.com/mba**

International Students

17% of students enrolled are international students.

Services and Facilities Counseling/support services, international student housing, international student organization, orientation, visa services. Financial aid is not available to international students.

Applying *Required:* TOEFL with recommended score of 600 (paper), proof of adequate funds, proof of health/immunizations.

International Student Contact Ms. Carol Swanberg, Director of Admissions and Financial Aid, Graduate School of Business, 1101 East 58th Street, Chicago, IL 60637-1513. **Phone:** 773-702-7369. **Fax:** 773-702-9085. **E-mail:** carol.swanberg@gsb.uchicago.edu.

■ APPLICATION

Required Application form, baccalaureate/first degree, essay, 2 letters of recommendation, personal statement, transcripts of college work. School will accept GMAT and GRE. **Recommended** Interview, resume/curriculum vitae, 3 years of work experience.

Deadlines and Fees *Deadlines:* 3/15 for fall, 3/15 for fall (international). *Application fee:* $150, $150 (international).

Application Contact Ms. Carol Swanberg, Director of Admissions and Financial Aid, Graduate School of Business, 1101 East 58th Street, Chicago, IL 60637-1513. **Phone:** 773-702-7369. **Fax:** 773-702-9085.

See full description on page 884.

University of Illinois at Chicago

Chicago, Illinois

COLLEGE OF BUSINESS ADMINISTRATION/MBA PROGRAMS

Graduate Business Faculty

Full-time: 70	Part-time: 39

Student Body

Total: 397	
Full-time: 101	Average Age: 26
Part-time: 296	Women: 38%

Admissions

Applications: 392	Average GMAT: 570
Admitted: 237	Average GPA: 3.3
Enrolled: 99	

Costs (1999–2000)

Full-time tuition: $10,416 per academic year (resident), $17,460 per academic year (nonresident)
Part-time tuition: $1818 per course (resident), $2992 per course (nonresident)

After Graduation (Class of 1998–99)

Employed within 3 months of graduation: 82%
Average starting salary: $56,500

Accreditation

AACSB—The International Association for Management Education

DEGREES MBA • MBA/MA • MBA/MIS • MBA/MPH • MBA/MS • MD/MBA

University of Illinois at Chicago (continued)

MBA—Master of Business Administration Full-time and part-time. 2-3 years work experience recommended. At least 54 total credits required. 16 to 72 months to complete program. *Concentrations:* accounting, decision sciences, economics, electronic commerce (e-commerce), entrepreneurship, finance, health care, information management, international business, management, management information systems, management systems analysis, marketing, operations management, organizational behavior/development, strategic management, statistics.

MBA/MA—MBA/MA in Economics Full-time and part-time. At least 72 total credits required. 30 to 72 months to complete program. *Concentrations:* economics.

MBA/MIS—Master of Business Administration/Master of Information Systems Full-time and part-time. At least 86 total credits required. 24 to 72 months to complete program. *Concentrations:* management information systems.

MBA/MPH—Master of Business Administration/Master of Public Health Full-time and part-time. At least 68 total credits required. 30 to 72 months to complete program. *Concentrations:* health care.

MBA/MS—MBA/MS in Accounting Full-time and part-time. At least 66 total credits required. 30 to 72 months to complete program. *Concentrations:* accounting.

MBA/MS—MBA/MS in Nursing Full-time and part-time. At least 67 total credits required. 24 to 72 months to complete program. *Concentrations:* health care.

MD/MBA—Doctor of Medicine/Master of Business Administration Full-time. Minimum of 60 months to complete program.

COSTS

Tuition, state resident: *Full-time* $10,416. *Part-time* $1818 per course. **Tuition, nonresident:** *Full-time* $17,460. *Part-time* $2992 per course. **Tuition, international:** *Full-time* $17,460. Tuition varies by number of courses or credits taken. **Graduate housing:** Room and board costs vary by campus location, number of occupants, and type of accommodation. *Typical cost:* $4300 (room only).

FINANCIAL AID (1999–2000)

25 students received aid, including fellowships, loans, research assistantships, teaching assistantships, and work study. Aid is available to part-time students. **Financial Aid Contact** Ms. Marsha Weiss, Director, Student Financial Aid, 1200 West Harrison, Suite 1892, Chicago, IL 60607. **Phone:** 312-996-3126. **Fax:** 312-996-3385. **E-mail:** mweiss@uic. edu.

RESOURCES AND SERVICES

Information about online services, personal computer policies, library resources, international exchange programs, internship programs, and placement services at this institution and others can be found at **www. petersons.com/mba**

International Students

13% of students enrolled are international students.

Services and Facilities Counseling/support services, ESL/language courses, international student organization, orientation, visa services. Financial aid is available to international students.

Applying *Required:* TOEFL with recommended score of 570 (paper), proof of adequate funds, proof of health/immunizations.

International Student Contact Dr. Joseph Cherian, Associate Dean, MBA Programs and Continuing Education, 815 West Van Buren, Suite 220, Chicago, IL 60607. **Phone:** 312-996-4573. **Fax:** 312-413-0338. **E-mail:** mba@uic.edu.

■ APPLICATION

Required GMAT, application form, baccalaureate/first degree, essay, 2 letters of recommendation, personal statement, resume/curriculum vitae, transcripts of college work. **Recommended** 2 years of work experience.

Deadlines and Fees *Deadlines:* 6/1 for fall, 11/15 for spring, 4/11 for summer, 4/1 for fall (international), 10/1 for spring (international), 3/1 for summer (international). *Application fee:* $40, $50 (international).

Application Contact Mr. Jack McCord, Associate Director, Marketing and Recruiting, 815 West Van Buren, Suite 220, Chicago, IL 60607. **Phone:** 312-996-4573. **Toll-free Phone:** 877-MBA-UIC1. **Fax:** 312-413-0338. **E-mail:** mba@uic.edu.

University of Illinois at Springfield

Springfield, Illinois

COLLEGE OF BUSINESS AND MANAGEMENT

Graduate Business Faculty
Full-time: 35   Part-time: 12

Student Body
Total: 377   Average Age: 33
Full-time: 72   Women: 42%
Part-time: 305

Admissions
Applications: 222   Average GMAT: 400
Admitted: 164   Average GPA: 3.13
Enrolled: 36

Costs (1999–2000)
Full-time tuition: N/R
Part-time tuition: $105 per credit hour (resident), $314 per credit hour (nonresident)

DEGREES MA • MBA • MS

MA—Master of Arts in Accountancy Full-time and part-time. At least 33 total credits required. 18 to 72 months to complete program. *Concentrations:* accounting.

MBA—Master of Business Administration Full-time and part-time. At least 48 total credits required. 24 to 72 months to complete program.

MS—Master of Science in Management Information Systems Full-time and part-time. *Distance learning option.* At least 44 total credits required. 24 to 72 months to complete program. *Concentrations:* management information systems.

COSTS

Tuition, state resident: *Part-time* $105 per credit hour. **Tuition, nonresident:** *Part-time* $314 per credit hour. Tuition varies by number of courses or credits taken. **Required fees:** *Full-time* $252. *Part-time* $70 per semester. Fees vary by number of courses or credits taken and campus location. **Graduate housing:** Room and board costs vary by number of occupants and type of accommodation. *Typical cost:* $2004 (room only).

FINANCIAL AID (1999–2000)

Research assistantships, scholarships, and work study. Aid is available to part-time students. Financial aid application deadline: 6/1. **Financial Aid Contact** Mr. Gerard Joseph, Director, Financial Assistance, F-20E, Springfield, IL 62794-9243. **Phone:** 217-206-6724. **Fax:** 217-206-6620. **E-mail:** joseph.gerard@uis.edu.

RESOURCES AND SERVICES

Information about online services, personal computer policies, library resources, international exchange programs, internship programs, and placement services at this institution and others can be found at **www. petersons.com/mba**

International Students

6% of students enrolled are international students.

Services and Facilities Counseling/support services, ESL/language courses, visa services, host family program; income tax seminar. Financial aid is available to international students.

Applying *Required:* TOEFL with recommended score of 550 (paper), proof of adequate funds, proof of health/immunizations.

International Student Contact Mr. Jonathan GoldbergBelle, Director, International Student Services, International Student Services J-167, Springfield, IL 62794-9243. **Phone:** 217-206-6678. **Fax:** 217-206-7280. **E-mail:** jgoldl@uis. edu.

■ APPLICATION

Required GMAT, application form, baccalaureate/first degree, essay, letter(s) of recommendation, transcripts of college work.

Deadlines and Fees Applications for domestic students are processed on a rolling basis. *Deadlines:* 6/1 for fall (international), 11/1 for spring (international), 4/1 for summer (international).

Application Contact Office of Enrollment Services, University of Illinois at Springfield, Springfield, IL 62794-9243. **Phone:** 217-206-6626. **Toll-free Phone:** 800-252-8533. **Fax:** 217-206-6620. **E-mail:** admissions@uis.edu.

University of Illinois at Urbana–Champaign

Urbana, Illinois

COLLEGE OF COMMERCE AND BUSINESS ADMINISTRATION

Graduate Business Faculty
Full-time: 109   Part-time: 49

Student Body
Total: 380
Full-time: 380
Average Age: 27
Women: 35%

Admissions
Applications: 950
Admitted: 480
Enrolled: 180
Average GMAT: 619
Average GPA: 3.4

Costs (1999–2000)
Full-time tuition: $11,846 per academic year (resident), $19,204 per academic year (nonresident)
Part-time tuition: N/R

After Graduation (Class of 1998–99)
Employed within 3 months of graduation: 91.5%
Average starting salary: $61,804

Accreditation
AACSB—The International Association for Management Education

DEGREES JD/MBA • MAS • MBA • MBA/MA • MBA/ME • MBA/MS • MD/MBA • MS • MSA • MSF • MSPE • MST

JD/MBA—Juris Doctor/Master of Business Administration Full-time. 85 to 86 total credits required. Minimum of 45 months to complete program. *Concentrations:* management.

MAS—Master of Accounting Science Full-time. At least 32 total credits required. Minimum of 12 months to complete program. *Concentrations:* accounting.

MBA—Executive MBA Full-time. At least 18 total credits required. Minimum of 18 months to complete program. *Concentrations:* management.

MBA—Master of Business Administration Full-time. At least 18 total credits required. Minimum of 21 months to complete program. *Concentrations:* accounting, agribusiness, entrepreneurship, environmental economics/management, finance, financial economics, financial management/planning, health care, human resources, information management, international economics, international finance, international management, management systems analysis, marketing, operations management, organizational management, risk management, strategic management, system management, technology management.

MBA/MA—Master of Business Administration/Master of Arts in Architecture Full-time. At least 20 total credits required. Minimum of 21 months to complete program. *Concentrations:* management.

MBA/MA—Master of Business Administration/Master of Arts in Journalism Full-time. 18 to 19 total credits required. 21 to 28 months to complete program. *Concentrations:* management.

MBA/ME—Master of Business Administration/Master of Education Full-time. 18 to 19 total credits required. 21 to 28 months to complete program. *Concentrations:* human resources, management.

MBA/MS—Master of Business Administration/Master of Science in Civil Engineering Full-time. 18 to 19 total credits required. 21 to 28 months to complete program. *Concentrations:* management.

MBA/MS—Master of Business Administration/Master of Science in Computer Science Full-time. 19 to 20 total credits required. 21 to 28 months to complete program. *Concentrations:* management.

MBA/MS—Master of Business Administration/Master of Science in Electrical Engineering Full-time. 18 to 19 total credits required. 21 to 28 months to complete program. *Concentrations:* management.

MBA/MS—Master of Business Administration/Master of Science in General Engineering Full-time. At least 18 total credits required. 21 to 28 months to complete program. *Concentrations:* management.

MBA/MS—Master of Business Administration/Master of Science in Industrial Engineering Full-time. 18 to 19 total credits required. 21 to 28 months to complete program. *Concentrations:* management.

MBA/MS—Master of Business Administration/Master of Science in Mechanical Engineering Full-time. 18 to 19 total credits required. 21 to 28 months to complete program. *Concentrations:* management.

MBA/MS—Master of Business Administration/Master of Science Full-time. 18 to 19 total credits required. 21 to 28 months to complete program. *Concentrations:* management.

MD/MBA—Doctor of Medicine/Master of Business Administration Full-time. At least 196 total credits required. Minimum of 57 months to complete program. *Concentrations:* management.

MS—Master of Science in Business Administration Full-time. 2-5 years of work experience required. At least 40 total credits required. 12 months to complete program. *Concentrations:* management.

MSA—Master of Science in Accountancy Full-time. At least 32 total credits required. Minimum of 12 months to complete program. *Concentrations:* accounting.

MSF—Master of Science in Finance Full-time. 10 to 12 total credits required. 12 to 24 months to complete program. *Concentrations:* banking, finance, financial economics, financial management/planning, insurance, international finance, real estate, risk management.

MSPE—Master of Science in Policy Economics Full-time. At least 10 total credits required. 12 to 24 months to complete program. *Concentrations:* developmental economics, economics, environmental economics/management, financial economics, industrial administration/management, international banking, international business, international economics, managerial economics, public policy and administration.

MST—Master of Science in Taxation Full-time. At least 32 total credits required. Minimum of 12 months to complete program. *Concentrations:* accounting, taxation.

COSTS
Tuition, state resident: *Full-time* $11,846. **Tuition, nonresident:** *Full-time* $19,204. **Tuition, international:** *Full-time* $19,204. **Required fees:** Fees vary by number of courses or credits taken. **Graduate housing:** Room and board costs vary by campus location, number of occupants, type of accommodation, and type of board plan. *Typical cost:* $7000 (including board).

FINANCIAL AID (1999–2000)
220 students received aid, including fellowships, grants, loans, and scholarships. Financial aid application deadline: 4/1. **Financial Aid Contact** Mrs. Camille Gilmore, Director of Recruiting, Admissions and Marketing, 1407 West Gregory Drive, 410 David Kinley Hall, Urbana, IL 61801. **Phone:** 217-244-7602. **Fax:** 217-333-1156.

RESOURCES AND SERVICES
Information about online services, personal computer policies, library resources, international exchange programs, internship programs, and placement services at this institution and others can be found at **www.petersons.com/mba**

International Students
45% of students enrolled are international students.

Services and Facilities Counseling/support services, ESL/language courses, visa services. Financial aid is available to international students.
Applying *Required:* TOEFL with recommended score of 550 (paper), proof of adequate funds, proof of health/immunizations.

International Student Contact Mrs. Camille Gilmore, Director of Recruiting, Admissions and Marketing, 1407 West Gregory Drive, 410 David Kinley Hall, Urbana, IL 61801. **Phone:** 217-244-7602. **Fax:** 217-333-1156. **E-mail:** mba@uiuc.edu.

■ APPLICATION
Required GMAT, application form, baccalaureate/first degree, essay, 3 letters of recommendation, personal statement, resume/curriculum vitae, transcripts of college work. School will accept GRE. **Recommended** Interview, 3 years of work experience.

Deadlines and Fees *Deadlines:* 4/1 for fall, 2/1 for fall (international). *Application fee:* $40, $50 (international).

Application Contact Mrs. Camille Gilmore, Director of Recruiting, Admissions and Marketing, 1407 West Gregory Drive, 410 David Kinley Hall, Urbana, IL 61801. **Phone:** 217-244-7602. **Toll-free Phone:** 800-MBA-UIUC. **Fax:** 217-333-1156. **E-mail:** mba@uiuc.edu.

See full description on page 906.

University of St. Francis

Joliet, Illinois

COLLEGE OF GRADUATE STUDIES

Graduate Business Faculty
Full-time: 6   Part-time: 150

Student Body
Total: 1,250
Part-time: 1,250
Average Age: 40

University of St. Francis (continued)

Admissions
Admitted: 348
Enrolled: 327

Average GPA: 3

Costs (1999–2000)
Full-time tuition: N/R
Part-time tuition: $400 per credit hour

After Graduation (Class of 1998–99)
Employed within 3 months of graduation: 100%

DEGREES MBA • MS

MBA—Master of Business Administration Full-time and part-time. *Distance learning option.* 2 years of management experience required. 36 to 48 total credits required. 12 to 72 months to complete program. *Concentrations:* health care, management, organizational behavior/development.

MS—MS in Continuing Education and Training Technology Full-time and part-time. 2 years of work experience required. At least 36 total credits required. 12 to 72 months to complete program.

MS—Master of Science in Continuing Education and Training Management Full-time and part-time. 2 years of work experience required. 36 to 40 total credits required. 12 to 72 months to complete program.

MS—Master of Science in Health Services Administration Full-time and part-time. *Distance learning option.* 2 years of health care experience required. At least 36 total credits required. 12 to 72 months to complete program.

MS—Master of Science in Management Full-time and part-time. *Distance learning option.* 2 years of management experience required. At least 36 total credits required. 12 to 72 months to complete program. *Concentrations:* health care, management, organizational behavior/development.

The M.B.A. at the University of St. Francis (USF) is for business professionals who seek top-management career advancement. The program has three concentrations: management, continuing education and training, and health services. The faculty has both academic credentials and real-world experience, and the curriculum includes theory but emphasizes application to the business world. A Business Advisory Board of executives, entrepreneurs, and educators ensures a current and relevant program. Technology is used by faculty members and students in class. Free computer training is available to students, as are online research services. The M.B.A. is 36-48 credit hours, depending on a student's undergraduate major and business experience. It can be completed in one to three years. All courses are offered in the evening or on weekends, with an average class size of 15 to 20 students. GRE or GMAT scores may not be required if the applicant has two years of business experience. The application process is simple and can proceed while a student begins the first class. Graduate assistantships and location coordinator positions are available to defray tuition costs. Student loans are available. Tuition can be paid in three interest-free installments or can be delayed for employment reimbursement. All courses are available on line through the USF Web site at http://www.stfrancis.edu.

COSTS
Tuition *Part-time:* $400 per credit hour. Tuition varies by academic program.

FINANCIAL AID (1999–2000)
Loans and research assistantships. Aid is available to part-time students. **Financial Aid Contact** Mr. Bruce Foote, Director, Financial Aid Office, 500 Wilcox, Joliet, IL 60435. **Phone:** 815-740-3403. **Fax:** 815-740-3537. **E-mail:** bfoote@stfrancis.edu.

RESOURCES AND SERVICES
Information about online services, personal computer policies, library resources, international exchange programs, internship programs, and placement services at this institution and others can be found at **www. petersons.com/mba**

International Students
Services and Facilities Financial aid is not available to international students. **Applying** *Required:* TOEFL with recommended score of 550 (paper), proof of adequate funds, proof of health/immunizations. **International Student Contact** Mr. Eric Gunnick, Associate Registrar, 500 Wilcox Street, Joliet, IL 60435-6169. **Phone:** 815-744-4245. **E-mail:** egunnick@stfrancis. edu.

■ APPLICATION
Required Application form, baccalaureate/first degree, essay, 2 letters of recommendation, personal statement, transcripts of college work, 2 years of work experience. **Recommended** Interview.
Deadlines and Fees *Application fee:* $25, $25 (international).

Application Contact Dr. Joy Thompson, Associate Dean, College of Graduate Studies, 500 Wilcox, Joliet, IL, 60435. **Phone:** 800-735-4723. **Fax:** 815-740-3537. **E-mail:** jthompson@stfrancis.edu.

Western Illinois University
Macomb, Illinois

COLLEGE OF BUSINESS AND TECHNOLOGY

Graduate Business Faculty
Full-time: 87

Student Body
Total: 132	Average Age: 24
Full-time: 85	Women: 42%
Part-time: 47	

Admissions
Applications: 250	Average GMAT: 530
Admitted: 125	Average GPA: 3.35
Enrolled: 75	

Costs (1999–2000)
Full-time tuition: N/R
Part-time tuition: $96 per credit (resident), $288 per credit (nonresident)

Accreditation
AACSB—The International Association for Management Education

DEGREE MBA

MBA—Master of Business Administration Full-time and part-time. *Distance learning option.* 33 to 60 total credits required. 12 to 24 months to complete program. *Concentrations:* accounting, decision sciences, economics, entrepreneurship, finance, human resources, information management, international business, logistics, management, management information systems, marketing, project management, taxation.

COSTS
Tuition, state resident: *Part-time* $96 per credit. **Tuition, nonresident:** *Part-time* $288 per credit. **Required fees:** Tuition and fees vary by number of courses or credits taken. **Graduate housing:** Room and board costs vary by number of occupants, type of accommodation, and type of board plan. *Typical cost:* $4193 (including board).

FINANCIAL AID (1999–2000)
45 students received aid, including research assistantships, scholarships, and teaching assistantships. **Financial Aid Contact** Mr. William Bushaw, Director of Financial Aid, 1 University Circle, Macomb, IL 61455-1390. **Phone:** 309-298-2446. **Fax:** 309-298-2353.

RESOURCES AND SERVICES
Information about online services, personal computer policies, library resources, international exchange programs, internship programs, and placement services at this institution and others can be found at **www. petersons.com/mba**

International Students
15% of students enrolled are international students.

Services and Facilities Counseling/support services, ESL/language courses, international student housing, visa services. Financial aid is not available to international students.
Applying *Required:* TOEFL with recommended score of 550 (paper), proof of adequate funds, proof of health/immunizations.

International Student Contact Mr. Steve Risch, Director of International Admissions, School of Graduate and International Studies, 1 University Circle, Macomb, IL 61455-1309. **Phone:** 309-298-1806.

■ APPLICATION
Required GMAT, application form, baccalaureate/first degree, transcripts of college work.

Deadlines and Fees Applications for domestic and international students are processed on a rolling basis.

Application Contact Dr. David Bloomberg, Director of MBA Program, College of Business and Technology, 1 University Circle, Macomb, IL 61455-1390. **Phone:** 309-298-2442. **Fax:** 309-298-1039. **E-mail:** dj_bloomberg@wiu.edu.

INDIANA

Ball State University

Muncie, Indiana

COLLEGE OF BUSINESS

Graduate Business Faculty
Full-time: 66

Student Body
Total: 177
Full-time: 34
Part-time: 143

Average Age: 29
Women: 20%

Admissions
Applications: 151
Admitted: 118
Enrolled: 79

Average GMAT: 540
Average GPA: 3.17

Costs (1999–2000)
Full-time tuition: N/R
Part-time tuition: $4300 per semester (resident), $11,000 per semester (nonresident)

Accreditation
AACSB—The International Association for Management Education

DEGREES MBA

MBA—Master of Business Administration in Applied Business Economics Full-time and part-time. At least 36 total credits required. 12 to 72 months to complete program. *Concentrations:* economics, managerial economics.

MBA—Master of Business Administration in Entrepreneurship Full-time and part-time. *Distance learning option.* At least 36 total credits required. 12 to 72 months to complete program. *Concentrations:* entrepreneurship.

MBA—Master of Business Administration in Finance Full-time and part-time. *Distance learning option.* At least 36 total credits required. 12 to 72 months to complete program. *Concentrations:* finance, financial management/planning.

MBA—Master of Business Administration in Human Resource Management Full-time and part-time. At least 36 total credits required. 12 to 72 months to complete program. *Concentrations:* human resources.

MBA—Master of Business Administration in Information Systems Full-time and part-time. At least 36 total credits required. 12 to 72 months to complete program. *Concentrations:* information management, management information systems, management systems analysis.

MBA—Master of Business Administration in Operations and Manufacturing Full-time and part-time. *Distance learning option.* At least 36 total credits required. 12 to 72 months to complete program. *Concentrations:* manufacturing management, operations management, production management.

COSTS

Tuition, state resident: *Part-time* $4300 per semester. **Tuition, nonresident:** *Part-time* $11,000 per semester. Tuition varies by number of courses or credits taken and campus location. **Required fees:** *Full-time* $500. *Part-time* $0 per semester. **Graduate housing:** Room and board costs vary by campus location, number of occupants, type of accommodation, and type of board plan. *Typical cost:* $5800 (including board).

FINANCIAL AID (1999–2000)

Loans, research assistantships, scholarships, and teaching assistantships. Aid is available to part-time students. **Financial Aid Contact** Clarence Casazza, Director of Scholarships and Financial Aid, Scholarships and Financial Aid, LU 245, Muncie, IN 47306. **Phone:** 765-285-5600. **Fax:** 765-285-2464. **E-mail:** 00ccasazza@bsu.edu.

RESOURCES AND SERVICES

Information about online services, personal computer policies, library resources, international exchange programs, internship programs, and placement services at this institution and others can be found at **www.petersons.com/mba**

International Students

10% of students enrolled are international students.

Services and Facilities Counseling/support services, ESL/language courses, international student organization, visa services. Financial aid is available to international students.
Applying *Required:* TOEFL with recommended score of 213 (computer) or 550 (paper), proof of adequate funds, proof of health/immunizations.

International Student Contact Jim Coffin, Director of International Programs, 708 North Calvert, Muncie, IN 47306. **Phone:** 765-285-5422. **Fax:** 765-285-3710. **E-mail:** jlcoffin@bsu.edu.

▪ APPLICATION

Required GMAT, application form, baccalaureate/first degree, resume/curriculum vitae, transcripts of college work. **Recommended** Personal statement.
Deadlines and Fees *Deadlines:* 1/1 for fall (international), 7/1 for spring (international). *Application fee:* $35, $40 (international).
Application Contact Tamara Estep, Director of Graduate Business Programs, College of Business, WB 146, Muncie, IN 47306. **Phone:** 765-285-1931. **Fax:** 765-285-8818. **E-mail:** bsumba@bsu.edu.

Bethel College

Mishawaka, Indiana

PROGRAM IN BUSINESS ADMINISTRATION

Graduate Business Faculty
Full-time: 5

Part-time: 3

Student Body
Total: 24
Part-time: 24

Average Age: 32
Women: 42%

Admissions
Applications: 12
Admitted: 11
Enrolled: 8

Average GMAT: 496
Average GPA: 3.29

Costs (1999–2000)
Full-time tuition: N/R
Part-time tuition: $300 per credit hour

DEGREE MBA

MBA—Master of Business Administration Part-time. At least 36 total credits required. 24 to 48 months to complete program. *Concentrations:* management.

COSTS

Tuition *Part-time:* $300 per credit hour.

FINANCIAL AID (1999–2000)

Financial Aid Contact Mr. Guy Fisher, Director of Financial Aid, 1001 West McKinley Avenue, Mishawaka, IN 46545-5591. **Phone:** 219-257-3317. **Fax:** 219-257-3326. **E-mail:** fisherg@bethel-in.edu.

RESOURCES AND SERVICES

Information about online services, personal computer policies, library resources, international exchange programs, internship programs, and placement services at this institution and others can be found at **www.petersons.com/mba**

International Students

17% of students enrolled are international students.

Services and Facilities Counseling/support services, visa services. Financial aid is not available to international students.
Applying *Required:* TOEFL with recommended score of 220 (computer) or 560 (paper), proof of adequate funds.
International Student Contact Ms. Andrea Helmuth, Director of Admissions, 1001 West McKinley Avenue, Mishawaka, IN 46545-5591. **Phone:** 219-257-3339. **Fax:** 219-257-3335. **E-mail:** helmut@bethel-in.edu.

▪ APPLICATION

Required GMAT, application form, baccalaureate/first degree, interview, personal statement, transcripts of college work, 2 years of work experience.
Deadlines and Fees Applications for domestic and international students are processed on a rolling basis. *Application fee:* $25, $25 (international).
Application Contact Dr. Bradley Smith, Director of MBA Program, 1001 West McKinley Avenue, Mishawaka, IN 46545-5591. **Phone:** 219-257-3363. **Fax:** 219-257-7617. **E-mail:** smithb@bethel-in.edu.

Butler University

Indianapolis, Indiana

COLLEGE OF BUSINESS ADMINISTRATION

Accreditation
AACSB—The International Association for Management Education

Butler University (continued)

DEGREE MBA

MBA—Master of Business Administration Full-time and part-time. 30 to 58 total credits required. 12 to 60 months to complete program. *Concentrations:* accounting, administration, finance, leadership, marketing.

RESOURCES AND SERVICES
Information about online services, personal computer policies, library resources, international exchange programs, internship programs, and placement services at this institution and others can be found at **www. petersons.com/mba**

International Students
Services and Facilities Counseling/support services, ESL/language courses, visa services. Financial aid is not available to international students.
International Student Contact Director, International Studies, 4600 Sunset Avenue, Indianapolis, IN 46208-3185. **Phone:** 317-940-9888. **Fax:** 317-940-6421.

■ APPLICATION
Application Contact William K. Templeton, Director of MBA Program, 4600 Sunset Avenue, Indianapolis, IN 46208-3485. **Phone:** 317-940-9221. **Fax:** 317-940-9455. **E-mail:** templeton@butler.edu.

Indiana Institute of Technology

Fort Wayne, Indiana

PROGRAM IN BUSINESS ADMINISTRATION

DEGREE MBA

MBA—Extended Studies Division MBA Full-time and part-time. 39 to 45 total credits required. 12 to 24 months to complete program. *Concentrations:* entrepreneurship, human resources, management, marketing.

RESOURCES AND SERVICES
Information about online services, personal computer policies, library resources, international exchange programs, internship programs, and placement services at this institution and others can be found at **www. petersons.com/mba**

International Students
Services and Facilities Counseling/support services, ESL/language courses. Financial aid is not available to international students.
International Student Contact Mr. Tom Filus, Director of Admissions, 1600 East Washington Boulevard, Fort Wayne, IN 46803. **Phone:** 219-422-5561 Ext. 2251. **E-mail:** filus@indtech.edu.

■ APPLICATION
Application Contact Mrs. Kathleen Stahl, Director of Admissions—Extended Studies Division, 1600 East Washington Boulevard, Fort Wayne, IN 46803. **Phone:** 219-422-5561 Ext. 2278. **Toll-free Phone:** 888-666-TECH. **Fax:** 219-422-1518. **E-mail:** stahl@indtech.edu.

Indiana State University

Terre Haute, Indiana

SCHOOL OF BUSINESS

Graduate Business Faculty
Full-time: 30   Part-time: 2

Student Body
Total: 142
Full-time: 22   Average Age: 37
Part-time: 120   Women: 43%

Admissions
Applications: 100   Average GMAT: 530
Admitted: 50   Average GPA: 3.1

Costs (1999–2000)
Full-time tuition: $1713 per academic year (resident), $4277 per academic year (nonresident)
Part-time tuition: $123 per credit hour (resident), $300 per credit hour (nonresident)

After Graduation (Class of 1998–99)
Employed within 3 months of graduation: 95%
Average starting salary: $42,000

Accreditation
AACSB—The International Association for Management Education

DEGREE MBA

MBA—Master of Business Administration Full-time and part-time. 32 to 72 total credits required. 18 to 60 months to complete program. *Concentrations:* electronic commerce (e-commerce), financial management/planning.

COSTS
Tuition, state resident: *Full-time* $1713. *Part-time* $123 per credit hour. **Tuition, nonresident:** *Full-time* $4277. *Part-time* $300 per credit hour.

FINANCIAL AID (1999–2000)
17 students received aid, including research assistantships. Financial aid application deadline: 3/1. **Financial Aid Contact** Dr. Dale Varble, Associate Dean and MBA Coordinator, School of Business, Terre Haute, IN 47809-5402. **Phone:** 812-237-2002. **Fax:** 812-237-8720. **E-mail:** mba@befac.indstate.edu.

RESOURCES AND SERVICES
Information about online services, personal computer policies, library resources, international exchange programs, internship programs, and placement services at this institution and others can be found at **www. petersons.com/mba**

International Students
25% of students enrolled are international students.

Services and Facilities Counseling/support services, ESL/language courses, housing location assistance, international student organization, orientation, visa services, academic advising. Financial aid is available to international students.
Applying *Required:* TOEFL with recommended score of 550 (paper), proof of adequate funds, proof of health/immunizations.
International Student Contact Dr. Gaston Fernandez, Director, International Student and Scholar Services, Erickson Hall 611, Terre Haute, IN 47809-1401. **Phone:** 812-237-2440. **Fax:** 812-237-3602. **E-mail:** iac@indstate.edu.

■ APPLICATION
Required GMAT, application form, baccalaureate/first degree, personal statement, transcripts of college work. School will accept GRE. **Recommended** Work experience.
Deadlines and Fees *Deadlines:* 7/1 for fall, 11/1 for spring, 5/1 for summer, 7/1 for fall (international), 11/1 for spring (international), 5/1 for summer (international). *Application fee:* $35, $35 (international).
Application Contact Mr. William Minnis, MBA Coordinator, School of Business, Terre Haute, IN 47809-5402. **Phone:** 812-237-2002. **Fax:** 812-237-8720. **E-mail:** mba@befac.indstate.edu.

Indiana University Bloomington

Bloomington, Indiana

KELLEY SCHOOL OF BUSINESS

Graduate Business Faculty
Full-time: 110   Part-time: 39

Student Body
Total: 558   Average Age: 28
Full-time: 558   Women: 27%

Admissions
Applications: 1,770   Average GMAT: 634
Admitted: 626   Average GPA: 3.3
Enrolled: 263

Costs (1999–2000)
Full-time tuition: $9339 per academic year (resident), $18,117 per academic year (nonresident)
Part-time tuition: N/R

After Graduation (Class of 1998–99)
Employed within 3 months of graduation: 95%
Average starting salary: $74,000

Accreditation
AACSB—The International Association for Management Education

DEGREES JD/MBA • MBA • MBA/MS

JD/MBA—Juris Doctor/Master of Business Administration Full-time. At least 118 total credits required. 48 to 84 months to complete program. *Concentrations:* economics, electronic commerce (e-commerce), finance, human resources, international management, management consulting, management information systems, marketing, new venture management, operations management.

MBA—Master of Business Administration Full-time. At least 54 total credits required. 15 to 84 months to complete program. *Concentrations:* economics, electronic commerce (e-commerce), finance, human resources, international management, management consulting, management information systems, marketing, new venture management, operations management.

MBA/MS—Master of Business Administration/Master of Science in East Asian Studies Full-time. At least 64 total credits required. 36 to 84 months to complete program.

MBA/MS—Master of Business Administration/Master of Science in Russian and East European Studies Full-time. At least 64 total credits required. 36 to 84 months to complete program.

MBA/MS—Master of Business Administration/Master of Science in West European Studies Full-time. At least 64 total credits required. 36 to 84 months to complete program.

Many M.B.A. programs give the impression that business is tidy, that it is neatly divided up into functional categories, that business decisions come with ample time frames built in, and that management problems lend themselves easily to textbook solutions. The Indiana M.B.A. is different. Business is not about theory and abstractions. It is about fast-paced life in the marketplace. The Indiana M.B.A. program takes the focus out of the classroom and puts it in the boardroom, or on the trading floor, or in the corridor after a high-powered meeting, or in the quiet of an office at 11 p.m. as solutions are finally discovered. That is business, and Indiana M.B.A. graduates are prepared to deal with it.

M.B.A. students at Indiana participate in a breakthrough M.B.A. curriculum. There are no academic barriers. Students maneuver within an M.B.A. structure that is based on integration, not fragmentation. Practically and philosophically, the program is about synthesis: gathering information, linking it together, and finding the connections. Teamwork—a common way of working in corporations these days—is a major focus among both the faculty members and the students.

The Kelley M.B.A. program at Indiana University is a leader in graduate management education—an innovator preparing for the twenty-first century of business.

COSTS
Tuition, state resident: *Full-time* $8779. **Tuition, nonresident:** *Full-time* $17,557. **Required fees:** *Full-time* $560. Tuition and fees vary by number of courses or credits taken and academic program. **Graduate housing:** Room and board costs vary by number of occupants, type of accommodation, and type of board plan. *Typical cost:* $6150 (including board).

FINANCIAL AID (1999–2000)
499 students received aid, including fellowships, loans, research assistantships, scholarships, and teaching assistantships. Financial aid application deadline: 3/1. **Financial Aid Contact** Mr. Eric Pfeffinger, Associate Director of Financial Aid, MBA, Kelley School of Business, Room 254, 1309 East 10th Street, Bloomington, IN 47405-1701. **Phone:** 812-855-8006. **Fax:** 812-855-9039. **E-mail:** epfeffin@indiana.edu.

RESOURCES AND SERVICES
Information about online services, personal computer policies, library resources, international exchange programs, internship programs, and placement services at this institution and others can be found at **www.petersons.com/mba**

International Students
25% of students enrolled are international students.
Services and Facilities Counseling/support services, ESL/language courses, housing location assistance, international student housing, international student organization, orientation, visa services. Financial aid is available to international students.
Applying *Required:* TOEFL with recommended score of 580 (paper), proof of adequate funds, proof of health/immunizations.
International Student Contact Ms. Christine Davis, Director of Graduate Student Services, Kelley School of Business, Room 254, 1309 East 10th Street, Bloomington, IN 47405-1701. **Phone:** 812-855-8006. **Fax:** 812-855-9039. **E-mail:** cdavis@indiana.edu.

■ APPLICATION
Required GMAT, application form, baccalaureate/first degree, essay, 2 letters of recommendation, personal statement, resume/curriculum vitae, transcripts of college work. **Recommended** Interview, work experience.

Deadlines and Fees *Deadlines:* 4/15 for fall, 3/1 for fall (international). *Application fee:* $75, $75 (international).
Application Contact Mr. James Holmen, Director of Admissions and Financial Aid, Kelley School of Business, Room 254, 1309 East 10th Street, Bloomington, IN 47405-1701. **Phone:** 812-855-8006. **Fax:** 812-855-9039. **E-mail:** mbaoffice@indiana.edu.

See full description on page 684.

Indiana University Kokomo
Kokomo, Indiana
DIVISION OF BUSINESS AND ECONOMICS
DEGREE MBA

MBA—Master of Business Administration Full-time and part-time. 35 to 59 total credits required. 24 to 48 months to complete program. *Concentrations:* management.

RESOURCES AND SERVICES
Information about online services, personal computer policies, library resources, international exchange programs, internship programs, and placement services at this institution and others can be found at **www.petersons.com/mba**

International Students
Services and Facilities Counseling/support services, ESL/language courses, visa services. Financial aid is not available to international students.
International Student Contact Mr. Kenneth A. Rogers, Associate Dean and Director, International Services, 306 Franklin, Bloomington, IN 46904-9003. **Phone:** 812-855-9086. **Fax:** 812-855-4418. **E-mail:** intlserv@indiana.edu.

■ APPLICATION
Application Contact Dr. Dilip Pendse, MBA Director, PO Box 9003, Kokomo, IN 46904-9003. **Phone:** 765-455-9279. **Fax:** 765-455-9348. **E-mail:** dpendse@iuk.edu.

Indiana University Northwest
Gary, Indiana
DIVISION OF BUSINESS AND ECONOMICS

Graduate Business Faculty
Full-time: 16 — Part-time: 4

Student Body
Total: 195 — Average Age: 30
Full-time: 9 — Women: 41%
Part-time: 186

Admissions
Applications: 93 — Average GMAT: 500
Admitted: 69 — Average GPA: 3.1
Enrolled: 60

Costs (1999–2000)
Full-time tuition: N/R
Part-time tuition: $147 per credit hour (resident), $344 per credit hour (nonresident)

Accreditation
AACSB—The International Association for Management Education

DEGREES M Acc • MBA

M Acc—Evening Master of Accountancy Part-time. At least 30 total credits required. 24 to 72 months to complete program. *Concentrations:* accounting.
MBA—Evening MBA Full-time and part-time. At least 54 total credits required. 30 to 72 months to complete program. *Concentrations:* finance, human resources, management, marketing, organizational behavior/development.

COSTS
Tuition, state resident: *Part-time* $147 per credit hour. **Tuition, nonresident:** *Part-time* $344 per credit hour. Tuition varies by academic program.

FINANCIAL AID (1999–2000)
7 students received aid, including loans, scholarships, and work study. Aid is available to part-time students. Financial aid application deadline: 7/15. **Financial Aid Contact** William Lee, Director, Financial Aid, 3400 Broadway, Gary, IN 46408-1197. **Phone:** 219-980-6778.

Indiana University Northwest (continued)

RESOURCES AND SERVICES

Information about online services, personal computer policies, library resources, international exchange programs, internship programs, and placement services at this institution and others can be found at **www.petersons.com/mba**

International Students

4% of students enrolled are international students.

Services and Facilities Visa services. Financial aid is not available to international students.

Applying *Required:* TOEFL, proof of adequate funds, proof of health/immunizations.

International Student Contact Anne Palmer, Senior Director of International Admissions, International Admissions, 300 North Jordan, Bloomington, IN 47405. **Phone:** 812-855-4306.

■ APPLICATION

Required GMAT, application form, baccalaureate/first degree, 1 letter of recommendation, personal statement, transcripts of college work.

Deadlines and Fees Applications for domestic and international students are processed on a rolling basis. *Application fee:* $25, $40 (international).

Application Contact Kathryn Lantz, Director, Undergraduate and Graduate Programs in Business, Division of Business and Economics, 3400 Broadway, Gary, IN 46408-1197. **Phone:** 219-980-6635. **Fax:** 219-980-6916. **E-mail:** kathryn@iunbus1.iun.indiana.edu.

Indiana University–Purdue University Fort Wayne

Fort Wayne, Indiana

SCHOOL OF BUSINESS AND MANAGEMENT SCIENCES

Accreditation
AACSB—The International Association for Management Education

DEGREES MBA • MPA

MBA—Master of Business Administration Full-time and part-time. 32 to 59 total credits required. 18 to 72 months to complete program. *Concentrations:* management, strategic management.

MPA—Master of Public Affairs At least 48 total credits required. *Concentrations:* health care, public management, public policy and administration.

RESOURCES AND SERVICES

Information about online services, personal computer policies, library resources, international exchange programs, internship programs, and placement services at this institution and others can be found at **www.petersons.com/mba**

International Students

Services and Facilities Counseling/support services, ESL/language courses, visa services. Financial aid is not available to international students.

International Student Contact Dr. Ali Rassuli, Director of Graduate Studies in Business, School of Business and Management Sciences, Neff 366, 2101 Coliseum Boulevard East, Fort Wayne, IN 46805-1499. **Phone:** 219-481-6498. **Fax:** 219-481-6879.

■ APPLICATION

Application Contact Ms. Lorrie Williams, Secretary, MBA Program, School of Business and Management Sciences, Neff 366, 2101 Coliseum Boulevard East, Fort Wayne, IN 46805-1499. **Phone:** 219-481-6498. **Fax:** 219-481-6879. **E-mail:** williaml@ipfw.edu.

Indiana University–Purdue University Indianapolis

Indianapolis, Indiana

SCHOOL OF BUSINESS

Graduate Business Faculty
Full-time: 28

Student Body
Total: 318
Part-time: 318

Average Age: 29
Women: 23%

Admissions
Applications: 124
Admitted: 75
Enrolled: 61

Average GMAT: 600
Average GPA: 3.3

Costs (1999–2000)
Full-time tuition: N/R
Part-time tuition: $250 per credit hour (resident), $500 per credit hour (nonresident)

DEGREES JD/MBA • MBA • MBA/MHA • MPA

JD/MBA—Juris Doctor/Master of Business Administration Full-time. At least 119 total credits required. 48 to 60 months to complete program. *Concentrations:* management.

MBA—Kelley Direct Online MBA *Distance learning option.* 48 total credits required. 24 months to complete program. *Concentrations:* business information science, management.

MBA—Master of Business Administration Part-time. 2 years of work experience required. At least 51 total credits required. 36 to 60 months to complete program. *Concentrations:* finance, management.

MBA/MHA—Master of Business Administration/Master of Health Administration Full-time and part-time. 36 to 48 months to complete program. *Concentrations:* health care, management.

MPA—Master of Professional Accountancy Full-time and part-time. At least 30 total credits required. Minimum of 12 months to complete program. *Concentrations:* accounting.

COSTS

Tuition, state resident: *Part-time* $250 per credit hour. **Tuition, nonresident:** *Part-time* $500 per credit hour. **Required fees:** Fees vary by number of courses or credits taken.

FINANCIAL AID (1999–2000)

10 students received aid, including loans and work study. Aid is available to part-time students. Financial aid application deadline: 3/1.
Financial Aid Contact Financial Aid, 425 University Boulevard, Room 103, Indianapolis, IN 46202. **Phone:** 317-278-3277. **Fax:** 317-274-5930.

RESOURCES AND SERVICES

Information about online services, personal computer policies, library resources, international exchange programs, internship programs, and placement services at this institution and others can be found at **www.petersons.com/mba**

International Students

6% of students enrolled are international students.

Services and Facilities Counseling/support services, ESL/language courses, international student housing, visa services. Financial aid is not available to international students.

Applying *Required:* TOEFL with recommended score of 550 (paper), proof of adequate funds, proof of health/immunizations.

International Student Contact International Affairs, 620 Union Drive, Room 207, Indianapolis, IN 46202-5167. **Phone:** 317-274-7294. **Fax:** 317-278-2213.

■ APPLICATION

Required GMAT, application form, baccalaureate/first degree, essay, 2 letters of recommendation, personal statement, resume/curriculum vitae, transcripts of college work. **Recommended** 2 years of work experience.

Deadlines and Fees *Deadlines:* 5/1 for fall, 11/1 for spring, 4/1 for fall (international), 10/1 for spring (international). *Application fee:* $35, $55 (international).

Application Contact Admissions, 801 West Michigan Street, #3028, Indianapolis, IN 46202-5151. **Phone:** 317-274-4895. **Fax:** 317-274-2483.

Indiana University South Bend

South Bend, Indiana

DIVISION OF BUSINESS AND ECONOMICS

Graduate Business Faculty
Full-time: 30

Part-time: 6

Student Body
Total: 242
Full-time: 43
Part-time: 199

Average Age: 31
Women: 36%

Admissions
Applications: 64
Admitted: 60
Enrolled: 46
Average GMAT: 507
Average GPA: 2.83

Costs (1999–2000)
Full-time tuition: N/R
Part-time tuition: $159 per credit hour (resident), $378 per credit hour (nonresident)

Accreditation
AACSB—The International Association for Management Education

DEGREES MBA • MS • MSA

MBA—Master of Business Administration Full-time and part-time. 36 to 51 total credits required. 24 to 60 months to complete program.
MS—Management Information Technology Full-time and part-time. 21 to 63 total credits required. 24 to 60 months to complete program.
MSA—Master of Science in Accounting Full-time and part-time. At least 30 total credits required. 24 to 60 months to complete program.

COSTS
Tuition, state resident: *Part-time* $159 per credit hour. **Tuition, nonresident:** *Part-time* $378 per credit hour. Tuition varies by number of courses or credits taken, campus location, and academic program. **Required fees:** Tuition and fees vary by number of courses or credits taken. **Graduate housing:** Room and board costs vary by number of occupants. *Typical cost:* $2700 (including board).

FINANCIAL AID (1999–2000)
Grants, loans, scholarships, and work study. Financial aid application deadline: 5/1. **Financial Aid Contact** Ms. Sally Schnakenberg, Receptionist, Financial Aid Office, IUSB, PO Box 7111, South Bend, IN 46634-7111. **Phone:** 219-237-2223.

RESOURCES AND SERVICES
Information about online services, personal computer policies, library resources, international exchange programs, internship programs, and placement services at this institution and others can be found at www.petersons.com/mba

International Students
21% of students enrolled are international students.
Services and Facilities Counseling/support services, ESL/language courses, international student housing, visa services.
Applying *Required:* TOEFL with recommended score of 550 (paper), proof of adequate funds. *Recommended:* TSE, TWE, proof of health/immunizations.
International Student Contact Ms. Gabrielle Robinson, International Center, IUSB, PO Box 7111, South Bend, IN 46634-7111. **Phone:** 219-237-4419.

■ APPLICATION
Required Application form, baccalaureate/first degree, 3 letters of recommendation, transcripts of college work. School will accept GMAT. **Recommended** Interview, personal statement, resume/curriculum vitae, work experience.
Deadlines and Fees *Deadlines:* 7/1 for fall, 11/1 for spring, 4/1 for summer, 7/1 for fall (international), 11/1 for spring (international), 4/1 for summer (international). *Application fee:* $35, $40 (international).
Application Contact Dr. Katherine Jackson, Director, Graduate Business Programs, IUSB PO Box 7111, South Bend, IN 46634-7111. **Phone:** 219-237-4138. **Fax:** 219-237-4866.

Indiana Wesleyan University
Marion, Indiana

DIVISION OF ADULT AND PROFESSIONAL STUDIES

Graduate Business Faculty
Full-time: 7
Part-time: 400

Student Body
Total: 1,150
Full-time: 1,150
Average Age: 36

Costs (1999–2000)
Full-time tuition: N/R
Part-time tuition: $250 per credit hour

After Graduation (Class of 1998–99)
Employed within 3 months of graduation: 98%

DEGREES MBA • MS

MBA—Master of Business Administration Full-time. *Distance learning option.* At least 46 total credits required. 24 to 60 months to complete program. *Concentrations:* management.
MS—Master of Science in Management Full-time. At least 36 total credits required. 24 to 60 months to complete program.

COSTS
Tuition *Part-time:* $250 per credit hour. Tuition varies by campus location and academic program.

FINANCIAL AID (1999–2000)
Financial Aid Contact Ms. Paula Cook, Assistant Director of Financial Aid, 4201 South Washington Street, Marion, IN 46953-4999. **Phone:** 765-674-6901.

RESOURCES AND SERVICES
Information about online services, personal computer policies, library resources, international exchange programs, internship programs, and placement services at this institution and others can be found at www.petersons.com/mba

■ APPLICATION
Required Application form, baccalaureate/first degree, essay, 2 letters of recommendation, personal statement, transcripts of college work, 3 years of work experience.
Deadlines and Fees Applications for domestic students are processed on a rolling basis. *Application fee:* $20.
Application Contact Division of Adult and Professional Studies, 4406 South Harmon Street, Marion, IN 46953. **Phone:** 765-677-2350.

Manchester College
North Manchester, Indiana

DEPARTMENT OF ACCOUNTING AND BUSINESS

DEGREE M Acc

M Acc—Master of Accountancy Full-time and part-time. At least 33 total credits required. 12 to 72 months to complete program. *Concentrations:* accounting.

RESOURCES AND SERVICES
Information about online services, personal computer policies, library resources, international exchange programs, internship programs, and placement services at this institution and others can be found at www.petersons.com/mba

International Students
Services and Facilities Counseling/support services, ESL/language courses. Financial aid is available to international students.

■ APPLICATION
Application Contact Ms. Janis Fahs, Chair, Department of Accounting and Business, 604 College Avenue, MC Box 138, North Manchester, IN 46962-1225. **Phone:** 219-982-5300. **Fax:** 219-982-5043. **E-mail:** jkfahs@manchester.edu.

Oakland City University
Oakland City, Indiana

SCHOOL OF ADULT PROGRAMS AND PROFESSIONAL STUDIES

Graduate Business Faculty
Full-time: 3
Part-time: 11

Student Body
Total: 69
Full-time: 69
Average Age: 35
Women: 25%

Admissions
Average GPA: 3.2

Costs (1999–2000)
Full-time tuition: N/R
Part-time tuition: $285 per credit hour

After Graduation (Class of 1998–99)
Employed within 3 months of graduation: 100%

DEGREE MS

Oakland City University (continued)

MS—Master of Science in Management Full-time. *Distance learning option.* At least 36 total credits required. 18 months to complete program. *Concentrations:* management, management science.

COSTS

Tuition *Part-time:* $285 per credit hour. Tuition varies by number of courses or credits taken.

FINANCIAL AID (1999–2000)

6 students received aid, including grants and scholarships. Financial aid application deadline: 3/1. **Financial Aid Contact** Mrs. Caren Richeson, Director, Financial Aid, 143 North Lucretia Street, Oakland City, IN 47660. **Phone:** 812-749-1224. **Fax:** 812-749-1233.

RESOURCES AND SERVICES

Information about online services, personal computer policies, library resources, international exchange programs, internship programs, and placement services at this institution and others can be found at **www. petersons.com/mba**

International Students

Services and Facilities Financial aid is available to international students. **Applying** *Required:* TOEFL with recommended score of 500 (paper). *Recommended:* Proof of adequate funds, proof of health/immunizations.

International Student Contact Dr. Jerry Phillips, Dean of Academic Affairs, 143 North Lucretia Street, Oakland City, IN 47660. **Phone:** 812-749-1238. **Fax:** 812-749-1233. **E-mail:** ocudean@comsource.net.

■ APPLICATION

Required GMAT, application form, baccalaureate/first degree, interview, 3 letters of recommendation, resume/curriculum vitae, transcripts of college work. School will accept GRE and MAT. **Recommended** Personal statement, work experience.

Deadlines and Fees *Application fee:* $25, $25 (international).

Application Contact Dr. Charles Nichols, Jr., Director, Master of Science in Management Program, 143 North Lucretia Street, Oakland City, IN 47660-1099. **Phone:** 812-749-1405. **Toll-free Phone:** 800-737-5126. **Fax:** 812-749-1294. **E-mail:** drnicholsocu@yahoo.com.

Purdue University

West Lafayette, Indiana

KRANNERT GRADUATE SCHOOL OF MANAGEMENT

Graduate Business Faculty
Full-time: 84	Part-time: 7

Student Body
Total: 359	Average Age: 27
Full-time: 359	Women: 23%

Admissions
Applications: 1,650	Average GMAT: 628
Admitted: 443	Average GPA: 3.27
Enrolled: 216	

Costs (1999–2000)
Full-time tuition: $9110 per academic year (resident), $17,670 per academic year (nonresident)
Part-time tuition: N/R

After Graduation (Class of 1998–99)
Employed within 3 months of graduation: 98%
Average starting salary: $68,000

Accreditation
AACSB—The International Association for Management Education

DEGREES MS

MS—Executive Master of Science in Management Part-time. *Distance learning option.* At least 48 total credits required. Minimum of 22 months to complete program.

MS—Master of Science in Human Resource Management Full-time. At least 62 total credits required. Minimum of 24 months to complete program. *Concentrations:* human resources, organizational behavior/development.

MS—Master of Science in Industrial Administration Full-time. At least 48 total credits required. Minimum of 11 months to complete program. *Concentrations:* industrial administration/management.

MS—Master of Science in Management Full-time. At least 60 total credits required. Minimum of 24 months to complete program. *Concentrations:* accounting, finance, human resources, international management, management information systems, manufacturing management, marketing, operations management, organizational behavior/development, strategic management.

COSTS

Tuition, state resident: *Full-time* $8560. **Tuition, nonresident:** *Full-time* $17,120. **Required fees:** *Full-time* $550. Tuition and fees vary by campus location and academic program. **Graduate housing:** Room and board costs vary by campus location, number of occupants, type of accommodation, and type of board plan. *Typical cost:* $4300 (room only).

FINANCIAL AID (1999–2000)

Fellowships, research assistantships, and teaching assistantships. Financial aid application deadline: 2/15. **Financial Aid Contact** Ms. Joyce Hall, Director, Division of Financial Aid, 1102 Schleman Hall, Room 305, West Lafayette, IN 47907-1102. **Phone:** 765-494-5050. **Fax:** 765-494-6707.

RESOURCES AND SERVICES

Information about online services, personal computer policies, library resources, international exchange programs, internship programs, and placement services at this institution and others can be found at **www. petersons.com/mba**

International Students

26% of students enrolled are international students.

Services and Facilities Counseling/support services, international student organization, orientation. Financial aid is not available to international students. **Applying** *Required:* TOEFL with recommended score of 230 (computer) or 575 (paper), proof of adequate funds, proof of health/immunizations.

International Student Contact Mr. Michael A. Brzezinski, Director, International Students and Scholars Office, 1101 Schleman Hall, Room 136, West Lafayette, IN 47907-1101. **Phone:** 765-494-5770. **Fax:** 765-494-6859.

■ APPLICATION

Required GMAT, application form, baccalaureate/first degree, essay, 2 letters of recommendation, personal statement, resume/curriculum vitae, transcripts of college work. **Recommended** Interview, work experience.

Deadlines and Fees Applications for domestic students are processed on a rolling basis. *Deadline:* 2/1 for fall (international). *Application fee:* $30, $30 (international).

Application Contact Dr. Ward Snearly, Director of Admissions, 1310 Krannert Building, West Lafayette, IN 47907-1310. **Phone:** 765-494-4365. **Fax:** 765-494-9841. **E-mail:** snearlyw@mgmt.purdue.edu.

See full description on page 774.

Purdue University Calumet

Hammond, Indiana

SCHOOL OF MANAGEMENT

Graduate Business Faculty
Full-time: 19	Part-time: 1

Student Body
Total: 206	Average Age: 32
Part-time: 206	Women: 25%

Admissions
Applications: 106	Average GMAT: 550
Admitted: 91	Average GPA: 2.75
Enrolled: 90	

Costs (1999–2000)
Full-time tuition: N/R
Part-time tuition: $128 per credit hour (resident), $280 per credit hour (nonresident)

DEGREES M Acc • MBA

M Acc—Master of Accountancy Part-time. At least 30 total credits required. Minimum of 24 months to complete program.

MBA—Executive MBA Part-time. 5 years of business experience and interview required. At least 42 total credits required. Minimum of 18 months to complete program.

MBA—Master of Business Administration Full-time and part-time. 36 to 51 total credits required. 30 to 42 months to complete program.

COSTS

Tuition, state resident: *Part-time* $128 per credit hour. **Tuition, nonresident:** *Part-time* $280 per credit hour. Tuition varies by number of courses or credits taken and academic program. **Required fees:** *Part-time* $20 per semester. Tuition and fees vary by number of courses or credits taken.

FINANCIAL AID (1999–2000)

15 students received aid, including grants and loans. Financial aid application deadline: 3/1. **Financial Aid Contact** Mary Ann Bishel, Director of Financial Aid, 2200 169th Street, Hammond, IN 46323-2094. **Phone:** 219-989-2301. **Fax:** 219-989-2771. **E-mail:** finaid@calumet. purdue.edu.

RESOURCES AND SERVICES

Information about online services, personal computer policies, library resources, international exchange programs, internship programs, and placement services at this institution and others can be found at **www. petersons.com/mba**

International Students

2% of students enrolled are international students.

Services and Facilities Counseling/support services, visa services. Financial aid is not available to international students.
Applying *Required:* TOEFL with recommended score of 550 (paper).
International Student Contact Ms. Marsha Gordon, Coordinator of Graduate School, 2200 169th Street, Hammond, IN 46323-2094. **Phone:** 219-989-2559. **Fax:** 219-989-2581. **E-mail:** gordon@calumet.purdue.edu.

■ APPLICATION

Required GMAT, baccalaureate/first degree, 3 letters of recommendation, personal statement, resume/curriculum vitae, transcripts of college work. **Recommended** Interview.
Deadlines and Fees *Deadlines:* 7/1 for fall, 10/1 for spring, 3/1 for summer, 7/1 for fall (international), 10/1 for spring (international), 3/1 for summer (international). *Application fee:* $30, $30 (international).
Application Contact Dr. Paul McGrath, MBA Advisor, Hammond, IN 46323-2094. **Phone:** 219-989-2425. **Fax:** 800-937-2101. **E-mail:** pmcgrat@calumet. purdue.edu.

University of Indianapolis

Indianapolis, Indiana

GRADUATE BUSINESS PROGRAMS

Graduate Business Faculty
Full-time: 3   Part-time: 15

Student Body
Total: 288
Full-time: 78   Average Age: 32
Part-time: 210   Women: 35%

Admissions
Average GMAT: 436   Average GPA: 2.9

Costs (1999–2000)
Full-time tuition: N/R
Part-time tuition: $280 per credit hour

Accreditation
ACBSP—The American Council of Business Schools and Programs

DEGREES M Acc • MBA

M Acc—Master of Accounting Part-time. At least 30 total credits required. 12 to 60 months to complete program. *Concentrations:* accounting.

MBA—Executive MBA Full-time. At least 40 total credits required. 20 to 22 months to complete program.

MBA—Master of Business Administration Part-time. At least 42 total credits required. 24 to 60 months to complete program. *Concentrations:* management.

COSTS

Tuition *Part-time:* $280 per credit hour. Tuition varies by number of courses or credits taken.

FINANCIAL AID (1999–2000)

Work study. **Financial Aid Contact** Mrs. Linda Handy, Director of Financial Aid, 1400 East Hanna Avenue, Indianapolis, IN 46227. **Phone:** 317-788-3217. **Fax:** 317-788-3300.

RESOURCES AND SERVICES

Information about online services, personal computer policies, library resources, international exchange programs, internship programs, and placement services at this institution and others can be found at **www. petersons.com/mba**

International Students

2% of students enrolled are international students.

Services and Facilities Counseling/support services, ESL/language courses. Financial aid is available to international students.
Applying *Required:* TOEFL with recommended score of 550 (paper), proof of adequate funds, proof of health/immunizations.
International Student Contact Ms. Mimi Chase, International Student Officer, 1400 East Hanna Avenue, Indianapolis, IN 46227. **Phone:** 317-788-3394. **Fax:** 317-788-3300.

■ APPLICATION

Required GMAT, GRE, application form, baccalaureate/first degree, interview, 2 letters of recommendation, transcripts of college work.
Deadlines and Fees Applications for domestic and international students are processed on a rolling basis. *Application fee:* $50, $50 (international).
Application Contact Dr. Renee Wachter, Associate Dean and Director, Graduate Business Programs, 1400 East Hanna Avenue, Indianapolis, IN 46227. **Phone:** 317-788-3370. **Toll-free Phone:** 800-232-8634. **Fax:** 317-788-3300.

University of Notre Dame

Notre Dame, Indiana

MENDOZA COLLEGE OF BUSINESS

Accreditation
AACSB—The International Association for Management Education

DEGREES JD/MBA • MBA • MS

JD/MBA—MBA/JD Joint Degree Program Full-time. At least 123 total credits required. Minimum of 48 months to complete program. *Concentrations:* accounting, banking, entrepreneurship, finance, human resources, international business, management, management consulting, management information systems, manufacturing management, marketing, marketing research.

MBA—Executive MBA Full-time. *Distance learning option.* At least 48 total credits required. Maximum of 24 months to complete program.

MBA—One-year MBA program Full-time. At least 44 total credits required. Minimum of 33 months to complete program. *Concentrations:* accounting, banking, entrepreneurship, finance, human resources, international banking, international business, management, management consulting, management information systems, manufacturing management, marketing, marketing research.

MBA—Two-year MBA program Full-time. 2 years of work experience required (3 preferred). 60 to 63 total credits required. Maximum of 22 months to complete program. *Concentrations:* accounting, banking, entrepreneurship, finance, human resources, international business, management, management consulting, management information systems, manufacturing management, marketing, marketing research.

MS—Master of Science in Accountancy Full-time and part-time. 30 to 36 total credits required. Minimum of 9 months to complete program. *Concentrations:* accounting, taxation.

MS—Master of Science in Administration Full-time and part-time. At least 48 total credits required. Maximum of 60 months to complete program. *Concentrations:* nonprofit management.

RESOURCES AND SERVICES

Information about online services, personal computer policies, library resources, international exchange programs, internship programs, and placement services at this institution and others can be found at **www. petersons.com/mba**

International Students

Services and Facilities Counseling/support services, ESL/language courses, visa services, host family program. Financial aid is available to international students.
International Student Contact Ms. Maureen A. Fitzgibbon, Director of International Student Affairs, 204A LaFortune Student Center, Notre Dame, IN 46556. **Phone:** 219-631-3825. **Fax:** 219-631-3162. **E-mail:** fitzgibbon.3@nd.edu.

■ APPLICATION

Application Contact Mr. Hayden Estrada, IV, Director of MBA Admissions, 276 College of Business Administration, PO Box 399, Notre Dame, IN 46556-0399. **Phone:** 219-631-8488. **Toll-free Phone:** 800-631-8488. **Fax:** 219-631-8800. **E-mail:** mba.1@nd.edu.

University of Saint Francis

Fort Wayne, Indiana

DEPARTMENT OF BUSINESS ADMINISTRATION

Graduate Business Faculty

Full-time: 3   Part-time: 3

Student Body

Total: 52   Average Age: 33
Full-time: 14   Women: 33%
Part-time: 38

Admissions

Applications: 24   Average GMAT: 511
Admitted: 16   Average GPA: 2.96
Enrolled: 9

Costs (1999–2000)

Full-time tuition: N/R
Part-time tuition: $367 per credit hour

After Graduation (Class of 1998–99)

Employed within 3 months of graduation: 99%

DEGREES MBA • MS

MBA—Master of Business Administration Full-time and part-time. 30 to 51 total credits required. 24 to 60 months to complete program. *Concentrations:* finance, international business, management, marketing.

MS—Master of Science in Business Administration Full-time and part-time. 30 to 45 total credits required. 18 to 60 months to complete program.

COSTS

Tuition *Part-time:* $367 per credit hour. **Required fees:** *Full-time* $95. *Part-time* $70 per hour. Tuition and fees vary by number of courses or credits taken. **Graduate housing:** Room and board costs vary by number of occupants. *Typical cost:* $4480 (including board).

FINANCIAL AID (1999–2000)

15 students received aid, including loans, research assistantships, scholarships, and work study. Aid is available to part-time students. Financial aid application deadline: 7/1. **Financial Aid Contact** Ms. Sherri Shockey, Director of Financial Aid, 2701 Spring Street, Fort Wayne, IN 46808-3994. **Phone:** 219-434-3283. **Fax:** 219-434-7526. **E-mail:** sshockey@sf.edu.

RESOURCES AND SERVICES

Information about online services, personal computer policies, library resources, international exchange programs, internship programs, and placement services at this institution and others can be found at **www.petersons.com/mba**

International Students

10% of students enrolled are international students.

Services and Facilities Counseling/support services, visa services. Financial aid is not available to international students.
Applying *Required:* TOEFL with recommended score of 550 (paper), proof of adequate funds, proof of health/immunizations.
International Student Contact Ms. Kathleen Benson-Chaney, International Student Advisor, 2701 Spring Street, Fort Wayne, IN 46808-3994. **Phone:** 219-434-3102. **Fax:** 219-434-3183.

■ APPLICATION

Required Application form, baccalaureate/first degree, transcripts of college work. School will accept GMAT.

Deadlines and Fees Applications for domestic students are processed on a rolling basis. *Deadlines:* 5/1 for fall (international), 9/15 for spring (international). *Application fee:* $20, $20 (international).

Application Contact Ms. Emily Guerrero, Adult Student Coordinator, 2701 Spring Street, Fort Wayne, IN 46808-3994. **Phone:** 219-434-7494. **Toll-free Phone:** 800-729-4738 (in-state), 800-729-4732 (out-of-state). **Fax:** 219-434-3183. **E-mail:** eguerrer@sf.edu.

University of Southern Indiana

Evansville, Indiana

SCHOOL OF BUSINESS

Accreditation

AACSB—The International Association for Management Education

DEGREES MBA • MS • MSA

MBA—Master of Business Administration Full-time and part-time. Competency in calculus and computer skills are recommended. At least 36 total credits required. 29 to 48 months to complete program.

MS—Master of Science in Industrial Management Full-time and part-time. At least 33 total credits required. 24 to 84 months to complete program.

MSA—Master of Science in Accountancy Competency in calculus and computer skills are recommended. At least 30 total credits required. Maximum of 84 months to complete program.

RESOURCES AND SERVICES

Information about online services, personal computer policies, library resources, international exchange programs, internship programs, and placement services at this institution and others can be found at **www.petersons.com/mba**

International Students

Services and Facilities Counseling/support services, ESL/language courses, international student organization, orientation, multicultural center. Financial aid is not available to international students.
International Student Contact Mrs. Heidi Gregori-Gahan, Director, International Students Services, 8600 University Boulevard, Evansville, IN 47712. **Phone:** 812-465-1248. **Fax:** 812-464-1960. **E-mail:** gahan@usi.edu.

■ APPLICATION

Application Contact Dr. Peggy F. Harrel, Director of Graduate Studies, 8600 University Boulevard, Evansville, IN 47712. **Phone:** 812-465-7015. **Fax:** 812-464-1956. **E-mail:** gssr@usi.edu.

IOWA

Clarke College

Dubuque, Iowa

PROGRAM IN MANAGEMENT

Graduate Business Faculty

Full-time: 5   Part-time: 2

Student Body

Total: 42   Average Age: 38
Full-time: 7   Women: 36%
Part-time: 35

Admissions

Applications: 16   Average GMAT: 555
Admitted: 16   Average GPA: 3.2
Enrolled: 12

Costs (1999–2000)

Full-time tuition: N/R
Part-time tuition: $366 per credit

DEGREE MSM

MSM—Master of Science in Management Full-time and part-time. At least 36 total credits required. 18 to 24 months to complete program. *Concentrations:* human resources, management, operations management.

COSTS

Tuition *Part-time:* $360 per credit. Tuition varies by class time, number of courses or credits taken, and academic program. **Required fees:** *Full-time* $54. *Part-time* $6 per credit. **Graduate housing:** Room and board costs vary by number of occupants, type of accommodation, and type of board plan. *Typical cost:* $5082 (including board), $2472 (room only).

FINANCIAL AID (1999–2000)

Loans. Aid is available to part-time students. **Financial Aid Contact** Mr. Mike Pope, Director of Financial Aid, 1550 Clarke Drive, Dubuque, IA 52001-3198. **Phone:** 319-588-6327. **Fax:** 319-588-6789. **E-mail:** mpope@clarke.edu.

RESOURCES AND SERVICES

Information about online services, personal computer policies, library resources, international exchange programs, internship programs, and

placement services at this institution and others can be found at **www. petersons.com/mba**

International Students
2% of students enrolled are international students.
Services and Facilities Counseling/support services, ESL/language courses, international student housing. Financial aid is not available to international students.
Applying *Required:* TOEFL with recommended score of 550 (paper), proof of adequate funds, proof of health/immunizations.
International Student Contact Mr. Omar Correa, Coordinator of International Admissions, 1550 Clarke Drive, Dubuque, IA 52001-3198. **Phone:** 319-588-6316. **Fax:** 319-588-6789. **E-mail:** ocorrea@clarke.edu.

■ **APPLICATION**

Required Application form, baccalaureate/first degree, essay, 2 letters of recommendation, personal statement, resume/curriculum vitae, transcripts of college work. School will accept GMAT, GRE, and MAT. **Recommended** Interview, work experience.
Deadlines and Fees *Application fee:* $25, $25 (international).
Application Contact John Wiemers, Coordinator of MSM Program, 1550 Clarke Drive, Dubuque, IA 52001-3198. **Phone:** 319-588-8143. **Toll-free Phone:** 800-383-2345. **Fax:** 319-588-6789. **E-mail:** jwiemers@clarke.edu.

Drake University

Des Moines, Iowa

COLLEGE OF BUSINESS AND PUBLIC ADMINISTRATION

Graduate Business Faculty
Full-time: 30 | Part-time: 6

Student Body
Total: 419 | Average Age: 29
Full-time: 67 | Women: 43%
Part-time: 352

Admissions
Applications: 148 | Average GMAT: 537
Admitted: 142 | Average GPA: 3.26
Enrolled: 98

Costs (1999–2000)
Full-time tuition: N/R
Part-time tuition: $340 per credit hour

After Graduation (Class of 1998–99)
Employed within 3 months of graduation: 100%

Accreditation
AACSB—The International Association for Management Education

DEGREES M Acc • MBA • MPA

M Acc—Master of Accountancy Full-time and part-time. At least 30 total credits required. 12 to 60 months to complete program.
MBA—Master of Business Administration Full-time and part-time. *Distance learning option.* At least 32 total credits required. 16 to 60 months to complete program.
MPA—Master of Public Administration Full-time and part-time. At least 36 total credits required. 16 to 60 months to complete program.

COSTS

Tuition *Part-time:* $340 per credit hour. Tuition varies by academic program.
Graduate housing: Room and board costs vary by number of occupants, type of accommodation, and type of board plan. *Typical cost:* $4870 (including board), $2570 (room only).

FINANCIAL AID (1999–2000)

25 students received aid, including research assistantships and work study. Aid is available to part-time students. Financial aid application deadline: 3/1. **Financial Aid Contact** Dr. John Parker, Dean, Student Financial Aid Services, 2507 University Avenue, Des Moines, IA 50311-4516. **Phone:** 515-271-2905.

RESOURCES AND SERVICES

Information about online services, personal computer policies, library resources, international exchange programs, internship programs, and placement services at this institution and others can be found at **www. petersons.com/mba**

International Students
Services and Facilities Counseling/support services, ESL/language courses, international student housing, international student organization, orientation, visa services. Financial aid is not available to international students.
Applying *Required:* TOEFL with recommended score of 213 (computer) or 550 (paper), proof of adequate funds, proof of health/immunizations.
International Student Contact Ms. Ann Martin, Graduate Admission Coordinator, 2507 University Avenue—Office of Graduate Admission, Des Moines, IA 50311. **Phone:** 515-271-3871. **Fax:** 515-271-2831. **E-mail:** ann.martin@drake.edu.

■ **APPLICATION**

Required GMAT, application form, baccalaureate/first degree, transcripts of college work. **Recommended** Resume/curriculum vitae.
Deadlines and Fees Applications for domestic and international students are processed on a rolling basis. *Application fee:* $25, $25 (international).
Application Contact Ms. Nancy Gabriel, Director of Graduate Programs, College of Business and Public Administration, 2507 University Avenue, Des Moines, IA 50311-4516. **Phone:** 515-271-2188. **Fax:** 515-271-4518. **E-mail:** cbpa.gradprograms@drake.edu.

Iowa State University of Science and Technology

Ames, Iowa

COLLEGE OF BUSINESS

Graduate Business Faculty
Full-time: 60

Student Body
Total: 246 | Average Age: 30
Full-time: 103 | Women: 35%
Part-time: 143

Admissions
Applications: 248 | Average GMAT: 588
Admitted: 163 | Average GPA: 3.28
Enrolled: 115

Costs (1999–2000)
Full-time tuition: $3526 per academic year (resident), $9962 per academic year (nonresident)
Part-time tuition: $240 per credit (resident), $598 per credit (nonresident)

After Graduation (Class of 1998–99)
Employed within 3 months of graduation: 82%
Average starting salary: $49,444

Accreditation
AACSB—The International Association for Management Education

DEGREES M Acc • MBA • MBA/MS • MS

M Acc—Master of Accounting Full-time and part-time. At least 32 total credits required. 12 to 36 months to complete program. *Concentrations:* accounting.
MBA—Evening MBA Part-time. At least 48 total credits required. 31 months to complete program. *Concentrations:* accounting, agribusiness, finance, human resources, management information systems, manufacturing management, marketing.
MBA—Full-time MBA Full-time. At least 48 total credits required. 21 months to complete program. *Concentrations:* accounting, agribusiness, finance, human resources, management information systems, manufacturing management, marketing.
MBA—Saturday MBA Part-time. At least 48 total credits required. 31 months to complete program. *Concentrations:* accounting, agribusiness, finance, human resources, management information systems, manufacturing management, marketing.
MBA/MS—Master of Business Administration/Master of Science in Community and Regional Planning Full-time. At least 73 total credits required. 33 months to complete program.
MBA/MS—Master of Business Administration/Master of Science in Statistics Full-time. At least 72 total credits required. 33 months to complete program.
MS—Master of Science in Business Full-time and part-time. At least 31 total credits required. 12 to 36 months to complete program. *Concentrations:* accounting, agribusiness, finance, management information systems, marketing, production management.

Iowa State University of Science and Technology (continued)

MS—Master of Science in Industrial Relations
Full-time and part-time. At least 36 total credits required. 12 to 36 months to complete program. *Concentrations:* industrial/labor relations.

COSTS
Tuition, state resident: *Full-time* $3308. *Part-time* $240 per credit. **Tuition, nonresident:** *Full-time* $9744. *Part-time* $598 per credit. **Required fees:** *Full-time* $218. *Part-time* $44 per semester. Tuition and fees vary by class time, number of courses or credits taken, and academic program. **Graduate housing:** Room and board costs vary by number of occupants, type of accommodation, and type of board plan. *Typical cost:* $4300 (including board).

FINANCIAL AID (1999–2000)
Loans, research assistantships, scholarships, and work study. Aid is available to part-time students. Financial aid application deadline: 5/1. **Financial Aid Contact** Mr. Earl Dowling, Director, Student Financial Aid Office, 12 Beardshear Hall, Ames, IA 50011. **Phone:** 515-294-2223. **Fax:** 515-294-0851.

RESOURCES AND SERVICES
Information about online services, personal computer policies, library resources, international exchange programs, internship programs, and placement services at this institution and others can be found at **www.petersons.com/mba**

International Students
22% of students enrolled are international students.

Services and Facilities Counseling/support services, ESL/language courses, housing location assistance, international student organization, language tutoring, orientation, visa services. Financial aid is available to international students.
Applying *Required:* TOEFL with recommended score of 230 (computer) or 570 (paper), proof of adequate funds.
International Student Contact Mr. Dennis Peterson, International Education Services, 4 Hamilton Hall, Ames, IA 50011. **Phone:** 515-294-1120. **Fax:** 515-294-8263. **E-mail:** intlserv@iastate.edu.

■ APPLICATION
Required GMAT, application form, baccalaureate/first degree, essay, 3 letters of recommendation, resume/curriculum vitae, transcripts of college work. **Recommended** 3 years of work experience.
Deadlines and Fees *Deadlines:* 5/1 for fall, 3/1 for fall (international). *Application fee:* $20, $50 (international).
Application Contact Mr. Ronald Ackerman, Director of Graduate Admissions, College of Business, 218 Carver Hall, Ames, IA 50011-2063. **Phone:** 515-294-8118. **Toll-free Phone:** 877-478-4622. **Fax:** 515-294-2446. **E-mail:** busgrad@iastate.edu.

See full description on page 692.

Maharishi University of Management
Fairfield, Iowa

SCHOOL OF BUSINESS AND PUBLIC ADMINISTRATION

Graduate Business Faculty
Full-time: 10 | Part-time: 4

Student Body
Total: 96
Full-time: 96 | Average Age: 25 / Women: 32%

Admissions
Applications: 105 | Enrolled: 91
Admitted: 91

Costs (1999–2000)
Full-time tuition: $16,320 per academic year
Part-time tuition: N/R

DEGREE MBA

MBA—Master of Business Administration Full-time and part-time. *Distance learning option.* 60 to 80 total credits required. 18 to 36 months to complete program.

COSTS
Tuition *Full-time:* $16,320. Tuition varies by class time, number of courses or credits taken, and academic program. **Graduate housing:** Room and board costs vary by number of occupants. *Typical cost:* $5200 (including board).

FINANCIAL AID (1999–2000)
96 students received aid, including loans, scholarships, and work study. Aid is available to part-time students. **Financial Aid Contact** Tom Rowe, Director, Financial Aid, 1000 North 4th Street, DB 1127, Fairfield, IA 52557-1127. **Phone:** 515-472-1156. **Fax:** 515-472-1133. **E-mail:** finaid@mum.edu.

RESOURCES AND SERVICES
Information about online services, personal computer policies, library resources, international exchange programs, internship programs, and placement services at this institution and others can be found at **www.petersons.com/mba**

International Students
97% of students enrolled are international students.

Services and Facilities Counseling/support services, ESL/language courses, international student housing, visa services. Financial aid is available to international students.
Applying *Required:* TOEFL with recommended score of 575 (paper), proof of adequate funds.
International Student Contact Ms. Elaine Christensen, Director of International Admissions, Office of Admissions, Fairfield, IA 52557. **Phone:** 515-472-1110. **Fax:** 515-472-1179. **E-mail:** echriste@mum.edu.

■ APPLICATION
Required Application form, baccalaureate/first degree, essay, 2 letters of recommendation, personal statement, transcripts of college work. School will accept GMAT. **Recommended** Interview, resume/curriculum vitae, work experience.
Deadlines and Fees Applications for domestic and international students are processed on a rolling basis. *Application fee:* $40, $40 (international).
Application Contact Mr. Paul Handelman, MBA Admissions Officer, Office of Admissions, Fairfield, IA 52557. **Phone:** 515-472-1110. **Fax:** 515-472-1179. **E-mail:** phandel@mum.edu.

St. Ambrose University
Davenport, Iowa

PROGRAM IN BUSINESS ADMINISTRATION

Graduate Business Faculty
Full-time: 30 | Part-time: 36

Student Body
Total: 535
Full-time: 130 | Average Age: 33 / Women: 45%
Part-time: 405

Admissions
Applications: 247 | Average GMAT: 540
Admitted: 230 | Average GPA: 2.5
Enrolled: 188

Costs (1999–2000)
Full-time tuition: N/R
Part-time tuition: $1296 per course

After Graduation (Class of 1998–99)
Employed within 3 months of graduation: 95%

Accreditation
ACBSP—The American Council of Business Schools and Programs

DEGREES M Acc • MBA

M Acc—Master of Accountancy Part-time. At least 30 total credits required. 30 to 60 months to complete program.
MBA—H.L. McLaughlin MBA Full-time and part-time. *Distance learning option.* At least 45 total credits required. 12 to 60 months to complete program. *Concentrations:* finance, human resources, management information systems, marketing, technology management.
MBA—Master of Business Administration in Health Care Part-time. At least 45 total credits required. 30 to 60 months to complete program.

COSTS
Tuition *Part-time:* $1296 per course. **Required fees:** Fees vary by campus location. **Graduate housing:** Room and board costs vary by campus location,

number of occupants, type of accommodation, and type of board plan. *Typical cost:* $5160 (including board), $2820 (room only).

FINANCIAL AID (1999–2000)
55 students received aid, including research assistantships. Financial aid application deadline: 3/1. **Financial Aid Contact** Mr. Jeff Griebel, Director, Financial Aid Office, 518 West Locust Street, Davenport, IA 52803-2898. **Phone:** 319-333-6314. **Fax:** 319-333-6297. **E-mail:** finaid@saunix.sau.edu.

RESOURCES AND SERVICES
Information about online services, personal computer policies, library resources, international exchange programs, internship programs, and placement services at this institution and others can be found at **www.petersons.com/mba**

International Students
2% of students enrolled are international students.
Services and Facilities Counseling/support services, ESL/language courses, multicultural club, international house(for meetings and social gatherings). Financial aid is not available to international students.
Applying *Required:* TOEFL with recommended score of 550 (paper), proof of adequate funds, proof of health/immunizations.
International Student Contact Mr. Allen Hubbell, Coordinator of International Student Programs, Admissions Office, 518 West Locust Street, Davenport, IA 52803-2898. **Phone:** 319-333-6309. **Fax:** 319-333-6297. **E-mail:** ahubbell@saunix.sau.edu.

■ APPLICATION
Required GMAT, application form, baccalaureate/first degree, 2 letters of recommendation, personal statement, transcripts of college work.
Deadlines and Fees Applications for domestic and international students are processed on a rolling basis. *Application fee:* $25, $25 (international).
Application Contact Dr. John Collis, Dean, College of Business, 518 West Locust Street, Davenport, IA 52803-2898. **Phone:** 319-333-6270. **Toll-free Phone:** 888-MBA-1-SAU. **Fax:** 319-333-6268. **E-mail:** jcollis@saunix.sau.edu.

See full description on page 800.

University of Dubuque
Dubuque, Iowa

SCHOOL OF BUSINESS

Graduate Business Faculty
Full-time: 3 | Part-time: 11

Student Body
Total: 129
Full-time: 10 | Average Age: 33
Part-time: 119 | Women: 32%

Admissions
Average GMAT: 475

Costs (1999–2000)
Full-time tuition: N/R
Part-time tuition: $340 per credit

After Graduation (Class of 1998–99)
Employed within 3 months of graduation: 99%

DEGREE MBA

MBA—Master of Business Administration Full-time and part-time. *Distance learning option.* At least 36 total credits required. 12 to 72 months to complete program. *Concentrations:* finance, management, quality management, aviation management.

COSTS
Tuition *Part-time:* $340 per credit. Tuition varies by number of courses or credits taken. **Graduate housing:** Room and board costs vary by number of occupants, type of accommodation, and type of board plan. *Typical cost:* $4620 (including board).

FINANCIAL AID (1999–2000)
Aid is available to part-time students. Financial aid application deadline: 4/1. **Financial Aid Contact** Timothy Kremer, Director, 2000 University Avenue, Dubuque, IA 52001-5050. **Phone:** 319-589-3396.

RESOURCES AND SERVICES
Information about online services, personal computer policies, library resources, international exchange programs, internship programs, and

placement services at this institution and others can be found at **www.petersons.com/mba**

International Students
47% of students enrolled are international students.
Services and Facilities Counseling/support services, ESL/language courses, international student housing, international student organization, orientation, visa services. Financial aid is not available to international students.
Applying *Required:* TOEFL with recommended score of 550 (paper), proof of adequate funds, proof of health/immunizations.
International Student Contact Ms. Raydora Drummer, Director of Multicultural Services, 2000 University Avenue, Dubuque, IA 52001-5050. **Phone:** 319-589-3253. **E-mail:** rdrummer@dbq.edu.

■ APPLICATION
Required GMAT, application form, baccalaureate/first degree, 3 letters of recommendation, transcripts of college work. **Recommended** Interview, personal statement, resume/curriculum vitae, work experience.
Deadlines and Fees Applications for domestic and international students are processed on a rolling basis. *Application fee:* $25, $25 (international).
Application Contact Mr. Thomas A. Tully, MBA Director, 2000 University Avenue, Dubuque, IA 52001-5050. **Phone:** 319-589-3300. **Toll-free Phone:** 800-722-5583. **Fax:** 319-589-3417. **E-mail:** ttully@dbq.edu.

The University of Iowa
Iowa City, Iowa

HENRY B. TIPPIE COLLEGE OF BUSINESS

Graduate Business Faculty
Full-time: 97 | Part-time: 24

Student Body
Total: 827
Full-time: 351 | Average Age: 31
Part-time: 476 | Women: 37%

Admissions
Applications: 744
Admitted: 379 | Average GMAT: 623
Enrolled: 240 | Average GPA: 3.3

Costs (1999–2000)
Full-time tuition: $4528 per academic year (resident), $11,962 per academic year (nonresident)
Part-time tuition: N/R

After Graduation (Class of 1998–99)
Employed within 3 months of graduation: 98%
Average starting salary: $65,960

Accreditation
AACSB—The International Association for Management Education

DEGREES JD/MBA • M Acc • MA • MBA • MBA/MA • MBA/MHA • MBA/MS

JD/MBA—Juris Doctor/Master of Business Administration Full-time. At least 123 total credits required. 48 months to complete program.

M Acc—Master of Accountancy Full-time and part-time. 30 to 69 total credits required. 12 to 30 months to complete program. *Concentrations:* accounting.

MA—Master of Arts in Management Information Systems Full-time and part-time. 48 total credits required. 24 months to complete program. *Concentrations:* management information systems.

MBA—Evening MBA Part-time. At least 45 total credits required. 36 to 120 months to complete program.

MBA—Executive MBA Part-time. 10 years of work experience (post graduation). At least 48 total credits required. 21 months to complete program.

MBA—Full-time MBA Full-time. At least 60 total credits required. 21 months to complete program. *Concentrations:* accounting, entrepreneurship, finance, human resources, management, management information systems, marketing, operations management, organizational behavior/development, production management.

MBA/MA—Master of Business Administration/Master of Arts in Library Science and Information Science Full-time and part-time. Minimum of 36 months to complete program.

MBA/MA—Master of Business Administration/Master of Arts in MIS Full-time. 75 to 78 total credits required. Minimum of 28 months to complete program.

The University of Iowa (continued)

MBA/MHA—Master of Business Administration/Master of Hospital Administration Full-time. At least 72 total credits required. Minimum of 28 months to complete program. *Concentrations:* health care.

MBA/MS—Master of Business Administration/Master of Science in Nursing Full-time and part-time. At least 61 total credits required. Minimum of 34 months to complete program.

COSTS

Tuition, state resident: *Full-time* $4316. **Tuition, nonresident:** *Full-time* $11,750. **Tuition, international:** *Full-time* $11,750. Tuition varies by class time, number of courses or credits taken, and academic program. **Required fees:** *Full-time* $212. Tuition and fees vary by academic program. **Graduate housing:** Room and board costs vary by type of accommodation and type of board plan. *Typical cost:* $8280 (including board).

FINANCIAL AID (1999–2000)

88 students received aid, including fellowships, research assistantships, scholarships, teaching assistantships, and work study. Aid is available to part-time students. Financial aid application deadline: 4/15. **Financial Aid Contact** Ms. Mary Spreen, Director of MBA Admissions and Financial Aid, Henry B. Tippie College of Business, 108 Pappajohn Business Building, Suite C140, Iowa City, IA 52242-1000. **Phone:** 319-335-1039. **Fax:** 319-335-3604. **E-mail:** mary-spreen@uiowa.edu.

RESOURCES AND SERVICES

Information about online services, personal computer policies, library resources, international exchange programs, internship programs, and placement services at this institution and others can be found at **www.petersons.com/mba**

International Students

23% of students enrolled are international students.

Services and Facilities Counseling/support services, ESL/language courses, housing location assistance, international student organization, language tutoring, orientation. Financial aid is available to international students.
Applying *Required:* TOEFL with recommended score of 600 (paper), proof of adequate funds, proof of health/immunizations.

International Student Contact Ms. Jane Van Voorhis, Assistant Director, Iowa Institute for International Business, 108 Pappajohn Business Administration Building, Suite W308, Iowa City, IA 52242-1000. **Phone:** 319-335-1379. **Fax:** 319-335-3604. **E-mail:** jane-van-voorhis@uiowa.edu.

■ APPLICATION

Required GMAT, application form, baccalaureate/first degree, essay, interview, 3 letters of recommendation, resume/curriculum vitae, transcripts of college work, 2 years of work experience.
Deadlines and Fees *Deadlines:* 7/15 for fall, 4/15 for fall (international). *Application fee:* $30, $50 (international).

Application Contact Ms. Mary Spreen, Director of MBA Admissions and Financial Aid, Henry B. Tippie College of Business, 108 Pappajohn Business Building, Suite C140, Iowa City, IA 52242-1000. **Phone:** 319-335-1039. **Toll-free Phone:** 800-MBA-IOWA. **Fax:** 319-335-3604. **E-mail:** mary-spreen@uiowa.edu.

See full description on page 908.

University of Northern Iowa

Cedar Falls, Iowa

SCHOOL OF BUSINESS ADMINISTRATION

Graduate Business Faculty
Full-time: 33

Student Body
Total: 81	Average Age: 34
Full-time: 27	Women: 31%
Part-time: 54	

Admissions
Applications: 59	Average GMAT: 580
Admitted: 48	Average GPA: 3
Enrolled: 32	

Costs (1999–2000)
Full-time tuition: $3510 per academic year (resident), $8358 per academic year (nonresident)
Part-time tuition: $184 per credit hour (resident), $454 per credit hour (nonresident)

After Graduation (Class of 1998–99)
Average starting salary: $48,400

Accreditation
AACSB—The International Association for Management Education

DEGREE MBA

MBA—Master of Business Administration Full-time and part-time. At least 31 total credits required. 10 to 70 months to complete program. *Concentrations:* management.

COSTS

Tuition, state resident: *Full-time* $3308. *Part-time* $184 per credit hour. **Tuition, nonresident:** *Full-time* $8156. *Part-time* $454 per credit hour. **Required fees:** *Full-time* $202. Tuition and fees vary by number of courses or credits taken. **Graduate housing:** Room and board costs vary by number of occupants, type of accommodation, and type of board plan. *Typical cost:* $4161 (including board).

FINANCIAL AID (1999–2000)

Scholarships and work study. Aid is available to part-time students. Financial aid application deadline: 3/1. **Financial Aid Contact** Mr. Roland Carrillo, Director of Financial Aid, Financial Office, Gilchrist 116, Cedar Falls, IA 50614-0024. **Phone:** 319-273-2701. **Fax:** 319-273-6950.

RESOURCES AND SERVICES

Information about online services, personal computer policies, library resources, international exchange programs, internship programs, and placement services at this institution and others can be found at **www.petersons.com/mba**

International Students

17% of students enrolled are international students.

Services and Facilities ESL/language courses, visa services. Financial aid is available to international students.
Applying *Required:* TOEFL with recommended score of 500 (paper), proof of adequate funds, proof of health/immunizations.

International Student Contact Director, International Student Office, Admissions, H33, Cedar Falls, IA 50614-0521. **Phone:** 319-273-6421. **Fax:** 319-273-2921. **E-mail:** international.admissions@uni.edu.

■ APPLICATION

Required GMAT, application form, baccalaureate/first degree, 2 letters of recommendation, personal statement, transcripts of college work.
Deadlines and Fees *Deadlines:* 7/20 for fall, 12/15 for spring, 5/1 for fall (international), 11/1 for spring (international). *Application fee:* $20, $50 (international).

Application Contact Ms. Nancy L. Hoffman, MBA Office, College of Business Administration, Suite 325, Cedar Falls, IA 50614-0123. **Phone:** 319-273-6243. **Fax:** 319-273-2922. **E-mail:** nancy.hoffman@uni.edu.

Upper Iowa University

Fayette, Iowa

PROGRAM IN BUSINESS LEADERSHIP

DEGREE MA

MA—Master of Arts in Business Leadership Full-time and part-time. *Distance learning option.* At least 36 total credits required. 12 to 60 months to complete program. *Concentrations:* human resources, management, organizational behavior/development, quality management.

RESOURCES AND SERVICES

Information about online services, personal computer policies, library resources, international exchange programs, internship programs, and placement services at this institution and others can be found at **www.petersons.com/mba**

International Students

Services and Facilities Counseling/support services.
International Student Contact Jerilyn Carlson, International Student Advisor, 605 Washington Street, PO Box 1857, Fayette, IA 52142-1857. **Phone:** 319-425-5701. **Fax:** 319-425-5771. **E-mail:** carlsonj@uiu.edu.

■ APPLICATION

Application Contact Dr. Patrick Langan, Director, Graduate Program, 605 Washington Street, PO Box 1857, Fayette, IA 52142-1857. **Phone:** 319-425-

5701. **Toll-free Phone:** 800-733-9298. **Fax:** 319-425-5358. **E-mail:** online@ uiu.edu.

KANSAS

Baker University

Baldwin City, Kansas

SCHOOL OF PROFESSIONAL AND GRADUATE STUDIES

Graduate Business Faculty
Full-time: 22   Part-time: 221

Student Body
Total: 802   Average Age: 34
Full-time: 680   Women: 50%
Part-time: 122

Admissions
Applications: 253   Enrolled: 251
Admitted: 251   Average GPA: 3.1

Costs (1999–2000)
Full-time tuition: N/R
Part-time tuition: $325 per credit

Accreditation
ACBSP—The American Council of Business Schools and Programs

DEGREES MBA • MS

MBA—Master of Business Administration Full-time. At least 44 total credits required. 24 to 72 months to complete program.

MS—Master of Science in Management Full-time. At least 36 total credits required. 18 to 72 months to complete program.

COSTS

Tuition *Part-time:* $325 per credit. Tuition varies by academic program.

FINANCIAL AID (1999–2000)

294 students received aid. Aid is available to part-time students.
Financial Aid Contact Ms. Sylvia Ellis, Associate Director of Financial Aid, 6600 College Boulevard, Suite 340, Overland Park, KS 66211. **Phone:** 913-491-4432. **Fax:** 913-491-0470. **E-mail:** sylvia@kc.idir.net.

RESOURCES AND SERVICES

Information about online services, personal computer policies, library resources, international exchange programs, internship programs, and placement services at this institution and others can be found at **www. petersons.com/mba**

International Students

0.5% of students enrolled are international students.

Services and Facilities ESL/language courses. Financial aid is not available to international students.
Applying *Required:* TOEFL with recommended score of 600 (paper), proof of adequate funds. *Recommended:* Proof of health/immunizations.
International Student Contact Ms. Kathy Marian, International Student Coordinator, Box 65, Baldwin City, KS 66006-0065. **E-mail:** marian@harvey.bakeru. edu.

■ APPLICATION

Required Application form, baccalaureate/first degree, 2 letters of recommendation, transcripts of college work, 2 years of work experience.
Deadlines and Fees Applications for domestic and international students are processed on a rolling basis. *Application fee:* $20, $20 (international).
Application Contact Ms. Kelly Wiedt, Director of Marketing, 6600 College Boulevard, Suite 340, Overland Park, KS 66211. **Phone:** 913-491-4432. **Fax:** 913-491-0470. **E-mail:** kelly.wiedt@apollogrp.edu.

Benedictine College

Atchison, Kansas

EXECUTIVE MASTER OF BUSINESS ADMINISTRATION

Graduate Business Faculty
Full-time: 3   Part-time: 7

Student Body
Total: 23   Average Age: 37
Full-time: 19   Women: 22%
Part-time: 4

Admissions
Applications: 21   Enrolled: 20
Admitted: 20

Costs (1999–2000)
Full-time tuition: $12,500 per academic year
Part-time tuition: N/R

After Graduation (Class of 1998–99)
Employed within 3 months of graduation: 100%

DEGREE EMBA

EMBA—Executive Master of Business Administration Part-time. At least 33 total credits required. 12 to 24 months to complete program.

COSTS

Tuition *Full-time:* $12,500.

FINANCIAL AID (1999–2000)

Loans. Aid is available to part-time students. Financial aid application deadline: 2/1. **Financial Aid Contact** Mr. Keith Jaloma, Director, Financial Aid, 1020 North 2nd Street, Atchison, KS 66002. **Phone:** 913-367-5340. **Fax:** 913-367-5462. **E-mail:** kjaloma@benedictine.edu.

RESOURCES AND SERVICES

Information about online services, personal computer policies, library resources, international exchange programs, internship programs, and placement services at this institution and others can be found at **www. petersons.com/mba**

International Students

9% of students enrolled are international students.

Services and Facilities Financial aid is not available to international students.
Applying *Required:* TOEFL with recommended score of 570 (paper).
International Student Contact Ms. Carol Shomin, Administrative Director— Executive MBA, 1020 North 2nd Street, Atchison, KS 66002. **Phone:** 913-367-5340 Ext. 2589. **Fax:** 913-367-1049. **E-mail:** emba@benedictine.edu.

■ APPLICATION

Required Application form, baccalaureate/first degree, essay, interview, 2 letters of recommendation, transcripts of college work, 5 years of work experience.
Deadlines and Fees *Deadlines:* 8/10 for fall, 1/1 for spring, 4/10 for summer, 8/10 for fall (international), 1/1 for spring (international), 4/10 for summer (international). *Application fee:* $100, $100 (international).
Application Contact Ms. Carol Shomin, Administrative Director—Executive MBA, 1020 North 2nd Street, Atchison, KS 66002. **Phone:** 913-367-5340 Ext. 2589. **Toll-free Phone:** 800-467-5340. **Fax:** 913-367-1049. **E-mail:** emba@benedictine. edu.

Emporia State University

Emporia, Kansas

SCHOOL OF BUSINESS

Graduate Business Faculty
Full-time: 30

Student Body
Total: 61   Average Age: 30
Full-time: 48   Women: 31%
Part-time: 13

Admissions
Applications: 79   Average GPA: 3.1
Average GMAT: 455

Costs (1999–2000)
Full-time tuition: N/R

Emporia State University (continued)

Part-time tuition: $115 per credit hour (resident), $282 per credit hour (nonresident)

After Graduation (Class of 1998–99)
Employed within 3 months of graduation: 90%
Average starting salary: $34,000

DEGREE MBA

MBA—Master of Business Administration Full-time and part-time. At least 36 total credits required. 12 to 84 months to complete program. *Concentrations:* accounting.

COSTS
Tuition, state resident: *Part-time* $115 per credit hour. **Tuition, nonresident:** *Part-time* $282 per credit hour. **Graduate housing:** Room and board costs vary by number of occupants, type of accommodation, and type of board plan. *Typical cost:* $3774 (including board).

FINANCIAL AID (1999–2000)
Financial Aid Contact Wilma Kasnic, Director of Financial Aid, Emporia, KS 66801. **Phone:** 316-341-5457. **Fax:** 316-341-6088. **E-mail:** kasnicwi@emporia. edu.

RESOURCES AND SERVICES
Information about online services, personal computer policies, library resources, international exchange programs, internship programs, and placement services at this institution and others can be found at **www. petersons.com/mba**

International Students
36% of students enrolled are international students.

Services and Facilities Counseling/support services, ESL/language courses, international student housing, visa services.
Applying *Required:* Proof of adequate funds, proof of health/immunizations. *Recommended:* TOEFL.

International Student Contact James Harter, Assistant Vice President for International Education, 1200 Commercial Street, ESU Box 4041, Emporia, KS 66801-5087. **Phone:** 316-341-5374. **Fax:** 316-341-5884. **E-mail:** oisa@ emporia.edu.

■ APPLICATION
Required GMAT, application form, baccalaureate/first degree, transcripts of college work. **Recommended** 3 letters of recommendation, personal statement.
Deadlines and Fees Applications for domestic and international students are processed on a rolling basis. *Application fee:* $30, $75 (international).
Application Contact Dr. Donald S. Miller, Director, MBA Program, School of Business, Emporia, KS 66801. **Phone:** 316-341-5456. **Fax:** 316-341-5892. **E-mail:** millerdo@emporia.edu.

See full description on page 644.

Fort Hays State University

Hays, Kansas

COLLEGE OF BUSINESS AND LEADERSHIP

Graduate Business Faculty
Full-time: 12

Student Body
Total: 114
Full-time: 67

Part-time: 47
Average Age: 31

Admissions
Applications: 121
Admitted: 109
Enrolled: 88

Average GMAT: 500
Average GPA: 3.19

Costs (1999–2000)
Full-time tuition: N/R
Part-time tuition: $96 per credit (resident), $254 per credit (nonresident)

After Graduation (Class of 1998–99)
Employed within 3 months of graduation: 95%

DEGREE MBA

MBA—Master of Business Administration Full-time and part-time. 30 to 54 total credits required. 12 to 24 months to complete program. *Concentrations:* accounting, management.

COSTS
Tuition, state resident: *Part-time* $96 per credit. **Tuition, nonresident:** *Part-time* $254 per credit. **Graduate housing:** Room and board costs vary by number of occupants, type of accommodation, and type of board plan. *Typical cost:* $3800 (including board).

FINANCIAL AID (1999–2000)
27 students received aid, including loans, research assistantships, scholarships, teaching assistantships, and work study. Aid is available to part-time students. Financial aid application deadline: 3/1. **Financial Aid Contact** Financial Aid Office, 600 Park Street, Hays, KS 67601-4099. **Phone:** 785-628-4408. **Fax:** 785-628-4014. **E-mail:** finaid@bigcat.fhsu. edu.

RESOURCES AND SERVICES
Information about online services, personal computer policies, library resources, international exchange programs, internship programs, and placement services at this institution and others can be found at **www. petersons.com/mba**

International Students
20% of students enrolled are international students.

Services and Facilities Counseling/support services, ESL/language courses, international student organization, language tutoring. Financial aid is available to international students.
Applying *Required:* TOEFL with recommended score of 550 (paper), proof of adequate funds, proof of health/immunizations.
International Student Contact Mr. Noppadon Moapichai, International Student Advisor, SH 208, Hays, KS 67601-4099. **Phone:** 785-628-4276. **Fax:** 785-628-4113. **E-mail:** nmoapich@fhsu.edu.

■ APPLICATION
Required GMAT, application form, baccalaureate/first degree, 2 letters of recommendation, personal statement, resume/curriculum vitae, transcripts of college work.
Deadlines and Fees Applications for domestic and international students are processed on a rolling basis. *Application fee:* $25, $35 (international).
Application Contact Dr. Thomas Jackson, Dean, Graduate School, 600 Park Street, Hays, KS 67601-4099. **Phone:** 785-628-4236. **Fax:** 785-628-4479. **E-mail:** ldonaldson@fhsu.edu.

Friends University

Wichita, Kansas

GRADUATE PROGRAMS

Graduate Business Faculty
Full-time: 4
Part-time: 3

Student Body
Total: 68
Full-time: 68

Average Age: 36
Women: 28%

Admissions
Applications: 38
Admitted: 30

Enrolled: 30

Costs (1999–2000)
Full-time tuition: N/R
Part-time tuition: $490 per credit hour

After Graduation (Class of 1998–99)
Employed within 3 months of graduation: 100%
Average starting salary: $48,000

DEGREES MBA • MMIS • MS

MBA—Executive MBA Full-time. At least 36 total credits required. 23 months to complete program.

MMIS—Master of Management Information Systems Full-time. At least 36 total credits required. 22 months to complete program.

MS—Master of Science in Management Full-time. At least 36 total credits required. 22 months to complete program.

COSTS
Tuition *Part-time:* $490 per credit hour. Tuition varies by academic program.

FINANCIAL AID (1999–2000)
33 students received aid, including loans. **Financial Aid Contact** Ms. Myra Pfannenstile, Director of Financial Aid, 2100 West University Street, Wichita, KS 67213. **Phone:** 800-794-6945 Ext. 5658. **Fax:** 316-295-5703. **E-mail:** apply4$@friends.edu.

RESOURCES AND SERVICES
Information about online services, personal computer policies, library resources, international exchange programs, internship programs, and placement services at this institution and others can be found at **www.petersons.com/mba**

International Students
Services and Facilities Financial aid is not available to international students.
Applying *Required:* TOEFL with recommended score of 550 (paper).
International Student Contact Dr. William Wunder, Director of Executive MBA Program, 2100 West University Street, Wichita, KS 67213. **Phone:** 800-794-6345 Ext. 5591. **Fax:** 316-264-6251. **E-mail:** wundew@friends.edu.

■ APPLICATION
Required Application form, baccalaureate/first degree, interview, letter(s) of recommendation, personal statement, resume/curriculum vitae, transcripts of college work, 4 years of work experience.
Deadlines and Fees *Deadlines:* 1/1 for winter, 6/1 for spring, 6/1 for summer. *Application fee:* $45, $65 (international).
Application Contact Dr. William Wunder, Director of Executive MBA Program, 2100 West University Street, Wichita, KS 67213. **Phone:** 316-295-5591. **Toll-free Phone:** 800-794-6945. **Fax:** 316-264-6251. **E-mail:** wundew@friends.edu.

Kansas State University
Manhattan, Kansas

COLLEGE OF BUSINESS ADMINISTRATION

Admissions
Average GMAT: 540   Average GPA: 3.57

Costs (1999–2000)
Full-time tuition: N/R
Part-time tuition: $167 per credit hour (resident), $395 per credit hour (nonresident)

After Graduation (Class of 1998–99)
Employed within 3 months of graduation: 85%
Average starting salary: $43,000

Accreditation
AACSB—The International Association for Management Education

DEGREES M Acc • MBA

M Acc—Master of Accountancy Full-time and part-time. At least 30 total credits required. 12 to 18 months to complete program. *Concentrations:* accounting.

MBA—Master of Business Administration Full-time and part-time. 40 to 52 total credits required. 24 months to complete program. *Concentrations:* agribusiness, finance, international business, management, marketing.

COSTS
Tuition, state resident: *Part-time* $101 per credit hour. **Tuition, nonresident:** *Part-time* $329 per credit hour. **Required fees:** *Full-time* $572. *Part-time* $66 per credit hour. Tuition and fees vary by number of courses or credits taken, academic program, and local reciprocity agreements. **Graduate housing:** Room and board costs vary by number of occupants, type of accommodation, and type of board plan. *Typical cost:* $6000 (room only).

FINANCIAL AID (1999–2000)
25 students received aid, including fellowships, grants, loans, research assistantships, scholarships, teaching assistantships, and work study. Aid is available to part-time students. Financial aid application deadline: 3/1. **Financial Aid Contact** Dr. Cynthia S. McCahon, Director of Graduate Studies, College of Business Administration, Calvin Hall #110, Manhattan, KS 66506-0501. **Phone:** 785-532-7190. **Fax:** 785-532-7216. **E-mail:** cmccahon@ksu.edu.

RESOURCES AND SERVICES
Information about online services, personal computer policies, library resources, international exchange programs, internship programs, and placement services at this institution and others can be found at **www.petersons.com/mba**

International Students
Services and Facilities Counseling/support services, ESL/language courses, housing location assistance, international student housing, international student organization, language tutoring, orientation, visa services. Financial aid is not available to international students.
Applying *Required:* TOEFL with recommended score of 213 (computer) or 550 (paper), proof of adequate funds.
International Student Contact Dr. Cynthia S. McCahon, Director of Graduate Studies, College of Business Administration, Calvin Hall #110, Manhattan, KS 66506-0501. **Phone:** 785-532-7190. **Fax:** 785-532-7216. **E-mail:** cmccahon@ksu.edu.

■ APPLICATION
Required GMAT, application form, baccalaureate/first degree, 3 letters of recommendation, personal statement, resume/curriculum vitae, transcripts of college work. **Recommended** Work experience.
Deadlines and Fees *Deadlines:* 7/1 for fall, 1/1 for spring, 3/1 for fall (international), 9/1 for spring (international). *Application fee:* $45, $45 (international).
Application Contact Dr. Cynthia S. McCahon, Director of Graduate Studies, College of Business Administration, Calvin Hall #110, Manhattan, KS 66506-0501. **Phone:** 785-532-7190. **Fax:** 785-532-7216. **E-mail:** cmccahon@ksu.edu.

Kansas Wesleyan University
Salina, Kansas

PROGRAM IN BUSINESS ADMINISTRATION

DEGREE MBA

MBA—Master of Business Administration Full-time. At least 30 total credits required. 18 to 84 months to complete program. *Concentrations:* health care.

RESOURCES AND SERVICES
Information about online services, personal computer policies, library resources, international exchange programs, internship programs, and placement services at this institution and others can be found at **www.petersons.com/mba**

International Students
Services and Facilities Counseling/support services.
International Student Contact International Office, 100 East Claflin, Salina, KS 67401-6196. **Phone:** 785-827-5541.

■ APPLICATION
Application Contact Chair, MBA Program, 100 East Claflin Avenue, Salina, KS 67401. **Phone:** 785-827-5541 Ext. 2238. **Toll-free Phone:** 800-874-1154 Ext. 2238.

MidAmerica Nazarene University
Olathe, Kansas

GRADUATE STUDIES IN MANAGEMENT

Graduate Business Faculty
Full-time: 5   Part-time: 3

Student Body
Total: 128   Average Age: 36
Full-time: 128   Women: 43%

Admissions
Applications: 46   Enrolled: 42
Admitted: 43   Average GPA: 3.36

Costs (1999–2000)
Full-time tuition: $6700 per academic year
Part-time tuition: N/R

DEGREE MBA

MBA—Master of Business Administration Full-time. At least 36 total credits required. 22 to 25 months to complete program.

COSTS
Tuition *Full-time:* $6700. Tuition varies by number of courses or credits taken.

MidAmerica Nazarene University (continued)

FINANCIAL AID (1999–2000)

30 students received aid. **Financial Aid Contact** Ms. Deb Ellis, Assistant Director of Fiscal Operations, 2030 East College Way, Olathe, KS 66062-1899. **Phone:** 913-791-3298. **Fax:** 913-791-3401. **E-mail:** dellis@mnu.edu.

RESOURCES AND SERVICES

Information about online services, personal computer policies, library resources, international exchange programs, internship programs, and placement services at this institution and others can be found at **www.petersons.com/mba**

International Students

2% of students enrolled are international students.

Services and Facilities Counseling/support services, ESL/language courses, visa services. Financial aid is available to international students.
Applying *Required:* TOEFL with recommended score of 600 (paper), proof of adequate funds. *Recommended:* Proof of health/immunizations.
International Student Contact Ms. Peggy Ulmet, International Student Advisor, 2030 East College Way, Olathe, KS 66062-1899. **Phone:** 913-782-3750 Ext. 181. **Fax:** 913-791-3285. **E-mail:** pulmet@mnu.edu.

■ APPLICATION

Required Application form, baccalaureate/first degree, essay, interview, 2 letters of recommendation, personal statement, transcripts of college work, 2 years of work experience.
Deadlines and Fees *Deadlines:* 8/1 for fall, 2/1 for spring. *Application fee:* $75, $75 (international).
Application Contact Dr. Mary Jones, Director, Graduate Studies in Management, 2030 East College Way, Olathe, KS 66062-1899. **Phone:** 913-791-3276. **Fax:** 913-791-3409. **E-mail:** mejones@mnu.edu.

Newman University

Wichita, Kansas

PROGRAM IN ORGANIZATIONAL LEADERSHIP

DEGREE MS

MS—Master of Science in Organizational Leadership At least 33 total credits required.

RESOURCES AND SERVICES

Information about online services, personal computer policies, library resources, international exchange programs, internship programs, and placement services at this institution and others can be found at **www.petersons.com/mba**

International Students

International Student Contact Kathi Samuels, Advisor, 3100 McCormick Avenue, Wichita, KS 67213-2097. **Phone:** 316-942-4291 Ext. 160. **E-mail:** samuelsk@newmanu.edu.

■ APPLICATION

Application Contact Coordinator of Graduate Admissions, 3100 McCormick Avenue, Wichita, KS 67213-2097. **Phone:** 316-942-4291 Ext. 355. **Toll-free Phone:** 316-945-NEWU.

Ottawa University

Ottawa, Kansas

GRADUATE STUDIES-KANSAS CITY

Graduate Business Faculty
Full-time: 6 — Part-time: 47

Student Body
Total: 253 — Average Age: 43
Full-time: 11 — Women: 77%
Part-time: 242

Admissions
Applications: 79 — Enrolled: 69
Admitted: 75

Costs (1999–2000)
Full-time tuition: N/R
Part-time tuition: $215 per credit hour

DEGREE MA

MA—Master of Arts in Human Resources Part-time. *Distance learning option.* At least 36 total credits required. Minimum of 24 months to complete program. *Concentrations:* human resources, management, management consulting.

COSTS

Tuition *Part-time:* $215 per credit hour. **Required fees:** Tuition and fees vary by campus location and academic program.

FINANCIAL AID (1999–2000)

Loans. Aid is available to part-time students. **Financial Aid Contact** Howard Fischer, Director of Financial Aid Operations, 2340 West Mission Lane, Phoenix, AZ 85021. **Phone:** 800-235-9586. **Fax:** 602-371-0035. **E-mail:** fischerh@ottawa.edu.

RESOURCES AND SERVICES

Information about online services, personal computer policies, library resources, international exchange programs, internship programs, and placement services at this institution and others can be found at **www.petersons.com/mba**

■ APPLICATION

Required Application form, baccalaureate/first degree, essay, interview, 3 letters of recommendation, personal statement, resume/curriculum vitae, transcripts of college work.
Deadlines and Fees Applications for domestic students are processed on a rolling basis.
Application Contact Dr. Gus Breytspraak, 10865 Grandview, Building 20, Overland Park, KS 66210. **Phone:** 913-451-1431. **Toll-free Phone:** 800-235-9586. **Fax:** 913-451-0806. **E-mail:** breytspraak@ottawa.edu.

Pittsburg State University

Pittsburg, Kansas

KELCE COLLEGE OF BUSINESS

Graduate Business Faculty
Full-time: 28

Student Body
Total: 86 — Average Age: 27
Full-time: 67 — Women: 31%
Part-time: 19

Admissions
Applications: 250 — Average GMAT: 516
Admitted: 125 — Average GPA: 3.3
Enrolled: 28

Costs (1999–2000)
Full-time tuition: $2604 per academic year (resident), $6620 per academic year (nonresident)
Part-time tuition: $111 per credit hour (resident), $278 per credit hour (nonresident)

After Graduation (Class of 1998–99)
Employed within 3 months of graduation: 96%
Average starting salary: $42,000

Accreditation
AACSB—The International Association for Management Education

DEGREE MBA

MBA—Master of Business Administration Full-time and part-time. *Distance learning option.* 34 to 70 total credits required. 12 to 72 months to complete program. *Concentrations:* accounting, management.

COSTS

Tuition, state resident: *Full-time* $2604. *Part-time* $111 per credit hour. **Tuition, nonresident:** *Full-time* $6620. *Part-time* $278 per credit hour. **Tuition, international:** *Full-time* $6620. **Graduate housing:** Room and board costs vary by number of occupants, type of accommodation, and type of board plan. *Typical cost:* $3747 (including board).

FINANCIAL AID (1999–2000)

24 students received aid, including research assistantships, scholarships, teaching assistantships, and work study. Financial aid application

deadline: 4/1. **Financial Aid Contact** Ms. Joanna McCormick, Director, Financial Aid, 1701 South Broadway, Pittsburg, KS 66762. **Phone:** 316-235-4240. **Fax:** 316-235-7515. **E-mail:** jmccormi@pittstate.edu.

RESOURCES AND SERVICES

Information about online services, personal computer policies, library resources, international exchange programs, internship programs, and placement services at this institution and others can be found at **www.petersons.com/mba**

International Students

53% of students enrolled are international students.

Services and Facilities Counseling/support services, ESL/language courses, international student organization. Financial aid is available to international students. **Applying** *Required:* TOEFL with recommended score of 550 (paper), proof of adequate funds.

International Student Contact Mr. Chuck Olcese, Director, International Student Services, 1701 South Broadway, Pittsburg, KS 66762. **Phone:** 316-235-4680. **Fax:** 316-235-4962. **E-mail:** colcese@pittstate.edu.

■ APPLICATION

Required GMAT, application form, baccalaureate/first degree, transcripts of college work. **Recommended** Letter(s) of recommendation, work experience.

Deadlines and Fees *Deadlines:* 7/15 for fall, 12/15 for spring, 5/1 for summer, 7/15 for fall (international), 12/15 for spring (international), 5/1 for summer (international). *Application fee:* $40 (international).

Application Contact Dr. Russell Hardin, Director of MBA Program, Kelce College of Business, Pittsburg, KS 66762. **Phone:** 316-235-4598. **Fax:** 316-235-4578. **E-mail:** jhardin@pittstate.edu.

Saint Mary College

Leavenworth, Kansas

DEPARTMENT OF BUSINESS, ECONOMICS AND ACCOUNTING

Graduate Business Faculty
Full-time: 4 — Part-time: 3

Student Body
Total: 64 — Average Age: 38
Full-time: 6 — Women: 41%
Part-time: 58

Admissions
Applications: 57 — Enrolled: 44
Admitted: 49 — Average GPA: 3.5

Costs (1999–2000)
Full-time tuition: N/R
Part-time tuition: $270 per credit hour

After Graduation (Class of 1998–99)
Employed within 3 months of graduation: 99%

DEGREES MBA • MS

MBA—Master of Business Administration Full-time and part-time. At least 36 total credits required. 18 to 60 months to complete program.

MS—Master of Science in Management Full-time and part-time. At least 36 total credits required. 18 to 24 months to complete program. *Concentrations:* health care, management.

COSTS

Tuition *Part-time:* $270 per credit hour. Tuition varies by campus location.

FINANCIAL AID (1999–2000)

Loans. **Financial Aid Contact** Ms. Judy Wiedower, Director of Financial Aid, 4100 South Fourth Street Trafficway, Leavenworth, KS 66048-5082. **Phone:** 913-758-6314. **Fax:** 913-758-6140. **E-mail:** wiedower@hub.smcks.edu.

RESOURCES AND SERVICES

Information about online services, personal computer policies, library resources, international exchange programs, internship programs, and placement services at this institution and others can be found at **www.petersons.com/mba**

International Students

2% of students enrolled are international students.

Services and Facilities Financial aid is not available to international students. **Applying** *Required:* TOEFL with recommended score of 550 (paper), proof of adequate funds, proof of health/immunizations.

International Student Contact Mrs. Wanda Owen, Associate Registrar, 4100 South Fourth Street Trafficway, Leavenworth, KS 66048-5082. **Phone:** 913-758-6121. **Fax:** 913-758-6140. **E-mail:** owenw@hub.smcks.edu.

■ APPLICATION

Required Application form, baccalaureate/first degree, essay, interview, 3 letters of recommendation, transcripts of college work. **Recommended** Personal statement.

Deadlines and Fees *Application fee:* $20, $20 (international).

Application Contact Mr. David Jones, Instructor in Business, 11413 Pflumm Road, Overland Park, KS 66215. **Phone:** 913-345-8288. **Fax:** 913-345-2802. **E-mail:** jonesd@hub.smcks.edu.

University of Kansas

Lawrence, Kansas

SCHOOL OF BUSINESS

Graduate Business Faculty
Full-time: 56 — Part-time: 4

Student Body
Total: 527 — Average Age: 29
Full-time: 226 — Women: 32%
Part-time: 301

Admissions
Applications: 290 — Average GMAT: 606
Admitted: 178 — Average GPA: 3.26
Enrolled: 129

Costs (1999–2000)
Full-time tuition: $5844 per academic year (resident), $13,808 per academic year (nonresident)
Part-time tuition: $201 per credit hour (resident)

After Graduation (Class of 1998–99)
Employed within 3 months of graduation: 93%
Average starting salary: $56,000

Accreditation
AACSB—The International Association for Management Education

DEGREES MBA • MS

MBA—Evening MBA Full-time and part-time. At least 48 total credits required. 36 to 60 months to complete program. *Concentrations:* finance, human resources, information management, international business, management, management science, marketing, strategic management, technology management.

MBA—Full-time MBA Full-time. At least 60 total credits required. 24 months to complete program. *Concentrations:* finance, human resources, information management, international business, management, management science, marketing, strategic management, technology management.

MS—Master of Science in Business I Full-time and part-time. At least 30 total credits required. 12 to 24 months to complete program. *Concentrations:* human resources, information management, international business, organizational behavior/development, strategic management, technology management.

MS—Master of Science in Business II Full-time and part-time. At least 64 total credits required. 24 to 48 months to complete program. *Concentrations:* information management.

COSTS

Tuition, state resident: *Full-time* $3516. *Part-time* $103 per credit hour. **Tuition, nonresident:** *Full-time* $11,480. **Required fees:** *Full-time* $2328. *Part-time* $98 per credit hour. Tuition and fees vary by number of courses or credits taken and campus location. **Graduate housing:** Room and board costs vary by number of occupants, type of accommodation, and type of board plan. *Typical cost:* $3950 (including board).

FINANCIAL AID (1999–2000)

40 students received aid, including fellowships, research assistantships, scholarships, and teaching assistantships. Financial aid application deadline: 3/1. **Financial Aid Contact** Mr. David Collins, Associate Director of Masters Programs, 206 Summerfield Hall, School of Business, Lawrence, KS 66045. **Phone:** 785-864-4254. **Fax:** 785-864-5328. **E-mail:** bschoolgrad@ukans.edu.

RESOURCES AND SERVICES

Information about online services, personal computer policies, library resources, international exchange programs, internship programs, and

University of Kansas (continued)

placement services at this institution and others can be found at **www.petersons.com/mba**

International Students
10% of students enrolled are international students.

Services and Facilities Counseling/support services, ESL/language courses, orientation, visa services. Financial aid is available to international students.
Applying *Required:* TOEFL with recommended score of 250 (computer) or 600 (paper), proof of adequate funds, proof of health/immunizations.
International Student Contact Mr. David Collins, Associate Director of Masters Programs, 206 Summerfield Hall, School of Business, Lawrence, KS 66045. **Phone:** 785-864-4254. **Fax:** 785-864-5328. **E-mail:** dcollins@ukans.edu.

■ APPLICATION
Required GMAT, application form, baccalaureate/first degree, essay, interview, 2 letters of recommendation, personal statement, resume/curriculum vitae, transcripts of college work. **Recommended** Work experience.
Deadlines and Fees *Deadlines:* 5/1 for fall, 10/1 for spring, 3/1 for summer, 5/1 for fall (international), 10/1 for spring (international), 3/1 for summer (international). *Application fee:* $50, $50 (international).
Application Contact Mr. David Collins, Associate Director of Masters Programs, 206 Summerfield Hall, School of Business, Lawrence, KS 66045. **Phone:** 785-864-4254. **Toll-free Phone:** 800-642-2425. **Fax:** 785-864-5328. **E-mail:** bschoolgrad@ukans.edu.

See full description on page 910.

Washburn University of Topeka
Topeka, Kansas

SCHOOL OF BUSINESS

Graduate Business Faculty
Full-time: 19 | Part-time: 4

Student Body
Total: 140
Full-time: 21 | Average Age: 30
Part-time: 119 | Women: 49%

Admissions
Applications: 43 | Average GMAT: 513
Admitted: 32 | Average GPA: 3.2
Enrolled: 26

Costs (1999–2000)
Full-time tuition: N/R
Part-time tuition: $139 per credit hour (resident), $286 per credit hour (nonresident)

After Graduation (Class of 1998–99)
Employed within 3 months of graduation: 96%
Average starting salary: $38,829

DEGREE MBA

MBA—Master of Business Administration Full-time and part-time. 30 to 55 total credits required. 12 to 72 months to complete program. *Concentrations:* accounting.

COSTS
Tuition, state resident: *Part-time* $139 per credit hour. **Tuition, nonresident:** *Part-time* $286 per credit hour. **Required fees:** *Full-time* $50. *Part-time* $13 per semester. Tuition and fees vary by number of courses or credits taken.

FINANCIAL AID (1999–2000)
30 students received aid, including loans, scholarships, and work study. Aid is available to part-time students. Financial aid application deadline: 3/1. **Financial Aid Contact** Ms. Annita Huff, Director, Financial Aid, 1700 SW College Avenue, Topeka, KS 66621. **Phone:** 785-231-1010 Ext. 1151. **Fax:** 785-231-1079. **E-mail:** zzahuff@washburn.edu.

RESOURCES AND SERVICES
Information about online services, personal computer policies, library resources, international exchange programs, internship programs, and placement services at this institution and others can be found at **www.petersons.com/mba**

International Students
14% of students enrolled are international students.

Services and Facilities Counseling/support services, ESL/language courses, housing location assistance, international student housing, visa services. Financial aid is not available to international students.
Applying *Required:* TOEFL with recommended score of 213 (computer) or 550 (paper), TWE with recommended score of 5, proof of adequate funds. *Recommended:* TSE.
International Student Contact Dr. William A. Langdon, Chair, Institute of International Programs, 1700 SW College Avenue. **Phone:** 785-231-1010 Ext. 1714. **Fax:** 785-231-1067. **E-mail:** zzisa@washburn.edu.

■ APPLICATION
Required GMAT, application form, baccalaureate/first degree, 2 letters of recommendation, transcripts of college work. School will accept GRE. **Recommended** Interview, personal statement, resume/curriculum vitae, work experience.
Deadlines and Fees *Deadlines:* 7/1 for fall, 11/15 for spring, 4/15 for summer, 7/1 for fall (international), 11/15 for spring (international), 4/15 for summer (international). *Application fee:* $40 (international).
Application Contact Dr. Russell Smith, Director, Graduate Programs, School of Business, 1700 SW College Avenue, Topeka, KS 66621. **Phone:** 785-231-1010 Ext. 1307. **Fax:** 785-231-1063. **E-mail:** mba@washburn.edu.

Wichita State University
Wichita, Kansas

W. FRANK BARTON SCHOOL OF BUSINESS

Graduate Business Faculty
Full-time: 42 | Part-time: 6

Student Body
Total: 235
Full-time: 57 | Average Age: 29
Part-time: 178 | Women: 40%

Admissions
Applications: 147 | Average GMAT: 514
Admitted: 95 | Average GPA: 3.29
Enrolled: 71

Costs (1999–2000)
Full-time tuition: N/R
Part-time tuition: $117 per credit (resident), $346 per credit (nonresident)

After Graduation (Class of 1998–99)
Employed within 3 months of graduation: 92%
Average starting salary: $54,000

Accreditation
AACSB—The International Association for Management Education

DEGREES MA • MBA • MBA/MS • MPA • MS

MA—Master of Arts in Economics Full-time and part-time. 30 to 39 total credits required. 18 to 72 months to complete program. *Concentrations:* managerial economics.

MBA—Executive MBA Part-time. At least 36 total credits required. 22 months to complete program.

MBA—Master of Business Administration Full-time and part-time. 30 to 58 total credits required. 15 to 72 months to complete program.

MBA/MS—Master of Science in Business/Master of Science in Nursing Full-time and part-time. At least 63 total credits required. 36 to 72 months to complete program.

MPA—Master of Public Accounting Full-time and part-time. At least 31 total credits required. 12 to 72 months to complete program. *Concentrations:* accounting.

MS—Master of Science in Business Full-time and part-time. 31 to 62 total credits required. 15 to 72 months to complete program. *Concentrations:* entrepreneurship, finance, human resources, management, marketing.

COSTS
Tuition, state resident: *Part-time* $117 per credit. **Tuition, nonresident:** *Part-time* $346 per credit. Tuition varies by academic program and local reciprocity agreements. **Graduate housing:** Room and board costs vary by number of occupants, type of accommodation, and type of board plan. *Typical cost:* $5300 (including board).

FINANCIAL AID (1999–2000)
50 students received aid, including fellowships, loans, scholarships, and teaching assistantships. Financial aid application deadline: 3/30.

Financial Aid Contact Ms. Deb Byers, Director, Financial Planning and Assistance, 1845 North Fairmount, Wichita, KS 67260-0024. **Phone:** 800-522-2978. **Fax:** 316-978-3396.

RESOURCES AND SERVICES
Information about online services, personal computer policies, library resources, international exchange programs, internship programs, and placement services at this institution and others can be found at **www.petersons.com/mba**

International Students
20% of students enrolled are international students.

Services and Facilities Counseling/support services, ESL/language courses, international student housing, international student organization, orientation, visa services. Financial aid is available to international students.
Applying *Required:* TOEFL with recommended score of 550 (paper), proof of adequate funds.
International Student Contact Mr. John Koppenhaver, Director, Office of International Program, 1845 North Fairmount, Wichita, KS 67260-0088. **Phone:** 316-978-3232. **Fax:** 316-978-3777. **E-mail:** koppenha@twsuvm.uc.twsu.edu.

■ APPLICATION
Required GMAT, application form, baccalaureate/first degree, transcripts of college work. **Recommended** Interview, resume/curriculum vitae, work experience.
Deadlines and Fees *Deadlines:* 7/1 for fall, 11/1 for spring, 4/30 for fall (international), 8/31 for spring (international). *Application fee:* $25, $50 (international).
Application Contact Dr. Donald Christensen, Director, Graduate Studies in Business, 1845 North Fairmount, Wichita, KS 67260-0048. **Phone:** 316-978-3230. **Fax:** 316-978-3767. **E-mail:** christen@twsuvm.uc.twsu.edu.

KENTUCKY

Bellarmine College
Louisville, Kentucky

W. FIELDING RUBEL SCHOOL OF BUSINESS

Graduate Business Faculty
Full-time: 15 — Part-time: 1

Student Body
Total: 209
Full-time: 49 — Average Age: 28
Part-time: 160 — Women: 43%

Admissions
Applications: 73 — Average GMAT: 505
Admitted: 69 — Average GPA: 3.15
Enrolled: 63

Costs (1999–2000)
Full-time tuition: N/R
Part-time tuition: N/R

After Graduation (Class of 1998–99)
Employed within 3 months of graduation: 100%

DEGREES MBA

MBA—Executive MBA Part-time. At least 42 total credits required. 16 months to complete program.
MBA—Weekend MBA Full-time and part-time. At least 42 total credits required. 22 months to complete program.
MBA—Weeknight MBA Full-time and part-time. At least 42 total credits required. 30 to 72 months to complete program.

FINANCIAL AID (1999–2000)
Work study. Aid is available to part-time students. Financial aid application deadline: 7/1. **Financial Aid Contact** Mr. David Wuinee, Director of Financial Aid, 2001 Newburg Road, Louisville, KY 40205-0671. **Phone:** 502-452-8131. **Fax:** 502-452-8002.

RESOURCES AND SERVICES
Information about online services, personal computer policies, library resources, international exchange programs, internship programs, and

placement services at this institution and others can be found at **www.petersons.com/mba**

International Students
1.0% of students enrolled are international students.
Services and Facilities Counseling/support services. Financial aid is not available to international students.
Applying *Required:* TOEFL, proof of adequate funds.
International Student Contact Laura Richardson, Director, MBA Programs, 2001 Newburg Road, Louisville, KY 40205-0671. **Phone:** 502-452-8258. **Fax:** 502-452-8013. **E-mail:** lrichardson@bellarmine.edu.

■ APPLICATION
Required GMAT, application form, baccalaureate/first degree, essay, 2 letters of recommendation, personal statement, resume/curriculum vitae, transcripts of college work. **Recommended** Work experience.
Deadlines and Fees Applications for domestic and international students are processed on a rolling basis. *Application fee:* $25, $25 (international).
Application Contact Laura Richardson, Director, MBA Programs, 2001 Newburg Road, Louisville, KY 40205-0671. **Phone:** 502-452-8258. **Fax:** 502-452-8013. **E-mail:** lrichardson@bellarmine.edu.

Brescia University
Owensboro, Kentucky

PROGRAM IN MANAGEMENT

Graduate Business Faculty
Full-time: 4 — Part-time: 1

Student Body
Total: 37
Part-time: 37 — Average Age: 36 / Women: 49%

Admissions
Applications: 30 — Average GMAT: 468
Admitted: 28 — Average GPA: 3.17
Enrolled: 22

Costs (1999–2000)
Full-time tuition: N/R
Part-time tuition: $200 per credit hour

DEGREE MSM

MSM—Master of Science in Management Part-time. At least 32 total credits required. 22 to 72 months to complete program. *Concentrations:* human resources, international business, international economics, leadership, organizational management, strategic management.

COSTS
Tuition *Part-time:* $200 per credit hour. Tuition varies by number of courses or credits taken.

FINANCIAL AID (1999–2000)
5 students received aid, including loans. Aid is available to part-time students. Financial aid application deadline: 3/1. **Financial Aid Contact** Mrs. Vivian Rinaldo, Student Financial Aid Director, 717 Frederica Street, Owensboro, KY 42301-3023. **Phone:** 270-686-4290 Ext. 290. **Fax:** 270-686-4266. **E-mail:** vivianp@brescia.edu.

RESOURCES AND SERVICES
Information about online services, personal computer policies, library resources, international exchange programs, internship programs, and placement services at this institution and others can be found at **www.petersons.com/mba**

International Students
3% of students enrolled are international students.
Services and Facilities Counseling/support services. Financial aid is not available to international students.
Applying *Required:* TOEFL with recommended score of 213 (computer) or 550 (paper), proof of adequate funds.
International Student Contact Dr. Barry McArdle, Dean of Student Development, 717 Frederica Street, Owensboro, KY 42301-3023. **Phone:** 270-686-4332 Ext. 332. **Fax:** 270-686-4266. **E-mail:** barrym@brescia.edu.

Brescia University (continued)

■ APPLICATION

Required Application form, baccalaureate/first degree, resume/curriculum vitae, transcripts of college work. School will accept GMAT. **Recommended** Interview, work experience.

Deadlines and Fees *Deadlines:* 8/19 for fall, 1/13 for spring, 8/19 for fall (international), 1/13 for winter (international). *Application fee:* $50, $50 (international).

Application Contact Mr. Rick Eber, Director of Admissions, Admissions Office, 717 Frederica Street, Owensboro, KY 42301-3023. **Phone:** 270-686-4241 Ext. 241. **Toll-free Phone:** 800-877-BRESCIA. **Fax:** 270-686-4201. **E-mail:** admissions@brescia.edu.

Eastern Kentucky University

Richmond, Kentucky

COLLEGE OF BUSINESS AND TECHNOLOGY

Graduate Business Faculty
Full-time: 17

Student Body

Total: 82	Average Age: 30
Full-time: 13	Women: 37%
Part-time: 69	

Admissions

Applications: 55	Average GMAT: 460
Admitted: 54	Average GPA: 3.06
Enrolled: 29	

Costs (1999–2000)
Full-time tuition: N/R
Part-time tuition: $145 per credit hour (resident), $391 per credit hour (nonresident)

After Graduation (Class of 1998–99)
Employed within 3 months of graduation: 90%

DEGREE MBA

MBA—Master of Business Administration Full-time and part-time. 30 to 48 total credits required. 12 to 84 months to complete program.

COSTS

Tuition, state resident: *Part-time* $145 per credit hour. **Tuition, nonresident:** *Part-time* $391 per credit hour. Tuition varies by number of courses or credits taken. **Graduate housing:** Room and board costs vary by campus location, number of occupants, type of accommodation, and type of board plan. *Typical cost:* $5000 (including board).

FINANCIAL AID (1999–2000)

12 students received aid, including research assistantships, teaching assistantships, and work study. Aid is available to part-time students. **Financial Aid Contact** Ms. Susan Luhman, Director, Student Financial Assistance, Coates Box 4A, Richmond, KY 40475-3101. **Phone:** 606-622-2361. **Fax:** 606-622-1020. **E-mail:** finaid@acs.eku.edu.

RESOURCES AND SERVICES

Information about online services, personal computer policies, library resources, international exchange programs, internship programs, and placement services at this institution and others can be found at **www.petersons.com/mba**

International Students

11% of students enrolled are international students.

Services and Facilities Counseling/support services, ESL/language courses. Financial aid is available to international students.
Applying *Required:* TOEFL with recommended score of 550 (paper), proof of adequate funds.
International Student Contact Dr. Neil Wright, Director of International Education, Case Annex, Room 181, Richmond, KY 40475-3140. **Phone:** 606-622-1478. **Fax:** 606-622-1020. **E-mail:** intwrigh@acs.eku.edu.

■ APPLICATION

Required Application form, baccalaureate/first degree, essay, personal statement, transcripts of college work. School will accept GMAT.
Deadlines and Fees *Deadlines:* 7/20 for fall, 11/20 for spring, 5/20 for summer, 7/20 for fall (international), 11/20 for spring (international), 5/20 for summer (international).

Application Contact Dr. Jack L. Dyer, MBA Director, 317 Combs Building, 521 Lancaster Avenue, Richmond, KY 40475-3102. **Phone:** 606-622-1775. **Toll-free Phone:** 800-465-9191. **Fax:** 606-622-1413. **E-mail:** cbomba@acs.eku.edu.

Morehead State University

Morehead, Kentucky

COLLEGE OF BUSINESS

Graduate Business Faculty

Full-time: 26	Part-time: 2

Student Body

Total: 381	Average Age: 25
Full-time: 131	Women: 47%
Part-time: 250	

Admissions

Applications: 129	Average GMAT: 489
Admitted: 109	Average GPA: 3.2

Costs (1999–2000)
Full-time tuition: $2640 per academic year (resident), $2640 per academic year (nonresident)
Part-time tuition: $177 per credit hour (resident), $177 per credit hour (nonresident)

Accreditation
ACBSP—The American Council of Business Schools and Programs

DEGREES MBA

MBA—Master of Business Administration in Bank Management Full-time and part-time. *Distance learning option.* At least 36 total credits required. Minimum of 12 months to complete program. *Concentrations:* banking.

MBA—Master of Business Administration in Computer Information Systems Full-time and part-time. *Distance learning option.* At least 36 total credits required. Minimum of 12 months to complete program.

MBA—Master of Business Administration in Human Resource Management Full-time and part-time. *Distance learning option.* At least 36 total credits required. Minimum of 12 months to complete program. *Concentrations:* banking, health care, human resources, management, management information systems.

COSTS

Tuition, state resident: *Full-time* $2640. *Part-time* $177 per credit hour. **Tuition, nonresident:** *Full-time* $2640. *Part-time* $177 per credit hour. Tuition varies by campus location. **Graduate housing:** Room and board costs vary by number of occupants and type of accommodation. *Typical cost:* $1476 (room only).

FINANCIAL AID (1999–2000)

Research assistantships, scholarships, teaching assistantships, and work study. Financial aid application deadline: 4/1. **Financial Aid Contact** Mr. Tim Rhodes, Director of Financial Aid, HM 305, Morehead, KY 40351. **Phone:** 606-783-2011. **Fax:** 606-783-2293. **E-mail:** t.rhodes@morehead-st.edu.

RESOURCES AND SERVICES

Information about online services, personal computer policies, library resources, international exchange programs, internship programs, and placement services at this institution and others can be found at **www.petersons.com/mba**

International Students

9% of students enrolled are international students.

Services and Facilities Counseling/support services, ESL/language courses, language tutoring. Financial aid is available to international students.
Applying *Required:* TOEFL with recommended score of 525 (paper), proof of adequate funds.
International Student Contact Mr. Clement Liew, International Student Coordinator, UPO 330, Morehead, KY 40351. **Phone:** 606-783-2759. **E-mail:** c.liew@morehead-st.edu.

■ APPLICATION

Required GMAT, application form, baccalaureate/first degree, transcripts of college work.

Application Contact Mr. Keith Moore, MBA Program Director, 213-D Combs Building, Morehead, KY 40351. **Phone:** 606-783-2183. **Fax:** 606-783-5025. **E-mail:** msu-mba@morehead-st.edu.

Murray State University

Murray, Kentucky

COLLEGE OF BUSINESS AND PUBLIC AFFAIRS

Graduate Business Faculty
Full-time: 26

Student Body
Total: 160
Full-time: 75
Part-time: 85

Average Age: 31
Women: 43%

Admissions
Applications: 121
Admitted: 91
Enrolled: 47

Average GMAT: 493
Average GPA: 3.15

Costs (1999–2000)
Full-time tuition: $2674 per academic year (resident), $7446 per academic year (nonresident)
Part-time tuition: $156 per hour (resident), $418 per hour (nonresident)

Accreditation
AACSB—The International Association for Management Education

DEGREES MBA • MPA • MS

MBA—Master of Business Administration Full-time and part-time. *Distance learning option.* At least 67 total credits required. 12 to 96 months to complete program. *Concentrations: accounting.*

MPA—Master of Public Administration Full-time and part-time. *Distance learning option.* At least 36 total credits required. 18 to 96 months to complete program.

MS—Master of Science in Economics Full-time and part-time. At least 30 total credits required. 18 to 96 months to complete program.

MS—Telecommunications Systems Management Full-time and part-time. At least 36 total credits required. 18 to 96 months to complete program.

COSTS

Tuition, state resident: *Full-time* $2674. *Part-time* $156 per hour. **Tuition, nonresident:** *Full-time* $7446. *Part-time* $418 per hour. **Tuition, international:** *Full-time* $7446. Tuition varies by number of courses or credits taken and local reciprocity agreements. **Required fees:** Tuition and fees vary by number of courses or credits taken. **Graduate housing:** Room and board costs vary by number of occupants, type of accommodation, and type of board plan. *Typical cost:* $2985 (including board), $1940 (room only).

FINANCIAL AID (1999–2000)

20 students received aid, including research assistantships, scholarships, teaching assistantships, and work study. Financial aid application deadline: 4/1. **Financial Aid Contact** Mr. Charles Vinson, Director, Student Financial Aid, PO Box 9, Murray, KY 42071. **Phone:** 270-762-2596. **Fax:** 270-762-3050. **E-mail:** charles.vinson@murraystate.edu.

RESOURCES AND SERVICES

Information about online services, personal computer policies, library resources, international exchange programs, internship programs, and placement services at this institution and others can be found at **www.petersons.com/mba**

International Students

30% of students enrolled are international students.

Services and Facilities Counseling/support services, ESL/language courses, visa services. Financial aid is not available to international students.
Applying *Required:* TOEFL with recommended score of 525 (paper), proof of adequate funds.
International Student Contact Dr. Michael Basile, Director, Institute for International Programs, PO Box 9, Murray, KY 42071. **Phone:** 270-762-4411. **Fax:** 270-762-3237. **E-mail:** michael.basile@murraystate.edu.

■ APPLICATION

Required GMAT, application form, baccalaureate/first degree, transcripts of college work.

Deadlines and Fees *Application fee:* $20, $20 (international).

Application Contact Dr. Nkombo Muuka, MBA Director, 109 Business Building, Murray, KY 42071. **Phone:** 270-762-6970. **Toll-free Phone:** 800-272-4678. **Fax:** 270-762-3482. **E-mail:** cbpa@murraystate.edu.

Northern Kentucky University

Highland Heights, Kentucky

COLLEGE OF BUSINESS

Graduate Business Faculty
Full-time: 16

Part-time: 6

Student Body
Total: 182
Full-time: 12
Part-time: 170

Average Age: 33
Women: 42%

Admissions
Applications: 65
Admitted: 43
Enrolled: 30

Average GMAT: 518
Average GPA: 3.11

Costs (1999–2000)
Full-time tuition: $2858 per academic year (resident), $7298 per academic year (nonresident)
Part-time tuition: $159 per semester hour (resident), $405 per semester hour (nonresident)

Accreditation
AACSB—The International Association for Management Education

DEGREES JD/MBA • M Acc • MBA

JD/MBA—Juris Doctor/Master of Business Administration Full-time and part-time. Separate admission to the Chase College of Law required. 106 to 118 total credits required. 33 to 60 months to complete program.

M Acc—Master of Accountancy Full-time and part-time. Undergraduate degree in accounting with accounting GPA of 2.9 or higher required. 30 total credits required. 12 to 96 months to complete program.

MBA—Master of Business Administration Full-time and part-time. 39 to 51 total credits required. 21 to 96 months to complete program. *Concentrations:* entrepreneurship, finance, international business, management information systems, marketing, project management.

COSTS

Tuition, state resident: *Full-time* $2300. *Part-time* $128 per semester hour. **Tuition, nonresident:** *Full-time* $6740. *Part-time* $374 per semester hour. **Tuition, international:** *Full-time* $6740. Tuition varies by academic program and local reciprocity agreements. **Required fees:** *Full-time* $558. *Part-time* $31 per semester hour. Tuition and fees vary by academic program. **Graduate housing:** Room and board costs vary by number of occupants, type of accommodation, and type of board plan. *Typical cost:* $5782 (including board), $4082 (room only).

FINANCIAL AID (1999–2000)

Loans, research assistantships, scholarships, and work study. Aid is available to part-time students. Financial aid application deadline: 4/1. **Financial Aid Contact** Dr. Peg Griffin, Coordinator of Graduate Programs, Louie B Nunn Drive, Highland Heights, KY 41099. **Phone:** 859-572-6364. **Fax:** 859-572-6670. **E-mail:** griffinp@nku.edu.

RESOURCES AND SERVICES

Information about online services, personal computer policies, library resources, international exchange programs, internship programs, and placement services at this institution and others can be found at **www.petersons.com/mba**

International Students

3% of students enrolled are international students.

Services and Facilities Counseling/support services, housing location assistance, international student housing, international student organization, language tutoring, orientation, visa services. Financial aid is available to international students.
Applying *Required:* TOEFL with recommended score of 213 (computer) or 550 (paper), proof of adequate funds, proof of health/immunizations.
International Student Contact Ms. Viki Kimball, Coordinator, International Student Affairs Office, University Center 366, Louie B Nunn Drive, Highland Heights, KY 41099. **Phone:** 859-572-6517. **Fax:** 859-572-6178. **E-mail:** isa@nku.edu.

■ APPLICATION

Required GMAT, application form, baccalaureate/first degree, transcripts of college work. **Recommended** 2 years of work experience.

Deadlines and Fees *Deadlines:* 8/1 for fall, 12/1 for spring, 5/1 for summer, 6/1 for fall (international), 10/1 for spring (international). *Application fee:* $25, $25 (international).

Application Contact Ms. Nina Thomas, Assistant Dean/MBA Program Director, College of Business, BEP Center 401, Highland Heights, KY 41099. **Phone:** 859-572-5165. **Fax:** 859-572-6177. **E-mail:** mbusiness@nku.edu.

Thomas More College

Crestview Hills, Kentucky

PROGRAM IN BUSINESS ADMINISTRATION

DEGREE MBA

MBA—Accelerated MBA Full-time. At least 45 total credits required. 24 months to complete program.

RESOURCES AND SERVICES

Information about online services, personal computer policies, library resources, international exchange programs, internship programs, and placement services at this institution and others can be found at **www.petersons.com/mba**

International Students

Services and Facilities Counseling/support services, ESL/language courses, international student organization, visa services. Financial aid is available to international students.
International Student Contact Ms. Mary Campbell, Director of International Services, Crestview Hills, KY 41017. **Phone:** 859-344-3337. **Fax:** 859-344-3607. **E-mail:** campbelm@thomasmore.edu.

■ APPLICATION

Application Contact Ms. Vicki Culbreth, TAP Program Representative, 2670 Chancellor Drive, Crestview Hills, KY 41017. **Phone:** 859-341-4554. **Fax:** 859-578-3589. **E-mail:** vxculbre@apollogrp.edu.

University of Kentucky

Lexington, Kentucky

CAROL MARTIN GATTON COLLEGE OF BUSINESS AND ECONOMICS

Graduate Business Faculty

Full-time: 75	Part-time: 16

Student Body

Total: 254	Average Age: 27
Full-time: 142	Women: 28%
Part-time: 112	

Admissions

Applications: 331	Average GMAT: 600
Admitted: 106	Average GPA: 3.3
Enrolled: 86	

Costs (1999–2000)
Full-time tuition: $3596 per academic year (resident), $10,116 per academic year (nonresident)
Part-time tuition: $188 per credit hour (resident), $550 per credit hour (nonresident)

After Graduation (Class of 1998–99)
Employed within 3 months of graduation: 98%
Average starting salary: $48,400

Accreditation
AACSB—The International Association for Management Education

DEGREES JD/MBA • MBA • MD/MBA • MS • Pharm D/MBA

JD/MBA—Juris Doctor/Master of Business Administration Full-time. At least 111 total credits required. 48 to 96 months to complete program.

MBA—Master of Business Administration Full-time and part-time. At least 36 total credits required. 18 to 96 months to complete program. *Concentrations:* accounting, international business, management information systems, marketing, production management.

MD/MBA—Doctor of Medicine/Master of Business Administration Full-time. At least 204 total credits required. 60 to 96 months to complete program.

MS—Master of Science in Accountancy Full-time and part-time. At least 30 total credits required. 12 to 96 months to complete program.

Pharm D/MBA—Doctor of Pharmacy/Master of Business Administration Full-time. At least 148 total credits required. Minimum of 48 months to complete program.

COSTS

Tuition, state resident: *Full-time* $3596. *Part-time* $188 per credit hour. **Tuition, nonresident:** *Full-time* $10,116. *Part-time* $550 per credit hour. Tuition varies by academic program and local reciprocity agreements. **Graduate housing:**

Room and board costs vary by number of occupants, type of accommodation, and type of board plan. *Typical cost:* $5834 (including board).

FINANCIAL AID (1999–2000)

72 students received aid, including fellowships, research assistantships, scholarships, and work study. Aid is available to part-time students. Financial aid application deadline: 3/1. **Financial Aid Contact** Dr. Susan Jordan, MBA Director, Gatton College of Business and Economics, Lexington, KY 40506-0034. **Phone:** 859-257-1306. **Fax:** 859-323-9971. **E-mail:** ukmba@uky.edu.

RESOURCES AND SERVICES

Information about online services, personal computer policies, library resources, international exchange programs, internship programs, and placement services at this institution and others can be found at **www.petersons.com/mba**

International Students

8% of students enrolled are international students.

Services and Facilities Counseling/support services, ESL/language courses, international student housing, international student organization, orientation, visa services. Financial aid is available to international students.
Applying *Required:* TOEFL with recommended score of 550 (paper), TWE with recommended score of 4.5, proof of adequate funds, proof of health/immunizations.
International Student Contact Ms. Carolyn Holmes, International Student Advisor, 204 Bradley Hall—Office of International Affairs, Lexington, KY 40506. **Phone:** 859-257-4067 Ext. 237. **E-mail:** holmes@ukcc.uky.edu.

■ APPLICATION

Required GMAT, application form, baccalaureate/first degree, 3 letters of recommendation, personal statement, resume/curriculum vitae, transcripts of college work. **Recommended** Work experience.
Deadlines and Fees *Deadlines:* 7/1 for fall, 2/1 for fall (international). *Application fee:* $30, $35 (international).
Application Contact Ms. Beverly Kemper, MBA Center, Gatton College of Business and Economics, Lexington, KY 40506-0034. **Phone:** 606-257-3592. **Toll-free Phone:** 859-257-7722 (in-state), 859-323-9971 (out-of-state). **Fax:** 606-257-3293.

See full description on page 912.

University of Louisville

Louisville, Kentucky

COLLEGE OF BUSINESS AND PUBLIC ADMINISTRATION

Graduate Business Faculty

Full-time: 63	Part-time: 12

Student Body

Total: 687	Average Age: 30
Full-time: 269	Women: 40%
Part-time: 418	

Admissions

Applications: 194	Average GMAT: 555
Admitted: 154	Average GPA: 3.27
Enrolled: 79	

Costs (1999–2000)
Full-time tuition: $3546 per academic year (resident), $10,066 per academic year (nonresident)
Part-time tuition: $207 per semester hour (resident), $592 per semester hour (nonresident)

After Graduation (Class of 1998–99)
Employed within 3 months of graduation: 90%
Average starting salary: $47,500

Accreditation
AACSB—The International Association for Management Education

DEGREES JD/MBA • M Acc • MBA • MD/MBA • ME/MBA

JD/MBA—Juris Doctor/Master of Business Administration Full-time. Up to 118 total credits required. 48 months to complete program.

M Acc—Master of Accountancy Full-time and part-time. At least 30 total credits required. Minimum of 12 months to complete program.

MBA—Integrative Master of Business Administration Full-time and part-time. At least 47 total credits required. 24 months to complete program.

MBA—Master of Business Administration Full-time and part-time. 36 to 48 total credits required. 12 to 72 months to complete program. *Concentrations:* entrepreneurship, health care.

MD/MBA—Doctor of Medicine/Master of Business Administration

ME/MBA—Master of Engineering/Master of Business Administration Full-time and part-time. Minimum of 36 months to complete program.

COSTS
Tuition, state resident: *Full-time* $3546. *Part-time* $207 per semester hour. **Tuition, nonresident:** *Full-time* $10,066. *Part-time* $592 per semester hour. **Tuition, international:** *Full-time* $10,066. **Required fees:** Tuition and fees vary by number of courses or credits taken and local reciprocity agreements. **Graduate housing:** Room and board costs vary by campus location, number of occupants, type of accommodation, and type of board plan. *Typical cost:* $4550 (including board), $3150 (room only).

FINANCIAL AID (1999–2000)
25 students received aid, including loans, research assistantships, scholarships, and work study. Aid is available to part-time students. Financial aid application deadline: 3/1. **Financial Aid Contact** Patricia Arauz, Director of Financial Aid, Financial Aid Office, Louisville, KY 40292. **Phone:** 502-852-8802. **Fax:** 502-852-0182.

RESOURCES AND SERVICES
Information about online services, personal computer policies, library resources, international exchange programs, internship programs, and placement services at this institution and others can be found at **www.petersons.com/mba**

International Students
21% of students enrolled are international students.

Services and Facilities Counseling/support services, ESL/language courses, international student housing, international student organization, orientation, visa services. Financial aid is not available to international students.
Applying *Required:* TOEFL with recommended score of 550 (paper), proof of adequate funds, proof of health/immunizations.
International Student Contact Ms. Sharolyn Pepper, International Student Coordinator, International Center, Louisville, KY 40292. **Phone:** 502-852-6602. **Fax:** 502-852-7216. **E-mail:** pepper@louisville.edu.

■ **APPLICATION**
Required GMAT, application form, baccalaureate/first degree, 2 letters of recommendation, personal statement, resume/curriculum vitae, transcripts of college work. **Recommended** Work experience.
Deadlines and Fees Applications for international students are processed on a rolling basis. *Deadlines:* 5/1 for fall, 9/1 for spring, 3/1 for summer. *Application fee:* $25, $25 (international).
Application Contact Dolores Calebs, Academic Counselor: Graduate Programs, CBPA Student Academic Support Services, Louisville, KY 40292. **Phone:** 502-852-3969. **Toll-free Phone:** 800-334-8635. **Fax:** 502-852-4901. **E-mail:** mba@gwise.louisville.edu.

See full description on page 914.

Western Kentucky University
Bowling Green, Kentucky

COLLEGE OF BUSINESS ADMINISTRATION

Accreditation
AACSB—The International Association for Management Education

DEGREES MA • MBA

MA—Master of Arts in Economics
MBA—Master of Business Administration Full-time and part-time. *Distance learning option.* 30 to 51 total credits required. 12 to 60 months to complete program.

RESOURCES AND SERVICES
Information about online services, personal computer policies, library resources, international exchange programs, internship programs, and placement services at this institution and others can be found at **www.petersons.com/mba**

International Students
Services and Facilities Counseling/support services, ESL/language courses, international student housing, international student organization, orientation, visa services. Financial aid is available to international students.
International Student Contact Ms. Joan Lindsey, International Student Advisor,

1 Big Red Way, Bowling Green, KY 42101-3576. **Phone:** 270-745-4858. **Fax:** 270-745-6144. **E-mail:** joan.lindsey@wku.edu.

■ **APPLICATION**
Application Contact Dr. Thomas Dillon, MBA Program Director, 1 Big Red Way, Bowling Green, KY 42101-3576. **Phone:** 270-745-6311. **Fax:** 270-745-3893. **E-mail:** thomas.dillon@wku.edu.

LOUISIANA

Louisiana State University and Agricultural and Mechanical College
Baton Rouge, Louisiana

E.J. OURSO COLLEGE OF BUSINESS ADMINISTRATION

Graduate Business Faculty
Full-time: 115 | Part-time: 36

Student Body
Total: 602
Full-time: 356
Part-time: 246
Average Age: 30
Women: 35%

Admissions
Applications: 700
Admitted: 250
Enrolled: 200
Average GMAT: 584
Average GPA: 3.3

Costs (1999–2000)
Full-time tuition: $2876 per academic year (resident), $8176 per academic year (nonresident)
Part-time tuition: N/R

After Graduation (Class of 1998–99)
Employed within 3 months of graduation: 84%
Average starting salary: $49,433

Accreditation
AACSB—The International Association for Management Education

DEGREES MBA • MPA • MS

MBA—Master of Business Administration Full-time and part-time. At least 60 total credits required. 24 to 60 months to complete program. *Concentrations:* decision sciences, economics, entrepreneurship, finance, health care, human resources, management information systems, marketing, public policy and administration, real estate.

MPA—Master of Public Administration Full-time and part-time. At least 42 total credits required. 24 to 60 months to complete program. *Concentrations:* public policy and administration.

MS—Master of Science Full-time and part-time. At least 36 total credits required. 12 to 60 months to complete program. *Concentrations:* accounting, decision sciences, economics, finance, information management, marketing.

The E. J. Ourso College of Business Administration at Louisiana State University (LSU) in Baton Rouge has a new M.B.A. curriculum that may be taken in one of three tracks. The full-time track is a two-year program that gives students 18 hours of electives beyond the functional core to develop a concentration in such areas as internal auditing, management information systems, real estate, human resource management, marketing, and finance. The part-time track is a four-year program in which students attend class two nights per week. The part-time program is designed for developing managers who are currently employed in the Baton Rouge area. The third option is the Executive M.B.A. program. This program meets on Fridays and Saturdays every other weekend and takes only 18 months to complete. The students in this program are professionals in the workforce and come to school to get the knowledge of advanced studies in management.

The college has been continually accredited by AACSB-The International Association for Management Education since 1930. LSU also has accreditation from the Southern Association of Colleges and Schools (SACS). The Center for Engineering and Business Administration houses the E. J. Ourso College

Louisiana State University and Agricultural and Mechanical College (continued)

of Business Administration on the LSU campus. The classes meet in multimedia classrooms that are equipped with Internet access.

COSTS

Tuition, state resident: *Full-time* $2876. **Tuition, nonresident:** *Full-time* $8176. **Tuition, international:** *Full-time* $8176. Tuition varies by number of courses or credits taken. **Graduate housing:** Room and board costs vary by campus location, number of occupants, type of accommodation, and type of board plan. *Typical cost:* $8000 (including board), $4800 (room only).

FINANCIAL AID (1999–2000)

210 students received aid, including fellowships, loans, research assistantships, scholarships, teaching assistantships, and work study. **Financial Aid Contact** Student Aid and Scholarships, 202 Himes Hall, Baton Rouge, LA 70803. **Phone:** 225-388-3103. **Fax:** 225-388-6300.

RESOURCES AND SERVICES

Information about online services, personal computer policies, library resources, international exchange programs, internship programs, and placement services at this institution and others can be found at **www. petersons.com/mba**

International Students

12% of students enrolled are international students.

Services and Facilities Counseling/support services, ESL/language courses, housing location assistance, international student organization, orientation, visa services. Financial aid is available to international students.
Applying *Required:* TOEFL with recommended score of 213 (computer) or 550 (paper), proof of adequate funds, proof of health/immunizations.
International Student Contact International Student Office, 108 Hatcher Hall, Baton Rouge, LA 70803-6302. **Phone:** 225-388-3191. **Fax:** 225-388-1413.

■ APPLICATION

Required GMAT, application form, baccalaureate/first degree, essay, 3 letters of recommendation, personal statement, transcripts of college work. **Recommended** Resume/curriculum vitae, work experience.
Deadlines and Fees *Deadlines:* 5/15 for fall, 5/15 for fall (international). *Application fee:* $25, $25 (international).
Application Contact Dr. P. David Shields, Director, Flores MBA Programs, MBA Office, E. J. Ourso College of Business Administration, 3307 CEBA, Baton Rouge, LA 70803-6302. **Phone:** 225-388-8867. **Fax:** 225-388-2421. **E-mail:** busmba@lsu.edu.

Louisiana Tech University

Ruston, Louisiana

COLLEGE OF ADMINISTRATION AND BUSINESS

Graduate Business Faculty
Full-time: 45 | Part-time: 7

Student Body
Total: 78
Full-time: 62 | Average Age: 27
Part-time: 16 | Women: 35%

Admissions
Applications: 116 | Average GMAT: 514
Admitted: 108 | Average GPA: 3.28
Enrolled: 74

Costs (1999–2000)
Full-time tuition: $2744 per academic year (resident), $6024 per academic year (nonresident)
Part-time tuition: N/R

Accreditation
AACSB—The International Association for Management Education

DEGREES MBA • MPA

MBA—Master of Business Administration Full-time and part-time. At least 30 total credits required. 12 to 72 months to complete program. *Concentrations:* accounting, economics, finance, international business, international management, management, marketing, quantitative analysis.

MPA—Master of Professional Accountancy Full-time and part-time. At least 30 total credits required. 12 to 72 months to complete program. *Concentrations:* accounting.

COSTS

Tuition, state resident: *Full-time* $2464. **Tuition, nonresident:** *Full-time* $5744. **Tuition, international:** *Full-time* $5904. **Required fees:** *Full-time* $280. *Part-time* $220 per year. Tuition and fees vary by number of courses or credits taken and campus location. **Graduate housing:** Room and board costs vary by number of occupants, type of accommodation, and type of board plan. *Typical cost:* $4040 (including board).

FINANCIAL AID (1999–2000)

Fellowships, grants, loans, research assistantships, and teaching assistantships. Aid is available to part-time students. Financial aid application deadline: 2/1. **Financial Aid Contact** Mr. Roger Vick, Director of Financial Aid, PO Box 7925 TS, Ruston, LA 71272. **Phone:** 318-257-2641. **Fax:** 318-257-2628.

RESOURCES AND SERVICES

Information about online services, personal computer policies, library resources, international exchange programs, internship programs, and placement services at this institution and others can be found at **www. petersons.com/mba**

International Students

27% of students enrolled are international students.

Services and Facilities Counseling/support services, housing location assistance, international student organization, language tutoring, orientation, visa services. Financial aid is available to international students.
Applying *Required:* TOEFL with recommended score of 213 (computer) or 550 (paper), proof of adequate funds, proof of health/immunizations.
International Student Contact Mr. Daniel Erickson, International Student Advisor, PO Box 3177 TS, Ruston, LA 71272. **Phone:** 318-257-4321. **Fax:** 318-257-4750. **E-mail:** daniel@vm.cc.latech.edu.

■ APPLICATION

Required GMAT, application form, baccalaureate/first degree, transcripts of college work.
Deadlines and Fees *Deadlines:* 8/1 for fall, 11/1 for winter, 2/1 for spring, 5/1 for summer, 6/1 for fall (international), 9/1 for winter (international), 12/1 for spring (international), 3/1 for summer (international). *Application fee:* $20, $30 (international).
Application Contact Dr. Gene H. Johnson, Associate Dean of Graduate Affairs and Academic Research, PO Box 10318, Ruston, LA 71272. **Phone:** 318-257-4528. **Fax:** 318-257-4253. **E-mail:** johnson@cab.latech.edu.

Loyola University New Orleans

New Orleans, Louisiana

JOSEPH A. BUTT, S.J., COLLEGE OF BUSINESS ADMINISTRATION

Graduate Business Faculty
Full-time: 18 | Part-time: 2

Student Body
Total: 133
Full-time: 12 | Average Age: 35
Part-time: 121 | Women: 30%

Admissions
Applications: 69 | Average GMAT: 575
Admitted: 55 | Average GPA: 3.08
Enrolled: 34

Costs (1999–2000)
Full-time tuition: N/R
Part-time tuition: $501 per credit hour

After Graduation (Class of 1998–99)
Employed within 3 months of graduation: 86%
Average starting salary: $53,333

Accreditation
AACSB—The International Association for Management Education

DEGREES JD/MBA • MBA • MQM

JD/MBA—Juris Doctor/Master of Business Administration Full-time and part-time. At least 105 total credits required. Maximum of 60 months to complete program.

MBA—Master of Business Administration Full-time and part-time. 33 to 56 total credits required. 12 to 84 months to complete program. *Concentrations:* accounting, finance, international business, management, quality management.

MQM—Master of Quality Management Part-time. 5 years of work experience required. At least 32 total credits required. 24 months to complete program.

COSTS

Tuition *Part-time:* $501 per credit hour. **Required fees:** *Full-time* $502. *Part-time* $130 per semester. Tuition and fees vary by academic program. **Graduate housing:** Room and board costs vary by number of occupants, type of accommodation, and type of board plan. *Typical cost:* $7188 (including board), $4388 (room only).

FINANCIAL AID (1999–2000)

33 students received aid, including loans, research assistantships, and work study. Aid is available to part-time students. Financial aid application deadline: 5/1. **Financial Aid Contact** Mr. Wallace Boudet, Director of Scholarships and Financial Aid, 6363 Saint Charles Avenue, Box 206, New Orleans, LA 70118. **Phone:** 504-865-3231. **Fax:** 504-865-3233. **E-mail:** wpboudet@loyno.edu.

RESOURCES AND SERVICES

Information about online services, personal computer policies, library resources, international exchange programs, internship programs, and placement services at this institution and others can be found at **www.petersons.com/mba**

International Students

11% of students enrolled are international students.

Services and Facilities Counseling/support services, ESL/language courses, international student housing, international student organization, language tutoring, visa services. Financial aid is not available to international students.

Applying *Required:* TOEFL with recommended score of 237 (computer) or 580 (paper), proof of adequate funds, proof of health/immunizations.

International Student Contact Ms. Debbie Danna, Director, International Student Affairs, 6363 Saint Charles Avenue, Box 205, New Orleans, LA 70118. **Phone:** 504-864-7550. **Fax:** 504-864-7428. **E-mail:** danna@loyno.edu.

■ APPLICATION

Required GMAT, application form, baccalaureate/first degree, essay, 2 letters of recommendation, resume/curriculum vitae, transcripts of college work. **Recommended** Work experience.

Deadlines and Fees *Deadlines:* 6/15 for fall (international), 11/30 for spring (international). *Application fee:* $50, $50 (international).

Application Contact Dr. Pamela Van Epps, Coordinator of Graduate and External Programs, College of Business Administration, 6363 Saint Charles Avenue, New Orleans, LA 70118. **Phone:** 504-864-7944. **Fax:** 504-864-7970. **E-mail:** vanepps@beta.edu.

McNeese State University

Lake Charles, Louisiana

COLLEGE OF BUSINESS

Graduate Business Faculty
Full-time: 16

Student Body
Total: 86
Full-time: 28
Part-time: 58

Average Age: 30
Women: 49%

Admissions
Applications: 33
Admitted: 26
Enrolled: 26

Average GMAT: 505
Average GPA: 3.11

Costs (1999–2000)
Full-time tuition: $1987 per academic year (resident), $3530 per academic year (nonresident)
Part-time tuition: $540 per semester (resident), $882 per semester (nonresident)

After Graduation (Class of 1998–99)
Employed within 3 months of graduation: 90%

Accreditation
AACSB—The International Association for Management Education

DEGREE MBA

MBA—Master of Business Administration Full-time and part-time. At least 57 total credits required. 18 to 48 months to complete program.

COSTS

Tuition, state resident: *Full-time* $1987. *Part-time* $540 per semester. **Tuition, nonresident:** *Full-time* $3530. *Part-time* $882 per semester. **Required fees:** Tuition and fees vary by number of courses or credits taken. **Graduate housing:** Room and board costs vary by number of occupants and type of accommodation. *Typical cost:* $2956 (including board).

FINANCIAL AID (1999–2000)

Research assistantships, teaching assistantships, and work study. Aid is available to part-time students. Financial aid application deadline: 5/1. **Financial Aid Contact** Ms. Taina Savoit, Director of Financial Aid, PO Box 93260, Lake Charles, LA 70609. **Phone:** 337-475-5065. **Fax:** 337-475-5068. **E-mail:** tsavoit@mcneese.edu.

RESOURCES AND SERVICES

Information about online services, personal computer policies, library resources, international exchange programs, internship programs, and placement services at this institution and others can be found at **www.petersons.com/mba**

International Students

17% of students enrolled are international students.

Services and Facilities Counseling/support services. Financial aid is available to international students.

Applying *Required:* TOEFL with recommended score of 525 (paper), proof of adequate funds, proof of health/immunizations.

International Student Contact Ms. Linda Finley, Admissions Counselor, PO Box 92495, Lake Charles, LA 70609. **Phone:** 337-475-5145. **Fax:** 337-475-5189. **E-mail:** lfinley@mcneese.edu.

■ APPLICATION

Required Application form, baccalaureate/first degree, transcripts of college work. School will accept GMAT.

Deadlines and Fees *Deadlines:* 5/1 for fall (international), 10/1 for spring (international), 3/1 for summer (international). *Application fee:* $20, $40 (international).

Application Contact Dr. Bruce Swindle, MBA Program Director, PO Box 91660, Lake Charles, LA 70609. **Phone:** 337-475-5576. **Toll-free Phone:** 800-662-3352. **Fax:** 337-475-5986. **E-mail:** mbaprog@mail.mcneese.edu.

Nicholls State University

Thibodaux, Louisiana

COLLEGE OF BUSINESS ADMINISTRATION

Graduate Business Faculty
Full-time: 37

Student Body
Total: 113
Full-time: 35
Part-time: 78

Average Age: 34
Women: 52%

Admissions
Applications: 42
Admitted: 40
Enrolled: 26

Average GMAT: 470
Average GPA: 3.1

Costs (1999–2000)
Full-time tuition: $2411 per academic year (resident), $6675 per academic year (nonresident)
Part-time tuition: $273 per credit hour (resident), $273 per credit hour (nonresident)

Accreditation
AACSB—The International Association for Management Education

DEGREE MBA

MBA—Master of Business Administration Full-time and part-time. 33 to 69 total credits required. 18 to 72 months to complete program.

COSTS

Tuition, state resident: *Full-time* $2136. *Part-time* $273 per credit hour. **Tuition, nonresident:** *Full-time* $6400. *Part-time* $273 per credit hour. Tuition varies by number of courses or credits taken. **Required fees:** *Full-time* $275. **Graduate housing:** Room and board costs vary by number of occupants. *Typical cost:* $2850 (including board).

FINANCIAL AID (1999–2000)

30 students received aid, including research assistantships. Financial aid application deadline: 8/17. **Financial Aid Contact** Ms. Allison Kleinpeter,

Nicholls State University (continued)

Director of Financial Aid, PO Box 2004, Thibodaux, LA 70310. **E-mail:** fa-aak@mail.nich.edu.

RESOURCES AND SERVICES

Information about online services, personal computer policies, library resources, international exchange programs, internship programs, and placement services at this institution and others can be found at **www.petersons.com/mba**

International Students

14% of students enrolled are international students.

Services and Facilities Counseling/support services, international student organization, visa services. Financial aid is not available to international students.
Applying *Required:* TOEFL with recommended score of 213 (computer) or 550 (paper), proof of adequate funds, proof of health/immunizations.
International Student Contact Mrs. Marilyn Gonzalez, Coordinator, International Student Affairs, PO Box 2004, Thibodaux, LA 70310. **Phone:** 504-448-7038. **Fax:** 504-448-4929. **E-mail:** esap-mag@mail.nich.edu.

■ APPLICATION

Required Application form, baccalaureate/first degree, transcripts of college work. School will accept GMAT.

Deadlines and Fees Applications for domestic and international students are processed on a rolling basis. *Application fee:* $10, $25 (international).

Application Contact Dr. J. B. Stroud, Jr., Director of Graduate Studies, PO Box 2015, Thibodaux, LA 70310. **Phone:** 504-449-7014. **Fax:** 504-448-4922. **E-mail:** ba-mba@mail.nich.edu.

Southeastern Louisiana University

Hammond, Louisiana

COLLEGE OF BUSINESS

Graduate Business Faculty
Full-time: 26 — Part-time: 2

Student Body
Total: 218
Full-time: 136
Part-time: 82
Average Age: 30
Women: 41%

Admissions
Applications: 108
Admitted: 104
Enrolled: 68
Average GMAT: 485
Average GPA: 3.1

Costs (1999–2000)
Full-time tuition: $2100 per academic year (resident), $6096 per academic year (nonresident)
Part-time tuition: $117 per credit hour (resident), $339 per credit hour (nonresident)

Accreditation
AACSB—The International Association for Management Education

DEGREE MBA

MBA—MBA Program Full-time and part-time. At least 33 total credits required. 12 to 72 months to complete program. *Concentrations:* accounting, marketing.

COSTS

Tuition, state resident: *Full-time* $2100. *Part-time* $117 per credit hour. **Tuition, nonresident:** *Full-time* $6096. *Part-time* $339 per credit hour. **Required fees:** Tuition and fees vary by number of courses or credits taken. **Graduate housing:** Room and board costs vary by campus location, number of occupants, type of accommodation, and type of board plan. *Typical cost:* $2770 (including board), $1250 (room only).

FINANCIAL AID (1999–2000)

164 students received aid, including fellowships, loans, research assistantships, scholarships, teaching assistantships, and work study. Aid is available to part-time students. Financial aid application deadline: 5/1. **Financial Aid Contact** Mr. Sal Loria, Director, Financial Aid, SLU 10768, Hammond, LA 70402. **Phone:** 504-549-2244. **Fax:** 504-549-5077. **E-mail:** sloria@selu.edu.

RESOURCES AND SERVICES

Information about online services, personal computer policies, library resources, international exchange programs, internship programs, and placement services at this institution and others can be found at **www.petersons.com/mba**

International Students

23% of students enrolled are international students.

Services and Facilities Counseling/support services, ESL/language courses, international student housing, international student organization, visa services. Financial aid is not available to international students.
Applying *Required:* TOEFL with recommended score of 525 (paper), proof of adequate funds, proof of health/immunizations.
International Student Contact Dr. Bradley S. O'Hara, Director, Graduate Business Programs, College of Business, SLU 10735, Hammond, LA 70402. **Phone:** 504-549-2146. **Fax:** 504-549-3977. **E-mail:** bohara@selu.edu.

■ APPLICATION

Required Application form, baccalaureate/first degree, transcripts of college work. School will accept GMAT.

Deadlines and Fees *Deadlines:* 7/15 for fall, 12/1 for spring, 5/1 for summer, 6/1 for fall (international), 10/1 for spring (international), 3/1 for summer (international). *Application fee:* $20, $30 (international).

Application Contact Mrs. Edna Smiley, Graduate Admissions Coordinator, Graduate Admissions Office, Enrollment Services, SLU 10752, Hammond, LA 70402. **Phone:** 504-549-5619. **Fax:** 504-549-5632. **E-mail:** esmiley@selu.edu.

Southern University and Agricultural and Mechanical College

Baton Rouge, Louisiana

COLLEGE OF BUSINESS

Graduate Business Faculty
Full-time: 8

Student Body
Total: 15
Full-time: 3
Part-time: 12
Average Age: 35
Women: 80%

Admissions
Applications: 17
Admitted: 14
Enrolled: 9
Average GMAT: 456
Average GPA: 3.1

Costs (1999–2000)
Full-time tuition: $2500 per academic year (resident), $6500 per academic year (nonresident)
Part-time tuition: N/R

Accreditation
AACSB—The International Association for Management Education

DEGREE MPA

MPA—Master of Public Accounting Full-time and part-time. At least 30 total credits required. Minimum of 12 months to complete program.

COSTS

Tuition, state resident: *Full-time* $2500. **Tuition, nonresident:** *Full-time* $6500. Tuition varies by number of courses or credits taken.

FINANCIAL AID (1999–2000)

2 students received aid, including teaching assistantships. Financial aid application deadline: 6/1. **Financial Aid Contact** Graduate School, Baton Rouge, LA 70813. **Phone:** 225-771-5642.

RESOURCES AND SERVICES

Information about online services, personal computer policies, library resources, international exchange programs, internship programs, and placement services at this institution and others can be found at **www.petersons.com/mba**

International Students

13% of students enrolled are international students.

Services and Facilities Counseling/support services, international student organization, orientation.
Applying *Required:* TOEFL.

■ APPLICATION

Required GMAT, application form, baccalaureate/first degree, letter(s) of recommendation, resume/curriculum vitae, transcripts of college work.

Deadlines and Fees *Deadlines:* 6/1 for fall, 11/1 for spring, 4/1 for summer, 6/1 for fall (international), 11/1 for spring (international), 4/1 for summer (international).

Application Contact Office of Graduate Studies, PO Box 9860, Southern Branch Post Office, Baton Rouge, LA 70813-9860. **Phone:** 225-771-5390. **Toll-free Phone:** 888-223-1460. **Fax:** 225-771-5723.

Tulane University
New Orleans, Louisiana

A. B. FREEMAN SCHOOL OF BUSINESS

Graduate Business Faculty
Full-time: 60 — Part-time: 35

Student Body
Total: 535
Full-time: 184 — Average Age: 28
Part-time: 351 — Women: 24%

Admissions
Applications: 424
Admitted: 179 — Average GMAT: 644
Enrolled: 78 — Average GPA: 3.4

Costs (1999–2000)
Full-time tuition: $25,390 per academic year
Part-time tuition: $783 per credit hour

After Graduation (Class of 1998–99)
Employed within 3 months of graduation: 94%
Average starting salary: $62,230

Accreditation
AACSB—The International Association for Management Education

DEGREES JD/M Acc • JD/MBA • M Acc • MBA • MBA/M Acc • MBA/MA • MBA/MPH • MM

JD/M Acc—Accounting/Law Full-time. Admittance to Tulane Law School required. At least 109 total credits required. 39 to 84 months to complete program. *Concentrations:* accounting, management information systems, taxation.

JD/MBA—Juris Doctor/Master of Business Administration Full-time. Admittance to Tulane Law School required. At least 125 total credits required. 45 to 84 months to complete program. *Concentrations:* accounting, finance, international management, management, management information systems, marketing, organizational behavior/development.

M Acc—Master of Accounting Full-time and part-time. At least 30 total credits required. 9 to 84 months to complete program. *Concentrations:* accounting, management information systems, taxation.

MBA—Asia Executive MBA Full-time. Five years management experience and English language proficiency. At least 60 total credits required. 13 to 84 months to complete program. *Concentrations:* management.

MBA—Chile Executive MBA Full-time. Joint admission to Universidad de Chile and Tulane; work and management experience; English proficiency. At least 60 total credits required. 13 to 84 months to complete program. *Concentrations:* management.

MBA—Executive MBA Full-time. *Distance learning option.* Seven years of work experience with at least five in management required. At least 48 total credits required. Minimum of 19 months to complete program. *Concentrations:* management.

MBA—Professional MBA Part-time. At least 55 total credits required. 36 to 84 months to complete program. *Concentrations:* accounting, finance, international management, management, management information systems, marketing, organizational behavior/development.

MBA—Master of Business Administration Full-time. At least 63 total credits required. 21 to 84 months to complete program. *Concentrations:* accounting, finance, international management, management, management information systems, marketing, organizational behavior/development.

MBA/M Acc—MBA/Accounting Full-time. At least 75 total credits required. 24 to 84 months to complete program. *Concentrations:* accounting, finance, international management, management, management information systems, marketing, organizational behavior/development, taxation.

MBA/MA—Master of Business Administration/Master of Arts in Latin American Studies Full-time. Admittance to Tulane Master of Arts Program required. At least 75 total credits required. 28 to 84 months to complete program. *Concentrations:* accounting, finance, international management, management, management information systems, marketing, organizational behavior/development.

MBA/MPH—Master of Business Administration/Master of Public Health in Health Systems Management Full-time. Admittance to Tulane School of Public Health and Tropical Medicine required. At least 93 total credits required. 33 to 84 months to complete program. *Concentrations:* accounting, finance, international management, management, management information systems, marketing, organizational behavior/development.

MM—Ecuador Executive Full-time. Joint admission to ESPOL and Tulane; work and management experience required; English proficiency. At least 36 total credits required. 21 to 84 months to complete program. *Concentrations:* international management.

COSTS

Tuition *Full-time:* $23,500. *Part-time:* $783 per credit hour. **Tuition, state resident:** *Full-time* $23,500. *Part-time* $783 per credit hour. **Tuition, nonresident:** *Full-time* $23,500. *Part-time* $783 per credit hour. **Tuition, international:** *Full-time* $23,500. **Required fees:** *Full-time* $1890. *Part-time* $42 per credit. Tuition and fees vary by class time, number of courses or credits taken, and academic program. **Graduate housing:** Room and board costs vary by number of occupants, type of accommodation, and type of board plan. *Typical cost:* $7070 (including board).

FINANCIAL AID (1999–2000)
145 students received aid, including fellowships, research assistantships, scholarships, teaching assistantships, and work study. Aid is available to part-time students. Financial aid application deadline: 4/15. **Financial Aid Contact** Mr. John Silbernagel, Assistant Dean for Admissions and Financial Aid, 7 McAlister Drive, Suite 400, New Orleans, LA 70118-5669. **Phone:** 504-865-5410. **Fax:** 504-865-6770. **E-mail:** john.silbernagel@tulane.edu.

RESOURCES AND SERVICES
Information about online services, personal computer policies, library resources, international exchange programs, internship programs, and placement services at this institution and others can be found at **www.petersons.com/mba**

International Students
37% of students enrolled are international students.

Services and Facilities Counseling/support services, ESL/language courses, housing location assistance, international student housing, international student organization, language tutoring, orientation, visa services. Financial aid is available to international students.

Applying *Required:* TOEFL with recommended score of 263 (computer) or 624 (paper), proof of adequate funds, proof of health/immunizations.

International Student Contact Ms. Janice Hughes, Director, International Programs, 7 McAlister Drive, Suite 451, New Orleans, LA 70118-5669. **Phone:** 504-865-5438. **Fax:** 504-862-8770. **E-mail:** jlhughes@mailhost.tcs.tulane.edu.

■ APPLICATION

Required GMAT, application form, baccalaureate/first degree, essay, interview, 2 letters of recommendation, resume/curriculum vitae, transcripts of college work. **Recommended** Work experience.

Deadlines and Fees Applications for domestic and international students are processed on a rolling basis. *Application fee:* $40, $50 (international).

Application Contact Mr. John Silbernagel, Assistant Dean for Admissions and Financial Aid, 7 McAlister Drive, Suite 400, New Orleans, LA 70118-5669. **Phone:** 504-865-5410. **Fax:** 504-865-6770. **E-mail:** john.silbernagel@tulane.edu.

See full description on page 858.

University of Louisiana at Lafayette
Lafayette, Louisiana

GRADUATE SCHOOL

Graduate Business Faculty
Full-time: 34 — Part-time: 2

Student Body
Total: 153
Full-time: 72 — Average Age: 30
Part-time: 81 — Women: 37%

University of Louisiana at Lafayette (continued)

Admissions
Applications: 119
Admitted: 87
Enrolled: 62

Average GMAT: 500
Average GPA: 3

Costs (1999–2000)
Full-time tuition: $2024 per academic year (resident), $7620 per academic year (nonresident)
Part-time tuition: N/R

After Graduation (Class of 1998–99)
Employed within 3 months of graduation: 100%
Average starting salary: $47,000

DEGREES MBA

MBA—Master of Business Administration in Health Care Administration Full-time and part-time. 39 to 48 total credits required. 18 to 72 months to complete program. *Concentrations:* accounting, economics, finance, health care, management, marketing.

MBA—Master of Business Administration Full-time and part-time. 33 to 42 total credits required. 18 to 72 months to complete program. *Concentrations:* accounting, economics, finance, management, marketing.

COSTS
Tuition, state resident: *Full-time* $2024. **Tuition, nonresident:** *Full-time* $7620. **Tuition, international:** *Full-time* $7400. Tuition varies by number of courses or credits taken and local reciprocity agreements. **Graduate housing:** Room and board costs vary by number of occupants, type of accommodation, and type of board plan. *Typical cost:* $2600 (including board).

FINANCIAL AID (1999–2000)
15 students received aid, including loans and research assistantships. Financial aid application deadline: 5/1. **Financial Aid Contact** Dr. Lewis Pyenson, Dean, Graduate School, Box 44610, Lafayette, LA 70504-4610. **Phone:** 337-482-6965. **Fax:** 337-482-6195. **E-mail:** lrp6914@louisiana.edu.

RESOURCES AND SERVICES
Information about online services, personal computer policies, library resources, international exchange programs, internship programs, and placement services at this institution and others can be found at **www.petersons.com/mba**

International Students
8% of students enrolled are international students.
Services and Facilities Counseling/support services, housing location assistance, international student housing, international student organization, orientation, visa services. Financial aid is available to international students.
Applying *Required:* TOEFL with recommended score of 550 (paper), proof of adequate funds, proof of health/immunizations.
International Student Contact Mr. Sekaran Murugaiah, Director, Box 43932, Lafayette, LA 70504-3932. **Phone:** 337-482-6819.

■ APPLICATION
Required Application form, baccalaureate/first degree, 3 letters of recommendation, resume/curriculum vitae, transcripts of college work. School will accept GMAT. **Recommended** Interview, personal statement, work experience.
Deadlines and Fees *Deadlines:* 6/15 for fall, 11/1 for spring, 4/15 for summer, 5/15 for fall (international), 10/1 for spring (international), 1/15 for summer (international). *Application fee:* $5, $15 (international).
Application Contact Dr. Lewis Pyenson, Dean, Graduate School, Box 44610, Lafayette, LA 70504-4610. **Phone:** 337-482-6965. **Fax:** 337-482-6195. **E-mail:** lrp6914@louisiana.edu.

University of Louisiana at Monroe

Monroe, Louisiana

COLLEGE OF BUSINESS ADMINISTRATION

Graduate Business Faculty
Full-time: 35

Student Body
Total: 82
Full-time: 62
Part-time: 20

Average Age: 28
Women: 44%

Admissions
Applications: 58
Admitted: 51
Enrolled: 28

Average GMAT: 510
Average GPA: 3.28

Costs (1999–2000)
Full-time tuition: $1016 per academic year (resident), $2979 per academic year (nonresident)
Part-time tuition: $110 per credit (resident), $110 per credit (nonresident)

DEGREE MBA

MBA—Master of Business Administration Full-time and part-time. 30 to 66 total credits required. 12 to 72 months to complete program. *Concentrations:* entrepreneurship, health care.

COSTS
Tuition, state resident: *Full-time* $1016. *Part-time* $110 per credit. **Tuition, nonresident:** *Full-time* $2979. *Part-time* $110 per credit. **Tuition, international:** *Full-time* $3995. Tuition varies by number of courses or credits taken. **Graduate housing:** Room and board costs vary by number of occupants and type of board plan. *Typical cost:* $2560 (including board).

FINANCIAL AID (1999–2000)
41 students received aid, including research assistantships, teaching assistantships, and work study. Financial aid application deadline: 7/1. **Financial Aid Contact** Mr. Charles R. Dobrinick, Director of Financial Aid, 700 University Drive, Monroe, LA 71209-0100. **Phone:** 318-342-5320. **E-mail:** dobrinic@spock.ulm.edu.

RESOURCES AND SERVICES
Information about online services, personal computer policies, library resources, international exchange programs, internship programs, and placement services at this institution and others can be found at **www.petersons.com/mba**

International Students
48% of students enrolled are international students.
Services and Facilities Counseling/support services, ESL/language courses, international student organization, language tutoring, orientation. Financial aid is available to international students.
Applying *Required:* TOEFL with recommended score of 213 (computer) or 550 (paper), proof of adequate funds, proof of health/immunizations.
International Student Contact Dr. William Rambin, International Student Coordinator, 700 University Drive, Monroe, LA 71209. **Phone:** 318-342-5223. **E-mail:** cnrambin@alpha.ulm.edu.

■ APPLICATION
Required GMAT, application form, baccalaureate/first degree, transcripts of college work. **Recommended** Interview, letter(s) of recommendation, personal statement, resume/curriculum vitae, work experience.
Deadlines and Fees Applications for domestic and international students are processed on a rolling basis. *Application fee:* $15, $25 (international).
Application Contact Ms. Jacqueline O'Neal, Director, MBA Program, 700 University Drive, Monroe, LA 71209-0100. **Phone:** 318-342-1100. **Fax:** 318-342-1101. **E-mail:** econeal@alpha.ulm.edu.

MAINE

Maine Maritime Academy

Castine, Maine

DEPARTMENT OF GRADUATE STUDIES

Graduate Business Faculty
Full-time: 5   Part-time: 11

Student Body
Total: 32
Full-time: 22   Average Age: 30
Part-time: 10   Women: 9%

Admissions
Applications: 23
Admitted: 21   Enrolled: 9
                                                      Average GPA: 3.2

Costs (1999–2000)
Full-time tuition: N/R
Part-time tuition: $365 per credit (resident), $365 per credit
   (nonresident)

After Graduation (Class of 1998–99)
Employed within 3 months of graduation: 100%

DEGREES MS

MS—Master of Science in Logistics Management Full-time and part-time. At least 45 total credits required. 11 to 60 months to complete program.

MS—Master of Science in Maritime Management Full-time and part-time. At least 45 total credits required. 11 to 60 months to complete program. *Concentrations:* international logistics, international management, international trade, logistics, management.

MS—Master of Science in Port Management Full-time and part-time. At least 45 total credits required. 11 to 60 months to complete program. *Concentrations:* international logistics, international trade, logistics, management.

COSTS

Tuition, state resident: *Part-time* $365 per credit. **Tuition, nonresident:** *Part-time* $365 per credit. **Required fees:** *Full-time* $360. **Graduate housing:** *Typical cost:* $5750 (room only).

FINANCIAL AID (1999–2000)

5 students received aid, including fellowships, loans, research assistantships, teaching assistantships, and work study. Aid is available to part-time students. **Financial Aid Contact** Ms. Gail Ryan, Director of Financial Aid, Pleasant Street, Castine, ME 04420. **Phone:** 207-326-2206. **Fax:** 207-326-2515. **E-mail:** admissns@bell.mma.edu.

RESOURCES AND SERVICES

Information about online services, personal computer policies, library resources, international exchange programs, internship programs, and placement services at this institution and others can be found at **www.petersons.com/mba**

International Students

28% of students enrolled are international students.

Services and Facilities Counseling/support services, housing location assistance, international student housing, orientation, visa services. Financial aid is not available to international students.

Applying *Required:* TOEFL, proof of adequate funds, proof of health/immunizations.

International Student Contact Mr. Harry Kaiserian, Jr., Registrar, Pleasant Street, Castine, ME 04420. **E-mail:** registra@bell.mma.edu.

■ APPLICATION

Required GMAT or GRE, application form, baccalaureate/first degree, 2 letters of recommendation, transcripts of college work. **Recommended** Essay, interview, personal statement, resume/curriculum vitae.

Deadlines and Fees Applications for domestic and international students are processed on a rolling basis. *Application fee:* $40, $40 (international).

Application Contact Mrs. Carolyn Ulrich, Administrative Assistant, Graduate Studies, Pleasant Street, Castine, ME 04420. **Phone:** 207-326-2485. **Toll-free Phone:** 800-464-6565 (in-state), 800-227-8465 (out-of-state). **Fax:** 207-326-2411. **E-mail:** gradschl@bell.mma.edu.

Thomas College

Waterville, Maine

PROGRAMS IN BUSINESS

Graduate Business Faculty
Full-time: 13   Part-time: 17

Student Body
Total: 135
Part-time: 135   Average Age: 36

Admissions
Applications: 40   Average GMAT: 514
Admitted: 40   Average GPA: 3.2
Enrolled: 40

Costs (1999–2000)
Full-time tuition: N/R
Part-time tuition: $470 per course

After Graduation (Class of 1998–99)
Employed within 3 months of graduation: 100%

DEGREES MBA • MS

MBA—Master of Business Administration Part-time. At least 36 total credits required. Minimum of 18 months to complete program.

MS—Master of Science in Taxation Part-time. At least 30 total credits required. Minimum of 18 months to complete program. *Concentrations:* taxation.

COSTS

Tuition *Part-time:* $470 per course. **Required fees:** Tuition and fees vary by academic program.

FINANCIAL AID (1999–2000)

Grants, loans, scholarships, and work study. Aid is available to part-time students. **Financial Aid Contact** Ms. Lisa Vashon, Director of Student Financial Services, 180 West River Road, Waterville, ME 04901. **Phone:** 207-859-1105. **Fax:** 207-877-0114. **E-mail:** sfs@thomas.edu.

RESOURCES AND SERVICES

Information about online services, personal computer policies, library resources, international exchange programs, internship programs, and placement services at this institution and others can be found at **www.petersons.com/mba**

International Students

Services and Facilities Financial aid is not available to international students. **Applying** *Required:* TOEFL, proof of health/immunizations.

■ APPLICATION

Required Baccalaureate/first degree, letter(s) of recommendation, personal statement, resume/curriculum vitae, transcripts of college work. School will accept GMAT. **Recommended** Essay.

Deadlines and Fees Applications for domestic and international students are processed on a rolling basis. *Application fee:* $40, $40 (international).

Application Contact Dr. Robert Whitcomb, Dean, 180 West River Road, Waterville, ME 04901. **Phone:** 207-859-1102. **Toll-free Phone:** 800-339-7001. **Fax:** 207-859-1114. **E-mail:** mba@thomas.edu.

University of Maine

Orono, Maine

THE MAINE BUSINESS SCHOOL

Graduate Business Faculty
Full-time: 15

Student Body
Total: 76   Average Age: 32
Full-time: 34   Women: 33%
Part-time: 42

Admissions
Applications: 63   Average GMAT: 528
Admitted: 54   Average GPA: 3.26
Enrolled: 26

Costs (1999–2000)
Full-time tuition: N/R
Part-time tuition: $198 per credit (resident), $562 per credit
   (nonresident)

University of Maine (continued)

After Graduation (Class of 1998–99)
Employed within 3 months of graduation: 85%

Accreditation
AACSB—The International Association for Management Education

DEGREE MBA

MBA—Master of Business Administration Full-time and part-time. 30 to 48 total credits required. 12 to 72 months to complete program. *Concentrations:* finance, management, marketing.

COSTS

Tuition, state resident: *Part-time* $198 per credit. **Tuition, nonresident:** *Part-time* $562 per credit. Tuition varies by number of courses or credits taken and local reciprocity agreements. **Required fees:** *Full-time* $388. *Part-time* $124 per year. Tuition and fees vary by number of courses or credits taken. **Graduate housing:** Room and board costs vary by number of occupants and type of board plan. *Typical cost:* $5256 (including board).

FINANCIAL AID (1999–2000)
Loans, research assistantships, scholarships, and work study. Financial aid application deadline: 3/1. **Financial Aid Contact** Ms. Peggy Crawford, Director of Student Aid, 5781 Wingate Hall, Orono, ME 04469-5781. **Phone:** 207-581-1324. **Fax:** 207-581-3261.

RESOURCES AND SERVICES
Information about online services, personal computer policies, library resources, international exchange programs, internship programs, and placement services at this institution and others can be found at **www.petersons.com/mba**

International Students
16% of students enrolled are international students.

Services and Facilities Counseling/support services, ESL/language courses, international student housing, visa services. Financial aid is available to international students.
Applying *Required:* TOEFL with recommended score of 213 (computer) or 550 (paper), proof of adequate funds, proof of health/immunizations.
International Student Contact Mrs. Karen Boucias, Director of International Programs, 100 Winslow Hall, Orono, ME 04469-5782. **Phone:** 207-581-2905. **Fax:** 207-581-2920. **E-mail:** umintprg@maine.edu.

■ APPLICATION
Required GMAT, application form, baccalaureate/first degree, essay, 3 letters of recommendation, personal statement, transcripts of college work. **Recommended** Resume/curriculum vitae.
Deadlines and Fees *Deadlines:* 7/15 for fall, 12/1 for spring, 3/15 for summer, 7/15 for fall (international), 12/1 for spring (international), 3/15 for summer (international). *Application fee:* $50, $50 (international).
Application Contact Ms. Caroline Dane, Assistant to the Director of the Graduate Program, 5723 Donald P. Corbett Business Building, Orono, ME 04469-5723. **Phone:** 207-581-1973. **Fax:** 207-581-1930. **E-mail:** mba@maine.edu.

See full description on page 916.

University of Southern Maine

Portland, Maine

SCHOOL OF BUSINESS

Graduate Business Faculty
Full-time: 14 | Part-time: 1

Student Body
Total: 133
Full-time: 13
Part-time: 120
Average Age: 32
Women: 37%

Admissions
Applications: 43
Admitted: 34
Enrolled: 26
Average GMAT: 558
Average GPA: 3.33

Costs (1999–2000)
Full-time tuition: N/R
Part-time tuition: $182 per credit hour (resident), $505 per credit hour (nonresident)

Accreditation
AACSB—The International Association for Management Education

DEGREE MBA

MBA—Master of Business Administration Full-time and part-time. 30 to 51 total credits required. 24 to 72 months to complete program.

COSTS
Tuition, state resident: *Part-time* $182 per credit hour. **Tuition, nonresident:** *Part-time* $505 per credit hour. Tuition varies by academic program and local reciprocity agreements. **Required fees:** *Part-time* $42.50 per course. Fees vary by number of courses or credits taken. **Graduate housing:** Room and board costs vary by campus location, number of occupants, and type of accommodation. *Typical cost:* $5796 (including board), $3418 (room only).

FINANCIAL AID (1999–2000)
Loans, research assistantships, scholarships, teaching assistantships, and work study. Aid is available to part-time students. Financial aid application deadline: 3/15. **Financial Aid Contact** Mr. Keith Dubois, Financial Aid Director, 37 College Avenue, Gorham, ME 04038. **Phone:** 207-780-5250.

RESOURCES AND SERVICES
Information about online services, personal computer policies, library resources, international exchange programs, internship programs, and placement services at this institution and others can be found at **www.petersons.com/mba**

International Students
2% of students enrolled are international students.

Services and Facilities Counseling/support services, ESL/language courses, international student housing, international student organization, visa services. Financial aid is available to international students.
Applying *Required:* TOEFL with recommended score of 213 (computer) or 550 (paper), proof of adequate funds, proof of health/immunizations.
International Student Contact Ms. Domenica Cipollone, Director, International Programs, PO Box 9300, Portland, ME 04104-9300. **Phone:** 207-780-4954. **Fax:** 207-780-4933. **E-mail:** domenica@usm.maine.edu.

■ APPLICATION
Required GMAT or GRE, application form, baccalaureate/first degree, essay, 3 letters of recommendation, resume/curriculum vitae, transcripts of college work.
Deadlines and Fees Applications for domestic and international students are processed on a rolling basis. *Application fee:* $25, $25 (international).
Application Contact Ms. Alice Cash, MBA Program Manager, PO Box 9300, Portland, ME 04104-9300. **Phone:** 207-780-4184. **Toll-free Phone:** 800-800-4USM Ext. 4184. **Fax:** 207-780-4662. **E-mail:** mba@usm.maine.edu.

MARYLAND

Bowie State University

Bowie, Maryland

BUSINESS PROGRAMS

Graduate Business Faculty
Full-time: 7 | Part-time: 6

Student Body
Total: 518 | Average Age: 34

Admissions
Enrolled: 72

Costs (1999–2000)
Full-time tuition: N/R
Part-time tuition: $195 per credit (resident), $368 per credit (nonresident)

DEGREES MA • MS

MA—Master of Arts in Administrative Management Full-time and part-time. At least 36 total credits required. 18 to 84 months to complete program. *Concentrations:* accounting, human resources, management, public management.

MA—Master of Arts in Human Resource Development Full-time and part-time. At least 39 total credits required. 18 to 84 months to complete program. *Concentrations:* human resources.

MA—Master of Arts in Organizational Communications Full-time and part-time. At least 36 total credits required. 18 to 84 months to complete program. *Concentrations:* organizational management.

MS—Master of Science in Management Information Systems Full-time and part-time. *Distance learning option.* At least 36 total credits required. 18 to 84 months to complete program. *Concentrations:* management information systems.

COSTS

Tuition, state resident: *Part-time* $195 per credit. **Tuition, nonresident:** *Part-time* $368 per credit. **Required fees:** *Full-time* $245. **Graduate housing:** Room and board costs vary by number of occupants, type of accommodation, and type of board plan. *Typical cost:* $4750 (including board).

FINANCIAL AID (1999–2000)

Fellowships, grants, loans, research assistantships, scholarships, and work study. Aid is available to part-time students. Financial aid application deadline: 4/1. **Financial Aid Contact** Mr. Donald Kiah, Acting Assistant Vice President of Enrollment, 14000 Jericho Park Road, Bowie, MD 20715. **Phone:** 301-464-7763. **Fax:** 301-464-7521. **E-mail:** dkiah@bowiestate.edu.

RESOURCES AND SERVICES

Information about online services, personal computer policies, library resources, international exchange programs, internship programs, and placement services at this institution and others can be found at **www. petersons.com/mba**

International Students

Services and Facilities Counseling/support services, visa services. Financial aid is not available to international students.
Applying *Required:* TOEFL with recommended score of 550 (paper), TWE with recommended score of 4, proof of adequate funds, proof of health/immunizations.
International Student Contact Dr. Anne Nedd, Director of the University College of Excellence, 14000 Jericho Park Road, Bowie, MD 20715. **Phone:** 301-464-7255. **E-mail:** anedd@bowiestate.edu.

■ APPLICATION

Required Application form, baccalaureate/first degree, transcripts of college work. **Recommended** Personal statement, work experience.
Deadlines and Fees *Deadlines:* 7/1 for fall, 12/1 for spring, 3/1 for fall (international), 8/1 for spring (international). *Application fee:* $40, $40 (international).
Application Contact Ms. Shawna Acker, Graduate Admissions Coordinator, School of Graduate Studies and Research, 14000 Jericho Park Road, Bowie, MD 20715-3318. **Phone:** 301-464-6561. **Fax:** 301-809-4076. **E-mail:** shawna. acker@bowiestate.edu.

College of Notre Dame of Maryland

Baltimore, Maryland

GRADUATE STUDIES

DEGREE MA

MA—Master of Arts in Management Full-time and part-time. At least 42 total credits required. 15 to 84 months to complete program. *Concentrations:* financial management/planning, human resources, management.

RESOURCES AND SERVICES

Information about online services, personal computer policies, library resources, international exchange programs, internship programs, and placement services at this institution and others can be found at **www. petersons.com/mba**

International Students

Services and Facilities Counseling/support services, ESL/language courses. Financial aid is not available to international students.
International Student Contact Sr. Miriam Jansen, Director, International Programs, 4701 North Charles Street, Baltimore, MD 21210-2476. **Phone:** 410-532-3183. **E-mail:** mjansen@ndm.edu.

■ APPLICATION

Application Contact Ms. Linda Herr, Graduate Studies Secretary, 4701 North Charles Street, Baltimore, MD 21210-2476. **Phone:** 410-532-5317. **Fax:** 410-532-5793. **E-mail:** gradadm@ndm.edu.

Frostburg State University

Frostburg, Maryland

COLLEGE OF BUSINESS

Graduate Business Faculty

Full-time: 14	Part-time: 12

Student Body

Total: 425	Average Age: 35
Full-time: 45	Women: 43%
Part-time: 380	

Admissions

Applications: 170	Enrolled: 94
Admitted: 148	

Costs (1999–2000)
Full-time tuition: $3060 per academic year (resident), $3546 per academic year (nonresident)
Part-time tuition: $180 per credit hour (resident), $208 per credit hour (nonresident)

DEGREES MBA • MBA/MS

MBA—Master of Business Administration Full-time and part-time. At least 48 total credits required. 12 to 72 months to complete program. *Concentrations:* management.

MBA/MS—Master of Business Administration/Master of Science in Nursing Administration Full-time and part-time. *Distance learning option.* At least 63 total credits required. 24 to 72 months to complete program. *Concentrations:* management.

COSTS

Tuition, state resident: *Full-time* $3060. *Part-time* $180 per credit hour. **Tuition, nonresident:** *Full-time* $3546. *Part-time* $208 per credit hour. **Required fees:** Tuition and fees vary by campus location and local reciprocity agreements. **Graduate housing:** Room and board costs vary by number of occupants, type of accommodation, and type of board plan. *Typical cost:* $2600 (including board).

FINANCIAL AID (1999–2000)

9 students received aid, including research assistantships and work study. **Financial Aid Contact** Dr. Robert Smith, Assistant Dean for Graduate Admissions and Records, Room 133, Hitchins Administration Building, Frostburg, MD 21532. **Phone:** 301-687-7053. **Fax:** 301-687-4597. **E-mail:** rsmith@frostburg.edu.

RESOURCES AND SERVICES

Information about online services, personal computer policies, library resources, international exchange programs, internship programs, and placement services at this institution and others can be found at **www. petersons.com/mba**

International Students

2% of students enrolled are international students.
Services and Facilities Counseling/support services, visa services. Financial aid is available to international students.
Applying *Required:* TOEFL with recommended score of 550 (paper), proof of adequate funds, proof of health/immunizations.
International Student Contact Mr. Robert Smith, Assistant Dean for Graduate Admissions and Records, Room 133, Hitchins Administration Building, Frostburg, MD 21532. **Phone:** 301-687-7053. **Fax:** 301-687-4597. **E-mail:** rsmith@ frostburg.edu.

■ APPLICATION

Required Application form, baccalaureate/first degree, transcripts of college work. **Recommended** Work experience.
Deadlines and Fees *Application fee:* $30, $30 (international).
Application Contact Dr. David Nicol, Chair, MBA Department, College of Business, Frostburg, MD 21532-1099. **Phone:** 301-687-4375. **Fax:** 301-687-4486. **E-mail:** mba@frostburg.edu.

See full description on page 660.

Hood College

Frederick, Maryland

DEPARTMENT OF ECONOMICS AND MANAGEMENT (INTERIM)

Graduate Business Faculty

Hood College (continued)

Full-time: 8
Part-time: 11

Student Body
Total: 145
Full-time: 8

Part-time: 137
Average Age: 33

Costs (1999–2000)
Full-time tuition: N/R
Part-time tuition: $295 per credit hour

After Graduation (Class of 1998–99)
Employed within 3 months of graduation: 100%
Average starting salary: $60,000

DEGREE MBA

MBA—Master of Business Administration Full-time and part-time. At least 36 total credits required. Maximum of 84 months to complete program. *Concentrations:* accounting, finance, human resources, information management, marketing, public management.

COSTS
Tuition *Part-time:* $295 per credit hour.

FINANCIAL AID (1999–2000)
Loans. Aid is available to part-time students. **Financial Aid Contact** Financial Aid Office, 401 Rosemont Avenue, Frederick, MD 21701-8575. **Phone:** 301-696-3411.

RESOURCES AND SERVICES
Information about online services, personal computer policies, library resources, international exchange programs, internship programs, and placement services at this institution and others can be found at **www.petersons.com/mba**

International Students
Services and Facilities Financial aid is not available to international students.
Applying *Required:* TOEFL with recommended score of 575 (paper), TWE with recommended score of 4.
International Student Contact Dr. Anita Jose, Director, MBA Program, 401 Rosemont Avenue, Frederick, MD 21701-8578. **Phone:** 301-696-3691. **Fax:** 301-696-3771. **E-mail:** ajose@hood.edu.

■ APPLICATION
Required Application form, baccalaureate/first degree, transcripts of college work. **Recommended** Resume/curriculum vitae, work experience.
Deadlines and Fees Applications for domestic and international students are processed on a rolling basis. *Application fee:* $30, $30 (international).
Application Contact Ms. Margo Rhoades, Graduate Enrollment Manager, 401 Rosemont Avenue, Frederick, MD 21701-8575. **Phone:** 301-696-3601. **E-mail:** mrhoades@hood.edu.

Johns Hopkins University

Baltimore, Maryland

SCHOOL OF PROFESSIONAL STUDIES IN BUSINESS AND EDUCATION

Graduate Business Faculty
Full-time: 15

Part-time: 246

Student Body
Total: 3,018
Full-time: 238
Part-time: 2,780

Average Age: 35
Women: 48%

Admissions
Applications: 927
Admitted: 734

Enrolled: 675
Average GPA: 3.25

Costs (1999–2000)
Full-time tuition: N/R
Part-time tuition: $430 per credit hour

DEGREES MBA • MS

MBA—Master of Business Administration Full-time and part-time. At least 51 total credits required. 24 to 72 months to complete program. *Concentrations:* electronic commerce (e-commerce), finance, human resources, international business, management, management information systems, marketing, real estate.

MS—Management and Community Development Full-time and part-time. Students must hold mid- to executive- level position within a police department. At least 45 total credits required. *Concentrations:* public policy and administration.
MS—Master of Science in Information and Telecommunications Systems Full-time and part-time. At least 48 total credits required. 24 to 72 months to complete program.
MS—Master of Science in Marketing Full-time and part-time. At least 48 total credits required. 24 to 72 months to complete program. *Concentrations:* marketing.
MS—Master of Science in Organization Development and Human Resources Full-time and part-time. At least 36 total credits required. 24 to 72 months to complete program. *Concentrations:* human resources, organizational behavior/development.
MS—Master of Science in Real Estate Full-time and part-time. At least 40 total credits required. 24 to 72 months to complete program. *Concentrations:* real estate.

COSTS
Tuition *Part-time:* $430 per credit hour. Tuition varies by number of courses or credits taken and campus location. **Required fees:** *Part-time* $45 per semester.

FINANCIAL AID (1999–2000)
455 students received aid, including loans and scholarships. Aid is available to part-time students. Financial aid application deadline: 6/1.
Financial Aid Contact Laura Donnelly, Director of Financial Aid, 7150 Gateway Drive, Suite A/B, Columbia, MD 21046-2101. **Phone:** 410-872-1230. **Fax:** 410-872-1250.

RESOURCES AND SERVICES
Information about online services, personal computer policies, library resources, international exchange programs, internship programs, and placement services at this institution and others can be found at **www.petersons.com/mba**

International Students
2% of students enrolled are international students.
Services and Facilities Counseling/support services, visa services. Financial aid is not available to international students.
Applying *Required:* TOEFL with recommended score of 220 (computer) or 650 (paper), proof of adequate funds, proof of health/immunizations.
International Student Contact Ms. Kathy Bovard, Director, Student Affairs, 6740 Alexander Bell Drive, Columbia, MD 21046-2101. **Phone:** 410-872-1210. **Fax:** 410-872-9061. **E-mail:** staffair@jhu.edu.

■ APPLICATION
Required Application form, baccalaureate/first degree, essay, 2 letters of recommendation, resume/curriculum vitae, transcripts of college work. **Recommended** Interview, work experience.
Deadlines and Fees Applications for domestic and international students are processed on a rolling basis. *Application fee:* $55, $55 (international).
Application Contact Ms. Barbara Shaffer, Director, Enrollment Management Services, 7150 Gateway Drive, Suite A/B, Columbia, MD 21046-2101. **Phone:** 410-872-1200. **Toll-free Phone:** 800-811-7585. **Fax:** 410-872-1251. **E-mail:** adr_mail@jhuvms.hcf.

See full description on page 694.

Loyola College in Maryland

Baltimore, Maryland

SELLINGER SCHOOL OF BUSINESS AND MANAGEMENT

Graduate Business Faculty
Full-time: 49

Part-time: 10

Student Body
Total: 1,025
Full-time: 239
Part-time: 786

Average Age: 31
Women: 34%

Admissions
Applications: 688
Admitted: 569
Enrolled: 490

Average GMAT: 531
Average GPA: 3.05

Costs (1999–2000)
Full-time tuition: $6930 per academic year
Part-time tuition: $385 per credit

Accreditation
AACSB—The International Association for Management Education

DEGREES MBA • MSF

MBA—Executive MBA Part-time. At least 51 total credits required. 21 months to complete program.

MBA—MBA Fellows Program Part-time. At least 51 total credits required. 33 months to complete program.

MBA—Master of Business Administration Full-time and part-time. At least 51 total credits required. 12 to 84 months to complete program. *Concentrations:* accounting, economics, finance, health care, international business, management, management information systems, marketing.

MSF—Master of Science in Finance Full-time and part-time. At least 42 total credits required. 12 to 84 months to complete program.

COSTS
Tuition *Full-time:* $6930. *Part-time:* $385 per credit. **Required fees:** *Part-time* $25 per semester. Tuition and fees vary by number of courses or credits taken and academic program.

FINANCIAL AID (1999–2000)
102 students received aid, including loans and scholarships. Aid is available to part-time students. **Financial Aid Contact** Mr. Mark Lindenmeyer, Director of Financial Aid, 4501 North Charles Street, Baltimore, MD 21210-2699. **Phone:** 410-617-2576. **Fax:** 410-617-5149.

RESOURCES AND SERVICES
Information about online services, personal computer policies, library resources, international exchange programs, internship programs, and placement services at this institution and others can be found at **www.petersons.com/mba**

International Students
5% of students enrolled are international students.
Services and Facilities Counseling/support services, ESL/language courses, visa services. Financial aid is not available to international students.
Applying *Required:* TOEFL with recommended score of 213 (computer) or 550 (paper), proof of adequate funds, proof of health/immunizations.
International Student Contact Dr. Joseph Healy, Director, International Program, 4501 North Charles Street, Baltimore, MD 21210-2699. **Phone:** 410-617-2910.

■ **APPLICATION**
Required GMAT, application form, baccalaureate/first degree, essay, personal statement, resume/curriculum vitae, transcripts of college work. **Recommended** Letter(s) of recommendation, 2 years of work experience.
Deadlines and Fees *Deadlines:* 8/20 for fall, 11/20 for spring, 5/20 for summer, 5/15 for fall (international), 8/15 for spring (international), 1/15 for summer (international). *Application fee:* $50, $50 (international).
Application Contact Mr. John White, Director, Graduate Business Programs, 4501 North Charles Street, Baltimore, MD 21210-2699. **Phone:** 410-617-5067. **Toll-free Phone:** 800-221-9107 Ext. 3067. **Fax:** 410-617-2005. **E-mail:** mba@loyola.edu.

See full description on page 712.

Morgan State University

Baltimore, Maryland

EARL G. GRAVES SCHOOL OF BUSINESS AND MANAGEMENT

Graduate Business Faculty
Full-time: 42   Part-time: 3

Student Body
Total: 109
Part-time: 109   Average Age: 28
    Women: 51%

Admissions
Applications: 105   Average GMAT: 468
Admitted: 60   Average GPA: 3.06
Enrolled: 37

Costs (1999–2000)
Full-time tuition: N/R
Part-time tuition: $226 per credit hour (resident), $390 per credit hour (nonresident)

After Graduation (Class of 1998–99)
Employed within 3 months of graduation: 89%
Average starting salary: $41,043

Accreditation
AACSB—The International Association for Management Education

DEGREE MBA

MBA—Master of Business Administration Part-time. *Distance learning option.* 30 to 60 total credits required. 16 to 60 months to complete program. *Concentrations:* accounting, finance, information management, international business, management, marketing, taxation, travel industry/tourism management.

COSTS
Tuition, state resident: *Part-time* $186 per credit hour. **Tuition, nonresident:** *Part-time* $350 per credit hour. Tuition varies by number of courses or credits taken. **Required fees:** *Part-time* $40 per credit hour.

FINANCIAL AID (1999–2000)
Financial Aid Contact Dr. James Waller, Director, Admissions and Financial Aid, Holmes Hall 206, 1700 East Cold Spring Lane, Baltimore, MD 21251. **Phone:** 443-885-3185.

RESOURCES AND SERVICES
Information about online services, personal computer policies, library resources, international exchange programs, internship programs, and placement services at this institution and others can be found at **www.petersons.com/mba**

International Students
Services and Facilities Counseling/support services, ESL/language courses, housing location assistance, international student organization, language tutoring, orientation, visa services.
Applying *Required:* TOEFL with recommended score of 600 (paper), proof of adequate funds.
International Student Contact Mr. Richard Kitson-Walters, International Student Services, Carter-Grant Wilson Building, 326 Cold Spring Lane and Hillen Road, Baltimore, MD 21251. **Phone:** 443-885-3078.

■ **APPLICATION**
Required GMAT, application form, baccalaureate/first degree, essay, 3 letters of recommendation, personal statement, transcripts of college work. **Recommended** Interview, resume/curriculum vitae.
Deadlines and Fees *Application fee:* $20, $20 (international).
Application Contact Dr. Mildred Glover, Assistant Dean and Director of Graduate Program, School of Business and Management, Cold Spring Lane and Hillen Road, Baltimore, MD 21251. **Phone:** 443-885-3396. **Fax:** 443-319-3651. **E-mail:** mba@moac.morgan.edu.

Mount Saint Mary's College and Seminary

Emmitsburg, Maryland

PROGRAM IN BUSINESS

Graduate Business Faculty
Full-time: 9   Part-time: 7

Student Body
Total: 135
Full-time: 19   Average Age: 32
Part-time: 116   Women: 35%

Admissions
Applications: 24   Average GMAT: 500
Admitted: 22   Average GPA: 3
Enrolled: 20

Costs (1999–2000)
Full-time tuition: N/R
Part-time tuition: $275 per credit

DEGREE MBA

MBA—Master of Business Administration Full-time and part-time. At least 36 total credits required. Maximum of 60 months to complete program. *Concentrations:* accounting, finance, management, marketing.

COSTS
Tuition *Part-time:* $270 per credit. **Required fees:** *Part-time* $5 per credit. Fees vary by number of courses or credits taken.

FINANCIAL AID (1999–2000)
30 students received aid, including loans and research assistantships. **Financial Aid Contact** Mr. Dave Reeder, Associate Director of Financial

Mount Saint Mary's College and Seminary (continued)

Aid, 16300 Old Emmitsburg Road, Emmitsburg, MD 21727. **Phone:** 301-447-5207. **Fax:** 301-447-5755. **E-mail:** reeder@msmary.edu.

RESOURCES AND SERVICES
Information about online services, personal computer policies, library resources, international exchange programs, internship programs, and placement services at this institution and others can be found at **www.petersons.com/mba**

International Students
9% of students enrolled are international students.

Services and Facilities Counseling/support services, ESL/language courses. Financial aid is available to international students.
Applying *Required:* TOEFL with recommended score of 550 (paper), proof of adequate funds, proof of health/immunizations.
International Student Contact Dr. Gertrude Conway, Professor of Philosophy, 16300 Old Emmitsburg Road, Emmitsburg, MD 21727. **Phone:** 301-447-5368. **Fax:** 301-447-5755. **E-mail:** conway@msmary.edu.

■ APPLICATION
Required GMAT, application form, baccalaureate/first degree, personal statement, transcripts of college work, 5 years of work experience. **Recommended** Resume/curriculum vitae.
Deadlines and Fees Applications for domestic and international students are processed on a rolling basis. *Application fee:* $35, $35 (international).
Application Contact Mrs. Sandy Kauffman, Administrative Assistant, Graduate Program, 16300 Old Emmitsburg Road, Emmitsburg, MD 21727. **Phone:** 301-447-5326. **Fax:** 301-447-5335. **E-mail:** kauffman@msmary.edu.

Salisbury State University

Salisbury, Maryland

FRANKLIN P. PERDUE SCHOOL OF BUSINESS

Graduate Business Faculty
Full-time: 26

Part-time: 4

Student Body
Total: 105
Full-time: 27

Part-time: 78
Women: 42%

Admissions
Applications: 40
Enrolled: 34

Average GMAT: 472
Average GPA: 3.3

Costs (1999–2000)
Full-time tuition: N/R
Part-time tuition: $172 per credit hour (resident), $340 per credit hour (nonresident)

Accreditation
AACSB—The International Association for Management Education

DEGREE MBA

MBA—Master of Business Administration Full-time and part-time. At least 63 total credits required. 12 to 84 months to complete program. *Concentrations:* accounting.

COSTS
Tuition, state resident: *Part-time* $168 per credit hour. **Tuition, nonresident:** *Part-time* $336 per credit hour. **Required fees:** *Part-time* $4 per credit hour. **Graduate housing:** Room and board costs vary by number of occupants, type of accommodation, and type of board plan. *Typical cost:* $7200 (including board), $4800 (room only).

FINANCIAL AID (1999–2000)
4 students received aid, including loans and research assistantships. Financial aid application deadline: 5/1. **Financial Aid Contact** Janine Vienna, Director, Graduate Business Program, Franklin P. Perdue School of Business, 1101 Camden Avenue, Salisbury, MD 21801-6837. **Phone:** 410-548-3983. **Fax:** 410-546-6208. **E-mail:** jmvienna@ssu.edu.

RESOURCES AND SERVICES
Information about online services, personal computer policies, library resources, international exchange programs, internship programs, and placement services at this institution and others can be found at **www.petersons.com/mba**

International Students
18% of students enrolled are international students.
Services and Facilities Counseling/support services, housing location assistance, international student housing, international student organization, language tutoring, orientation. Financial aid is available to international students.
Applying *Required:* TOEFL with recommended score of 550 (paper), proof of adequate funds, proof of health/immunizations.
International Student Contact Janine Vienna, Director, Graduate Business Program, 1101 Camden Avenue, Salisbury, MD 21801-6837. **Phone:** 410-548-3983. **Fax:** 410-546-6208. **E-mail:** jmvienna@ssu.edu.

■ APPLICATION
Required GMAT, application form, baccalaureate/first degree, 2 letters of recommendation, personal statement, resume/curriculum vitae, transcripts of college work. **Recommended** Work experience.
Deadlines and Fees *Deadlines:* 7/15 for fall, 11/15 for winter, 12/15 for spring, 5/1 for summer, 4/1 for fall (international), 9/1 for winter (international), 10/1 for spring (international), 2/1 for summer (international). *Application fee:* $30, $30 (international).
Application Contact Janine Vienna, Director, Graduate Business Program, Franklin P. Perdue School of Business, 1101 Camden Avenue, Salisbury, MD 21801-6837. **Phone:** 410-548-3983. **Fax:** 410-546-6208. **E-mail:** jmvienna@ssu.edu.

Towson University

Towson, Maryland

COLLEGE OF GRADUATE EDUCATION AND RESEARCH

Graduate Business Faculty
Full-time: 10

Student Body
Total: 137
Full-time: 32
Part-time: 105

Average Age: 29
Women: 80%

Admissions
Applications: 86

Enrolled: 84

Costs (1999–2000)
Full-time tuition: $3510 per academic year (resident), $6948 per academic year (nonresident)
Part-time tuition: $195 per credit hour (resident), $386 per credit hour (nonresident)

Accreditation
AACSB—The International Association for Management Education

DEGREE MS

MS—Master of Science in Human Resource Development Full-time and part-time. At least 36 total credits required. 18 to 84 months to complete program. *Concentrations:* human resources.

COSTS
Tuition, state resident: *Full-time* $3510. *Part-time* $195 per credit hour. **Tuition, nonresident:** *Full-time* $6948. *Part-time* $386 per credit hour. **Required fees:** Tuition and fees vary by academic program. **Graduate housing:** Room and board costs vary by number of occupants, type of accommodation, and type of board plan. *Typical cost:* $5850 (room only).

FINANCIAL AID (1999–2000)
9 students received aid, including grants, loans, scholarships, and work study. Aid is available to part-time students. Financial aid application deadline: 4/1. **Financial Aid Contact** Ms. Fran Musotto, Graduate Office Supervisor, 8000 York Road, Towson, MD 21252-0001. **Phone:** 410-830-2501. **Fax:** 410-830-4675. **E-mail:** petgrad@towson.edu.

RESOURCES AND SERVICES
Information about online services, personal computer policies, library resources, international exchange programs, internship programs, and placement services at this institution and others can be found at **www.petersons.com/mba**

International Students
4% of students enrolled are international students.
Services and Facilities Counseling/support services, ESL/language courses, visa services.
Applying *Required:* TOEFL with recommended score of 550 (paper), proof of adequate funds, proof of health/immunizations.

International Student Contact Ms. Jan Schmitt, International Graduate Admissions Coordinator, 8000 York Road, Towson, MD 21252-0001. **Phone:** 410-830-2501. **Fax:** 410-830-4675. **E-mail:** petgrad@towson.edu.

■ **APPLICATION**

Required Application form, baccalaureate/first degree, essay, transcripts of college work.

Deadlines and Fees Applications for domestic and international students are processed on a rolling basis. *Application fee:* $40, $100 (international).

Application Contact Ms. Fran Musotto, Graduate Office Supervisor, 800 York Road, Towson, MD 21252-0001. **Phone:** 410-830-2501. **Toll-free Phone:** 888-486-4675. **Fax:** 410-830-4675. **E-mail:** petgrad@towson.edu.

University of Baltimore

Baltimore, Maryland

SCHOOL OF BUSINESS

Graduate Business Faculty
Full-time: 50 | Part-time: 25

Student Body
Total: 810
Full-time: 321 | Average Age: 28
Part-time: 489 | Women: 57%

Admissions
Applications: 290
Admitted: 223 | Average GMAT: 518
Enrolled: 169 | Average GPA: 3.2

Costs (1999–2000)
Full-time tuition: N/R
Part-time tuition: $264 per credit (resident), $393 per credit (nonresident)

Accreditation
AACSB—The International Association for Management Education

DEGREES JD/MBA • MBA • MBA/MS • MS • PhD/MBA • Pharm D/MBA

JD/MBA—Juris Doctor/Master of Business Administration Full-time and part-time. 102 to 123 total credits required. 36 to 84 months to complete program. *Concentrations:* entrepreneurship, finance, human resources, international business, management, management information systems, marketing, technology management.

MBA—Advantage MBA Full-time. At least 48 total credits required. 12 months to complete program. *Concentrations:* finance, health care, management, management information systems, marketing.

MBA—Chinese Executive MBA Full-time. At least 48 total credits required. 12 months to complete program. *Concentrations:* finance, health care, management, management information systems, marketing.

MBA—Flex MBA Full-time and part-time. *Distance learning option.* 30 to 51 total credits required. 12 to 84 months to complete program. *Concentrations:* decision sciences, entrepreneurship, finance, health care, human resources, international business, management, management information systems, marketing, technology management.

MBA—Professional Saturday MBA Part-time. At least 48 total credits required. 23 months to complete program. *Concentrations:* finance, health care, management, management information systems, marketing.

MBA—Web MBA Full-time and part-time. *Distance learning option.* At least 48 total credits required. 24 months to complete program. *Concentrations:* management.

MBA/MS—Master of Business Administration/Master of Science in Nursing Full-time and part-time. At least 66 total credits required. 24 to 84 months to complete program. *Concentrations:* health care.

MS—MS in Marketing and Venturing Part-time. At least 48 total credits required. 24 to 48 months to complete program. *Concentrations:* entrepreneurship, marketing.

MS—Master of Science in Accounting Full-time and part-time. 30 to 51 total credits required. 12 to 84 months to complete program. *Concentrations:* accounting.

MS—Master of Science in Finance Full-time and part-time. 30 to 42 total credits required. 12 to 84 months to complete program. *Concentrations:* finance.

MS—Master of Science in Information Systems Full-time and part-time. 33 to 45 total credits required. 12 to 84 months to complete program. *Concentrations:* management information systems.

MS—Master of Science in Taxation Full-time and part-time. At least 30 total credits required. 12 to 84 months to complete program. *Concentrations:* taxation.

PhD/MBA—Doctor of Philosophy in Nursing/Master of Business Administration Full-time and part-time. At least 85 total credits required. 24 to 84 months to complete program. *Concentrations:* health care.

Pharm D/MBA—Doctor of Pharmacy/Master of Business Administration Full-time and part-time. At least 155 total credits required. 24 to 84 months to complete program. *Concentrations:* health care.

COSTS

Tuition, state resident: *Part-time* $264 per credit. **Tuition, nonresident:** *Part-time* $393 per credit. **Required fees:** Tuition and fees vary by number of courses or credits taken, academic program, and local reciprocity agreements.

FINANCIAL AID (1999–2000)

Loans, research assistantships, scholarships, and work study. Aid is available to part-time students. **Financial Aid Contact** Director of Financial Aid, 1420 North Charles Street, Baltimore, MD 21201-5779. **Phone:** 410-837-4763. **Fax:** 410-837-4820.

RESOURCES AND SERVICES

Information about online services, personal computer policies, library resources, international exchange programs, internship programs, and placement services at this institution and others can be found at www.petersons.com/mba

International Students

6% of students enrolled are international students.

Services and Facilities Counseling/support services, orientation, visa services. Financial aid is available to international students.

Applying *Required:* TOEFL with recommended score of 213 (computer) or 550 (paper), proof of adequate funds. *Recommended:* Proof of health/immunizations.

International Student Contact Ms. Wendy Burgess, Director, International Services, 1420 North Charles Street, Baltimore, MD 21201-5779. **Phone:** 410-837-4756. **Fax:** 410-837-4793. **E-mail:** admissions@ubmail.ubalt.edu.

■ **APPLICATION**

Required GMAT, application form, baccalaureate/first degree, 2 letters of recommendation, personal statement, resume/curriculum vitae, transcripts of college work. School will accept GRE. **Recommended** Work experience.

Deadlines and Fees *Deadlines:* 7/15 for fall, 12/1 for spring, 4/1 for summer, 6/1 for fall (international), 12/1 for spring (international), 4/1 for summer (international). *Application fee:* $30, $30 (international).

Application Contact Ms. Lorna Hills, Assistant Director of Admissions, 1420 North Charles Street, Baltimore, MD 21201-5779. **Phone:** 877-277-5982. **Toll-free Phone:** 877-APPLYUB. **Fax:** 410-837-4793. **E-mail:** admissions@ubmail.ubalt.edu.

See full description on page 868.

University of Maryland, College Park

College Park, Maryland

ROBERT H. SMITH SCHOOL OF BUSINESS

Graduate Business Faculty
Full-time: 80 | Part-time: 46

Student Body
Total: 955
Full-time: 521 | Average Age: 27
Part-time: 434 | Women: 31%

Admissions
Applications: 1,938
Admitted: 577 | Average GMAT: 647
Enrolled: 360 | Average GPA: 3.34

Costs (1999–2000)
Full-time tuition: $11,967 per academic year (resident), $17,025 per academic year (nonresident)
Part-time tuition: $582 per credit hour (resident), $582 per credit hour (nonresident)

After Graduation (Class of 1998–99)
Employed within 3 months of graduation: 95.5%
Average starting salary: $68,000

Accreditation
AACSB—The International Association for Management Education

University of Maryland, College Park (continued)

DEGREES JD/MBA • MBA • MBA/MPM • MBA/MS • MBA/MSW • MS

JD/MBA—Juris Doctor/Master of Business Administration Full-time and part-time. At least 108 total credits required. 36 to 60 months to complete program.

MBA—Master of Business Administration Full-time and part-time. At least 54 total credits required. 18 to 60 months to complete program. *Concentrations:* accounting, entrepreneurship, finance, human resources, international business, logistics, management information systems, management science, marketing.

MBA/MPM—Master of Business Administration/Master of Public Management Full-time and part-time. At least 66 total credits required. 28 to 60 months to complete program.

MBA/MS—Master of Business Administration/Master of Science Full-time and part-time. At least 66 total credits required. 21 to 60 months to complete program. *Concentrations:* business information science, finance, logistics, management science.

MBA/MSW—Master of Business Administration/Master of Social Work Full-time and part-time. At least 88 total credits required. 28 to 60 months to complete program.

MS—Master of Science Full-time and part-time. At least 30 total credits required. 12 to 60 months to complete program. *Concentrations:* accounting, finance, financial information systems, management information systems, management science, organizational behavior/development.

COSTS

Tuition, state resident: *Full-time* $10,467. *Part-time* $582 per credit hour. **Tuition, nonresident:** *Full-time* $15,525. *Part-time* $582 per credit hour. **Tuition, international:** *Full-time* $15,525. **Required fees:** *Full-time* $1500. *Part-time* $1000 per year. Tuition and fees vary by number of courses or credits taken and campus location.

FINANCIAL AID (1999–2000)

210 students received aid, including fellowships, grants, research assistantships, scholarships, teaching assistantships, and work study. Financial aid application deadline: 2/1. **Financial Aid Contact** Ms. Nicole Roop, Financial Aid Department, Lee Building, College Park, MD 20742. **Phone:** 301-314-8313.

RESOURCES AND SERVICES

Information about online services, personal computer policies, library resources, international exchange programs, internship programs, and placement services at this institution and others can be found at **www. petersons.com/mba**

International Students

21% of students enrolled are international students.

Services and Facilities Counseling/support services, ESL/language courses, international student organization, orientation, visa services. Financial aid is available to international students.

Applying *Required:* TOEFL with recommended score of 250 (computer) or 600 (paper), proof of adequate funds, proof of health/immunizations. *Recommended:* TWE with recommended score of 4.

International Student Contact Ms. Valerie Woolston, Director of International Education Services, Mitchell Building, 3rd Floor, College Park, MD 20742. **Phone:** 301-314-7740. **Fax:** 301-314-9347.

■ **APPLICATION**

Required GMAT, application form, baccalaureate/first degree, essay, 2 letters of recommendation, personal statement, resume/curriculum vitae, transcripts of college work. School will accept GRE. **Recommended** Work experience.

Deadlines and Fees *Deadlines:* 12/15 for fall, 2/1 for winter, 3/15 for spring, 5/1 for summer, 12/15 for fall (international), 2/1 for winter (international). *Application fee:* $50, $50 (international).

Application Contact Ms. Sabrina White, Director MBA/MS Admission, The Robert H. Smith School of Business, 2308 Van Munching Hall, College Park, MD 20742. **Phone:** 301-405-2278. **Fax:** 301-314-9862. **E-mail:** mba_info@ rhsmith.umd.edu.

See full description on page 918.

University of Maryland University College

College Park, Maryland

GRADUATE SCHOOL OF MANAGEMENT AND TECHNOLOGY

Graduate Business Faculty
Part-time: 137

Student Body
Total: 3,865
Full-time: 281
Part-time: 3,584

Average Age: 37
Women: 48%

Admissions
Applications: 1,273
Admitted: 1,263

Enrolled: 736

Costs (1999–2000)
Full-time tuition: N/R
Part-time tuition: $281 per credit (resident), $382 per credit (nonresident)

DEGREES MBA • MIM • MS

MBA—Master of Business Administration Part-time. *Distance learning option.* Internet access required. At least 42 total credits required. 24 to 60 months to complete program.

MIM—Executive Master of International Management Full-time. 5 years of mid- or senior-level management experience required. At least 36 total credits required. 18 months to complete program.

MIM—Master of International Management Full-time and part-time. *Distance learning option.* 36 to 39 total credits required. 16 to 84 months to complete program. *Concentrations:* international finance, international marketing, international trade.

MS—Executive Master of Science in Computer Systems Management Full-time. 5 years of mid- or senior-level management experience required. At least 36 total credits required. 18 months to complete program. *Concentrations:* information management.

MS—Executive Master of Science in Management Full-time. 5 years of mid- or senior-level management experience required. At least 36 total credits required. 16 months to complete program.

MS—Executive Master of Science in Technology Management Full-time. 5 years of mid- or senior-level management experience required. At least 36 total credits required. 16 months to complete program.

MS—Executive Master of Science in Telecommunications Management Full-time. 5 years of mid- or senior-level management experience required. At least 36 total credits required. 18 months to complete program. *Concentrations:* telecommunications management.

MS—Master of Science in Computer Systems Management Full-time and part-time. *Distance learning option.* 36 to 39 total credits required. 16 to 84 months to complete program. *Concentrations:* information management.

MS—Master of Science in Environmental Management Full-time and part-time. *Distance learning option.* 36 to 39 total credits required. 16 to 84 months to complete program. *Concentrations:* environmental economics/management.

MS—Master of Science in Management Full-time and part-time. *Distance learning option.* 36 to 39 total credits required. 16 to 84 months to complete program. *Concentrations:* contract management, finance, health care, human resources, management, management information systems, marketing, nonprofit management.

MS—Master of Science in Technology Management Full-time and part-time. *Distance learning option.* 36 to 39 total credits required. 16 to 84 months to complete program. *Concentrations:* technology management.

MS—Master of Science in Telecommunications Management Full-time and part-time. 36 to 39 total credits required. 16 to 84 months to complete program. *Concentrations:* telecommunications management.

COSTS

Tuition, state resident: *Part-time* $281 per credit. **Tuition, nonresident:** *Part-time* $382 per credit. Tuition varies by academic program.

FINANCIAL AID (1999–2000)

Grants, loans, scholarships, and work study. Aid is available to part-time students. Financial aid application deadline: 6/1. **Financial Aid Contact** Coordinator, Graduate Services, Graduate Admissions and Advising, 3501 University Boulevard East, Adelphi, MD 20783. **Phone:** 301-985-7155. **Fax:** 301-985-7175. **E-mail:** gradinfo@nova.umuc.edu.

RESOURCES AND SERVICES

Information about online services, personal computer policies, library resources, international exchange programs, internship programs, and placement services at this institution and others can be found at **www. petersons.com/mba**

International Students

5% of students enrolled are international students.

Services and Facilities Counseling/support services, visa services. Financial aid is not available to international students.

Applying *Required:* TOEFL with recommended score of 580 (paper), TWE with recommended score of 4, proof of adequate funds.

International Student Contact Ms. Julie Xiang, Coordinator, Graduate Services, Graduate Admissions and Advising, 3501 University Boulevard East, Adelphi, MD 20783. **Phone:** 301-985-7155. **Fax:** 301-985-7175. **E-mail:** gradinfo@nova.umuc.edu.

■ APPLICATION

Required Application form, baccalaureate/first degree, personal statement, transcripts of college work. **Recommended** Work experience.

Deadlines and Fees *Application fee:* $50, $50 (international).

Application Contact Coordinator, Graduate Services, Graduate Admissions and Advising, 3501 University Boulevard East, Adelphi, MD 20783. **Phone:** 301-985-7155. **Fax:** 301-985-7175. **E-mail:** gradinfo@nova.umuc.edu.

MASSACHUSETTS

American International College

Springfield, Massachusetts

SCHOOL OF BUSINESS ADMINISTRATION

Graduate Business Faculty

Full-time: 11	Part-time: 15

Student Body

Total: 75	
Full-time: 25	Average Age: 28
Part-time: 50	Women: 40%

Admissions

Applications: 50	Enrolled: 25
Admitted: 40	Average GPA: 3.3

Costs (1999–2000)
Full-time tuition: $10,160 per academic year
Part-time tuition: $405 per hour

DEGREES MBA • MS

MBA—Master of Business Administration Full-time and part-time. 36 to 54 total credits required. 12 to 18 months to complete program. *Concentrations:* accounting, finance, international business, management, marketing, materials management.

MS—Master of Science in Accounting and Taxation Full-time and part-time. 30 to 60 total credits required. 10 to 20 months to complete program. *Concentrations:* accounting, taxation.

COSTS

Tuition *Full-time:* $10,160. *Part-time:* $405 per hour. **Graduate housing:** Room and board costs vary by number of occupants. *Typical cost:* $7112 (including board).

FINANCIAL AID (1999–2000)

40 students received aid, including fellowships, grants, loans, scholarships, and work study. Aid is available to part-time students. Financial aid application deadline: 5/1. **Financial Aid Contact** Dr. Lee C. Sirois, Director of Financial Aid, 1000 State Street, Springfield, MA 01109-3189. **Phone:** 413-747-6259. **Fax:** 413-737-2803.

RESOURCES AND SERVICES

Information about online services, personal computer policies, library resources, international exchange programs, internship programs, and placement services at this institution and others can be found at **www. petersons.com/mba**

International Students

16% of students enrolled are international students.

Services and Facilities Counseling/support services, ESL/language courses, visa services. Financial aid is not available to international students.

Applying *Required:* TOEFL with recommended score of 550 (paper), proof of adequate funds, proof of health/immunizations.

International Student Contact Dr. Trudy Somers, Dean, School of Business Administration, 1000 State Street, Box 2A, Springfield, MA 01109-3189. **Phone:** 413-747-6230. **Fax:** 413-737-2803. **E-mail:** business@www.aic.edu.

■ APPLICATION

Required Application form, baccalaureate/first degree, 2 letters of recommendation, transcripts of college work.

Deadlines and Fees Applications for domestic and international students are processed on a rolling basis. *Application fee:* $25, $40 (international).

Application Contact Dr. Trudy Somers, Dean, School of Business Administration, 1000 State Street, Box 2A, Springfield, MA 01109-3189. **Phone:** 413-747-6230. **Fax:** 413-737-2803. **E-mail:** business@www.aic.edu.

See full description on page 542.

Anna Maria College

Paxton, Massachusetts

PROGRAM IN BUSINESS ADMINISTRATION

Graduate Business Faculty

Full-time: 5	Part-time: 20

Student Body

Total: 200	Part-time: 180
Full-time: 20	Average Age: 35

Admissions

Average GMAT: 550	Average GPA: 2.6

Costs (1999–2000)
Full-time tuition: N/R
Part-time tuition: $775 per course

After Graduation (Class of 1998–99)
Employed within 3 months of graduation: 90%

DEGREES MBA

MBA—Master of Business Administration in Health Care Administration Full-time and part-time. *Distance learning option.* At least 45 total credits required. 18 to 60 months to complete program. *Concentrations:* health care.

MBA—Master of Business Administration Full-time and part-time. At least 45 total credits required. 18 to 60 months to complete program. *Concentrations:* entrepreneurship, finance, leadership, marketing.

COSTS

Tuition *Part-time:* $775 per course.

FINANCIAL AID (1999–2000)

Financial Aid Contact Ms. Laurie Peltier, Director of Admissions, 50 Sunset Lane, Paxton, MA 01612-1198. **Phone:** 508-849-3367. **Fax:** 508-849-3362. **E-mail:** lpeltier@annamaria.edu.

RESOURCES AND SERVICES

Information about online services, personal computer policies, library resources, international exchange programs, internship programs, and placement services at this institution and others can be found at **www. petersons.com/mba**

International Students

Services and Facilities Counseling/support services, ESL/language courses.

Applying *Required:* TOEFL with recommended score of 500 (paper), proof of adequate funds, proof of health/immunizations.

International Student Contact Mr. Bernard Wood, Director of Business Programs, 50 Sunset Lane, Paxton, MA 01612-1198. **Phone:** 508-849-3307. **Fax:** 508-849-3362. **E-mail:** bwood@annamaria.edu.

■ APPLICATION

Required Application form, baccalaureate/first degree, interview, 2 letters of recommendation, personal statement, resume/curriculum vitae, transcripts of college work. School will accept GMAT or GRE or MAT.

Deadlines and Fees Applications for domestic and international students are processed on a rolling basis. *Application fee:* $30, $30 (international).

Anna Maria College (continued)

Application Contact Ms. Laurie Peltier, Director of Admissions, 50 Sunset Lane, Paxton, MA 01612-1198. **Phone:** 508-849-3367. **Fax:** 508-849-3362. **E-mail:** lpeltier@annamaria.edu.

Arthur D. Little School of Management

Chestnut Hill, Massachusetts

GRADUATE PROGRAM

Graduate Business Faculty
Full-time: 6   Part-time: 18

Student Body
Total: 54   Average Age: 32
Full-time: 54   Women: 22%

Admissions
Applications: 126   Average GMAT: 550
Admitted: 118   Average GPA: 3
Enrolled: 58

Costs (1999–2000)
Full-time tuition: $32,000 per academic year
Part-time tuition: N/R

After Graduation (Class of 1998–99)
Employed within 3 months of graduation: 80%
Average starting salary: $85,000

DEGREE MSM

MSM—Master of Science in Management Full-time. At least 53 total credits required. 11 months to complete program. *Concentrations:* finance, industrial administration/management, international business, international finance, international management, international marketing, management, management science, marketing, strategic management.

Arthur D. Little (ADL), a leading international consulting firm, is the only corporation to create an accredited graduate business program. Beginning in 1964, the Arthur D. Little School of Management developed a Master of Science in Management Program especially designed for experienced international managers. This intensive one-year program provides 65 participants with a curriculum distinguished by its practical, problem-solving orientation and multicultural learning environment. The program is enhanced by its use of an actual four-month management consulting project with ADL or a key client and business simulation exercises.

Students work side by side with the faculty, which is composed of international business school professors and ADL senior consultants. The faculty's working knowledge of leading-edge business issues reinforces the importance of blending leading academic theory with actual management practice. The professional experience of the participants, typically seven to eight years, further complements the learning.

With a truly international class (90 percent of students are international and come from twenty-two countries), the M.S.M. program emphasizes global issues, cross-cultural awareness, and team building. Graduates are equipped with the knowledge and problem-solving skills that will allow them to lead their organizations into the future.

As a result of the School's strategic alliance with Boston College's (BC) Carroll School of Management, the program is housed on BC's 148-acre Chestnut Hill campus and at ADL headquarters in Cambridge. Metropolitan Boston, the educational capital of the U.S., provides participants with a wide array of cultural and recreational activities. The area offers a variety of housing to suit any lifestyle.

COSTS
Tuition *Full-time:* $32,000.

FINANCIAL AID (1999–2000)
Fellowships, grants, and scholarships. Financial aid application deadline: 6/1. **Financial Aid Contact** Mr. Mark Challis, Finance Administrator, 194 Beacon Street, Chestnut Hill, MA 02467-3853. **Phone:** 617-498-6347. **Fax:** 617-498-7086.

RESOURCES AND SERVICES
Information about online services, personal computer policies, library resources, international exchange programs, internship programs, and placement services at this institution and others can be found at **www.petersons.com/mba**

International Students
93% of students enrolled are international students.

Services and Facilities Counseling/support services, visa services. Financial aid is available to international students.

Applying *Required:* TOEFL with recommended score of 550 (paper), proof of adequate funds, proof of health/immunizations.

International Student Contact Ms. Martha Bayliss Whyte, Assistant Dean, 194 Beacon Street, Chestnut Hill, MA 02467-3853. **Phone:** 617-552-2879. **Fax:** 617-552-2051. **E-mail:** adlsom@adlittle.com.

■ APPLICATION
Required GMAT, application form, baccalaureate/first degree, essay, 2 letters of recommendation, personal statement, resume/curriculum vitae, transcripts of college work, 5 years of work experience. **Recommended** Interview.

Deadlines and Fees *Deadlines:* 6/15 for fall, 6/15 for fall (international). *Application fee:* $50, $50 (international).

Application Contact Mr. William Makris, Chairman, Admission Committee, 194 Beacon Street, Chestnut Hill, MA 02467-3853. **Phone:** 617-552-2877. **Fax:** 617-552-2051. **E-mail:** adlsom@adlittle.com.

See full description on page 550.

Assumption College

Worcester, Massachusetts

DEPARTMENT OF BUSINESS STUDIES

Graduate Business Faculty
Full-time: 15   Part-time: 7

Student Body
Total: 154   Average Age: 27
Full-time: 4   Women: 51%
Part-time: 150

Admissions
Applications: 50   Enrolled: 44
Admitted: 46   Average GMAT: 475

Costs (1999–2000)
Full-time tuition: N/R
Part-time tuition: $322 per credit

DEGREE MBA

MBA—Master of Business Administration Part-time. 36 to 60 total credits required. 30 to 84 months to complete program. *Concentrations:* accounting, finance, health care, human resources, international business, management, marketing.

The Assumption M.B.A. Program has been designed to provide professional preparation for men and women currently employed who wish to study on a part-time basis (typically one or two courses per semester). The primary goal of the program is to provide an opportunity for qualified persons to develop the knowledge, skills, abilities, and competencies that constitute a foundation for career growth and development in business, government, or other organizational environments.

In the program, stress is placed on effective decision making and the development and implementation of organized strategy at all levels. While including required study in the key functional areas of management, the program offers ample flexibility so that students can concentrate their study in a chosen area by completing one of the available concentrations. Alternatively, students may design a package of elective courses that tailor the program to their individual needs.

Small classes taught by full-time Assumption faculty members, each of whom has practical business experience, and by adjunct instructors who actively practice in their fields provide a rich and personally focused graduate learning experience.

COSTS
Tuition *Part-time:* $322 per credit.

FINANCIAL AID (1999–2000)
4 students received aid, including loans and research assistantships. Aid is available to part-time students. Financial aid application deadline: 3/1. **Financial Aid Contact** Ms. Dana Mignogna, Graduate Financial Aid Administrator, Financial Aid Department, 500 Salisbury Street, Worcester,

MA 01609-1296. **Phone:** 508-767-7154. **Fax:** 508-767-7356. **E-mail:** dmignogn@assumption.edu.

RESOURCES AND SERVICES
Information about online services, personal computer policies, library resources, international exchange programs, internship programs, and placement services at this institution and others can be found at **www.petersons.com/mba**

International Students
3% of students enrolled are international students.

Services and Facilities Counseling/support services, ESL/language courses, international student organization, language tutoring. Financial aid is not available to international students.
Applying *Required:* TOEFL with recommended score of 500 (paper), proof of adequate funds, proof of health/immunizations.

■ APPLICATION

Required GMAT, application form, baccalaureate/first degree, 2 letters of recommendation, personal statement, transcripts of college work. **Recommended** Essay, resume/curriculum vitae, work experience.

Deadlines and Fees Applications for domestic and international students are processed on a rolling basis. *Application fee:* $30, $30 (international).
Application Contact Mr. Frank Marino, MBA Advisor, Department of Business Studies, 500 Salisbury Street, PO Box 15005, Worcester, MA 01609-1296. **Phone:** 508-767-7255. **Fax:** 508-767-7252. **E-mail:** mba@assumption.edu.

Babson College
Wellesley, Babson Park, Massachusetts

F. W. OLIN GRADUATE SCHOOL OF BUSINESS

Graduate Business Faculty
Full-time: 110   Part-time: 37

Student Body
Total: 1,730   Average Age: 28
Full-time: 480   Women: 31%
Part-time: 1,250

Admissions
Applications: 782   Average GMAT: 637
Admitted: 336   Average GPA: 3.1
Enrolled: 150

Costs (1999–2000)
Full-time tuition: $23,662 per academic year
Part-time tuition: $2208 per course

After Graduation (Class of 1998–99)
Employed within 3 months of graduation: 95%
Average starting salary: $68,450

Accreditation
AACSB—The International Association for Management Education

DEGREES MBA

MBA—Evening MBA Full-time and part-time. At least 60 total credits required. 48 to 96 months to complete program. *Concentrations:* international business.
MBA—One-year MBA Full-time. At least 45 total credits required. Minimum of 12 months to complete program. *Concentrations:* international business.
MBA—Two-year MBA Full-time. At least 62 total credits required. Minimum of 21 months to complete program. *Concentrations:* international business.

Babson's graduate school building (Olin Hall) opened in the fall of 1996. The building was designed to meet the requirements of the new Two-Year M.B.A. curriculum. The facility includes designated rooms for each first-year mentor team, where the team members can work on their group assignments and, on occasion, host their business mentor representatives. In addition, there are six interactive classrooms, one large classroom for 100 students, a lecture hall for 200, and a computer lab. An adjacent area containing temporary offices for faculty members to use while they teach in a module enhances faculty communication.

Students use entrepreneurial hatchery space for business start-ups and new product development. Other rooms are designed for group study, seminars, and the Graduate Student Association (GSA). The Cutler Investment Management Center, which opened in March 2000, provides students, faculty members, and alumni with sophisticated technological tools and information resources to compete in any area of financial services. Home to the Babson

College Fund, the center reflects Babson's commitment to providing a practice-based environment for people involved in the study of capital markets.

Babson's long tradition of emphasizing the global aspects of business continues today with the international concentration and the thriving Global Management Program. The international concentration is available to all M.B.A. program participants.

COSTS
Tuition *Full-time:* $23,662. *Part-time:* $2208 per course. **Required fees:** Tuition and fees vary by academic program. **Graduate housing:** Room and board costs vary by number of occupants, type of accommodation, and type of board plan. *Typical cost:* $10,594 (including board), $7488 (room only).

FINANCIAL AID (1999–2000)
213 students received aid, including fellowships, grants, loans, research assistantships, scholarships, and work study. Financial aid application deadline: 4/15. **Financial Aid Contact** Ms. Melissa Shaak, Director, Financial Aid, Babson College, Hollister Hall, Babson Park, MA 02457-0310. **Phone:** 781-239-4219. **Fax:** 781-239-5510. **E-mail:** shaak@babson.edu.

RESOURCES AND SERVICES
Information about online services, personal computer policies, library resources, international exchange programs, internship programs, and placement services at this institution and others can be found at **www.petersons.com/mba**

International Students
6% of students enrolled are international students.

Services and Facilities Counseling/support services, housing location assistance, international student housing, international student organization, orientation, visa services, partners program for spouses, office of international programs. Financial aid is available to international students.
Applying *Required:* TOEFL with recommended score of 250 (computer) or 600 (paper), proof of adequate funds, proof of health/immunizations.
International Student Contact Mr. Amir Reza, International Student Advisor, International Programs, Babson Park, MA 02457-0130. **Phone:** 781-239-5506. **Fax:** 781-239-5232. **E-mail:** areza@babson.edu.

■ APPLICATION

Required GMAT, application form, baccalaureate/first degree, essay, interview, 2 letters of recommendation, personal statement, resume/curriculum vitae, transcripts of college work, 2 years of work experience.

Deadlines and Fees *Deadlines:* 3/1 for fall, 3/1 for fall (international). *Application fee:* $50, $50 (international).
Application Contact Ms. Luisa Boverini, Associate Director, MBA Admission, F. W. Olin Graduate School of Business, Olin Hall, Babson Park, MA 02457. **Phone:** 781-239-5591. **Toll-free Phone:** 800-488-4512. **Fax:** 781-239-4194. **E-mail:** mbaadmission@babson.edu.

See full description on page 554.

Bentley College
Waltham, Massachusetts

THE ELKIN B. McCALLUM GRADUATE SCHOOL OF BUSINESS

Graduate Business Faculty
Full-time: 224   Part-time: 162

Student Body
Total: 1,500   Average Age: 31
Full-time: 314   Women: 45%
Part-time: 1,186

Admissions
Applications: 900   Average GMAT: 539
Admitted: 601   Average GPA: 3.2
Enrolled: 340

Costs (1999–2000)
Full-time tuition: $17,145 per academic year
Part-time tuition: $2135 per course

After Graduation (Class of 1998–99)
Employed within 3 months of graduation: 94%
Average starting salary: $64,000

Accreditation
AACSB—The International Association for Management Education

DEGREES IAMBA • MBA • MS

Bentley College (continued)

IAMBA—Information Age Master of Business Administration Full-time. Interview and resume/curriculum vitae required. At least 58 total credits required. 24 months to complete program. *Concentrations:* accounting, business ethics, economics, entrepreneurship, finance, international business, management, management information systems, marketing, operations management, quantitative analysis, taxation, technology management.

MBA—Self-Paced Master of Business Administration Full-time and part-time. 30 to 57 total credits required. 12 to 84 months to complete program. *Concentrations:* accounting, business ethics, economics, entrepreneurship, finance, international business, management, management information systems, marketing, operations management, quantitative analysis, taxation, technology management.

MS—Accounting Information Systems Full-time and part-time. 30 to 39 total credits required. 12 to 84 months to complete program.

MS—Corporate Finance Full-time and part-time. 30 to 57 total credits required. 12 to 84 months to complete program.

MS—Global Financial Analysis Full-time and part-time. 30 to 36 total credits required. 24 to 84 months to complete program.

MS—Human Factors in Information Design Part-time. At least 30 total credits required. 24 to 60 months to complete program.

MS—Information Age Marketing Full-time and part-time. At least 30 total credits required. 12 to 60 months to complete program.

MS—Master of Science in Accountancy Full-time and part-time. 30 to 60 total credits required. 12 to 84 months to complete program.

MS—Master of Science in Computer Information Systems Full-time and part-time. 30 to 36 total credits required. 12 to 84 months to complete program.

MS—Personal Financial Planning Full-time and part-time. 30 to 36 total credits required. 12 to 84 months to complete program.

MS—Taxation Full-time and part-time. *Distance learning option.* 30 to 36 total credits required. 12 to 84 months to complete program.

The Bentley College McCallum Graduate School of Business M.B.A. prepares students by integrating strategic business processes and information technology applications, which are critical to effective management and business operations. Students become skilled in managing processes, analyzing information, and bringing people together—skills that are crucial in achieving success.

The Information Age M.B.A. is designed for full-time students with some professional work experience who want to be ready for the management challenges of today's technology-driven workplace. The Self-Paced M.B.A. emphasizes choice and flexibility and is designed to meet the needs of working professionals. The One-Year M.B.A. is a fast-track program for those with an undergraduate business degree. Students can customize their program by selecting from thirteen areas of concentration, including accounting systems, business data analysis, business economics, business ethics, change management, e-business, entrepreneurial studies, finance, information age marketing, international business, management, management information systems, and management of operations and technology. An advanced graduate business certificate is also offered. Students should contact Kimberly Nauen at 781-891-2108 or 800-442-4723 (toll-free) or visit the Web site (http://www.bentley.edu/graduate) for more information.

COSTS

Tuition *Full-time:* $17,080. *Part-time:* $2135 per course. Tuition varies by academic program. **Required fees:** *Full-time* $65. *Part-time* $32.50 per semester. Fees vary by number of courses or credits taken. **Graduate housing:** Room and board costs vary by number of occupants, type of accommodation, and type of board plan. *Typical cost:* $9725 (including board).

FINANCIAL AID (1999–2000)

376 students received aid, including grants, research assistantships, scholarships, and work study. Aid is available to part-time students. Financial aid application deadline: 4/15. **Financial Aid Contact** Ms. Donna Kendall, Director of Financial Assistance, Rauch 108, Waltham, MA 02452-4705. **Phone:** 781-891-3168. **Fax:** 781-891-2448. **E-mail:** finaid@bentley.edu.

RESOURCES AND SERVICES

Information about online services, personal computer policies, library resources, international exchange programs, internship programs, and placement services at this institution and others can be found at **www.petersons.com/mba**

International Students

12% of students enrolled are international students.

Services and Facilities Counseling/support services, ESL/language courses, international student housing, visa services, one-on-one tutoring. Financial aid is available to international students.

Applying *Required:* TOEFL with recommended score of 580 (paper), proof of adequate funds, proof of health/immunizations.

International Student Contact Ms. Barbara Lombardi, International Student Advisor, Adamain Academic Graduate Center 160, Waltham, MA 02452-4705. **Phone:** 781-891-2929. **Fax:** 781-891-2819.

■ APPLICATION

Required GMAT, application form, baccalaureate/first degree, essay, 2 letters of recommendation, personal statement, transcripts of college work. **Recommended** Interview, resume/curriculum vitae.

Deadlines and Fees *Deadlines:* 6/1 for fall, 11/1 for spring, 3/1 for summer, 3/1 for fall (international), 10/1 for spring (international), 3/1 for summer (international). *Application fee:* $50, $50 (international).

Application Contact Ms. Kim Naven, Director of Graduate Admissions, The Elkin B. McCallum Graduate School of Business, 175 Forest Street, Waltham, MA 02452-4705. **Phone:** 781-891-2108. **Fax:** 781-891-2464. **E-mail:** knaven@bentley.edu.

See full description on page 564.

Boston College

Chestnut Hill, Massachusetts

THE GRADUATE SCHOOL OF THE WALLACE E. CARROLL SCHOOL OF MANAGEMENT

Graduate Business Faculty

Full-time: 90	Part-time: 26

Student Body

Total: 927	Average Age: 27
Full-time: 219	Women: 33%
Part-time: 708	

Admissions

Applications: 1,206	Average GMAT: 645
Admitted: 675	Average GPA: 3.3
Enrolled: 290	

Costs (1999–2000)
Full-time tuition: $23,268 per academic year
Part-time tuition: $748 per credit hour

After Graduation (Class of 1998–99)
Employed within 3 months of graduation: 97.3%
Average starting salary: $67,174

Accreditation
AACSB—The International Association for Management Education

DEGREES JD/MBA • MBA • MBA/MA • MBA/MS • MBA/MSF • MBA/MSW • MS • PhD/MBA

JD/MBA—Juris Doctor/Master of Business Administration Full-time. Must take LSAT. 110 to 116 total credits required. 40 to 45 months to complete program.

MBA—Master of Business Administration Full-time and part-time. 43 to 55 total credits required. 15 to 72 months to complete program. *Concentrations:* accounting, entrepreneurship, finance, international management, management, management consulting, management information systems, marketing, operations management, organizational behavior/development, strategic management.

MBA/MA—Master of Business Administration/Master of Arts in Hispanic Studies Full-time. 67 to 73 total credits required. 28 to 33 months to complete program.

MBA/MA—Master of Business Administration/Master of Arts in Italian Studies Full-time. 67 to 73 total credits required. 28 to 33 months to complete program.

MBA/MA—Master of Business Administration/Master of Arts in Linguistics Full-time. 67 to 73 total credits required. 28 to 33 months to complete program.

MBA/MA—Master of Business Administration/Master of Arts in Mathematics Full-time. 67 to 73 total credits required. 28 to 33 months to complete program.

MBA/MA—Master of Business Administration/Master of Arts in Political Science Full-time. 67 to 73 total credits required. 28 to 33 months to complete program.

MBA/MA—Master of Business Administration/Master of Arts in Russian Full-time. 67 to 73 total credits required. 28 to 33 months to complete program.

MBA/MA—Master of Business Administration/Master of Arts in Slavic Studies Full-time. 67 to 73 total credits required. 28 to 33 months to complete program.

MBA/MA—Masters of Business Administration/Master of Arts in French Studies Full-time. 67 to 73 total credits required. 28 to 33 months to complete program.

MBA/MS—Master of Business Administration/Master of Science in Biology Full-time. 67 to 73 total credits required. 28 to 33 months to complete program.

MBA/MS—Master of Business Administration/Master of Science in Geology/Geophysics Full-time. 67 to 73 total credits required. 28 to 33 months to complete program.

MBA/MS—Master of Business Administration/Master of Science in Nursing Full-time. 74 to 80 total credits required. 33 to 36 months to complete program.

MBA/MSF—Master of Business Administration/Master of Science in Finance Full-time and part-time. 67 to 85 total credits required. 24 to 108 months to complete program.

MBA/MSW—Master of Business Administration/Master of Social Work Full-time. 104 to 110 total credits required. 28 to 33 months to complete program.

MS—Master of Science in Finance Full-time and part-time. 24 to 30 total credits required. 11 to 36 months to complete program. *Concentrations:* finance.

PhD/MBA—Doctor of Philosophy in Sociology/Master of Business Administration Full-time. 77 to 83 total credits required. 52 to 57 months to complete program.

COSTS

Tuition *Full-time:* $23,188. *Part-time:* $748 per credit hour. **Required fees:** *Full-time* $80. *Part-time* $15 per semester. Tuition and fees vary by number of courses or credits taken.

FINANCIAL AID (1999–2000)

90 students received aid, including fellowships, grants, loans, research assistantships, scholarships, and work study. Financial aid application deadline: 3/1. **Financial Aid Contact** Mr. Robert Carpenter, Program Director, Student Employment, Financial Aid Office, Lyons Hall 120, 140 Commonwealth Avenue, Chestnut Hill, MA 02467-3808. **Phone:** 617-552-3300. **Fax:** 617-552-4889. **E-mail:** robert.carpenter@bc.edu.

RESOURCES AND SERVICES

Information about online services, personal computer policies, library resources, international exchange programs, internship programs, and placement services at this institution and others can be found at **www.petersons.com/mba**

International Students

13% of students enrolled are international students.

Services and Facilities Counseling/support services, housing location assistance, international student organization, orientation, visa services. Financial aid is available to international students.
Applying *Required:* TOEFL with recommended score of 250 (computer) or 600 (paper), proof of adequate funds, proof of health/immunizations.

International Student Contact Ms. Jean Donnelly, Assistant Director of Admissions, Fulton Hall 315, 140 Commonwealth Avenue, Chestnut Hill, MA 02467-3808. **Phone:** 617-552-3920. **Fax:** 617-552-8078. **E-mail:** bcmba@bc.edu.

▪ APPLICATION

Required GMAT, application form, baccalaureate/first degree, essay, 2 letters of recommendation, resume/curriculum vitae, transcripts of college work. **Recommended** Work experience.

Deadlines and Fees *Deadlines:* 4/1 for fall, 3/1 for fall (international). *Application fee:* $50, $50 (international).

Application Contact Ms. Shelley Conley, Director, MBA Admissions, the Graduate School of the Wallace E. Carroll School of Management, 140 Commonwealth Avenue, Fulton 315, Chestnut Hill, MA 02467-3808. **Phone:** 617-552-3920. **Fax:** 617-552-8078.

See full description on page 570.

Boston University

Boston, Massachusetts

SCHOOL OF MANAGEMENT

Graduate Business Faculty
Full-time: 105   Part-time: 15

Student Body
Total: 1,159
Full-time: 540   Average Age: 28
Part-time: 619   Women: 37%

Admissions
Applications: 1,166   Enrolled: 225
Admitted: 515   Average GMAT: 630

Average GPA: 3.15

Costs (1999–2000)
Full-time tuition: $24,496 per academic year
Part-time tuition: $743 per credit

After Graduation (Class of 1998–99)
Employed within 3 months of graduation: 90%
Average starting salary: $65,236

Accreditation
AACSB—The International Association for Management Education

DEGREES JD/MBA • MBA • MBA/MA • MBA/MS • MS

JD/MBA—Juris Doctor/Master of Business Administration Full-time. At least 124 total credits required. 36 to 72 months to complete program. *Concentrations:* health care.

MBA—Executive MBA Full-time. 10 years of work experience and company sponsorship required. At least 64 total credits required. 17 months to complete program.

MBA—Master of Business with Concentration in Health Care Management Full-time and part-time. At least 64 total credits required. 14 to 72 months to complete program.

MBA—Master of Business with Concentration in Public and Nonprofit Management Full-time and part-time. At least 64 total credits required. 14 to 72 months to complete program. *Concentrations:* public and private management.

MBA—Master of Business Administration Full-time and part-time. At least 64 total credits required. 14 to 72 months to complete program. *Concentrations:* entrepreneurship, finance, international business, international management, management information systems, marketing, operations management, organizational behavior/development.

MBA/MA—Master of Business Administration/Master of Arts in Economics Full-time and part-time. At least 80 total credits required. 24 to 72 months to complete program.

MBA/MA—Master of Business Administration/Master of Arts in International Relations Full-time and part-time. At least 80 total credits required. 24 to 72 months to complete program.

MBA/MA—Master of Business Administration/Master of Arts in Medical Sciences Full-time and part-time. At least 80 total credits required. 24 to 72 months to complete program. *Concentrations:* health care.

MBA/MS—Master of Business Administration/Master of Science in Manufacturing Engineering Full-time and part-time. At least 80 total credits required. 24 to 72 months to complete program.

MBA/MS—Master of Business Administration/Master of Science in Television Management Full-time and part-time. At least 80 total credits required. 24 to 72 months to complete program.

MBA/MS—Master of Business/Master of Science in Management Information Systems Full-time. At least 84 total credits required. 24 to 72 months to complete program.

MBA/MS—Master of Business/Science in Public Health Full-time and part-time. At least 85 total credits required. 36 to 72 months to complete program. *Concentrations:* actuarial science, entrepreneurship.

MS—Master of Science in Investment Management Part-time. 18 months to complete program. *Concentrations:* finance.

MS—Master of Science in Management Information Systems Full-time. At least 48 total credits required. 12 months to complete program.

COSTS

Tuition *Full-time:* $23,770. *Part-time:* $743 per credit. **Required fees:** *Full-time* $726. *Part-time* $60 per semester. Tuition and fees vary by number of courses or credits taken and academic program.

FINANCIAL AID (1999–2000)

294 students received aid, including loans, research assistantships, scholarships, teaching assistantships, and work study. Aid is available to part-time students. Financial aid application deadline: 3/15. **Financial Aid Contact** Ms. Ia Vang, Assistant Director of Graduate Admissions and Financial Aid, 595 Commonwealth Avenue, Boston, MA 02215. **Phone:** 617-353-2670. **Fax:** 617-353-7368. **E-mail:** mba@bu.edu.

RESOURCES AND SERVICES

Information about online services, personal computer policies, library resources, international exchange programs, internship programs, and placement services at this institution and others can be found at **www.petersons.com/mba**

International Students

26% of students enrolled are international students.

Services and Facilities Counseling/support services, ESL/language courses, international student housing, international student organization, orientation, visa

Boston University (continued)

services. Financial aid is available to international students.
Applying *Required:* TOEFL with recommended score of 250 (computer) or 600 (paper), proof of adequate funds, proof of health/immunizations.
International Student Contact Ms. Dawn Galolo, Assistant Director of Graduate Admissions, 595 Commonwealth Avenue, Boston, MA 02215. **Phone:** 617-353-2670. **Fax:** 617-353-7368. **E-mail:** mba@bu.edu.

■ APPLICATION

Required GMAT, application form, baccalaureate/first degree, essay, 2 letters of recommendation, resume/curriculum vitae, transcripts of college work. **Recommended** Interview, 2 years of work experience.
Deadlines and Fees *Deadlines:* 4/15 for fall, 11/15 for spring, 3/1 for fall (international). *Application fee:* $75, $75 (international).
Application Contact Mr. Peter Kelly, Director of Graduate Admissions and Financial Aid, 595 Commonwealth Avenue, Boston, MA 02215. **Phone:** 617-353-9112. **Fax:** 617-353-7368. **E-mail:** mba@bu.edu.

See full description on page 572.

Brandeis University

Waltham, Massachusetts

GRADUATE SCHOOL OF INTERNATIONAL ECONOMICS AND FINANCE

Graduate Business Faculty

Full-time: 20	Part-time: 13

Student Body

Total: 165	Average Age: 24

Admissions

Applications: 283	Average GMAT: 600
Admitted: 171	Average GPA: 3.5
Enrolled: 81	

Costs (1999–2000)
Full-time tuition: $25,392 per academic year
Part-time tuition: $2280 per course

After Graduation (Class of 1998–99)
Employed within 3 months of graduation: 85%
Average starting salary: $59,000

DEGREES MA • MBA • MS

MA—Master of Arts in International Economics and Finance Full-time. At least 64 total credits required. 12 to 24 months to complete program. *Concentrations:* international business, international economics, international finance.

MBA—International MBA Full-time. 2-3 years of work experience required. At least 64 total credits required. Minimum of 24 months to complete program.

MS—Master of Science in Finance Part-time. 2-3 years of work experience required. Up to 44 total credits required. Minimum of 15 months to complete program. *Concentrations:* finance, international finance.

The Brandeis University Graduate School of International Economics and Finance Master of Business Administration/International (MBAi) Program offers an education in business administration with a strong international focus and solid analytical foundations. Intended for students with several years' work experience, the MBAi prepares students for careers in a wide variety of international areas, such as multinational enterprises, small- and medium-sized firms operating across borders, or consulting firms that service international companies. Many graduates are employed in finance by leading financial services firms, securities companies, and commercial and investment banks. Students receive in-depth training in technical analysis and strategic issues and gain an understanding of managerial issues. Students must show mastery of a major language other than English and spend a semester studying outside of the United States at one of twenty-two exchange schools. During their studies, they work in multicultural teams; emphasis is placed on acquiring an appreciation for international differences in values and behavior, which are critically important in today's workplace.

The internationally focused curriculum, language requirement, study-abroad component, and multicultural aspects of the Brandeis MBAi distinguish it sharply from "generic" M.B.A. degrees. MBAi students receive training in all the major subjects included in a traditional M.B.A., such as economics, accounting, control, finance, marketing, operations, organizational behavior, and business policy. But they learn these subjects in an international context. Case

examples are derived from international firms, and analytical models involve international applications.

COSTS

Tuition *Full-time:* $25,392. *Part-time:* $2280 per course. Tuition varies by academic program. **Graduate housing:** Room and board costs vary by number of occupants and type of accommodation. *Typical cost:* $3800 (room only).

FINANCIAL AID (1999–2000)

Financial Aid Contact Geraldine F. Koch, Assistant Dean for Admissions and Financial Aid, MS-032, Waltham, MA 02454-9110. **Phone:** 781-736-4829. **Fax:** 781-736-2263. **E-mail:** gerrikoch@brandeis.edu.

RESOURCES AND SERVICES

Information about online services, personal computer policies, library resources, international exchange programs, internship programs, and placement services at this institution and others can be found at **www.petersons.com/mba**

International Students

Services and Facilities Counseling/support services, housing location assistance, international student housing, international student organization, language tutoring, orientation, visa services.
Applying *Required:* TOEFL with recommended score of 600 (paper), proof of adequate funds, proof of health/immunizations.
International Student Contact Ms. Tara Rohatghi, Assistant Director, International Students and Scholars Office, Kutz Hall, 415 South Street, Waltham, MA 02454-9110. **Phone:** 781-736-3480. **Fax:** 781-736-3484.

■ APPLICATION

Required Application form, baccalaureate/first degree, essay, 3 letters of recommendation, personal statement, resume/curriculum vitae, transcripts of college work, work experience. School will accept GMAT and GRE. **Recommended** Interview.
Deadlines and Fees *Deadlines:* 2/15 for fall, 2/15 for fall (international). *Application fee:* $50, $50 (international).
Application Contact Geraldine F. Koch, Assistant Dean for Admissions and Financial Aid, MS-032, PO Box 9110, Waltham, MA 02454-9110. **Phone:** 781-736-4829. **Toll-free Phone:** 800-878-8866. **Fax:** 781-736-2263. **E-mail:** gerrikoch@brandeis.edu.

See full description on page 576.

Brandeis University

Waltham, Massachusetts

HELLER GRADUATE SCHOOL

Graduate Business Faculty

Full-time: 39	Part-time: 18

Student Body

Total: 34	Average Age: 28
Full-time: 31	Women: 71%
Part-time: 3	

Admissions

Applications: 65	Average GMAT: 575
Admitted: 45	Average GPA: 3.4
Enrolled: 34	

Costs (1999–2000)
Full-time tuition: $26,253 per academic year
Part-time tuition: $1400 per course

After Graduation (Class of 1998–99)
Employed within 3 months of graduation: 80%

DEGREES MBA • MM

MBA—Human Services Full-time and part-time. 15 to 36 months to complete program. *Concentrations:* health care, nonprofit management, public and private management, public management, public policy and administration.

MM—Human Services Full-time and part-time. 15 to 36 months to complete program. *Concentrations:* health care, nonprofit management, public and private management, public management, public policy and administration.

COSTS

Tuition *Full-time:* $26,253. *Part-time:* $1400 per course. **Tuition, international:** *Full-time* $26,253. **Required fees:** Tuition and fees vary by number of courses or credits taken and academic program.

FINANCIAL AID (1999–2000)

34 students received aid, including fellowships, loans, research assistantships, scholarships, and teaching assistantships. Aid is available to part-time students. Financial aid application deadline: 2/15. **Financial Aid Contact** Ms. Lisa Sherry, Admissions Officer, PO Box 9110, MS 035, Waltham, MA 02454. **Phone:** 781-736-3820. **Fax:** 781-736-3881. **E-mail:** sherry@brandeis.edu.

RESOURCES AND SERVICES

Information about online services, personal computer policies, library resources, international exchange programs, internship programs, and placement services at this institution and others can be found at **www. petersons.com/mba**

International Students

26% of students enrolled are international students.

Services and Facilities Counseling/support services, ESL/language courses, housing location assistance, international student housing, international student organization, language tutoring, orientation, visa services. Financial aid is available to international students.

Applying *Required:* TOEFL with recommended score of 600 (paper), proof of adequate funds, proof of health/immunizations.

International Student Contact Ms. Lisa Sherry, Admissions Office, PO Box 9110, MS 035, Waltham, MA 02454. **Phone:** 781-736-3820. **Fax:** 781-736-3881. **E-mail:** sherry@brandeis.edu.

■ APPLICATION

Required GMAT or GRE, application form, baccalaureate/first degree, essay, letter(s) of recommendation, personal statement, resume/curriculum vitae, transcripts of college work. **Recommended** Interview, 2 years of work experience.

Deadlines and Fees *Deadlines:* 2/15 for summer, 2/15 for summer (international). *Application fee:* $50, $50 (international).

Application Contact Ms. Lisa Sherry, Admissions Office, PO Box 9110, MS 035, Waltham, MA 02454. **Phone:** 781-736-3820. **Fax:** 781-736-3881. **E-mail:** sherry@brandis.edu.

See full description on page 578.

Cambridge College

Cambridge, Massachusetts

PROGRAM IN MANAGEMENT

Student Body

Total: 160	Average Age: 35
Full-time: 128	Women: 60%
Part-time: 32	

Admissions

Applications: 110	Enrolled: 83
Admitted: 95	

Costs (1999–2000)

Full-time tuition: N/R
Part-time tuition: $315 per credit

DEGREE MM

MM—Graduate Program in Management Full-time and part-time. 26 to 35 total credits required. Minimum of 12 months to complete program. *Concentrations:* entrepreneurship, health care, human resources, leadership, nonprofit management, organizational behavior/development.

COSTS

Tuition *Part-time:* $315 per credit. **Required fees:** *Full-time* $180. Tuition and fees vary by academic program.

FINANCIAL AID (1999–2000)

3 students received aid, including teaching assistantships and work study. Financial aid application deadline: 9/10. **Financial Aid Contact** Ms. Gerri Major, Director of Financial Aid, 1000 Massachusetts Avenue, Cambridge, MA 02138. **Phone:** 617-868-1000 Ext. 137. **Fax:** 617-349-3545. **E-mail:** finaid@idea.cambridge.edu.

RESOURCES AND SERVICES

Information about online services, personal computer policies, library resources, international exchange programs, internship programs, and placement services at this institution and others can be found at **www. petersons.com/mba**

International Students

9% of students enrolled are international students.

Services and Facilities Counseling/support services, ESL/language courses. Financial aid is not available to international students.

International Student Contact Ms. Jacqueline Tynes, Senior Enrollment Representative, 1000 Massachusetts Avenue, Cambridge, MA 02138. **Phone:** 617-868-1000 Ext. 140. **Fax:** 617-349-3545. **E-mail:** admitt@idea.cambridge.edu.

■ APPLICATION

Required Application form, baccalaureate/first degree, essay, interview, 1 letter of recommendation, personal statement, resume/curriculum vitae, transcripts of college work, 5 years of work experience.

Deadlines and Fees Applications for domestic and international students are processed on a rolling basis. *Application fee:* $30, $30 (international).

Application Contact Mr. James McDaniel, Senior Enrollment Representative, 1000 Massachusetts Avenue, Cambridge, MA 02138. **Phone:** 617-868-1000. **Fax:** 617-349-3545. **E-mail:** admitt@idea.cambridge.edu.

Clark University

Worcester, Massachusetts

GRADUATE SCHOOL OF MANAGEMENT

Graduate Business Faculty

Full-time: 18	Part-time: 7

Student Body

Total: 344	Part-time: 218
Full-time: 126	Women: 44%

Admissions

Applications: 353	Average GMAT: 565
Admitted: 242	Average GPA: 3.2
Enrolled: 91	

Costs (1999–2000)

Full-time tuition: $19,990 per academic year
Part-time tuition: $1990 per course

After Graduation (Class of 1998–99)

Employed within 3 months of graduation: 95%

Accreditation

AACSB—The International Association for Management Education

DEGREES MBA • MSF

MBA—Master of Business Administration in Health Services Full-time and part-time. At least 57 total credits required. 12 to 72 months to complete program. *Concentrations:* health care.

MBA—Master of Business Administration Full-time and part-time. At least 57 total credits required. 12 to 72 months to complete program. *Concentrations:* accounting, entrepreneurship, environmental economics/management, finance, health care, human resources, international business, management information systems, marketing.

MSF—Master of Science in Finance Full-time and part-time. At least 60 total credits required. 12 to 72 months to complete program.

COSTS

Tuition *Full-time:* $19,990. *Part-time:* $1990 per course.

FINANCIAL AID (1999–2000)

57 students received aid, including loans, research assistantships, scholarships, teaching assistantships, and work study. Aid is available to part-time students. Financial aid application deadline: 5/31. **Financial Aid Contact** Mr. John Brandon, Director of Admissions, Graduate School of Management, 950 Main Street, Worcester, MA 01610-1477. **Phone:** 508-793-7406. **Fax:** 508-793-8822. **E-mail:** clarkmba@clarku.edu.

RESOURCES AND SERVICES

Information about online services, personal computer policies, library resources, international exchange programs, internship programs, and placement services at this institution and others can be found at **www. petersons.com/mba**

International Students

26% of students enrolled are international students.

Services and Facilities Counseling/support services, ESL/language courses, housing location assistance, international student housing, international student organization, orientation, visa services. Financial aid is available to international students.

Applying *Required:* TOEFL with recommended score of 213 (computer) or 550 (paper), proof of adequate funds, proof of health/immunizations.

Clark University (continued)

International Student Contact Mr. David Elwell, Director, International Students and Scholars Office, 950 Main Street, Worcester, MA 01610-1477. **Phone:** 508-793-7750.

■ **APPLICATION**

Required GMAT, application form, baccalaureate/first degree, essay, 2 letters of recommendation, personal statement, resume/curriculum vitae, transcripts of college work. **Recommended** Interview.

Deadlines and Fees *Deadlines:* 6/1 for fall, 12/1 for spring, 6/1 for fall (international), 12/1 for spring (international). *Application fee:* $40, $40 (international).

Application Contact Mr. John Brandon, Director of Admissions, Graduate School of Management, 950 Main Street, Worcester, MA 01610-1477. **Phone:** 508-793-7406. **Fax:** 508-793-8822. **E-mail:** clarkmba@clarku.edu.

See full description on page 598.

Emerson College
Boston, Massachusetts

SCHOOL OF COMMUNICATION, MANAGEMENT, AND PUBLIC POLICY

Graduate Business Faculty
Full-time: 27 — Part-time: 15

Student Body
Total: 327 — Average Age: 27

Admissions
Applications: 316 — Enrolled: 100
Admitted: 212 — Average GPA: 3.1

Costs (1999–2000)
Full-time tuition: $14,112 per academic year
Part-time tuition: $588 per credit

After Graduation (Class of 1998–99)
Employed within 3 months of graduation: 96%
Average starting salary: $33,000

DEGREES MA

MA—Health Communication Full-time and part-time. At least 48 total credits required. 18 to 30 months to complete program. *Concentrations:* health care.

MA—Master of Arts in Global Marketing Communication and Advertising Full-time. At least 40 total credits required. 12 months to complete program. *Concentrations:* advertising, international marketing, marketing, public relations.

MA—Master of Arts in Integrated Marketing Communications Full-time and part-time. At least 44 total credits required. 12 to 24 months to complete program. *Concentrations:* advertising, marketing, public relations, sports/entertainment management.

MA—Master of Arts in Management and Organizational Communication Full-time and part-time. At least 44 total credits required. 12 to 24 months to complete program. *Concentrations:* human resources, leadership, management, nonprofit organization, organizational behavior/development, organizational management.

COSTS

Tuition *Full-time:* $14,112. *Part-time:* $588 per credit. **Required fees:** Tuition and fees vary by number of courses or credits taken.

FINANCIAL AID (1999–2000)
48 students received aid, including fellowships, research assistantships, and teaching assistantships. Aid is available to part-time students. Financial aid application deadline: 4/1. **Financial Aid Contact** Director of Financial Aid and Student Employment, 120 Boylston Street, Boston, MA 02116-1511. **Phone:** 617-824-8655.

RESOURCES AND SERVICES
Information about online services, personal computer policies, library resources, international exchange programs, internship programs, and placement services at this institution and others can be found at **www.petersons.com/mba**

International Students

Services and Facilities Counseling/support services, ESL/language courses, visa services. Financial aid is available to international students.
Applying *Required:* TOEFL with recommended score of 550 (paper), proof of adequate funds, proof of health/immunizations.

International Student Contact Ms. Lynn Terrell, Director of Graduate Admission, 120 Boylston Street, Boston, MA 02116-1511. **Phone:** 617-824-8610. **Fax:** 617-824-8614. **E-mail:** gradapp@emerson.edu.

■ **APPLICATION**

Required Application form, baccalaureate/first degree, essay, 3 letters of recommendation, personal statement, resume/curriculum vitae, transcripts of college work. School will accept GMAT and GRE.

Deadlines and Fees Applications for domestic and international students are processed on a rolling basis. *Application fee:* $45, $75 (international).

Application Contact Ms. Lynn Terrell, Director, Office of Graduate Admission, 120 Boylston Street, Boston, MA 02116-1511. **Phone:** 617-824-8610. **Fax:** 617-824-8614. **E-mail:** gradapp@emerson.edu.

See full description on page 638.

Emmanuel College
Boston, Massachusetts

CENTER FOR ADULT STUDIES

Graduate Business Faculty
Part-time: 40

Student Body
Total: 265 — Average Age: 32
Full-time: 40 — Women: 60%
Part-time: 225

Admissions
Applications: 40 — Enrolled: 30
Admitted: 36 — Average GPA: 3.4

Costs (1999–2000)
Full-time tuition: N/R
Part-time tuition: $1290 per course

After Graduation (Class of 1998–99)
Employed within 3 months of graduation: 95%

DEGREES MA • MS

MA—Master of Arts in Human Resources Management Full-time and part-time. At least 36 total credits required. 24 to 60 months to complete program. *Concentrations:* human resources.

MS—Master of Science in Management Full-time and part-time. At least 36 total credits required. 24 to 60 months to complete program. *Concentrations:* leadership, management.

COSTS

Tuition *Part-time:* $1290 per course.

FINANCIAL AID (1999–2000)
10 students received aid, including loans. Aid is available to part-time students. **Financial Aid Contact** Financial Aid Office, 400 The Fenway, Boston, MA 02115. **Phone:** 617-735-9725.

RESOURCES AND SERVICES
Information about online services, personal computer policies, library resources, international exchange programs, internship programs, and placement services at this institution and others can be found at **www.petersons.com/mba**

International Students

2% of students enrolled are international students.

Services and Facilities Counseling/support services, international student housing, international student organization, orientation, visa services. Financial aid is not available to international students.

Applying *Required:* TOEFL with recommended score of 550 (paper), proof of adequate funds, proof of health/immunizations.

International Student Contact Renee Loaza-Damergi, International Student Office, 400 The Fenway, Boston, MA 02115. **Phone:** 617-735-9884.

■ **APPLICATION**

Required Application form, baccalaureate/first degree, essay, interview, 2 letters of recommendation, personal statement, resume/curriculum vitae, transcripts of college work, 3 years of work experience.

Deadlines and Fees Applications for domestic and international students are processed on a rolling basis. *Application fee:* $50, $50 (international).

Application Contact Valerie Healey, Center for Adult Studies, 400 The Fenway, Boston, MA 02115. **Phone:** 617-735-9902. **Toll-free Phone:** 800-331-3227. **Fax:** 617-735-9708.

International Students

37% of students enrolled are international students.

Services and Facilities Counseling/support services, ESL/language courses. Financial aid is not available to international students.

Applying *Required:* TOEFL with recommended score of 600 (paper), proof of adequate funds.

International Student Contact Ms. Danielle Ashbrook Guichard, Acting Director and Associate Dean, 77 Massachusetts Avenue, 5-106, Cambridge, MA 02139. **Phone:** 617-253-3795. **Fax:** 617-258-5483. **E-mail:** iso-help@mit. edu.

■ APPLICATION

Required GMAT, application form, baccalaureate/first degree, essay, 2 letters of recommendation, personal statement, resume/curriculum vitae, transcripts of college work. **Recommended** Work experience.

Deadlines and Fees *Deadlines:* 12/1 for fall, 2/2 for winter, 12/1 for fall (international). *Application fee:* $150, $175 (international).

Application Contact Mr. Rod Garcia, Director of Master's Admissions, 50 Memorial Drive, E52-126, Cambridge, MA 02142. **Phone:** 617-253-3730. **Fax:** 617-253-6405. **E-mail:** mbaadmissions@sloan.mit.edu.

Nichols College

Dudley, Massachusetts

GRADUATE PROGRAM IN BUSINESS ADMINISTRATION

Graduate Business Faculty
Full-time: 15 Part-time: 12

Student Body
Total: 365
Full-time: 5 Average Age: 29
Part-time: 360 Women: 45%

Admissions
Applications: 75 Enrolled: 69
Admitted: 72 Average GPA: 3.2

Costs (1999–2000)
Full-time tuition: N/R
Part-time tuition: $1082 per course

DEGREE MBA

MBA—Master of Business Administration Full-time and part-time. At least 36 total credits required. 15 to 72 months to complete program. *Concentrations:* accounting, economics, finance, international business, management, marketing.

COSTS

Tuition *Part-time:* $1082 per course.

FINANCIAL AID (1999–2000)

Financial Aid Contact Ms. Diane Gillepsie, Director of Financial Aid, Dudley, MA 01571-5000. **Phone:** 508-213-2276. **Fax:** 508-213-2490. **E-mail:** gillesdl@nichols.edu.

RESOURCES AND SERVICES

Information about online services, personal computer policies, library resources, international exchange programs, internship programs, and placement services at this institution and others can be found at **www.petersons.com/mba**

International Students

2% of students enrolled are international students.

Services and Facilities Counseling/support services, language tutoring. Financial aid is not available to international students.

Applying *Required:* TOEFL with recommended score of 550 (paper), proof of adequate funds.

International Student Contact Mr. Joseph A. Symock, Director for the MBA Program, PO Box 5000, Dudley, MA 01571. **E-mail:** symockja@nichols.edu.

■ APPLICATION

Required Application form, baccalaureate/first degree, essay, interview, 2 letters of recommendation, personal statement, resume/curriculum vitae, transcripts of college work.

Deadlines and Fees Applications for domestic and international students are processed on a rolling basis. *Application fee:* $25, $25 (international).

Application Contact Mr. Joseph A. Symock, Director for the MBA Program, PO Box 5000, Dudley, MA 01571. **Phone:** 508-213-2207. **Fax:** 508-213-2490. **E-mail:** symockja@nichols.edu.

Northeastern University

Boston, Massachusetts

GRADUATE SCHOOL OF BUSINESS ADMINISTRATION

Graduate Business Faculty
Full-time: 85 Part-time: 35

Student Body
Total: 963
Full-time: 403 Average Age: 31
Part-time: 560 Women: 36%

Admissions
Applications: 738
Admitted: 589 Average GMAT: 580
Enrolled: 209 Average GPA: 3.2

Costs (1999–2000)
Full-time tuition: $22,150 per academic year
Part-time tuition: $550 per credit

After Graduation (Class of 1998–99)
Employed within 3 months of graduation: 84%
Average starting salary: $63,154

Accreditation
AACSB—The International Association for Management Education

DEGREES MBA • MBA/MS • MS • MST

MBA—Cooperative Education MBA Full-time. At least 80 total credits required. 21 months to complete program. *Concentrations:* management.

MBA—Executive MBA Part-time. At least 80 total credits required. 18 months to complete program.

MBA—High Technology MBA Part-time. At least 80 total credits required. 21 months to complete program.

MBA—Part-Time MBA Part-time. At least 80 total credits required. 30 to 84 months to complete program.

MBA/MS—Graduate School of Professional Accounting—Accounting Program Full-time. At least 97 total credits required. 15 months to complete program.

MS—Master of Science in Finance Full-time and part-time. At least 42 total credits required. 12 to 48 months to complete program.

MST—Graduate School of Professional Accounting—Graduate Taxation Program Full-time and part-time. *Distance learning option.* At least 42 total credits required. 12 to 48 months to complete program.

COSTS

Tuition *Full-time:* $22,000. *Part-time:* $550 per credit. Tuition varies by number of courses or credits taken and academic program. **Required fees:** *Full-time* $150. **Graduate housing:** Room and board costs vary by number of occupants, type of accommodation, and type of board plan. *Typical cost:* $10,380 (including board).

FINANCIAL AID (1999–2000)

17 students received aid, including fellowships, loans, research assistantships, teaching assistantships, and work study. Aid is available to part-time students. Financial aid application deadline: 3/1. **Financial Aid Contact** Mr. William Mcgarrigle, Associate Director, Graduate Financial Aid, 410 Richards Hall, Boston, MA 02115. **Phone:** 617-373-5899.

RESOURCES AND SERVICES

Information about online services, personal computer policies, library resources, international exchange programs, internship programs, and placement services at this institution and others can be found at **www.petersons.com/mba**

International Students

9% of students enrolled are international students.

Services and Facilities Counseling/support services, ESL/language courses, housing location assistance, international student housing, international student organization, language tutoring, orientation, visa services. Financial aid is not available to international students.

Applying *Required:* TOEFL with recommended score of 250 (computer) or 600 (paper), proof of adequate funds, proof of health/immunizations.

International Student Contact Mr. Salvatore Mazzone, Assistant Director, International Student Office, 206 Ell Building, 360 Huntington Avenue, Boston, MA 02115. **Phone:** 617-373-2310. **Fax:** 617-373-8788.

Northeastern University (continued)

▪ APPLICATION

Required GMAT, application form, baccalaureate/first degree, essay, interview, 2 letters of recommendation, personal statement, resume/curriculum vitae, transcripts of college work. **Recommended** 3 years of work experience.

Deadlines and Fees *Deadlines:* 6/15 for fall, 12/15 for spring, 6/15 for fall (international), 12/15 for spring (international). *Application fee:* $50, $50 (international).

Application Contact Ms. Melaine Mace-Kairouz, Administrative Assistant, 350 Dodge Hall, Boston, MA 02115. **Phone:** 617-373-5992. **Fax:** 617-373-8564. **E-mail:** gsba@cba.neu.edu.

See full description on page 746.

Salem State College

Salem, Massachusetts

PROGRAM IN BUSINESS ADMINISTRATION

Graduate Business Faculty

Full-time: 21	Part-time: 2

Student Body

Total: 165	Average Age: 35
Full-time: 17	Women: 42%
Part-time: 148	

Admissions

Applications: 28	Average GMAT: 465
Admitted: 22	Average GPA: 2.78
Enrolled: 17	

Costs (1999–2000)
Full-time tuition: N/R
Part-time tuition: $170 per credit hour (resident), $260 per credit hour (nonresident)

DEGREE MBA

MBA—Master of Business Administration Part-time. At least 54 total credits required. 24 to 72 months to complete program.

COSTS

Tuition, state resident: *Part-time* $140 per credit hour. **Tuition, nonresident:** *Part-time* $230 per credit hour. **Required fees:** *Part-time* $30 per credit hour.

FINANCIAL AID (1999–2000)

5 students received aid, including loans, research assistantships, and work study. Aid is available to part-time students. Financial aid application deadline: 4/15. **Financial Aid Contact** Ms. Janet Lundstrom, Director, Financial Aid, 352 Lafayette Street, Salem, MA 01970-5353. **Phone:** 978-542-6112. **Fax:** 978-542-6876.

RESOURCES AND SERVICES

Information about online services, personal computer policies, library resources, international exchange programs, internship programs, and placement services at this institution and others can be found at **www.petersons.com/mba**

International Students

4% of students enrolled are international students.

Services and Facilities Counseling/support services, ESL/language courses, housing location assistance, international student organization, language tutoring, orientation, visa services, cultural programming. Financial aid is not available to international students.
Applying *Required:* TOEFL with recommended score of 213 (computer) or 550 (paper), proof of adequate funds, proof of health/immunizations.

International Student Contact Dr. Donald Ross, Jr., Director, Center for International Education, 352 Lafayette Street, Salem, MA 01970-5353. **Phone:** 978-542-6351. **Fax:** 978-542-7104. **E-mail:** donald.ross@salem.mass.edu.

▪ APPLICATION

Required GMAT, application form, baccalaureate/first degree, interview, 3 letters of recommendation, personal statement, resume/curriculum vitae, transcripts of college work.

Deadlines and Fees *Deadlines:* 7/1 for fall, 11/1 for spring, 7/1 for fall (international), 11/1 for spring (international). *Application fee:* $25, $25 (international).

Application Contact A. Richard Anderson, Coordinator, Graduate Programs in Business, 352 Lafayette Street, Salem, MA 01970-5353. **Phone:** 978-542-6320. **Fax:** 978-542-7215. **E-mail:** richard.anderson@salem.mass.edu.

Simmons College

Boston, Massachusetts

GRADUATE SCHOOL OF MANAGEMENT

Graduate Business Faculty

Full-time: 12	Part-time: 4

Student Body

Total: 232	Average Age: 31
Full-time: 45	Women: 100%
Part-time: 187	

Admissions

Applications: 215	Average GMAT: 560
Admitted: 144	Average GPA: 3.2
Enrolled: 115	

Costs (1999–2000)
Full-time tuition: N/R
Part-time tuition: $620 per credit hour

After Graduation (Class of 1998–99)
Employed within 3 months of graduation: 85%
Average starting salary: $70,000

DEGREE MBA

MBA—Master of Business Administration Full-time and part-time. At least 45 total credits required. 11 to 60 months to complete program. *Concentrations:* management.

COSTS

Tuition *Part-time:* $620 per credit hour. Tuition varies by number of courses or credits taken. **Graduate housing:** *Typical cost:* $10,000 (including board).

FINANCIAL AID (1999–2000)

42 students received aid, including grants, loans, research assistantships, scholarships, and work study. Aid is available to part-time students. Financial aid application deadline: 3/1. **Financial Aid Contact** Ms. Nicole Cunningham, Financial Aid Assistant, 300 The Fenway, Boston, MA 02115. **Phone:** 617-521-2037. **E-mail:** financialaid@simmons.edu.

RESOURCES AND SERVICES

Information about online services, personal computer policies, library resources, international exchange programs, internship programs, and placement services at this institution and others can be found at **www.petersons.com/mba**

International Students

Services and Facilities Counseling/support services, ESL/language courses, housing location assistance, international student housing, language tutoring, orientation, visa services. Financial aid is available to international students.
Applying *Required:* TOEFL with recommended score of 550 (paper), proof of adequate funds, proof of health/immunizations.

International Student Contact Ms. Jean Dixan, MBA Admissions Office, 409 Commonwealth Avenue, Boston, MA 02215. **Phone:** 617-521-3846. **Fax:** 617-521-3880. **E-mail:** jean.dixan@simmons.edu.

▪ APPLICATION

Required GMAT, application form, essay, 3 letters of recommendation, personal statement, resume/curriculum vitae, transcripts of college work, 2 years of work experience. **Recommended** Baccalaureate/first degree, interview.

Deadlines and Fees *Deadlines:* 6/30 for fall, 11/15 for spring, 6/30 for fall (international), 11/15 for spring (international). *Application fee:* $75, $75 (international).

Application Contact Ms. Andrea Bruce, Director of MBA Admissions and Marketing, 409 Commonwealth Avenue, Boston, MA 02215. **Phone:** 617-521-3829. **Toll-free Phone:** 800-597-1622. **Fax:** 617-521-3880. **E-mail:** andrea.bruce@simmons.edu.

See full description on page 824.

Suffolk University

Boston, Massachusetts

FRANK SAWYER SCHOOL OF MANAGEMENT

Graduate Business Faculty

Full-time: 39	Part-time: 45

Student Body
Total: 1,177
Full-time: 133
Part-time: 1,044

Average Age: 30
Women: 48%

Admissions
Applications: 669
Admitted: 562

Enrolled: 326
Average GPA: 3.11

Costs (1999–2000)
Full-time tuition: $19,590 per academic year
Part-time tuition: $1947 per course

After Graduation (Class of 1998–99)
Employed within 3 months of graduation: 91%
Average starting salary: $59,000

Accreditation
AACSB—The International Association for Management Education

DEGREES JD/MBA • MBA • MS

JD/MBA—Juris Doctor/Master of Business Administration Full-time and part-time. *Distance learning option.* At least 109 total credits required. 48 to 60 months to complete program.

MBA—Executive MBA Full-time. 34 to 49 total credits required. 15 to 30 months to complete program. *Concentrations:* accounting, business law, entrepreneurship, finance, human resources, international business, management, management information systems, marketing, nonprofit management, organizational behavior/development, organizational management, public management, public policy and administration.

MBA—Master of Business Administration in Health Full-time and part-time. *Distance learning option.* 30 to 45 total credits required. 10 to 60 months to complete program.

MBA—On-line MBA Full-time and part-time. *Distance learning option.* 34 to 51 total credits required. 10 to 60 months to complete program.

MBA—Master of Business Administration Full-time and part-time. *Distance learning option.* 34 to 51 total credits required. 10 to 60 months to complete program. *Concentrations:* accounting, business law, entrepreneurship, finance, financial economics, human resources, management, management information systems, marketing, nonprofit management, organizational behavior/development, organizational management, public management, public policy and administration.

MS—Master of Science in Accounting Full-time and part-time. 30 to 48 total credits required. 10 to 60 months to complete program. *Concentrations:* accounting.

MS—Master of Science in Finance Full-time and part-time. 30 to 44 total credits required. 12 to 60 months to complete program. *Concentrations:* finance.

MS—Master of Science in Financial Services and Banking Full-time and part-time. 30 to 44 total credits required. 12 to 60 months to complete program. *Concentrations:* banking, finance.

MS—Master of Science in Taxation Full-time and part-time. 21 to 39 total credits required. 10 to 60 months to complete program. *Concentrations:* taxation.

COSTS
Tuition *Full-time:* $19,470. *Part-time:* $1947 per course. Tuition varies by number of courses or credits taken and academic program. **Required fees:** *Full-time* $120. *Part-time* $30 per semester. Tuition and fees vary by number of courses or credits taken.

FINANCIAL AID (1999–2000)
270 students received aid, including fellowships, grants, loans, research assistantships, and work study. Aid is available to part-time students. Financial aid application deadline: 3/15. **Financial Aid Contact** Christine Perry, Director of Financial Aid, 8 Ashburton Place, Boston, MA 02108-2770. **Phone:** 617-573-8470. **Fax:** 617-720-3579. **E-mail:** cperry@acad.suffolk.edu.

RESOURCES AND SERVICES
Information about online services, personal computer policies, library resources, international exchange programs, internship programs, and placement services at this institution and others can be found at **www. petersons.com/mba**

International Students
8% of students enrolled are international students.
Services and Facilities Counseling/support services, ESL/language courses, housing location assistance, international student organization, orientation, visa services, international student advising office. Financial aid is available to international students.
Applying *Required:* TOEFL with recommended score of 213 (computer) or 550 (paper), proof of adequate funds, proof of health/immunizations.

International Student Contact Arthur Levine, Associate Director—International Student Advising Office, 8 Ashburton Place, Boston, MA 02108-2770. **Phone:** 617-573-8154. **Fax:** 617-742-2651. **E-mail:** alevine@admin.suffolk.edu.

■ **APPLICATION**

Required GMAT, application form, baccalaureate/first degree, essay, 2 letters of recommendation, personal statement, resume/curriculum vitae, transcripts of college work. **Recommended** Work experience.

Deadlines and Fees *Deadlines:* 6/15 for fall, 11/15 for spring, 4/15 for summer, 6/15 for fall (international), 11/15 for spring (international), 4/15 for summer (international). *Application fee:* $50, $50 (international).

Application Contact Ms. Judith Reynolds, Director of Graduate Admission, 8 Ashburton Place, Boston, MA 02108-2770. **Phone:** 617-573-8302. **Toll-free Phone:** 800-6SUFFOL. **Fax:** 617-523-0116. **E-mail:** grad.admission@admin. suffolk.edu.

See full description on page 840.

University of Massachusetts Amherst

Amherst, Massachusetts

ISENBERG SCHOOL OF MANAGEMENT

Graduate Business Faculty
Full-time: 55

Student Body
Total: 372
Full-time: 81
Part-time: 291

Average Age: 27
Women: 44%

Admissions
Applications: 370
Admitted: 154
Enrolled: 128

Average GMAT: 635
Average GPA: 3.3

Costs (1999–2000)
Full-time tuition: $5642 per academic year (resident), $12,758 per academic year (nonresident)
Part-time tuition: $400 per credit (resident), $400 per credit (nonresident)

After Graduation (Class of 1998–99)
Employed within 3 months of graduation: 94%
Average starting salary: $69,200

Accreditation
AACSB—The International Association for Management Education

DEGREES MBA • MBA/MS

MBA—Professional Master of Business Administration Full-time and part-time. *Distance learning option.* At least 37 total credits required. 12 to 48 months to complete program. *Concentrations:* management, nonprofit management.

MBA/MS—Master of Business Administration/Master of Science in Accounting Full-time. *Distance learning option.* At least 55 total credits required. 24 months to complete program. *Concentrations:* accounting, electronic commerce (e-commerce), entrepreneurship, finance, management, marketing, nonprofit management.

COSTS
Tuition, state resident: *Full-time* $2640. *Part-time* $400 per credit. **Tuition, nonresident:** *Full-time* $9756. *Part-time* $400 per credit. **Tuition, international:** *Full-time* $9756. Tuition varies by academic program and local reciprocity agreements. **Required fees:** *Full-time* $3002. *Part-time* $20 per course. Tuition and fees vary by academic program. **Graduate housing:** Room and board costs vary by number of occupants, type of accommodation, and type of board plan. *Typical cost:* $4790 (including board), $2638 (room only).

FINANCIAL AID (1999–2000)
69 students received aid, including fellowships, loans, research assistantships, scholarships, teaching assistantships, and work study. Aid is available to part-time students. Financial aid application deadline: 3/1. **Financial Aid Contact** Financial Aid Services, 255 Whitmore Building, Amherst, MA 01003. **Phone:** 413-545-0801. **Fax:** 413-545-1722. **E-mail:** a.peramba@dpc.umass.edu.

RESOURCES AND SERVICES
Information about online services, personal computer policies, library resources, international exchange programs, internship programs, and

University of Massachusetts Amherst (continued)

placement services at this institution and others can be found at **www. petersons.com/mba**

International Students

9% of students enrolled are international students.

Services and Facilities Counseling/support services, ESL/language courses, housing location assistance, international student housing, international student organization, language tutoring, orientation, visa services, writing center. Financial aid is available to international students.

Applying *Required:* TOEFL with recommended score of 250 (computer) or 600 (paper), proof of adequate funds, proof of health/immunizations.

International Student Contact Patricia Vokbus, Deputy Director of International Programs Office, William S. Clark International Center, Amherst, MA 01003. **Phone:** 413-545-2843. **Fax:** 413-545-1201. **E-mail:** fso@ipo.umass.edu.

■ APPLICATION

Required GMAT, application form, baccalaureate/first degree, 2 letters of recommendation, personal statement, resume/curriculum vitae, transcripts of college work, 3 years of work experience. **Recommended** Interview.

Deadlines and Fees *Deadlines:* 2/1 for fall, 2/1 for fall (international). *Application fee:* $25, $40 (international).

Application Contact Heather Miller, Director of the Office of Graduate Programs, 209 Isenberg School of Management, Amherst, MA 01003-4910. **Phone:** 413-545-5608. **Fax:** 413-545-3858. **E-mail:** gradprog@som.umass.edu.

See full description on page 920.

University of Massachusetts Boston

Boston, Massachusetts

COLLEGE OF MANAGEMENT

Graduate Business Faculty

Full-time: 49	Part-time: 6

Student Body

Total: 383	Average Age: 27
Full-time: 66	Women: 46%
Part-time: 317	

Admissions

Applications: 315	Average GMAT: 560
Admitted: 85	Average GPA: 3.22
Enrolled: 72	

Costs (1999–2000)
Full-time tuition: N/R
Part-time tuition: $110 per credit (resident), $369 per credit (nonresident)

After Graduation (Class of 1998–99)
Employed within 3 months of graduation: 90%

DEGREES MBA • MBA/MS

MBA—Master of Business Administration Full-time and part-time. 33 to 57 total credits required. 18 to 60 months to complete program. *Concentrations:* accounting, electronic commerce (e-commerce), environmental economics/management, finance, human resources, international management, management information systems, marketing, operations management.

MBA/MS—Master of Business Administration/Master of Science in Nursing Full-time and part-time. Must be RN. 48 to 69 total credits required. 24 to 60 months to complete program. *Concentrations:* accounting, electronic commerce (e-commerce), environmental economics/management, finance, human resources, international management, management information systems, marketing, operations management.

COSTS

Tuition, state resident: *Part-time* $110 per credit. **Tuition, nonresident:** *Part-time* $369 per credit. **Required fees:** *Full-time* $1700. *Part-time* $200 per course. Tuition and fees vary by number of courses or credits taken.

FINANCIAL AID (1999–2000)

Loans, research assistantships, and teaching assistantships. Aid is available to part-time students. Financial aid application deadline: 3/1.
Financial Aid Contact Ms. Ernestine Whiting, Director of Financial Aid,

100 Morrissey Boulevard, Boston, MA 02125-3393. **Phone:** 617-287-6300. **Fax:** 617-287-6323. **E-mail:** ernestine.whiting@umb.edu.

RESOURCES AND SERVICES

Information about online services, personal computer policies, library resources, international exchange programs, internship programs, and placement services at this institution and others can be found at **www. petersons.com/mba**

International Students

13% of students enrolled are international students.

Services and Facilities Counseling/support services, ESL/language courses, housing location assistance, international student housing, international student organization, language tutoring, orientation, visa services. Financial aid is not available to international students.

Applying *Required:* TOEFL with recommended score of 600 (paper), proof of adequate funds, proof of health/immunizations. *Recommended:* TWE.

International Student Contact Mrs. Peggy Roldan, Admissions Officer, 100 Morrissey Boulevard, Boston, MA 02125-3393. **Phone:** 617-287-6401. **Fax:** 617-287-6236. **E-mail:** peggy.roldan@umb.edu.

■ APPLICATION

Required Application form, baccalaureate/first degree, essay, 3 letters of recommendation, personal statement, resume/curriculum vitae, transcripts of college work. School will accept GMAT.

Deadlines and Fees *Deadlines:* 6/1 for fall, 11/1 for spring, 5/1 for fall (international), 10/1 for spring (international). *Application fee:* $25, $40 (international).

Application Contact Mr. Daniel Robb, Assistant Dean of College of Management, 100 Morrissey Boulevard, Boston, MA 02125-3393. **Phone:** 617-287-7720. **Fax:** 617-287-7725. **E-mail:** mba@umb.edu.

University of Massachusetts Dartmouth

North Dartmouth, Massachusetts

CHARLTON COLLEGE OF BUSINESS

Graduate Business Faculty

Full-time: 43	Part-time: 1

Student Body

Total: 63	Average Age: 31
Full-time: 24	Women: 48%
Part-time: 39	

Admissions

Applications: 49	Enrolled: 20
Admitted: 43	Average GMAT: 481

Costs (1999–2000)
Full-time tuition: $4959 per academic year (resident), $10,733 per academic year (nonresident)
Part-time tuition: $86 per credit (resident), $327 per credit (nonresident)

Accreditation
AACSB—The International Association for Management Education

DEGREE MBA

MBA—Master of Business Administration Full-time and part-time. At least 30 total credits required. 12 to 60 months to complete program. *Concentrations:* management.

COSTS

Tuition, state resident: *Full-time* $2071. *Part-time* $86 per credit. **Tuition, nonresident:** *Full-time* $7845. *Part-time* $327 per credit. **Tuition, international:** *Full-time* $7845. Tuition varies by class time, number of courses or credits taken, and local reciprocity agreements. **Required fees:** *Full-time* $2888. Fees vary by class time, number of courses or credits taken, academic program, and local reciprocity agreements. **Graduate housing:** Room and board costs vary by type of board plan. *Typical cost:* $3292 (room only).

FINANCIAL AID (1999–2000)

Loans, research assistantships, and teaching assistantships. Aid is available to part-time students. Financial aid application deadline: 3/1.
Financial Aid Contact Mr. Gerald Coutinho, Director of Financial Aid, 285 Old Westport Road, North Dartmouth, MA 02747-2300. **Phone:** 508-999-8632. **Fax:** 508-999-8935. **E-mail:** financialaid@umassd.edu.

RESOURCES AND SERVICES
Information about online services, personal computer policies, library resources, international exchange programs, internship programs, and placement services at this institution and others can be found at **www.petersons.com/mba**

International Students
32% of students enrolled are international students.

Services and Facilities Counseling/support services, ESL/language courses, housing location assistance, orientation, visa services. Financial aid is not available to international students.
Applying *Required:* TOEFL with recommended score of 173 (computer) or 500 (paper), proof of adequate funds.
International Student Contact Dr. Richard Panofsky, Associate Vice Chancellor for Academic Affairs/Graduate Studies, 285 Old Westport Road, North Dartmouth, MA 02747-2300. **Phone:** 508-999-8029. **Fax:** 508-999-8183. **E-mail:** rpanofsky@umassd.edu.

■ APPLICATION
Required GMAT, application form, baccalaureate/first degree, 2 letters of recommendation, personal statement, resume/curriculum vitae, transcripts of college work.
Deadlines and Fees *Deadlines:* 6/1 for fall, 10/1 for spring, 4/1 for fall (international), 8/1 for spring (international). *Application fee:* $20, $40 (international).
Application Contact Ms. Carol Novo, Coordinator of Graduate Admissions, 285 Old Westport Road, North Dartmouth, MA 02747-2300. **Phone:** 508-999-8026. **Fax:** 508-999-8183. **E-mail:** graduate@umassd.edu.

University of Massachusetts Lowell
Lowell, Massachusetts

COLLEGE OF MANAGEMENT

Graduate Business Faculty
Full-time: 31 — Part-time: 5

Student Body
Total: 312
Full-time: 30 — Average Age: 26
Part-time: 282 — Women: 32%

Admissions
Applications: 181 — Average GMAT: 520
Admitted: 150 — Average GPA: 3
Enrolled: 126

Costs (1999–2000)
Full-time tuition: N/R
Part-time tuition: $89 per credit hour (resident), $312 per credit hour (nonresident)

After Graduation (Class of 1998–99)
Employed within 3 months of graduation: 85%

Accreditation
AACSB—The International Association for Management Education

DEGREES MBA • MMS

MBA—Master of Business Administration Full-time and part-time. 2 years work experience. 42 total credits required. 18 to 56 months to complete program. *Concentrations:* finance, health care, information management, management, management information systems, marketing.
MMS—Master of Management Science in Manufacturing Full-time and part-time. At least 33 total credits required. 18 to 56 months to complete program. *Concentrations:* profit management, technology management.

COSTS
Tuition, state resident: *Part-time* $89 per credit hour. **Tuition, nonresident:** *Part-time* $312 per credit hour. **Required fees:** *Part-time* $128 per credit. Tuition and fees vary by academic program. **Graduate housing:** Room and board costs vary by number of occupants. *Typical cost:* $4066 (including board).

FINANCIAL AID (1999–2000)
6 students received aid, including fellowships, loans, research assistantships, teaching assistantships, and work study. Aid is available to part-time students. Financial aid application deadline: 6/1. **Financial Aid Contact** Ms. Carole King, Program Coordinator, 1 University Avenue,

Lowell, MA 01854-2881. **Phone:** 978-934-4237. **E-mail:** carole_king@uml.edu.

RESOURCES AND SERVICES
Information about online services, personal computer policies, library resources, international exchange programs, internship programs, and placement services at this institution and others can be found at **www.petersons.com/mba**

International Students
8% of students enrolled are international students.

Services and Facilities Counseling/support services, ESL/language courses, housing location assistance, international student housing, international student organization. Financial aid is available to international students.
Applying *Required:* TOEFL with recommended score of 213 (computer) or 550 (paper), proof of adequate funds, proof of health/immunizations.
International Student Contact Ms. Anne Dean, Staff Assistant, Graduate School International Office, 1 University Avenue, Lowell, MA 01854-2881. **Phone:** 978-934-2386.

■ APPLICATION
Required GMAT, GMAT or GRE, baccalaureate/first degree, 3 letters of recommendation, personal statement, transcripts of college work.
Deadlines and Fees Applications for domestic and international students are processed on a rolling basis. *Application fee:* $20, $35 (international).
Application Contact Ms. Kathleen Rourke, Assistant to the Director of MBA Program, 1 University Avenue, Lowell, MA 01854-2881. **Phone:** 978-934-2848. **Fax:** 978-934-4017. **E-mail:** mba_mms@uml.edu.

Western New England College
Springfield, Massachusetts

SCHOOL OF BUSINESS

Graduate Business Faculty
Full-time: 30 — Part-time: 19

Student Body
Total: 1,108
Part-time: 1,108 — Average Age: 29
— Women: 35%

Admissions
Applications: 140 — Enrolled: 120
Admitted: 120 — Average GPA: 2.9

Costs (1999–2000)
Full-time tuition: N/R
Part-time tuition: $379 per semester hour

DEGREES MBA • MS

MBA—Accelerated MBA Part-time. 3 years of professional work experience required. At least 33 total credits required. Minimum of 18 months to complete program.
MBA—Weekend MBA Part-time. 3 years of professional work experience required. At least 30 total credits required. 12 months to complete program.
MBA—Master of Business Administration Part-time. At least 36 total credits required. 24 to 96 months to complete program. *Concentrations:* accounting, finance, health care, human resources, international business, management information systems, marketing.
MS—Master of Science in Accounting Part-time. At least 51 total credits required. 36 to 96 months to complete program. *Concentrations:* accounting.
MS—Master of Science in Information Systems Part-time. At least 33 total credits required. 36 to 96 months to complete program. *Concentrations:* management information systems.

COSTS
Tuition *Part-time:* $379 per semester hour. Tuition varies by class time, campus location, and academic program. **Required fees:** Tuition and fees vary by academic program.

FINANCIAL AID (1999–2000)
Loans. Aid is available to part-time students. Financial aid application deadline: 8/15. **Financial Aid Contact** Mr. Rodney Pease, Director of Student Administrative Services, 1215 Wilbraham Road, Springfield, MA 01119-2654. **Phone:** 413-796-2080. **Fax:** 413-796-2081. **E-mail:** rpease@wnec.edu.

RESOURCES AND SERVICES
Information about online services, personal computer policies, library resources, international exchange programs, internship programs, and

Western New England College (continued)

placement services at this institution and others can be found at **www. petersons.com/mba**

International Students

Services and Facilities Counseling/support services. Financial aid is not available to international students.

Applying *Required:* TOEFL, proof of adequate funds.

International Student Contact Mr. Harold Neunder, Administrative Director of Continuing Education, 1215 Wilbraham Road, Springfield, MA 01119-2654. **Phone:** 413-782-1750. **Fax:** 413-782-1779. **E-mail:** hneunder@wnec.edu.

■ APPLICATION

Required Application form, baccalaureate/first degree, personal statement, resume/curriculum vitae, transcripts of college work. School will accept GMAT.

Deadlines and Fees *Application fee:* $30, $30 (international).

Application Contact Mr. Harold Neunder, Administrative Director of Continuing Education, 1215 Wilbraham Road, Springfield, MA 01119-2654. **Phone:** 413-782-1249. **Toll-free Phone:** 800-325-1122. **Fax:** 413-782-1779. **E-mail:** hneunder@wnec.edu.

Worcester Polytechnic Institute

Worcester, Massachusetts

DEPARTMENT OF MANAGEMENT

Graduate Business Faculty

Full-time: 18	Part-time: 7

Student Body

Total: 282	Average Age: 33
Full-time: 19	Women: 28%
Part-time: 263	

Admissions

Applications: 85	Average GMAT: 575
Admitted: 73	Average GPA: 3.1
Enrolled: 58	

Costs (1999–2000)

Full-time tuition: N/R
Part-time tuition: $703 per credit

After Graduation (Class of 1998–99)

Employed within 3 months of graduation: 100%
Average starting salary: $65,000

DEGREES MBA • MS

MBA—Master of Business Administration Full-time and part-time. *Distance learning option.* 31 to 49 total credits required. 11 to 96 months to complete program. *Concentrations:* construction management, electronic commerce (e-commerce), entrepreneurship, management, management information systems, manufacturing management, marketing, new venture management, operations management, production management, project management, technology management.

MS—Master of Science in Marketing and Technological Innovation Full-time and part-time. At least 30 total credits required. 11 to 96 months to complete program. *Concentrations:* electronic commerce (e-commerce), entrepreneurship, marketing, new venture management, technology management.

MS—Master of Science in Operations and Information Technology Full-time and part-time. At least 30 total credits required. 11 to 96 months to complete program. *Concentrations:* management information systems, operations management, production management.

V*irtually every company relies on technology—to manage complexity, reduce costs, improve quality, and bring new products to market faster. Sometimes they even create new technologies. Worcester Polytechnic Institute (WPI), the nation's third-oldest private technological university, has been offering highly flexible, highly relevant M.B.A. and master's programs in management for more than two decades. Each is distinguished by a strong technology management focus and a global perspective. WPI graduates know how to leverage technological innovation to grow their companies, and in doing so, they leverage their own career growth. This is why WPI management graduates have an outstanding record of success in the business community.*

In addition to the Master of Business Administration, WPI offers Master of Science in Marketing and Technological Innovation and Master of Science in Operations and Information Technology degrees as well as a variety of graduate certificate programs.

WPI's student-friendly options include full- or part-time study at WPI campuses in Worcester and Waltham, Massachusetts, and worldwide via its Advanced Distance Learning Network. Curriculum and career planning, through a committed, involved academic adviser, are an integral part of the WPI experience and help prepare graduates for the unique management challenges of a technology-driven environment.

COSTS

Tuition *Part-time:* $703 per credit. **Required fees:** *Full-time* $50. Tuition and fees vary by number of courses or credits taken.

FINANCIAL AID (1999–2000)

8 students received aid, including fellowships, loans, and research assistantships. Financial aid application deadline: 2/15. **Financial Aid Contact** Mr. Norman D. Wilkinson, Director of Graduate Management Programs, 100 Institute Road, Worcester, MA 01609-2280. **Phone:** 508-831-5218. **Fax:** 508-831-5720. **E-mail:** wpigmp@wpi.edu.

RESOURCES AND SERVICES

Information about online services, personal computer policies, library resources, international exchange programs, internship programs, and placement services at this institution and others can be found at **www. petersons.com/mba**

International Students

23% of students enrolled are international students.

Services and Facilities Counseling/support services, ESL/language courses, housing location assistance, international student housing, international student organization, language tutoring, orientation, visa services. Financial aid is available to international students.

Applying *Required:* TOEFL with recommended score of 213 (computer) or 550 (paper), proof of adequate funds, proof of health/immunizations.

International Student Contact Dr. Tom Thomsen, Director, International Students and Scholars, 28 Trowbridge Road, Worcester, MA 01609-2280. **Phone:** 508-831-6030. **Fax:** 508-831-6032. **E-mail:** hartvig@wpi.edu.

■ APPLICATION

Required GMAT, application form, baccalaureate/first degree, essay, 3 letters of recommendation, personal statement, transcripts of college work. School will accept GRE. **Recommended** Resume/curriculum vitae, 2 years of work experience.

Deadlines and Fees Applications for domestic and international students are processed on a rolling basis. *Application fee:* $50, $50 (international).

Application Contact Mr. Norman D. Wilkinson, Director of Graduate Management Programs, 100 Institute Road, Worcester, MA 01609-2280. **Phone:** 508-831-5218. **Fax:** 508-831-5720. **E-mail:** wpigmp@wpi.edu.

See full description on page 1022.

MICHIGAN

Andrews University

Berrien Springs, Michigan

SCHOOL OF BUSINESS

Graduate Business Faculty

Full-time: 16	Part-time: 4

Student Body

Total: 50	Average Age: 29
Full-time: 32	Women: 40%
Part-time: 18	

Admissions

Applications: 110	Enrolled: 16
Admitted: 77	Average GPA: 3.12

Costs (1999–2000)

Full-time tuition: N/R
Part-time tuition: $300 per quarter hour

DEGREES MBA • MS

MBA—Master of Business Administration Full-time and part-time. At least 48 total credits required. 12 to 48 months to complete program. *Concentrations:* accounting, health care, management.

MS—Master of Science in Administration Full-time and part-time. At least 48 total credits required. 12 to 48 months to complete program. *Concentrations:* manufacturing management, nonprofit management.

COSTS

Tuition *Part-time:* $300 per quarter hour. **Graduate housing:** Room and board costs vary by number of occupants, type of accommodation, and type of board plan. *Typical cost:* $6210 (including board), $4680 (room only).

FINANCIAL AID (1999–2000)

35 students received aid, including fellowships, research assistantships, scholarships, and work study. **Financial Aid Contact** Ms. Ellen Murdick, Director of Financial Aid, Berrien Springs, MI 49104. **Phone:** 800-253-2874. **Fax:** 616-471-6161.

RESOURCES AND SERVICES

Information about online services, personal computer policies, library resources, international exchange programs, internship programs, and placement services at this institution and others can be found at **www.petersons.com/mba**

International Students

66% of students enrolled are international students.

Services and Facilities Counseling/support services, ESL/language courses, housing location assistance, international student organization, orientation. Financial aid is available to international students.

Applying *Required:* TOEFL with recommended score of 213 (computer) or 550 (paper), proof of adequate funds, proof of health/immunizations.

International Student Contact Mr. Najeeb Nakhle, Director of International Student Affairs, Berrien Springs, MI 49104. **Phone:** 800-253-2874. **E-mail:** nakhle@andrews.edu.

■ APPLICATION

Required GMAT, GRE, application form, baccalaureate/first degree, 3 letters of recommendation, personal statement, transcripts of college work.

Deadlines and Fees Applications for domestic and international students are processed on a rolling basis. *Application fee:* $40, $40 (international).

Application Contact Dr. Charles Tidwell, Graduate Advisor, School of Business, Berrien Springs, MI 49104. **Phone:** 616-471-3632. **Toll-free Phone:** 800-253-2874. **Fax:** 616-471-6158. **E-mail:** tidwell@andrews.edu.

Aquinas College

Grand Rapids, Michigan

GRADUATE SCHOOL OF MANAGEMENT

Graduate Business Faculty
Full-time: 16 | Part-time: 16

Student Body
Total: 227
Full-time: 10 | Average Age: 37
Part-time: 217 | Women: 55%

Admissions
Applications: 83 | Average GMAT: 484
Admitted: 80 | Average GPA: 3.63
Enrolled: 73

Costs (1999–2000)
Full-time tuition: N/R
Part-time tuition: $320 per credit hour

After Graduation (Class of 1998–99)
Employed within 3 months of graduation: 91%
Average starting salary: $38,900

DEGREE MM

MM—Master of Management Full-time and part-time. At least 39 total credits required. 18 to 48 months to complete program. *Concentrations:* arts administration/management, health care, international business, marketing, organizational behavior/development.

COSTS

Tuition *Part-time:* $320 per credit hour.

FINANCIAL AID (1999–2000)

60 students received aid, including scholarships. Aid is available to part-time students. Financial aid application deadline: 6/15. **Financial Aid Contact** Mr. David Steffee, Director of Financial Aid, 1607 Robinson

Road, SE, Grand Rapids, MI 49506-1799. **Phone:** 616-459-8281 Ext. 5127. **Fax:** 616-732-4435. **E-mail:** steffdav@aquinas.edu.

RESOURCES AND SERVICES

Information about online services, personal computer policies, library resources, international exchange programs, internship programs, and placement services at this institution and others can be found at **www.petersons.com/mba**

International Students

Services and Facilities Visa services. Financial aid is not available to international students.

Applying *Required:* TOEFL with recommended score of 213 (computer) or 550 (paper), proof of adequate funds, proof of health/immunizations.

International Student Contact Mr. Mark Campbell, Assistant Director of Admissions, 1607 Robinson Road, SE, Grand Rapids, MI 49506-1799. **Phone:** 616-459-8281 Ext. 5208. **Fax:** 616-732-4435. **E-mail:** campbmar@aquinas.edu.

■ APPLICATION

Required GMAT, application form, baccalaureate/first degree, essay, interview, 3 letters of recommendation, personal statement, transcripts of college work, 2 years of work experience.

Deadlines and Fees Applications for domestic and international students are processed on a rolling basis. *Application fee:* $35, $35 (international).

Application Contact Dr. Larry Pfaff, Dean, School of Management, 1607 Robinson Road, SE, Grand Rapids, MI 49506-1799. **Phone:** 616-459-8281 Ext. 8002. **Toll-free Phone:** 800-748-0350. **Fax:** 616-732-4489. **E-mail:** pfafflaw@aquinas.edu.

Baker College Center for Graduate Studies

Flint, Michigan

PROGRAMS IN BUSINESS

Graduate Business Faculty
Full-time: 8 | Part-time: 117

Student Body
Total: 730
Full-time: 225 | Part-time: 505
| Average Age: 39

Admissions
Applications: 892
Admitted: 758 | Average GMAT: 520
Enrolled: 730 | Average GPA: 3.06

Costs (1999–2000)
Full-time tuition: $6600 per academic year
Part-time tuition: $220 per quarter hour

After Graduation (Class of 1998–99)
Employed within 3 months of graduation: 99%

DEGREE MBA

MBA—Master of Business Administration Full-time and part-time. *Distance learning option.* At least 50 total credits required. 15 to 48 months to complete program. *Concentrations:* health care, human resources, industrial administration/management, international business, leadership, management, marketing, sports/entertainment management.

COSTS

Tuition *Full-time:* $6600. *Part-time:* $220 per quarter hour.

FINANCIAL AID (1999–2000)

420 students received aid, including grants and loans. Aid is available to part-time students. **Financial Aid Contact** Mrs. Krista McGuire, Graduate Director of Financial Aid, 1050 West Bristol Road, Flint, MI 48507-5508. **Phone:** 800-469-3165. **Fax:** 810-766-4399. **E-mail:** mcguir_k@corpfl.baker.edu.

RESOURCES AND SERVICES

Information about online services, personal computer policies, library resources, international exchange programs, internship programs, and placement services at this institution and others can be found at **www.petersons.com/mba**

Baker College Center for Graduate Studies (continued)

International Students

Services and Facilities Counseling/support services, international student housing, visa services. Financial aid is not available to international students.
Applying *Required:* TOEFL with recommended score of 213 (computer) or 550 (paper), proof of adequate funds. *Recommended:* Proof of health/immunizations.
International Student Contact Ms. Dawn Prueter, Registrar, 1050 West Bristol Road, Flint, MI 48507-5508. **Phone:** 810-766-4390. **Fax:** 810-766-4399.

■ APPLICATION

Required Application form, baccalaureate/first degree, essay, 3 letters of recommendation, personal statement, resume/curriculum vitae, transcripts of college work, 3 years of work experience. School will accept GMAT or GRE or MAT.
Deadlines and Fees Applications for domestic and international students are processed on a rolling basis. *Application fee:* $25, $25 (international).
Application Contact Mr. Chuck Gurden, Director of Graduate Admissions, 1050 West Bristol Road, Flint, MI 48507-5508. **Phone:** 810-766-4390. **Toll-free Phone:** 800-469-3165. **Fax:** 810-766-4399. **E-mail:** gurden_c@corpfl.baker.edu.

See full description on page 556.

Central Michigan University

Mount Pleasant, Michigan

COLLEGE OF BUSINESS ADMINISTRATION

Accreditation
AACSB—The International Association for Management Education

DEGREES MBA • MBE

MBA—Master of Business Administration Full-time and part-time. At least 30 total credits required. 12 to 50 months to complete program. *Concentrations:* accounting, finance, human resources, international business, management information systems, marketing.
MBE—Master of Business Education Full-time and part-time. At least 36 total credits required. 12 to 84 months to complete program.

RESOURCES AND SERVICES

Information about online services, personal computer policies, library resources, international exchange programs, internship programs, and placement services at this institution and others can be found at **www. petersons.com/mba**

International Students

Services and Facilities Counseling/support services, ESL/language courses, visa services. Financial aid is not available to international students.
International Student Contact Mr. Christopher Viers, Associate Director, Center for Education, Bovee University Center, Mt. Pleasant, MI 48859. **Phone:** 517-774-4308. **Fax:** 517-774-3690.

■ APPLICATION

Application Contact Dr. Daniel Vetter, Director, Graduate Business Studies, College of Business Administration, 112 Grawn Hall, Mount Pleasant, MI 48859. **Phone:** 517-774-3150. **Fax:** 517-774-2372. **E-mail:** daniel.e.vetter@cmich. edu.

Eastern Michigan University

Ypsilanti, Michigan

COLLEGE OF BUSINESS

Graduate Business Faculty

Full-time: 83	Part-time: 2

Student Body

Total: 781	
Full-time: 237	Average Age: 29
Part-time: 544	Women: 49%

Admissions

Applications: 300	
Admitted: 200	Average GMAT: 500
Enrolled: 100	Average GPA: 3.08

Costs (1999–2000)
Full-time tuition: $5200 per academic year (resident), $11,250 per academic year (nonresident)

Part-time tuition: $157 per credit hour (resident), $350 per credit hour (nonresident)

After Graduation (Class of 1998–99)
Employed within 3 months of graduation: 98%
Average starting salary: $35,500

Accreditation
AACSB—The International Association for Management Education

DEGREES MBA • MS

MBA—Master of Business Administration Full-time and part-time. 33 to 57 total credits required. 12 to 72 months to complete program. *Concentrations:* accounting, finance, human resources, international business, management, management information systems, marketing, operations management, organizational behavior/development, production management, strategic management.
MS—Master of Science in Accounting Full-time and part-time. 30 to 60 total credits required. 12 to 72 months to complete program. *Concentrations:* accounting, taxation.
MS—Master of Science in Human Resources/Organizational Development Full-time and part-time. 30 to 60 total credits required. 12 to 72 months to complete program. *Concentrations:* human resources, organizational behavior/development.
MS—Master of Science in Information Systems Full-time and part-time. 30 to 60 total credits required. 12 to 72 months to complete program. *Concentrations:* management information systems.

COSTS

Tuition, state resident: *Full-time* $5200. *Part-time* $157 per credit hour. **Tuition, nonresident:** *Full-time* $11,250. *Part-time* $350 per credit hour. Tuition varies by local reciprocity agreements. **Graduate housing:** Room and board costs vary by number of occupants, type of accommodation, and type of board plan. *Typical cost:* $6600 (including board).

FINANCIAL AID (1999–2000)

100 students received aid, including fellowships, research assistantships, and work study. Aid is available to part-time students. Financial aid application deadline: 3/15. **Financial Aid Contact** Office of Financial Aid, 403 Pierce Hall, Ypsilanti, MI 48197. **Phone:** 734-487-0455.

RESOURCES AND SERVICES

Information about online services, personal computer policies, library resources, international exchange programs, internship programs, and placement services at this institution and others can be found at **www. petersons.com/mba**

International Students

30% of students enrolled are international students.

Services and Facilities Counseling/support services, ESL/language courses, international student housing, visa services. Financial aid is not available to international students.
Applying *Required:* TOEFL with recommended score of 213 (computer) or 500 (paper), TWE with recommended score of 5, proof of adequate funds, proof of health/immunizations.
International Student Contact Mr. Paul Webb, Director, Foreign Student Affairs Office, 208 Goodison, Ypsilanti, MI 48197. **Phone:** 734-487-3116.

■ APPLICATION

Required Application form, baccalaureate/first degree, essay, personal statement, transcripts of college work. School will accept GMAT. **Recommended** Work experience.
Deadlines and Fees *Deadlines:* 5/15 for fall, 11/1 for winter, 3/15 for spring, 4/15 for summer, 5/1 for fall (international), 10/15 for winter (international), 3/1 for spring (international), 4/1 for summer (international). *Application fee:* $30, $30 (international).
Application Contact Dr. L. Christie Montgomery, Coordinator, Graduate Business Programs, 401 Gary M. Owen Building, Ypsilanti, MI 48197. **Phone:** 734-487-4444. **Fax:** 734-480-0618. **E-mail:** cob.grad@emich.edu.

Ferris State University

Big Rapids, Michigan

COLLEGE OF BUSINESS

Graduate Business Faculty

Full-time: 6	Part-time: 5

Student Body

Total: 150	Part-time: 59
Full-time: 91	Average Age: 31

Admissions

Applications: 120
Admitted: 75
Enrolled: 52

Women: 32%

Average GMAT: 540
Average GPA: 3.1

Costs (1999–2000)

Full-time tuition: N/R
Part-time tuition: $230 per credit hour (resident), $470 per credit hour (nonresident)

DEGREE MS

MS—Master of Science in Information Systems Management Full-time and part-time. *Distance learning option.* 31 to 34 total credits required. 12 to 60 months to complete program. *Concentrations:* information management, quality management.

COSTS

Tuition, state resident: *Part-time* $230 per credit hour. **Tuition, nonresident:** *Part-time* $470 per credit hour. Tuition varies by number of courses or credits taken, academic program, and local reciprocity agreements. **Required fees:** Tuition and fees vary by number of courses or credits taken and local reciprocity agreements. **Graduate housing:** Room and board costs vary by campus location, type of accommodation, and type of board plan. *Typical cost:* $4792 (including board).

FINANCIAL AID (1999–2000)

20 students received aid, including fellowships, grants, research assistantships, scholarships, teaching assistantships, and work study. Aid is available to part-time students. Financial aid application deadline: 4/1. **Financial Aid Contact** Robert Bopp, Financial Aid Director, 901 State Street, Big Rapids, MI 49307. **Phone:** 616-592-2110.

RESOURCES AND SERVICES

Information about online services, personal computer policies, library resources, international exchange programs, internship programs, and placement services at this institution and others can be found at **www.petersons.com/mba**

International Students

47% of students enrolled are international students.

Services and Facilities Counseling/support services, ESL/language courses, housing location assistance, international student housing, international student organization, orientation, visa services. Financial aid is available to international students.

Applying *Required:* TOEFL with recommended score of 550 (paper), proof of adequate funds, proof of health/immunizations.

International Student Contact Dr. Paul Landen, Coordinator, International Student Support, 901 State Street, Big Rapids, MI 49307. **Phone:** 231-591-2406. **Fax:** 616-592-2400.

■ APPLICATION

Required Application form, baccalaureate/first degree, essay, 3 letters of recommendation, personal statement, resume/curriculum vitae, transcripts of college work. School will accept GMAT or GRE.

Deadlines and Fees *Deadlines:* 7/1 for fall, 11/1 for winter, 4/1 for spring, 4/1 for summer, 7/1 for fall (international), 11/1 for winter (international), 4/1 for summer (international). *Application fee:* $20, $20 (international).

Application Contact Dr. Greg Gogolin, Coordinator, MSISM, Business 114, Big Rapids, MI 49307-2289. **Phone:** 231-591-2168. **Toll-free Phone:** 800-453-7747 (in-state), 800-433-7747 (out-of-state). **Fax:** 231-591-2973. **E-mail:** ism@ferris.edu.

See full description on page 652.

Grand Valley State University

Allendale, Michigan

SEIDMAN SCHOOL OF BUSINESS

Graduate Business Faculty

Full-time: 30

Part-time: 3

Student Body

Total: 321
Full-time: 29
Part-time: 292

Average Age: 33
Women: 32%

Admissions

Applications: 165
Admitted: 141
Enrolled: 117

Average GMAT: 573
Average GPA: 3.3

Costs (1999–2000)

Full-time tuition: N/R
Part-time tuition: $187 per credit (resident), $394 per credit (nonresident)

After Graduation (Class of 1998–99)

Employed within 3 months of graduation: 98%

Accreditation

AACSB—The International Association for Management Education

DEGREES MBA • MBA/MSN • MS

MBA—Master of Business Administration Full-time and part-time. 33 to 50 total credits required. 12 to 96 months to complete program.

MBA/MSN—Master of Business Administration/Master of Science in Nursing 63 total credits required.

MS—Master of Science in Taxation Full-time and part-time. 33 to 45 total credits required. 12 to 96 months to complete program.

COSTS

Tuition, state resident: *Part-time* $187 per credit. **Tuition, nonresident:** *Part-time* $394 per credit. Tuition varies by number of courses or credits taken. **Graduate housing:** *Typical cost:* $5000 (including board).

FINANCIAL AID (1999–2000)

16 students received aid, including fellowships, loans, research assistantships, scholarships, and work study. Aid is available to part-time students. Financial aid application deadline: 4/1. **Financial Aid Contact** Mr. Ken Fridsma, Director, Financial Aid, 100 STU, Allendale, MI 49401. **Phone:** 616-895-3234. **Fax:** 616-895-3180. **E-mail:** fridsmak@gvsu.edu.

RESOURCES AND SERVICES

Information about online services, personal computer policies, library resources, international exchange programs, internship programs, and placement services at this institution and others can be found at **www.petersons.com/mba**

International Students

5% of students enrolled are international students.

Services and Facilities Counseling/support services, ESL/language courses, housing location assistance, visa services. Financial aid is not available to international students.

Applying *Required:* TOEFL with recommended score of 550 (paper), proof of adequate funds, proof of health/immunizations.

International Student Contact Ms. Marche Haddad, Director, Global Programs, International Affairs, 104 STU, Allendale, MI 49401. **Phone:** 616-895-3898. **Fax:** 616-895-3899. **E-mail:** haddadm@gvsu.edu.

■ APPLICATION

Required Application form, baccalaureate/first degree, essay, transcripts of college work. School will accept GMAT.

Deadlines and Fees *Deadlines:* 8/1 for fall, 12/1 for winter, 4/1 for spring, 6/1 for fall (international), 12/1 for winter (international), 4/1 for spring (international). *Application fee:* $20, $20 (international).

Application Contact Ms. Claudia Bajema, MBA Program Director, 401 West Fulton, Grand Rapids, MI 49504. **Phone:** 616-336-7387. **Fax:** 616-336-7389. **E-mail:** bajemac@gvsu.edu.

Kettering University

Flint, Michigan

GRADUATE SCHOOL

Graduate Business Faculty

Full-time: 13

Part-time: 2

Student Body

Total: 535
Full-time: 1
Part-time: 534

Average Age: 32
Women: 24%

Admissions

Enrolled: 535

Costs (1999–2000)

Full-time tuition: N/R
Part-time tuition: $1230 per course

After Graduation (Class of 1998–99)

Employed within 3 months of graduation: 100%

Accreditation
ACBSP—The American Council of Business Schools and Programs

DEGREES MS

MS—Master of Science in Manufacturing Management Part-time. *Distance learning option.* At least 54 total credits required. 36 to 72 months to complete program. *Concentrations:* manufacturing management.

MS—Master of Science in Operations Management Part-time. *Distance learning option.* At least 48 total credits required. 24 to 60 months to complete program. *Concentrations:* operations management.

COSTS
Tuition *Part-time:* $1230 per course. **Tuition, state resident:** *Part-time* $45 per course. **Graduate housing:** *Typical cost:* $7500 (including board).

FINANCIAL AID (1999–2000)
14 students received aid, including fellowships, loans, research assistantships, and teaching assistantships. Aid is available to part-time students. **Financial Aid Contact** Melissa Ruterbusch, Director of Financial Aid, 1700 West Third Avenue, Flint, MI 48504-4898. **Phone:** 810-762-7859. **Fax:** 810-762-9807. **E-mail:** mruterbu@kettering.edu.

RESOURCES AND SERVICES
Information about online services, personal computer policies, library resources, international exchange programs, internship programs, and placement services at this institution and others can be found at **www.petersons.com/mba**

International Students
2% of students enrolled are international students.

Services and Facilities Counseling/support services, visa services. Financial aid is available to international students.
Applying *Required:* TOEFL with recommended score of 580 (paper), proof of adequate funds, proof of health/immunizations.
International Student Contact Celia Bandl, Director, International Programs and Governmental Activities, 1700 West Third Avenue, Flint, MI 48504-4898. **Phone:** 810-762-9869. **Fax:** 810-762-9755. **E-mail:** cbandl@kettering.edu.

■ APPLICATION
Required Application form, baccalaureate/first degree, transcripts of college work.
Deadlines and Fees *Deadlines:* 7/15 for fall, 11/1 for winter, 7/15 for fall (international), 11/1 for winter (international).
Application Contact Ms. Betty Bedore, Coordinator of Graduate Publications, 1700 West Third Avenue, Flint, MI 48504. **Phone:** 810-762-7494. **Fax:** 810-762-9935. **E-mail:** bbedore@kettering.edu.

Lawrence Technological University
Southfield, Michigan

COLLEGE OF MANAGEMENT

Accreditation
ACBSP—The American Council of Business Schools and Programs

DEGREES CIMBA • MBA • MS

CIMBA—Career Integrated Master of Business Administration Part-time. *Distance learning option.* At least 36 total credits required. 18 to 24 months to complete program.

MBA—Master of Business Administration Full-time and part-time. At least 36 total credits required. 18 to 84 months to complete program. *Concentrations:* human resources, international business, management information systems, operations management.

MS—Master of Science in Industrial Operations Full-time and part-time. At least 30 total credits required. 18 to 84 months to complete program.

MS—Master of Science in Information Systems Full-time and part-time. At least 30 total credits required. 18 to 84 months to complete program.

RESOURCES AND SERVICES
Information about online services, personal computer policies, library resources, international exchange programs, internship programs, and placement services at this institution and others can be found at **www.petersons.com/mba**

International Students
Services and Facilities ESL/language courses, international student housing.
International Student Contact Mr. Frank de Hesselle, Director, International Student Affairs, 21000 West Ten Mile Road, Southfield, MI 48075. **Phone:** 248-204-3160 Ext. 3179. **Fax:** 248-204-3188. **E-mail:** dehesselle@ltu.edu.

■ APPLICATION
Application Contact Ms. Patricia Leto, Graduate Admissions Counselor, 21000 West Ten Mile Road, Southfield, MI 48075-1058. **Phone:** 248-204-3160 Ext. 3187. **Toll-free Phone:** 800-CALL-LTU. **Fax:** 248-204-3188. **E-mail:** leto@ltu.edu.

See full description on page 706.

Madonna University
Livonia, Michigan

PROGRAM IN BUSINESS ADMINISTRATION

Graduate Business Faculty

Full-time: 14	Part-time: 18

Student Body

Total: 218	
Full-time: 54	Average Age: 36
Part-time: 164	Women: 54%

Admissions

Applications: 60	Average GMAT: 400
Admitted: 48	Average GPA: 3.1
Enrolled: 40	

Costs (1999–2000)
Full-time tuition: N/R
Part-time tuition: $288 per credit hour

After Graduation (Class of 1998–99)
Employed within 3 months of graduation: 95%
Average starting salary: $40,000

DEGREES MBA • MSBA

MBA—Master of Business Administration Full-time and part-time. At least 40 total credits required. Minimum of 24 months to complete program.

MSBA—Master of Science in Business Administration in International Business Full-time and part-time. At least 36 total credits required. 24 to 72 months to complete program.

MSBA—Master of Science in Business Administration in Leadership Studies Full-time and part-time. *Distance learning option.* At least 36 total credits required. 24 to 72 months to complete program. *Concentrations:* international business, leadership.

MSBA—Master of Science in Business Administration in Quality and Operations Management Full-time and part-time. *Distance learning option.* At least 36 total credits required. 24 to 72 months to complete program.

COSTS
Tuition *Part-time:* $288 per credit hour. **Graduate housing:** *Typical cost:* $4168 (including board).

FINANCIAL AID (1999–2000)
Grants and scholarships. Financial aid application deadline: 8/1.
Financial Aid Contact Ms. Kathy Durham, Secretary, 36600 Schoolcraft Road, Livonia, MI 48150-1173. **Phone:** 734-432-5663. **Fax:** 734-432-5344. **E-mail:** durham@smtp.munet.edu.

RESOURCES AND SERVICES
Information about online services, personal computer policies, library resources, international exchange programs, internship programs, and placement services at this institution and others can be found at **www.petersons.com/mba**

International Students
Services and Facilities Counseling/support services, ESL/language courses, international student housing, visa services. Financial aid is not available to international students.
Applying *Required:* TOEFL with recommended score of 530 (paper), proof of adequate funds, proof of health/immunizations.
International Student Contact Mr. Jonathan Swift, Director, Center for International Studies, 36600 Schoolcraft Road, Livonia, MI 48150-1173. **Phone:** 734-432-5636. **Fax:** 734-432-5393. **E-mail:** swift@smtp.munet.edu.

■ APPLICATION

Required Application form, baccalaureate/first degree, interview, 2 letters of recommendation, personal statement, transcripts of college work. School will accept GMAT and GRE. **Recommended** Resume/curriculum vitae, work experience.

Application Contact Mrs. Sandra Kellums, Coordinator of Graduate Admissions and Records, 36600 Schoolcraft Road, Livonia, MI 48150-1173. **Phone:** 734-432-5666. **Fax:** 734-432-5862. **E-mail:** kellums@smtp.munet.edu.

Michigan State University

East Lansing, Michigan

ELI BROAD GRADUATE SCHOOL OF MANAGEMENT

Graduate Business Faculty
Full-time: 136

Student Body
Total: 266
Full-time: 266

Average Age: 28
Women: 29%

Admissions
Applications: 956
Admitted: 215
Enrolled: 111

Average GMAT: 638
Average GPA: 3.35

Costs (1999–2000)
Full-time tuition: $9800 per academic year (resident), $13,800 per academic year (nonresident)
Part-time tuition: N/R

After Graduation (Class of 1998–99)
Employed within 3 months of graduation: 95%
Average starting salary: $66,810

Accreditation
AACSB—The International Association for Management Education

DEGREES EMBA • MBA • MS

EMBA—Executive Master of Business Administration in Advanced Management Part-time. At least 43 total credits required. Maximum of 21 months to complete program.

MBA—Full-time Master of Business Administration Full-time. At least 57 total credits required. Maximum of 21 months to complete program. *Concentrations:* accounting, electronic commerce (e-commerce), finance, human resources, international business, international management, leadership, logistics, management, management information systems, marketing, operations management, travel industry/tourism management, transportation and logistics.

MBA—Master of Business Administration in Integrative Management Part-time. At least 45 total credits required. Maximum of 17 months to complete program.

MS—Master of Science in Business Management of Manufacturing Full-time. At least 39 total credits required. Maximum of 21 months to complete program. *Concentrations:* management.

MS—Master of Science in Food Service Management Full-time. At least 30 total credits required. Maximum of 21 months to complete program.

MS—Master of Science in Professional Accounting Full-time. At least 31 total credits required. Maximum of 21 months to complete program. *Concentrations:* accounting, management information systems, taxation.

COSTS

Tuition, state resident: *Full-time* $9800. **Tuition, nonresident:** *Full-time* $13,800. **Tuition, international:** *Full-time* $13,800. **Graduate housing:** Room and board costs vary by campus location, number of occupants, type of accommodation, and type of board plan. *Typical cost:* $4100 (including board).

FINANCIAL AID (1999–2000)

160 students received aid, including fellowships, loans, research assistantships, scholarships, teaching assistantships, and work study. Aid is available to part-time students. Financial aid application deadline: 4/1. **Financial Aid Contact** Office of Financial Aid, 252 Student Services Building, East Lansing, MI 48824-1113. **Phone:** 517-353-5940. **Fax:** 517-432-1155. **E-mail:** ofa00@msu.edu.

RESOURCES AND SERVICES

Information about online services, personal computer policies, library resources, international exchange programs, internship programs, and placement services at this institution and others can be found at **www.petersons.com/mba**

International Students

36% of students enrolled are international students.

Services and Facilities Counseling/support services, ESL/language courses, housing location assistance, international student housing, international student organization, orientation, visa services. Financial aid is available to international students.

Applying *Required:* TOEFL with recommended score of 600 (paper), proof of adequate funds.

International Student Contact Office of International Students and Scholars, 103 International Center, East Lansing, MI 48824. **Phone:** 517-353-1720. **Fax:** 517-355-4657.

■ APPLICATION

Required GMAT, application form, baccalaureate/first degree, essay, interview, 2 letters of recommendation, resume/curriculum vitae, transcripts of college work, 2 years of work experience.

Deadlines and Fees *Deadlines:* 6/15 for fall, 4/1 for fall (international). *Application fee:* $30, $40 (international).

Application Contact Mr. Randall Dean, Director, MBA Admissions, 215 Eppley Center, East Lansing, MI 48824-1121. **Phone:** 517-355-7604. **Toll-free Phone:** 800-4-MSU-MBA. **Fax:** 517-353-1649.

See full description on page 726.

Michigan Technological University

Houghton, Michigan

SCHOOL OF BUSINESS AND ECONOMICS

Graduate Business Faculty
Full-time: 24

Student Body
Total: 4
Full-time: 4

Average Age: 29
Women: 25%

Admissions
Applications: 7
Admitted: 6

Enrolled: 2

Costs (1999–2000)
Full-time tuition: N/R
Part-time tuition: $182 per credit hour (resident), $417 per credit hour (nonresident)

After Graduation (Class of 1998–99)
Employed within 3 months of graduation: 100%

DEGREE MS

MS—Master of Science in Mineral Economics Full-time and part-time. At least 45 total credits required. 9 to 60 months to complete program. *Concentrations:* resources management.

COSTS

Tuition, state resident: *Part-time* $182 per credit hour. **Tuition, nonresident:** *Part-time* $417 per credit hour. Tuition varies by number of courses or credits taken and local reciprocity agreements. **Required fees:** Fees vary by academic program. **Graduate housing:** Room and board costs vary by number of occupants, type of accommodation, and type of board plan. *Typical cost:* $4420 (including board).

FINANCIAL AID (1999–2000)

4 students received aid, including work study. Aid is available to part-time students. **Financial Aid Contact** Dr. Gary Campbell, Professor of Mineral Economics, 1400 Townsend Drive, Houghton, MI 49931-1295. **Phone:** 906-487-2808. **Fax:** 906-487-2944. **E-mail:** gacampbe@mtu.edu.

RESOURCES AND SERVICES

Information about online services, personal computer policies, library resources, international exchange programs, internship programs, and placement services at this institution and others can be found at **www.petersons.com/mba**

International Students

50% of students enrolled are international students.

Services and Facilities Counseling/support services, visa services. Financial aid is available to international students.

Applying *Required:* TOEFL with recommended score of 520 (paper), proof of adequate funds.

Michigan Technological University (continued)

International Student Contact Ms. Mary Brunner, Associate Director, International Services, 1400 Townsend Drive, Houghton, MI 49931-1295. **Phone:** 906-487-2160. **Fax:** 906-487-1891. **E-mail:** mbrunner@mtu.edu.

■ **APPLICATION**

Required GMAT or GRE, application form, baccalaureate/first degree, personal statement, resume/curriculum vitae, transcripts of college work. **Recommended** 3 letters of recommendation.

Deadlines and Fees Applications for domestic and international students are processed on a rolling basis. *Application fee:* $35, $35 (international).

Application Contact Dr. Gary Campbell, Professor of Mineral Economics, 1400 Townsend Drive, Houghton, MI 49931-1295. **Phone:** 906-487-2808. **Fax:** 906-487-2944. **E-mail:** gacampbe@mtu.edu.

Northwood University

Midland, Michigan

RICHARD DEVOS GRADUATE SCHOOL OF MANAGEMENT

Graduate Business Faculty

Full-time: 5	Part-time: 4

Student Body

Total: 207	
Full-time: 42	Average Age: 33
Part-time: 165	Women: 29%

Admissions

Applications: 200	Enrolled: 95
Admitted: 130	Average GPA: 3

Costs (1999–2000)
Full-time tuition: $18,000 per academic year
Part-time tuition: $20,000 per degree program

After Graduation (Class of 1998–99)
Employed within 3 months of graduation: 80%
Average starting salary: $79,000

DEGREES MBA

MBA—Executive MBA Part-time. Interview, management experience, and 5 years of work experience required. At least 40 total credits required. Minimum of 30 months to complete program.

MBA—Full-time MBA Full-time. At least 65 total credits required. Minimum of 15 months to complete program.

MBA—Managerial MBA 3-5 years of work experience. 35 to 45 total credits required. 15 to 60 months to complete program. *Concentrations:* management.

The DeVos Graduate School is looking for candidates that value education. There are other business programs, even M.B.A. options, that are easier and faster. With case analysis and discussion as the cornerstone of learning, the DeVos M.B.A. programs are designed for serious students who recognize the need for additional management training and plan to use this opportunity to aid in advancing their careers and organizations.

DeVos faculty members aspire to provide candidates with the highest standard of personal and professional growth. They combine their premier academic credentials with significant business experience. They also realize that, in the real world, managers are put to the test. That is why the faculty embraces Northwood's policy of no tenure. They are measured as businesses will measure the M.B.A. graduates—through a continual critique of their performance.

The DeVos Graduate School is housed within a state-of-the-art complex on the Northwood University campus in Midland, Michigan. This facility houses four discussion-oriented classrooms, including a multimedia classroom; breakout rooms; a computer lab; a student lounge; and faculty and administrative offices. The entire graduate school is designed specifically to suit the M.B.A. program's highly interactive environment.

For further information, contact the Graduate School by telephone at 800-MBA-9000 (toll-free) or e-mail at mba@northwood.edu or visit its Web site at http://www.northwood.edu/mba.

COSTS

Tuition *Full-time:* $18,000. *Part-time:* $20,000 per degree program. **Graduate housing:** *Typical cost:* $5492 (including board); $2769 (room only).

FINANCIAL AID (1999–2000)

61 students received aid, including grants, loans, scholarships, and work study. Aid is available to part-time students. Financial aid application deadline: 2/15. **Financial Aid Contact** Ms. Nancy Vaughn, Assistant Director of Financial Aid, 4000 Whiting Drive, Midland, MI 48640-2398. **Phone:** 517-837-4454. **Fax:** 517-837-4111. **E-mail:** vaughn@northwood.edu.

RESOURCES AND SERVICES

Information about online services, personal computer policies, library resources, international exchange programs, internship programs, and placement services at this institution and others can be found at **www.petersons.com/mba**

International Students

13% of students enrolled are international students.

Services and Facilities Counseling/support services, ESL/language courses, housing location assistance, orientation, visa services. Financial aid is available to international students.

Applying *Required:* TOEFL with recommended score of 610 (paper), proof of adequate funds.

International Student Contact Mr. Rusty Beckham, Director of Marketing, 4000 Whiting Drive, Midland, MI 48640. **Phone:** 517-837-4488. **Fax:** 517-837-4800. **E-mail:** mba@northwood.edu.

■ **APPLICATION**

Required GMAT, application form, baccalaureate/first degree, essay, interview, personal statement, resume/curriculum vitae, transcripts of college work, work experience.

Deadlines and Fees Applications for domestic and international students are processed on a rolling basis. *Application fee:* $25, $25 (international).

Application Contact Mr. Rusty Beckham, Director of Marketing, 4000 Whiting Drive, Midland, MI 48640. **Phone:** 517-837-4488. **Toll-free Phone:** 800-MBA-9000 (in-state), 517-837-4488 (out-of-state). **Fax:** 517-837-4800. **E-mail:** mba@northwood.edu.

See full description on page 752.

Oakland University

Rochester, Michigan

SCHOOL OF BUSINESS ADMINISTRATION

Graduate Business Faculty

Full-time: 52	Part-time: 28

Student Body

Total: 568	
Full-time: 46	Average Age: 29
Part-time: 522	Women: 35%

Admissions

Applications: 146	Average GMAT: 560
Admitted: 126	Average GPA: 3.2
Enrolled: 84	

Costs (1999–2000)
Full-time tuition: N/R
Part-time tuition: $227 per credit (resident), $489 per credit (nonresident)

After Graduation (Class of 1998–99)
Employed within 3 months of graduation: 98%
Average starting salary: $50,000

Accreditation
AACSB—The International Association for Management Education

DEGREES EMBA • M Acc • MBA • PMC

EMBA—Executive MBA in Health Care Management Part-time. 5 years of health care work experience required. At least 39 total credits required. Minimum of 21 months to complete program.

M Acc—Master of Accounting Full-time and part-time. At least 33 total credits required. 12 to 72 months to complete program.

MBA—Master of Business Administration Full-time and part-time. At least 36 total credits required. 12 to 72 months to complete program. *Concentrations:* accounting, economics, entrepreneurship, finance, health care, human resources, international business, management information systems, marketing, operations management.

PMC—Post-Master's Certificate Full-time and part-time. At least 15 total credits required. 8 to 72 months to complete program. *Concentrations:* accounting, economics, entrepreneurship, finance, health care, human resources, international business, management information systems, marketing, operations management.

Oakland University is a comprehensive, state-assisted institution of approximately 15,000 students that offers a diverse set of academic programs, from baccalaureate to doctoral levels. Located between the cities of Pontiac and Rochester (at the intersection of I-75 and M-59), Oakland University is easily accessible to millions of Detroit metropolitan area residents. Undergraduate programs and the M.B.A. are accredited by AACSB-The International Association for Management Education. Oakland University is among four universities in Michigan that have also achieved AACSB accreditation for their undergraduate accounting program.

The M.B.A. program provides a solid foundation in the functional areas of business, with special emphasis on the management of information resources. Nine concentrations allow students to tailor the program to their career goals. Course work includes real-life cases and applications to assist students with the development of problem-solving skills. A Master of Accounting and post-master's certificate programs are also offered through the School of Business Administration. Classes are held in the evening in Rochester and Birmingham or on Saturday mornings (Rochester only) to accommodate the working adult. Oakland University's graduate business programs are open to both individuals who hold bachelor's degrees in business and nonbusiness majors. Women and minorities are encouraged to apply.

COSTS

Tuition, state resident: *Part-time* $227 per credit. **Tuition, nonresident:** *Part-time* $489 per credit. Tuition varies by number of courses or credits taken. **Required fees:** *Part-time* $287 per semester. Fees vary by campus location. **Graduate housing:** Room and board costs vary by number of occupants, type of accommodation, and type of board plan. *Typical cost:* $6995 (including board).

FINANCIAL AID (1999–2000)

Loans, research assistantships, and work study. Financial aid application deadline: 3/1. **Financial Aid Contact** Mr. Lee Anderson, Director, Financial Aid, 161 North Foundation Hall, Rochester, MI 48309-4401. **Phone:** 248-370-3370. **E-mail:** anderson@oakland.edu.

RESOURCES AND SERVICES

Information about online services, personal computer policies, library resources, international exchange programs, internship programs, and placement services at this institution and others can be found at **www. petersons.com/mba**

International Students

Services and Facilities Counseling/support services, ESL/language courses, visa services. Financial aid is available to international students.
Applying *Required:* TOEFL with recommended score of 550 (paper), proof of adequate funds. *Recommended:* Proof of health/immunizations.
International Student Contact Ms. Lisa Heap-Seguchi, Interim Director, International Student Services, 157 North Foundation Hall, Rochester, MI 48309-4401. **Phone:** 248-370-3266. **Fax:** 248-370-3351. **E-mail:** seguchi@oakland. edu.

■ APPLICATION

Required GMAT, application form, baccalaureate/first degree, transcripts of college work. **Recommended** Personal statement, resume/curriculum vitae, 2 years of work experience.
Deadlines and Fees *Deadlines:* 8/1 for fall, 12/1 for winter, 4/1 for spring, 6/1 for summer, 5/1 for fall (international), 9/1 for winter (international). *Application fee:* $30, $30 (international).
Application Contact Ms. Gloria Schatz, Program Assistant, Office of Graduate Business Programs, 416 Varner Hall, Rochester, MI 48309-4493. **Phone:** 248-370-3287. **Fax:** 248-370-4604. **E-mail:** gbp@oakland.edu.

Saginaw Valley State University

University Center, Michigan

COLLEGE OF BUSINESS AND MANAGEMENT

Graduate Business Faculty
Full-time: 26

Student Body
Total: 109
Full-time: 18
Part-time: 91

Average Age: 30
Women: 44%

Admissions
Applications: 39
Admitted: 39
Enrolled: 21

Average GMAT: 480
Average GPA: 3

Costs (1999–2000)
Full-time tuition: N/R
Part-time tuition: $167 per credit hour (resident), $327 per credit hour (nonresident)

DEGREE MBA

MBA—Master of Business Administration Full-time and part-time. 31 to 47 total credits required. 12 to 72 months to complete program. *Concentrations:* accounting, economics, finance, international business, management, marketing.

COSTS

Tuition, state resident: *Part-time* $167 per credit hour. **Tuition, nonresident:** *Part-time* $327 per credit hour. **Required fees:** Tuition and fees vary by number of courses or credits taken. **Graduate housing:** Room and board costs vary by number of occupants, type of accommodation, and type of board plan. *Typical cost:* $4800 (including board).

FINANCIAL AID (1999–2000)

50 students received aid, including fellowships, loans, research assistantships, and work study. Aid is available to part-time students.
Financial Aid Contact Ms. Cindy Munger, Acting Director, Scholarships and Student Financial Aid, 7400 Bay Road, 160 Wickes Hall, University Center, MI 48710. **Phone:** 517-790-4103. **Fax:** 517-790-0180. **E-mail:** clm@svsu.edu.

RESOURCES AND SERVICES

Information about online services, personal computer policies, library resources, international exchange programs, internship programs, and placement services at this institution and others can be found at **www. petersons.com/mba**

International Students

17% of students enrolled are international students.

Services and Facilities Counseling/support services, ESL/language courses, housing location assistance, international student organization, orientation, visa services. Financial aid is not available to international students.
Applying *Required:* TOEFL with recommended score of 525 (paper), proof of adequate funds, proof of health/immunizations.
International Student Contact Mr. Lee H. Pelton, Special Assistant to the President for International Programs, 7400 Bay Road, University Center, MI 48710. **Phone:** 517-790-4268. **Fax:** 517-249-1666. **E-mail:** pelton@tardis.svsu.edu.

■ APPLICATION

Required GMAT, application form, baccalaureate/first degree, essay, 2 letters of recommendation, personal statement, resume/curriculum vitae, transcripts of college work. **Recommended** Interview, work experience.
Deadlines and Fees *Application fee:* $25, $25 (international).
Application Contact Dr. Jill Wetmore, Assistant Dean, College of Business and Management, 7400 Bay Road, Curtis Hall 320, University Center, MI 48710. **Phone:** 517-790-4064. **Fax:** 517-249-1960. **E-mail:** cbmdean@tardis.svsu.edu.

Siena Heights University

Adrian, Michigan

GRADUATE STUDIES

DEGREES MA

MA—Master of Arts in Health Care Administration Full-time and part-time. At least 36 total credits required. 24 to 84 months to complete program.

MA—Master of Arts in Human Resource Development Full-time and part-time. At least 36 total credits required. 24 to 84 months to complete program. *Concentrations:* human resources.

RESOURCES AND SERVICES

Information about online services, personal computer policies, library resources, international exchange programs, internship programs, and placement services at this institution and others can be found at **www. petersons.com/mba**

International Students

Services and Facilities Counseling/support services. Financial aid is not available to international students.
International Student Contact Dr. Robert Gordon, Dean of Graduate Studies

Siena Heights University (continued)

and Life Long Learning, 1247 East Siena Heights Drive, Adrian, MI 49221-1796. **Phone:** 517-264-7666. **Fax:** 517-264-7714. **E-mail:** rgordon@sienahts.edu.

■ **APPLICATION**

Application Contact Dr. C. Patrick Palmer, Associate Professor of Human Resource Development, 1247 East Sienna Heights, Adrian, MI 49221-1796. **Phone:** 517-264-7606 Ext. 7606. **Toll-free Phone:** 800-521-0009. **Fax:** 517-264-7704. **E-mail:** ppalmer@sienahts.edu.

Spring Arbor College

Spring Arbor, Michigan

SCHOOL OF BUSINESS AND MANAGEMENT

Graduate Business Faculty
Full-time: 3 | Part-time: 11

Student Body
Total: 103 | Average Age: 38
Full-time: 38 | Women: 50%
Part-time: 65

Admissions
Applications: 17 | Enrolled: 15
Admitted: 15 | Average GPA: 2.99

Costs (1999–2000)
Full-time tuition: N/R
Part-time tuition: $265 per credit hour

DEGREE MBA

MBA—Master of Business Administration Full-time and part-time. 36 to 54 total credits required. 20 to 72 months to complete program.

COSTS

Tuition *Part-time:* $265 per credit hour.

FINANCIAL AID (1999–2000)

15 students received aid, including grants and work study. Aid is available to part-time students. Financial aid application deadline: 8/25. **Financial Aid Contact** Lois Hardy, Director of Financial Aid, 106 East Main, Spring Arbor, MI 49283. **Phone:** 517-750-6463. **Fax:** 517-750-6620. **E-mail:** loish@admit.arbor.edu.

RESOURCES AND SERVICES

Information about online services, personal computer policies, library resources, international exchange programs, internship programs, and placement services at this institution and others can be found at **www.petersons.com/mba**

International Students

Services and Facilities Counseling/support services, ESL/language courses. **Applying** *Required:* TOEFL with recommended score of 550 (paper), proof of adequate funds.

International Student Contact Carla Koontz, Director of International Students, 106 East Main, Spring Arbor, MI 49283-9799. **Phone:** 517-750-1200 Ext. 1334. **Fax:** 517-750-1536. **E-mail:** ckoontz@admin.arbor.edu.

■ **APPLICATION**

Required Application form, baccalaureate/first degree, essay, 2 letters of recommendation, transcripts of college work, 3 years of work experience.
Deadlines and Fees *Application fee:* $45, $45 (international).
Application Contact Yvette Saint-Blakely, Admissions Representative, 106 East Main, Spring Arbor, MI 49283. **Phone:** 517-750-6536. **Fax:** 517-750-6624. **E-mail:** yvettesb@admin.arbor.edu.

University of Detroit Mercy

Detroit, Michigan

COLLEGE OF BUSINESS ADMINISTRATION

Graduate Business Faculty
Full-time: 33 | Part-time: 20

Student Body
Total: 487 | Average Age: 31
Full-time: 69 | Women: 41%
Part-time: 418

Admissions
Applications: 300 | Average GMAT: 520
Admitted: 225 | Average GPA: 3.1
Enrolled: 166

Costs (1999–2000)
Full-time tuition: N/R
Part-time tuition: $545 per credit hour

After Graduation (Class of 1998–99)
Employed within 3 months of graduation: 95%
Average starting salary: $57,000

Accreditation
AACSB—The International Association for Management Education

DEGREES MBA • MS

MBA—Master of Business Administration Full-time and part-time. 35 to 53 total credits required. 12 to 60 months to complete program. *Concentrations:* accounting, decision sciences, developmental economics, economics, finance, human resources, international and area business studies, international trade, management, management information systems, management science, marketing, operations management, quantitative analysis.

MS—Master of Science in Computer and Information Systems Full-time and part-time. 33 to 36 total credits required. 12 to 60 months to complete program.

MS—Master of Science in Product Development Full-time. Maximum of 24 months to complete program.

COSTS

Tuition *Part-time:* $545 per credit hour. **Required fees:** Tuition and fees vary by number of courses or credits taken. **Graduate housing:** Room and board costs vary by number of occupants, type of accommodation, and type of board plan. *Typical cost:* $5000 (including board), $3200 (room only).

FINANCIAL AID (1999–2000)

Loans, research assistantships, and work study. Aid is available to part-time students. Financial aid application deadline: 8/1. **Financial Aid Contact** Ms. Anne Watson, Director of Financial Aid, 4001 West McNichols Road, Detroit, MI 48219-0900. **Phone:** 313-993-3350.

RESOURCES AND SERVICES

Information about online services, personal computer policies, library resources, international exchange programs, internship programs, and placement services at this institution and others can be found at **www.petersons.com/mba**

International Students

18% of students enrolled are international students.

Services and Facilities Counseling/support services, ESL/language courses, housing location assistance, international student housing, international student organization, orientation, visa services. Financial aid is not available to international students.

Applying *Required:* Proof of adequate funds, proof of health/immunizations.

International Student Contact Dr. David Kent, Director for International Admissions, 4001 West McNichols Road, Detroit, MI 48219-0900. **Phone:** 313-993-1205. **Fax:** 313-993-1192.

■ **APPLICATION**

Required GMAT, application form, baccalaureate/first degree, transcripts of college work. **Recommended** Essay, letter(s) of recommendation, personal statement, resume/curriculum vitae.

Deadlines and Fees Applications for domestic students are processed on a rolling basis. *Deadlines:* 5/1 for fall (international), 9/1 for spring (international), 1/1 for summer (international). *Application fee:* $30, $50 (international).

Application Contact Dr. Bahman Mirshab, Associate Dean for Graduate Business Programs, College of Business Administration, 4001 West McNichols Road, Detroit, MI 48219-0900. **Phone:** 313-993-1202. **Fax:** 313-993-1673. **E-mail:** mba@udmercy.edu.

University of Michigan

Ann Arbor, Michigan

SCHOOL OF BUSINESS ADMINISTRATION

Graduate Business Faculty
Full-time: 129 | Part-time: 77

Student Body

Total: 1,927
Full-time: 879
Part-time: 1,048

Average Age: 28
Women: 25%

Admissions

Applications: 4,246
Enrolled: 573

Average GMAT: 675
Average GPA: 3.3

Costs (1999–2000)

Full-time tuition: $21,684 per academic year (resident), $26,684 per academic year (nonresident)

Part-time tuition: $700 per credit hour (resident), $700 per credit hour (nonresident)

After Graduation (Class of 1998–99)

Employed within 3 months of graduation: 100%

Accreditation

AACSB—The International Association for Management Education

DEGREES MBA • MBA/M Arch • MBA/MA • MBA/MEM • MBA/MHSA • MBA/MM • MBA/MPP • MBA/MS • MBA/MSW

MBA—Evening MBA Part-time. At least 60 total credits required. 36 to 120 months to complete program. *Concentrations:* accounting, Asian business studies, entrepreneurship, finance, human resources, international and area business studies, international business, international management, management information systems, marketing, operations management, organizational behavior/development, production management, public policy and administration, real estate, strategic management.

MBA—Full-time MBA Full-time. At least 60 total credits required. 24 months to complete program. *Concentrations:* accounting, Asian business studies, entrepreneurship, finance, human resources, international and area business studies, international business, international management, Japanese business studies, management information systems, marketing, operations management, production management, public policy and administration, real estate, strategic management.

MBA/M Arch—Master of Business Administration/Master of Architecture Full-time. At least 90 total credits required. 36 months to complete program.

MBA/MA—Master of Business Administration/Master of Arts in Chinese Studies Full-time. At least 70 total credits required. 36 months to complete program.

MBA/MA—Master of Business Administration/Master of Arts in Japanese Studies Full-time. At least 70 total credits required. 36 months to complete program.

MBA/MA—Master of Business Administration/Master of Arts in Japanese Studies Full-time. At least 120 total credits required. 48 months to complete program.

MBA/MA—Master of Business Administration/Master of Arts in Modern Middle Eastern and North African Studies Full-time. At least 81 total credits required. 36 months to complete program.

MBA/MA—Master of Business Administration/Master of Arts in Russian and East European Studies Full-time. At least 75 total credits required. 30 to 36 months to complete program.

MBA/MA—Master of Business Administration/Master of Arts in South and Southeast Asian Studies Full-time. At least 69 total credits required. 30 to 36 months to complete program.

MBA/MEM—Master of Business Administration/Master of Engineering in Manufacturing Full-time. At least 66 total credits required. 30 months to complete program.

MBA/MHSA—Master of Business Administration/Master of Health Services Administration Full-time. At least 90 total credits required. 36 months to complete program.

MBA/MM—Master of Business Administration/Master of Music Full-time. At least 65 total credits required. 24 months to complete program.

MBA/MPP—Master of Business Administration/Master of Public Policy Full-time. At least 84 total credits required. 36 months to complete program.

MBA/MS—Master of Business Administration/Master of Science in Construction Engineering & Management Full-time. At least 69 total credits required. 30 months to complete program.

MBA/MS—Master of Business Administration/Master of Science in Engineering Full-time. At least 69 total credits required. 24 to 30 months to complete program.

MBA/MS—Master of Business Administration/Master of Science in Industrial and Operations Engineering Full-time. At least 65 total credits required. 30 months to complete program.

MBA/MS—Master of Business Administration/Master of Science in Nursing Administration Full-time. At least 70 total credits required. 30 months to complete program.

MBA/MSW—Master of Business Administration/Master of Social Work Full-time. At least 85 total credits required. 36 months to complete program.

COSTS

Tuition, state resident: *Full-time* $21,684. *Part-time* $700 per credit hour. **Tuition, nonresident:** *Full-time* $26,684. *Part-time* $700 per credit hour. Tuition varies by class time and academic program. **Graduate housing:** Room and board costs vary by campus location, number of occupants, type of accommodation, and type of board plan. *Typical cost:* $7950 (including board).

FINANCIAL AID (1999–2000)

775 students received aid, including fellowships, loans, research assistantships, scholarships, teaching assistantships, and work study. Aid is available to part-time students. Financial aid application deadline: 3/1. **Financial Aid Contact** Mrs. Heidi Sisson, Manager, Financial Aid and Scholarships, 701 Tappan Street, Ann Arbor, MI 48109-1234. **Phone:** 734-764-5139. **Fax:** 734-763-7804. **E-mail:** umbsfinaid@umich.edu.

RESOURCES AND SERVICES

Information about online services, personal computer policies, library resources, international exchange programs, internship programs, and placement services at this institution and others can be found at **www.petersons.com/mba**

International Students

24% of students enrolled are international students.

Services and Facilities Counseling/support services, ESL/language courses, international student housing, international student organization, orientation, visa services. Financial aid is available to international students.

Applying *Required:* TOEFL with recommended score of 600 (paper), proof of adequate funds. *Recommended:* TSE, TWE.

International Student Contact Ms. Renee Peterson, Manager, International Exchange Program, 701 Tappan Street, Ann Arbor, MI 48109-1234. **Phone:** 734-936-3916. **Fax:** 734-763-7804. **E-mail:** reneep@umich.edu.

■ APPLICATION

Required GMAT, application form, baccalaureate/first degree, essay, 2 letters of recommendation, personal statement, resume/curriculum vitae, transcripts of college work. **Recommended** Interview, 2 years of work experience.

Deadlines and Fees *Deadlines:* 11/1 for fall, 11/1 for fall (international). *Application fee:* $125, $125 (international).

Application Contact Ms. Kristina Nebel, Director, Admissions, 701 Tappan Street, Ann Arbor, MI 48109-1234. **Phone:** 734-647-4929. **Fax:** 734-763-7804. **E-mail:** umbusmba@umich.edu.

University of Michigan–Dearborn

Dearborn, Michigan

SCHOOL OF MANAGEMENT

Graduate Business Faculty

Full-time: 30

Part-time: 3

Student Body

Total: 334
Full-time: 17
Part-time: 317

Average Age: 31
Women: 22%

Admissions

Applications: 127
Admitted: 84
Enrolled: 62

Average GMAT: 554
Average GPA: 3.27

Costs (1999–2000)

Full-time tuition: N/R
Part-time tuition: $259 per credit (resident), $748 per credit (nonresident)

Accreditation

AACSB—The International Association for Management Education

DEGREES MBA • MBA/MS • MS

MBA—MBA Program Full-time and part-time. 36 to 63 total credits required. 20 to 84 months to complete program. *Concentrations:* accounting, finance, human resources, international business, management, marketing.

MBA/MS—Master of Business Administration/Master of Science in Engineering Full-time and part-time. At least 66 total credits required. 24 to 84 months to complete program. *Concentrations:* accounting, finance, human resources, international business, management, marketing.

University of Michigan–Dearborn (continued)

MS—Master of Science in Accounting Full-time and part-time. At least 30 total credits required. 10 to 84 months to complete program. *Concentrations:* accounting.

MS—Master of Science in Finance Full-time and part-time. At least 30 total credits required. 10 to 84 months to complete program. *Concentrations:* finance.

COSTS

Tuition, state resident: *Part-time* $259 per credit. **Tuition, nonresident:** *Part-time* $748 per credit. Tuition varies by number of courses or credits taken. **Required fees:** *Part-time* $150 per course. Fees vary by number of courses or credits taken and academic program.

FINANCIAL AID (1999–2000)

Loans, scholarships, and work study. Aid is available to part-time students. Financial aid application deadline: 2/1. **Financial Aid Contact** Mr. John Mason, Director, Financial Aid Office, 4901 Evergreen Road, Dearborn, MI 48128-1491. **Phone:** 313-593-5300. **E-mail:** jamason@ umd.umich.edu.

RESOURCES AND SERVICES

Information about online services, personal computer policies, library resources, international exchange programs, internship programs, and placement services at this institution and others can be found at **www. petersons.com/mba**

International Students

Services and Facilities Counseling/support services, ESL/language courses, visa services. Financial aid is not available to international students. **Applying** *Required:* TOEFL with recommended score of 222 (computer) or 560 (paper), proof of adequate funds, proof of health/immunizations. **International Student Contact** Ms. Mary Howard, Graduate Programs Associate, 4901 Evergreen Road, Dearborn, MI 48128-1491. **Phone:** 313-593-5348. **Fax:** 313-593-4071. **E-mail:** mbhoward@umd.umich.edu.

■ APPLICATION

Required GMAT, application form, baccalaureate/first degree, 1 letter of recommendation, personal statement, resume/curriculum vitae, transcripts of college work, 2 years of work experience.

Deadlines and Fees Applications for domestic and international students are processed on a rolling basis. *Application fee:* $55, $55 (international).

Application Contact MBA Program Director, School of Management, 4901 Evergreen Road, Dearborn, MI 48128-1491. **Phone:** 313-593-5460. **Fax:** 313-593-4071. **E-mail:** gradbusiness@umd.umich.edu.

University of Michigan–Flint

Flint, Michigan

SCHOOL OF MANAGEMENT

Graduate Business Faculty
Full-time: 15

Part-time: 9

Student Body
Total: 230
Part-time: 230

Average Age: 29
Women: 37%

Admissions
Applications: 53
Admitted: 44
Enrolled: 37

Average GMAT: 530
Average GPA: 3.1

Costs (1999–2000)
Full-time tuition: N/R
Part-time tuition: $2126 per semester (resident), $2126 per semester (nonresident)

After Graduation (Class of 1998–99)
Employed within 3 months of graduation: 90%

Accreditation
AACSB—The International Association for Management Education

DEGREE MBA

MBA—Master of Business Administration Part-time. At least 48 total credits required. 30 to 70 months to complete program.

COSTS

Tuition, state resident: *Part-time* $2126 per semester. **Tuition, nonresident:** *Part-time* $2126 per semester. **Required fees:** *Part-time* $206 per year.

FINANCIAL AID (1999–2000)

25 students received aid, including grants, loans, scholarships, and work study. Aid is available to part-time students. Financial aid application deadline: 3/15. **Financial Aid Contact** Mr. Mark Delorey, Financial Aid Director, 277 University Pavilion, Flint, MI 48502-1950. **Phone:** 810-762-3444. **Fax:** 810-766-6757.

RESOURCES AND SERVICES

Information about online services, personal computer policies, library resources, international exchange programs, internship programs, and placement services at this institution and others can be found at **www. petersons.com/mba**

International Students

Services and Facilities Financial aid is not available to international students. **Applying** *Required:* TOEFL with recommended score of 213 (computer) or 550 (paper).

International Student Contact Ms. Janet McIntire, Coordinator of MBA Admissions and Student Services, School of Management, 364 CROB 303 East Kearlsey Street, Flint, MI 48502-1950. **Phone:** 810-762-3163. **Fax:** 810-762-3282. **E-mail:** jmcintir@flint.umich.edu.

■ APPLICATION

Required GMAT, application form, baccalaureate/first degree, 3 letters of recommendation, personal statement, resume/curriculum vitae, transcripts of college work, 3 years of work experience.

Deadlines and Fees *Deadlines:* 7/1 for fall, 11/1 for winter, 6/1 for fall (international), 10/1 for winter (international). *Application fee:* $20.

Application Contact Ms. Janet McIntire, Coordinator of MBA Admissions and Student Services, School of Management, 364 CROB 303 East Kearsley Street, Flint, MI 48502-1950. **Phone:** 810-762-3163. **Fax:** 810-762-3282. **E-mail:** jmcintir@flint.umich.edu.

See full description on page 924.

Walsh College of Accountancy and Business Administration

Troy, Michigan

GRADUATE PROGRAMS

Graduate Business Faculty
Full-time: 11

Part-time: 82

Student Body
Total: 1,750
Full-time: 61
Part-time: 1,689

Average Age: 33
Women: 49%

Admissions
Applications: 548
Admitted: 506

Enrolled: 353
Average GPA: 3

Costs (1999–2000)
Full-time tuition: $5394 per academic year
Part-time tuition: $283 per credit hour

After Graduation (Class of 1998–99)
Employed within 3 months of graduation: 85%
Average starting salary: $36,000

DEGREES MAE • MBA • MS

MAE—Master of Arts in Economics Full-time and part-time. *Distance learning option.* 12 to 36 total credits required. 12 to 60 months to complete program. *Concentrations:* economics.

MBA—The Walsh MBA Full-time and part-time. *Distance learning option.* GMAT score required. 36 to 51 total credits required. 12 to 60 months to complete program. *Concentrations:* accounting, finance, financial economics, information management, marketing, taxation.

MS—Master of Science in Finance Full-time and part-time. At least 36 total credits required. 12 to 60 months to complete program. *Concentrations:* banking, economics, finance, financial economics, financial management/planning, international finance.

MS—**Master of Science in Leadership and Innovation** Full-time and part-time. *Distance learning option.* At least 36 total credits required. 24 months to complete program. *Concentrations:* information management.

MS—**Master of Science in Management** Full-time and part-time. *Distance learning option.* At least 36 total credits required. 12 to 60 months to complete program. *Concentrations:* human resources, international management, marketing, operations management, technology management.

MS—**Master of Science in Professional Accountancy** Full-time and part-time. 36 to 51 total credits required. 12 to 60 months to complete program. *Concentrations:* accounting.

MS—**Master of Science in Taxation** Full-time and part-time. At least 35 total credits required. 12 to 60 months to complete program. *Concentrations:* taxation.

COSTS

Tuition *Full-time:* $5094. *Part-time:* $283 per credit hour. **Required fees:** *Full-time* $300.

FINANCIAL AID (1999–2000)

Grants, loans, scholarships, and work study. Aid is available to part-time students. **Financial Aid Contact** Mr. Howard Thomas, Director, Student Financial Resources, 3838 Livernois, PO Box 7006, Troy, MI 48007-7006. **Phone:** 248-689-8282 Ext. 285. **Fax:** 248-524-2520. **E-mail:** hthomas@walshcol.edu.

RESOURCES AND SERVICES

Information about online services, personal computer policies, library resources, international exchange programs, internship programs, and placement services at this institution and others can be found at **www.petersons.com/mba**

International Students

3% of students enrolled are international students.

Services and Facilities Counseling/support services, international student organization. Financial aid is available to international students.

Applying *Required:* TOEFL with recommended score of 213 (computer) or 550 (paper), proof of adequate funds.

International Student Contact Ms. Diane Zalapi, Director, Admissions and New Student Recruitment, 3838 Livernois Road, Troy, MI 48007-7006. **Phone:** 248-689-8282 Ext. 294. **Fax:** 248-689-0938. **E-mail:** admissions@walshcol.edu.

■ APPLICATION

Required Application form, baccalaureate/first degree, resume/curriculum vitae, transcripts of college work, 2 years of work experience.

Deadlines and Fees Applications for domestic and international students are processed on a rolling basis. *Application fee:* $25, $25 (international).

Application Contact Ms. Diane Zalapi, Director, Admissions and New Student Recruitment, 3838 Livernois Road, PO Box 7006, Troy, MI 48007-7006. **Phone:** 248-689-8282 Ext. 294. **Fax:** 248-689-0938. **E-mail:** dzalapi@walshcollege.edu.

See full description on page 1002.

Wayne State University

Detroit, Michigan

SCHOOL OF BUSINESS ADMINISTRATION

Graduate Business Faculty

Full-time: 56	Part-time: 38

Student Body

Total: 1,739	
Full-time: 181	Average Age: 28
Part-time: 1,558	Women: 42%

Admissions

Applications: 543	Average GMAT: 535
Admitted: 412	Average GPA: 3.2
Enrolled: 294	

Costs (1999–2000)
Full-time tuition: $4718 per academic year (resident), $9802 per academic year (nonresident)
Part-time tuition: $175 per credit (resident), $387 per credit (nonresident)

After Graduation (Class of 1998–99)
Employed within 3 months of graduation: 95%
Average starting salary: $55,223

Accreditation
AACSB—The International Association for Management Education

DEGREES MBA • MS

MBA—Master of Business Administration Full-time and part-time. At least 36 total credits required. 12 to 72 months to complete program. *Concentrations:* accounting, entrepreneurship, finance, human resources, industrial/labor relations, international business, management, management information systems, managerial economics, marketing, quality management, taxation.

MS—Master of Science in Taxation Full-time and part-time. At least 36 total credits required. 12 to 72 months to complete program. *Concentrations:* taxation.

COSTS

Tuition, state resident: *Full-time* $4718. *Part-time* $175 per credit. **Tuition, nonresident:** *Full-time* $9802. *Part-time* $387 per credit. **Tuition, international:** *Full-time* $9802. Tuition varies by number of courses or credits taken. **Graduate housing:** Room and board costs vary by number of occupants and type of accommodation. *Typical cost:* $6000 (room only).

FINANCIAL AID (1999–2000)

Research assistantships, scholarships, teaching assistantships, and work study. Aid is available to part-time students. **Financial Aid Contact** Mr. Kevin Culler, Interim Director, Office of Scholarships and Financial Aid, Newberry Joy Student Services Building, 3 West Helen, Detroit, MI 48202. **Phone:** 313-577-3378. **Fax:** 313-577-6648.

RESOURCES AND SERVICES

Information about online services, personal computer policies, library resources, international exchange programs, internship programs, and placement services at this institution and others can be found at **www.petersons.com/mba**

International Students

Services and Facilities Counseling/support services, ESL/language courses, international student housing. Financial aid is not available to international students. **Applying** *Required:* TOEFL with recommended score of 550 (paper), proof of adequate funds, proof of health/immunizations.

International Student Contact Christopher Viers, Director, International Services Office, 5460 Cass, 2nd Floor, Detroit, MI 48202. **Phone:** 313-577-3422. **Fax:** 313-577-2962. **E-mail:** af8383@wayne.edu.

■ APPLICATION

Required Application form, baccalaureate/first degree, transcripts of college work. School will accept GMAT.

Deadlines and Fees *Deadlines:* 8/1 for fall, 12/1 for winter, 4/1 for spring, 4/1 for summer, 7/1 for fall (international), 11/1 for winter (international), 3/1 for spring (international), 3/1 for summer (international). *Application fee:* $20, $30 (international).

Application Contact Ms. Linda Zaddach, Assistant Dean of Student Affairs, 5201 Cass, Room 200, Prentis Building, Detroit, MI 48202. **Phone:** 313-577-4510. **Toll-free Phone:** 800-910-EARN. **Fax:** 313-577-5299. **E-mail:** l.s.zaddach@wayne.edu.

See full description on page 1008.

Western Michigan University

Kalamazoo, Michigan

HAWORTH COLLEGE OF BUSINESS

Accreditation
AACSB—The International Association for Management Education

DEGREES MBA • MS

MBA—Professional MBA Full-time and part-time. *Distance learning option.* At least 48 total credits required. 12 to 36 months to complete program.

MBA—Master of Business Administration Full-time and part-time. *Distance learning option.* At least 48 total credits required. Minimum of 15 months to complete program. *Concentrations:* accounting, economics, finance, management, management information systems, marketing.

MS—Master of Science in Accountancy Full-time and part-time. At least 66 total credits required. Minimum of 18 months to complete program.

RESOURCES AND SERVICES

Information about online services, personal computer policies, library resources, international exchange programs, internship programs, and placement services at this institution and others can be found at **www.petersons.com/mba**

International Students

Services and Facilities Counseling/support services, ESL/language courses, housing location assistance, international student housing, orientation, visa services.

Western Michigan University (continued)

Financial aid is not available to international students.
International Student Contact Ms. Jolene Jackson, Director, International Student Services, 414 Ellsworth Hall, Kalamazoo, MI 49008. **Phone:** 616-387-5865. **Fax:** 616-387-5899. **E-mail:** jolene.jackson@wmich.edu.

■ **APPLICATION**

Application Contact Mrs. Michele M. Moe, Director, HCOB Academic Advising and Admissions, 2130 Arnold Schneider Hall, Kalamazoo, MI 49008. **Phone:** 616-387-5075. **Fax:** 616-387-5710. **E-mail:** michele.moe@wmich.edu.

MINNESOTA

Capella University

Minneapolis, Minnesota

SCHOOL OF BUSINESS

Admissions
Average GPA: 3
Costs (1999–2000)
Full-time tuition: N/R
Part-time tuition: $925 per course

DEGREES MBA • MS

MBA—Master of Business Administration *Distance learning option.* At least 52 total credits required. 12 to 60 months to complete program. *Concentrations:* electronic commerce (e-commerce), entrepreneurship, finance, international business, leadership, marketing, technology management.

MS—Master of Science in Organization and Management *Distance learning option.* At least 48 total credits required. 12 to 60 months to complete program. *Concentrations:* electronic commerce (e-commerce), entrepreneurship, finance, international business, leadership, marketing, organizational management, technology management, telecommunications management.

COSTS

Tuition *Part-time:* $925 per course. Tuition varies by academic program.

FINANCIAL AID (1999–2000)

61 students received aid, including loans. Aid is available to part-time students. **Financial Aid Contact** Ms. Bonnie Clayton, Director of Financial Aid, 330 Second Avenue South, Suite 550, Minneapolis, MN 55401. **Fax:** 612-337-5396. **E-mail:** bclayton@capella.edu.

RESOURCES AND SERVICES

Information about online services, personal computer policies, library resources, international exchange programs, internship programs, and placement services at this institution and others can be found at **www.petersons.com/mba**

International Students

Services and Facilities Financial aid is not available to international students.
Applying *Required:* TOEFL with recommended score of 213 (computer) or 550 (paper), proof of adequate funds.
International Student Contact Amanda Lenzmeier, Enrollment Services Associate, 330 Second Avenue South, Suite 550, Minneapolis, MN 55401. **Phone:** 800-987-2282 Ext. 247. **Fax:** 612-339-8022. **E-mail:** alenzmeier@capella.edu.

■ **APPLICATION**

Required Application form, baccalaureate/first degree, essay, personal statement, resume/curriculum vitae, transcripts of college work. **Recommended** Interview, work experience.
Deadlines and Fees *Deadlines:* 9/5 for fall, 12/5 for winter, 3/5 for spring, 6/5 for summer, 9/5 for fall (international), 12/5 for winter (international), 3/5 for spring (international), 6/5 for summer (international). *Application fee:* $50, $150 (international).
Application Contact Ms. Sarah Peterson, Associate Director of Enrollment Services—School of Business, 330 Second Avenue South, Suite 550, Minneapolis, MN 55401. **Phone:** 800-987-2282 Ext. 347. **Fax:** 612-339-8022. **E-mail:** speterson@capella.edu.

College of St. Catherine

St. Paul, Minnesota

PROGRAM IN ORGANIZATIONAL LEADERSHIP

Graduate Business Faculty
Full-time: 5   Part-time: 4
Student Body
Total: 105   Average Age: 37
Part-time: 105   Women: 91%
Admissions
Applications: 26   Enrolled: 25
Admitted: 26
Costs (1999–2000)
Full-time tuition: N/R
Part-time tuition: $456 per credit

DEGREE MA

MA—Master of Arts in Organizational Leadership Full-time and part-time. At least 36 total credits required. Minimum of 30 months to complete program. *Concentrations:* accounting, leadership.

COSTS

Tuition *Part-time:* $456 per credit. Tuition varies by number of courses or credits taken and academic program. **Graduate housing:** Room and board costs vary by number of occupants, type of accommodation, and type of board plan. *Typical cost:* $4700 (including board).

FINANCIAL AID (1999–2000)

23 students received aid, including grants, loans, and research assistantships. Aid is available to part-time students. Financial aid application deadline: 4/1. **Financial Aid Contact** Ms. Pamela Johnson, Director, Enrollment, Student Services and Financial Aid, Mailstop F-11, St. Paul, MN 55105. **Phone:** 651-690-6540. **E-mail:** pjohnson@stkate.edu.

RESOURCES AND SERVICES

Information about online services, personal computer policies, library resources, international exchange programs, internship programs, and placement services at this institution and others can be found at **www.petersons.com/mba**

International Students

1.0% of students enrolled are international students.
Services and Facilities Counseling/support services, ESL/language courses, international student organization, visa services. Financial aid is available to international students.
Applying *Required:* TOEFL with recommended score of 500 (paper), proof of adequate funds, proof of health/immunizations.
International Student Contact Ms. June Noronha, Associate Dean for Multi-cultural Education, 2004 Randolph Avenue #F-29, Saint Paul, MN 55105. **Phone:** 651-690-6784. **Fax:** 651-690-8824. **E-mail:** jnoronha@stkate.edu.

■ **APPLICATION**

Required Application form, baccalaureate/first degree, essay, 2 letters of recommendation, personal statement, resume/curriculum vitae, transcripts of college work, 2 years of work experience. School will accept GMAT, GRE, and MAT.
Deadlines and Fees Applications for domestic and international students are processed on a rolling basis. *Application fee:* $25, $25 (international).
Application Contact Admissions Office, 2004 Randolph Avenue, St. Paul, MN 55105-1789. **Phone:** 651-690-6505.

The College of St. Scholastica

Duluth, Minnesota

PROGRAM IN MANAGEMENT

Graduate Business Faculty
Full-time: 8   Part-time: 1
Student Body
Total: 135   Average Age: 39
Full-time: 4   Women: 56%
Part-time: 131
Admissions
Applications: 64   Enrolled: 58
Admitted: 64

Costs (1999–2000)
Full-time tuition: N/R
Part-time tuition: $536 per credit

After Graduation (Class of 1998–99)
Employed within 3 months of graduation: 99%

DEGREE MA

MA—Master of Arts in Management Full-time and part-time. At least 32 total credits required. 12 to 84 months to complete program. *Concentrations:* management, organizational behavior/development, strategic management.

COSTS

Tuition *Part-time:* $536 per credit. Tuition varies by academic program. **Graduate housing:** Room and board costs vary by number of occupants, type of accommodation, and type of board plan. *Typical cost:* $4864 (including board).

FINANCIAL AID (1999–2000)
33 students received aid, including loans. Aid is available to part-time students. **Financial Aid Contact** Mr. Jon Erickson, Student Financial Planning Counselor, 1200 Kenwood Avenue, Duluth, MN 55811. **Phone:** 218-723-6397. **Fax:** 218-723-5991.

RESOURCES AND SERVICES
Information about online services, personal computer policies, library resources, international exchange programs, internship programs, and placement services at this institution and others can be found at **www.petersons.com/mba**

International Students
2% of students enrolled are international students.

Services and Facilities Counseling/support services. Financial aid is not available to international students.
Applying *Required:* TOEFL with recommended score of 575 (paper), proof of adequate funds, proof of health/immunizations.
International Student Contact Mr. Oliver Meyer, Assistant Director of Admissions, 1200 Kenwood Avenue, Duluth, MN 55811. **Phone:** 218-723-6045. **Fax:** 218-723-6290. **E-mail:** omeyer@css.edu.

■ APPLICATION

Required Application form, baccalaureate/first degree, essay, interview, transcripts of college work, 2 years of work experience.
Deadlines and Fees Applications for domestic and international students are processed on a rolling basis. *Application fee:* $50, $50 (international).
Application Contact Mr. George Smith, Program Director, Management Department, 1200 Kenwood Avenue, Duluth, MN 55811. **Phone:** 218-723-6651. **Toll-free Phone:** 800-447-5444. **Fax:** 218-723-5991. **E-mail:** gsmith@css.edu.

Concordia University at St. Paul

St. Paul, Minnesota

PROGRAM IN ORGANIZATIONAL MANAGEMENT

DEGREE MA

MA—Master of Arts in Organizational Development

RESOURCES AND SERVICES
Information about online services, personal computer policies, library resources, international exchange programs, internship programs, and placement services at this institution and others can be found at **www.petersons.com/mba**

International Students
International Student Contact International Student Program, 275 Syndicate Street North, St. Paul, MN 55104-5494. **Phone:** 651-641-8272.

■ APPLICATION

Application Contact Graduate Studies, 275 Syndicate Street North, St. Paul, MN 55104-5494. **Phone:** 651-641-8897.

Metropolitan State University

St. Paul, Minnesota

COLLEGE OF MANAGEMENT

Graduate Business Faculty

Full-time: 15	Part-time: 36

Student Body

Total: 215	Average Age: 36
Full-time: 88	Women: 51%
Part-time: 127	

Admissions

Applications: 63	Average GMAT: 510
Admitted: 33	Average GPA: 3.15
Enrolled: 18	

Costs (1999–2000)
Full-time tuition: N/R
Part-time tuition: $145 per credit (resident), $226 per credit (nonresident)

DEGREES MBA • MMA

MBA—Master of Business Administration Full-time and part-time. At least 42 total credits required. 12 to 60 months to complete program. *Concentrations:* accounting, economics, entrepreneurship, finance, human resources, international business, management, management information systems, marketing, organizational behavior/development.

MMA—Master of Management and Administration Full-time and part-time. At least 40 total credits required. 12 to 60 months to complete program. *Concentrations:* nonprofit management, public policy and administration.

COSTS

Tuition, state resident: *Part-time* $139 per credit. **Tuition, nonresident:** *Part-time* $220 per credit. Tuition varies by local reciprocity agreements. **Required fees:** *Full-time* $405. *Part-time* $6.33 per credit. Fees vary by number of courses or credits taken.

FINANCIAL AID (1999–2000)
24 students received aid, including research assistantships and work study. Financial aid application deadline: 6/30. **Financial Aid Contact** Mr. Jim Cleaveland, Director, Financial Aid, 700 East 7th Street, St. Paul, MN 55106-5000. **Phone:** 651-772-7670. **Fax:** 651-772-3716. **E-mail:** jim-cleaveland@metrostate.edu.

RESOURCES AND SERVICES
Information about online services, personal computer policies, library resources, international exchange programs, internship programs, and placement services at this institution and others can be found at **www.petersons.com/mba**

International Students
14% of students enrolled are international students.

Services and Facilities Counseling/support services, ESL/language courses, international student organization, orientation, visa services. Financial aid is available to international students.
Applying *Required:* TOEFL with recommended score of 213 (computer) or 550 (paper), proof of adequate funds, proof of health/immunizations.
International Student Contact Dr. Saleha Suleman, International Student Coordinator/Advisor, 700 East 7th Street, St. Paul, MN 55106-5000. **Phone:** 651-772-7720. **Fax:** 651-772-7528. **E-mail:** saleha.suleman@metrostate.edu.

■ APPLICATION

Required GMAT, application form, baccalaureate/first degree, essay, 2 letters of recommendation, personal statement, resume/curriculum vitae, transcripts of college work. School will accept GRE. **Recommended** 3 years of work experience.
Deadlines and Fees Applications for domestic students are processed on a rolling basis. *Deadlines:* 7/15 for fall (international), 11/15 for spring (international), 3/15 for summer (international). *Application fee:* $20, $20 (international).
Application Contact Ms. Gloria Marcus, Admissions Advisor, 730 Hennepin Avenue #818, Minneapolis, MN 55403-1896. **Phone:** 612-373-2724. **Fax:** 612-373-2888. **E-mail:** gloria.marcus@metrostate.edu.

St. Cloud State University

St. Cloud, Minnesota

G.R. HERBERGER COLLEGE OF BUSINESS

Graduate Business Faculty

Full-time: 61	Part-time: 18

Student Body

Total: 73	Part-time: 33
Full-time: 40	Women: 33%

St. Cloud State University (continued)

Admissions
Applications: 53
Admitted: 44
Enrolled: 27

Average GMAT: 534
Average GPA: 3.26

Costs (1999–2000)
Full-time tuition: $3564 per academic year (resident), $5411 per academic year (nonresident)
Part-time tuition: N/R

After Graduation (Class of 1998–99)
Employed within 3 months of graduation: 80%
Average starting salary: $35,000

Accreditation
AACSB—The International Association for Management Education

DEGREE MBA

MBA—Master of Business Administration Full-time and part-time. At least 36 total credits required. 18 to 63 months to complete program. *Concentrations:* accounting, economics, finance, human resources, insurance, international business, management, management information systems, marketing, real estate, taxation.

COSTS
Tuition, state resident: *Full-time* $3564. **Tuition, nonresident:** *Full-time* $5411. Tuition varies by local reciprocity agreements. **Graduate housing:** Room and board costs vary by number of occupants, type of accommodation, and type of board plan. *Typical cost:* $3212 (including board).

FINANCIAL AID (1999–2000)
Loans, research assistantships, teaching assistantships, and work study. Financial aid application deadline: 3/1. **Financial Aid Contact** Frank Loncorich, Director, Financial Aid, 720 4th Avenue South, St. Cloud, MN 56301-4498. **Phone:** 320-255-2047. **Fax:** 320-654-5424. **E-mail:** finaid@stcloudstate.edu.

RESOURCES AND SERVICES
Information about online services, personal computer policies, library resources, international exchange programs, internship programs, and placement services at this institution and others can be found at www.petersons.com/mba

International Students
37% of students enrolled are international students.
Services and Facilities Counseling/support services, ESL/language courses, housing location assistance, international student organization, language tutoring, orientation. Financial aid is available to international students.
Applying *Required:* TOEFL with recommended score of 550 (paper), proof of adequate funds, proof of health/immunizations.
International Student Contact Chunsheng Zhang, Assistant Vice President for Academic Affairs/ International Studies, 720 4th Avenue South, St. Cloud, MN 56301-4498. **Phone:** 320-255-4287. **Fax:** 320-255-4223. **E-mail:** intstudy@stcloudstate.edu.

■ APPLICATION
Required GMAT, application form, baccalaureate/first degree, 3 letters of recommendation, transcripts of college work. **Recommended** Personal statement.
Deadlines and Fees Applications for domestic and international students are processed on a rolling basis. *Application fee:* $20, $20 (international).
Application Contact Ms. Kathy Meyer, Graduate Admissions Manager, 720 4th Avenue South, St. Cloud, MN 56301-4498. **Phone:** 320-255-2113. **Fax:** 320-654-5371. **E-mail:** grads@condor.stcloudstate.edu.

Saint Mary's University of Minnesota

Winona, Minnesota

GRADUATE SCHOOL

Graduate Business Faculty
Full-time: 2

Part-time: 42

Student Body
Total: 320

Average Age: 32

Admissions
Average GPA: 3

Costs (1999–2000)
Full-time tuition: N/R
Part-time tuition: $225 per credit

DEGREES MA • MA/MS

MA—Master of Arts in International Business Full-time and part-time. GMAT score required. 41 total credits required. 15 to 60 months to complete program. *Concentrations:* international and area business studies, international business, international management.

MA—Master of Arts in Management Full-time and part-time. 35 total credits required. 24 to 60 months to complete program. *Concentrations:* management.

MA—Master of Arts in Management/Health Human Services Administration Full-time and part-time. At least 48 total credits required. 28 to 60 months to complete program. *Concentrations:* health care, management, public management, public policy and administration.

MA/MS—Master of Arts in Management/Master of Science in Telecommunications Full-time and part-time. 57 total credits required. 28 to 60 months to complete program. *Concentrations:* management, technology management, telecommunications management.

COSTS
Tuition *Part-time:* $225 per credit. **Required fees:** Tuition and fees vary by campus location and academic program.

FINANCIAL AID (1999–2000)
Aid is available to part-time students. **Financial Aid Contact** Ms. Tracey Steine, Assistant Director, Financial Aid, 700 Terrace Heights, Winona, MN 55987-1399. **Phone:** 507-457-1790. **Fax:** 507-457-1633. **E-mail:** tsteine@smumn.edu.

RESOURCES AND SERVICES
Information about online services, personal computer policies, library resources, international exchange programs, internship programs, and placement services at this institution and others can be found at www.petersons.com/mba

International Students
Services and Facilities Health insurance. Financial aid is not available to international students.
Applying *Required:* TOEFL with recommended score of 550 (paper), proof of adequate funds, proof of health/immunizations.
International Student Contact John Pyle, Dean of Enrollment Management and Student Services, 2500 Park Avenue, Minneapolis, MN 55404-4403. **Phone:** 612-874-9877. **Fax:** 612-728-5121. **E-mail:** tcadmissions@smumn.edu.

■ APPLICATION
Required Application form, baccalaureate/first degree, interview, 2 letters of recommendation, personal statement, resume/curriculum vitae, transcripts of college work. **Recommended** Work experience.
Deadlines and Fees Applications for domestic and international students are processed on a rolling basis. *Application fee:* $20, $20 (international).
Application Contact Ms. Carolyn Verret, Director of Master of Arts in Management and International Business, School of Graduate Studies, 2500 Park Avenue, Minneapolis, MN 55404-4403. **Phone:** 612-728-5135. **Toll-free Phone:** 800-328-4827. **Fax:** 612-728-5121. **E-mail:** cverret@smumn.edu.

Southwest State University

Marshall, Minnesota

DEPARTMENT OF BUSINESS ADMINISTRATION

Graduate Business Faculty
Full-time: 10

Student Body
Total: 45
Part-time: 45

Women: 51%

Admissions
Applications: 20
Admitted: 15

Enrolled: 13
Average GPA: 3

Costs (1999–2000)
Full-time tuition: N/R
Part-time tuition: $135 per credit (resident), $214 per credit (nonresident)

After Graduation (Class of 1998–99)
Employed within 3 months of graduation: 95%

DEGREE MS

MS—Master of Science in Management Part-time. *Distance learning option.* 33 to 37 total credits required. 30 to 84 months to complete program. *Concentrations:* management.

COSTS

Tuition, state resident: *Part-time* $135 per credit. **Tuition, nonresident:** *Part-time* $214 per credit. **Required fees:** *Part-time* $21 per credit hour.

FINANCIAL AID (1999–2000)

Research assistantships. Aid is available to part-time students. **Financial Aid Contact** Ms. Connie Smisek, Assistant Director of Financial Aid, Financial Aid Office, 1501 State Street, Marshall, MN 56258. **Phone:** 507-537-7329. **E-mail:** smisekci@southwest.msus.edu.

RESOURCES AND SERVICES

Information about online services, personal computer policies, library resources, international exchange programs, internship programs, and placement services at this institution and others can be found at **www.petersons.com/mba**

International Students

Services and Facilities Counseling/support services, ESL/language courses, visa services.
Applying *Required:* TOEFL.
International Student Contact Richard Shearer, Admissions Office, 1501 State Street, Marshall, MN 56258-1598. **Phone:** 507-537-6286. **E-mail:** shearerr@southwest.msus.edu.

■ APPLICATION

Required GMAT, application form, baccalaureate/first degree, essay, 2 letters of recommendation, transcripts of college work, 2 years of work experience. **Recommended** Interview.
Deadlines and Fees Applications for domestic and international students are processed on a rolling basis. *Application fee:* $20.
Application Contact Stacy Ball, Graduate Program Director—Management, Admissions Office, 1501 State Street, Marshall, MN 56258-1598. **Phone:** 507-537-6286. **Fax:** 507-537-6227. **E-mail:** ball@southwest.msus.edu.

University of Minnesota, Duluth

Duluth, Minnesota

SCHOOL OF BUSINESS AND ECONOMICS

Graduate Business Faculty
Full-time: 30

Student Body
Total: 36
Full-time: 7
Part-time: 29

Average Age: 30
Women: 31%

Admissions
Applications: 24
Admitted: 15
Enrolled: 14

Average GMAT: 550
Average GPA: 3.25

Costs (1999–2000)
Full-time tuition: $7100 per academic year (resident), $7100 per academic year (nonresident)
Part-time tuition: $429 per credit (resident), $429 per credit (nonresident)

Accreditation
AACSB—The International Association for Management Education

DEGREE MBA

MBA—Evening MBA Full-time and part-time. At least 32 total credits required. 24 to 84 months to complete program.

COSTS

Tuition, state resident: *Full-time* $7000. *Part-time* $425 per credit. **Tuition, nonresident:** *Full-time* $7000. *Part-time* $425 per credit. **Required fees:** *Full-time* $100. *Part-time* $4 per credit. Tuition and fees vary by number of courses or credits taken. **Graduate housing:** Room and board costs vary by campus location, number of occupants, type of accommodation, and type of board plan. *Typical cost:* $7000 (including board).

FINANCIAL AID (1999–2000)

Financial Aid Contact Ms. Brenda Herzig, Director of Financial Aid, 21 Campus Center, Duluth, MN 55812-2496. **Phone:** 218-726-8000. **Fax:** 218-726-8532. **E-mail:** finaid@d.umn.edu.

RESOURCES AND SERVICES

Information about online services, personal computer policies, library resources, international exchange programs, internship programs, and placement services at this institution and others can be found at **www.petersons.com/mba**

International Students

11% of students enrolled are international students.
Services and Facilities Counseling/support services, ESL/language courses, international student organization.
Applying *Required:* TOEFL with recommended score of 550 (paper), TWE with recommended score of 4, proof of adequate funds, proof of health/immunizations.
International Student Contact Ms. Karin Robbins, International Student Advisor, 60 Campus Center, 10 University Drive, Duluth, MN 55812-2496. **Phone:** 218-726-8962. **Fax:** 218-726-6244. **E-mail:** krobbin1@d.umn.edu.

■ APPLICATION

Required GMAT or GRE, application form, baccalaureate/first degree, personal statement, transcripts of college work. School will accept GMAT and GRE. **Recommended** Work experience.
Deadlines and Fees *Deadlines:* 7/15 for fall, 11/1 for spring, 5/1 for summer, 7/15 for fall (international), 11/1 for spring (international), 5/1 for summer (international). *Application fee:* $50, $55 (international).
Application Contact Ms. M. J. Leone, 431 Darland Administration Building, Duluth, MN 55812-2496. **Phone:** 218-726-7523. **Toll-free Phone:** 800-232-1339. **Fax:** 218-726-6970. **E-mail:** grad@d.umn.edu.

University of Minnesota, Twin Cities Campus

Minneapolis, Minnesota

CARLSON SCHOOL OF MANAGEMENT

Graduate Business Faculty
Full-time: 117

Part-time: 40

Student Body
Total: 1,586
Full-time: 558
Part-time: 1,028

Average Age: 27
Women: 38%

Admissions
Applications: 1,635
Admitted: 828
Enrolled: 529

Average GMAT: 643
Average GPA: 3.3

Costs (1999–2000)
Full-time tuition: $12,407 per academic year (resident), $17,423 per academic year (nonresident)
Part-time tuition: $474 per credit (resident), $692 per credit (nonresident)

After Graduation (Class of 1998–99)
Employed within 3 months of graduation: 93%
Average starting salary: $69,000

Accreditation
AACSB—The International Association for Management Education

DEGREES EMBA • MA • MBA • MBT • MHA • MS

EMBA—Carlson Executive Development MBA Part-time. 8 years of work experience required. At least 48 total credits required. Minimum of 20 months to complete program. *Concentrations:* management.

MA—Master of Arts in Human Resources and Industrial Relations Full-time and part-time. At least 48 total credits required. 12 to 84 months to complete program. *Concentrations:* human resources, industrial/labor relations.

MBA—Day MBA Full-time. At least 60 total credits required. 21 months to complete program. *Concentrations:* accounting, electronic commerce (e-commerce), entrepreneurship, finance, information management, international business, marketing, operations management, strategic management.

MBA—Evening MBA Part-time. 38 to 60 total credits required. 18 to 60 months to complete program. *Concentrations:* accounting, entrepreneurship, finance,

University of Minnesota, Twin Cities Campus (continued)

information management, international business, marketing, operations management, strategic management.

MBT—Master of Business Taxation Full-time and part-time. At least 30 total credits required. 12 to 84 months to complete program. *Concentrations:* taxation.

MHA—Master of Healthcare Administration Full-time and part-time. At least 61 total credits required. 21 months to complete program. *Concentrations:* health care.

MS—Master of Science in Management of Technology Part-time. At least 35 total credits required. Minimum of 21 months to complete program.

The Carlson School of Management is strategically poised to provide an excellent M.B.A. experience at a great value. With its new building and integrated curriculum, the School is well equipped to handle the technological and cross-functional demands of today's business organization. The Twin Cities (Minneapolis-St. Paul) business community, a powerhouse of Fortune 500 companies, has direct influence on the School's strategic goals and activities. CEOs participate in the Executive Mentor program and Top Management Perspectives course. Progressive companies participate in the nation's oldest consulting project, the E-Business Practicum, the Growth Fund, and the Product Design and Development experiential options. The MIS area is ranked third in the nation by U.S. News & World Report. Marketing, operations, and finance receive special recognition from peers. Quality guru Joseph Juran awarded his foundation's assets to the Quality Leadership Center. An alumnus donated $2.5 million to the Entrepreneurship Program to support an expanded curriculum and mentorship program emphasizing high technology. Through the Financial Markets Laboratory, students select and invest more than $4 million in companies. Faculty members bring their international experiences into the classroom. Furthermore, the School has alliances with thirteen top business schools around the world. With an average salary offer of $73,666, the Carlson School is an excellent investment.

COSTS

Tuition, state resident: *Full-time* $11,607. *Part-time* $474 per credit. **Tuition, nonresident:** *Full-time* $16,623. *Part-time* $692 per credit. **Tuition, international:** *Full-time* $16,623. Tuition varies by class time, number of courses or credits taken, academic program, and local reciprocity agreements. **Required fees:** *Full-time* $800. *Part-time* $100 per semester. Tuition and fees vary by class time, number of courses or credits taken, and academic program. **Graduate housing:** Room and board costs vary by campus location, number of occupants, type of accommodation, and type of board plan. *Typical cost:* $5500 (including board).

FINANCIAL AID (1999–2000)

Fellowships, grants, loans, research assistantships, scholarships, teaching assistantships, and work study. Aid is available to part-time students. Financial aid application deadline: 3/1. **Financial Aid Contact** Ms. Sheryl Spivey, Director, Financial Aid, 210 Fraser Hall, 106 Pleasant Street, SE, Minneapolis, MN 55455-0422. **Phone:** 612-624-1665. **Fax:** 612-624-9584. **E-mail:** spive001@tc.omn.edu.

RESOURCES AND SERVICES

Information about online services, personal computer policies, library resources, international exchange programs, internship programs, and placement services at this institution and others can be found at **www.petersons.com/mba**

International Students

11% of students enrolled are international students.

Services and Facilities Counseling/support services, ESL/language courses, housing location assistance, international student housing, international student organization, orientation, visa services. Financial aid is not available to international students.

Applying *Required:* TOEFL with recommended score of 240 (computer) or 580 (paper), proof of adequate funds, proof of health/immunizations.

International Student Contact Ms. Kay Thomas, Director, International Student and Scholar Services, 20 Nicholson Hall, Minneapolis, MN 55455. **E-mail:** kthomas@maroon.tc.umn.edu.

■ APPLICATION

Required GMAT, application form, baccalaureate/first degree, essay, letter(s) of recommendation, personal statement, resume/curriculum vitae, transcripts of college work. **Recommended** Interview, work experience.

Deadlines and Fees *Deadlines:* 3/1 for fall, 2/15 for fall (international). *Application fee:* $60, $90 (international).

Application Contact Ms. Ruth Pechauer, MBA Recruiting Coordinator, 2-210 Carlson School of Management, 321 19th Avenue South, Minneapolis, MN

55455. **Phone:** 612-625-5555. **Fax:** 612-626-7785. **E-mail:** rpechauer@csom.umn.edu.

See full description on page 926.

University of St. Thomas

St. Paul, Minnesota

GRADUATE SCHOOL OF BUSINESS

Graduate Business Faculty

Full-time: 34	Part-time: 140

Student Body

Total: 2,630	Average Age: 32
Full-time: 208	Women: 46%
Part-time: 2,422	

Admissions

Applications: 1,122	Average GMAT: 517
Admitted: 935	Average GPA: 3
Enrolled: 634	

Costs (1999–2000)
Full-time tuition: N/R
Part-time tuition: $437 per credit hour

After Graduation (Class of 1998–99)
Employed within 3 months of graduation: 98%

DEGREES MBA • MBC • MIM • MS

MBA—Accounting MBA Full-time. Not for undergraduates who majored in accounting. At least 57 total credits required. 15 months to complete program. *Concentrations:* accounting.

MBA—Day MBA Full-time. At least 47 total credits required. Minimum of 24 months to complete program. *Concentrations:* accounting, contract management, finance, health care, information management, insurance, management, manufacturing management, marketing, new venture management, nonprofit management, real estate, risk management, sports/entertainment management.

MBA—Evening MBA Full-time and part-time. 2 years of work experience required. 37 to 44 total credits required. Minimum of 18 months to complete program. *Concentrations:* accounting, contract management, finance, health care, information management, insurance, management, manufacturing management, marketing, new venture management, nonprofit management, real estate, risk management, sports/entertainment management.

MBA—Executive MBA Part-time. 4 years of management experience required. At least 42 total credits required. 30 months to complete program.

MBA—MBA in Human Resource Management Full-time and part-time. 2 years of work experience required. 46 to 53 total credits required. Minimum of 24 months to complete program. *Concentrations:* human resources.

MBA—MBA in Medical Group Management Part-time. *Distance learning option.* 5 years of work experience required. At least 54 total credits required. 27 months to complete program. *Concentrations:* health care.

MBC—Master of Business Communication Full-time and part-time. 2 years of work experience required; writing assessment. At least 42 total credits required. Minimum of 36 months to complete program. *Concentrations:* public relations.

MIM—Master of International Management Full-time and part-time. 42 to 49 total credits required. Minimum of 24 months to complete program. *Concentrations:* human resources, information management, international finance, international marketing, manufacturing management.

MS—Master of Science in Real Estate Appraisal Part-time. MAI or AACI designation, or working toward completion. At least 39 total credits required. Minimum of 36 months to complete program.

COSTS

Tuition *Part-time:* $437 per credit hour. Tuition varies by academic program. **Graduate housing:** Room and board costs vary by number of occupants, type of accommodation, and type of board plan. *Typical cost:* $5700 (including board), $3400 (room only).

FINANCIAL AID (1999–2000)

355 students received aid, including grants, loans, research assistantships, and scholarships. Aid is available to part-time students. Financial aid application deadline: 5/15. **Financial Aid Contact** Mr. Wayne Vernon, Graduate Financial Aid Counselor, 2115 Summit Avenue, CHC 156, St. Paul, MN 55105. **Phone:** 651-962-6594. **Fax:** 651-962-6599. **E-mail:** wrvernon@stthomas.edu.

RESOURCES AND SERVICES

Information about online services, personal computer policies, library resources, international exchange programs, internship programs, and placement services at this institution and others can be found at **www. petersons.com/mba**

International Students

5% of students enrolled are international students.

Services and Facilities Counseling/support services, ESL/language courses, housing location assistance, international student organization, orientation, visa services, mentor program. Financial aid is available to international students.
Applying *Required:* TOEFL with recommended score of 550 (paper), proof of adequate funds, proof of health/immunizations.

International Student Contact Mrs. Eleni Hoffhines, Coordinator, International Admissions, 2115 Summit Avenue, 44C1, St. Paul, MN 55105-1096. **Phone:** 651-962-6450. **Fax:** 651-962-5199. **E-mail:** evhoffhines@stthomas.edu.

■ APPLICATION

Required Application form, baccalaureate/first degree, essay, personal statement, resume/curriculum vitae, transcripts of college work. School will accept GMAT, GRE, and MAT. **Recommended** 2 years of work experience.

Deadlines and Fees *Application fee:* $30, $30 (international).

Application Contact Ms. Martha Ballard, Director, Student and Faculty Services, 1000 LaSalle Avenue, TMH 251, Minneapolis, MN 55403-2005. **Phone:** 651-962-4220. **Toll-free Phone:** 800-328-6819. **Fax:** 651-962-4260. **E-mail:** mba@stthomas.edu.

See full description on page 954.

MISSISSIPPI

Delta State University

Cleveland, Mississippi

COLLEGE OF BUSINESS

Graduate Business Faculty
Full-time: 37   Part-time: 5

Student Body
Total: 136	
Full-time: 45	Average Age: 30
Part-time: 91	Women: 49%

Admissions
Applications: 63	Average GMAT: 500
Admitted: 62	Average GPA: 3.2
Enrolled: 56	

Costs (1999–2000)
Full-time tuition: N/R
Part-time tuition: N/R

After Graduation (Class of 1998–99)
Employed within 3 months of graduation: 90%
Average starting salary: $28,000

Accreditation
ACBSP—The American Council of Business Schools and Programs

DEGREES MBA • MCA • MPA

MBA—Executive MBA Full-time. At least 33 total credits required. 24 months to complete program. *Concentrations:* management.

MBA—Master of Business Administration Full-time and part-time. At least 36 total credits required. 12 to 72 months to complete program. *Concentrations:* finance, human resources, information management, management, marketing, sports/entertainment management.

MCA—Master of Commercial Aviation Full-time. At least 30 total credits required. 12 to 72 months to complete program. *Concentrations:* travel industry/tourism management.

MPA—Master of Professional Accountancy Full-time and part-time. At least 30 total credits required. 12 to 72 months to complete program. *Concentrations:* accounting.

COSTS

Required fees: Tuition and fees vary by class time and number of courses or credits taken. **Graduate housing:** Room and board costs vary by campus location, number of occupants, and type of accommodation. *Typical cost:* $2596 (including board).

FINANCIAL AID (1999–2000)

33 students received aid, including fellowships, loans, scholarships, and work study. Aid is available to part-time students. **Financial Aid Contact** Mrs. Ann Margaret Mullins, Director of Student Financial Assistance, Box 3154, Cleveland, MS 38733. **Phone:** 662-846-4670.

RESOURCES AND SERVICES

Information about online services, personal computer policies, library resources, international exchange programs, internship programs, and placement services at this institution and others can be found at **www. petersons.com/mba**

International Students

2% of students enrolled are international students.

Services and Facilities International student organization, orientation. Financial aid is not available to international students.
Applying *Required:* TOEFL with recommended score of 550 (paper), proof of adequate funds, proof of health/immunizations.

International Student Contact Dr. Mary Jean Lush, Director, Graduate, Nontraditional, and International Programs, College of Business, Box 3295, Cleveland, MS 38733. **Phone:** 662-846-4181. **Fax:** 662-846-4215. **E-mail:** mjlush@dsu.deltast.edu.

■ APPLICATION

Required GMAT, application form, baccalaureate/first degree, resume/curriculum vitae, transcripts of college work. School will accept GRE and MAT.

Deadlines and Fees Applications for domestic and international students are processed on a rolling basis.

Application Contact Dr. Mary Jean Lush, Director, Graduate, Nontraditional, and International Programs, Box 3295, Cleveland, MS 38733. **Phone:** 662-846-4234. **Fax:** 662-846-4215. **E-mail:** gradbus@dsu.deltast.edu.

Jackson State University

Jackson, Mississippi

SCHOOL OF BUSINESS

Graduate Business Faculty
Full-time: 21

Student Body
Total: 67	Average Age: 30
Full-time: 30	Women: 60%
Part-time: 37	

Admissions
Average GMAT: 450	Average GPA: 3

Costs (1999–2000)
Full-time tuition: $2688 per academic year (resident), $5546 per academic year (nonresident)
Part-time tuition: $150 per hour (resident), $150 per hour (nonresident)

After Graduation (Class of 1998–99)
Employed within 3 months of graduation: 84%
Average starting salary: $30,000

Accreditation
AACSB—The International Association for Management Education

DEGREES MBA • MBE • MPA • MSSM

MBA—Master of Business Administration Full-time and part-time. At least 36 total credits required. 12 to 96 months to complete program.

MBE—Master of Business Education Full-time. At least 27 total credits required. 12 to 96 months to complete program.

MPA—Master of Professional Accountancy Full-time and part-time. At least 30 total credits required. 12 to 96 months to complete program. *Concentrations:* accounting.

MSSM—Master of Science in Systems Management Full-time. *Distance learning option.* At least 32 total credits required. 12 to 96 months to complete program.

Jackson State University (continued)

COSTS

Tuition, state resident: *Full-time* $2688. *Part-time* $150 per hour. **Tuition, nonresident:** *Full-time* $5546. *Part-time* $150 per hour. **Tuition, international:** *Full-time* $5546. Tuition varies by number of courses or credits taken. **Graduate housing:** Room and board costs vary by number of occupants and type of board plan. *Typical cost:* $3566 (including board).

FINANCIAL AID (1999–2000)

9 students received aid, including fellowships, research assistantships, scholarships, teaching assistantships, and work study. Financial aid application deadline: 5/1. **Financial Aid Contact** Dr. Jesse Pennington, Director of Graduate Programs, School of Business, PO Box 18660, Jackson, MS 39217. **Phone:** 601-432-6315. **Fax:** 601-432-6882.

RESOURCES AND SERVICES

Information about online services, personal computer policies, library resources, international exchange programs, internship programs, and placement services at this institution and others can be found at **www. petersons.com/mba**

International Students

12% of students enrolled are international students.

Services and Facilities Counseling/support services, ESL/language courses. Financial aid is not available to international students.
Applying *Required:* TOEFL with recommended score of 525 (paper), proof of adequate funds, proof of health/immunizations.
International Student Contact Ms. Kathy Sims, International Student Advisor, 1400 John R Lynch Street, Jackson, MS 39217. **Phone:** 601-979-3791. **Fax:** 601-979-3388.

■ APPLICATION

Required GMAT, application form, baccalaureate/first degree, 3 letters of recommendation, transcripts of college work.

Deadlines and Fees Applications for domestic and international students are processed on a rolling basis.

Application Contact Dr. Jesse Pennington, Director of Graduate Programs, School of Business, PO Box 18660, Jackson, MS 39217. **Phone:** 601-432-6315. **Toll-free Phone:** 800-848-6817. **Fax:** 601-432-6882.

Millsaps College

Jackson, Mississippi

SCHOOL OF MANAGEMENT

Graduate Business Faculty
Full-time: 21 — Part-time: 2

Student Body
Total: 107
Full-time: 34 — Average Age: 27
Part-time: 73 — Women: 36%

Admissions
Applications: 64
Admitted: 42 — Average GMAT: 560
Enrolled: 30 — Average GPA: 3.15

Costs (1999–2000)
Full-time tuition: N/R
Part-time tuition: $570 per semester hour

After Graduation (Class of 1998–99)
Employed within 3 months of graduation: 70%
Average starting salary: $42,000

Accreditation
AACSB—The International Association for Management Education

DEGREES M Acc • MBA

M Acc—Master of Accountancy Full-time and part-time. 30 to 48 total credits required. 12 to 72 months to complete program. *Concentrations:* accounting.

MBA—Master of Business Administration Full-time and part-time. 30 to 48 total credits required. 12 to 72 months to complete program. *Concentrations:* accounting, decision sciences, finance, health care, management, marketing.

COSTS

Tuition *Part-time:* $560 per semester hour. **Required fees:** *Part-time* $10 per semester hour. Tuition and fees vary by number of courses or credits taken.

FINANCIAL AID (1999–2000)

81 students received aid, including loans, research assistantships, and scholarships. Aid is available to part-time students. Financial aid application deadline: 7/15. **Financial Aid Contact** Anne L. McDonald, Director of Graduate Business Admissions, 1701 North State Street, Jackson, MS 39210-0001. **Phone:** 601-974-1253. **Fax:** 601-974-1260. **E-mail:** mbamacc@millsaps.edu.

RESOURCES AND SERVICES

Information about online services, personal computer policies, library resources, international exchange programs, internship programs, and placement services at this institution and others can be found at **www. petersons.com/mba**

International Students

6% of students enrolled are international students.

Services and Facilities Counseling/support services, orientation, visa services, advising, outplacement. Financial aid is available to international students.
Applying *Required:* TOEFL with recommended score of 550 (paper), proof of adequate funds.
International Student Contact Anne L. McDonald, Director of Graduate Business Admissions, 1701 North State Street, Jackson, MS 39210. **Phone:** 601-974-1253. **Fax:** 601-974-1260. **E-mail:** mbamacc@millsaps.edu.

■ APPLICATION

Required GMAT, application form, baccalaureate/first degree, essay, 2 letters of recommendation, personal statement, transcripts of college work. **Recommended** Interview, resume/curriculum vitae, 3 years of work experience.

Deadlines and Fees *Deadlines:* 7/1 for fall, 11/15 for spring, 4/15 for summer, 5/30 for fall (international), 10/1 for spring (international), 3/1 for summer (international). *Application fee:* $25, $25 (international).

Application Contact Anne L. McDonald, Director of Graduate Business Admissions, 1701 North State Street, Jackson, MS 39210-0001. **Phone:** 601-974-1253. **Toll-free Phone:** 800-352-1050 Ext. 1253. **Fax:** 601-974-1260. **E-mail:** mbamacc@millsaps.edu.

See full description on page 728.

Mississippi College

Clinton, Mississippi

SCHOOL OF BUSINESS ADMINISTRATION

Graduate Business Faculty
Full-time: 19 — Part-time: 6

Student Body
Total: 196 — Part-time: 171
Full-time: 25 — Average Age: 35

Admissions
Applications: 96 — Average GMAT: 451
Admitted: 88 — Average GPA: 3.28
Enrolled: 80

Costs (1999–2000)
Full-time tuition: N/R
Part-time tuition: $290 per hour

After Graduation (Class of 1998–99)
Employed within 3 months of graduation: 98%

Accreditation
ACBSP—The American Council of Business Schools and Programs

DEGREES JD/MBA • MBA

JD/MBA—JD/MBA program Full-time. At least 103 total credits required. Minimum of 42 months to complete program. *Concentrations:* accounting, commerce.

MBA—Master of Business Administration Full-time and part-time. At least 30 total credits required. 12 to 60 months to complete program. *Concentrations:* accounting, taxation.

COSTS

Tuition *Part-time:* $290 per hour. **Required fees:** *Part-time* $179 per semester.

FINANCIAL AID (1999–2000)

Research assistantships, scholarships, and work study. Aid is available to part-time students. Financial aid application deadline: 2/1. **Financial Aid Contact** Ms. Mary Givhan, Director of Financial Aid, Box 4066, Clinton,

MS 39058. **Phone:** 601-925-3319. **Fax:** 601-925-3950. **E-mail:** givhan@mc.edu.

RESOURCES AND SERVICES
Information about online services, personal computer policies, library resources, international exchange programs, internship programs, and placement services at this institution and others can be found at **www.petersons.com/mba**

International Students
2% of students enrolled are international students.

Services and Facilities Counseling/support services, ESL/language courses. Financial aid is not available to international students.
Applying *Required:* TOEFL with recommended score of 550 (paper), proof of health/immunizations. *Recommended:* Proof of adequate funds.
International Student Contact Dr. Debbie Norris, Dean of Graduate School, Box 4029, Clinton, MS 39058. **Phone:** 601-925-3260. **Fax:** 601-925-3889. **E-mail:** dnorris@mc.edu.

■ APPLICATION
Required GMAT, application form, baccalaureate/first degree, essay, personal statement, transcripts of college work.
Deadlines and Fees *Deadlines:* 7/31 for fall, 6/30 for fall (international). *Application fee:* $25, $75 (international).
Application Contact Dr. Gerald Lee, Director, MBA Program, Box 4014, Clinton, MS 39058. **Phone:** 601-925-3220. **Fax:** 601-925-3954. **E-mail:** glee@mc.edu.

Mississippi State University
Mississippi State, Mississippi

COLLEGE OF BUSINESS AND INDUSTRY

Graduate Business Faculty
Full-time: 58

Student Body
Total: 280
Full-time: 179
Part-time: 101

Average Age: 29
Women: 46%

Admissions
Applications: 189
Admitted: 141
Enrolled: 43

Average GMAT: 526
Average GPA: 3.29

Costs (1999–2000)
Full-time tuition: $3017 per academic year (resident), $6119 per academic year (nonresident)
Part-time tuition: $168 per credit (resident), $340 per credit (nonresident)

After Graduation (Class of 1998–99)
Employed within 3 months of graduation: 85%
Average starting salary: $35,000

Accreditation
AACSB—The International Association for Management Education

DEGREES MBA • MPA • MSBA • MSIS • MTX
MBA—Master of Business Administration Full-time and part-time. At least 30 total credits required. 12 to 72 months to complete program. *Concentrations:* public management.

MPA—Master of Professional Accountancy Full-time and part-time. At least 30 total credits required. 12 to 72 months to complete program.

MSBA—Master of Science in Business Administration Full-time and part-time. At least 30 total credits required. 12 to 72 months to complete program. *Concentrations:* economics, finance.

MSIS—Master of Science in Information Systems At least 30 total credits required. 12 to 72 months to complete program. *Concentrations:* information systems.

MTX—Master of Taxation Full-time and part-time. At least 30 total credits required. 12 to 72 months to complete program.

COSTS
Tuition, state resident: *Full-time* $3017. *Part-time* $168 per credit. **Tuition, nonresident:** *Full-time* $6119. *Part-time* $340 per credit. Tuition varies by number of courses or credits taken. **Graduate housing:** Room and board costs vary by number of occupants, type of accommodation, and type of board plan. *Typical cost:* $5735 (including board), $1800 (room only).

FINANCIAL AID (1999–2000)
110 students received aid, including fellowships, loans, research assistantships, scholarships, teaching assistantships, and work study. Aid is available to part-time students. **Financial Aid Contact** Mr. Bruce Crain, Director of Financial Aid, PO Box 6035, Mississippi State, MS 39762. **Phone:** 662-325-2450. **Fax:** 662-325-0702.

RESOURCES AND SERVICES
Information about online services, personal computer policies, library resources, international exchange programs, internship programs, and placement services at this institution and others can be found at **www.petersons.com/mba**

International Students
25% of students enrolled are international students.

Services and Facilities Counseling/support services, ESL/language courses, housing location assistance, international student housing, international student organization, orientation, visa services. Financial aid is available to international students.
Applying *Required:* TOEFL with recommended score of 233 (computer) or 575 (paper), proof of adequate funds, proof of health/immunizations.
International Student Contact Ms. Helen Zuercher, Director of International Services, Mail Stop 9742, Mississippi State, MS 39762-9742. **Phone:** 662-325-8929. **Fax:** 662-325-8583. **E-mail:** hzuercher@iso.msstate.edu.

■ APPLICATION
Required GMAT, application form, baccalaureate/first degree, 3 letters of recommendation, personal statement, transcripts of college work. School will accept GRE and MAT.
Deadlines and Fees *Deadlines:* 7/1 for fall, 11/1 for spring, 4/1 for summer, 7/1 for fall (international), 11/1 for spring (international), 4/1 for summer (international). *Application fee:* $25, $25 (international).
Application Contact Dr. Barbara Spencer, Director of Graduate Studies in Business, PO Box 5288, Mississippi State, MS 39762. **Phone:** 662-325-1891. **Fax:** 662-325-8161.

See full description on page 730.

University of Mississippi
Oxford, University, Mississippi

SCHOOL OF BUSINESS ADMINISTRATION

Graduate Business Faculty
Full-time: 58

Student Body
Total: 65
Full-time: 65

Average Age: 25

Admissions
Applications: 241
Admitted: 58
Enrolled: 26

Average GMAT: 560
Average GPA: 3.4

Costs (1999–2000)
Full-time tuition: $3052 per academic year (resident), $6154 per academic year (nonresident)
Part-time tuition: $509 per course (resident), $1026 per course (nonresident)

After Graduation (Class of 1998–99)
Employed within 3 months of graduation: 100%
Average starting salary: $45,600

Accreditation
AACSB—The International Association for Management Education

DEGREES MA • MBA

MA—Master of Arts in Economics Full-time and part-time. At least 30 total credits required. 12 to 60 months to complete program.

MBA—Master of Business Administration Full-time and part-time. At least 49 total credits required. 18 to 26 months to complete program. *Concentrations:* accounting, banking, economics, finance, financial management/planning, human resources, information management, insurance, international business, management, management information systems, managerial economics, marketing, operations management, organizational behavior/development, quantitative analysis, real estate, system management.

University of Mississippi (continued)

COSTS

Tuition, state resident: *Full-time* $3052. *Part-time* $509 per course. **Tuition, nonresident:** *Full-time* $6154. *Part-time* $1026 per course. **Tuition, international:** *Full-time* $6154. **Required fees:** Tuition and fees vary by number of courses or credits taken. **Graduate housing:** Room and board costs vary by campus location, number of occupants, and type of accommodation. *Typical cost:* $2670 (room only).

FINANCIAL AID (1999–2000)

35 students received aid, including fellowships, research assistantships, and work study. Financial aid application deadline: 4/1. **Financial Aid Contact** Mr. Larry Ridgeway, Director of Financial Aid, Old Chemistry Building, Room 25, University, MS 38677. **Phone:** 601-232-7175. **Fax:** 601-234-8155.

RESOURCES AND SERVICES

Information about online services, personal computer policies, library resources, international exchange programs, internship programs, and placement services at this institution and others can be found at **www.petersons.com/mba**

International Students

22% of students enrolled are international students.

Services and Facilities Counseling/support services, visa services. Financial aid is available to international students.

Applying *Required:* TOEFL with recommended score of 600 (paper), proof of adequate funds, proof of health/immunizations.

International Student Contact Ms. Tanta Owen, Foreign Student Advisor, Office of International Programs, Room 23, Y Building, University, MS 38677. **Phone:** 601-232-7404.

■ APPLICATION

Required Application form, baccalaureate/first degree, 2 letters of recommendation, personal statement, transcripts of college work. School will accept GMAT. **Recommended** Essay, resume/curriculum vitae, work experience.

Deadlines and Fees *Deadlines:* 4/15 for spring, 4/15 for summer. *Application fee:* $25, $25 (international).

Application Contact Dr. John Holleman, Director of MBA Administration, School of Business Administration, Office of the Dean, University, MS 38677. **Phone:** 601-232-5483. **Fax:** 601-232-5821. **E-mail:** holleman@bus.olemiss.edu.

See full description on page 928.

University of Southern Mississippi

Hattiesburg, Mississippi

COLLEGE OF BUSINESS ADMINISTRATION

Graduate Business Faculty
Full-time: 20

Student Body

Total: 88	Average Age: 28.5
Full-time: 40	Women: 28%
Part-time: 48	

Admissions

Applications: 102	Average GMAT: 524
Admitted: 68	Average GPA: 3.35
Enrolled: 44	

Costs (1999–2000)
Full-time tuition: $3868 per academic year (resident), $7220 per academic year (nonresident)
Part-time tuition: $137 per semester hour (resident), $172 per semester hour (nonresident)

After Graduation (Class of 1998–99)
Employed within 3 months of graduation: 70%
Average starting salary: $40,000

Accreditation
AACSB—The International Association for Management Education

DEGREES MBA • MPA

MBA—Professional MBA Full-time and part-time. $25 application fee required for out-of-state applicants. At least 36 total credits required. 24 to 72 months to complete program. *Concentrations:* finance, financial management/planning, management information systems, marketing.

MBA—Master of Business Administration Full-time and part-time. $25 application fee required for out-of-state applicants. At least 36 total credits required. 12 to 72 months to complete program. *Concentrations:* accounting, finance, international business, management, management information systems, marketing.

MPA—Master of Professional Accountancy Full-time and part-time. $25 application fee required for out-of-state applicants. At least 30 total credits required. 12 to 72 months to complete program. *Concentrations:* accounting.

COSTS

Tuition, state resident: *Full-time* $3868. *Part-time* $137 per semester hour. **Tuition, nonresident:** *Full-time* $7220. *Part-time* $172 per semester hour. Tuition varies by number of courses or credits taken. **Graduate housing:** Room and board costs vary by campus location, number of occupants, type of accommodation, and type of board plan. *Typical cost:* $4128 (including board), $2571 (room only).

FINANCIAL AID (1999–2000)

30 students received aid, including loans, research assistantships, scholarships, and work study. Aid is available to part-time students. Financial aid application deadline: 3/15. **Financial Aid Contact** Jim Gibson, Director of Financial Aid, Box 5101, Hattiesburg, MS 39406-5101. **Phone:** 601-266-4774. **E-mail:** james.b.gibson@usm.edu.

RESOURCES AND SERVICES

Information about online services, personal computer policies, library resources, international exchange programs, internship programs, and placement services at this institution and others can be found at **www.petersons.com/mba**

International Students

15% of students enrolled are international students.

Services and Facilities Counseling/support services, ESL/language courses, international student organization, orientation. Financial aid is available to international students.

Applying *Required:* TOEFL with recommended score of 250 (computer) or 525 (paper), proof of adequate funds, proof of health/immunizations.

International Student Contact Ms. Barbara Whitt, Director, International Student Affairs, Box 5151, Hattiesburg, MS 39406-5151. **Phone:** 601-266-4841. **Fax:** 601-266-5839. **E-mail:** barbara.whitt@usm.edu.

■ APPLICATION

Required GMAT, application form, baccalaureate/first degree, essay, 3 letters of recommendation, personal statement, transcripts of college work. **Recommended** Resume/curriculum vitae, work experience.

Deadlines and Fees *Deadlines:* 7/15 for fall, 11/15 for spring, 4/15 for summer, 7/1 for fall (international), 11/1 for spring (international), 4/1 for summer (international).

Application Contact Ms. Sue A. Fayard, Manager, Graduate Business Programs, Box 5096, Hattiesburg, MS 39406-5096. **Phone:** 601-266-4653. **Fax:** 601-266-4639. **E-mail:** fayard@cba.usm.edu.

MISSOURI

Avila College

Kansas City, Missouri

DEPARTMENT OF BUSINESS AND ECONOMICS

Graduate Business Faculty
Full-time: 8   Part-time: 10

Student Body
Total: 113
Full-time: 17   Average Age: 32
Part-time: 96   Women: 59%

Admissions
Applications: 64   Average GMAT: 495
Admitted: 42   Average GPA: 3.3
Enrolled: 42

Costs (1999–2000)
Full-time tuition: N/R
Part-time tuition: $313 per credit hour

DEGREE MBA

MBA—Master of Business Administration Full-time and part-time. 30 to 48 total credits required. 12 to 84 months to complete program. *Concentrations:* accounting, finance, health care, international business, management, management information systems, marketing.

COSTS

Tuition *Part-time:* $310 per credit hour. Tuition varies by number of courses or credits taken. **Required fees:** *Part-time* $3 per credit hour. Fees vary by class time. **Graduate housing:** Room and board costs vary by number of occupants, type of accommodation, and type of board plan. *Typical cost:* $4800 (including board).

FINANCIAL AID (1999–2000)

Loans. Aid is available to part-time students. Financial aid application deadline: 7/31. **Financial Aid Contact** Christal Williams, Financial Aid Specialist, 11901 Wornall Road, Kansas City, MO 54145-1698. **Phone:** 816-942-8400 Ext. 2347. **E-mail:** borderscd@mail.avila.edu.

RESOURCES AND SERVICES

Information about online services, personal computer policies, library resources, international exchange programs, internship programs, and placement services at this institution and others can be found at **www. petersons.com/mba**

International Students

9% of students enrolled are international students.

Services and Facilities Counseling/support services, ESL/language courses, international student organization. Financial aid is not available to international students.
Applying *Required:* TOEFL with recommended score of 550 (paper), proof of adequate funds.
International Student Contact Bruce Inwards, ILCP Coordinator and ESL Lecturer, 11901 Wornall Road, Kansas City, MO 64145-1698. **Phone:** 816-942-8400 Ext. 2372.

■ APPLICATION

Required GMAT, application form, baccalaureate/first degree, interview, personal statement, transcripts of college work.
Deadlines and Fees Applications for domestic and international students are processed on a rolling basis. *Application fee:* $20, $20 (international).
Application Contact Don Miller, MBA Recruiter, 11901 Wornall Road, Kansas City, MO 64145-1698. **Phone:** 816-942-8400 Ext. 2321. **Fax:** 816-942-3362. **E-mail:** millerdl@mail.avila.ed.

Central Missouri State University

Warrensburg, Missouri

HARMON COLLEGE OF BUSINESS ADMINISTRATION

Graduate Business Faculty

Full-time: 65   Part-time: 3

Student Body
Total: 110

Admissions
Average GMAT: 500   Average GPA: 3

Costs (1999–2000)
Full-time tuition: N/R
Part-time tuition: $164 per credit hour (resident), $328 per credit hour (nonresident)

After Graduation (Class of 1998–99)
Employed within 3 months of graduation: 85%
Average starting salary: $39,500

Accreditation
AACSB—The International Association for Management Education

DEGREES MA • MBA • MS

MA—Master of Arts in Economics Full-time and part-time. 32 to 45 total credits required. Minimum of 18 months to complete program. *Concentrations:* economics.
MBA—Master of Business Administration Full-time and part-time. 33 to 45 total credits required. Minimum of 18 months to complete program. *Concentrations:* accounting, finance, information management, management, marketing.
MS—Master of Science in Information Technology Full-time and part-time. 33 to 45 total credits required. Minimum of 18 months to complete program. *Concentrations:* information management.

COSTS

Tuition, state resident: *Part-time* $164 per credit hour. **Tuition, nonresident:** *Part-time* $328 per credit hour. Tuition varies by number of courses or credits taken. **Graduate housing:** Room and board costs vary by number of occupants, type of accommodation, and type of board plan. *Typical cost:* $2200 (including board).

FINANCIAL AID (1999–2000)

Loans, research assistantships, scholarships, teaching assistantships, and work study. Aid is available to part-time students. Financial aid application deadline: 3/1. **Financial Aid Contact** Dr. Kim Andrews, Director of Graduate Programs, College of Business and Economics, Warrensburg, MO 64093. **Phone:** 660-543-8597. **Fax:** 660-543-8350. **E-mail:** andrews@cmsu1.cmsu.edu.

RESOURCES AND SERVICES

Information about online services, personal computer policies, library resources, international exchange programs, internship programs, and placement services at this institution and others can be found at **www. petersons.com/mba**

International Students

Services and Facilities Counseling/support services, ESL/language courses, housing location assistance, international student organization, orientation. Financial aid is available to international students.
Applying *Required:* TOEFL with recommended score of 550 (paper), proof of health/immunizations.
International Student Contact Dr. Joy Stevenson, International Student Advisor, Warrensburg, MO 64093. **Phone:** 660-543-4195. **Fax:** 660-543-4201. **E-mail:** stevenson@cmsu1.cmsu.edu.

■ APPLICATION

Required Application form, baccalaureate/first degree, transcripts of college work. School will accept GMAT. **Recommended** Interview, letter(s) of recommendation, personal statement.
Deadlines and Fees Applications for domestic and international students are processed on a rolling basis.
Application Contact Dr. Kim Andrews, Director of Graduate Programs, College of Business and Economics, Warrensburg, MO 64093. **Phone:** 660-543-8597. **Toll-free Phone:** 888-219-1980. **Fax:** 660-543-8350. **E-mail:** andrews@cmsu1.cmsu.edu.

Columbia College

Columbia, Missouri

PROGRAM IN BUSINESS ADMINISTRATION

Graduate Business Faculty
Full-time: 7   Part-time: 7

Columbia College (continued)

Student Body
Total: 62
Full-time: 24
Part-time: 38

Average Age: 33
Women: 56%

Admissions
Applications: 14
Admitted: 14

Enrolled: 14

Costs (1999–2000)
Full-time tuition: $5400 per academic year
Part-time tuition: $180 per credit hour

DEGREE MBA

MBA—Program in Business Administration Full-time and part-time. Baccalaureate earned in Business Administration or completion of core undergraduate courses. At least 36 total credits required. Minimum of 15 months to complete program. *Concentrations:* management.

COSTS
Tuition *Full-time:* $5400. *Part-time:* $180 per credit hour. **Graduate housing:** Room and board costs vary by number of occupants and type of board plan. *Typical cost:* $4399 (including board), $2767 (room only).

FINANCIAL AID (1999–2000)
16 students received aid, including loans. Aid is available to part-time students. Financial aid application deadline: 3/15. **Financial Aid Contact** Ms. Sharon Abernathy, Director, Financial Aid, 1001 Rogers Street, Columbia, MO 65216. **Phone:** 573-875-7360. **Fax:** 573-875-7209. **E-mail:** saabernathy@email.ccis.edu.

RESOURCES AND SERVICES
Information about online services, personal computer policies, library resources, international exchange programs, internship programs, and placement services at this institution and others can be found at **www.petersons.com/mba**

International Students
10% of students enrolled are international students.
Services and Facilities ESL/language courses. Financial aid is not available to international students.
Applying *Required:* TOEFL with recommended score of 550 (paper), proof of adequate funds.
International Student Contact Ms. Britta Wright, International Programs Coordinator, 1001 Rogers Street, Columbia, MO 65216. **Phone:** 573-875-7686. **Fax:** 573-875-7209. **E-mail:** blwright@email.ccis.edu.

■ APPLICATION
Required Application form, baccalaureate/first degree, essay, 3 letters of recommendation, personal statement, transcripts of college work. **Recommended** Work experience.
Deadlines and Fees Applications for domestic and international students are processed on a rolling basis. *Application fee:* $25, $50 (international).
Application Contact Ms. Regina Morin, Director of Admissions, 1001 Rogers Street, Columbia, MO 65216. **Phone:** 573-875-7354. **Toll-free Phone:** 800-231-2391 Ext. 7352. **Fax:** 573-875-7209. **E-mail:** rmmorin@email.ccis.edu.

Drury University

Springfield, Missouri

BREECH SCHOOL OF BUSINESS ADMINISTRATION

Graduate Business Faculty
Full-time: 10

Student Body
Total: 53
Full-time: 5
Part-time: 48

Average Age: 30
Women: 51%

Admissions
Applications: 70
Admitted: 32
Enrolled: 24

Average GMAT: 530
Average GPA: 3.4

Costs (1999–2000)
Full-time tuition: $8420 per academic year
Part-time tuition: $270 per credit hour

After Graduation (Class of 1998–99)
Employed within 3 months of graduation: 100%

Accreditation
ACBSP—The American Council of Business Schools and Programs

DEGREE MBA

MBA—Master of Business Administration Full-time and part-time. At least 55 total credits required. 12 to 84 months to complete program.

COSTS
Tuition *Full-time:* $8370. *Part-time:* $270 per credit hour. **Required fees:** *Full-time* $50. *Part-time* $50 per degree program. **Graduate housing:** Room and board costs vary by number of occupants, type of accommodation, and type of board plan. *Typical cost:* $4100 (including board).

FINANCIAL AID (1999–2000)
6 students received aid, including research assistantships and scholarships. Aid is available to part-time students. Financial aid application deadline: 7/1. **Financial Aid Contact** Dr. Thomas Zimmerer, Director, Breech School of Business Administration, 900 North Benton Avenue, Springfield, MO 65802-3791. **Phone:** 417-873-7241. **Fax:** 417-873-7537.

RESOURCES AND SERVICES
Information about online services, personal computer policies, library resources, international exchange programs, internship programs, and placement services at this institution and others can be found at **www.petersons.com/mba**

International Students
8% of students enrolled are international students.
Services and Facilities Counseling/support services, ESL/language courses, visa services. Financial aid is not available to international students.
Applying *Required:* TOEFL with recommended score of 550 (paper), proof of adequate funds, proof of health/immunizations.
International Student Contact Ms. Cheryl Jones, Director of International Student Services, 900 North Benton Avenue, Springfield, MO 65802-3791. **Phone:** 417-873-7885. **E-mail:** cjones@drury.edu.

■ APPLICATION
Required GMAT, application form, baccalaureate/first degree, personal statement, transcripts of college work. **Recommended** Interview, letter(s) of recommendation, resume/curriculum vitae, work experience.
Deadlines and Fees *Deadlines:* 7/15 for fall, 11/15 for spring, 6/1 for summer, 6/15 for fall (international), 10/15 for spring (international), 6/1 for summer (international). *Application fee:* $25, $25 (international).
Application Contact Mr. Alan Foltz, Assistant Director, Breech School of Business Administration, 900 North Benton Avenue, Springfield, MO 65802-3791. **Phone:** 417-873-7385. **Fax:** 417-873-7537. **E-mail:** afoltz@drury.edu.

Fontbonne College

St. Louis, Missouri

DEPARTMENT OF BUSINESS ADMINISTRATION

Graduate Business Faculty
Full-time: 7

Part-time: 85

Student Body
Total: 332

Costs (1999–2000)
Full-time tuition: N/R
Part-time tuition: $360 per credit hour

DEGREES M Mgt • MBA

M Mgt—Options (accelerated adult) Part-time. 3 years work experience required. At least 36 total credits required. 18 to 19 months to complete program.

MBA—Options Accelerated MBA Part-time. 3 years work experience required. At least 43 total credits required. 24 months to complete program.

MBA—Weekend MBA Part-time. At least 30 total credits required. 12 to 72 months to complete program.

COSTS
Tuition *Part-time:* $360 per credit hour. **Required fees:** Fees vary by academic program.

FINANCIAL AID (1999–2000)

Financial Aid Contact Ms. Nicole Moore, Director of Financial Aid, 6800 Wydown Boulevard, St. Louis, MO 63130. **Phone:** 314-889-1496. **Fax:** 314-889-1451. **E-mail:** nmoore@fontbonne.edu.

RESOURCES AND SERVICES

Information about online services, personal computer policies, library resources, international exchange programs, internship programs, and placement services at this institution and others can be found at **www. petersons.com/mba**

International Students

Services and Facilities Counseling/support services, ESL/language courses, visa services. Financial aid is not available to international students.
Applying *Required:* TOEFL with recommended score of 600 (paper), proof of adequate funds.
International Student Contact Robert Miller, Coordinator of International Students, 6800 Wydown Boulevard, St. Louis, MO 63105-3098. **Phone:** 314-889-4509. **Fax:** 314-889-1451. **E-mail:** rmiller@fontbonne.edu.

■ APPLICATION

Required Application form, baccalaureate/first degree, 2 letters of recommendation, transcripts of college work.
Deadlines and Fees Applications for domestic and international students are processed on a rolling basis. *Application fee:* $20, $20 (international).
Application Contact Ms. Cindy Bluestone, Marketing Manager, Options, 6800 Wydown Boulevard, St. Louis, MO 63105-3098. **Phone:** 314-863-2220. **Fax:** 314-863-0917. **E-mail:** cbbushue@apollogrp.edu.

Lincoln University

Jefferson City, Missouri

COLLEGE OF BUSINESS AND PROFESSIONAL STUDIES

Graduate Business Faculty
Full-time: 4

Student Body
Total: 25
Average Age: 33
Women: 56%

Admissions
Applications: 27
Admitted: 27
Enrolled: 25
Average GMAT: 390
Average GPA: 3

Costs (1999–2000)
Full-time tuition: $2948 per academic year (resident), $5756 per academic year (nonresident)
Part-time tuition: $117 per credit hour (resident), $234 per credit hour (nonresident)

DEGREE MBA

MBA—Master of Business Administration in Management Full-time and part-time. At least 36 total credits required. 18 to 60 months to complete program. *Concentrations:* accounting, management.

COSTS

Tuition, state resident: *Full-time* $2808. *Part-time* $117 per credit hour. **Tuition, nonresident:** *Full-time* $5616. *Part-time* $234 per credit hour. **Required fees:** *Full-time* $140. Tuition and fees vary by number of courses or credits taken. **Graduate housing:** Room and board costs vary by number of occupants. *Typical cost:* $1835 (including board).

FINANCIAL AID (1999–2000)

Financial Aid Contact Financial Aid Office, 820 Chestnut, Jefferson City, MO 65102-0029. **Phone:** 573-681-6156.

RESOURCES AND SERVICES

Information about online services, personal computer policies, library resources, international exchange programs, internship programs, and placement services at this institution and others can be found at **www. petersons.com/mba**

International Students

24% of students enrolled are international students.

Services and Facilities Counseling/support services, ESL/language courses, international student organization, language tutoring, orientation, ymca facilities—free membership. Financial aid is not available to international students.
Applying *Required:* TOEFL with recommended score of 500 (paper), proof of adequate funds, proof of health/immunizations.

International Student Contact Mr. Edward R. Wilkerson, Director, Residential Life and Commuter Student Affairs, 820 Chestnut, Jefferson City, MO 65102. **Phone:** 573-681-5478. **Fax:** 573-681-5479.

■ APPLICATION

Required Application form, baccalaureate/first degree, 3 letters of recommendation, personal statement, transcripts of college work. School will accept GMAT.
Deadlines and Fees *Deadlines:* 7/1 for fall, 12/1 for spring, 5/1 for summer, 7/1 for fall (international), 12/1 for spring (international), 5/1 for summer (international). *Application fee:* $17, $17 (international).
Application Contact Dr. Vera Stanojevic, Dean, Graduate Studies, 820 Chestnut, Jefferson City, MO 65102-0029. **Phone:** 573-681-5074. **Fax:** 573-681-5078. **E-mail:** hanlind@lincoln.edu.

Lindenwood University

St. Charles, Missouri

DEPARTMENT OF BUSINESS ADMINISTRATION

Graduate Business Faculty
Full-time: 12
Part-time: 57

Student Body
Total: 417
Full-time: 288
Part-time: 129
Average Age: 34
Women: 52%

Admissions
Applications: 60
Admitted: 55
Enrolled: 52

Costs (1999–2000)
Full-time tuition: N/R
Part-time tuition: $260 per credit

DEGREES MA • MBA • MBA/MS • MS

MA—Master of Arts in Human Service Agency Management Full-time and part-time. At least 39 total credits required. Minimum of 12 months to complete program.

MBA—Traditional MBA Full-time and part-time. 36 to 48 total credits required. 12 to 60 months to complete program. *Concentrations:* accounting, finance, human resources, international business, management, management information systems, marketing, nonprofit management.

MBA/MS—Master of Business Administration/Master of Science in Administration Full-time and part-time. At least 42 total credits required. 12 to 60 months to complete program. *Concentrations:* management, marketing.

MS—Master of Science in Health Management Full-time and part-time. At least 48 total credits required. 12 to 60 months to complete program.

MS—Master of Science in Human Resource Management Full-time and part-time. At least 48 total credits required. 12 to 60 months to complete program.

MS—Master of Science in Management Full-time and part-time. At least 36 total credits required. 12 to 60 months to complete program. *Concentrations:* financial management/planning, international business, management, marketing, public management.

MS—Master of Science in Marketing Full-time and part-time. At least 36 total credits required. 12 to 60 months to complete program.

COSTS

Tuition *Part-time:* $260 per credit. Tuition varies by number of courses or credits taken.

FINANCIAL AID (1999–2000)

Grants, loans, scholarships, and work study. Aid is available to part-time students. **Financial Aid Contact** Mr. John Guffey, Associate Director of Graduate and Adult Professional Admissions and MBA Program, 209 South Kingshighway, St. Charles, MO 63301. **Phone:** 636-949-4933. **Fax:** 636-949-4910.

RESOURCES AND SERVICES

Information about online services, personal computer policies, library resources, international exchange programs, internship programs, and placement services at this institution and others can be found at **www. petersons.com/mba**

International Students

24% of students enrolled are international students.

Services and Facilities International student housing. Financial aid is available to international students.

Lindenwood University (continued)

Applying *Required:* TOEFL with recommended score of 550 (paper), proof of adequate funds.

International Student Contact Ms. Jeanne Murabito, Dean of Academic Services, 209 South Kingshighway, St. Charles, MO 63301. **Phone:** 636-949-4978. **Fax:** 636-949-4910. **E-mail:** murabito@lindenwood.edu.

■ APPLICATION

Required Application form, baccalaureate/first degree, 1 letter of recommendation, resume/curriculum vitae, transcripts of college work. **Recommended** Interview.

Application Contact Mr. John Guffey, Associate Director of Graduate and Adult Professional Admissions and MBA Program, 209 South Kingshighway, St. Charles, MO 63301. **Phone:** 636-949-4933. **Fax:** 636-949-4910. **E-mail:** admissions@lindenwood.edu.

Maryville University of Saint Louis

St. Louis, Missouri

THE JOHN E. SIMON SCHOOL OF BUSINESS

Graduate Business Faculty
Full-time: 14   Part-time: 3

Student Body
Total: 191   Average Age: 34
Full-time: 26   Women: 52%
Part-time: 165

Admissions
Applications: 76   Average GMAT: 488
Admitted: 66   Average GPA: 3.15
Enrolled: 53

Costs (1999–2000)
Full-time tuition: $13,000 per academic year
Part-time tuition: $386 per credit hour

After Graduation (Class of 1998–99)
Employed within 3 months of graduation: 95%

DEGREE MBA

MBA—Master of Business Administration Full-time and part-time. At least 36 total credits required. Maximum of 60 months to complete program. *Concentrations:* accounting, electronic commerce (e-commerce), health care, international business, management, management information systems, marketing.

COSTS

Tuition *Full-time:* $12,880. *Part-time:* $386 per credit hour. **Tuition, international:** *Full-time* $12,880. **Required fees:** *Full-time* $120. *Part-time* $60 per semester. Tuition and fees vary by number of courses or credits taken. **Graduate housing:** Room and board costs vary by number of occupants. *Typical cost:* $5600 (including board).

FINANCIAL AID (1999–2000)

Grants and work study. **Financial Aid Contact** Ms. Martha Harbaugh, Director of Financial Aid, 13550 Conway Road, St. Louis, MO 63141-7299. **Phone:** 314-529-9360. **Fax:** 314-542-9085. **E-mail:** fin_aid@maryville.edu.

RESOURCES AND SERVICES

Information about online services, personal computer policies, library resources, international exchange programs, internship programs, and placement services at this institution and others can be found at **www.petersons.com/mba**

International Students

8% of students enrolled are international students.

Services and Facilities Counseling/support services, ESL/language courses, housing location assistance, international student housing, international student organization, orientation, visa services, health services. Financial aid is not available to international students.

Applying *Required:* TOEFL with recommended score of 213 (computer) or 550 (paper), proof of adequate funds, proof of health/immunizations.

International Student Contact Ms. Liga Abolins, Director of International Programs and ESL, 13550 Conway Road, St. Louis, MO 63141-7299. **Phone:** 314-529-9649. **Fax:** 314-529-9384. **E-mail:** intl@maryville.edu.

■ APPLICATION

Required GMAT, application form, baccalaureate/first degree, personal statement, transcripts of college work. **Recommended** Work experience.

Deadlines and Fees Applications for domestic and international students are processed on a rolling basis. *Application fee:* $35, $35 (international).

Application Contact Ms. Kathy Dougherty, MBA Admissions and Enrollment Director, 13550 Conway Road, St. Louis, MO 63141-7299. **Phone:** 314-529-9382. **Toll-free Phone:** 800-627-9855. **Fax:** 314-529-9975. **E-mail:** business@maryville.edu.

Northwest Missouri State University

Maryville, Missouri

COLLEGE OF PROFESSIONAL AND APPLIED STUDIES

Graduate Business Faculty
Full-time: 16

Student Body
Total: 72   Average Age: 30
Full-time: 28   Women: 53%
Part-time: 44

Admissions
Applications: 24   Average GMAT: 481
Admitted: 24   Average GPA: 3.2
Enrolled: 17

Costs (1999–2000)
Full-time tuition: N/R
Part-time tuition: $108 per credit (resident), $190 per credit (nonresident)

After Graduation (Class of 1998–99)
Employed within 3 months of graduation: 95%
Average starting salary: $27,000

Accreditation
ACBSP—The American Council of Business Schools and Programs

DEGREES MBA

MBA—Master of Business Administration in Accounting Full-time and part-time. At least 33 total credits required. 12 to 96 months to complete program.

MBA—Master of Business Administration in Agricultural Economics Full-time and part-time. At least 36 total credits required. 12 to 96 months to complete program.

MBA—Master of Business Administration in Management Information Systems Full-time and part-time. At least 33 total credits required. 12 to 96 months to complete program.

MBA—Master of Business Administration Full-time and part-time. At least 33 total credits required. 12 to 96 months to complete program.

COSTS

Tuition, state resident: *Part-time* $105 per credit. **Tuition, nonresident:** *Part-time* $187 per credit. **Required fees:** *Part-time* $3 per credit. Tuition and fees vary by number of courses or credits taken. **Graduate housing:** Room and board costs vary by number of occupants and type of board plan. *Typical cost:* $3780 (including board).

FINANCIAL AID (1999–2000)

25 students received aid, including loans, research assistantships, scholarships, teaching assistantships, and work study. Financial aid application deadline: 3/1. **Financial Aid Contact** Mr. Del Morley, Director of Financial Assistance, 800 University Drive, Maryville, MO 64468. **Phone:** 660-562-1363. **Fax:** 660-562-1900. **E-mail:** 0700277@mail.nwmissouri.edu.

RESOURCES AND SERVICES

Information about online services, personal computer policies, library resources, international exchange programs, internship programs, and placement services at this institution and others can be found at **www.petersons.com/mba**

International Students

17% of students enrolled are international students.

Services and Facilities Counseling/support services, ESL/language courses, visa services. Financial aid is not available to international students.

Applying *Required:* TOEFL with recommended score of 550 (paper), proof of adequate funds.

International Student Contact Mr. Kent Porterfield, Assistant Vice-President, Student Affairs, 800 University Drive, Maryville, MO 64468. **Phone:** 660-562-1219. **Fax:** 660-562-1439. **E-mail:** 0700415@mail.nwmissouri.edu.

■ APPLICATION

Required GMAT, application form, baccalaureate/first degree, essay, personal statement, transcripts of college work.

Deadlines and Fees *Deadlines:* 7/1 for fall, 12/1 for spring, 5/1 for summer, 5/15 for fall (international), 11/1 for spring (international), 4/1 for summer (international).

Application Contact Mrs. Becky Smith, Executive Secretary-College of Professional and Applied Studies, 800 University Drive, Maryville, MO 64468. **Phone:** 660-562-1277. **Toll-free Phone:** 800-633-1175. **Fax:** 660-562-1484. **E-mail:** beckys@mail.nwmissouri.edu.

Rockhurst University

Kansas City, Missouri

SCHOOL OF MANAGEMENT

Graduate Business Faculty
Full-time: 21   Part-time: 11

Student Body
Total: 536   Average Age: 31
Full-time: 28   Women: 41%
Part-time: 508

Admissions
Applications: 200   Enrolled: 125
Admitted: 158

Costs (1999–2000)
Full-time tuition: N/R
Part-time tuition: $350 per credit hour

After Graduation (Class of 1998–99)
Employed within 3 months of graduation: 70%
Average starting salary: $30,000

DEGREES EMBA • MBA

EMBA—Executive MBA Part-time. Company or organization sponsorship and recommendations required. At least 45 total credits required. 24 months to complete program. *Concentrations:* management.

MBA—Master of Business Administration Full-time and part-time. *Distance learning option.* At least 36 total credits required. 12 to 72 months to complete program. *Concentrations:* accounting, finance, human resources, industrial/labor relations, international business, management, marketing.

COSTS

Tuition *Part-time:* $350 per credit hour. Tuition varies by academic program. **Required fees:** *Part-time* $15 per semester. **Graduate housing:** Room and board costs vary by number of occupants, type of accommodation, and type of board plan. *Typical cost:* $4950 (including board).

FINANCIAL AID (1999–2000)

61 students received aid, including loans. Aid is available to part-time students. Financial aid application deadline: 4/1. **Financial Aid Contact** Mr. Paul Gordon, Director of Financial Aid, 1100 Rockhurst Road, Kansas City, MO 64110-2561. **Phone:** 816-501-4100. **E-mail:** paul.gordon@rockhurst.edu.

RESOURCES AND SERVICES

Information about online services, personal computer policies, library resources, international exchange programs, internship programs, and placement services at this institution and others can be found at **www.petersons.com/mba**

International Students

0.9% of students enrolled are international students.

Services and Facilities Counseling/support services, visa services. Financial aid is not available to international students.

Applying *Required:* TOEFL with recommended score of 550 (paper), proof of adequate funds, proof of health/immunizations.

International Student Contact Ms. Donette Alonzo, Director of International Student Services, 1100 Rockhurst Road, Kansas City, MO 64110-2561. **Phone:** 816-501-4821. **E-mail:** donette.alonzo@rockhurst.edu.

■ APPLICATION

Required GMAT, application form, baccalaureate/first degree, transcripts of college work. **Recommended** Interview, work experience.

Deadlines and Fees Applications for domestic and international students are processed on a rolling basis.

Application Contact Mrs. Susan Black, Director of Recruitment for School of Management, 1100 Rockhurst Road, Kansas City, MO 64110-2561. **Phone:** 816-501-4654. **Fax:** 816-501-4650. **E-mail:** susan.black@rockhurst.edu.

Saint Louis University

St. Louis, Missouri

SCHOOL OF BUSINESS AND ADMINISTRATION

Graduate Business Faculty
Full-time: 55   Part-time: 20

Student Body
Total: 345   Average Age: 27
Full-time: 143   Women: 29%
Part-time: 202

Admissions
Applications: 364   Average GMAT: 601
Admitted: 149   Average GPA: 3.15
Enrolled: 61

Costs (1999–2000)
Full-time tuition: $22,038 per academic year
Part-time tuition: $630 per credit

Accreditation
AACSB—The International Association for Management Education

DEGREES EMIB • JD/MBA • M Acc • MBA • MBA/MS • MF

EMIB—Executive Master of International Business Part-time. At least 36 total credits required. 24 months to complete program.

JD/MBA—Juris Doctor/Master of Business Administration Full-time. At least 130 total credits required. 42 to 60 months to complete program.

M Acc—Master of Accountancy Full-time and part-time. 30 to 63 total credits required. 12 to 60 months to complete program.

MBA—Master of Business Administration Full-time and part-time. 39 to 57 total credits required. 12 to 60 months to complete program. *Concentrations:* accounting, economics, entrepreneurship, finance, international business, management, management information systems, marketing, supply chain management.

MBA/MS—Master of Business Administration/Master of Science in Nursing Full-time and part-time. At least 73 total credits required. 36 to 60 months to complete program.

MF—Master of Finance Full-time and part-time. 30 to 48 total credits required. 12 to 60 months to complete program.

*S*aint Louis University's (SLU) School of Business and Administration has a long and proud tradition of providing a sound academic foundation for the professional practice of business. For more than fifty years, SLU's M.B.A. program has provided students with important analytical skills and functional principles, but today's environment demands more. SLU M.B.A. students prepare for the business environment of tomorrow through an academically challenging, values-based curriculum that emphasizes adaptability to change, practical training, and personal and professional development.

The Saint Louis University M.B.A. program is designed to produce professional business and organizational leaders who can adapt to perform effectively and ethically in a fast-changing, global environment. Throughout the program, global issues are woven into the course work. Through electives, students have the opportunity to select areas of emphasis, which range from entrepreneurship to international business to a specialization in a functional area.

COSTS

Tuition *Full-time:* $22,000. *Part-time:* $630 per credit. Tuition varies by academic program. **Required fees:** *Full-time* $38. *Part-time* $19 per semester. Fees vary by number of courses or credits taken. **Graduate housing:** Room and board costs vary by campus location, number of occupants, type of accommodation, and type of board plan. *Typical cost:* $7900 (including board).

FINANCIAL AID (1999–2000)

30 students received aid, including fellowships, research assistantships, scholarships, teaching assistantships, and work study. Financial aid application deadline: 4/15. **Financial Aid Contact** Mr. Hal Deuser, Director, Financial Aid, 221 North Grand, St. Louis, MO 63103-9945. **Phone:** 314-977-2350.

Saint Louis University (continued)

RESOURCES AND SERVICES
Information about online services, personal computer policies, library resources, international exchange programs, internship programs, and placement services at this institution and others can be found at **www. petersons.com/mba**

International Students
21% of students enrolled are international students.

Services and Facilities Counseling/support services, ESL/language courses, housing location assistance, international student housing, international student organization, orientation, visa services, graduate writing center, international intramural league. Financial aid is available to international students.
Applying *Required:* TOEFL with recommended score of 213 (computer) or 550 (paper), TWE with recommended score of 4.5, proof of adequate funds, proof of health/immunizations.
International Student Contact Ms. Frances Hsieh, Foreign Student Advisor, 221 North Grand, St. Louis, MO 63103-9945. **Phone:** 314-977-2318. **Fax:** 314-977-3412. **E-mail:** intlprg@slu.edu.

■ APPLICATION
Required GMAT, application form, baccalaureate/first degree, essay, 2 letters of recommendation, personal statement, resume/curriculum vitae, transcripts of college work. **Recommended** Interview, 2 years of work experience.
Deadlines and Fees *Deadlines:* 4/15 for fall, 11/15 for winter, 11/15 for spring, 4/15 for summer, 4/15 for fall (international), 11/15 for winter (international), 11/15 for spring (international), 4/15 for summer (international). *Application fee:* $55, $55 (international).
Application Contact Mr. Casey Crane, Manager, MBA Admission, School of Business, 3674 Lindell Boulevard, St. Louis, MO 63108. **Phone:** 314-977-2013. **Fax:** 314-977-1416. **E-mail:** mba@slu.edu.

Southeast Missouri State University

Cape Girardeau, Missouri

COLLEGE OF BUSINESS

Graduate Business Faculty
Full-time: 45

Student Body

Total: 85	
Full-time: 25	Average Age: 29
Part-time: 60	Women: 47%

Admissions

Applications: 60	Average GMAT: 525
Admitted: 50	Average GPA: 3.3
Enrolled: 40	

Costs (1999–2000)
Full-time tuition: N/R
Part-time tuition: $120 per credit hour (resident), $205 per credit hour (nonresident)

After Graduation (Class of 1998–99)
Employed within 3 months of graduation: 95%

DEGREE MBA

MBA—Master of Business Administration Full-time and part-time. 33 to 63 total credits required. 12 to 72 months to complete program. *Concentrations:* accounting, management.

COSTS
Tuition, state resident: *Part-time* $120 per credit hour. **Tuition, nonresident:** *Part-time* $205 per credit hour. Tuition varies by number of courses or credits taken.
Graduate housing: Room and board costs vary by number of occupants, type of accommodation, and type of board plan. *Typical cost:* $5000 (including board).

FINANCIAL AID (1999–2000)
30 students received aid, including loans, research assistantships, scholarships, teaching assistantships, and work study. Aid is available to part-time students. **Financial Aid Contact** Mrs. Karen Walker, Director, Financial Aid Services, Financial Aid Office, Cape Girardeau, MT 63701.

Phone: 573-651-2039. **Fax:** 573-651-5155. **E-mail:** financialaid@ semovm.semo.edu.

RESOURCES AND SERVICES
Information about online services, personal computer policies, library resources, international exchange programs, internship programs, and placement services at this institution and others can be found at **www. petersons.com/mba**

International Students
24% of students enrolled are international students.

Services and Facilities Counseling/support services, ESL/language courses, housing location assistance, international student organization, orientation, visa services. Financial aid is available to international students.
Applying *Required:* TOEFL with recommended score of 213 (computer) or 550 (paper), proof of adequate funds, proof of health/immunizations.
International Student Contact Dr. Peter Gordon, Director, International Business Programs, International Business Office, One University Plaza, Cape Girardeau, MO 63701. **Phone:** 573-651-2914. **Fax:** 573-651-5032. **E-mail:** pgordon@ semovm.semo.edu.

■ APPLICATION
Required Application form, baccalaureate/first degree, transcripts of college work. School will accept GMAT.
Deadlines and Fees Applications for domestic and international students are processed on a rolling basis. *Application fee:* $20, $50 (international).
Application Contact Dr. Kenneth Heischmidt, Director, MBA Program, MBA Office, Cape Girardeau, MO 63701. **Phone:** 573-651-5116. **Fax:** 573-651-5032. **E-mail:** mba@semovm.semo.edu.

Southwest Baptist University

Bolivar, Missouri

COLLEGE OF BUSINESS AND COMPUTER SCIENCE

Accreditation
ACBSP—The American Council of Business Schools and Programs

DEGREE MS

MS—Master of Science in Administration Full-time and part-time. At least 36 total credits required. Minimum of 14 months to complete program. *Concentrations:* accounting, business studies, health care.

RESOURCES AND SERVICES
Information about online services, personal computer policies, library resources, international exchange programs, internship programs, and placement services at this institution and others can be found at **www. petersons.com/mba**

International Students
Services and Facilities Financial aid is available to international students.
International Student Contact Mrs. Rhonda Agee, Director of Graduate Programs, 1600 University Avenue, Bolivar, MO 65613-2597. **Phone:** 417-328-2000. **Fax:** 417-328-1887. **E-mail:** wsbus@sbuniv.edu.

■ APPLICATION
Application Contact Mrs. Rhonda Agee, Director of Graduate Programs, Bolivar, MO 65613-2597. **Phone:** 417-328-2000. **Fax:** 417-328-1887. **E-mail:** wsbus@ sbuniv.edu.

Southwest Missouri State University

Springfield, Missouri

COLLEGE OF BUSINESS ADMINISTRATION

Graduate Business Faculty

Full-time: 79	Part-time: 3

Student Body

Total: 257	
Full-time: 150	Average Age: 25
Part-time: 107	Women: 47%

Admissions

Applications: 200	Enrolled: 140
Admitted: 165	Average GMAT: 520

Average GPA: 3.33

Costs (1999–2000)
Full-time tuition: $3070 per academic year (resident), $5970 per academic year (nonresident)
Part-time tuition: $115 per credit (resident), $230 per credit (nonresident)

Accreditation
AACSB—The International Association for Management Education

DEGREES M Acc • MBA • MHA

M Acc—Master of Accountancy Full-time and part-time. 33 to 57 total credits required. 12 to 96 months to complete program. *Concentrations:* accounting.

MBA—Master of Business Administration Full-time and part-time. 33 to 57 total credits required. 12 to 96 months to complete program. *Concentrations:* accounting, finance, financial management/planning, information management, international business, management, management information systems, marketing, transportation and logistics.

MHA—Master of Health Administration Full-time and part-time. 42 to 60 total credits required. 24 to 96 months to complete program. *Concentrations:* health care.

Southwest Missouri State University's (SMSU) M.B.A. degree, which is accredited by AACSB-The International Association for Management Education, integrates a variety of courses offered by the five departments of the College of Business Administration. The program is designed specifically for students who hold undergraduate degrees in the arts, the sciences, engineering, and law, as well as business administration. Students with little or no undergraduate work in business normally require five semesters to complete the program. Students with appropriate prior academic preparation in business and economics and a strong work ethic may complete the program in one calendar year.

A strength of the SMSU M.B.A. program is its emphasis on the individual. The program empowers students to tailor their educational experience according to their goals. Emphasis areas are available in traditional business disciplines such as marketing, management, accounting, and finance. A techno-M.B.A. is also available. The design of the program allows students to structure a concentration that is consistent with their individual career goals and needs. The program is designed to offer an outstanding combination of resources that provides students with unequaled educational value. Students and faculty members work closely together to build a cooperative environment that promotes continuous improvement and lifelong learning. M.B.A. faculty members recognize that their major responsibilities are teaching and working with students, but they are also actively involved in their areas of professional expertise.

State-of-the-art David D. Glass Hall, home of the College of Business Administration, includes a variety of special-purpose classrooms as well as six computer laboratories.

COSTS
Tuition, state resident: *Full-time* $2700. *Part-time* $115 per credit. **Tuition, nonresident:** *Full-time* $5600. *Part-time* $230 per credit. **Required fees:** *Full-time* $370. *Part-time* $185 per semester. Tuition and fees vary by number of courses or credits taken and academic program. **Graduate housing:** Room and board costs vary by number of occupants, type of accommodation, and type of board plan. *Typical cost:* $4000 (including board).

FINANCIAL AID (1999–2000)
Loans, research assistantships, scholarships, and work study. Aid is available to part-time students. Financial aid application deadline: 3/31. **Financial Aid Contact** Mr. Todd Morriss, Director, Office of Student Financial Aid, 901 South National, Springfield, MO 65804. **Phone:** 417-836-5262. **Fax:** 417-836-4842. **E-mail:** rtm290t@mail.smsu.edu.

RESOURCES AND SERVICES
Information about online services, personal computer policies, library resources, international exchange programs, internship programs, and placement services at this institution and others can be found at **www.petersons.com/mba**

International Students
30% of students enrolled are international students.

Services and Facilities Counseling/support services, ESL/language courses, housing location assistance, international student housing, international student organization, language tutoring, orientation, visa services, international friends hosting program. Financial aid is available to international students.
Applying *Required:* TOEFL with recommended score of 213 (computer) or 550 (paper), proof of adequate funds.
International Student Contact Ms. Jan Swann, Coordinator—International Student Services, Car 302, 901 South National, Springfield, MO 65804. **Phone:** 417-

836-6618. **Fax:** 417-836-7656. **E-mail:** internationalstudentservices@mail.smsu.edu.

■ APPLICATION
Required GMAT, application form, baccalaureate/first degree, personal statement, transcripts of college work.

Deadlines and Fees Applications for domestic students are processed on a rolling basis. *Deadlines:* 4/15 for fall (international), 9/1 for spring (international), 4/1 for summer (international). *Application fee:* $25, $25 (international).

Application Contact Dr. Michael Fields, Associate Dean, 901 South National, Springfield, MO 65804-0094. **Phone:** 417-836-5646. **Fax:** 417-836-4407. **E-mail:** dmf603f@mail.smsu.edu.

Stephens College
Columbia, Missouri
DEPARTMENT OF BUSINESS ADMINISTRATION
DEGREE MBA

MBA—Master of Business Administration *Distance learning option.* At least 36 total credits required. 18 to 84 months to complete program. *Concentrations:* entrepreneurship, health care, information management, management.

RESOURCES AND SERVICES
Information about online services, personal computer policies, library resources, international exchange programs, internship programs, and placement services at this institution and others can be found at **www.petersons.com/mba**

International Students
Services and Facilities Financial aid is not available to international students. **International Student Contact** Dr. Joan Rines, Director of Graduate Programs, 1200 East Broadway, Campus Box 2083, Columbia, MO 65215. **E-mail:** grad@wc.stephens.edu.

■ APPLICATION
Application Contact Dr. Joan Rines, Director of Graduate Programs, 1200 East Broadway, Campus Box 2083, Columbia, MO 65215. **Toll-free Phone:** 800-388-7579. **Fax:** 573-876-7248. **E-mail:** grad@wc.stephens.edu.

Truman State University
Kirksville, Missouri
DIVISION OF BUSINESS AND ACCOUNTANCY

Graduate Business Faculty
Full-time: 16

Student Body
Total: 20
Full-time: 20
Average Age: 22
Women: 60%

Admissions
Applications: 28
Admitted: 24
Enrolled: 14
Average GMAT: 580
Average GPA: 3.4

Costs (1999–2000)
Full-time tuition: $4000 per academic year (resident), $7000 per academic year (nonresident)
Part-time tuition: $165 per hour (resident), $300 per hour (nonresident)

After Graduation (Class of 1998–99)
Employed within 3 months of graduation: 100%
Average starting salary: $43,000

Accreditation
AACSB—The International Association for Management Education

DEGREE M Acc

M Acc—Master of Accountancy Full-time and part-time. 30 to 42 total credits required. 12 to 24 months to complete program. *Concentrations:* accounting, taxation.

COSTS
Tuition, state resident: *Full-time* $4000. *Part-time* $165 per hour. **Tuition, nonresident:** *Full-time* $7000. *Part-time* $300 per hour. Tuition varies by number of courses or credits taken. **Graduate housing:** Room and board costs vary by

Truman State University (continued)

number of occupants and type of accommodation. *Typical cost:* $4200 (including board).

FINANCIAL AID (1999–2000)
10 students received aid, including research assistantships, teaching assistantships, and work study. Financial aid application deadline: 5/1. **Financial Aid Contact** Ms. Melinda Wood, Financial Aid Director, East Normal Street, Kirksville, MO 63501-4221. **Phone:** 660-785-4130.

RESOURCES AND SERVICES
Information about online services, personal computer policies, library resources, international exchange programs, internship programs, and placement services at this institution and others can be found at **www. petersons.com/mba**

International Students
15% of students enrolled are international students.

Services and Facilities Counseling/support services, international student housing. Financial aid is not available to international students.

Applying *Required:* TOEFL with recommended score of 560 (paper), proof of adequate funds, proof of health/immunizations.

International Student Contact Melanee Crist, International Student Advisor, East Normal Street, Kirksville, MO 63501-4221. **Phone:** 660-785-4215.

■ APPLICATION
Required GMAT, application form, baccalaureate/first degree, 3 letters of recommendation, personal statement, resume/curriculum vitae, transcripts of college work.

Deadlines and Fees *Deadlines:* 6/1 for fall, 11/1 for spring, 6/1 for fall (international), 11/1 for spring (international).

Application Contact Dr. Jeffrey Romine, Coordinator of Graduate Studies, Division of Business and Accountancy, East Normal Street, Kirksville, MO 63501-4221. **Phone:** 660-785-4378. **Fax:** 660-785-7471. **E-mail:** jromine@truman. edu.

See full description on page 856.

University of Missouri–Columbia

Columbia, Missouri

COLLEGE OF BUSINESS

Graduate Business Faculty
Full-time: 18	Part-time: 9

Student Body
Total: 155	
Full-time: 155	Average Age: 26
	Women: 34%

Admissions
Applications: 215	Average GMAT: 610
Admitted: 126	Average GPA: 3.35
Enrolled: 70	

Costs (1999–2000)
Full-time tuition: N/R
Part-time tuition: $168 per credit hour (resident), $505 per credit hour (nonresident)

After Graduation (Class of 1998–99)
Employed within 3 months of graduation: 96%
Average starting salary: $49,400

Accreditation
AACSB—The International Association for Management Education

DEGREES JD/MBA • MBA • MBA/MHA • MBA/MS

JD/MBA—Juris Doctor/Master of Business Administration Full-time and part-time. 48 to 54 months to complete program.

MBA—Master of Business Administration Full-time and part-time. 32 to 56 total credits required. 12 to 24 months to complete program. *Concentrations:* advertising, agricultural economics, economics, finance, human resources, legal administration, management, management information systems, management science, marketing, public relations, quality management.

MBA/MHA—Master of Business Administration/Master of Health Administration Full-time and part-time.

MBA/MS—Master of Business Administration/Master of Science in Industrial Engineering Full-time and part-time.

COSTS
Tuition, state resident: *Part-time* $168 per credit hour. **Tuition, nonresident:** *Part-time* $505 per credit hour. Tuition varies by number of courses or credits taken, academic program, and local reciprocity agreements. **Required fees:** *Full-time* $600. Fees vary by number of courses or credits taken, campus location, and academic program. **Graduate housing:** Room and board costs vary by campus location, number of occupants, type of accommodation, and type of board plan. *Typical cost:* $4500 (including board).

FINANCIAL AID (1999–2000)
75 students received aid, including fellowships, loans, research assistantships, scholarships, teaching assistantships, and work study. **Financial Aid Contact** Ms. Barbara Schneider, Coordinator of Recruiting and Admissions, 303 Middlebush Hall, Columbia, MO 65211. **Phone:** 573-882-2750. **Fax:** 573-882-0365. **E-mail:** grad@bpa.missouri.edu.

RESOURCES AND SERVICES
Information about online services, personal computer policies, library resources, international exchange programs, internship programs, and placement services at this institution and others can be found at **www. petersons.com/mba**

International Students
24% of students enrolled are international students.

Services and Facilities Counseling/support services, ESL/language courses, housing location assistance, international student housing, international student organization, language tutoring, orientation, visa services. Financial aid is available to international students.

Applying *Required:* TOEFL with recommended score of 550 (paper), proof of adequate funds, proof of health/immunizations.

International Student Contact Ms. Becky Brandt, Assistant Director of Admissions, 123 Jesse Hall, Columbia, MO 65211. **Phone:** 573-882-3754. **Fax:** 573-882-7887. **E-mail:** inter@missouri.edu.

■ APPLICATION
Required GMAT, application form, baccalaureate/first degree, resume/curriculum vitae, transcripts of college work. **Recommended** Work experience.

Deadlines and Fees *Deadlines:* 8/1 for fall, 12/1 for winter, 5/1 for summer, 7/1 for fall (international), 11/1 for winter (international), 4/1 for summer (international). *Application fee:* $25, $50 (international).

Application Contact Ms. Barbara Schneider, Coordinator of Recruiting and Admissions, 303 Middlebush Hall, Columbia, MO 65211. **Phone:** 573-882-2750. **Fax:** 573-882-0365. **E-mail:** grad@bpa.missouri.edu.

See full description on page 930.

University of Missouri–Kansas City

Kansas City, Missouri

SCHOOL OF BUSINESS AND PUBLIC ADMINISTRATION

Graduate Business Faculty
Full-time: 44	Part-time: 12

Student Body
Total: 725	
Full-time: 198	Average Age: 31
Part-time: 527	Women: 49%

Admissions
Applications: 462	Average GMAT: 555
Admitted: 290	Average GPA: 3.3
Enrolled: 218	

Costs (1999–2000)
Full-time tuition: N/R
Part-time tuition: $188 per credit hour (resident), $525 per credit hour (nonresident)

After Graduation (Class of 1998–99)
Employed within 3 months of graduation: 90%
Average starting salary: $48,000

Accreditation
AACSB—The International Association for Management Education

DEGREES MBA • MPA • MS

MBA—Executive MBA Part-time. At least 48 total credits required. 21 months to complete program. *Concentrations:* management.

MBA—Master of Business Administration Full-time and part-time. 30 to 60 total credits required. 12 to 84 months to complete program. *Concentrations:* entrepreneurship, finance, human resources, international business, management, management information systems, marketing, operations management, organizational behavior/development, quantitative analysis.

MPA—Master of Public Administration Full-time and part-time. At least 36 total credits required. 12 to 84 months to complete program. *Concentrations:* city/urban administration, health care, human resources, nonprofit management, organizational behavior/development.

MS—Master of Science in Accounting Full-time and part-time. 30 to 60 total credits required. 12 to 84 months to complete program. *Concentrations:* accounting.

COSTS

Tuition, state resident: *Part-time* $168 per credit hour. **Tuition, nonresident:** *Part-time* $505 per credit hour. Tuition varies by number of courses or credits taken and local reciprocity agreements. **Required fees:** *Part-time* $20 per credit hour. Tuition and fees vary by number of courses or credits taken. **Graduate housing:** Room and board costs vary by number of occupants and type of board plan. *Typical cost:* $4865 (including board).

FINANCIAL AID (1999–2000)

Fellowships, loans, research assistantships, scholarships, teaching assistantships, and work study. Aid is available to part-time students. Financial aid application deadline: 3/1. **Financial Aid Contact** Mr. Patrick McTee, Director of Financial Aid, 5100 Rockhill Road, Kansas City, MO 64110-2499. **Phone:** 816-235-1154. **Fax:** 816-235-5511.

RESOURCES AND SERVICES

Information about online services, personal computer policies, library resources, international exchange programs, internship programs, and placement services at this institution and others can be found at **www.petersons.com/mba**

International Students

16% of students enrolled are international students.

Services and Facilities Counseling/support services, ESL/language courses, international student organization, orientation, visa services. Financial aid is available to international students.

Applying *Required:* TOEFL with recommended score of 213 (computer) or 550 (paper), proof of adequate funds, proof of health/immunizations.

International Student Contact Dr. Ravi Kallur, Director of International Student Affairs Office, 5100 Rockhill Road, Kansas City, MO 64110-2499. **Phone:** 816-235-1017. **Fax:** 816-235-1717. **E-mail:** is90@umkc.edu.

■ APPLICATION

Required GMAT or GRE, application form, baccalaureate/first degree, personal statement, transcripts of college work. School will accept GMAT and GRE.

Deadlines and Fees Applications for domestic students are processed on a rolling basis. *Deadlines:* 4/1 for fall (international), 10/1 for winter (international), 4/1 for summer (international). *Application fee:* $25, $25 (international).

Application Contact Bloch School Student Services, 5100 Rockhill Road, Kansas City, MO 64110-2499. **Phone:** 816-235-2215. **Fax:** 816-235-2708.

University of Missouri–St. Louis

St. Louis, Missouri

COLLEGE OF BUSINESS ADMINISTRATION

Graduate Business Faculty
Full-time: 32   Part-time: 4

Student Body
Total: 369   Average Age: 27
Full-time: 89   Women: 40%
Part-time: 280

Admissions
Applications: 216   Average GMAT: 565
Admitted: 141   Average GPA: 3.04
Enrolled: 80

Costs (1999–2000)
Full-time tuition: $5994 per academic year (resident), $16,104 per academic year (nonresident)
Part-time tuition: $168 per credit hour (resident), $505 per credit hour (nonresident)

After Graduation (Class of 1998–99)
Employed within 3 months of graduation: 93%
Average starting salary: $41,000

Accreditation
AACSB—The International Association for Management Education

DEGREES M Acc • MBA • MS

M Acc—Master of Accounting Full-time and part-time. 30 to 69 total credits required. 18 to 72 months to complete program. *Concentrations:* accounting, taxation.

MBA—Professional MBA On-Line Part-time. *Distance learning option.* 3 years of work experience required. At least 48 total credits required. 23 months to complete program.

MBA—Master of Business Administration Full-time and part-time. 39 to 54 total credits required. 18 to 72 months to complete program. *Concentrations:* accounting, finance, human resources, management information systems, marketing, operations management.

MS—Master of Science in Management Information Systems Full-time and part-time. 30 to 48 total credits required. 18 to 72 months to complete program. *Concentrations:* economics, management information systems, telecommunications management.

The M.B.A. program at the University of Missouri (UM)-St. Louis is designed to develop a well-rounded business professional rather than a narrowly trained specialist. The underlying philosophy of all of the graduate business programs at UM-St. Louis is to combine high-quality students with an active and well-trained faculty in a rigorous course of study. The result is a challenging educational program with demanding instruction in state-of-the-art research-based management education. This means that students receive the most recent knowledge relating to whatever topics they are studying. UM-St. Louis has a truly excellent and diverse business school faculty that strikes a balance among multiple purposes. Faculty members understand and accept the importance of blending research with teaching and theory with practice. Business students have access to four computerized classrooms and two case rooms with laptop computers at each seating position. Most other classrooms have computerized workstations for the instructors, which allow for Internet connections and video and/or software-aided presentations.

Full-time students can complete the 39- to 54-hour M.B.A. program in eighteen months to two years by taking evening courses. Part-time students generally take two to five years to complete the program. The Professional M.B.A. On-Line format for the degree is a 48-hour lockstep program that students complete in twenty-three months. Students attend on-campus sessions one weekend per month; the remainder of the course interaction is conducted through the Internet.

COSTS

Tuition, state resident: *Full-time* $5034. *Part-time* $168 per credit hour. **Tuition, nonresident:** *Full-time* $15,144. *Part-time* $505 per credit hour. **Required fees:** *Full-time* $960. *Part-time* $32 per hour. Tuition and fees vary by academic program. **Graduate housing:** Room and board costs vary by number of occupants and type of accommodation. *Typical cost:* $5000 (including board).

FINANCIAL AID (1999–2000)

95 students received aid, including research assistantships. Aid is available to part-time students. Financial aid application deadline: 4/1. **Financial Aid Contact** Mr. Anthony Georges, Director, Financial Aid, 8001 Natural Bridge Road, St. Louis, MO 63121-4499. **Phone:** 314-516-5526. **Fax:** 314-516-5408. **E-mail:** financialaid@umsl.edu.

RESOURCES AND SERVICES

Information about online services, personal computer policies, library resources, international exchange programs, internship programs, and placement services at this institution and others can be found at **www.petersons.com/mba**

International Students

13% of students enrolled are international students.

Services and Facilities Counseling/support services, ESL/language courses, international student housing, international student organization, orientation, visa services. Financial aid is not available to international students.

Applying *Required:* TOEFL with recommended score of 213 (computer) or 550 (paper), proof of adequate funds, proof of health/immunizations.

International Student Contact Mr. Leonard Trudo, International Admissions Officer, Office of International Student Services, 8001 Natural Bridge Road, St. Louis, MO 63121-4499. **Phone:** 314-516-5229. **Fax:** 314-516-5636. **E-mail:** iss@umsl.edu.

■ APPLICATION

Required GMAT, application form, baccalaureate/first degree, 2 letters of recommendation, personal statement, transcripts of college work. **Recommended** Essay, interview, resume/curriculum vitae, work experience.

University of Missouri–St. Louis (continued)

Deadlines and Fees *Deadlines:* 7/1 for fall, 11/1 for winter, 5/1 for spring, 5/1 for summer, 5/1 for fall (international), 10/1 for winter (international), 3/1 for summer (international). *Application fee:* $25, $40 (international).

Application Contact Director, Graduate Programs in Business, 8001 Natural Bridge Road, St. Louis, MO 63121-4499. **Phone:** 314-516-5885. **Fax:** 314-516-6420. **E-mail:** mba@umsl.edu.

Washington University in St. Louis

St. Louis, Missouri

JOHN M. OLIN SCHOOL OF BUSINESS

Graduate Business Faculty

Full-time: 73	Part-time: 15

Student Body

Total: 664	Average Age: 29
Full-time: 298	Women: 24%
Part-time: 366	

Admissions

Applications: 1,481	Average GMAT: 624
Admitted: 456	Average GPA: 3.2
Enrolled: 230	

Costs (1999–2000)
Full-time tuition: $25,990 per academic year
Part-time tuition: $715 per credit hour

After Graduation (Class of 1998–99)
Employed within 3 months of graduation: 100%
Average starting salary: $70,000

Accreditation
AACSB—The International Association for Management Education

DEGREES MBA

MBA—Executive MBA Part-time. At least 60 total credits required. 21 months to complete program.

MBA—Executive MBA in Health Services Part-time. At least 60 total credits required. 20 months to complete program.

MBA—Executive MBA in Manufacturing, Operations, and Operations Part-time. At least 60 total credits required. 20 months to complete program.

MBA—Full-time MBA Full-time. At least 60 total credits required. 21 months to complete program. *Concentrations:* accounting, finance, international business, management, marketing, operations management, organizational behavior/development, strategic management.

MBA—Professional MBA Part-time. At least 54 total credits required. 36 to 60 months to complete program. *Concentrations:* accounting, finance, international business, management, marketing, operations management, organizational behavior/development, strategic management.

COSTS

Tuition *Full-time:* $25,870. *Part-time:* $715 per credit hour. **Required fees:** *Full-time* $120. Tuition and fees vary by class time, number of courses or credits taken, and academic program. **Graduate housing:** Room and board costs vary by type of accommodation. *Typical cost:* $14,850 (including board).

FINANCIAL AID (1999–2000)

391 students received aid, including fellowships, grants, research assistantships, scholarships, teaching assistantships, and work study. Aid is available to part-time students. Financial aid application deadline: 3/31. **Financial Aid Contact** Ms. Cynthia Gregory, Assistant Director of Financial Aid, 1 Brookings Drive, Campus Box 1133, St. Louis, MO 63130-4899. **Phone:** 314-935-7301. **Fax:** 314-935-6309. **E-mail:** mba@olin.wustl.edu.

RESOURCES AND SERVICES

Information about online services, personal computer policies, library resources, international exchange programs, internship programs, and placement services at this institution and others can be found at **www.petersons.com/mba**

International Students
17% of students enrolled are international students.

Services and Facilities Counseling/support services, ESL/language courses, housing location assistance, international student housing, international student organization, language tutoring, orientation, visa services. Financial aid is available to international students.

Applying *Required:* TOEFL with recommended score of 590 (paper), proof of adequate funds, proof of health/immunizations.

International Student Contact Ms. Kathy Steiner-Lang, Director, International Office, Campus Box 1083, One Brookings Drive, St. Louis, MO 63130-4899. **Phone:** 314-935-5910. **Fax:** 314-935-4075. **E-mail:** stix@artsci.wustl.edu.

■ APPLICATION

Required GMAT, application form, baccalaureate/first degree, essay, 2 letters of recommendation, personal statement, resume/curriculum vitae, transcripts of college work. **Recommended** Interview, work experience.

Deadlines and Fees *Deadlines:* 12/14 for fall, 1/11 for winter, 2/15 for spring, 3/29 for summer, 12/14 for fall (international), 1/11 for winter (international), 2/15 for spring (international), 3/29 for summer (international). *Application fee:* $80, $80 (international).

Application Contact Ms. Pamela Wiese, Director of MBA Admissions, 1 Brookings Drive, Campus Box 1133, St. Louis, MO 63130-4899. **Phone:** 314-935-7301. **Toll-free Phone:** 888-622-5115. **Fax:** 314-935-6309. **E-mail:** mba@olin.wustl.edu.

See full description on page 1006.

Webster University

St. Louis, Missouri

SCHOOL OF BUSINESS AND TECHNOLOGY

Graduate Business Faculty

Full-time: 14	Part-time: 96

Student Body

Total: 9,304	Part-time: 6,825
Full-time: 2,479	Average Age: 35

Admissions

Applications: 3,362	Enrolled: 2,914
Admitted: 3,104	

Costs (1999–2000)
Full-time tuition: N/R
Part-time tuition: $368 per credit hour

DEGREES MA • MA/MBA • MBA • MS

MA—Master of Arts in Business Full-time and part-time. At least 36 total credits required.

MA—Master of Arts in Health Care Management Full-time and part-time. At least 36 total credits required. *Concentrations:* health care.

MA—Master of Arts in Human Resources Management Full-time and part-time. At least 36 total credits required. *Concentrations:* human resources.

MA—Master of Arts in Public Administration Full-time and part-time. At least 36 total credits required. *Concentrations:* public policy and administration.

MA/MBA—Master of Arts in Computer Resources and Information Management/Master of Business Administration Full-time and part-time. 36 to 48 total credits required.

MA/MBA—Master of Arts in Finance/Master of Business Administration Full-time and part-time. 36 to 48 total credits required. *Concentrations:* finance.

MA/MBA—Master of Arts in Health Services Management/Master of Business Administration Full-time and part-time. 39 to 51 total credits required. *Concentrations:* health care.

MA/MBA—Master of Arts in Human Resources Development/Master of Business Administration Full-time and part-time. 36 to 48 total credits required. *Concentrations:* human resources.

MA/MBA—Master of Arts in International Business/Master of Business Administration Full-time and part-time. 36 to 48 total credits required. *Concentrations:* international business.

MA/MBA—Master of Arts in Management/Master of Business Administration Full-time and part-time. 36 to 48 total credits required. *Concentrations:* management.

MA/MBA—Master of Arts in Marketing Management/Master of Business Administration Full-time and part-time. 36 to 48 total credits required. *Concentrations:* marketing.

MA/MBA—Master of Arts in Procurement and Acquisitions/Master of Business Administration Full-time and part-time. 36 to 48 total credits required.

MA/MBA—Master of Arts in Security Management/Master of Business Administration Full-time and part-time. 36 to 51 total credits required.

MA/MBA—Master of Arts in Telecommunication/Master of Business Administration Full-time and part-time. 36 to 48 total credits required. *Concentrations:* telecommunications management.

MBA—Master of Business Administration Full-time and part-time. *Distance learning option.* 36 to 48 total credits required.

MS—Master of Science in Computer Science/Distributed Systems Full-time and part-time. At least 36 total credits required.

MS—Master of Science in Environmental Management Full-time and part-time. Minimum of 36 months to complete program. *Concentrations:* environmental economics/management.

MS—Master of Science in Space Systems Operations Management Full-time and part-time. Minimum of 36 months to complete program. *Concentrations:* management science.

COSTS

Tuition *Part-time:* $368 per credit hour. Tuition varies by campus location. **Graduate housing:** Room and board costs vary by number of occupants, type of accommodation, and type of board plan. *Typical cost:* $4190 (room only).

FINANCIAL AID (1999–2000)

Loans, research assistantships, scholarships, teaching assistantships, and work study. Aid is available to part-time students. **Financial Aid Contact** Mr. Jonathan Gruett, Director, Kirk House, 211 Edgar Road, Webster Groves, MO 63119-3194. **Phone:** 314-968-6903. **Fax:** 314-968-7125. **E-mail:** gruettjo@webster.edu.

RESOURCES AND SERVICES

Information about online services, personal computer policies, library resources, international exchange programs, internship programs, and placement services at this institution and others can be found at **www. petersons.com/mba**

International Students

7% of students enrolled are international students.

Services and Facilities ESL/language courses, orientation, visa services, international student advisor. Financial aid is available to international students. **Applying** *Required:* TOEFL, proof of adequate funds, proof of health/immunizations. *Recommended:* TSE, TWE.

International Student Contact Mr. Charlie Beech, Assistant Vice President, International Enrollment Center, 538 Garden, West, Webster Groves, MO 63119-3194. **Phone:** 314-961-2660 Ext. 7609. **Fax:** 314-968-7119. **E-mail:** beechce@webster.edu.

■ APPLICATION

Required Application form, baccalaureate/first degree, interview, transcripts of college work.

Deadlines and Fees Applications for domestic and international students are processed on a rolling basis. *Application fee:* $25, $50 (international).

Application Contact Mr. Robert Chamberlin, Director, Enrollment Services Center, 107 Sverdrup 8300 Big Bend Boulevard, Webster Groves, MO 63119-3194. **Phone:** 314-968-7462. **Toll-free Phone:** 800-981-9801. **Fax:** 314-968-7166. **E-mail:** chamberc@webster.edu.

William Woods University

Fulton, Missouri

COLLEGE OF GRADUATE AND ADULT STUDIES

DEGREE MBA

MBA—Master of Business Administration Full-time. At least 36 total credits required. 18 months to complete program. *Concentrations:* management.

RESOURCES AND SERVICES

Information about online services, personal computer policies, library resources, international exchange programs, internship programs, and placement services at this institution and others can be found at **www. petersons.com/mba**

International Students

Services and Facilities ESL/language courses, international student housing. Financial aid is not available to international students.
International Student Contact Mr. Tom Frankman, Director of Academic Affairs, 200 West 12th Street, Fulton, MO 65251. **Phone:** 573-592-1149. **Fax:** 573-592-1164.

■ APPLICATION

Application Contact Ms. Julie Howar, Recruitment Representative, 200 West 12th Street, Fulton, MO 65251. **Phone:** 800-995-3199. **Fax:** 573-592-1164.

MONTANA

Montana State University–Bozeman

Bozeman, Montana

COLLEGE OF BUSINESS

Graduate Business Faculty
Full-time: 9

Student Body
Total: 34   Women: 65%
Full-time: 34

Admissions
Applications: 23   Average GMAT: 488
Admitted: 23   Average GPA: 3.53
Enrolled: 22

Costs (1999–2000)
Full-time tuition: $4249 per academic year (resident), $9998 per academic year (nonresident)
Part-time tuition: $185 per credit (resident), $424 per credit (nonresident)

After Graduation (Class of 1998–99)
Employed within 3 months of graduation: 36%
Average starting salary: $34,213

Accreditation
AACSB—The International Association for Management Education

DEGREE MP Ac

MP Ac—Master of Professional Accountancy Full-time and part-time. At least 30 total credits required. 12 to 48 months to complete program. *Concentrations:* accounting.

COSTS

Tuition, state resident: *Full-time* $4249. *Part-time* $185 per credit. **Tuition, nonresident:** *Full-time* $9998. *Part-time* $424 per credit. Tuition varies by number of courses or credits taken and local reciprocity agreements. **Required fees:** Tuition and fees vary by number of courses or credits taken. **Graduate housing:** Room and board costs vary by number of occupants, type of accommodation, and type of board plan. *Typical cost:* $4650 (including board).

FINANCIAL AID (1999–2000)

19 students received aid, including fellowships, loans, scholarships, and teaching assistantships. Financial aid application deadline: 3/1.
Financial Aid Contact Mr. James Craig, Director of Financial Aid Services, 135 Strand Union Building, PO Box 174160, Bozeman, MT 59717-4160. **Phone:** 406-994-2845. **E-mail:** finaid@montana.edu.

RESOURCES AND SERVICES

Information about online services, personal computer policies, library resources, international exchange programs, internship programs, and placement services at this institution and others can be found at **www. petersons.com/mba**

International Students

Services and Facilities Counseling/support services, ESL/language courses, international student housing, orientation, visa services, job finding service, financial services assistance. Financial aid is not available to international students.
Applying *Required:* TOEFL with recommended score of 213 (computer) or 550 (paper), TSE with recommended score of 50, proof of adequate funds, proof of health/immunizations.

International Student Contact Dr. Norman Peterson, Director of International Programs, 400 Culbertson Hall, PO Box 170226, Bozeman, MT 59717-0226. **Phone:** 406-994-4031. **Fax:** 406-994-1619.

■ APPLICATION

Required Application form, baccalaureate/first degree, essay, 3 letters of recommendation, transcripts of college work. School will accept GMAT, GRE, and GMAT or GRE.

Deadlines and Fees *Deadlines:* 3/1 for fall, 10/1 for spring, 2/15 for summer, 3/1 for fall (international), 8/15 for spring (international), 1/1 for summer (international). *Application fee:* $50, $50 (international).

Application Contact Office of Student Services, College of Business, 338 Reid Hall, PO Box 173040, Bozeman, MT 59717-3040. **Phone:** 406-994-4681. **Fax:** 406-994-6206. **E-mail:** busgrad@montana.edu.

The University of Montana–Missoula

Missoula, Montana

SCHOOL OF BUSINESS ADMINISTRATION

Graduate Business Faculty
Full-time: 27   Part-time: 11

Student Body
Total: 157
Full-time: 93   Average Age: 30
Part-time: 64   Women: 46%

Admissions
Applications: 129   Average GMAT: 560
Admitted: 104   Average GPA: 3.27
Enrolled: 93

Costs (1999–2000)
Full-time tuition: $4151 per academic year (resident), $9694 per academic year (nonresident)
Part-time tuition: $150 per credit (resident), $370 per credit (nonresident)

After Graduation (Class of 1998–99)
Employed within 3 months of graduation: 95%
Average starting salary: $30,250

Accreditation
AACSB—The International Association for Management Education

DEGREES M Acct • MBA

M Acct—Master of Accounting Full-time and part-time. At least 30 total credits required. 12 to 60 months to complete program. *Concentrations:* accounting.
MBA—Off-campus MBA Part-time. *Distance learning option.* At least 32 total credits required. 24 to 60 months to complete program. *Concentrations:* management.
MBA—Master of Business Administration Full-time and part-time. At least 32 total credits required. 12 to 60 months to complete program. *Concentrations:* management.

COSTS

Tuition, state resident: *Full-time* $4151. *Part-time* $150 per credit. **Tuition, nonresident:** *Full-time* $9694. *Part-time* $370 per credit. **Tuition, international:** *Full-time* $14,471. Tuition varies by class time and number of courses or credits taken. **Required fees:** Tuition and fees vary by class time. **Graduate housing:** Room and board costs vary by campus location, number of occupants, type of accommodation, and type of board plan. *Typical cost:* $5720 (including board).

FINANCIAL AID (1999–2000)

Loans, research assistantships, scholarships, teaching assistantships, and work study. Aid is available to part-time students. Financial aid application deadline: 3/1. **Financial Aid Contact** Mr. Myron Hanson, Director, Financial Aid Office, Financial Aid Office, Missoula, MT 59812. **Phone:** 406-243-5373. **Fax:** 406-243-4930. **E-mail:** hanson@selway.umt.edu.

RESOURCES AND SERVICES

Information about online services, personal computer policies, library resources, international exchange programs, internship programs, and placement services at this institution and others can be found at **www.petersons.com/mba**

International Students

8% of students enrolled are international students.
Services and Facilities Counseling/support services, ESL/language courses, international student organization. Financial aid is available to international students.
Applying *Required:* TOEFL with recommended score of 237 (computer) or 580 (paper), proof of adequate funds, proof of health/immunizations.
International Student Contact Ms. Eftychia Koehn, Director, Foreign Student Office, Foreign Student Office, Missoula, MT 59812-0002. **Phone:** 406-243-2226. **Fax:** 406-243-6115. **E-mail:** ekoehn@selway.umt.edu.

■ APPLICATION

Required GMAT, application form, baccalaureate/first degree, 3 letters of recommendation, transcripts of college work. **Recommended** Resume/curriculum vitae.
Deadlines and Fees *Deadlines:* 3/1 for fall, 9/1 for spring, 3/1 for summer, 3/1 for fall (international), 9/1 for spring (international), 3/1 for summer (international). *Application fee:* $45, $45 (international).
Application Contact Ms. Kathleen Spritzer, Administrative Assistant, School of Business Administration, Missoula, MT 59812-1216. **Phone:** 406-243-4983. **Fax:** 406-243-2086. **E-mail:** kathleen.spritzer@business.umt.edu.

NEBRASKA

Bellevue University

Bellevue, Nebraska

COLLEGE OF BUSINESS

Costs (1999–2000)
Full-time tuition: $9000 per academic year   Part-time tuition: $250 per credit

DEGREE MBA

MBA—Master of Business Administration Full-time and part-time. *Distance learning option.* At least 36 total credits required. 16 to 32 months to complete program. *Concentrations:* accounting, international business, management information systems.

COSTS

Tuition *Full-time:* $9000. *Part-time:* $250 per credit. **Tuition, international:** *Full-time* $9000.

FINANCIAL AID (1999–2000)

Scholarships. **Financial Aid Contact** Mr. Jon Dotterer, Director of Financial Aid, 1000 Galvin Road South, Bellevue, NE 68005. **Phone:** 402-293-3763. **Fax:** 402-293-2062.

RESOURCES AND SERVICES

Information about online services, personal computer policies, library resources, international exchange programs, internship programs, and placement services at this institution and others can be found at **www.petersons.com/mba**

International Students

Services and Facilities Counseling/support services, ESL/language courses, international student housing, visa services. Financial aid is not available to international students.
Applying *Required:* TOEFL with recommended score of 460 (paper), proof of adequate funds.
International Student Contact Mr. Ron Psota, International Student Coordinator, 1000 Galvin Road South, Bellevue, NE 68005. **Phone:** 402-293-3759. **Fax:** 402-293-3819. **E-mail:** rep@scholars.bellevue.edu.

■ APPLICATION

Required Application form, baccalaureate/first degree, essay, 2 letters of recommendation, personal statement, transcripts of college work. School will accept GMAT, GRE, and MAT. **Recommended** 3 years of work experience.
Deadlines and Fees Applications for domestic and international students are processed on a rolling basis. *Application fee:* $50, $50 (international).
Application Contact Ms. Elizabeth Wall, Graduate Enrollment Coordinator, 1000 Galvin Road South, Bellevue, NE 68005. **Phone:** 402-293-3702. **Fax:** 402-293-3730. **E-mail:** online-g@scholars.bellevue.edu.

See full description on page 562.

Chadron State College

Chadron, Nebraska

DEPARTMENT OF BUSINESS AND ECONOMICS

Graduate Business Faculty
Full-time: 12

Student Body

Total: 14
Full-time: 4
Part-time: 10

Average Age: 34
Women: 29%

Admissions

Applications: 14
Admitted: 14

Enrolled: 14
Average GPA: 3.27

Costs (1999–2000)

Full-time tuition: $2212 per academic year (resident), $4090 per academic year (nonresident)
Part-time tuition: $104 per credit hour (resident), $183 per credit hour (nonresident)

DEGREE MBA

MBA—Master of Business Administration Full-time and part-time. *Distance learning option.* At least 36 total credits required. 12 to 84 months to complete program.

COSTS

Tuition, state resident: *Full-time* $1878. *Part-time* $78 per credit hour. **Tuition, nonresident:** *Full-time* $3756. *Part-time* $157 per credit hour. **Tuition, international:** *Full-time* $3756. Tuition varies by number of courses or credits taken and local reciprocity agreements. **Required fees:** *Full-time* $334. *Part-time* $26 per credit hour. **Graduate housing:** Room and board costs vary by number of occupants, type of accommodation, and type of board plan. *Typical cost:* $3300 (including board), $1566 (room only).

FINANCIAL AID (1999–2000)

Loans, research assistantships, scholarships, and teaching assistantships. Aid is available to part-time students. Financial aid application deadline: 6/1. **Financial Aid Contact** Ms. Sherry Douglas, Director of Financial Aid, 1000 Main Street, Chadron, NE 69337. **Phone:** 308-432-6230. **Fax:** 308-432-6229. **E-mail:** sdouglas@csc.edu.

RESOURCES AND SERVICES

Information about online services, personal computer policies, library resources, international exchange programs, internship programs, and placement services at this institution and others can be found at **www. petersons.com/mba**

International Students

Services and Facilities Counseling/support services. Financial aid is available to international students.
Applying *Required:* TOEFL with recommended score of 550 (paper), proof of adequate funds, proof of health/immunizations.
International Student Contact Mr. Dale Williamson, Registrar, 1000 Main Street, Chadron, NE 69337. **Phone:** 308-432-6221. **Fax:** 308-432-6229. **E-mail:** dwilliamson@csc.edu.

■ APPLICATION

Required GMAT, application form, baccalaureate/first degree, 3 letters of recommendation, personal statement, transcripts of college work.

Deadlines and Fees Applications for domestic students are processed on a rolling basis. *Deadlines:* 6/1 for fall (international), 10/1 for spring (international). *Application fee:* $15, $15 (international).

Application Contact Ms. Mary Burke, Graduate Office, 1000 Main Street, Chadron, NE 69337. **Phone:** 308-432-6214. **Fax:** 308-432-6454. **E-mail:** mburke@csc.edu.

Creighton University

Omaha, Nebraska

EUGENE C. EPPLEY COLLEGE OF BUSINESS ADMINISTRATION

Graduate Business Faculty

Full-time: 21

Part-time: 3

Student Body

Total: 186
Full-time: 45
Part-time: 141

Average Age: 28
Women: 30%

Admissions

Applications: 36
Admitted: 35
Enrolled: 23

Average GMAT: 530
Average GPA: 3.2

Costs (1999–2000)

Full-time tuition: $8644 per academic year
Part-time tuition: $447 per credit

After Graduation (Class of 1998–99)

Employed within 3 months of graduation: 97%
Average starting salary: $45,700

Accreditation

AACSB—The International Association for Management Education

DEGREES JD/MBA • JD/MS • MBA • MBA/INR • MBA/MCS • MBA/MS • MS

JD/MBA—Juris Doctor/Master of Business Administration Full-time and part-time. At least 33 total credits required. 33 to 72 months to complete program. *Concentrations:* management.

JD/MS—Doctor of Jurisprudence/Master of Science in Electronic Commerce Full-time and part-time. 109 to 130 total credits required. 33 to 72 months to complete program. *Concentrations:* electronic commerce (e-commerce).

MBA—Master of Business Administration Full-time and part-time. 33 to 56 total credits required. 12 to 72 months to complete program. *Concentrations:* management.

MBA/INR—Master of Business Administration/Master of International Relations Full-time and part-time. 54 to 77 total credits required. 24 to 72 months to complete program. *Concentrations:* management.

MBA/MCS—Master of Business Administration/Master of Computer Science Full-time and part-time. 51 to 74 total credits required. 24 to 72 months to complete program. *Concentrations:* management.

MBA/MS—Master of Business Administration/Master of Science in Information Technology Management Full-time and part-time. 48 to 77 total credits required. 24 to 72 months to complete program. *Concentrations:* information management, management, management information systems, technology management.

MS—Master of Science in Electronic Commerce Full-time and part-time. 33 to 54 total credits required. 18 to 72 months to complete program. *Concentrations:* commerce, information management, management information systems, marketing, technology management.

MS—Master of Science in Information Technology Management Full-time and part-time. 33 to 62 total credits required. 12 to 72 months to complete program. *Concentrations:* information management, management information systems, technology management.

COSTS

Tuition *Full-time:* $8046. *Part-time:* $447 per credit. **Required fees:** *Full-time* $598. *Part-time* $50 per semester. **Graduate housing:** Room and board costs vary by number of occupants, type of accommodation, and type of board plan. *Typical cost:* $5500 (including board).

FINANCIAL AID (1999–2000)

22 students received aid, including research assistantships and scholarships. Aid is available to part-time students. Financial aid application deadline: 3/1. **Financial Aid Contact** Mr. Robert Walker, Director, Financial Aid, 2500 California Plaza, Omaha, NE 68178. **Phone:** 402-280-2731. **Fax:** 402-280-2895. **E-mail:** rwalker@creighton.edu.

RESOURCES AND SERVICES

Information about online services, personal computer policies, library resources, international exchange programs, internship programs, and placement services at this institution and others can be found at **www. petersons.com/mba**

International Students

13% of students enrolled are international students.
Services and Facilities Counseling/support services, ESL/language courses, visa services. Financial aid is available to international students.
Applying *Required:* TOEFL with recommended score of 550 (paper), proof of adequate funds, proof of health/immunizations. *Recommended:* TSE.
International Student Contact Ms. Susi Rachouh, Assistant Director of International Programs, 2500 California Plaza, Omaha, NE 68178. **Phone:** 402-280-2059. **Fax:** 402-280-2211. **E-mail:** rachouh@creighton.edu.

■ APPLICATION

Required Application form, baccalaureate/first degree, essay, 3 letters of recommendation, personal statement, transcripts of college work. School will accept GMAT. **Recommended** Resume/curriculum vitae, work experience.

Deadlines and Fees *Application fee:* $40, $40 (international).

Application Contact Ms. Gail Hafer, Coordinator of Graduate Business Programs, College of Business Administration, 2500 California Plaza, Omaha, NE 68178. **Phone:** 402-280-2853. **Fax:** 402-280-2172. **E-mail:** cobagrad@creighton.edu.

University of Nebraska at Kearney

Kearney, Nebraska

COLLEGE OF BUSINESS AND TECHNOLOGY

DEGREE MBA

MBA—Master of Business Administration Full-time and part-time. At least 36 total credits required. Minimum of 24 months to complete program. *Concentrations:* accounting, human resources, management information systems.

RESOURCES AND SERVICES

Information about online services, personal computer policies, library resources, international exchange programs, internship programs, and placement services at this institution and others can be found at **www. petersons.com/mba**

International Students

Services and Facilities Counseling/support services, international student housing. Financial aid is not available to international students.
International Student Contact Mr. Jerald Fox, Director, International Education, 2113 Founders Hall, Kearney, NE 68849. **Phone:** 308-865-8246. **Fax:** 308-865-8160. **E-mail:** fox@platte.unk.edu.

■ APPLICATION

Application Contact MBA Office, West Center E106, Kearney, NE 68849-4580. **Phone:** 308-865-8346. **Fax:** 308-865-8310. **E-mail:** mbaoffice@unk.edu.

University of Nebraska at Omaha

Omaha, Nebraska

COLLEGE OF BUSINESS ADMINISTRATION

Graduate Business Faculty
Full-time: 56 — Part-time: 10

Student Body
Total: 305
Full-time: 32
Part-time: 273
Average Age: 30
Women: 44%

Admissions
Applications: 58
Admitted: 53
Enrolled: 40
Average GMAT: 535
Average GPA: 3.36

Costs (1999–2000)
Full-time tuition: N/R
Part-time tuition: $112 per credit (resident), $252 per credit (nonresident)

Accreditation
AACSB—The International Association for Management Education

DEGREES MBA

MBA—Executive MBA Part-time. *Distance learning option.* 6 years of professional-level work experience required. At least 48 total credits required. 24 months to complete program. *Concentrations:* management.

MBA—Master of Business Administration Full-time and part-time. 36 to 45 total credits required. 15 to 72 months to complete program.

COSTS

Tuition, state resident: *Part-time* $112 per credit. **Tuition, nonresident:** *Part-time* $252 per credit. **Required fees:** *Part-time* $56 per semester. Fees vary by number of courses or credits taken. **Graduate housing:** *Typical cost:* $3000 (room only).

FINANCIAL AID (1999–2000)

15 students received aid, including loans, research assistantships, scholarships, and work study. Aid is available to part-time students. Financial aid application deadline: 3/1. **Financial Aid Contact** Mr. Randy Sell, Director, Financial Aid, Dodge Street, Omaha, NE 68182. **Phone:** 402-554-2327. **E-mail:** randy_sell@unomaha.edu.

RESOURCES AND SERVICES

Information about online services, personal computer policies, library resources, international exchange programs, internship programs, and placement services at this institution and others can be found at **www. petersons.com/mba**

International Students
10% of students enrolled are international students.

Services and Facilities Counseling/support services, ESL/language courses, housing location assistance, international student organization, orientation, visa services. Financial aid is not available to international students.
Applying *Required:* TOEFL with recommended score of 213 (computer) or 550 (paper), proof of adequate funds, proof of health/immunizations. *Recommended:* TWE.
International Student Contact Ms. Sharon Emery, International Student Advisor, 6001 Dodge Street, Omaha, NE 68182. **Phone:** 402-554-2293. **Fax:** 402-554-2949. **E-mail:** sharon_emery@unomaha.edu.

■ APPLICATION

Required GMAT or GRE, application form, baccalaureate/first degree, resume/curriculum vitae, transcripts of college work. **Recommended** Work experience.
Deadlines and Fees *Deadlines:* 7/1 for fall, 12/1 for spring, 4/1 for summer, 7/1 for fall (international), 12/1 for spring (international), 4/1 for summer (international). *Application fee:* $35, $35 (international).
Application Contact Ms. Lex Kaczmarek, Assistant Director, MBA Program, Dodge Street, Omaha, NE 68182-0048. **Phone:** 402-554-2303. **Toll-free Phone:** 800-858-8648. **Fax:** 402-554-3747. **E-mail:** lex_kaczmarek@unomaha.edu.

University of Nebraska–Lincoln

Lincoln, Nebraska

COLLEGE OF BUSINESS ADMINISTRATION

Graduate Business Faculty
Full-time: 48 — Part-time: 4

Student Body
Total: 160
Full-time: 72
Part-time: 88
Average Age: 32
Women: 34%

Admissions
Applications: 301
Admitted: 130
Enrolled: 86
Average GMAT: 580
Average GPA: 3.4

Costs (1999–2000)
Full-time tuition: $3282 per academic year (resident), $7350 per academic year (nonresident)
Part-time tuition: $116 per credit hour (resident), $285 per credit hour (nonresident)

After Graduation (Class of 1998–99)
Employed within 3 months of graduation: 95%
Average starting salary: $45,000

Accreditation
AACSB—The International Association for Management Education

DEGREES JD/MBA • MA • MBA • MBA/M Arch • MPA

JD/MBA—Juris Doctor/Master of Business Administration Full-time and part-time. At least 100 total credits required. 48 to 72 months to complete program.

MA—Master of Arts in Business Full-time and part-time. GRE required. At least 36 total credits required. 12 to 72 months to complete program. *Concentrations:* finance, management, marketing.

MBA—Master of Business Administration Full-time and part-time. *Distance learning option.* At least 48 total credits required. 18 to 72 months to complete program. *Concentrations:* agribusiness, electronic commerce (e-commerce), finance, human resources, international business, management information systems, marketing, strategic management.

MBA/M Arch—Master of Business Administration/Master of Architecture Full-time and part-time. At least 72 total credits required. 36 to 60 months to complete program.

MPA—Master of Professional Accountancy Full-time and part-time. At least 36 total credits required. 12 to 72 months to complete program.

The College of Business Administration at the University of Nebraska-Lincoln (UNL) is pleased to announce a new M.B.A. program as part of the J. D. Edwards Honors Program in Computer Science and Management. The M.B.A. in information and software systems combines 48 credit hours of business and computer science courses. The program is designed to produce well-rounded, highly skilled graduates who have the advantage of using computers to solve business problems from the inside out.

Named after one of America's most successful software development firms, the J. D. Edwards program was funded by a multimillion-dollar gift from the company's cofounder and chairman, C. Edward McVaney, and his wife, Carole. This small, highly selective program takes education in information and software systems into the next millennium by offering a curriculum that is rich in computing foundations, information technology, and business essentials. Classes are taught by renowned faculty members. Selected students receive a $20,000-per-year assistantship and full tuition waiver. For more information, students should visit the College's Web site at http://www.cba.unl.edu.

COSTS

Tuition, state resident: *Full-time* $2772. *Part-time* $116 per credit hour. **Tuition, nonresident:** *Full-time* $6840. *Part-time* $285 per credit hour. **Tuition, international:** *Full-time* $5165. Tuition varies by number of courses or credits taken, campus location, and local reciprocity agreements. **Required fees:** *Full-time* $510. *Part-time* $238 per year. Tuition and fees vary by number of courses or credits taken and campus location. **Graduate housing:** Room and board costs vary by number of occupants and type of board plan. *Typical cost:* $4070 (including board), $1880 (room only).

FINANCIAL AID (1999–2000)

Fellowships, research assistantships, scholarships, teaching assistantships, and work study. Aid is available to part-time students. Financial aid application deadline: 3/31. **Financial Aid Contact** Scholarships and Financial Aid, 16 Administration Building, Lincoln, NE 68588-0411. **Phone:** 402-472-2030. **E-mail:** scholsa@cwis.unl.edu.

RESOURCES AND SERVICES

Information about online services, personal computer policies, library resources, international exchange programs, internship programs, and placement services at this institution and others can be found at **www.petersons.com/mba**

International Students

12% of students enrolled are international students.

Services and Facilities Counseling/support services, ESL/language courses, housing location assistance, international student housing, international student organization, language tutoring, orientation, visa services, travel services. Financial aid is available to international students.

Applying *Required:* TOEFL with recommended score of 213 (computer) or 550 (paper), proof of adequate funds, proof of health/immunizations.

International Student Contact Mr. Peter Levitov, Associate Dean of International Affairs, 1237 R Street, Lincoln, NE 68588-0221. **Phone:** 402-472-5358. **E-mail:** plevitov1@unl.edu.

■ APPLICATION

Required GMAT, application form, baccalaureate/first degree, 3 letters of recommendation, transcripts of college work. **Recommended** Work experience.

Deadlines and Fees *Deadlines:* 6/15 for fall, 11/15 for spring, 4/15 for summer, 5/15 for fall (international), 10/15 for spring (international), 3/15 for summer (international). *Application fee:* $35, $35 (international).

Application Contact Judith Shutts, Graduate Advisor, CBA 126, Lincoln, NE 68588-0405. **Phone:** 402-472-2338. **Fax:** 402-472-5180. **E-mail:** cgraduate@unlnotes.unl.edu.

Wayne State College

Wayne, Nebraska

DIVISION OF BUSINESS

Graduate Business Faculty
Full-time: 19

Student Body
Total: 69
Part-time: 69

Average Age: 35
Women: 51%

Admissions
Average GMAT: 500

Average GPA: 3

Costs (1999–2000)
Full-time tuition: N/R
Part-time tuition: $282 per course (resident), $517 per course (nonresident)

After Graduation (Class of 1998–99)
Employed within 3 months of graduation: 95%

DEGREE MBA

MBA—Master of Business Administration Full-time and part-time. *Distance learning option.* At least 36 total credits required. 18 to 84 months to complete program.

COSTS

Tuition, state resident: *Part-time* $282 per course. **Tuition, nonresident:** *Part-time* $517 per course.

FINANCIAL AID (1999–2000)

10 students received aid, including teaching assistantships. Aid is available to part-time students. Financial aid application deadline: 5/1. **Financial Aid Contact** Bonnie Scranton, Director of Financial Aid, 1111 Main Street, Wayne, NE 68787. **Phone:** 402-375-7000.

RESOURCES AND SERVICES

Information about online services, personal computer policies, library resources, international exchange programs, internship programs, and placement services at this institution and others can be found at **www.petersons.com/mba**

International Students

3% of students enrolled are international students.

Services and Facilities Counseling/support services.
Applying *Required:* TOEFL with recommended score of 550 (paper), proof of adequate funds.

International Student Contact Curt Frye, Vice President, Student Services, 111 Main Street, Wayne, NJ 68787. **Phone:** 402-375-7000.

■ APPLICATION

Required GMAT, application form, baccalaureate/first degree, transcripts of college work.

Deadlines and Fees Applications for domestic and international students are processed on a rolling basis. *Application fee:* $10, $10 (international).

Application Contact MBA Office, 1111 Main Street, Wayne, NE 68787. **Phone:** 402-375-7245.

NEVADA

University of Nevada, Las Vegas

Las Vegas, Nevada

COLLEGE OF BUSINESS

Graduate Business Faculty
Full-time: 90

Student Body
Total: 203
Full-time: 48

Part-time: 155

Admissions
Applications: 115
Admitted: 43
Enrolled: 35

Average GMAT: 582
Average GPA: 3.15

Costs (1999–2000)
Full-time tuition: N/R
Part-time tuition: $100 per credit hour (resident), $205 per credit hour (nonresident)

Accreditation
AACSB—The International Association for Management Education

DEGREES MA • MBA • MS

MA—Master of Arts in Economics Full-time and part-time. At least 30 total credits required. 12 to 72 months to complete program.

MBA—Master of Business Administration Full-time and part-time. At least 48 total credits required. 12 to 72 months to complete program. *Concentrations:* finance, management information systems, marketing.

MS—Master of Science in Accountancy Full-time and part-time. At least 30 total credits required. 12 to 72 months to complete program.

University of Nevada, Las Vegas (continued)

COSTS

Tuition, state resident: *Part-time* $100 per credit hour. **Tuition, nonresident:** *Part-time* $205 per credit hour. Tuition varies by number of courses or credits taken and local reciprocity agreements.

FINANCIAL AID (1999–2000)

Fellowships, grants, research assistantships, scholarships, and teaching assistantships. Financial aid application deadline: 3/1. **Financial Aid Contact** Ms. Judy Belanger, Director, Student Financial Services, 4505 Maryland Parkway, Las Vegas, NV 89154-2016. **Phone:** 702-895-3697. **Fax:** 720-895-1353.

RESOURCES AND SERVICES

Information about online services, personal computer policies, library resources, international exchange programs, internship programs, and placement services at this institution and others can be found at **www.petersons.com/mba**

International Students

Services and Facilities Counseling/support services, ESL/language courses, housing location assistance, language tutoring, orientation, visa services. Financial aid is not available to international students.
Applying *Required:* TOEFL with recommended score of 213 (computer) or 550 (paper), proof of adequate funds, proof of health/immunizations.
International Student Contact Dr. Nasser Daneshvary, Associate Dean, College of Business, Las Vegas, NV 89154-6031. **Phone:** 702-895-3655. **Fax:** 702-895-4090. **E-mail:** cobmba@ccmail.nevada.edu.

■ APPLICATION

Required Application form, baccalaureate/first degree, essay, 2 letters of recommendation, personal statement, resume/curriculum vitae, transcripts of college work. School will accept GMAT. **Recommended** Interview, work experience.
Deadlines and Fees *Deadlines:* 6/1 for fall, 11/15 for spring, 5/1 for fall (international), 10/1 for spring (international). *Application fee:* $40, $55 (international).
Application Contact Dr. Nasser Daneshvary, Associate Dean, 4505 Maryland Parkway, Las Vegas, NV 89154-6031. **Phone:** 702-895-3655. **Fax:** 702-895-4090. **E-mail:** cobmba@ccmail.nevada.edu.

See full description on page 932.

University of Nevada, Reno

Reno, Nevada

COLLEGE OF BUSINESS ADMINISTRATION

Accreditation
AACSB—The International Association for Management Education

DEGREES M Ac • MA • MBA • MS

M Ac—Master of Accountancy At least 30 total credits required.

MA—Master of Arts in Economics Full-time and part-time. At least 32 total credits required. 24 to 72 months to complete program.

MBA—Master of Business Administration Full-time and part-time. 2 years of work experience required. At least 51 total credits required. 36 to 72 months to complete program.

MS—Master of Science in Economics Full-time and part-time. At least 32 total credits required. 24 to 72 months to complete program.

RESOURCES AND SERVICES

Information about online services, personal computer policies, library resources, international exchange programs, internship programs, and placement services at this institution and others can be found at **www.petersons.com/mba**

International Students

Services and Facilities Counseling/support services, ESL/language courses, international student housing. Financial aid is available to international students.
International Student Contact Ms. Linda Brunson, Office of International Students and Scholars, Reno, NV 89557. **Phone:** 775-784-6874. **Fax:** 775-784-4105. **E-mail:** lbrunson@unr.edu.

■ APPLICATION

Application Contact Ms. Vicki Krentz, Associate Director of Graduate Studies, Reno, NV 89557. **Phone:** 775-784-4912. **Fax:** 775-784-1773.

See full description on page 934.

NEW HAMPSHIRE

Antioch New England Graduate School

Keene, New Hampshire

DEPARTMENT OF ORGANIZATION AND MANAGEMENT

Graduate Business Faculty

Full-time: 1	Part-time: 10

Student Body

Total: 116	Average Age: 41
Full-time: 99	Women: 72%
Part-time: 17	

Admissions

Applications: 44	Enrolled: 38
Admitted: 41	Average GPA: 3

Costs (1999–2000)
Full-time tuition: $12,865 per academic year
Part-time tuition: $410 per credit

After Graduation (Class of 1998–99)
Employed within 3 months of graduation: 95%
Average starting salary: $35,000

DEGREES ME • MHSA • MS

ME—Master of Education in Administration and Supervision Full-time and part-time. At least 40 total credits required. Minimum of 15 months to complete program. *Concentrations:* leadership, management, management consulting, nonprofit management, organizational behavior/development, organizational management.

MHSA—Master of Human Services Administration Full-time and part-time. At least 40 total credits required. Minimum of 15 months to complete program. *Concentrations:* human resources, leadership, management, nonprofit management, organizational behavior/development, organizational management.

MS—Master of Science in Management Full-time and part-time. At least 50 total credits required. Minimum of 20 months to complete program. *Concentrations:* human resources, leadership, management, organizational behavior/development, organizational management.

COSTS

Tuition *Full-time:* $12,700. *Part-time:* $410 per credit. Tuition varies by number of courses or credits taken and academic program. **Required fees:** *Full-time* $165. *Part-time* $55 per semester.

FINANCIAL AID (1999–2000)

70 students received aid, including fellowships, loans, scholarships, and work study. **Financial Aid Contact** Michelle Chamley, Director, Financial Aid Office, 40 Avon Street, Keene, NH 03431-3516. **Phone:** 603-357-3122 Ext. 263. **Fax:** 603-357-0718. **E-mail:** mchamley@antiochne.edu.

RESOURCES AND SERVICES

Information about online services, personal computer policies, library resources, international exchange programs, internship programs, and placement services at this institution and others can be found at **www.petersons.com/mba**

International Students

Services and Facilities Counseling/support services. Financial aid is not available to international students.
Applying *Required:* TOEFL with recommended score of 213 (computer) or 550 (paper), TWE with recommended score of 5, proof of adequate funds, proof of health/immunizations.
International Student Contact Robbie Hertneky, Director of Admissions, 40 Avon Street, Keene, NH 03431-3516. **Phone:** 603-357-6265. **Fax:** 603-357-0718. **E-mail:** rhertneky@antiochne.edu.

■ APPLICATION

Required Application form, baccalaureate/first degree, essay, interview, 3 letters of recommendation, personal statement, resume/curriculum vitae, transcripts of college work, work experience.
Deadlines and Fees *Deadlines:* 8/1 for fall, 12/1 for spring, 8/1 for fall (international), 12/1 for spring (international). *Application fee:* $40, $40 (international).

Application Contact Robbie Hertneky, Director of Admissions, 40 Avon Street, Keene, NH 03431-3516. **Phone:** 603-357-6265. **Fax:** 603-357-0718. **E-mail:** rhertneky@antiochne.edu.

Dartmouth College

Hanover, New Hampshire

THE TUCK SCHOOL OF BUSINESS AT DARTMOUTH

Graduate Business Faculty
Full-time: 40 | Part-time: 14

Student Body
Total: 377
Full-time: 377 | Average Age: 28
| Women: 32%

Admissions
Applications: 2,689 | Average GMAT: 682
Admitted: 359 | Average GPA: 3.4
Enrolled: 189

Costs (1999–2000)
Full-time tuition: $27,150 per academic year
Part-time tuition: N/R

After Graduation (Class of 1998–99)
Employed within 3 months of graduation: 100%
Average starting salary: $84,212

Accreditation
AACSB—The International Association for Management Education

DEGREES MBA • MBA/MALD • MBA/MPA • MD/MBA • ME/MBA

MBA—Master of Business Administration Full-time. 24 to 60 months to complete program.

MBA/MALD—Joint Program in Conjunction with Fletcher School of Law at Tufts University Full-time. 36 to 60 months to complete program.

MBA/MPA—Joint Program in Conjunction with Kennedy School at Harvard University Full-time.

MD/MBA—Joint Program in Conjunction with Dartmouth Medical School Full-time. 72 to 84 months to complete program.

ME/MBA—Joint Program in Conjunction with Dartmouth's Thayer School of Engineering Full-time. 36 to 60 months to complete program.

COSTS

Tuition *Full-time:* $27,150. **Graduate housing:** Room and board costs vary by number of occupants and type of accommodation. *Typical cost:* $9950 (including board), $5200 (room only).

FINANCIAL AID (1999–2000)

242 students received aid, including fellowships, loans, scholarships, and work study. Financial aid application deadline: 3/1. **Financial Aid Contact** Elizabeth Roberto, Financial Aid Officer, 100 Tuck Hall, Hanover, NH 03755-9000. **Phone:** 603-646-3748. **Fax:** 603-646-1308. **E-mail:** elizabeth.e.roberto@dartmouth.edu.

RESOURCES AND SERVICES

Information about online services, personal computer policies, library resources, international exchange programs, internship programs, and placement services at this institution and others can be found at **www. petersons.com/mba**

International Students
26% of students enrolled are international students.
Services and Facilities Counseling/support services, ESL/language courses, housing location assistance, international student organization, language tutoring, orientation, visa services. Financial aid is available to international students.
Applying *Required:* TOEFL, proof of adequate funds, proof of health/immunizations.
International Student Contact Ms. Sally O. Jaeger, Director of Admissions, Tuck School of Business, 100 Tuck Hall, Hanover, NH 03755-9000. **Phone:** 603-646-3162. **Fax:** 603-646-1441. **E-mail:** sally.jaeger@dartmouth.edu.

■ APPLICATION

Required GMAT, application form, baccalaureate/first degree, essay, 2 letters of recommendation, personal statement, transcripts of college work. **Recommended** Interview, work experience.
Deadlines and Fees *Deadlines:* 12/3 for fall, 1/18 for winter, 2/18 for spring, 4/21 for summer, 12/3 for fall (international), 1/18 for winter (international),

2/18 for spring (international), 4/21 for summer (international). *Application fee:* $150, $150 (international).
Application Contact Ms. Sally O. Jaeger, Director of Admissions, Tuck School of Business, 100 Tuck Hall, Hanover, NH 03755. **Phone:** 603-646-3162. **Fax:** 603-646-1441. **E-mail:** tuck.admissions@dartmouth.edu.

See full description on page 620.

New England College

Henniker, New Hampshire

PROGRAM IN ORGANIZATIONAL MANAGEMENT

Graduate Business Faculty
Part-time: 10

Student Body
Total: 35 | Average Age: 35

Admissions
Applications: 43 | Enrolled: 35
Admitted: 40

Costs (1999–2000)
Full-time tuition: N/R
Part-time tuition: $195 per credit

DEGREE MS

MS—Master of Science in Organizational Management Full-time and part-time. At least 40 total credits required. Minimum of 24 months to complete program.

COSTS

Tuition *Part-time:* $195 per credit. **Required fees:** *Part-time* $35 per semester.

FINANCIAL AID (1999–2000)

Aid is available to part-time students. **Financial Aid Contact** Sara Gardner, Administrative Assistant, Financial Aid, 7 Main Street, Henniker, NH 03242-3293. **Phone:** 603-428-2488. **Fax:** 603-428-2266. **E-mail:** slg@nec1.nec.edu.

RESOURCES AND SERVICES

Information about online services, personal computer policies, library resources, international exchange programs, internship programs, and placement services at this institution and others can be found at **www. petersons.com/mba**

International Students
Services and Facilities Visa services.
Applying *Required:* Proof of adequate funds.
International Student Contact Rebecca W. Matte, International Student Advisor, 7 Main Street, Henniker, NH 03242-3293. **Phone:** 603-428-2241. **E-mail:** rwm@nec1.nec.edu.

■ APPLICATION

Required Application form, baccalaureate/first degree, essay, interview, 3 letters of recommendation, personal statement, resume/curriculum vitae, transcripts of college work.
Deadlines and Fees *Application fee:* $25, $25 (international).
Application Contact Linda Connor, Office Manager, Graduate and Continuing Studies, 7 Main Street, Henniker, NH 03242. **Phone:** 603-428-2252. **Fax:** 603-428-8123. **E-mail:** lcc@bill.nec.edu.

New Hampshire College

Manchester, New Hampshire

GRADUATE SCHOOL OF BUSINESS

Graduate Business Faculty
Full-time: 27 | Part-time: 107

Student Body
Total: 2,544
Full-time: 495 | Average Age: 32
Part-time: 2,049 | Women: 42%

Costs (1999–2000)
Full-time tuition: N/R
Part-time tuition: $999 per course

New Hampshire College (continued)

After Graduation (Class of 1998–99)
Employed within 3 months of graduation: 92%

Accreditation
ACBSP—The American Council of Business Schools and Programs

DEGREES MBA • MS

MBA—Master of Business Administration Full-time and part-time. *Distance learning option.* At least 42 total credits required. 12 to 96 months to complete program. *Concentrations:* accounting, finance, health care, industrial/labor relations, international business, management information systems, manufacturing management, marketing, operations management, taxation.
MS—Master of Science in Accounting Full-time and part-time. At least 51 total credits required. 18 to 96 months to complete program. *Concentrations:* taxation.
MS—Master of Science in Business Education Full-time and part-time. At least 30 total credits required. 9 to 96 months to complete program.
MS—Master of Science in Computer Information Systems Full-time and part-time. At least 48 total credits required. 18 to 96 months to complete program.
MS—Master of Science in Finance Full-time and part-time. At least 57 total credits required. 18 to 96 months to complete program.
MS—Master of Science in International Business Full-time and part-time. At least 42 total credits required. 12 to 96 months to complete program.

COSTS

Tuition *Part-time:* $999 per course. **Required fees:** *Full-time* $540. **Graduate housing:** Room and board costs vary by type of accommodation. *Typical cost:* $9052 (including board).

FINANCIAL AID (1999–2000)

Financial Aid Contact Ms. Christine McGuire, Financial Aid Administrator, 2500 North River Road, Manchester, NH 03106-1045. **Phone:** 603-645-9645. **Fax:** 603-645-9665. **E-mail:** mcguirch@nhc.edu.

RESOURCES AND SERVICES

Information about online services, personal computer policies, library resources, international exchange programs, internship programs, and placement services at this institution and others can be found at **www. petersons.com/mba**

International Students

15% of students enrolled are international students.

Services and Facilities Counseling/support services, ESL/language courses, international student organization, orientation, visa services.
Applying *Required:* TOEFL with recommended score of 550 (paper), proof of adequate funds, proof of health/immunizations.
International Student Contact Dr. George Commenator, Director, Center for International Education, 2500 North River Road, Manchester, NH 03106-1045. **Phone:** 603-668-2211 Ext. 2242. **Fax:** 603-645-9603. **E-mail:** commenge@nhc.edu.

■ APPLICATION

Required Application form, baccalaureate/first degree, transcripts of college work. School will accept GMAT. **Recommended** Work experience.
Deadlines and Fees Applications for domestic and international students are processed on a rolling basis.
Application Contact Ms. Patricia Gerard, Assistant Dean, Academic and Administrative Services, 2500 North River Road, Manchester, NH 03106-1045. **Phone:** 603-644-3102 Ext. 3417. **Fax:** 603-644-3150. **E-mail:** henleypa@nhc.edu.

See full description on page 738.

Plymouth State College

Plymouth, New Hampshire

DEPARTMENT OF GRADUATE STUDIES IN BUSINESS

Graduate Business Faculty

Full-time: 22	Part-time: 4

Student Body

Total: 81	Average Age: 35
Full-time: 7	Women: 40%
Part-time: 74	

Admissions

Applications: 62	Enrolled: 57
Admitted: 60	Average GMAT: 469

Average GPA: 2.99

Costs (1999–2000)
Full-time tuition: N/R
Part-time tuition: $273 per credit (resident), $299 per credit (nonresident)

DEGREE MBA

MBA—Master of Business Administration in General Management Full-time and part-time. At least 36 total credits required. 9 to 36 months to complete program. *Concentrations:* management.

COSTS

Tuition, state resident: *Part-time* $273 per credit. **Tuition, nonresident:** *Part-time* $299 per credit. Tuition varies by number of courses or credits taken. **Graduate housing:** Room and board costs vary by number of occupants, type of accommodation, and type of board plan. *Typical cost:* $4500 (including board).

FINANCIAL AID (1999–2000)

Loans, scholarships, and teaching assistantships. Aid is available to part-time students. **Financial Aid Contact** Mr. Maurice Day, II, Financial Aid Officer, Speare Administration Building, Room 108, Plymouth, NH 03264. **Phone:** 603-535-2873. **Fax:** 603-535-2627. **E-mail:** mday@mail.plymouth.edu.

RESOURCES AND SERVICES

Information about online services, personal computer policies, library resources, international exchange programs, internship programs, and placement services at this institution and others can be found at **www. petersons.com/mba**

International Students

12% of students enrolled are international students.

Services and Facilities Counseling/support services, international student housing, visa services. Financial aid is not available to international students.
Applying *Required:* TOEFL with recommended score of 500 (paper), proof of adequate funds.
International Student Contact Ms. Karen Hammond, Assistant to the Director, Office of Graduate Studies in Business, Mary Taylor House, MSC #11, Plymouth, NH 03264. **Phone:** 603-535-2835. **Fax:** 603-535-2648. **E-mail:** khammond@mail.plymouth.edu.

■ APPLICATION

Required Application form, baccalaureate/first degree, essay, 3 letters of recommendation, personal statement, resume/curriculum vitae, transcripts of college work. School will accept GMAT.
Deadlines and Fees Applications for domestic and international students are processed on a rolling basis. *Application fee:* $25, $35 (international).
Application Contact Ms. Karen Hammond, Assistant to the Director, Office of Graduate Studies in Business, Mary Taylor House, MSC #11, Plymouth, NH 03264. **Phone:** 603-535-2835. **Toll-free Phone:** 800-367-4723. **Fax:** 603-535-2648. **E-mail:** khammond@mail.plymouth.edu.

See full description on page 768.

Rivier College

Nashua, New Hampshire

DEPARTMENT OF BUSINESS ADMINISTRATION

Graduate Business Faculty

Full-time: 6	Part-time: 29

Student Body

Total: 309	Average Age: 30
Full-time: 11	Women: 45%
Part-time: 298	

Admissions

Applications: 122	Enrolled: 119
Admitted: 119	Average GPA: 2.8

Costs (1999–2000)
Full-time tuition: N/R
Part-time tuition: $972 per course

DEGREES MBA • MS

MBA—Master of Business Administration Full-time and part-time. 36 to 45 total credits required. 24 to 60 months to complete program. *Concentrations:* accounting, health care, marketing, quality management.

282

MS—Computer Information Systems Full-time and part-time. 39 to 45 total credits required. 24 to 60 months to complete program. *Concentrations:* management systems analysis.

MS—Master of Science in Human Resources Management Full-time and part-time. 39 to 48 total credits required. 24 to 60 months to complete program. *Concentrations:* human resources.

COSTS
Tuition *Part-time:* $972 per course. Tuition varies by number of courses or credits taken.

FINANCIAL AID (1999–2000)
23 students received aid, including loans. Aid is available to part-time students. **Financial Aid Contact** Mr. Paul Henderson, Director, 420 Main Street, Nashua, NH 03060-5086. **Phone:** 603-888-1311 Ext. 8534. **E-mail:** finaid@rivier.edu.

RESOURCES AND SERVICES
Information about online services, personal computer policies, library resources, international exchange programs, internship programs, and placement services at this institution and others can be found at **www.petersons.com/mba**

International Students
2% of students enrolled are international students.

Services and Facilities Counseling/support services, ESL/language courses.
Applying *Required:* TOEFL with recommended score of 600 (paper), proof of adequate funds.

■ APPLICATION
Required Application form, baccalaureate/first degree, interview, 3 letters of recommendation, transcripts of college work. **Recommended** Work experience.
Deadlines and Fees *Deadlines:* 7/1 for fall (international), 11/1 for spring (international), 4/1 for summer (international). *Application fee:* $25, $25 (international).
Application Contact Chair, Department of Business Administration, 420 Main Street, Nashua, NH 03060-5086. **Phone:** 603-888-1311 Ext. 8237. **Fax:** 603-888-0237.

University of New Hampshire
Durham, New Hampshire
WHITTEMORE SCHOOL OF BUSINESS AND ECONOMICS

Graduate Business Faculty
Full-time: 43   Part-time: 3

Student Body
Total: 220
Full-time: 77   Average Age: 32
Part-time: 143   Women: 29%

Admissions
Applications: 134   Average GMAT: 568
Admitted: 117   Average GPA: 3
Enrolled: 89

Costs (1999–2000)
Full-time tuition: $6947 per academic year (resident), $15,837 per academic year (nonresident)
Part-time tuition: $1150 per course (resident), $1350 per course (nonresident)

After Graduation (Class of 1998–99)
Employed within 3 months of graduation: 85%
Average starting salary: $49,500

Accreditation
AACSB—The International Association for Management Education

DEGREES MBA • MS

MBA—Executive Master of Business Administration Full-time. Interview required. At least 54 total credits required. 19 months to complete program. *Concentrations:* management.

MBA—Full-time Day Master of Business Administration Full-time. 2 years of work experience required. At least 60 total credits required. 24 to 36 months to complete program. *Concentrations:* accounting, finance, management, marketing, operations management.

MBA—Part-time Evening Master of Business Administration Part-time. At least 60 total credits required. 36 to 72 months to complete program. *Concentrations:* accounting, finance, management, marketing, operations management.

MS—Master of Science in Accounting Full-time and part-time. At least 30 total credits required. 12 to 24 months to complete program. *Concentrations:* accounting.

COSTS
Tuition, state resident: *Full-time* $6050. *Part-time* $1150 per course. **Tuition, nonresident:** *Full-time* $14,940. *Part-time* $1350 per course. Tuition varies by class time, number of courses or credits taken, academic program, and local reciprocity agreements. **Required fees:** *Full-time* $897. *Part-time* $175 per trimester. Tuition and fees vary by class time, number of courses or credits taken, and academic program. **Graduate housing:** Room and board costs vary by number of occupants, type of accommodation, and type of board plan. *Typical cost:* $5154 (including board), $3176 (room only).

FINANCIAL AID (1999–2000)
27 students received aid, including research assistantships, scholarships, teaching assistantships, and work study. Aid is available to part-time students. Financial aid application deadline: 3/1. **Financial Aid Contact** Mr. George Abraham, Director, Graduate and Executive Programs, 15 College Road, McConnell Hall, Room 116, Durham, NH 03824-3593. **Phone:** 603-862-1367. **Fax:** 603-862-4468. **E-mail:** wsbe.grad.program@unh.edu.

RESOURCES AND SERVICES
Information about online services, personal computer policies, library resources, international exchange programs, internship programs, and placement services at this institution and others can be found at **www.petersons.com/mba**

International Students
6% of students enrolled are international students.

Services and Facilities Counseling/support services, ESL/language courses, international student housing, orientation, visa services. Financial aid is available to international students.
Applying *Required:* TOEFL with recommended score of 213 (computer) or 550 (paper), proof of adequate funds, proof of health/immunizations. *Recommended:* TWE.
International Student Contact Dr. Leila Paje-Manalo, Office for International Students and Scholars, Hood House, Durham, NH 03824. **Phone:** 603-862-1508. **Fax:** 603-862-0169. **E-mail:** 11pm@christa.unh.edu.

■ APPLICATION
Required GMAT, application form, baccalaureate/first degree, essay, 3 letters of recommendation, personal statement, transcripts of college work.
Deadlines and Fees *Deadlines:* 7/1 for fall, 3/1 for fall (international). *Application fee:* $50, $50 (international).
Application Contact Mr. George Abraham, Director, Graduate and Executive Programs, 15 College Road, McConnell Hall, Room 116, Durham, NH 03824-3593. **Phone:** 603-862-1367. **Fax:** 603-862-4468. **E-mail:** wsbe.grad.program@unh.edu.

NEW JERSEY

College of Saint Elizabeth
Morristown, New Jersey
DEPARTMENT OF BUSINESS ADMINISTRATION/ECONOMICS

Admissions
Average GPA: 3.5
Costs (1999–2000)
Full-time tuition: N/R
Part-time tuition: N/R

DEGREES MS

MS—Health Care Management Part-time. At least 33 total credits required. 24 to 72 months to complete program. *Concentrations:* health care.

MS—Management Part-time. At least 33 total credits required. 24 to 72 months to complete program. *Concentrations:* human resources, strategic management.

College of Saint Elizabeth (continued)

RESOURCES AND SERVICES
Information about online services, personal computer policies, library resources, international exchange programs, internship programs, and placement services at this institution and others can be found at **www. petersons.com/mba**

International Students
Services and Facilities Counseling/support services.
Applying *Required:* TOEFL with recommended score of 210 (computer) or 550 (paper), proof of adequate funds, proof of health/immunizations.
International Student Contact Mr. Thomas Sirinides, Director, International Student Services, 2 Convent Road, Morristown, NJ 07960. **Phone:** 973-290-4227. **E-mail:** sirge@liza.st-elizabeth.edu.

■ APPLICATION
Required Application form, baccalaureate/first degree, essay, 3 letters of recommendation, personal statement, transcripts of college work. **Recommended** Resume/curriculum vitae.
Deadlines and Fees *Application fee:* $35.
Application Contact Dr. Peter Schneider, Chairman, 2 Convent Road, Morristown, NJ 07960. **Phone:** 973-290-4082. **Fax:** 973-290-4177. **E-mail:** pschnei735@aol.com.

Fairleigh Dickinson University, Teaneck–Hackensack Campus

Teaneck, New Jersey

SAMUEL J. SILBERMAN COLLEGE OF BUSINESS ADMINISTRATION

DEGREES EMBA • HEMBA • MBA • MS

EMBA—Executive Master of Business Administration Part-time. At least 48 total credits required.

HEMBA—Executive Master of Business Administration in Health Systems Management Part-time. Up to 48 total credits required.

MBA—Master of Business Administration in Global Management Full-time. At least 48 total credits required. 12 months to complete program.

MBA—Master of Business Administration in Pharmaceutical-Chemical Studies Full-time and part-time. Up to 60 total credits required. *Concentrations:* health care.

MBA—Master of Business Administration Full-time and part-time. 34 to 60 total credits required. *Concentrations:* accounting, entrepreneurship, finance, human resources, international business, management, management information systems, marketing.

MS—Master of Science in Taxation Full-time and part-time. At least 36 total credits required. *Concentrations:* taxation.

RESOURCES AND SERVICES
Information about online services, personal computer policies, library resources, international exchange programs, internship programs, and placement services at this institution and others can be found at **www. petersons.com/mba**

International Students
Services and Facilities Counseling/support services, ESL/language courses, international student housing, visa services. Financial aid is available to international students.
International Student Contact Office of International Affairs, 1000 River Road, Teaneck, NJ 07666. **Phone:** 201-692-2205. **Fax:** 201-692-2560. **E-mail:** global@mailbox.fdu.edu.

■ APPLICATION
Application Contact Mr. Andrew Nelson, Office of Adult and Graduate Admission, 1000 River Road, Teaneck, NJ 07666. **Phone:** 201-692-2551. **Toll-free Phone:** 800-338-8803. **E-mail:** graduate-adult@hrserv.fdu.edu.

See full description on page 650.

Georgian Court College

Lakewood, New Jersey

PROGRAM IN BUSINESS ADMINISTRATION

Graduate Business Faculty

Full-time: 7

Part-time: 5

Student Body
Total: 127
Full-time: 16
Part-time: 111

Average Age: 33
Women: 68%

Costs (1999–2000)
Full-time tuition: N/R
Part-time tuition: $375 per credit

Accreditation
ACBSP—The American Council of Business Schools and Programs

DEGREE MBA

MBA—Master of Business Administration Full-time and part-time. At least 63 total credits required. Maximum of 72 months to complete program.

COSTS
Tuition *Part-time:* $375 per credit. **Required fees:** *Full-time* $66. *Part-time* $33 per semester.

FINANCIAL AID (1999–2000)
10 students received aid, including grants, loans, and work study. Aid is available to part-time students. **Financial Aid Contact** Ms. Susan Barschow, Director of Financial Aid, 900 Lakewood Avenue, Lakewood, NJ 08701-2697. **Phone:** 732-364-2200 Ext. 258. **Fax:** 732-367-3920. **E-mail:** barschow@georgian.edu.

RESOURCES AND SERVICES
Information about online services, personal computer policies, library resources, international exchange programs, internship programs, and placement services at this institution and others can be found at **www. petersons.com/mba**

International Students
0.8% of students enrolled are international students.
Services and Facilities Counseling/support services. Financial aid is not available to international students.
Applying *Required:* TOEFL with recommended score of 550 (paper), proof of adequate funds, proof of health/immunizations.
International Student Contact Sr. Virginia Hasson, Interim Dean of the Graduate School, 900 Lakewood Avenue, Lakewood, NJ 08701-2697. **Phone:** 732-367-1717. **Fax:** 732-364-0583. **E-mail:** admissions-grad@georgian.edu.

■ APPLICATION
Required GMAT, application form, baccalaureate/first degree, 3 letters of recommendation, transcripts of college work. **Recommended** Interview.
Deadlines and Fees *Deadlines:* 6/1 for fall, 12/1 for spring, 3/1 for fall (international), 7/15 for spring (international). *Application fee:* $40, $40 (international).
Application Contact Sr. Virginia Hasson, Interim Dean of the Graduate School, Lakewood, NJ 08701-2697. **Phone:** 732-367-1717. **E-mail:** admissions-grad@georgian.edu.

Kean University

Union, New Jersey

SCHOOL OF BUSINESS, GOVERNMENT, AND TECHNOLOGY

Graduate Business Faculty
Full-time: 65

Part-time: 15

Student Body
Total: 122
Full-time: 22

Part-time: 100
Women: 34%

Admissions
Applications: 32
Admitted: 29
Enrolled: 25

Average GMAT: 500
Average GPA: 3.25

Costs (1999–2000)
Full-time tuition: N/R
Part-time tuition: $268 per credit (resident), $329 per credit (nonresident)

After Graduation (Class of 1998–99)
Employed within 3 months of graduation: 95%

DEGREE MS

MS—Master of Science in Management Information Systems Full-time and part-time. At least 36 total credits required. 16 to 72 months to complete program.

Concentrations: electronic commerce (e-commerce), management information systems, management science, marketing.

COSTS

Tuition, state resident: *Part-time* $268 per credit. **Tuition, nonresident:** *Part-time* $329 per credit. Tuition varies by number of courses or credits taken.

FINANCIAL AID (1999–2000)

Loans and research assistantships. Aid is available to part-time students. **Financial Aid Contact** Mr. Alfred Brown, Office of Financial Aid, Administration Building, 1st Floor, Union, NJ 07083. **Phone:** 908-527-2050. **Fax:** 908-289-4150. **E-mail:** albrown@turbo.kean.edu.

RESOURCES AND SERVICES

Information about online services, personal computer policies, library resources, international exchange programs, internship programs, and placement services at this institution and others can be found at **www.petersons.com/mba**

International Students

18% of students enrolled are international students.

Services and Facilities Counseling/support services, ESL/language courses, international student housing, international student organization, language tutoring, orientation, visa services. Financial aid is not available to international students.
Applying *Recommended:* TOEFL.

International Student Contact Mr. Willfredo Vega, Professional Services Specialist, 1000 Morris Avenue, Union, NJ 07083. **Phone:** 908-527-2015. **Fax:** 908-351-5187. **E-mail:** wvega@turbo.kean.edu.

■ APPLICATION

Required Application form, baccalaureate/first degree, essay, 2 letters of recommendation, personal statement, transcripts of college work. **Recommended** Interview, resume/curriculum vitae.

Deadlines and Fees *Deadlines:* 6/1 for fall, 11/1 for spring, 3/15 for fall (international), 11/1 for spring (international). *Application fee:* $35, $35 (international).

Application Contact Thomas Abraham, Program Coordinator, 1000 Morris Avenue, Union, NJ 07083. **Phone:** 908-527-2492. **Fax:** 908-289-7439. **E-mail:** msmis@turbo.kean.edu.

Monmouth University

West Long Branch, New Jersey

SCHOOL OF BUSINESS ADMINISTRATION

Graduate Business Faculty

Full-time: 26	Part-time: 3

Student Body

Total: 284	Average Age: 32
Full-time: 39	Women: 42%
Part-time: 245	

Admissions

Applications: 143	Enrolled: 86
Admitted: 138	

Costs (1999–2000)

Full-time tuition: $8754 per academic year
Part-time tuition: $456 per credit

After Graduation (Class of 1998–99)

Employed within 3 months of graduation: 95%

Accreditation

AACSB—The International Association for Management Education

DEGREES MBA

MBA—Master of Business Administration in Health Care Management Full-time and part-time. 33 to 51 total credits required. 12 to 60 months to complete program. *Concentrations:* health care.
MBA—Master of Business Administration Full-time and part-time. 30 to 48 total credits required. 12 to 60 months to complete program.

COSTS

Tuition *Full-time:* $8206. *Part-time:* $456 per credit. **Required fees:** *Full-time* $548. *Part-time* $548 per year. Tuition and fees vary by number of courses or credits taken. **Graduate housing:** Room and board costs vary by number of occupants, type of accommodation, and type of board plan. *Typical cost:* $6682 (including board), $3376 (room only).

FINANCIAL AID (1999–2000)

32 students received aid, including fellowships and loans. Financial aid application deadline: 9/1. **Financial Aid Contact** Ms. Claire Alasio, Director, Financial Aid, 400 Cedar Avenue, West Long Branch, NJ 07764-1898. **Phone:** 732-571-3463. **Fax:** 732-263-5577.

RESOURCES AND SERVICES

Information about online services, personal computer policies, library resources, international exchange programs, internship programs, and placement services at this institution and others can be found at **www.petersons.com/mba**

International Students

2% of students enrolled are international students.

Services and Facilities Counseling/support services, ESL/language courses, visa services. Financial aid is available to international students.
Applying *Required:* TOEFL with recommended score of 525 (paper), proof of adequate funds, proof of health/immunizations.

International Student Contact Office of Graduate and Adult Enrollment Services, 400 Cedar Avenue, West Long Branch, NJ 07764-1898. **Phone:** 732-571-3452. **Fax:** 732-263-5123.

■ APPLICATION

Required GMAT, application form, baccalaureate/first degree, transcripts of college work. **Recommended** Resume/curriculum vitae.

Deadlines and Fees *Deadlines:* 8/1 for fall, 12/15 for spring, 5/7 for summer, 7/15 for fall (international), 11/15 for spring (international), 4/7 for summer (international). *Application fee:* $35, $35 (international).

Application Contact Office of Graduate and Adult Enrollment Services, 400 Cedar Avenue, West Long Branch, NJ 07764-1898. **Phone:** 732-571-3452.

Montclair State University

Upper Montclair, New Jersey

SCHOOL OF BUSINESS

Graduate Business Faculty

Full-time: 42	Part-time: 2

Student Body

Total: 260	Average Age: 31
Full-time: 48	Women: 44%
Part-time: 212	

Admissions

Applications: 142	Average GMAT: 509
Admitted: 62	Average GPA: 3.1
Enrolled: 53	

Costs (1999–2000)

Full-time tuition: $5834 per academic year (resident), $7634 per academic year (nonresident)
Part-time tuition: $220 per credit (resident), $295 per credit (nonresident)

Accreditation

AACSB—The International Association for Management Education

DEGREE MBA

MBA—Master of Business Administration Full-time and part-time. 33 to 54 total credits required. 24 to 96 months to complete program. *Concentrations:* accounting, economics, finance, international business, management, management information systems, marketing.

Montclair State University's M.B.A. program gives students the decision-making and problem-solving skills they need to prepare them for today's dynamic global economy. Students develop practical expertise through team projects, hands-on courses in technology, case analyses, presentations, and interactions with leading executives.

The program, which is accredited by AACSB-The International Association of Management Education, is composed of 54 credits of required and elective courses. Students may concentrate in one of seven areas or select from an array of advanced courses that provide a broad general education. Advanced standing is given to students with appropriate prior preparation. Evening and Saturday classes allow working professionals to obtain an M.B.A. degree without interrupting their careers. Class size averages about 20 students, which allows for a maximum of interaction and participation.

Most students in the program are full-time professionals who bring to the classroom their real-world business knowledge and experience. Montclair State

Montclair State University (continued)

graduates are well rounded, self-motivated, and entrepreneurial. Equipped with an education built on standards of excellence, alumni enjoy tremendous opportunities for a rich and rewarding career.

The University is set on a beautiful, 200-acre hilltop campus just 14 miles from New York City. The campus is conveniently located near highways and commuter rail and bus lines.

COSTS

Tuition, state resident: *Full-time* $5280. *Part-time* $220 per credit. **Tuition, nonresident:** *Full-time* $7080. *Part-time* $295 per credit. **Tuition, international:** *Full-time* $7080. **Required fees:** *Full-time* $554. *Part-time* $23.1 per credit hour. **Graduate housing:** Room and board costs vary by number of occupants, type of accommodation, and type of board plan. *Typical cost:* $8229 (including board).

FINANCIAL AID (1999–2000)

30 students received aid, including loans, research assistantships, scholarships, teaching assistantships, and work study. Aid is available to part-time students. Financial aid application deadline: 3/1. **Financial Aid Contact** Ms. Ifeyinwa Okobi, Office of Student Financial Aid, Upper Montclair, NJ 07043-1624. **Phone:** 973-655-4461.

RESOURCES AND SERVICES

Information about online services, personal computer policies, library resources, international exchange programs, internship programs, and placement services at this institution and others can be found at **www.petersons.com/mba**

International Students

15% of students enrolled are international students.

Services and Facilities Counseling/support services, ESL/language courses, international student organization, language tutoring, orientation, visa services. Financial aid is not available to international students.
Applying *Required:* TOEFL with recommended score of 213 (computer) or 550 (paper), proof of adequate funds, proof of health/immunizations.
International Student Contact Ms. Jacqueline Leighton, Director, International Services, Valley Road and Normal Avenue, Upper Montclair, NJ 07043-1624. **Phone:** 973-655-4253. **Fax:** 973-655-7726. **E-mail:** international.services@montclair.edu.

■ APPLICATION

Required GMAT, application form, baccalaureate/first degree, essay, 2 letters of recommendation, personal statement, transcripts of college work. **Recommended** Interview, resume/curriculum vitae, work experience.

Deadlines and Fees Applications for domestic and international students are processed on a rolling basis. *Application fee:* $40, $40 (international).

Application Contact Mr. Ray Ortegon, Director of Enrollment Management and Recruitment, The Graduate School, Upper Montclair, NJ 07043-1624. **Phone:** 973-655-5147. **Toll-free Phone:** 800-331-9207. **Fax:** 973-655-7869. **E-mail:** graduate.school@montclair.edu.

New Jersey Institute of Technology

Newark, New Jersey

SCHOOL OF MANAGEMENT

Graduate Business Faculty
Full-time: 27   Part-time: 15

Student Body
Total: 500   Part-time: 375
Full-time: 125   Average Age: 32

Admissions
Applications: 150   Average GMAT: 500
Admitted: 130   Average GPA: 3.2
Enrolled: 97

Costs (1999–2000)
Full-time tuition: N/R
Part-time tuition: $505 per credit (resident), $651 per credit (nonresident)

After Graduation (Class of 1998–99)
Employed within 3 months of graduation: 100%

Accreditation
AACSB—The International Association for Management Education

DEGREES MBA • MS

MBA—Executive Master of Business Administration in Management of Technology Part-time. 48 total credits required. 18 months to complete program. *Concentrations:* management information systems, strategic management.
MBA—MBA in Management of Technology Full-time and part-time. Minimum GMAT score of 550 required. 48 to 60 total credits required. 18 to 84 months to complete program. *Concentrations:* electronic commerce (e-commerce), logistics, management, management information systems, operations management, technology management.
MS—Master of Science in Management Full-time and part-time. 36 to 48 total credits required. 12 to 84 months to complete program. *Concentrations:* accounting, electronic commerce (e-commerce), finance, human resources, international business, management, management information systems, marketing.

COSTS

Tuition, state resident: *Part-time* $388 per credit. **Tuition, nonresident:** *Part-time* $534 per credit. Tuition varies by academic program. **Required fees:** *Part-time* $117 per credit. Fees vary by class time and academic program. **Graduate housing:** Room and board costs vary by number of occupants, type of accommodation, and type of board plan. *Typical cost:* $7200 (including board).

FINANCIAL AID (1999–2000)

15 students received aid, including fellowships, loans, research assistantships, teaching assistantships, and work study. Financial aid application deadline: 3/15. **Financial Aid Contact** Director, Financial Aid Department, University Heights, Newark, NJ 07102-1982. **Phone:** 973-596-3479.

RESOURCES AND SERVICES

Information about online services, personal computer policies, library resources, international exchange programs, internship programs, and placement services at this institution and others can be found at **www.petersons.com/mba**

International Students

50% of students enrolled are international students.

Services and Facilities Counseling/support services, ESL/language courses, housing location assistance, international student housing, international student organization, language tutoring, orientation, visa services. Financial aid is available to international students.
Applying *Required:* TOEFL with recommended score of 213 (computer) or 550 (paper), proof of adequate funds, proof of health/immunizations.
International Student Contact Jinan Jaber-Linsalata, Director, International Student and Faculty Services, University Heights, Newark, NJ 07102-1982. **Phone:** 973-596-2451. **E-mail:** jinan.jaber-linsalata@njit.edu.

■ APPLICATION

Required GMAT, application form, baccalaureate/first degree, interview, 2 letters of recommendation, transcripts of college work. **Recommended** Essay, personal statement, resume/curriculum vitae, 5 years of work experience.

Deadlines and Fees *Deadlines:* 6/5 for fall, 10/15 for spring, 6/5 for fall (international), 10/15 for spring (international).

Application Contact Mr. Stuart Lipper, Director of Graduate Programs, School of Management, University Heights, Newark, NJ 07102-1982. **Phone:** 973-596-6378. **Fax:** 973-596-3074. **E-mail:** lipper@njit.edu.

The Richard Stockton College of New Jersey

Pomona, New Jersey

PROGRAM IN BUSINESS STUDIES

Graduate Business Faculty
Full-time: 24

Student Body
Total: 76   Average Age: 30
Full-time: 1   Women: 53%
Part-time: 75

Admissions
Applications: 30   Average GMAT: 450
Admitted: 20   Average GPA: 3
Enrolled: 18

Costs (1999–2000)
Full-time tuition: N/R
Part-time tuition: $260 per credit (resident), $349 per credit
(nonresident)

DEGREE MBS

MBS—Master of Business Studies Full-time and part-time. At least 30 total credits required. 12 to 36 months to complete program. *Concentrations:* accounting, management, management information systems, marketing.

COSTS
Tuition, state resident: *Part-time* $225 per credit. **Tuition, nonresident:** *Part-time* $314 per credit. **Required fees:** *Part-time* $35 per credit.

FINANCIAL AID (1999–2000)
Loans. **Financial Aid Contact** Ms. Jeanne Lewis, Director of Financial Aid, PO Box 195, Pomona, NJ 08240-0195. **Phone:** 609-652-4201. **Fax:** 609-748-5517.

RESOURCES AND SERVICES
Information about online services, personal computer policies, library resources, international exchange programs, internship programs, and placement services at this institution and others can be found at **www. petersons.com/mba**

International Students
Services and Facilities Counseling/support services.
Applying *Required:* TOEFL with recommended score of 550 (paper), proof of adequate funds, proof of health/immunizations.
International Student Contact Dr. Lewis Leitner, Head of the MBA Program, PO Box 195, Pomona, NJ 08240-0195. **Phone:** 609-652-4519. **Fax:** 609-652-4858. **E-mail:** lewis.leitner@stockton.edu.

■ APPLICATION
Required GMAT, application form, baccalaureate/first degree, letter(s) of recommendation, personal statement, resume/curriculum vitae, transcripts of college work. School will accept GRE.

Deadlines and Fees *Application fee:* $35, $35 (international).

Application Contact Dr. Lewis Leitner, Head of the MBS Program, PO Box 195, Pomona, NJ 08240-0195. **Phone:** 609-652-4519. **Fax:** 609-652-4858. **E-mail:** lewis.leitner@stockton.edu.

Rider University
Lawrenceville, New Jersey

COLLEGE OF BUSINESS ADMINISTRATION

Graduate Business Faculty
Full-time: 43   Part-time: 6

Student Body
Total: 351
Full-time: 45   Average Age: 28
Part-time: 306   Women: 46%

Admissions
Applications: 87
Admitted: 61   Average GMAT: 533
Enrolled: 53   Average GPA: 3.18

Costs (1999–2000)
Full-time tuition: $8460 per academic year
Part-time tuition: $480 per credit hour

After Graduation (Class of 1998–99)
Employed within 3 months of graduation: 96%

Accreditation
AACSB—The International Association for Management Education

DEGREES M Acc • MBA

M Acc—Master of Accountancy Full-time and part-time. 30 to 57 total credits required. 12 to 60 months to complete program. *Concentrations:* accounting, finance, health care, international banking, management, marketing.

MBA—Master of Business Administration Full-time and part-time. 30 to 51 total credits required. 12 to 60 months to complete program. *Concentrations:* accounting, economics, finance, health care, international business, management, marketing, organizational management.

COSTS
Tuition *Full-time:* $8460. *Part-time:* $470 per credit hour. **Required fees:** *Part-time* $10 per credit hour. Tuition and fees vary by number of courses or credits taken. **Graduate housing:** Room and board costs vary by number of occupants, type of accommodation, and type of board plan. *Typical cost:* $6500 (including board).

FINANCIAL AID (1999–2000)
7 students received aid, including research assistantships. Financial aid application deadline: 5/1. **Financial Aid Contact** Mr. Shawn Murphy, Associate Director—Student Financial Services, 2083 Lawrenceville Road, Lawrenceville, NJ 08648-3099. **Phone:** 609-896-5360. **Fax:** 609-895-6645. **E-mail:** grdsrv@rider.edu.

RESOURCES AND SERVICES
Information about online services, personal computer policies, library resources, international exchange programs, internship programs, and placement services at this institution and others can be found at **www. petersons.com/mba**

International Students
5% of students enrolled are international students.

Services and Facilities Counseling/support services, housing location assistance, orientation, visa services. Financial aid is not available to international students.
Applying *Required:* TOEFL with recommended score of 240 (computer) or 585 (paper), proof of adequate funds, proof of health/immunizations.
International Student Contact Mr. Tom Kelly, Associate Dean, College of Business Administration, 2083 Lawrenceville Road, Lawrenceville, NJ 08648-3099. **Phone:** 609-896-5127. **Fax:** 609-896-5304. **E-mail:** grdsrv@rider.edu.

■ APPLICATION
Required GMAT, application form, baccalaureate/first degree, transcripts of college work. **Recommended** Essay, interview, letter(s) of recommendation, personal statement, resume/curriculum vitae, work experience.

Deadlines and Fees *Deadlines:* 8/1 for fall, 12/1 for spring, 5/1 for summer, 8/1 for fall (international), 12/1 for spring (international), 5/1 for summer (international). *Application fee:* $35, $35 (international).

Application Contact Dr. John Carpenter, Dean, 2083 Lawrenceville Road, Lawrenceville, NJ 08648-3099. **Phone:** 609-896-5036. **Fax:** 609-896-5261. **E-mail:** grdsrv@rider.edu.

Rowan University
Glassboro, New Jersey

COLLEGE OF BUSINESS

Graduate Business Faculty
Full-time: 17

Student Body
Total: 91   Average Age: 34
Full-time: 6   Women: 51%
Part-time: 85

Admissions
Applications: 16   Average GMAT: 535
Admitted: 11   Average GPA: 3.42

Costs (1999–2000)
Full-time tuition: $6686 per academic year (resident), $10,238 per academic year (nonresident)
Part-time tuition: $281 per credit (resident), $429 per credit (nonresident)

DEGREE MBA

MBA—Master of Business Administration Full-time and part-time. 36 to 57 total credits required. 12 to 72 months to complete program.

The Master of Business Administration (M.B.A.) Program at Rowan University provides a contemporary graduate business education to professionals of diverse fields and academic backgrounds. The M.B.A. curriculum emphasizes communication skills, critical thinking, information technology, quantitative analysis, and the international nature of business. Students learn to be team leaders and team players.

There is an average student-teacher ratio of 15:1 and the convenience of evening and Saturday classes for working professionals. Classes are taught by professors, not teaching assistants. The campus is easily accessible to students in the southern New Jersey, northern Delaware, and Philadelphia metropolitan areas. Rowan's College of Business has one of the finest computer facilities in this tristate area.

Students enrolled in the M.B.A. Program are required to complete a total of eleven graduate courses, nine required and two elective. Prospective M.B.A. students who do not have the required foundation courses may enroll as Pre-M.B.A. students while completing the necessary foundation courses. The maximum number of foundation courses required of Pre-M.B.A. students is seven.

All M.B.A. students must maintain a 3.0 GPA. Students are expected to make steady progress toward the completion of their degree. A full-time student may complete the degree requirements in one year. Part-time students are allowed a maximum of six years to complete all graduate courses.

COSTS

Tuition, state resident: *Full-time* $5904. *Part-time* $246 per credit. **Tuition, nonresident:** *Full-time* $9456. *Part-time* $394 per credit. **Required fees:** *Full-time* $782. *Part-time* $35 per credit. Tuition and fees vary by number of courses or credits taken. **Graduate housing:** Room and board costs vary by number of occupants and type of accommodation. *Typical cost:* $5326 (including board).

FINANCIAL AID (1999–2000)

Research assistantships and work study. Aid is available to part-time students. **Financial Aid Contact** Financial Aid Office, Memorial Hall, 201 Mullica Hill Road, Glassboro, NJ 08028-1701. **Phone:** 856-256-4250. **Fax:** 856-256-4413.

RESOURCES AND SERVICES

Information about online services, personal computer policies, library resources, international exchange programs, internship programs, and placement services at this institution and others can be found at **www. petersons.com/mba**

International Students

7% of students enrolled are international students.

Services and Facilities Counseling/support services, ESL/language courses. Financial aid is not available to international students.
Applying *Required:* TOEFL with recommended score of 213 (computer) or 550 (paper), proof of adequate funds, proof of health/immunizations.
International Student Contact Ms. Margaret Van Brunt, Assistant to the Dean of the College of Business, College of Business, Bunce Hall, 201 Mullica Hill Road, Glassboro, NJ 08028-1701. **Phone:** 856-256-4047. **Fax:** 856-256-4439. **E-mail:** vanbrunt@rowan.edu.

■ APPLICATION

Required GMAT, application form, baccalaureate/first degree, essay, 2 letters of recommendation, personal statement, resume/curriculum vitae, transcripts of college work. **Recommended** Work experience.

Deadlines and Fees Applications for domestic and international students are processed on a rolling basis. *Application fee:* $50, $50 (international).

Application Contact Ms. Margaret Van Brunt, Assistant to the Dean of the College of Business, College of Business, Bunce Hall, Glassboro, NJ 08028-1701. **Phone:** 856-256-4047. **Fax:** 856-256-4439. **E-mail:** mirchandani@rowan.edu.

Rutgers, The State University of New Jersey, Camden

Camden, New Jersey

SCHOOL OF BUSINESS

Graduate Business Faculty
Full-time: 32   Part-time: 6

Student Body
Total: 264
Full-time: 40   Average Age: 28
Part-time: 224   Women: 28%

Admissions
Applications: 158   Average GMAT: 563
Admitted: 134   Average GPA: 3.2
Enrolled: 83

Costs (1999–2000)
Full-time tuition: $9000 per academic year (resident), $13,420 per academic year (nonresident)
Part-time tuition: $372 per credit (resident), $556 per credit (nonresident)

After Graduation (Class of 1998–99)
Employed within 3 months of graduation: 98%
Average starting salary: $57,000

Accreditation
AACSB—The International Association for Management Education

DEGREES JD/MBA • MBA

JD/MBA—Juris Doctor/Master of Business Administration Full-time and part-time. LSAT score required. 108 to 120 total credits required. 36 to 60 months to complete program. *Concentrations:* business law.

MBA—Master of Business Administration Full-time and part-time. At least 60 total credits required. 18 to 24 months to complete program. *Concentrations:* accounting, finance, health care, human resources, international business, management, management information systems, marketing.

COSTS

Tuition, state resident: *Full-time* $9000. *Part-time* $372 per credit. **Tuition, nonresident:** *Full-time* $13,420. *Part-time* $556 per credit. Tuition varies by academic program and local reciprocity agreements. **Required fees:** Fees vary by campus location and academic program. **Graduate housing:** Room and board costs vary by campus location, number of occupants, type of accommodation, and type of board plan. *Typical cost:* $6471 (including board).

FINANCIAL AID (1999–2000)

22 students received aid, including loans, research assistantships, and work study. Aid is available to part-time students. **Financial Aid Contact** Mr. Richard Woodland, Director, Financial Aid, Camden Campus, 401 Cooper Street, Camden, NJ 08102-1401. **Phone:** 609-225-6039. **Fax:** 609-225-6074. **E-mail:** rwoodlan@camden.rutgers.edu.

RESOURCES AND SERVICES

Information about online services, personal computer policies, library resources, international exchange programs, internship programs, and placement services at this institution and others can be found at **www. petersons.com/mba**

International Students

15% of students enrolled are international students.

Services and Facilities Counseling/support services, housing location assistance, international student housing, international student organization, visa services. Financial aid is available to international students.
Applying *Required:* TOEFL with recommended score of 550 (paper), proof of adequate funds, proof of health/immunizations.
International Student Contact Ms. Janice Edwards, Associate Director of Graduate Admissions, Camden Campus, Office of Graduate Admissions, Camden, NJ 08102-1401. **Phone:** 609-225-6104. **Fax:** 609-225-6498. **E-mail:** edwards@camuga.rutgers.edu.

■ APPLICATION

Required GMAT, application form, baccalaureate/first degree, 3 letters of recommendation, personal statement, transcripts of college work. **Recommended** Work experience.

Deadlines and Fees *Application fee:* $40, $40 (international).

Application Contact Dr. Izzet Kenis, MBA Program Director, Rutgers University, School of Business, MBA Program, Camden, NJ 08102-1401. **Phone:** 609-225-6216. **Fax:** 609-225-6231. **E-mail:** kenis@crab.rutgers.edu.

Rutgers, The State University of New Jersey, Newark

Newark, New Jersey

GRADUATE SCHOOL OF MANAGEMENT

Graduate Business Faculty
Full-time: 136   Part-time: 62

Student Body
Total: 1,474
Full-time: 375   Average Age: 28
Part-time: 1,099   Women: 30%

Admissions
Applications: 919   Average GMAT: 587
Admitted: 442   Average GPA: 3.17
Enrolled: 308

Costs (1999–2000)
Full-time tuition: $10,382 per academic year (resident), $14,996 per academic year (nonresident)

Part-time tuition: $388 per credit (resident), $581 per credit (nonresident)

After Graduation (Class of 1998–99)
Employed within 3 months of graduation: 74%
Average starting salary: $70,025

Accreditation
AACSB—The International Association for Management Education

DEGREES M Acc • MBA • MF

M Acc—Master of Accountancy in Taxation Part-time. At least 30 total credits required. 10 to 30 months to complete program. *Concentrations:* taxation.

MBA—Executive MBA Full-time. 10 years of work experience required. At least 54 total credits required. 20 months to complete program. *Concentrations:* accounting, entrepreneurship, finance, human resources, information management, international business, management, management information systems, management science, marketing, operations management.

MBA—MBA in Professional Accounting Full-time. At least 62 total credits required. 14 months to complete program. *Concentrations:* accounting.

MBA—Master of Business Administration in Management Full-time and part-time. At least 60 total credits required. 15 to 24 months to complete program. *Concentrations:* accounting, electronic commerce (e-commerce), entrepreneurship, finance, health care, human resources, international business, international management, leadership, management, marketing, marketing research, nonprofit management, nonprofit organization, operations management, quantitative analysis, strategic management, supply chain management, technology management.

MF—Quantitative Financial Management Full-time. 30 total credits required. *Concentrations:* finance.

COSTS

Tuition, state resident: *Full-time* $9394. *Part-time* $388 per credit. **Tuition, nonresident:** *Full-time* $14,008. *Part-time* $581 per credit. **Required fees:** *Full-time* $988. *Part-time* $165 per semester. Tuition and fees vary by number of courses or credits taken and academic program. **Graduate housing:** Room and board costs vary by campus location, number of occupants, type of accommodation, and type of board plan. *Typical cost:* $8200 (including board), $5500 (room only).

FINANCIAL AID (1999–2000)

215 students received aid, including fellowships, grants, loans, scholarships, and work study. Financial aid application deadline: 3/15. **Financial Aid Contact** Mr. Glenn Berman, Director of Admissions, 190 University Avenue, Newark, NJ 07102-1894. **Phone:** 973-353-1234. **Fax:** 973-353-1592. **E-mail:** gberman@rbs.rutgers.edu.

RESOURCES AND SERVICES

Information about online services, personal computer policies, library resources, international exchange programs, internship programs, and placement services at this institution and others can be found at **www. petersons.com/mba**

International Students

14% of students enrolled are international students.

Services and Facilities Counseling/support services, ESL/language courses, housing location assistance, international student housing, orientation, visa services. Financial aid is not available to international students.
Applying *Required:* TOEFL with recommended score of 250 (computer) or 600 (paper), proof of adequate funds, proof of health/immunizations.

International Student Contact Ms. Patricia Rotonda, Assistant Dean, Student Services, Engelhard Hall, 190 University Avenue, Newark, NJ 07102-1813. **Phone:** 973-353-5482. **Fax:** 973-353-1057. **E-mail:** protonda@gsmack.rutgers.edu.

■ APPLICATION

Required GMAT, application form, baccalaureate/first degree, essay, 2 letters of recommendation, resume/curriculum vitae, transcripts of college work. **Recommended** Work experience.

Deadlines and Fees *Deadlines:* 6/1 for fall, 11/15 for spring, 5/1 for summer, 3/15 for fall (international), 3/15 for summer (international). *Application fee:* $50, $50 (international).

Application Contact Mr. Glenn Berman, Director of Admissions, 190 University Avenue, Newark, NJ 07102-1894. **Phone:** 973-353-1234. **Fax:** 973-353-1592. **E-mail:** gberman@rbs.rutgers.edu.

See full description on page 796.

Rutgers, The State University of New Jersey, New Brunswick

New Brunswick, New Jersey

SCHOOL OF MANAGEMENT AND LABOR RELATIONS

Graduate Business Faculty
Full-time: 26   Part-time: 4

Student Body
Total: 202   Average Age: 31
Full-time: 78   Women: 70%
Part-time: 124

Admissions
Applications: 149   Average GMAT: 422
Admitted: 94   Average GPA: 3.27
Enrolled: 49

Costs (1999–2000)
Full-time tuition: $7543 per academic year (resident), $10,703 per academic year (nonresident)
Part-time tuition: $279 per credit (resident), $412 per credit (nonresident)

After Graduation (Class of 1998–99)
Employed within 3 months of graduation: 90%
Average starting salary: $47,200

DEGREES MHRM • MLIR

MHRM—Master of Human Resources Management Full-time and part-time. *Distance learning option.* At least 48 total credits required. 18 to 60 months to complete program. *Concentrations:* human resources.

MLIR—Master of Labor and Industrial Relations Full-time and part-time. At least 39 total credits required. 12 to 60 months to complete program. *Concentrations:* industrial/labor relations.

COSTS

Tuition, state resident: *Full-time* $6776. *Part-time* $279 per credit. **Tuition, nonresident:** *Full-time* $9936. *Part-time* $412 per credit. Tuition varies by number of courses or credits taken and academic program. **Required fees:** *Full-time* $767. *Part-time* $109 per semester. **Graduate housing:** Room and board costs vary by number of occupants, type of accommodation, and type of board plan. *Typical cost:* $4012 (including board).

FINANCIAL AID (1999–2000)

Fellowships, research assistantships, teaching assistantships, and work study. **Financial Aid Contact** Office of Financial Aid, Records Hall, New Brunswick, NJ 08903. **Phone:** 732-932-7755. **Fax:** 732-932-7385.

RESOURCES AND SERVICES

Information about online services, personal computer policies, library resources, international exchange programs, internship programs, and placement services at this institution and others can be found at **www. petersons.com/mba**

International Students

32% of students enrolled are international students.

Services and Facilities Counseling/support services, ESL/language courses, orientation. Financial aid is available to international students.
Applying *Required:* TOEFL with recommended score of 575 (paper), proof of adequate funds, proof of health/immunizations.

International Student Contact Ms. Marcy Cohen, Director, International Faculty and Student Services Center, 180 College Avenue, New Brunswick, NJ 08903. **Phone:** 732-932-7015. **Fax:** 732-932-7992. **E-mail:** marcohen@rci.rutgers.edu.

■ APPLICATION

Required GMAT or GRE, application form, baccalaureate/first degree, personal statement, 3 letters of recommendation, transcripts of college work. **Recommended** Resume/curriculum vitae, work experience.

Deadlines and Fees *Deadlines:* 5/1 for fall, 11/1 for spring, 3/1 for summer, 4/1 for fall (international), 11/1 for spring (international). *Application fee:* $50, $50 (international).

Application Contact Ms. Judy von Loewe, Graduate Program Coordinator, Janice Levin Building, 94 Rockafeller Road, Piscataway, NJ 08854-8054. **Phone:** 732-445-5973. **Fax:** 732-445-2830. **E-mail:** mhrm@rci.rutgers.edu.

Saint Peter's College

Jersey City, New Jersey

MBA PROGRAMS

Graduate Business Faculty
Full-time: 16   Part-time: 17

Student Body
Total: 252   Average Age: 33
Full-time: 23   Women: 46%
Part-time: 229

Admissions
Applications: 102   Enrolled: 55
Admitted: 77

Costs (1999–2000)
Full-time tuition: $9558 per academic year
Part-time tuition: $531 per credit

After Graduation (Class of 1998–99)
Employed within 3 months of graduation: 91%
Average starting salary: $55,000

DEGREES MBA • MS

MBA—MBA in Finance Full-time and part-time. At least 48 total credits required. 12 to 60 months to complete program. *Concentrations:* finance.

MBA—MBA in Marketing Full-time and part-time. At least 48 total credits required. 12 to 60 months to complete program. *Concentrations:* marketing.

MBA—Master of Business Administration in International Business Full-time and part-time. At least 48 total credits required. 12 to 60 months to complete program. *Concentrations:* international business.

MBA—Master of Business Administration in Management Full-time and part-time. At least 48 total credits required. 12 to 60 months to complete program. *Concentrations:* management.

MBA—Master of Business Administration in Management Information Systems Full-time and part-time. At least 48 total credits required. 12 to 60 months to complete program. *Concentrations:* management information systems.

MS—Master of Science in Accountancy Full-time and part-time. At least 30 total credits required. 10 to 60 months to complete program. *Concentrations:* accounting.

COSTS

Tuition *Full-time:* $9558. *Part-time:* $531 per credit.

FINANCIAL AID (1999–2000)

165 students received aid, including loans and work study. Aid is available to part-time students. Financial aid application deadline: 3/15. **Financial Aid Contact** Ms. Rebecca Royal, Director of Financial Aid, 2641 Kennedy Boulevard, Jersey City, NJ 07306-5997. **Phone:** 201-915-9308. **Fax:** 201-434-6878.

RESOURCES AND SERVICES

Information about online services, personal computer policies, library resources, international exchange programs, internship programs, and placement services at this institution and others can be found at **www.petersons.com/mba**

International Students

5% of students enrolled are international students.

Services and Facilities Counseling/support services, housing location assistance, language tutoring, visa services. Financial aid is available to international students.

Applying *Required:* TOEFL with recommended score of 550 (paper), proof of adequate funds, proof of health/immunizations.

International Student Contact Ms. Barbara Bertsch, Graduate Admissions Coordinator, 2641 Kennedy Boulevard, Jersey City, NJ 07306-5997. **Phone:** 201-915-9213 Ext. 9216. **Fax:** 201-432-5860. **E-mail:** admissions@spcvxa.spc.edu.

▪ APPLICATION

Required Application form, baccalaureate/first degree, 3 letters of recommendation, personal statement, transcripts of college work. School will accept GMAT and MAT.

Deadlines and Fees Applications for domestic and international students are processed on a rolling basis. *Application fee:* $20, $20 (international).

Application Contact Ms. Barbara Bertsch, Graduate Admissions Representative, 2641 Kennedy Boulevard, Jersey City, NJ 07306-5997. **Phone:** 201-915-9216. **Fax:** 201-432-5860. **E-mail:** admissions@spcvxa.spc.edu.

See full description on page 808.

Seton Hall University

South Orange, New Jersey

W. PAUL STILLMAN SCHOOL OF BUSINESS

Graduate Business Faculty
Full-time: 57   Part-time: 32

Student Body
Total: 631   Average Age: 27
Full-time: 96   Women: 36%
Part-time: 535

Admissions
Applications: 277   Average GMAT: 560
Admitted: 229   Average GPA: 3.2
Enrolled: 152

Costs (1999–2000)
Full-time tuition: $15,233 per academic year
Part-time tuition: $622 per credit

After Graduation (Class of 1998–99)
Employed within 3 months of graduation: 67%
Average starting salary: $54,000

Accreditation
AACSB—The International Association for Management Education

DEGREES JD/MBA • MBA • MBA/MHA • MBA/MS • MBA/MSN • MS

JD/MBA—Juris Doctor/Master of Business Administration Full-time. 48 to 60 months to complete program. *Concentrations:* accounting, economics, finance, human resources, management, management information systems, marketing, quantitative analysis, sports/entertainment management.

MBA—Day/Evening Full-time and part-time. 30 to 42 total credits required. 18 to 60 months to complete program. *Concentrations:* accounting, environmental economics/management, finance, management, management information systems, management systems analysis, marketing, sports/entertainment management, system management.

MBA—Evening MBA *Concentrations:* accounting, environmental economics/management, finance, management, management information systems, management systems analysis, marketing, sports/entertainment management, system management.

MBA/MHA—Master of Business Administration/Master of Hospital Administration Full-time and part-time. 60 total credits required. 30 to 60 months to complete program.

MBA/MS—Master of Business Administration/Master of Science in International Business Part-time. At least 78 total credits required. 30 to 60 months to complete program. *Concentrations:* accounting, economics, finance, human resources, management, management information systems, marketing, quantitative analysis, sports/entertainment management.

MBA/MSN—Master of Business Administration/Master of Science in Nursing Full-time and part-time. 54 total credits required. 24 to 60 months to complete program.

MS—Master of Science in Accounting Part-time. At least 30 total credits required. 12 to 60 months to complete program.

MS—Master of Science in International Business Part-time. At least 33 total credits required. 18 to 60 months to complete program.

MS—Master of Science in Professional Accounting Part-time. At least 30 total credits required. 12 to 60 months to complete program.

MS—Master of Science in Taxation Part-time. *Distance learning option.* At least 30 total credits required. 12 to 60 months to complete program.

COSTS

Tuition *Full-time:* $14,928. *Part-time:* $622 per credit. **Required fees:** *Full-time* $305. *Part-time* $285 per semester. Tuition and fees vary by number of courses or credits taken. **Graduate housing:** Room and board costs vary by number of occupants, type of accommodation, and type of board plan. *Typical cost:* $9790 (including board), $7584 (room only).

FINANCIAL AID (1999–2000)

Loans, research assistantships, teaching assistantships, and work study. Aid is available to part-time students. **Financial Aid Contact** Mr. Richard Bishop, Director, Financial Aid Office, Financial Aid Office, Bayley Hall,

---

South Orange, NJ 07079. **Phone:** 973-761-9348. **Fax:** 973-761-7954. **E-mail:** bishopric@shu.edu.

RESOURCES AND SERVICES
Information about online services, personal computer policies, library resources, international exchange programs, internship programs, and placement services at this institution and others can be found at **www.petersons.com/mba**

International Students
Services and Facilities Counseling/support services, ESL/language courses, housing location assistance, international student organization, orientation, visa services. Financial aid is not available to international students.
Applying *Required:* TOEFL with recommended score of 550 (paper), proof of adequate funds, proof of health/immunizations. *Recommended:* TWE with recommended score of 5.
International Student Contact Ms. Geri Sabia, Director/International Programs, Presidents Hall, South Orange, NJ 07079. **Phone:** 973-761-9081. **Fax:** 973-275-2383. **E-mail:** sabiager@shu.edu.

■ APPLICATION
Required GMAT, application form, baccalaureate/first degree, essay, 3 letters of recommendation, personal statement, resume/curriculum vitae, transcripts of college work, 2 years of work experience. **Recommended** Interview.
Deadlines and Fees *Deadlines:* 6/1 for fall, 10/1 for spring, 6/1 for fall (international), 10/1 for spring (international). *Application fee:* $50, $50 (international).
Application Contact Ms. Lorrie Dougherty, Director of Graduate Admissions and Career Development, Stillman School of Business, 400 South Orange Avenue, South Orange, NJ 07079-2692. **Phone:** 973-761-9220. **Fax:** 973-761-9208. **E-mail:** doughelo@shu.edu.

See full description on page 822.

Stevens Institute of Technology
Hoboken, New Jersey

WESLEY J. HOWE SCHOOL OF TECHNOLOGY MANAGEMENT

Graduate Business Faculty
Full-time: 21 — Part-time: 16

Student Body
Total: 1,020
Full-time: 50 — Average Age: 26
Part-time: 970 — Women: 31%

Admissions
Applications: 472 — Enrolled: 346
Admitted: 422

Costs (1999–2000)
Full-time tuition: $14,520 per academic year
Part-time tuition: $605 per credit hour

DEGREES ME/MM • MS • MSIS • MSM • MTM

ME/MM—Master of Engineering/Master of Management Full-time and part-time. At least 30 total credits required. Maximum of 36 months to complete program.

MS—Master of Science in Telecommunications Full-time and part-time. *Distance learning option.* At least 36 total credits required. 12 to 36 months to complete program.

MSIS—Master of Science in Information Systems Full-time and part-time. At least 36 total credits required. 20 to 36 months to complete program. *Concentrations:* economics, information management, project management, telecommunications management.

MSM—Master of Science in Management Full-time and part-time. At least 36 total credits required. 12 to 36 months to complete program. *Concentrations:* information management, project management, technology management.

MTM—Master of Technology Management Part-time. 5 years industry experience. At least 44 total credits required. 20 months to complete program.

COSTS
Tuition *Full-time:* $14,520. *Part-time:* $605 per credit hour. **Tuition, international:** *Full-time* $14,520. Tuition varies by number of courses or credits taken and academic program. **Required fees:** *Part-time* $80 per semester. **Graduate housing:** Room and board costs vary by number of occupants, type of accommodation, and type of board plan. *Typical cost:* $9150 (including board), $3946 (room only).

FINANCIAL AID (1999–2000)
Fellowships, loans, research assistantships, teaching assistantships, and work study. Aid is available to part-time students. **Financial Aid Contact** David Sheridan, Dean of Enrollment Services, Castle Point on Hudson, Hoboken, NJ 07030. **Phone:** 201-216-5201. **Fax:** 201-216-8030. **E-mail:** dsherida@stevens-tech.edu.

RESOURCES AND SERVICES
Information about online services, personal computer policies, library resources, international exchange programs, internship programs, and placement services at this institution and others can be found at **www.petersons.com/mba**

International Students
9% of students enrolled are international students.
Services and Facilities Counseling/support services, ESL/language courses, international student organization, visa services. Financial aid is available to international students.
Applying *Required:* TOEFL with recommended score of 550 (paper).
International Student Contact Mr. Ronald D. Lorton, Manager of International Student Services and Scholar Services, Castle Point on Hudson, Hoboken, NJ 07030. **Phone:** 201-216-5189. **Fax:** 201-216-8333. **E-mail:** rlorton@stevens-tech.edu.

■ APPLICATION
Required Application form, baccalaureate/first degree, 2 letters of recommendation, transcripts of college work. **Recommended** Personal statement, resume/curriculum vitae, 1 year of work experience.
Deadlines and Fees *Application fee:* $45, $45 (international).
Application Contact Dr. James Tietjen, Dean, Wesley J. Howe School of Technology Management, Castle Point on the Hudson, Hoboken, NJ 07030. **Phone:** 201-216-5386. **Fax:** 201-216-5385. **E-mail:** jtietjen@stevens-tech.edu.

Thomas Edison State College
Trenton, New Jersey

GRADUATE STUDIES

Graduate Business Faculty
Part-time: 18

Student Body
Total: 124
Part-time: 124 — Average Age: 41
 — Women: 44%

Admissions
Enrolled: 56

Costs (1999–2000)
Full-time tuition: N/R
Part-time tuition: $298 per credit (resident), $298 per credit (nonresident)

DEGREE MSM

MSM—Master of Science in Management Part-time. *Distance learning option.* At least 36 total credits required. Minimum of 18 months to complete program. *Concentrations:* management.

COSTS
Tuition, state resident: *Part-time* $298 per credit. **Tuition, nonresident:** *Part-time* $298 per credit.

FINANCIAL AID (1999–2000)
Loans. Aid is available to part-time students. **Financial Aid Contact** Ms. Carmen Panlilio, Director of Financial Aid and Veterans Affairs, 101 West State Street, Trenton, NJ 08608-1176. **Phone:** 609-633-9780. **Fax:** 609-777-2956. **E-mail:** cpanlilio@call.tesc.edu.

RESOURCES AND SERVICES
Information about online services, personal computer policies, library resources, international exchange programs, internship programs, and placement services at this institution and others can be found at **www.petersons.com/mba**

International Students
Services and Facilities Financial aid is not available to international students.
Applying *Required:* TOEFL with recommended score of 500 (paper).
International Student Contact Dr. Esther Taitsman, Director of Masters of Science in Management, 101 West State Street, Trenton, NJ 08608-1176. **Phone:** 609-292-5143. **Fax:** 609-984-8447. **E-mail:** msm@call.tesc.edu.

Thomas Edison State College (continued)

■ APPLICATION

Required Application form, baccalaureate/first degree, essay, 2 letters of recommendation, personal statement, transcripts of college work, 3 years of work experience. **Recommended** Resume/curriculum vitae.

Deadlines and Fees *Deadlines:* 7/30 for fall, 11/30 for winter, 3/30 for summer, 7/30 for fall (international), 11/30 for winter (international), 3/30 for summer (international). *Application fee:* $75, $75 (international).

Application Contact Dr. Esther Taitsman, Director of Masters of Science in Management, 101 West State Street, Trenton, NJ 08608-1176. **Phone:** 609-984-1150. **Fax:** 609-777-2956. **E-mail:** msm@call.tesc.edu.

William Paterson University of New Jersey

Wayne, New Jersey

COLLEGE OF BUSINESS

Graduate Business Faculty
Full-time: 10	Part-time: 4

Student Body
Total: 140	Part-time: 135
Full-time: 5	Women: 50%

Admissions
Applications: 75	Average GMAT: 485
Admitted: 45	Average GPA: 2.86
Enrolled: 30	

Costs (1999–2000)
Full-time tuition: N/R
Part-time tuition: $230 per credit (resident), $327 per credit (nonresident)

DEGREE MBA

MBA—Master of Business Administration Part-time. At least 60 total credits required. 24 to 72 months to complete program. *Concentrations:* finance, management, marketing, sports/entertainment management.

COSTS

Tuition, state resident: *Part-time* $230 per credit. **Tuition, nonresident:** *Part-time* $327 per credit.

FINANCIAL AID (1999–2000)

Loans, research assistantships, and teaching assistantships. Aid is available to part-time students. **Financial Aid Contact** Director, Graduate Services, Department of Graduate Studies, Raubinger Hall, 300 Pompton Road, Wayne, NJ 07470-8420. **Phone:** 973-720-2237. **Fax:** 973-720-2035.

RESOURCES AND SERVICES

Information about online services, personal computer policies, library resources, international exchange programs, internship programs, and placement services at this institution and others can be found at **www.petersons.com/mba**

International Students

14% of students enrolled are international students.

Services and Facilities Counseling/support services, ESL/language courses, international student housing, visa services. Financial aid is not available to international students.

Applying *Required:* TOEFL with recommended score of 550 (paper), proof of adequate funds, proof of health/immunizations.

International Student Contact Department of Graduate Studies, Raubinger Hall, 300 Pompton Road, Wayne, NJ 07470-8420. **Phone:** 973-720-2237. **Fax:** 973-720-2035.

■ APPLICATION

Required GMAT, application form, baccalaureate/first degree, essay, 2 letters of recommendation, transcripts of college work.

Deadlines and Fees *Application fee:* $35, $35 (international).

Application Contact Director, Graduate Services, Department of Graduate Studies, Raubinger Hall, 300 Pompton Road, Wayne, NJ 07470-8420. **Phone:** 973-720-2237. **Fax:** 973-720-2035.

NEW MEXICO

College of Santa Fe

Santa Fe, New Mexico

DEPARTMENT OF BUSINESS ADMINISTRATION

Graduate Business Faculty
Full-time: 6	Part-time: 12

Student Body
Total: 76	Average Age: 38
Full-time: 27	Women: 72%
Part-time: 49	

Admissions
Applications: 23	Enrolled: 14
Admitted: 23	Average GPA: 3.2

Costs (1999–2000)
Full-time tuition: N/R
Part-time tuition: $251 per credit

DEGREE MBA

MBA—Master of Business Administration Full-time and part-time. At least 36 total credits required. 12 to 60 months to complete program. *Concentrations:* finance, human resources, management information systems.

COSTS

Tuition *Part-time:* $251 per credit. **Graduate housing:** Room and board costs vary by number of occupants, type of accommodation, and type of board plan. *Typical cost:* $4892 (including board).

FINANCIAL AID (1999–2000)

Scholarships and work study. Aid is available to part-time students. **Financial Aid Contact** Mr. Dale Reinhart, Director of Admissions and Enrollment Management, 1600 St. Michael's Drive, Santa Fe, NM 87505. **Phone:** 505-473-6133. **Fax:** 505-473-6129.

RESOURCES AND SERVICES

Information about online services, personal computer policies, library resources, international exchange programs, internship programs, and placement services at this institution and others can be found at **www.petersons.com/mba**

International Students

Services and Facilities Counseling/support services. Financial aid is not available to international students.

International Student Contact Mr. Andy Lovato, Director, Career Placement/International Student Advisor, 1600 St. Michael's Drive, Santa Fe, NM 87505-7634. **Phone:** 505-473-6294. **Fax:** 505-473-6121.

■ APPLICATION

Required Application form, baccalaureate/first degree, interview, 2 letters of recommendation, transcripts of college work. **Recommended** Work experience.

Deadlines and Fees Applications for domestic and international students are processed on a rolling basis. *Application fee:* $25, $25 (international).

Application Contact Dr. Ali Arshad, Chair, Business Administration Department, 1600 Saint Michael's Drive, Santa Fe, NM 87505-7634. **Phone:** 505-473-6211. **Toll-free Phone:** 800-456-2673. **Fax:** 505-473-6504. **E-mail:** aarshad@csf.edu.

Eastern New Mexico University

Portales, New Mexico

COLLEGE OF BUSINESS

Graduate Business Faculty
Full-time: 16	Part-time: 1

Student Body
Total: 37	Average Age: 35
Full-time: 5	Women: 51%
Part-time: 32	

Admissions
Applications: 33	Average GMAT: 530
Admitted: 31	Average GPA: 3.29
Enrolled: 10	

Costs (1999–2000)
Full-time tuition: $1761 per academic year (resident), $6639 per academic year (nonresident)
Part-time tuition: $108 per credit hour (resident), $311 per credit hour (nonresident)

After Graduation (Class of 1998–99)
Employed within 3 months of graduation: 100%
Average starting salary: $36,000

Accreditation
ACBSP—The American Council of Business Schools and Programs

DEGREE MBA

MBA—Master of Business Administration Full-time and part-time. *Distance learning option.* 2 years of work experience required. At least 33 total credits required. 15 to 60 months to complete program. *Concentrations:* management.

COSTS
Tuition, state resident: *Full-time* $1482. *Part-time* $85 per credit hour. **Tuition, nonresident:** *Full-time* $6360. *Part-time* $288 per credit hour. Tuition varies by campus location and local reciprocity agreements. **Required fees:** *Full-time* $279. *Part-time* $23 per credit hour. **Graduate housing:** Room and board costs vary by campus location, number of occupants, type of accommodation, and type of board plan. *Typical cost:* $3250 (including board), $1450 (room only).

FINANCIAL AID (1999–2000)
9 students received aid, including fellowships, research assistantships, teaching assistantships, and work study. Aid is available to part-time students. Financial aid application deadline: 3/1. **Financial Aid Contact** Ms. Julie Poorman, Student Financial Aid, Station 20, Portales, NM 88130. **Phone:** 505-562-2194.

RESOURCES AND SERVICES
Information about online services, personal computer policies, library resources, international exchange programs, internship programs, and placement services at this institution and others can be found at **www. petersons.com/mba**

International Students
14% of students enrolled are international students.

Services and Facilities Counseling/support services. Financial aid is not available to international students.
Applying *Required:* TOEFL with recommended score of 550 (paper), proof of adequate funds, proof of health/immunizations.
International Student Contact Mrs. Pat Dodd, Admissions Specialist III, Station 7, Portales, NM 88130. **Phone:** 505-562-2225. **Fax:** 505-562-2168. **E-mail:** pat.dodd@enmu.edu.

■ APPLICATION
Required GMAT, application form, baccalaureate/first degree, personal statement, transcripts of college work, 2 years of work experience. School will accept GRE.
Deadlines and Fees Applications for domestic and international students are processed on a rolling basis. *Application fee:* $10, $10 (international).

New Mexico Highlands University
Las Vegas, New Mexico

SCHOOL OF BUSINESS

Graduate Business Faculty
Full-time: 15 Part-time: 9

Student Body
Total: 52
Full-time: 26 Average Age: 30
Part-time: 26 Women: 58%

Admissions
Applications: 42 Average GMAT: 450
Admitted: 37 Average GPA: 3.3
Enrolled: 36

Costs (1999–2000)
Full-time tuition: N/R
Part-time tuition: $72 per credit hour (resident), $72 per credit hour (nonresident)

After Graduation (Class of 1998–99)
Employed within 3 months of graduation: 67%
Average starting salary: $33,000

DEGREE MBA

MBA—Master of Business Administration Full-time and part-time. *Distance learning option.* 45 to 54 total credits required. 24 to 36 months to complete program. *Concentrations:* management, nonprofit management, technology management.

COSTS
Tuition, state resident: *Part-time* $72 per credit hour. **Tuition, nonresident:** *Part-time* $72 per credit hour. Tuition varies by number of courses or credits taken, campus location, and academic program. **Required fees:** Tuition and fees vary by academic program. **Graduate housing:** Room and board costs vary by number of occupants, type of accommodation, and type of board plan. *Typical cost:* $4000 (including board).

FINANCIAL AID (1999–2000)
5 students received aid, including fellowships, loans, research assistantships, scholarships, teaching assistantships, and work study. Aid is available to part-time students. **Financial Aid Contact** Director of Financial Aid, Felix Martinez Building, Las Vegas, NM 87701. **Phone:** 505-454-0584.

RESOURCES AND SERVICES
Information about online services, personal computer policies, library resources, international exchange programs, internship programs, and placement services at this institution and others can be found at **www. petersons.com/mba**

International Students
6% of students enrolled are international students.

Services and Facilities Counseling/support services, ESL/language courses. Financial aid is not available to international students.
Applying *Required:* TOEFL with recommended score of 525 (paper), proof of adequate funds.
International Student Contact Lyn DeMartin, Director of International Programs, Las Vegas, NM 87701. **Phone:** 505-454-3344 Ext. 3058.

■ APPLICATION
Required Application form, baccalaureate/first degree, 3 letters of recommendation, personal statement, resume/curriculum vitae, transcripts of college work. School will accept GMAT. **Recommended** Interview.
Deadlines and Fees Applications for domestic and international students are processed on a rolling basis. *Application fee:* $15, $15 (international).
Application Contact Dr. Margaret Young, Dean, School of Business, Las Vegas, NM 87701. **Phone:** 505-454-3115. **Fax:** 505-454-3354. **E-mail:** busmba@nmhu.edu.

New Mexico State University
Las Cruces, New Mexico

COLLEGE OF BUSINESS ADMINISTRATION AND ECONOMICS

Graduate Business Faculty
Full-time: 46 Part-time: 16

Student Body
Total: 130
Full-time: 81 Average Age: 29
Part-time: 49 Women: 34%

Admissions
Applications: 72 Average GMAT: 492
Admitted: 52 Average GPA: 3.25
Enrolled: 29

Costs (1999–2000)
Full-time tuition: $2682 per academic year (resident), $8376 per academic year (nonresident)
Part-time tuition: $112 per credit (resident), $112 per credit (nonresident)

Accreditation
AACSB—The International Association for Management Education

DEGREE MBA

MBA—Master of Business Administration Full-time and part-time. Minimum GMAT 400 and minimum GPA x GMAT = 1400. 30 to 54 total credits required. 18 to 40 months to complete program.

New Mexico State University (continued)

COSTS

Tuition, state resident: *Full-time* $2682. *Part-time* $112 per credit. **Tuition, nonresident:** *Full-time* $8376. *Part-time* $112 per credit. **Tuition, international:** *Full-time* $8376. **Required fees:** Tuition and fees vary by number of courses or credits taken and local reciprocity agreements. **Graduate housing:** Room and board costs vary by number of occupants, type of accommodation, and type of board plan. *Typical cost:* $4600 (including board).

FINANCIAL AID (1999–2000)

24 students received aid, including fellowships, research assistantships, scholarships, teaching assistantships, and work study. **Financial Aid Contact** Mr. Lydia Bruner, Director, Financial Aid, PO Box 30001/Dept 5100, Las Cruces, NM 88003. **Phone:** 505-646-2447. **Fax:** 505-646-7381. **E-mail:** lbruner@nmsu.edu.

RESOURCES AND SERVICES

Information about online services, personal computer policies, library resources, international exchange programs, internship programs, and placement services at this institution and others can be found at **www. petersons.com/mba**

International Students

22% of students enrolled are international students.

Services and Facilities Counseling/support services, ESL/language courses, housing location assistance, international student housing, international student organization, language tutoring, orientation, visa services, sponsored student assistance. Financial aid is not available to international students.

Applying *Required:* TOEFL with recommended score of 197 (computer) or 530 (paper).

International Student Contact Ms. Christina R. Fridenstina, Coordinator, Foreign Students/Immigration Services, Center for International Programs, Box 3567, Las Cruces, NM 88003. **Phone:** 505-646-2017. **Fax:** 505-646-2558. **E-mail:** cip@nmsu.edu.

■ APPLICATION

Required GMAT, application form, baccalaureate/first degree, resume/curriculum vitae, transcripts of college work.

Deadlines and Fees *Deadlines:* 7/1 for fall, 11/1 for spring, 4/1 for summer, 3/1 for fall (international), 10/1 for spring (international). *Application fee:* $15, $35 (international).

Application Contact Dr. R. Wayne Headrick, Director, MBA Program, 114 Guthrie Hall, MSC 3GSP, Las Cruces, NM 88003-8001. **Phone:** 505-646-8003. **Fax:** 505-646-7977. **E-mail:** mba@nmsu.edu.

University of New Mexico

Albuquerque, New Mexico

ROBERT O. ANDERSON GRADUATE SCHOOL OF MANAGEMENT

Graduate Business Faculty

Full-time: 52	Part-time: 48

Student Body

Total: 460	Women: 44%
Average Age: 33	

Admissions

Applications: 163	Average GMAT: 560
Admitted: 110	Average GPA: 3.3
Enrolled: 91	

Costs (1999–2000)
Full-time tuition: N/R
Part-time tuition: $129 per credit hour (resident), $129 per credit hour (nonresident)

After Graduation (Class of 1998–99)
Employed within 3 months of graduation: 85%
Average starting salary: $50,000

Accreditation
AACSB—The International Association for Management Education

DEGREES JD/MBA • MBA • MBA/MA • MS

JD/MBA—Juris Doctor/Master of Business Administration Full-time. At least 129 total credits required. 60 to 96 months to complete program. *Concentrations:* management.

MBA—Executive MBA Full-time. At least 50 total credits required. 24 months to complete program. *Concentrations:* management.

MBA—Master of Business Administration Full-time and part-time. At least 48 total credits required. 12 to 60 months to complete program.

MBA—Master of Business Administration Full-time and part-time. At least 57 total credits required. 12 to 60 months to complete program. *Concentrations:* accounting, entrepreneurship, finance, human resources, international business, management, management information systems, marketing, operations management, public policy and administration, taxation, technology management.

MBA/MA—Master of Business Administration/Master of Arts in Latin American Studies Full-time and part-time. 72 total credits required. 53 to 72 months to complete program. *Concentrations:* international management.

MS—Master of Science in Accounting Full-time and part-time. 33 total credits required. 24 to 60 months to complete program. *Concentrations:* accounting.

COSTS

Tuition, state resident: *Part-time* $129 per credit hour. **Tuition, nonresident:** *Part-time* $129 per credit hour. Tuition varies by class time and number of courses or credits taken. **Required fees:** *Full-time* $60. *Part-time* $35 per semester. Tuition and fees vary by number of courses or credits taken. **Graduate housing:** Room and board costs vary by number of occupants, type of accommodation, and type of board plan. *Typical cost:* $7000 (including board).

FINANCIAL AID (1999–2000)

75 students received aid, including fellowships, loans, research assistantships, scholarships, and work study. Aid is available to part-time students. Financial aid application deadline: 5/1. **Financial Aid Contact** Mr. Ron Martinez, Director, Mesa Vista Hall, Room 1035, Albuquerque, NM 87131. **Phone:** 505-277-5017. **Fax:** 505-277-6326.

RESOURCES AND SERVICES

Information about online services, personal computer policies, library resources, international exchange programs, internship programs, and placement services at this institution and others can be found at **www. petersons.com/mba**

International Students

17% of students enrolled are international students.

Services and Facilities Counseling/support services, ESL/language courses, housing location assistance, orientation, visa services. Financial aid is not available to international students.

Applying *Required:* TOEFL with recommended score of 220 (computer) or 550 (paper), proof of adequate funds, proof of health/immunizations.

International Student Contact Ms. Cynthia Stuart, Director of Admissions, Student Services Center, Room 140, Albuquerque, NM 87131. **Phone:** 505-277-5829. **Fax:** 505-277-6686. **E-mail:** cstuart@unm.edu.

■ APPLICATION

Required Application form, baccalaureate/first degree, essay, 3 letters of recommendation, personal statement, resume/curriculum vitae, transcripts of college work. School will accept GMAT. **Recommended** 2 years of work experience.

Deadlines and Fees *Deadlines:* 6/1 for fall, 11/1 for spring, 4/1 for summer, 5/1 for fall (international), 10/1 for spring (international), 3/1 for summer (international). *Application fee:* $25, $25 (international).

Application Contact Ms. Loyola Chastain, MBA Program Manager, Anderson Graduate School of Management, Albuquerque, NM 87131-1221. **Phone:** 505-277-3147. **Fax:** 505-277-9356. **E-mail:** lchast@unm.edu.

Western New Mexico University

Silver City, New Mexico

DEPARTMENT OF BUSINESS ADMINISTRATION AND ECONOMICS

Graduate Business Faculty

Full-time: 7	Part-time: 2

Student Body

Total: 58	Average Age: 30
Full-time: 3	Women: 52%
Part-time: 55	

Admissions

Applications: 30	Average GMAT: 500
Admitted: 30	Average GPA: 3.42
Enrolled: 30	

Costs (1999–2000)
Full-time tuition: N/R
Part-time tuition: $60 per credit hour (resident), $60 per credit hour (nonresident)

After Graduation (Class of 1998–99)
Employed within 3 months of graduation: 80%

DEGREE MBA

MBA—Master of Business Administration Full-time and part-time. At least 36 total credits required. 18 to 84 months to complete program.

COSTS

Tuition, state resident: *Part-time* $60 per credit hour. **Tuition, nonresident:** *Part-time* $60 per credit hour. Tuition varies by number of courses or credits taken, campus location, and local reciprocity agreements. **Graduate housing:** Room and board costs vary by number of occupants, type of accommodation, and type of board plan. *Typical cost:* $3100 (including board).

FINANCIAL AID (1999–2000)

Fellowships, loans, and work study. Financial aid application deadline: 4/1. **Financial Aid Contact** Charles Kelly, Financial Aid Director, PO Box 680, Silver City, NM 88062. **Phone:** 505-538-6173. **Fax:** 505-538-6155.

RESOURCES AND SERVICES

Information about online services, personal computer policies, library resources, international exchange programs, internship programs, and placement services at this institution and others can be found at **www.petersons.com/mba**

International Students

2% of students enrolled are international students.

Services and Facilities International student advisor. Financial aid is available to international students.
Applying *Required:* TOEFL with recommended score of 550 (paper), proof of adequate funds, proof of health/immunizations.
International Student Contact Mr. Michael Alecksen, Director of Admissions, PO Box 680, Silver City, NM 88062. **Phone:** 505-538-6106. **Fax:** 505-538-6155.

■ APPLICATION

Required GMAT, application form, baccalaureate/first degree, transcripts of college work.
Deadlines and Fees Applications for domestic and international students are processed on a rolling basis. *Application fee:* $10, $10 (international).
Application Contact Mr. Michael Alecksen, Director of Admissions, PO Box 680, Silver City, NM 88062. **Phone:** 505-538-6106. **Fax:** 505-538-6155.

NEW YORK

Adelphi University

Garden City, New York

SCHOOL OF BUSINESS

Graduate Business Faculty
Full-time: 25   Part-time: 23

Student Body
Total: 335   Average Age: 28
Full-time: 43   Women: 58%
Part-time: 292

Admissions
Applications: 112   Average GMAT: 450
Admitted: 110   Average GPA: 2.8
Enrolled: 97

Costs (1999–2000)
Full-time tuition: $17,000 per academic year
Part-time tuition: $650 per credit

DEGREES MBA • MS

MBA—MBA-CPA Program Full-time and part-time. 57 to 90 total credits required. 30 to 72 months to complete program. *Concentrations:* accounting.
MBA—Master of Business Administration Full-time and part-time. *Distance learning option.* 33 to 66 total credits required. 12 to 72 months to complete program. *Concentrations:* accounting, banking, finance, health care, human resources, international business, management, marketing.

MS—Master of Science in Accounting Full-time and part-time. 30 to 45 total credits required. 12 to 72 months to complete program. *Concentrations:* accounting.
MS—Master of Science in Finance and Banking Full-time and part-time. 30 to 51 total credits required. 12 to 72 months to complete program. *Concentrations:* banking, finance.

COSTS

Tuition *Full-time:* $16,600. *Part-time:* $500 per credit. **Tuition, international:** *Full-time* $16,600. **Required fees:** *Full-time* $400. *Part-time* $150 per credit. Fees vary by campus location. **Graduate housing:** Room and board costs vary by type of accommodation and type of board plan. *Typical cost:* $7180 (including board), $3590 (room only).

FINANCIAL AID (1999–2000)

4 students received aid, including research assistantships. Financial aid application deadline: 3/1. **Financial Aid Contact** Ms. Gloria Gebhardt, Manager, Office of Student Financial Services, Garden City, NY 11530. **Phone:** 516-877-3070. **Fax:** 516-877-3039.

RESOURCES AND SERVICES

Information about online services, personal computer policies, library resources, international exchange programs, internship programs, and placement services at this institution and others can be found at **www.petersons.com/mba**

International Students

10% of students enrolled are international students.

Services and Facilities Counseling/support services, ESL/language courses, international student housing, visa services. Financial aid is available to international students.
Applying *Required:* TOEFL with recommended score of 550 (paper), proof of adequate funds, proof of health/immunizations.
International Student Contact Ms. Renate Las Manis, Director, International Student Service, Garden City, NY 11530. **Phone:** 516-877-4990. **E-mail:** lasmanis@adelphi.edu.

■ APPLICATION

Required Application form, baccalaureate/first degree, essay, 2 letters of recommendation, transcripts of college work. School will accept GMAT. **Recommended** Personal statement, resume/curriculum vitae, work experience.
Deadlines and Fees *Deadlines:* 8/15 for fall, 12/15 for spring, 5/15 for summer, 5/1 for fall (international), 3/1 for summer (international). *Application fee:* $50, $50 (international).
Application Contact Ms. Jennifer Spiegel, Associate Director of Graduate Admissions, Office of Admission, Garden City, NY 11530. **Phone:** 516-877-3050. **Toll-free Phone:** 800-Adelphi. **Fax:** 516-877-3244. **E-mail:** spiegel@adelphi.edu.

See full description on page 536.

Alfred University

Alfred, New York

COLLEGE OF BUSINESS

Graduate Business Faculty
Full-time: 14   Part-time: 2

Student Body
Total: 54   Average Age: 25
Full-time: 14   Women: 41%
Part-time: 40

Admissions
Applications: 30   Average GMAT: 505
Admitted: 17   Average GPA: 3.09
Enrolled: 14

Costs (1999–2000)
Full-time tuition: $23,020 per academic year
Part-time tuition: $446 per credit hour

DEGREE MBA

MBA—MBA Program Full-time and part-time. 30 to 55 total credits required. 10 to 60 months to complete program.

COSTS

Tuition *Full-time:* $22,444. *Part-time:* $446 per credit hour. Tuition varies by number of courses or credits taken. **Required fees:** *Full-time* $576. *Part-time* $27 per year. **Graduate housing:** Room and board costs vary by campus loca-

Alfred University (continued)

tion, number of occupants, type of accommodation, and type of board plan. *Typical cost:* $6500 (including board), $4000 (room only).

FINANCIAL AID (1999–2000)

14 students received aid, including research assistantships. **Financial Aid Contact** Mr. Earl Pierce, Financial Aid Office, Alumni Hall, 26 North Main Street, Alfred, NY 14802. **Phone:** 607-871-2159. **Fax:** 607-871-2198. **E-mail:** finaid@alfred.edu.

RESOURCES AND SERVICES

Information about online services, personal computer policies, library resources, international exchange programs, internship programs, and placement services at this institution and others can be found at **www. petersons.com/mba**

International Students

4% of students enrolled are international students.

Services and Facilities Counseling/support services, ESL/language courses, international student organization, orientation. Financial aid is available to international students.

Applying *Required:* TOEFL with recommended score of 243 (computer) or 590 (paper), proof of adequate funds, proof of health/immunizations.

International Student Contact Mr. Daryl Conte, Assistant Dean of Students, Saxon Drive, Alfred, NY 14802. **Phone:** 607-871-2134. **Fax:** 607-871-2339. **E-mail:** conted@alfred.edu.

■ APPLICATION

Required GMAT, application form, baccalaureate/first degree, 2 letters of recommendation, personal statement, transcripts of college work. **Recommended** Work experience.

Deadlines and Fees Applications for domestic and international students are processed on a rolling basis. *Application fee:* $50, $50 (international).

Application Contact Ms. Lori Hollenbeck, Assistant Dean, College of Business, Saxon Drive, Alfred, NY 14802. **Phone:** 607-871-2630. **Fax:** 607-871-2114. **E-mail:** hollenl@alfred.edu.

See full description on page 538.

Audrey Cohen College

New York, New York

SCHOOL FOR BUSINESS

Graduate Business Faculty

Full-time: 3	Part-time: 11

Student Body

Total: 14	
Full-time: 14	Average Age: 27
	Women: 57%

Admissions

Applications: 43	Average GMAT: 580
Admitted: 16	Average GPA: 3.2
Enrolled: 14	

Costs (1999–2000)

Full-time tuition: $22,314 per academic year
Part-time tuition: N/R

After Graduation (Class of 1998–99)

Employed within 3 months of graduation: 100%
Average starting salary: $42,000

DEGREE MBA

MBA—MBA in Media Management Full-time. At least 51 total credits required. 12 to 36 months to complete program. *Concentrations:* arts administration/management, information management, new venture management, telecommunications management.

COSTS

Tuition *Full-time:* $22,314. **Tuition, nonresident:** *Full-time* $22,314. Tuition varies by number of courses or credits taken and academic program.

FINANCIAL AID (1999–2000)

12 students received aid, including loans, research assistantships, and scholarships. Financial aid application deadline: 8/1. **Financial Aid Contact** Mr. Steven K. Lenhart, Director of Admissions, Marketing and Recruitment, 75 Varick Street, New York, NY 10013-1919. **Phone:** 212-343-1234 Ext. 2700. **E-mail:** slenhart@audreycohen.edu.

RESOURCES AND SERVICES

Information about online services, personal computer policies, library resources, international exchange programs, internship programs, and placement services at this institution and others can be found at **www. petersons.com/mba**

International Students

14% of students enrolled are international students.

Services and Facilities Counseling/support services, international student organization, orientation, visa services. Financial aid is available to international students.

Applying *Required:* TOEFL with recommended score of 660 (paper), proof of adequate funds, proof of health/immunizations.

International Student Contact Mr. Steven K. Lenhart, Director of Admissions and Recruitment, 75 Varick Street, New York, NY 10013-1919. **Phone:** 212-343-1234 Ext. 2700. **Fax:** 212-343-8470. **E-mail:** slenhart@audreycohen. edu.

■ APPLICATION

Required Application form, baccalaureate/first degree, essay, interview, 2 letters of recommendation, personal statement, resume/curriculum vitae, transcripts of college work. School will accept GMAT, GRE, and GMAT or GRE or MAT. **Recommended** 3 years of work experience.

Deadlines and Fees *Deadlines:* 7/5 for fall, 11/1 for spring, 6/1 for fall (international), 10/15 for spring (international). *Application fee:* $45, $45 (international).

Application Contact Mr. Steven K. Lenhart, Director of Admissions, Marketing and Recruitment, 75 Varick Street, New York, NY 10013-1919. **Phone:** 212-343-1234 Ext. 2700. **Fax:** 212-343-8470. **E-mail:** slenhart@audreycohen. edu.

Bernard M. Baruch College of the City University of New York

New York, New York

ZICKLIN SCHOOL OF BUSINESS

Graduate Business Faculty

Full-time: 127	Part-time: 59

Student Body

Total: 1,980	Average Age: 28
Full-time: 823	Women: 38%
Part-time: 1,157	

Admissions

Applications: 1,930	Average GMAT: 580
Admitted: 1,066	Average GPA: 3.2
Enrolled: 604	

Costs (1999–2000)

Full-time tuition: $4350 per academic year (resident), $7600 per academic year (nonresident)
Part-time tuition: $185 per credit (resident), $320 per credit (nonresident)

After Graduation (Class of 1998–99)

Employed within 3 months of graduation: 88%
Average starting salary: $53,000

Accreditation

AACSB—The International Association for Management Education

DEGREES EMBA • JD/MBA • MBA • MS

EMBA—Executive MBA Full-time. At least 54 total credits required. 24 months to complete program. *Concentrations:* strategic management.

JD/MBA—Juris Doctor/Master of Business Administration Full-time and part-time. At least 131 total credits required. 42 to 72 months to complete program.

MBA—Accelerated Part-Time MBA Program Part-time. At least 54 total credits required. 28 months to complete program. *Concentrations:* accounting, entrepreneurship, finance, international business, management information systems, marketing.

MBA—Master of Business Administration Full-time and part-time. At least 64 total credits required. 24 to 72 months to complete program. *Concentrations:* electronic commerce (e-commerce).

MBA—Master of Business Administration Full-time and part-time. At least 54 total credits required. 24 to 72 months to complete program. *Concentrations:* accounting, advertising, decision sciences, economics, entrepreneurship, finance, health care, human resources, international business, international marketing, management, management information systems, marketing, operations management, organizational behavior/development, quantitative analysis, taxation.

MS—Executive Master of Science in Finance Full-time. At least 30 total credits required. 12 months to complete program.

MS—Executive Master of Science in Taxation Full-time. At least 30 total credits required. 18 months to complete program.

MS—Master of Science in Accountancy Full-time and part-time. 30 to 60 total credits required. 18 to 72 months to complete program.

MS—Master of Science in Business Computer Information Systems Full-time and part-time. 36 to 53 total credits required. 18 to 72 months to complete program.

MS—Master of Science in Marketing *Concentrations:* electronic commerce (e-commerce).

MS—Master of Science in Marketing Full-time and part-time. At least 30 total credits required. 18 to 72 months to complete program.

MS—Master of Science in Operations Research Full-time and part-time. Fall admission only for FT program; fall or spring admission for PT program. 30 to 49 total credits required. 18 to 72 months to complete program.

MS—Master of Science in Statistics Part-time. Fall admission only; PT program only. 36 to 55 total credits required. 36 to 72 months to complete program.

MS—Master of Science in Taxation Part-time. Fall admission only; PT program only. At least 30 total credits required. 30 to 72 months to complete program.

COSTS

Tuition, state resident: *Full-time* $4350. *Part-time* $185 per credit. **Tuition, nonresident:** *Full-time* $7600. *Part-time* $320 per credit. **Required fees:** Tuition and fees vary by class time and academic program.

FINANCIAL AID (1999–2000)

120 students received aid, including fellowships, loans, research assistantships, scholarships, teaching assistantships, and work study. Financial aid application deadline: 3/1. **Financial Aid Contact** Mr. James Murphy, Director of Financial Aid, 17 Lexington Avenue, Box H-0725, New York, NY 10010. **Phone:** 212-802-2240. **E-mail:** financial_aid @ baruch.cuny.edu.

RESOURCES AND SERVICES

Information about online services, personal computer policies, library resources, international exchange programs, internship programs, and placement services at this institution and others can be found at **www.petersons.com/mba**

International Students

25% of students enrolled are international students.

Services and Facilities Counseling/support services, ESL/language courses, housing location assistance, international student organization, orientation, visa services, english communication immersion program. Financial aid is available to international students.

Applying *Required:* TOEFL with recommended score of 570 (paper), TWE with recommended score of 4.5, proof of adequate funds, proof of health/immunizations.

International Student Contact Mr. Stephen Goldberg, Director, International Students Office, 17 Lexington Avenue, Box F-1711, New York, NY 10010. **Phone:** 212-802-2350. **E-mail:** issc@baruch.cuny.edu.

■ APPLICATION

Required GMAT, application form, baccalaureate/first degree, essay, 2 letters of recommendation, personal statement, resume/curriculum vitae, transcripts of college work. School will accept GRE. **Recommended** Work experience.

Deadlines and Fees *Deadlines:* 3/1 for fall, 11/1 for spring, 3/1 for fall (international), 11/1 for spring (international). *Application fee:* $40, $40 (international).

Application Contact Mr. Michael Wynne, Office of Graduate Admissions, 17 Lexington Avenue, Box H-0880, New York, NY 10010-5585. **Phone:** 212-802-2330. **Fax:** 212-802-2335. **E-mail:** graduate_admissions@baruch.cuny.edu.

See full description on page 566.

Canisius College

Buffalo, New York

WEHLE SCHOOL OF BUSINESS

Graduate Business Faculty
Full-time: 29   Part-time: 10

Student Body
Total: 387   Average Age: 31
Full-time: 58   Women: 37%
Part-time: 329

Admissions
Applications: 186   Average GMAT: 510
Admitted: 139   Average GPA: 3
Enrolled: 83

Costs (1999–2000)
Full-time tuition: N/R
Part-time tuition: $555 per credit hour

Accreditation
AACSB—The International Association for Management Education

DEGREES MBA • MSTM

MBA—Master of Business Administration in Professional Accounting Part-time. At least 61 total credits required. Maximum of 72 months to complete program.

MBA—One-Year MBA Full-time. 48 total credits required. 12 months to complete program.

MBA—Master of Business Administration Full-time and part-time. At least 51 total credits required. 24 to 60 months to complete program. *Concentrations:* accounting, finance, management, management information systems, marketing.

MSTM—Master of Science in Telecommunications Management Part-time. At least 36 total credits required. 24 to 60 months to complete program.

COSTS

Tuition *Part-time:* $545 per credit hour. Tuition varies by academic program. **Required fees:** *Part-time* $10 per credit hour. **Graduate housing:** Room and board costs vary by number of occupants, type of accommodation, and type of board plan. *Typical cost:* $5500 (including board).

FINANCIAL AID (1999–2000)

193 students received aid, including loans, research assistantships, and scholarships. Aid is available to part-time students. Financial aid application deadline: 6/15. **Financial Aid Contact** Mr. Curt Gaume, Director of Financial Aid, 2001 Main Street, Buffalo, NY 14208-1098. **Phone:** 716-888-2300.

RESOURCES AND SERVICES

Information about online services, personal computer policies, library resources, international exchange programs, internship programs, and placement services at this institution and others can be found at **www.petersons.com/mba**

International Students

4% of students enrolled are international students.

Services and Facilities Counseling/support services, ESL/language courses, housing location assistance, international student housing, international student organization, language tutoring, orientation, visa services. Financial aid is not available to international students.

Applying *Required:* TOEFL with recommended score of 200 (computer) or 500 (paper), proof of adequate funds, proof of health/immunizations.

International Student Contact Ms. Ester Northman, Director, International Student Programs, 2001 Main Street, Buffalo, NY 14208-1098. **E-mail:** northman@canisius.edu.

■ APPLICATION

Required GMAT, application form, baccalaureate/first degree, essay, personal statement, transcripts of college work. School will accept GRE. **Recommended** Letter(s) of recommendation, resume/curriculum vitae.

Deadlines and Fees Applications for domestic and international students are processed on a rolling basis. *Application fee:* $25, $25 (international).

Application Contact Ms. Laura McEwen, Dean of Graduate Business Programs, 2001 Main Street, Buffalo, NY 14208-1098. **Phone:** 716-888-2140. **Fax:** 716-888-2525. **E-mail:** mcewenl@canisius.edu.

Clarkson University

Potsdam, New York

SCHOOL OF BUSINESS

Graduate Business Faculty
Full-time: 30   Part-time: 3

Student Body
Total: 124   Average Age: 26
Full-time: 89   Women: 35%
Part-time: 35

Admissions
Applications: 167   Average GMAT: 560
Admitted: 124   Average GPA: 3.3
Enrolled: 89

Clarkson University (continued)

Costs (1999–2000)
Full-time tuition: $21,984 per academic year
Part-time tuition: $687 per credit hour

After Graduation (Class of 1998–99)
Employed within 3 months of graduation: 80%
Average starting salary: $48,200

Accreditation
AACSB—The International Association for Management Education

DEGREES MBA • MS

MBA—Master of Business Administration Full-time and part-time. At least 32 total credits required. 12 to 24 months to complete program.

MS—Master of Science in Management Systems Full-time and part-time. At least 30 total credits required. 12 to 24 months to complete program. *Concentrations:* business information science, human resources, manufacturing management.

COSTS
Tuition *Full-time:* $21,984. *Part-time:* $687 per credit hour. **Tuition, international:** *Full-time* $21,984. **Graduate housing:** Room and board costs vary by campus location, type of accommodation, and type of board plan. *Typical cost:* $5500 (including board).

FINANCIAL AID (1999–2000)
87 students received aid, including research assistantships and teaching assistantships. Aid is available to part-time students. **Financial Aid Contact** Michelle Y. Bonville, Associate Director of Graduate Business Programs, CU Box 5770, 207 Snell Hall, Potsdam, NY 13699-5770. **Phone:** 315-268-6613. **Fax:** 315-268-3810. **E-mail:** bonvillm@clarkson. edu.

RESOURCES AND SERVICES
Information about online services, personal computer policies, library resources, international exchange programs, internship programs, and placement services at this institution and others can be found at **www. petersons.com/mba**

International Students
26% of students enrolled are international students.

Services and Facilities Counseling/support services, ESL/language courses, international student organization, orientation, visa services. Financial aid is available to international students.
Applying *Required:* TOEFL with recommended score of 600 (paper), TSE with recommended score of 50, proof of adequate funds, proof of health/immunizations.
International Student Contact Ms. Mary Theis, Director, International Students, Box 5645, Potsdam, NY 13699. **E-mail:** theism@clarkson.edu.

■ APPLICATION
Required GMAT, application form, baccalaureate/first degree, essay, 3 letters of recommendation, resume/curriculum vitae, transcripts of college work. **Recommended** Interview, personal statement, work experience.
Deadlines and Fees Applications for domestic students are processed on a rolling basis. *Application fee:* $25, $35 (international).
Application Contact Michelle Y. Bonville, Associate Director of Graduate Business Programs, CU Box 5770, 207 Snell Hall, Potsdam, NY 13699-5770. **Phone:** 315-268-6613. **Fax:** 315-268-3810. **E-mail:** bonvillm@clarkson.edu.

See full description on page 596.

College of Insurance
New York, New York

PROGRAM IN BUSINESS ADMINISTRATION

Graduate Business Faculty
Full-time: 10 | Part-time: 25

Student Body
| Total: 87 | Part-time: 56 |
| Full-time: 31 | Average Age: 28 |

Admissions
| Average GMAT: 500 | Average GPA: 3 |

Costs (1999–2000)
Full-time tuition: N/R
Part-time tuition: $624 per credit

After Graduation (Class of 1998–99)
Employed within 3 months of graduation: 87%
Average starting salary: $50,000

DEGREES MBA • MS

MBA—Traditional MBA Full-time and part-time. At least 51 total credits required. 12 to 48 months to complete program. *Concentrations:* actuarial science, finance, insurance, risk management.

MS—Master of Science Full-time and part-time. At least 36 total credits required. 12 to 48 months to complete program.

COSTS
Tuition *Part-time:* $624 per credit. **Required fees:** *Full-time* $480. Tuition and fees vary by number of courses or credits taken. **Graduate housing:** Room and board costs vary by number of occupants and type of board plan. *Typical cost:* $9414 (including board), $7220 (room only).

FINANCIAL AID (1999–2000)
54 students received aid, including grants, loans, research assistantships, and work study. Aid is available to part-time students. Financial aid application deadline: 5/15. **Financial Aid Contact** Ms. Marjorie Melikian, Director of Financial Aid, 101 Murray Street, New York, NY 10007. **Phone:** 212-815-9222. **Fax:** 212-964-3381.

RESOURCES AND SERVICES
Information about online services, personal computer policies, library resources, international exchange programs, internship programs, and placement services at this institution and others can be found at **www. petersons.com/mba**

International Students
39% of students enrolled are international students.

Services and Facilities Counseling/support services, ESL/language courses, international student housing, international student organization, orientation, visa services. Financial aid is not available to international students.
Applying *Required:* TOEFL with recommended score of 550 (paper), proof of adequate funds, proof of health/immunizations.
International Student Contact Ms. Theresa C. Marro, Administrative Director, Enrollment, and International Student Services, 101 Murray Street, New York, NY 10007. **Phone:** 212-815-9232. **Fax:** 212-964-3381. **E-mail:** admissions@ tci.edu.

■ APPLICATION
Required Application form, baccalaureate/first degree, 2 letters of recommendation, personal statement, transcripts of college work. School will accept GMAT. **Recommended** Interview, resume/curriculum vitae.
Deadlines and Fees Applications for international students are processed on a rolling basis. *Deadlines:* 8/1 for fall, 12/1 for spring. *Application fee:* $30, $50 (international).
Application Contact Ms. Theresa C. Marro, Administrative Director, Enrollment and International Student Affairs, 101 Murray Street, New York, NY 10007. **Phone:** 212-815-9232. **Fax:** 212-964-3381. **E-mail:** admissions@tci.edu.

The College of Saint Rose
Albany, New York

SCHOOL OF BUSINESS

Graduate Business Faculty
Full-time: 13

Student Body
Total: 133	Average Age: 32
Full-time: 15	Women: 52%
Part-time: 118	

Admissions
Applications: 74	Average GMAT: 497
Admitted: 66	Average GPA: 3.1
Enrolled: 52	

Costs (1999–2000)
Full-time tuition: N/R
Part-time tuition: $351 per credit

After Graduation (Class of 1998–99)
Employed within 3 months of graduation: 96%
Average starting salary: $42,500

Accreditation
ACBSP—The American Council of Business Schools and Programs

DEGREES JD/MBA • MBA • MS

JD/MBA—Juris Doctor/Master of Business Administration Full-time and part-time. At least 102 total credits required. 36 to 48 months to complete program.

MBA—Accelerated MBA Part-time. At least 36 total credits required. 24 months to complete program.

MBA—One-year MBA Full-time. At least 36 total credits required. 12 months to complete program.

MBA—Part-time MBA Part-time. At least 36 total credits required. 24 to 96 months to complete program.

MS—Master of Science in Accounting Full-time and part-time. At least 30 total credits required. 12 to 96 months to complete program. *Concentrations:* accounting.

COSTS

Tuition *Part-time:* $351 per credit. **Graduate housing:** Room and board costs vary by type of board plan. *Typical cost:* $6034 (including board).

FINANCIAL AID (1999–2000)

23 students received aid, including loans, research assistantships, scholarships, and work study. Aid is available to part-time students. Financial aid application deadline: 3/1. **Financial Aid Contact** Mr. James Vallee, Director of Financial Aid, 432 Western Avenue, Albany, NY 12203. **Phone:** 518-454-5168.

RESOURCES AND SERVICES

Information about online services, personal computer policies, library resources, international exchange programs, internship programs, and placement services at this institution and others can be found at **www.petersons.com/mba**

International Students

3% of students enrolled are international students.

Services and Facilities Counseling/support services, housing location assistance, international student housing, international student organization, language tutoring, orientation, visa services, international student health insurance, assistance with preparation of appropriate tax forms. Financial aid is available to international students.

Applying *Required:* TOEFL with recommended score of 550 (paper), proof of adequate funds, proof of health/immunizations.

International Student Contact Ms. Alice Torda, Director of International Programs, 432 Western Avenue, Albany, NY 12203.

■ APPLICATION

Required Application form, baccalaureate/first degree, essay, 2 letters of recommendation, personal statement, resume/curriculum vitae, transcripts of college work. School will accept GMAT.

Deadlines and Fees *Deadlines:* 7/15 for fall, 12/1 for spring, 4/1 for summer, 7/15 for fall (international), 12/1 for spring (international), 4/1 for summer (international). *Application fee:* $30, $30 (international).

Application Contact Ann Tully, Director of Graduate Admissions, Adult and Continuing Education, 432 Western Avenue, Albany, NY 12203. **Phone:** 518-454-5143. **E-mail:** mba@mail.strose.edu.

See full description on page 604.

Columbia University

New York, New York

GRADUATE SCHOOL OF BUSINESS

Graduate Business Faculty
Full-time: 117   Part-time: 81

Student Body
Total: 1,256
Full-time: 1,256   Average Age: 27
                          Women: 36%

Admissions
Applications: 5,719   Average GMAT: 700
Admitted: 658   Average GPA: 3.45
Enrolled: 487

Costs (1999–2000)
Full-time tuition: $29,174 per academic year
Part-time tuition: N/R

After Graduation (Class of 1998–99)
Employed within 3 months of graduation: 100%
Average starting salary: $136,000

Accreditation
AACSB—The International Association for Management Education

DEGREES DDS/MBA • EdD/MBA • JD/MBA • MBA • MBA/MIA • MBA/MPH • MBA/MS • MD/MBA

DDS/MBA—Doctor of Dental Surgery/Master of Business Administration Full-time. Students must complete 5 terms of full-time matriculation at the Dental School prior to entering the Business School. Minimum of 54 months to complete program.

EdD/MBA—Doctor of Educational Leadership and Management/Master of Business Administration Full-time. Must apply and be admitted to both schools. At least 90 total credits required. Minimum of 27 months to complete program.

JD/MBA—Juris Doctor/Master of Business Administration Full-time. Must apply and be admitted to both schools. At least 118 total credits required. Minimum of 21 months to complete program.

MBA—Executive MBA Full-time. Must have company sponsorship and 5 or more years of organizational experience. At least 60 total credits required. Minimum of 19 months to complete program.

MBA—Executive MBA-Global (with London Business School) Full-time. Through one application process, students will be admitted to both Columbia and London Business Schools. At least 60 total credits required. Minimum of 19 months to complete program.

MBA—Master of Business Administration Full-time. At least 60 total credits required. 16 to 20 months to complete program. *Concentrations:* accounting, economics, entrepreneurship, finance, human resources, information management, international business, management, management information systems, management science, marketing, nonprofit management, operations management, public management, real estate, sports/entertainment management, telecommunications management.

MBA/MIA—Master of Business Administration/Master of International Affairs Full-time. Must apply and be admitted to both schools. At least 90 total credits required. Minimum of 27 months to complete program.

MBA/MPH—Master of Business Administration/Master of Public Health Full-time. Must apply and be admitted to both schools. At least 80 total credits required. Minimum of 24 months to complete program.

MBA/MS—Master of Business Administration/Master of Science in Industrial Engineering Full-time. Must apply and be admitted to both schools. At least 69 total credits required. Minimum of 21 months to complete program.

MBA/MS—Master of Business Administration/Master of Science in Journalism Full-time. Must apply and be admitted to both schools. At least 75 total credits required. Minimum of 21 months to complete program.

MBA/MS—Master of Business Administration/Master of Science in Mining Engineering Full-time. Must apply and be admitted to both schools. At least 75 total credits required. Minimum of 21 months to complete program.

MBA/MS—Master of Business Administration/Master of Science in Nursing Full-time. Must apply and be admitted to both schools. At least 75 total credits required. Minimum of 21 months to complete program.

MBA/MS—Master of Business Administration/Master of Science in Operations Research Full-time. Must apply and be admitted to both schools. At least 69 total credits required. Minimum of 21 months to complete program.

MBA/MS—Master of Business Administration/Master of Science in Social Work Full-time. Must apply and be admitted to both schools. At least 90 total credits required. Minimum of 27 months to complete program.

MBA/MS—Master of Business Administration/Master of Science in Urban Planning Full-time. Must apply and be admitted to both schools. At least 90 total credits required. Minimum of 27 months to complete program.

MD/MBA—Doctor of Medicine/Master of Business Administration Full-time. Students must begin matriculation at the Medical School. Minimum of 54 months to complete program.

COSTS

Tuition *Full-time:* $27,780. **Required fees:** *Full-time* $1394. **Graduate housing:** Room and board costs vary by number of occupants and type of accommodation. *Typical cost:* $10,360 (including board).

FINANCIAL AID (1999–2000)

Fellowships, grants, loans, scholarships, and work study. Financial aid application deadline: 2/1. **Financial Aid Contact** Ms. Kathleen Swan, Director of Financial Aid, Graduate School of Business, 218 Uris Hall, 3022 Broadway, New York, NY 10027. **Phone:** 212-854-4057. **Fax:** 212-854-1809. **E-mail:** kswan@claven.gsb.columbia.edu.

RESOURCES AND SERVICES

Information about online services, personal computer policies, library resources, international exchange programs, internship programs, and placement services at this institution and others can be found at **www.petersons.com/mba**

Columbia University (continued)

International Students
28% of students enrolled are international students.

Services and Facilities Counseling/support services, international student housing, visa services, student organizations for specific geographic regions . Financial aid is available to international students.

Applying *Required:* TOEFL with recommended score of 253 (computer) or 610 (paper), proof of adequate funds, proof of health/immunizations.

International Student Contact Ms. Pascale Pritsios, Associate Director for the Jerome A. Chazen Institute of International Business, Graduate School of Business, 214 Uris Hall, 3022 Broadway, New York, NY 10027. **Phone:** 212-854-4750. **Fax:** 212-222-9821. **E-mail:** ppritsio@claven.gsb.columbia.edu.

■ APPLICATION

Required GMAT, application form, baccalaureate/first degree, essay, 2 letters of recommendation, personal statement, resume/curriculum vitae, transcripts of college work, 2 years of work experience.

Deadlines and Fees *Deadlines:* 4/20 for fall, 10/1 for spring, 3/1 for fall (international), 10/1 for spring (international). *Application fee:* $160, $160 (international).

Application Contact Ms. Linda Meehan, Assistant Dean and Executive Director of Admissions and Financial Aid, Graduate School of Business, 216 Uris Hall, 3022 Broadway, New York, NY 10027. **Phone:** 212-854-1961. **Fax:** 212-662-6754. **E-mail:** apply@claven.gsb.columbia.edu.

See full description on page 610.

Cornell University

Ithaca, New York

PROFESSIONAL FIELD OF THE JOHNSON GRADUATE SCHOOL OF MANAGEMENT

Graduate Business Faculty

Full-time: 49	Part-time: 12

Student Body

Total: 560	Average Age: 29
Full-time: 560	Women: 25%

Admissions

Applications: 3,036	Average GMAT: 675
Admitted: 586	Average GPA: 3.45
Enrolled: 314	

Costs (1999–2000)
Full-time tuition: $25,648 per academic year
Part-time tuition: N/R

After Graduation (Class of 1998–99)
Employed within 3 months of graduation: 90%
Average starting salary: $80,246

Accreditation
AACSB—The International Association for Management Education

DEGREES JD/MBA • MBA • MBA/MA • MBA/MILR • ME/MBA

JD/MBA—Juris Doctor/Master of Business Administration Full-time. Minimum of 48 months to complete program.

MBA—Executive MBA Part-time. 8 years of full-time professional and substantial management experience and employer sponsorship required. At least 60 total credits required. Minimum of 18 months to complete program.

MBA—Master of Business Administration, Twelve-Month Option Full-time. Graduate science or technical degree required. At least 60 total credits required. Minimum of 12 months to complete program.

MBA—Master of Business Administration Full-time. At least 60 total credits required. Minimum of 18 months to complete program.

MBA/MA—Master of Business Administration/Master of Arts in Asian Studies Full-time. Minimum of 72 months to complete program.

MBA/MILR—Master of Business Administration/Master of Industrial and Labor Relations Full-time. Minimum of 48 months to complete program.

ME/MBA—Master of Engineering/Master of Business Administration Full-time. Minimum of 60 months to complete program.

COSTS

Tuition *Full-time:* $25,600. Tuition varies by academic program. **Required fees:** *Full-time* $48. **Graduate housing:** Room and board costs vary by campus location, number of occupants, type of accommodation, and type of board plan. *Typical cost:* $7500 (including board).

FINANCIAL AID (1999–2000)
213 students received aid, including fellowships, grants, loans, scholarships, and teaching assistantships. Financial aid application deadline: 1/15. **Financial Aid Contact** Ms. Ann Richards, Director of Financial Aid and Associate Director of Admission Operations, Sage Hall, Ithaca, NY 14853-6201. **Phone:** 607-255-9395. **Fax:** 607-225-0065. **E-mail:** mba@cornell.edu.

RESOURCES AND SERVICES
Information about online services, personal computer policies, library resources, international exchange programs, internship programs, and placement services at this institution and others can be found at **www.petersons.com/mba**

International Students
24% of students enrolled are international students.

Services and Facilities Counseling/support services, ESL/language courses, international student organization, orientation, visa services. Financial aid is available to international students.

Applying *Required:* TOEFL with recommended score of 600 (paper), proof of adequate funds, proof of health/immunizations. *Recommended:* TWE with recommended score of 4.

International Student Contact Ms. Harriet Peters, Director of Advising and Student Activities, 106 Sage Hall, Ithaca, NY 14853-6201. **Phone:** 607-255-9437. **Fax:** 607-255-6731. **E-mail:** hap1@cornell.edu.

■ APPLICATION

Required GMAT, application form, baccalaureate/first degree, essay, 2 letters of recommendation, personal statement, resume/curriculum vitae, transcripts of college work, 3 years of work experience.

Deadlines and Fees *Deadlines:* 11/15 for fall, 1/15 for winter, 3/15 for spring, 11/15 for fall (international), 1/15 for winter (international), 3/15 for spring (international). *Application fee:* $150, $150 (international).

Application Contact Ms. Natalie Grinblatt, Director of Admissions, 111 Sage Hall, Ithaca, NY 14853-6201. **Phone:** 607-255-4526. **Toll-free Phone:** 800-847-2082. **Fax:** 607-255-0065. **E-mail:** mba@cornell.edu.

See full description on page 614.

Dowling College

Oakdale, New York

SCHOOL OF BUSINESS

Graduate Business Faculty

Full-time: 19	Part-time: 64

Student Body

Total: 826	Average Age: 33
Full-time: 342	Women: 42%
Part-time: 484	

Admissions

Applications: 487	Enrolled: 242
Admitted: 459	

Costs (1999–2000)
Full-time tuition: N/R
Part-time tuition: $495 per credit

DEGREES MBA

MBA—Aviation Management MBA Full-time and part-time. At least 36 total credits required. 12 to 36 months to complete program.

MBA—Banking and Finance MBA Full-time and part-time. At least 36 total credits required. 12 to 36 months to complete program. *Concentrations:* banking, finance, international banking, international finance.

MBA—General Management MBA Full-time and part-time. At least 36 total credits required. 12 to 36 months to complete program. *Concentrations:* management.

MBA—Information Systems Management Full-time and part-time. Up to 36 total credits required. 12 to 36 months to complete program. *Concentrations:* information management.

MBA—Public Management MBA Full-time and part-time. At least 36 total credits required. 12 to 36 months to complete program. *Concentrations:* public management.

MBA—Saturday Accelerated MBA Full-time. At least 36 total credits required. 16 months to complete program. *Concentrations:* banking, finance, international banking, international finance, management.

MBA—Total Quality Management MBA Full-time and part-time. At least 36 total credits required. 12 to 36 months to complete program. *Concentrations:* quality management.

COSTS

Tuition *Part-time:* $495 per credit. Tuition varies by class time, number of courses or credits taken, campus location, and academic program. **Required fees:** *Full-time* $275. Tuition and fees vary by number of courses or credits taken and campus location. **Graduate housing:** Room and board costs vary by campus location, number of occupants, and type of accommodation. *Typical cost:* $5150 (room only).

FINANCIAL AID (1999–2000)

181 students received aid, including grants, research assistantships, scholarships, and work study. Aid is available to part-time students. Financial aid application deadline: 6/30. **Financial Aid Contact** Ms. Nancy Brewer, Director, Enrollment Services for Financial Aid, Idle Hour Boulevard, Oakdale, NY 11769-1999. **Phone:** 800-369-5464. **Fax:** 516-563-3827. **E-mail:** brewern@dowling.edu.

RESOURCES AND SERVICES

Information about online services, personal computer policies, library resources, international exchange programs, internship programs, and placement services at this institution and others can be found at **www.petersons.com/mba**

International Students

11% of students enrolled are international students.

Services and Facilities Counseling/support services, ESL/language courses, visa services. Financial aid is not available to international students.
Applying *Required:* TOEFL with recommended score of 550 (paper), proof of adequate funds, proof of health/immunizations. *Recommended:* TSE, TWE.
International Student Contact Ms. Mirka Pangracova, Coordinator, Enrollment Services—Fortunoff Hall, 206, Idle Hour Boulevard, Oakdale, NY 11769-1999. **Phone:** 516-244-5097. **Fax:** 516-563-3827. **E-mail:** pangracm@dowling.edu.

■ APPLICATION

Required GMAT, application form, baccalaureate/first degree, 2 letters of recommendation, resume/curriculum vitae, transcripts of college work. **Recommended** 3 years of work experience.
Deadlines and Fees Applications for domestic and international students are processed on a rolling basis. *Application fee:* $25.
Application Contact Mr. Herbert Armstrong, Assistant Dean, Idle Hour Boulevard, Oakdale, NY 11769-5098. **Phone:** 516-244-3193. **Toll-free Phone:** 800-DOWLING. **Fax:** 516-244-5098. **E-mail:** armstroh@dowling.edu.

D'Youville College

Buffalo, New York

DEPARTMENT OF BUSINESS

Graduate Business Faculty
Full-time: 3

Student Body

Total: 18	Part-time: 14
Full-time: 4	Women: 61%

Admissions

Applications: 11	Enrolled: 6
Admitted: 11	

Costs (1999–2000)
Full-time tuition: N/R
Part-time tuition: $405 per credit

DEGREE MS

MS—Master of Science in International Business Full-time and part-time. *Distance learning option.* 38 to 44 total credits required. 24 to 60 months to complete program.

COSTS

Tuition *Part-time:* $405 per credit. Tuition varies by number of courses or credits taken. **Graduate housing:** Room and board costs vary by number of occupants and type of board plan. *Typical cost:* $5380 (including board).

FINANCIAL AID (1999–2000)

Scholarships. Aid is available to part-time students. Financial aid application deadline: 8/1. **Financial Aid Contact** Mr. Joseph Syracuse, Graduate Admissions Director, 320 Porter Avenue, Buffalo, NY 14201-1084. **Phone:** 716-881-7676. **Fax:** 716-881-7790. **E-mail:** syracujc@dyc.edu.

RESOURCES AND SERVICES

Information about online services, personal computer policies, library resources, international exchange programs, internship programs, and placement services at this institution and others can be found at **www.petersons.com/mba**

International Students

11% of students enrolled are international students.

Services and Facilities Counseling/support services, international student housing.
Applying *Required:* TOEFL with recommended score of 550 (paper), proof of adequate funds, proof of health/immunizations.
International Student Contact Mr. Joseph Syracuse, Graduate Admissions Director, 320 Porter Avenue, Buffalo, NY 14201-1084. **Phone:** 716-881-7676. **Fax:** 716-881-7790. **E-mail:** syracujc@dyc.edu.

■ APPLICATION

Required Application form, baccalaureate/first degree, interview, letter(s) of recommendation, transcripts of college work. School will accept GMAT and GRE.
Recommended Essay, resume/curriculum vitae, work experience.
Deadlines and Fees Applications for domestic and international students are processed on a rolling basis. *Application fee:* $25, $25 (international).
Application Contact Mr. Joseph Syracuse, Graduate Admissions Director, 320 Porter Avenue, Buffalo, NY 14201-1084. **Phone:** 716-881-7676. **Toll-free Phone:** 800-777-3921. **Fax:** 716-881-7790. **E-mail:** syracujc@dyc.edu.

Fordham University

New York, New York

COLLEGE OF BUSINESS ADMINISTRATION

Graduate Business Faculty

Full-time: 85	Part-time: 180

Student Body

Total: 1,569	Part-time: 1,162
Full-time: 407	Average Age: 27

Admissions

Applications: 934	Average GMAT: 600
Admitted: 620	Average GPA: 3.1
Enrolled: 314	

Costs (1999–2000)
Full-time tuition: N/R
Part-time tuition: $620 per credit

After Graduation (Class of 1998–99)
Employed within 3 months of graduation: 90%
Average starting salary: $75,000

Accreditation
AACSB—The International Association for Management Education

DEGREES MBA • MS • MTaxA

MBA—Deming Scholars MBA Full-time. At least 60 total credits required. 18 months to complete program. *Concentrations:* quality management.

MBA—Global Professional MBA Full-time and part-time. 45 to 78 total credits required. 12 to 72 months to complete program. *Concentrations:* accounting, finance, information management, management, marketing, quality management.

MBA—Master of Business Administration Full-time and part-time. 45 to 69 total credits required. 12 to 72 months to complete program. *Concentrations:* accounting, finance, information management, management, marketing, quality management.

MS—Master of Science in Taxation Full-time and part-time. 39 to 54 total credits required. 12 to 72 months to complete program. *Concentrations:* taxation.

MTaxA—Master of Taxation and Accounting Full-time. 66 to 99 total credits required. 18 to 24 months to complete program. *Concentrations:* accounting, taxation.

COSTS

Tuition *Part-time:* $620 per credit. **Required fees:** Tuition and fees vary by number of courses or credits taken. **Graduate housing:** *Typical cost:* $12,000 (room only).

Fordham University (continued)

FINANCIAL AID (1999–2000)
185 students received aid, including fellowships, loans, research assistantships, scholarships, and teaching assistantships. Financial aid application deadline: 5/1. **Financial Aid Contact** Ms. Kathy Pattison, Assistant Dean, Admissions and Financial Aid, 33 West 60th Street, Fourth Floor, New York, NY 10023. **Phone:** 212-636-6200. **Fax:** 212-636-7076. **E-mail:** admissionsgb@fordham.edu.

RESOURCES AND SERVICES
Information about online services, personal computer policies, library resources, international exchange programs, internship programs, and placement services at this institution and others can be found at www.petersons.com/mba

International Students
11% of students enrolled are international students.

Services and Facilities Counseling/support services, ESL/language courses, international student organization, orientation, visa services. Financial aid is available to international students.
Applying *Required:* TOEFL with recommended score of 250 (computer) or 600 (paper), proof of adequate funds, proof of health/immunizations.
International Student Contact Ms. Kathy Pattison, Assistant Dean, Admissions and Financial Aid, 33 West 60th Street, Fourth Floor, New York, NY 10023. **Phone:** 212-636-6200. **Fax:** 212-636-7076. **E-mail:** admissionsgb@fordham.edu.

■ APPLICATION
Required GMAT, application form, baccalaureate/first degree, essay, 2 letters of recommendation, personal statement, resume/curriculum vitae, transcripts of college work. **Recommended** Interview, 2 years of work experience.

Deadlines and Fees Applications for domestic and international students are processed on a rolling basis. *Application fee:* $65, $65 (international).

Application Contact Ms. Kathy Pattison, Assistant Dean, Admissions and Financial Aid, 33 West 60th Street, Fourth Floor, New York, NY 10023. **Phone:** 212-636-6200. **Toll-free Phone:** 800-825-4422. **Fax:** 212-636-7076. **E-mail:** admissionsgb@fordham.edu.

See full description on page 658.

Hofstra University
Hempstead, New York

FRANK G. ZARB SCHOOL OF BUSINESS

Graduate Business Faculty
Full-time: 48 — Part-time: 2

Student Body
Total: 650
Full-time: 180 — Average Age: 26
Part-time: 470 — Women: 39%

Admissions
Applications: 500
Admitted: 290 — Average GMAT: 570
Enrolled: 185 — Average GPA: 3.2

Costs (1999–2000)
Full-time tuition: N/R
Part-time tuition: $474 per credit

After Graduation (Class of 1998–99)
Employed within 3 months of graduation: 92%
Average starting salary: $64,500

Accreditation
AACSB—The International Association for Management Education

DEGREES MBA • MS

MBA—Executive MBA Part-time. 7 years of work experience required. At least 48 total credits required. 20 months to complete program. *Concentrations:* management.

MBA—Master of Business Administration Full-time and part-time. 42 to 66 total credits required. 12 to 60 months to complete program. *Concentrations:* accounting, finance, international business, management, management information systems, marketing, taxation.

MS—Master of Science in Accounting Full-time and part-time. BA in accounting or equivalent required. 30 to 36 total credits required. 12 to 36 months to complete program. *Concentrations:* accounting.

MS—Master of Science in Accounting Information Systems Full-time and part-time. BA in accounting or equivalent required. 30 to 36 total credits required. 12 to 36 months to complete program. *Concentrations:* financial information systems.

MS—Master of Science in Accounting and Taxation Full-time and part-time. BA in accounting or equivalent required. 30 to 36 total credits required. 12 to 36 months to complete program. *Concentrations:* accounting, taxation.

MS—Master of Science in Computer Information Systems Full-time and part-time. 30 to 36 total credits required. 12 to 36 months to complete program. *Concentrations:* management information systems.

MS—Master of Science in Finance Full-time and part-time. 30 to 36 total credits required. 12 to 36 months to complete program. *Concentrations:* finance.

MS—Master of Science in Human Resources Management Full-time and part-time. 30 to 36 total credits required. 12 to 36 months to complete program. *Concentrations:* human resources.

MS—Master of Science in Marketing Research Full-time and part-time. 30 to 36 total credits required. 12 to 36 months to complete program. *Concentrations:* marketing research.

MS—Master of Science in Taxation Full-time and part-time. BA in accounting or equivalent required. 30 to 36 total credits required. 12 to 36 months to complete program. *Concentrations:* taxation.

COSTS
Tuition *Part-time:* $474 per credit. **Required fees:** *Full-time* $520. *Part-time* $350 per year. Fees vary by number of courses or credits taken. **Graduate housing:** Room and board costs vary by campus location, number of occupants, type of accommodation, and type of board plan. *Typical cost:* $8500 (including board).

FINANCIAL AID (1999–2000)
50 students received aid, including fellowships, grants, research assistantships, scholarships, and work study. Financial aid application deadline: 4/1. **Financial Aid Contact** Ms. Susan McTiernan, Associate Dean for Graduate Programs, 134 Hofstra University, Hempstead, NY 11549-1090. **Phone:** 516-463-5683. **Fax:** 516-463-5268. **E-mail:** bizsmm@hofstra.edu.

RESOURCES AND SERVICES
Information about online services, personal computer policies, library resources, international exchange programs, internship programs, and placement services at this institution and others can be found at www.petersons.com/mba

International Students
8% of students enrolled are international students.

Services and Facilities Counseling/support services, ESL/language courses, housing location assistance, international student housing, international student organization, language tutoring, orientation, visa services. Financial aid is not available to international students.
Applying *Required:* TOEFL with recommended score of 580 (paper), proof of adequate funds, proof of health/immunizations.
International Student Contact Ann Nastasi, Director of International Students' Office, 200 Hofstra University, Hempstead, NY 11549. **Phone:** 516-467-6796. **Fax:** 516-463-6921. **E-mail:** dnsamn@hofstra.edu.

■ APPLICATION
Required GMAT, application form, baccalaureate/first degree, essay, 2 letters of recommendation, personal statement, resume/curriculum vitae, transcripts of college work.

Deadlines and Fees Applications for domestic and international students are processed on a rolling basis. *Application fee:* $40, $75 (international).

Application Contact Office of Graduate Admissions, 100 Hofstra University, Hempstead, NY 11549-1090. **Phone:** 516-463-6700. **Fax:** 516-560-7660. **E-mail:** hofstra@hofstra.edu.

See full description on page 676.

Iona College
New Rochelle, New York

HAGAN SCHOOL OF BUSINESS

Graduate Business Faculty
Full-time: 35 — Part-time: 18

Student Body

Total: 292

Full-time: 41

Part-time: 251

Average Age: 30

Women: 43%

Admissions

Applications: 134

Admitted: 119

Enrolled: 80

Average GMAT: 487

Average GPA: 3.2

Costs (1999–2000)

Full-time tuition: N/R

Part-time tuition: $515 per credit

After Graduation (Class of 1998–99)

Employed within 3 months of graduation: 96%

Accreditation

AACSB—The International Association for Management Education

DEGREE MBA

MBA—Master of Business Administration Full-time and part-time. *Distance learning option.* 33 to 57 total credits required. 18 to 72 months to complete program. *Concentrations:* finance, human resources, management, management information systems, marketing.

COSTS

Tuition *Part-time:* $515 per credit. **Required fees:** *Part-time* $45 per trimester.

FINANCIAL AID (1999–2000)

48 students received aid, including loans, scholarships, and work study. Aid is available to part-time students. **Financial Aid Contact** Student Financial Services, 715 North Avenue, New Rochelle, NY 10801-1890. **Phone:** 914-633-2497.

RESOURCES AND SERVICES

Information about online services, personal computer policies, library resources, international exchange programs, internship programs, and placement services at this institution and others can be found at **www.petersons.com/mba**

International Students

2% of students enrolled are international students.

Services and Facilities Counseling/support services. Financial aid is available to international students.

Applying *Required:* TOEFL with recommended score of 550 (paper), proof of adequate funds, proof of health/immunizations.

International Student Contact Mr. Geoffrey Rhet, International Student Advisor, 715 North Avenue, New Rochelle, NY 10801. **Phone:** 914-633-2502.

■ APPLICATION

Required GMAT, application form, baccalaureate/first degree, essay, 2 letters of recommendation, personal statement, transcripts of college work. **Recommended** Interview, resume/curriculum vitae, work experience.

Deadlines and Fees Applications for domestic and international students are processed on a rolling basis. *Application fee:* $50, $50 (international).

Application Contact Ms. Carol Shea, Director of MBA Admissions, 715 North Avenue, New Rochelle, NY 10801-1890. **Phone:** 914-633-2289. **Toll-free Phone:** 800-231-IONA. **Fax:** 914-633-2012. **E-mail:** cshea@iona.edu.

See full description on page 690.

Lehman College of the City University of New York

Bronx, New York

DEPARTMENT OF ECONOMICS AND ACCOUNTING

DEGREES MS • MSED

MS—Master of Science in Accounting Full-time and part-time. GMAT required. At least 30 total credits required. 12 to 60 months to complete program.

MSED—Master of Science in Business Education Full-time and part-time. 30 to 36 total credits required. Maximum of 60 months to complete program.

RESOURCES AND SERVICES

Information about online services, personal computer policies, library resources, international exchange programs, internship programs, and placement services at this institution and others can be found at **www.petersons.com/mba**

International Students

Services and Facilities Financial aid is not available to international students. **International Student Contact** Ms. Ann O'Sullivan, Coordinator of International Student Services, 250 Bedford Park Boulevard West, Bronx, NY 10468-1589. **Phone:** 718-960-7274. **Fax:** 718-960-8712. **E-mail:** sullivan@alpha.lehman.cuny.edu.

■ APPLICATION

Application Contact Office of Graduate Admissions, Shuster Hall, Room 158, Bronx, NY 10468-1589. **Phone:** 718-960-8713. **Toll-free Phone:** 877-LEHMAN-1. **Fax:** 718-960-8712. **E-mail:** enroll@lehman.cuny.edu.

Le Moyne College

Syracuse, New York

DEPARTMENT OF BUSINESS

Graduate Business Faculty

Full-time: 26

Part-time: 2

Student Body

Total: 380

Full-time: 5

Part-time: 375

Average Age: 34

Women: 42%

Admissions

Applications: 84

Admitted: 55

Enrolled: 53

Average GMAT: 500

Average GPA: 3

Costs (1999–2000)

Full-time tuition: N/R

Part-time tuition: $399 per credit hour

After Graduation (Class of 1998–99)

Employed within 3 months of graduation: 99%

DEGREES MBA

MBA—Master of Business Administration Part-time. At least 54 total credits required. 24 to 72 months to complete program. *Concentrations:* accounting, human resources, leadership, management information systems.

MBA—Master of Business Administration Part-time. 51 total credits required. 24 to 72 months to complete program.

COSTS

Tuition *Part-time:* $399 per credit hour. Tuition varies by number of courses or credits taken.

FINANCIAL AID (1999–2000)

9 students received aid, including loans and research assistantships. Aid is available to part-time students. **Financial Aid Contact** William Cheetham, Financial Aid Director, 1419 Salt Springs Road, Syracuse, NY 13214-1399. **Phone:** 315-445-4400.

RESOURCES AND SERVICES

Information about online services, personal computer policies, library resources, international exchange programs, internship programs, and placement services at this institution and others can be found at **www.petersons.com/mba**

International Students

1% of students enrolled are international students.

Services and Facilities Counseling/support services, visa services.

Applying *Required:* TOEFL with recommended score of 550 (paper), proof of adequate funds, proof of health/immunizations.

International Student Contact Dr. Norbert Henry, Director of Adult Education, 1419 Salt Springs Road, Syracuse, NY 13214-1399. **Phone:** 315-445-4144. **E-mail:** henry@maple.lemoyne.edu.

■ APPLICATION

Required GMAT, application form, baccalaureate/first degree, interview, 2 letters of recommendation, resume/curriculum vitae, transcripts of college work, 2 years of work experience.

Deadlines and Fees Applications for domestic and international students are processed on a rolling basis.

Application Contact Dr. Wally J. Elmer, Professor and MBA Director, 1419 Salt Springs Road, Syracuse, NY 13214-1399. **Phone:** 315-445-4786. **Fax:** 315-445-4787. **E-mail:** elmer@maple.lemoyne.edu.

Long Island University, Brooklyn Campus

Brooklyn, New York

SCHOOL OF BUSINESS AND PUBLIC ADMINISTRATION

Graduate Business Faculty
Full-time: 25   Part-time: 27

Student Body
Total: 212   Average Age: 30
Full-time: 91   Women: 50%
Part-time: 121

Admissions
Average GMAT: 480   Average GPA: 3

Costs (1999–2000)
Full-time tuition: N/R
Part-time tuition: $505 per credit

After Graduation (Class of 1998–99)
Employed within 3 months of graduation: 85%

DEGREES MBA • MPA • MS • MSHR

MBA—Generic MBA Full-time and part-time. 30 to 54 total credits required. 18 to 72 months to complete program.

MBA—MBA for Certified Public Accountants Full-time and part-time. 30 to 78 total credits required. 18 to 72 months to complete program.

MBA—Master of Business Administration Full-time and part-time. 30 to 54 total credits required. 18 to 72 months to complete program. *Concentrations:* accounting, finance, international business, management, marketing, taxation.

MPA—Master of Public Administration Full-time and part-time. 36 to 48 total credits required. 18 to 72 months to complete program.

MS—Master of Science in Accounting Full-time and part-time. At least 36 total credits required. 18 to 72 months to complete program.

MS—Master of Science in Taxation Full-time and part-time. At least 36 total credits required. 18 to 72 months to complete program.

MSHR—Master of Science in Human Resources Full-time and part-time. 36 to 48 total credits required. 18 to 72 months to complete program. *Concentrations:* human resources.

COSTS

Tuition *Part-time:* $505 per credit. Tuition varies by number of courses or credits taken. **Required fees:** *Full-time* $150.

FINANCIAL AID (1999–2000)

25 students received aid, including fellowships, grants, loans, research assistantships, scholarships, and work study. Aid is available to part-time students. **Financial Aid Contact** Ms. Rose Iannicelli, Director of Financial Aid, One University Plaza, Brooklyn, NY 11201-8423. **Phone:** 718-488-3320. **Fax:** 718-488-3343. **E-mail:** yanni@joshua.liu.edu.

RESOURCES AND SERVICES

Information about online services, personal computer policies, library resources, international exchange programs, internship programs, and placement services at this institution and others can be found at **www.petersons.com/mba**

International Students

9% of students enrolled are international students.

Services and Facilities Counseling/support services, ESL/language courses, international student housing, international student organization, language tutoring, orientation. Financial aid is available to international students.

Applying *Required:* TOEFL with recommended score of 600 (paper), proof of adequate funds, proof of health/immunizations.

International Student Contact Mr. Steven Chin, Director of International Student Services, One University Plaza, Brooklyn, NY 11201-8423. **Phone:** 718-488-1216. **E-mail:** schin@hornet_liu.edu.

■ APPLICATION

Required GMAT, application form, baccalaureate/first degree, letter(s) of recommendation, personal statement, resume/curriculum vitae, transcripts of college work. **Recommended** Essay.

Deadlines and Fees *Deadlines:* 7/15 for fall, 1/1 for winter, 5/15 for spring, 5/15 for summer, 7/1 for fall (international), 12/15 for winter (international), 5/1 for summer (international). *Application fee:* $30, $30 (international).

Application Contact Mr. Alan Chaves, Dean of Admissions, One University Plaza, Brooklyn, NY 11201-8423. **Phone:** 800-548-7526. **Fax:** 718-797-2399. **E-mail:** attend@liu.edu.

Long Island University, C.W. Post Campus

Brookville, New York

COLLEGE OF MANAGEMENT

Graduate Business Faculty
Full-time: 41   Part-time: 69

Student Body
Total: 461   Average Age: 29
Full-time: 129   Women: 40%
Part-time: 332

Admissions
Applications: 325   Average GMAT: 500
Admitted: 277   Average GPA: 2.8
Enrolled: 196

Costs (1999–2000)
Full-time tuition: N/R
Part-time tuition: $525 per credit

After Graduation (Class of 1998–99)
Employed within 3 months of graduation: 95%

DEGREES JD/MBA • MBA • MS

JD/MBA—Dual JD/MBA Full-time and part-time. 102 to 117 total credits required. 48 to 72 months to complete program.

MBA—Accelerated International MBA Full-time. At least 36 total credits required. 18 to 60 months to complete program. *Concentrations:* international business.

MBA—Master of Business Administration Full-time and part-time. 36 to 60 total credits required. 18 to 60 months to complete program. *Concentrations:* finance, international business, logistics, management, management information systems, marketing.

MS—Master of Science in Accountancy Full-time and part-time. 36 to 60 total credits required. 18 to 60 months to complete program. *Concentrations:* accounting, taxation.

MS—Master of Science in Taxation Full-time and part-time. 36 to 60 total credits required. 18 to 60 months to complete program. *Concentrations:* human resources, taxation.

COSTS

Tuition *Part-time:* $525 per credit. Tuition varies by number of courses or credits taken and academic program. **Required fees:** *Part-time* $95 per semester. Tuition and fees vary by number of courses or credits taken. **Graduate housing:** Room and board costs vary by number of occupants, type of accommodation, and type of board plan. *Typical cost:* $5890 (including board).

FINANCIAL AID (1999–2000)

280 students received aid, including fellowships, grants, loans, research assistantships, teaching assistantships, and work study. Aid is available to part-time students. **Financial Aid Contact** Mrs. Joanne Graziano, Director, Financial Aid, 720 Northern Boulevard, Brookville, NY 11548-1300. **Phone:** 516-299-2338. **Fax:** 516-299-3833.

RESOURCES AND SERVICES

Information about online services, personal computer policies, library resources, international exchange programs, internship programs, and placement services at this institution and others can be found at **www.petersons.com/mba**

International Students

20% of students enrolled are international students.

Services and Facilities Counseling/support services, ESL/language courses, international student housing, visa services. Financial aid is not available to international students.

Applying *Required:* TOEFL with recommended score of 173 (computer) or 550 (paper), proof of adequate funds, proof of health/immunizations.

International Student Contact Ms. Sarah Evans, Assistant Director, International Admissions, 720 Northern Boulevard, Brookville, NY 11548-1300. **Phone:** 516-299-2900. **Fax:** 516-299-2137.

■ APPLICATION

Required GMAT, application form, baccalaureate/first degree, essay, 2 letters of recommendation, personal statement, resume/curriculum vitae, transcripts of college work. **Recommended** Interview, work experience.

Deadlines and Fees *Deadlines:* 8/15 for fall, 12/15 for spring, 4/15 for summer, 7/15 for fall (international), 11/15 for spring (international), 5/15 for summer (international). *Application fee:* $30, $30 (international).

Application Contact Mrs. Beth Carson, Associate Director, Graduate Admissions, 720 Northern Boulevard, Brookville, NY 11548-1300. **Phone:** 516-299-2900. **Fax:** 516-299-2137. **E-mail:** admissions@collegehall.liunet.edu.

Manhattan College
Riverdale, New York

SCHOOL OF BUSINESS

DEGREE MBA

MBA—Master of Business Administration Full-time and part-time. 39 to 57 total credits required. 12 to 60 months to complete program. *Concentrations:* finance, international business, management, marketing.

RESOURCES AND SERVICES

Information about online services, personal computer policies, library resources, international exchange programs, internship programs, and placement services at this institution and others can be found at www. petersons.com/mba

International Students

International Student Contact Ms. Debra Damico, International Student Advisor, Manhattan College Parkway, Riverdale, NY 10471. **Phone:** 718-862-7213. **Fax:** 718-862-8016. **E-mail:** damico@manhattan.edu.

■ APPLICATION

Application Contact Mr. Alfred R. Manduley, Director, MBA Program, Manhattan College Parkway, Riverdale, NY 10471. **Phone:** 718-862-7290. **Fax:** 718-862-8023. **E-mail:** amandule@manhattan.edu.

Manhattanville College
Purchase, New York

SCHOOL OF GRADUATE AND PROFESSIONAL STUDIES

Graduate Business Faculty

Full-time: 4	Part-time: 38

Student Body

Total: 235	Average Age: 36
Part-time: 235	Women: 87%

Admissions

Applications: 60	Enrolled: 45
Admitted: 50	Average GPA: 3.1

Costs (1999–2000)
Full-time tuition: N/R
Part-time tuition: $420 per credit

DEGREES MS

MS—Master of Science in Leadership and Strategic Management Part-time. At least 39 total credits required. 24 to 60 months to complete program. *Concentrations:* leadership, strategic management.

MS—Master of Science in Organizational Management and Human Resource Development Part-time. At least 36 total credits required. 18 to 60 months to complete program. *Concentrations:* human resources, organizational management.

COSTS

Tuition *Part-time:* $420 per credit.

FINANCIAL AID (1999–2000)

Financial Aid Contact Ms. Darlene Huszar, Associate Director of Financial Aid, 2900 Purchase Street, Purchase, NY 10577-2132. **Phone:** 914-323-5357. **Fax:** 914-323-5382.

RESOURCES AND SERVICES

Information about online services, personal computer policies, library resources, international exchange programs, internship programs, and placement services at this institution and others can be found at www. petersons.com/mba

International Students

4% of students enrolled are international students.

Services and Facilities Counseling/support services, ESL/language courses, international student housing, international student advisor. Financial aid is not available to international students.

Applying *Required:* TOEFL with recommended score of 600 (paper), proof of adequate funds, proof of health/immunizations.

International Student Contact Ms. L.A. Adams, International Student Advisor, 2900 Purchase Street, Purchase, NY 10577-2132. **Phone:** 914-323-5168. **Fax:** 914-323-5494. **E-mail:** laadams@mville.edu.

■ APPLICATION

Required Application form, baccalaureate/first degree, essay, interview, 2 letters of recommendation, personal statement, resume/curriculum vitae, transcripts of college work, 2 years of work experience.

Deadlines and Fees Applications for domestic and international students are processed on a rolling basis. *Application fee:* $45, $45 (international).

Application Contact Dr. Donald Richards, Director of MS Program and Associate Dean, 2900 Purchase Street, Purchase, NY 10577-2123. **Phone:** 914-694-3425. **Fax:** 914-694-3488. **E-mail:** richardsd@mville.edu.

Marist College
Poughkeepsie, New York

SCHOOL OF MANAGEMENT

Graduate Business Faculty

Full-time: 20	Part-time: 2

Student Body

Total: 143	Part-time: 138
Full-time: 5	Women: 36%

Admissions

Applications: 65	Average GMAT: 522
Admitted: 60	Average GPA: 3.2
Enrolled: 48	

Costs (1999–2000)
Full-time tuition: N/R
Part-time tuition: $462 per credit hour

After Graduation (Class of 1998–99)
Employed within 3 months of graduation: 100%
Average starting salary: $69,000

DEGREE MBA

MBA—Master of Business Administration Full-time and part-time. *Distance learning option.* 30 to 51 total credits required. 12 to 84 months to complete program. *Concentrations:* accounting, finance, health care, human resources, management, management information systems.

COSTS

Tuition *Part-time:* $462 per credit hour. **Required fees:** *Part-time* $30 per semester.

FINANCIAL AID (1999–2000)

7 students received aid, including scholarships and work study. Aid is available to part-time students. Financial aid application deadline: 8/15. **Financial Aid Contact** Ms. Jean Theobald, Director, Graduate Admissions, 3399 North Road, Dyson Center, Poughkeepsie, NY 12601-1387. **Phone:** 845-575-3800. **Fax:** 845-575-3640. **E-mail:** eileen.bull@marist.edu.

RESOURCES AND SERVICES

Information about online services, personal computer policies, library resources, international exchange programs, internship programs, and placement services at this institution and others can be found at www. petersons.com/mba

International Students

Services and Facilities Counseling/support services, ESL/language courses, visa services. Financial aid is not available to international students.

Applying *Required:* TOEFL with recommended score of 550 (paper), proof of adequate funds, proof of health/immunizations. *Recommended:* TWE with recommended score of 4.

International Student Contact Ms. Jean Theobald, Director, Graduate Admissions, 3399 North Road, Dyson 149, Poughkeepsie, NY 12601-1387. **Phone:** 845-575-3530. **Fax:** 845-575-3640. **E-mail:** graduate@marist.edu.

Marist College (continued)

■ APPLICATION

Required GMAT, application form, baccalaureate/first degree, transcripts of college work. **Recommended** Work experience.

Deadlines and Fees Applications for domestic and international students are processed on a rolling basis. *Application fee:* $30, $30 (international).

Application Contact Ms. Jean Theobald, Director, Graduate Admissions, 3399 North Road, Dyson Center, Poughkeepsie, NY 12601-1387. **Phone:** 845-575-3530. **Fax:** 845-575-3640. **E-mail:** graduate@marist.edu.

Medaille College

Buffalo, New York

PROGRAM IN BUSINESS ADMINISTRATION

Graduate Business Faculty

Full-time: 11	Part-time: 3

Student Body

Total: 78	Average Age: 36
Full-time: 41	Women: 58%
Part-time: 37	

Admissions

Applications: 39	Enrolled: 27
Admitted: 34	Average GPA: 3.15

Costs (1999–2000)
Full-time tuition: $10,740 per academic year
Part-time tuition: $448 per credit

After Graduation (Class of 1998–99)
Employed within 3 months of graduation: 100%

DEGREES MBA

MBA—ACCEL Full-time. Minimum 3 years work experience required. At least 43 total credits required. 24 to 72 months to complete program.

MBA—Master of Business Administration Full-time and part-time. Minimum 3 years of work experience required. At least 45 total credits required. 12 to 72 months to complete program. *Concentrations:* human resources, strategic management.

COSTS

Tuition *Full-time:* $10,440. *Part-time:* $435 per credit. **Tuition, international:** *Full-time* $10,440. **Required fees:** *Full-time* $300. *Part-time* $13 per credit. Tuition and fees vary by number of courses or credits taken, campus location, and academic program. **Graduate housing:** Room and board costs vary by number of occupants. *Typical cost:* $5300 (including board).

FINANCIAL AID (1999–2000)

37 students received aid, including loans and work study. Aid is available to part-time students. Financial aid application deadline: 4/15. **Financial Aid Contact** Rachel Barker, Director of Financial Aid, 18 Agassiz Circle, Buffalo, NY 14214. **Phone:** 716-884-3281 Ext. 256. **Fax:** 716-884-0291. **E-mail:** rbarker@medaille.edu.

RESOURCES AND SERVICES

Information about online services, personal computer policies, library resources, international exchange programs, internship programs, and placement services at this institution and others can be found at **www. petersons.com/mba**

International Students

Services and Facilities Counseling/support services. Financial aid is not available to international students.
Applying *Required:* TOEFL, proof of adequate funds, proof of health/immunizations.
International Student Contact Mr. Clayton Steen, Graduate Admissions Counselor, 18 Agassiz Circle, Buffalo, NY 14214. **Phone:** 716-884-3281 Ext. 203. **Fax:** 716-884-0291. **E-mail:** csteen@medaille.edu.

■ APPLICATION

Required GMAT, application form, baccalaureate/first degree, essay, 2 letters of recommendation, resume/curriculum vitae, transcripts of college work, 3 years of work experience. School will accept GRE. **Recommended** Interview.

Deadlines and Fees Applications for domestic and international students are processed on a rolling basis. *Application fee:* $35, $35 (international).

Application Contact Mr. Clayton Steen, Graduate Admissions Counselor, 18 Agassiz Circle, Buffalo, NY 14214. **Phone:** 716-884-3281 Ext. 203. **Toll-free Phone:** 800-292-1582. **Fax:** 716-884-0291. **E-mail:** csteen@medaille.edu.

Mercy College

Dobbs Ferry, New York

PROGRAM IN HUMAN RESOURCE MANAGEMENT

DEGREES MBA • MS

MBA—Master of Business Administration Full-time and part-time. *Distance learning option.* 33 to 57 total credits required. 24 to 60 months to complete program. *Concentrations:* accounting, finance, international business, management, marketing.

MS—Master of Science in Human Resource Management Full-time and part-time. At least 36 total credits required. 12 to 60 months to complete program. *Concentrations:* human resources, organizational management.

RESOURCES AND SERVICES

Information about online services, personal computer policies, library resources, international exchange programs, internship programs, and placement services at this institution and others can be found at **www. petersons.com/mba**

International Students

Services and Facilities Counseling/support services, ESL/language courses, international student housing, visa services. Financial aid is not available to international students.
International Student Contact International Student Advisor, 555 Broadway, Dobbs Ferry, NY 10522-1189. **Phone:** 914-674-7233.

■ APPLICATION

Application Contact Mr. Wayne Cioffari, Director, MBA Program, 555 Broadway, Dobbs Ferry, NY 10522-1189. **Phone:** 914-674-7481 Ext. 500. **Toll-free Phone:** 800-MERCY-NY. **Fax:** 914-674-7488. **E-mail:** wcioffari@mercynet.edu.

Mount Saint Mary College

Newburgh, New York

DIVISION OF BUSINESS

Graduate Business Faculty

Full-time: 7	Part-time: 8

Student Body

Total: 82	Average Age: 34
Full-time: 3	Women: 48%
Part-time: 79	

Admissions

Applications: 150	Average GMAT: 480
Admitted: 35	Average GPA: 3.21
Enrolled: 25	

Costs (1999–2000)
Full-time tuition: N/R
Part-time tuition: $389 per credit

After Graduation (Class of 1998–99)
Employed within 3 months of graduation: 100%
Average starting salary: $40,000

DEGREE MBA

MBA—Master of Business Administration Full-time and part-time. *Distance learning option.* 34 to 55 total credits required. 24 to 72 months to complete program.

COSTS

Tuition *Part-time:* $389 per credit.

FINANCIAL AID (1999–2000)

3 students received aid, including loans and work study. Aid is available to part-time students. Financial aid application deadline: 3/15. **Financial Aid Contact** Mrs. Susan Twomey, Director, Financial Aid, Financial Aid Office, Room 116, Aguinas Hall, Newburgh, NY 12550. **Phone:** 914-569-3195. **E-mail:** twomey@msmc.edu.

RESOURCES AND SERVICES

Information about online services, personal computer policies, library resources, international exchange programs, internship programs, and

placement services at this institution and others can be found at **www. petersons.com/mba**

International Students
4% of students enrolled are international students.

Services and Facilities Counseling/support services, international student housing, visa services. Financial aid is not available to international students.
Applying *Required:* TOEFL, proof of adequate funds, proof of health/immunizations.

International Student Contact Dr. James Griesemer, Coordinator, MBA Program, Division of Business, 330 Powell Avenue, Newburgh, NY 12550-3494. **Phone:** 914-569-3120. **Fax:** 914-569-3885. **E-mail:** grieseme@msmc.edu.

■ **APPLICATION**

Required GMAT, application form, baccalaureate/first degree, interview, 3 letters of recommendation, personal statement, transcripts of college work. **Recommended** Resume/curriculum vitae, work experience.

Deadlines and Fees Applications for domestic and international students are processed on a rolling basis. *Application fee:* $20, $20 (international).

Application Contact Dr. James Griesemer, Coordinator, MBA Program, 330 Powell Avenue, Newburgh, NY 12550-3494. **Phone:** 914-569-3582. **Toll-free Phone:** 800-558-0942. **Fax:** 914-569-3885. **E-mail:** grieseme@msmc.edu.

Nazareth College of Rochester

Rochester, New York

PROGRAM IN MANAGEMENT

Graduate Business Faculty
Full-time: 6	Part-time: 8

Student Body
Total: 108	Average Age: 37
Part-time: 108	Women: 54%

Admissions
Admitted: 43	Average GPA: 3
Enrolled: 42	

Costs (1999–2000)
Full-time tuition: N/R
Part-time tuition: $456 per credit hour

DEGREE MS

MS—Master of Science in Management Part-time. At least 33 total credits required. 15 to 60 months to complete program. *Concentrations:* management.

COSTS

Tuition *Part-time:* $456 per credit hour.

FINANCIAL AID (1999–2000)

Aid is available to part-time students. **Financial Aid Contact** Dr. Bruce Woolley, Director of Financial Aid, 4245 East Avenue, Rochester, NY 14618-3790. **Phone:** 716-389-2310. **Fax:** 716-586-2452. **E-mail:** bcwoolle@naz.edu.

RESOURCES AND SERVICES

Information about online services, personal computer policies, library resources, international exchange programs, internship programs, and placement services at this institution and others can be found at **www. petersons.com/mba**

International Students
0.9% of students enrolled are international students.

Services and Facilities Counseling/support services.
Applying *Required:* TOEFL with recommended score of 550 (paper), proof of adequate funds, proof of health/immunizations.

International Student Contact Ms. Shirley Pilot, Graduate Student Advisor, 4245 East Avenue, Rochester, NY 14618-3790. **Phone:** 716-389-2819. **Fax:** 716-586-2452. **E-mail:** sjpilot@naz.edu.

■ **APPLICATION**

Required Application form, baccalaureate/first degree, essay, interview, 2 letters of recommendation, personal statement, resume/curriculum vitae, transcripts of college work. **Recommended** Work experience.

Deadlines and Fees *Application fee:* $40, $40 (international).

Application Contact Mr. Gerard Zappia, Chairperson, Business Department, 4245 East Avenue, Rochester, NY 14618-3790. **Phone:** 716-389-2570. **Fax:** 716-586-2452. **E-mail:** gfzappia@naz.edu.

New School University

New York, New York

ROBERT J. MILANO GRADUATE SCHOOL OF MANAGEMENT AND URBAN POLICY

Graduate Business Faculty
Full-time: 22	Part-time: 110

Student Body
Total: 780	Average Age: 31
Full-time: 164	Women: 75%
Part-time: 616	

Admissions
Applications: 408	Enrolled: 286
Admitted: 369	Average GPA: 3.2

Costs (1999–2000)
Full-time tuition: N/R
Part-time tuition: $690 per credit

After Graduation (Class of 1998–99)
Employed within 3 months of graduation: 90%
Average starting salary: $40,000

DEGREES MS

MS—Master of Science in Health Services Management and Policy Full-time and part-time. *Distance learning option.* At least 42 total credits required. Minimum of 24 months to complete program. *Concentrations:* health care.

MS—Master of Science in Human Resources Management Full-time and part-time. *Distance learning option.* At least 42 total credits required. Minimum of 24 months to complete program. *Concentrations:* human resources, organizational management.

MS—Master of Science in Nonprofit Management Full-time and part-time. *Distance learning option.* At least 42 total credits required. Minimum of 24 months to complete program. *Concentrations:* nonprofit management.

MS—Master of Science in Organizational Change Management Full-time and part-time. *Distance learning option.* At least 42 total credits required. Minimum of 24 months to complete program.

MS—Master of Science in Urban Policy Analysis and Management Full-time and part-time. *Distance learning option.* At least 42 total credits required. Minimum of 24 months to complete program. *Concentrations:* public policy and administration.

COSTS

Tuition *Part-time:* $690 per credit. **Required fees:** Tuition and fees vary by number of courses or credits taken and academic program. **Graduate housing:** Room and board costs vary by type of accommodation and type of board plan. *Typical cost:* $9200 (including board).

FINANCIAL AID (1999–2000)

215 students received aid, including fellowships, grants, loans, scholarships, teaching assistantships, and work study. Aid is available to part-time students. **Financial Aid Contact** Ms. Heather Ward, Office of Financial Aid, 65 Fifth Avenue, New York, NY 10011. **Phone:** 212-229-8930. **Fax:** 212-229-8935. **E-mail:** wardh@newschool.edu.

RESOURCES AND SERVICES

Information about online services, personal computer policies, library resources, international exchange programs, internship programs, and placement services at this institution and others can be found at **www. petersons.com/mba**

International Students
4% of students enrolled are international students.

Services and Facilities Counseling/support services, ESL/language courses, housing location assistance, orientation, visa services. Financial aid is available to international students.
Applying *Required:* TOEFL with recommended score of 600 (paper), proof of adequate funds, proof of health/immunizations.

International Student Contact Mr. Gary St. Fleur, International Student Advisor, 65 Fifth Avenue, Office of Student Affairs, New York, NY 10003. **Phone:** 212-229-5712. **Fax:** 212-229-8935. **E-mail:** mgsinfo@newschool.edu.

■ **APPLICATION**

Required Application form, baccalaureate/first degree, essay, interview, 2 letters of recommendation, personal statement, transcripts of college work. **Recommended** Resume/curriculum vitae.

Deadlines and Fees Applications for domestic and international students are processed on a rolling basis. *Application fee:* $30, $30 (international).

New School University (continued)

Application Contact Ms. Emily Woolf Economou, Director of Admissions, 72 Fifth Avenue, New York, NY 10011. **Phone:** 212-229-5462. **Toll-free Phone:** 877-645-2661. **Fax:** 212-229-8935. **E-mail:** mgsinfo@newschool.edu.

See full description on page 740.

New York Institute of Technology

Old Westbury, New York

SCHOOL OF MANAGEMENT

Graduate Business Faculty

Full-time: 20	Part-time: 82

Student Body

Total: 654	Average Age: 34
Full-time: 230	Women: 44%
Part-time: 424	

Admissions

Applications: 374	Average GMAT: 450
Admitted: 300	Average GPA: 3.05
Enrolled: 190	

Costs (1999–2000)
Full-time tuition: $8100 per academic year
Part-time tuition: $450 per credit

After Graduation (Class of 1998–99)
Employed within 3 months of graduation: 90%

DEGREES DO/MBA • MBA • MS

DO/MBA—Doctor of Osteopathy/Master of Business Administration Full-time and part-time. *Distance learning option.* Minimum of 60 months to complete program. *Concentrations:* health care, management.

MBA—Executive MBA Full-time and part-time. 56 total credits required. *Concentrations:* accounting, business policy/strategy, international business, international finance, management, management information systems, managerial economics, marketing.

MBA—Master of Business Administration Full-time and part-time. *Distance learning option.* 36 to 54 total credits required. 12 to 60 months to complete program. *Concentrations:* accounting, finance, health care, international business, management, management information systems, marketing.

MS—Master of Science in Human Resource Management and Labor Relations Full-time and part-time. *Distance learning option.* Up to 42 total credits required. 12 to 60 months to complete program. *Concentrations:* human resources, industrial/labor relations.

COSTS

Tuition *Full-time:* $8100. *Part-time:* $450 per credit. Tuition varies by number of courses or credits taken. **Graduate housing:** Room and board costs vary by campus location, number of occupants, type of accommodation, and type of board plan. *Typical cost:* $6510 (including board), $3480 (room only).

FINANCIAL AID (1999–2000)

462 students received aid, including fellowships, loans, research assistantships, and scholarships. Aid is available to part-time students. **Financial Aid Contact** Mr. James Newell, Director of Financial Aid, PO Box 8000, Old Westbury, NY 11568. **Phone:** 516-686-7680. **Fax:** 516-686-7997. **E-mail:** jnewell@nyit.edu.

RESOURCES AND SERVICES

Information about online services, personal computer policies, library resources, international exchange programs, internship programs, and placement services at this institution and others can be found at **www. petersons.com/mba**

International Students

32% of students enrolled are international students.

Services and Facilities Counseling/support services, ESL/language courses, international student housing, international student organization, visa services. Financial aid is available to international students.

Applying *Required:* TOEFL with recommended score of 575 (paper), proof of adequate funds, proof of health/immunizations.

International Student Contact Ms. Barbara Multari, International Student Advisor, PO Box 8000, Old Westbury, NY 11568. **Phone:** 516-686-7585. **Fax:** 516-626-0673.

■ APPLICATION

Required GMAT, application form, baccalaureate/first degree, essay, transcripts of college work. **Recommended** Work experience.

Deadlines and Fees Applications for international students are processed on a rolling basis. *Application fee:* $50, $50 (international).

Application Contact Dr. Stephen Hartman, Director, MBA Program, PO Box 8000, Old Westbury, NY 11568. **Phone:** 516-686-7972. **E-mail:** shartman@nyit.edu.

See full description on page 742.

New York University

New York, New York

LEONARD N. STERN SCHOOL OF BUSINESS

Graduate Business Faculty

Full-time: 206	Part-time: 99

Student Body

Total: 3,266	Average Age: 28
Full-time: 1,174	Women: 35%
Part-time: 2,092	

Admissions

Applications: 4,360	Average GMAT: 686
Admitted: 786	Average GPA: 3.4
Enrolled: 418	

Costs (1999–2000)
Full-time tuition: $29,000 per academic year
Part-time tuition: $1050 per credit

After Graduation (Class of 1998–99)
Employed within 3 months of graduation: 98%
Average starting salary: $77,722

Accreditation
AACSB—The International Association for Management Education

DEGREES JD/MBA • MA/MBA • MBA • MBA/MPA • MBA/MS • MS

JD/MBA—Juris Doctor/Master of Business Administration Full-time. At least 122 total credits required. 48 to 72 months to complete program. *Concentrations:* accounting, economics, finance, international business, management, management information systems, marketing, operations management, quantitative analysis, taxation.

MA/MBA—Master of Arts in French Studies/Master of Business Administration Full-time and part-time. At least 80 total credits required. 28 to 72 months to complete program. *Concentrations:* accounting, economics, finance, international business, management, management information systems, marketing, operations management, quantitative analysis, taxation.

MA/MBA—Master of Arts in Politics/Master of Business Administration Full-time and part-time. At least 76 total credits required. 28 to 72 months to complete program. *Concentrations:* accounting, economics, finance, international business, management, management information systems, marketing, operations management, quantitative analysis, taxation.

MBA—Executive MBA Full-time. At least 72 total credits required. 22 months to complete program. *Concentrations:* finance, management.

MBA—Master of Business Administration Full-time and part-time. At least 60 total credits required. 16 to 72 months to complete program. *Concentrations:* accounting, economics, finance, international business, management, management information systems, marketing, operations management, quantitative analysis, taxation.

MBA/MPA—Master of Business Administration/Master of Public Administration Full-time and part-time. At least 95 total credits required. Maximum of 36 months to complete program.

MBA/MS—Master of Science in Biology/Master of Business Administration Full-time and part-time. At least 86 total credits required. Maximum of 36 months to complete program.

MS—Master of Science Full-time and part-time. 36 to 58 total credits required. 18 to 48 months to complete program. *Concentrations:* accounting, management information systems, quantitative analysis.

COSTS

Tuition *Full-time:* $29,000. *Part-time:* $1050 per credit. **Graduate housing:** *Typical cost:* $20,518 (including board).

FINANCIAL AID (1999–2000)

998 students received aid, including fellowships, research assistantships, scholarships, teaching assistantships, and work study. Financial aid application deadline: 12/15. **Financial Aid Contact** Angelica Capeci, Assistant Financial Aid, 44 West 4th Street, MEC 10-160, New York, NY 10012-1126. **Phone:** 212-998-0790. **Fax:** 212-995-4225. **E-mail:** fin-aid@stern.nyu.edu.

RESOURCES AND SERVICES

Information about online services, personal computer policies, library resources, international exchange programs, internship programs, and placement services at this institution and others can be found at **www.petersons.com/mba**

International Students

Services and Facilities Counseling/support services, ESL/language courses, housing location assistance, international student housing, international student organization, language tutoring, orientation, visa services. Financial aid is available to international students.

Applying *Required:* TOEFL with recommended score of 250 (computer) or 600 (paper), proof of adequate funds, proof of health/immunizations.

International Student Contact Tricia Brown, Associate Director, International Programs, 44 West 4 Street, Suite 10-87, New York, NY 10012. **Phone:** 212-998-0915. **Fax:** 212-995-4238. **E-mail:** tbrown@stern.nyu.edu.

■ APPLICATION

Required GMAT, application form, baccalaureate/first degree, essay, 2 letters of recommendation, resume/curriculum vitae, transcripts of college work, 2 years of work experience. **Recommended** Interview.

Deadlines and Fees *Deadlines:* 3/15 for fall, 3/15 for fall (international). *Application fee:* $100, $100 (international).

Application Contact Mr. John Lyon, Director, MBA Admissions, 44 West 4th Street, Suite 10-160, New York, NY 10012-1126. **Phone:** 212-998-0600. **Fax:** 212-995-4231. **E-mail:** sternmba@stern.nyu.edu.

Pace University, New York City Campus

New York, New York

LUBIN SCHOOL OF BUSINESS

Graduate Business Faculty

Full-time: 114	Part-time: 57

Student Body

Total: 1,854	
Full-time: 524	Average Age: 31
Part-time: 1,330	Women: 44%

Admissions

Applications: 1,307	Average GMAT: 518
Admitted: 803	Average GPA: 3.15
Enrolled: 371	

Costs (1999–2000)

Full-time tuition: N/R
Part-time tuition: $575 per credit

After Graduation (Class of 1998–99)

Employed within 3 months of graduation: 95%
Average starting salary: $56,000

Accreditation

AACSB—The International Association for Management Education

DEGREES JD/MBA • MBA • MS

JD/MBA—Juris Doctor/Master of Business Administration Full-time and part-time. At least 129 total credits required. 48 to 72 months to complete program.

MBA—Executive MBA Full-time. *Distance learning option.* Experienced executives. At least 51 total credits required. 21 months to complete program. *Concentrations:* management.

MBA—One-year MBA in Finance Full-time. 36 to 40 total credits required. 12 months to complete program. *Concentrations:* finance.

MBA—Master of Business Administration Full-time and part-time. 36 to 84 total credits required. 24 to 60 months to complete program. *Concentrations:* accounting, economics, finance, international business, management, management information systems, management science, marketing, taxation.

MS—Master of Science Full-time and part-time. 30 to 60 total credits required. 12 to 60 months to complete program. *Concentrations:* accounting, economics, finance, management science, taxation.

COSTS

Tuition *Part-time:* $575 per credit. **Required fees:** *Part-time* $180 per semester. Fees vary by number of courses or credits taken. **Graduate housing:** Room and board costs vary by number of occupants and type of board plan. *Typical cost:* $7200 (including board).

FINANCIAL AID (1999–2000)

775 students received aid, including grants, loans, research assistantships, scholarships, and work study. Aid is available to part-time students. Financial aid application deadline: 5/15. **Financial Aid Contact** Ms. Ann Prisco, University Director of Financial Aid, 1 Pace Plaza, New York, NY 10038. **Phone:** 212-346-1300. **Fax:** 212-346-1750. **E-mail:** aprisco@pace.edu.

RESOURCES AND SERVICES

Information about online services, personal computer policies, library resources, international exchange programs, internship programs, and placement services at this institution and others can be found at **www.petersons.com/mba**

International Students

19% of students enrolled are international students.

Services and Facilities Counseling/support services, ESL/language courses, international student housing, visa services. Financial aid is available to international students.

Applying *Required:* TOEFL with recommended score of 550 (paper), proof of adequate funds, proof of health/immunizations.

International Student Contact Ms. Deirdre Sato, Director of International Students and Scholars, 861 Bedford Road-Campus Center, Pleasantville, NY 10570-2799. **Phone:** 914-773-3447. **Fax:** 914-773-3783. **E-mail:** dsato@pace.edu.

■ APPLICATION

Required GMAT, application form, baccalaureate/first degree, essay, 2 letters of recommendation, personal statement, resume/curriculum vitae, transcripts of college work.

Deadlines and Fees *Deadlines:* 7/31 for fall, 11/30 for spring, 5/1 for summer, 7/1 for fall (international), 11/1 for spring (international), 4/1 for summer (international). *Application fee:* $60, $60 (international).

Application Contact Ms. Joanna Broda, Director of Graduate Admission, Office of Graduate Admission, 1 Martine Avenue, White Plains, NY 10606-1909. **Phone:** 914-422-4283. **Toll-free Phone:** 800-874-7223. **Fax:** 914-422-4287. **E-mail:** gradwp@pace.edu.

See full description on page 758.

Polytechnic University, Manhattan Graduate Center

New York, New York

DEPARTMENT OF MANAGEMENT

Admissions

Applications: 125	Admitted: 93

Costs (1999–2000)

Full-time tuition: N/R
Part-time tuition: N/R

DEGREES MOT • MS

MOT—MOT Executive Program Full-time and part-time. 36 total credits required. 16 months to complete program. *Concentrations:* electronic commerce (e-commerce), entrepreneurship, financial information systems, new venture management, research and development administration, technology management.

MS—Financial Engineering Full-time and part-time. 36 total credits required. 12 to 60 months to complete program. *Concentrations:* banking, finance, financial economics, financial information systems, technology management, financial engineering.

MS—TIM Program Management Full-time and part-time. 36 total credits required. 16 months to complete program. *Concentrations:* electronic commerce (e-commerce), entrepreneurship, financial information systems, information management, management information systems, telecommunications management.

Polytechnic University, Manhattan Graduate Center (continued)

COSTS

Full-time tuition 18,600 per year; tuition for the FE program is $725 per credit.

FINANCIAL AID (1999–2000)

Loans. **Financial Aid Contact** Office of Financial Aid, Six Metrotech Center, Brooklyn, NY 11201. **Phone:** 718-260-3300.

RESOURCES AND SERVICES

Information about online services, personal computer policies, library resources, international exchange programs, internship programs, and placement services at this institution and others can be found at **www. petersons.com/mba**

International Students

Services and Facilities Counseling/support services, housing location assistance, orientation. Financial aid is available to international students.
Applying *Required:* TOEFL, proof of health/immunizations.
International Student Contact Mr. Michael Gendel, International Student Advisor, Six Metrotech Center, Brooklyn, NY 11201. **Phone:** 718-260-3445. **Fax:** 718-260-3446. **E-mail:** mgendel@poly.edu.

■ APPLICATION

Required Application form, baccalaureate/first degree, essay, interview, 2 letters of recommendation, resume/curriculum vitae, transcripts of college work, work experience. School will accept GMAT or GRE. **Recommended** Personal statement.
Deadlines and Fees *Deadlines:* 5/31 for fall, 5/31 for fall (international). *Application fee:* $50, $50 (international).
Application Contact Mel Horwitch, Department Chair, 55 Broad Street, Suite 13B, New York, NY 10004. **Phone:** 212-547-7030 Ext. 202. **Fax:** 212-547-7029. **E-mail:** horwitch@poly.edu.

Polytechnic University, Brooklyn Campus

Brooklyn, New York

DEPARTMENT OF MANAGEMENT

Graduate Business Faculty
Full-time: 8   Part-time: 20
Costs (1999–2000)
Full-time tuition: N/R
Part-time tuition: $725 per credit hour

DEGREES MS • MSM

MS—Master of Science in Organizational Behavior Full-time and part-time. *Distance learning option.* At least 36 total credits required. 12 to 60 months to complete program. *Concentrations:* human resources, organizational behavior/development.
MSM—Master of Science in Management Full-time and part-time. *Distance learning option.* At least 36 total credits required. 12 to 60 months to complete program. *Concentrations:* construction management, electronic commerce (e-commerce), entrepreneurship, human resources, information management, management information systems, operations management, organizational behavior/development, technology management, telecommunications management.

COSTS

Tuition *Part-time:* $725 per credit hour. Tuition varies by academic program. **Required fees:** *Full-time* $600. *Part-time* $300 per semester.

FINANCIAL AID (1999–2000)

Loans. **Financial Aid Contact** Office of Financial Aid, Six Metrotech Center, Brooklyn, NY 11201. **Phone:** 718-260-3300.

RESOURCES AND SERVICES

Information about online services, personal computer policies, library resources, international exchange programs, internship programs, and placement services at this institution and others can be found at **www. petersons.com/mba**

International Students

Services and Facilities Counseling/support services, international student organization, visa services. Financial aid is available to international students.
Applying *Required:* TOEFL, proof of health/immunizations.

International Student Contact Mr. Michael Gendel, International Student Advisor, Six Metrotech Center, Brooklyn, NY 11201. **Phone:** 718-260-3445. **Fax:** 718-260-3446. **E-mail:** mgendel@poly.edu.

■ APPLICATION

Required Application form, baccalaureate/first degree, essay, 2 letters of recommendation, transcripts of college work. School will accept GMAT and GRE. **Recommended** Interview, personal statement, work experience.
Deadlines and Fees Applications for domestic and international students are processed on a rolling basis. *Application fee:* $45, $45 (international).
Application Contact Prof. Barry Blecherman, Assistant Professor and Program Director, MSM Management Program, Department of Management, Six Metrotech Center, Brooklyn, NY 11201. **Phone:** 718-260-3398. **Fax:** 718-260-3874. **E-mail:** blecherm@poly.edu.

See full description on page 770.

Polytechnic University, Brooklyn Campus

Brooklyn, New York

MSM EXTENSION ISRAEL

Graduate Business Faculty
Full-time: 5   Part-time: 20
Student Body
Total: 180   Part-time: 90
Full-time: 90   Women: 40%
Costs (1999–2000)
Full-time tuition: 40,000 Israeli New shekels per academic year
Part-time tuition: N/R

DEGREE MSM

MSM—Master of Science Full-time and part-time. *Distance learning option.* 36 total credits required. 12 to 60 months to complete program. *Concentrations:* construction management, electronic commerce (e-commerce), human resources, information management, management information systems, operations management, organizational behavior/development, technology management, telecommunications management.

COSTS

Tuition *Full-time:* 40,000 Israeli New shekels. Tuition varies by academic program.

FINANCIAL AID (1999–2000)

Loans. Aid is available to part-time students. **Financial Aid Contact** Office of Financial Aid, Six Metrotech Center, Brooklyn, NY 11201. **Phone:** 718-260-3300.

RESOURCES AND SERVICES

Information about online services, personal computer policies, library resources, international exchange programs, internship programs, and placement services at this institution and others can be found at **www. petersons.com/mba**

International Students

Services and Facilities Counseling/support services, visa services. Financial aid is available to international students.
Applying *Required:* TOEFL, proof of health/immunizations. *Recommended:* IELT.
International Student Contact Mr. Michael Gendel, International Student Advisor, Six Metrotech Center, Brooklyn, NY 11201. **Phone:** 718-260-3445. **Fax:** 718-260-3446. **E-mail:** mgendel@poly.edu.

■ APPLICATION

Required Application form, baccalaureate/first degree, essay, 2 letters of recommendation, transcripts of college work. School will accept GMAT and GRE. **Recommended** Interview, personal statement, work experience.
Deadlines and Fees Applications for domestic and international students are processed on a rolling basis. *Application fee:* $50, $50 (international).
Application Contact Prof. Harold Kaufman, Professor and Program Director, MSM Management Program in Israel, Department of Management, Six Metro Center, Brooklyn, NY 11201. **Phone:** 718-260-3485. **Fax:** 718-260-3874. **E-mail:** hkaufman@poly.edu.

Polytechnic University, Farmingdale Campus

Farmingdale, New York

DEPARTMENT OF MANAGEMENT

Graduate Business Faculty
Full-time: 8   Part-time: 20

Costs (1999–2000)
Full-time tuition: N/R
Part-time tuition: $725 per credit hour

DEGREE MSM

MSM—Master of Science in Management Full-time and part-time. *Distance learning option.* At least 36 total credits required. 12 to 60 months to complete program. *Concentrations:* construction management, electronic commerce (e-commerce), entrepreneurship, human resources, information management, management information systems, operations management, organizational behavior/development, technology management, telecommunications management.

COSTS

Tuition *Part-time:* $725 per credit hour. Tuition varies by academic program.
Required fees: *Full-time* $600. *Part-time* $300 per semester.

FINANCIAL AID (1999–2000)

Loans. Aid is available to part-time students. **Financial Aid Contact** Office of Financial Aid, Six Metrotech Center, Brooklyn, NY 11201. **Phone:** 718-260-3300.

RESOURCES AND SERVICES

Information about online services, personal computer policies, library resources, international exchange programs, internship programs, and placement services at this institution and others can be found at **www. petersons.com/mba**

International Students

Services and Facilities Counseling/support services, visa services. Financial aid is available to international students.
Applying *Required:* TOEFL, proof of health/immunizations.
International Student Contact Mr. Michael Gendel, International Student Advisor, Six Metrotech Center, Brooklyn, NY 11201. **Phone:** 718-260-3445. **Fax:** 718-260-3446. **E-mail:** mgendel@poly.edu.

■ APPLICATION

Required Application form, baccalaureate/first degree, essay, 2 letters of recommendation, transcripts of college work. School will accept GMAT and GRE.
Recommended Interview, personal statement, work experience.
Deadlines and Fees Applications for domestic and international students are processed on a rolling basis. *Application fee:* $45, $45 (international).
Application Contact Prof. Barry Blecherman, Assistant Professor and Program Director, MSM Management Program, Department of Management, Six Metrotech Center, Brooklyn, NY 11201. **Phone:** 718-260-3398. **Fax:** 718-260-3874. **E-mail:** blecherm@poly.edu.

Polytechnic University, Westchester Graduate Center

Hawthorne, New York

DIVISION OF MANAGEMENT

Graduate Business Faculty
Full-time: 8   Part-time: 20

Student Body
Total: 206
Part-time: 206   Women: 15%

Costs (1999–2000)
Full-time tuition: N/R
Part-time tuition: $725 per credit hour

DEGREE MSM

MSM—Master of Science in Management Full-time and part-time. *Distance learning option.* At least 36 total credits required. 12 to 60 months to complete program. *Concentrations:* construction management, electronic commerce

---

(e-commerce), entrepreneurship, human resources, information management, management information systems, operations management, organizational behavior/development, technology management, telecommunications management.

COSTS

Tuition *Part-time:* $725 per credit hour. Tuition varies by academic program.
Required fees: *Full-time* $600. *Part-time* $300 per semester.

FINANCIAL AID (1999–2000)

Loans. Aid is available to part-time students. **Financial Aid Contact** Office of Financial Aid, Six Metrotech Center, Brooklyn, NY 11201. **Phone:** 718-260-3300.

RESOURCES AND SERVICES

Information about online services, personal computer policies, library resources, international exchange programs, internship programs, and placement services at this institution and others can be found at **www. petersons.com/mba**

International Students

Services and Facilities Counseling/support services, visa services. Financial aid is available to international students.
Applying *Required:* TOEFL, proof of health/immunizations.
International Student Contact Mr. Michael Gendel, International Student Advisor, Six Metrotech Center, Brooklyn, NY 11201. **Phone:** 718-260-3445. **Fax:** 718-260-3446. **E-mail:** mgendel@poly.edu.

■ APPLICATION

Required Application form, baccalaureate/first degree, essay, 2 letters of recommendation, transcripts of college work. School will accept GMAT and GRE.
Recommended Interview, personal statement, work experience.
Deadlines and Fees Applications for domestic and international students are processed on a rolling basis. *Application fee:* $45, $45 (international).
Application Contact Prof. Barry Blecherman, Assistant Professor and Program Director, MSM Management Program, Department of Management, Six Metrotech Center, Brooklyn, NY 11201. **Phone:** 718-260-3398. **Fax:** 718-260-3874. **E-mail:** blecherm@poly.edu.

Pratt Institute

Brooklyn, New York

PROGRAM IN FACILITIES MANAGEMENT

DEGREE MS

MS—Master of Science in Facilities Management Full-time and part-time. At least 50 total credits required. Minimum of 24 months to complete program.

RESOURCES AND SERVICES

Information about online services, personal computer policies, library resources, international exchange programs, internship programs, and placement services at this institution and others can be found at **www. petersons.com/mba**

International Students

Services and Facilities Counseling/support services, ESL/language courses, international student housing, visa services, networking club. Financial aid is not available to international students.
International Student Contact Ms. Jane Bush, Director—International Student Affairs, 200 Willoughby Avenue, Brooklyn, NY 11205-3899. **Phone:** 718-636-3674. **Fax:** 718-636-3497. **E-mail:** jbush@pratt.edu.

■ APPLICATION

Application Contact Prof. Mary Matthews, Chairperson—Facilities Management Department, 295 Lafayette Street, Room 440, New York, NY 10012. **Phone:** 212-461-6018. **Toll-free Phone:** 800-331-0834. **Fax:** 212-461-6028. **E-mail:** mjmcmfm@soho.pratt.edu.

Rensselaer Polytechnic Institute

Troy, New York

LALLY SCHOOL OF MANAGEMENT AND TECHNOLOGY

Graduate Business Faculty
Full-time: 57   Part-time: 2

Student Body
Total: 2,001
Full-time: 231   Average Age: 28
Part-time: 1,770   Women: 27%

Rensselaer Polytechnic Institute (continued)

Admissions
Applications: 506
Admitted: 345
Enrolled: 275

Average GMAT: 632
Average GPA: 3.2

Costs (1999–2000)
Full-time tuition: $22,205 per academic year
Part-time tuition: $700 per credit hour

After Graduation (Class of 1998–99)
Employed within 3 months of graduation: 92%
Average starting salary: $62,655

Accreditation
AACSB—The International Association for Management Education

DEGREES JD/MBA • MBA • MBA/MS • MS

JD/MBA—Juris Doctor/Master of Business Administration Full-time and part-time. At least 60 total credits required. 48 to 60 months to complete program. *Concentrations:* business information science, business policy/strategy, decision sciences, electronic commerce (e-commerce), entrepreneurship, environmental economics/management, finance, financial information systems, information management, management, management consulting, management information systems, management science, manufacturing management, marketing, new venture management, operations management, production management, quality management, quantitative analysis, research and development administration, statistics, technology management.

MBA—Executive Master of Business Administration Part-time. At least 48 total credits required. 24 months to complete program. *Concentrations:* leadership, management.

MBA—Master of Business Administration Full-time and part-time. *Distance learning option.* At least 60 total credits required. 18 to 24 months to complete program. *Concentrations:* business information science, business policy/strategy, decision sciences, electronic commerce (e-commerce), entrepreneurship, environmental economics/management, finance, financial information systems, information management, management, management consulting, management information systems, management science, manufacturing management, marketing, new venture management, operations management, production management, quality management, quantitative analysis, research and development administration, statistics, technology management.

MBA/MS—Master of Business Administration/Master of Science in Engineering Full-time and part-time. *Distance learning option.* At least 72 total credits required. 30 to 36 months to complete program. *Concentrations:* business information science, business policy/strategy, decision sciences, electronic commerce (e-commerce), entrepreneurship, environmental economics/management, finance, financial information systems, information management, management, management consulting, management information systems, management science, manufacturing management, marketing, new venture management, operations management, production management, quality management, quantitative analysis, research and development administration, statistics, technology management.

MS—Master of Science in Environmental Management and Policy Full-time and part-time. At least 45 total credits required. 18 to 24 months to complete program.

MS—Master of Science in Management Full-time and part-time. *Distance learning option.* At least 30 total credits required. 9 to 18 months to complete program. *Concentrations:* business information science, business policy/strategy, electronic commerce (e-commerce), entrepreneurship, environmental economics/management, finance, financial information systems, information management, management, management consulting, management information systems, management science, management systems analysis, marketing, new venture management, operations management, production management, quality management, quantitative analysis, statistics.

COSTS
Tuition *Full-time:* $21,000. *Part-time:* $700 per credit hour. Tuition varies by number of courses or credits taken. **Required fees:** *Full-time* $1205. **Graduate housing:** Room and board costs vary by number of occupants, type of accommodation, and type of board plan. *Typical cost:* $7859 (including board).

FINANCIAL AID (1999–2000)
126 students received aid, including fellowships, loans, research assistantships, scholarships, and teaching assistantships. Financial aid application deadline: 2/1. **Financial Aid Contact** Mr. Zamiul Haque, Director, MBA/MS Admissions, Lally School of Management and Technology, Pittsburgh Building Room 3208, Troy, NY 12180-3590. **Phone:** 518-276-6809. **Fax:** 518-276-2665. **E-mail:** management@rpi.edu.

RESOURCES AND SERVICES
Information about online services, personal computer policies, library resources, international exchange programs, internship programs, and placement services at this institution and others can be found at **www.petersons.com/mba**

International Students
5% of students enrolled are international students.

Services and Facilities Counseling/support services, ESL/language courses, international student housing, visa services, pre-mba program through kaplan. Financial aid is available to international students.
Applying *Required:* TOEFL with recommended score of 600 (paper), proof of adequate funds, proof of health/immunizations.
International Student Contact Ms. Jane Havis, Assistant Dean, International Student Services, RPI 4043 Troy Building, Troy, NY 12180-3590. **Phone:** 518-276-6561. **Fax:** 518-276-4839. **E-mail:** havisj@rpi.edu.

■ APPLICATION
Required GMAT, application form, baccalaureate/first degree, essay, 2 letters of recommendation, personal statement, resume/curriculum vitae, transcripts of college work. School will accept GRE. **Recommended** Interview, work experience.
Deadlines and Fees Applications for domestic students are processed on a rolling basis. *Deadline:* 6/1 for fall (international). *Application fee:* $50, $50 (international).
Application Contact Mr. Zamiul Haque, Director, MBA/MS Admissions, Lally School of Management and Technology, Pittsburgh Building Room 3208, Troy, NY 12180-3590. **Phone:** 518-276-6809. **Fax:** 518-276-2665. **E-mail:** management@rpi.edu.

See full description on page 782.

Roberts Wesleyan College
Rochester, New York

DIVISION OF BUSINESS AND MANAGEMENT

Graduate Business Faculty
Full-time: 4

Part-time: 12

Student Body
Total: 56
Full-time: 56

Average Age: 37
Women: 55%

Admissions
Applications: 34
Admitted: 30

Enrolled: 24
Average GPA: 3.25

Costs (1999–2000)
Full-time tuition: N/R
Part-time tuition: $493 per credit hour

After Graduation (Class of 1998–99)
Employed within 3 months of graduation: 100%

DEGREE MS

MS—MS in Management Full-time. At least 36 total credits required. Minimum of 17 months to complete program. *Concentrations:* entrepreneurship, nonprofit management, organizational management.

COSTS
Tuition *Part-time:* $493 per credit hour. **Required fees:** *Full-time* $215. Tuition and fees vary by academic program. **Graduate housing:** *Typical cost:* $3174 (including board), $1774 (room only).

FINANCIAL AID (1999–2000)
30 students received aid, including loans. Aid is available to part-time students. **Financial Aid Contact** Mr. Steve Field, Director of Financial Aid, Rochester, NY 14624-1997. **Phone:** 716-594-6150. **Fax:** 716-594-6036. **E-mail:** fields@roberts.edu.

RESOURCES AND SERVICES
Information about online services, personal computer policies, library resources, international exchange programs, internship programs, and placement services at this institution and others can be found at **www.petersons.com/mba**

International Students
5% of students enrolled are international students.

Services and Facilities Counseling/support services, ESL/language courses, visa services. Financial aid is available to international students.

Applying *Required:* TOEFL with recommended score of 550 (paper), proof of adequate funds, proof of health/immunizations.

■ APPLICATION

Required Application form, baccalaureate/first degree, essay, 2 letters of recommendation, transcripts of college work, 2 years of work experience.

Deadlines and Fees Applications for domestic and international students are processed on a rolling basis. *Application fee:* $35, $35 (international).

Application Contact Mrs. Monica Mattioli, Marketing Director, Division of Business, 2301 Westside Drive, Rochester, NY 14624-1997. **Phone:** 716-594-6600. **Fax:** 716-594-6585. **E-mail:** msm@roberts.edu.

Rochester Institute of Technology

Rochester, New York

COLLEGE OF BUSINESS

Graduate Business Faculty
Full-time: 40   Part-time: 33

Student Body
Total: 441   Average Age: 31
Full-time: 216   Women: 33%
Part-time: 225

Admissions
Applications: 376   Average GMAT: 572
Admitted: 277   Average GPA: 3.1
Enrolled: 181

Costs (1999–2000)
Full-time tuition: $19,605 per academic year
Part-time tuition: $546 per credit hour

After Graduation (Class of 1998–99)
Employed within 3 months of graduation: 92%
Average starting salary: $49,559

Accreditation
AACSB—The International Association for Management Education

DEGREES EMBA • MBA • MS

EMBA—Executive MBA Part-time. At least 72 total credits required. 24 months to complete program.

MBA—Master of Business Administration Full-time and part-time. At least 72 total credits required. 12 to 84 months to complete program. *Concentrations:* accounting, decision sciences, finance, human resources, international business, leadership, management, management information systems, marketing, marketing research, operations management, organizational behavior/development, production management, quality management, technology management.

MS—Master of Science Full-time and part-time. GRE required. At least 48 total credits required. 12 to 84 months to complete program. *Concentrations:* finance, manufacturing management.

COSTS

Tuition *Full-time:* $19,461. *Part-time:* $546 per credit hour. Tuition varies by number of courses or credits taken and academic program. **Required fees:** *Full-time* $144. Tuition and fees vary by number of courses or credits taken. **Graduate housing:** Room and board costs vary by number of occupants, type of accommodation, and type of board plan. *Typical cost:* $5040 (including board).

FINANCIAL AID (1999–2000)

122 students received aid, including grants, loans, research assistantships, scholarships, and work study. Aid is available to part-time students. Financial aid application deadline: 8/1. **Financial Aid Contact** Ms. Verna Hazen, Director of Financial Aid, One Lomb Memorial Drive, Rochester, NY 14623-5604. **Phone:** 716-475-2186. **Fax:** 716-475-7270. **E-mail:** vjhsfa@rit.edu.

RESOURCES AND SERVICES

Information about online services, personal computer policies, library resources, international exchange programs, internship programs, and placement services at this institution and others can be found at **www.petersons.com/mba**

International Students

24% of students enrolled are international students.

Services and Facilities Counseling/support services, ESL/language courses, international student housing, international student organization, orientation, visa services. Financial aid is available to international students.

Applying *Required:* TOEFL with recommended score of 230 (computer) or 570 (paper), proof of adequate funds, proof of health/immunizations.

International Student Contact Mr. Jeffrey Cox, Program Coordinator, International Students, One Lomb Memorial Drive, Rochester, NY 14623-5604. **Phone:** 716-475-7433. **Fax:** 716-475-7419. **E-mail:** jwccst@rit.edu.

■ APPLICATION

Required GMAT, application form, baccalaureate/first degree, personal statement, transcripts of college work. **Recommended** Resume/curriculum vitae.

Deadlines and Fees *Deadlines:* 8/1 for fall, 10/31 for winter, 1/31 for spring, 5/1 for summer, 7/15 for fall (international), 10/15 for winter (international), 1/15 for spring (international), 4/17 for summer (international). *Application fee:* $40, $40 (international).

Application Contact Ms. Mildred Portela, Graduate Business Programs, 105 Lomb Memorial Drive, Rochester, NY 14623-5604. **Phone:** 716-475-6221. **Fax:** 716-475-7450. **E-mail:** gradbus@rit.edu.

See full description on page 790.

Sage Graduate School

Troy, New York

DIVISION OF MANAGEMENT, COMMUNICATIONS AND LEGAL STUDIES

Graduate Business Faculty
Full-time: 7   Part-time: 11

Student Body
Total: 101   Average Age: 35
Full-time: 9   Women: 56%
Part-time: 92

Admissions
Applications: 24   Enrolled: 16
Admitted: 24   Average GPA: 2.75

Costs (1999–2000)
Full-time tuition: N/R
Part-time tuition: $388 per credit hour

After Graduation (Class of 1998–99)
Average starting salary: $50,000

DEGREES JD/MBA • MBA • MBA/MS • MS

JD/MBA—Combined MBA/JD (Albany Law) Full-time and part-time. 75 to 87 total credits required. 60 to 72 months to complete program. *Concentrations:* human resources, management, marketing, strategic management.

MBA—Professional Master of Business Administration Full-time and part-time. 36 to 48 total credits required. 24 to 72 months to complete program. *Concentrations:* finance, human resources, management, marketing.

MBA/MS—Master of Business Administration/Master of Science in Nursing Full-time and part-time. At least 66 total credits required. 24 to 84 months to complete program. *Concentrations:* health care, management, marketing.

MS—Master of Science in Health Services Administration Full-time and part-time. At least 39 total credits required. 24 to 72 months to complete program. *Concentrations:* health care.

MS—Master of Science in Public Administration Full-time and part-time. At least 39 total credits required. 24 to 72 months to complete program. *Concentrations:* public policy and administration.

COSTS

Tuition *Part-time:* $388 per credit hour. **Required fees:** *Part-time* $100 per year. **Graduate housing:** Room and board costs vary by number of occupants and type of board plan. *Typical cost:* $3500 (including board), $1600 (room only).

FINANCIAL AID (1999–2000)

Financial Aid Contact Ms. Lisa Kuban, Assistant Director of Student Financial Services, 65 First Street, Troy, NY 12180. **Phone:** 518-244-2341. **Fax:** 518-244-2460. **E-mail:** kubanl@sage.edu.

RESOURCES AND SERVICES

Information about online services, personal computer policies, library resources, international exchange programs, internship programs, and

placement services at this institution and others can be found at **www. petersons.com/mba**

International Students

1.0% of students enrolled are international students.

Services and Facilities Visa services.

Applying *Required:* TOEFL with recommended score of 550 (paper), proof of adequate funds, proof of health/immunizations.

International Student Contact Ms. Melissa Robertson, Associate Director of Graduate Admissions, 45 Ferry Street, Troy, NY 12180-4115. **Phone:** 518-244-2443. **Fax:** 518-244-2460. **E-mail:** roberm@sage.edu.

■ APPLICATION

Required Application form, baccalaureate/first degree, essay, 2 letters of recommendation, personal statement, resume/curriculum vitae, transcripts of college work. **Recommended** Interview, 1 year of work experience.

Deadlines and Fees Applications for domestic and international students are processed on a rolling basis. *Application fee:* $40, $40 (international).

Application Contact Ms. Melissa Robertson, Associate Director of Graduate Admissions, 45 Ferry Street, Troy, NY 12180-4115. **Phone:** 518-244-2264. **Toll-free Phone:** 800-999-3772. **Fax:** 518-244-4571. **E-mail:** roberm@sage.edu.

St. Bonaventure University

St. Bonaventure, New York

SCHOOL OF BUSINESS

Graduate Business Faculty

Full-time: 21	Part-time: 4

Student Body

Total: 210	
Full-time: 117	Average Age: 28
Part-time: 93	Women: 50%

Admissions

Applications: 80	Average GMAT: 480
Admitted: 72	Average GPA: 3.2
Enrolled: 66	

Costs (1999–2000)
Full-time tuition: $8460 per academic year
Part-time tuition: $470 per credit hour

After Graduation (Class of 1998–99)
Employed within 3 months of graduation: 100%
Average starting salary: $40,000

DEGREES MBA

MBA—Evening MBA Part-time. 30 to 51 total credits required. 12 to 72 months to complete program. *Concentrations:* accounting, finance, international business, management, marketing.

MBA—One-year MBA Full-time. 30 to 51 total credits required. Minimum of 12 months to complete program. *Concentrations:* accounting, finance, international business, management, marketing.

MBA—Weekend MBA Part-time. 30 to 51 total credits required. 12 to 72 months to complete program. *Concentrations:* accounting, finance, international business, management, marketing.

COSTS

Tuition *Full-time:* $8460. *Part-time:* $470 per credit hour. Tuition varies by number of courses or credits taken. **Graduate housing:** Room and board costs vary by campus location, number of occupants, type of accommodation, and type of board plan. *Typical cost:* $5630 (including board), $2760 (room only).

FINANCIAL AID (1999–2000)

5 students received aid, including research assistantships. **Financial Aid Contact** Ms. Mary Piccioli, Director of Financial Aid, Hopkins Hall, St. Bonaventure, NY 14778. **Phone:** 716-375-2528. **Fax:** 716-375-2005. **E-mail:** mpiccioli@sbu.edu.

RESOURCES AND SERVICES

Information about online services, personal computer policies, library resources, international exchange programs, internship programs, and placement services at this institution and others can be found at **www. petersons.com/mba**

International Students

1.0% of students enrolled are international students.

Services and Facilities Counseling/support services, housing location assistance, international student organization. Financial aid is not available to international students.

Applying *Required:* TOEFL with recommended score of 250 (computer) or 600 (paper), proof of adequate funds, proof of health/immunizations.

International Student Contact Ms. Alice Sayegh, Director of Foreign Studies, RC 221B, St. Bonaventure, NY 14778. **Phone:** 716-375-2574. **Fax:** 716-375-2381. **E-mail:** asayegh@sbu.edu.

■ APPLICATION

Required GMAT, application form, baccalaureate/first degree, 2 letters of recommendation, transcripts of college work.

Deadlines and Fees Applications for domestic and international students are processed on a rolling basis. *Application fee:* $35, $35 (international).

Application Contact Prof. Brian C. McAllister, Director, MBA Program, PO Box BS, St. Bonaventure, NY 14778. **Phone:** 716-375-2098. **Fax:** 716-375-2191. **E-mail:** bmac@sbu.edu.

St. John Fisher College

Rochester, New York

SCHOOL OF ADULT AND GRADUATE EDUCATION

Graduate Business Faculty
Full-time: 20

Student Body

Total: 157	Average Age: 32
Full-time: 15	Women: 48%
Part-time: 142	

Admissions

Applications: 47	Average GMAT: 469
Admitted: 38	Average GPA: 3.18
Enrolled: 25	

Costs (1999–2000)
Full-time tuition: $15,600 per academic year
Part-time tuition: $550 per credit hour

After Graduation (Class of 1998–99)
Employed within 3 months of graduation: 90%
Average starting salary: $32,000

DEGREE MBA

MBA—Master of Business Administration Full-time and part-time. At least 54 total credits required. 12 to 48 months to complete program. *Concentrations:* accounting, industrial/labor relations, management.

T*he primary goal of St. John Fisher College's Business Division programs is to prepare professionally competent and ethically responsible graduates for careers in local and regional business organizations. Business Division programs strive to provide a learning environment that develops values-centered leaders who are prepared to succeed in the competitive, diverse, and rapidly changing business environment of the Rochester region. The curricula build upon a liberal arts foundation that is guided by the motto of the College's Basilian founders: "Teach me goodness, discipline, and knowledge."*

The purpose of Fisher's M.B.A. program is to prepare students to excel in the managerial roles they will occupy in the twenty-first-century organization. A Fisher M.B.A. develops competencies in multiple management disciplines and draws upon an integrated perspective to address issues of modern management. Aligned with the College's long-standing tradition as a values-based institution of higher learning, the M.B.A. program grounds students in ethical theory, which becomes infused with decision making in the context of business management. The 54-credit-hour program prepares students to function effectively in small and midsize businesses, the backbone of the business community in the Rochester area.

COSTS

Tuition *Full-time:* $15,600. *Part-time:* $550 per credit hour. Tuition varies by academic program. **Graduate housing:** Room and board costs vary by number of occupants and type of board plan. *Typical cost:* $6500 (including board).

FINANCIAL AID (1999–2000)

5 students received aid, including loans and work study. Aid is available to part-time students. Financial aid application deadline: 8/15. **Financial Aid Contact** Mrs. Angela Monnat, Director of Financial Aid, 3690 East

Avenue, Rochester, NY 14618-3597. **Phone:** 716-385-8042. **Fax:** 716-385-8094. **E-mail:** monnat@sjfc.edu.

RESOURCES AND SERVICES
Information about online services, personal computer policies, library resources, international exchange programs, internship programs, and placement services at this institution and others can be found at **www.petersons.com/mba**

International Students
3% of students enrolled are international students.

Services and Facilities Counseling/support services, ESL/language courses. Financial aid is not available to international students.
Applying *Required:* TOEFL with recommended score of 575 (paper), proof of adequate funds, proof of health/immunizations.
International Student Contact Mr. Steven Hoskins, Director of Graduate Admissions, 3690 East Avenue, Rochester, NY 14618-3597. **Phone:** 716-385-8161. **Fax:** 716-385-8344. **E-mail:** hoskins@sjfc.edu.

■ APPLICATION
Required Application form, baccalaureate/first degree, essay, 2 letters of recommendation, personal statement, resume/curriculum vitae, transcripts of college work. School will accept GMAT. **Recommended** Interview.
Deadlines and Fees *Deadlines:* 8/1 for fall, 11/15 for spring, 4/15 for summer, 8/1 for fall (international), 11/15 for spring (international), 4/15 for summer (international). *Application fee:* $30, $30 (international).
Application Contact Mr. Steven Hoskins, Director of Graduate Admissions, 3690 East Avenue, Rochester, NY 14618-3597. **Phone:** 716-385-8161. **Fax:** 716-385-8344. **E-mail:** hoskins@sjfc.edu.

St. John's University
Jamaica, New York

PETER J. TOBIN COLLEGE OF BUSINESS ADMINISTRATION

Graduate Business Faculty
Full-time: 99   Part-time: 34

Student Body
Total: 933
Full-time: 144   Average Age: 30
Part-time: 789   Women: 41%

Admissions
Applications: 521   Average GMAT: 490
Admitted: 358   Average GPA: 3.1
Enrolled: 213

Costs (1999–2000)
Full-time tuition: $15,270 per academic year
Part-time tuition: $630 per credit

After Graduation (Class of 1998–99)
Employed within 3 months of graduation: 95%
Average starting salary: $60,000

Accreditation
AACSB—The International Association for Management Education

DEGREES JD/MBA • MBA • MS

JD/MBA—Juris Doctor/Master of Business Administration Full-time. 115 to 155 total credits required. Minimum of 36 months to complete program. *Concentrations:* accounting, decision sciences, economics, finance, international finance, management, management information systems, marketing, taxation.

MBA—Master of Business Administration in Accounting Full-time and part-time. 39 to 78 total credits required. 16 to 60 months to complete program. *Concentrations:* accounting.

MBA—Master of Business Administration in Computer Information Systems Full-time and part-time. 36 to 66 total credits required. 12 to 60 months to complete program. *Concentrations:* management information systems.

MBA—Master of Business Administration in Decision Sciences Full-time and part-time. 36 to 66 total credits required. 12 to 60 months to complete program. *Concentrations:* decision sciences.

MBA—Master of Business Administration in Economics Full-time and part-time. 36 to 66 total credits required. 12 to 60 months to complete program. *Concentrations:* economics.

MBA—Master of Business Administration in Executive Management Full-time and part-time. 36 to 66 total credits required. 12 to 60 months to complete program. *Concentrations:* management.

MBA—Master of Business Administration in Finance Full-time and part-time. 36 to 66 total credits required. 12 to 60 months to complete program. *Concentrations:* finance.

MBA—Master of Business Administration in Financial Services Full-time and part-time. 36 to 66 total credits required. 12 to 60 months to complete program. *Concentrations:* finance.

MBA—Master of Business Administration in International Business Full-time and part-time. 36 to 66 total credits required. 12 to 60 months to complete program. *Concentrations:* international business.

MBA—Master of Business Administration in International Finance Full-time and part-time. 36 to 66 total credits required. 12 to 60 months to complete program. *Concentrations:* international finance.

MBA—Master of Business Administration in Marketing Management Full-time and part-time. 36 to 66 total credits required. 12 to 60 months to complete program. *Concentrations:* marketing.

MBA—Master of Business Administration in Taxation Full-time and part-time. 39 to 76 total credits required. 16 to 60 months to complete program. *Concentrations:* taxation.

MS—Master of Science in Forecasting and Planning Full-time and part-time. 36 to 66 total credits required. 12 to 60 months to complete program.

MS—Master of Science in Purchasing and Supply Leadership Full-time and part-time. 30 to 66 total credits required. 12 to 60 months to complete program.

MS—Master of Science in Taxation Full-time and part-time. 31 to 66 total credits required. 12 to 60 months to complete program. *Concentrations:* taxation.

COSTS
Tuition *Full-time:* $15,120. *Part-time:* $630 per credit. **Required fees:** *Full-time* $150. *Part-time* $75 per semester. **Graduate housing:** Room and board costs vary by campus location, number of occupants, type of accommodation, and type of board plan. *Typical cost:* $8550 (including board), $5300 (room only).

FINANCIAL AID (1999–2000)
446 students received aid, including loans, research assistantships, and scholarships. Aid is available to part-time students. Financial aid application deadline: 3/1. **Financial Aid Contact** Mr. Jorge Rodriguez, Assistant Vice President and Executive Director, 8000 Utopia Parkway, Jamaica, NY 11439. **Phone:** 718-990-2000. **Fax:** 718-990-5945.

RESOURCES AND SERVICES
Information about online services, personal computer policies, library resources, international exchange programs, internship programs, and placement services at this institution and others can be found at **www.petersons.com/mba**

International Students
16% of students enrolled are international students.

Services and Facilities Counseling/support services, ESL/language courses, visa services. Financial aid is not available to part-time students.
Applying *Required:* TOEFL with recommended score of 500 (paper), proof of adequate funds, proof of health/immunizations.
International Student Contact Mrs. June Sadowski-Devarez, Assistant Dean-International Student Services, 8000 Utopia Parkway, SJH Room 116, Jamaica, NY 11439. **Phone:** 718-990-6083. **Fax:** 718-990-2070. **E-mail:** sadowskj@stjohns.edu.

■ APPLICATION
Required GMAT, application form, baccalaureate/first degree, essay, 2 letters of recommendation, personal statement, transcripts of college work. **Recommended** Interview, resume/curriculum vitae.
Deadlines and Fees Applications for domestic students are processed on a rolling basis. *Deadlines:* 6/1 for fall (international), 11/1 for spring (international). *Application fee:* $40, $40 (international).
Application Contact Ms. Sheila Russell, Assistant Director of MBA Admissions, 8000 Utopia Parkway, Jamaica, NY 11439. **Phone:** 718-990-1345 Ext. 5736. **Toll-free Phone:** 888-9STJOHNS. **Fax:** 718-990-5242.

See full description on page 802.

St. Thomas Aquinas College
Sparkill, New York

DIVISION OF BUSINESS ADMINISTRATION

Graduate Business Faculty
Full-time: 7   Part-time: 8

Student Body
Total: 59
Part-time: 59   Average Age: 29
          Women: 36%

St. Thomas Aquinas College (continued)

Admissions
Applications: 37
Admitted: 29
Enrolled: 23

Average GMAT: 500
Average GPA: 3.2

Costs (1999–2000)
Full-time tuition: $9900 per academic year
Part-time tuition: $405 per credit

After Graduation (Class of 1998–99)
Employed within 3 months of graduation: 100%

DEGREE MBA

MBA—Master of Business Administration Full-time and part-time. At least 60 total credits required. 12 to 60 months to complete program. *Concentrations:* finance, management, marketing.

COSTS
Tuition *Full-time:* $9900. *Part-time:* $405 per credit. Tuition varies by number of courses or credits taken.

FINANCIAL AID (1999–2000)
7 students received aid. Aid is available to part-time students. Financial aid application deadline: 2/15. **Financial Aid Contact** Ms. Anna Maria Chrissotimos, Director of Financial Aid, 125 Route 340, Sparkill, NY 10976-1050. **Phone:** 914-398-4097. **Fax:** 914-398-4224.

RESOURCES AND SERVICES
Information about online services, personal computer policies, library resources, international exchange programs, internship programs, and placement services at this institution and others can be found at **www. petersons.com/mba**

International Students
Services and Facilities Counseling/support services, visa services. Financial aid is not available to international students.
Applying *Required:* TOEFL with recommended score of 500 (paper), proof of adequate funds, proof of health/immunizations.
International Student Contact Ms. Elizabeth Ward, Director of International Student Center, 125 Route 340, Sparkill, NY 10976-1050. **Phone:** 914-398-4100. **Fax:** 914-398-4224.

■ APPLICATION
Required Application form, baccalaureate/first degree, essay, 3 letters of recommendation, personal statement, resume/curriculum vitae, transcripts of college work. School will accept GMAT. **Recommended** Interview.
Deadlines and Fees *Application fee:* $35, $35 (international).
Application Contact Mr. Gregg Meyer, Dean of Enrollment Management, 125 Route 340, Sparkill, NY 10976-1050. **Phone:** 914-398-4100. **Fax:** 914-398-4224. **E-mail:** gmeyer@stac.edu.

Siena College
Loudonville, New York

SCHOOL OF BUSINESS

Graduate Business Faculty
Full-time: 9

Student Body
Total: 22
Full-time: 8
Part-time: 14

Average Age: 22
Women: 45%

Admissions
Applications: 17
Admitted: 17
Enrolled: 13

Average GMAT: 558
Average GPA: 3.1

Costs (1999–2000)
Full-time tuition: N/R
Part-time tuition: $350 per credit hour

After Graduation (Class of 1998–99)
Employed within 3 months of graduation: 100%

DEGREE MBA

MBA—Master of Business Administration in Professional Accountancy Full-time and part-time. At least 33 total credits required. 12 to 30 months to complete program. *Concentrations:* accounting.

COSTS
Tuition *Part-time:* $350 per credit hour. **Required fees:** *Part-time* $25 per semester.

FINANCIAL AID (1999–2000)
8 students received aid, including loans. Aid is available to part-time students. Financial aid application deadline: 4/15. **Financial Aid Contact** Ms. Mary Lawyer, Director, Financial Aid Office, 515 Loudon Road, Loudonville, NY 12211-1462. **Phone:** 518-783-2427. **Fax:** 518-783-2410. **E-mail:** mlawyer@siena.edu.

RESOURCES AND SERVICES
Information about online services, personal computer policies, library resources, international exchange programs, internship programs, and placement services at this institution and others can be found at **www. petersons.com/mba**

International Students
Services and Facilities Counseling/support services, visa services. Financial aid is not available to international students.
Applying *Required:* TOEFL with recommended score of 550 (paper), proof of adequate funds, proof of health/immunizations. *Recommended:* TSE, TWE.
International Student Contact Dr. Leonard Stokes, Director, MBA Program, 515 Loudon Road, Loudonville, NY 12211-1462. **Phone:** 518-786-5026. **Fax:** 518-786-5040. **E-mail:** stokes@siena.edu.

■ APPLICATION
Required GMAT, application form, baccalaureate/first degree, essay, 2 letters of recommendation, personal statement, resume/curriculum vitae, transcripts of college work. School will accept GRE and MAT. **Recommended** Interview.
Deadlines and Fees *Deadlines:* 5/31 for fall, 10/31 for spring, 5/31 for fall (international), 10/31 for spring (international). *Application fee:* $50, $50 (international).
Application Contact Dr. Leonard Stokes, Director, MBA Program, 515 Loudon Road, Loudonville, NY 12211-1462. **Phone:** 518-786-5026. **Fax:** 518-786-5040. **E-mail:** stokes@siena.edu.

State University of New York at Albany
Albany, New York

SCHOOL OF BUSINESS

Graduate Business Faculty
Full-time: 48

Part-time: 15

Student Body
Total: 374
Full-time: 163
Part-time: 211

Average Age: 24
Women: 47%

Admissions
Applications: 405
Admitted: 211
Enrolled: 115

Average GMAT: 591
Average GPA: 3.3

Costs (1999–2000)
Full-time tuition: $5100 per academic year (resident), $8416 per academic year (nonresident)
Part-time tuition: $213 per credit hour (resident), $351 per credit hour (nonresident)

After Graduation (Class of 1998–99)
Employed within 3 months of graduation: 100%
Average starting salary: $55,000

Accreditation
AACSB—The International Association for Management Education

DEGREES MBA • MS

MBA—Evening MBA Part-time. *Distance learning option.* 2 years of work experience. At least 60 total credits required. 24 to 60 months to complete program. *Concentrations:* finance, human resources, management information systems, marketing.

MBA—Evening MBA Part-time. At least 49 total credits required. 36 to 72 months to complete program. *Concentrations:* management.

Peterson's Guide to MBA Programs 2001

MBA—Executive MBA Full-time and part-time. *Distance learning option.* 3 years of work experience. At least 60 total credits required. 12 to 24 months to complete program. *Concentrations:* accounting, management systems analysis, real estate.

MBA—Master of Business Administration Full-time. 63 total credits required. 24 to 36 months to complete program. *Concentrations:* finance, human resources, management information systems, marketing.

MBA—Weekend MBA Part-time. At least 39 total credits required. 21 to 72 months to complete program.

MBA—Master of Business Administration Full-time. 63 total credits required. 24 to 36 months to complete program. *Concentrations:* finance, human resources, management information systems, marketing.

MBA—Master of Business Administration Part-time. At least 44 total credits required. 24 to 48 months to complete program.

MBA—Master of Business Administration Full-time. At least 63 total credits required. 21 months to complete program. *Concentrations:* finance, management information systems, marketing.

MS—Master of Science in Accounting Part-time. At least 63 total credits required. 21 months to complete program. *Concentrations:* accounting.

MS—Master of Science in Accounting Full-time and part-time. Degree in accounting required. At least 30 total credits required. 9 to 72 months to complete program. *Concentrations:* accounting, information management.

MS—Master of Science in Taxation Full-time and part-time. At least 39 total credits required. 12 to 72 months to complete program. *Concentrations:* taxation.

COSTS

Tuition, state resident: *Full-time* $5100. *Part-time* $213 per credit hour. **Tuition, nonresident:** *Full-time* $8416. *Part-time* $351 per credit hour. **Required fees:** Fees vary by number of courses or credits taken. **Graduate housing:** Room and board costs vary by number of occupants, type of accommodation, and type of board plan. *Typical cost:* $5400 (including board).

FINANCIAL AID (1999–2000)

25 students received aid, including fellowships, research assistantships, and work study. Financial aid application deadline: 4/1. **Financial Aid Contact** Mr. Dennis Tillman, Director of Financial Aid, Office of Financial Aid, CCB52—1400 Washington Avenue, Albany, NY 12222. **Phone:** 518-442-5480. **Fax:** 518-442-5295. **E-mail:** faodbt@safnet.albany.edu.

RESOURCES AND SERVICES

Information about online services, personal computer policies, library resources, international exchange programs, internship programs, and placement services at this institution and others can be found at **www.petersons.com/mba**

International Students

7% of students enrolled are international students.

Services and Facilities Counseling/support services, ESL/language courses, international student housing, international student organization, visa services. Financial aid is not available to international students.
Applying *Required:* TOEFL with recommended score of 580 (paper), proof of adequate funds, proof of health/immunizations.

International Student Contact Mr. Steven Thomson, Director of International Student Services, ULB-66 1400 Washington Avenue, Albany, NY 12222. **Phone:** 518-442-5495. **Fax:** 518-442-5390. **E-mail:** ssvsat@safnet.albany.edu.

■ APPLICATION

Required GMAT, application form, baccalaureate/first degree, essay, 3 letters of recommendation, personal statement, transcripts of college work. School will accept GRE. **Recommended** Resume/curriculum vitae, 1 year of work experience.
Deadlines and Fees Applications for domestic and international students are processed on a rolling basis. *Application fee:* $50, $50 (international).

Application Contact Albina Grignon, Assistant Dean for Student Services, 1400 Washington Avenue, Albany, NY 12222. **Phone:** 518-442-4961. **Toll-free Phone:** 800-UALBANY. **Fax:** 518-442-3944. **E-mail:** a.grignon@albany.edu.

State University of New York at Binghamton

Binghamton, New York

SCHOOL OF MANAGEMENT

Graduate Business Faculty

Full-time: 33   Part-time: 21

Student Body

Total: 323	Average Age: 26
Full-time: 263	Women: 42%
Part-time: 60	

Admissions

Applications: 359	Average GMAT: 551
Admitted: 284	Average GPA: 3.3
Enrolled: 112	

Costs (1999–2000)

Full-time tuition: $6115 per academic year (resident), $9431 per academic year (nonresident)
Part-time tuition: $213 per credit hour (resident), $351 per credit hour (nonresident)

After Graduation (Class of 1998–99)

Employed within 3 months of graduation: 85%
Average starting salary: $48,000

Accreditation

AACSB—The International Association for Management Education

DEGREES   EMBA • MBA • MS

EMBA—Executive Master of Business Administration in Health Care Full-time. Up to 54 total credits required. Maximum of 21 months to complete program.

MBA—Master of Business Administration Full-time and part-time. 36 to 68 total credits required. 9 to 57 months to complete program. *Concentrations:* accounting, finance, management information systems, marketing, operations management, organizational behavior/development.

MS—Master of Science in Accounting Full-time and part-time. 32 to 66 total credits required. 9 to 57 months to complete program. *Concentrations:* accounting.

COSTS

Tuition, state resident: *Full-time* $5100. *Part-time* $213 per credit hour. **Tuition, nonresident:** *Full-time* $8416. *Part-time* $351 per credit hour. Tuition varies by number of courses or credits taken. **Required fees:** *Full-time* $1015. **Graduate housing:** Room and board costs vary by number of occupants, type of accommodation, and type of board plan. *Typical cost:* $6666 (including board), $3980 (room only).

FINANCIAL AID (1999–2000)

35 students received aid, including fellowships, grants, loans, research assistantships, scholarships, teaching assistantships, and work study. Financial aid application deadline: 2/15. **Financial Aid Contact** Mr. Richard Reeves-Ellington, Associate Dean, School of Management, Binghamton, NY 13902-6000. **Phone:** 607-777-2315. **Fax:** 607-777-4872.

RESOURCES AND SERVICES

Information about online services, personal computer policies, library resources, international exchange programs, internship programs, and placement services at this institution and others can be found at **www.petersons.com/mba**

International Students

38% of students enrolled are international students.

Services and Facilities Counseling/support services, ESL/language courses, housing location assistance, international student organization, language tutoring, orientation, visa services. Financial aid is available to international students.
Applying *Required:* TOEFL with recommended score of 230 (computer) or 570 (paper), proof of adequate funds, proof of health/immunizations.

International Student Contact Ms. Ellen Badger, Director, International Student and Scholar Services, PO Box 6000, Binghamton, NY 13902-6000. **Phone:** 607-777-2510. **Fax:** 607-777-2889. **E-mail:** ebadger@binghamton.edu.

■ APPLICATION

Required GMAT, application form, baccalaureate/first degree, 2 letters of recommendation, personal statement, transcripts of college work. **Recommended** Resume/curriculum vitae, work experience.
Deadlines and Fees Applications for domestic and international students are processed on a rolling basis. *Application fee:* $50, $50 (international).

Application Contact Alesia Wheeler, Assistant Director, MBA/MS Program, PO Box 6000, Binghamton, NY 13902-6000. **Phone:** 607-777-2316. **Fax:** 607-777-4872. **E-mail:** awheeler@binghamton.edu.

See full description on page 832.

State University of New York at Buffalo

Buffalo, New York

SCHOOL OF MANAGEMENT

Graduate Business Faculty
Full-time: 57

Part-time: 8

Student Body
Total: 694
Full-time: 471
Part-time: 223

Average Age: 30
Women: 41%

Admissions
Applications: 915
Admitted: 372
Enrolled: 238

Average GMAT: 600
Average GPA: 3.2

Costs (1999–2000)
Full-time tuition: $5950 per academic year (resident), $9266 per academic year (nonresident)
Part-time tuition: $425 per credit (resident), $425 per credit (nonresident)

After Graduation (Class of 1998–99)
Employed within 3 months of graduation: 80%
Average starting salary: $46,185

Accreditation
AACSB—The International Association for Management Education

DEGREES JD/MBA • MBA • MBA/M Arch • MBA/MS • MD/MBA • Pharm D/MBA

JD/MBA—Juris Doctor/Master of Business Administration Full-time. At least 96 total credits required. 48 to 72 months to complete program. *Concentrations:* accounting, finance, health care, human resources, international business, management, management information systems, manufacturing management, marketing.

MBA—Executive MBA Part-time. At least 48 total credits required. 22 months to complete program. *Concentrations:* management.

MBA—Full-time MBA Full-time. At least 60 total credits required. 12 to 48 months to complete program. *Concentrations:* accounting, electronic commerce (e-commerce), finance, health care, human resources, international business, management, management consulting, management information systems, manufacturing management, marketing.

MBA—Professional MBA Part-time. Minimum of 3 years of relevant post-baccalaureate work experience required. At least 48 total credits required. 36 months to complete program. *Concentrations:* management.

MBA/M Arch—Master of Business Administration/Master of Architecture Full-time. At least 96 total credits required. 48 to 72 months to complete program. *Concentrations:* accounting, finance, health care, human resources, international business, management, management information systems, manufacturing management, marketing.

MBA/MS—Master of Business Administration/Master of Science in Geography Full-time. At least 78 total credits required. 36 to 48 months to complete program. *Concentrations:* accounting, finance, health care, human resources, international business, management, management information systems, manufacturing management, marketing.

MD/MBA—Doctor of Medicine/Master of Business Administration Full-time. At least 180 total credits required. 60 months to complete program.

Pharm D/MBA—Doctor of Pharmacy/Master of Business Administration Full-time. At least 231 total credits required. 84 months to complete program.

COSTS
Tuition, state resident: *Full-time* $5100. *Part-time* $425 per credit. **Tuition, nonresident:** *Full-time* $8416. *Part-time* $425 per credit. Tuition varies by number of courses or credits taken. **Required fees:** *Full-time* $850. Fees vary by number of courses or credits taken and academic program. **Graduate housing:** Room and board costs vary by campus location, number of occupants, type of accommodation, and type of board plan. *Typical cost:* $6880 (including board).

FINANCIAL AID (1999–2000)
207 students received aid, including fellowships, grants, loans, research assistantships, scholarships, teaching assistantships, and work study. Aid is available to part-time students. Financial aid application deadline: 2/15. **Financial Aid Contact** Dr. Joanne Plunkett, Director, Student Finances and Records, Hayes C, Buffalo, NY 14214. **Phone:** 716-829-3724. **Fax:** 716-829-2022. **E-mail:** jplunkett@sfr.buffalo.edu.

RESOURCES AND SERVICES
Information about online services, personal computer policies, library resources, international exchange programs, internship programs, and placement services at this institution and others can be found at **www.petersons.com/mba**

International Students
34% of students enrolled are international students.

Services and Facilities Counseling/support services, ESL/language courses, language tutoring, visa services. Financial aid is not available to international students.

Applying *Required:* TOEFL with recommended score of 213 (computer) or 550 (paper), TSE with recommended score of 50, proof of adequate funds, proof of health/immunizations.

International Student Contact Ms. Ellen Dussourd, Director, International Student Scholar Services, 210 Talbert Hall, Buffalo, NY 14260. **Phone:** 716-645-2258. **Fax:** 716-645-6197. **E-mail:** disspird@acsu.buffalo.edu.

■ APPLICATION
Required GMAT, application form, baccalaureate/first degree, essay, 2 letters of recommendation, personal statement, transcripts of college work. **Recommended** Resume/curriculum vitae, work experience.

Deadlines and Fees *Deadlines:* 7/1 for fall, 4/1 for fall (international). *Application fee:* $50, $50 (international).

Application Contact Dr. Katherine Ferguson, Assistant Dean and Administrative Director of the MBA Program, 206 Jacobs Management Center, Buffalo, NY 14260. **Phone:** 716-645-3204. **Fax:** 716-645-2341. **E-mail:** som-mba@buffalo.edu.

See full description on page 834.

State University of New York at New Paltz

New Paltz, New York

SCHOOL OF BUSINESS

Graduate Business Faculty
Full-time: 10

Student Body
Total: 102
Full-time: 44
Part-time: 58

Average Age: 36
Women: 46%

Admissions
Applications: 38
Admitted: 34
Enrolled: 22

Average GMAT: 478
Average GPA: 3.3

Costs (1999–2000)
Full-time tuition: N/R
Part-time tuition: $213 per credit (resident), $351 per credit (nonresident)

DEGREE MBA

MBA—Master of Business Administration Full-time and part-time. 36 to 57 total credits required. 18 to 84 months to complete program. *Concentrations:* accounting, finance, international business, marketing.

COSTS
Tuition, state resident: *Part-time* $213 per credit. **Tuition, nonresident:** *Part-time* $351 per credit. Tuition varies by local reciprocity agreements. **Required fees:** Fees vary by number of courses or credits taken. **Graduate housing:** Room and board costs vary by number of occupants and type of board plan. *Typical cost:* $5246 (including board).

FINANCIAL AID (1999–2000)
10 students received aid, including fellowships and teaching assistantships. **Financial Aid Contact** Mr. Daniel Sistarenik, Director of Financial Aid, 75 South Manheim Boulevard, Suite 9, New Paltz, NY 12561-2443. **Phone:** 914-257-3250. **Fax:** 914-257-3568. **E-mail:** sistared@npum.newpaltz.edu.

RESOURCES AND SERVICES
Information about online services, personal computer policies, library resources, international exchange programs, internship programs, and placement services at this institution and others can be found at **www.petersons.com/mba**

International Students

35% of students enrolled are international students.

Services and Facilities Counseling/support services, ESL/language courses, international student housing, international student organization, language tutoring, orientation, visa services. Financial aid is available to international students.

Applying *Required:* TOEFL with recommended score of 550 (paper), proof of adequate funds, proof of health/immunizations.

International Student Contact Ms. Jean Whitlow, Assistant Director of Business Programs, 75 South Manheim Boulevard, Suite 9, New Paltz, NY 12561-2443. **Phone:** 845-257-2930. **Fax:** 845-257-3737. **E-mail:** whitlowj@newpaltz.edu.

■ APPLICATION

Required Application form, baccalaureate/first degree, essay, 3 letters of recommendation, personal statement, transcripts of college work. School will accept GMAT. **Recommended** Interview, resume/curriculum vitae.

Deadlines and Fees Applications for domestic and international students are processed on a rolling basis. *Application fee:* $50, $50 (international).

Application Contact Ms. Jean Whitlow, Assistant Director of Business Programs, 75 South Manheim Boulevard, Suite 9, New Paltz, NY 12561-2443. **Phone:** 845-257-2930. **Fax:** 845-257-3737. **E-mail:** whitlowj@matrix.newpaltz.edu.

State University of New York at Oswego

Oswego, New York

SCHOOL OF BUSINESS

Graduate Business Faculty
Full-time: 16 — Part-time: 3

Student Body
Total: 121
Full-time: 46
Part-time: 75

Average Age: 32
Women: 53%

Admissions
Applications: 75
Admitted: 71
Enrolled: 64

Average GMAT: 510
Average GPA: 3.1

Costs (1999–2000)
Full-time tuition: $5100 per academic year (resident), $8416 per academic year (nonresident)
Part-time tuition: $213 per credit (resident), $351 per credit (nonresident)

DEGREES MBA

MBA—Master of Business Administration/Accounting Full-time and part-time. At least 36 total credits required. 12 to 72 months to complete program. *Concentrations:* accounting.

MBA—Master of Business Administration Full-time and part-time. 36 to 54 total credits required. 12 to 72 months to complete program.

COSTS

Tuition, state resident: *Full-time* $5100. *Part-time* $213 per credit. **Tuition, nonresident:** *Full-time* $8416. *Part-time* $351 per credit. Tuition varies by number of courses or credits taken. **Graduate housing:** Room and board costs vary by number of occupants and type of board plan. *Typical cost:* $5460 (including board).

FINANCIAL AID (1999–2000)

12 students received aid, including research assistantships and teaching assistantships. Aid is available to part-time students. Financial aid application deadline: 4/1. **Financial Aid Contact** Margaret Sternberg, Director of Financial Aid, 206 Culkin Hall, Oswego, NY 13126. **Phone:** 315-341-2248. **Fax:** 315-341-3696. **E-mail:** finaid@oswego.edu.

RESOURCES AND SERVICES

Information about online services, personal computer policies, library resources, international exchange programs, internship programs, and placement services at this institution and others can be found at **www.petersons.com/mba**

International Students

6% of students enrolled are international students.

Services and Facilities Counseling/support services, ESL/language courses, international student housing, visa services. Financial aid is not available to inter-

national students.

Applying *Required:* TOEFL with recommended score of 550 (paper), proof of adequate funds, proof of health/immunizations.

International Student Contact International Student Advisor, Office of International Studies, Rich Hall, Oswego, NY 13126. **Phone:** 315-341-5775. **Fax:** 315-341-2488. **E-mail:** oliver@oswego.edu.

■ APPLICATION

Required GMAT, application form, baccalaureate/first degree, essay, 3 letters of recommendation, personal statement, transcripts of college work. **Recommended** Resume/curriculum vitae.

Deadlines and Fees Applications for domestic and international students are processed on a rolling basis. *Application fee:* $50, $50 (international).

Application Contact Mr. Charles A. Spector, MMA Director, School of Business, Swetman Hall, Oswego, NY 13126. **Phone:** 315-341-2911. **Fax:** 315-341-5440.

State University of New York at Stony Brook

Stony Brook, New York

W. AVERELL HARRIMAN SCHOOL FOR MANAGEMENT AND POLICY

Graduate Business Faculty
Full-time: 9 — Part-time: 30

Student Body
Total: 103
Full-time: 56
Part-time: 47

Average Age: 29
Women: 45%

Admissions
Applications: 155
Admitted: 103
Enrolled: 58

Average GMAT: 550
Average GPA: 3.3

Costs (1999–2000)
Full-time tuition: $5712 per academic year (resident), $9028 per academic year (nonresident)
Part-time tuition: $213 per credit hour (resident), $351 per credit hour (nonresident)

DEGREES MS

MS—Master of Science in Accounting Full-time and part-time. At least 30 total credits required. Minimum of 9 months to complete program.

MS—Master of Science in Management and Policy Full-time and part-time. At least 60 total credits required. Maximum of 60 months to complete program. *Concentrations:* health care, human resources, management information systems.

COSTS

Tuition, state resident: *Full-time* $5100. *Part-time* $213 per credit hour. **Tuition, nonresident:** *Full-time* $8416. *Part-time* $351 per credit hour. Tuition varies by number of courses or credits taken. **Required fees:** *Full-time* $612. *Part-time* $22 per credit. Fees vary by class time, number of courses or credits taken, and academic program. **Graduate housing:** Room and board costs vary by number of occupants, type of accommodation, and type of board plan. *Typical cost:* $5350 (including board).

FINANCIAL AID (1999–2000)

70 students received aid, including fellowships, research assistantships, teaching assistantships, and work study. Financial aid application deadline: 4/15. **Financial Aid Contact** Mrs. Ana Maria Torres, Director, Office of Financial Aid and Student Employment, Stony Brook, NY 11794-0851. **Phone:** 631-632-6840. **Fax:** 631-632-9525. **E-mail:** amtorres@notes.cc.sunysb.edu.

RESOURCES AND SERVICES

Information about online services, personal computer policies, library resources, international exchange programs, internship programs, and placement services at this institution and others can be found at **www.petersons.com/mba**

International Students

58% of students enrolled are international students.

Services and Facilities Counseling/support services, ESL/language courses, international student housing, orientation, visa services. Financial aid is available to international students.

State University of New York at Stony Brook (continued)

Applying *Required:* TOEFL with recommended score of 213 (computer) or 550 (paper), proof of adequate funds, proof of health/immunizations.
International Student Contact Dr. Elizabeth Barnum, Director of Foreign Student Services, Stony Brook, NY 11794-4433. **Phone:** 631-632-7040. **Fax:** 631-632-7243. **E-mail:** ebarnum@notes.cc.sunysb.edu.

■ **APPLICATION**

Required GMAT or GRE, application form, baccalaureate/first degree, 3 letters of recommendation, personal statement, transcripts of college work. **Recommended** Resume/curriculum vitae.
Deadlines and Fees *Deadlines:* 1/15 for fall, 10/1 for spring, 4/15 for fall (international), 11/1 for spring (international). *Application fee:* $50, $50 (international).
Application Contact Office of Student Services, W. Averell Harriman School for Management and Policy, Stony Brook, NY 11794-3775. **Phone:** 631-632-7296. **Fax:** 631-632-8181. **E-mail:** oss@notes.cc.sunysb.edu.

See full description on page 836.

State University of New York College at Oneonta

Oneonta, New York

DEPARTMENT OF ECONOMICS AND BUSINESS

Graduate Business Faculty
Full-time: 8

Student Body
Total: 17
Full-time: 8
Part-time: 9
Women: 53%

Admissions
Applications: 1
Admitted: 1
Average GMAT: 616
Average GPA: 2.36

Costs (1999–2000)
Full-time tuition: N/R
Part-time tuition: $213 per credit (resident), $351 per credit (nonresident)

DEGREE MS

MS—MS in Business Economics Full-time and part-time. At least 30 total credits required. Minimum of 30 months to complete program.

COSTS

Tuition, state resident: *Part-time* $213 per credit. **Tuition, nonresident:** *Part-time* $351 per credit. **Graduate housing:** *Typical cost:* $5456 (including board), $3006 (room only).

FINANCIAL AID (1999–2000)

Grants, loans, scholarships, and work study. Aid is available to part-time students. **Financial Aid Contact** Bill Goodhue, Director of Financial Aid, 123 Netzer Administration Building, Oneonta, NY 13820-4015. **Phone:** 607-436-2532. **Fax:** 607-436-2659. **E-mail:** goodhuew@oneonta.edu.

RESOURCES AND SERVICES

Information about online services, personal computer policies, library resources, international exchange programs, internship programs, and placement services at this institution and others can be found at www.petersons.com/mba

International Students

6% of students enrolled are international students.
Services and Facilities Counseling/support services, ESL/language courses, international student housing. Financial aid is not available to international students. **Applying** *Required:* TOEFL with recommended score of 500 (paper), proof of health/immunizations. *Recommended:* Proof of adequate funds.
International Student Contact David Jervis, Ravine Parkway, Oneonta, NY 13820-4015. **Phone:** 607-436-3369. **Fax:** 607-436-2475. **E-mail:** jervisdt@oneonta.edu.

■ **APPLICATION**

Required GMAT, application form, baccalaureate/first degree, 3 letters of recommendation, resume/curriculum vitae, transcripts of college work.
Deadlines and Fees Applications for domestic and international students are processed on a rolling basis. *Application fee:* $50, $50 (international).

Application Contact Wade Thomas, Director of Master of Science in Business Economics, Ravine Parkway, Oneonta, NY 13820-4015. **Phone:** 607-436-3458. **Fax:** 607-436-2543. **E-mail:** thomaswl@oneonta.edu.

State University of New York Empire State College

Saratoga Springs, New York

GRADUATE STUDIES

Graduate Business Faculty
Full-time: 1
Part-time: 10

Student Body
Total: 106
Full-time: 3
Part-time: 103
Average Age: 41
Women: 47%

Admissions
Applications: 50
Admitted: 45
Enrolled: 33

Costs (1999–2000)
Full-time tuition: N/R
Part-time tuition: $213 per credit (resident), $351 per credit (nonresident)

DEGREES MA • MBA

MA—Master of Arts in Business and Policy Studies Full-time and part-time. *Distance learning option.* At least 36 total credits required. 24 to 72 months to complete program.

MBA—Master of Business Administration *Distance learning option.* Minimum 3-5 years of managerial experience required. 20 to 60 total credits required. 48 to 72 months to complete program.

COSTS

Tuition, state resident: *Part-time* $213 per credit. **Tuition, nonresident:** *Part-time* $351 per credit. **Required fees:** Tuition and fees vary by number of courses or credits taken and academic program.

FINANCIAL AID (1999–2000)

Fellowships, loans, and work study. Financial aid application deadline: 7/1. **Financial Aid Contact** Ms. Eileen Corrigan, Director, Financial Aid, 2 Union Avenue, Saratoga Springs, NY 12866. **Phone:** 518-587-2100 Ext. 221.

RESOURCES AND SERVICES

Information about online services, personal computer policies, library resources, international exchange programs, internship programs, and placement services at this institution and others can be found at www.petersons.com/mba

International Students

2% of students enrolled are international students.
Services and Facilities Financial aid is not available to international students. **Applying** *Required:* TOEFL with recommended score of 250 (computer) or 600 (paper), proof of adequate funds, proof of health/immunizations.
International Student Contact Dean for International Programs, 320 Broadway, Saratoga Springs, NY 12866-4390. **Phone:** 518-587-2100 Ext. 231. **Fax:** 518-581-8306. **E-mail:** ken.abrams@esc.edu.

■ **APPLICATION**

Required Application form, baccalaureate/first degree, essay, 3 letters of recommendation, personal statement, resume/curriculum vitae, transcripts of college work.
Deadlines and Fees *Deadlines:* 8/15 for fall, 1/15 for spring, 8/15 for fall (international), 1/15 for spring (international). *Application fee:* $50, $50 (international).
Application Contact Dr. Alan Belasen, MBA Faculty Members, 28 Union Avenue, Saratoga Springs, NY 12866. **Phone:** 518-587-2100 Ext. 207. **Toll-free Phone:** 800-GOTOESC. **E-mail:** alan.belasen@esc.edu.

See full description on page 838.

State University of New York Institute of Technology at Utica/Rome

Utica, New York

SCHOOL OF MANAGEMENT

Graduate Business Faculty
Full-time: 13

Student Body
Total: 127
Full-time: 36
Part-time: 91

Average Age: 35
Women: 43%

Admissions
Applications: 64
Admitted: 44
Enrolled: 32

Average GMAT: 490
Average GPA: 3.3

Costs (1999–2000)
Full-time tuition: $5701 per academic year (resident), $9017 per academic year (nonresident)
Part-time tuition: $230 per credit hour (resident), $368 per credit hour (nonresident)

After Graduation (Class of 1998–99)
Employed within 3 months of graduation: 90%
Average starting salary: $54,000

DEGREES MS

MS—Master of Science in Accountancy Full-time and part-time. *Distance learning option.* At least 33 total credits required. Minimum of 12 months to complete program.

MS—Master of Science in Business Management Full-time and part-time. At least 33 total credits required. Minimum of 12 months to complete program. *Concentrations:* accounting, finance, health care, human resources, management science, system management.

COSTS

Tuition, state resident: *Full-time* $5100. *Part-time* $213 per credit hour. **Tuition, nonresident:** *Full-time* $8416. *Part-time* $351 per credit hour. **Tuition, international:** *Full-time* $8416. **Required fees:** *Full-time* $601. *Part-time* $17 per credit hour. Tuition and fees vary by number of courses or credits taken. **Graduate housing:** Room and board costs vary by number of occupants and type of board plan. *Typical cost:* $6100 (including board), $3900 (room only).

FINANCIAL AID (1999–2000)

56 students received aid, including fellowships, grants, loans, research assistantships, scholarships, teaching assistantships, and work study. Aid is available to part-time students. Financial aid application deadline: 6/15. **Financial Aid Contact** Mr. Edward Hutchinson, Director of Financial Aid, PO Box 3050, Utica, NY 13504-3050. **Phone:** 315-792-7210. **Fax:** 315-792-7837. **E-mail:** seah@sunyit.edu.

RESOURCES AND SERVICES

Information about online services, personal computer policies, library resources, international exchange programs, internship programs, and placement services at this institution and others can be found at **www.petersons.com/mba**

International Students

2% of students enrolled are international students.
Services and Facilities Counseling/support services, ESL/language courses, housing location assistance, international student organization, orientation, visa services. Financial aid is not available to international students.
Applying *Required:* TOEFL with recommended score of 213 (computer) or 550 (paper), proof of adequate funds, proof of health/immunizations.
International Student Contact Ms. Marybeth Lyons, Director of Admissions, PO Box 3050, Utica, NY 13504-3050. **Phone:** 315-792-7500. **Fax:** 315-792-7837. **E-mail:** smbl@sunyit.edu.

■ APPLICATION

Required Application form, baccalaureate/first degree, 1 letter of recommendation, transcripts of college work. School will accept GMAT. **Recommended** Interview.
Deadlines and Fees Applications for domestic and international students are processed on a rolling basis. *Application fee:* $50, $50 (international).

Application Contact Ms. Marybeth Lyons, Director of Admissions, PO Box 3050, Utica, NY 13504-3050. **Phone:** 315-792-7500. **Toll-free Phone:** 800-SUNYTEC. **Fax:** 315-792-7837. **E-mail:** smbl@sunyit.edu.

State University of New York Maritime College

Throggs Neck, New York

PROGRAM IN TRANSPORTATION MANAGEMENT

DEGREE MS

MS—Master of Science in Transportation Management Full-time and part-time. 33 to 57 total credits required. Maximum of 60 months to complete program. *Concentrations:* business law, environmental economics/management, international economics, international logistics, logistics, management information systems, management systems analysis, managerial economics, operations management, organizational behavior/development, port/maritime management, system management.

RESOURCES AND SERVICES

Information about online services, personal computer policies, library resources, international exchange programs, internship programs, and placement services at this institution and others can be found at **www.petersons.com/mba**

International Students

Services and Facilities ESL/language courses. Financial aid is not available to international students.
International Student Contact Pamela Dettmer, Assistant Administrator, 6 Pennyfield Avenue, Bronx, NY 10465. **Phone:** 718-409-7285. **Fax:** 718-409-7359.

■ APPLICATION

Application Contact Pamela Dettmer, Assistant Administrator, 6 Pennyfield Avenue, Bronx, NY 10465. **Phone:** 718-409-7285. **Fax:** 718-409-7359.

Syracuse University

Syracuse, New York

SCHOOL OF MANAGEMENT

Graduate Business Faculty
Full-time: 58

Part-time: 11

Student Body
Total: 556
Full-time: 195
Part-time: 361

Average Age: 28
Women: 30%

Admissions
Applications: 700
Admitted: 170
Enrolled: 106

Average GMAT: 602
Average GPA: 3.2

Costs (1999–2000)
Full-time tuition: $19,412 per academic year
Part-time tuition: $613 per credit

After Graduation (Class of 1998–99)
Employed within 3 months of graduation: 97%
Average starting salary: $70,000

Accreditation
AACSB—The International Association for Management Education

DEGREES EMBA • JD/MBA • JD/MS • MBA • MBA/MS • MS

EMBA—Executive Master of Business Administration Part-time. At least 54 total credits required. 22 months to complete program.

JD/MBA—Juris Doctor/Master of Business Administration Full-time and part-time. At least 119 total credits required. 44 to 84 months to complete program. *Concentrations:* accounting, entrepreneurship, finance, human resources, international business, logistics, management, marketing, new venture management, supply chain management, technology management.

JD/MS—Juris Doctor/Master of Science in Accounting Full-time and part-time. 101 to 131 total credits required. 28 to 84 months to complete program. *Concentrations:* accounting, finance.

Syracuse University (continued)

JD/MS—Juris Doctor/Master of Science in Finance Full-time and part-time. At least 91 total credits required. 24 to 84 months to complete program. *Concentrations:* sports/entertainment management.

MBA—Master of Business Administration Full-time and part-time. *Distance learning option.* 36 to 60 total credits required. 11 to 84 months to complete program. *Concentrations:* accounting, entrepreneurship, finance, human resources, international business, logistics, management, marketing, new venture management, supply chain management, technology management.

MBA/MS—Master of Business Administration/Master of Science in Media Management Full-time and part-time. At least 82 total credits required. 24 to 84 months to complete program. *Concentrations:* accounting, entrepreneurship, finance, human resources, international business, logistics, management, marketing, new venture management, sports/entertainment management, supply chain management, technology management.

MS—Master of Science in Accounting Full-time and part-time. 30 to 63 total credits required. 8 to 84 months to complete program. *Concentrations:* accounting.

MS—Master of Science in Finance Full-time and part-time. 30 to 64 total credits required. 8 to 84 months to complete program. *Concentrations:* finance.

MS—Master of Science in Media Management Full-time and part-time. At least 42 total credits required. 12 to 84 months to complete program. *Concentrations:* sports/entertainment management.

COSTS

Tuition *Full-time:* $19,003. *Part-time:* $613 per credit. Tuition varies by number of courses or credits taken. **Required fees:** *Full-time* $409. Fees vary by class time and academic program. **Graduate housing:** Room and board costs vary by campus location, number of occupants, type of accommodation, and type of board plan. *Typical cost:* $9706 (including board).

FINANCIAL AID (1999–2000)

60 students received aid, including fellowships, grants, loans, research assistantships, scholarships, teaching assistantships, and work study. Financial aid application deadline: 3/1. **Financial Aid Contact** Ms. Paula A. Charland, Assistant Dean for MBA and Master's Enrollment, Suite 100, School of Management, Syracuse, NY 13244-2130. **Phone:** 315-443-9214. **Fax:** 315-443-9517. **E-mail:** mbainfo@som.syr.edu.

RESOURCES AND SERVICES

Information about online services, personal computer policies, library resources, international exchange programs, internship programs, and placement services at this institution and others can be found at **www.petersons.com/mba**

International Students

20% of students enrolled are international students.

Services and Facilities Counseling/support services, ESL/language courses, housing location assistance, international student housing, international student organization, language tutoring, orientation, visa services. Financial aid is available to international students.

Applying *Required:* TOEFL with recommended score of 237 (computer) or 580 (paper), proof of adequate funds, proof of health/immunizations.

International Student Contact Dr. Patricia A. Burak, Director, Office of International Services, 310 Walnut Place, Syracuse, NY 13244-2380. **Phone:** 315-443-2457. **Fax:** 315-443-3091. **E-mail:** paburak@mailbox.syr.edu.

■ APPLICATION

Required GMAT, application form, baccalaureate/first degree, essay, 2 letters of recommendation, resume/curriculum vitae, transcripts of college work, 1 year of work experience. **Recommended** Interview.

Deadlines and Fees *Deadlines:* 5/1 for fall, 12/1 for spring, 5/1 for fall (international), 12/1 for spring (international). *Application fee:* $40, $40 (international).

Application Contact Ms. Paula A. Charland, Assistant Dean for MBA and Master's Enrollment, Suite 100, School of Management, Syracuse, NY 13244-2130. **Phone:** 315-443-9214. **Fax:** 315-443-9517. **E-mail:** mbainfo@som.syr.edu.

See full description on page 842.

Union College

Schenectady, New York

GRADUATE MANAGEMENT INSTITUTE

Graduate Business Faculty
Full-time: 11   Part-time: 10

Student Body
Total: 218   Part-time: 150
Full-time: 68   Average Age: 27

Admissions
Applications: 63   Average GMAT: 570
Admitted: 58   Average GPA: 3.2
Enrolled: 38

Costs (1999–2000)
Full-time tuition: $14,190 per academic year
Part-time tuition: $1560 per course

DEGREES MBA

MBA—Master of Business Administration in Health Systems Administration Full-time and part-time. At least 60 total credits required. 24 to 72 months to complete program.

MBA—Master of Business Administration Full-time and part-time. At least 60 total credits required. 24 to 72 months to complete program. *Concentrations:* management.

COSTS

Tuition *Full-time:* $14,040. *Part-time:* $1560 per course. **Required fees:** *Full-time* $150.

FINANCIAL AID (1999–2000)

35 students received aid, including fellowships, loans, research assistantships, and scholarships. Financial aid application deadline: 4/1. **Financial Aid Contact** Ms. Rhonda Sheehan, Graduate Management Institute, Schenectady, NY 12308. **Phone:** 518-388-6238. **Fax:** 518-388-6754. **E-mail:** sheehanr@union.edu.

RESOURCES AND SERVICES

Information about online services, personal computer policies, library resources, international exchange programs, internship programs, and placement services at this institution and others can be found at **www.petersons.com/mba**

International Students

5% of students enrolled are international students.

Services and Facilities Counseling/support services, ESL/language courses, housing location assistance, international student organization, visa services. Financial aid is available to international students.

Applying *Required:* TOEFL with recommended score of 550 (paper), proof of adequate funds, proof of health/immunizations.

International Student Contact Ms. Rhonda Sheehan, Administrative Assistant, Graduate Management Institute, Schenectady, NY 12308. **Phone:** 518-388-6238. **Fax:** 518-388-6754. **E-mail:** sheehanr@union.edu.

■ APPLICATION

Required GMAT, application form, baccalaureate/first degree, essay, 3 letters of recommendation, resume/curriculum vitae, transcripts of college work.

Deadlines and Fees Applications for domestic students are processed on a rolling basis. *Deadline:* 5/1 for fall (international). *Application fee:* $50, $50 (international).

Application Contact Ms. Rhonda Sheehan, Graduate Management Institute, Schenectady, NY 12308. **Phone:** 518-388-6238. **Fax:** 518-388-6754. **E-mail:** sheehanr@union.edu.

See full description on page 860.

University of Rochester

Rochester, New York

WILLIAM E. SIMON GRADUATE SCHOOL OF BUSINESS ADMINISTRATION

Graduate Business Faculty
Full-time: 55   Part-time: 8

Student Body
Total: 858   Part-time: 253
Full-time: 605   Average Age: 29

Admissions
Applications: 1,473   Average GMAT: 647
Admitted: 443   Average GPA: 3.2
Enrolled: 165

Costs (1999–2000)
Full-time tuition: $27,024 per academic year
Part-time tuition: $882 per credit hour

After Graduation (Class of 1998–99)
Employed within 3 months of graduation: 99%
Average starting salary: $71,415

Accreditation
AACSB—The International Association for Management Education

DEGREES MBA • MBA/MS • MD/MBA • MS

MBA—Executive MBA Full-time. At least 66 total credits required. 18 to 22 months to complete program.

MBA—Master of Business Administration Full-time and part-time. At least 67 total credits required. 18 to 22 months to complete program. *Concentrations:* accounting, economics, electronic commerce (e-commerce), entrepreneurship, finance, health care, international management, management information systems, marketing, operations management, public policy and administration, strategic management.

MBA/MS—Biotech MBA/Master of Science in Microbiology Full-time and part-time. At least 80 total credits required. 24 to 28 months to complete program. *Concentrations:* accounting, economics, electronic commerce (e-commerce), entrepreneurship, finance, health care, international management, management information systems, marketing, operations management, public policy and administration, strategic management.

MBA/MS—Master of Business Administration/Master of Science in Nursing Full-time and part-time. At least 85 total credits required. 27 to 28 months to complete program. *Concentrations:* accounting, economics, electronic commerce (e-commerce), entrepreneurship, finance, health care, international management, management information systems, marketing, operations management, public policy and administration, strategic management.

MBA/MS—Master of Business Administration/Master of Science in Public Health Full-time and part-time. At least 85 total credits required. 24 to 28 months to complete program. *Concentrations:* accounting, economics, electronic commerce (e-commerce), entrepreneurship, finance, health care, international management, management information systems, marketing, operations management, public policy and administration, strategic management.

MD/MBA—Doctor of Medicine/Master of Business Administration Full-time and part-time. *Concentrations:* accounting, economics, electronic commerce (e-commerce), entrepreneurship, finance, health care, international management, management information systems, marketing, operations management, public policy and administration, strategic management.

MS—Master of Science in Finance Full-time and part-time. At least 36 total credits required. 9 to 12 months to complete program. *Concentrations:* finance.

MS—Master of Science in Information Systems Management Full-time and part-time. At least 39 total credits required. 9 to 12 months to complete program. *Concentrations:* management information systems.

MS—Master of Science in Manufacturing Management Full-time and part-time. At least 39 total credits required. 9 to 12 months to complete program. *Concentrations:* manufacturing management.

MS—Master of Science in Service Management Full-time and part-time. At least 39 total credits required. 9 to 12 months to complete program.

Consistent with its philosophy of training for the future, the internationally integrated M.B.A. program at the William E. Simon Graduate School of Business Administration at the University of Rochester is constantly refining its curricular content to reflect changes in the marketplace. Among new offerings recently introduced are a concentration in health-care management and a brand management specialization within the marketing concentration. This specialization has been developed in cooperation with leading organizations such as the Procter & Gamble Company. The Simon School also introduced a brand new concentration in electronic commerce in September 1999. Managing in this environment requires an understanding of not only the technological infrastructure needed for e-commerce but also the processes needed to support it in the logistical, financial, and service aspects. The concentration allows students to analyze e-commerce from marketing and economics-based perspectives. An appreciation of similarities and differences across countries' legal systems, market structures, and methods of corporate governance prepare the Simon M.B.A. graduate to enter the global arena. Another crucial element for success in tomorrow's workplace is the demonstrated ability to interact quickly and effectively with coworkers from diverse backgrounds. The fifty different countries represented at Rochester provide an invaluable workshop for developing those skills. Together with annual team training and individual study team evaluation meetings throughout the first year, the School has added specially trained second-year M.B.A. mentors to the team-building infrastructure. As both geographic awareness and rapidly changing technology define changes in business, the Simon School faculty and administration respond with careful curricular adjustments to stay on the cutting edge of business school education.

COSTS
Tuition *Full-time:* $26,460. *Part-time:* $882 per credit hour. Tuition varies by number of courses or credits taken. **Required fees:** *Full-time* $564. *Part-time* $70 per quarter. **Graduate housing:** Room and board costs vary by number of occupants and type of accommodation. *Typical cost:* $7695 (including board).

FINANCIAL AID (1999–2000)
4 students received aid, including fellowships, loans, research assistantships, scholarships, and teaching assistantships. Financial aid application deadline: 3/1. **Financial Aid Contact** Ms. Pamela Black-Colton, Assistant Dean for MBA Admissions and Administration, William E. Simon Graduate School of Business Administration, Rochester, NY 14627-0107. **Phone:** 716-275-3533. **Fax:** 716-271-3907. **E-mail:** mbaadm@mail.simon.rochester.edu.

RESOURCES AND SERVICES
Information about online services, personal computer policies, library resources, international exchange programs, internship programs, and placement services at this institution and others can be found at **www.petersons.com/mba**

International Students
36% of students enrolled are international students.

Services and Facilities Counseling/support services, ESL/language courses, international student organization, orientation, visa services. Financial aid is available to international students.
Applying *Required:* TOEFL with recommended score of 250 (computer) or 600 (paper), proof of adequate funds, proof of health/immunizations.
International Student Contact Ms. Barbara Harris-Smith, Director, International Student Affairs, Morey 209, Rochester, NY 14627-0447. **Phone:** 716-275-2866. **Fax:** 716-244-4503. **E-mail:** bhs@troi.cc.rochester.edu.

■ APPLICATION
Required GMAT, application form, baccalaureate/first degree, essay, 2 letters of recommendation, personal statement, resume/curriculum vitae, transcripts of college work. **Recommended** Interview, work experience.
Deadlines and Fees *Deadlines:* 6/1 for fall, 11/1 for winter, 6/1 for fall (international), 11/1 for winter (international). *Application fee:* $75, $75 (international).
Application Contact Ms. Pamela Black-Colton, Assistant Dean for MBA Admissions and Administration, William E. Simon Graduate School of Business Administration, Rochester, NY 14627-0107. **Phone:** 716-275-3533. **Fax:** 716-271-3907. **E-mail:** mbaadm@simon.rochester.edu.

See full description on page 952.

Wagner College
Staten Island, New York

DEPARTMENT OF BUSINESS ADMINISTRATION

DEGREES MBA

MBA—Executive MBA Full-time. 5 years of management experience required. At least 36 total credits required. Minimum of 18 months to complete program.
MBA—Master of Business Administration Full-time and part-time. 36 to 48 total credits required. 18 to 60 months to complete program. *Concentrations:* finance, international business, management, marketing.

RESOURCES AND SERVICES
Information about online services, personal computer policies, library resources, international exchange programs, internship programs, and placement services at this institution and others can be found at **www.petersons.com/mba**

International Students
Services and Facilities ESL/language courses. Financial aid is not available to international students.
International Student Contact Ms. Tracy Ehrhardt, Senior Associate Director of Admissions, 1 Campus Road, Staten Island, NY 10301-4495. **Phone:** 800-221-1010. **Fax:** 718-390-3105. **E-mail:** adm@wagner.edu.

■ APPLICATION
Application Contact Mr. Angelo Araimo, Dean of Admissions, One Campus Road, Staten Island, NY 10301. **Phone:** 718-390-3411. **Fax:** 718-390-3105. **E-mail:** adm@wagner.edu.

NORTH CAROLINA

Appalachian State University

Boone, North Carolina

JOHN A. WALKER COLLEGE OF BUSINESS

Graduate Business Faculty
Full-time: 47

Student Body
Total: 98
Full-time: 47
Part-time: 51

Average Age: 28
Women: 39%

Admissions
Applications: 94
Admitted: 74
Enrolled: 49

Average GMAT: 505
Average GPA: 3.2

Costs (1999–2000)
Full-time tuition: N/R
Part-time tuition: $230 per course (resident), $1920 per course (nonresident)

After Graduation (Class of 1998–99)
Employed within 3 months of graduation: 99%
Average starting salary: $38,000

Accreditation
AACSB—The International Association for Management Education

DEGREES MA • MBA • MS

MA—Master of Arts in Industrial Organizational Psychology and Human Resources Full-time and part-time. At least 30 total credits required. 12 to 24 months to complete program.

MBA—Master of Business Administration Full-time and part-time. At least 39 total credits required. Minimum of 12 months to complete program.

MS—Master of Science in Accounting Full-time and part-time. At least 30 total credits required. 12 to 24 months to complete program. *Concentrations:* accounting, taxation.

COSTS

Tuition, state resident: *Part-time* $230 per course. **Tuition, nonresident:** *Part-time* $1920 per course. **Required fees:** Tuition and fees vary by number of courses or credits taken. **Graduate housing:** Room and board costs vary by number of occupants and type of accommodation. *Typical cost:* $3200 (room only).

FINANCIAL AID (1999–2000)

Fellowships, research assistantships, teaching assistantships, and work study. Aid is available to part-time students. **Financial Aid Contact** Ms. Sandi McGuire, Assistant Director, Financial Aid Office, John E. Thomas Academic Support, Boone, NC 28608. **Phone:** 828-262-2190. **Fax:** 828-262-2585.

RESOURCES AND SERVICES

Information about online services, personal computer policies, library resources, international exchange programs, internship programs, and placement services at this institution and others can be found at **www. petersons.com/mba**

International Students
4% of students enrolled are international students.

Services and Facilities Counseling/support services, ESL/language courses, international student housing. Financial aid is available to international students.
Applying *Required:* TOEFL with recommended score of 550 (paper), proof of health/immunizations.
International Student Contact Dr. Robert White, Assistant Director of International Programs, Office of International Programs, IG Greer Hall, Boone, NC 28608. **Phone:** 828-262-2046. **Fax:** 828-262-4037. **E-mail:** whitera@conrad. appstate.edu.

▪ APPLICATION

Required Application form, baccalaureate/first degree, essay, 3 letters of recommendation, transcripts of college work. School will accept GMAT. **Recommended** Interview, personal statement, resume/curriculum vitae, work experience.
Deadlines and Fees *Deadlines:* 4/15 for fall, 4/15 for fall (international). *Application fee:* $35, $35 (international).

Application Contact Dr. Rickey C. Kirkpatrick, Assistant Dean of Graduate Studies and External Programs, PO Box 32037, Boone, NC 28608. **Phone:** 828-262-2922. **Fax:** 828-262-2925. **E-mail:** kirkprc@conrad.appstate.edu.

Campbell University

Buies Creek, North Carolina

LUNDY-FETTERMAN SCHOOL OF BUSINESS

Graduate Business Faculty
Full-time: 10

Part-time: 4

Student Body
Total: 178
Full-time: 17
Part-time: 161

Average Age: 28
Women: 41%

Admissions
Applications: 127
Admitted: 74
Enrolled: 62

Average GMAT: 490
Average GPA: 3.1

Costs (1999–2000)
Full-time tuition: N/R
Part-time tuition: $190 per semester hour

After Graduation (Class of 1998–99)
Employed within 3 months of graduation: 70%
Average starting salary: $34,000

DEGREE MBA

MBA—Master of Business Administration Full-time and part-time. 30 to 57 total credits required. 18 to 60 months to complete program.

COSTS

Tuition *Part-time:* $190 per semester hour. **Required fees:** Tuition and fees vary by number of courses or credits taken and campus location. **Graduate housing:** Room and board costs vary by number of occupants, type of accommodation, and type of board plan. *Typical cost:* $5000 (including board).

FINANCIAL AID (1999–2000)

36 students received aid, including loans. Aid is available to part-time students. **Financial Aid Contact** Ms. Peggy Mason, Director of Financial Aid, PO Box 36, Buies Creek, NC 27506. **Phone:** 910-893-1310. **Fax:** 910-893-1288.

RESOURCES AND SERVICES

Information about online services, personal computer policies, library resources, international exchange programs, internship programs, and placement services at this institution and others can be found at **www. petersons.com/mba**

International Students
8% of students enrolled are international students.

Services and Facilities Counseling/support services, international student housing, international student organization, orientation. Financial aid is not available to international students.
Applying *Required:* TOEFL with recommended score of 550 (paper), proof of adequate funds, proof of health/immunizations.
International Student Contact Mr. Allen Huggins, Director of International Admissions, PO Box 546, Buies Creek, NC 27506. **Phone:** 910-893-1415. **Fax:** 910-893-1288.

▪ APPLICATION

Required GMAT, application form, baccalaureate/first degree, 3 letters of recommendation, transcripts of college work.

Deadlines and Fees Applications for domestic and international students are processed on a rolling basis. *Application fee:* $20, $20 (international).

Application Contact Mr. Jim Farthing Jr., Director of Graduate Admissions, PO Box 546, Buies Creek, NC 27506. **Phone:** 910-893-1306 Ext. 1318. **Fax:** 910-893-1288.

Duke University

Durham, North Carolina

FUQUA SCHOOL OF BUSINESS

Graduate Business Faculty

Full-time: 68   Part-time: 16

Student Body
Total: 668   Average Age: 28
Full-time: 668   Women: 33%

Admissions
Applications: 3,484   Average GMAT: 676
Admitted: 665   Average GPA: 3.33
Enrolled: 331

Costs (1999–2000)
Full-time tuition: $27,671 per academic year
Part-time tuition: N/R

After Graduation (Class of 1998–99)
Employed within 3 months of graduation: 99%
Average starting salary: $81,356

Accreditation
AACSB—The International Association for Management Education

DEGREES MBA

MBA—The Duke MBA Full-time. 85 total credits required. 24 months to complete program. *Concentrations:* health care, management.

MBA—The Duke MBA—Cross Continent Full-time. *Distance learning option.* 48 total credits required. 21 months to complete program.

MBA—The Duke MBA -Global Executive Full-time. *Distance learning option.* 45 total credits required. 20 months to complete program.

MBA—The Duke MBA -Weekend Executive Full-time. 45 total credits required. 20 months to complete program. *Concentrations:* management.

COSTS

Tuition *Full-time:* $26,200. **Required fees:** *Full-time* $1471. Tuition and fees vary by academic program.

FINANCIAL AID (1999–2000)

447 students received aid, including loans, scholarships, and work study. Financial aid application deadline: 3/1. **Financial Aid Contact** Mr. Paul West, Director of Financial Aid, Fuqua School of Business, Box 90128, Durham, NC 27708-0128. **Phone:** 919-660-7803. **Fax:** 919-681-6243. **E-mail:** pdw1@mail.duke.edu.

RESOURCES AND SERVICES

Information about online services, personal computer policies, library resources, international exchange programs, internship programs, and placement services at this institution and others can be found at **www.petersons.com/mba**

International Students

27% of students enrolled are international students.

Services and Facilities Counseling/support services, ESL/language courses, housing location assistance, international student organization, orientation, visa services. Financial aid is available to international students.

Applying *Required:* TOEFL with recommended score of 250 (computer) or 660 (paper), proof of adequate funds, proof of health/immunizations.

International Student Contact Ms. Katie Joyce, Director of the International Center, Fuqua School of Business at Duke University, Box 90126, Durham, NC 27708-0126. **Phone:** 919-660-7980. **Fax:** 919-681-6243. **E-mail:** joyce@mail.duke.edu.

■ APPLICATION

Required GMAT, application form, baccalaureate/first degree, essay, 2 letters of recommendation, personal statement, resume/curriculum vitae, transcripts of college work. **Recommended** Interview, 5 years of work experience.

Deadlines and Fees *Deadline:* 4/26 for fall (international). *Application fee:* $150, $150 (international).

Application Contact Ms. Liz Riley, Director of Admissions, Fuqua School of Business, Box 90104, Durham, NC 27708-0104. **Phone:** 919-660-7705. **Fax:** 919-681-8026. **E-mail:** fuqua-admissions@mail.duke.edu.

East Carolina University

Greenville, North Carolina

SCHOOL OF BUSINESS

Graduate Business Faculty
Full-time: 60   Part-time: 2

Student Body
Total: 377   Part-time: 131
Full-time: 246   Average Age: 28

                             Women: 46%

Admissions
Applications: 191   Average GMAT: 508
Admitted: 163   Average GPA: 3.12
Enrolled: 106

Costs (1999–2000)
Full-time tuition: $2018 per academic year (resident), $4223 per academic year (nonresident)
Part-time tuition: $757 per semester (resident), $3594 per semester (nonresident)

After Graduation (Class of 1998–99)
Employed within 3 months of graduation: 83%
Average starting salary: $40,100

Accreditation
AACSB—The International Association for Management Education

DEGREES MBA • MD/MBA • MSA

MBA—Master of Business Administration Full-time and part-time. 30 to 60 total credits required. 10 to 20 months to complete program. *Concentrations:* health care, international management, management information systems, travel industry/tourism management, hospitality management.

MD/MBA—Doctor of Medicine/Master of Business Administration Full-time and part-time. Must be enrolled in an accredited medical school or be a medical resident. At least 42 total credits required. 12 months to complete program. *Concentrations:* health care.

MSA—Master of Science in Accounting Full-time and part-time. 30 to 60 total credits required. 10 to 20 months to complete program. *Concentrations:* taxation.

COSTS

Tuition, state resident: *Full-time* $1012. *Part-time* $380 per semester. **Tuition, nonresident:** *Full-time* $3217. *Part-time* $3217 per semester. Tuition varies by number of courses or credits taken. **Required fees:** *Full-time* $1006. *Part-time* $377 per semester. **Graduate housing:** Room and board costs vary by number of occupants, type of accommodation, and type of board plan. *Typical cost:* $5590 (including board).

FINANCIAL AID (1999–2000)

120 students received aid, including research assistantships, scholarships, teaching assistantships, and work study. Aid is available to part-time students. Financial aid application deadline: 6/1. **Financial Aid Contact** Dr. Rose Mary Stelma, Director, Student Financial Aid, Greenville, NC 27858-4353. **Phone:** 252-328-6610. **Fax:** 252-328-4347.

RESOURCES AND SERVICES

Information about online services, personal computer policies, library resources, international exchange programs, internship programs, and placement services at this institution and others can be found at **www.petersons.com/mba**

International Students

9% of students enrolled are international students.

Services and Facilities Counseling/support services, international student organization, orientation, visa services. Financial aid is available to international students.

Applying *Required:* TOEFL with recommended score of 213 (computer) or 550 (paper), proof of adequate funds, proof of health/immunizations.

International Student Contact Dr. Linda McGowan, Overseas Opportunities Coordinator, International Affairs, Greenville, NC 27858-4353. **Phone:** 252-328-1937. **Fax:** 252-328-4813. **E-mail:** mcgowanl@mail.ecu.edu.

■ APPLICATION

Required Application form, baccalaureate/first degree, transcripts of college work. School will accept GMAT. **Recommended** Work experience.

Deadlines and Fees *Deadlines:* 6/1 for fall, 10/15 for spring, 3/15 for summer, 6/1 for fall (international), 10/15 for spring, 3/15 for summer (international). *Application fee:* $40, $40 (international).

Application Contact Dr. Frederick Niswander, Assistant Dean for Graduate Programs, School of Business, Greenville, NC 27858-4353. **Phone:** 252-328-6970. **Fax:** 252-328-2106. **E-mail:** gradbus@mail.ecu.edu.

See full description on page 630.

Elon College

Elon College, North Carolina

MARTHA AND SPENCER LOVE SCHOOL OF BUSINESS

Graduate Business Faculty
Full-time: 22

Student Body
Total: 96
Full-time: 18
Part-time: 78

Average Age: 32
Women: 38%

Admissions
Applications: 37
Admitted: 32
Enrolled: 27

Average GMAT: 525
Average GPA: 3.2

Costs (1999–2000)
Full-time tuition: N/R
Part-time tuition: $291 per credit hour

DEGREE MBA

MBA—Master of Business Administration Full-time and part-time. At least 39 total credits required. 21 to 72 months to complete program. *Concentrations:* leadership.

COSTS

Tuition *Part-time:* $291 per credit hour. Tuition varies by academic program.

FINANCIAL AID (1999–2000)

8 students received aid, including loans and work study. Aid is available to part-time students. Financial aid application deadline: 8/1. **Financial Aid Contact** Mr. Joel Speckhard, Director of Financial Planning, 2700 Campus Box, Elon College, NC 27244. **Phone:** 800-334-8448 Ext. 2. **Fax:** 336-538-3986. **E-mail:** speckhar@elon.edu.

RESOURCES AND SERVICES

Information about online services, personal computer policies, library resources, international exchange programs, internship programs, and placement services at this institution and others can be found at **www. petersons.com/mba**

International Students

Services and Facilities Counseling/support services, visa services, writing center, healthcare, international student advisor. Financial aid is not available to international students.
Applying *Required:* TOEFL with recommended score of 213 (computer) or 550 (paper), proof of adequate funds, proof of health/immunizations.
International Student Contact Mr. Greg Zaiser, Director of Graduate Admissions, 2750 Campus Box, Elon College, NC 27244. **Phone:** 800-334-8448 Ext. 3. **Fax:** 336-538-3986. **E-mail:** gradadm@elon.edu.

■ APPLICATION

Required GMAT, application form, baccalaureate/first degree, 3 letters of recommendation, personal statement, transcripts of college work, 2 years of work experience. **Recommended** Interview, resume/curriculum vitae.
Deadlines and Fees Applications for domestic and international students are processed on a rolling basis. *Application fee:* $35, $35 (international).
Application Contact Mr. Greg Zaiser, Director of Graduate Admissions, Office of Graduate Admissions, 2750 Campus Box, Elon College, NC 27244. **Phone:** 336-584-2474. **Toll-free Phone:** 800-334-8444 Ext. 3 (in-state), 336-584-2474 (out-of-state). **Fax:** 336-538-3986. **E-mail:** gradadm@elon.edu.

Fayetteville State University

Fayetteville, North Carolina

PROGRAM IN BUSINESS ADMINISTRATION

Graduate Business Faculty
Full-time: 29

Student Body
Total: 100
Full-time: 10
Part-time: 90

Average Age: 33
Women: 47%

Admissions
Applications: 160
Admitted: 80
Enrolled: 60

Average GMAT: 490
Average GPA: 3.3

Costs (1999–2000)
Full-time tuition: $1334 per academic year (resident), $8176 per academic year (nonresident)
Part-time tuition: $90 per credit (resident), $478 per credit (nonresident)

After Graduation (Class of 1998–99)
Employed within 3 months of graduation: 90%
Average starting salary: $40,000

DEGREE MBA

MBA—Master of Business Administration Full-time and part-time. 36 to 54 total credits required. 12 to 72 months to complete program. *Concentrations:* accounting, entrepreneurship, finance, international management, management, marketing.

COSTS

Tuition, state resident: *Full-time* $1334. *Part-time* $90 per credit. **Tuition, nonresident:** *Full-time* $8176. *Part-time* $478 per credit. Tuition varies by number of courses or credits taken.

FINANCIAL AID (1999–2000)

4 students received aid, including loans, research assistantships, and teaching assistantships. Aid is available to part-time students. Financial aid application deadline: 5/15. **Financial Aid Contact** Lois N. McKoy, Director, Financial Aid Office, 1200 Murchison Road, Fayetteville, NC 28301. **Phone:** 910-486-1325. **Fax:** 910-486-1111. **E-mail:** lmckoy@uncfsu.edu.

RESOURCES AND SERVICES

Information about online services, personal computer policies, library resources, international exchange programs, internship programs, and placement services at this institution and others can be found at **www. petersons.com/mba**

International Students

10% of students enrolled are international students.

Services and Facilities Counseling/support services, visa services. Financial aid is not available to international students.
Applying *Required:* TOEFL with recommended score of 550 (paper), proof of adequate funds.
International Student Contact Dr. Asad Tavakoli, MBA Director, 1200 Murchison Road, Fayetteville, NC 28301. **Phone:** 910-486-1197. **Fax:** 910-486-1033. **E-mail:** tavakoli@sbe1.uncfsu.edu.

■ APPLICATION

Required GMAT, application form, baccalaureate/first degree, 2 letters of recommendation, transcripts of college work.
Deadlines and Fees *Deadlines:* 7/30 for fall, 12/15 for spring, 4/30 for summer, 7/15 for fall (international), 12/1 for spring (international), 4/15 for summer (international). *Application fee:* $20, $20 (international).
Application Contact Dr. Asad Tavakoli, MBA Director, 1200 Murchison Road, Fayetteville, NC 28303. **Phone:** 910-486-1197. **Fax:** 910-486-1033. **E-mail:** mba@sbe1.uncfsu.edu.

Gardner-Webb University

Boiling Springs, North Carolina

SCHOOL OF BUSINESS

Graduate Business Faculty
Full-time: 13

Student Body
Total: 257
Full-time: 257

Average Age: 33
Women: 51%

Admissions
Applications: 77
Admitted: 77
Enrolled: 72

Average GMAT: 450
Average GPA: 3.15

Costs (1999–2000)
Full-time tuition: N/R
Part-time tuition: $230 per credit hour

DEGREE MBA

MBA—Master of Business Administration Full-time and part-time. At least 36 total credits required. 24 to 72 months to complete program. *Concentrations:* finance, health care, human resources, international business, management information systems.

COSTS

Tuition *Part-time:* $230 per credit hour. Tuition varies by number of courses or credits taken. **Graduate housing:** Room and board costs vary by number of occupants, type of accommodation, and type of board plan. *Typical cost:* $4630 (including board).

FINANCIAL AID (1999–2000)

28 students received aid, including loans. Aid is available to part-time students. **Financial Aid Contact** Mr. Mike Roebuck, Director of Financial Aid, Boiling Springs, NC 28017. **Phone:** 704-406-4497. **Fax:** 704-406-5102. **E-mail:** mroebuck@gardner-webb.edu.

RESOURCES AND SERVICES

Information about online services, personal computer policies, library resources, international exchange programs, internship programs, and placement services at this institution and others can be found at **www. petersons.com/mba**

International Students

Services and Facilities Counseling/support services, international student housing, i-20 processing. Financial aid is not available to international students.
Applying *Required:* TOEFL with recommended score of 500 (paper), proof of adequate funds, proof of health/immunizations.
International Student Contact Mrs. Melissa Swofford, Director of Admissions-MBA, Campus Box 7272, Boiling Springs, NC 28017. **Phone:** 704-406-4489. **Fax:** 704-406-3895. **E-mail:** mswofford@gardner-webb.edu.

■ APPLICATION

Required GMAT, application form, baccalaureate/first degree, interview, 3 letters of recommendation, resume/curriculum vitae, transcripts of college work. **Recommended** Work experience.
Deadlines and Fees Applications for domestic and international students are processed on a rolling basis. *Application fee:* $25, $25 (international).
Application Contact Mrs. Melissa Swofford, Director of Admissions-MBA, Campus Box 7272, Boiling Springs, NC 28017. **Phone:** 704-434-4489. **Fax:** 704-434-3895. **E-mail:** mswofford@gardner-webb.edu.

High Point University

High Point, North Carolina

GRADUATE STUDIES

Graduate Business Faculty
Full-time: 16

Student Body
Total: 173	Average Age: 32
Full-time: 19	Women: 50%
Part-time: 154	

Admissions
Applications: 49	Average GPA: 3
Admitted: 39	

Costs (1999–2000)
Full-time tuition: $5824 per academic year
Part-time tuition: $318 per credit

After Graduation (Class of 1998–99)
Employed within 3 months of graduation: 100%

DEGREES MBA • MS

MBA—Master of Business Administration Full-time and part-time. At least 37 total credits required. 24 to 60 months to complete program. *Concentrations:* accounting, international business.

MS—Master of Science in International Management Full-time and part-time. At least 37 total credits required. 24 to 60 months to complete program.

MS—Master of Science in Management Full-time and part-time. At least 37 total credits required. 24 to 60 months to complete program.

COSTS

Tuition *Full-time:* $5724. *Part-time:* $318 per credit. Tuition varies by number of courses or credits taken. **Required fees:** *Full-time* $100. *Part-time* $50 per semester. **Graduate housing:** Room and board costs vary by number of occupants, type of accommodation, and type of board plan. *Typical cost:* $5770 (including board), $2480 (room only).

FINANCIAL AID (1999–2000)

27 students received aid, including loans. Aid is available to part-time students. Financial aid application deadline: 3/1. **Financial Aid Contact**

Ms. Dana Kelly, Director of Financial Aid, University Station, Montlieu Avenue, High Point, NC 27262-3598. **Phone:** 336-841-9124. **Fax:** 336-888-6382. **E-mail:** finaid@highpoint.edu.

RESOURCES AND SERVICES

Information about online services, personal computer policies, library resources, international exchange programs, internship programs, and placement services at this institution and others can be found at **www. petersons.com/mba**

International Students

5% of students enrolled are international students.

Services and Facilities Housing location assistance, orientation. Financial aid is not available to international students.
Applying *Required:* TOEFL with recommended score of 550 (paper), proof of adequate funds.
International Student Contact Dr. Alberta Herron, Dean of Graduate Studies, University Station, Montlieu Avenue, High Point, NC 27262-3598. **Phone:** 336-841-9198. **Fax:** 336-841-4599. **E-mail:** graduate@highpoint.edu.

■ APPLICATION

Required GMAT, application form, baccalaureate/first degree, 3 letters of recommendation, personal statement, transcripts of college work.
Deadlines and Fees *Deadlines:* 4/15 for fall, 10/15 for spring, 3/15 for summer, 4/15 for fall (international), 10/15 for spring (international), 3/15 for summer (international). *Application fee:* $35, $50 (international).
Application Contact Dr. Alberta Herron, Dean of Graduate Studies, University Station, Montlieu Avenue, High Point, NC 27262-3598. **Phone:** 336-841-9198. **Fax:** 336-841-4599. **E-mail:** graduate@highpoint.edu.

Lenoir-Rhyne College

Hickory, North Carolina

DEPARTMENT OF BUSINESS

Graduate Business Faculty
Full-time: 6	Part-time: 2

Student Body
Total: 34	Average Age: 35
Part-time: 34	Women: 41%

Admissions
Applications: 12	Enrolled: 12
Admitted: 12	Average GMAT: 513

Costs (1999–2000)
Full-time tuition: N/R
Part-time tuition: $225 per credit hour

DEGREE MBA

MBA—Master of Business Administration Part-time. At least 36 total credits required. 24 to 72 months to complete program.

COSTS

Tuition *Part-time:* $225 per credit hour. Tuition varies by academic program.
Graduate housing: *Typical cost:* $4700 (including board).

FINANCIAL AID (1999–2000)

Loans. **Financial Aid Contact** Ms. Rachel Nichols, Director of Financial Aid, PO Box 7419, Hickory, NC 28603. **Phone:** 828-328-7041. **E-mail:** allenr@lrc.edu.

RESOURCES AND SERVICES

Information about online services, personal computer policies, library resources, international exchange programs, internship programs, and placement services at this institution and others can be found at **www. petersons.com/mba**

International Students

Services and Facilities Counseling/support services, ESL/language courses, housing location assistance, international student housing, international student organization, orientation, visa services. Financial aid is not available to international students.
Applying *Required:* TOEFL with recommended score of 550 (paper), proof of adequate funds.
International Student Contact Dr. Marion Love, Director of International Student Services, PO Box 7160, Hickory, NC 28603. **Phone:** 828-328-7160. **Fax:** 828-328-7365. **E-mail:** iso@lrc.edu.

Lenoir-Rhyne College (continued)

■ APPLICATION

Required GMAT, application form, baccalaureate/first degree, essay, 3 letters of recommendation, personal statement, transcripts of college work, 2 years of work experience.

Deadlines and Fees Applications for domestic and international students are processed on a rolling basis. *Application fee:* $25, $25 (international).

Application Contact Graduate Office, PO Box 7420, Hickory, NC 28603. **Phone:** 828-328-7275. **Fax:** 828-328-7348.

Meredith College

Raleigh, North Carolina

JOHN E. WEEMS GRADUATE SCHOOL

Graduate Business Faculty
Full-time: 6   Part-time: 4

Student Body
Total: 98
Full-time: 61   Average Age: 28
Part-time: 37   Women: 100%

Admissions
Applications: 25   Average GMAT: 500
Admitted: 18   Average GPA: 3
Enrolled: 13

Costs (1999–2000)
Full-time tuition: $4950 per academic year
Part-time tuition: $275 per credit hour

DEGREE MBA

MBA—Master of Business Administration Full-time and part-time. At least 36 total credits required. 24 to 72 months to complete program.

COSTS

Tuition *Full-time:* $4950. *Part-time:* $275 per credit hour.

FINANCIAL AID (1999–2000)

Grants and loans. Aid is available to part-time students. Financial aid application deadline: 2/15. **Financial Aid Contact** Mr. William Cox, Director of Financial Assistance, 3800 Hillsborough Street, Raleigh, NC 27607-5298. **Phone:** 919-760-8327. **Fax:** 919-760-2373. **E-mail:** coxw@meredith.edu.

RESOURCES AND SERVICES

Information about online services, personal computer policies, library resources, international exchange programs, internship programs, and placement services at this institution and others can be found at **www. petersons.com/mba**

International Students

2% of students enrolled are international students.

Services and Facilities Counseling/support services. Financial aid is available to international students.

Applying *Required:* TOEFL with recommended score of 173 (computer) or 500 (paper), proof of adequate funds, proof of health/immunizations.

International Student Contact Ms. Carrol Snodgrass, Administrative Assistant, 3800 Hillsborough Street, Raleigh, NC 27607-5298. **Phone:** 919-760-8423. **Fax:** 919-760-2898. **E-mail:** snodgrassc@meredith.edu.

■ APPLICATION

Required GMAT, application form, baccalaureate/first degree, interview, 2 letters of recommendation, resume/curriculum vitae, transcripts of college work, 2 years of work experience.

Deadlines and Fees *Deadlines:* 8/1 for fall, 12/1 for spring, 5/1 for summer, 8/1 for fall (international), 12/1 for spring (international), 5/1 for summer (international). *Application fee:* $50, $50 (international).

Application Contact Ms. Carrol Snodgrass, Administrative Assistant, 3800 Hillsborough Street, Raleigh, NC 27607-5298. **Phone:** 919-760-8423. **Fax:** 919-760-2898. **E-mail:** snodgrassc@meredith.edu.

Montreat College

Montreat, North Carolina

BUSINESS DIVISION

DEGREE MBA

MBA—Master of Business Administration Full-time. 36 to 48 total credits required. Minimum of 24 months to complete program.

RESOURCES AND SERVICES

Information about online services, personal computer policies, library resources, international exchange programs, internship programs, and placement services at this institution and others can be found at **www. petersons.com/mba**

International Students

Services and Facilities Financial aid is not available to international students.

■ APPLICATION

Application Contact Ms. Yvette Harrold, Director of Promotions, 4135 South Stream Boulevard, Suite 200, Charlotte, NC 28217. **Phone:** 704-327-3390 Ext. 101. **Fax:** 704-357-0176. **E-mail:** yharrol@montreat.edu.

North Carolina Central University

Durham, North Carolina

SCHOOL OF BUSINESS

Graduate Business Faculty
Full-time: 24

Student Body
Total: 34   Average Age: 27
Full-time: 15   Women: 18%
Part-time: 19

Admissions
Applications: 22   Average GMAT: 481
Admitted: 16   Average GPA: 3.01
Enrolled: 15

Costs (1999–2000)
Full-time tuition: $2151 per academic year (resident), $9421 per academic year (nonresident)
Part-time tuition: N/R

After Graduation (Class of 1998–99)
Employed within 3 months of graduation: 80%

Accreditation
ACBSP—The American Council of Business Schools and Programs

DEGREES JD/MBA • MBA • MBA/MIS

JD/MBA—Juris Doctor/Master of Business Administration Full-time and part-time. 103 to 130 total credits required. 48 to 72 months to complete program.

MBA—Master of Business Administration Full-time and part-time. 33 to 63 total credits required. 24 to 72 months to complete program. *Concentrations:* accounting, finance, marketing.

MBA/MIS—Master of Business Administration/Master of Information Science Full-time and part-time. At least 48 total credits required. 36 to 72 months to complete program.

COSTS

Tuition, state resident: *Full-time* $982. **Tuition, nonresident:** *Full-time* $8252. **Required fees:** *Full-time* $1169. Tuition and fees vary by number of courses or credits taken. **Graduate housing:** Room and board costs vary by campus location, number of occupants, type of accommodation, and type of board plan. *Typical cost:* $1200 (room only).

FINANCIAL AID (1999–2000)

14 students received aid, including loans, research assistantships, scholarships, teaching assistantships, and work study. Aid is available to part-time students. **Financial Aid Contact** Ms. Sharon Oliver, Assistant Vice-Chancellor for Scholarships and Student Aid, 1801 Fayetteville Street, Durham, NC 27707-3129. **Phone:** 919-560-6202.

RESOURCES AND SERVICES
Information about online services, personal computer policies, library resources, international exchange programs, internship programs, and placement services at this institution and others can be found at **www. petersons.com/mba**

International Students
21% of students enrolled are international students.

Services and Facilities Counseling/support services. Financial aid is available to international students.

Applying *Required:* TOEFL with recommended score of 500 (paper), proof of adequate funds, proof of health/immunizations.

International Student Contact Ms. Phyllis Shumate, Director of Diversity and Multicultural Services and Foreign Student Advisor, 1801 Fayetteville Street, Durham, NC 27707-3129. **E-mail:** pshumate@wpo.nccu.edu.

■ APPLICATION
Required GMAT, application form, baccalaureate/first degree, 2 letters of recommendation, personal statement, transcripts of college work. **Recommended** Interview.

Deadlines and Fees *Deadlines:* 6/1 for fall, 11/1 for spring, 6/1 for fall (international), 11/1 for spring (international). *Application fee:* $30, $30 (international).

Application Contact Dr. Mary Phillips, Associate Dean of Graduate Programs, 1801 Fayetteville Street, Durham, NC 27707-3129. **Phone:** 919-560-6120. **Fax:** 919-560-6163.

North Carolina State University
Raleigh, North Carolina
COLLEGE OF MANAGEMENT

Graduate Business Faculty
Full-time: 95

Part-time: 15

Student Body
Total: 400
Full-time: 208
Part-time: 192

Average Age: 30
Women: 37%

Admissions
Applications: 340
Average GMAT: 615

Average GPA: 3.16

Costs (1999–2000)
Full-time tuition: $2470 per academic year (resident), $11,636 per academic year (nonresident)
Part-time tuition: $886 per semester (resident), $4323 per semester (nonresident)

After Graduation (Class of 1998–99)
Employed within 3 months of graduation: 95%
Average starting salary: $54,000

Accreditation
AACSB—The International Association for Management Education

DEGREES M Acc • M Econ • MA • MS

M Acc—Master of Accounting Full-time. At least 30 total credits required. 12 to 72 months to complete program. *Concentrations:* accounting.

M Econ—Master of Economics Full-time and part-time. At least 30 total credits required. 12 to 72 months to complete program. *Concentrations:* economics.

MA—Master of Arts in Economics Full-time and part-time. At least 30 total credits required. 12 to 72 months to complete program. *Concentrations:* economics.

MS—Master of Science in Management Full-time and part-time. At least 42 total credits required. 16 to 72 months to complete program. *Concentrations:* financial management/planning, management information systems, operations management, technology management.

COSTS
Tuition, state resident: *Full-time* $1578. *Part-time* $592 per semester. **Tuition, nonresident:** *Full-time* $10,744. *Part-time* $4029 per semester. Tuition varies by class time and number of courses or credits taken. **Required fees:** *Full-time* $892. *Part-time* $294 per semester. Tuition and fees vary by number of courses or credits taken. **Graduate housing:** Room and board costs vary by number of occupants, type of accommodation, and type of board plan. *Typical cost:* $8776 (including board).

FINANCIAL AID (1999–2000)
Fellowships, research assistantships, and teaching assistantships. Financial aid application deadline: 4/1. **Financial Aid Contact** Ms. Julia Rice Mallette, Director, Financial Aid, Box 7302, Raleigh, NC 27695. **Phone:** 919-515-2334. **Fax:** 919-515-8422. **E-mail:** julie_rice@ncsu.edu.

RESOURCES AND SERVICES
Information about online services, personal computer policies, library resources, international exchange programs, internship programs, and placement services at this institution and others can be found at **www. petersons.com/mba**

International Students
Services and Facilities Counseling/support services, ESL/language courses, international student housing, orientation, visa services. Financial aid is available to international students.

Applying *Required:* TOEFL with recommended score of 250 (computer) or 600 (paper), proof of adequate funds, proof of health/immunizations.

International Student Contact Mr. Michael Bustle, Director, International Student Office, Box 7306, Raleigh, NC 27695. **Phone:** 919-515-2961. **Fax:** 919-515-1402. **E-mail:** michael_bustle@ncsu.edu.

■ APPLICATION
Required GMAT, application form, baccalaureate/first degree, 3 letters of recommendation, personal statement, resume/curriculum vitae, transcripts of college work, work experience.

Deadlines and Fees *Deadlines:* 4/1 for fall, 4/1 for fall (international). *Application fee:* $55, $55 (international).

Application Contact Ms. Pamela Bostic, Assistant Director, MSM Program, Box 7229, Raleigh, NC 27695. **Phone:** 919-515-5584. **Fax:** 919-515-5073. **E-mail:** msm@ncsu.edu.

See full description on page 744.

Pfeiffer University
Misenheimer, North Carolina
PROGRAM IN BUSINESS ADMINISTRATION

Graduate Business Faculty
Full-time: 25

Part-time: 15

Student Body
Total: 814
Average Age: 29

Women: 55%

Costs (1999–2000)
Full-time tuition: N/R
Part-time tuition: $265 per credit hour

After Graduation (Class of 1998–99)
Employed within 3 months of graduation: 95%

DEGREES MBA • MSOM

MBA—Master of Business Administration Full-time and part-time. *Distance learning option.* At least 36 total credits required. 18 to 60 months to complete program. *Concentrations:* entrepreneurship, finance, international business, management, marketing.

MSOM—Master of Science in Organizational Management with health concentration Full-time and part-time. *Distance learning option.* At least 36 total credits required. 18 to 60 months to complete program. *Concentrations:* health care, organizational management.

MSOM—Master of Science in Organization and Management Full-time and part-time. *Distance learning option.* At least 36 total credits required. 18 to 60 months to complete program.

COSTS
Tuition *Part-time:* $265 per credit hour.

FINANCIAL AID (1999–2000)
30 students received aid, including loans, teaching assistantships, and work study. Aid is available to part-time students. **Financial Aid Contact** Mr. Gordon Peck, Misenheimer Campus, Charlotte, NC 28209. **Phone:** 704-521-9116. **Fax:** 704-521-8617.

RESOURCES AND SERVICES
Information about online services, personal computer policies, library resources, international exchange programs, internship programs, and placement services at this institution and others can be found at **www. petersons.com/mba**

Pfeiffer University (continued)

International Students

5% of students enrolled are international students.

Services and Facilities Counseling/support services, ESL/language courses, housing location assistance, international student housing, orientation, visa services. Financial aid is not available to international students.

Applying *Required:* TOEFL with recommended score of 500 (paper), proof of adequate funds, proof of health/immunizations.

International Student Contact Dr. Robert Spear, Director of MBA Programs, 4701 Park road, Charlotte, NC 28209. **Phone:** 704-521-9116. **Fax:** 704-521-8617. **E-mail:** rks@pfeiffer.edu.

■ APPLICATION

Required Application form, baccalaureate/first degree, interview, 3 letters of recommendation, transcripts of college work. School will accept GMAT, GRE, and MAT. **Recommended** Essay, resume/curriculum vitae, 4 years of work experience.

Deadlines and Fees Applications for domestic and international students are processed on a rolling basis. *Application fee:* $75, $75 (international).

Application Contact Dr. Muhammad Abdullah, Director of MBA Programs, 4701 Park Road, Charlotte, NC 28209. **Phone:** 704-521-9116 Ext. 253. **Fax:** 704-521-8617. **E-mail:** mabdulla@pfeiffer.edu.

Queens College

Charlotte, North Carolina

MCCOLL SCHOOL OF BUSINESS

Graduate Business Faculty
Full-time: 7   Part-time: 4

Student Body
Total: 289
Full-time: 95   Average Age: 31
Part-time: 194   Women: 33%

Admissions
Applications: 105   Average GMAT: 560
Admitted: 75   Average GPA: 2.9
Enrolled: 62

Costs (1999–2000)
Full-time tuition: $18,500 per academic year
Part-time tuition: $310 per credit hour

After Graduation (Class of 1998–99)
Employed within 3 months of graduation: 99.9%

Accreditation
ACBSP—The American Council of Business Schools and Programs

DEGREES MBA

MBA—Executive MBA Full-time. 5 to 7 years work/management experience. At least 54 total credits required. 24 months to complete program.

MBA—Master of Business Administration Full-time and part-time. 33 to 45 total credits required. 24 to 60 months to complete program.

COSTS

Tuition *Full-time:* $18,500. *Part-time:* $310 per credit hour. **Required fees:** *Part-time* $20 per semester. Tuition and fees vary by class time and academic program.

FINANCIAL AID (1999–2000)

131 students received aid, including fellowships and loans. Aid is available to part-time students. **Financial Aid Contact** Mr. Tony Carter, Director of Financial Aid, 1900 Selwyn Avenue, Charlotte, NC 28274-0001. **Phone:** 704-337-2225. **Fax:** 704-337-2403. **E-mail:** cartert@rex.queens.edu.

RESOURCES AND SERVICES

Information about online services, personal computer policies, library resources, international exchange programs, internship programs, and placement services at this institution and others can be found at **www.petersons.com/mba**

International Students

1% of students enrolled are international students.

Services and Facilities Financial aid is not available to international students.
Applying *Required:* TOEFL with recommended score of 550 (paper), proof of adequate funds, proof of health/immunizations.

International Student Contact Ms. Katie Wireman, McColl School MBA, Director of Admissions, 1900 Selwyn, Charlotte, NC 28274-0002. **Phone:** 704-337-2224. **Fax:** 704-337-2403.

■ APPLICATION

Required GMAT, application form, baccalaureate/first degree, essay, 2 letters of recommendation, personal statement, resume/curriculum vitae, transcripts of college work.

Deadlines and Fees Applications for domestic and international students are processed on a rolling basis. *Application fee:* $50, $50 (international).

Application Contact Ms. Katie Wireman, McColl School MBA, Director of Admissions, 1900 Selwyn, Charlotte, NC 28274-0002. **Phone:** 704-337-2224. **Fax:** 704-337-2403. **E-mail:** wiremank@rex.queens.edu.

The University of North Carolina at Chapel Hill

Chapel Hill, North Carolina

KENAN-FLAGLER BUSINESS SCHOOL

Graduate Business Faculty
Full-time: 115

Student Body
Total: 522   Average Age: 28
Full-time: 522   Women: 31%

Admissions
Applications: 1,860   Average GMAT: 640
Admitted: 538   Average GPA: 3.3
Enrolled: 278

Costs (1999–2000)
Full-time tuition: $8403 per academic year (resident), $20,353 per academic year (nonresident)
Part-time tuition: N/R

After Graduation (Class of 1998–99)
Employed within 3 months of graduation: 97%
Average starting salary: $78,232

Accreditation
AACSB—The International Association for Management Education

DEGREES JD/MBA • MAC • MBA • MBA/MHA • MBA/MRP

JD/MBA—Juris Doctor/Master of Business Administration Full-time. At least 123 total credits required. Minimum of 48 months to complete program.

MAC—Master of Accounting Full-time. At least 48 total credits required. 12 months to complete program.

MBA—Corporate MBA Full-time. *Distance learning option.* Maximum of 20 months to complete program.

MBA—Executive MBA Full-time. At least 57 total credits required. Maximum of 24 months to complete program.

MBA—Master of Business Administration Full-time. At least 59 total credits required. 24 months to complete program. *Concentrations:* electronic commerce (e-commerce), entrepreneurship, finance, international business, management, management consulting, marketing, new venture management, operations management, real estate, supply chain management.

MBA/MHA—Master of Business Administration/Master of Health Administration Full-time. At least 110 total credits required. Minimum of 36 months to complete program.

MBA/MRP—Master of Business Administration/Master of Regional Planning Full-time. At least 107 total credits required. Minimum of 36 months to complete program.

COSTS

Tuition, state resident: *Full-time* $8403. **Tuition, nonresident:** *Full-time* $20,353. Tuition varies by class time, number of courses or credits taken, campus location, and academic program. **Required fees:** Tuition and fees vary by campus location and academic program.

FINANCIAL AID (1999–2000)

Fellowships, loans, research assistantships, and teaching assistantships. Aid is available to part-time students. Financial aid application deadline: 2/15. **Financial Aid Contact** Office of Scholarship and Student Aid, CB

2300 Vance Hall, Chapel Hill, NC 27599-2300. **Phone:** 919-962-4163. **Fax:** 919-962-2716.

RESOURCES AND SERVICES
Information about online services, personal computer policies, library resources, international exchange programs, internship programs, and placement services at this institution and others can be found at **www.petersons.com/mba**

International Students
31% of students enrolled are international students.

Services and Facilities Counseling/support services, international student organization, orientation, speakers, programs. Financial aid is not available to international students.
Applying *Required:* TOEFL with recommended score of 600 (paper), proof of adequate funds, proof of health/immunizations.
International Student Contact Ms. Alison Jesse, Associate Director, MBA Admissions/Student Services, CB 3490 McColl Building, Chapel Hill, NC 27599-3490. **Phone:** 919-962-9830. **Fax:** 919-962-0898. **E-mail:** mba_info@unc.edu.

■ APPLICATION
Required Application form, baccalaureate/first degree, essay, interview, 3 letters of recommendation, personal statement, resume/curriculum vitae, transcripts of college work, 2 years of work experience. School will accept GMAT.
Deadlines and Fees *Deadlines:* 10/22 for fall, 11/19 for winter, 1/14 for spring, 3/10 for summer, 3/6 for fall (international). *Application fee:* $60, $60 (international).
Application Contact Sherrylyn Wallace, Director, MBA Admissions, CB 3490 McColl Building, Chapel Hill, NC 27599-3490. **Phone:** 919-962-3236. **Fax:** 919-962-0898. **E-mail:** mba_info@unc.edu.

The University of North Carolina at Charlotte

Charlotte, North Carolina

COLLEGE OF BUSINESS ADMINISTRATION

Graduate Business Faculty
Full-time: 68

Student Body
Total: 445
Full-time: 82
Part-time: 363

Average Age: 30
Women: 35%

Admissions
Applications: 234
Admitted: 164
Enrolled: 118

Average GMAT: 549
Average GPA: 3.2

Costs (1999–2000)
Full-time tuition: $1940 per academic year (resident), $9210 per academic year (nonresident)
Part-time tuition: $372 per course (resident), $2189 per course (nonresident)

After Graduation (Class of 1998–99)
Employed within 3 months of graduation: 94%
Average starting salary: $72,400

Accreditation
AACSB—The International Association for Management Education

DEGREES M Acc • MBA • MS

M Acc—Master of Accounting Full-time and part-time. At least 30 total credits required. 12 to 72 months to complete program. *Concentrations:* accounting, taxation.

MBA—Master of Business Administration Full-time and part-time. At least 42 total credits required. 24 to 72 months to complete program. *Concentrations:* banking, economics, finance, information management, management, technology management.

MS—Master of Science in Economics Full-time and part-time. At least 30 total credits required. 12 to 72 months to complete program. *Concentrations:* economics, finance.

T*he primary objective of the Belk College of Business Administration's M.B.A. program at the University of North Carolina at Charlotte is to develop leaders for positions in the complex organizations of the future. The program began in 1970 and is AACSB—The International Association of Management Education accredited. Courses are scheduled in the evening to accommodate part-time students. A part-time student can complete the program in three years. Full-time students can complete the program in two years. The curriculum stresses the universal characteristics of management and their applications in a wide variety of organizations. Management problems and issues are examined from economic, technological, and behavioral perspectives. Concentrations are offered in business finance, economics, financial institutions/ commercial banking, information and technology management, and management. Students who do not choose a structured concentration may propose a self-structured concentration in a significant area of interest.*

COSTS
Tuition, state resident: *Full-time* $1940. *Part-time* $372 per course. **Tuition, nonresident:** *Full-time* $9210. *Part-time* $2189 per course. **Tuition, international:** *Full-time* $9210. Tuition varies by number of courses or credits taken. **Graduate housing:** Room and board costs vary by number of occupants, type of accommodation, and type of board plan. *Typical cost:* $4500 (including board), $2400 (room only).

FINANCIAL AID (1999–2000)
100 students received aid, including grants, loans, research assistantships, teaching assistantships, and work study. Aid is available to part-time students. Financial aid application deadline: 4/1. **Financial Aid Contact** Student Financial Aid Office, 9201 University City Boulevard, Charlotte, NC 28223. **Phone:** 704-547-2461. **Fax:** 704-547-3132.

RESOURCES AND SERVICES
Information about online services, personal computer policies, library resources, international exchange programs, internship programs, and placement services at this institution and others can be found at **www.petersons.com/mba**

International Students
11% of students enrolled are international students.

Services and Facilities Counseling/support services, ESL/language courses, international student housing, visa services. Financial aid is not available to international students.
Applying *Required:* TOEFL with recommended score of 550 (paper), proof of adequate funds, proof of health/immunizations.
International Student Contact Peggie Reid, International Admissions, Denny Building, Room 211, 9201 University City Boulevard, Charlotte, NC 28223-0001. **Phone:** 704-547-2694. **Fax:** 704-510-6340. **E-mail:** intnladm@email.uncc.edu.

■ APPLICATION
Required GMAT, application form, baccalaureate/first degree, 3 letters of recommendation, personal statement, transcripts of college work. **Recommended** Resume/curriculum vitae, work experience.
Deadlines and Fees Applications for domestic students are processed on a rolling basis. *Deadlines:* 5/1 for fall (international), 10/1 for spring (international), 4/1 for summer (international). *Application fee:* $35, $35 (international).
Application Contact Ms. Johnna Watson, Assistant Dean for Enrollment Services, Graduate Admissions, 9201 University City Boulevard, Charlotte, NC 28223-0001. **Phone:** 704-547-3366. **Fax:** 704-547-3219. **E-mail:** gradadm@email.uncc.edu.

The University of North Carolina at Greensboro

Greensboro, North Carolina

JOSEPH M. BRYAN SCHOOL OF BUSINESS AND ECONOMICS

Graduate Business Faculty
Full-time: 76

Part-time: 12

Student Body
Total: 242
Full-time: 87
Part-time: 155

Average Age: 29
Women: 29%

Admissions
Applications: 184
Admitted: 153
Enrolled: 92

Average GMAT: 570
Average GPA: 3.3

The University of North Carolina at Greensboro (continued)

Costs (1999–2000)
Full-time tuition: $2778 per academic year (resident), $13,666 per academic year (nonresident)
Part-time tuition: $1139 per semester (resident), $6833 per semester (nonresident)

After Graduation (Class of 1998–99)
Employed within 3 months of graduation: 100%

Accreditation
AACSB—The International Association for Management Education

DEGREE MBA

MBA—Evening MBA Full-time and part-time. 36 to 48 total credits required. 24 to 60 months to complete program.

COSTS
Tuition, state resident: *Full-time* $2778. *Part-time* $1139 per semester. **Tuition, nonresident:** *Full-time* $13,666. *Part-time* $6833 per semester. **Tuition, international:** *Full-time* $13,666. **Required fees:** Tuition and fees vary by number of courses or credits taken. **Graduate housing:** Room and board costs vary by campus location, number of occupants, type of accommodation, and type of board plan. *Typical cost:* $4000 (including board).

FINANCIAL AID (1999–2000)
Fellowships, grants, research assistantships, teaching assistantships, and work study. Financial aid application deadline: 3/15. **Financial Aid Contact** Ms. Deborah Tollefson, Director, Financial Aid, 723 Kenilworth Street, Greensboro, NC 27412-5001. **Phone:** 336-334-5702. **Fax:** 336-334-3010. **E-mail:** tdnagy@friday.uncg.edu.

RESOURCES AND SERVICES
Information about online services, personal computer policies, library resources, international exchange programs, internship programs, and placement services at this institution and others can be found at **www. petersons.com/mba**

International Students
13% of students enrolled are international students.
Services and Facilities Counseling/support services, ESL/language courses, international student housing, international student organization, orientation, visa services, international festival. Financial aid is available to international students.
Applying *Required:* TOEFL with recommended score of 213 (computer) or 550 (paper), proof of adequate funds, proof of health/immunizations.
International Student Contact Ms. Martha Trigonis, International Programs Center, 1000 Spring Garden Street, Greensboro, NC 27412-5001. **Phone:** 336-334-5404. **Fax:** 336-334-5406. **E-mail:** trigonis@uncg.edu.

■ APPLICATION
Required GMAT, application form, baccalaureate/first degree, essay, 3 letters of recommendation, personal statement, resume/curriculum vitae, transcripts of college work. **Recommended** Interview, 2 years of work experience.
Deadlines and Fees *Deadlines:* 7/1 for fall, 11/1 for spring, 5/1 for fall (international), 10/1 for spring (international). *Application fee:* $35, $35 (international).
Application Contact Dr. Catherine Holderness, Associate Director for MBA Student Services, Bryan Building, Room 220, 1000 Spring Garden Street, Greensboro, NC 27412-5001. **Phone:** 336-334-5390. **Fax:** 336-334-4209. **E-mail:** c_holder@uncg.edu.

See full description on page 938.

The University of North Carolina at Pembroke

Pembroke, North Carolina

GRADUATE STUDIES

Graduate Business Faculty
Full-time: 18	Part-time: 1

Student Body
Total: 84	Average Age: 34
Full-time: 3	Women: 45%
Part-time: 81	

Admissions
Applications: 119	Average GPA: 3
Average GMAT: 350	

Costs (1999–2000)
Full-time tuition: $1317 per academic year (resident), $4461 per academic year (nonresident)
Part-time tuition: $246 per course (resident), $2063 per course (nonresident)

DEGREES MBA • MS

MBA—Master of Business Administration Full-time and part-time. At least 36 total credits required. 12 to 60 months to complete program.

MS—Master of Science in Public Management Full-time and part-time. At least 39 total credits required. 24 to 60 months to complete program. *Concentrations:* public and private management, public management.

COSTS
Tuition, state resident: *Full-time* $982. *Part-time* $246 per course. **Tuition, nonresident:** *Full-time* $4126. *Part-time* $2063 per course. **Tuition, international:** *Full-time* $4126. **Required fees:** *Full-time* $335. *Part-time* $83 per semester. Tuition and fees vary by number of courses or credits taken. **Graduate housing:** Room and board costs vary by number of occupants, type of accommodation, and type of board plan. *Typical cost:* $3755 (including board), $1078 (room only).

FINANCIAL AID (1999–2000)
25 students received aid, including loans and research assistantships. Aid is available to part-time students. Financial aid application deadline: 4/15. **Financial Aid Contact** Mr. Bruce Blackmon, Director of Financial Aid, Pembroke, NC 28372-1510. **Phone:** 910-521-6366. **Fax:** 910-521-6497. **E-mail:** blackmon@farmer.uncp.edu.

RESOURCES AND SERVICES
Information about online services, personal computer policies, library resources, international exchange programs, internship programs, and placement services at this institution and others can be found at **www. petersons.com/mba**

International Students
Services and Facilities Counseling/support services, international student organization. Financial aid is not available to international students.
Applying *Required:* TOEFL, proof of adequate funds.
International Student Contact Dr. W. Bruce Ezell, Jr., Dean of Graduate Studies, PO Box 1510, Pembroke, NC 28372-1510. **Phone:** 910-521-6271. **Fax:** 910-521-6497. **E-mail:** ezell@farmer.uncp.edu.

■ APPLICATION
Required Application form, baccalaureate/first degree, essay, 3 letters of recommendation, transcripts of college work. School will accept GMAT and GMAT or GRE or MAT.
Deadlines and Fees Applications for domestic students are processed on a rolling basis. *Deadlines:* 3/1 for fall (international), 9/1 for spring (international). *Application fee:* $25, $25 (international).
Application Contact Dr. W. Bruce Ezell, Jr., Dean of Graduate Studies, PO Box 1510, Pembroke, NC 28372-1510. **Phone:** 910-521-6271. **Fax:** 910-521-6497. **E-mail:** ezell@farmer.uncp.edu.

Wake Forest University

Winston-Salem, North Carolina

BABCOCK GRADUATE SCHOOL OF MANAGEMENT

Graduate Business Faculty
Full-time: 40	Part-time: 14

Student Body
Total: 662	Average Age: 27
Full-time: 236	Women: 26%
Part-time: 426	

Admissions
Applications: 727	Average GMAT: 633
Admitted: 339	Average GPA: 3.2
Enrolled: 193	

Costs (1999–2000)
Full-time tuition: $21,300 per academic year
Part-time tuition: $2050 per course

After Graduation (Class of 1998–99)
Employed within 3 months of graduation: 96%
Average starting salary: $65,000

Accreditation
AACSB—The International Association for Management Education

DEGREES JD/MBA • MBA • MD/MBA

JD/MBA—Juris Doctor/Master of Business Administration Full-time. At least 123 total credits required. 44 months to complete program. *Concentrations:* finance, marketing, operations management, organizational behavior/development.

MBA—Evening MBA Part-time. At least 48 total credits required. 22 to 60 months to complete program. *Concentrations:* finance, marketing, operations management, organizational behavior/development.

MBA—Evening MBA-Charlotte Part-time. At least 54 total credits required. 24 months to complete program. *Concentrations:* finance, marketing, operations management, organizational behavior/development.

MBA—Executive MBA Part-time. At least 51 total credits required. 22 months to complete program. *Concentrations:* finance, marketing, operations management, organizational behavior/development.

MBA—Full-time MBA Full-time. At least 64 total credits required. 22 months to complete program. *Concentrations:* entrepreneurship, finance, management consulting, marketing, operations management.

MD/MBA—Doctor of Medicine/Master of Business Administration Full-time. 248 total credits required. 60 months to complete program. *Concentrations:* finance, marketing, operations management, organizational behavior/development.

COSTS

Tuition *Full-time:* $21,200. *Part-time:* $2050 per course. **Required fees:** *Full-time* $100.

FINANCIAL AID (1999–2000)

351 students received aid, including loans, research assistantships, and scholarships. Aid is available to part-time students. Financial aid application deadline: 3/1. **Financial Aid Contact** Ms. Donna Agee, Assistant Director, Admissions and Financial Aid, Babcock Graduate School of Management, PO Box 7659, Winston-Salem, NC 27109-7659. **Phone:** 336-758-4424. **Fax:** 336-758-5830. **E-mail:** donna.agee@mba.wfu.edu.

RESOURCES AND SERVICES

Information about online services, personal computer policies, library resources, international exchange programs, internship programs, and placement services at this institution and others can be found at **www.petersons.com/mba**

International Students

8% of students enrolled are international students.

Services and Facilities Counseling/support services, housing location assistance, international student housing, orientation, visa services. Financial aid is available to international students.

Applying *Required:* TOEFL with recommended score of 600 (paper), proof of adequate funds, proof of health/immunizations.

International Student Contact Ms. Donna Agee, Assistant Director, Admissions and Financial Aid, Babcock Graduate School of Management, PO Box 7659, Winston-Salem, NC 27109-7659. **Phone:** 336-758-4424. **Fax:** 336-758-5830. **E-mail:** donna.agee@mba.wfu.edu.

■ **APPLICATION**

Required GMAT, application form, baccalaureate/first degree, essay, 2 letters of recommendation, resume/curriculum vitae, transcripts of college work. **Recommended** Interview, work experience.

Deadlines and Fees Applications for domestic and international students are processed on a rolling basis. *Application fee:* $75, $75 (international).

Application Contact Ms. Cathy Caesar, Staff Assistant, Babcock Graduate School of Management, PO Box 7659, Winston-Salem, NC 27109-7659. **Phone:** 336-758-5422. **Toll-free Phone:** 800-772-1622. **Fax:** 336-758-5830. **E-mail:** admissions@mba.wfu.edu.

See full description on page 1000.

Western Carolina University

Cullowhee, North Carolina

COLLEGE OF BUSINESS

Graduate Business Faculty
Full-time: 39

Student Body
Total: 96
Full-time: 40
Part-time: 56
Average Age: 28
Women: 36%

Admissions
Applications: 71
Admitted: 59
Enrolled: 29
Average GMAT: 505
Average GPA: 3.4

Costs (1999–2000)
Full-time tuition: $1957 per academic year (resident), $9227 per academic year (nonresident)
Part-time tuition: N/R

After Graduation (Class of 1998–99)
Employed within 3 months of graduation: 90%

Accreditation
AACSB—The International Association for Management Education

DEGREES M Acc • MBA • MPM

M Acc—Master of Accountancy Full-time and part-time. Will accept the GMAT or the GRE. At least 51 total credits required. 12 to 36 months to complete program. *Concentrations:* accounting.

MBA—Master of Business Administration Full-time and part-time. At least 48 total credits required. 16 to 48 months to complete program. *Concentrations:* health care, human resources, project management.

MPM—Master of Project Management Part-time. *Distance learning option.* Resume, 1 letter of recommendation, working experience. At least 42 total credits required. 24 to 36 months to complete program. *Concentrations:* project management.

COSTS

Tuition, state resident: *Full-time* $982. **Tuition, nonresident:** *Full-time* $8252. Tuition varies by class time and number of courses or credits taken. **Required fees:** *Full-time* $975. Fees vary by class time, number of courses or credits taken, and academic program. **Graduate housing:** Room and board costs vary by number of occupants, type of accommodation, and type of board plan. *Typical cost:* $5000 (including board), $3140 (room only).

FINANCIAL AID (1999–2000)

70 students received aid, including fellowships, grants, loans, research assistantships, scholarships, teaching assistantships, and work study. Aid is available to part-time students. Financial aid application deadline: 3/31. **Financial Aid Contact** Ms. Nancy Dillard, Acting Director, Student Financial Aid, 230 HF Robinson Building, Cullowhee, NC 28723. **Phone:** 828-227-7290. **Fax:** 828-227-7042. **E-mail:** dillard@wcu.edu.

RESOURCES AND SERVICES

Information about online services, personal computer policies, library resources, international exchange programs, internship programs, and placement services at this institution and others can be found at **www.petersons.com/mba**

International Students

22% of students enrolled are international students.

Services and Facilities Counseling/support services, housing location assistance, international student housing, international student organization, orientation, visa services. Financial aid is available to international students.

Applying *Required:* TOEFL with recommended score of 550 (paper), proof of adequate funds, proof of health/immunizations.

International Student Contact Mr. Richard Cameron, International Student Advisor, 460 HF Robinson Administration Building, Cullowhee, NC 28723. **Phone:** 828-227-7234. **Fax:** 828-227-7036. **E-mail:** cameron@wcu.edu.

■ **APPLICATION**

Required GMAT, application form, baccalaureate/first degree, transcripts of college work.

Deadlines and Fees Applications for domestic and international students are processed on a rolling basis. *Application fee:* $35, $35 (international).

Application Contact Ms. Faye Deitz, Student Services Assistant, MBA Program, 112 Forsyth Building, Cullowhee, NC 28723. **Phone:** 828-227-3588. **Fax:** 828-227-7414. **E-mail:** fdeitz@wcu.edu.

Wingate University

Wingate, North Carolina

SCHOOL OF BUSINESS AND ECONOMICS

Graduate Business Faculty
Full-time: 8
Part-time: 1

Student Body
Total: 80
Part-time: 80
Average Age: 29
Women: 40%

Wingate University (continued)

Admissions
Applications: 28
Admitted: 24
Enrolled: 24

Average GMAT: 425
Average GPA: 3.25

Costs (1999–2000)
Full-time tuition: N/R
Part-time tuition: $750 per course

After Graduation (Class of 1998–99)
Employed within 3 months of graduation: 100%

Accreditation
ACBSP—The American Council of Business Schools and Programs

DEGREE MBA

MBA—Master of Business Administration Part-time. At least 33 total credits required. 24 to 72 months to complete program. *Concentrations:* management.

COSTS
Tuition *Part-time:* $750 per course.

FINANCIAL AID (1999–2000)
5 students received aid, including loans. Aid is available to part-time students. Financial aid application deadline: 8/1.

RESOURCES AND SERVICES
Information about online services, personal computer policies, library resources, international exchange programs, internship programs, and placement services at this institution and others can be found at www.petersons.com/mba

International Students
4% of students enrolled are international students.

Services and Facilities Financial aid is not available to international students.
Applying *Required:* TOEFL with recommended score of 550 (paper), proof of adequate funds, proof of health/immunizations.

■ APPLICATION
Required Application form, baccalaureate/first degree, 2 letters of recommendation, personal statement, transcripts of college work, 1 year of work experience. School will accept GMAT.

Deadlines and Fees Applications for domestic and international students are processed on a rolling basis. *Application fee:* $25, $50 (international).

Application Contact Mrs. Kathryn Rowell, MBA Coordinator, Campus Box 3000, Wingate, NC 28174. **Phone:** 704-233-8148. **Fax:** 704-233-8146. **E-mail:** karowe@wingate.edu.

NORTH DAKOTA

Minot State University
Minot, North Dakota

COLLEGE OF BUSINESS

Graduate Business Faculty
Full-time: 13

Student Body
Total: 40
Full-time: 5
Part-time: 35

Average Age: 28
Women: 65%

Admissions
Applications: 34
Admitted: 31
Enrolled: 27

Average GMAT: 495
Average GPA: 3.62

Costs (1999–2000)
Full-time tuition: $5380 per academic year (resident), $14,364 per academic year (nonresident)
Part-time tuition: $112 per credit (resident), $299 per credit (nonresident)

After Graduation (Class of 1998–99)
Employed within 3 months of graduation: 90%
Average starting salary: $37,500

DEGREE MS

MS—Master of Science in Management Full-time and part-time. *Distance learning option.* At least 33 total credits required. 18 to 72 months to complete program. *Concentrations:* management information systems, organizational management.

COSTS
Tuition, state resident: *Full-time* $5380. *Part-time* $112 per credit. **Tuition, nonresident:** *Full-time* $14,364. *Part-time* $299 per credit. **Tuition, international:** *Full-time* $14,364. **Required fees:** *Part-time* $11.7 per semester hour. Tuition and fees vary by number of courses or credits taken. **Graduate housing:** Room and board costs vary by number of occupants, type of accommodation, and type of board plan. *Typical cost:* $2765 (including board), $1154 (room only).

FINANCIAL AID (1999–2000)
15 students received aid, including research assistantships, scholarships, and teaching assistantships. Aid is available to part-time students. Financial aid application deadline: 2/15. **Financial Aid Contact** Mr. Dale Gehring, Financial Aid Director, 500 University Avenue West, Minot, ND 58707. **Phone:** 701-858-3862. **Fax:** 701-839-6933. **E-mail:** gehringd@minotstateu.edu.

RESOURCES AND SERVICES
Information about online services, personal computer policies, library resources, international exchange programs, internship programs, and placement services at this institution and others can be found at www.petersons.com/mba

International Students
3% of students enrolled are international students.

Services and Facilities Counseling/support services, housing location assistance, international student organization. Financial aid is available to international students.
Applying *Required:* TOEFL with recommended score of 550 (paper), proof of adequate funds, proof of health/immunizations.
International Student Contact Ms. Rolaunda Walker, International Student Specialist, 500 University Avenue West, Minot, ND 58707. **E-mail:** walkerro@minotstateu.edu.

■ APPLICATION
Required GMAT or GRE, application form, baccalaureate/first degree, essay, 3 letters of recommendation, transcripts of college work. **Recommended** Work experience.

Deadlines and Fees Applications for domestic and international students are processed on a rolling basis. *Application fee:* $30, $30 (international).

Application Contact Ms. Tammy White, Administrative Assistant-Graduate Programs, 500 University Avenue West, Minot, ND 58707. **Phone:** 701-858-3250. **Toll-free Phone:** 800-777-0750. **Fax:** 701-839-6933. **E-mail:** whitet@minotstateu.edu.

North Dakota State University
Fargo, North Dakota

COLLEGE OF BUSINESS ADMINISTRATION

Graduate Business Faculty
Full-time: 17

Part-time: 1

Student Body
Total: 71
Full-time: 18
Part-time: 53

Average Age: 29
Women: 46%

Admissions
Applications: 49
Admitted: 31
Enrolled: 25

Average GMAT: 550
Average GPA: 3.28

Costs (1999–2000)
Full-time tuition: N/R
Part-time tuition: $116 per credit (resident), $286 per credit (nonresident)

After Graduation (Class of 1998–99)
Employed within 3 months of graduation: 100%
Average starting salary: $28,000

DEGREE MBA

MBA—Master of Business Administration Full-time and part-time. At least 60 total credits required. 12 to 84 months to complete program. *Concentrations:* accounting, finance, management, marketing.

COSTS

Tuition, state resident: *Part-time* $116 per credit. **Tuition, nonresident:** *Part-time* $286 per credit. Tuition varies by number of courses or credits taken and local reciprocity agreements. **Required fees:** Fees vary by academic program. **Graduate housing:** Room and board costs vary by number of occupants, type of accommodation, and type of board plan. *Typical cost:* $3034 (including board).

FINANCIAL AID (1999–2000)

14 students received aid, including loans, research assistantships, scholarships, and work study. Aid is available to part-time students. Financial aid application deadline: 3/15. **Financial Aid Contact** Mr. Paul Brown, MBA Program Director, Box 5137 Putnam Hall, Fargo, ND 58105. **Phone:** 701-231-7681. **Fax:** 701-231-7508. **E-mail:** paul_brown@ndsu.nodak.edu.

RESOURCES AND SERVICES

Information about online services, personal computer policies, library resources, international exchange programs, internship programs, and placement services at this institution and others can be found at **www.petersons.com/mba**

International Students

11% of students enrolled are international students.

Services and Facilities Counseling/support services, ESL/language courses. Financial aid is available to international students.
Applying *Required:* TOEFL with recommended score of 550 (paper), proof of adequate funds, proof of health/immunizations.
International Student Contact Ms. Virginia Packwood, Director of International Programs, Ceres Hall, Fargo, ND 58105. **Phone:** 701-231-7895. **Fax:** 701-231-1014.

■ APPLICATION

Required GMAT, application form, baccalaureate/first degree, 3 letters of recommendation, personal statement, transcripts of college work.

Deadlines and Fees *Deadlines:* 4/1 for fall (international), 8/1 for spring (international). *Application fee:* $25, $25 (international).

Application Contact Mr. Paul Brown, MBA Program Director, Box 5137 Putnam Hall, Fargo, ND 58105. **Phone:** 701-231-7681. **Toll-free Phone:** 800-488-6578. **Fax:** 701-231-7508. **E-mail:** paul_brown@ndsu.nodak.edu.

OHIO

Ashland University

Ashland, Ohio

COLLEGE OF BUSINESS ADMINISTRATION AND ECONOMICS

Graduate Business Faculty
Full-time: 18 — Part-time: 11

Student Body
Total: 465
Full-time: 164 — Average Age: 34
Part-time: 301 — Women: 38%

Admissions
Applications: 157 — Enrolled: 122
Admitted: 135 — Average GPA: 3.21

Costs (1999–2000)
Full-time tuition: N/R
Part-time tuition: $385 per credit hour

After Graduation (Class of 1998–99)
Employed within 3 months of graduation: 99%

Accreditation
ACBSP—The American Council of Business Schools and Programs

DEGREE MBA

MBA—Executive MBA Part-time. 36 to 55 total credits required. 24 to 60 months to complete program. *Concentrations:* management.

COSTS

Tuition *Part-time:* $385 per credit hour.

FINANCIAL AID (1999–2000)

Financial Aid Contact Mr. Steve Howell, Director, Financial Aid, Ashland, OH 44805. **Phone:** 419-289-5002. **Fax:** 419-289-5333. **E-mail:** showell@ashland.edu.

RESOURCES AND SERVICES

Information about online services, personal computer policies, library resources, international exchange programs, internship programs, and placement services at this institution and others can be found at **www.petersons.com/mba**

International Students

4% of students enrolled are international students.

Services and Facilities Counseling/support services, ESL/language courses, international student organization, orientation, visa services, writing center. Financial aid is not available to international students.
Applying *Required:* TOEFL with recommended score of 550 (paper), proof of adequate funds, proof of health/immunizations.
International Student Contact Mr. Thomas Koop, Director, International Student Services, Ashland, OH 44805. **Phone:** 419-289-5068. **Fax:** 419-289-5989. **E-mail:** tkoop@ashland.edu.

■ APPLICATION

Required Application form, baccalaureate/first degree, letter(s) of recommendation, personal statement, resume/curriculum vitae, transcripts of college work, 2 years of work experience. **Recommended** Interview.

Deadlines and Fees *Deadlines:* 8/1 for fall, 12/15 for spring, 4/1 for summer, 8/1 for fall (international), 12/15 for spring (international), 4/1 for summer (international). *Application fee:* $25, $25 (international).

Application Contact Mr. Stephen W. Krispinsky, Executive Director, MBA Program, 21 Miller Hall, Ashland, OH 44805. **Phone:** 419-289-5236. **Toll-free Phone:** 800-882-1548. **Fax:** 419-289-5910. **E-mail:** skrispin@ashland.edu.

Baldwin-Wallace College

Berea, Ohio

DIVISION OF BUSINESS ADMINISTRATION

Graduate Business Faculty
Full-time: 26 — Part-time: 22

Student Body
Total: 418
Full-time: 29 — Average Age: 27
Part-time: 389 — Women: 45%

Admissions
Applications: 230 — Average GMAT: 485
Admitted: 162 — Average GPA: 3
Enrolled: 153

Costs (1999–2000)
Full-time tuition: $10,600 per academic year
Part-time tuition: $1590 per course

DEGREES EMBA • HCEMBA • IMBA • MBA

EMBA—Executive Master of Business Administration Part-time. 38 to 44 total credits required. 24 to 48 months to complete program. *Concentrations:* health care, management.

HCEMBA—Health Care Executive Master of Business Administration Part-time. 38 to 44 total credits required. 24 to 48 months to complete program.

IMBA—International Master of Business Administration Full-time and part-time. 40 to 58 total credits required. 12 to 48 months to complete program. *Concentrations:* international management.

MBA—Master of Business Administration Part-time. 40 to 55 total credits required. 24 to 48 months to complete program. *Concentrations:* management.

Baldwin-Wallace College (B-W) offers four distinct programs: the M.B.A. in systems management, the M.B.A. in international management, the M.B.A. in executive management, and the M.B.A. in executive health care management. B-W's M.B.A. programs feature the distinctive systems approach, which focuses on how various business disciplines work together. These programs take a strategic view of management, focusing on decisions

Baldwin-Wallace College (continued)

that influence long-term business success. The M.B.A. programs at B-W emphasize problem solving, effective communication, group dynamics, team leadership, human resource awareness, and international awareness. Evening and Saturday formats allow working professionals the opportunity to seek a graduate degree without interrupting their careers. All of B-W's graduate programs can be completed part-time in two years. The M.B.A. in international management offers a full-time format, which can be completed in 1½ years. The College also offers advanced graduate certificates in business management and international management. The M.B.A. programs at B-W provide enrollment opportunities throughout the academic year.

COSTS

Tuition *Full-time:* $10,600. *Part-time:* $1590 per course. Tuition varies by number of courses or credits taken and academic program. **Graduate housing:** Room and board costs vary by type of accommodation. *Typical cost:* $7200 (room only).

FINANCIAL AID (1999–2000)

78 students received aid, including fellowships, research assistantships, scholarships, teaching assistantships, and work study. **Financial Aid Contact** George Rolleston, Director of Financial Aid, 275 Eastland Road, Berea, OH 44017-2088. **Phone:** 440-826-2108.

RESOURCES AND SERVICES

Information about online services, personal computer policies, library resources, international exchange programs, internship programs, and placement services at this institution and others can be found at **www.petersons.com/mba**

International Students

9% of students enrolled are international students.

Services and Facilities Counseling/support services, ESL/language courses, international student housing. Financial aid is available to international students.
Applying *Required:* TOEFL with recommended score of 500 (paper), proof of adequate funds.
International Student Contact Peggy Shepard, Graduate Business Coordinator, 275 Eastland Road, Berea, OH 44017-2088. **Phone:** 440-826-2196. **Fax:** 440-826-3868. **E-mail:** pshepard@bw.edu.

■ APPLICATION

Required GMAT, application form, baccalaureate/first degree, 2 letters of recommendation, resume/curriculum vitae, transcripts of college work, 2 years of work experience. School will accept GRE. **Recommended** Interview, personal statement.
Deadlines and Fees Applications for domestic and international students are processed on a rolling basis. *Application fee:* $15, $15 (international).
Application Contact Peggy Shepard, Graduate Business Coordinator, 275 Eastland Road, Berea, OH 44017-2088. **Phone:** 440-826-2196. **Fax:** 440-826-3868. **E-mail:** pshepard@bw.edu.

See full description on page 558.

Bowling Green State University

Bowling Green, Ohio

COLLEGE OF BUSINESS ADMINISTRATION

Graduate Business Faculty

Full-time: 67	Part-time: 9

Student Body

Total: 198	Average Age: 31
Full-time: 65	Women: 27%
Part-time: 133	

Admissions

Applications: 156	Average GMAT: 550
Admitted: 125	Average GPA: 3.2
Enrolled: 69	

Costs (1999–2000)
Full-time tuition: $6362 per academic year (resident), $11,910 per academic year (nonresident)
Part-time tuition: $298 per credit hour (resident), $562 per credit hour (nonresident)

After Graduation (Class of 1998–99)
Average starting salary: $43,800

Accreditation
AACSB—The International Association for Management Education

DEGREES M Acc • MBA • MBA/MOD • MOD

M Acc—Master of Accountancy Full-time. At least 30 total credits required. 12 to 72 months to complete program.
MBA—Executive MBA Part-time. At least 36 total credits required. 31 to 72 months to complete program.
MBA—Full-time MBA Full-time. 47 to 57 total credits required. 14 to 18 months to complete program. *Concentrations:* finance, management information systems, marketing, supply chain management.
MBA—Part-time MBA Part-time. 42 to 54 total credits required. 45 to 72 months to complete program. *Concentrations:* finance, management information systems, marketing, supply chain management.
MBA/MOD—Master of Business Administration/Master of Organization Development Full-time and part-time. 38 to 69 total credits required. 30 to 72 months to complete program.
MOD—Executive Master of Organization Development Part-time. At least 30 total credits required. 18 to 72 months to complete program.
MOD—Master of Organizational Development Full-time. At least 33 total credits required. 18 to 72 months to complete program.

COSTS

Tuition, state resident: *Full-time* $6362. *Part-time* $298 per credit hour. **Tuition, nonresident:** *Full-time* $11,910. *Part-time* $562 per credit hour. Tuition varies by number of courses or credits taken, academic program, and local reciprocity agreements.

FINANCIAL AID (1999–2000)

49 students received aid, including loans, research assistantships, teaching assistantships, and work study. Aid is available to part-time students. Financial aid application deadline: 2/15. **Financial Aid Contact** Ms. Carmen Castro-Rivera, Director, Graduate Studies in Business, College of Business Administration, Room 369 BA, Bowling Green, OH 43403. **Phone:** 419-372-2488. **Fax:** 419-372-2875. **E-mail:** mba-info@cba.bgsu.edu.

RESOURCES AND SERVICES

Information about online services, personal computer policies, library resources, international exchange programs, internship programs, and placement services at this institution and others can be found at **www.petersons.com/mba**

International Students

26% of students enrolled are international students.

Services and Facilities Counseling/support services, ESL/language courses, housing location assistance, international student organization, orientation, visa services. Financial aid is available to international students.
Applying *Required:* TOEFL with recommended score of 550 (paper), proof of adequate funds, proof of health/immunizations.
International Student Contact Mr. Jeff Grilliot, Director of International Programs, Offenhauer West, Bowling Green, OH 43403. **E-mail:** jgrilli@bgnet.bgsu.edu.

■ APPLICATION

Required GMAT, application form, baccalaureate/first degree, 2 letters of recommendation, personal statement, resume/curriculum vitae, transcripts of college work. **Recommended** Interview, work experience.
Deadlines and Fees *Deadlines:* 6/1 for fall, 10/1 for spring, 2/15 for summer, 1/15 for summer (international). *Application fee:* $30, $30 (international).
Application Contact Ms. Carmen Castro-Rivera, Director, Graduate Studies in Business, College of Business Administration, Room 369 BA, Bowling Green, OH 43403. **Phone:** 419-372-2488. **Toll-free Phone:** 800-BGSU-MBA. **Fax:** 419-372-2875. **E-mail:** mba-info@cba.bgsu.edu.

See full description on page 574.

Case Western Reserve University

Cleveland, Ohio

WEATHERHEAD SCHOOL OF MANAGEMENT

Graduate Business Faculty

Full-time: 99	Part-time: 12

Student Body

Total: 1,447	Average Age: 28
Full-time: 723	Women: 37%
Part-time: 724	

Admissions

Applications: 784	Enrolled: 212
Admitted: 475	Average GMAT: 620

Average GPA: 3.2

Costs (1999–2000)
Full-time tuition: $22,900 per academic year
Part-time tuition: $955 per credit hour

After Graduation (Class of 1998–99)
Employed within 3 months of graduation: 98%
Average starting salary: $68,300

Accreditation
AACSB—The International Association for Management Education

DEGREES JD/MBA • M Acc • MBA • MBA/M Acc • MBA/MS • MBA/MSMIS • MBA/MSN • MIM/MBA • MSM-ORM-OR/MBA • MSM-SC/MBA • MSMIS

JD/MBA—Juris Doctor/Master of Business Administration Full-time. 115 to 131 total credits required. 36 to 48 months to complete program. *Concentrations:* accounting, banking, economics, electronic commerce (e-commerce), entrepreneurship, finance, health care, human resources, international management, management, management information systems, marketing, nonprofit management, operations management, organizational behavior/development, supply chain management, technology management.

M Acc—Master of Accountancy Full-time and part-time. 36 to 48 total credits required. 11 to 21 months to complete program. *Concentrations:* accounting, taxation.

MBA—42-hour MBA Program Part-time. At least 42 total credits required. 24 to 36 months to complete program. *Concentrations:* accounting, banking, economics, electronic commerce (e-commerce), entrepreneurship, finance, health care, human resources, international management, management, management information systems, marketing, nonprofit management, operations management, organizational behavior/development, supply chain management, technology management.

MBA—47-hour MBA Full-time. Undergraduate degree in business granted within last 10 years required. At least 47 total credits required. 11 to 39 months to complete program. *Concentrations:* accounting, banking, economics, electronic commerce (e-commerce), entrepreneurship, finance, health care, human resources, international management, management, management information systems, marketing, nonprofit management, operations management, organizational behavior/development, supply chain management, technology management.

MBA—51-hour MBA Program Part-time. At least 51 total credits required. 39 months to complete program. *Concentrations:* accounting, banking, economics, electronic commerce (e-commerce), entrepreneurship, finance, health care, human resources, international management, management, management information systems, marketing, nonprofit management, operations management, organizational behavior/development, supply chain management, technology management.

MBA—63-hour MBA Program Full-time. At least 63 total credits required. 21 months to complete program. *Concentrations:* accounting, banking, economics, electronic commerce (e-commerce), entrepreneurship, finance, health care, human resources, international management, management, management information systems, marketing, nonprofit management, operations management, organizational behavior/development, supply chain management, technology management.

MBA—Executive MBA Full-time. 10 years minimum work experience; company sponsorship. At least 45 total credits required. 24 months to complete program.

MBA/M Acc—Master of Business Administration/Master of Accounting Full-time and part-time. At least 67 total credits required. 24 to 48 months to complete program. *Concentrations:* accounting, banking, economics, electronic commerce (e-commerce), health care, human resources, management, management information systems, marketing, nonprofit management, operations management, organizational behavior/development, supply chain management, technology management.

MBA/MS—Master of Business Administration/Master of Science in Applied Social Sciences Full-time and part-time. 93 to 105 total credits required. 36 to 48 months to complete program. *Concentrations:* accounting, arts administration/management, banking, economics, electronic commerce (e-commerce), entrepreneurship, finance, health care, human resources, international management, management, management information systems, marketing, nonprofit management, operations management, organizational behavior/development, supply chain management, technology management.

MBA/MS—Master of Business Administration/Master of Science in Applied Social Sciences Full-time and part-time. 93 to 105 total credits required. 36 to 48 months to complete program. *Concentrations:* accounting, arts administration/management, banking, economics, electronic commerce (e-commerce), entrepreneurship, finance, health care, human resources, international management, management, management information systems, marketing, nonprofit management, operations management, organizational behavior/development, supply chain management, technology management.

MBA/MSMIS—Master of Business Administration/Master of Science in Management Information Systems Full-time and part-time. 66 to 76 total credits required. 27 to 60 months to complete program. *Concentrations:* accounting,

banking, economics, electronic commerce (e-commerce), entrepreneurship, finance, health care, human resources, international management, management, management information systems, marketing, nonprofit management, operations management, organizational behavior/development, supply chain management, technology management.

MBA/MSN—Master of Business Administration/Master of Science in Nursing Full-time and part-time. 78 to 104 total credits required. 29 to 48 months to complete program. *Concentrations:* accounting, banking, economics, electronic commerce (e-commerce), entrepreneurship, finance, health care, human resources, international management, management, management information systems, marketing, nonprofit management, operations management, organizational behavior/development, supply chain management, technology management.

MIM/MBA—Master of International Management/Master of Business Administration Full-time. 66 to 78 total credits required. 21 to 24 months to complete program. *Concentrations:* accounting, banking, economics, electronic commerce (e-commerce), entrepreneurship, finance, health care, human resources, international management, management, management information systems, marketing, nonprofit management, operations management, organizational behavior/development, supply chain management, technology management.

MSM-ORM-OR/MBA—Master of Science in Management in Operations Research/Master of Business Administration Full-time and part-time. At least 36 total credits required. 11 to 60 months to complete program. *Concentrations:* accounting, banking, economics, electronic commerce (e-commerce), entrepreneurship, finance, health care, human resources, international management, management, management information systems, marketing, nonprofit management, operations management, organizational behavior/development, supply chain management, technology management.

MSM-SC/MBA—Master of Science in Management in Supply Chain/Master of Business Administration Full-time and part-time. At least 36 total credits required. 11 to 60 months to complete program. *Concentrations:* accounting, banking, economics, electronic commerce (e-commerce), entrepreneurship, finance, health care, human resources, international management, management, management information systems, marketing, nonprofit management, operations management, organizational behavior/development, supply chain management, technology management.

MSMIS—Master of Science in Management Information Systems Full-time and part-time. At least 42 total credits required. 11 to 21 months to complete program. *Concentrations:* management information systems.

COSTS
Tuition *Full-time:* $22,900. *Part-time:* $955 per credit hour. Tuition varies by class time, number of courses or credits taken, and academic program. **Graduate housing:** Room and board costs vary by campus location, number of occupants, type of accommodation, and type of board plan. *Typical cost:* $12,175 (including board), $9340 (room only).

FINANCIAL AID (1999–2000)
1,000 students received aid, including fellowships, grants, loans, scholarships, and work study. Financial aid application deadline: 3/16. **Financial Aid Contact** Ms. Pam Chamar, Assistant Director, Academic Support Services, Weatherhead School of Management, 10900 Euclid Avenue, Cleveland, OH 44106-7235. **Phone:** 216-368-2030 Ext. 5098. **Fax:** 216-368-0703. **E-mail:** pxc3@po.cwru.edu.

RESOURCES AND SERVICES
Information about online services, personal computer policies, library resources, international exchange programs, internship programs, and placement services at this institution and others can be found at www.petersons.com/mba

International Students
25% of students enrolled are international students.

Services and Facilities Counseling/support services, ESL/language courses, housing location assistance, international student organization, orientation, visa services, special pre-mba language and culture course. Financial aid is available to international students.

Applying *Required:* TOEFL with recommended score of 243 (computer) or 590 (paper), proof of adequate funds, proof of health/immunizations.

International Student Contact Mr. Todd Llyod, Associate Director of Admissions and International Programs, Weatherhead School of Management, 10900 Euclid Avenue, 310 Enterprise Hall, Cleveland, OH 44106-7235. **Phone:** 216-368-2030 Ext. 6992. **Fax:** 216-368-5548. **E-mail:** tll9@po.cwru.edu.

■ APPLICATION
Required GMAT, application form, baccalaureate/first degree, essay, interview, 2 letters of recommendation, resume/curriculum vitae, transcripts of college work, 2 years of work experience.

Deadlines and Fees *Deadlines:* 4/13 for fall, 12/1 for spring, 4/13 for summer, 3/16 for fall (international), 3/16 for summer (international). *Application fee:* $50, $50 (international).

Case Western Reserve University (continued)

Application Contact Ms. Christine Gill, Director of Marketing and Admissions, 10900 Euclid Avenue, 310 Enterprise Hall, Cleveland, OH 44106-7235. **Phone:** 216-368-2030 Ext. 3761. **Fax:** 216-368-5548. **E-mail:** questions@exchange.som.cwru.edu.

See full description on page 586.

Cleveland State University

Cleveland, Ohio

JAMES J. NANCE COLLEGE OF BUSINESS ADMINISTRATION

Graduate Business Faculty
Full-time: 80

Student Body
Total: 979	Average Age: 28
Full-time: 162	Women: 39%
Part-time: 817	

Admissions
Applications: 520	Average GMAT: 513
Admitted: 461	Average GPA: 3.12
Enrolled: 285	

Costs (1999–2000)
Full-time tuition: $5590 per academic year (resident), $11,050 per academic year (nonresident)
Part-time tuition: $215 per credit hour (resident), $425 per credit hour (nonresident)

After Graduation (Class of 1998–99)
Employed within 3 months of graduation: 92%
Average starting salary: $52,000

Accreditation
AACSB—The International Association for Management Education

DEGREES JD/MBA • MAFIS • MBA • MCIS • MLRHR

JD/MBA—Juris Doctor/Master of Business Administration Full-time and part-time. 110 to 139 total credits required. 42 to 72 months to complete program. *Concentrations:* legal administration, management.

MAFIS—Master of Accountancy and Financial Information Systems Full-time and part-time. 33 to 79 total credits required. 12 to 72 months to complete program. *Concentrations:* actuarial science, financial information systems, management information systems.

MBA—Accelerated MBA Part-time. At least 31 total credits required. Minimum of 12 months to complete program. *Concentrations:* finance, human resources, management, marketing, organizational behavior/development.

MBA—Executive MBA Part-time. At least 54 total credits required. Minimum of 22 months to complete program. *Concentrations:* management.

MBA—Master of Business Administration in Health Administration Full-time and part-time. 34 to 66 total credits required. 12 to 72 months to complete program. *Concentrations:* organizational behavior/development, organizational management, public and private management, public management.

MBA—Master of Business Administration Full-time and part-time. 31 to 69 total credits required. 6 to 72 months to complete program. *Concentrations:* accounting, advertising, banking, finance, human resources, industrial/labor relations, information management, international and area business studies, management, management information systems, marketing, operations management, organizational behavior/development, quality management, real estate.

MCIS—Master of Computer and Information Science Full-time and part-time. 30 to 57 total credits required. 12 to 72 months to complete program. *Concentrations:* business information science, information management, management information systems, technology management.

MLRHR—Master of Labor Relations and Human Resources Full-time and part-time. 34 to 46 total credits required. 12 to 72 months to complete program. *Concentrations:* human resources, industrial/labor relations, management, organizational behavior/development, organizational management.

COSTS

Tuition, state resident: *Full-time* $5590. *Part-time* $215 per credit hour. **Tuition, nonresident:** *Full-time* $11,050. *Part-time* $425 per credit hour. **Required fees:** Tuition and fees vary by number of courses or credits taken. **Graduate housing:** Room and board costs vary by number of occupants and type of board plan. *Typical cost:* $7200 (including board).

FINANCIAL AID (1999–2000)

Research assistantships and work study. **Financial Aid Contact** Director, Financial Aid, 2344 Euclid Avenue, Cleveland, OH 44115. **Phone:** 216-687-3764. **Fax:** 216-687-9247.

RESOURCES AND SERVICES

Information about online services, personal computer policies, library resources, international exchange programs, internship programs, and placement services at this institution and others can be found at **www.petersons.com/mba**

International Students

22% of students enrolled are international students.

Services and Facilities Counseling/support services, ESL/language courses, housing location assistance, international student organization, orientation, visa services. Financial aid is available to international students.
Applying *Required:* TOEFL with recommended score of 195 (computer) or 525 (paper), proof of adequate funds, proof of health/immunizations. *Recommended:* TSE, TWE.
International Student Contact Mr. George Burke, Director, Center for International Services and Programs, 2344 Euclid Avenue, Room 103, Cleveland, OH 44115. **Phone:** 216-687-5234. **Fax:** 216-687-5441. **E-mail:** gburke@csuohio.edu.

■ APPLICATION

Required GMAT, GRE, application form, baccalaureate/first degree, transcripts of college work.
Deadlines and Fees *Deadlines:* 7/15 for fall, 12/1 for spring, 4/1 for summer, 5/15 for fall (international), 11/1 for spring (international), 3/15 for summer (international). *Application fee:* $25, $25 (international).
Application Contact Mr. Bruce Gottschalk, Administrator, MBA Programs, 1860 East 18th Street, Business Building Room 219, Cleveland, OH 44114. **Phone:** 216-687-3731. **Fax:** 216-687-5311. **E-mail:** b.gottschalk@csuohio.edu.

See full description on page 602.

Franciscan University of Steubenville

Steubenville, Ohio

DEPARTMENT OF BUSINESS

Graduate Business Faculty
Full-time: 8	Part-time: 4

Student Body
Total: 61	Part-time: 56
Full-time: 5	Women: 41%

Admissions
Applications: 21	Average GMAT: 473
Admitted: 20	Average GPA: 3
Enrolled: 18	

Costs (1999–2000)
Full-time tuition: N/R
Part-time tuition: $280 per credit

DEGREE MBA

MBA—Master of Business Administration Full-time and part-time. At least 40 total credits required. Minimum of 15 months to complete program. *Concentrations:* accounting.

COSTS

Tuition *Part-time:* $280 per credit. **Graduate housing:** Room and board costs vary by type of board plan. *Typical cost:* $5070 (including board), $2400 (room only).

FINANCIAL AID (1999–2000)

39 students received aid, including grants, loans, scholarships, and work study. Aid is available to part-time students. Financial aid application deadline: 7/1. **Financial Aid Contact** Mr. John Herrmann, Associate Director, Financial Aid, Enrollment Services, 1235 University Boulevard, Steubenville, OH 43952-1763. **Phone:** 740-283-6211. **Fax:** 740-284-5456. **E-mail:** jherrmann@franuniv.edu.

RESOURCES AND SERVICES

Information about online services, personal computer policies, library resources, international exchange programs, internship programs, and

placement services at this institution and others can be found at **www. petersons.com/mba**

International Students
2% of students enrolled are international students.

Services and Facilities Counseling/support services, housing location assistance, international student organization, language tutoring, orientation. Financial aid is available to international students.
Applying *Required:* TOEFL with recommended score of 550 (paper), proof of adequate funds.
International Student Contact Mr. Mark McGuire, Director of Graduate Enrollment, Admissions Department, University Boulevard, Steubenville, OH 43952-1763. **Phone:** 740-283-6226 Ext. 6461. **Fax:** 740-284-5456. **E-mail:** mmcguire@franuniv.edu.

■ APPLICATION
Required Application form, baccalaureate/first degree, 3 letters of recommendation, personal statement, transcripts of college work. School will accept GMAT. **Recommended** Essay, interview, resume/curriculum vitae.
Deadlines and Fees *Application fee:* $20, $20 (international).
Application Contact Mr. Mark McGuire, Director of Graduate Enrollment, Admissions Department, University Boulevard, Steubenville, OH 43952-6701. **Phone:** 740-283-6226 Ext. 6461. **Toll-free Phone:** 800-783-6220. **Fax:** 740-284-5456. **E-mail:** mmcguire@franuniv.edu.

Franklin University
Columbus, Ohio

GRADUATE SCHOOL OF BUSINESS

Graduate Business Faculty

Full-time: 10	Part-time: 15

Student Body

Total: 661	Average Age: 34
Full-time: 465	Women: 51%
Part-time: 196	

Admissions

Applications: 303	Enrolled: 194
Admitted: 257	

Costs (1999–2000)
Full-time tuition: $6165 per academic year
Part-time tuition: $290 per credit

DEGREES MBA • MS

MBA—Master of Business Administration Full-time and part-time. *Distance learning option.* At least 42 total credits required. 17 to 24 months to complete program. *Concentrations:* health care, international business, organizational management, technology management.

MS—Master of Science in Human Services Management Full-time and part-time. At least 38 total credits required. Minimum of 24 months to complete program.

MS—Master of Science in Marketing and Communication Full-time and part-time. At least 36 total credits required. Minimum of 24 months to complete program.

COSTS
Tuition *Full-time:* $6090. *Part-time:* $290 per credit. **Tuition, international:** *Full-time* $6090. **Required fees:** *Full-time* $75. *Part-time* $25 per trimester.

FINANCIAL AID (1999–2000)
225 students received aid, including loans, scholarships, and work study. Financial aid application deadline: 5/30. **Financial Aid Contact** Karen Smith, Director of Financial Aid, 201 South Grant Avenue, Columbus, OH 43215-5399. **Phone:** 614-341-6303. **Fax:** 614-224-8027. **E-mail:** smithka@franklin.edu.

RESOURCES AND SERVICES
Information about online services, personal computer policies, library resources, international exchange programs, internship programs, and placement services at this institution and others can be found at **www. petersons.com/mba**

International Students
4% of students enrolled are international students.

Services and Facilities Counseling/support services, ESL/language courses. Financial aid is available to international students.

Applying *Required:* TOEFL with recommended score of 550 (paper), proof of adequate funds, proof of health/immunizations.
International Student Contact Patrick Schumer, International Student Services Associate, 201 South Grant Avenue, Columbus, OH 43215. **Phone:** 614-341-6309. **Fax:** 614-224-8027. **E-mail:** schumerp@franklin.edu.

■ APPLICATION
Required Application form, baccalaureate/first degree, essay, 2 letters of recommendation, personal statement, transcripts of college work, 4 years of work experience.
Deadlines and Fees Applications for domestic and international students are processed on a rolling basis. *Application fee:* $30, $40 (international).
Application Contact Jill Bettinger, MBA Student Services Associate, 201 South Grant Avenue, Columbus, OH 43215. **Phone:** 614-341-6398. **Toll-free Phone:** 877-341-6300. **Fax:** 614-221-7723. **E-mail:** bettingj@franklin.edu.

Heidelberg College
Tiffin, Ohio

DEPARTMENT OF BUSINESS ADMINISTRATION

DEGREE MBA

MBA—Graduate Studies in Business Full-time and part-time. At least 37 total credits required. 12 to 72 months to complete program. *Concentrations:* management.

RESOURCES AND SERVICES
Information about online services, personal computer policies, library resources, international exchange programs, internship programs, and placement services at this institution and others can be found at **www. petersons.com/mba**

International Students
Services and Facilities Counseling/support services, ESL/language courses, international student housing.
International Student Contact Mr. Lewis Miller, Director, International Programs, 310 East Market Street, Tiffin, OH 44883. **Phone:** 419-448-2207. **E-mail:** lmiller@heidelberg.edu.

■ APPLICATION
Application Contact Dr. Henry Rennie, Director, Graduate Studies in Business, 310 East Market Street, Tiffin, OH 44883. **Phone:** 419-448-2221. **Fax:** 419-448-2236. **E-mail:** hrennie@heidelberg.edu.

John Carroll University
University Heights, Ohio

JOHN M. AND MARY JO BOLER SCHOOL OF BUSINESS

Accreditation
AACSB—The International Association for Management Education

DEGREE MBA

MBA—Master of Business Administration Full-time and part-time. At least 36 total credits required. 24 to 72 months to complete program. *Concentrations:* accounting, economics, finance, international business, logistics, management, marketing.

RESOURCES AND SERVICES
Information about online services, personal computer policies, library resources, international exchange programs, internship programs, and placement services at this institution and others can be found at **www. petersons.com/mba**

International Students
Services and Facilities Financial aid is not available to international students.

■ APPLICATION
Application Contact Dr. James M. Daley, Associate Dean and Director, MBA Program, 20700 North Park Boulevard, University Heights, OH 44118-4581. **Phone:** 216-397-4507. **Fax:** 216-397-1728. **E-mail:** jdaley@jcvaxa.jcu.edu.

Kent State University

Kent, Ohio

GRADUATE SCHOOL OF MANAGEMENT

Graduate Business Faculty
Full-time: 56   Part-time: 2

Student Body
Total: 432
Full-time: 184   Average Age: 26
Part-time: 248   Women: 41%

Admissions
Applications: 218   Average GMAT: 540
Admitted: 178   Average GPA: 3.25
Enrolled: 88

Costs (1999–2000)
Full-time tuition: $5334 per academic year (resident), $10,238 per academic year (nonresident)
Part-time tuition: $243 per credit (resident), $466 per credit (nonresident)

After Graduation (Class of 1998–99)
Employed within 3 months of graduation: 85%
Average starting salary: $41,300

Accreditation
AACSB—The International Association for Management Education

DEGREES MA • MBA • MBA/MLS • MBA/MS • MS

MA—Master of Arts in Economics Full-time and part-time. At least 30 total credits required. 12 to 72 months to complete program. *Concentrations:* economics, financial economics.

MBA—Executive MBA Full-time. Interview, work experience five (5) years minimum. 45 total credits required. 26 months to complete program.

MBA—Master of Business Administration Full-time and part-time. 39 to 60 total credits required. 12 to 72 months to complete program. *Concentrations:* finance, human resources, international business, management information systems, marketing.

MBA/MLS—Master of Business Administration/Master of Library Science Full-time and part-time. 70 total credits required. 36 to 72 months to complete program.

MBA/MS—Master of Business Administration/Master of Science in Nursing Full-time and part-time. 70 total credits required. 36 to 72 months to complete program.

MS—Master of Science in Accounting Full-time and part-time. 30 to 53 total credits required. 12 to 72 months to complete program. *Concentrations:* accounting.

COSTS

Tuition, state resident: *Full-time* $5334. *Part-time* $243 per credit. **Tuition, nonresident:** *Full-time* $10,238. *Part-time* $466 per credit. **Tuition, international:** *Full-time* $10,238. Tuition varies by number of courses or credits taken and campus location. **Graduate housing:** Room and board costs vary by number of occupants, type of accommodation, and type of board plan. *Typical cost:* $5320 (including board).

FINANCIAL AID (1999–2000)

60 students received aid, including fellowships, loans, research assistantships, teaching assistantships, and work study. Financial aid application deadline: 4/1. **Financial Aid Contact** Ms. Helen Suchy, Assistant Director, Student Financial Aid Office, PO Box 5190, Kent, OH 44242-0001. **Phone:** 330-672-2972. **Fax:** 330-672-4014.

RESOURCES AND SERVICES

Information about online services, personal computer policies, library resources, international exchange programs, internship programs, and placement services at this institution and others can be found at **www. petersons.com/mba**

International Students

13% of students enrolled are international students.
Services and Facilities Counseling/support services, ESL/language courses, international student housing, orientation, visa services. Financial aid is available to international students.
Applying *Required:* TOEFL with recommended score of 213 (computer) or 550 (paper), proof of adequate funds, proof of health/immunizations.

International Student Contact Mr. Ted McKown, II, Assistant Director for International Admissions, Office of Admissions, Kent, OH 44242. **Phone:** 330-672-2444. **Fax:** 330-672-2499. **E-mail:** tmckown@admissions.kent.edu.

■ APPLICATION

Required GMAT, application form, baccalaureate/first degree, essay, 3 letters of recommendation, resume/curriculum vitae, transcripts of college work.
Deadlines and Fees *Deadlines:* 7/1 for fall, 12/15 for spring, 5/15 for summer, 4/1 for fall (international). *Application fee:* $30, $30 (international).
Application Contact Ms. Louise Ditchey, Director, Master's Program, Graduate School of Management, PO Box 5190, Kent, OH 44242-0001. **Phone:** 330-672-2282. **Fax:** 330-672-7303. **E-mail:** gradbus@bsa3.kent.edu.

Lake Erie College

Painesville, Ohio

DIVISION OF MANAGEMENT STUDIES

Graduate Business Faculty
Full-time: 6   Part-time: 4

Student Body
Total: 90   Average Age: 35
Part-time: 90   Women: 66%

Admissions
Applications: 28   Enrolled: 27
Admitted: 28

Costs (1999–2000)
Full-time tuition: $16,102 per academic year
Part-time tuition: $445 per credit hour

After Graduation (Class of 1998–99)
Employed within 3 months of graduation: 98%

DEGREE MBA

MBA—Master of Business Administration Full-time and part-time. At least 36 total credits required. 16 to 84 months to complete program. *Concentrations:* health care, management.

COSTS

Tuition *Full-time:* $15,210. *Part-time:* $415 per credit hour. **Required fees:** *Full-time* $892. *Part-time* $30 per credit hour. **Graduate housing:** *Typical cost:* $5260 (including board), $2900 (room only).

FINANCIAL AID (1999–2000)

Financial Aid Contact Mrs. Ann Marie Gruber, Director of Financial Aid, 391 West Washington Street, Painesville, OH 44077-3389. **Phone:** 440-639-7814. **Fax:** 440-352-3533. **E-mail:** rford@lec.edu.

RESOURCES AND SERVICES

Information about online services, personal computer policies, library resources, international exchange programs, internship programs, and placement services at this institution and others can be found at **www. petersons.com/mba**

International Students

Services and Facilities Counseling/support services. Financial aid is not available to international students.
Applying *Required:* TOEFL with recommended score of 590 (paper), proof of adequate funds, proof of health/immunizations.

International Student Contact Dr. Maria de la Camara, Associate Dean of Arts and Sciences, 391 West Washington Street, Painesville, OH 44077-3389. **Phone:** 440-639-7854. **Fax:** 440-352-3533. **E-mail:** dlcamara@lakeerie.edu.

■ APPLICATION

Required Application form, baccalaureate/first degree, essay, interview, personal statement, resume/curriculum vitae, transcripts of college work, 2 years of work experience.
Deadlines and Fees Applications for domestic and international students are processed on a rolling basis. *Application fee:* $25, $25 (international).
Application Contact Mrs. Susan Fogarty, Associate Director of Admissions, 391 West Washington Street, Painesville, OH 44077-3389. **Phone:** 440-639-7882. **Toll-free Phone:** 800-916-0904. **Fax:** 440-352-3533. **E-mail:** sfogarty@lec.edu.

Malone College

Canton, Ohio

GRADUATE SCHOOL

Graduate Business Faculty
Full-time: 10   Part-time: 3

Student Body
Total: 89   Average Age: 37

Costs (1999–2000)
Full-time tuition: N/R
Part-time tuition: $350 per credit

DEGREE MBA

MBA—Master of Business Administration Part-time. At least 37 total credits required. Minimum of 24 months to complete program.

COSTS

Tuition *Part-time:* $350 per credit.

FINANCIAL AID (1999–2000)

Loans. Aid is available to part-time students. Financial aid application deadline: 8/1. **Financial Aid Contact** Mr. Mike Bole, Financial Aid Office, 515 25th Street, NW, Canton, OH 44709-3897. **Phone:** 330-471-8160. **Fax:** 330-471-8478. **E-mail:** gradschool@malone.edu.

RESOURCES AND SERVICES

Information about online services, personal computer policies, library resources, international exchange programs, internship programs, and placement services at this institution and others can be found at **www. petersons.com/mba**

■ APPLICATION

Required GMAT, application form, baccalaureate/first degree, interview, 2 letters of recommendation, transcripts of college work. School will accept GRE. **Recommended** Work experience.

Deadlines and Fees Applications for domestic and international students are processed on a rolling basis. *Application fee:* $20, $20 (international).

Application Contact Mr. Dan DePasquale, Director of Graduate Student Services, 515 25th Street, NW, Canton, OH 44709-3897. **Phone:** 800-257-4723 Ext. 8381. **Fax:** 330-471-8343. **E-mail:** gradschool@malone.edu.

The McGregor School of Antioch University

Yellow Springs, Ohio

DEPARTMENT OF MANAGEMENT

Graduate Business Faculty
Full-time: 4   Part-time: 22

Student Body
Total: 80   Average Age: 33
Full-time: 80   Women: 60%

Admissions
Enrolled: 25   Average GPA: 3.1

Costs (1999–2000)
Full-time tuition: $9344 per academic year
Part-time tuition: N/R

After Graduation (Class of 1998–99)
Employed within 3 months of graduation: 98%

DEGREE MA

MA—Master of Arts in Management Full-time. 64 total credits required. 18 months to complete program. *Concentrations:* management.

COSTS

Tuition *Full-time:* $9344.

FINANCIAL AID (1999–2000)

Financial Aid Contact Ms. Kathy John, Financial Aid Director, 800 Livermore Street, Yellow Springs, OH 45387-1609. **Phone:** 973-767-6321 Ext. 6778. **Fax:** 937-767-6461. **E-mail:** kjohn@mcgregor.antioch.edu.

RESOURCES AND SERVICES

Information about online services, personal computer policies, library resources, international exchange programs, internship programs, and placement services at this institution and others can be found at **www. petersons.com/mba**

International Students

8% of students enrolled are international students.

Services and Facilities Financial aid is not available to international students. **International Student Contact** Mrs. Carol Hangan, Admissions Officer, Office of Admissions, 800 Livermore Street, Yellow Springs, OH 45387-1609. **Phone:** 937-767-6321 Ext. 6940. **Fax:** 937-767-6461. **E-mail:** changan@mcgregor. edu.

■ APPLICATION

Required Application form, baccalaureate/first degree, interview, 2 letters of recommendation, personal statement, transcripts of college work, 3 years of work experience. **Recommended** Resume/curriculum vitae.

Deadlines and Fees *Application fee:* $50, $50 (international).

Application Contact Mrs. Carol Hangan, Admissions Officer, Office of Admissions, 800 Livermore Street, Yellow Springs, OH 45387-1609. **Phone:** 937-767-6321 Ext. 6940. **Fax:** 937-767-6461. **E-mail:** changan@mcgregor.edu.

Miami University

Oxford, Ohio

RICHARD T. FARMER SCHOOL OF BUSINESS ADMINISTRATION

Graduate Business Faculty
Full-time: 100   Part-time: 8

Student Body
Total: 104   Average Age: 26
Full-time: 53   Women: 38%
Part-time: 51

Admissions
Applications: 177   Average GMAT: 560
Admitted: 81   Average GPA: 3.12
Enrolled: 51

Costs (1999–2000)
Full-time tuition: $7316 per academic year (resident), $13,970 per academic year (nonresident)
Part-time tuition: $278 per credit (resident), $555 per credit (nonresident)

After Graduation (Class of 1998–99)
Employed within 3 months of graduation: 81%
Average starting salary: $45,823

Accreditation
AACSB—The International Association for Management Education

DEGREES M Acc • MA • MBA

M Acc—Master of Accountancy Full-time. At least 30 total credits required. 12 months to complete program. *Concentrations:* accounting.

MA—Master of Arts in Economics Full-time. At least 30 total credits required. 12 months to complete program. *Concentrations:* economics.

MBA—Master of Business Administration Full-time and part-time. 37 to 58 total credits required. 12 to 36 months to complete program. *Concentrations:* finance, management, management information systems, marketing.

COSTS

Tuition, state resident: *Full-time* $5190. *Part-time* $216 per credit. **Tuition, nonresident:** *Full-time* $11,844. *Part-time* $493 per credit. **Required fees:** *Full-time* $2126. *Part-time* $62 per credit. Tuition and fees vary by number of courses or credits taken and campus location. **Graduate housing:** Room and board costs vary by number of occupants, type of accommodation, and type of board plan. *Typical cost:* $3735 (room only).

FINANCIAL AID (1999–2000)

82 students received aid, including fellowships, loans, and research assistantships. Financial aid application deadline: 3/1. **Financial Aid Contact** Mrs. Judy Barille, Director of MBA Programs, Richard T. Farmer School of Business Administration, Oxford, OH 45056. **Phone:** 513-529-6643. **Fax:** 513-529-2487. **E-mail:** barillja@muohio.edu.

RESOURCES AND SERVICES

Information about online services, personal computer policies, library resources, international exchange programs, internship programs, and

Miami University (continued)

placement services at this institution and others can be found at **www. petersons.com/mba**

International Students

17% of students enrolled are international students.

Services and Facilities Counseling/support services, ESL/language courses, housing location assistance, international student housing, international student organization, orientation, visa services. Financial aid is available to international students.

Applying *Required:* TOEFL with recommended score of 220 (computer) or 550 (paper), TWE with recommended score of 4, proof of adequate funds, proof of health/immunizations.

International Student Contact Mr. Donald Nelson, Director, International Programs, Langstroth House, Oxford, OH 45056. **Phone:** 513-529-5628. **Fax:** 513-529-7383.

■ APPLICATION

Required GMAT, application form, baccalaureate/first degree, essay, interview, 2 letters of recommendation, resume/curriculum vitae, transcripts of college work. School will accept GRE. **Recommended** Personal statement, work experience.

Deadlines and Fees *Deadlines:* 7/15 for fall, 12/1 for spring, 4/15 for summer, 7/1 for fall (international). *Application fee:* $35, $35 (international).

Application Contact Mrs. Judy Barille, Director of MBA Programs, Richard T. Farmer School of Business Administration, Oxford, OH 45056. **Phone:** 513-529-6643. **Fax:** 513-529-2487. **E-mail:** barillja@muohio.edu.

The Ohio State University

Columbus, Ohio

MAX M. FISHER COLLEGE OF BUSINESS

Graduate Business Faculty
Full-time: 95

Part-time: 5

Student Body
Total: 468
Full-time: 285
Part-time: 183

Average Age: 28
Women: 30%

Admissions
Applications: 1,235
Admitted: 405
Enrolled: 249

Average GMAT: 638
Average GPA: 3.26

Costs (1999–2000)
Full-time tuition: $6744 per academic year (resident), $15,879 per academic year (nonresident)
Part-time tuition: N/R

After Graduation (Class of 1998–99)
Employed within 3 months of graduation: 98%
Average starting salary: $77,111

Accreditation
AACSB—The International Association for Management Education

DEGREES MBA • MLHR

MBA—Evening MBA Part-time. At least 60 total credits required. 21 months to complete program.

MBA—Full-time MBA Full-time. At least 96 total credits required. 18 to 22 months to complete program. *Concentrations:* accounting, finance, human resources, international business, logistics, management consulting, management information systems, marketing, operations management, real estate.

MLHR—Master of Labor and Human Resources Full-time and part-time. 45 to 50 total credits required. 12 to 15 months to complete program.

COSTS

Tuition, state resident: *Full-time* $6744. **Tuition, nonresident:** *Full-time* $15,879. Tuition varies by number of courses or credits taken and academic program. **Graduate housing:** Room and board costs vary by campus location, number of occupants, type of accommodation, and type of board plan. *Typical cost:* $7000 (including board).

FINANCIAL AID (1999–2000)

78 students received aid, including fellowships, loans, research assistantships, scholarships, teaching assistantships, and work study. Financial aid application deadline: 1/15. **Financial Aid Contact** Ms. Michelle Jacobson, Interim Director, Graduate Programs Office, 2108 Neil

Avenue, Gerlach Hall, Columbus, OH 43210. **Phone:** 614-292-8511. **Fax:** 614-292-9006. **E-mail:** jacobson.1@osu.edu.

RESOURCES AND SERVICES

Information about online services, personal computer policies, library resources, international exchange programs, internship programs, and placement services at this institution and others can be found at **www. petersons.com/mba**

International Students

22% of students enrolled are international students.

Services and Facilities Counseling/support services, ESL/language courses, international student housing, international student organization, visa services. Financial aid is available to international students.

Applying *Required:* TOEFL with recommended score of 240 (computer) or 600 (paper), proof of adequate funds, proof of health/immunizations.

International Student Contact Mr. John Greisberger, Director-International Education, Oxley Hall, 1712 Neil Avenue, Columbus, OH 43210. **Phone:** 614-292-6101. **Fax:** 614-292-4725. **E-mail:** greisberger.1@osu.edu.

■ APPLICATION

Required GMAT, application form, baccalaureate/first degree, essay, 3 letters of recommendation, personal statement, resume/curriculum vitae, transcripts of college work. **Recommended** Interview, 3 years of work experience.

Deadlines and Fees *Deadlines:* 4/30 for fall, 4/30 for fall (international). *Application fee:* $30, $40 (international).

Application Contact Ms. Laura Lembo, Associate Director, Recruitment and Admissions, 2108 Neil Avenue, 100 Gerlach Hall, Columbus, OH 43210. **Phone:** 614-292-8511. **Fax:** 614-292-9006. **E-mail:** cobgrd@cob.ohio-state.edu.

Ohio University

Athens, Ohio

COLLEGE OF BUSINESS

Graduate Business Faculty
Full-time: 58

Part-time: 10

Student Body
Total: 93
Full-time: 53
Part-time: 40

Average Age: 25
Women: 33%

Admissions
Applications: 178
Admitted: 113
Enrolled: 53

Average GMAT: 536
Average GPA: 3.38

Costs (1999–2000)
Full-time tuition: $7672 per academic year (resident), $13,236 per academic year (nonresident)
Part-time tuition: $238 per credit hour (resident), $457 per credit hour (nonresident)

After Graduation (Class of 1998–99)
Employed within 3 months of graduation: 97%

Accreditation
AACSB—The International Association for Management Education

DEGREES MBA • MS

MBA—Executive MBA Part-time. At least 64 total credits required. 21 months to complete program.

MBA—MBA Without Boundaries Part-time. *Distance learning option.* At least 72 total credits required. 24 months to complete program.

MBA—Master of Business Administration Full-time. At least 72 total credits required. 12 to 15 months to complete program.

MS—Master of Science in Accountancy Full-time and part-time. At least 48 total credits required. 9 months to complete program.

COSTS

Tuition, state resident: *Full-time* $7672. *Part-time* $238 per credit hour. **Tuition, nonresident:** *Full-time* $13,236. *Part-time* $457 per credit hour. Tuition varies by number of courses or credits taken. **Required fees:** Fees vary by number of courses or credits taken and campus location. **Graduate housing:** Room and board costs vary by number of occupants, type of accommodation, and type of board plan. *Typical cost:* $5680 (including board).

FINANCIAL AID (1999–2000)

48 students received aid, including loans, scholarships, teaching assistantships, and work study. Financial aid application deadline: 3/1. **Financial Aid Contact** Ms. Jan Ross, Assistant Director, Copeland Hall 514, Athens, OH 45701-2979. **Phone:** 740-593-2007. **Fax:** 740-597-2995. **E-mail:** rossj@ohiou.edu.

RESOURCES AND SERVICES

Information about online services, personal computer policies, library resources, international exchange programs, internship programs, and placement services at this institution and others can be found at **www.petersons.com/mba**

International Students

23% of students enrolled are international students.

Services and Facilities Counseling/support services, ESL/language courses, orientation. Financial aid is available to international students.
Applying *Required:* TOEFL with recommended score of 600 (paper), proof of adequate funds. *Recommended:* TWE.

International Student Contact Dr. Alan Boyd, Director, International Student and Faculty Services, Scott Quad 172, Athens, OH 45701-2979. **Phone:** 740-593-4330. **Fax:** 740-593-4328.

■ APPLICATION

Required GMAT, application form, baccalaureate/first degree, essay, 3 letters of recommendation, transcripts of college work. **Recommended** Interview, personal statement, resume/curriculum vitae, 2 years of work experience.
Deadlines and Fees *Deadlines:* 3/1 for fall, 3/1 for fall (international). *Application fee:* $30, $30 (international).

Application Contact Ms. Jan Ross, Assistant Director, Graduate Programs, Copeland Hall 514, Athens, OH 45701-2979. **Phone:** 740-593-2007. **Fax:** 740-597-2995. **E-mail:** rossj@ohiou.edu.

See full description on page 756.

Otterbein College

Westerville, Ohio

DEPARTMENT OF BUSINESS, ACCOUNTING AND ECONOMICS

Graduate Business Faculty
Full-time: 9   Part-time: 10

Student Body
Total: 171   Average Age: 32

Admissions
Applications: 76   Average GMAT: 530
Admitted: 61   Average GPA: 3.14

Costs (1999–2000)
Full-time tuition: N/R
Part-time tuition: $210 per credit

DEGREE MBA

MBA—Master of Business Administration Full-time and part-time. At least 64 total credits required. Minimum of 24 months to complete program.

COSTS

Tuition *Part-time:* $210 per credit.

FINANCIAL AID (1999–2000)

Loans. Aid is available to part-time students. **Financial Aid Contact** Financial Aid Office, Westerville, OH 43081-2006. **Phone:** 614-823-1502.

RESOURCES AND SERVICES

Information about online services, personal computer policies, library resources, international exchange programs, internship programs, and placement services at this institution and others can be found at **www.petersons.com/mba**

International Students

8% of students enrolled are international students.

Services and Facilities Counseling/support services, ESL/language courses, international student organization, orientation, visa services.
Applying *Required:* TOEFL with recommended score of 550 (paper). *Recommended:* Proof of adequate funds, proof of health/immunizations.

International Student Contact Charles Vedder, Director of International Student Programs, Student Affairs Office, Westerville, OH 43081-2006. **Phone:** 614-823-1312. **Fax:** 614-823-3299. **E-mail:** cvedder@otterbein.edu.

■ APPLICATION

Required GMAT, application form, baccalaureate/first degree, 3 letters of recommendation, personal statement, resume/curriculum vitae, transcripts of college work, work experience. **Recommended** Interview.
Deadlines and Fees *Application fee:* $35, $35 (international).

Application Contact Peggy Sibila, Assistant Director, Graduate Programs Office, One Otterbein College, 208 Roush Hall, Westerville, OH 43081. **Phone:** 614-823-3270. **Fax:** 614-823-3208. **E-mail:** psibila@otterbein.edu.

Tiffin University

Tiffin, Ohio

PROGRAM IN BUSINESS ADMINISTRATION

Graduate Business Faculty
Full-time: 17   Part-time: 5

Student Body
Total: 144   Average Age: 30
Full-time: 126   Women: 35%
Part-time: 18

Admissions
Applications: 270   Enrolled: 164
Admitted: 170   Average GPA: 3.4

Costs (1999–2000)
Full-time tuition: $6600 per academic year
Part-time tuition: N/R

After Graduation (Class of 1998–99)
Employed within 3 months of graduation: 100%
Average starting salary: $34,500

Accreditation
ACBSP—The American Council of Business Schools and Programs

DEGREE MBA

MBA—Executive Management MBA Full-time and part-time. At least 33 total credits required. 24 to 72 months to complete program. *Concentrations:* management.

COSTS

Tuition *Full-time:* $6600. **Required fees:** Tuition and fees vary by number of courses or credits taken.

FINANCIAL AID (1999–2000)

40 students received aid, including loans. Aid is available to part-time students. Financial aid application deadline: 7/31. **Financial Aid Contact** Ms. Deb Brickner, Director of Financial Aid, 155 Miami Street, Tiffin, OH 44883-2161. **Phone:** 800-968-6446 Ext. 3357. **Fax:** 419-443-5006. **E-mail:** dbrickner@tiffin.edu.

RESOURCES AND SERVICES

Information about online services, personal computer policies, library resources, international exchange programs, internship programs, and placement services at this institution and others can be found at **www.petersons.com/mba**

International Students

9% of students enrolled are international students.

Services and Facilities Counseling/support services, international student housing. Financial aid is not available to international students.
Applying *Required:* TOEFL with recommended score of 550 (paper), proof of adequate funds, proof of health/immunizations.

International Student Contact Ms. Alice Nichols, Registrar, 155 Miami Street, Tiffin, OH 44883-2161. **Phone:** 800-968-6446 Ext. 3416. **Fax:** 419-443-5006. **E-mail:** anichols@tiffin.edu.

■ APPLICATION

Required Application form, baccalaureate/first degree, essay, personal statement, transcripts of college work. **Recommended** Interview, resume/curriculum vitae, work experience.
Deadlines and Fees *Deadlines:* 8/1 for fall, 12/1 for spring, 7/1 for fall (international). *Application fee:* $30, $30 (international).

Application Contact Mr. Darby Roggow, Director of Graduate Studies, 155 Miami Street, Tiffin, OH 44883-2161. **Phone:** 419-448-3310. **Toll-free Phone:** 800-968-6446 Ext. 3310. **Fax:** 419-443-5002. **E-mail:** droggow@tiffin.edu.

The University of Akron

Akron, Ohio

COLLEGE OF BUSINESS ADMINISTRATION

Graduate Business Faculty
Full-time: 46   Part-time: 9

Student Body
Total: 470
Full-time: 182   Average Age: 30
Part-time: 288   Women: 36%

Admissions
Applications: 307   Average GMAT: 570
Admitted: 239   Average GPA: 3.2
Enrolled: 143

Costs (1999–2000)
Full-time tuition: N/R
Part-time tuition: $186 per credit (resident), $353 per credit
(nonresident)

After Graduation (Class of 1998–99)
Average starting salary: $51,223

Accreditation
AACSB—The International Association for Management Education

DEGREES JD/M Tax • JD/MBA • M Tax • MBA • MSA • MSM

JD/M Tax—Juris Doctor/Master of Taxation Full-time and part-time. 98 to 116 total credits required. 36 to 96 months to complete program. *Concentrations:* taxation.

JD/MBA—Juris Doctor/Master of Business Administration Full-time and part-time. 103 to 124 total credits required. 36 to 96 months to complete program. *Concentrations:* accounting, entrepreneurship, finance, health care, international business, management, marketing.

M Tax—Master of Taxation Full-time and part-time. 30 to 48 total credits required. 12 to 72 months to complete program. *Concentrations:* taxation.

MBA—Master of Business Administration Full-time and part-time. 34 to 58 total credits required. 12 to 72 months to complete program. *Concentrations:* accounting, electronic commerce (e-commerce), entrepreneurship, finance, health care, international business, international finance, management, marketing, materials management, supply chain management, technology management.

MSA—Master of Science in Accountancy Full-time and part-time. 33 to 57 total credits required. 12 to 72 months to complete program. *Concentrations:* accounting.

MSM—Master of Science in Management Full-time and part-time. 33 to 57 total credits required. 12 to 72 months to complete program. *Concentrations:* human resources, management information systems.

COSTS

Tuition, state resident: *Part-time* $186 per credit. **Tuition, nonresident:** *Part-time* $353 per credit. **Required fees:** *Full-time* $22. *Part-time* $22 per year. Tuition and fees vary by number of courses or credits taken.

FINANCIAL AID (1999–2000)

90 students received aid, including fellowships, research assistantships, scholarships, teaching assistantships, and work study. Aid is available to part-time students. Financial aid application deadline: 3/15. **Financial Aid Contact** Miss Myra Weakland, Assistant Director, Graduate Programs in Business, 259 South Broadway, Room 412, Akron, OH 44325-4805. **Phone:** 330-972-7043. **Fax:** 330-972-6588. **E-mail:** gradcba@uakron. edu.

RESOURCES AND SERVICES

Information about online services, personal computer policies, library resources, international exchange programs, internship programs, and placement services at this institution and others can be found at **www. petersons.com/mba**

International Students

21% of students enrolled are international students.
Services and Facilities Counseling/support services, ESL/language courses, housing location assistance, international student housing, international student organization, language tutoring, orientation, visa services. Financial aid is available to international students.
Applying *Required:* TOEFL with recommended score of 213 (computer) or 550 (paper), proof of adequate funds, proof of health/immunizations. *Recommended:* TSE with recommended score of 50.

International Student Contact Ms. Theresa M. McCune, Admissions Credentials Evaluator, International Programs, Akron, OH 44325-3101. **Phone:** 330-972-6349. **Fax:** 330-972-8604. **E-mail:** international@uakron.edu.

■ APPLICATION

Required GMAT, application form, baccalaureate/first degree, 2 letters of recommendation, personal statement, resume/curriculum vitae, transcripts of college work. **Recommended** Essay, work experience.
Deadlines and Fees *Deadlines:* 8/1 for fall, 12/15 for spring, 6/1 for summer, 6/15 for fall (international), 11/1 for spring (international), 4/1 for summer (international). *Application fee:* $25, $50 (international).
Application Contact Miss Myra Weakland, Assistant Director, Graduate Programs in Business, 259 South Broadway, Room 412, Akron, OH 44325-4805. **Phone:** 330-972-7043. **Fax:** 330-972-6588. **E-mail:** gradcba@uakron.edu.

University of Cincinnati

Cincinnati, Ohio

COLLEGE OF BUSINESS ADMINISTRATION

Accreditation
AACSB—The International Association for Management Education

DEGREES JD/MBA • MBA • MBA/MA • MBA/MS • MD/MBA • MS

JD/MBA—Juris Doctor/Master of Business Administration Full-time. At least 134 total credits required. 42 to 84 months to complete program.

MBA—Master of Business Administration Full-time and part-time. At least 66 total credits required. 12 to 52 months to complete program. *Concentrations:* construction management, finance, information management, international business, management, marketing, operations management, quantitative analysis, real estate, technology management.

MBA/MA—Master of Business Administration/Master of Arts in Arts Administration Full-time and part-time. At least 122 total credits required. 36 to 84 months to complete program.

MBA/MS—Master of Business Administration/Master of Science in Industrial Engineering Full-time and part-time. At least 87 total credits required. 24 to 84 months to complete program.

MD/MBA—Doctor of Medicine/Master of Business Administration Full-time. At least 147 total credits required. 60 months to complete program.

MS—Master of Science in Quantitative Analysis Full-time and part-time. At least 45 total credits required. 12 to 24 months to complete program.

RESOURCES AND SERVICES

Information about online services, personal computer policies, library resources, international exchange programs, internship programs, and placement services at this institution and others can be found at **www. petersons.com/mba**

International Students

Services and Facilities Counseling/support services, international student housing, visa services. Financial aid is available to international students.
International Student Contact Ms. Penny Chapman, Academic Advisor, 103 Lindner Hall, Cincinnati, OH 45221. **Phone:** 513-556-7022. **Fax:** 513-556-4891. **E-mail:** penny.chapman@uc.edu.

■ APPLICATION

Application Contact Ms. Julie Dixon, Assistant Dean of Graduate Programs, 103 Lindner Hall, Cincinnati, OH 45221-0020. **Phone:** 513-556-7024. **Toll-free Phone:** 888-738-2622. **Fax:** 513-556-4891. **E-mail:** julie.dixon@uc.edu.

University of Dayton

Dayton, Ohio

SCHOOL OF BUSINESS ADMINISTRATION

Graduate Business Faculty
Full-time: 55   Part-time: 21

Student Body
Total: 437
Full-time: 178   Average Age: 29
Part-time: 259   Women: 39%

Admissions
Applications: 140   Average GMAT: 549
Admitted: 126   Average GPA: 3.07
Enrolled: 101

Costs (1999–2000)
Full-time tuition: $7920 per academic year
Part-time tuition: $440 per credit

After Graduation (Class of 1998–99)
Employed within 3 months of graduation: 95%

Accreditation
AACSB—The International Association for Management Education

DEGREES JD/MBA • MBA

JD/MBA—Juris Doctor/Master of Business Administration Full-time and part-time. 105 to 127 total credits required. 42 to 60 months to complete program. *Concentrations:* accounting, finance, international business, management information systems, marketing, operations management.

MBA—Master of Business Administration Full-time and part-time. 30 to 52 total credits required. 12 to 60 months to complete program. *Concentrations:* accounting, finance, international business, management information systems, marketing, operations management.

COSTS
Tuition *Full-time:* $7920. *Part-time:* $440 per credit. Tuition varies by number of courses or credits taken. **Required fees:** *Part-time* $25 per semester. Fees vary by campus location.

FINANCIAL AID (1999–2000)
Fellowships, grants, loans, research assistantships, and scholarships. Aid is available to part-time students. Financial aid application deadline: 3/15. **Financial Aid Contact** Ms. Joyce Wilkins, Director, Office of Financial Aid, 300 College Park Avenue, Dayton, OH 45469-1621. **Phone:** 937-229-4311. **Fax:** 937-229-4545. **E-mail:** wilkins@kahn.admin.udayton.edu.

RESOURCES AND SERVICES
Information about online services, personal computer policies, library resources, international exchange programs, internship programs, and placement services at this institution and others can be found at **www.petersons.com/mba**

International Students
Services and Facilities Counseling/support services, ESL/language courses, housing location assistance, international student organization, language tutoring, orientation, visa services. Financial aid is available to international students.
Applying *Required:* TOEFL with recommended score of 213 (computer) or 550 (paper), proof of adequate funds, proof of health/immunizations.
International Student Contact Mr. Kevin O'Keefe, International Student Advisor, 300 College Park Avenue, Dayton, OH 45469-1481. **Phone:** 937-229-2748. **Fax:** 937-229-2766.

■ APPLICATION
Required GMAT, application form, baccalaureate/first degree, resume/curriculum vitae, transcripts of college work. **Recommended** Essay, letter(s) of recommendation, personal statement, work experience.
Deadlines and Fees Applications for domestic students are processed on a rolling basis. *Deadlines:* 3/1 for fall (international), 7/1 for winter (international). *Application fee:* $30, $30 (international).
Application Contact Dr. Charles E. Wells, Associate Dean and Director, MBA Program, 300 College Park Avenue, Dayton, OH 45469-2234. **Phone:** 937-229-3733. **Fax:** 937-229-3882. **E-mail:** mba@udayton.edu.

The University of Findlay
Findlay, Ohio

MBA PROGRAM

Graduate Business Faculty

Full-time: 4	Part-time: 8

Student Body

Total: 387 — Average Age: 30

Admissions

Average GMAT: 350 — Average GPA: 3.1

Costs (1999–2000)
Full-time tuition: N/R
Part-time tuition: $313 per credit hour

After Graduation (Class of 1998–99)
Employed within 3 months of graduation: 100%
Average starting salary: $45,000

DEGREE MBA

MBA—Master of Business Administration Full-time and part-time. *Distance learning option.* At least 33 total credits required. 12 to 60 months to complete program. *Concentrations:* health care, organizational management, public management, sports/entertainment management.

COSTS
Tuition *Part-time:* $313 per credit hour. **Graduate housing:** *Typical cost:* $2755 (including board).

FINANCIAL AID (1999–2000)
Loans, research assistantships, and work study. Aid is available to part-time students. Financial aid application deadline: 4/15. **Financial Aid Contact** Arman Habegger, Financial Aid Director, 1000 North Main Street, Findlay, OH 45840-3653.

RESOURCES AND SERVICES
Information about online services, personal computer policies, library resources, international exchange programs, internship programs, and placement services at this institution and others can be found at **www.petersons.com/mba**

International Students
9% of students enrolled are international students.
Services and Facilities Counseling/support services, ESL/language courses, international student housing. Financial aid is available to international students.
Applying *Required:* TOEFL with recommended score of 525 (paper), proof of adequate funds, proof of health/immunizations.
International Student Contact Denise Bunge, International Student Office, 1000 North Main Street, Findlay, OH 45840. **Phone:** 419-424-4558. **Fax:** 419-424-5507. **E-mail:** bunge@mail.findlay.edu.

■ APPLICATION
Required GMAT, application form, baccalaureate/first degree, interview, 3 letters of recommendation, transcripts of college work, 1 year of work experience.
Deadlines and Fees *Application fee:* $25.
Application Contact Dr. Ahmed El-Zayaty, MBA Program Director, 1000 North Main Street, Findlay, OH 45840-3653. **Phone:** 419-424-4897. **Fax:** 419-424-6781. **E-mail:** el-zayaty@mail.findlay.edu.

University of Toledo
Toledo, Ohio

COLLEGE OF BUSINESS ADMINISTRATION

Graduate Business Faculty

Full-time: 65	Part-time: 6

Student Body

Total: 280	Average Age: 30
Full-time: 79	Women: 36%
Part-time: 201	

Admissions

Applications: 227	Average GMAT: 511
Admitted: 198	Average GPA: 2.97
Enrolled: 76	

Costs (1999–2000)
Full-time tuition: $6462 per academic year (resident), $12,832 per academic year (nonresident)
Part-time tuition: $229 per credit hour (resident), $594 per credit hour (nonresident)

After Graduation (Class of 1998–99)
Employed within 3 months of graduation: 98%

Accreditation
AACSB—The International Association for Management Education

DEGREES MBA • MS

MBA—Executive MBA Full-time. At least 42 total credits required. Maximum of 15 months to complete program. *Concentrations:* entrepreneurship, management, technology management.

MBA—Master of Business Administration Full-time and part-time. 36 to 60 total credits required. 12 to 72 months to complete program. *Concentrations:* accounting, finance, human resources, international business, management, management information systems, marketing, operations management.

University of Toledo (continued)

MS—Master of Science in Accounting Full-time and part-time. At least 30 total credits required. 12 to 72 months to complete program. *Concentrations:* accounting.

MS—Master of Science in Manufacturing Management Full-time and part-time. At least 55 total credits required. 24 to 72 months to complete program. *Concentrations:* manufacturing management.

COSTS

Tuition, state resident: *Full-time* $6462. *Part-time* $229 per credit hour. **Tuition, nonresident:** *Full-time* $12,832. *Part-time* $594 per credit hour. **Required fees:** Tuition and fees vary by number of courses or credits taken, academic program, and local reciprocity agreements. **Graduate housing:** Room and board costs vary by campus location, number of occupants, type of accommodation, and type of board plan. *Typical cost:* $4538 (including board), $3218 (room only).

FINANCIAL AID (1999–2000)

73 students received aid, including fellowships, research assistantships, scholarships, and teaching assistantships. Aid is available to part-time students. Financial aid application deadline: 3/1. **Financial Aid Contact** Dr. Paula Compton, Director of Financial Aid, 2801 West Bancroft, Toledo, OH 43606-3398. **Phone:** 419-530-7746. **Fax:** 419-530-7757.

RESOURCES AND SERVICES

Information about online services, personal computer policies, library resources, international exchange programs, internship programs, and placement services at this institution and others can be found at **www. petersons.com/mba**

International Students

29% of students enrolled are international students.

Services and Facilities Counseling/support services, ESL/language courses, housing location assistance, international student housing, international student organization, orientation, visa services. Financial aid is available to international students.

Applying *Required:* TOEFL with recommended score of 550 (paper), proof of adequate funds, proof of health/immunizations.

International Student Contact Ms. Dawn Malone, Director of International Admissions, Office of International Services, Rocket Hall 1060, Toledo, OH 43606-3390. **Phone:** 419-530-1201. **Fax:** 419-530-1202. **E-mail:** intlsvs@utnet.utoledo. edu.

■ APPLICATION

Required GMAT, application form, baccalaureate/first degree, 3 letters of recommendation, personal statement, transcripts of college work. School will accept GRE. **Recommended** Resume/curriculum vitae.

Deadlines and Fees *Deadlines:* 8/1 for fall, 11/15 for spring, 4/15 for summer, 5/1 for fall (international), 10/1 for spring (international), 3/1 for summer (international). *Application fee:* $30, $30 (international).

Application Contact Dr. Bruce Kuhlman, Director of Graduate Programs, College of Business Administration, Office of Graduate Studies in Business, Toledo, OH 43606-3390. **Phone:** 419-530-2775. **Fax:** 419-530-7260. **E-mail:** bruce. kuhlman@utoledo.edu.

See full description on page 980.

Walsh University

North Canton, Ohio

PROGRAM IN MANAGEMENT

DEGREE MA

MA—Master of Arts in Management Part-time. At least 36 total credits required. 24 to 60 months to complete program. *Concentrations:* accounting, business law, financial management/planning, legal administration, management information systems, managerial economics, marketing research, organizational behavior/development, organizational management, project management, public relations, quantitative analysis, strategic management.

RESOURCES AND SERVICES

Information about online services, personal computer policies, library resources, international exchange programs, internship programs, and placement services at this institution and others can be found at **www. petersons.com/mba**

International Students

Services and Facilities Counseling/support services, ESL/language courses. Financial aid is not available to international students.

International Student Contact Ms. Lori Brindisi, Director of International Student Development, 2020 Easton Street, NW, North Canton, OH 44720-3396. **Phone:** 330-490-7130. **Fax:** 330-499-8518. **E-mail:** brindisi@alex.walsh.edu.

■ APPLICATION

Application Contact Director of Admissions, 2020 Easton Street, NW, North Canton, OH 44720-3396. **Phone:** 330-490-7171. **Fax:** 330-490-7165. **E-mail:** admissions@alex.walsh.edu.

Wright State University

Dayton, Ohio

COLLEGE OF BUSINESS AND ADMINISTRATION

Graduate Business Faculty
Full-time: 54

Student Body
Total: 429	Average Age: 30
Full-time: 134	Women: 36%
Part-time: 295	

Admissions
Applications: 134	Average GMAT: 538
Admitted: 111	Average GPA: 3.18
Enrolled: 65	

Costs (1999–2000)
Full-time tuition: $5568 per academic year (resident), $9696 per academic year (nonresident)
Part-time tuition: $175 per credit (resident), $302 per credit (nonresident)

Accreditation
AACSB—The International Association for Management Education

DEGREES M Acc • MBA • MBA/MS • MS

M Acc—Master of Accountancy Full-time and part-time. 45 to 108 total credits required. 12 to 60 months to complete program.

MBA—Master of Business Administration Full-time and part-time. 51 to 74 total credits required. 12 to 60 months to complete program. *Concentrations:* economics, finance, international business, logistics, management, management information systems, marketing, operations management, project management.

MBA/MS—Master of Business Administration/Master of Science in Nursing Full-time and part-time. 90 to 104 total credits required. 24 to 60 months to complete program.

MBA/MS—Master of Business Administration/Master of Science in Social and Applied Economics Full-time and part-time. 81 to 104 total credits required. 18 to 60 months to complete program.

MS—Master of Science in Social and Applied Economics Full-time and part-time. 48 to 60 total credits required. 12 to 60 months to complete program.

COSTS

Tuition, state resident: *Full-time* $5568. *Part-time* $175 per credit. **Tuition, nonresident:** *Full-time* $9696. *Part-time* $302 per credit. **Tuition, international:** *Full-time* $9696. **Graduate housing:** Room and board costs vary by number of occupants, type of accommodation, and type of board plan. *Typical cost:* $5000 (including board).

FINANCIAL AID (1999–2000)

Fellowships, loans, research assistantships, teaching assistantships, and work study. Aid is available to part-time students. **Financial Aid Contact** Mr. David Darr, Director of Financial Aid, Colonel Glenn Highway, Dayton, OH 45435. **Phone:** 937-775-5721. **Fax:** 937-775-5795. **E-mail:** dave.darr@wright.edu.

RESOURCES AND SERVICES

Information about online services, personal computer policies, library resources, international exchange programs, internship programs, and placement services at this institution and others can be found at **www. petersons.com/mba**

International Students

17% of students enrolled are international students.

Services and Facilities Counseling/support services, ESL/language courses, housing location assistance, international student organization, orientation. Financial aid is not available to international students.

Applying *Required:* TOEFL with recommended score of 550 (paper), proof of adequate funds.

International Student Contact Mr. Steven Lyons, Director of International Student Programs, Colonel Glenn Highway, Dayton, OH 45435. **Phone:** 937-775-5745. **Fax:** 937-775-5795. **E-mail:** steven.lyons@wright.edu.

■ **APPLICATION**

Required GMAT, application form, baccalaureate/first degree, resume/curriculum vitae, transcripts of college work.

Deadlines and Fees Applications for domestic and international students are processed on a rolling basis. *Application fee:* $25, $25 (international).

Application Contact Mr. James Crawford, Director of Graduate Programs in Business, College of Business and Administration, 110 Rike Hall, Dayton, OH 45435. **Phone:** 937-775-2437. **Fax:** 937-775-3545. **E-mail:** james.crawford@wright.edu.

See full description on page 1024.

Xavier University

Cincinnati, Ohio

COLLEGE OF BUSINESS ADMINISTRATION

Graduate Business Faculty
Full-time: 45   Part-time: 20

Student Body
Total: 1,105
Full-time: 224   Average Age: 28
Part-time: 881   Women: 34%

Admissions
Applications: 377
Admitted: 339   Average GMAT: 540
Enrolled: 255   Average GPA: 3.2

Costs (1999–2000)
Full-time tuition: N/R
Part-time tuition: $420 per credit

After Graduation (Class of 1998–99)
Average starting salary: $46,000

Accreditation
AACSB—The International Association for Management Education

DEGREES MBA • MBA/MHSA • MBA/MSN

MBA—Executive MBA Part-time. At least 48 total credits required. 19 months to complete program.

MBA—On-Site MBA Part-time. At least 48 total credits required. 22 months to complete program.

MBA—Master of Business Administration Full-time and part-time. 36 to 55 total credits required. 12 to 72 months to complete program. *Concentrations:* accounting, entrepreneurship, finance, human resources, international business, management information systems, marketing, quality management.

MBA/MHSA—Master of Business Administration/Master of Health Services Administration Full-time and part-time. 92 to 105 total credits required. 36 to 72 months to complete program.

MBA/MSN—Master of Business Administration/Master of Science in Nursing Full-time and part-time. 56 to 65 total credits required. 36 to 72 months to complete program.

*T**he M.B.A. programs of Williams College of Business, which are accredited by AACSB-The International Association for Management Education, get the results students demand. Offered in four distinct formats, each program delivers the academic knowledge and skills to develop executives and leaders. The Evening Program offers flexibility, convenience, and a real-world approach. Adaptable for full-time or part-time study, its highly integrated team-based curriculum allows students to tailor their course sequence and specialize in nine areas of study while completing their degree in two to three years. The Weekend Program meets the needs of working professionals who are not able to attend courses during the week. This cohort curriculum gets students their degrees in two years. The Executive Program fulfills the unique educational needs of highly experienced professionals. This nineteen-month course of study includes an international study trip, limited class size, and a peer-based learning environment with the top faculty members of the College. The On-Site Program works with sponsoring organizations to deliver a curriculum at a location that is convenient to their employees. It is an excellent way for organizations to promote focused team building through team learning. Two dual-degree options, with health services administration and nursing, are also offered. Each program gives students a highly pertinent and*

valuable educational experience while providing a measurable return on their self-investment.

COSTS

Tuition *Part-time:* $420 per credit. Tuition varies by number of courses or credits taken and academic program. **Required fees:** Tuition and fees vary by academic program.

FINANCIAL AID (1999–2000)

Grants, loans, research assistantships, and scholarships. Aid is available to part-time students. Financial aid application deadline: 3/1. **Financial Aid Contact** Mr. Paul Calme, Director of Financial Aid, 3800 Victory Parkway, Cincinnati, OH 45207-5411. **Phone:** 513-742-3142. **Fax:** 513-745-2806. **E-mail:** calme@xu.edu.

RESOURCES AND SERVICES

Information about online services, personal computer policies, library resources, international exchange programs, internship programs, and placement services at this institution and others can be found at **www.petersons.com/mba**

International Students

2% of students enrolled are international students.

Services and Facilities Counseling/support services, ESL/language courses, international student housing, international student organization, orientation, visa services. Financial aid is available to international students.

Applying *Required:* TOEFL with recommended score of 213 (computer) or 550 (paper), proof of adequate funds. *Recommended:* Proof of health/immunizations.

International Student Contact Ms. Katherine Hammett, Director of International Student Services, 3800 Victory Parkway, Cincinnati, OH 45207-2171. **Phone:** 513-745-2864. **Fax:** 513-745-2876. **E-mail:** hammett@xu.edu.

■ **APPLICATION**

Required GMAT, application form, baccalaureate/first degree, resume/curriculum vitae, transcripts of college work. **Recommended** 2 letters of recommendation, 3 years of work experience.

Deadlines and Fees Applications for domestic and international students are processed on a rolling basis. *Application fee:* $35, $35 (international).

Application Contact Ms. Jennifer Bush, Director of MBA Enrollment Services, 3800 Victory Parkway, Cincinnati, OH 45207-3221. **Phone:** 513-745-3525. **Fax:** 513-745-2929. **E-mail:** xumba@xu.edu.

Youngstown State University

Youngstown, Ohio

WARREN P. WILLIAMSON JR. COLLEGE OF BUSINESS ADMINISTRATION

Graduate Business Faculty
Full-time: 23   Part-time: 3

Student Body
Total: 155
Full-time: 86   Average Age: 29
Part-time: 69   Women: 43%

Admissions
Applications: 35   Average GMAT: 510
Admitted: 33   Average GPA: 3.15
Enrolled: 28

Costs (1999–2000)
Full-time tuition: N/R
Part-time tuition: $550 per course (resident), $750 per course (nonresident)

Accreditation
AACSB—The International Association for Management Education
ACBSP—The American Council of Business Schools and Programs

DEGREES MBA

MBA—Executive MBA Full-time. 5 years of professional work experience required. At least 72 total credits required. 24 months to complete program.

MBA—Master of Business Administration Full-time and part-time. At least 52 total credits required. 12 to 72 months to complete program. *Concentrations:* accounting, finance, management, marketing.

COSTS

Tuition, state resident: *Part-time* $550 per course. **Tuition, nonresident:** *Part-time* $750 per course. Tuition varies by number of courses or credits taken and

Youngstown State University (continued)

local reciprocity agreements. **Graduate housing:** Room and board costs vary by campus location, number of occupants, type of accommodation, and type of board plan. *Typical cost:* $4800 (including board).

FINANCIAL AID (1999–2000)
42 students received aid, including fellowships, grants, loans, research assistantships, scholarships, teaching assistantships, and work study. Aid is available to part-time students. **Financial Aid Contact** Ms. Beth Bartlett, Administrative Assistant, 410 Wick Avenue, Youngstown, OH 44555-0002.

RESOURCES AND SERVICES
Information about online services, personal computer policies, library resources, international exchange programs, internship programs, and placement services at this institution and others can be found at **www. petersons.com/mba**

International Students
7% of students enrolled are international students.

Services and Facilities Counseling/support services, ESL/language courses, international student organization, language tutoring. Financial aid is available to international students.
Applying *Required:* TOEFL with recommended score of 550 (paper), proof of adequate funds.
International Student Contact Dr. Silvia Hyre, Director, Center for International Studies, Phelps Building, Youngstown, OH 44555. **E-mail:** amspecol@ysub.ysu.edu.

■ **APPLICATION**
Required GMAT, application form, baccalaureate/first degree, personal statement, resume/curriculum vitae, transcripts of college work. **Recommended** Interview, letter(s) of recommendation.
Deadlines and Fees *Deadlines:* 8/15 for fall, 11/15 for winter, 2/15 for spring, 5/15 for summer, 1/15 for fall (international), 3/15 for winter (international), 6/15 for spring (international). *Application fee:* $30, $75 (international).
Application Contact Ms. Linda Mohn, MBA Program Coordinator, One University Plaza, Youngstown, OH 44555-0002. **Phone:** 330-742-3069. **Toll-free Phone:** 800-336-9978. **Fax:** 330-742-1459. **E-mail:** ljmohn@cc.ysu.edu.

OKLAHOMA

Cameron University

Lawton, Oklahoma

SCHOOL OF GRADUATE AND PROFESSIONAL STUDIES

Graduate Business Faculty
Full-time: 12 | Part-time: 7

Student Body
Total: 229
Full-time: 52 | Average Age: 35
Part-time: 177 | Women: 46%

Admissions
Applications: 241 | Average GMAT: 493
Admitted: 241 | Average GPA: 3
Enrolled: 212

Costs (1999–2000)
Full-time tuition: $1494 per academic year (resident), $3456 per academic year (nonresident)
Part-time tuition: $83 per credit (resident), $192 per credit (nonresident)

DEGREE MBA

MBA—Master of Business Administration Full-time and part-time. *Distance learning option.* 33 to 45 total credits required. 12 to 72 months to complete program.

COSTS

Tuition, state resident: *Full-time* $1494. *Part-time* $83 per credit. **Tuition, nonresident:** *Full-time* $3456. *Part-time* $192 per credit. **Tuition, international:** *Full-time* $3456. Tuition varies by local reciprocity agreements. **Required fees:** Fees vary by campus location. **Graduate housing:** Room and board costs vary

by number of occupants and type of board plan. *Typical cost:* $3602 (including board).

FINANCIAL AID (1999–2000)
35 students received aid, including loans, research assistantships, scholarships, and work study. Aid is available to part-time students. Financial aid application deadline: 4/15. **Financial Aid Contact** Ms. Caryn Pacheco, Director of Financial Aid, 2800 West Gore Boulevard, Lawton, OK 73505-6377. **Phone:** 580-581-2293. **Fax:** 580-581-5514. **E-mail:** carynp@cameron.edu.

RESOURCES AND SERVICES
Information about online services, personal computer policies, library resources, international exchange programs, internship programs, and placement services at this institution and others can be found at **www. petersons.com/mba**

International Students
4% of students enrolled are international students.

Services and Facilities Counseling/support services. Financial aid is not available to international students.
Applying *Required:* TOEFL with recommended score of 213 (computer) or 550 (paper), proof of adequate funds.
International Student Contact Ms. Zoe Durant, Director, Admissions and Registrar, 2800 West Gore Boulevard, Lawton, OK 73505-6377. **Phone:** 580-581-2288. **Fax:** 580-581-5514. **E-mail:** zoed@cameron.edu.

■ **APPLICATION**
Required Application form, baccalaureate/first degree, transcripts of college work. School will accept GMAT.
Deadlines and Fees Applications for domestic and international students are processed on a rolling basis. *Application fee:* $15, $15 (international).
Application Contact Dr. Jack Amyx, International Business Studies/MBA, 2800 West Gore Boulevard, Lawton, OK 73505-6377. **Phone:** 580-581-2267. **Fax:** 580-581-2253. **E-mail:** jacka@cameron.edu.

Northeastern State University

Tahlequah, Oklahoma

COLLEGE OF BUSINESS AND INDUSTRY

Graduate Business Faculty
Full-time: 51 | Part-time: 30

Student Body
Total: 75
Part-time: 75 | Average Age: 34
 | Women: 53%

Admissions
Applications: 80
Admitted: 70 | Enrolled: 53
 | Average GMAT: 450

Costs (1999–2000)
Full-time tuition: N/R
Part-time tuition: $80 per credit hour (resident), $188 per credit hour (nonresident)

Accreditation
ACBSP—The American Council of Business Schools and Programs

DEGREE MBA

MBA—Master of Business Administration Full-time and part-time. At least 32 total credits required. 12 to 18 months to complete program. *Concentrations:* management.

COSTS

Tuition, state resident: *Part-time* $80 per credit hour. **Tuition, nonresident:** *Part-time* $188 per credit hour. Tuition varies by class time, number of courses or credits taken, campus location, and academic program. **Required fees:** Tuition and fees vary by campus location.

FINANCIAL AID (1999–2000)
Work study. Financial aid application deadline: 3/1. **Financial Aid Contact** Bill McFarland, Director, Student Financial Services, 600 North Grand, Tahlequah, OK 74464. **Phone:** 918-456-5511 Ext. 3407. **Fax:** 918-458-2150.

RESOURCES AND SERVICES
Information about online services, personal computer policies, library resources, international exchange programs, internship programs, and

placement services at this institution and others can be found at **www.petersons.com/mba**

International Students
7% of students enrolled are international students.

Services and Facilities Counseling/support services, international student housing. Financial aid is available to international students.

Applying *Required:* TOEFL with recommended score of 550 (paper), proof of adequate funds.

International Student Contact Kimbra Scott, International Student Coordinator, President's Office, Tahlequah, OK 74464. **Phone:** 918-458-2000. **Fax:** 918-458-2015. **E-mail:** ranallo@cherokee.nsuok.edu.

■ APPLICATION

Required GMAT, application form, baccalaureate/first degree, transcripts of college work. **Recommended** Essay, interview, letter(s) of recommendation, personal statement, resume/curriculum vitae, work experience.

Deadlines and Fees *Deadlines:* 7/1 for fall, 12/1 for winter, 1/1 for spring, 5/1 for summer, 7/1 for fall (international), 12/1 for winter (international), 1/1 for spring (international), 5/1 for summer (international).

Application Contact Dr. Thomas Carment, MBA Program Coordinator, NSU College of Business and Industry, Tahlequah, OK 74464. **Phone:** 918-456-5511 Ext. 2905. **Toll-free Phone:** 800-722-9614. **Fax:** 918-458-2337. **E-mail:** carment@cherokee.nsuok.edu.

Oklahoma City University
Oklahoma City, Oklahoma

SCHOOL OF MANAGEMENT AND BUSINESS SCIENCES

Graduate Business Faculty
Full-time: 34   Part-time: 25

Student Body
Total: 1,068
Full-time: 547
Part-time: 521
Average Age: 30
Women: 37%

Admissions
Applications: 321
Admitted: 202
Enrolled: 179
Average GPA: 3.25

Costs (1999–2000)
Full-time tuition: N/R
Part-time tuition: $390 per credit hour

DEGREES MBA • MSA

MBA—Executive MBA Full-time and part-time. 36 to 39 total credits required. 20 to 60 months to complete program. *Concentrations:* management.

MBA—Master of Business Administration Full-time and part-time. 36 to 39 total credits required. 20 to 60 months to complete program. *Concentrations:* arts administration/management, finance, health care, international finance, international marketing, management, management information systems, marketing, public management.

MSA—Master of Science in Accounting Full-time and part-time. At least 30 total credits required. 20 to 60 months to complete program. *Concentrations:* accounting.

COSTS

Tuition *Part-time:* $390 per credit hour. Tuition varies by number of courses or credits taken and academic program. **Required fees:** *Full-time* $135. Tuition and fees vary by academic program. **Graduate housing:** Room and board costs vary by number of occupants, type of accommodation, and type of board plan. *Typical cost:* $4530 (including board), $2020 (room only).

FINANCIAL AID (1999–2000)

Fellowships, loans, scholarships, and work study. Aid is available to part-time students. **Financial Aid Contact** Mrs. Laura Rahhal, Director of Graduate Admissions, 2501 North Blackwelder, Oklahoma City, OK 73106. **Phone:** 405-521-5351. **Fax:** 405-521-5356. **E-mail:** lrahhal1@okcu.edu.

RESOURCES AND SERVICES

Information about online services, personal computer policies, library resources, international exchange programs, internship programs, and placement services at this institution and others can be found at **www.petersons.com/mba**

International Students
52% of students enrolled are international students.

Services and Facilities Counseling/support services, ESL/language courses, international student housing, international student organization, language tutoring, orientation, visa services.

Applying *Required:* TOEFL with recommended score of 550 (paper), proof of adequate funds, proof of health/immunizations.

International Student Contact Ms. Julie Sinclair, Director of International Student Office, 2501 North Blackwelder, Oklahoma City, OK 73106. **Phone:** 405-521-5358. **Fax:** 405-521-5946. **E-mail:** jsinclair@okcu.edu.

■ APPLICATION

Required Application form, baccalaureate/first degree, 2 letters of recommendation, personal statement, transcripts of college work. **Recommended** Interview.

Deadlines and Fees Applications for domestic and international students are processed on a rolling basis. *Application fee:* $35, $70 (international).

Application Contact Mrs. Laura Rahhal, Director of Graduate Admissions, 2501 North Blackwelder, Oklahoma City, OK 73106. **Phone:** 405-521-5351. **Toll-free Phone:** 800-633-7242. **Fax:** 405-521-5356. **E-mail:** lrahhal@okcu.edu.

Oklahoma State University
Stillwater, Oklahoma

COLLEGE OF BUSINESS ADMINISTRATION

Graduate Business Faculty
Full-time: 86

Student Body
Total: 350
Full-time: 140
Part-time: 210
Average Age: 26
Women: 30%

Admissions
Applications: 700
Admitted: 400
Enrolled: 275
Average GMAT: 600

Costs (1999–2000)
Full-time tuition: $1896 per academic year (resident), $6421 per academic year (nonresident)
Part-time tuition: $86 per credit (resident), $275 per credit (nonresident)

Accreditation
AACSB—The International Association for Management Education

DEGREES MBA • MS • MSTM

MBA—Master of Business Administration Full-time and part-time. *Distance learning option.* 38 to 50 total credits required. 18 to 24 months to complete program. *Concentrations:* accounting, economics, electronic commerce (e-commerce), finance, human resources, international business, management, management information systems, marketing, operations management, telecommunications management.

MS—Master of Science—Accounting Full-time and part-time. 24 to 32 total credits required. 12 to 60 months to complete program.

MS—Master of Science—Economics Full-time and part-time. 30 to 33 total credits required. 12 to 60 months to complete program.

MSTM—Master of Science in Telecommunications Management Full-time and part-time. *Distance learning option.* 33 to 35 total credits required. 12 to 60 months to complete program. *Concentrations:* management, technology management.

COSTS

Tuition, state resident: *Full-time* $1896. *Part-time* $86 per credit. **Tuition, nonresident:** *Full-time* $6421. *Part-time* $275 per credit. Tuition varies by number of courses or credits taken.

FINANCIAL AID (1999–2000)

Research assistantships, scholarships, teaching assistantships, and work study. Aid is available to part-time students. **Financial Aid Contact** Financial Aid Office, Hanner Hall, Stillwater, OK 74078. **Phone:** 405-744-6604. **Fax:** 405-744-6438.

RESOURCES AND SERVICES

Information about online services, personal computer policies, library resources, international exchange programs, internship programs, and placement services at this institution and others can be found at **www.petersons.com/mba**

International Students
20% of students enrolled are international students.

Services and Facilities Counseling/support services, ESL/language courses, visa services. Financial aid is available to international students.

Oklahoma State University (continued)

Applying *Required:* TOEFL with recommended score of 575 (paper), proof of adequate funds, proof of health/immunizations.

International Student Contact Ms. Lou Hara, Senior International Admissions Specialist, Graduate College, 202 Whitehurst, Stillwater, OK 74078-1019. **Phone:** 800-227-8732.

■ APPLICATION

Required GMAT, application form, baccalaureate/first degree, essay, 3 letters of recommendation, personal statement, resume/curriculum vitae, transcripts of college work. School will accept GRE. **Recommended** Work experience.

Deadlines and Fees *Deadlines:* 7/1 for fall, 11/1 for spring, 3/1 for fall (international), 6/1 for spring (international). *Application fee:* $25, $25 (international).

Application Contact Mr. Peter Rosen, Assistant Director, MBA Program, College of Business Administration, 102 Gundersen Hall, Stillwater, OK 74078-0555. **Phone:** 405-744-2951. **Fax:** 405-744-7474. **E-mail:** mba-osu@okway.okstate. edu.

Oral Roberts University

Tulsa, Oklahoma

SCHOOL OF BUSINESS

Student Body

Total: 61	Average Age: 31
Full-time: 31	Women: 46%
Part-time: 30	

Admissions

Applications: 48	Average GMAT: 500
Admitted: 40	Average GPA: 3.2
Enrolled: 30	

Costs (1999–2000)
Full-time tuition: $5216 per academic year
Part-time tuition: $272 per credit

DEGREES M Mgt • MBA

M Mgt—Master of Management Full-time and part-time. *Distance learning option.* At least 35 total credits required. Minimum of 18 months to complete program. *Concentrations:* human resources, nonprofit management.

MBA—Master of Business Administration Full-time and part-time. At least 36 total credits required. 18 to 60 months to complete program. *Concentrations:* accounting, finance, international business, management, marketing.

COSTS

Tuition *Full-time:* $4896. *Part-time:* $272 per credit. **Required fees:** *Full-time* $320. *Part-time* $80 per semester. Fees vary by number of courses or credits taken.

FINANCIAL AID (1999–2000)

Loans, research assistantships, scholarships, and work study. Aid is available to part-time students. Financial aid application deadline: 7/15. **Financial Aid Contact** Mrs. Barbara Thompson, Financial Aid Coordinator, Adult Learning Service Center, 7777 South Lewis Avenue, Tulsa, OK 74171-0001. **Phone:** 918-4956602. **Fax:** 918-495-7965. **E-mail:** bthompson@oru.edu.

RESOURCES AND SERVICES

Information about online services, personal computer policies, library resources, international exchange programs, internship programs, and placement services at this institution and others can be found at **www. petersons.com/mba**

International Students

33% of students enrolled are international students.

Services and Facilities Counseling/support services, ESL/language courses, international student organization, visa services. Financial aid is available to international students.

Applying *Required:* TOEFL with recommended score of 213 (computer) or 550 (paper), proof of adequate funds, proof of health/immunizations.

International Student Contact Graduate Business Representative, Adult Learning Service Center, 7777 South Lewis Avenue, Tulsa, OK 74171-0001. **Phone:** 918-495-6117. **Fax:** 918-495-7965. **E-mail:** alsc@oru.edu.

■ APPLICATION

Required Application form, baccalaureate/first degree, essay, 3 letters of recommendation, personal statement, transcripts of college work. School will accept GMAT. **Recommended** Resume/curriculum vitae.

Deadlines and Fees Applications for domestic students are processed on a rolling basis. *Deadline:* 5/1 for summer (international). *Application fee:* $35, $35 (international).

Application Contact Graduate Business Representative, Adult Learning Service Center, 7777 South Lewis Avenue, Tulsa, OK 74171-0001. **Phone:** 918-495-6117. **Toll-free Phone:** 800-6437976. **Fax:** 918-495-7965. **E-mail:** alsc@oru. edu.

Southeastern Oklahoma State University

Durant, Oklahoma

SCHOOL OF BUSINESS

DEGREE MBA

MBA—Master of Business Administration Full-time and part-time. 36 to 57 total credits required. 12 to 72 months to complete program.

RESOURCES AND SERVICES

Information about online services, personal computer policies, library resources, international exchange programs, internship programs, and placement services at this institution and others can be found at **www. petersons.com/mba**

International Students

Services and Facilities Financial aid is not available to international students. **International Student Contact** Dr. Doug McMillan, Dean, Graduate School, Fifth Avenue, Box 4111, Durant, OK 74701. **Phone:** 580-924-0121 Ext. 2428. **Fax:** 580-920-7472.

■ APPLICATION

Application Contact Dr. Doug McMillan, Dean, Graduate School, Fifth Avenue, Box 4111, Durant, OK 74701. **Phone:** 580-924-0121 Ext. 2428. **Fax:** 580-920-7472.

Southern Nazarene University

Bethany, Oklahoma

SCHOOL OF BUSINESS

Graduate Business Faculty

Full-time: 5	Part-time: 11

Student Body

Total: 148	Average Age: 36
Full-time: 148	Women: 54%

Admissions

Average GMAT: 492	Average GPA: 3.1

Costs (1999–2000)
Full-time tuition: $1300 per academic year
Part-time tuition: N/R

DEGREES MBA • MS

MBA—Master of Business Administration Full-time. At least 38 total credits required. 18 months to complete program. *Concentrations:* management.

MS—Master of Science in Management Full-time. At least 32 total credits required. 15 months to complete program. *Concentrations:* management.

COSTS

Tuition *Full-time:* $1300. **Required fees:** Tuition and fees vary by number of courses or credits taken, campus location, and academic program.

FINANCIAL AID (1999–2000)

Financial Aid Contact Mrs. Margaret Rohlmeier, Assistant Financial Aid Director, 6729 Northwest 39th Expressway, Bethany, OK 73008-2694. **Phone:** 405-491-6685. **Fax:** 405-491-6302. **E-mail:** mrohlmi@snu.edu.

RESOURCES AND SERVICES

Information about online services, personal computer policies, library resources, international exchange programs, internship programs, and

placement services at this institution and others can be found at **www. petersons.com/mba**

International Students

Services and Facilities Visa services. Financial aid is available to international students.
Applying *Required:* TOEFL with recommended score of 550 (paper). *Recommended:* Proof of adequate funds, proof of health/immunizations.
International Student Contact Ms. Kathy Mueller, International Admissions Assistant, 6729 NW 39 Expressway, Bethany, OK 73008. **Phone:** 405-491-6386. **Fax:** 405-491-6320. **E-mail:** kmueller@snu.edu.

■ APPLICATION

Required GMAT, application form, baccalaureate/first degree, essay, interview, 3 letters of recommendation, personal statement, resume/curriculum vitae, transcripts of college work, 2 years of work experience.
Deadlines and Fees Applications for domestic and international students are processed on a rolling basis. *Application fee:* $25, $35 (international).
Application Contact Dr. Scott Morris, Director, MSM/MBA, School of Business—Graduate Studies in Management, 6729 Northwest 39th Expressway, Bethany, OK 73008-2694. **Phone:** 405-491-6358. **Fax:** 405-491-6384. **E-mail:** smorris@snu.edu.

Southwestern Oklahoma State University

Weatherford, Oklahoma

SCHOOL OF BUSINESS

Graduate Business Faculty
Full-time: 7

Student Body
Total: 23
Part-time: 23
Average Age: 28
Women: 43%

Admissions
Average GMAT: 480

Costs (1999–2000)
Full-time tuition: N/R
Part-time tuition: $74 per credit (resident), $188 per credit (nonresident)

DEGREE MBA

MBA—Master of Business Administration Part-time. At least 33 total credits required. 24 to 60 months to complete program.

COSTS

Tuition, state resident: *Part-time* $74 per credit. **Tuition, nonresident:** *Part-time* $188 per credit. Tuition varies by academic program.

FINANCIAL AID (1999–2000)

Loans, research assistantships, and work study. **Financial Aid Contact** Director, Financial Aid, 100 Campus Drive, Weatherford, OK 73096. **Phone:** 580-774-3022. **Fax:** 580-774-3795.

RESOURCES AND SERVICES

Information about online services, personal computer policies, library resources, international exchange programs, internship programs, and placement services at this institution and others can be found at **www. petersons.com/mba**

International Students

17% of students enrolled are international students.
Services and Facilities International student organization, orientation. Financial aid is available to international students.
Applying *Required:* TOEFL with recommended score of 550 (paper), proof of adequate funds, proof of health/immunizations.
International Student Contact Mr. Bob Klaassen, Admissions Director and Registrar, 100 Campus Drive, Weatherford, OK 73096. **Phone:** 580-774-3777. **Fax:** 580-774-3795. **E-mail:** klaassb@swosu.edu.

■ APPLICATION

Required GMAT, application form, baccalaureate/first degree, 2 letters of recommendation, transcripts of college work.
Deadlines and Fees *Application fee:* $15, $15 (international).

Application Contact Dr. Elizabeth Ferrell, Assistant Professor, 100 Campus Drive, Weatherford, OK 73096-3098. **Phone:** 580-774-3040. **Fax:** 580-774-7067. **E-mail:** ferrelm@swosu.edu.

University of Central Oklahoma

Edmond, Oklahoma

COLLEGE OF BUSINESS ADMINISTRATION

Graduate Business Faculty
Full-time: 74
Part-time: 44

Student Body
Total: 582
Full-time: 290
Part-time: 292
Average Age: 34
Women: 43%

Admissions
Applications: 163
Admitted: 162
Enrolled: 138
Average GMAT: 440
Average GPA: 2.8

Costs (1999–2000)
Full-time tuition: $1485 per academic year (resident), $2259 per academic year (nonresident)
Part-time tuition: $82.50 per credit (resident), $126 per credit (nonresident)

After Graduation (Class of 1998–99)
Average starting salary: $31,825

Accreditation
ACBSP—The American Council of Business Schools and Programs

DEGREE MBA

MBA—Master of Business Administration Full-time and part-time. At least 36 total credits required. 36 to 60 months to complete program. *Concentrations:* accounting, decision sciences, economics, finance, international business, management, management information systems, operations management.

COSTS

Tuition, state resident: *Full-time* $1188. *Part-time* $66 per credit. **Tuition, nonresident:** *Full-time* $1962. *Part-time* $109 per credit. **Tuition, international:** *Full-time* $1962. **Required fees:** *Full-time* $297. *Part-time* $16.50 per credit. Tuition and fees vary by number of courses or credits taken. **Graduate housing:** Room and board costs vary by number of occupants, type of accommodation, and type of board plan. *Typical cost:* $2950 (including board).

FINANCIAL AID (1999–2000)

Research assistantships, scholarships, and work study. Aid is available to part-time students. **Financial Aid Contact** Ms. Sheila Fugett, Director, Financial Aid, 100 North University Drive, Edmond, OK 73034-5209. **Phone:** 405-974-2303.

RESOURCES AND SERVICES

Information about online services, personal computer policies, library resources, international exchange programs, internship programs, and placement services at this institution and others can be found at **www. petersons.com/mba**

International Students

Services and Facilities Counseling/support services, ESL/language courses, international student housing, international student organization, language tutoring, orientation, visa services. Financial aid is not available to international students.
Applying *Required:* TOEFL with recommended score of 550 (paper), proof of adequate funds, proof of health/immunizations.
International Student Contact Dr. Ronald Paddack, Director, International Student Services, 100 North University Drive, Edmond, OK 73034. **Phone:** 405-974-2374. **E-mail:** int-offc@aixl.ucok.edu.

■ APPLICATION

Required Application form, baccalaureate/first degree, transcripts of college work. School will accept GMAT or GRE.
Deadlines and Fees Applications for domestic students are processed on a rolling basis. *Deadlines:* 7/1 for fall (international), 4/1 for summer (international). *Application fee:* $20, $20 (international).
Application Contact Ms. Gloria Auth, Director, MBA Program, 100 North University Drive, Edmond, OK 73034-5209. **Phone:** 405-974-2422. **Fax:** 405-974-3821. **E-mail:** mba@ucok.edu.

University of Oklahoma

Norman, Oklahoma

MICHAEL F. PRICE COLLEGE OF BUSINESS

Graduate Business Faculty
Full-time: 28   Part-time: 3

Student Body
Total: 326   Average Age: 27
Full-time: 156   Women: 35%
Part-time: 170

Admissions
Applications: 228   Enrolled: 75
Admitted: 130   Average GMAT: 600

Costs (1999–2000)
Full-time tuition: N/R
Part-time tuition: $92 per credit hour (resident), $266 per credit hour (nonresident)

Accreditation
AACSB—The International Association for Management Education

DEGREES JD/MBA • M Acc • MBA

JD/MBA—Juris Doctor/Master of Business Administration Full-time. At least 126 total credits required. 48 to 72 months to complete program.

M Acc—Master of Accountancy Full-time and part-time. 36 to 49 total credits required. 18 to 72 months to complete program.

MBA—Master of Business Administration Full-time and part-time. At least 53 total credits required. 21 to 72 months to complete program. *Concentrations:* accounting, finance, health care, international business, management, management information systems, marketing.

COSTS

Tuition, state resident: *Part-time* $92 per credit hour. **Tuition, nonresident:** *Part-time* $266 per credit hour. **Required fees:** Fees vary by class time, number of courses or credits taken, and academic program.

FINANCIAL AID (1999–2000)

Fellowships, loans, research assistantships, scholarships, and teaching assistantships. **Financial Aid Contact** Dr. Alice Watkins, Associate Director of Graduate Programs in Business, 307 West Brooks, Room 105K, Norman, OK 73019-0450. **Phone:** 405-325-4107. **Fax:** 405-325-1957. **E-mail:** awatkins@ou.edu.

RESOURCES AND SERVICES

Information about online services, personal computer policies, library resources, international exchange programs, internship programs, and placement services at this institution and others can be found at **www. petersons.com/mba**

International Students

Services and Facilities Counseling/support services, ESL/language courses, international student housing, international student organization, visa services. Financial aid is available to international students.
Applying *Required:* TOEFL with recommended score of 550 (paper), proof of adequate funds, proof of health/immunizations. *Recommended:* TSE.

International Student Contact Lee Savage, Director of International Student Programs, International Student Services, Norman, OK 73019. **Phone:** 405-325-3163.

■ APPLICATION

Required GMAT, application form, baccalaureate/first degree, 3 letters of recommendation, personal statement, resume/curriculum vitae, transcripts of college work. **Recommended** Interview.

Deadlines and Fees Applications for domestic students are processed on a rolling basis. *Deadline:* 4/1 for fall (international). *Application fee:* $25, $50 (international).

Application Contact Dr. Alice Watkins, Associate Director of Graduate Programs in Business, 307 West Brooks, Room 105K, Norman, OK 73019-0450. **Phone:** 405-325-4107. **Fax:** 405-325-1957. **E-mail:** awatkins@ou.edu.

University of Tulsa

Tulsa, Oklahoma

COLLEGE OF BUSINESS ADMINISTRATION

Accreditation
AACSB—The International Association for Management Education

DEGREES MBA • MS/MAIS • MS/MTax

MBA—Master of Business Administration Full-time and part-time. 30 to 60 total credits required. 15 to 72 months to complete program. *Concentrations:* accounting, finance, management.

MS/MAIS—Master of Science/Master of Accounting and Information Systems Full-time and part-time. Undergraduate degree in accounting or management information systems preferred. At least 30 total credits required. 15 to 96 months to complete program.

MS/MTax—Master of Science/Master of Taxation Full-time and part-time. At least 36 total credits required. 15 to 96 months to complete program.

RESOURCES AND SERVICES

Information about online services, personal computer policies, library resources, international exchange programs, internship programs, and placement services at this institution and others can be found at **www. petersons.com/mba**

International Students

Services and Facilities Counseling/support services, ESL/language courses, international student organization.
International Student Contact Ms. Pam Smith, Dean of International Services and Programs, 600 South College Avenue, Tulsa, OK 74104-3126. **Phone:** 918-631-2329. **Fax:** 918-631-3322. **E-mail:** pamela-smith@utulsa.edu.

■ APPLICATION

Application Contact Ms. Bodil Mills, Administrative Assistant, 600 South College Avenue, BAH 308, Tulsa, OK 74104-3126. **Phone:** 918-631-2242. **Fax:** 918-631-2142. **E-mail:** bodil-mills@utulsa.edu.

OREGON

George Fox University

Newberg, Oregon

DEPARTMENT OF BUSINESS AND ECONOMICS

Graduate Business Faculty
Full-time: 8   Part-time: 1

Student Body
Total: 94   Average Age: 35
Part-time: 94   Women: 45%

Admissions
Applications: 58   Enrolled: 53
Admitted: 54   Average GPA: 3.57

Costs (1999–2000)
Full-time tuition: N/R
Part-time tuition: $22,530 per degree program

DEGREE MBA

MBA—Master of Business Administration Part-time. 2 years of work experience required. At least 40 total credits required. 24 months to complete program. *Concentrations:* management.

COSTS

Tuition *Part-time:* $22,530 per degree program.

FINANCIAL AID (1999–2000)

66 students received aid, including loans. Aid is available to part-time students. Financial aid application deadline: 8/1. **Financial Aid Contact** Monika Keller, Financial Aid Counselor, 414 North Meridian, Newberg, OR 97132. **Phone:** 800-765-4369 Ext. 2233. **Fax:** 503-537-3867. **E-mail:** mkeller@georgefox.edu.

RESOURCES AND SERVICES

Information about online services, personal computer policies, library resources, international exchange programs, internship programs, and placement services at this institution and others can be found at **www.petersons.com/mba**

International Students

Services and Facilities Financial aid is not available to international students. **Applying** *Required:* TOEFL with recommended score of 550 (paper), proof of adequate funds, proof of health/immunizations.

International Student Contact Ms. Jan Cain, Graduate Admissions Counselor, 414 North Meridian, Newberg, OR 97132-2697. **Phone:** 503-554-2261. **Fax:** 503-554-3867.

■ APPLICATION

Required Application form, baccalaureate/first degree, essay, interview, 3 letters of recommendation, personal statement, transcripts of college work, 2 years of work experience. **Recommended** Resume/curriculum vitae.

Deadlines and Fees *Deadlines:* 7/1 for fall, 11/15 for spring, 7/1 for fall (international), 11/15 for spring (international). *Application fee:* $25, $25 (international).

Application Contact Ms. Jan Cain, Graduate Admissions Counselor, 414 North Meridian, Newberg, OR 97132-2697. **Phone:** 503-554-2261. **Fax:** 503-554-3867.

Marylhurst University

Marylhurst, Oregon

GRADUATE PROGRAM IN MANAGEMENT

DEGREE MBA

MBA—Master of Business Administration Full-time and part-time. *Distance learning option.* 45 to 50 total credits required. 12 to 60 months to complete program. *Concentrations:* finance, information management, marketing, organizational behavior/development.

RESOURCES AND SERVICES

Information about online services, personal computer policies, library resources, international exchange programs, internship programs, and placement services at this institution and others can be found at **www.petersons.com/mba**

International Students

Services and Facilities Counseling/support services, ESL/language courses, international student housing, visa services. Financial aid is not available to international students.
International Student Contact Mr. Wade Bird, Credentials Evaluator, PO Box 261, Marylhurst, OR 97036-0261. **Phone:** 503-699-6268. **Fax:** 503-636-9526. **E-mail:** wbird@marylhurst.edu.

■ APPLICATION

Application Contact Dr. Bonita Kolb, Chair, Graduate Business and Management, P7600 Pacific Highway, PO Box 261, Marylhurst, OR 97036-0261. **Phone:** 503-699-6318. **Toll-free Phone:** 800-634-9982. **Fax:** 503-636-9526. **E-mail:** bkolb@marylhurst.edu.

See full description on page 720.

Oregon Graduate Institute of Science and Technology

Beaverton, Oregon

DEPARTMENT OF MANAGEMENT IN SCIENCE AND TECHNOLOGY

Graduate Business Faculty

Full-time: 3	Part-time: 24

Student Body

Total: 82	
Full-time: 2	Average Age: 36
Part-time: 80	Women: 23%

Admissions

Applications: 17	
Admitted: 16	Average GPA: 3
Enrolled: 13	

Costs (1999–2000)
Full-time tuition: N/R
Part-time tuition: $520 per credit

DEGREE MSM

MSM—Master of Science in Management of Science and Technology Full-time and part-time. *Distance learning option.* GMAT or GRE required if undergraduate GPA is less than 3.0. At least 52 total credits required. 18 to 60 months to complete program. *Concentrations:* financial information systems, technology management.

COSTS

Tuition *Part-time:* $520 per credit. Tuition varies by class time and number of courses or credits taken.

FINANCIAL AID (1999–2000)

Financial Aid Contact Director, Student Services, 20000 NW Walker Road, Beaverton, OR 97006-8921. **Phone:** 503-748-1166. **Fax:** 503-748-1285. **E-mail:** admissions@admin.ogi.edu.

RESOURCES AND SERVICES

Information about online services, personal computer policies, library resources, international exchange programs, internship programs, and placement services at this institution and others can be found at **www.petersons.com/mba**

International Students

1% of students enrolled are international students.

Services and Facilities Financial aid is not available to international students. **Applying** *Required:* TOEFL with recommended score of 625 (paper), proof of adequate funds. *Recommended:* Proof of health/immunizations.

International Student Contact Alison Roache-Jones, Admissions Manager, 20000 Northwest Walker Road, Beaverton, OR 97006. **Phone:** 503-748-7636. **Fax:** 503-748-1285. **E-mail:** admissions@admin.ogi.edu.

■ APPLICATION

Required Application form, baccalaureate/first degree, 3 letters of recommendation, personal statement, transcripts of college work, 2 years of work experience. School will accept GMAT and GRE.

Deadlines and Fees Applications for domestic and international students are processed on a rolling basis. *Application fee:* $50, $50 (international).

Application Contact Ms. Victoria Tyler, MST Department Administrator, 20000 Northwest Walker Road, Beaverton, OR 97006. **Phone:** 503-748-1335. **Toll-free Phone:** 800-685-2423. **Fax:** 503-748-1268. **E-mail:** vtyler@admin.ogi.edu.

Oregon State University

Corvallis, Oregon

COLLEGE OF BUSINESS

Graduate Business Faculty

Full-time: 31	Part-time: 2

Student Body

Total: 81	
Full-time: 56	Average Age: 27
Part-time: 25	Women: 47%

Admissions

Applications: 181	
Admitted: 68	Average GMAT: 565
Enrolled: 47	Average GPA: 3.26

Costs (1999–2000)
Full-time tuition: $6489 per academic year (resident), $11,061 per academic year (nonresident)
Part-time tuition: N/R

After Graduation (Class of 1998–99)
Employed within 3 months of graduation: 95%
Average starting salary: $40,000

Accreditation
AACSB—The International Association for Management Education

DEGREE MBA

MBA—Master of Business Administration Full-time and part-time. 58 to 72 total credits required. 11 to 15 months to complete program. *Concentrations:* management.

Oregon State University (continued)

COSTS

Tuition, state resident: *Full-time* $6489. **Tuition, nonresident:** *Full-time* $11,061. **Tuition, international:** *Full-time* $11,061. Tuition varies by class time and number of courses or credits taken. **Required fees:** Fees vary by number of courses or credits taken and academic program. **Graduate housing:** Room and board costs vary by number of occupants, type of accommodation, and type of board plan. *Typical cost:* $6780 (including board).

FINANCIAL AID (1999–2000)

Fellowships, loans, research assistantships, scholarships, teaching assistantships, and work study. Financial aid application deadline: 2/1. **Financial Aid Contact** Keith McCreight, Director, Financial Aid Office, OSU Financial Aid Office, AdS A218, Corvallis, OR 97331. **Phone:** 541-737-2241. **Fax:** 541-737-4494. **E-mail:** mccreigk@ccmail.orst.edu.

RESOURCES AND SERVICES

Information about online services, personal computer policies, library resources, international exchange programs, internship programs, and placement services at this institution and others can be found at **www.petersons.com/mba**

International Students

26% of students enrolled are international students.

Services and Facilities Counseling/support services, ESL/language courses, housing location assistance, international student housing, international student organization, language tutoring, orientation, visa services. Financial aid is available to international students.

Applying *Required:* TOEFL with recommended score of 233 (computer) or 575 (paper), proof of adequate funds, proof of health/immunizations. *Recommended:* TSE.

International Student Contact Dr. John G. Van de Water, Dean, International Education, 444 Snell, International Education, Corvallis, OR 97331. **Phone:** 541-737-3006. **Fax:** 541-737-6482. **E-mail:** vandewaj@ccmail.orst.edu.

■ APPLICATION

Required GMAT, application form, baccalaureate/first degree, 3 letters of recommendation, personal statement, transcripts of college work. **Recommended** Resume/curriculum vitae, work experience.

Deadlines and Fees *Deadlines:* 3/1 for fall, 12/1 for winter, 3/1 for spring, 5/15 for summer, 3/1 for fall (international), 9/15 for winter (international), 12/15 for spring (international), 3/15 for summer (international). *Application fee:* $50, $50 (international).

Application Contact Ms. Fran Saveriano, MBA Program Coordinator, 210 Bexell Hall, Corvallis, OR 97331-2603. **Phone:** 541-737-3150. **Toll-free Phone:** 800-228-3187. **Fax:** 541-737-4890. **E-mail:** saveriano@bus.orst.edu.

Portland State University

Portland, Oregon

SCHOOL OF BUSINESS ADMINISTRATION

Graduate Business Faculty

Full-time: 60	Part-time: 22

Student Body

Total: 398	Average Age: 30
Full-time: 127	Women: 37%
Part-time: 271	

Admissions

Applications: 251	Average GMAT: 602
Admitted: 120	Average GPA: 3.2
Enrolled: 104	

Costs (1999–2000)
Full-time tuition: $6291 per academic year (resident), $10,766 per academic year (nonresident)
Part-time tuition: $200 per credit hour (resident), $200 per credit hour (nonresident)

After Graduation (Class of 1998–99)
Employed within 3 months of graduation: 80%
Average starting salary: $63,464

Accreditation
AACSB—The International Association for Management Education

DEGREES EMP • MBA • MIM • MSFA

EMP—Engineering Management Program Full-time and part-time. At least 50 total credits required. 12 to 48 months to complete program.
MBA—Master of Business Administration Full-time and part-time. *Distance learning option.* At least 72 total credits required. 12 to 60 months to complete program. *Concentrations:* finance, international business, technology management.
MIM—Master of International Management Full-time and part-time. At least 66 total credits required. 12 to 60 months to complete program.
MSFA—Master of Science in Financial Analysis Full-time and part-time. At least 49 total credits required. 12 to 24 months to complete program.

COSTS

Tuition, state resident: *Full-time* $6291. *Part-time* $200 per credit hour. **Tuition, nonresident:** *Full-time* $10,766. *Part-time* $200 per credit hour. Tuition varies by number of courses or credits taken and local reciprocity agreements. **Required fees:** Fees vary by number of courses or credits taken and academic program. **Graduate housing:** Room and board costs vary by campus location, number of occupants, type of accommodation, and type of board plan. *Typical cost:* $10,000 (room only).

FINANCIAL AID (1999–2000)

Financial Aid Contact Ms. Kathy Goff, Assistant Director of Financial Aid, Student Financial Aid Office, PO Box 751, Portland, OR 97207-0751. **Phone:** 503-725-3461.

RESOURCES AND SERVICES

Information about online services, personal computer policies, library resources, international exchange programs, internship programs, and placement services at this institution and others can be found at **www.petersons.com/mba**

International Students

16% of students enrolled are international students.

Services and Facilities Counseling/support services, ESL/language courses, international student housing, orientation, visa services.

Applying *Required:* TOEFL with recommended score of 213 (computer) or 550 (paper), proof of adequate funds, proof of health/immunizations.

International Student Contact Dawn White, Director, International Education Services, PO Box 751, Portland, OR 97207. **Phone:** 503-725-5075. **E-mail:** whited@pdx.edu.

■ APPLICATION

Required GMAT, application form, baccalaureate/first degree, resume/curriculum vitae, transcripts of college work, 2 years of work experience. **Recommended** Letter(s) of recommendation, personal statement.

Deadlines and Fees *Deadlines:* 4/1 for fall, 8/1 for winter, 3/1 for fall (international), 7/1 for winter (international). *Application fee:* $50, $50 (international).

Application Contact Pam Mitchell, Graduate Programs Administrator, School of Business Administration, PO Box 751, Portland, OR 97207-0751. **Phone:** 503-725-4733. **Fax:** 503-725-5850. **E-mail:** pamm@sba.pdx.edu.

See full description on page 772.

University of Oregon

Eugene, Oregon

CHARLES H. LUNDQUIST COLLEGE OF BUSINESS

Graduate Business Faculty

Full-time: 49	Part-time: 12

Student Body

Total: 178	Average Age: 27
Full-time: 178	Women: 26%

Admissions

Applications: 316	Average GMAT: 619
Admitted: 158	Average GPA: 3.36
Enrolled: 83	

Costs (1999–2000)
Full-time tuition: $8350 per academic year (resident), $13,009 per academic year (nonresident)
Part-time tuition: N/R

After Graduation (Class of 1998–99)
Employed within 3 months of graduation: 94%
Average starting salary: $54,000

Accreditation
AACSB—The International Association for Management Education

DEGREES JD/MBA • M Acct • MBA

JD/MBA— Full-time. At least 120 total credits required. Minimum of 48 months to complete program.

M Acct—Master of Accounting Full-time. At least 45 total credits required. Minimum of 12 months to complete program.

MBA—MBA Program Full-time. 48 to 72 total credits required. 15 to 24 months to complete program. *Concentrations:* entrepreneurship, finance, international business, management, marketing, sports/entertainment management.

COSTS

Tuition, state resident: *Full-time* $6750. **Tuition, nonresident:** *Full-time* $11,409. **Tuition, international:** *Full-time* $11,409. Tuition varies by class time and number of courses or credits taken. **Required fees:** *Full-time* $1600. Fees vary by number of courses or credits taken and academic program. **Graduate housing:** Room and board costs vary by number of occupants, type of accommodation, and type of board plan. *Typical cost:* $7700 (including board).

FINANCIAL AID (1999–2000)

Fellowships, loans, research assistantships, scholarships, teaching assistantships, and work study. **Financial Aid Contact** Ms. Wendy Mitchell, Director of Master's Programs, Charles H. Lundquist College of Business, 1208 University of Oregon, Eugene, OR 97403-1208. **Phone:** 541-546-3306. **Fax:** 541-348-3347. **E-mail:** mbainfo@biz.uoregon.edu.

RESOURCES AND SERVICES

Information about online services, personal computer policies, library resources, international exchange programs, internship programs, and placement services at this institution and others can be found at **www. petersons.com/mba**

International Students

26% of students enrolled are international students.

Services and Facilities Counseling/support services, ESL/language courses, housing location assistance, international student housing, international student organization, language tutoring, orientation, visa services. Financial aid is not available to international students.

Applying *Required:* TOEFL with recommended score of 575 (paper), proof of adequate funds, proof of health/immunizations.

International Student Contact Ms. Wendy Mitchell, Assistant Dean, Academic Programs, Charles H. Lundquist College of Business, Eugene, OR 97403-1208. **Phone:** 541-346-3306. **Fax:** 541-346-3347. **E-mail:** mbainfo@biz.uoregon. edu.

■ **APPLICATION**

Required Application form, baccalaureate/first degree, essay, 2 letters of recommendation, resume/curriculum vitae, transcripts of college work. School will accept GMAT. **Recommended** Interview, work experience.

Deadlines and Fees *Deadlines:* 4/15 for fall, 2/15 for fall (international). *Application fee:* $50, $50 (international).

Application Contact Ms. Wendy Mitchell, Assistant Dean, Academic Programs, Charles H. Lundquist College of Business, 1208 University of Oregon, Eugene, OR 97403-1208. **Phone:** 541-346-3306. **Fax:** 541-346-3347. **E-mail:** mbainfo@biz.uoregon.edu.

University of Portland

Portland, Oregon

DR. ROBERT B. PAMPLIN, JR. SCHOOL OF BUSINESS

Graduate Business Faculty
Full-time: 27 — Part-time: 3

Student Body
Total: 95
Full-time: 30 — Average Age: 32
Part-time: 65 — Women: 41%

Admissions
Applications: 92
Admitted: 61 — Average GMAT: 525
Enrolled: 31 — Average GPA: 3.2

Costs (1999–2000)
Full-time tuition: N/R
Part-time tuition: $563 per credit hour

Accreditation
AACSB—The International Association for Management Education

DEGREES MB • MBA

MB—Master of Business Administration Part-time. At least 30 total credits required. Maximum of 72 months to complete program. *Concentrations:* accounting, economics, entrepreneurship, international and area business studies, management, marketing.

MBA—Master of Business Administration Full-time and part-time. 30 to 54 total credits required. 12 to 72 months to complete program. *Concentrations:* finance, international business, management, marketing.

COSTS

Tuition *Part-time:* $563 per credit hour. Tuition varies by academic program. **Graduate housing:** Room and board costs vary by number of occupants, type of accommodation, and type of board plan. *Typical cost:* $5190 (including board).

FINANCIAL AID (1999–2000)

6 students received aid, including loans, research assistantships, scholarships, and work study. Aid is available to part-time students. Financial aid application deadline: 3/15. **Financial Aid Contact** Ms. Tracy Reisinger, Director of Financial Aid, 5000 North Willamette Boulevard, Portland, OR 97203-5798. **Phone:** 503-943-7311. **Fax:** 503-943-7399. **E-mail:** reisinge@up.edu.

RESOURCES AND SERVICES

Information about online services, personal computer policies, library resources, international exchange programs, internship programs, and placement services at this institution and others can be found at **www. petersons.com/mba**

International Students

31% of students enrolled are international students.

Services and Facilities Counseling/support services, ESL/language courses, international student organization. Financial aid is available to international students. **Applying** *Required:* TOEFL with recommended score of 570 (paper), proof of adequate funds.

International Student Contact Mr. Michael Pelley, Director of International Programs, 5000 North Willamette Boulevard, Portland, OR 97203-5798. **Phone:** 503-943-7367. **Fax:** 503-943-7399. **E-mail:** pelley@up.edu.

■ **APPLICATION**

Required Application form, baccalaureate/first degree, essay, 2 letters of recommendation, personal statement, transcripts of college work. School will accept GMAT. **Recommended** Work experience.

Deadlines and Fees *Deadlines:* 8/1 for fall, 12/1 for spring, 4/1 for summer, 5/1 for fall (international). *Application fee:* $40, $40 (international).

Application Contact Dr. Todd Shank, Associate Dean/Director, 5000 North Willamette Boulevard, Portland, OR 97203-5798. **Phone:** 503-943-7224. **Toll-free Phone:** 800-227-4566 Ext. 7224. **Fax:** 503-943-8041. **E-mail:** mba-up@up.edu.

Willamette University

Salem, Oregon

GEO. H. ATKINSON GRADUATE SCHOOL OF MANAGEMENT

Graduate Business Faculty
Full-time: 14 — Part-time: 6

Student Body
Total: 159
Full-time: 137 — Average Age: 26
Part-time: 22 — Women: 42%

Admissions
Applications: 129
Admitted: 120 — Average GMAT: 550
Enrolled: 70 — Average GPA: 3.2

Costs (1999–2000)
Full-time tuition: $16,010 per academic year
Part-time tuition: $532 per credit

After Graduation (Class of 1998–99)
Employed within 3 months of graduation: 80%
Average starting salary: $49,000

Accreditation
AACSB—The International Association for Management Education

DEGREES JD/MBA • MBA

JD/MBA—Juris Doctor/Master of Business Administration Full-time. At least 120 total credits required. 48 months to complete program. *Concentrations:*

Willamette University (continued)

accounting, finance, human resources, information management, international management, management, management science, marketing, organizational behavior/development, public management, public policy and administration, quantitative analysis.

MBA—Accelerated Program Full-time and part-time. Degree from AACSB-accredited business program, 3.5 cumulative GPA, and 2 years of work experience. 30 to 60 total credits required. 9 to 26 months to complete program. *Concentrations:* accounting, finance, human resources, information management, international management, management, management science, marketing, organizational behavior/development, public management, public policy and administration, quantitative analysis.

MBA—Master of Business Administration Full-time and part-time. At least 60 total credits required. 26 to 60 months to complete program. *Concentrations:* accounting, finance, human resources, information management, international management, management, management science, marketing, organizational behavior/development, public management, public policy and administration, quantitative analysis.

COSTS

Tuition *Full-time:* $15,960. *Part-time:* $532 per credit. **Tuition, international:** *Full-time* $15,960. **Required fees:** *Full-time* $50. *Part-time* $12.50 per semester. Tuition and fees vary by number of courses or credits taken and academic program. **Graduate housing:** Room and board costs vary by number of occupants, type of accommodation, and type of board plan. *Typical cost:* $6500 (room only).

FINANCIAL AID (1999–2000)

116 students received aid, including loans, research assistantships, scholarships, and work study. Aid is available to part-time students.
Financial Aid Contact Zofia Miller, Assistant Director of Financial Aid, 900 State Street, Salem, OR 97301. **Phone:** 503-370-5416. **Fax:** 503-370-6588. **E-mail:** zmiller@willamette.edu.

RESOURCES AND SERVICES

Information about online services, personal computer policies, library resources, international exchange programs, internship programs, and placement services at this institution and others can be found at **www.petersons.com/mba**

International Students

23% of students enrolled are international students.

Services and Facilities Counseling/support services, housing location assistance, international student organization, visa services. Financial aid is available to international students.
Applying *Required:* TOEFL with recommended score of 213 (computer) or 550 (paper), proof of adequate funds, proof of health/immunizations.
International Student Contact Donna McElroy, Director, International Student and Faculty Services, 900 State Street, Salem, OR 97301-3931. **Phone:** 503-375-5404. **Fax:** 503-370-6407. **E-mail:** dmcelroy@willamette.edu.

■ APPLICATION

Required GMAT or GRE, application form, baccalaureate/first degree, essay, 2 letters of recommendation, personal statement, resume/curriculum vitae, transcripts of college work. **Recommended** Interview.

Deadlines and Fees Applications for domestic and international students are processed on a rolling basis. *Application fee:* $50, $50 (international).

Application Contact Judy O'Neill, Assistant Dean/Director of Admissions, 900 State Street, Salem, OR 97301-3931. **Phone:** 503-370-6167. **Fax:** 503-370-3011. **E-mail:** joneill@willamette.edu.

See full description on page 1018.

PENNSYLVANIA

Allentown College of St. Francis de Sales

Center Valley, Pennsylvania

DEPARTMENT OF BUSINESS

Graduate Business Faculty

Full-time: 10	Part-time: 15

Student Body

Total: 565	Average Age: 35
Full-time: 3	Women: 62%
Part-time: 562	

Admissions

Applications: 133	Average GMAT: 530
Admitted: 119	Average GPA: 3.2
Enrolled: 89	

Costs (1999–2000)
Full-time tuition: N/R
Part-time tuition: $415 per credit

After Graduation (Class of 1998–99)
Employed within 3 months of graduation: 99%
Average starting salary: $45,000

DEGREE MBA

MBA—Master of Business Administration Full-time and part-time. *Distance learning option.* 33 to 48 total credits required. 12 to 84 months to complete program. *Concentrations:* accounting, electronic commerce (e-commerce), finance, health care, management, marketing, system management.

COSTS

Tuition *Part-time:* $415 per credit. Tuition varies by number of courses or credits taken.

RESOURCES AND SERVICES

Information about online services, personal computer policies, library resources, international exchange programs, internship programs, and placement services at this institution and others can be found at **www.petersons.com/mba**

International Students

2% of students enrolled are international students.

Services and Facilities Counseling/support services, ESL/language courses, language tutoring, orientation. Financial aid is not available to international students.
Applying *Required:* TOEFL, proof of adequate funds.

■ APPLICATION

Required GMAT, application form, baccalaureate/first degree, 3 letters of recommendation, personal statement, transcripts of college work, 2 years of work experience. School will accept GRE. **Recommended** Interview, resume/curriculum vitae.

Deadlines and Fees Applications for domestic and international students are processed on a rolling basis. *Application fee:* $35, $35 (international).

Application Contact Dr. Mohamed A. S. Latib, Director, MBA Program, 2755 Station Avenue, Center Valley, PA 18034-9568. **Phone:** 610-282-1100 Ext. 1365. **Toll-free Phone:** 888-MBA-EXCEL. **Fax:** 610-282-2254. **E-mail:** mba@email.allencol.edu.

The American College

Bryn Mawr, Pennsylvania

RICHARD D. IRWIN GRADUATE SCHOOL

Graduate Business Faculty

Full-time: 23	Part-time: 4

Student Body

Total: 940	Average Age: 45
Part-time: 940	Women: 33%

Admissions
Applications: 130   Enrolled: 125

Costs (1999–2000)
Full-time tuition: N/R
Part-time tuition: $525 per course

DEGREE MS

MS—Master of Science in Financial Services Full-time and part-time. *Distance learning option.* At least 36 total credits required. Maximum of 84 months to complete program. *Concentrations:* financial management/planning.

COSTS

Tuition *Part-time:* $525 per course.

FINANCIAL AID (1999–2000)
Scholarships. **Financial Aid Contact** M. Donald Wright, Director, Richard D. Irwin Graduate School, 270 South Bryn Mawr Avenue, Bryn Mawr, PA 19010-2105. **E-mail:** donw@amercoll.edu.

RESOURCES AND SERVICES
Information about online services, personal computer policies, library resources, international exchange programs, internship programs, and placement services at this institution and others can be found at **www.petersons.com/mba**

International Students
3% of students enrolled are international students.

Services and Facilities Financial aid is not available to international students.
International Student Contact Joanne Patterson, Associate Director—Graduate Administration, 270 South Bryn Mawr Avenue, Bryn Mawr, PA 19010. **Phone:** 610-526-1366. **Fax:** 610-526-1310. **E-mail:** joannep@amercoll.edu.

■ APPLICATION

Required Application form, baccalaureate/first degree, personal statement, transcripts of college work.
Deadlines and Fees Applications for domestic and international students are processed on a rolling basis. *Application fee:* $275, $275 (international).
Application Contact Joanne Patterson, Associate Director, Graduate School Administration, 270 South Bryn Mawr Avenue, Bryn Mawr, PA 19010-2105. **Phone:** 610-526-1366. **Fax:** 610-526-1310. **E-mail:** joannep@amercoll.edu.

Bloomsburg University of Pennsylvania

Bloomsburg, Pennsylvania

COLLEGE OF BUSINESS

Graduate Business Faculty
Full-time: 25

Student Body
Total: 69   Average Age: 34
Full-time: 14   Women: 36%
Part-time: 55

Admissions
Applications: 15   Average GMAT: 510
Admitted: 15   Average GPA: 3.04
Enrolled: 15

Costs (1999–2000)
Full-time tuition: $3780 per academic year (resident), $6614 per academic year (nonresident)
Part-time tuition: $210 per credit hour (resident), $367 per credit hour (nonresident)

After Graduation (Class of 1998–99)
Employed within 3 months of graduation: 100%

DEGREE MBA

MBA—Master of Business Administration Full-time and part-time. 36 to 51 total credits required. 12 to 72 months to complete program.

COSTS

Tuition, state resident: *Full-time* $3780. *Part-time* $210 per credit hour. **Tuition, nonresident:** *Full-time* $6614. *Part-time* $367 per credit hour. Tuition varies by number of courses or credits taken. **Required fees:** Fees vary by number of courses or credits taken and campus location. **Graduate housing:** Room and

board costs vary by number of occupants, type of accommodation, and type of board plan. *Typical cost:* $3842 (including board), $2232 (room only).

FINANCIAL AID (1999–2000)
Loans, research assistantships, and work study. **Financial Aid Contact** Thomas M. Lyons, 400 East Second Street, Bloomsburg, PA 17815-1905. **Phone:** 570-389-4279. **Fax:** 570-389-4795.

RESOURCES AND SERVICES
Information about online services, personal computer policies, library resources, international exchange programs, internship programs, and placement services at this institution and others can be found at **www.petersons.com/mba**

International Students
9% of students enrolled are international students.

Services and Facilities Counseling/support services, housing location assistance, international student housing, international student organization, orientation, visa services.
Applying *Required:* TOEFL with recommended score of 550 (paper), proof of adequate funds, proof of health/immunizations.
International Student Contact Dr. Madhau Sharma, Director, International Education, 400 East Second Street, Bloomsburg, PA 17815-1905. **Phone:** 570-389-4830. **E-mail:** msharma@bloomu.edu.

■ APPLICATION

Required GMAT, application form, baccalaureate/first degree, 3 letters of recommendation, resume/curriculum vitae, transcripts of college work. School will accept GRE. **Recommended** Interview.
Deadlines and Fees Applications for domestic students are processed on a rolling basis. *Application fee:* $30, $30 (international).
Application Contact Dr. Patrick Schloss, Assistant Vice President and Dean of Graduate Studies and Research, 400 East Second Street, Bloomsburg, PA 17815-1905. **Phone:** 570-389-4015. **Fax:** 570-389-3054. **E-mail:** mba@bloomu.edu.

California University of Pennsylvania

California, Pennsylvania

SCHOOL OF GRADUATE STUDIES

Graduate Business Faculty
Part-time: 10

Student Body
Total: 75   Average Age: 33
Full-time: 35   Women: 49%
Part-time: 40

Admissions
Applications: 34   Average GMAT: 470
Admitted: 24   Average GPA: 3.25
Enrolled: 20

Costs (1999–2000)
Full-time tuition: $4794 per academic year (resident), $7624 per academic year (nonresident)
Part-time tuition: $210 per credit (resident), $367 per credit (nonresident)

After Graduation (Class of 1998–99)
Employed within 3 months of graduation: 87%
Average starting salary: $23,000

DEGREE MS

MS—Master of Science in Business Administration Full-time and part-time. At least 39 total credits required. 20 to 72 months to complete program.

COSTS

Tuition, state resident: *Full-time* $3780. *Part-time* $210 per credit. **Tuition, nonresident:** *Full-time* $6610. *Part-time* $367 per credit. **Required fees:** *Full-time* $1014. Tuition and fees vary by number of courses or credits taken. **Graduate housing:** Room and board costs vary by number of occupants, type of accommodation, and type of board plan. *Typical cost:* $4526 (including board).

California University of Pennsylvania (continued)

FINANCIAL AID (1999–2000)

10 students received aid, including research assistantships. Financial aid application deadline: 8/1. **Financial Aid Contact** Mr. Robert Thorn, Director of Financial Aid, 250 University Avenue, California, PA 15419-1394. **Phone:** 724-938-4415. **E-mail:** thorn@cup.edu.

RESOURCES AND SERVICES

Information about online services, personal computer policies, library resources, international exchange programs, internship programs, and placement services at this institution and others can be found at **www.petersons.com/mba**

International Students

16% of students enrolled are international students.

Services and Facilities Counseling/support services. Financial aid is not available to international students.

Applying *Required:* TOEFL with recommended score of 550 (paper), proof of adequate funds, proof of health/immunizations.

International Student Contact Dr. Nancy Tait, International Student Advisor, 250 University Avenue, California, PA 15419-1394. **Phone:** 724-938-4056. **E-mail:** tait@cup.edu.

■ APPLICATION

Required GMAT, application form, baccalaureate/first degree, transcripts of college work.

Deadlines and Fees Applications for domestic and international students are processed on a rolling basis. *Application fee:* $25, $25 (international).

Application Contact Dr. Donald Thompson, Dean of Graduate Studies and Research, 250 University Avenue, California, PA 15419-1394. **Phone:** 724-938-4187. **Fax:** 724-938-5712. **E-mail:** gradschool@cup.edu.

Carnegie Mellon University

Pittsburgh, Pennsylvania

GRADUATE SCHOOL OF INDUSTRIAL ADMINISTRATION

Graduate Business Faculty

Full-time: 84	Part-time: 32

Student Body

Total: 641	Average Age: 28
Full-time: 457	Women: 24%
Part-time: 184	

Admissions

Applications: 1,415	Average GMAT: 653
Admitted: 421	Average GPA: 3.2
Enrolled: 244	

Costs (1999–2000)
Full-time tuition: $25,130 per academic year
Part-time tuition: $250 per unit

After Graduation (Class of 1998–99)
Employed within 3 months of graduation: 93%
Average starting salary: $86,980

Accreditation
AACSB—The International Association for Management Education

DEGREES JD/MS • MS

JD/MS—Juris Doctor/Master of Science in Industrial Administration Full-time. At least 247 total credits required. 48 months to complete program.

MS—Master of Science in Computational Finance Full-time and part-time. *Distance learning option.* At least 48 total credits required. 12 to 24 months to complete program. *Concentrations:* finance, quantitative analysis.

MS—Master of Science in Electronic Commerce Full-time. At least 60 total credits required. 12 months to complete program.

MS—Master of Science in Industrial Administration Full-time and part-time. At least 68 total credits required. 16 to 24 months to complete program. *Concentrations:* accounting, economics, entrepreneurship, finance, international business, management information systems, marketing, operations management, organizational behavior/development, quantitative analysis, strategic management.

MS—Master of Science in Information Networking Full-time. At least 48 total credits required. *Concentrations:* information management, management information systems, management systems analysis, telecommunications management.

COSTS

Tuition *Full-time:* $25,000. *Part-time:* $250 per unit. **Required fees:** *Full-time* $130. *Part-time* $130 per year. **Graduate housing:** Room and board costs vary by campus location, number of occupants, type of accommodation, and type of board plan. *Typical cost:* $9400 (including board).

FINANCIAL AID (1999–2000)

350 students received aid, including fellowships, loans, teaching assistantships, and work study. Financial aid application deadline: 6/1. **Financial Aid Contact** Ms. Lauren Tracey, Associate Director of Financial Aid and Admissions, Graduate School of Industrial Administration, Pittsburgh, PA 15213-3890. **Phone:** 412-268-7581. **Fax:** 412-268-4209. **E-mail:** laurent@cmu.edu.

RESOURCES AND SERVICES

Information about online services, personal computer policies, library resources, international exchange programs, internship programs, and placement services at this institution and others can be found at **www.petersons.com/mba**

International Students

29% of students enrolled are international students.

Services and Facilities Counseling/support services, ESL/language courses, visa services. Financial aid is not available to international students.

Applying *Required:* TOEFL with recommended score of 600 (paper), proof of adequate funds.

International Student Contact Ms. Wendy Hermann, Director, Student Affairs, Graduate School of Industrial Administration, Pittsburgh, PA 15213-3890. **Phone:** 412-268-3167. **Fax:** 412-268-6837. **E-mail:** hermann@andrew.cmu.edu.

■ APPLICATION

Required GMAT, application form, baccalaureate/first degree, essay, 3 letters of recommendation, resume/curriculum vitae, transcripts of college work. **Recommended** Interview, work experience.

Deadlines and Fees *Deadlines:* 3/10 for fall, 3/10 for fall (international). *Application fee:* $60, $60 (international).

Application Contact Ms. Laurie Stewart, Director of Admissions, Graduate School of Industrial Administration, Pittsburgh, PA 15213-3890. **Phone:** 412-268-2272. **Toll-free Phone:** 800-850-GSIA. **Fax:** 412-268-4209. **E-mail:** gsia-admisions@andrew.cmu.edu.

See full description on page 584.

Chatham College

Pittsburgh, Pennsylvania

PROGRAM IN MANAGEMENT

DEGREE MM

MM—Master of Management Full-time and part-time. 30 to 51 total credits required. Minimum of 12 months to complete program.

RESOURCES AND SERVICES

Information about online services, personal computer policies, library resources, international exchange programs, internship programs, and placement services at this institution and others can be found at **www.petersons.com/mba**

International Students

Services and Facilities Counseling/support services, ESL/language courses, international student housing, international student organization, orientation, visa services. Financial aid is not available to international students.

International Student Contact International Admissions Counselor, Woodland Road, Pittsburgh, PA 15232-2826. **Phone:** 412-365-1618.

■ APPLICATION

Application Contact Dr. Mark Sanford, Academic Advisor for Evening and Weekend Studies, Woodland Road, Pittsburgh, PA 15232. **Phone:** 412-365-1858. **Toll-free Phone:** 800-837-1290. **Fax:** 412-365-1720. **E-mail:** admissions@chatham.edu.

Clarion University of Pennsylvania

Clarion, Pennsylvania

COLLEGE OF BUSINESS ADMINISTRATION

Graduate Business Faculty
Full-time: 40

Student Body
Total: 40
Full-time: 26
Part-time: 14

Average Age: 31
Women: 38%

Admissions
Applications: 50
Admitted: 44
Enrolled: 26

Average GMAT: 520
Average GPA: 3.29

Costs (1999–2000)
Full-time tuition: $3780 per academic year (resident), $6610 per academic year (nonresident)
Part-time tuition: $210 per credit (resident), $367 per credit (nonresident)

Accreditation
AACSB—The International Association for Management Education

DEGREE MBA

MBA—Master of Business Administration Full-time and part-time. At least 33 total credits required. 11 to 72 months to complete program. *Concentrations:* accounting, economics, finance, management, marketing.

COSTS

Tuition, state resident: *Full-time* $3780. *Part-time* $210 per credit. **Tuition, nonresident:** *Full-time* $6610. *Part-time* $367 per credit. **Tuition, international:** *Full-time* $6236. Tuition varies by number of courses or credits taken. **Graduate housing:** Room and board costs vary by number of occupants and type of board plan. *Typical cost:* $3712 (including board), $2300 (room only).

FINANCIAL AID (1999–2000)

22 students received aid, including research assistantships and work study. Aid is available to part-time students. Financial aid application deadline: 4/15. **Financial Aid Contact** Mr. Kenneth Grugel, Director of Financial Aid, Egbert Hall, Clarion, PA 16214. **Phone:** 814-393-2315. **Fax:** 814-393-2520. **E-mail:** kgrugel@clarion.edu.

RESOURCES AND SERVICES

Information about online services, personal computer policies, library resources, international exchange programs, internship programs, and placement services at this institution and others can be found at **www.petersons.com/mba**

International Students

13% of students enrolled are international students.

Services and Facilities Counseling/support services, international student housing, international student organization, orientation. Financial aid is not available to international students.

Applying *Required:* TOEFL with recommended score of 550 (paper), proof of adequate funds.

International Student Contact Ms. Linda Heineman, Foreign Student Advisor, International Programs Office, Clarion, PA 16214. **Phone:** 814-393-2340. **Fax:** 814-393-2341. **E-mail:** heineman@mail.clarion.edu.

■ APPLICATION

Required GMAT, application form, baccalaureate/first degree, 3 letters of recommendation, resume/curriculum vitae, transcripts of college work. **Recommended** Personal statement.

Deadlines and Fees Applications for domestic students are processed on a rolling basis. *Deadlines:* 4/1 for fall (international), 7/1 for spring (international). *Application fee:* $25, $25 (international).

Application Contact Dr. Robert Balough, Director of MBA Program, 302 Still Hall, Clarion, PA 16214. **Phone:** 814-393-2605. **Toll-free Phone:** 800-841-8975. **Fax:** 814-393-1910. **E-mail:** mba@clarion.edu.

See full description on page 594.

College Misericordia

Dallas, Pennsylvania

DIVISION OF BEHAVIORAL SCIENCE, EDUCATION, AND BUSINESS

Graduate Business Faculty
Full-time: 3

Part-time: 12

Student Body
Total: 92
Part-time: 92

Average Age: 35
Women: 71%

Admissions
Applications: 50
Admitted: 32

Enrolled: 32
Average GPA: 3

Costs (1999–2000)
Full-time tuition: N/R
Part-time tuition: $430 per credit

After Graduation (Class of 1998–99)
Employed within 3 months of graduation: 100%

DEGREE MS

MS—Master of Science in Organizational Management Full-time and part-time. At least 36 total credits required. 12 to 60 months to complete program. *Concentrations:* human resources, management, nonprofit management.

COSTS

Tuition *Part-time:* $430 per credit. Tuition varies by number of courses or credits taken and academic program.

FINANCIAL AID (1999–2000)

10 students received aid, including fellowships, loans, research assistantships, teaching assistantships, and work study. Aid is available to part-time students. **Financial Aid Contact** Peg Charnick, Director of Financial Aid, 301 Lake Street, Dallas, PA 18612-1098. **Phone:** 570-674-6280.

RESOURCES AND SERVICES

Information about online services, personal computer policies, library resources, international exchange programs, internship programs, and placement services at this institution and others can be found at **www.petersons.com/mba**

International Students

Services and Facilities Financial aid is available to international students. **International Student Contact** Ms. Laree Brown, Outreach Specialist, Office of Adult Education, 301 Lake Street, Dallas, PA 18612-1098. **Phone:** 570-674-6451.

■ APPLICATION

Required Application form, baccalaureate/first degree, essay, 3 letters of recommendation, transcripts of college work, 2 years of work experience. School will accept GRE and MAT. **Recommended** Interview.

Deadlines and Fees Applications for domestic and international students are processed on a rolling basis. *Application fee:* $25, $25 (international).

Application Contact Ms. Larree Brown, Outreach Specialist, Office of Adult Education, 301 Lake Street, Dallas, PA 18612-1098. **Phone:** 570-674-6451. **Toll-free Phone:** 800-852-7675.

Drexel University

Philadelphia, Pennsylvania

COLLEGE OF BUSINESS AND ADMINISTRATION

Graduate Business Faculty
Full-time: 84

Part-time: 30

Student Body
Total: 816
Full-time: 302
Part-time: 514

Average Age: 26
Women: 45%

Admissions
Applications: 809
Admitted: 475
Enrolled: 232

Average GMAT: 563
Average GPA: 3.23

Drexel University (continued)

Costs (1999–2000)
Full-time tuition: N/R
Part-time tuition: $511 per credit

Accreditation
AACSB—The International Association for Management Education

DEGREES MBA • MS

MBA—Master of Business Administration Full-time and part-time. *Distance learning option.* 48 to 72 total credits required. 12 to 84 months to complete program. *Concentrations:* accounting, decision sciences, economics, electronic commerce (e-commerce), finance, financial management/planning, international business, management, management information systems, marketing, marketing research, operations management, organizational behavior/development, organizational management, production management, taxation.

MS—Master of Science in Accounting Full-time and part-time. 48 to 72 total credits required. 12 to 84 months to complete program. *Concentrations:* accounting.

MS—Master of Science in Decision Sciences Full-time and part-time. 48 to 72 total credits required. 12 to 84 months to complete program. *Concentrations:* decision sciences.

MS—Master of Science in Finance Full-time and part-time. 48 to 72 total credits required. 12 to 84 months to complete program. *Concentrations:* finance.

MS—Master of Science in Taxation Full-time and part-time. 48 to 72 total credits required. 12 to 84 months to complete program. *Concentrations:* taxation.

COSTS
Tuition *Part-time:* $511 per credit. Tuition varies by number of courses or credits taken. **Graduate housing:** *Typical cost:* $7254 (including board).

FINANCIAL AID (1999–2000)
33 students received aid, including fellowships, research assistantships, and teaching assistantships. Financial aid application deadline: 3/1.
Financial Aid Contact Mr. Robert Forest, Assistant Director, Graduate Financial Aid, 3141 Chestnut Street, Philadelphia, PA 19104-2875. **Phone:** 215-895-1627. **Fax:** 215-895-6903. **E-mail:** robert.d.forest@drexel.edu.

RESOURCES AND SERVICES
Information about online services, personal computer policies, library resources, international exchange programs, internship programs, and placement services at this institution and others can be found at **www.petersons.com/mba**

International Students
32% of students enrolled are international students.
Services and Facilities Counseling/support services, ESL/language courses, international student housing, visa services. Financial aid is available to international students.
Applying *Required:* TOEFL with recommended score of 570 (paper), proof of adequate funds, proof of health/immunizations.
International Student Contact Mr. Jef Davis, Director, International Students and Scholars Office, Creese Student Center-Room 210, 3141 Chestnut Streets, Philadelphia, PA 19104. **Phone:** 215-895-2502. **Fax:** 215-895-6617. **E-mail:** jef@drexel.edu.

■ APPLICATION
Required GMAT, application form, baccalaureate/first degree, essay, 2 letters of recommendation, personal statement, transcripts of college work. **Recommended** Resume/curriculum vitae.
Deadlines and Fees *Deadlines:* 8/31 for fall, 11/30 for winter, 3/1 for spring, 5/31 for summer, 6/20 for fall (international), 9/25 for winter (international), 1/1 for spring (international), 3/31 for summer (international). *Application fee:* $35, $35 (international).
Application Contact Ms. Dawn Alli, Associate Director of Graduate Admissions, Office of Graduate Admissions, 3141 Chestnut Street, Philadelphia, PA 19104-2875. **Phone:** 215-895-6704. **Toll-free Phone:** 800-2DREXEL. **Fax:** 215-895-5939. **E-mail:** da32@drexel.edu.

See full description on page 626.

Duquesne University

Pittsburgh, Pennsylvania

GRADUATE SCHOOL OF BUSINESS ADMINISTRATION

Graduate Business Faculty

Full-time: 46   Part-time: 12
Student Body
Total: 672   Average Age: 31
Full-time: 134   Women: 40%
Part-time: 538

Admissions
Applications: 241   Average GMAT: 520
Admitted: 182   Average GPA: 3.1
Enrolled: 101

Costs (1999–2000)
Full-time tuition: N/R
Part-time tuition: $588 per credit

After Graduation (Class of 1998–99)
Employed within 3 months of graduation: 99%
Average starting salary: $50,000

Accreditation
AACSB—The International Association for Management Education

DEGREES JD/MBA • MBA • MBA/MA • MBA/MHMS • MBA/MLS • MBA/MS • MBA/MSTax • MS

JD/MBA—Juris Doctor/Master of Business Administration Full-time and part-time. Must apply to the Graduate School of Business Administration and the Law School. At least 126 total credits required. 36 to 72 months to complete program.

MBA—Master of Business Administration Full-time and part-time. At least 56 total credits required. 18 to 72 months to complete program. *Concentrations:* accounting, business ethics, economics, environmental economics/management, finance, health care, human resources, international business, international management, management information systems, marketing, taxation.

MBA/MA—Master of Business Administration/Master of Arts in Liberal Studies Full-time and part-time. Must apply to Graduate School of Business Administration and Graduate School of Arts. At least 68 total credits required. 24 to 72 months to complete program. *Concentrations:* accounting.

MBA/MHMS—Master of Business Administration/Master of Health Management Systems Full-time and part-time. Must apply to Graduate School of Business Administration and School of Health Sciences. At least 67 total credits required. 24 to 72 months to complete program.

MBA/MLS—Master of Business Administration/Master of Liberal Studies Full-time and part-time. 69 to 72 total credits required. 24 to 72 months to complete program.

MBA/MS—Master of Business Administration/Master of Science in Environmental Science Management Full-time and part-time. Must apply to Graduate School of Business Administration and Graduate School of Sciences. 64 to 68 total credits required. 24 to 72 months to complete program.

MBA/MS—Master of Business Administration/Master of Science in Industrial Pharmacy Full-time. Must apply to Graduate School of Business Administration and School of Pharmacy. At least 75 total credits required. 24 to 72 months to complete program.

MBA/MS—Master of Business Administration/Master of Science in Information Systems Management Full-time and part-time. At least 80 total credits required. 24 to 72 months to complete program. *Concentrations:* accounting, business ethics, economics, environmental economics/management, finance, health care, human resources, international business, international management, management information systems, marketing, real estate, taxation.

MBA/MS—Master of Business Administration/Master of Science in Nursing Full-time and part-time. Must apply to Graduate School of Business Administration and School of Nursing. At least 74 total credits required. 24 to 72 months to complete program.

MBA/MSTax—Master of Business Administration/Master of Science in Taxation Full-time and part-time. At least 62 total credits required. 24 to 72 months to complete program.

MS—Master of Science in Information Systems Management Full-time and part-time. At least 56 total credits required. 18 to 72 months to complete program.

MS—Master of Science in Taxation Full-time and part-time. At least 36 total credits required. 12 to 72 months to complete program.

Duquesne University's John F. Donahue Graduate School of Business Administration challenges students to reach their potential in a dynamic, intellectually exciting environment that is driven by a century-long commitment to professional and personal ethics, teaching excellence, continuous improvement, scholarship, and creative academic-business partnerships. The School prepares leaders who can blend technical competence with a broad-based renaissance education.

The distinctive curriculum focuses on total quality, ethics, the integration of disciplines, communications, the management of technology, and an increased

global perspective. The application of these issues through the use of real business problems responds to employers' strongly expressed need for graduates who can immediately add value in real-world situations. A comprehensive reading program helps students relate specific business disciplines to the world at large, reflecting a renaissance approach to graduate education. Executive faculty members, executives-in-residence, and advisory boards of business professionals supplement the academic capabilities of a faculty with a roster of outstanding executives who participate in the classroom experience.

The Donahue Graduate School of Business Administration provides professional management education of uncompromised quality through instructional excellence in a dynamic environment of change and continuous improvement that offers students excitement, opportunity, and the chance to grow.

COSTS

Tuition *Part-time:* $535 per credit. **Required fees:** *Part-time* $53 per credit. Tuition and fees vary by number of courses or credits taken and campus location. **Graduate housing:** Room and board costs vary by number of occupants. *Typical cost:* $6314 (including board).

FINANCIAL AID (1999–2000)

27 students received aid, including research assistantships. Aid is available to part-time students. Financial aid application deadline: 7/1. **Financial Aid Contact** Mr. Frank Dutkovich, Director, Financial Aid, 600 Forbes Avenue, Pittsburgh, PA 15282. **Phone:** 412-396-6607.

RESOURCES AND SERVICES

Information about online services, personal computer policies, library resources, international exchange programs, internship programs, and placement services at this institution and others can be found at www.petersons.com/mba

International Students

10% of students enrolled are international students.

Services and Facilities Counseling/support services, ESL/language courses, international student organization, visa services. Financial aid is not available to international students.

Applying *Required:* TOEFL with recommended score of 550 (paper), proof of adequate funds, proof of health/immunizations. *Recommended:* TSE, TWE.

International Student Contact Ms. Valentina DeSilva, International Student Advisor, 601 Duquesne Union, Pittsburgh, PA 15282. **Phone:** 412-396-6113. **Fax:** 412-396-5178. **E-mail:** oia@duq2.cc.duq.edu.

■ APPLICATION

Required GMAT, application form, baccalaureate/first degree, 2 letters of recommendation, personal statement, transcripts of college work. **Recommended** Interview, resume/curriculum vitae, work experience.

Deadlines and Fees *Deadlines:* 6/1 for fall, 11/1 for spring, 3/1 for summer, 6/1 for fall (international), 11/1 for spring (international), 3/1 for summer (international). *Application fee:* $40, $40 (international).

Application Contact Ms. Patricia Moore, Assistant Director, Graduate Program, John F. Donahue Graduate School of Business, 600 Forbes Avenue, Pittsburgh, PA 15282. **Phone:** 412-396-6276. **Fax:** 412-396-5304. **E-mail:** moorep@duq2.cc.duq.edu.

See full description on page 628.

Eastern College

St. Davids, Pennsylvania

GRADUATE BUSINESS PROGRAMS

DEGREES M Div/MS • MBA • MBA/M Div • MBA/MS

M Div/MS—Master of Divinity/Master of Science in Economic Development Full-time and part-time. At least 116 total credits required. Maximum of 84 months to complete program.

MBA—Fast-track MBA Full-time. At least 39 total credits required. Minimum of 22 months to complete program. *Concentrations:* management.

MBA—Global MBA Full-time and part-time. At least 36 total credits required. 12 to 84 months to complete program. *Concentrations:* accounting, economics, finance, management, marketing.

MBA/M Div—Master of Business Administration/Master of Divinity Full-time and part-time. At least 116 total credits required. Maximum of 84 months to complete program. *Concentrations:* accounting, economics, finance, international development management, management.

MBA/MS—Fast Track Executive MBA/Master of Science in Health Administration Full-time and part-time. Five years full-time professional work experience or three years post-baccalaureate full-time professional work. 33 to 39 total

credits required. 22 to 84 months to complete program. *Concentrations:* health care.

MBA/MS—Master of Business Administration/Master of Science in Economic Development Full-time and part-time. At least 39 total credits required. 18 to 84 months to complete program. *Concentrations:* international development management.

MBA/MS—Master of Business Administration/Master of Science in Non-Profit Management Full-time and part-time. At least 36 total credits required. 24 to 84 months to complete program. *Concentrations:* nonprofit management.

RESOURCES AND SERVICES

Information about online services, personal computer policies, library resources, international exchange programs, internship programs, and placement services at this institution and others can be found at www.petersons.com/mba

International Students

Services and Facilities Counseling/support services, international student organization. Financial aid is available to international students.

International Student Contact Ms. Lisa Pappas, International Student Advisor, 1300 Eagle Road, St. Davids, PA 19087-3696. **Phone:** 610-341-1454. **Fax:** 610-341-1705.

■ APPLICATION

Application Contact Tia Booth, Graduate Admissions Representative, 1300 Eagle Road, St. Davids, PA 19087-3696. **Phone:** 610-341-5972. **Fax:** 610-341-1466. **E-mail:** gradm@eastern.edu.

See full description on page 632.

Gannon University

Erie, Pennsylvania

SCHOOL OF BUSINESS

DEGREES MBA • MBA/MS • MPA

MBA—Master of Business Administration Full-time and part-time. 30 to 48 total credits required. 12 to 72 months to complete program. *Concentrations:* accounting, finance, human resources, marketing, public policy and administration.

MBA/MS—Master of Business Administration/Master of Science in Nursing Full-time and part-time. At least 69 total credits required. 24 to 72 months to complete program. *Concentrations:* accounting, finance, human resources, marketing, public policy and administration.

MPA—Master of Public Administration Full-time and part-time. At least 36 total credits required. 12 to 36 months to complete program. *Concentrations:* accounting, finance, marketing, public management, public policy and administration.

RESOURCES AND SERVICES

Information about online services, personal computer policies, library resources, international exchange programs, internship programs, and placement services at this institution and others can be found at www.petersons.com/mba

International Students

Services and Facilities Counseling/support services.

International Student Contact Dr. Marjorie Krebs, Professor, Mental Health/Psychology, University Square, Erie, PA 16541. **Phone:** 814-871-7721.

■ APPLICATION

Application Contact Dr. Robert Wallace, Director of MBA Programs, Dahlkemper School of Business, University Square, Erie, PA 16541. **Phone:** 814-871-7565. **E-mail:** wallace002@gannon.edu.

Geneva College

Beaver Falls, Pennsylvania

DEPARTMENT OF BUSINESS, ACCOUNTING AND MANAGEMENT

Graduate Business Faculty
Full-time: 8

Student Body

Total: 18	Average Age: 32
Part-time: 18	Women: 50%

Admissions

Applications: 20	Enrolled: 18
Admitted: 18	Average GPA: 3.2

Geneva College (continued)

Costs (1999–2000)
Full-time tuition: $1260 per academic year
Part-time tuition: $420 per credit

DEGREE MBA

MBA—Master of Business Administration Full-time and part-time. At least 36 total credits required. 12 to 72 months to complete program.

COSTS

Tuition *Full-time:* $1260. *Part-time:* $420 per credit.

FINANCIAL AID (1999–2000)
Loans. **Financial Aid Contact** Ms. Paula DeAngelis, Financial Aid Special Programs Coordinator, 3200 College Avenue, Beaver Falls, PA 15010-3599. **Phone:** 724-847-5680. **Fax:** 724-847-6776. **E-mail:** pdeangel@geneva.edu.

RESOURCES AND SERVICES
Information about online services, personal computer policies, library resources, international exchange programs, internship programs, and placement services at this institution and others can be found at **www.petersons.com/mba**

International Students
11% of students enrolled are international students.

Services and Facilities Counseling/support services, ESL/language courses. Financial aid is not available to international students.
Applying *Required:* TOEFL, proof of adequate funds, proof of health/immunizations.
International Student Contact Dr. Robin Ware, Director of Graduate Student Services, 3200 College Avenue, Beaver Falls, PA 15010-3599. **Phone:** 724-847-6697. **Fax:** 724-847-6101. **E-mail:** rjware@geneva.edu.

■ APPLICATION
Required GMAT, application form, baccalaureate/first degree, 2 letters of recommendation, resume/curriculum vitae, transcripts of college work. School will accept GRE.
Deadlines and Fees Applications for domestic and international students are processed on a rolling basis.
Application Contact Dr. Robin Ware, Director of Graduate Student Services, 3200 College Avenue, Beaver Falls, PA 15010-3599. **Phone:** 724-847-6697. **Toll-free Phone:** 800-847-8255. **Fax:** 724-847-6101. **E-mail:** rjware@geneva.edu.

Grove City College
Grove City, Pennsylvania
PROGRAM IN ACCOUNTING

Graduate Business Faculty
Full-time: 4 — Part-time: 1

Student Body
Total: 11 — Part-time: 6
Full-time: 5 — Women: 64%

Admissions
Applications: 8 — Enrolled: 6
Admitted: 8 — Average GPA: 3

Costs (1999–2000)
Full-time tuition: N/R
Part-time tuition: $296 per credit

DEGREE MA

MA—Master of Arts in Accounting Full-time and part-time. At least 30 total credits required. 12 to 24 months to complete program. *Concentrations:* accounting.

COSTS
Tuition *Part-time:* $296 per credit.

FINANCIAL AID (1999–2000)
6 students received aid, including scholarships. **Financial Aid Contact** Mrs. Patty Peterson, Director of Financial Aid, 100 Campus Drive, Grove City, PA 16127-2104. **Phone:** 724-458-2163.

RESOURCES AND SERVICES
Information about online services, personal computer policies, library resources, international exchange programs, internship programs, and placement services at this institution and others can be found at **www.petersons.com/mba**

International Students
Services and Facilities Counseling/support services. Financial aid is available to international students.
Applying *Required:* TOEFL with recommended score of 550 (paper), proof of adequate funds, proof of health/immunizations.
International Student Contact Mr. Jeffrey Mincey, Director of Admissions, 100 Campus Drive, Grove City, PA 16127-2104. **Phone:** 724-458-2100. **Fax:** 724-458-3395.

■ APPLICATION
Required Application form, baccalaureate/first degree, essay, 2 letters of recommendation, transcripts of college work.
Deadlines and Fees Applications for domestic and international students are processed on a rolling basis. *Application fee:* $30, $30 (international).
Application Contact Office of Admissions, 100 Campus Drive, Grove City, PA 16127-2104. **Phone:** 724-458-2100. **Fax:** 724-458-3395.

Indiana University of Pennsylvania
Indiana, Pennsylvania
EBERLY COLLEGE OF BUSINESS AND INFORMATION TECHNOLOGY

Graduate Business Faculty
Full-time: 71 — Part-time: 10

Student Body
Total: 160 — Average Age: 29
Full-time: 120 — Women: 40%
Part-time: 40

Admissions
Applications: 210 — Average GMAT: 525
Admitted: 140 — Average GPA: 3.1
Enrolled: 85

Costs (1999–2000)
Full-time tuition: $4403 per academic year (resident), $7233 per academic year (nonresident)
Part-time tuition: $210 per credit (resident), $367 per credit (nonresident)

After Graduation (Class of 1998–99)
Employed within 3 months of graduation: 85%
Average starting salary: $45,000

DEGREES MBA • ME

MBA—Executive MBA Part-time. Minimum of 4 years work experience. 51 total credits required. 24 months to complete program.

MBA—Master of Business Administration Full-time and part-time. 2 years of work experience recommended. 33 to 51 total credits required. 12 to 24 months to complete program.

ME—Master of Education in Business Full-time and part-time. 30 to 45 total credits required. 12 to 18 months to complete program.

COSTS
Tuition, state resident: *Full-time* $3780. *Part-time* $210 per credit. **Tuition, nonresident:** *Full-time* $6610. *Part-time* $367 per credit. Tuition varies by number of courses or credits taken. **Required fees:** *Full-time* $623. *Part-time* $228 per year. **Graduate housing:** *Typical cost:* $3800 (including board).

FINANCIAL AID (1999–2000)
Research assistantships and work study. **Financial Aid Contact** Dr. Krish Krishnan, Director, MBA Program, Eberly College of Business and Information Technology, Indiana, PA 15705. **Phone:** 724-357-2522. **Fax:** 724-357-6232. **E-mail:** krishnan@iup.edu.

RESOURCES AND SERVICES
Information about online services, personal computer policies, library resources, international exchange programs, internship programs, and placement services at this institution and others can be found at **www.petersons.com/mba**

International Students

Services and Facilities Counseling/support services, international student housing. Financial aid is available to international students.
Applying *Required:* TOEFL with recommended score of 200 (computer) or 530 (paper), proof of adequate funds.
International Student Contact Dr. Krish Krishnan, Director, MBA Program, Eberly College of Business and Information Technology, Indiana, PA 15705. **Phone:** 724-357-2522. **Fax:** 724-357-6232. **E-mail:** krishnan@iup.edu.

▪ APPLICATION

Required GMAT, application form, baccalaureate/first degree, essay, 2 letters of recommendation, personal statement, transcripts of college work. **Recommended** Resume/curriculum vitae.
Deadlines and Fees Applications for domestic students are processed on a rolling basis. *Deadlines:* 7/1 for fall (international), 11/1 for spring (international). *Application fee:* $30, $30 (international).
Application Contact Dr. Krish Krishnan, Director, MBA Program, Eberly College of Business and Information Technology, Indiana, PA 15705. **Phone:** 724-357-2522. **Toll-free Phone:** 800-487-4746. **Fax:** 724-357-6232. **E-mail:** krishnan@iup.edu.

King's College

Wilkes-Barre, Pennsylvania

WILLIAM G. MCGOWAN SCHOOL OF BUSINESS

Graduate Business Faculty
Full-time: 6   Part-time: 2

Student Body
Total: 97
Part-time: 97   Average Age: 35
                                                  Women: 58%

Admissions
Applications: 22   Average GMAT: 450
Admitted: 20   Average GPA: 3.32
Enrolled: 19

Costs (1999–2000)
Full-time tuition: N/R
Part-time tuition: $480 per credit hour

DEGREES MS

MS—Master of Science in Finance Part-time. At least 30 total credits required. Maximum of 84 months to complete program. *Concentrations:* accounting, finance, taxation.

MS—Master of Science in Health Care Administration Part-time. 42 to 45 total credits required. Maximum of 84 months to complete program. *Concentrations:* health care.

COSTS

Tuition *Part-time:* $480 per credit hour.

RESOURCES AND SERVICES

Information about online services, personal computer policies, library resources, international exchange programs, internship programs, and placement services at this institution and others can be found at **www. petersons.com/mba**

International Students

Services and Facilities Counseling/support services, ESL/language courses, visa services. Financial aid is not available to international students.
Applying *Required:* TOEFL with recommended score of 600 (paper), proof of adequate funds. *Recommended:* Proof of health/immunizations.
International Student Contact Dr. Elizabeth S. Lott, Director of Graduate Programs, 133 North River Street, Wilkes-Barre, PA 18711-0801. **Phone:** 570-208-5991. **Fax:** 570-825-9049. **E-mail:** eslott@kings.edu.

▪ APPLICATION

Required GMAT, application form, baccalaureate/first degree, 2 letters of recommendation, transcripts of college work. **Recommended** Resume/curriculum vitae, work experience.
Deadlines and Fees Applications for domestic and international students are processed on a rolling basis. *Application fee:* $35, $35 (international).
Application Contact Dr. Elizabeth S. Lott, Director of Graduate Programs, Graduate Division, 133 North River Street, Wilkes-Barre, PA 18711-0801. **Phone:** 570-208-5991. **Fax:** 570-825-9049. **E-mail:** eslott@kings.edu.

Kutztown University of Pennsylvania

Kutztown, Pennsylvania

COLLEGE OF BUSINESS

DEGREES MBA

MBA—Health Care Executive MBA Part-time. *Distance learning option.* At least 36 total credits required. Minimum of 18 months to complete program. *Concentrations:* health care.

MBA—International Executive MBA Part-time. *Distance learning option.* At least 36 total credits required. Minimum of 18 months to complete program. *Concentrations:* international business.

MBA—Master of Business Administration Full-time and part-time. *Distance learning option.* At least 36 total credits required. 12 to 72 months to complete program. *Concentrations:* entrepreneurship, finance, health care, human resources, international business, logistics, marketing.

RESOURCES AND SERVICES

Information about online services, personal computer policies, library resources, international exchange programs, internship programs, and placement services at this institution and others can be found at **www. petersons.com/mba**

International Students

Services and Facilities Counseling/support services, ESL/language courses, international student housing, visa services. Financial aid is available to international students.
International Student Contact Dean of Academic Services, Stratton Administration Building, Room 124, Kutztown, PA 19530. **Phone:** 610-683-4215. **Fax:** 610-683-1356.

▪ APPLICATION

Application Contact Dean, College of Business, DF 119, Kutztown, PA 19530. **Phone:** 610-683-4576. **Fax:** 610-683-4573.

La Roche College

Pittsburgh, Pennsylvania

GRADUATE AND CONTINUING EDUCATION OFFICE

Graduate Business Faculty
Full-time: 3   Part-time: 15

Student Body
Total: 107
Full-time: 6   Average Age: 35
Part-time: 101   Women: 75%

Admissions
Applications: 38   Enrolled: 34
Admitted: 34

Costs (1999–2000)
Full-time tuition: N/R
Part-time tuition: $420 per credit

Accreditation
ACBSP—The American Council of Business Schools and Programs

DEGREE MS

MS—Master of Science in Human Resources Management Full-time and part-time. At least 42 total credits required. 12 to 72 months to complete program. *Concentrations:* human resources.

COSTS

Tuition *Part-time:* $420 per credit. Tuition varies by number of courses or credits taken and academic program. **Graduate housing:** *Typical cost:* $6130 (including board), $3760 (room only).

FINANCIAL AID (1999–2000)

Loans. Aid is available to part-time students. Financial aid application deadline: 5/1. **Financial Aid Contact** Ms. Janet McLaughlin, Director of

La Roche College (continued)

Financial Aid, 9000 Babcock Boulevard, Pittsburgh, PA 15237-5898. **Phone:** 412-536-1122. **Fax:** 412-536-1072. **E-mail:** mclaugj1@laroche. edu.

RESOURCES AND SERVICES
Information about online services, personal computer policies, library resources, international exchange programs, internship programs, and placement services at this institution and others can be found at **www. petersons.com/mba**

International Students
2% of students enrolled are international students.
Services and Facilities Counseling/support services, ESL/language courses. Financial aid is not available to international students.
Applying *Required:* TOEFL with recommended score of 550 (paper), proof of adequate funds, proof of health/immunizations.
International Student Contact Dr. Igor Jourin, Assistant to the Dean for Multicultural Education, 9000 Babcock Boulevard, Pittsburgh, PA 15237. **Phone:** 412-536-1294. **Fax:** 412-536-1290. **E-mail:** jourini1@laroche.edu.

■ APPLICATION
Required Application form, baccalaureate/first degree, essay, 2 letters of recommendation, personal statement, resume/curriculum vitae, transcripts of college work. School will accept GMAT, GRE, and MAT. **Recommended** Work experience.
Deadlines and Fees Applications for domestic students are processed on a rolling basis. *Application fee:* $25, $25 (international).
Application Contact Ms. Renee Kozlowski, Associate Director of Admissions, 9000 Babcock Boulevard, Pittsburgh, PA 15237. **Phone:** 412-536-1265. **Fax:** 412-536-1283. **E-mail:** kozlowr1@laroche.edu.

La Salle University
Philadelphia, Pennsylvania
SCHOOL OF BUSINESS ADMINISTRATION

Accreditation
AACSB—The International Association for Management Education

DEGREES EMBA • MBA • MS
EMBA—Executive MBA Program for Science and Technology Part-time. Minimum of 20 months to complete program.
MBA—Master of Business Administration Full-time and part-time. 33 to 48 total credits required. 12 to 64 months to complete program. *Concentrations:* accounting, finance, health care, human resources, international business, management, management information systems, marketing.
MS—Master of Science in Global Management of Techonology

RESOURCES AND SERVICES
Information about online services, personal computer policies, library resources, international exchange programs, internship programs, and placement services at this institution and others can be found at **www. petersons.com/mba**

International Students
Services and Facilities Counseling/support services, visa services. Financial aid is not available to international students.
International Student Contact Ms. Elaine Mshomba, Director, International Student Services, 1900 West Olney Avenue, Philadelphia, PA 19141-1199. **Phone:** 215-951-1948. **Fax:** 215-951-5009. **E-mail:** mshombae@lasalle.edu.

■ APPLICATION
Application Contact Mr. Brian Niles, Director, Marketing and Graduate Enrollment, 1900 West Olney Avenue, Philadelphia, PA 19141. **Phone:** 215-951-1100. **Fax:** 215-951-1886. **E-mail:** niles@lasalle.edu.

Lebanon Valley College
Annville, Pennsylvania
MBA PROGRAM
Graduate Business Faculty
Full-time: 8   Part-time: 40

Student Body
Total: 258   Average Age: 34
Part-time: 258   Women: 36%
Admissions
Average GMAT: 495
Costs (1999–2000)
Full-time tuition: N/R
Part-time tuition: $299 per credit
After Graduation (Class of 1998–99)
Employed within 3 months of graduation: 100%

DEGREE MBA
MBA—Master of Business Administration Full-time and part-time. 2 years of work experience required. At least 36 total credits required. Maximum of 84 months to complete program.

COSTS
Tuition *Part-time:* $299 per credit.

FINANCIAL AID (1999–2000)
4 students received aid. **Financial Aid Contact** Mrs. Heather Richardson, Assistant Director of Financial Aid, PO Box R, Annville, PA 17003-0501. **Phone:** 717-867-6181. **Fax:** 717-867-6026. **E-mail:** finaid@lvc.edu.

RESOURCES AND SERVICES
Information about online services, personal computer policies, library resources, international exchange programs, internship programs, and placement services at this institution and others can be found at **www. petersons.com/mba**

■ APPLICATION
Required GMAT, application form, baccalaureate/first degree, interview, resume/curriculum vitae, transcripts of college work, 2 years of work experience.
Deadlines and Fees Applications for domestic and international students are processed on a rolling basis. *Application fee:* $25.
Application Contact Mrs. Cheryl L. Batdorf, Assistant Director, MBA Program, 101 North College Avenue, Annville, PA 17003-0501. **Phone:** 717-867-6335. **Fax:** 717-867-6018. **E-mail:** mentzer@lvc.edu.

Lehigh University
Bethlehem, Pennsylvania
COLLEGE OF BUSINESS AND ECONOMICS
Graduate Business Faculty
Full-time: 52   Part-time: 9
Student Body
Total: 330   Average Age: 32
Full-time: 58   Women: 28%
Part-time: 272
Admissions
Applications: 257   Average GMAT: 601
Admitted: 126   Average GPA: 3.2
Enrolled: 94
Costs (1999–2000)
Full-time tuition: $21,984 per academic year
Part-time tuition: $610 per credit hour
After Graduation (Class of 1998–99)
Employed within 3 months of graduation: 95%
Average starting salary: $66,800

Accreditation
AACSB—The International Association for Management Education

DEGREES MBA • MBA/M Eng • MS
MBA—Master of Business Administration Full-time and part-time. *Distance learning option.* 42 total credits required. 18 to 24 months to complete program. *Concentrations:* finance, international business, management, marketing, supply chain management, technology management, engineering.
MBA—Master of Business Administration Full-time and part-time. *Distance learning option.* GMAT required. At least 36 total credits required. 12 to 18 months to complete program. *Concentrations:* finance, international business, management, marketing, supply chain management, technology management.
MBA/M Eng—Master of Business Administration and Engineering Full-time and part-time. *Distance learning option.* 45 total credits required. 18 to 24 months to complete program. *Concentrations:* finance, international business, man-

agement, marketing, supply chain management, technology management, engineering.

MS—Master of Science in Economics Part-time. At least 30 total credits required. 12 months to complete program.

COSTS

Tuition *Full-time:* $21,960. *Part-time:* $610 per credit hour. **Tuition, international:** *Full-time* $21,960. **Required fees:** *Full-time* $24. *Part-time* $6 per quarter hour. Tuition and fees vary by number of courses or credits taken. **Graduate housing:** Room and board costs vary by type of accommodation. *Typical cost:* $5400 (room only).

FINANCIAL AID (1999–2000)

67 students received aid, including fellowships, loans, research assistantships, scholarships, and teaching assistantships. Aid is available to part-time students. Financial aid application deadline: 2/1. **Financial Aid Contact** Ms. Kathleen A. Trexler, Associate Dean and Director of the MBA Program, 621 Taylor Street, Bethlehem, PA 18015. **Phone:** 610-758-3418. **Fax:** 610-758-5283. **E-mail:** kat3@lehigh.edu.

RESOURCES AND SERVICES

Information about online services, personal computer policies, library resources, international exchange programs, internship programs, and placement services at this institution and others can be found at **www.petersons.com/mba**

International Students

5% of students enrolled are international students.

Services and Facilities Counseling/support services, ESL/language courses, housing location assistance, international student housing, international student organization, language tutoring, orientation, visa services. Financial aid is available to international students.

Applying *Required:* TOEFL with recommended score of 570 (paper), proof of adequate funds, proof of health/immunizations. *Recommended:* TSE.

International Student Contact Giselle Nansteel, International Students and Scholars Office, 5 East Packer Avenue, Whitaker Labs, Bethlehem, PA 18015. **Phone:** 610-758-4859.

■ APPLICATION

Required Application form, baccalaureate/first degree, essay, 2 letters of recommendation, personal statement, transcripts of college work, 2 years of work experience. School will accept GMAT and GMAT or GRE.

Deadlines and Fees *Deadlines:* 7/15 for fall, 12/1 for spring, 4/30 for summer, 7/15 for fall (international), 12/1 for spring (international), 4/30 for summer (international). *Application fee:* $40, $40 (international).

Application Contact Ms. Mary Theresa Taglang, Director of Recruitment and Admissions, 621 Taylor Street, Bethlehem, PA 18015. **Phone:** 610-758-5280. **Fax:** 610-758-5283. **E-mail:** mttu@lehigh.edu.

See full description on page 708.

Marywood University

Scranton, Pennsylvania

DEPARTMENT OF BUSINESS AND MANAGERIAL SCIENCE

Graduate Business Faculty
Full-time: 11 — Part-time: 9

Student Body
Total: 124
Part-time: 124 — Average Age: 31 — Women: 47%

Admissions
Applications: 45 — Average GMAT: 495
Admitted: 38 — Average GPA: 2.9
Enrolled: 35

Costs (1999–2000)
Full-time tuition: $9162 per academic year
Part-time tuition: $499 per credit

After Graduation (Class of 1998–99)
Employed within 3 months of graduation: 97%
Average starting salary: $45,000

DEGREES MBA • MS

MBA—Master of Business Administration in Finance/Investment Full-time and part-time. At least 36 total credits required. 24 to 84 months to complete program. *Concentrations:* finance.

MBA—Master of Business Administration in General Management Full-time and part-time. At least 36 total credits required. 24 to 84 months to complete program. *Concentrations:* management.

MBA—Master of Business Administration in Management Information Systems Full-time and part-time. At least 36 total credits required. 24 to 84 months to complete program. *Concentrations:* management information systems.

MS—Master of Science in Management Information Systems Full-time and part-time. At least 36 total credits required. 24 to 84 months to complete program. *Concentrations:* management information systems.

COSTS

Tuition *Full-time:* $8982. *Part-time:* $499 per credit. Tuition varies by number of courses or credits taken. **Required fees:** *Full-time* $180. **Graduate housing:** Room and board costs vary by number of occupants, type of accommodation, and type of board plan. *Typical cost:* $6540 (including board).

FINANCIAL AID (1999–2000)

Loans, research assistantships, scholarships, and teaching assistantships. Aid is available to part-time students. Financial aid application deadline: 3/10. **Financial Aid Contact** Mr. Stanley F. Skrutski, Director, Financial Aid, 2300 Adams Avenue, Scranton, PA 18509. **Phone:** 570-348-6211 Ext. 6225. **Fax:** 570-348-1817. **E-mail:** skrutski@ac.marywood.edu.

RESOURCES AND SERVICES

Information about online services, personal computer policies, library resources, international exchange programs, internship programs, and placement services at this institution and others can be found at **www.petersons.com/mba**

International Students

0.8% of students enrolled are international students.

Services and Facilities Counseling/support services, ESL/language courses, housing location assistance, international student housing, orientation, visa services. Financial aid is not available to international students.

Applying *Required:* TOEFL with recommended score of 550 (paper), proof of adequate funds, proof of health/immunizations.

International Student Contact Ms. Ann Boland-Chase, Registrar, 2300 Adams Avenue, Scranton, PA 18509-1598. **Phone:** 570-348-6280. **Fax:** 570-961-4758. **E-mail:** boland-chase@ac.marywood.edu.

■ APPLICATION

Required Application form, baccalaureate/first degree, 2 letters of recommendation, transcripts of college work. School will accept GMAT.

Deadlines and Fees Applications for domestic and international students are processed on a rolling basis. *Application fee:* $20, $20 (international).

Application Contact Dr. Samir P. Dagher, Executive Director and Chairman, 2300 Adams Avenue, Scranton, PA 18509-1598. **Phone:** 570-348-6274. **Toll-free Phone:** 800-338-4207. **Fax:** 570-961-4762. **E-mail:** dagher@ac.marywood.edu.

Moravian College

Bethlehem, Pennsylvania

DEPARTMENT OF ECONOMICS AND BUSINESS

Graduate Business Faculty
Full-time: 10 — Part-time: 5

Student Body
Total: 86
Full-time: 1 — Average Age: 34
Part-time: 85 — Women: 38%

Admissions
Applications: 31 — Average GMAT: 500
Admitted: 25 — Average GPA: 3
Enrolled: 22

Costs (1999–2000)
Full-time tuition: N/R
Part-time tuition: $1380 per course

DEGREE MBA

MBA—The Moravian MBA Part-time. 30 to 62 total credits required. 12 to 84 months to complete program. *Concentrations:* management.

COSTS

Tuition *Part-time:* $1380 per course.

Moravian College (continued)

RESOURCES AND SERVICES
Information about online services, personal computer policies, library resources, international exchange programs, internship programs, and placement services at this institution and others can be found at **www.petersons.com/mba**

International Students
Services and Facilities Financial aid is not available to international students.
Applying *Required:* TOEFL with recommended score of 550 (paper), proof of adequate funds.
International Student Contact Dr. Santo D. Marabella, Director, The Moravian MBA, 1200 Main Street, Bethleham, PA 18018. **Phone:** 610-807-4444. **Fax:** 610-861-1466. **E-mail:** mba@moravian.edu.

▪ APPLICATION
Required GMAT, application form, baccalaureate/first degree, 2 letters of recommendation, transcripts of college work. **Recommended** Interview, work experience.
Deadlines and Fees Applications for domestic and international students are processed on a rolling basis. *Application fee:* $40, $40 (international).
Application Contact Dr. Santo D. Marabella, Director, The Moravian MBA, 1200 Main Street, Bethlehem, PA 18018. **Phone:** 610-807-4444. **Fax:** 610-861-1466. **E-mail:** mba@moravian.edu.

The Pennsylvania State University at Erie, The Behrend College
Erie, Pennsylvania

PROGRAM IN BUSINESS ADMINISTRATION

Graduate Business Faculty
Full-time: 22

Student Body
Total: 139
Full-time: 4
Part-time: 135

Average Age: 33
Women: 35%

Admissions
Applications: 46
Admitted: 41
Enrolled: 36

Average GMAT: 520
Average GPA: 3.2

Costs (1999–2000)
Full-time tuition: $8225 per academic year (resident), $15,521 per academic year (nonresident)
Part-time tuition: $337 per credit (resident), $641 per credit (nonresident)

DEGREE MBA

MBA—Master of Business Administration Full-time and part-time. *Distance learning option.* At least 48 total credits required. 18 to 96 months to complete program. *Concentrations:* accounting, economics, finance, management information systems, marketing.

COSTS
Tuition, state resident: *Full-time* $8088. *Part-time* $337 per credit. **Tuition, nonresident:** *Full-time* $15,384. *Part-time* $641 per credit. Tuition varies by number of courses or credits taken, campus location, academic program, and local reciprocity agreements. **Required fees:** *Full-time* $137. Tuition and fees vary by number of courses or credits taken and local reciprocity agreements.

FINANCIAL AID (1999–2000)
15 students received aid, including loans, scholarships, and work study. Aid is available to part-time students. Financial aid application deadline: 2/15. **Financial Aid Contact** Ms. Jane Brady, Assistant Director of Admissions and Financial Aid, Station Road, Erie, PA 16563. **Phone:** 814-898-6162. **Fax:** 814-898-6044. **E-mail:** jub9@psu.edu.

RESOURCES AND SERVICES
Information about online services, personal computer policies, library resources, international exchange programs, internship programs, and placement services at this institution and others can be found at **www.petersons.com/mba**

International Students
1% of students enrolled are international students.
Services and Facilities Counseling/support services, housing location assistance, orientation, visa services. Financial aid is not available to international students.
Applying *Required:* TOEFL with recommended score of 213 (computer) or 550 (paper), proof of adequate funds, proof of health/immunizations.
International Student Contact Ms. Janique Caffie, Director of Educational Equity Program, Station Road, Erie, PA 16563. **Phone:** 814-898-6111. **Fax:** 814-898-6024. **E-mail:** juc3@psu.edu.

▪ APPLICATION
Required GMAT, application form, baccalaureate/first degree, essay, 3 letters of recommendation, personal statement, transcripts of college work. **Recommended** 3 years of work experience.
Deadlines and Fees *Deadlines:* 8/1 for fall, 12/15 for spring, 4/15 for summer, 2/1 for fall (international), 10/1 for spring (international), 2/1 for summer (international). *Application fee:* $40, $40 (international).
Application Contact Ms. Jane Brady, Assistant Director of Admissions and Financial Aid, Station Road, Erie, PA 16563. **Phone:** 814-898-6100. **Fax:** 814-898-6044. **E-mail:** jub9@psu.edu.

The Pennsylvania State University Great Valley Campus
Malvern, Pennsylvania

GRADUATE STUDIES AND CONTINUING EDUCATION

Graduate Business Faculty
Full-time: 14

Part-time: 27

Student Body
Total: 535
Full-time: 10
Part-time: 525

Average Age: 37
Women: 40%

Admissions
Applications: 166
Admitted: 132
Enrolled: 120

Average GMAT: 540
Average GPA: 3.11

Costs (1999–2000)
Full-time tuition: N/R
Part-time tuition: $362 per credit (resident), $641 per credit (nonresident)

After Graduation (Class of 1998–99)
Employed within 3 months of graduation: 99%

DEGREES MBA • MBA/MSIS

MBA—MBA in Health Care Policy, Administration, and Management Part-time. At least 42 total credits required. 16 to 72 months to complete program. *Concentrations:* health care, management information systems.

MBA—MBA in Management Part-time. At least 42 total credits required. 16 to 72 months to complete program. *Concentrations:* electronic commerce (e-commerce), entrepreneurship, finance, health care, human resources, management, management information systems, marketing.

MBA/MSIS—Concurrent Master's Programs in Business and Information Science Part-time. At least 65 total credits required. 36 to 72 months to complete program. *Concentrations:* electronic commerce (e-commerce), entrepreneurship, finance, health care, human resources, management, management information systems, marketing.

COSTS
Tuition, state resident: *Part-time* $362 per credit. **Tuition, nonresident:** *Part-time* $641 per credit. **Required fees:** *Part-time* $34 per course. Fees vary by number of courses or credits taken.

FINANCIAL AID (1999–2000)
Fellowships, grants, loans, research assistantships, scholarships, and work study. Aid is available to part-time students. **Financial Aid Contact** Ms. Ruth Smiley, Financial Aid Counselor, Penn State Great Valley, 30 East Swedesford Road, Malvern, PA 19355. **Phone:** 610-648-3248. **Fax:** 610-648-3366. **E-mail:** finances@gv.psu.edu.

RESOURCES AND SERVICES
Information about online services, personal computer policies, library resources, international exchange programs, internship programs, and placement services at this institution and others can be found at **www. petersons.com/mba**

International Students
0.9% of students enrolled are international students.

Services and Facilities Financial aid is not available to international students.
International Student Contact Ms. Sharon Kauffman, Graduate Enrollment Coordinator, 30 East Swedesford Road, Malvern, PA 19355-1488. **Phone:** 610-648-3248. **Fax:** 610-648-3366. **E-mail:** gvmba@psu.edu.

■ APPLICATION
Required GMAT, application form, baccalaureate/first degree, 2 letters of recommendation, personal statement, resume/curriculum vitae, transcripts of college work, 3 years of work experience.

Deadlines and Fees *Deadlines:* 7/31 for fall, 11/30 for spring, 4/30 for fall (international), 7/30 for spring (international). *Application fee:* $45, $45 (international).

Application Contact Ms. Sharon Kauffman, Graduate Enrollment Coordinator, 30 East Swedesford Road, Malvern, PA 19355. **Phone:** 610-648-3248. **Fax:** 610-648-3366. **E-mail:** gvmba@psu.edu.

The Pennsylvania State University Harrisburg Campus of the Capital College

Middletown, Pennsylvania

SCHOOL OF BUSINESS ADMINISTRATION

Graduate Business Faculty

Full-time: 28	Part-time: 1

Student Body

Total: 209	Average Age: 27
Full-time: 11	Women: 35%
Part-time: 198	

Admissions

Applications: 71	Average GMAT: 550
Admitted: 64	Average GPA: 3.18
Enrolled: 57	

Costs (1999–2000)
Full-time tuition: $3143 per academic year (resident), $5769 per academic year (nonresident)
Part-time tuition: $337 per credit (resident), $641 per credit (nonresident)

After Graduation (Class of 1998–99)
Employed within 3 months of graduation: 100%
Average starting salary: $45,000

Accreditation
AACSB—The International Association for Management Education

DEGREES MBA • MS

MBA—Master of Business Administration Full-time and part-time. At least 30 total credits required. 18 to 72 months to complete program.

MS—Master of Science in Information Systems Full-time and part-time. At least 30 total credits required. 18 to 72 months to complete program. *Concentrations:* management information systems.

COSTS
Tuition, state resident: *Full-time* $3143. *Part-time* $337 per credit. **Tuition, nonresident:** *Full-time* $5769. *Part-time* $641 per credit. **Tuition, international:** *Full-time* $5769. Tuition varies by academic program. **Required fees:** Fees vary by number of courses or credits taken. **Graduate housing:** Room and board costs vary by campus location, number of occupants, type of accommodation, and type of board plan. *Typical cost:* $4650 (including board).

FINANCIAL AID (1999–2000)
8 students received aid, including fellowships, research assistantships, scholarships, and work study. Aid is available to part-time students.
Financial Aid Contact Ms. Carolyn Julian, Student Aid Advisor, 777 West Harrisburg Pike, Middletown, PA 17057-4898. **Phone:** 717-948-6307. **Fax:** 717-948-6261. **E-mail:** czb3@psu.edu.

RESOURCES AND SERVICES
Information about online services, personal computer policies, library resources, international exchange programs, internship programs, and placement services at this institution and others can be found at **www. petersons.com/mba**

International Students
Services and Facilities Counseling/support services, housing location assistance, international student organization. Financial aid is not available to international students.
Applying *Required:* TOEFL with recommended score of 550 (paper), proof of adequate funds, proof of health/immunizations.
International Student Contact Ms. Donna Howard, International Student Advisor, 777 West Harrisburg Pike, Middletown, PA 17057-4898. **Phone:** 717-948-6025. **Fax:** 717-948-6261. **E-mail:** djh1@psu.edu.

■ APPLICATION
Required GMAT, application form, baccalaureate/first degree, essay, personal statement, transcripts of college work.

Deadlines and Fees *Deadlines:* 7/18 for fall, 11/18 for spring, 4/18 for summer, 4/18 for fall (international), 7/18 for spring (international), 11/18 for summer (international). *Application fee:* $40, $40 (international).

Application Contact Admissions, 777 West Harrisburg Pike, Middletown, PA 17057-4898. **Phone:** 717-948-6250. **Toll-free Phone:** 800-222-2056. **Fax:** 717-948-6325. **E-mail:** rrl1@psu.edu.

The Pennsylvania State University University Park Campus

State College, University Park, Pennsylvania

THE MARY JEAN AND FRANK P. SMEAL COLLEGE OF BUSINESS ADMINISTRATION

Graduate Business Faculty

Full-time: 103	Part-time: 42

Student Body

Total: 235	Average Age: 29
Full-time: 235	Women: 29%

Admissions

Applications: 1,131	Average GMAT: 608
Admitted: 303	Average GPA: 3.27
Enrolled: 115	

Costs (1999–2000)
Full-time tuition: $8558 per academic year (resident), $15,788 per academic year (nonresident)
Part-time tuition: N/R

After Graduation (Class of 1998–99)
Employed within 3 months of graduation: 98%
Average starting salary: $73,200

Accreditation
AACSB—The International Association for Management Education

DEGREES MBA • MBA/MHA • MMM

MBA—Full-time MBA Full-time. At least 48 total credits required. 16 to 21 months to complete program. *Concentrations:* electronic commerce (e-commerce), entrepreneurship, finance, insurance, logistics, management, management information systems, manufacturing management, marketing, new venture management, real estate, supply chain management.

MBA/MHA—Master of Business Administration/Master of Health Administration Full-time. At least 63 total credits required. 21 months to complete program. *Concentrations:* health care.

MMM—Master of Quality and Manufacturing Management Full-time. At least 30 total credits required. 9 months to complete program. *Concentrations:* manufacturing management, quality management.

COSTS
Tuition, state resident: *Full-time* $7932. **Tuition, nonresident:** *Full-time* $15,162. **Tuition, international:** *Full-time* $15,162. **Required fees:** *Full-time* $626. **Graduate housing:** Room and board costs vary by campus location, number of occupants, type of accommodation, and type of board plan. *Typical cost:* $5950 (including board), $3190 (room only).

The Pennsylvania State University University Park Campus (continued)

FINANCIAL AID (1999–2000)
Fellowships, grants, research assistantships, scholarships, teaching assistantships, and work study. Financial aid application deadline: 2/1. **Financial Aid Contact** Mr. Paul Simenson, Office of Student Aid, 314 Shields Building, University Park, PA 16802-1220. **Phone:** 814-865-6301. **Fax:** 814-863-0322. **E-mail:** pms2@studentaid.psu.edu.

RESOURCES AND SERVICES
Information about online services, personal computer policies, library resources, international exchange programs, internship programs, and placement services at this institution and others can be found at **www. petersons.com/mba**

International Students
27% of students enrolled are international students.

Services and Facilities Counseling/support services, ESL/language courses, international student organization, orientation, visa services. Financial aid is available to international students.
Applying *Required:* TOEFL with recommended score of 600 (paper), proof of adequate funds, proof of health/immunizations.
International Student Contact Ms. Masume Assaf, Assistant Director for International Programs, 222 Boucke Building, University Park, PA 16802-5900. **Phone:** 814-865-6348. **Fax:** 814-865-3336. **E-mail:** assaf@psu.edu.

■ APPLICATION
Required GMAT, application form, baccalaureate/first degree, essay, interview, letter(s) of recommendation, resume/curriculum vitae, transcripts of college work, 2 years of work experience.
Deadlines and Fees *Deadlines:* 6/1 for fall, 3/1 for fall (international). *Application fee:* $40, $40 (international).
Application Contact Ms. Toni Irvin, Director of Marketing, Recruitment and Admissions, MBA Program, The Smeal College of Business Administration, 106 Business Administration Building, University Park, PA 16802-3000. **Phone:** 814-863-0474. **Toll-free Phone:** 800-379-3446. **Fax:** 814-863-8072. **E-mail:** smealmba@psu.edu.

See full description on page 762.

Philadelphia College of Bible
Langhorne, Pennsylvania

ORGANIZATIONAL LEADERSHIP PROGRAM

Graduate Business Faculty
Full-time: 1   Part-time: 6

Student Body
Total: 45
Full-time: 15   Average Age: 36
Part-time: 30   Women: 31%

Admissions
Applications: 24   Enrolled: 15
Admitted: 19

Costs (1999–2000)
Full-time tuition: $5140 per academic year
Part-time tuition: $285 per credit

After Graduation (Class of 1998–99)
Employed within 3 months of graduation: 100%

DEGREE MSOL

MSOL—Master of Science in Organizational Leadership Full-time and part-time. At least 44 total credits required. Minimum of 9 months to complete program.

COSTS
Tuition *Full-time:* $5130. *Part-time:* $285 per credit. **Required fees:** *Full-time* $10. *Part-time* $10 per year.

FINANCIAL AID (1999–2000)
7 students received aid, including scholarships. Aid is available to part-time students. **Financial Aid Contact** Ms. Leslie Seip, Director, Graduate Student Services, 200 Manor Avenue, Langhorne, PA 19047. **Phone:** 800-572-2472. **Fax:** 215-702-4359. **E-mail:** lseip@pcb.edu.

RESOURCES AND SERVICES
Information about online services, personal computer policies, library resources, international exchange programs, internship programs, and placement services at this institution and others can be found at **www. petersons.com/mba**

International Students
11% of students enrolled are international students.

Services and Facilities Counseling/support services, ESL/language courses, international student housing. Financial aid is available to international students.
Applying *Required:* TOEFL with recommended score of 550 (paper), proof of adequate funds, proof of health/immunizations.
International Student Contact Mr. Eric Wenger, International Admissions Counselor, 200 Manor Avenue, Langhorne, PA 19047. **Phone:** 215-702-4258. **Fax:** 215-702-4248. **E-mail:** ewenger@pcb.edu.

■ APPLICATION
Required Application form, baccalaureate/first degree, essay, 3 letters of recommendation, personal statement, transcripts of college work, work experience. **Recommended** Interview.
Deadlines and Fees Applications for domestic and international students are processed on a rolling basis. *Application fee:* $25, $25 (international).
Application Contact Dr. Jay Desko, Associate Dean, Graduate School, 200 Manor Avenue, Langhorne, PA 19047. **Phone:** 215-702-4272. **Toll-free Phone:** 800-572-2472. **Fax:** 215-702-4359. **E-mail:** jdesko@pcb.edu.

Philadelphia University
Philadelphia, Pennsylvania

SCHOOL OF BUSINESS

Graduate Business Faculty
Full-time: 30   Part-time: 38

Student Body
Total: 407
Full-time: 115   Average Age: 27
Part-time: 292   Women: 49%

Admissions
Applications: 143   Average GMAT: 470
Admitted: 112   Average GPA: 3.2
Enrolled: 54

Costs (1999–2000)
Full-time tuition: N/R
Part-time tuition: $497 per credit

DEGREES MBA • MBA/MS • MS

MBA—Master of Business Administration Full-time and part-time. 33 to 52 total credits required. 12 to 84 months to complete program. *Concentrations:* accounting, finance, health care, international business, management, marketing, taxation.

MBA/MS—Master of Business Administration/Master of Science in Instructional Technology Full-time and part-time. 54 to 73 total credits required. 30 to 84 months to complete program. *Concentrations:* management information systems, technology management.

MBA/MS—Master of Business Administration/Master of Science in Taxation Full-time and part-time. 53 to 72 total credits required. 30 to 84 months to complete program. *Concentrations:* accounting, taxation.

MS—Master of Science in Taxation Full-time and part-time. At least 33 total credits required. 18 to 84 months to complete program. *Concentrations:* taxation.

COSTS
Tuition *Part-time:* $497 per credit. Tuition varies by academic program.

FINANCIAL AID (1999–2000)
Research assistantships, scholarships, and work study. Aid is available to part-time students. **Financial Aid Contact** Ms. Lisa Cooper, Director of Financial Aid, School House Lane and Henry Avenue, Philadelphia, PA 19144. **Phone:** 215-951-2940. **E-mail:** cooperl@philau.edu.

RESOURCES AND SERVICES
Information about online services, personal computer policies, library resources, international exchange programs, internship programs, and placement services at this institution and others can be found at **www. petersons.com/mba**

International Students

Services and Facilities Counseling/support services, ESL/language courses, visa services. Financial aid is available to international students.
Applying *Required:* TOEFL with recommended score of 550 (paper), proof of adequate funds, proof of health/immunizations.
International Student Contact Ms. Hannah Bar-Giora, International Student Advisor, School House Lane and Henry Avenue, Philadelphia, PA 19144. **Phone:** 215-951-2660. **E-mail:** bargiorah@philau.edu.

■ APPLICATION

Required Application form, baccalaureate/first degree, 2 letters of recommendation, personal statement, resume/curriculum vitae, transcripts of college work. School will accept GMAT. **Recommended** Interview.
Deadlines and Fees Applications for domestic and international students are processed on a rolling basis. *Application fee:* $35, $35 (international).
Application Contact Mr. William Firman, Jr., Director of Graduate Admissions, School House Lane and Henry Avenue, Philadelphia, PA 19144. **Phone:** 215-951-2943. **Fax:** 215-951-2907. **E-mail:** firmanw@philau.edu.
See full description on page 766.

Point Park College

Pittsburgh, Pennsylvania

DEPARTMENT OF BUSINESS

Graduate Business Faculty
Full-time: 12 | Part-time: 15

Student Body
Total: 164
Full-time: 118 | Average Age: 27
Part-time: 46 | Women: 42%

Admissions
Applications: 146 | Average GMAT: 482
Admitted: 126 | Average GPA: 3.29
Enrolled: 87

Costs (1999–2000)
Full-time tuition: $6624 per academic year
Part-time tuition: $378 per credit

After Graduation (Class of 1998–99)
Employed within 3 months of graduation: 73%
Average starting salary: $29,300

DEGREES MBA

MBA—Accelerated MBA Full-time and part-time. At least 36 total credits required. 12 to 24 months to complete program.
MBA—International MBA Full-time and part-time. 39 to 45 total credits required. 16 to 72 months to complete program. *Concentrations:* international business.

COSTS

Tuition *Full-time:* $6624. *Part-time:* $368 per credit. **Required fees:** *Part-time* $10 per credit. **Graduate housing:** Room and board costs vary by number of occupants and type of board plan. *Typical cost:* $5334 (including board), $2550 (room only).

FINANCIAL AID (1999–2000)

11 students received aid, including grants, loans, research assistantships, and scholarships. Aid is available to part-time students.
Financial Aid Contact Sandra Cronin, Director, Financial Aid, 201 Wood Street, Pittsburgh, PA 15222. **Phone:** 412-392-3935. **Fax:** 412-391-1980 **E-mail:** scronin@ppc.edu.

RESOURCES AND SERVICES

Information about online services, personal computer policies, library resources, international exchange programs, internship programs, and placement services at this institution and others can be found at www.petersons.com/mba

International Students

10% of students enrolled are international students.
Services and Facilities Counseling/support services, ESL/language courses, international student housing, visa services. Financial aid is available to international students.
Applying *Required:* TOEFL with recommended score of 500 (paper), proof of adequate funds.

International Student Contact Ms. Cynthia Kuo, Coordinator, International Student Development, 201 Wood Street, Pittsburgh, PA 15222-1984. **Phone:** 412-392-3903. **Fax:** 412-391-1980.

■ APPLICATION

Required GMAT, application form, baccalaureate/first degree, 2 letters of recommendation, personal statement, transcripts of college work. **Recommended** Resume/curriculum vitae.
Deadlines and Fees Applications for domestic and international students are processed on a rolling basis. *Application fee:* $30, $30 (international).
Application Contact Ms. Kathy Ballas, Director of Accredited and Graduate Enrollment, Graduate Admissions, 201 Wood Street, Pittsburgh, PA 15222-1984. **Phone:** 412-392-3808. **Fax:** 412-392-6164. **E-mail:** kballas@ppc.edu.

Robert Morris College

Moon Township, Pennsylvania

PROGRAM IN BUSINESS ADMINISTRATION

Graduate Business Faculty
Full-time: 18 | Part-time: 25

Student Body
Total: 421 | Average Age: 33
Part-time: 421 | Women: 40%

Admissions
Applications: 298 | Average GMAT: 462
Admitted: 208 | Average GPA: 3.09
Enrolled: 154

Costs (1999–2000)
Full-time tuition: N/R
Part-time tuition: $386 per credit

DEGREES MBA • MS

MBA—Master of Business Administration Part-time. At least 33 total credits required. *Concentrations:* management.
MS—Master of Science Part-time. At least 33 total credits required. *Concentrations:* accounting, business education, finance, health care, management, management information systems, marketing, sports/entertainment management, taxation.

COSTS

Tuition *Part-time:* $370 per credit. Tuition varies by academic program. **Required fees:** *Part-time* $16 per credit. **Graduate housing:** Room and board costs vary by number of occupants and type of board plan. *Typical cost:* $6320 (including board), $3720 (room only).

FINANCIAL AID (1999–2000)

Aid is available to part-time students. Financial aid application deadline: 5/1. **Financial Aid Contact** Mrs. Janet Lawson, Manager of Financial Aid, 881 Narrows Run Road, Moon Township, PA 15108-1189. **Phone:** 412-262-8267. **Fax:** 412-262-8601. **E-mail:** lawson@robert-morris.edu.

RESOURCES AND SERVICES

Information about online services, personal computer policies, library resources, international exchange programs, internship programs, and placement services at this institution and others can be found at www.petersons.com/mba

International Students

Services and Facilities Counseling/support services. Financial aid is not available to international students.
Applying *Required:* TOEFL with recommended score of 500 (paper), proof of adequate funds.
International Student Contact Ms. Darcy Tannehill, Associate Dean of Enrollment Management, 6th Avenue, Pittsburgh, PA 15219-3099. **Phone:** 412-227-6808. **Fax:** 412-281-5539. **E-mail:** tannehil@robert-morris.edu.

■ APPLICATION

Required Application form, baccalaureate/first degree, essay, interview, 2 letters of recommendation, transcripts of college work. School will accept GMAT, GRE, and MAT.
Deadlines and Fees Applications for domestic and international students are processed on a rolling basis. *Application fee:* $25, $25 (international).
Application Contact Ms. Kelli Laurenzi, Recruiting Coordinator, Enrollment Management, 881 Narrows Run Road, Moon Township, PA 15108-1189. **Phone:**

Robert Morris College (continued)

412-262-8535. **Toll-free Phone:** 762-762-0097 (in-state), 800-762-0097 (out-of-state). **Fax:** 412-299-2425.

See full description on page 788.

Rosemont College
Rosemont, Pennsylvania

DIVISION OF ACCELERATED DEGREE PROGRAMS

Student Body
Total: 85

Costs (1999–2000)
Full-time tuition: N/R
Part-time tuition: $1305 per course

DEGREES MBA • MS • MSM

MBA—Accelerated MBA Full-time and part-time. Minimum of three years of progressive managerial experience. At least 36 total credits required. Minimum of 12 months to complete program.

MS—Master of Science in Arts and Cultural Management At least 30 total credits required. Minimum of 12 months to complete program.

MSM—Master of Science in Management Full-time and part-time. At least 36 total credits required. Minimum of 12 months to complete program.

COSTS
Tuition *Part-time:* $1305 per course.

FINANCIAL AID (1999–2000)
Loans. **Financial Aid Contact** Financial Aid Office, 1400 Montgomery Avenue, Rosemont, PA 19010-1699. **Phone:** 610-527-0200 Ext. 2220. **Fax:** 610-527-1041.

RESOURCES AND SERVICES
Information about online services, personal computer policies, library resources, international exchange programs, internship programs, and placement services at this institution and others can be found at **www. petersons.com/mba**

International Students
Services and Facilities ESL/language courses, international student organization, orientation. Financial aid is not available to international students.
Applying *Required:* TOEFL with recommended score of 500 (paper), proof of adequate funds.
International Student Contact Ms. Dianne Rotwitt, 1400 Montgomery Avenue, Rosemont, PA 19010-1699. **Phone:** 610-527-0200 Ext. 2428. **Fax:** 610-527-0341. **E-mail:** darotwitt@juno.com.

■ APPLICATION
Required Application form, baccalaureate/first degree, essay, interview, 2 letters of recommendation, personal statement, transcripts of college work, 3 years of work experience.
Deadlines and Fees *Application fee:* $50, $50 (international).
Application Contact Mrs. Rennie Andrews, MSM Coordinator, Rosemont, PA 19010-1699. **Phone:** 610-527-0200 Ext. 2380. **Fax:** 610-527-2958. **E-mail:** randrews@rosemont.edu.

Saint Francis College
Loretto, Pennsylvania

BUSINESS ADMINISTRATION PROGRAM

Graduate Business Faculty
Full-time: 7 — Part-time: 8

Student Body
Total: 130 — Average Age: 33
Full-time: 6 — Women: 36%
Part-time: 124

Admissions
Average GMAT: 520 — Average GPA: 3.2

Costs (1999–2000)
Full-time tuition: $7938 per academic year
Part-time tuition: $441 per credit

After Graduation (Class of 1998–99)
Employed within 3 months of graduation: 95%
Average starting salary: $35,000

DEGREE MBA

MBA—Master of Business Administration Full-time and part-time. 36 to 60 total credits required. 12 to 60 months to complete program. *Concentrations:* accounting, finance, health care, human resources, industrial administration/management, industrial/labor relations, management, marketing.

COSTS
Tuition *Full-time:* $7938. *Part-time:* $441 per credit. **Required fees:** Tuition and fees vary by academic program.

FINANCIAL AID (1999–2000)
12 students received aid, including research assistantships and work study. **Financial Aid Contact** Mr. Vincent Frank, Financial Aid Director, Padua Hall, Loretto, PA 15940. **Phone:** 814-472-3010.

RESOURCES AND SERVICES
Information about online services, personal computer policies, library resources, international exchange programs, internship programs, and placement services at this institution and others can be found at **www. petersons.com/mba**

International Students
Services and Facilities Counseling/support services. Financial aid is available to international students.
Applying *Required:* TOEFL with recommended score of 500 (paper), proof of adequate funds, proof of health/immunizations.

■ APPLICATION
Required Application form, baccalaureate/first degree, essay, 3 letters of recommendation, transcripts of college work. School will accept GMAT. **Recommended** Interview, resume/curriculum vitae.
Deadlines and Fees Applications for domestic and international students are processed on a rolling basis. *Application fee:* $30, $30 (international).
Application Contact Dr. Randy L. Frye, Director, MBA Program, 225A Scotus Hall, Loretto, PA 15940. **Phone:** 814-472-3087. **Toll-free Phone:** 800-457-6300 (in-state), 800-542-5732 (out-of-state). **Fax:** 814-472-3044. **E-mail:** rfrye@sfcpa.edu.

Saint Joseph's University
Philadelphia, Pennsylvania

ERIVAN K. HAUB SCHOOL OF BUSINESS

Graduate Business Faculty
Full-time: 60 — Part-time: 19

Student Body
Total: 947 — Average Age: 29
Full-time: 70 — Women: 37%
Part-time: 877

Admissions
Applications: 207 — Average GMAT: 510
Admitted: 157 — Average GPA: 3
Enrolled: 120

Costs (1999–2000)
Full-time tuition: $16,610 per academic year
Part-time tuition: $510 per credit

After Graduation (Class of 1998–99)
Employed within 3 months of graduation: 90%

Accreditation
AACSB—The International Association for Management Education

DEGREES EMBA • MBA • MS

EMBA—Executive MBA Full-time. At least 48 total credits required. Maximum of 21 months to complete program.

MBA—Pharmaceutical MBA Part-time. At least 33 total credits required. 8 to 60 months to complete program.

MBA—Master of Business Administration Full-time and part-time. *Distance learning option.* At least 48 total credits required. 30 to 48 months to complete program. *Concentrations:* accounting, finance, health care, international business, international marketing, management, management information systems, marketing.

MS—Master of Science in Environmental Protection/Safety Management Full-time and part-time. At least 36 total credits required. 18 to 60 months to complete program.

MS—Master of Science in Program-Food Marketing Part-time. At least 32 total credits required. 8 to 60 months to complete program.

MS—Master of Science in Public Safety Full-time and part-time. At least 36 total credits required. 18 to 60 months to complete program.

COSTS

Tuition *Full-time:* $16,610. *Part-time:* $510 per credit.

FINANCIAL AID (1999–2000)

Work study. Aid is available to part-time students. **Financial Aid Contact** Ms. Felicia Korenstein, Financial Aid Counselor, 5600 City Avenue, Philadelphia, PA 19131. **Phone:** 610-660-1344.

RESOURCES AND SERVICES

Information about online services, personal computer policies, library resources, international exchange programs, internship programs, and placement services at this institution and others can be found at **www. petersons.com/mba**

International Students

Services and Facilities Counseling/support services, ESL/language courses, visa services. Financial aid is not available to international students.
Applying *Required:* TOEFL with recommended score of 213 (computer) or 550 (paper), proof of adequate funds.
International Student Contact Dr. Thomas Buckley, Director, Office for International Programs, 5600 City Avenue, Philadelphia, PA 19131. **Phone:** 610-660-1836.

■ APPLICATION

Required GMAT, application form, baccalaureate/first degree, essay, 2 letters of recommendation, resume/curriculum vitae, transcripts of college work.
Deadlines and Fees *Deadlines:* 7/15 for fall, 11/15 for spring, 4/15 for summer, 7/15 for fall (international), 11/15 for spring (international), 4/15 for summer (international). *Application fee:* $35, $35 (international).
Application Contact Ms. Adele Foley, Associate Dean/Director, MBA Programs, 5600 City Avenue, Philadelphia, PA 19131. **Phone:** 610-660-1690. **Fax:** 610-660-1599.

See full description on page 804.

Seton Hill College

Greensburg, Pennsylvania

PROGRAM IN MANAGEMENT

Graduate Business Faculty
Full-time: 4 | Part-time: 4

Student Body
Total: 55
Part-time: 55 | Average Age: 37 | Women: 67%

Admissions
Applications: 26 | Enrolled: 21
Admitted: 23

Costs (1999–2000)
Full-time tuition: $6500 per academic year
Part-time tuition: $360 per credit

DEGREE MSM

MSM—**Master of Science in Management** Full-time and part-time. 36 to 39 total credits required. 24 to 60 months to complete program. *Concentrations:* management.

COSTS

Tuition *Full-time:* $6480. *Part-time:* $360 per credit. **Tuition, international:** *Full-time* $6480. **Required fees:** *Full-time* $20. **Graduate housing:** *Typical cost:* $5050 (including board).

FINANCIAL AID (1999–2000)

Scholarships. Aid is available to part-time students. **Financial Aid Contact** Ms. Maryann Dudas, Director of Financial Aid, Seton Hill Drive, Greensburg, PA 15601. **Phone:** 724-838-4275. **Fax:** 724-830-1294. **E-mail:** dudas@setonhill.edu.

RESOURCES AND SERVICES

Information about online services, personal computer policies, library resources, international exchange programs, internship programs, and placement services at this institution and others can be found at **www. petersons.com/mba**

International Students

Services and Facilities Counseling/support services, international student organization, orientation. Financial aid is available to international students.
Applying *Required:* TOEFL with recommended score of 550 (paper).
International Student Contact Ms. Sadie Lopez Alicea, Graduate Program Advisor, Seton Hill Drive, Greensburg, PA 15601. **Phone:** 724-838-4283. **Fax:** 724-830-1294. **E-mail:** alicea@setonhill.edu.

■ APPLICATION

Required Application form, baccalaureate/first degree, 3 letters of recommendation, personal statement, resume/curriculum vitae, transcripts of college work. **Recommended** 2 years of work experience.
Deadlines and Fees Applications for domestic and international students are processed on a rolling basis. *Application fee:* $30.
Application Contact Ms. Sadie Lopez Alicea, Graduate Program Advisor, Seton Hill Drive, Greensburg, PA 15601. **Phone:** 724-838-4283. **Toll-free Phone:** 800-826-6234. **Fax:** 724-830-1294. **E-mail:** alicea@setonhill.edu.

Slippery Rock University of Pennsylvania

Slippery Rock, Pennsylvania

COLLEGE OF INFORMATION SCIENCE AND BUSINESS ADMINISTRATION

Graduate Business Faculty
Full-time: 5

Student Body
Total: 16
Full-time: 3 | Average Age: 25
Part-time: 13 | Women: 50%

Admissions
Applications: 14 | Enrolled: 5
Admitted: 5 | Average GPA: 3

Costs (1999–2000)
Full-time tuition: $5348 per academic year (resident), $11,776 per academic year (nonresident)
Part-time tuition: $210 per credit (resident), $367 per credit (nonresident)

Accreditation
ACBSP—The American Council of Business Schools and Programs

DEGREES MPA • MS

MPA—**Master of Public Administration** Full-time and part-time. At least 42 total credits required. Minimum of 24 months to complete program.

MS—**Master of Science in Accounting** Full-time and part-time. At least 30 total credits required. Minimum of 24 months to complete program. *Concentrations:* accounting.

COSTS

Tuition, state resident: *Full-time* $4483. *Part-time* $210 per credit. **Tuition, nonresident:** *Full-time* $10,911. *Part-time* $367 per credit. **Tuition, international:** *Full-time* $7032. **Required fees:** *Full-time* $865. *Part-time* $452 per semester. Tuition and fees vary by number of courses or credits taken. **Graduate housing:** Room and board costs vary by campus location, number of occupants, type of accommodation, and type of board plan. *Typical cost:* $3810 (including board), $2038 (room only).

FINANCIAL AID (1999–2000)

Grants, loans, research assistantships, scholarships, and work study. Aid is available to part-time students. **Financial Aid Contact** Ms. Patricia Hladio, Financial Aid Office, 14 Maltby Avenue, Slippery Rock, PA 16057. **Phone:** 724-738-2044. **Fax:** 724-738-2922.

RESOURCES AND SERVICES

Information about online services, personal computer policies, library resources, international exchange programs, internship programs, and placement services at this institution and others can be found at **www. petersons.com/mba**

Slippery Rock University of Pennsylvania (continued)

International Students

13% of students enrolled are international students.

Services and Facilities Counseling/support services, ESL/language courses, housing location assistance, international student organization. Financial aid is available to international students.

Applying *Required:* TOEFL with recommended score of 550 (paper), proof of adequate funds, proof of health/immunizations.

International Student Contact Ms. Pamela Frigot, Director of International Studies, 14 Maltby Avenue, Slippery Rock, PA 16057. **Phone:** 724-738-2057. **Fax:** 724-738-2959. **E-mail:** pamela.frigot@sru.edu.

■ APPLICATION

Required Application form, baccalaureate/first degree, interview, letter(s) of recommendation, transcripts of college work. School will accept GMAT or GRE. **Recommended** Work experience.

Deadlines and Fees *Deadlines:* 7/1 for fall, 11/1 for spring, 3/1 for summer, 6/1 for fall (international), 10/1 for spring (international). *Application fee:* $25, $25 (international).

Application Contact Ms. Carla Hradisky-Coffelt, Director of Graduate Admissions and Recruitment, 14 Maltby Avenue, Slippery Rock, PA 16057. **Phone:** 724-738-2051 Ext. 2112. **Fax:** 724-738-2908. **E-mail:** carla.hradisky@sru.edu.

Temple University

Philadelphia, Pennsylvania

FOX SCHOOL OF BUSINESS AND MANAGEMENT

Graduate Business Faculty

Full-time: 79   Part-time: 20

Student Body

Total: 1,188   Average Age: 31
Full-time: 340   Women: 41%
Part-time: 848

Admissions

Applications: 788   Average GMAT: 540
Admitted: 428   Average GPA: 3.1
Enrolled: 233

Costs (1999–2000)

Full-time tuition: $8642 per academic year (resident), $12,002 per academic year (nonresident)
Part-time tuition: $348 per credit (resident), $488 per credit (nonresident)

After Graduation (Class of 1998–99)

Employed within 3 months of graduation: 93%
Average starting salary: $67,000

Accreditation

AACSB—The International Association for Management Education

DEGREES DDS/MBA • EMBA • IMBA • JD/MBA • MBA • MBA/MS • MS • MSBA

DDS/MBA—Doctor of Dental Medicine/Master of Business Administration Full-time. 36 months to complete program.

EMBA—Executive MBA Full-time. 48 total credits required. 21 months to complete program.

IMBA—Master of Business Administration in International Business Full-time. 30 to 48 total credits required. 11 to 14 months to complete program. *Concentrations:* international management.

JD/MBA—Juris Doctor/Master of Business Administration Full-time and part-time. 36 months to complete program.

MBA—Master of Business Administration Full-time and part-time. *Distance learning option.* 30 to 48 total credits required. 12 to 72 months to complete program. *Concentrations:* accounting, electronic commerce (e-commerce), finance, health care, human resources, international business, management, management information systems, marketing, strategic management.

MBA/MS—International Master of Business Administration/Master of Science Full-time. 60 total credits required. 16 months to complete program. *Concentrations:* economics, finance, financial management/planning, human resources, international management.

MBA/MS—MBA/MS in E-Business Full-time. 48 to 66 total credits required. 21 to 24 months to complete program. *Concentrations:* electronic commerce (e-commerce), management information systems.

MBA/MS—Master of Business Administration in Health Care Management/Master of Science in Health Care Financial Management Full-time and part-time. 42 to 81 total credits required. 17 to 72 months to complete program. *Concentrations:* financial management/planning, health care.

MS—Master of Science Full-time and part-time. At least 30 total credits required. 12 to 72 months to complete program. *Concentrations:* actuarial science, electronic commerce (e-commerce), statistics.

MSBA—Master of Science in Business Administration Full-time and part-time. 30 to 48 total credits required. 12 to 72 months to complete program. *Concentrations:* economics, finance, health care, human resources, information systems.

Temple University's M.B.A. program provides students with the skills and knowledge identified by business leaders as essential for success. Accredited by AACSB-The International Association for Management Education, the program focuses on team-based, quality-oriented, and cross-functional models of management. Students develop practical expertise through case analyses and presentations, interaction with business practitioners, and team projects.

The new M.B.A. curriculum comprises sixteen courses (six core and ten advanced level) and offers ten areas of concentration, including e-business. A 6-credit capstone course links the curriculum with industry, including financial services, health care, information technology, pharmaceuticals/biotechnology, and tourism.

Evening classes and part- or full-time study at Temple University Center City (1616 Walnut Street) and Temple Fort Washington (in suburban Montgomery County) make the program convenient to the working professionals who comprise 80 percent of the 1,188 M.B.A. students. M.B.A. core courses are currently available online. The M.B.A./M.S. in e-business is a twenty-one-month, full-time, day program. Students are required to complete a four-month paid internship.

A variety of professional development activities, including personal career counseling, a resume databank, on- and off-campus recruiting, a mentor program, an Executives in Residence program, and workshops, foster career preparation and opportunities. In addition, the new curriculum includes professional development modules that all graduate students are encouraged to attend. Temple's Fox School of Business and Management is a major supplier of managerial talent to the Philadelphia region, the nation's fifth-largest metropolitan area. Its extensive network includes 40,000 alumni, most of whom live and work in the region. Regional business leaders, including alumni, are actively involved in the M.B.A. program. They sponsor consulting projects and internships, serve as mentors and guest speakers, and offer input on curriculum. For more information, students should visit the University's Web site at http://www.sbm.temple.edu.

COSTS

Tuition, state resident: *Full-time* $8352. *Part-time* $348 per credit. **Tuition, nonresident:** *Full-time* $11,712. *Part-time* $488 per credit. **Tuition, international:** *Full-time* $11,712. Tuition varies by academic program. **Required fees:** *Full-time* $290. *Part-time* $290 per year. Fees vary by number of courses or credits taken. **Graduate housing:** Room and board costs vary by number of occupants, type of accommodation, and type of board plan. *Typical cost:* $11,450 (including board), $9450 (room only).

FINANCIAL AID (1999–2000)

20 students received aid, including fellowships, loans, research assistantships, scholarships, teaching assistantships, and work study. Financial aid application deadline: 3/15. **Financial Aid Contact** Mr. John Morris, Director, 2nd Floor Conwell Hall, Philadelphia, PA 19122. **Phone:** 215-204-1405. **Fax:** 215-204-5897.

RESOURCES AND SERVICES

Information about online services, personal computer policies, library resources, international exchange programs, internship programs, and placement services at this institution and others can be found at **www.petersons.com/mba**

International Students

17% of students enrolled are international students.

Services and Facilities Counseling/support services, ESL/language courses, housing location assistance, international student organization, orientation, visa services. Financial aid is available to international students.

Applying *Required:* TOEFL with recommended score of 230 (computer) or 575 (paper), proof of adequate funds, proof of health/immunizations.

International Student Contact Mr. Martyn Miller, Director, 203 Vivacqua Hall, PO Box 2843, Philadelphia, PA 19122-6083. **Phone:** 215-204-7708. **Fax:** 215-204-6166.

■ APPLICATION

Required GMAT, application form, baccalaureate/first degree, 2 letters of recommendation, personal statement, resume/curriculum vitae, transcripts of college work, 2 years of work experience.

Deadlines and Fees *Deadlines:* 4/15 for fall, 9/30 for spring, 3/15 for summer, 1/5 for fall (international), 9/1 for spring (international), 1/15 for summer (international). *Application fee:* $40, $40 (international).

Application Contact Ms. Pamela Jenkins, Associate Director, MBA and MS Programs, 1810 North 13th Street, Speakman Hall, Room 5, Philadelphia, PA 19122. **Phone:** 215-204-4562. **Fax:** 215-204-8300. **E-mail:** pamj@sbm.temple.edu.

See full description on page 844.

University of Pennsylvania

Philadelphia, Pennsylvania

WHARTON SCHOOL

Graduate Business Faculty
Full-time: 190   Part-time: 59

Student Body
Total: 1,545
Full-time: 1,545   Average Age: 28
     Women: 30%

Admissions
Applications: 8,434
Admitted: 1,064   Average GMAT: 691
Enrolled: 780   Average GPA: 3.5

Costs (1999–2000)
Full-time tuition: $28,116 per academic year
Part-time tuition: N/R

After Graduation (Class of 1998–99)
Employed within 3 months of graduation: 96.2%

Accreditation
AACSB—The International Association for Management Education

DEGREES MBA • MBA/MA

MBA—Executive MBA Full-time. At least 19 total credits required. 23 months to complete program. *Concentrations:* accounting, finance, health care, information management, insurance, management, marketing, operations management, public policy and administration, real estate, risk management.

MBA—Master of Business Administration Full-time. At least 19 total credits required. Minimum of 21 months to complete program. *Concentrations:* accounting, electronic commerce (e-commerce), entrepreneurship, finance, health care, human resources, information management, insurance, international banking, international management, management, marketing, operations management, public policy and administration, real estate, strategic management, statistics.

MBA/MA—Lauder Institute of Management and International Studies Full-time. At least 19 total credits required. 24 months to complete program. *Concentrations:* accounting, Asian business studies, Chinese business studies, electronic commerce (e-commerce), entrepreneurship, European business studies, finance, health care, human resources, information management, insurance, international and area business studies, international banking, international business, international economics, international finance, international management, international marketing, international trade, Japanese business studies, Latin American business studies, management, marketing, operations management, public policy and administration, real estate, strategic management, statistics.

COSTS
Tuition *Full-time:* $25,632. **Required fees:** *Full-time* $2484. **Graduate housing:** Room and board costs vary by campus location, number of occupants, type of accommodation, and type of board plan. *Typical cost:* $11,100 (including board).

FINANCIAL AID (1999–2000)
916 students received aid, including fellowships, grants, loans, research assistantships, scholarships, teaching assistantships, and work study.
Financial Aid Contact Ms. Sharon Brooks, Associate Director, Financial Aid, 102 Vance Hall, Philadelphia, PA 19104-6362. **Phone:** 215-898-6183. **Fax:** 215-898-0120. **E-mail:** mba.admissions@wharton.upenn.edu.

RESOURCES AND SERVICES
Information about online services, personal computer policies, library resources, international exchange programs, internship programs, and

placement services at this institution and others can be found at **www.petersons.com/mba**

International Students
33% of students enrolled are international students.

Services and Facilities Counseling/support services, ESL/language courses, international student housing, orientation, visa services. Financial aid is available to international students.
Applying *Required:* TOEFL.
International Student Contact Ms. Amy Orlov, Director of Graduate Student Affairs, 216 Vance Hall, Philadelphia, PA 19104-6361. **Phone:** 215-898-4968. **Fax:** 215-898-0425. **E-mail:** orlova@wharton.upenn.edu.

■ APPLICATION

Required GMAT, application form, baccalaureate/first degree, essay, 2 letters of recommendation, transcripts of college work. **Recommended** Interview, 2 years of work experience.

Deadlines and Fees *Deadlines:* 4/10 for spring, 4/10 for spring (international). *Application fee:* $160, $160 (international).

Application Contact Ms. Rosemaria Martinelli, Director, MBA Admissions and Financial Aid, 3733 Spruce Street, 102 Vance Hall, Philadelphia, PA 19104-6361. **Phone:** 215-898-6183. **Fax:** 215-898-0120. **E-mail:** mba.admissions@wharton.upenn.edu.

See full description on page 944.

University of Pittsburgh

Pittsburgh, Pennsylvania

JOSEPH M. KATZ GRADUATE SCHOOL OF BUSINESS

Graduate Business Faculty
Full-time: 70   Part-time: 10

Student Body
Total: 762   Part-time: 565
Full-time: 197   Average Age: 27

Admissions
Applications: 1,141   Average GMAT: 582
Admitted: 577   Average GPA: 3.14
Enrolled: 349

Costs (1999–2000)
Full-time tuition: $20,627 per academic year (resident), $32,324 per academic year (nonresident)
Part-time tuition: $481 per credit (resident), $901 per credit (nonresident)

After Graduation (Class of 1998–99)
Employed within 3 months of graduation: 95%
Average starting salary: $65,085

Accreditation
AACSB—The International Association for Management Education

DEGREES JD/MBA • MBA • MBA/MA • MBA/MHA • MBA/MIB • MBA/MPIA • MBA/MS

JD/MBA—Juris Doctor/Master of Business Administration Full-time and part-time. At least 119 total credits required. 42 to 72 months to complete program.

MBA—Full-time MBA Full-time and part-time. At least 50 total credits required. 11 to 48 months to complete program. *Concentrations:* accounting, finance, human resources, management, management information systems, marketing, operations management.

MBA/MA—Master of Business Administration/Master of Arts Full-time and part-time. At least 82.5 total credits required. 48 to 72 months to complete program. *Concentrations:* international and area business studies.

MBA/MHA—Master of Business Administration/Master of Health Administration At least 73 total credits required. 21 to 72 months to complete program.

MBA/MIB—Master of Business Administration/Master of International Business Full-time and part-time. At least 74 total credits required. 21 to 72 months to complete program. *Concentrations:* international business, public management.

MBA/MPIA—Master of Business Administration/Master of Public and International Affairs Full-time and part-time. At least 78 total credits required. 24 to 72 months to complete program.

MBA/MS—Master of Business Administration/Master of Science in Management of Information Systems Full-time and part-time. At least 74 total credits required. 21 to 72 months to complete program. *Concentrations:* management information systems.

University of Pittsburgh (continued)

COSTS

Tuition, state resident: *Full-time* $16,629. *Part-time* $481 per credit. **Tuition, nonresident:** *Full-time* $28,326. *Part-time* $901 per credit. **Required fees:** *Full-time* $3998. *Part-time* $90 per term. Tuition and fees vary by class time and number of courses or credits taken.

FINANCIAL AID (1999–2000)

Fellowships, loans, scholarships, and work study. Financial aid application deadline: 12/1. **Financial Aid Contact** Ms. Kelly Wilson, Director of the Office of Enrollment Management, 276 Mervis Hall, Pittsburgh, PA 15260. **Phone:** 412-648-1700. **Fax:** 412-648-1659. **E-mail:** mba-admissions@katz.pitt.edu.

RESOURCES AND SERVICES

Information about online services, personal computer policies, library resources, international exchange programs, internship programs, and placement services at this institution and others can be found at **www. petersons.com/mba**

International Students

10% of students enrolled are international students.

Services and Facilities Counseling/support services, ESL/language courses, visa services. Financial aid is available to international students.
Applying *Required:* TOEFL with recommended score of 600 (paper), proof of adequate funds.
International Student Contact Ms. Kelly Wilson, Director of the Office of Enrollment Management, 276 Mervis Hall, Pittsburgh, PA 15260. **Phone:** 412-648-1700. **Fax:** 412-648-1659. **E-mail:** tst@vms.cis.pitt.edu.

■ APPLICATION

Required GMAT, application form, baccalaureate/first degree, essay, 2 letters of recommendation, resume/curriculum vitae, transcripts of college work. **Recommended** Interview, 2 years of work experience.
Deadlines and Fees *Deadlines:* 4/15 for fall, 2/15 for fall (international). *Application fee:* $50, $50 (international).
Application Contact Ms. Kelly Wilson, Director of the Office of Enrollment Management, 276 Mervis Hall, Pittsburgh, PA 15260. **Phone:** 412-648-1700. **Fax:** 412-648-1659. **E-mail:** mba-admissions@katz.pitt.edu.

See full description on page 946.

The University of Scranton

Scranton, Pennsylvania

PROGRAM IN BUSINESS ADMINISTRATION

Graduate Business Faculty
Full-time: 50

Student Body

Total: 140	Average Age: 30
Full-time: 42	Women: 46%
Part-time: 98	

Admissions

Applications: 76	Average GMAT: 510
Admitted: 71	Average GPA: 3.2
Enrolled: 29	

Costs (1999–2000)
Full-time tuition: N/R
Part-time tuition: $515 per credit

Accreditation
AACSB—The International Association for Management Education

DEGREE MBA

MBA—Master of Business Administration Full-time and part-time. At least 36 total credits required. 18 to 72 months to complete program. *Concentrations:* accounting, finance, international business, management information systems, marketing, operations management.

COSTS

Tuition *Part-time:* $515 per credit. Tuition varies by academic program. **Graduate housing:** Room and board costs vary by campus location, number of occupants, type of accommodation, and type of board plan. *Typical cost:* $7500 (including board).

FINANCIAL AID (1999–2000)

Teaching assistantships and work study. Aid is available to part-time students. Financial aid application deadline: 3/1. **Financial Aid Contact** Mr. William R. Burke, Director of Financial Aid, The Graduate School, Scranton, PA 18510-4689. **Phone:** 570-941-7700. **Fax:** 570-941-6369. **E-mail:** burkew1@uofs.edu.

RESOURCES AND SERVICES

Information about online services, personal computer policies, library resources, international exchange programs, internship programs, and placement services at this institution and others can be found at **www. petersons.com/mba**

International Students

30% of students enrolled are international students.

Services and Facilities Counseling/support services, ESL/language courses, international student housing, international student organization, orientation. Financial aid is not available to international students.
Applying *Required:* TOEFL with recommended score of 173 (computer) or 500 (paper), proof of adequate funds.
International Student Contact Mr. Peter J. Blazes, Director of International Student Affairs, Scranton, PA 18510-4632. **Phone:** 570-941-7575. **Fax:** 570-941-5995. **E-mail:** blazesp1@scranton.edu.

■ APPLICATION

Required Application form, baccalaureate/first degree, 3 letters of recommendation, personal statement, transcripts of college work. School will accept GMAT. **Recommended** Resume/curriculum vitae.
Deadlines and Fees *Application fee:* $35, $35 (international).
Application Contact Mr. James L. Goonan, Director of Graduate Admissions, The Graduate School, Scranton, PA 18510-4632. **Phone:** 570-941-6304. **Toll-free Phone:** 800-366-4723. **Fax:** 570-941-5995. **E-mail:** goonanj1@uofs.edu.

Villanova University

Villanova, Pennsylvania

COLLEGE OF COMMERCE AND FINANCE

Graduate Business Faculty

Full-time: 40	Part-time: 7

Student Body

Total: 588	Average Age: 29
Full-time: 42	Women: 35%
Part-time: 546	

Admissions

Average GMAT: 590	Average GPA: 3.2

Costs (1999–2000)
Full-time tuition: $12,996 per academic year
Part-time tuition: $510 per credit

Accreditation
AACSB—The International Association for Management Education

DEGREES EMBA • JD/MBA • M Tax • MBA

EMBA—EMBA Program Part-time. *Distance learning option.* Minimum of 21 months to complete program.

JD/MBA—JD/MBA Program Full-time and part-time. *Distance learning option.* 36 to 120 months to complete program.

M Tax—Master of Taxation Full-time and part-time. *Distance learning option.* At least 24 total credits required. 12 to 60 months to complete program.

MBA—The MBA Program Full-time and part-time. *Distance learning option.* 33 to 51 total credits required. 19 to 84 months to complete program. *Concentrations:* finance, management information systems, marketing.

COSTS

Tuition *Full-time:* $12,936. *Part-time:* $510 per credit. Tuition varies by academic program. **Required fees:** *Full-time* $60. *Part-time* $30 per semester.

FINANCIAL AID (1999–2000)

21 students received aid, including research assistantships. Financial aid application deadline: 3/31. **Financial Aid Contact** Mr. George Walter, Director of Financial Assistance, Kennedy Hall, 800 Lancaster Avenue, Villanova, PA 19085. **Phone:** 610-519-6456. **Fax:** 610-519-7599. **E-mail:** gwalter@email.vill.edu.

RESOURCES AND SERVICES

Information about online services, personal computer policies, library resources, international exchange programs, internship programs, and placement services at this institution and others can be found at **www.petersons.com/mba**

International Students

1% of students enrolled are international students.

Services and Facilities Counseling/support services. Financial aid is available to international students.

Applying *Required:* TOEFL with recommended score of 600 (paper), proof of adequate funds, proof of health/immunizations.

International Student Contact Mr. Stephen McWilliams, Director of International/Human Services, Corr Hall, 800 Lancaster Avenue, Villanova, PA 19085. **Phone:** 610-519-4095. **E-mail:** smcwilli@email.vill.edu.

■ APPLICATION

Required GMAT, application form, baccalaureate/first degree, essay, 2 letters of recommendation, transcripts of college work. **Recommended** Personal statement, resume/curriculum vitae, 1 year of work experience.

Deadlines and Fees *Deadlines:* 6/30 for fall, 11/15 for spring, 3/31 for summer, 6/30 for fall (international), 11/15 for spring (international), 3/31 for summer (international). *Application fee:* $40, $40 (international).

Application Contact Ms. Melinda German, Director, Graduate Studies in Business, Room 112-Bartley Hall, Villanova, PA 19085-1699. **Phone:** 610-519-4336. **Fax:** 610-519-6273. **E-mail:** mba@email.villanova.edu.

See full description on page 994.

Waynesburg College

Waynesburg, Pennsylvania

PROGRAM IN BUSINESS ADMINISTRATION

DEGREES MBA

MBA—Executive MBA Full-time and part-time. Minimum age requirement: 25. At least 36 total credits required. 12 to 84 months to complete program. *Concentrations:* finance, health care, leadership.

MBA—Master of Business Administration Full-time and part-time. Minimum age requirement: 25. At least 36 total credits required. 12 to 84 months to complete program. *Concentrations:* management.

RESOURCES AND SERVICES

Information about online services, personal computer policies, library resources, international exchange programs, internship programs, and placement services at this institution and others can be found at **www.petersons.com/mba**

International Students

Services and Facilities Counseling/support services, international student housing, international student organization. Financial aid is not available to international students.

International Student Contact Mr. Charles Trump, International Coordinator, 51 West College Street, Waynesburg, PA 15370-1222. **Phone:** 724-852-3260 Ext. 260. **Fax:** 724-627-6416. **E-mail:** ctrump@waynesburg.edu.

■ APPLICATION

Application Contact Ms. Hope Hamel, Department of Business Administration, Hanna Hall, 51 West College Street, Waynesburg, PA 15370. **Phone:** 724-852-3267. **Toll-free Phone:** 888-481-6029. **E-mail:** hhamel@waynesburg.edu.

West Chester University of Pennsylvania

West Chester, Pennsylvania

SCHOOL OF BUSINESS AND PUBLIC AFFAIRS

Graduate Business Faculty

Full-time: 10 — Part-time: 8

Student Body

Total: 300 — Average Age: 32
Full-time: 25 — Women: 33%
Part-time: 275

Admissions

Applications: 100 — Average GMAT: 500
Admitted: 90 — Average GPA: 3
Enrolled: 87

Costs (1999–2000)

Full-time tuition: $4464 per academic year (resident), $7294 per academic year (nonresident)
Part-time tuition: $210 per credit (resident), $367 per credit (nonresident)

After Graduation (Class of 1998–99)

Employed within 3 months of graduation: 100%

DEGREES MBA

MBA—Evening MBA Full-time and part-time. At least 36 total credits required. Maximum of 72 months to complete program. *Concentrations:* economics, finance, management.

MBA—Executive MBA Part-time. 5 years of management experience required. At least 36 total credits required. 24 to 72 months to complete program. *Concentrations:* management.

MBA—Technology and Electronic Commerce MBA Part-time. 3 years of work experience required. At least 36 total credits required. 24 to 72 months to complete program. *Concentrations:* electronic commerce (e-commerce), technology management.

COSTS

Tuition, state resident: *Full-time* $3780. *Part-time* $210 per credit. **Tuition, nonresident:** *Full-time* $6610. *Part-time* $367 per credit. **Tuition, international:** *Full-time* $6610. Tuition varies by number of courses or credits taken. **Required fees:** *Full-time* $684. *Part-time* $39 per credit hour. Fees vary by number of courses or credits taken and campus location.

FINANCIAL AID (1999–2000)

Research assistantships. Aid is available to part-time students. Financial aid application deadline: 2/15. **Financial Aid Contact** Office of Financial Aid, University Avenue and High Street, West Chester, PA 19383. **Phone:** 610-436-2627. **Fax:** 610-436-2574. **E-mail:** finaid@wcupa.edu.

RESOURCES AND SERVICES

Information about online services, personal computer policies, library resources, international exchange programs, internship programs, and placement services at this institution and others can be found at **www.petersons.com/mba**

International Students

7% of students enrolled are international students.

Services and Facilities Counseling/support services, ESL/language courses, visa services. Financial aid is available to international students.

Applying *Required:* TOEFL with recommended score of 550 (paper), proof of adequate funds, proof of health/immunizations.

International Student Contact Mr. Berry Degler, Assistant Director, University Avenue and High Street, West Chester, PA 19383. **Phone:** 610-436-3515. **Fax:** 610-436-3426. **E-mail:** bdegler@wcupa.edu.

■ APPLICATION

Required GMAT, application form, baccalaureate/first degree, 2 letters of recommendation, personal statement, resume/curriculum vitae, transcripts of college work. **Recommended** Interview, 3 years of work experience.

Deadlines and Fees Applications for domestic and international students are processed on a rolling basis. *Application fee:* $25, $25 (international).

Application Contact Dr. Randall LaSalle, Director of MBA Program, University Avenue and High Street, Anderson Hall, West Chester, PA 19383. **Phone:** 610-436-2608. **Fax:** 610-436-2439. **E-mail:** rlasalle@wcupa.edu.

Widener University

Chester, Pennsylvania

SCHOOL OF BUSINESS ADMINISTRATION

Graduate Business Faculty

Full-time: 39 — Part-time: 13

Student Body

Total: 528 — Average Age: 31
Full-time: 54 — Women: 49%
Part-time: 474

Admissions

Applications: 254 — Average GMAT: 510
Admitted: 231 — Average GPA: 3.2
Enrolled: 149

Widener University (continued)

Costs (1999–2000)
Full-time tuition: N/R
Part-time tuition: $520 per credit

Accreditation
AACSB—The International Association for Management Education

DEGREES JD/MBA • MBA • ME/MBA • MS • Psy D/MBA • Psy D/MHA • PsyD/MS

JD/MBA—Juris Doctor/Master of Business Administration Full-time and part-time. 48 to 84 months to complete program.

MBA—Master of Business Administration in Health and Medical Services Administration Full-time and part-time. 40 to 59 total credits required. 15 to 84 months to complete program. *Concentrations:* health care.

MBA—Master of Business Administration Full-time and part-time. 36 to 56 total credits required. 15 to 84 months to complete program. *Concentrations:* accounting, economics, finance, financial management/planning, human resources, international business, management, management information systems, marketing, taxation.

ME/MBA—Master of Engineering/Master of Business Administration Full-time and part-time. 60 to 68 total credits required. 27 to 84 months to complete program.

MS—Master of Science in Accounting Information Systems Full-time and part-time. GMAT not required for Certified Public Accountants. 33 to 60 total credits required. 15 to 84 months to complete program.

MS—Master of Science in Health Administration Full-time and part-time. 37 to 52 total credits required. 15 to 84 months to complete program. *Concentrations:* health care.

MS—Master of Science in Human Resources Management Full-time and part-time. May substitute GRE or MAT for GMAT. 33 to 38 total credits required. 15 to 84 months to complete program.

MS—Master of Science in Information Systems Full-time and part-time. 33 to 39 total credits required. 15 to 84 months to complete program. *Concentrations:* management information systems.

MS—Master of Science in Taxation Full-time and part-time. GMAT not required for Certified Public Accountants. 33 to 54 total credits required. 15 to 84 months to complete program. *Concentrations:* financial management/planning, taxation.

Psy D/MBA—Doctor of Clinical Psychology/Master of Business Administration Full-time. 120 to 160 total credits required. 60 months to complete program. *Concentrations:* health care, management.

Psy D/MHA—Doctor of Clinical Psychology/Master of Health Administration Full-time. 120 to 160 total credits required. 60 months to complete program.

PsyD/MS—Doctor of Clinical Psychology/Master of Science in Human Resources Management Full-time. 60 months to complete program.

COSTS
Tuition *Part-time:* $520 per credit. **Tuition, international:** *Full-time* $12,500. **Required fees:** *Part-time* $25 per semester.

FINANCIAL AID (1999–2000)
150 students received aid, including loans, research assistantships, and work study. Aid is available to part-time students. Financial aid application deadline: 5/1. **Financial Aid Contact** Ms. Mary Cay Reilly, Associate Director, Financial Aid, One University Place, Chester, PA 19013-5792. **Phone:** 610-499-4174. **Fax:** 610-876-9751. **E-mail:** financial.aid@widener.edu.

RESOURCES AND SERVICES
Information about online services, personal computer policies, library resources, international exchange programs, internship programs, and placement services at this institution and others can be found at **www.petersons.com/mba**

International Students
3% of students enrolled are international students.

Services and Facilities Counseling/support services, ESL/language courses, housing location assistance, international student organization, visa services. Financial aid is not available to international students.
Applying *Required:* TOEFL with recommended score of 213 (computer) or 550 (paper), proof of adequate funds, proof of health/immunizations. *Recommended:* TSE, TWE.
International Student Contact Ms. Lois Fuller, Director, International Student Services, One University Place, Chester, PA 19013-5792. **E-mail:** lois.j.fuller@widener.edu.

■ APPLICATION
Required GMAT, application form, baccalaureate/first degree, essay, 2 letters of recommendation, transcripts of college work. **Recommended** Resume/curriculum vitae, work experience.
Deadlines and Fees *Deadlines:* 8/1 for fall, 12/1 for spring, 4/1 for summer, 6/1 for fall (international), 10/1 for spring (international), 2/1 for summer (international). *Application fee:* $25, $325 (international).
Application Contact Ms. Lisa Bussom, Assistant Dean, Graduate Programs in Business, One University Place, Chester, PA 19013-5792. **Phone:** 610-499-4305. **Fax:** 610-499-4615. **E-mail:** gradbus.advise@widener.edu.

See full description on page 1014.

Wilkes University
Wilkes-Barre, Pennsylvania

COLLEGE OF ARTS, SCIENCES AND PROFESSIONAL STUDIES

Graduate Business Faculty
Full-time: 12   Part-time: 5

Student Body
Total: 178   Average Age: 29
Full-time: 13   Women: 45%
Part-time: 165

Admissions
Applications: 80   Average GMAT: 450
Admitted: 60   Average GPA: 3
Enrolled: 50

Costs (1999–2000)
Full-time tuition: N/R
Part-time tuition: $490 per credit

After Graduation (Class of 1998–99)
Employed within 3 months of graduation: 99%

DEGREE MBA

MBA—Master of Business Administration Full-time and part-time. 36 to 48 total credits required. 18 to 36 months to complete program. *Concentrations:* accounting, entrepreneurship, finance, human resources, international and area business studies, management, marketing.

COSTS
Tuition *Part-time:* $490 per credit. **Graduate housing:** *Typical cost:* $7102 (including board).

FINANCIAL AID (1999–2000)
7 students received aid, including research assistantships. Financial aid application deadline: 2/28. **Financial Aid Contact** Mrs. Rachael Lohman, Director, Financial Aid, Student Services Building, Wilkes-Barre, PA 18766. **Phone:** 570-831-4346. **E-mail:** fao@wilkes1.wilkes.edu.

RESOURCES AND SERVICES
Information about online services, personal computer policies, library resources, international exchange programs, internship programs, and placement services at this institution and others can be found at **www.petersons.com/mba**

International Students
2% of students enrolled are international students.

Services and Facilities Counseling/support services, ESL/language courses, international student housing, visa services. Financial aid is not available to international students.
Applying *Required:* TOEFL with recommended score of 550 (paper), proof of adequate funds, proof of health/immunizations.
International Student Contact Ms. Barbara King, Coordinator for International Students, Wilkes University, Conyngham Center, Wilkes-Barre, PA 18766. **Phone:** 570-831-4107. **E-mail:** king@wilkes1.wilkes.edu.

■ APPLICATION
Required Application form, baccalaureate/first degree, 2 letters of recommendation, transcripts of college work. School will accept GMAT. **Recommended** Resume/curriculum vitae, work experience.
Deadlines and Fees Applications for domestic and international students are processed on a rolling basis. *Application fee:* $30, $30 (international).
Application Contact C. Russel Havey, MBA Program Director, College of Arts, Sciences and Professional Studies, Wilkes-Barre, PA 18766. **Phone:** 570-408-4701. **Toll-free Phone:** 800-WILKESU Ext. 4701. **E-mail:** mbaprog@wilkes1.wilkes.edu.

York College of Pennsylvania
York, Pennsylvania

DEPARTMENT OF BUSINESS ADMINISTRATION

Graduate Business Faculty
Full-time: 18   Part-time: 1

Student Body
Total: 238
Full-time: 52   Average Age: 33
Part-time: 186   Women: 37%

Admissions
Applications: 65
Admitted: 60   Average GMAT: 494
Enrolled: 43   Average GPA: 3.27

Costs (1999–2000)
Full-time tuition: N/R
Part-time tuition: $300 per credit hour

After Graduation (Class of 1998–99)
Employed within 3 months of graduation: 89%
Average starting salary: $28,000

DEGREE MBA

MBA—Master of Business Administration Full-time and part-time. At least 33 total credits required. 12 to 84 months to complete program. *Concentrations:* accounting, health care, human resources, information management, management, marketing.

COSTS

Tuition *Part-time:* $300 per credit hour. **Required fees:** *Full-time* $185. *Part-time* $80 per semester. Tuition and fees vary by number of courses or credits taken.

FINANCIAL AID (1999–2000)
26 students received aid, including loans and scholarships. Aid is available to part-time students. Financial aid application deadline: 4/15. **Financial Aid Contact** Mr. Calvin Williams, Director of Financial Aid, York, PA 17405-7199. **Phone:** 717-846-7788 Ext. 1226.

RESOURCES AND SERVICES
Information about online services, personal computer policies, library resources, international exchange programs, internship programs, and placement services at this institution and others can be found at **www.petersons.com/mba**

International Students
4% of students enrolled are international students.

Services and Facilities Counseling/support services. Financial aid is not available to international students.
Applying *Required:* TOEFL with recommended score of 530 (paper), proof of adequate funds, proof of health/immunizations.
International Student Contact Ms. Nancy Spataro, Director of Admissions, York, PA 17405-7199. **Phone:** 717-846-7788 Ext. 1600.

■ APPLICATION

Required Application form, baccalaureate/first degree, transcripts of college work. School will accept GMAT.

Deadlines and Fees *Deadlines:* 7/15 for fall, 12/15 for spring, 4/15 for summer, 7/15 for fall (international), 12/15 for spring (international), 4/15 for summer (international). *Application fee:* $30, $30 (international).

Application Contact Mr. John Barbor, Coordinator, MBA Program, York, PA 17405-7199. **Phone:** 717-815-1491. **Toll-free Phone:** 800-455-8018. **Fax:** 717-849-1619. **E-mail:** jbarbor@ycp.edu.

RHODE ISLAND

Bryant College
Smithfield, Rhode Island

GRADUATE SCHOOL

Graduate Business Faculty
Full-time: 30   Part-time: 5

Student Body
Total: 490
Full-time: 38   Average Age: 32
Part-time: 452   Women: 40%

Admissions
Applications: 202
Admitted: 135   Average GMAT: 530
Enrolled: 117   Average GPA: 3.21

Costs (1999–2000)
Full-time tuition: N/R
Part-time tuition: $1100 per course

Accreditation
AACSB—The International Association for Management Education

DEGREES MBA • MSA • MST

MBA—Master of Business Administration Full-time and part-time. *Distance learning option.* 48 to 54 total credits required. 18 to 72 months to complete program. *Concentrations:* accounting, finance, management, management information systems, marketing, operations management.

MSA—Master of Science in Accounting Full-time and part-time. 30 to 54 total credits required. 24 to 72 months to complete program. *Concentrations:* accounting.

MST—Master of Science in Taxation Part-time. At least 30 total credits required. 30 to 72 months to complete program. *Concentrations:* taxation.

High-quality, flexibility, and value define the Bryant College M.B.A. courses. They are offered with working professionals in mind, are scheduled throughout the year, and meet one evening per week for 2¼ hours at 5:20 or 7:45 p.m. Most students earn their advanced degrees on a part-time basis while working full-time, and complete degree requirements in three to six years. Full-time study is also available, and students may move from part-time to full-time status at various times throughout the program, as life circumstances change.

Bryant faculty members are accomplished academics and experienced practitioners. Class size averages 20 students, giving students the opportunity to learn with and from other working professionals. The classroom becomes a living case study as students apply their experiences to discussions and group projects.

The Hodgson Memorial Library, considered one of the region's most extensive business libraries, is conveniently located in the College's Unistructure. With an impressive blend of print and electronic resources, the library holds more than 140,000 items in various formats—books, bound journals, audiovisual materials, and microform—and also offers LEXIS-NEXIS, DIALOG (offering access to 5,000 data resources), and the BRIDGE Information Systems Selective Ticker Service, which provides market data and investment analysis.

COSTS

Tuition *Part-time:* $1100 per course. Tuition varies by academic program. **Graduate housing:** Room and board costs vary by number of occupants and type of board plan. *Typical cost:* $8050 (including board), $5200 (room only).

FINANCIAL AID (1999–2000)
66 students received aid, including fellowships, loans, research assistantships, and scholarships. Aid is available to part-time students. **Financial Aid Contact** Mr. John Canning, Director of Financial Aid, 1150 Douglas Pike, Smithfield, RI 02917-1284. **Phone:** 401-232-6020. **Fax:** 401-232-6319. **E-mail:** jcanning@bryant.edu.

RESOURCES AND SERVICES
Information about online services, personal computer policies, library resources, international exchange programs, internship programs, and placement services at this institution and others can be found at **www.petersons.com/mba**

International Students
2% of students enrolled are international students.

Services and Facilities Intercultural center. Financial aid is not available to international students.
Applying *Required:* TOEFL, proof of adequate funds, proof of health/immunizations.

International Student Contact Ms. Kathleen Sullivan, Director, Intercultural Center, 1150 Douglas Pike, Smithfield, RI 02917-1284. **Phone:** 401-232-6946. **Fax:** 401-232-6362. **E-mail:** ksulliva@bryant.edu.

Bryant College (continued)

■ APPLICATION

Required GMAT, application form, baccalaureate/first degree, essay, 1 letter of recommendation, personal statement, resume/curriculum vitae, transcripts of college work. **Recommended** Interview, 3 years of work experience.

Deadlines and Fees *Deadlines:* 7/15 for fall, 11/15 for spring, 4/1 for summer, 4/1 for fall (international), 11/15 for spring (international), 3/1 for summer (international). *Application fee:* $60, $80 (international).

Application Contact Ms. Catherine Pastille, Assistant Director for Graduate Admission, 1150 Douglas Pike, Smithfield, RI 02917-1284. **Phone:** 401-232-6230. **Fax:** 401-232-6494. **E-mail:** gradprog@bryant.edu.

See full description on page 582.

Johnson & Wales University

Providence, Rhode Island

THE ALAN SHAWN FEINSTEIN GRADUATE SCHOOL

Graduate Business Faculty
Full-time: 17

Part-time: 14

Student Body
Total: 575
Full-time: 450
Part-time: 125

Average Age: 27
Women: 43%

Admissions
Applications: 431
Admitted: 319

Enrolled: 217

Costs (1999–2000)
Full-time tuition: N/R
Part-time tuition: $212 per quarter hour

After Graduation (Class of 1998–99)
Employed within 3 months of graduation: 76%
Average starting salary: $28,000

DEGREES MBA

MBA—Master of Business Administration in Global Business Full-time and part-time. At least 54 total credits required. 12 to 18 months to complete program. *Concentrations:* accounting, financial management/planning, international trade, management, organizational management.

MBA—Master of Business Administration in Hospitality Administration Full-time and part-time. At least 54 total credits required. 12 to 18 months to complete program.

COSTS

Tuition *Part-time:* $212 per quarter hour. Tuition varies by class time. **Graduate housing:** Room and board costs vary by type of accommodation and type of board plan. *Typical cost:* $5970 (including board).

FINANCIAL AID (1999–2000)

216 students received aid, including grants, loans, and scholarships. **Financial Aid Contact** Ms. Lynn Robinson, Director, Financial Aid, 8 Abbott Park Place, Providence, RI 02903-3703. **Phone:** 401-598-4648. **Fax:** 401-598-1040. **E-mail:** gradadm@jwu.edu.

RESOURCES AND SERVICES

Information about online services, personal computer policies, library resources, international exchange programs, internship programs, and placement services at this institution and others can be found at **www.petersons.com/mba**

International Students

44% of students enrolled are international students.

Services and Facilities Counseling/support services, ESL/language courses, international student housing, visa services. Financial aid is available to international students.

Applying *Required:* TOEFL with recommended score of 550 (paper), proof of adequate funds.

International Student Contact Ms. Janine DeVellis, International Student Advisor, International Office, 8 Abbott Park Place, Providence, RI 02903-3703. **Phone:** 401-598-1074. **Fax:** 401-598-4773. **E-mail:** gradadm@jwu.edu.

■ APPLICATION

Required Application form, baccalaureate/first degree, 3 letters of recommendation, transcripts of college work. School will accept GMAT, GRE, and MAT. **Recommended** Interview, resume/curriculum vitae, work experience.

Deadlines and Fees Applications for domestic and international students are processed on a rolling basis.

Application Contact Dr. Allan Freedman, Director, Graduate Admissions, 8 Abbott Park Place, Providence, RI 02903-3703. **Phone:** 401-598-1015. **Toll-free Phone:** 800-342-5598 Ext. 1015. **Fax:** 401-598-4773. **E-mail:** gradadm@jwu.edu.

See full description on page 696.

Providence College

Providence, Rhode Island

DEPARTMENT OF BUSINESS ADMINISTRATION

Graduate Business Faculty
Full-time: 19

Part-time: 10

Student Body
Total: 277
Full-time: 10
Part-time: 267

Average Age: 28
Women: 27%

Admissions
Applications: 48
Admitted: 37
Enrolled: 37

Average GMAT: 500
Average GPA: 3

Costs (1999–2000)
Full-time tuition: $8640 per academic year
Part-time tuition: $750 per course

DEGREE MBA

MBA—Master of Business Administration Full-time and part-time. At least 36 total credits required. 12 to 60 months to complete program. *Concentrations:* accounting, economics, finance, international business, marketing, public policy and administration, quantitative analysis.

COSTS

Tuition *Full-time:* $8640. *Part-time:* $750 per course. Tuition varies by number of courses or credits taken.

FINANCIAL AID (1999–2000)

7 students received aid, including research assistantships. **Financial Aid Contact** Mr. Herbert D'Arcy, Jr., Executive Director, Financial Aid Office, River Avenue and Eaton Street, Providence, RI 02918-0001. **Phone:** 401-865-2602. **Fax:** 401-865-2057. **E-mail:** hdarcy@providence.edu.

RESOURCES AND SERVICES

Information about online services, personal computer policies, library resources, international exchange programs, internship programs, and placement services at this institution and others can be found at **www.petersons.com/mba**

International Students

2% of students enrolled are international students.

Services and Facilities Counseling/support services. Financial aid is not available to international students.

Applying *Required:* TOEFL with recommended score of 550 (paper), proof of adequate funds.

International Student Contact Dr. John Hogan, International Student Advisor, River Avenue and Eaton Street, Providence, RI 02918-0001. **Phone:** 401-865-2676. **E-mail:** jhogan@providence.edu.

■ APPLICATION

Required GMAT, application form, baccalaureate/first degree, 2 letters of recommendation, personal statement, transcripts of college work. **Recommended** Resume/curriculum vitae.

Deadlines and Fees Applications for domestic and international students are processed on a rolling basis. *Application fee:* $50, $50 (international).

Application Contact Dr. John Shaw, Director, Master of Business Administration Program, River Avenue and Eaton Street, Providence, RI 02918-0001. **Phone:** 401-865-2333. **Fax:** 401-865-2978. **E-mail:** jshaw@providence.edu.

Salve Regina University

Newport, Rhode Island

GRADUATE SCHOOL

Graduate Business Faculty
Full-time: 4   Part-time: 10

Student Body
Total: 123
Full-time: 19   Average Age: 39
Part-time: 104   Women: 41%

Admissions
Applications: 53   Enrolled: 28
Admitted: 38   Average GMAT: 555

Costs (1999–2000)
Full-time tuition: $5720 per academic year
Part-time tuition: $300 per credit

DEGREES MA • MBA • MS

MA—Master of Arts in Human Resource Management Full-time and part-time. At least 36 total credits required. 24 to 60 months to complete program. *Concentrations:* human resources.

MBA—Master of Business Administration Full-time and part-time. *Distance learning option.* At least 36 total credits required. 24 to 60 months to complete program. *Concentrations:* accounting, finance, management, management information systems.

MS—Master of Science in Accounting Full-time and part-time. At least 42 total credits required. 24 to 60 months to complete program. *Concentrations:* accounting.

MS—Master of Science in Information Systems Science Full-time and part-time. At least 36 total credits required. 24 to 60 months to complete program. *Concentrations:* management information systems.

MS—Master of Science in Management *Distance learning option.* At least 36 total credits required. 24 to 60 months to complete program. *Concentrations:* insurance, management.

COSTS

Tuition *Full-time:* $5400. *Part-time:* $300 per credit. Tuition varies by number of courses or credits taken. **Required fees:** *Full-time* $320. *Part-time* $35 per semester.

FINANCIAL AID (1999–2000)

17 students received aid, including loans. Aid is available to part-time students. Financial aid application deadline: 3/1. **Financial Aid Contact** Ms. Aida Mirante, Director of Financial Aid and Veterans Affairs, 100 Ochre Point Avenue, Newport, RI 02840-4192. **Phone:** 401-341-2901. **Fax:** 401-341-2928. **E-mail:** mirantea@salve.edu.

RESOURCES AND SERVICES

Information about online services, personal computer policies, library resources, international exchange programs, internship programs, and placement services at this institution and others can be found at **www.petersons.com/mba**

International Students

Services and Facilities ESL/language courses. Financial aid is not available to international students.
Applying *Required:* TOEFL with recommended score of 550 (paper), proof of adequate funds.

International Student Contact Mrs. Laura McPhie Oliveira, Dean of Enrollment Services, 100 Ochre Point Avenue, Newport, RI 02840-4192. **Phone:** 401-847-6650 Ext. 2908. **Fax:** 401-848-2823. **E-mail:** sruadmis@salve.edu.

■ APPLICATION

Required Application form, baccalaureate/first degree, 2 letters of recommendation, personal statement, transcripts of college work. School will accept GMAT, GRE, and MAT. **Recommended** Resume/curriculum vitae.

Deadlines and Fees Applications for domestic and international students are processed on a rolling basis. *Application fee:* $35, $35 (international).

Application Contact Mr. John Britton, Director of Graduate MBA Program, 100 Ochre Point Avenue, Newport, RI 02840-4192. **Phone:** 401-341-3140. **Toll-free Phone:** 888-GO-SALVE. **Fax:** 401-341-2993. **E-mail:** brittonj@salve.edu.

See full description on page 812.

University of Rhode Island

Kingston, Rhode Island

COLLEGE OF BUSINESS ADMINISTRATION

Graduate Business Faculty
Full-time: 55

Student Body
Total: 227
Full-time: 18   Average Age: 29
Part-time: 209   Women: 32%

Admissions
Applications: 116   Average GMAT: 549
Admitted: 84   Average GPA: 3.1
Enrolled: 63

Costs (1999–2000)
Full-time tuition: $8683 per academic year (resident), $22,194 per academic year (nonresident)
Part-time tuition: $197 per credit (resident), $562 per credit (nonresident)

After Graduation (Class of 1998–99)
Employed within 3 months of graduation: 90%
Average starting salary: $57,000

Accreditation
AACSB—The International Association for Management Education

DEGREES MBA • MS

MBA—Executive MBA Part-time. 49 total credits required. 18 months to complete program. *Concentrations:* management.

MBA—Full-time MBA Full-time. 49 total credits required. 12 months to complete program. *Concentrations:* accounting, finance, international business, management, management information systems, marketing.

MBA—Part-time MBA Part-time. 36 to 54 total credits required. 24 to 48 months to complete program. *Concentrations:* accounting, finance, international business, management, management information systems, marketing.

MS—Master of Science in Accounting Full-time and part-time. 30 to 69 total credits required. 12 to 48 months to complete program.

COSTS

Tuition, state resident: *Full-time* $7283. *Part-time* $197 per credit. **Tuition, nonresident:** *Full-time* $20,794. *Part-time* $562 per credit. **Required fees:** *Full-time* $1400. *Part-time* $50 per semester. Tuition and fees vary by number of courses or credits taken and academic program. **Graduate housing:** Room and board costs vary by number of occupants and type of accommodation. *Typical cost:* $5400 (room only).

FINANCIAL AID (1999–2000)

Fellowships, loans, research assistantships, scholarships, and work study. Aid is available to part-time students. Financial aid application deadline: 2/1. **Financial Aid Contact** Financial Aid Office, Roosevelt Hall, Kingston, RI 02881. **Phone:** 401-874-2314. **Fax:** 401-874-2002.

RESOURCES AND SERVICES

Information about online services, personal computer policies, library resources, international exchange programs, internship programs, and placement services at this institution and others can be found at **www.petersons.com/mba**

International Students

3% of students enrolled are international students.

Services and Facilities Counseling/support services, housing location assistance, international student housing, international student organization, orientation, visa services. Financial aid is not available to international students.
Applying *Required:* TOEFL with recommended score of 231 (computer) or 575 (paper), proof of adequate funds, proof of health/immunizations.

International Student Contact International Students and Scholars Office, 37 Lower College Road, Kingston, RI 02881. **Phone:** 401-874-2395. **Fax:** 401-789-5298. **E-mail:** issoff@uriacc.uri.edu.

■ APPLICATION

Required GMAT, application form, baccalaureate/first degree, essay, 2 letters of recommendation, personal statement, transcripts of college work. **Recommended** Resume/curriculum vitae.

Deadlines and Fees *Deadlines:* 7/15 for fall, 11/15 for spring, 4/15 for fall (international), 11/15 for spring (international). *Application fee:* $30, $45 (international).

University of Rhode Island (continued)

Application Contact Ms. Lisa Hadzekyriakides, Coordinator, MBA Programs, 210 Ballentine Hall, 7 Lippitt Road, Kingston, RI 02881-0802. **Phone:** 401-874-5000. **Fax:** 401-874-7047. **E-mail:** hadz@uri.edu.

See full description on page 950.

SOUTH CAROLINA

Charleston Southern University

Charleston, South Carolina

PROGRAM IN BUSINESS

Graduate Business Faculty
Full-time: 12   Part-time: 2

Student Body
Total: 117   Average Age: 31
Full-time: 11   Women: 50%
Part-time: 106

Admissions
Applications: 47   Average GMAT: 450
Enrolled: 38   Average GPA: 2.91

Costs (1999–2000)
Full-time tuition: N/R
Part-time tuition: $192 per credit hour

After Graduation (Class of 1998–99)
Employed within 3 months of graduation: 95%

DEGREE MBA

MBA—Master of Business Administration Full-time and part-time. 30 to 36 total credits required. 12 to 72 months to complete program. *Concentrations:* accounting, finance, health care, management information systems, organizational behavior/development.

COSTS

Tuition *Part-time:* $192 per credit hour. Tuition varies by number of courses or credits taken. **Graduate housing:** Room and board costs vary by number of occupants. *Typical cost:* $6405 (including board).

FINANCIAL AID (1999–2000)

29 students received aid, including loans and research assistantships. Aid is available to part-time students. Financial aid application deadline: 4/15. **Financial Aid Contact** Ms. Ellen Green, Director, Financial Aid, PO Box 118087, Charleston, SC 29423-8087. **Phone:** 843-863-7050. **Fax:** 843-863-7070. **E-mail:** egreen@csuniv.edu.

RESOURCES AND SERVICES

Information about online services, personal computer policies, library resources, international exchange programs, internship programs, and placement services at this institution and others can be found at **www.petersons.com/mba**

International Students

2% of students enrolled are international students.
Services and Facilities Counseling/support services. Financial aid is available to international students.
Applying *Required:* TOEFL with recommended score of 550 (paper), proof of adequate funds, proof of health/immunizations.
International Student Contact Ms. Barbara Mead, Assistant Dean of Students/ International Services Director, PO Box 118087, Charleston, SC 29423-8087. **Phone:** 843-863-8009. **Fax:** 843-863-7021. **E-mail:** bmead@csuniv.edu.

■ APPLICATION

Required GMAT, application form, baccalaureate/first degree, 2 letters of recommendation, personal statement, transcripts of college work.
Deadlines and Fees Applications for domestic and international students are processed on a rolling basis. *Application fee:* $25, $25 (international).
Application Contact Ms. Heather Marie Brooks, Director of Evening Colleges and Graduate Admissions, PO Box 118087, Charleston, SC 29423-8087. **Phone:** 843-863-7525. **Fax:** 843-863-7070. **E-mail:** hbrooks@csuniv.edu.

The Citadel, The Military College of South Carolina

Charleston, South Carolina

COLLEGE OF GRADUATE AND PROFESSIONAL STUDIES

Accreditation
AACSB—The International Association for Management Education

DEGREE MBA

MBA—Master of Business Administration Full-time and part-time. At least 39 total credits required. 24 to 72 months to complete program.

RESOURCES AND SERVICES

Information about online services, personal computer policies, library resources, international exchange programs, internship programs, and placement services at this institution and others can be found at **www.petersons.com/mba**

■ APPLICATION

Application Contact College of Graduate and Professional Studies, 171 Moultrie Street, Charleston, SC 29409. **Phone:** 843-953-5089. **Toll-free Phone:** 800-868-1842. **Fax:** 843-953-7630.

Clemson University

Clemson, South Carolina

COLLEGE OF BUSINESS AND PUBLIC AFFAIRS

Graduate Business Faculty
Full-time: 103   Part-time: 2

Student Body
Total: 342   Average Age: 27
Full-time: 120   Women: 35%
Part-time: 222

Admissions
Applications: 273   Average GMAT: 591
Admitted: 142   Average GPA: 3.27
Enrolled: 60

Costs (1999–2000)
Full-time tuition: $3870 per academic year (resident), $9646 per academic year (nonresident)
Part-time tuition: $245 per credit hour (resident), $490 per credit hour (nonresident)

After Graduation (Class of 1998–99)
Employed within 3 months of graduation: 85%
Average starting salary: $53,300

Accreditation
AACSB—The International Association for Management Education

DEGREES MBA

MBA—Full-time MBA Full-time. 1 year of work experience preferred. At least 62 total credits required. 21 months to complete program. *Concentrations:* accounting, business information science, economics, electronic commerce (e-commerce), entrepreneurship, finance, human resources, industrial administration/ management, information management, international business, management, management information systems, marketing, operations management, production management, public policy and administration, technology management.
MBA—Part-time MBA Part-time. 2 years of work experience required. At least 43 total credits required. 21 to 72 months to complete program.

COSTS

Tuition, state resident: *Full-time* $3680. *Part-time* $245 per credit hour. **Tuition, nonresident:** *Full-time* $9456. *Part-time* $490 per credit hour. Tuition varies by number of courses or credits taken, campus location, and academic program. **Required fees:** *Full-time* $190. Tuition and fees vary by campus location and academic program. **Graduate housing:** Room and board costs vary by number of occupants, type of accommodation, and type of board plan. *Typical cost:* $3900 (room only).

FINANCIAL AID (1999–2000)

55 students received aid, including fellowships, loans, and research assistantships. Financial aid application deadline: 1/15. **Financial Aid**

Contact Financial Aid Office, G01 Sikes Hall, Clemson, SC 29634. **Phone:** 864-656-2280. **Fax:** 864-656-1831. **E-mail:** finaid@clemson.edu.

RESOURCES AND SERVICES
Information about online services, personal computer policies, library resources, international exchange programs, internship programs, and placement services at this institution and others can be found at **www.petersons.com/mba**

International Students
18% of students enrolled are international students.

Services and Facilities Counseling/support services, housing location assistance, international student organization, orientation, visa services. Financial aid is available to international students.
Applying *Required:* TOEFL with recommended score of 213 (computer) or 550 (paper), proof of adequate funds, proof of health/immunizations.
International Student Contact International Services and Diversity Programs, E 208 Martin Hall, Clemson, SC 29634. **Phone:** 864-656-2357. **Fax:** 864-656-4187.

■ **APPLICATION**

Required GMAT, application form, baccalaureate/first degree, 2 letters of recommendation, resume/curriculum vitae, transcripts of college work. **Recommended** 1 year of work experience.

Deadlines and Fees *Deadlines:* 6/15 for fall, 4/15 for fall (international). *Application fee:* $40, $40 (international).

Application Contact Director of Admissions, MBA Programs, Box 341315, MBA Office, Clemson, SC 29634-1315. **Phone:** 864-656-3975. **Fax:** 864-656-0947. **E-mail:** mba@clemson.edu.

See full description on page 600.

Francis Marion University

Florence, South Carolina
SCHOOL OF BUSINESS

Graduate Business Faculty
Full-time: 20
Student Body
Total: 71 — Average Age: 31
Full-time: 10 — Women: 46%
Part-time: 61
Admissions
Applications: 34 — Average GMAT: 485
Admitted: 26 — Average GPA: 3
Enrolled: 26
Costs (1999–2000)
Full-time tuition: $2715 per academic year (resident), $5430 per academic year (nonresident)
Part-time tuition: $181 per hour (resident), $362 per hour (nonresident)

After Graduation (Class of 1998–99)
Employed within 3 months of graduation: 100%
Average starting salary: $42,000

Accreditation
AACSB—The International Association for Management Education

DEGREES MBA

MBA—Health Management MBA Full-time and part-time. *Distance learning option.* 36 to 42 total credits required. 24 to 72 months to complete program. *Concentrations:* health care, management.

MBA—Master of Business Administration Full-time and part-time. 36 total credits required. 18 to 72 months to complete program.

COSTS

Tuition, state resident: *Full-time* $2715. *Part-time* $181 per hour. **Tuition, nonresident:** *Full-time* $5430. *Part-time* $362 per hour. **Required fees:** *Part-time* $75 per semester. **Graduate housing:** Room and board costs vary by number of occupants, type of accommodation, and type of board plan. *Typical cost:* $3550 (including board).

FINANCIAL AID (1999–2000)
5 students received aid, including research assistantships and scholarships. Aid is available to part-time students. Financial aid application deadline: 3/1. **Financial Aid Contact** Mr. Scott Brown,

Director of Financial Assistance, Box 100547, Florence, SC 29501-0547. **Phone:** 843-661-1190.

RESOURCES AND SERVICES
Information about online services, personal computer policies, library resources, international exchange programs, internship programs, and placement services at this institution and others can be found at **www.petersons.com/mba**

International Students
13% of students enrolled are international students.

Services and Facilities Counseling/support services, ESL/language courses, housing location assistance, international student organization, language tutoring, orientation. Financial aid is available to international students.
Applying *Required:* TOEFL with recommended score of 550 (paper), proof of adequate funds, proof of health/immunizations.
International Student Contact Graduate Office, Box 100547, Florence, SC 29501-0547. **Phone:** 843-661-1281.

■ **APPLICATION**

Required GMAT, application form, baccalaureate/first degree, essay, 2 letters of recommendation, personal statement, transcripts of college work. **Recommended** Interview.

Deadlines and Fees Applications for domestic and international students are processed on a rolling basis. *Application fee:* $25, $25 (international).

Application Contact Dr. Barry O'Brien, Director, MBA Program, Box 100547, Florence, SC 29501-0547. **Phone:** 843-661-1419. **Fax:** 843-661-1432. **E-mail:** bobrien@fmarion.edu.

South Carolina State University

Orangeburg, South Carolina
DEPARTMENT OF AGRIBUSINESS AND ECONOMICS

Graduate Business Faculty
Full-time: 8
Student Body
Total: 7 — Average Age: 24
Full-time: 5 — Women: 29%
Part-time: 2
Admissions
Average GMAT: 400 — Average GPA: 2.8
Costs (1999–2000)
Full-time tuition: $3654 per academic year (resident), $7192 per academic year (nonresident)
Part-time tuition: $203 per credit (resident), $400 per credit (nonresident)

After Graduation (Class of 1998–99)
Employed within 3 months of graduation: 100%
Average starting salary: $28,000

DEGREE MS

MS—Master of Science in Agribusiness Full-time and part-time. At least 33 total credits required. Maximum of 72 months to complete program. *Concentrations:* agribusiness, agricultural economics.

COSTS

Tuition, state resident: *Full-time* $3654. *Part-time* $203 per credit. **Tuition, nonresident:** *Full-time* $7192. *Part-time* $400 per credit. **Graduate housing:** Room and board costs vary by number of occupants and type of accommodation. *Typical cost:* $7500 (including board).

FINANCIAL AID (1999–2000)
7 students received aid, including fellowships, loans, research assistantships, scholarships, and work study. **Financial Aid Contact** Dr. Nelson Modeste, Chairman, Department of Agribusiness and Economics, Orangeburg, SC 29117. **Phone:** 803-536-8076. **Fax:** 803-533-3639. **E-mail:** nmodeste@scsu.edu.

RESOURCES AND SERVICES
Information about online services, personal computer policies, library resources, international exchange programs, internship programs, and placement services at this institution and others can be found at **www.petersons.com/mba**

International Students
14% of students enrolled are international students.

SOUTH CAROLINA

South Carolina State University (continued)

Services and Facilities Counseling/support services, international student organization, visa services. Financial aid is not available to international students.
Applying *Required:* TOEFL with recommended score of 550 (paper), proof of adequate funds, proof of health/immunizations.
International Student Contact Mrs. Carolyn G. Free, Director, Minority and International Programs, PO Box 8123, Orangeburg, SC 29117. **Phone:** 803-536-8402. **Fax:** 803-536-8990. **E-mail:** zs_cfree@scsu.edu.

■ **APPLICATION**

Required Application form, baccalaureate/first degree, essay, 3 letters of recommendation, personal statement, transcripts of college work. School will accept GMAT, GRE, and MAT.
Deadlines and Fees *Deadlines:* 7/10 for fall, 11/10 for spring, 5/1 for summer, 7/10 for fall (international), 11/10 for spring (international), 5/1 for summer (international). *Application fee:* $25, $25 (international).
Application Contact Dr. Nelson Modeste, Chairman, Department of Agribusiness and Economics, Orangeburg, SC 29117. **Phone:** 803-536-8076. **Fax:** 803-533-3639. **E-mail:** nmodeste@scsu.edu.

University of Charleston, South Carolina

Charleston, South Carolina

SCHOOL OF BUSINESS AND ECONOMICS

Graduate Business Faculty
Full-time: 25

Student Body
Total: 28
Full-time: 12
Part-time: 16

Average Age: 30
Women: 64%

Admissions
Applications: 16
Admitted: 10
Enrolled: 9

Average GMAT: 551
Average GPA: 3.41

Costs (1999–2000)
Full-time tuition: N/R
Part-time tuition: $145 per credit hour (resident), $298 per credit hour (nonresident)

DEGREE MS

MS—Master of Science in Accountancy Full-time and part-time. At least 30 total credits required. 24 to 60 months to complete program. *Concentrations:* accounting.

COSTS

Tuition, state resident: *Part-time* $145 per credit hour. **Tuition, nonresident:** *Part-time* $298 per credit hour.

FINANCIAL AID (1999–2000)

6 students received aid, including fellowships, research assistantships, and work study. Aid is available to part-time students. Financial aid application deadline: 4/1. **Financial Aid Contact** Mr. Donald Griggs, Director, Office of Financial Assistance and Veterans Affairs, Charleston, SC 29424-0001. **Phone:** 843-953-5540. **Fax:** 843-953-7192. **E-mail:** financialaid@cofc.edu.

RESOURCES AND SERVICES

Information about online services, personal computer policies, library resources, international exchange programs, internship programs, and placement services at this institution and others can be found at **www.petersons.com/mba**

International Students

4% of students enrolled are international students.

Services and Facilities Counseling/support services, ESL/language courses, housing location assistance, international student housing, language tutoring, orientation, visa services. Financial aid is not available to international students.
Applying *Required:* TOEFL with recommended score of 550 (paper), proof of adequate funds, proof of health/immunizations.
International Student Contact Ms. Laura Hines, Director of Graduate Services, Randolph Hall, Charleston, SC 29424-0001. **Phone:** 843-953-5614. **Fax:** 843-953-1434. **E-mail:** gradsch@cofc.edu.

■ **APPLICATION**

Required GMAT, application form, baccalaureate/first degree, transcripts of college work.
Deadlines and Fees Applications for domestic and international students are processed on a rolling basis. *Application fee:* $35, $35 (international).
Application Contact Graduate School Office, Randolph Hall, Charleston, SC 29424-0001. **Phone:** 843-953-5614. **Fax:** 843-953-1434. **E-mail:** gradsch@cofc.edu.

University of South Carolina

Columbia, South Carolina

THE DARLA MOORE SCHOOL OF BUSINESS

Graduate Business Faculty
Full-time: 117

Part-time: 20

Student Body
Total: 956
Full-time: 599
Part-time: 357

Average Age: 27
Women: 36%

Admissions
Applications: 1,225
Admitted: 741
Enrolled: 458

Average GMAT: 600
Average GPA: 3.3

Costs (1999–2000)
Full-time tuition: $4014 per academic year (resident), $8528 per academic year (nonresident)
Part-time tuition: $202 per credit hour (resident), $428 per credit hour (nonresident)

After Graduation (Class of 1998–99)
Employed within 3 months of graduation: 81%
Average starting salary: $60,500

Accreditation
AACSB—The International Association for Management Education

DEGREES IMBA • JD/M Acc • JD/MA • JD/MBA • JD/MHR • JD/MIBS • JD/MS • M Acc • M Tax • MA • MA/MBA • MBA • MHR • MIBS • MS

IMBA—International Master of Business Administration Full-time. 2 years work experience. At least 48 total credits required. Minimum of 15 months to complete program. *Concentrations:* accounting, entrepreneurship, finance, international business, international finance, international management, international marketing, international trade, management, management information systems, management science, marketing, operations management, organizational management, strategic management.
JD/M Acc—Juris Doctor/Master of Accountancy Full-time. 48 to 60 total credits required. 36 to 48 months to complete program. *Concentrations:* accounting, business law.
JD/MA—Juris Doctor/Master of Arts in Economics Full-time. 48 to 60 total credits required. 36 to 48 months to complete program. *Concentrations:* business law, economics.
JD/MBA—Juris Doctor/Master of Business Administration Full-time. 2 year work experience. At least 54 total credits required. Minimum of 48 months to complete program. *Concentrations:* business law, management.
JD/MHR—Juris Doctor/Master of Human Resources Full-time. 48 to 60 total credits required. 36 to 48 months to complete program. *Concentrations:* business law, human resources, industrial administration/management, industrial/labor relations.
JD/MIBS—Juris Doctor/Master of International Business Studies Full-time. 2 years work experience. At least 60 total credits required. Minimum of 48 months to complete program. *Concentrations:* business law, international business.
JD/MS—Juris Doctor/Master of Science in Business Administration Full-time. 48 to 60 total credits required. 36 to 48 months to complete program. *Concentrations:* business law, management information systems, management science, marketing, operations management.
M Acc—Master of Accountancy Full-time. At least 30 total credits required. 12 to 18 months to complete program. *Concentrations:* accounting.
M Tax—Master of Taxation Full-time. At least 36 total credits required. 12 to 18 months to complete program. *Concentrations:* taxation.
MA—Master of Arts in Economics Full-time. At least 30 total credits required. 12 to 15 months to complete program. *Concentrations:* economics.
MA/MBA—Master of Arts in English/Master of Business Administration Full-time. At least 51 total credits required. 36 to 48 months to complete program.

382

Peterson's Guide to MBA Programs 2001

Concentrations: management, management information systems, management science, marketing, operations management.

MBA—Professional MBA Program Part-time. *Distance learning option.* At least 54 total credits required. Minimum of 31 months to complete program. *Concentrations:* accounting, entrepreneurship, finance, international business, management, management information systems, management science, marketing, operations management, organizational management, strategic management.

MBA—Master of Business Administration Full-time. 2 years work experience. At least 54 total credits required. 21 to 24 months to complete program. *Concentrations:* accounting, entrepreneurship, finance, international business, management, management information systems, management science, marketing, operations management, organizational management, strategic management.

MHR—Master of Human Resources Full-time. At least 42 total credits required. 18 to 24 months to complete program. *Concentrations:* human resources, industrial administration/management, industrial/labor relations.

MIBS—Master of International Business Studies Full-time. 2 years work experience. At least 60 total credits required. 24 to 36 months to complete program. *Concentrations:* accounting, entrepreneurship, finance, international business, international finance, international management, international marketing, international trade, management, management information systems, management science, marketing, operations management, organizational management, strategic management.

MS—Master of Science in Business Administration Full-time. 30 to 36 total credits required. 12 to 15 months to complete program. *Concentrations:* management information systems, management science, marketing, operations management.

Innovation has been the key to the success of the Darla Moore School of Business at the University of South Carolina. The School has a long history of keeping pace with the ever-changing global economic environment through a blend of academic preparation and real-world experience. Three distinctive degree programs with global opportunities are offered. The Master of International Business Studies (M.I.B.S.) degree program features an integrated business curriculum, formal language training (eight languages), cultural studies, and a six-month overseas internship. The Master of Business Administration (M.B.A.) degree program provides international study opportunities at thirteen locations. The International Master of Business Administration (I.M.B.A.) degree program combines the best of European and American management education in a unique partnership between the University of South Carolina and the Vienna Business and Economics University. By emphasizing foreign languages, cultural studies, overseas internships, and study-abroad programs, the Darla Moore School of Business has earned international recognition. The School believes that global understanding and competency are essential for business students who must operate in a world of few boundaries and constant change.

COSTS
Tuition, state resident: *Full-time* $4014. *Part-time* $202 per credit hour. **Tuition, nonresident:** *Full-time* $8528. *Part-time* $428 per credit hour. Tuition varies by class time, number of courses or credits taken, and local reciprocity agreements. **Required fees:** Fees vary by class time, number of courses or credits taken, academic program, and local reciprocity agreements. **Graduate housing:** Room and board costs vary by campus location, number of occupants, type of accommodation, and type of board plan. *Typical cost:* $12,000 (including board).

FINANCIAL AID (1999–2000)
300 students received aid, including fellowships, loans, research assistantships, scholarships, teaching assistantships, and work study. Financial aid application deadline: 2/1. **Financial Aid Contact** Ms. Libby Shropshier, Director of Graduate Administrative and Financial Affairs, Columbia, SC 29208. **Phone:** 803-777-6845. **Fax:** 803-777-0414. **E-mail:** shropshier@darla.badm.sc.edu.

RESOURCES AND SERVICES
Information about online services, personal computer policies, library resources, international exchange programs, internship programs, and placement services at this institution and others can be found at **www.petersons.com/mba**

International Students
21% of students enrolled are international students.
Services and Facilities Counseling/support services, ESL/language courses, housing location assistance, international student housing, international student organization, visa services. Financial aid is available to international students.
Applying *Required:* TOEFL with recommended score of 600 (paper), proof of adequate funds, proof of health/immunizations.
International Student Contact Ms. Patricia Willer, Director of International Programs for Students, James F. Byrne Building, Suite 123, Columbia, SC 29208. **Phone:** 803-777-7461. **Fax:** 803-777-0462. **E-mail:** d800033@vm.sc.edu.

■ APPLICATION
Required Application form, baccalaureate/first degree, essay, 2 letters of recommendation, personal statement, resume/curriculum vitae, transcripts of college work. School will accept GMAT and GRE. **Recommended** Interview, 2 years of work experience.

Deadlines and Fees *Deadlines:* 2/1 for fall, 12/1 for spring, 5/1 for summer, 1/1 for fall (international), 11/1 for spring (international), 4/1 for summer (international). *Application fee:* $35, $35 (international).

Application Contact Ms. Reena Lichtenfeld, Managing Director of Admissions, Graduate Division, Darla Moore School of Business, Columbia, SC 29208. **Phone:** 803-777-6749. **Fax:** 803-777-0414. **E-mail:** rlichten@darla.badm.sc.edu.

See full description on page 960.

Winthrop University
Rock Hill, South Carolina

SCHOOL OF BUSINESS ADMINISTRATION

Accreditation
AACSB—The International Association for Management Education

DEGREES MBA

MBA—Executive MBA Full-time. At least 51 total credits required. Minimum of 24 months to complete program.

MBA—Master of Business Administration in Accounting Full-time and part-time. *Distance learning option.* At least 33 total credits required. Minimum of 18 months to complete program. *Concentrations:* accounting.

MBA—Master of Business Administration Full-time and part-time. *Distance learning option.* At least 39 total credits required. Minimum of 18 months to complete program.

RESOURCES AND SERVICES
Information about online services, personal computer policies, library resources, international exchange programs, internship programs, and placement services at this institution and others can be found at **www.petersons.com/mba**

International Students
Services and Facilities Counseling/support services, visa services. Financial aid is not available to international students.
International Student Contact Ms. LeeAnne Johnson, International Student Advisor, 204 Tillman, Rock Hill, SC 29733. **Phone:** 803-323-3440. **Fax:** 803-323-2340. **E-mail:** johnsonl@winthrop.edu.

■ APPLICATION
Application Contact Ms. Peggy Hager, Director of Graduate Studies, College of Business Administration, Rock Hill, SC 29733. **Phone:** 803-323-2409. **Fax:** 803-323-2539. **E-mail:** hagerp@mail.winthrop.edu.

SOUTH DAKOTA

Black Hills State University

Spearfish, South Dakota

COLLEGE OF BUSINESS AND TECHNOLOGY

Graduate Business Faculty
Full-time: 4

Student Body

Total: 4	Average Age: 36
Full-time: 3	Women: 75%
Part-time: 1	

Admissions

Applications: 3	Enrolled: 3
Admitted: 3	

Costs (1999–2000)
Full-time tuition: N/R
Part-time tuition: $88.6 per credit (resident), $261 per credit
(nonresident)

DEGREE MS

MS—Master of Science in Tourism and Hospitality Management Full-time and part-time. *Distance learning option.* At least 36 total credits required. 24 to 72 months to complete program. *Concentrations:* travel industry/tourism management.

COSTS

Tuition, state resident: *Part-time* $88.60 per credit. **Tuition, nonresident:** *Part-time* $261 per credit. Tuition varies by campus location and local reciprocity agreements. **Required fees:** *Part-time* $47 per credit hour. Tuition and fees vary by campus location. **Graduate housing:** Room and board costs vary by number of occupants, type of accommodation, and type of board plan. *Typical cost:* $2785 (including board).

FINANCIAL AID (1999–2000)

1 student received aid, including fellowships, scholarships, and work study. Aid is available to part-time students. Financial aid application deadline: 3/1. **Financial Aid Contact** Ms. Deb Henriksen, Financial Aid Director, 1200 University Street, Unit 9502, Spearfish, SD 57799-9502. **Phone:** 605-642-6343 Ext. 6581. **Fax:** 605-642-6024. **E-mail:** dhendri@mystic.bhsu.edu.

RESOURCES AND SERVICES

Information about online services, personal computer policies, library resources, international exchange programs, internship programs, and placement services at this institution and others can be found at **www.petersons.com/mba**

International Students

25% of students enrolled are international students.

Services and Facilities Counseling/support services. Financial aid is not available to international students.
Applying *Required:* TOEFL with recommended score of 520 (paper), proof of adequate funds, proof of health/immunizations.
International Student Contact Dr. George Earley, Director of Graduate Studies/Assessment, 1200 University Street, Unit 9076, Spearfish, SD 57799-9076. **Phone:** 605-642-6270. **E-mail:** gearley@mystic.bhsu.edu.

■ APPLICATION

Required GRE, application form, baccalaureate/first degree, transcripts of college work. **Recommended** 3 letters of recommendation, resume/curriculum vitae, work experience.
Deadlines and Fees Applications for domestic and international students are processed on a rolling basis. *Application fee:* $15, $115 (international).
Application Contact Dr. George Earley, Director of Graduate Studies/Assessment, 1200 University Street, Unit 9076, Spearfish, SD 57799-9076. **Phone:** 605-642-6270. **E-mail:** gearley@mystic.bhsu.edu.

University of South Dakota

Vermillion, South Dakota

SCHOOL OF BUSINESS

Graduate Business Faculty
Full-time: 40

Student Body

Total: 219	Part-time: 137
Full-time: 82	Women: 39%

Admissions

Average GMAT: 518	Average GPA: 3.2

Costs (1999–2000)
Full-time tuition: N/R
Part-time tuition: $203 per credit (resident), $382 per credit
(nonresident)

Accreditation
AACSB—The International Association for Management Education

DEGREES MBA • MPA

MBA—Master of Business Administration Full-time and part-time. At least 33 total credits required. 12 to 84 months to complete program. *Concentrations:* management, management information systems.
MPA—Master of Professional Accountancy Full-time and part-time. At least 30 total credits required. 12 to 84 months to complete program. *Concentrations:* accounting.

COSTS

Tuition, state resident: *Part-time* $150 per credit. **Tuition, nonresident:** *Part-time* $329 per credit. **Required fees:** *Part-time* $53 per credit. Tuition and fees vary by class time, campus location, and local reciprocity agreements. **Graduate housing:** *Typical cost:* $3037 (including board).

FINANCIAL AID (1999–2000)

Research assistantships and work study. Aid is available to part-time students. **Financial Aid Contact** Clarence Schumacher, Director, Financial Aid, 414 East Clark Street, Vermillion, SD 57069-2390. **Phone:** 605-677-5446.

RESOURCES AND SERVICES

Information about online services, personal computer policies, library resources, international exchange programs, internship programs, and placement services at this institution and others can be found at **www.petersons.com/mba**

International Students

5% of students enrolled are international students.

Services and Facilities Counseling/support services, ESL/language courses, visa services. Financial aid is not available to international students.
Applying *Required:* TOEFL with recommended score of 550 (paper), proof of adequate funds, proof of health/immunizations. *Recommended:* TWE.
International Student Contact International Student Advising, 414 East Clark Street, Vermillion, SD 57069-2390. **Phone:** 605-677-6305.

■ APPLICATION

Required GMAT, application form, baccalaureate/first degree, 2 letters of recommendation, transcripts of college work. **Recommended** Personal statement.
Deadlines and Fees *Deadlines:* 7/15 for fall, 11/1 for spring, 3/15 for summer, 7/15 for fall (international), 11/1 for spring (international), 3/15 for summer (international). *Application fee:* $15, $15 (international).
Application Contact Diane Duin, Director, Graduate Business Programs, 414 East Clark Street, Vermillion, SD 57069-2390. **Phone:** 605-677-5232. **Fax:** 605-677-5058. **E-mail:** dduin@usd.edu.

TENNESSEE

Belmont University

Nashville, Tennessee

JACK C. MASSEY GRADUATE SCHOOL OF BUSINESS

Graduate Business Faculty
Full-time: 20 — Part-time: 9

Student Body
Total: 225 — Average Age: 32
Part-time: 225 — Women: 47%

Admissions
Applications: 82 — Average GMAT: 530
Admitted: 58 — Average GPA: 3
Enrolled: 41

Costs (1999–2000)
Full-time tuition: N/R
Part-time tuition: $1600 per course

After Graduation (Class of 1998–99)
Employed within 3 months of graduation: 100%

DEGREES M Acc • MBA • MBA/M Acc

M Acc—Executive Master of Accountancy Full-time and part-time. At least 30 total credits required. 12 to 36 months to complete program. *Concentrations:* accounting.

MBA—Executive MBA Full-time and part-time. 34 to 49 total credits required. 15 to 48 months to complete program. *Concentrations:* accounting, finance, health care, management, operations management.

MBA/M Acc—Executive MBA, Master of Accounting Full-time and part-time. At least 63 total credits required. Minimum of 36 months to complete program. *Concentrations:* accounting, management.

COSTS

Tuition *Part-time:* $1600 per course. **Graduate housing:** *Typical cost:* $2600 (including board).

FINANCIAL AID (1999–2000)

17 students received aid, including research assistantships. Aid is available to part-time students. Financial aid application deadline: 6/15. **Financial Aid Contact** Financial Aid Office, 1900 Belmont Boulevard, Nashville, TN 37212-3757. **Phone:** 615-460-6403. **Fax:** 615-460-5541.

RESOURCES AND SERVICES

Information about online services, personal computer policies, library resources, international exchange programs, internship programs, and placement services at this institution and others can be found at **www. petersons.com/mba**

International Students

0.9% of students enrolled are international students.
Services and Facilities International student housing.
Applying *Required:* TOEFL with recommended score of 550 (paper), proof of adequate funds, proof of health/immunizations.
International Student Contact Ms. Kathy Skinner, Director of International Student Services, 1900 Belmont Boulevard, Nashville, TN 37212-3757. **E-mail:** skinnerk@mail.belmont.edu.

■ APPLICATION

Required GMAT, application form, baccalaureate/first degree, essay, 2 letters of recommendation, personal statement, resume/curriculum vitae, transcripts of college work, 2 years of work experience. **Recommended** Interview.

Deadlines and Fees *Deadlines:* 6/15 for fall, 12/1 for spring, 3/15 for summer, 6/15 for fall (international), 12/1 for spring (international), 3/15 for summer (international). *Application fee:* $50, $50 (international).

Application Contact Mr. Randy Raggio, Director, Jack C. Massey Graduate School of Business, 1900 Belmont Boulevard, Nashville, TN 37212-3757. **Phone:** 615-460-6660. **Fax:** 615-460-6455. **E-mail:** mckays@belmont.edu.

Christian Brothers University

Memphis, Tennessee

SCHOOL OF BUSINESS

Graduate Business Faculty
Full-time: 16 — Part-time: 1

Student Body
Total: 198 — Average Age: 32
Full-time: 42 — Women: 49%
Part-time: 156

Admissions
Applications: 132 — Average GMAT: 520
Admitted: 121 — Average GPA: 3.01
Enrolled: 86

Costs (1999–2000)
Full-time tuition: N/R
Part-time tuition: $375 per credit hour

After Graduation (Class of 1998–99)
Employed within 3 months of graduation: 100%

DEGREES MBA

MBA—Executive MBA Full-time. At least 48 total credits required. 20 months to complete program. *Concentrations:* management.

MBA—Master of Business Administration Full-time and part-time. At least 30 total credits required. 12 to 60 months to complete program. *Concentrations:* finance, information management, management, marketing.

COSTS

Tuition *Part-time:* $375 per credit hour. **Required fees:** *Part-time* $50 per semester. Tuition and fees vary by academic program. **Graduate housing:** *Typical cost:* $6500 (including board).

FINANCIAL AID (1999–2000)

Loans. Aid is available to part-time students. **Financial Aid Contact** Mr. Jim Shannon, Student Financial Resources Director, 650 East Parkway South, Memphis, TN 38104-5581. **Phone:** 901-321-3306. **E-mail:** ushannon@cbu.edu.

RESOURCES AND SERVICES

Information about online services, personal computer policies, library resources, international exchange programs, internship programs, and placement services at this institution and others can be found at **www. petersons.com/mba**

International Students

1% of students enrolled are international students.
Services and Facilities Financial aid is not available to international students.
Applying *Required:* TOEFL with recommended score of 550 (paper), proof of adequate funds. *Recommended:* Proof of health/immunizations.
International Student Contact Ms. Karen Conway, Director, Student Services, 650 East Parkway South, Memphis, TN 38104-5581. **Phone:** 901-321-3566. **E-mail:** kconway@cbu.edu.

■ APPLICATION

Required GMAT, application form, baccalaureate/first degree, 2 letters of recommendation, transcripts of college work.

Deadlines and Fees Applications for domestic and international students are processed on a rolling basis. *Application fee:* $25, $25 (international).

Application Contact Mr. James Rhodes, Director, MBA Program, 650 East Parkway South, Memphis, TN 38104-5581. **Phone:** 901-321-3319. **Fax:** 901-321-3566. **E-mail:** mba@cbu.edu.

Cumberland University

Lebanon, Tennessee

PROGRAM IN BUSINESS ADMINISTRATION

Graduate Business Faculty
Full-time: 6 — Part-time: 1

Student Body
Total: 80 — Average Age: 33
Part-time: 80 — Women: 50%

Cumberland University (continued)

Admissions

Applications: 40
Admitted: 25

Enrolled: 20
Average GMAT: 480

Costs (1999–2000)

Full-time tuition: N/R
Part-time tuition: $595 per hour

DEGREE MBA

MBA—Master of Business Administration Full-time and part-time. At least 36 total credits required. 36 to 48 months to complete program.

COSTS

Tuition *Part-time:* $595 per hour.

FINANCIAL AID (1999–2000)

Loans, research assistantships, and work study. Aid is available to part-time students. **Financial Aid Contact** Financial Aid Office, One Cumberland Square, Lebanon, TN 37087-3554. **Phone:** 615-444-2562 Ext. 222. **Fax:** 615-444-2569.

RESOURCES AND SERVICES

Information about online services, personal computer policies, library resources, international exchange programs, internship programs, and placement services at this institution and others can be found at **www.petersons.com/mba**

International Students

4% of students enrolled are international students.

Services and Facilities Counseling/support services. Financial aid is not available to international students.
International Student Contact Ms. Pace Pope, Administrative Assistant, One Cumberland Square, Lebanon, TN 37087-3554. **Phone:** 615-444-2562 Ext. 1224. **Fax:** 615-444-2569. **E-mail:** ppope@cumberland.edu.

■ APPLICATION

Required Application form, baccalaureate/first degree, interview, 3 letters of recommendation, transcripts of college work, 1 year of work experience. School will accept GMAT and GRE. **Recommended** Resume/curriculum vitae.

Deadlines and Fees *Deadlines:* 8/10 for fall, 1/3 for spring, 5/9 for summer, 8/10 for fall (international), 1/3 for spring (international), 5/9 for summer (international). *Application fee:* $50, $50 (international).

Application Contact Stephanie Walker, Director of Admissions, One Cumberland Square, Lebanon, TN 37087. **Phone:** 615-444-2562 Ext. 1220. **Toll-free Phone:** 800-467-0562. **Fax:** 615-444-2569. **E-mail:** swalker@cumberland.edu.

David Lipscomb University

Nashville, Tennessee

BUSINESS ADMINISTRATION PROGRAM

Graduate Business Faculty

Full-time: 11

Part-time: 3

Student Body

Total: 58
Full-time: 8
Part-time: 50

Average Age: 30
Women: 40%

Admissions

Applications: 92
Admitted: 69
Enrolled: 58

Average GMAT: 491
Average GPA: 3.11

Costs (1999–2000)

Full-time tuition: $15,720 per academic year
Part-time tuition: $435 per semester hour

Accreditation

ACBSP—The American Council of Business Schools and Programs

DEGREE MBA

MBA—MBA Program Full-time and part-time. 36 to 48 total credits required. 12 to 42 months to complete program. *Concentrations:* accounting, financial management/planning, health care, leadership, nonprofit management.

COSTS

Tuition *Full-time:* $15,660. *Part-time:* $435 per semester hour. **Tuition, international:** *Full-time* $15,660. **Required fees:** *Full-time* $60. *Part-time* $30 per semester.

FINANCIAL AID (1999–2000)

22 students received aid, including loans, research assistantships, and scholarships. Aid is available to part-time students. Financial aid application deadline: 3/1. **Financial Aid Contact** Mrs. Tamera Spivey, Financial Aid Counselor, 3901 Granny White Pike, Nashville, TN 37204-3951. **Phone:** 615-269-1000. **Fax:** 615-269-1804. **E-mail:** tamera.spivey@lipscomb.edu.

RESOURCES AND SERVICES

Information about online services, personal computer policies, library resources, international exchange programs, internship programs, and placement services at this institution and others can be found at **www.petersons.com/mba**

International Students

3% of students enrolled are international students.

Services and Facilities Counseling/support services, visa services. Financial aid is available to international students.
Applying *Required:* TOEFL with recommended score of 230 (computer) or 570 (paper), proof of adequate funds, proof of health/immunizations.
International Student Contact Dr. Doy hollman, International Student Advisor, 3901 Granny White Pike, Nashville, TN 37204-3951. **Phone:** 615-279-6154. **E-mail:** doy.hollman@lipscomb.edu.

■ APPLICATION

Required GMAT, application form, baccalaureate/first degree, essay, interview, 2 letters of recommendation, transcripts of college work. **Recommended** Resume/curriculum vitae.

Deadlines and Fees Applications for domestic students are processed on a rolling basis. *Deadlines:* 3/1 for fall (international), 7/1 for winter (international), 9/19 for spring (international), 12/4 for summer (international). *Application fee:* $50, $75 (international).

Application Contact Mrs. Beth Sedberry, Assistant to the Director of MBA Admissions, 3901 Granny White Pike, Nashville, TN 37204-3951. **Phone:** 615-279-5969. **Toll-free Phone:** 800-333-4358. **Fax:** 615-269-1818. **E-mail:** beth.sedberry@lipscomb.edu.

East Tennessee State University

Johnson City, Tennessee

COLLEGE OF BUSINESS

Graduate Business Faculty

Full-time: 37

Student Body

Total: 220
Full-time: 65
Part-time: 155

Average Age: 32
Women: 42%

Admissions

Applications: 152
Admitted: 98
Enrolled: 73

Average GMAT: 538
Average GPA: 3.1

Costs (1999–2000)

Full-time tuition: N/R
Part-time tuition: $129 per credit hour (resident), $340 per credit hour (nonresident)

After Graduation (Class of 1998–99)

Employed within 3 months of graduation: 80%

Accreditation

AACSB—The International Association for Management Education

DEGREES M Acc • MBA • MPM

M Acc—Master of Accounting Full-time and part-time. *Distance learning option.* At least 33 total credits required. 12 to 72 months to complete program. *Concentrations:* accounting.

MBA—Master of Business Administration Full-time and part-time. *Distance learning option.* At least 39 total credits required. 16 to 72 months to complete program.

MPM—Master of Public Management Full-time and part-time. *Distance learning option.* At least 45 total credits required. 20 to 72 months to complete program. *Concentrations:* city/urban administration, public management, public policy and administration.

COSTS

Tuition, state resident: *Part-time* $129 per credit hour. **Tuition, nonresident:** *Part-time* $340 per credit hour. **Required fees:** Tuition and fees vary by number of courses or credits taken. **Graduate housing:** Room and board costs vary by campus location, number of occupants, type of accommodation, and type of board plan. *Typical cost:* $3480 (including board), $1890 (room only).

FINANCIAL AID (1999–2000)

49 students received aid, including research assistantships and scholarships. Financial aid application deadline: 5/15. **Financial Aid Contact** Ms. Margaret Miller, Director of Financial Aid, PO Box 70722, Johnson City, TN 37614. **Phone:** 423-439-4300. **E-mail:** finaid@etsu.edu.

RESOURCES AND SERVICES

Information about online services, personal computer policies, library resources, international exchange programs, internship programs, and placement services at this institution and others can be found at **www.petersons.com/mba**

International Students

9% of students enrolled are international students.

Services and Facilities Counseling/support services, ESL/language courses, housing location assistance, international student organization, visa services. Financial aid is available to international students.
Applying *Required:* TOEFL with recommended score of 550 (paper), proof of adequate funds, proof of health/immunizations.
International Student Contact Ms. Maria Costa, International Student Counselor, PO Box 70668, Johnson City, TN 37614. **Phone:** 423-439-4429. **Fax:** 423-439-7131. **E-mail:** costa@etsu.edu.

■ APPLICATION

Required GMAT, application form, baccalaureate/first degree, essay, personal statement, transcripts of college work. School will accept GRE. **Recommended** Letter(s) of recommendation, 2 years of work experience.
Deadlines and Fees *Deadlines:* 6/1 for fall, 5/1 for fall (international), 10/1 for spring (international). *Application fee:* $25, $35 (international).
Application Contact Dr. Ronald Green, Director of Graduate Studies for the College of Business, PO Box 70699, Johnson City, TN 37614. **Phone:** 423-439-5314. **Fax:** 423-439-5274. **E-mail:** greenr@etsu.edu.

Lincoln Memorial University

Harrogate, Tennessee
PROGRAM IN BUSINESS ADMINISTRATION

Graduate Business Faculty
Full-time: 6   Part-time: 7

Student Body
Total: 46
Full-time: 1   Average Age: 27
Part-time: 45   Women: 35%

Admissions
Applications: 48   Enrolled: 3
Admitted: 17   Average GPA: 3

Costs (1999–2000)
Full-time tuition: $7746 per academic year
Part-time tuition: $215 per semester hour

DEGREE MBA

MBA—Master of Business Administration in Management Full-time and part-time. At least 36 total credits required. 18 to 84 months to complete program. *Concentrations:* management.

COSTS

Tuition *Full-time:* $7746. *Part-time:* $215 per semester hour. **Tuition, international:** *Full-time* $7746. Tuition varies by number of courses or credits taken. **Graduate housing:** Room and board costs vary by number of occupants, type of accommodation, and type of board plan. *Typical cost:* $3900 (including board).

FINANCIAL AID (1999–2000)

9 students received aid, including loans and scholarships. Aid is available to part-time students. Financial aid application deadline: 4/1. **Financial Aid Contact** Mrs. Christy Graham, Financial Aid Director, Cumberland Gap Parkway, Harrogate, TN 37752. **Phone:** 800-325-0900 Ext. 6388. **Fax:** 423-869-4825. **E-mail:** finaid@inetlmu.lmunet.edu.

RESOURCES AND SERVICES

Information about online services, personal computer policies, library resources, international exchange programs, internship programs, and placement services at this institution and others can be found at **www.petersons.com/mba**

International Students

Services and Facilities Counseling/support services, housing location assistance, international student organization. Financial aid is not available to international students.
Applying *Required:* TOEFL with recommended score of 500 (paper), proof of adequate funds, proof of health/immunizations.
International Student Contact Mr. Conrad Daniels, Dean of Admissions, Cumberland Gap Parkway, Harrogate, TN 37752. **Phone:** 423-869-6279. **Fax:** 423-869-6250. **E-mail:** admissions@inetlmu.lmunet.edu.

■ APPLICATION

Required GMAT, application form, baccalaureate/first degree, interview, 3 letters of recommendation, transcripts of college work. **Recommended** Essay.
Deadlines and Fees Applications for domestic and international students are processed on a rolling basis. *Application fee:* $25, $25 (international).
Application Contact Dr. Fred Bedelle, Dean, School of Graduate Studies, Cumberland Gap Parkway, Harrogate, TN 37752. **Phone:** 423-869-6223. **Toll-free Phone:** 800-325-0900. **Fax:** 423-869-6261. **E-mail:** fbedelle@yahoo.com.

Middle Tennessee State University

Murfreesboro, Tennessee
COLLEGE OF BUSINESS

Graduate Business Faculty
Full-time: 53

Student Body
Total: 375
Full-time: 24   Average Age: 26
Part-time: 351   Women: 38%

Admissions
Applications: 86   Average GMAT: 496
Admitted: 74   Average GPA: 2.6
Enrolled: 63

Costs (1999–2000)
Full-time tuition: N/R
Part-time tuition: $129 per credit hour (resident), $340 per credit hour (nonresident)

After Graduation (Class of 1998–99)
Employed within 3 months of graduation: 90%
Average starting salary: $35,000

Accreditation
AACSB—The International Association for Management Education

DEGREES MA • MBA • MS

MA—Master of Arts in Economics Full-time and part-time. At least 33 total credits required. 12 to 72 months to complete program. *Concentrations:* economics, industrial/labor relations.

MBA—Master of Business Administration Full-time and part-time. *Distance learning option.* 36 to 60 total credits required. 12 to 72 months to complete program. *Concentrations:* electronic commerce (e-commerce), entrepreneurship, health care, human resources, industrial administration/management, international business.

MS—Master of Science in Accounting and Information Systems Full-time and part-time. *Distance learning option.* 30 to 60 total credits required. 12 to 72 months to complete program. *Concentrations:* accounting, electronic commerce (e-commerce), management information systems.

COSTS

Tuition, state resident: *Part-time* $129 per credit hour. **Tuition, nonresident:** *Part-time* $340 per credit hour. **Required fees:** *Full-time* $1000. *Part-time* $50 per semester. Tuition and fees vary by academic program. **Graduate housing:** Room and board costs vary by type of accommodation and type of board plan. *Typical cost:* $3000 (including board), $2000 (room only).

FINANCIAL AID (1999–2000)

40 students received aid, including teaching assistantships. Financial aid application deadline: 5/1. **Financial Aid Contact** Financial Aid Office,

Middle Tennessee State University (continued)

MTSU Box 290, Murfreesboro, TN 37132. **Phone:** 615-898-2830. **Fax:** 615-898-4736.

RESOURCES AND SERVICES
Information about online services, personal computer policies, library resources, international exchange programs, internship programs, and placement services at this institution and others can be found at **www. petersons.com/mba**

International Students
11% of students enrolled are international students.

Services and Facilities Counseling/support services, housing location assistance, international student organization, language tutoring, orientation. Financial aid is available to international students.
Applying *Required:* TOEFL with recommended score of 525 (paper), proof of adequate funds, proof of health/immunizations.
International Student Contact Dr. Tech Wubneh, Director, International Programs and Services Office, 202 Cope Administration Building, Murfreesboro, TN 37132. **Phone:** 615-898-2238. **Fax:** 615-898-5178. **E-mail:** twubnch@mtsu. edu.

■ APPLICATION
Required GMAT, application form, baccalaureate/first degree, transcripts of college work.
Deadlines and Fees Applications for domestic students are processed on a rolling basis. *Deadlines:* 5/1 for fall (international), 9/1 for spring (international), 2/1 for summer (international). *Application fee:* $25, $30 (international).
Application Contact Dr. Troy Festervand, Director, Graduate Business Studies, MTSU Box 290, Murfreesboro, TN 37132. **Phone:** 615-898-2964. **Fax:** 615-904-8491. **E-mail:** fester@mtsu.edu.

Rhodes College

Memphis, Tennessee

DEPARTMENT OF ECONOMICS/BUSINESS ADMINISTRATION

Graduate Business Faculty

Full-time: 6	Part-time: 2

Student Body

Total: 14	Women: 43%
Full-time: 14	

Admissions

Applications: 10	Enrolled: 9
Admitted: 9	

Costs (1999–2000)
Full-time tuition: $18,561 per academic year
Part-time tuition: N/R

DEGREE MS

MS—Master of Science in Accounting Full-time and part-time. At least 30 total credits required. Minimum of 9 months to complete program.

COSTS
Tuition *Full-time:* $18,561.

FINANCIAL AID (1999–2000)
Loans and scholarships. Aid is available to part-time students. **Financial Aid Contact** Dr. Pam Church, Director of Master's Program, 2000 North Parkway, Memphis, TN 38112-1690. **Phone:** 901-843-3920. **Fax:** 901-843-3798. **E-mail:** church@rhodes.edu.

RESOURCES AND SERVICES
Information about online services, personal computer policies, library resources, international exchange programs, internship programs, and placement services at this institution and others can be found at **www. petersons.com/mba**

International Students
Services and Facilities Counseling/support services, ESL/language courses, international student housing, visa services. Financial aid is available to international students.
Applying *Required:* TOEFL with recommended score of 550 (paper).
International Student Contact Ms. Katharine Owen-Richardson, Director of International Programs, 2000 North Parkway, Memphis, TN 38112-1690. **Phone:** 901-843-3403. **E-mail:** owen@rhodes.edu.

■ APPLICATION
Required GMAT, application form, baccalaureate/first degree, 2 letters of recommendation, transcripts of college work.
Deadlines and Fees *Deadlines:* 3/1 for fall, 3/1 for fall (international).
Application Contact Dr. Pam Church, Director of Master's Program, Memphis, TN. **Phone:** 901-843-3920. **Fax:** 901-843-3798. **E-mail:** church@rhodes.edu.

Southern Adventist University

Collegedale, Tennessee

SCHOOL OF BUSINESS AND MANAGEMENT

Graduate Business Faculty

Full-time: 4	Part-time: 1

Student Body

Total: 26	Average Age: 36
Full-time: 5	Women: 35%
Part-time: 21	

Admissions

Applications: 30	Average GMAT: 550
Admitted: 28	Average GPA: 3.35
Enrolled: 26	

Costs (1999–2000)
Full-time tuition: N/R
Part-time tuition: $280 per hour

After Graduation (Class of 1998–99)
Employed within 3 months of graduation: 100%

DEGREES MBA • MBA/MSN

MBA—Accounting Full-time and part-time. *Distance learning option.* At least 36 total credits required. 12 to 60 months to complete program. *Concentrations:* accounting.
MBA—Healthcare Administration Full-time and part-time. At least 36 total credits required. 12 to 60 months to complete program. *Concentrations:* health care, hospitality management.
MBA—Management Full-time and part-time. *Distance learning option.* At least 36 total credits required. 12 to 60 months to complete program. *Concentrations:* management.
MBA/MSN—Master of Business Administration/Master of Science in Nursing Full-time and part-time. At least 56 total credits required. 18 to 72 months to complete program. *Concentrations:* health care, management.

COSTS
Tuition *Part-time:* $280 per hour. **Graduate housing:** Room and board costs vary by number of occupants and type of accommodation. *Typical cost:* $1780 (room only).

FINANCIAL AID (1999–2000)
6 students received aid, including loans.

RESOURCES AND SERVICES
Information about online services, personal computer policies, library resources, international exchange programs, internship programs, and placement services at this institution and others can be found at **www. petersons.com/mba**

International Students
23% of students enrolled are international students.

Services and Facilities ESL/language courses. Financial aid is not available to international students.
Applying *Required:* TOEFL with recommended score of 600 (paper), proof of adequate funds, proof of health/immunizations.
International Student Contact Ms. Linda Wilhelm, MBA Admissions Coordinator for School of Business and Management, School of Business and Management, PO Box 370, Collegedale, TN 37315. **Phone:** 423-238-2751. **Fax:** 423-238-3151. **E-mail:** sbm@southern.edu.

■ APPLICATION
Required GMAT, application form, baccalaureate/first degree, essay, letter(s) of recommendation, transcripts of college work. **Recommended** Personal statement, resume/curriculum vitae.
Deadlines and Fees Applications for domestic and international students are processed on a rolling basis. *Application fee:* $25.
Application Contact Ms. Linda Wilhelm, MBA Admissions Coordinator for School of Business and Management, School of Business and Management, PO Box

370, Collegedale, TN 37315. **Phone:** 423-238-2751. **Toll-free Phone:** 800-SOUTHERN. **Fax:** 423-238-3151. **E-mail:** sbm@southern.edu.

Tennessee State University

Nashville, Tennessee

COLLEGE OF BUSINESS

Graduate Business Faculty
Full-time: 24

Part-time: 1

Student Body
Total: 160

Full-time: 40

Part-time: 120

Average Age: 30

Women: 38%

Admissions
Applications: 75

Admitted: 50

Enrolled: 45

Average GMAT: 520

Average GPA: 2.8

Costs (1999–2000)
Full-time tuition: N/R

Part-time tuition: $155 per credit (resident), $379 per credit (nonresident)

Accreditation
AACSB—The International Association for Management Education

DEGREE MBA

MBA—Master of Business Administration Full-time and part-time. At least 34 total credits required. 9 to 72 months to complete program.

COSTS

Tuition, state resident: *Part-time* $155 per credit. **Tuition, nonresident:** *Part-time* $379 per credit. **Graduate housing:** Room and board costs vary by number of occupants and type of board plan. *Typical cost:* $3600 (including board), $2680 (room only).

FINANCIAL AID (1999–2000)
9 students received aid, including research assistantships and work study. Financial aid application deadline: 6/1. **Financial Aid Contact** Mr. Wilson Lee, Director of Financial Aid, 3500 John A. Merritt Boulevard, Nashville, TN 37209-1561. **Phone:** 615-963-5000.

RESOURCES AND SERVICES
Information about online services, personal computer policies, library resources, international exchange programs, internship programs, and placement services at this institution and others can be found at **www.petersons.com/mba**

International Students
16% of students enrolled are international students.

Services and Facilities Counseling/support services, housing location assistance, international student organization, orientation. Financial aid is available to international students.

Applying *Required:* TOEFL with recommended score of 500 (paper).

International Student Contact Mrs. Shirley Wingfield, Student Advisor, 3500 John A. Merritt Boulevard, Nashville, TN 37209-1561. **Phone:** 615-963-5000.

■ APPLICATION

Required GMAT, application form, baccalaureate/first degree, transcripts of college work.

Deadlines and Fees *Application fee:* $25, $25 (international).

Application Contact Dr. George Bruce Hartmann, MBA Coordinator, School of Business, 3500 John A. Merritt Boulevard, Nashville, TN 37209-1561. **Phone:** 615-963-7146. **Fax:** 615-963-7139. **E-mail:** ghartmann@tnstate.edu.

Tennessee Technological University

Cookeville, Tennessee

COLLEGE OF BUSINESS ADMINISTRATION

Graduate Business Faculty
Full-time: 28

Student Body
Total: 118

Full-time: 62

Part-time: 56

Average Age: 27

Women: 38%

Admissions
Applications: 61

Admitted: 53

Enrolled: 37

Average GMAT: 523

Average GPA: 3.2

Costs (1999–2000)
Full-time tuition: $3082 per academic year (resident), $5116 per academic year (nonresident)

Part-time tuition: $154 per hour (resident), $224 per hour (nonresident)

After Graduation (Class of 1998–99)
Employed within 3 months of graduation: 100%

Average starting salary: $37,500

Accreditation
AACSB—The International Association for Management Education

DEGREE MBA

MBA—Master of Business Administration Full-time and part-time. At least 36 total credits required. 12 to 72 months to complete program. *Concentrations:* accounting, management, management information systems.

COSTS

Tuition, state resident: *Full-time* $3082. *Part-time* $154 per hour. **Tuition, nonresident:** *Full-time* $5116. *Part-time* $224 per hour. **Required fees:** Tuition and fees vary by number of courses or credits taken. **Graduate housing:** Room and board costs vary by number of occupants, type of accommodation, and type of board plan. *Typical cost:* $4300 (including board), $2154 (room only).

FINANCIAL AID (1999–2000)
57 students received aid, including fellowships, loans, research assistantships, scholarships, and teaching assistantships. Aid is available to part-time students. Financial aid application deadline: 4/1. **Financial Aid Contact** Dr. Virginia Moore, Associate Dean and Director of MBA Studies, PO Box 5023, Cookeville, TN 38505. **Phone:** 931-372-3600. **Fax:** 931-372-6249. **E-mail:** mbastudies@tntech.edu.

RESOURCES AND SERVICES
Information about online services, personal computer policies, library resources, international exchange programs, internship programs, and placement services at this institution and others can be found at **www.petersons.com/mba**

International Students
6% of students enrolled are international students.

Services and Facilities Counseling/support services, ESL/language courses, international student organization, orientation, visa services. Financial aid is available to international students.

Applying *Required:* TOEFL with recommended score of 550 (paper), proof of adequate funds, proof of health/immunizations.

International Student Contact Ms. Caroline Dudney, Director of International Student Affairs, North Dixie Avenue, Cookeville, TN 38505. **Phone:** 931-372-3634. **Fax:** 931-372-6249. **E-mail:** edudney@tntech.edu.

■ APPLICATION

Required GMAT, application form, baccalaureate/first degree, 1 letter of recommendation, transcripts of college work. **Recommended** Interview.

Deadlines and Fees *Deadlines:* 5/1 for fall (international), 10/1 for spring (international), 3/1 for summer (international). *Application fee:* $25, $30 (international).

Application Contact Dr. Virginia Moore, Associate Dean and Director of MBA Studies, PO Box 5023, Cookeville, TN 38505. **Phone:** 931-372-3600. **Fax:** 931-372-6249. **E-mail:** mbastudies@tntech.edu.

Trevecca Nazarene University

Nashville, Tennessee

MAJOR IN ORGANIZATIONAL MANAGEMENT

Student Body
Total: 91

Full-time: 91

Average Age: 34

Women: 58%

Admissions
Applications: 31

Admitted: 30

Enrolled: 25

Average GMAT: 450

Average GPA: 2.98

Trevecca Nazarene University (continued)

Costs (1999–2000)
Full-time tuition: $6763 per academic year
Part-time tuition: N/R

DEGREE MA

MA—Master of Arts in Organizational Management Full-time. At least 38 total credits required. Maximum of 20 months to complete program.

COSTS
Tuition *Full-time:* $6763.

FINANCIAL AID (1999–2000)
Grants and loans. **Financial Aid Contact** Eddie White, Financial Aid, 333 Murfreesboro Road, Nashville, TN 37210-2834. **Phone:** 615-248-1242.

RESOURCES AND SERVICES
Information about online services, personal computer policies, library resources, international exchange programs, internship programs, and placement services at this institution and others can be found at **www.petersons.com/mba**

International Students
Services and Facilities Counseling/support services, housing location assistance.
Applying *Required:* TOEFL with recommended score of 173 (computer) or 500 (paper), proof of adequate funds.
International Student Contact Ms. Patty Cook, Director of Admissions, Enrollment Services, 333 Murfreesboro Road, Nashville, TN 37210-2834. **Phone:** 615-248-1320.

■ APPLICATION
Required GMAT, application form, baccalaureate/first degree, essay, 3 letters of recommendation, resume/curriculum vitae, transcripts of college work. **Recommended** Work experience.
Deadlines and Fees *Deadlines:* 7/15 for fall, 2/15 for spring. *Application fee:* $25, $25 (international).
Application Contact Ms. Charmion Richards, Assistant to the Director, 333 Murfreesboro Road, Nashville, TN 37210-2834. **Phone:** 615-248-1535. **Fax:** 615-248-1700. **E-mail:** crichards@trevecca.edu.

Tusculum College

Greeneville, Tennessee

PROGRAM IN ORGANIZATIONAL MANAGEMENT

DEGREE MA

MA—Master of Arts in Organizational Management Full-time and part-time. At least 36 total credits required. 18 to 60 months to complete program. *Concentrations:* organizational management.

RESOURCES AND SERVICES
Information about online services, personal computer policies, library resources, international exchange programs, internship programs, and placement services at this institution and others can be found at **www.petersons.com/mba**

International Students
International Student Contact Mr. Don Stout, Executive Director, 60 Shiloh Road, Greeneville, TN 37743-9997. **Phone:** 423-636-7330. **Fax:** 423-638-5181. **E-mail:** dstout@tusculum.edu.

■ APPLICATION
Application Contact Mr. Don Stout, Executive Director, PO Box 5689, Greeneville, TN 37743-9997. **Phone:** 423-636-7330. **Fax:** 423-638-5181. **E-mail:** dstout@tusculum.edu.

Union University

Jackson, Tennessee

SCHOOL OF BUSINESS ADMINISTRATION

Graduate Business Faculty
Full-time: 14   Part-time: 3

Student Body
Total: 163   Average Age: 32

Admissions
Enrolled: 163   Average GMAT: 512

Costs (1999–2000)
Full-time tuition: $6600 per academic year
Part-time tuition: N/R

DEGREE MBA

MBA—Master of Business Administration Full-time and part-time. At least 37 total credits required. 24 months to complete program. *Concentrations:* management.

*L*ocated in west Tennessee, Union University is a private Christian institution that offers the M.B.A. on both its Jackson and Germantown campuses. Union has a tradition of academic excellence at both the undergraduate and graduate level.

The Union M.B.A. is designed to meet the needs of students who must continue their full-time careers while obtaining the M.B.A. A cohort format is used, whereby students take all the same courses together in lock-step fashion. A new cohort begins each August and February with approximately 20-30 students. The entire program is scheduled in advance. The classes meet one night per week for 4 hours for approximately twenty-four months. There are no prerequisites for students with at least two years of relevant work experience. Students without work experience must take a core of undergraduate business courses.

The M.B.A. courses incorporate case studies, team projects, research, and class discussion as well as lecture for maximum learning potential.

All courses are taught by Union University faculty members. No video or audio instruction is used in place of faculty members.

COSTS
Tuition *Full-time:* $6600. **Required fees:** Tuition and fees vary by number of courses or credits taken. **Graduate housing:** Room and board costs vary by campus location, number of occupants, type of accommodation, and type of board plan. *Typical cost:* $3680 (including board).

FINANCIAL AID (1999–2000)
32 students received aid, including loans. Aid is available to part-time students. Financial aid application deadline: 2/1. **Financial Aid Contact** Mr. Don Morris, Assistant Vice President and Director of Financial Aid, 1050 Union University Drive, Jackson, TN 38305. **Phone:** 901-661-5015. **Fax:** 901-661-5017. **E-mail:** dmorris@uu.edu.

RESOURCES AND SERVICES
Information about online services, personal computer policies, library resources, international exchange programs, internship programs, and placement services at this institution and others can be found at **www.petersons.com/mba**

International Students
Services and Facilities Counseling/support services, ESL/language courses. Financial aid is not available to international students.
Applying *Required:* TOEFL with recommended score of 560 (paper), proof of adequate funds, proof of health/immunizations.
International Student Contact Ms. Angela Earl, Enrollment Counselor, 1050 Union University Drive, Jackson, TN 38305. **Phone:** 901-661-5001. **Fax:** 901-661-5017. **E-mail:** aearl@uu.edu.

■ APPLICATION
Required GMAT, application form, baccalaureate/first degree, transcripts of college work. **Recommended** 2 years of work experience.
Deadlines and Fees *Application fee:* $25, $25 (international).
Application Contact Mrs. Barbara Perry, MBA Director, 1050 Union University Drive, Jackson, TN 38305. **Phone:** 901-661-5363. **Fax:** 901-661-5101. **E-mail:** bperry@uu.edu.

The University of Memphis

Memphis, Tennessee

FOGELMAN COLLEGE OF BUSINESS AND ECONOMICS

Graduate Business Faculty
Full-time: 95   Part-time: 56

Student Body
Total: 790   Average Age: 29
Full-time: 426   Women: 39%
Part-time: 364

Admissions

Applications: 453
Admitted: 301
Enrolled: 234

Average GMAT: 530
Average GPA: 3.3

Costs (1999–2000)

Full-time tuition: $3436 per academic year (resident), $8600 per academic year (nonresident)
Part-time tuition: $176 per credit hour (resident), $402 per credit hour (nonresident)

After Graduation (Class of 1998–99)

Employed within 3 months of graduation: 90%
Average starting salary: $33,000

Accreditation

AACSB—The International Association for Management Education

DEGREES JD/MBA • MA • MBA • MS

JD/MBA—Juris Doctor/Master of Business Administration Full-time and part-time. At least 54 total credits required. 12 to 36 months to complete program.

MA—Master of Arts in Economics Full-time and part-time. At least 33 total credits required. 12 to 72 months to complete program. *Concentrations:* economics.

MBA—Executive MBA Full-time. At least 48 total credits required. 22 months to complete program.

MBA—International MBA Full-time. At least 56 total credits required. 24 months to complete program.

MBA—Master of Business Administration Full-time and part-time. 33 to 54 total credits required. 12 to 72 months to complete program. *Concentrations:* accounting, economics, finance, management, management information systems, marketing, operations management.

MS—Master of Science in Accounting Full-time and part-time. 30 to 51 total credits required. 12 to 72 months to complete program. *Concentrations:* accounting, system management, taxation.

MS—Master of Science in Business Administration Full-time and part-time. At least 33 total credits required. 12 to 72 months to complete program. *Concentrations:* finance, management, management information systems, marketing, real estate.

COSTS

Tuition, state resident: *Full-time* $3368. *Part-time* $172 per credit hour. **Tuition, nonresident:** *Full-time* $8532. *Part-time* $398 per credit hour. Tuition varies by number of courses or credits taken and local reciprocity agreements. **Required fees:** *Full-time* $68. *Part-time* $4 per credit hour. **Graduate housing:** Room and board costs vary by campus location, number of occupants, type of accommodation, and type of board plan. *Typical cost:* $4100 (including board).

FINANCIAL AID (1999–2000)

148 students received aid, including fellowships, research assistantships, scholarships, and teaching assistantships. **Financial Aid Contact** Bob Boone, Assistant Director, Student Financial Aid, Student Financial Aid Office, 312 Scates Hall, Memphis, TN 38152. **Phone:** 901-678-4825. **Fax:** 901-678-3590.

RESOURCES AND SERVICES

Information about online services, personal computer policies, library resources, international exchange programs, internship programs, and placement services at this institution and others can be found at **www.petersons.com/mba**

International Students

27% of students enrolled are international students.

Services and Facilities Counseling/support services, ESL/language courses, visa services. Financial aid is not available to international students.
Applying *Required:* TOEFL with recommended score of 550 (paper), proof of adequate funds, proof of health/immunizations.
International Student Contact Dr. Craig Langstraat, Interim Assistant Dean for Academic Programs, Fogelman College of Business and Economics, Room 426, Memphis, TN 38152. **Phone:** 901-678-3721. **Fax:** 901-678-4705. **E-mail:** fcbegp@cc.memphis.edu.

■ APPLICATION

Required GMAT, application form, baccalaureate/first degree, transcripts of college work. School will accept GRE. **Recommended** Essay, letter(s) of recommendation, personal statement.
Deadlines and Fees *Deadlines:* 8/1 for fall, 12/1 for spring, 5/1 for summer, 5/1 for fall (international), 9/15 for spring (international), 2/1 for summer (international). *Application fee:* $25, $50 (international).

Application Contact Dr. Craig Langstraat, Interim Assistant Dean for Academic Programs, Fogelman College of Business and Economics, Memphis, TN 38152. **Phone:** 901-678-3721. **Fax:** 901-678-4705. **E-mail:** fcbegp@cc.memphis.edu.

The University of Tennessee

Knoxville, Tennessee

COLLEGE OF BUSINESS ADMINISTRATION

Graduate Business Faculty

Full-time: 100

Student Body

Total: 527
Full-time: 482
Part-time: 45

Average Age: 30
Women: 32%

Admissions

Applications: 1,057
Admitted: 384
Enrolled: 237

Average GMAT: 625
Average GPA: 3.34

Costs (1999–2000)

Full-time tuition: $3806 per academic year (resident), $9874 per academic year (nonresident)
Part-time tuition: N/R

After Graduation (Class of 1998–99)

Employed within 3 months of graduation: 100%
Average starting salary: $62,537

Accreditation

AACSB—The International Association for Management Education

DEGREES JD/MBA • M Acc • MA • MBA • MS

JD/MBA—Juris Doctor/Master of Business Administration Full-time. 125 total credits required. 48 to 58 months to complete program. *Concentrations:* economics, entrepreneurship, environmental economics/management, finance, international business, management, manufacturing management, marketing, strategic management, transportation and logistics.

M Acc—Accounting Full-time. At least 30 total credits required. 12 to 16 months to complete program. *Concentrations:* accounting.

MA—Economics Full-time. At least 30 total credits required. 12 to 16 months to complete program. *Concentrations:* economics.

MBA—Business Administration Full-time. At least 54 total credits required. 22 months to complete program. *Concentrations:* economics, entrepreneurship, environmental economics/management, finance, international business, management, manufacturing management, marketing, statistics, transportation and logistics.

MBA—Executive MBA Part-time. At least 45 total credits required. 12 to 19 months to complete program.

MS—Management Science Full-time and part-time. At least 40 total credits required. 20 to 24 months to complete program.

MS—Statistics Full-time. At least 33 total credits required. 15 to 24 months to complete program.

The Master of Business Administration program at the University of Tennessee begins with this simple question: "What does every manager need to know?" It is a question that requires two years of long days, longer nights, and countless weekends to answer. The answer lies in action and hands-on, experiential learning and, once mastered, charts a new course for University of Tennessee graduates.

The School of Business offers an M.B.A. degree with concentrations in economics, finance, global business, logistics and transportation, management, management of information systems, marketing, new venture analysis and entrepreneurship, operations management, and statistics. The program is geared toward the full-time student, with admission in the fall semester only. An internship is also required. A B.A./M.B.A., a J.D./M.B.A., and an M.S./M.B.A. in industrial engineering are also offered. In addition, the College offers an Executive M.B.A., a Physician's Executive M.B.A. program, and a part-time Professional M.B.A.

Also offered by the College are master's programs in accounting, economics, management science, and statistics. A Ph.D. program in business administration, with concentrations in accounting, finance, logistics and transportation, management, marketing, or statistics, is offered as well.

COSTS

Tuition, state resident: *Full-time* $3306. **Tuition, nonresident:** *Full-time* $9374. Tuition varies by local reciprocity agreements. **Required fees:** *Full-time* $500.

Graduate housing: Room and board costs vary by campus location, number of occupants, and type of accommodation. *Typical cost:* $3500 (room only).

FINANCIAL AID (1999–2000)

100 students received aid, including fellowships, loans, research assistantships, teaching assistantships, and work study. Financial aid application deadline: 3/1. **Financial Aid Contact** Mr. Jeff Gerkin, Financial Aid Director, 115 Student Services Building, Knoxville, TN 37996-0210. **Phone:** 865-974-3131. **Fax:** 865-974-2175. **E-mail:** jgerkin@utk.edu.

RESOURCES AND SERVICES

Information about online services, personal computer policies, library resources, international exchange programs, internship programs, and placement services at this institution and others can be found at **www.petersons.com/mba**

International Students

19% of students enrolled are international students.

Services and Facilities Counseling/support services, ESL/language courses, international student housing, international student organization, orientation, visa services. Financial aid is available to international students.

Applying *Required:* TOEFL with recommended score of 550 (paper), proof of adequate funds.

International Student Contact Dr. James Gehlhar, Director, Center for International Education, 1620 Melrose, Knoxville, TN 37996-3531. **Phone:** 865-974-3177. **Fax:** 865-974-2985. **E-mail:** gehlhar@utk.edu.

■ APPLICATION

Required GMAT, application form, baccalaureate/first degree, essay, 2 letters of recommendation, transcripts of college work. **Recommended** Interview, personal statement, resume/curriculum vitae, work experience.

Deadlines and Fees *Deadlines:* 3/1 for fall, 3/1 for fall (international). *Application fee:* $35, $35 (international).

Application Contact Ms. Donna Potts, MBA Admissions Director, 527 Stokely Management Center, Knoxville, TN 37996-0552. **Phone:** 865-974-5033. **Fax:** 865-974-3826. **E-mail:** mba@utk.edu.

See full description on page 968.

The University of Tennessee at Chattanooga

Chattanooga, Tennessee

DEPARTMENT OF COMPUTER SCIENCE

Graduate Business Faculty

Full-time: 21	Part-time: 5

Student Body

Total: 456	
Full-time: 94	Average Age: 32
Part-time: 362	Women: 46%

Admissions

Applications: 213	
Admitted: 157	Average GMAT: 500
Enrolled: 74	Average GPA: 3.2

Costs (1999–2000)
Full-time tuition: $2478 per academic year (resident), $6078 per academic year (nonresident)
Part-time tuition: $480 per course (resident), $1137 per course (nonresident)

After Graduation (Class of 1998–99)
Employed within 3 months of graduation: 75%
Average starting salary: $25,000

Accreditation
AACSB—The International Association for Management Education

DEGREES EMBA • M Acc • MBA

EMBA—Executive Master of Business Administration Full-time. *Distance learning option.* 31 to 49 total credits required. 18 to 24 months to complete program.

M Acc—Master of Accountancy Part-time. 30 to 57 total credits required. 24 to 72 months to complete program. *Concentrations:* accounting.

MBA—Master of Business Administration Part-time. *Distance learning option.* 31 to 49 total credits required. 24 to 72 months to complete program. *Concentrations:* accounting, economics, entrepreneurship, finance, health care, human resources, international management, management information systems, marketing, operations management, organizational management.

COSTS

Tuition, state resident: *Full-time* $2478. *Part-time* $480 per course. **Tuition, nonresident:** *Full-time* $6078. *Part-time* $1137 per course. Tuition varies by number of courses or credits taken. **Required fees:** Fees vary by number of courses or credits taken and academic program. **Graduate housing:** Room and board costs vary by number of occupants and type of accommodation. *Typical cost:* $2000 (room only).

FINANCIAL AID (1999–2000)

250 students received aid, including fellowships, grants, loans, research assistantships, scholarships, and work study. Aid is available to part-time students. Financial aid application deadline: 4/1. **Financial Aid Contact** MBA Director, College of Business Administration, 615 McCallie Avenue, Chattanooga, TN 37403-2598. **Phone:** 423-755-4210.

RESOURCES AND SERVICES

Information about online services, personal computer policies, library resources, international exchange programs, internship programs, and placement services at this institution and others can be found at **www.petersons.com/mba**

International Students

7% of students enrolled are international students.

Services and Facilities Counseling/support services, ESL/language courses, international student housing, visa services. Financial aid is not available to international students.

Applying *Required:* TOEFL with recommended score of 500 (paper), proof of adequate funds, proof of health/immunizations.

International Student Contact Ms. Nancy Amberson, Graduate International Specialist, 615 McCallie Avenue, Chattanooga, TN 37403-2598. **Phone:** 423-785-2110.

■ APPLICATION

Required GMAT, application form, baccalaureate/first degree, transcripts of college work.

Deadlines and Fees Applications for domestic and international students are processed on a rolling basis. *Application fee:* $25, $25 (international).

Application Contact Ms. Kimberly Gee, Director of Graduate Programs, College of Business Administration, 615 McCallie Avenue, Chattanooga, TN 37403-2504. **Phone:** 423-755-4210. **Toll-free Phone:** 800-532-3028. **Fax:** 423-785-2329. **E-mail:** kim-gee@utc.edu.

The University of Tennessee at Martin

Martin, Tennessee

SCHOOL OF BUSINESS ADMINISTRATION

Graduate Business Faculty
Full-time: 27

Student Body

Total: 206	Average Age: 28
Full-time: 47	Women: 52%
Part-time: 159	

Admissions

Applications: 83	
Admitted: 82	Average GMAT: 496
Enrolled: 61	Average GPA: 3.19

Costs (1999–2000)
Full-time tuition: $3332 per academic year (resident), $5260 per academic year (nonresident)
Part-time tuition: $187 per credit (resident), $293 per credit (nonresident)

After Graduation (Class of 1998–99)
Employed within 3 months of graduation: 99%

Accreditation
AACSB—The International Association for Management Education

DEGREES M Acc • MBA

M Acc—Master of Accountancy Full-time and part-time. *Distance learning option.* At least 30 total credits required. 9 to 72 months to complete program.

MBA—Master of Business Administration Full-time and part-time. *Distance learning option.* At least 30 total credits required. 9 to 72 months to complete program.

COSTS

Tuition, state resident: *Full-time* $3332. *Part-time* $187 per credit. **Tuition, nonresident:** *Full-time* $5260. *Part-time* $293 per credit. **Required fees:** Tuition and fees vary by number of courses or credits taken and local reciprocity agreements. **Graduate housing:** Room and board costs vary by number of occupants, type of accommodation, and type of board plan. *Typical cost:* $3744 (including board).

FINANCIAL AID (1999–2000)

9 students received aid, including fellowships and research assistantships. Aid is available to part-time students. Financial aid application deadline: 3/1. **Financial Aid Contact** Mr. Randy Hall, Executive Director of Student Financial Assistance, University Street, Martin, TN 38238-1000. **Phone:** 901-587-7040. **Fax:** 901-587-7036. **E-mail:** rhall@utm.edu.

RESOURCES AND SERVICES

Information about online services, personal computer policies, library resources, international exchange programs, internship programs, and placement services at this institution and others can be found at **www.petersons.com/mba**

International Students

Services and Facilities Counseling/support services.
Applying *Required:* TOEFL with recommended score of 197 (computer) or 525 (paper), proof of adequate funds, proof of health/immunizations.

International Student Contact Ms. Sandra Baker, Director, International Programs, 144 Gooch Hall, Martin, TN 38238-1000. **Phone:** 901-587-7340. **Fax:** 901-587-7322. **E-mail:** sbaker@utm.edu.

■ APPLICATION

Required GMAT, application form, baccalaureate/first degree, transcripts of college work.

Deadlines and Fees Applications for domestic and international students are processed on a rolling basis. *Application fee:* $25, $50 (international).

Application Contact Dr. Richard B. Griffin, Coordinator of Graduate Programs in Business Administration, School of Business Administration, Martin, TN 38238-1000. **Phone:** 901-587-7208. **Toll-free Phone:** 888-293-5822. **Fax:** 901-587-7241. **E-mail:** bagrad@utm.edu.

Vanderbilt University

Nashville, Tennessee

OWEN GRADUATE SCHOOL OF MANAGEMENT

Graduate Business Faculty
Full-time: 42 — Part-time: 21

Student Body
Total: 560
Full-time: 560
Average Age: 30
Women: 25%

Admissions
Applications: 1,249
Admitted: 533
Enrolled: 291
Average GMAT: 630
Average GPA: 3.1

Costs (1999–2000)
Full-time tuition: $25,350 per academic year
Part-time tuition: N/R

After Graduation (Class of 1998–99)
Employed within 3 months of graduation: 97%
Average starting salary: $75,000

Accreditation
AACSB—The International Association for Management Education

DEGREES JD/MBA • MBA • MBA/MA • MBA/ME • MBA/MSN • MD/MBA

JD/MBA—Juris Doctor/Master of Business Administration Full-time. At least 151 total credits required. 40 months to complete program. *Concentrations:* accounting, finance, human resources, management information systems, marketing, operations management, organizational management.

MBA—Executive MBA Program Full-time. Minimum of 5 years of work experience (including management experience) required. At least 50 total credits required. 21 months to complete program. *Concentrations:* management.

MBA—Master of Business Administration Full-time. At least 60 total credits required. 20 months to complete program. *Concentrations:* accounting, finance, human resources, management information systems, operations management, organizational management.

MBA/MA—MBA/MA in Latin American Studies Program Full-time. At least 72 total credits required. 25 to 30 months to complete program. *Concentrations:* accounting, finance, human resources, management information systems, marketing, operations management, organizational management.

MBA/ME—Master of Business Administration/Masters of Engineering Full-time. At least 72 total credits required. 25 to 30 months to complete program. *Concentrations:* management, management information systems, operations management, technology management.

MBA/MSN—Master of Business Administration/Master of Science in Nursing Full-time. At least 69 total credits required. 25 to 30 months to complete program. *Concentrations:* accounting, finance, human resources, management, management information systems, marketing, operations management, organizational management.

MD/MBA—Doctor of Medicine/Master of Business Administration Full-time. At least 60 total credits required. 50 months to complete program.

COSTS

Tuition *Full-time:* $25,100. Tuition varies by academic program. **Required fees:** *Full-time* $250. **Graduate housing:** Room and board costs vary by number of occupants, type of accommodation, and type of board plan. *Typical cost:* $8850 (including board), $2450 (room only).

FINANCIAL AID (1999–2000)

281 students received aid, including fellowships, loans, scholarships, and work study. **Financial Aid Contact** Ms. Elizabeth Powitzkey, Associate Director of Student Services and Admissions, 401 21st Avenue South, Nashville, TN 37203. **Phone:** 615-322-6469. **Fax:** 615-343-1175. **E-mail:** elizabeth.powitzkey@owen.vanderbilt.edu.

RESOURCES AND SERVICES

Information about online services, personal computer policies, library resources, international exchange programs, internship programs, and placement services at this institution and others can be found at **www.petersons.com/mba**

International Students

21% of students enrolled are international students.

Services and Facilities Counseling/support services, ESL/language courses, international student housing, visa services. Financial aid is available to international students.
Applying *Required:* TOEFL, proof of adequate funds, proof of health/immunizations.

International Student Contact Ms. Christie St. John, Manager, International Relations, Owen Graduate School of Management, 401 21st Avenue South, Nashville, TN 37203. **Phone:** 615-322-6469. **Fax:** 615-343-1175. **E-mail:** admissions@owen.vanderbilt.edu.

■ APPLICATION

Required GMAT, application form, baccalaureate/first degree, essay, interview, 2 letters of recommendation, resume/curriculum vitae, transcripts of college work. **Recommended** Work experience.

Deadlines and Fees *Deadlines:* 11/15 for fall, 2/1 for winter, 3/15 for spring, 11/15 for fall (international), 2/1 for winter (international), 3/15 for spring (international). *Application fee:* $75, $75 (international).

Application Contact Mr. Todd Reale, Director of MBA Program and Admissions, Owen Graduate School of Management, 401 21st Avenue South, Nashville, TN 37203. **Phone:** 615-322-6469. **Toll-free Phone:** 800-288-OWEN. **Fax:** 615-343-1175. **E-mail:** admissions@owen.vanderbilt.edu.

See full description on page 992.

TEXAS

Abilene Christian University

Abilene, Texas

COLLEGE OF BUSINESS ADMINISTRATION

Graduate Business Faculty
Full-time: 8

Student Body
Total: 16
Full-time: 14
Part-time: 2

Average Age: 23
Women: 50%

Admissions
Applications: 14
Admitted: 14
Enrolled: 13

Average GMAT: 515
Average GPA: 3

Costs (1999–2000)
Full-time tuition: $8216 per academic year
Part-time tuition: $327 per credit hour

After Graduation (Class of 1998–99)
Employed within 3 months of graduation: 100%
Average starting salary: $39,500

Accreditation
ACBSP—The American Council of Business Schools and Programs

DEGREES M Acc • MBA

M Acc—Master of Accountancy Full-time and part-time. At least 30 total credits required. 12 to 60 months to complete program.

MBA—Master of Business Administration Full-time and part-time. At least 40 total credits required. 12 to 72 months to complete program. *Concentrations:* accounting, information management, management, nonprofit management.

COSTS

Tuition *Full-time:* $7848. *Part-time:* $327 per credit hour. **Required fees:** *Full-time* $368. **Graduate housing:** Room and board costs vary by number of occupants, type of accommodation, and type of board plan. *Typical cost:* $5350 (including board).

FINANCIAL AID (1999–2000)

11 students received aid, including loans, research assistantships, scholarships, teaching assistantships, and work study. Aid is available to part-time students. Financial aid application deadline: 3/1. **Financial Aid Contact** Gary West, Director of Student Financial Services, ACU Box 29007, Abilene, TX 79699-9007. **Phone:** 915-674-2643. **Fax:** 915-674-2130.

RESOURCES AND SERVICES

Information about online services, personal computer policies, library resources, international exchange programs, internship programs, and placement services at this institution and others can be found at **www.petersons.com/mba**

International Students

Services and Facilities Counseling/support services, ESL/language courses, international student organization, visa services. Financial aid is available to international students.
Applying *Required:* TOEFL with recommended score of 500 (paper), proof of adequate funds, proof of health/immunizations.
International Student Contact Mr. Ted Presley, Executive Director for International and Intercultural Education, ACU Box 28226, Abilene, TX 79699. **Phone:** 915-674-2710. **Fax:** 915-674-2966. **E-mail:** prestleyt@acu.edu.

■ APPLICATION

Required GMAT, application form, baccalaureate/first degree, essay, 3 letters of recommendation, personal statement, transcripts of college work. **Recommended** 2 years of work experience.
Deadlines and Fees Applications for domestic and international students are processed on a rolling basis. *Application fee:* $25, $45 (international).
Application Contact Mr. Bill Fowler, Chair, Department of Accounting and Finance, ACU Box 29305, Abilene, TX 79699-9305. **Phone:** 915-674-2080. **Toll-free Phone:** 800-395-4723. **Fax:** 915-674-2564. **E-mail:** bill.fowler@coba.acu.edu.

Amber University

Garland, Texas

DEPARTMENT OF BUSINESS ADMINISTRATION

Graduate Business Faculty
Full-time: 16

Part-time: 45

Student Body
Total: 396
Full-time: 40
Part-time: 356

Average Age: 35
Women: 40%

Admissions
Applications: 325
Admitted: 320

Enrolled: 300
Average GPA: 3

Costs (1999–2000)
Full-time tuition: $3960 per academic year
Part-time tuition: $495 per course

After Graduation (Class of 1998–99)
Employed within 3 months of graduation: 90%

DEGREES MBA

MBA—General Business MBA Full-time and part-time. *Distance learning option.* At least 36 total credits required.

MBA—Master of Business Administration in Management Full-time and part-time. *Distance learning option.* At least 36 total credits required. *Concentrations:* management.

COSTS

Tuition *Full-time:* $3960. *Part-time:* $495 per course.

FINANCIAL AID (1999–2000)

Financial Aid Contact Ms. Melinda Reagan, Vice President for Administrative Services, 1700 Eastgate, Garland, TX 75041. **Phone:** 972-279-6511 Ext. 122. **Fax:** 972-279-9773. **E-mail:** rea@ambernet.amberu.edu.

RESOURCES AND SERVICES

Information about online services, personal computer policies, library resources, international exchange programs, internship programs, and placement services at this institution and others can be found at **www.petersons.com/mba**

International Students

Services and Facilities Financial aid is not available to international students.
International Student Contact Dr. Jo Lynn Loyd, Dean For Strategic Planning, 1700 Eastgate, Garland, TX 75041. **Phone:** 972-279-6511 Ext. 126. **Fax:** 972-279-9773. **E-mail:** jloyd@ambernet.amberu.edu.

■ APPLICATION

Required Application form, baccalaureate/first degree, transcripts of college work.
Deadlines and Fees *Deadlines:* 8/1 for fall, 11/10 for winter, 2/1 for spring, 5/1 for summer, 8/1 for fall (international), 11/1 for winter (international), 2/1 for spring (international), 5/1 for summer (international). *Application fee:* $25, $25 (international).
Application Contact Ms. Marge Massey, Manager of Admissions, 1700 Eastgate, Garland, TX 75041. **Phone:** 972-279-6511 Ext. 167. **Fax:** 972-279-9773. **E-mail:** massey@ambernet.amberu.edu.

Angelo State University

San Angelo, Texas

DEPARTMENT OF BUSINESS ADMINISTRATION

Graduate Business Faculty
Full-time: 13

Student Body
Total: 88
Full-time: 35
Part-time: 53

Average Age: 32
Women: 35%

Admissions
Applications: 29
Admitted: 25

Enrolled: 22
Average GMAT: 503

Costs (1999–2000)
Full-time tuition: N/R
Part-time tuition: $36 per credit (resident), $249 per credit (nonresident)

Accreditation
ACBSP—The American Council of Business Schools and Programs

DEGREES MBA

MBA—Master of Business Administration in Accounting Full-time and part-time. At least 36 total credits required. 18 to 72 months to complete program. *Concentrations:* accounting.

MBA—Master of Business Administration in Management Full-time and part-time. At least 39 total credits required. 18 to 72 months to complete program. *Concentrations:* management.

COSTS

Tuition, state resident: *Part-time* $36 per credit. **Tuition, nonresident:** *Part-time* $249 per credit. **Required fees:** Tuition and fees vary by class time, number of courses or credits taken, and local reciprocity agreements. **Graduate housing:** Room and board costs vary by number of occupants, type of accommodation, and type of board plan. *Typical cost:* $4318 (including board).

FINANCIAL AID (1999–2000)

12 students received aid, including fellowships, research assistantships, scholarships, teaching assistantships, and work study. Aid is available to part-time students. Financial aid application deadline: 8/1. **Financial Aid Contact** Mr. James B. Parker, Financial Aid Director, PO Box 11015, San Angelo, TX 76909. **Phone:** 915-942-2246. **Fax:** 915-942-2082. **E-mail:** j.parker@angelo.edu.

RESOURCES AND SERVICES

Information about online services, personal computer policies, library resources, international exchange programs, internship programs, and placement services at this institution and others can be found at **www.petersons.com/mba**

International Students

3% of students enrolled are international students.

Services and Facilities Counseling/support services. Financial aid is available to international students.
Applying *Required:* TOEFL with recommended score of 550 (paper), proof of adequate funds, proof of health/immunizations.
International Student Contact Ms. Mitzie Keeling, Admissions Counselor/International Student Advisor, PO Box 11014, San Angelo, TX 76909. **Phone:** 915-942-2041 Ext. 242. **Fax:** 915-942-2078. **E-mail:** mitzie.keeling@angelo.edu.

■ APPLICATION

Required GMAT, application form, baccalaureate/first degree, resume/curriculum vitae, transcripts of college work.

Deadlines and Fees *Deadlines:* 8/7 for fall, 1/2 for spring, 5/10 for summer, 6/10 for fall (international), 11/1 for spring (international), 3/15 for summer (international). *Application fee:* $25, $50 (international).

Application Contact Dr. Carol Diminnie, Graduate Dean, PO Box 10025, San Angelo, TX 76909. **Phone:** 915-942-2169. **Fax:** 915-942-2194. **E-mail:** graduate.school@angelo.edu.

Baylor University

Waco, Texas

HANKAMER SCHOOL OF BUSINESS

Graduate Business Faculty
Full-time: 115

Student Body
Total: 175   Average Age: 25
Full-time: 175   Women: 34%

Admissions
Applications: 147   Average GMAT: 605
Admitted: 96   Average GPA: 3.13
Enrolled: 49

Costs (1999–2000)
Full-time tuition: $18,490 per academic year
Part-time tuition: $355 per course

After Graduation (Class of 1998–99)
Employed within 3 months of graduation: 98%
Average starting salary: $51,000

Accreditation
AACSB—The International Association for Management Education

DEGREES JD/M Tax • JD/MBA • M Acc • M Tax • MBA • MBA/MSIS • MS

JD/M Tax—Juris Doctor/Master of Taxation Full-time and part-time. At least 126 total credits required. 36 to 60 months to complete program. *Concentrations:* accounting, taxation.

JD/MBA—Juris Doctor/Master of Business Administration Full-time. 140 to 158 total credits required. 48 to 60 months to complete program.

M Acc—Master of Accountancy Full-time and part-time. At least 33 total credits required. 12 to 60 months to complete program. *Concentrations:* accounting, taxation.

M Tax—Master of Taxation Full-time and part-time. At least 33 total credits required. 12 to 60 months to complete program. *Concentrations:* taxation.

MBA—Executive MBA, Dallas Part-time. 8 years work experience. At least 47 total credits required. 21 months to complete program.

MBA—Executive MBA, Waco Part-time. 5 years work experience. At least 47 total credits required. 21 months to complete program.

MBA—Master of Business Administration Full-time. 53 to 71 total credits required. 16 to 21 months to complete program. *Concentrations:* accounting, economics, electronic commerce (e-commerce), entrepreneurship, finance, information management, international and area business studies, management, management information systems, marketing, system management.

MBA/MSIS—Master of Business Administration/Master of Science in Information Systems Full-time. 71 to 88 total credits required. 21 to 24 months to complete program. *Concentrations:* information management, system management.

MS—Master of Science in Information Systems Full-time and part-time. 36 to 54 total credits required. 12 to 60 months to complete program. *Concentrations:* information management, system management.

COSTS

Tuition *Full-time:* $13,490. *Part-time:* $355 per course. **Required fees:** *Full-time* $5000. Tuition and fees vary by number of courses or credits taken and academic program. **Graduate housing:** Room and board costs vary by number of occupants, type of accommodation, and type of board plan. *Typical cost:* $4800 (including board).

FINANCIAL AID (1999–2000)

70 students received aid, including fellowships, loans, research assistantships, scholarships, teaching assistantships, and work study.
Financial Aid Contact Mr. Cliff Neel, Assistant Vice President and Director of Financial Aid, PO Box 97028, Waco, TX 76798-7028. **Phone:** 254-710-2611. **E-mail:** cliff_neel@baylor.edu.

RESOURCES AND SERVICES

Information about online services, personal computer policies, library resources, international exchange programs, internship programs, and placement services at this institution and others can be found at **www.petersons.com/mba**

International Students

14% of students enrolled are international students.

Services and Facilities Counseling/support services, ESL/language courses, orientation, visa services, membership in graduate business association. Financial aid is available to international students.
Applying *Required:* TOEFL with recommended score of 250 (computer) or 600 (paper), proof of adequate funds, proof of health/immunizations.
International Student Contact Dr. June Rose Garrott, Advisor of International Students, PO Box 97381, Waco, TX 76798-7381. **Phone:** 254-710-1461. **Fax:** 254-710-1468. **E-mail:** junerose-garrott@baylor.edu.

■ APPLICATION

Required GMAT, application form, baccalaureate/first degree, essay, 2 letters of recommendation, personal statement, resume/curriculum vitae, transcripts of college work. **Recommended** Interview, work experience.

Deadlines and Fees *Deadlines:* 7/1 for fall, 11/1 for spring, 4/1 for summer, 7/1 for fall (international), 11/1 for spring (international), 4/1 for summer (international). *Application fee:* $50, $50 (international).

Application Contact Ms. Laurie Wilson, Director of Graduate Business Admissions, PO Box 98013, Waco, TX 76798-8013. **Phone:** 254-710-3718. **Toll-free Phone:** 800-583-0622. **Fax:** 254-710-1066. **E-mail:** laurie_wilson@baylor.edu.

See full description on page 560.

Dallas Baptist University

Dallas, Texas

GRADUATE SCHOOL OF BUSINESS

Graduate Business Faculty

Dallas Baptist University
(continued)

Full-time: 15
Part-time: 22

Student Body
Total: 445
Full-time: 84
Part-time: 361

Average Age: 37
Women: 50%

Admissions
Applications: 323
Admitted: 239

Enrolled: 170
Average GPA: 3

Costs (1999–2000)
Full-time tuition: $5364 per academic year
Part-time tuition: $298 per credit

Accreditation
ACBSP—The American Council of Business Schools and Programs

DEGREES MA • MBA

MA—Master of Arts in Organizational Management Full-time and part-time. 36 to 45 total credits required. Maximum of 72 months to complete program. *Concentrations:* human resources, management.

MBA—Master of Business Administration Full-time and part-time. *Distance learning option.* 36 to 60 total credits required. Maximum of 72 months to complete program. *Concentrations:* accounting, finance, health care, international business, management, management information systems, marketing, technology management.

COSTS

Tuition *Full-time:* $5364. *Part-time:* $298 per credit. Tuition varies by number of courses or credits taken.

FINANCIAL AID (1999–2000)

81 students received aid, including grants, loans, scholarships, and work study. Aid is available to part-time students. **Financial Aid Contact** Mr. Rick Renshaw, Director of Financial Aid, 3000 Mountain Creek Parkway, Dallas, TX 75211-9299. **Phone:** 214-333-5363. **Fax:** 214-333-5586. **E-mail:** rickr@dbu.edu.

RESOURCES AND SERVICES

Information about online services, personal computer policies, library resources, international exchange programs, internship programs, and placement services at this institution and others can be found at **www.petersons.com/mba**

International Students

Services and Facilities Counseling/support services, ESL/language courses, housing location assistance, international student organization, language tutoring, orientation, visa services. Financial aid is not available to international students. **Applying** *Required:* TOEFL with recommended score of 213 (computer) or 550 (paper), proof of adequate funds, proof of health/immunizations. **International Student Contact** Mr. Jacky Wong Chan, Coordinator of International Student Services, 3000 Mountain Creek Parkway, Dallas, TX 75211-9299. **Phone:** 214-333-5427. **Fax:** 214-333-5409. **E-mail:** globalinfo@dbu.edu.

■ APPLICATION

Required GMAT, application form, baccalaureate/first degree, 2 letters of recommendation, personal statement, resume/curriculum vitae, transcripts of college work. **Recommended** 2 years of work experience.

Deadlines and Fees Applications for domestic and international students are processed on a rolling basis. *Application fee:* $25, $25 (international).

Application Contact Mr. Kerry Webb, Director of Graduate Programs, 3000 Mountain Creek Parkway, Dallas, TX 75211-9299. **Phone:** 214-333-5242. **Fax:** 214-333-5579. **E-mail:** graduate@dbu.edu.

Hardin-Simmons University

Abilene, Texas

SCHOOL OF BUSINESS AND FINANCE

Graduate Business Faculty
Full-time: 6

Student Body
Total: 7
Full-time: 1
Part-time: 6

Average Age: 35
Women: 29%

Admissions
Applications: 7
Admitted: 7
Enrolled: 7

Average GMAT: 615
Average GPA: 2.78

Costs (1999–2000)
Full-time tuition: $5715 per academic year
Part-time tuition: $300 per credit

Accreditation
ACBSP—The American Council of Business Schools and Programs

DEGREES MBA

MBA—MBA-Non-Thesis Full-time and part-time. At least 36 total credits required. 15 to 60 months to complete program.
MBA—MBA-Thesis Full-time and part-time. At least 30 total credits required. 12 to 60 months to complete program.

COSTS

Tuition *Full-time:* $5400. *Part-time:* $300 per credit. **Tuition, international:** *Full-time* $5400. Tuition varies by number of courses or credits taken. **Required fees:** *Full-time* $315. *Part-time* $50 per semester. Fees vary by class time, number of courses or credits taken, and academic program. **Graduate housing:** Room and board costs vary by number of occupants, type of accommodation, and type of board plan. *Typical cost:* $3336 (including board).

FINANCIAL AID (1999–2000)

1 student received aid, including loans, research assistantships, scholarships, and work study. **Financial Aid Contact** Mr. Shane Davidson, Associate VP for Enrollment Services, Financial Aid Office, Box 16075, Abilene, TX 79698. **Phone:** 915-670-1206. **Fax:** 915-670-1527. **E-mail:** enroll@hsutx.edu.

RESOURCES AND SERVICES

Information about online services, personal computer policies, library resources, international exchange programs, internship programs, and placement services at this institution and others can be found at **www.petersons.com/mba**

International Students

Services and Facilities Counseling/support services. Financial aid is available to international students.
Applying *Required:* TOEFL with recommended score of 550 (paper), proof of adequate funds, proof of health/immunizations.
International Student Contact Dr. Dan McAlexander, Dean of Graduate Studies, Office of Graduate Studies, Box 16210, Abilene, TX 79698-6210. **Phone:** 915-670-1298. **Fax:** 915-670-1564. **E-mail:** gradoff@hsutx.edu.

■ APPLICATION

Required GMAT, application form, baccalaureate/first degree, essay, 3 letters of recommendation, resume/curriculum vitae, transcripts of college work. **Recommended** Interview, work experience.

Deadlines and Fees Applications for domestic and international students are processed on a rolling basis. *Application fee:* $25, $100 (international).

Application Contact Dr. Dan McAlexander, Dean of Graduate Studies, Office of Graduate Studies, Box 16210, Abilene, TX 79698-6210. **Phone:** 915-670-1298. **Toll-free Phone:** 888-478-1222. **Fax:** 915-670-1564. **E-mail:** gradoff@hsutx.edu.

Houston Baptist University

Houston, Texas

COLLEGE OF BUSINESS AND ECONOMICS

Graduate Business Faculty
Full-time: 24

Part-time: 35

Student Body
Total: 312
Full-time: 225

Part-time: 87
Women: 47%

Admissions
Applications: 150
Admitted: 101
Enrolled: 85

Average GMAT: 530
Average GPA: 2.5

Costs (1999–2000)
Full-time tuition: N/R
Part-time tuition: $1110 per course

DEGREES MBA • MS

MBA—Professional Master of Business Administration Full-time and part-time. 42 to 51 total credits required. 24 to 60 months to complete program. *Concentrations:* management consulting, management systems analysis, marketing research.

MS—Master of Science in Accountancy and Information Technology Full-time and part-time. At least 54 total credits required. Minimum of 24 months to complete program.

MS—Master of Science in Human Resource Management Full-time and part-time. At least 42 total credits required. 24 to 60 months to complete program. *Concentrations:* human resources.

MS—Master of Science in Management Computing and Systems Full-time. At least 42 total credits required. Minimum of 24 months to complete program. *Concentrations:* management science.

COSTS

Tuition *Part-time:* $1110 per course. Tuition varies by number of courses or credits taken and academic program. **Required fees:** *Part-time* $235 per quarter. **Graduate housing:** Room and board costs vary by number of occupants, type of accommodation, and type of board plan. *Typical cost:* $4049 (including board).

FINANCIAL AID (1999–2000)

Grants and loans. Aid is available to part-time students. Financial aid application deadline: 4/1. **Financial Aid Contact** Sherry Byrd, Director, Financial Aid, 7502 Fondren Road, Houston, TX 77074-3298. **Phone:** 281-649-3204. **Fax:** 281-649-3303.

RESOURCES AND SERVICES

Information about online services, personal computer policies, library resources, international exchange programs, internship programs, and placement services at this institution and others can be found at **www.petersons.com/mba**

International Students

3% of students enrolled are international students.

Services and Facilities Counseling/support services, ESL/language courses, orientation, visa services. Financial aid is available to international students. **Applying** *Required:* TOEFL with recommended score of 213 (computer) or 550 (paper).

International Student Contact Ms. Ida Thompson, Director of Admission for Graduate Programs, Houston, TX 77074-3298. **Phone:** 281-649-3302. **Fax:** 281-649-3011. **E-mail:** ithompson@hbu.edu.

■ APPLICATION

Required GMAT, application form, baccalaureate/first degree, 3 letters of recommendation, personal statement, resume/curriculum vitae, transcripts of college work. **Recommended** Work experience.

Deadlines and Fees *Deadlines:* 8/1 for fall, 11/1 for winter, 2/1 for spring, 5/1 for summer. *Application fee:* $50, $100 (international).

Application Contact Ms. Ida Thompson, Director of Admission for Graduate Programs, 7502 Fondren Road, Houston, TX 77074-3298. **Phone:** 281-649-3302. **Fax:** 281-649-3011. **E-mail:** ithompson@hbu.edu.

Lamar University

Beaumont, Texas

COLLEGE OF BUSINESS

Graduate Business Faculty
Full-time: 19

Student Body
Total: 81
Full-time: 29
Part-time: 52
Average Age: 32
Women: 42%

Admissions
Applications: 125
Admitted: 56
Enrolled: 23
Average GMAT: 530
Average GPA: 3.2

Costs (1999–2000)
Full-time tuition: $1294 per academic year (resident), $5128 per academic year (nonresident)
Part-time tuition: $186 per course (resident), $813 per course (nonresident)

After Graduation (Class of 1998–99)
Employed within 3 months of graduation: 80%
Average starting salary: $45,000

Accreditation
AACSB—The International Association for Management Education

DEGREE MBA

MBA—Master of Business Administration Full-time and part-time. 30 to 66 total credits required. 12 to 72 months to complete program. *Concentrations:* accounting, management.

COSTS

Tuition, state resident: *Full-time* $1044. *Part-time* $186 per course. **Tuition, nonresident:** *Full-time* $4878. *Part-time* $813 per course. **Required fees:** *Full-time* $250. *Part-time* $150 per semester. Tuition and fees vary by number of courses or credits taken. **Graduate housing:** Room and board costs vary by number of occupants, type of accommodation, and type of board plan. *Typical cost:* $3800 (including board).

FINANCIAL AID (1999–2000)

15 students received aid, including fellowships, grants, loans, research assistantships, scholarships, teaching assistantships, and work study. Aid is available to part-time students. **Financial Aid Contact** Ellen Nystrom, Director of Financial Aid, PO Box 10042, Beaumont, TX 77710-0042. **Phone:** 409-880-2302.

RESOURCES AND SERVICES

Information about online services, personal computer policies, library resources, international exchange programs, internship programs, and placement services at this institution and others can be found at **www.petersons.com/mba**

International Students

21% of students enrolled are international students.

Services and Facilities Counseling/support services, ESL/language courses, housing location assistance, international student organization, orientation, visa services.
Applying *Required:* TOEFL with recommended score of 525 (paper), proof of adequate funds, proof of health/immunizations.

International Student Contact Ms. Sandy Drane, International Student Advisor, PO Box 10009, Beaumont, TX 77710-0009. **Phone:** 409-880-8349.

■ APPLICATION

Required GMAT, application form, baccalaureate/first degree, transcripts of college work. **Recommended** Interview, letter(s) of recommendation, personal statement, resume/curriculum vitae.

Deadlines and Fees *Deadlines:* 5/1 for fall, 10/1 for spring, 3/1 for summer, 3/15 for fall (international), 10/1 for spring (international), 3/1 for summer (international).

Application Contact Dr. Robert Swerdlow, Associate Dean, College of Business, PO Box 10059, Beaumont, TX 77710-0059. **Phone:** 409-880-8604. **Fax:** 409-880-8088. **E-mail:** swerdlowra@hal.lamar.edu.

LeTourneau University

Longview, Texas

PROGRAM IN BUSINESS ADMINISTRATION

Graduate Business Faculty
Full-time: 5
Part-time: 53

Student Body
Total: 274
Full-time: 274
Average Age: 36
Women: 42%

Admissions
Applications: 324
Admitted: 274
Enrolled: 274
Average GPA: 3

Costs (1999–2000)
Full-time tuition: $7329 per academic year
Part-time tuition: N/R

After Graduation (Class of 1998–99)
Employed within 3 months of graduation: 90%

DEGREE MBA

MBA—Master of Business Administration Full-time. 3 years of work experience required, minimum age requirement: 23. At least 39 total credits required. 20 to 60 months to complete program. *Concentrations:* electronic commerce (e-commerce), finance, human resources, international business, management, marketing.

LeTourneau University (continued)

COSTS
Tuition *Full-time:* $7329.

FINANCIAL AID (1999–2000)
250 students received aid, including loans. **Financial Aid Contact** Ms. Delinda Hall, Director of Financial Aid, PO Box 7001, Longview, TX 75607-7001. **Phone:** 800-388-5327 Ext. 3430. **Fax:** 903-233-3411. **E-mail:** halll@letu.edu.

RESOURCES AND SERVICES
Information about online services, personal computer policies, library resources, international exchange programs, internship programs, and placement services at this institution and others can be found at **www. petersons.com/mba**

International Students
3% of students enrolled are international students.

Services and Facilities Financial aid is not available to international students.
Applying *Required:* TOEFL with recommended score of 500 (paper).
International Student Contact Dr. Donald Connors, Assistant Vice President, Graduate, Adult, and Continuing Studies, PO Box 7001, Longview, TX 75607-7001. **Phone:** 903-233-3250 Ext. 3207. **Fax:** 903-233-3227. **E-mail:** connorsd@letu.edu.

■ APPLICATION
Required Application form, baccalaureate/first degree, 2 letters of recommendation, resume/curriculum vitae, transcripts of college work, 3 years of work experience.
Deadlines and Fees Applications for domestic and international students are processed on a rolling basis. *Application fee:* $50, $50 (international).
Application Contact Chris Fontaine, Graduate Admissions Counselor, PO Box 7668, Longview, TX 75607-7668. **Phone:** 903-233-3250 Ext. 3140. **Fax:** 903-233-3227.

Midwestern State University

Wichita Falls, Texas

COLLEGE OF BUSINESS ADMINISTRATION

Graduate Business Faculty
Full-time: 19 — Part-time: 1

Student Body
Total: 76
Full-time: 16 — Average Age: 31
Part-time: 60 — Women: 43%

Admissions
Applications: 20 — Average GMAT: 450
Admitted: 18 — Average GPA: 3
Enrolled: 15

Costs (1999–2000)
Full-time tuition: N/R
Part-time tuition: $42 per hour (resident), $222 per hour (nonresident)

Accreditation
ACBSP—The American Council of Business Schools and Programs

DEGREE MBA

MBA—Master of Business Administration Full-time and part-time. *Distance learning option.* 36 to 60 total credits required. 12 to 72 months to complete program. *Concentrations:* management.

COSTS
Tuition, state resident: *Part-time* $42 per hour. **Tuition, nonresident:** *Part-time* $222 per hour. Tuition varies by number of courses or credits taken and local reciprocity agreements. **Graduate housing:** Room and board costs vary by type of board plan. *Typical cost:* $4400 (including board).

FINANCIAL AID (1999–2000)
8 students received aid, including loans, research assistantships, scholarships, teaching assistantships, and work study. Aid is available to part-time students. **Financial Aid Contact** Dr. Henry Van Geem, Jr., Advisor, MBA Program, 3410 Taft Boulevard, Wichita Falls, TX 76308-2096. **Phone:** 940-397-4367. **Fax:** 940-397-4280. **E-mail:** fvangemh@nexus.mwsu.edu.

RESOURCES AND SERVICES
Information about online services, personal computer policies, library resources, international exchange programs, internship programs, and placement services at this institution and others can be found at **www. petersons.com/mba**

International Students
11% of students enrolled are international students.

Services and Facilities Counseling/support services, ESL/language courses. Financial aid is not available to international students.
Applying *Required:* TOEFL with recommended score of 550 (paper), proof of adequate funds, proof of health/immunizations.
International Student Contact Mr. Uli Bauer, International Student Advisor—International Programs, 3410 Taft Boulevard, Wichita Falls, TX 76308-1096. **Phone:** 940-397-4208. **E-mail:** fbaueru@nexus.mwsu.edu.

■ APPLICATION
Required Application form, baccalaureate/first degree, transcripts of college work. School will accept GMAT.
Deadlines and Fees *Deadlines:* 8/7 for fall, 12/15 for spring, 5/15 for summer, 4/1 for fall (international), 8/1 for spring (international), 1/1 for summer (international).
Application Contact Dr. Henry Van Geem, Jr., Advisor, MBA Program, 3410 Taft Boulevard, Wichita Falls, TX 76308-2096. **Phone:** 940-397-4367. **Fax:** 940-397-4280. **E-mail:** fvangemh@nexus.mwsu.edu.

Our Lady of the Lake University of San Antonio

San Antonio, Texas

SCHOOL OF BUSINESS AND PUBLIC ADMINISTRATION

Graduate Business Faculty
Full-time: 23 — Part-time: 24

Student Body
Total: 606 — Average Age: 37
Part-time: 606 — Women: 50%

Admissions
Applications: 62 — Average GMAT: 440
Admitted: 61 — Average GPA: 3.1
Enrolled: 55

Costs (1999–2000)
Full-time tuition: N/R
Part-time tuition: $448 per credit hour

After Graduation (Class of 1998–99)
Employed within 3 months of graduation: 100%

Accreditation
ACBSP—The American Council of Business Schools and Programs

DEGREES MBA

MBA—Master of Business Administration in Electronic Commerce Management Part-time. 3 years of management or professional experience required. 36 to 57 total credits required. 24 to 72 months to complete program. *Concentrations:* electronic commerce (e-commerce).

MBA—Master of Business Administration in Health Care Management Part-time. 3 years of management or professional experience required. 36 to 54 total credits required. 24 to 72 months to complete program. *Concentrations:* health care.

MBA—Master of Business Administration Part-time. 3 years of management or professional experience required. 36 to 54 total credits required. 24 to 72 months to complete program. *Concentrations:* finance, international business, management.

COSTS
Tuition *Part-time:* $410 per credit hour. **Required fees:** *Part-time* $38 per credit hour.

FINANCIAL AID (1999–2000)
Fellowships and loans. Aid is available to part-time students. Financial aid application deadline: 4/15. **Financial Aid Contact** Ms. Terri McKinney, Director of Financial Aid, 411 Southwest 24th Street, San Antonio, TX 78207-4689. **Phone:** 210-434-6711 Ext. 319. **E-mail:** mckit@lake.ollusa.edu.

RESOURCES AND SERVICES

Information about online services, personal computer policies, library resources, international exchange programs, internship programs, and placement services at this institution and others can be found at **www. petersons.com/mba**

International Students

0.8% of students enrolled are international students.

Services and Facilities Counseling/support services, ESL/language courses, international student organization, visa services. Financial aid is not available to international students.

Applying *Required:* TOEFL with recommended score of 550 (paper), proof of adequate funds.

International Student Contact Ms. Carol Graham, International Student Advisor, 411 Southwest 24th Street, San Antonio, TX 78207-4689. **Phone:** 210-434-6711 Ext. 322. **Fax:** 210-431-4065. **E-mail:** grahc@lake.ollusa.edu.

■ APPLICATION

Required GMAT or GRE or MAT, application form, baccalaureate/first degree, interview, 2 letters of recommendation, resume/curriculum vitae, transcripts of college work, 3 years of work experience.

Deadlines and Fees *Deadlines:* 8/15 for fall, 1/5 for spring, 4/15 for summer, 8/15 for fall (international), 1/5 for spring (international), 4/15 for summer (international). *Application fee:* $25, $25 (international).

Application Contact Mr. Quentin Korte, Director, Graduate Programs, 411 Southwest 24th Street, San Antonio, TX 78207-4689. **Phone:** 210-434-6711 Ext. 412. **Fax:** 210-434-0821. **E-mail:** kortb@lake.ollusa.edu.

Prairie View A&M University

Prairie View, Texas

COLLEGE OF BUSINESS

Graduate Business Faculty
Full-time: 13

Student Body
Total: 77
Full-time: 10
Part-time: 67
Average Age: 29
Women: 51%

Admissions
Applications: 52
Admitted: 29
Enrolled: 22
Average GMAT: 430
Average GPA: 2.86

Costs (1999–2000)
Full-time tuition: $1844 per academic year (resident), $5660 per academic year (nonresident)
Part-time tuition: $120 per credit (resident), $254 per credit (nonresident)

After Graduation (Class of 1998–99)
Employed within 3 months of graduation: 95%
Average starting salary: $52,100

DEGREE MBA

MBA—Master of Business Administration Full-time and part-time. 36 to 57 total credits required. 12 to 60 months to complete program. *Concentrations:* management.

COSTS

Tuition, state resident: *Full-time* $756. *Part-time* $120 per credit. **Tuition, nonresident:** *Full-time* $4572. *Part-time* $254 per credit. Tuition varies by number of courses or credits taken. **Required fees:** *Full-time* $1088. *Part-time* $544 per semester. **Graduate housing:** Room and board costs vary by number of occupants and type of board plan. *Typical cost:* $9000 (including board).

FINANCIAL AID (1999–2000)

5 students received aid, including loans, scholarships, and work study. Financial aid application deadline: 3/1. **Financial Aid Contact** Mr. A.D. James, Director of Financial Aid, PO Box 2967, Prairie View, TX 77446. **Phone:** 409-857-4723. **Fax:** 409-857-2425. **E-mail:** ad_james@pvamu. edu.

RESOURCES AND SERVICES

Information about online services, personal computer policies, library resources, international exchange programs, internship programs, and placement services at this institution and others can be found at **www. petersons.com/mba**

International Students

13% of students enrolled are international students.

Services and Facilities Counseling/support services, visa services. Financial aid is not available to international students.

Applying *Required:* TOEFL with recommended score of 220 (computer) or 550 (paper), proof of adequate funds, proof of health/immunizations.

International Student Contact Ms. Evelyn McGinty, Immigration Service Coordinator, PO Box 5, Prairie View, TX 77446. **Phone:** 409-857-2327. **Fax:** 409-857-2100. **E-mail:** evelyn_mcginty@pvamu.edu.

■ APPLICATION

Required GMAT, application form, baccalaureate/first degree, 3 letters of recommendation, personal statement, resume/curriculum vitae, transcripts of college work.

Deadlines and Fees Applications for domestic and international students are processed on a rolling basis. *Application fee:* $25, $25 (international).

Application Contact Dr. Peter Sutanto, MBA Program Coordinator, College of Business, PO Box 638, Prairie View, TX 77446-0638. **Phone:** 409-857-4310. **Fax:** 409-857-2797. **E-mail:** peter_sutanto@pvamu.edu.

Rice University

Houston, Texas

JESSE H. JONES GRADUATE SCHOOL OF MANAGEMENT

Graduate Business Faculty
Full-time: 35
Part-time: 40

Student Body
Total: 297
Full-time: 297
Average Age: 28
Women: 27%

Admissions
Applications: 540
Admitted: 253
Enrolled: 159
Average GMAT: 640
Average GPA: 3.2

Costs (1999–2000)
Full-time tuition: $18,050 per academic year
Part-time tuition: N/R

After Graduation (Class of 1998–99)
Employed within 3 months of graduation: 98%
Average starting salary: $71,000

Accreditation
AACSB—The International Association for Management Education

DEGREES MBA • MD/MBA • ME/MBA

MBA—Executive MBA Part-time. 10 years of work experience and GMAT required. At least 60 total credits required. 21 months to complete program. *Concentrations:* management.

MBA—Master of Business Administration Full-time. GMAT required. At least 60 total credits required. 21 months to complete program. *Concentrations:* entrepreneurship, finance, international management, management, management information systems, marketing, strategic management.

MD/MBA—Doctor of Medicine/Master of Business Administration Full-time. Must be accepted into program at Baylor College of Medicine. At least 48 total credits required. 60 months to complete program. *Concentrations:* management.

ME/MBA—Master of Engineering/Master of Business Administration Full-time. Undergraduate engineering degree and GRE required. At least 76 total credits required. 24 months to complete program. *Concentrations:* management.

COSTS

Tuition *Full-time:* $17,500. **Required fees:** *Full-time* $550. **Graduate housing:** Room and board costs vary by number of occupants, type of accommodation, and type of board plan. *Typical cost:* $8000 (including board).

FINANCIAL AID (1999–2000)

183 students received aid, including loans, scholarships, and work study. Financial aid application deadline: 6/1. **Financial Aid Contact** Ms. Elizabeth Bandy, Assistant Director of Financial Aid, Office of Financial Aid, MS-12, PO Box 1892, Houston, TX 77251-1892. **Phone:** 713-348-4958. **Fax:** 713-348-5921. **E-mail:** fina@rice.edu.

RESOURCES AND SERVICES

Information about online services, personal computer policies, library resources, international exchange programs, internship programs, and placement services at this institution and others can be found at **www. petersons.com/mba**

Rice University (continued)

International Students

Services and Facilities Counseling/support services, ESL/language courses, international student housing, orientation, visa services. Financial aid is not available to international students.

Applying *Required:* TOEFL with recommended score of 250 (computer) or 600 (paper), proof of adequate funds, proof of health/immunizations. *Recommended:* TWE.

International Student Contact Dr. Adria Baker, Director, International Services, 6100 Main Street, A102, Abercrombie, MS 365, Houston, TX 77005-1892. **Phone:** 713-348-6095. **Fax:** 713-348-5199. **E-mail:** abaker@rice.edu.

■ APPLICATION

Required GMAT, application form, baccalaureate/first degree, essay, interview, 3 letters of recommendation, resume/curriculum vitae, transcripts of college work, 2 years of work experience. **Recommended** Personal statement.

Deadlines and Fees *Deadlines:* 4/6 for fall, 4/6 for fall (international). *Application fee:* $100, $100 (international).

Application Contact Mr. Peter Veruki, Executive Director of Career Planning and Admissions, Jesse H. Jones Graduate School of Management MS-531, PO Box 1892, Houston, TX 77251-1892. **Phone:** 713-348-4918. **Toll-free Phone:** 888-844-4773. **Fax:** 713-348-6147. **E-mail:** enterjgs@rice.edu.

See full description on page 784.

St. Edward's University

Austin, Texas

THE COLLEGE OF PROFESSIONAL AND GRADUATE STUDIES

Graduate Business Faculty

Full-time: 9	Part-time: 19

Student Body

Total: 530	Average Age: 32
Full-time: 69	Women: 42%
Part-time: 461	

Admissions

Applications: 210	Average GMAT: 503
Admitted: 174	Average GPA: 3
Enrolled: 138	

Costs (1999–2000)
Full-time tuition: $7236 per academic year
Part-time tuition: $402 per credit hour

DEGREE MBA

MBA—Master of Business Administration Full-time and part-time. 36 to 57 total credits required. 12 to 72 months to complete program. *Concentrations:* accounting, contract management, electronic commerce (e-commerce), finance, human resources, international business, management, management information systems, marketing, nonprofit management, operations management, public management, public policy and administration, sports/entertainment management, telecommunications management.

COSTS

Tuition *Full-time:* $7236. *Part-time:* $402 per credit hour. **Tuition, international:** *Full-time* $7236. **Graduate housing:** Room and board costs vary by number of occupants and type of accommodation. *Typical cost:* $5000 (including board).

FINANCIAL AID (1999–2000)

134 students received aid, including loans, scholarships, and work study. Aid is available to part-time students. Financial aid application deadline: 6/30. **Financial Aid Contact** Ms. Doris Constantine, Director of Student Financial Services, 3001 South Congress Avenue, Austin, TX 78704-6489. **Phone:** 512-448-8525. **Fax:** 512-416-5837. **E-mail:** doris@admin.stedwards.edu.

RESOURCES AND SERVICES

Information about online services, personal computer policies, library resources, international exchange programs, internship programs, and placement services at this institution and others can be found at **www.petersons.com/mba**

International Students

11% of students enrolled are international students.

Services and Facilities Counseling/support services, orientation, visa services. Financial aid is not available to international students.

Applying *Required:* TOEFL with recommended score of 550 (paper), proof of adequate funds.

International Student Contact Ms. Karen Easterday, Coordinator, International Education Services, 3001 South Congress Avenue, Austin, TX 78704-6489. **Phone:** 512-448-8531. **Fax:** 512-448-8492. **E-mail:** karene@admin.stedwards.edu.

■ APPLICATION

Required GMAT or GRE, application form, baccalaureate/first degree, essay, personal statement, resume/curriculum vitae, transcripts of college work. **Recommended** Letter(s) of recommendation, 3 years of work experience.

Deadlines and Fees *Deadlines:* 8/1 for fall, 12/1 for spring, 4/15 for summer, 8/1 for fall (international), 12/1 for spring (international), 4/15 for summer (international). *Application fee:* $35, $50 (international).

Application Contact Mr. Thomas Evans, Director, Center for Academic Progress, 3001 South Congress Avenue, Austin, TX 78704-6489. **Phone:** 512-448-8600. **Fax:** 512-448-8492. **E-mail:** tome@admin.stedwards.edu.

St. Mary's University of San Antonio

San Antonio, Texas

SCHOOL OF BUSINESS ADMINISTRATION

Graduate Business Faculty

Full-time: 29	Part-time: 13

Student Body

Total: 198	Average Age: 29
Full-time: 20	Women: 35%
Part-time: 178	

Admissions

Applications: 35	Average GMAT: 487
Admitted: 30	Average GPA: 3.12
Enrolled: 29	

Costs (1999–2000)
Full-time tuition: N/R
Part-time tuition: $404 per credit hour

After Graduation (Class of 1998–99)
Employed within 3 months of graduation: 99%

Accreditation
AACSB—The International Association for Management Education

DEGREES M Acc • MBA

M Acc—Master of Accounting Full-time and part-time. At least 30 total credits required. 18 to 60 months to complete program. *Concentrations:* accounting, taxation.

MBA—Master of Business Administration Full-time and part-time. 33 to 39 total credits required. 18 to 60 months to complete program. *Concentrations:* finance, international business, management.

COSTS

Tuition *Part-time:* $404 per credit hour. Tuition varies by number of courses or credits taken. **Required fees:** *Part-time* $90 per semester. **Graduate housing:** Room and board costs vary by number of occupants and type of board plan. *Typical cost:* $2165 (including board), $1465 (room only).

FINANCIAL AID (1999–2000)

5 students received aid, including grants, loans, research assistantships, scholarships, and work study. Financial aid application deadline: 3/1. **Financial Aid Contact** Mr. David Krause, Director, Financial Assistance, Office of Financial Assistance, 1 Camino Santa Maria, San Antonio, TX 78228. **Phone:** 210-436-3141. **Fax:** 210-431-2221. **E-mail:** dkrause@alvin.stmarytx.edu.

RESOURCES AND SERVICES

Information about online services, personal computer policies, library resources, international exchange programs, internship programs, and placement services at this institution and others can be found at **www.petersons.com/mba**

International Students

15% of students enrolled are international students.

Services and Facilities Counseling/support services, ESL/language courses, language tutoring. Financial aid is not available to international students.

Applying *Required:* TOEFL with recommended score of 133 (computer) or 550 (paper), proof of adequate funds, proof of health/immunizations.

International Student Contact Ms. Karen Johnson, Coordinator, International Student Services, 1 Camino Santa Maria, San Antonio, TX 78228-8507. **Phone:** 210-431-2093. **Fax:** 210-436-3300. **E-mail:** kditzler@alvin.stmarytx.edu.

■ **APPLICATION**

Required GMAT, application form, baccalaureate/first degree, 2 letters of recommendation, resume/curriculum vitae, transcripts of college work. **Recommended** Essay, interview, personal statement.

Deadlines and Fees Applications for domestic and international students are processed on a rolling basis. *Application fee:* $15, $15 (international).

Application Contact Dr. Thomas Hamilton, MBA Program Director, School of Business and Administration, 1 Camino Santa Maria, San Antonio, TX 78228-8607. **Phone:** 210-431-2027. **Fax:** 210-436-3620. **E-mail:** mba@stmarytx.edu.

Sam Houston State University

Huntsville, Texas

COLLEGE OF BUSINESS ADMINISTRATION

Graduate Business Faculty
Full-time: 38

Student Body
Total: 201
Full-time: 78
Part-time: 123

Average Age: 25
Women: 56%

Admissions
Applications: 81
Admitted: 72
Enrolled: 47

Average GMAT: 493
Average GPA: 3.09

Costs (1999–2000)
Full-time tuition: $795 per academic year (resident), $2739 per academic year (nonresident)
Part-time tuition: $94 per credit (resident), $308 per credit (nonresident)

After Graduation (Class of 1998–99)
Employed within 3 months of graduation: 90%
Average starting salary: $48,500

Accreditation
AACSB—The International Association for Management Education

DEGREE MBA

MBA—Master of Business Administration Full-time and part-time. *Distance learning option.* At least 36 total credits required. 12 to 72 months to complete program. *Concentrations:* accounting, economics, finance, management, management information systems, marketing.

COSTS

Tuition, state resident: *Full-time* $342. *Part-time* $40 per credit. **Tuition, nonresident:** *Full-time* $2286. *Part-time* $254 per credit. **Tuition, international:** *Full-time* $2286. Tuition varies by number of courses or credits taken. **Required fees:** *Full-time* $453. *Part-time* $54 per credit. Fees vary by number of courses or credits taken and campus location. **Graduate housing:** Room and board costs vary by number of occupants, type of accommodation, and type of board plan. *Typical cost:* $3500 (including board), $1800 (room only).

FINANCIAL AID (1999–2000)

Loans, research assistantships, and work study. **Financial Aid Contact** Mr. Douglas Wright, Financial Aid Counselor, PO Box 2328, Huntsville, TX 77341-2328. **Phone:** 936-294-1724. **Fax:** 936-294-3668. **E-mail:** sfa_clww@shsu.edu.

RESOURCES AND SERVICES

Information about online services, personal computer policies, library resources, international exchange programs, internship programs, and placement services at this institution and others can be found at www.petersons.com/mba

International Students

7% of students enrolled are international students.

Services and Facilities Counseling/support services, ESL/language courses, housing location assistance, orientation, visa services. Financial aid is available to international students.

Applying *Required:* TOEFL with recommended score of 213 (computer) or 550 (paper), proof of adequate funds, proof of health/immunizations.

International Student Contact Dr. Don Bumpass, Coordinator of Graduate Studies, PO Box 2478, Huntsville, TX 77341-2056. **Phone:** 936-294-1971. **Fax:** 936-294-1271. **E-mail:** grs_dlb@shsu.edu.

■ **APPLICATION**

Required GMAT, application form, baccalaureate/first degree, transcripts of college work.

Deadlines and Fees *Deadlines:* 8/1 for fall, 12/1 for spring, 6/15 for summer, 7/1 for fall (international), 11/1 for spring (international), 4/1 for summer (international). *Application fee:* $20, $20 (international).

Application Contact Dr. Mitchell Muehsam, MBA Director, PO Box 2056, Huntsville, TX 77341-2056. **Phone:** 936-294-1246. **Fax:** 936-294-3612. **E-mail:** eco_mjm@shsu.edu.

Southern Methodist University

Dallas, Texas

EDWIN L. COX SCHOOL OF BUSINESS

Graduate Business Faculty
Full-time: 79

Part-time: 26

Student Body
Total: 897
Full-time: 232
Part-time: 665

Average Age: 28
Women: 26%

Admissions
Applications: 487
Admitted: 200
Enrolled: 110

Average GMAT: 640
Average GPA: 3.2

Costs (1999–2000)
Full-time tuition: $22,994 per academic year
Part-time tuition: $803 per credit hour

After Graduation (Class of 1998–99)
Employed within 3 months of graduation: 91%
Average starting salary: $67,385

Accreditation
AACSB—The International Association for Management Education

DEGREES JD/MBA • MBA • MBA/MA • MSA

JD/MBA—Juris Doctor/Master of Business Administration Full-time. At least 150 total credits required. 54 months to complete program. *Concentrations:* accounting, business policy/strategy, electronic commerce (e-commerce), finance, legal administration, management information systems, organizational behavior/development, real estate.

MBA—Executive MBA Program Full-time. Minimum 10 years of work experience required. At least 60 total credits required. Minimum of 21 months to complete program. *Concentrations:* accounting, business law, business policy/strategy, electronic commerce (e-commerce), finance, insurance, international business, marketing, organizational behavior/development, real estate.

MBA—Full-Time MBA Program Full-time. At least 56 total credits required. 24 months to complete program. *Concentrations:* accounting, business policy/strategy, finance, management information systems, organizational behavior/development, real estate.

MBA—Professional MBA Program Part-time. Applicants must be employed. At least 56 total credits required. 36 to 72 months to complete program. *Concentrations:* accounting, business law, business policy/strategy, electronic commerce (e-commerce), finance, information management, insurance, marketing, organizational behavior/development, real estate.

MBA/MA—Master of Business Administration/Master of Arts in Administration Full-time. At least 75 total credits required. 24 months to complete program. *Concentrations:* accounting, arts administration/management, business policy/strategy, electronic commerce (e-commerce), finance, management information systems, organizational behavior/development, real estate.

MSA—Master of Science in Accounting Program Full-time. At least 30 total credits required. 9 months to complete program. *Concentrations:* accounting.

COSTS

Tuition *Full-time:* $21,330. *Part-time:* $711 per credit hour. **Required fees:** *Full-time* $1664. *Part-time* $92 per credit hour. **Graduate housing:** Room and board costs vary by number of occupants, type of accommodation, and type of board plan. *Typical cost:* $7249 (including board), $5435 (room only).

FINANCIAL AID (1999–2000)

484 students received aid, including grants, loans, research assistantships, and scholarships. Aid is available to part-time students.

Southern Methodist University (continued)

Financial aid application deadline: 3/31. **Financial Aid Contact** Mr. Mike Novak, Executive Director, Division of Enrollment Services, PO Box 750181, Dallas, TX 75275-0181. **Phone:** 214-768-3417. **Fax:** 214-768-0202. **E-mail:** enrol_serv@mail.smu.edu.

RESOURCES AND SERVICES
Information about online services, personal computer policies, library resources, international exchange programs, internship programs, and placement services at this institution and others can be found at **www. petersons.com/mba**

International Students
13% of students enrolled are international students.

Services and Facilities Counseling/support services, ESL/language courses, housing location assistance, international student organization, orientation, visa services. Financial aid is available to international students.
Applying *Required:* TOEFL with recommended score of 250 (computer) or 600 (paper), proof of adequate funds, proof of health/immunizations.
International Student Contact Ms. Linda Kao, Director of International Programs, PO Box 750333, Dallas, TX 75275-0333. **Phone:** 214-768-2630. **Fax:** 214-768-3956. **E-mail:** mbainfo@mail.cox.smu.edu.

■ APPLICATION
Required GMAT, application form, baccalaureate/first degree, essay, 2 letters of recommendation, personal statement, resume/curriculum vitae, transcripts of college work. **Recommended** Interview, 2 years of work experience.
Deadlines and Fees *Deadlines:* 11/30 for fall, 11/30 for fall (international). *Application fee:* $50, $50 (international).
Application Contact Director of MBA Admissions, PO Box 750333, Dallas, TX 75275-0333. **Phone:** 214-768-2630. **Toll-free Phone:** 800-472-3622. **Fax:** 214-768-3956. **E-mail:** mbainfo@mail.cox.smu.edu.

See full description on page 830.

Southwestern Adventist University

Keene, Texas

PROGRAM IN BUSINESS ADMINISTRATION

Graduate Business Faculty
Full-time: 6   Part-time: 6

Student Body
Total: 31   Part-time: 21
Full-time: 10

Admissions
Applications: 8   Average GMAT: 450
Admitted: 6   Average GPA: 3.25
Enrolled: 4

Costs (1999–2000)
Full-time tuition: N/R
Part-time tuition: $285 per credit

After Graduation (Class of 1998–99)
Employed within 3 months of graduation: 100%
Average starting salary: $40,000

DEGREE MBA

MBA—Master of Business Administration Full-time and part-time. At least 36 total credits required. Maximum of 60 months to complete program.

COSTS
Tuition *Part-time:* $285 per credit. **Graduate housing:** Room and board costs vary by number of occupants, type of accommodation, and type of board plan. *Typical cost:* $4550 (including board).

FINANCIAL AID (1999–2000)
2 students received aid, including grants, loans, scholarships, teaching assistantships, and work study. Aid is available to part-time students. Financial aid application deadline: 7/31. **Financial Aid Contact** Miss Patricia Norwood, Assistant Financial Vice President, PO Box 567, Keene, TX 76059. **Phone:** 817-645-3921 Ext. 223. **Fax:** 817-556-4744. **E-mail:** norwoodp@cosmic.swau.edu.

RESOURCES AND SERVICES
Information about online services, personal computer policies, library resources, international exchange programs, internship programs, and placement services at this institution and others can be found at **www. petersons.com/mba**

International Students
Services and Facilities Counseling/support services, ESL/language courses, visa services. Financial aid is available to international students.
Applying *Required:* TOEFL with recommended score of 520 (paper), proof of adequate funds.
International Student Contact Dr. Tom Bunch, Vice President Student Services, PO Box 567, Keene, TX 76059. **Phone:** 817-645-3921 Ext. 221. **Fax:** 817-556-4744. **E-mail:** buncht@cosmic.swau.edu.

■ APPLICATION
Required GMAT or GRE, application form, baccalaureate/first degree, 2 letters of recommendation, transcripts of college work. **Recommended** Interview, work experience.
Deadlines and Fees Applications for domestic and international students are processed on a rolling basis.
Application Contact Ms. Laura Yanez, Graduate Studies Counselor, PO Box 567, Keene, TX 76059. **Phone:** 817-645-3921 Ext. 724. **Toll-free Phone:** 800-433-2240 Ext. 724. **Fax:** 817-556-4744. **E-mail:** yanezl@cosmic.swau.edu.

Southwest Texas State University

San Marcos, Texas

SCHOOL OF BUSINESS

Graduate Business Faculty
Full-time: 47   Part-time: 1

Student Body
Total: 319   Average Age: 32
Full-time: 94   Women: 43%
Part-time: 225

Admissions
Applications: 147   Average GMAT: 560
Admitted: 110   Average GPA: 3
Enrolled: 85

Costs (1999–2000)
Full-time tuition: $2564 per academic year (resident), $7652 per academic year (nonresident)
Part-time tuition: N/R

After Graduation (Class of 1998–99)
Employed within 3 months of graduation: 96%

Accreditation
AACSB—The International Association for Management Education

DEGREE MBA

MBA—Master of Business Administration Full-time and part-time. At least 60 total credits required. 12 to 72 months to complete program. *Concentrations:* management.

COSTS
Tuition, state resident: *Full-time* $912. **Tuition, nonresident:** *Full-time* $6000. **Tuition, international:** *Full-time* $6000. Tuition varies by number of courses or credits taken. **Required fees:** *Full-time* $1652. Fees vary by number of courses or credits taken and campus location. **Graduate housing:** Room and board costs vary by number of occupants, type of accommodation, and type of board plan. *Typical cost:* $2847 (including board).

FINANCIAL AID (1999–2000)
Loans, research assistantships, scholarships, teaching assistantships, and work study. Aid is available to part-time students. Financial aid application deadline: 4/1. **Financial Aid Contact** Ms. Mariko Gomez, Director, Financial Assistance, 601 University Drive, San Marcos, TX 78666. **Phone:** 512-245-2315. **Fax:** 512-245-7920. **E-mail:** mg01@swt. edu.

RESOURCES AND SERVICES
Information about online services, personal computer policies, library resources, international exchange programs, internship programs, and placement services at this institution and others can be found at **www. petersons.com/mba**

International Students
13% of students enrolled are international students.

Services and Facilities Counseling/support services, ESL/language courses, housing location assistance, orientation, visa services. Financial aid is available to international students.

Applying *Required:* TOEFL with recommended score of 550 (paper), proof of adequate funds, proof of health/immunizations.

International Student Contact Dr. Diana Sellers, Director, Office for International Students, 601 University Drive, San Marcos, TX 78666. **Phone:** 512-245-7966. **Fax:** 512-245-3752. **E-mail:** dsll@swt.edu.

■ APPLICATION

Required GMAT, application form, baccalaureate/first degree, transcripts of college work.

Deadlines and Fees *Deadlines:* 6/15 for fall, 10/15 for spring, 4/15 for summer, 6/15 for fall (international), 10/15 for spring (international), 4/15 for summer (international). *Application fee:* $25, $75 (international).

Application Contact Dr. Robert Olney, Director of Graduate Business Programs, Graduate School of Business, 601 University Drive, San Marcos, TX 78666. **Phone:** 512-245-3591. **Fax:** 512-245-8375. **E-mail:** ro02@swt.edu.

Stephen F. Austin State University
Nacogdoches, Texas

COLLEGE OF BUSINESS

Graduate Business Faculty
Full-time: 52 — Part-time: 7

Student Body
Total: 58 — Average Age: 27
Full-time: 8 — Women: 40%
Part-time: 50

Admissions
Applications: 38 — Average GMAT: 495
Admitted: 33 — Average GPA: 3
Enrolled: 33

Costs (1999–2000)
Full-time tuition: N/R
Part-time tuition: $120 per course (resident), $744 per course (nonresident)

Accreditation
AACSB—The International Association for Management Education

DEGREES MBA • MPA

MBA—Master of Business Administration Full-time and part-time. 36 to 57 total credits required. 12 to 72 months to complete program. *Concentrations:* management.

MPA—Master of Professional Accountancy Full-time and part-time. At least 156 total credits required. 60 to 72 months to complete program. *Concentrations:* accounting.

COSTS

Tuition, state resident: *Part-time* $120 per course. **Tuition, nonresident:** *Part-time* $744 per course. **Required fees:** Tuition and fees vary by number of courses or credits taken. **Graduate housing:** Room and board costs vary by type of accommodation and type of board plan. *Typical cost:* $4600 (including board).

FINANCIAL AID (1999–2000)
Loans, research assistantships, scholarships, teaching assistantships, and work study. Aid is available to part-time students. Financial aid application deadline: 4/1. **Financial Aid Contact** Mr. Michael O'Rear, Director of Financial Aid, PO Box 13052, Nacogdoches, TX 75962. **Phone:** 936-468-2403. **Fax:** 936-468-1048. **E-mail:** morear@sfasu.edu.

RESOURCES AND SERVICES
Information about online services, personal computer policies, library resources, international exchange programs, internship programs, and placement services at this institution and others can be found at **www.petersons.com/mba**

International Students
2% of students enrolled are international students.

Services and Facilities Counseling/support services. Financial aid is not available to international students.

Applying *Required:* TOEFL with recommended score of 550 (paper), TWE with recommended score of 3.5, proof of adequate funds, proof of health/immunizations.

International Student Contact Ms. Stacy Wilson, International Student Advisor, PO Box 13051, Nacogdoches, TX 75962. **Phone:** 936-468-2504. **Fax:** 936-468-3849. **E-mail:** swilson@sfasu.edu.

■ APPLICATION

Required GMAT, application form, baccalaureate/first degree, transcripts of college work. **Recommended** 2 years of work experience.

Deadlines and Fees *Deadlines:* 7/20 for fall, 12/10 for spring, 5/1 for summer, 6/1 for fall (international), 11/1 for spring (international), 4/1 for summer (international).

Application Contact Dr. Violet C. Rogers, MBA Director, PO Box 13004, Nacogdoches, TX 75962. **Phone:** 936-468-3101. **Fax:** 936-468-1560. **E-mail:** mba@sfasu.edu.

Tarleton State University
Stephenville, Texas

COLLEGE OF BUSINESS ADMINISTRATION

Graduate Business Faculty
Full-time: 11

Student Body
Total: 143 — Part-time: 106
Full-time: 37 — Women: 40%

Admissions
Applications: 90 — Enrolled: 70
Admitted: 86 — Average GMAT: 451

Costs (1999–2000)
Full-time tuition: N/R
Part-time tuition: $70 per credit hour (resident), $272 per credit hour (nonresident)

Accreditation
ACBSP—The American Council of Business Schools and Programs

DEGREE MBA

MBA—Master of Business Administration Full-time and part-time. At least 36 total credits required. 18 to 72 months to complete program. *Concentrations:* accounting, agribusiness, finance, management, management information systems, marketing.

COSTS

Tuition, state resident: *Part-time* $70 per credit hour. **Tuition, nonresident:** *Part-time* $272 per credit hour. **Required fees:** Tuition and fees vary by number of courses or credits taken. **Graduate housing:** Room and board costs vary by campus location, type of accommodation, and type of board plan. *Typical cost:* $3422 (including board).

FINANCIAL AID (1999–2000)
Grants, loans, research assistantships, scholarships, teaching assistantships, and work study. Aid is available to part-time students. Financial aid application deadline: 6/1. **Financial Aid Contact** Ms. Betty Murray, Financial Aid Director, Box T-0310, Stephenville, TX 76402. **Phone:** 254-968-9070. **Fax:** 254-968-9600. **E-mail:** finaid@tarleton.edu.

RESOURCES AND SERVICES
Information about online services, personal computer policies, library resources, international exchange programs, internship programs, and placement services at this institution and others can be found at **www.petersons.com/mba**

International Students
2% of students enrolled are international students.

Services and Facilities ESL/language courses, international student housing.
International Student Contact Dr. Fred Koestler, Director, Box T-0770, Tarleton Station, Stephenville, TX 76402. **Phone:** 254-968-9632. **Fax:** 254-968-9618. **E-mail:** koestle@tarleton.edu.

■ APPLICATION

Required Application form, baccalaureate/first degree, transcripts of college work. School will accept GMAT or GRE.

Deadlines and Fees *Application fee:* $25, $25 (international).

Tarleton State University (continued)

Application Contact Dr. Linda Jones, Graduate Office/Dean, Box T-0350, Stephenville, TX 76402. **Phone:** 254-968-9104. **Toll-free Phone:** 800-OUR-GRAD. **Fax:** 254-968-9670. **E-mail:** gradoffice@tarleton.edu.

Texas A&M International University

Laredo, Texas

GRADUATE SCHOOL OF INTERNATIONAL TRADE AND BUSINESS ADMINISTRATION

Graduate Business Faculty
Full-time: 32	Part-time: 6

Student Body
Total: 282	Average Age: 28
Full-time: 106	Women: 37%
Part-time: 176	

Admissions
Applications: 194	Average GMAT: 480
Admitted: 161	Average GPA: 3.24
Enrolled: 78	

Costs (1999–2000)
Full-time tuition: $3344 per academic year (resident), $9825 per academic year (nonresident)
Part-time tuition: N/R

DEGREES MBA • MPA • MS

MBA—MBA in Spanish Part-time. Program offered in Spanish. At least 36 total credits required. 12 to 60 months to complete program. *Concentrations:* management.

MBA—Master of Business Administration in International Banking Full-time and part-time. At least 36 total credits required. 12 to 60 months to complete program. *Concentrations:* international banking.

MBA—Master of Business Administration in International Trade Full-time and part-time. At least 36 total credits required. 12 to 60 months to complete program. *Concentrations:* international trade.

MBA—Master of Business Administration Full-time and part-time. At least 36 total credits required. 12 to 60 months to complete program.

MPA—Master of Professional Accountancy Full-time and part-time. At least 36 total credits required. 12 to 60 months to complete program. *Concentrations:* accounting.

MS—Master of Science in Information Systems Full-time and part-time. At least 36 total credits required. 12 to 60 months to complete program.

MS—Master of Science in International Logistics Full-time and part-time. At least 36 total credits required. 12 to 60 months to complete program.

COSTS
Tuition, state resident: *Full-time* $2472. **Tuition, nonresident:** *Full-time* $8952. **Tuition, international:** *Full-time* $8952. Tuition varies by number of courses or credits taken and local reciprocity agreements. **Required fees:** *Full-time* $873. Tuition and fees vary by number of courses or credits taken. **Graduate housing:** Room and board costs vary by number of occupants and type of accommodation. *Typical cost:* $4750 (room only).

FINANCIAL AID (1999–2000)
184 students received aid, including fellowships, loans, research assistantships, scholarships, and work study. Aid is available to part-time students. **Financial Aid Contact** Ms. Kriztella Lopez, Director of Graduate Student Services, 5201 University Boulevard, Laredo, TX 78041-1900. **Phone:** 956-326-2770. **Fax:** 956-326-2769. **E-mail:** kriztella@tamiu.edu.

RESOURCES AND SERVICES
Information about online services, personal computer policies, library resources, international exchange programs, internship programs, and placement services at this institution and others can be found at **www.petersons.com/mba**

International Students
42% of students enrolled are international students.
Services and Facilities Counseling/support services, ESL/language courses, housing location assistance, international student organization, language tutoring, orientation, visa services. Financial aid is available to international students.

Applying *Required:* TOEFL with recommended score of 550 (paper), proof of adequate funds, proof of health/immunizations.
International Student Contact Mr. David VerMilyea, Director of Student Development, 5201 University Boulevard, Laredo, TX 78041-1900. **Phone:** 956-326-2280. **Fax:** 956-326-2279. **E-mail:** deverm@tamiu.edu.

■ APPLICATION
Required GMAT or GRE, application form, baccalaureate/first degree, transcripts of college work.
Deadlines and Fees *Deadlines:* 7/1 for fall, 11/1 for spring, 4/1 for summer, 6/1 for fall (international), 10/1 for spring (international), 3/1 for summer (international).
Application Contact Ms. Kriztella Lopez, Director of Graduate Student Services, 5201 University Boulevard, Laredo, TX 78041-1900. **Phone:** 956-326-2770. **Fax:** 956-326-2769. **E-mail:** kriztella@tamiu.edu.

See full description on page 846.

Texas A&M University

College Station, Texas

LOWRY MAYS GRADUATE SCHOOL OF BUSINESS

Graduate Business Faculty
Full-time: 149	Part-time: 14

Student Body
Total: 600	Average Age: 28
Full-time: 600	Women: 40%

Admissions
Applications: 530	Average GMAT: 619
Admitted: 156	Average GPA: 3.3
Enrolled: 88	

Costs (1999–2000)
Full-time tuition: $2595 per academic year (resident), $8319 per academic year (nonresident)
Part-time tuition: N/R

After Graduation (Class of 1998–99)
Employed within 3 months of graduation: 98%
Average starting salary: $64,500

Accreditation
AACSB—The International Association for Management Education

DEGREES MBA • MS

MBA—Executive Master of Business Administration Part-time. At least 53 total credits required. 24 months to complete program.

MBA—Master of Business Administration Full-time. At least 53 total credits required. 16 to 21 months to complete program. *Concentrations:* accounting, entrepreneurship, finance, financial information systems, financial management/planning, human resources, information management, international and area business studies, international business, international management, leadership, management consulting, management information systems, manufacturing management, marketing, new venture management, operations management, organizational behavior/development, production management, real estate, strategic management, technology management, telecommunications management.

MS—Master of Science in Accounting Full-time. At least 36 total credits required. 12 to 24 months to complete program. *Concentrations:* accounting, taxation.

MS—Master of Science in Finance Full-time. At least 36 total credits required. 12 to 24 months to complete program. *Concentrations:* finance, real estate.

MS—Master of Science in Land Economics and Real Estate Full-time. At least 36 total credits required. 12 to 34 months to complete program. *Concentrations:* real estate.

MS—Master of Science in Life Cycle Engineering and Operations Management Full-time. *Distance learning option.* At least 36 total credits required. 12 to 24 months to complete program. *Concentrations:* manufacturing management, operations management, production management.

MS—Master of Science in Management Full-time. At least 36 total credits required. 12 to 24 months to complete program. *Concentrations:* human resources, organizational behavior/development.

MS—Master of Science in Management Information Systems Full-time. At least 36 total credits required. 12 to 24 months to complete program. *Concentrations:* management information systems, management systems analysis, operations management, system management, technology management.

MS—Master of Science in Marketing Full-time. At least 36 total credits required. 12 to 24 months to complete program. *Concentrations:* marketing, marketing research.

COSTS
Tuition, state resident: *Full-time* $2014. Tuition, nonresident: *Full-time* $7738. Required fees: *Full-time* $581. Tuition and fees vary by number of courses or credits taken. Graduate housing: Room and board costs vary by campus location, number of occupants, type of accommodation, and type of board plan. *Typical cost:* $8242 (including board), $5562 (room only).

FINANCIAL AID (1999–2000)
69 students received aid, including fellowships, loans, research assistantships, scholarships, teaching assistantships, and work study. Financial aid application deadline: 2/1. Financial Aid Contact Ms. Anna Hines, Financial Aid Counselor, Student Financial Aid Office, College Station, TX 77843. Phone: 409-845-3981. Fax: 409-847-9061.

RESOURCES AND SERVICES
Information about online services, personal computer policies, library resources, international exchange programs, internship programs, and placement services at this institution and others can be found at www.petersons.com/mba

International Students
28% of students enrolled are international students.

Services and Facilities Counseling/support services, ESL/language courses, housing location assistance, international student housing, international student organization, orientation, visa services. Financial aid is available to international students.
Applying *Required:* TOEFL with recommended score of 250 (computer) or 600 (paper), proof of adequate funds, proof of health/immunizations.
International Student Contact Ms. Susan Whiting, Academic Advisor, 212 Wehner, College Station, TX 77843-4117. Phone: 409-845-4714. Fax: 409-862-2393. E-mail: swhiting@tamu.edu.

■ APPLICATION
Required Application form, baccalaureate/first degree, essay, interview, 3 letters of recommendation, resume/curriculum vitae, transcripts of college work, 2 years of work experience. School will accept GMAT.
Deadlines and Fees *Deadlines:* 5/1 for fall, 2/1 for fall (international). *Application fee:* $50, $75 (international).
Application Contact Ms. Wendy Blake, Assistant Director, Mays MBA Program, 212 Wehner, College Station, TX 77843-4117. Phone: 409-845-4714. Fax: 409-862-2393. E-mail: wblake@tamu.edu.

Texas A&M University–Commerce
Commerce, Texas
COLLEGE OF BUSINESS AND TECHNOLOGY

Graduate Business Faculty
Full-time: 22 | Part-time: 1

Student Body
Total: 253
Full-time: 88 — Average Age: 31
Part-time: 165 — Women: 43%

Admissions
Applications: 175
Admitted: 150 — Average GMAT: 505
Enrolled: 125 — Average GPA: 3.2

Costs (1999–2000)
Full-time tuition: $2381 per academic year (resident), $8801 per academic year (nonresident)
Part-time tuition: N/R

After Graduation (Class of 1998–99)
Employed within 3 months of graduation: 82%
Average starting salary: $48,000

Accreditation
AACSB—The International Association for Management Education

DEGREE MBA

MBA—Master of Business Administration Full-time and part-time. *Distance learning option.* 36 to 48 total credits required. 12 to 72 months to complete program. *Concentrations:* accounting, economics, finance, human resources, international business, management, management information systems, marketing, technology management.

COSTS
Tuition, state resident: *Full-time* $2381. Tuition, nonresident: *Full-time* $8801. Tuition varies by number of courses or credits taken and local reciprocity agreements. Required fees: Tuition and fees vary by number of courses or credits taken. Graduate housing: Room and board costs vary by number of occupants, type of accommodation, and type of board plan. *Typical cost:* $2075 (including board), $1200 (room only).

FINANCIAL AID (1999–2000)
18 students received aid, including loans, research assistantships, scholarships, and work study. Financial Aid Contact Dr. Robert Seay, Director, Graduate Programs in Business, PO Box 3011, Commerce, TX 75429-3011. Phone: 903-886-5100. Fax: 903-886-5114. E-mail: robert_seay@tamu-commerce.edu.

RESOURCES AND SERVICES
Information about online services, personal computer policies, library resources, international exchange programs, internship programs, and placement services at this institution and others can be found at www.petersons.com/mba

International Students
32% of students enrolled are international students.

Services and Facilities Counseling/support services, international student housing, visa services. Financial aid is not available to international students.
Applying *Required:* TOEFL with recommended score of 500 (paper), proof of adequate funds.
International Student Contact Ms. Patsy Pope, International Student Advisor, Commerce, TX 75429-3011. Phone: 903-886-5097. Fax: 903-886-5199. E-mail: patsy_pope@tamu-commerce.edu.

■ APPLICATION
Required GMAT, application form, baccalaureate/first degree, transcripts of college work. Recommended Interview, letter(s) of recommendation, personal statement, resume/curriculum vitae, work experience.
Deadlines and Fees *Deadlines:* 8/15 for fall, 12/15 for spring, 5/15 for summer, 6/1 for fall (international), 11/1 for spring (international), 3/15 for summer (international). *Application fee:* $25 (international).
Application Contact Dr. Robert Seay, Director of Graduate Programs in Business, PO Box 3011, Commerce, TX 75429-3011. Phone: 903-886-5190. Fax: 903-886-5114. E-mail: mba@tamu-commerce.edu.

See full description on page 848.

Texas A&M University–Corpus Christi
Corpus Christi, Texas
COLLEGE OF BUSINESS ADMINISTRATION

Graduate Business Faculty
Full-time: 31 | Part-time: 5

Student Body
Total: 148
Full-time: 49 — Average Age: 32
Part-time: 99 — Women: 48%

Admissions
Applications: 61
Admitted: 53 — Average GMAT: 526
Enrolled: 49 — Average GPA: 3.2

Costs (1999–2000)
Full-time tuition: N/R
Part-time tuition: $340 per course (resident), $985 per course (nonresident)

Accreditation
AACSB—The International Association for Management Education

DEGREES M Acc • MBA

M Acc—Master of Accountancy Full-time and part-time. 36 to 60 total credits required. 12 to 72 months to complete program.

Texas A&M University–Corpus Christi (continued)

MBA—Master of Business Administration Full-time and part-time. 30 to 48 total credits required. 12 to 72 months to complete program. *Concentrations:* health care, international business.

COSTS

Tuition, state resident: *Part-time* $120 per course. **Tuition, nonresident:** *Part-time* $765 per course. **Required fees:** *Part-time* $220 per course. Tuition and fees vary by number of courses or credits taken. **Graduate housing:** Room and board costs vary by number of occupants and type of accommodation. *Typical cost:* $5106 (including board).

FINANCIAL AID (1999–2000)

Grants, loans, scholarships, and work study. Aid is available to part-time students. Financial aid application deadline: 4/1. **Financial Aid Contact** Ms. Dolly Zeriali, Director, Financial Assistance, 6300 Ocean Drive, Corpus Christi, TX 78412. **Phone:** 361-994-2417. **Fax:** 361-994-6095. **E-mail:** dzeriali@falcon.tamucc.edu.

RESOURCES AND SERVICES

Information about online services, personal computer policies, library resources, international exchange programs, internship programs, and placement services at this institution and others can be found at **www.petersons.com/mba**

International Students

3% of students enrolled are international students.

Services and Facilities Counseling/support services, ESL/language courses, international student housing, international student organization. Financial aid is available to international students.
Applying *Required:* TOEFL with recommended score of 213 (computer) or 550 (paper), proof of adequate funds.
International Student Contact Ms. Beatrice Ramirez, Assistant Director of Admissions, 6300 Ocean Drive, Corpus Christi, TX 78412. **Phone:** 361-825-5924. **Fax:** 361-825-5887. **E-mail:** ramirez@falcon.tamucc.edu.

■ APPLICATION

Required GMAT, application form, baccalaureate/first degree, interview, personal statement, transcripts of college work.
Deadlines and Fees *Deadlines:* 7/15 for fall, 11/15 for spring, 5/15 for summer, 5/1 for fall (international), 9/1 for spring (international), 2/1 for summer (international). *Application fee:* $10, $30 (international).
Application Contact Ms. Betsy O'Lavin, Director of Master's Programs, College of Business, 6300 Ocean Drive, Corpus Christi, TX 78412-5503. **Phone:** 361-994-2655. **Toll-free Phone:** 800-482-6822. **Fax:** 361-994-2725. **E-mail:** eolavin@falcon.tamucc.edu.

Texas A&M University–Kingsville

Kingsville, Texas

COLLEGE OF BUSINESS ADMINISTRATION

Accreditation
ACBSP—The American Council of Business Schools and Programs

DEGREES MBA • MPA • MS

MBA—Master of Business Administration Full-time and part-time. At least 36 total credits required. 12 to 60 months to complete program. *Concentrations:* accounting, finance, management, marketing.
MPA—Master of Professional Accountancy Full-time and part-time. At least 36 total credits required. 12 to 60 months to complete program. *Concentrations:* accounting.
MS—Master of Science in Business Administration Full-time and part-time. At least 36 total credits required. 12 to 60 months to complete program.

RESOURCES AND SERVICES

Information about online services, personal computer policies, library resources, international exchange programs, internship programs, and placement services at this institution and others can be found at **www.petersons.com/mba**

International Students

Services and Facilities Counseling/support services, ESL/language courses. Financial aid is available to international students.

International Student Contact Dr. Mark Walsh, Director-Office of International Programs, Campus Box 163, Kingsville, TX 78363. **Phone:** 361-593-3994. **Fax:** 361-593-3984. **E-mail:** m-walsh2@tamuk.edu.

■ APPLICATION

Application Contact Dr. Robert Diersing, Coordinator of CBA Graduate Programs, Campus Box 182, Kingsville, TX 78363. **Phone:** 361-593-3802. **Fax:** 361-593-3708. **E-mail:** r-diersing@tamuk.edu.

Texas A&M University–Texarkana

Texarkana, Texas

DIVISION OF BEHAVIORAL SCIENCES AND BUSINESS ADMINISTRATION

Graduate Business Faculty
Full-time: 10 — Part-time: 6

Student Body
Total: 88 — Average Age: 32

Admissions
Applications: 29 — Enrolled: 22
Admitted: 22 — Average GMAT: 520

Costs (1999–2000)
Full-time tuition: $2196 per academic year (resident), $7368 per academic year (nonresident)
Part-time tuition: N/R

After Graduation (Class of 1998–99)
Employed within 3 months of graduation: 89%
Average starting salary: $31,500

DEGREES MBA • MS • MSA

MBA—Master of Business Administration Full-time and part-time. At least 36 total credits required. Maximum of 60 months to complete program.
MS—Master of Science in Business Administration Full-time and part-time. At least 36 total credits required. Maximum of 60 months to complete program.
MSA—Master of Science in Accounting Full-time and part-time. At least 36 total credits required. Maximum of 60 months to complete program.

COSTS

Tuition, state resident: *Full-time* $1884. **Tuition, nonresident:** *Full-time* $7056. Tuition varies by number of courses or credits taken and local reciprocity agreements. **Required fees:** *Full-time* $312. Tuition and fees vary by number of courses or credits taken.

FINANCIAL AID (1999–2000)

Grants and scholarships. Aid is available to part-time students. Financial aid application deadline: 3/15. **Financial Aid Contact** Ms. Marilyn Raney, Director of Financial Aid and Veteran Services, 2600 North Robison Road, Texarkana, TX 75501. **Phone:** 903-223-3060. **Fax:** 903-832-8890. **E-mail:** marilyn.raney@tamut.edu.

RESOURCES AND SERVICES

Information about online services, personal computer policies, library resources, international exchange programs, internship programs, and placement services at this institution and others can be found at **www.petersons.com/mba**

International Students

Services and Facilities Financial aid is not available to international students.
Applying *Required:* TOEFL with recommended score of 550 (paper), proof of adequate funds, proof of health/immunizations.
International Student Contact Mrs. Patricia Black, Director of Admissions and Registrar, PO Box 5518, Texarkana, TX 75503. **Phone:** 903-223-3068. **Fax:** 903-223-3140. **E-mail:** pat.black@tamut.edu.

■ APPLICATION

Required GMAT, application form, baccalaureate/first degree, 3 letters of recommendation, transcripts of college work.
Deadlines and Fees *Deadlines:* 7/15 for fall, 12/1 for spring, 4/15 for summer, 6/15 for fall (international), 11/1 for spring (international), 3/15 for summer (international). *Application fee:* $25 (international).
Application Contact Dr. John Johnson, Dean, Graduate School, PO Box 5518, Texarkana, TX 75505-5518. **Phone:** 903-223-3003. **Fax:** 903-832-8890. **E-mail:** john.johnson@tamut.edu.

Texas Christian University

Fort Worth, Texas

M. J. NEELEY SCHOOL OF BUSINESS

Graduate Business Faculty
Full-time: 31

Part-time: 1

Student Body
Total: 282
Full-time: 164
Part-time: 118

Average Age: 27
Women: 30%

Admissions
Applications: 508
Admitted: 237
Enrolled: 116

Average GMAT: 580
Average GPA: 3.1

Costs (1999–2000)
Full-time tuition: $12,025 per academic year
Part-time tuition: $390 per credit

After Graduation (Class of 1998–99)
Employed within 3 months of graduation: 99%
Average starting salary: $52,200

Accreditation
AACSB—The International Association for Management Education

DEGREES EMBA • M Acc • MBA

EMBA—Executive Master of Business Administration 8 years of experience, at least 5 of which are managerial. At least 51 total credits required. 21 months to complete program.

M Acc—Master of Accounting Full-time. At least 30 total credits required. 9 to 24 months to complete program. *Concentrations:* accounting.

MBA—Master of Business Administration Full-time and part-time. At least 48 total credits required. 24 to 36 months to complete program. *Concentrations:* accounting, electronic commerce (e-commerce), entrepreneurship, finance, international business, management, management consulting, marketing.

COSTS

Tuition *Full-time:* $9360. *Part-time:* $390 per credit. **Required fees:** *Full-time* $2665. *Part-time* $1800 per year. Tuition and fees vary by number of courses or credits taken and academic program.

FINANCIAL AID (1999–2000)

200 students received aid, including fellowships, grants, loans, research assistantships, scholarships, and work study. Aid is available to part-time students. Financial aid application deadline: 5/1. **Financial Aid Contact** Ms. Debbie Mar, Coordinator, Graduate Financial Aid, PO Box 297012, Fort Worth, TX 76129. **Phone:** 817-257-7872. **Fax:** 817-257-7462. **E-mail:** d.mar@tcu.edu.

RESOURCES AND SERVICES

Information about online services, personal computer policies, library resources, international exchange programs, internship programs, and placement services at this institution and others can be found at **www.petersons.com/mba**

International Students

22% of students enrolled are international students.

Services and Facilities Counseling/support services, ESL/language courses, housing location assistance, international student organization, orientation, visa services. Financial aid is available to international students.
Applying *Required:* TOEFL with recommended score of 213 (computer) or 550 (paper), proof of adequate funds, proof of health/immunizations.
International Student Contact Mr. John Singletorn, Director of International Student Services, PO Box 297003, Fort Worth, TX 76129. **Phone:** 817-921-7292. **Fax:** 817-921-7333. **E-mail:** jsingletorn@tcu.edu.

■ APPLICATION

Required GMAT, application form, baccalaureate/first degree, essay, 3 letters of recommendation, transcripts of college work. **Recommended** Interview, resume/curriculum vitae, work experience.
Deadlines and Fees Applications for domestic and international students are processed on a rolling basis. *Application fee:* $50, $50 (international).
Application Contact Ms. Peggy Conway, Director of MBA Admissions, PO Box 298540, Fort Worth, TX 76129. **Phone:** 817-257-7531. **Toll-free Phone:** 800-828-3764 Ext. 7531. **Fax:** 817-257-6431. **E-mail:** mbainfo@tcu.edu.

See full description on page 850.

Texas Southern University

Houston, Texas

JESSE H. JONES SCHOOL OF BUSINESS

Graduate Business Faculty
Full-time: 21

Part-time: 4

Student Body
Total: 79
Full-time: 40
Part-time: 39

Average Age: 28
Women: 47%

Admissions
Applications: 55
Admitted: 42
Enrolled: 34

Average GMAT: 416
Average GPA: 3.07

Costs (1999–2000)
Full-time tuition: N/R
Part-time tuition: $452 per course (resident), $1028 per course (nonresident)

After Graduation (Class of 1998–99)
Employed within 3 months of graduation: 100%
Average starting salary: $50,000

DEGREES MBA • MPA

MBA—Master of Business Administration Full-time and part-time. 33 to 63 total credits required. 18 to 72 months to complete program.
MPA—Master of Professional Accountancy Full-time and part-time. At least 36 total credits required. 24 to 72 months to complete program.

COSTS

Tuition, state resident: *Part-time* $452 per course. **Tuition, nonresident:** *Part-time* $1028 per course. Tuition varies by number of courses or credits taken. **Graduate housing:** Room and board costs vary by number of occupants and type of accommodation. *Typical cost:* $3400 (including board).

FINANCIAL AID (1999–2000)

4 students received aid, including research assistantships, teaching assistantships, and work study. Financial aid application deadline: 5/1.
Financial Aid Contact Mr. Albert Tezno, Director of Financial Aid, 3100 Cleburne Avenue, Houston, TX 77004. **Phone:** 713-313-4384. **Fax:** 713-313-1859. **E-mail:** aidaajtezno@tsu.edu.

RESOURCES AND SERVICES

Information about online services, personal computer policies, library resources, international exchange programs, internship programs, and placement services at this institution and others can be found at **www.petersons.com/mba**

International Students

34% of students enrolled are international students.

Services and Facilities Counseling/support services, ESL/language courses. Financial aid is available to international students.
Applying *Required:* TOEFL with recommended score of 550 (paper), proof of adequate funds, proof of health/immunizations.
International Student Contact Dr. Iris Perkins, Director/International Student Affairs, 3100 Cleburne Avenue, Houston, TX 77004-4584. **Phone:** 713-313-7896. **Fax:** 713-313-1878. **E-mail:** iafaiwperkin@tsu.edu.

■ APPLICATION

Required GMAT, application form, baccalaureate/first degree, transcripts of college work.
Deadlines and Fees *Deadlines:* 7/15 for fall, 11/15 for spring, 5/1 for summer, 7/15 for fall (international), 11/15 for spring (international), 5/1 for summer (international). *Application fee:* $35, $75 (international).
Application Contact Ms. Bobbie Richardson, MBA Coordinator, 3100 Cleburne Avenue, Houston, TX 77004-4584. **Phone:** 713-313-7309. **Fax:** 713-313-7705. **E-mail:** richardson_bj@tsu.edu.

Texas Tech University

Lubbock, Texas

COLLEGE OF BUSINESS ADMINISTRATION

Graduate Business Faculty
Full-time: 57

Texas Tech University *(continued)*

Student Body
Total: 399
Full-time: 319
Part-time: 80

Average Age: 26
Women: 36%

Admissions
Applications: 298
Admitted: 177
Enrolled: 104

Average GMAT: 550
Average GPA: 3.31

Costs (1999–2000)
Full-time tuition: $1968 per academic year (resident), $7032 per academic year (nonresident)
Part-time tuition: $72 per credit (resident), $285 per credit (nonresident)

After Graduation (Class of 1998–99)
Employed within 3 months of graduation: 63%
Average starting salary: $42,515

Accreditation
AACSB—The International Association for Management Education

DEGREES JD/MBA • MBA • MBA/MA • MBA/MS • MD/MBA • MS • MSA

JD/MBA—Juris Doctor/Master of Business Administration Full-time. At least 114 total credits required. 36 to 72 months to complete program. *Concentrations:* legal administration.

MBA—General MBA Full-time and part-time. 36 to 48 total credits required. 12 to 72 months to complete program. *Concentrations:* agribusiness, entrepreneurship, finance, international business, management, management information systems, marketing.

MBA—Master of Business Administration in Health Organization Management Full-time and part-time. 42 to 54 total credits required. 15 to 72 months to complete program. *Concentrations:* health care.

MBA/MA—MBA/MA in Foreign Language Full-time and part-time. At least 60 total credits required. Maximum of 72 months to complete program.

MBA/MA—Master of Business Administration/Master of Arts in Architecture Full-time. At least 36 total credits required. Maximum of 72 months to complete program.

MBA/MS—Master of Business Administration/Master of Science in Nursing Full-time. At least 96 total credits required. Maximum of 72 months to complete program. *Concentrations:* health care.

MD/MBA—Doctor of Medicine/Master of Business Administration *Concentrations:* health care.

MS—Master of Science in Business Administration Full-time and part-time. At least 36 total credits required. 12 to 72 months to complete program. *Concentrations:* banking, finance, management information systems, marketing, production management, telecommunications management.

MS—Master of Science in Health Organization Management Full-time and part-time. 50 to 62 total credits required. Maximum of 72 months to complete program. *Concentrations:* health care, management information systems.

MSA—Master of Science in Accounting Full-time and part-time. 36 to 80 total credits required. 12 to 72 months to complete program. *Concentrations:* taxation.

Texas Tech University's College of Business Administration offers joint programs in cooperation with other departments on campus. One of the most prominent programs is the M.B.A./Health Organization Management (HOM) offered in conjunction with the School of Medicine. The M.B.A./HOM program is one of eleven in the nation that has been dually accredited by AACSB-The International Association for Management Education and the Accrediting Commission on Education for Health Services Administration (ACEHSA).

The Master of Business Administration/Master of Science in Nursing is offered in association with the Texas Tech University Health Sciences School of Nursing and allows students to obtain both degrees with certification in HOM. In the summer of 1998, the College of Business launched the M.D./M.B.A., offering a new joint-degree program that allows students to receive M.B.A. and M.D. degrees concurrently.

The other highly regarded joint-degree programs are the J.D./M.B.A. and the J.D./M.S.A., which are conducted in cooperation with the School of Law. These programs allow law students to complete their M.B.A. or M.S.A. degrees concurrently with their law program. The degree plan enables the students to reduce the duration of the programs by 12 hours each.

In addition, there are two other joint-degree programs with the College of Business, one of which is the M.B.A./Master of Architecture program with the College of Architecture. The second program is an M.B.A./Master of Arts in foreign language (French, German, and Spanish). This joint degree is in conjunction with the College of Arts and Sciences.

As the newest addition to Texas Tech's global tradition, the TTU/Universidad Anahuac joint program is a direct response to increasing business transactions between the United States and Mexico. Located in the capital, Mexico City, Universidad Anahuac maintains well-established networks with domestic and worldwide firms and is therefore positioned as a valuable gateway to an exciting international career.

COSTS
Tuition, state resident: *Full-time* $1968. *Part-time* $72 per credit. **Tuition, nonresident:** *Full-time* $7032. *Part-time* $285 per credit. Tuition varies by number of courses or credits taken, academic program, and local reciprocity agreements. **Required fees:** Tuition and fees vary by number of courses or credits taken. **Graduate housing:** Room and board costs vary by number of occupants and type of accommodation. *Typical cost:* $5058 (including board).

FINANCIAL AID (1999–2000)
Fellowships, loans, research assistantships, scholarships, teaching assistantships, and work study. Aid is available to part-time students. Financial aid application deadline: 4/15. **Financial Aid Contact** Mr. Earl Hudgins, Director of Financial Aid, Box 45011, Lubbock, TX 79409-5011. **Phone:** 806-742-3681. **Fax:** 806-742-0880. **E-mail:** a7adu@techmail.admin.edu.

RESOURCES AND SERVICES
Information about online services, personal computer policies, library resources, international exchange programs, internship programs, and placement services at this institution and others can be found at **www.petersons.com/mba**

International Students
22% of students enrolled are international students.

Services and Facilities Counseling/support services, ESL/language courses, international student organization, orientation. Financial aid is not available to international students.

Applying *Required:* TOEFL with recommended score of 213 (computer) or 550 (paper), proof of adequate funds, proof of health/immunizations. **International Student Contact** Dr. Dale Duhan, Director, Box 42101, Lubbock, TX 79409-2101. **Phone:** 806-742-3114. **Fax:** 806-742-3958. **E-mail:** duhan@ba.ttu.edu.

■ APPLICATION
Required GMAT, application form, baccalaureate/first degree, essay, 3 letters of recommendation, resume/curriculum vitae, transcripts of college work. **Recommended** Interview, work experience.

Deadlines and Fees Applications for domestic students are processed on a rolling basis. *Deadlines:* 4/30 for fall (international), 10/1 for spring (international), 2/15 for summer (international). *Application fee:* $25, $50 (international).

Application Contact Ms. Nancy Dodge, Director, Graduate Services Center, Box 42101, Lubbock, TX 79409-2101. **Phone:** 806-742-3184. **Fax:** 806-742-3958. **E-mail:** ndodge@ba.ttu.edu.

See full description on page 852.

Texas Wesleyan University
Fort Worth, Texas

SCHOOL OF BUSINESS

DEGREE MBA

MBA—Master of Business Administration Full-time and part-time. At least 36 total credits required. 18 to 36 months to complete program. *Concentrations:* accounting, human resources, international business, management information systems, organizational management.

RESOURCES AND SERVICES
Information about online services, personal computer policies, library resources, international exchange programs, internship programs, and placement services at this institution and others can be found at **www.petersons.com/mba**

International Students
Services and Facilities Counseling/support services, ESL/language courses, international student housing, visa services. Financial aid is available to international students.
International Student Contact Ms. Helena Bussell, Assistant to Provost for International Programs, 1201 Wesleyan, Fort Worth, TX 76105-1536. **Phone:** 817-531-4220. **Fax:** 817-531-4288. **E-mail:** bussellh@txwes.edu.

■ APPLICATION

Application Contact Dr. J. Lee Whittington, Director of Graduate Programs, School of Business, 1201 Wesleyan, Fort Worth, TX 76105-1536. **Phone:** 817-531-6500 Ext. 6562. **Fax:** 817-531-6585. **E-mail:** jlee@txwes.edu.

Texas Woman's University

Denton, Texas

DEPARTMENT OF BUSINESS AND ECONOMICS

DEGREE MBA

MBA—Master of Business Administration Full-time and part-time. At least 36 total credits required. 12 to 36 months to complete program.

RESOURCES AND SERVICES

Information about online services, personal computer policies, library resources, international exchange programs, internship programs, and placement services at this institution and others can be found at **www. petersons.com/mba**

International Students

Services and Facilities Counseling/support services. Financial aid is available to international students.
International Student Contact Ms. Leslie Thomas, Coordinator, Box 425738, Denton, TX 76204. **Phone:** 940-898-3048.

■ APPLICATION

Application Contact Dr. Adelaide Griffin, Chair, Department of Business and Economics, Box 425738, Denton, TX 76204. **Phone:** 940-898-2111. **Fax:** 940-898-2120. **E-mail:** agriffin@twu.edu.

University of Dallas

Irving, Texas

GRADUATE SCHOOL OF MANAGEMENT

Graduate Business Faculty
Full-time: 22 — Part-time: 85

Student Body
Total: 1,641
Full-time: 280 — Average Age: 32
Part-time: 1,361 — Women: 42%

Admissions
Applications: 683
Admitted: 578 — Average GMAT: 550
Enrolled: 428 — Average GPA: 3.1

Costs (1999–2000)
Full-time tuition: $10,629 per academic year
Part-time tuition: $399 per credit hour

DEGREES M Mgt • MBA

M Mgt—Master of Management Full-time and part-time. At least 30 total credits required. 12 to 72 months to complete program. *Concentrations:* entrepreneurship, finance, financial management/planning, health care, human resources, industrial administration/management, international business, international management, international marketing, logistics, management information systems, marketing, nonprofit management, sports/entertainment management, technology management, telecommunications management.

MBA—Master of Business Administration Full-time and part-time. At least 49 total credits required. 12 to 72 months to complete program. *Concentrations:* entrepreneurship, finance, financial management/planning, health care, human resources, industrial administration/management, international business, international management, international marketing, logistics, management, management information systems, marketing, nonprofit management, sports/entertainment management, technology management, telecommunications management.

COSTS

Tuition *Full-time:* $10,557. *Part-time:* $391 per credit hour. Tuition varies by number of courses or credits taken. **Required fees:** *Full-time* $72. *Part-time* $8 per credit hour. **Graduate housing:** Room and board costs vary by number of occupants, type of accommodation, and type of board plan. *Typical cost:* $5186 (including board).

FINANCIAL AID (1999–2000)

270 students received aid, including loans and work study. Aid is available to part-time students. Financial aid application deadline: 2/15. **Financial Aid Contact** Mr. Larry Webb, Director of Enrollment, 1845 East Northgate Drive, Irving, TX 75062-4799. **Phone:** 972-721-5266. **Fax:** 972-721-5017. **E-mail:** lwebb@acad.udallas.edu.

RESOURCES AND SERVICES

Information about online services, personal computer policies, library resources, international exchange programs, internship programs, and placement services at this institution and others can be found at **www. petersons.com/mba**

International Students

22% of students enrolled are international students.

Services and Facilities Counseling/support services, ESL/language courses, international student organization. Financial aid is not available to international students.
Applying *Required:* TOEFL with recommended score of 520 (paper), proof of adequate funds. *Recommended:* Proof of health/immunizations.
International Student Contact Ms. Marilyn White, Director of International Student Services, 1845 East Northgate Drive, Irving, TX 75062-4799. **Phone:** 972-721-5059. **Fax:** 972-721-4009. **E-mail:** mwhite@gsm.udallas.edu.

■ APPLICATION

Required GMAT, application form, baccalaureate/first degree, 2 letters of recommendation, resume/curriculum vitae, transcripts of college work. **Recommended** Personal statement, 5 years of work experience.
Deadlines and Fees Applications for domestic and international students are processed on a rolling basis. *Application fee:* $25, $50 (international).
Application Contact Ms. Roxanne Del Rio, Director of Graduate School of Management Admissions, 1845 East Northgate Drive, Irving, TX 75062-4799. **Phone:** 972-721-5198. **Fax:** 972-721-4009. **E-mail:** admiss@gsm.udallas.edu.

See full description on page 892.

University of Houston

Houston, Texas

COLLEGE OF BUSINESS ADMINISTRATION

Accreditation
AACSB—The International Association for Management Education

DEGREES JD/MBA • MBA • MBA/MA • MBA/MIM • MBA/MS • MS

JD/MBA—Juris Doctor/Master of Business Administration Full-time and part-time. At least 115 total credits required. 36 to 48 months to complete program. *Concentrations:* accounting, entrepreneurship, finance, international business, management, management information systems, marketing, operations management, quantitative analysis, taxation.

MBA—Executive MBA/Professional MBA Full-time and part-time. At least 54 total credits required. 24 to 36 months to complete program.

MBA—Master of Business Administration Full-time and part-time. At least 54 total credits required. 12 to 60 months to complete program. *Concentrations:* accounting, entrepreneurship, finance, international business, management, management information systems, marketing, operations management.

MBA/MA—Master of Business Administration/Master of Arts in Spanish Full-time and part-time. At least 78 total credits required. 24 to 36 months to complete program. *Concentrations:* accounting, entrepreneurship, finance, international business, management, management information systems, marketing, operations management, quantitative analysis, taxation.

MBA/MIM—Master of Business Administration/Master of International Management Full-time and part-time. 54 to 66 total credits required. 24 to 36 months to complete program.

MBA/MS—Master of Business Administration/Master of Science in Industrial Engineering Full-time and part-time. At least 78 total credits required. 24 to 36 months to complete program. *Concentrations:* accounting, entrepreneurship, finance, international business, management, management information systems, marketing, operations management, quantitative analysis, taxation.

MS—Master of Science in Accountancy Full-time and part-time. At least 36 total credits required. 18 to 60 months to complete program. *Concentrations:* accounting, taxation.

MS—Master of Science in Finance Full-time and part-time. 36 to 54 total credits required. 18 to 36 months to complete program. *Concentrations:* finance.

RESOURCES AND SERVICES

Information about online services, personal computer policies, library resources, international exchange programs, internship programs, and

University of Houston (continued)

placement services at this institution and others can be found at **www. petersons.com/mba**

International Students

Services and Facilities Counseling/support services. Financial aid is available to international students.
International Student Contact Ms. Anita Gaines, Director, International Student Services and Scholar Services, 4800 Calhoun, Houston, TX 77204. **Phone:** 713-743-5072. **Fax:** 713-743-5079. **E-mail:** againes@uh.edu.

■ APPLICATION

Application Contact Office of Student Services, College of Business Administration, 4800 Calhoun, Houston, TX 77204-6282. **Phone:** 713-743-4900. **Fax:** 713-743-4942. **E-mail:** oss@cba.uh.edu.

University of Houston–Clear Lake

Houston, Texas

SCHOOL OF BUSINESS AND PUBLIC ADMINISTRATION

Graduate Business Faculty
Full-time: 54

Part-time: 39

Student Body
Total: 886
Full-time: 372
Part-time: 514

Average Age: 32
Women: 48%

Admissions
Applications: 397
Admitted: 313
Enrolled: 220

Average GMAT: 550
Average GPA: 3.1

Costs (1999–2000)
Full-time tuition: N/R
Part-time tuition: $167 per credit hour (resident), $301 per credit hour (nonresident)

Accreditation
AACSB—The International Association for Management Education

DEGREES MBA • MS

MBA—Master of Business Administration Full-time and part-time. 36 to 57 total credits required. 24 to 60 months to complete program. *Concentrations:* entrepreneurship, environmental economics/management, human resources, international business, management information systems, technology management.
MS—Master of Science in Accounting Full-time and part-time. 36 to 69 total credits required. 24 to 60 months to complete program. *Concentrations:* accounting.
MS—Master of Science in Finance Full-time and part-time. 36 to 57 total credits required. 24 to 60 months to complete program. *Concentrations:* finance, health care.
MS—Master of Science in Management Information Systems Full-time and part-time. 36 to 57 total credits required. 24 to 60 months to complete program. *Concentrations:* management information systems.

COSTS

Tuition, state resident: *Part-time* $120 per credit hour. **Tuition, nonresident:** *Part-time* $254 per credit hour. Tuition varies by number of courses or credits taken. **Required fees:** *Full-time* $242. *Part-time* $47 per credit hour. Fees vary by number of courses or credits taken and academic program.

FINANCIAL AID (1999–2000)

Loans, scholarships, teaching assistantships, and work study. Aid is available to part-time students. Financial aid application deadline: 5/1.
Financial Aid Contact Director of Financial Aid and Veterans' Affairs, 2700 Bay Area Boulevard, Houston, TX 77058-1098. **Phone:** 281-283-2485. **Fax:** 281-283-2502.

RESOURCES AND SERVICES

Information about online services, personal computer policies, library resources, international exchange programs, internship programs, and placement services at this institution and others can be found at **www. petersons.com/mba**

International Students

18% of students enrolled are international students.
Services and Facilities Counseling/support services, international student housing, international student organization, orientation. Financial aid is not available to international students.
Applying *Required:* TOEFL with recommended score of 550 (paper), proof of adequate funds.
International Student Contact Ms. Kathryn Dickerson, International Student Advisor, 2700 Bay Area Boulevard, Houston, TX 77058. **Phone:** 281-283-2506. **Fax:** 281-283-2530. **E-mail:** dickersonk@uhcl.cl.uh.edu.

■ APPLICATION

Required Application form, baccalaureate/first degree, transcripts of college work. School will accept GMAT and GRE. **Recommended** Personal statement, resume/curriculum vitae.
Deadlines and Fees *Deadlines:* 8/1 for fall, 12/1 for spring, 5/1 for summer, 6/1 for fall (international), 10/1 for spring (international), 3/1 for summer (international). *Application fee:* $30, $70 (international).
Application Contact Ms. Karen Carter, Academic Advisor, School of Business and Public Administration, Houston, TX 77058-1098. **Phone:** 281-283-3110. **Fax:** 281-283-3951. **E-mail:** carter@cl.uh.edu.

University of Houston–Victoria

Victoria, Texas

SCHOOL OF BUSINESS ADMINISTRATION

DEGREES MBA

Master of Science in Product Development Full-time. Maximum of 24 months to complete program.

MBA—Master of Business Administration Full-time and part-time. *Distance learning option.* At least 54 total credits required. 21 to 60 months to complete program. *Concentrations:* management.

RESOURCES AND SERVICES

Information about online services, personal computer policies, library resources, international exchange programs, internship programs, and placement services at this institution and others can be found at **www. petersons.com/mba**

International Students

Services and Facilities Counseling/support services, visa services. Financial aid is not available to international students.
International Student Contact Richard Phillips, Director of Enrollment, 2506 East Red River, Victoria, TX 77901-4450. **Phone:** 361-788-6297. **Fax:** 361-572-9377. **E-mail:** phillips@jade.vic.uh.edu.

■ APPLICATION

Application Contact Jane Mims, Coordinator of MBA Programs, 2506 East Red River, Victoria, TX 77901-4450. **Phone:** 361-582-1182. **Fax:** 361-582-1192. **E-mail:** mimsj@jade.vic.uh.edu.

University of Mary Hardin-Baylor

Belton, Texas

SCHOOL OF BUSINESS

DEGREE MBA

MBA—Master of Business Administration Full-time and part-time. At least 36 total credits required. 12 to 60 months to complete program. *Concentrations:* management.

RESOURCES AND SERVICES

Information about online services, personal computer policies, library resources, international exchange programs, internship programs, and placement services at this institution and others can be found at **www. petersons.com/mba**

International Students

Services and Facilities Counseling/support services, ESL/language courses, visa services. Financial aid is not available to international students.
International Student Contact Mr. Reed Harris, Director of International Students,

UMHB Station Box 8421, 950 College Street, Belton, TX 76513. **Phone:** 254-295-4949. **Fax:** 254-295-4535.

■ **APPLICATION**

Application Contact Dr. Lee Baldwin, Dean, School of Business, UMHB Station Box 8018, 900 College Street, Belton, TX 76513-2599. **Phone:** 254-295-4644. **Fax:** 254-295-4651. **E-mail:** lbaldwin@umhb.edu.

University of North Texas

Denton, Texas

COLLEGE OF BUSINESS ADMINISTRATION

Graduate Business Faculty
Full-time: 94

Student Body
Total: 580
Full-time: 185
Part-time: 395
Average Age: 31

Admissions
Applications: 229
Admitted: 117
Enrolled: 74
Average GMAT: 540
Average GPA: 2.95

Costs (1999–2000)
Full-time tuition: N/R
Part-time tuition: $151 per credit hour (resident), $285 per credit hour (nonresident)

Accreditation
AACSB—The International Association for Management Education

DEGREES MBA • MS

MBA—Master of Business Administration Full-time and part-time. 36 to 48 total credits required. Maximum of 72 months to complete program. *Concentrations:* finance, financial management/planning, human resources, management, marketing, production management.

MS—Master of Science in Accounting Full-time and part-time. At least 36 total credits required. Maximum of 72 months to complete program.

MS—Master of Science 30 to 45 total credits required. Maximum of 72 months to complete program. *Concentrations:* finance, management information systems, management science, real estate.

COSTS

Tuition, state resident: *Part-time* $151 per credit hour. **Tuition, nonresident:** *Part-time* $285 per credit hour. **Required fees:** Tuition and fees vary by number of courses or credits taken. **Graduate housing:** *Typical cost:* $3664 (including board).

FINANCIAL AID (1999–2000)

Fellowships, loans, research assistantships, scholarships, teaching assistantships, and work study. **Financial Aid Contact** Financial Aid Office, PO Box 311370, Denton, TX 76203-1370. **Phone:** 940-565-2302. **Fax:** 940-565-2738.

RESOURCES AND SERVICES

Information about online services, personal computer policies, library resources, international exchange programs, internship programs, and placement services at this institution and others can be found at **www.petersons.com/mba**

International Students

Services and Facilities Counseling/support services, ESL/language courses, international student housing, visa services. Financial aid is not available to international students.
Applying *Required:* TOEFL with recommended score of 550 (paper), proof of adequate funds, proof of health/immunizations.
International Student Contact International Office, PO Box 311067, Denton, TX 76203-1067. **Phone:** 940-565-2442. **Fax:** 940-565-4822. **E-mail:** intl@isp.unt.edu.

■ **APPLICATION**

Required Application form, baccalaureate/first degree, transcripts of college work. School will accept GMAT and GRE.
Deadlines and Fees Applications for domestic and international students are processed on a rolling basis. *Application fee:* $25, $50 (international).
Application Contact Mrs. Denise Galubenski, Graduate Degree Program Advisor, PO Box 311160, Denton, TX 76203-1160. **Phone:** 940-565-2110. **Fax:** 940-565-4640. **E-mail:** galubens@cobaf.unt.edu.

University of St. Thomas

Houston, Texas

CAMERON SCHOOL OF BUSINESS

Accreditation
ACBSP—The American Council of Business Schools and Programs

DEGREES MBA • MBA/MS • MIB • MSA

MBA—Master of Business Administration Full-time and part-time. At least 36 total credits required. Maximum of 72 months to complete program. *Concentrations:* accounting, finance, international business, management information systems, marketing.

MBA/MS—Master of Business Administration/Master of Science in Accounting Full-time and part-time. At least 60 total credits required. Maximum of 72 months to complete program. *Concentrations:* accounting.

MIB—Master of International Business Full-time and part-time. At least 36 total credits required. Maximum of 72 months to complete program.

MSA—Master of Science in Accounting Full-time and part-time. At least 36 total credits required. Maximum of 72 months to complete program. *Concentrations:* accounting.

RESOURCES AND SERVICES

Information about online services, personal computer policies, library resources, international exchange programs, internship programs, and placement services at this institution and others can be found at **www.petersons.com/mba**

International Students

Services and Facilities Counseling/support services, visa services. Financial aid is not available to international students.
International Student Contact Deacon Richard Glor, Registrar/International Student Advisor, 3800 Montrose Boulevard, Houston, TX 77006-4694. **Phone:** 713-525-2150. **Fax:** 713-525-3558. **E-mail:** glor@stthom.edu.

■ **APPLICATION**

Application Contact Dr. Yhi-Min Ho, Cameron School of Business, 3800 Montrose Boulevard, Houston, TX 77006-4694. **Phone:** 713-525-2100. **Fax:** 713-525-2110. **E-mail:** yhiminho@stthom.edu.

The University of Texas at Arlington

Arlington, Texas

COLLEGE OF BUSINESS ADMINISTRATION

Graduate Business Faculty
Full-time: 64

Student Body
Total: 849
Full-time: 362
Part-time: 487
Average Age: 30
Women: 40%

Admissions
Applications: 790
Admitted: 322
Enrolled: 200
Average GMAT: 556
Average GPA: 3.25

Costs (1999–2000)
Full-time tuition: $4521 per academic year (resident), $11,331 per academic year (nonresident)
Part-time tuition: $1001 per semester (resident), $2357 per semester (nonresident)

Accreditation
AACSB—The International Association for Management Education

DEGREES MA • MBA • MPA • MS

MA—Master of Arts in Economics Full-time and part-time. 30 to 36 total credits required. 12 to 14 months to complete program. *Concentrations:* economics.

MBA—Online Master of Business Administration Part-time. *Distance learning option.* 36 to 48 total credits required. 14 to 24 months to complete program.

MBA—Master of Business Administration Full-time and part-time. *Distance learning option.* 36 to 48 total credits required. 12 to 24 months to complete program. *Concentrations:* accounting, decision sciences, economics, electronic commerce (e-commerce), finance, health care, international business, management, management information systems, management science, management systems analysis, marketing, operations management, real estate, system management, technology management.

MPA—Master of Professional Accountancy Full-time and part-time. 39 to 60 total credits required. 14 to 24 months to complete program. *Concentrations:* accounting.

MS—Master of Science in Accounting Full-time and part-time. 36 to 75 total credits required. 14 to 28 months to complete program. *Concentrations:* accounting, system management.

MS—Master of Science in Health Care Administration Full-time and part-time. GRE required. 36 to 42 total credits required. 12 to 24 months to complete program. *Concentrations:* health care.

MS—Master of Science in Human Resource Management Full-time and part-time. 30 to 63 total credits required. 12 to 24 months to complete program. *Concentrations:* human resources, industrial/labor relations.

MS—Master of Science in Information Systems Full-time and part-time. 30 to 60 total credits required. 14 to 24 months to complete program. *Concentrations:* electronic commerce (e-commerce), information management, management information systems, management systems analysis, system management, technology management.

MS—Master of Science in Marketing Research Full-time and part-time. 36 to 63 total credits required. 12 to 24 months to complete program. *Concentrations:* marketing research.

MS—Master of Science in Real Estate Full-time and part-time. 30 to 57 total credits required. 12 to 24 months to complete program. *Concentrations:* real estate.

MS—Master of Science in Taxation Full-time and part-time. 36 to 75 total credits required. 14 to 28 months to complete program. *Concentrations:* taxation.

COSTS

Tuition, state resident: *Full-time* $4521. *Part-time* $1001 per semester. **Tuition, nonresident:** *Full-time* $11,331. *Part-time* $2357 per semester. **Required fees:** Tuition and fees vary by number of courses or credits taken and local reciprocity agreements. **Graduate housing:** Room and board costs vary by number of occupants, type of accommodation, and type of board plan. *Typical cost:* $4500 (including board).

FINANCIAL AID (1999–2000)

Financial Aid Contact Ms. Judy Schneider, Director of Financial Aid, UTA Box 19199, Arlington, TX 76019-0199. **Phone:** 817-272-3561. **Fax:** 817-272-3555. **E-mail:** fao@uta.edu.

RESOURCES AND SERVICES

Information about online services, personal computer policies, library resources, international exchange programs, internship programs, and placement services at this institution and others can be found at **www.petersons.com/mba**

International Students

27% of students enrolled are international students.

Services and Facilities Counseling/support services, ESL/language courses, housing location assistance, international student organization, orientation.

Applying *Required:* TOEFL with recommended score of 213 (computer) or 550 (paper), proof of adequate funds, proof of health/immunizations.

International Student Contact Dr. Judy Young, Director of International Office, UTA Box 19028, Arlington, TX 76019. **Phone:** 817-272-2355. **Fax:** 817-272-5005. **E-mail:** international@uta.edu.

▪ APPLICATION

Required Application form, baccalaureate/first degree, essay, 3 letters of recommendation, personal statement, transcripts of college work. School will accept GMAT. **Recommended** Resume/curriculum vitae, work experience.

Deadlines and Fees *Deadlines:* 6/15 for fall, 10/15 for spring, 3/15 for summer, 4/1 for fall (international), 9/1 for spring (international), 1/1 for summer (international). *Application fee:* $25, $50 (international).

Application Contact Ms. Alisa Johnson, Director for Graduate Business Services, UTA Box 19376, Arlington, TX 76019-0376. **Phone:** 817-272-3005. **Fax:** 817-272-5799. **E-mail:** admit@uta.edu.

See full description on page 970.

The University of Texas at Austin

Austin, Texas

GRADUATE SCHOOL OF BUSINESS

Graduate Business Faculty
Full-time: 174

Student Body
Total: 741	Average Age: 29
Full-time: 741	Women: 25%

Admissions
Applications: 3,389	Average GMAT: 675
Admitted: 751	Average GPA: 3.4
Enrolled: 388	

Costs (1999–2000)
Full-time tuition: $7568 per academic year (resident), $18,788 per academic year (nonresident)
Part-time tuition: N/R

After Graduation (Class of 1998–99)
Employed within 3 months of graduation: 96%
Average starting salary: $75,573

Accreditation
AACSB—The International Association for Management Education

DEGREES JD/MBA • MA • MBA • MBA/MA • MBA/MPA • MBA/MS • MPA

JD/MBA—Juris Doctor/Master of Business Administration Full-time. At least 134 total credits required. 48 to 60 months to complete program. *Concentrations:* accounting, electronic commerce (e-commerce), entrepreneurship, environmental economics/management, finance, human resources, information management, management, management information systems, marketing, operations management, strategic management, technology management.

MA—Master of Arts in Human Resources Development Leadership Full-time. Minimum 5 years of business experience required; must be currently working. At least 36 total credits required. 22 months to complete program.

MBA—Executive MBA Full-time. At least 42 total credits required. 22 months to complete program.

MBA—Executive MBA in Mexico City Full-time. Minimum 5 years of business experience required. At least 36 total credits required. 22 months to complete program.

MBA—Master of Business Administration Full-time. At least 60 total credits required. 24 months to complete program. *Concentrations:* accounting, electronic commerce (e-commerce), entrepreneurship, finance, human resources, information management, management, management information systems, marketing, operations management, strategic management, technology management.

MBA/MA—Master of Business Administration/Master of Arts in Asian Studies Full-time. 66 to 69 total credits required. 36 to 48 months to complete program. *Concentrations:* accounting, electronic commerce (e-commerce), entrepreneurship, finance, human resources, information management, management, management information systems, marketing, operations management, strategic management, technology management.

MBA/MA—Master of Business Administration/Master of Arts in Communications Full-time. At least 72 total credits required. 36 to 48 months to complete program. *Concentrations:* accounting, electronic commerce (e-commerce), entrepreneurship, finance, human resources, information management, management, management information systems, marketing, operations management, strategic management, technology management.

MBA/MA—Master of Business Administration/Master of Arts in Latin American Studies Full-time. At least 72 total credits required. 36 to 48 months to complete program. *Concentrations:* accounting, electronic commerce (e-commerce), entrepreneurship, finance, human resources, information management, management, management information systems, marketing, operations management, strategic management, technology management.

MBA/MA—Master of Business Administration/Master of Arts in Middle Eastern Studies Full-time. At least 69 total credits required. 36 to 48 months to complete program. *Concentrations:* accounting, decision sciences, electronic commerce (e-commerce), entrepreneurship, human resources, information management, management, management information systems, marketing, operations management, strategic management, technology management.

MBA/MA—Master of Business Administration/Master of Arts in Post-Soviet/Eastern European Studies Full-time. At least 69 total credits required. 36 to 48 months to complete program. *Concentrations:* accounting, decision sciences, electronic commerce (e-commerce), entrepreneurship, human resources, information management, management, management information systems, marketing, operations management, strategic management, technology management.

MBA/MPA—Master of Business Administration/Master of Professional Accounting Full-time. At least 72 total credits required. 36 to 48 months to complete program. *Concentrations:* accounting, entrepreneurship, environmental economics/management, finance, human resources, information management, management, management information systems, marketing, operations management, strategic management, taxation.

MBA/MPA—Master of Business Administration/Master of Public Affairs Full-time. At least 75 total credits required. 36 to 48 months to complete program. *Concentrations:* accounting, decision sciences, entrepreneurship, environmental economics/management, human resources, information management, management, management information systems, marketing, operations management, public policy and administration, strategic management.

MBA/MS—Master of Business Administration/Master of Science in Manufacturing Systems Engineering Full-time. At least 72 total credits required. 36 to 48 months to complete program. *Concentrations:* accounting, electronic commerce (e-commerce), entrepreneurship, finance, human resources, information management, management, management information systems, marketing, operations management, strategic management, technology management.

MBA/MS—Master of Business Administration/Master of Science in Nursing Full-time. At least 72 total credits required. 36 to 48 months to complete program. *Concentrations:* accounting, decision sciences, electronic commerce (e-commerce), entrepreneurship, human resources, information management, management, management information systems, marketing, operations management, strategic management, technology management.

MPA—Master of Professional Accountancy Full-time. 36 to 60 total credits required. 12 to 24 months to complete program. *Concentrations:* accounting, information management, taxation.

COSTS

Tuition, state resident: *Full-time* $3600. **Tuition, nonresident:** *Full-time* $14,820. **Tuition, international:** *Full-time* $14,820. **Required fees:** *Full-time* $3968. Tuition and fees vary by number of courses or credits taken and academic program.

FINANCIAL AID (1999–2000)

797 students received aid, including fellowships, grants, loans, research assistantships, scholarships, and teaching assistantships. Financial aid application deadline: 3/31. **Financial Aid Contact** Mrs. Mary Gielstra, Financial Aid Officer, Graduate School of Business, CBA 2.316, Austin, TX 78712. **Phone:** 512-471-7612. **Fax:** 512-471-4131. **E-mail:** mary.gielstra@bus.utexas.edu.

RESOURCES AND SERVICES

Information about online services, personal computer policies, library resources, international exchange programs, internship programs, and placement services at this institution and others can be found at **www.petersons.com/mba**

International Students

24% of students enrolled are international students.

Services and Facilities Counseling/support services, ESL/language courses, international student housing, international student organization, language tutoring, orientation, visa services. Financial aid is available to international students.

Applying *Required:* TOEFL with recommended score of 600 (paper), proof of adequate funds, proof of health/immunizations.

International Student Contact Ms. Linda Butler, International Student Advisor, International Office, PO Drawer A, Austin, TX 78713-7206. **Phone:** 512-471-1211. **Fax:** 512-471-8848. **E-mail:** lindab@mail.utexas.edu.

▪ APPLICATION

Required GMAT, application form, baccalaureate/first degree, essay, 2 letters of recommendation, personal statement, resume/curriculum vitae, transcripts of college work, 2 years of work experience.

Deadlines and Fees *Deadlines:* 4/15 for fall, 2/1 for fall (international). *Application fee:* $125, $125 (international).

Application Contact Dr. Carl Harris, Director of Admission, MBA Programs, Graduate School of Business, CBA 2.316, Austin, TX 78712-1172. **Phone:** 512-471-7612. **Fax:** 512-471-4243. **E-mail:** texasmba@bus.utexas.edu.

See full description on page 972.

The University of Texas at Brownsville

Brownsville, Texas

SCHOOL OF BUSINESS

Graduate Business Faculty
Full-time: 16 | Part-time: 1

Student Body
Total: 185
Full-time: 10 — Average Age: 28
Part-time: 175 — Women: 41%

Admissions
Applications: 50 — Average GMAT: 450
Admitted: 45 — Average GPA: 3.2
Enrolled: 30

Costs (1999–2000)
Full-time tuition: $1540 per academic year (resident), $4464 per academic year (nonresident)
Part-time tuition: $229 per course (resident), $892 per course (nonresident)

After Graduation (Class of 1998–99)
Employed within 3 months of graduation: 90%

Accreditation
ACBSP—The American Council of Business Schools and Programs

DEGREE MBA

MBA—Master of Business Administration Full-time and part-time. *Distance learning option.* 30 to 48 total credits required. 12 to 84 months to complete program.

COSTS

Tuition, state resident: *Full-time* $1540. *Part-time* $229 per course. **Tuition, nonresident:** *Full-time* $4464. *Part-time* $892 per course. **Tuition, international:** *Full-time* $5464. Tuition varies by number of courses or credits taken and local reciprocity agreements.

FINANCIAL AID (1999–2000)

30 students received aid, including loans and scholarships. Aid is available to part-time students. **Financial Aid Contact** Mr. Albert Barreda, Director of Financial Aid, Financial Aid Office, 80 Fort Brown, Brownsville, TX 78520-4991. **Phone:** 956-544-8277. **Fax:** 956-544-8229.

RESOURCES AND SERVICES

Information about online services, personal computer policies, library resources, international exchange programs, internship programs, and placement services at this institution and others can be found at **www.petersons.com/mba**

International Students

32% of students enrolled are international students.

Services and Facilities Counseling/support services, ESL/language courses, visa services. Financial aid is not available to international students.

Applying *Required:* TOEFL with recommended score of 550 (paper), proof of adequate funds, proof of health/immunizations.

International Student Contact Ms. Thelma Sullivan, International Student Counselor, 80 Fort Brown, Brownsville, TX 78520. **Phone:** 956-983-7092. **E-mail:** thelma@utbl.utb.edu.

▪ APPLICATION

Required Application form, baccalaureate/first degree, 2 letters of recommendation, transcripts of college work. School will accept GMAT.

Deadlines and Fees Applications for domestic and international students are processed on a rolling basis. *Application fee:* $15, $15 (international).

Application Contact Dr. Karl Kampschroeder, MBA Program Director, 80 Fort Brown, Brownsville, TX 78520-4991. **Phone:** 956-983-7302. **Fax:** 956-548-8736. **E-mail:** kfkamps@utbl.utb.edu.

The University of Texas at Dallas

Richardson, Texas

SCHOOL OF MANAGEMENT

Graduate Business Faculty
Full-time: 68   Part-time: 31

Student Body
Total: 1,207
Full-time: 348   Average Age: 31
Part-time: 859   Women: 41%

Admissions
Applications: 559   Average GMAT: 523
Admitted: 483   Average GPA: 3.2
Enrolled: 336

Costs (1999–2000)
Full-time tuition: $4393 per academic year (resident), $10,225 per
   academic year (nonresident)
Part-time tuition: $169 per semester hour (resident), $385 per semester
   hour (nonresident)

After Graduation (Class of 1998–99)
Average starting salary: $47,000

DEGREES MA • MBA • MS

MA—Master of Arts in International Management Full-time and part-time.
Distance learning option. At least 36 total credits required. 12 to 60 months to
complete program. *Concentrations:* international development management, international management.

MBA—Cohort MBA Full-time. At least 48 total credits required. 16 months to
complete program. *Concentrations:* finance, management information systems,
managerial economics, marketing, organizational behavior/development, technology management.

MBA—Executive MBA Part-time. At least 48 total credits required. 24 months
to complete program.

MBA—Master of Business Administration Full-time and part-time. *Distance learning option.* At least 48 total credits required. 12 to 60 months to complete
program. *Concentrations:* accounting, finance, information management, managerial economics, marketing, operations management, organizational behavior/
development, public policy and administration, strategic management.

MS—Alliance for Medical Management Education Part-time. *Distance learning
option.* 18 to 36 total credits required. 15 to 22 months to complete program.
Concentrations: accounting, finance, health care, information management,
organizational behavior/development.

MS—Master of Science in Accounting Full-time and part-time. At least 36 total
credits required. 12 to 60 months to complete program. *Concentrations:*
accounting.

MS—Master of Science in Management and Administration Full-time and part-
time. At least 36 total credits required. 12 to 60 months to complete program.
Concentrations: finance, information management, management information
systems, managerial economics, marketing, operations management, organizational
behavior/development, public policy and administration, strategic management.

The University of Texas at Dallas School of Management (SOM) is a
*metropolitan research and teaching institution that offers master's
programs ranging from a Cohort M.B.A. (full-time) to a highly popular
part-time M.B.A. curriculum and Master of Science degrees in a variety of
concentrations. In addition, the School offers a Master of Science in accountancy
with an emphasis on management information systems, a Master of Arts in
international management, and extensive executive education programs.*

*Located in the North Dallas Telecom Corridor, the School's programs attract
young, mid-level managers and upper-level professionals seeking continuing
management development. The curriculum focuses on global business issues,
change management, and management of technology. SOM's active relationships with corporate partners and the advisory council enhance the student's
educational experiences and influence placement opportunities.*

COSTS

Tuition, state resident: *Full-time* $4393. *Part-time* $76 per semester hour. **Tuition,
nonresident:** *Full-time* $10,225. *Part-time* $292 per semester hour. **Tuition, international:** *Full-time* $10,225. Tuition varies by number of courses or credits taken,
academic program, and local reciprocity agreements. **Required fees:** *Part-time*
$93 per semester hour.

FINANCIAL AID (1999–2000)
65 students received aid, including fellowships, research assistantships,
teaching assistantships, and work study. Aid is available to part-time
students. Financial aid application deadline: 11/1. **Financial Aid
Contact** Maria Ramos, Director of Financial Aid, MC 12, PO Box 830688,
Richardson, TX 75083-0688. **Phone:** 972-883-4021. **Fax:** 972-883-
2947. **E-mail:** ramos@utdallas.edu.

RESOURCES AND SERVICES
Information about online services, personal computer policies, library
resources, international exchange programs, internship programs, and
placement services at this institution and others can be found at **www.
petersons.com/mba**

International Students
32% of students enrolled are international students.

Services and Facilities Counseling/support services, international student housing, visa services.
Applying *Required:* TOEFL with recommended score of 550 (paper), proof of
adequate funds, proof of health/immunizations.
International Student Contact Jean Stuart, Director of Admissions and Records,
PO Box 830688, MC 11, Richardson, TX 75083-0688. **Phone:** 972-883-
4189. **Fax:** 972-883-4010.

■ APPLICATION
Required GMAT, application form, baccalaureate/first degree, 3 letters of recommendation, personal statement, resume/curriculum vitae, transcripts of college
work. **Recommended** Work experience.
Deadlines and Fees *Deadlines:* 7/15 for fall, 12/1 for spring, 5/1 for summer,
6/1 for fall (international), 10/1 for spring (international), 4/1 for summer
(international). *Application fee:* $25, $75 (international).
Application Contact Dr. Gary Horton, Head of Advising, School of Management, Richardson, TX 75083-0688. **Phone:** 972-883-2701. **Fax:** 972-883-
6425. **E-mail:** grad-admission@utdallas.edu.

See full description on page 974.

The University of Texas at El Paso

El Paso, Texas

COLLEGE OF BUSINESS ADMINISTRATION

Graduate Business Faculty
Full-time: 40

Student Body
Total: 245   Average Age: 32
Full-time: 60   Women: 38%
Part-time: 185

Admissions
Applications: 65

Costs (1999–2000)
Full-time tuition: $2350 per academic year (resident), $7294 per
   academic year (nonresident)
Part-time tuition: $409 per course (resident), $1033 per course
   (nonresident)

Accreditation
AACSB—The International Association for Management Education

DEGREES M Acc • MBA • MS

M Acc—Master of Accountancy Full-time and part-time. 36 to 78 total credits
required. 16 to 72 months to complete program. *Concentrations:* accounting,
taxation.

MBA—Master of Business Administration Full-time and part-time. *Distance learning option.* 36 to 51 total credits required. 16 to 72 months to complete program.
Concentrations: accounting, economics, finance, health care, human resources,
international business, management, management information systems.

MS—Master of Science in Economics Full-time and part-time. 30 to 36 total
credits required. 16 to 72 months to complete program. *Concentrations:* economics, financial economics, international economics.

COSTS

Tuition, state resident: *Full-time* $2350. *Part-time* $409 per course. **Tuition,
nonresident:** *Full-time* $7294. *Part-time* $1033 per course. Tuition varies by
local reciprocity agreements.

FINANCIAL AID (1999–2000)

Fellowships, research assistantships, teaching assistantships, and work study. Aid is available to part-time students. Financial aid application deadline: 3/1. **Financial Aid Contact** Ms. Linda Gonzalez-Hensgen, Director of Financial Aid, West Union 202, El Paso, TX 79968. **Phone:** 915-747-5204. **Fax:** 915-747-5631. **E-mail:** gonzalez@utep.edu.

RESOURCES AND SERVICES

Information about online services, personal computer policies, library resources, international exchange programs, internship programs, and placement services at this institution and others can be found at **www. petersons.com/mba**

International Students

Services and Facilities Counseling/support services, ESL/language courses, international student organization, orientation, visa services. Financial aid is available to international students.

Applying *Required:* TOEFL with recommended score of 600 (paper), proof of adequate funds, proof of health/immunizations.

International Student Contact Mr. Eric Piel, Director, International Student Office, 203 Union East, El Paso, TX 79968. **Phone:** 915-747-5664. **Fax:** 915-747-5794. **E-mail:** epiel@miners.utep.edu.

■ APPLICATION

Required GMAT, application form, baccalaureate/first degree, transcripts of college work.

Deadlines and Fees *Deadlines:* 7/1 for fall, 11/1 for spring, 4/1 for summer, 7/1 for fall (international), 11/1 for spring (international), 4/1 for summer (international). *Application fee:* $15, $65 (international).

Application Contact Ms. Maria Hanlin, Graduate Advisor, College of Business Administration, Room 102, 500 West University Avenue, El Paso, TX 79968. **Phone:** 915-747-5174. **Fax:** 915-747-5147. **E-mail:** coba@utep.edu.

The University of Texas at San Antonio

San Antonio, Texas

COLLEGE OF BUSINESS

Graduate Business Faculty

Full-time: 72	Part-time: 25

Student Body

Total: 530	Part-time: 347
Full-time: 183	Women: 37%

Admissions

Applications: 177	Average GMAT: 540
Admitted: 138	Average GPA: 3
Enrolled: 82	

Costs (1999–2000)

Full-time tuition: N/R
Part-time tuition: $110 per credit hour (resident), $326 per credit hour (nonresident)

After Graduation (Class of 1998–99)

Employed within 3 months of graduation: 65%
Average starting salary: $52,500

Accreditation

AACSB—The International Association for Management Education

DEGREES M Tax • MA • MBA • MS • MSMOT

M Tax—Master of Taxation Full-time and part-time. 30 to 60 total credits required. 12 to 72 months to complete program.

MA—Master of Arts in Economics Full-time and part-time. 33 to 48 total credits required. 12 to 72 months to complete program.

MBA—Executive MBA Full-time. At least 42 total credits required. 21 months to complete program.

MBA—Master of Business Administration in International Business Full-time and part-time. 39 to 63 total credits required. 12 to 72 months to complete program.

MBA—Master of Business Administration Full-time and part-time. 33 to 57 total credits required. 12 to 72 months to complete program. *Concentrations:* accounting, economics, finance, health care, human resources, management information systems, management science, marketing, taxation, technology management.

MS—Master of Science in Accounting Full-time and part-time. 30 to 60 total credits required. 12 to 72 months to complete program.

MS—Master of Science in Finance Full-time and part-time. 33 to 48 total credits required. 12 to 72 months to complete program.

MS—Master of Science in Information Technology Full-time and part-time. 33 to 51 total credits required. 12 to 72 months to complete program.

MSMOT—Master of Science in Management of Technology Full-time and part-time. At least 30 total credits required. 12 to 72 months to complete program.

COSTS

Tuition, state resident: *Part-time* $110 per credit hour. **Tuition, nonresident:** *Part-time* $326 per credit hour. Tuition varies by number of courses or credits taken.

FINANCIAL AID (1999–2000)

Grants, loans, research assistantships, scholarships, and work study. Aid is available to part-time students. Financial aid application deadline: 3/31. **Financial Aid Contact** Mr. Robert W. Evans, Student Financial Aid, 6900 North Loop 1604 West, San Antonio, TX 78249-0687. **Phone:** 210-458-4154. **Fax:** 210-458-4638.

RESOURCES AND SERVICES

Information about online services, personal computer policies, library resources, international exchange programs, internship programs, and placement services at this institution and others can be found at **www. petersons.com/mba**

International Students

8% of students enrolled are international students.

Services and Facilities Counseling/support services, ESL/language courses, housing location assistance, international student housing, international student organization, orientation, visa services. Financial aid is available to international students.

Applying *Required:* TOEFL with recommended score of 500 (paper), proof of adequate funds. *Recommended:* Proof of health/immunizations.

International Student Contact Ms. Magie Mata, Graduate Admissions Supervisor, 6900 North Loop 1604 West, San Antonio, TX 78249-0603. **Phone:** 210-458-4330. **Fax:** 210-458-4332.

■ APPLICATION

Required GMAT, application form, baccalaureate/first degree, transcripts of college work. **Recommended** Personal statement.

Deadlines and Fees *Deadlines:* 7/1 for fall, 12/1 for spring, 5/1 for summer, 4/1 for fall (international), 9/1 for spring (international), 4/1 for summer (international). *Application fee:* $25, $25 (international).

Application Contact Ms. Katherine Pope, Graduate Advisor, College of Business, 6900 North Loop 1604 West, San Antonio, TX 78249-0631. **Phone:** 210-458-4641. **Toll-free Phone:** 800-669-0919. **Fax:** 210-458-4398. **E-mail:** mbainfo@lonestar.utsa.edu.

See full description on page 976.

The University of Texas at Tyler

Tyler, Texas

SCHOOL OF BUSINESS ADMINISTRATION

Graduate Business Faculty

Full-time: 15	Part-time: 1

Student Body

Total: 101	Average Age: 32
Full-time: 2	Women: 41%
Part-time: 99	

Admissions

Applications: 45	Average GMAT: 507
Admitted: 35	Average GPA: 3.2
Enrolled: 35	

Costs (1999–2000)

Full-time tuition: N/R
Part-time tuition: $337 per course (resident), $967 per course (nonresident)

After Graduation (Class of 1998–99)

Employed within 3 months of graduation: 95%

Accreditation

AACSB—The International Association for Management Education

DEGREES MBA

The University of Texas at Tyler (continued)

MBA—Master of Business Administration Health Care Track Full-time and part-time. *Distance learning option.* At least 30 total credits required. 12 to 45 months to complete program.

MBA—Master of Business Administration Online Full-time and part-time. *Distance learning option.* At least 42 total credits required. 12 to 48 months to complete program.

MBA—Master of Business Administration Full-time and part-time. *Distance learning option.* At least 30 total credits required. 12 to 45 months to complete program. *Concentrations:* accounting, finance, management, marketing.

COSTS

Tuition, state resident: *Part-time* $337 per course. **Tuition, nonresident:** *Part-time* $967 per course. **Required fees:** Tuition and fees vary by number of courses or credits taken. **Graduate housing:** *Typical cost:* $2263 (room only).

FINANCIAL AID (1999–2000)

Research assistantships, scholarships, and work study. Financial aid application deadline: 7/1. **Financial Aid Contact** Financial Aid, 3900 University Boulevard, Tyler, TX 75799-0001. **Phone:** 903-566-7180. **Fax:** 903-566-7183. **E-mail:** ghill@mail.uttyl.edu.

RESOURCES AND SERVICES

Information about online services, personal computer policies, library resources, international exchange programs, internship programs, and placement services at this institution and others can be found at **www.petersons.com/mba**

International Students

5% of students enrolled are international students.

Services and Facilities Counseling/support services. Financial aid is not available to international students.

Applying *Required:* TOEFL with recommended score of 550 (paper), proof of adequate funds.

International Student Contact Ms. Nina Rogers, Registrar, 3900 University Boulevard, Tyler, TX 75799-0001. **Phone:** 903-566-7439. **Fax:** 903-566-7068. **E-mail:** nrogers@mail.uttyl.edu.

■ APPLICATION

Required GMAT, application form, baccalaureate/first degree, transcripts of college work.

Deadlines and Fees Applications for domestic and international students are processed on a rolling basis.

Application Contact Dr. Mary Fischer, Director of Graduate Programs in Business, 3900 University Boulevard, Tyler, TX 75799. **Phone:** 903-566-7433. **Fax:** 903-566-7372. **E-mail:** mary_fischer@mail.uttyl.edu.

The University of Texas–Pan American

Edinburg, Texas

COLLEGE OF BUSINESS ADMINISTRATION

Graduate Business Faculty
Full-time: 17

Student Body
Total: 227
Full-time: 70
Part-time: 157

Average Age: 33
Women: 38%

Admissions
Applications: 78
Admitted: 72
Enrolled: 38

Average GMAT: 470
Average GPA: 3.04

Costs (1999–2000)
Full-time tuition: $1570 per academic year (resident), $6658 per academic year (nonresident)
Part-time tuition: $54 per credit hour (resident), $248 per credit hour (nonresident)

After Graduation (Class of 1998–99)
Employed within 3 months of graduation: 90%

Accreditation
AACSB—The International Association for Management Education

DEGREES MBA

MBA—Physicians MBA Program Part-time. 30 to 33 total credits required. 24 months to complete program.

MBA—Weekend MBA Full-time. At least 33 total credits required. 24 months to complete program.

MBA—Master of Business Administration Full-time and part-time. 30 to 48 total credits required. 18 to 84 months to complete program.

COSTS

Tuition, state resident: *Full-time* $1570. *Part-time* $54 per credit hour. **Tuition, nonresident:** *Full-time* $6658. *Part-time* $248 per credit hour. **Required fees:** Tuition and fees vary by number of courses or credits taken. **Graduate housing:** Room and board costs vary by number of occupants, type of accommodation, and type of board plan. *Typical cost:* $2049 (including board).

FINANCIAL AID (1999–2000)

Fellowships, research assistantships, teaching assistantships, and work study. Aid is available to part-time students. Financial aid application deadline: 4/15. **Financial Aid Contact** Mr. Arnold Trejo, Director of Financial Aid, 1201 West University Drive, Edinburg, TX 78539. **Phone:** 956-381-2501. **Fax:** 956-381-2392. **E-mail:** atrejo@panam.edu.

RESOURCES AND SERVICES

Information about online services, personal computer policies, library resources, international exchange programs, internship programs, and placement services at this institution and others can be found at **www.petersons.com/mba**

International Students

17% of students enrolled are international students.

Services and Facilities Counseling/support services, ESL/language courses, visa services.

Applying *Required:* TOEFL with recommended score of 500 (paper), proof of adequate funds.

International Student Contact Mr. Santiago Villanueva, Assistant Dean/International Students, 1201 West University Drive, Edinburg, TX 78539. **Phone:** 956-381-2647. **Fax:** 956-381-2661. **E-mail:** svb3e2@panam.edu.

■ APPLICATION

Required GMAT, application form, baccalaureate/first degree, essay, 3 letters of recommendation, personal statement, transcripts of college work. **Recommended** Interview, work experience.

Deadlines and Fees *Deadlines:* 8/1 for fall, 11/1 for spring, 5/1 for summer, 7/1 for fall (international), 10/1 for spring (international), 4/1 for summer (international).

Application Contact Dr. Jane LeMaster, Director of MBA Programs, 1201 West University, Edinburg, TX 78539. **Phone:** 956-381-3313. **Fax:** 956-381-2970. **E-mail:** jlemaster@panam.edu.

University of the Incarnate Word

San Antonio, Texas

COLLEGE OF PROFESSIONAL STUDIES

Graduate Business Faculty
Full-time: 14

Part-time: 13

Student Body
Total: 230
Full-time: 43
Part-time: 187

Average Age: 32
Women: 58%

Admissions
Applications: 108
Admitted: 101
Enrolled: 63

Average GMAT: 428
Average GPA: 3.09

Costs (1999–2000)
Full-time tuition: N/R
Part-time tuition: $395 per credit hour

Accreditation
ACBSP—The American Council of Business Schools and Programs

DEGREES MBA • MBA/MSN

MBA—Master of Business Administration Full-time and part-time. 36 to 45 total credits required. 12 to 86 months to complete program. *Concentrations:* international business, sports/entertainment management.

MBA/MSN—Master of Business Administration/Master of Science in Nursing Full-time and part-time. At least 66 total credits required. 24 to 86 months to complete program.

COSTS

Tuition *Part-time:* $395 per credit hour. Tuition varies by number of courses or credits taken. **Graduate housing:** Room and board costs vary by number of occupants, type of accommodation, and type of board plan. *Typical cost:* $4870 (including board).

FINANCIAL AID (1999–2000)

62 students received aid, including loans and work study. Aid is available to part-time students. Financial aid application deadline: 5/31. **Financial Aid Contact** Ms. Lisa Blazer, Director of Financial Assistance, 4301 Broadway, Box 308, San Antonio, TX 78209-6397. **Phone:** 210-829-6008. **Fax:** 210-283-5053. **E-mail:** blazer@universe. uiwtx.edu.

RESOURCES AND SERVICES

Information about online services, personal computer policies, library resources, international exchange programs, internship programs, and placement services at this institution and others can be found at **www. petersons.com/mba**

International Students

10% of students enrolled are international students.

Services and Facilities Counseling/support services, ESL/language courses, international student housing, visa services. Financial aid is not available to international students.

Applying *Required:* TOEFL with recommended score of 560 (paper), proof of adequate funds, proof of health/immunizations.

International Student Contact Constance Kuwamoto, Assistant Director to Academic Services, 4301 Broadway, Box 31, San Antonio, TX 78209-6397. **Phone:** 210-829-3929.

■ APPLICATION

Required GMAT, application form, baccalaureate/first degree, transcripts of college work. **Recommended** Interview, personal statement, resume/curriculum vitae, work experience.

Deadlines and Fees Applications for domestic students are processed on a rolling basis. *Deadlines:* 6/1 for fall (international), 10/1 for spring (international), 2/1 for summer (international). *Application fee:* $20, $20 (international).

Application Contact Ms. Andrea Cyterski, Director of Admissions, Office of Admissions, 4301 Broadway, San Antonio, TX 78209. **Phone:** 210-829-6005. **Toll-free Phone:** 800-749-WORD. **Fax:** 210-829-3921. **E-mail:** cyterski@universe. uiwtx.edu.

Wayland Baptist University

Plainview, Texas

GRADUATE PROGRAMS

Graduate Business Faculty

Full-time: 12	Part-time: 9

Student Body

Total: 178	
Full-time: 22	Average Age: 37
Part-time: 156	Women: 31%

Admissions

Applications: 50	Average GMAT: 425
Admitted: 46	Average GPA: 3.32
Enrolled: 40	

Costs (1999–2000)
Full-time tuition: N/R
Part-time tuition: $245 per credit hour

DEGREES MA • MBA

MA—Master of Arts in Management Full-time and part-time. At least 36 total credits required. 12 to 72 months to complete program. *Concentrations:* management.

MBA—Master of Business Administration Full-time and part-time. At least 36 total credits required. 12 to 72 months to complete program. *Concentrations:* health care, human resources, management, management information systems.

COSTS

Tuition *Part-time:* $245 per credit hour. Tuition varies by campus location. **Required fees:** *Full-time* $350. *Part-time* $40 per semester. Fees vary by number of courses or credits taken and campus location. **Graduate housing:** Room and board costs vary by number of occupants, type of accommodation, and type of board plan. *Typical cost:* $2944 (including board).

FINANCIAL AID (1999–2000)

48 students received aid, including grants, loans, scholarships, and work study. Aid is available to part-time students. Financial aid application deadline: 5/1. **Financial Aid Contact** Ms. Julie Hacker, Director of Financial Aid, 1900 West Seventh Street, WBU 597, Plainview, TX 79072-6998. **Phone:** 806-296-4713. **Fax:** 806-296-4531. **E-mail:** hackerj@mail.wbu.edu.

RESOURCES AND SERVICES

Information about online services, personal computer policies, library resources, international exchange programs, internship programs, and placement services at this institution and others can be found at **www. petersons.com/mba**

International Students

0.6% of students enrolled are international students.

Services and Facilities Counseling/support services. Financial aid is available to international students.

Applying *Required:* TOEFL with recommended score of 500 (paper), proof of adequate funds, proof of health/immunizations.

International Student Contact Dr. Donna Wiley, Student Services Office Manager, WBU-643, Plainview, TX 79072. **Phone:** 806-296-4724. **Fax:** 806-291-4311. **E-mail:** wileyd@mail.wbu.edu.

■ APPLICATION

Required GMAT or GRE or MAT, application form, baccalaureate/first degree, personal statement, transcripts of college work.

Deadlines and Fees Applications for international students are processed on a rolling basis. *Application fee:* $35, $35 (international).

Application Contact Dr. Glenn Saul, Vice President of Academic Services, 1900 West Seventh, WBU 529, Plainview, TX 79072. **Phone:** 806-296-4574. **Fax:** 806-296-4596. **E-mail:** saulg@mail.wbu.edu.

West Texas A&M University

Canyon, Texas

T. BOONE PICKENS COLLEGE OF BUSINESS

Graduate Business Faculty

Full-time: 10	Part-time: 8

Student Body

Total: 188	
Full-time: 54	Average Age: 30
Part-time: 134	Women: 35%

Admissions

Applications: 51	Average GMAT: 510
Admitted: 50	Average GPA: 2.5
Enrolled: 49	

Costs (1999–2000)
Full-time tuition: $2160 per academic year (resident), $7992 per academic year (nonresident)
Part-time tuition: $60 per credit hour (resident), $222 per credit hour (nonresident)

Accreditation
ACBSP—The American Council of Business Schools and Programs

DEGREES MBA • MPA • MS

MBA—Master of Business Administration Full-time and part-time. *Distance learning option.* At least 36 total credits required. 24 to 60 months to complete program. *Concentrations:* accounting, management, management information systems.

MPA—Master of Professional Accountancy Full-time and part-time. *Distance learning option.* At least 36 total credits required. 24 to 60 months to complete program. *Concentrations:* accounting.

MS—Master of Science in Finance and Economics Full-time and part-time. *Distance learning option.* At least 36 total credits required. 24 to 60 months to complete program. *Concentrations:* economics, finance.

West Texas A&M University (continued)

COSTS

Tuition, state resident: *Full-time* $2160. *Part-time* $60 per credit hour. **Tuition, nonresident:** *Full-time* $7992. *Part-time* $222 per credit hour. **Required fees:** Tuition and fees vary by number of courses or credits taken and local reciprocity agreements. **Graduate housing:** Room and board costs vary by number of occupants and type of board plan. *Typical cost:* $3500 (including board).

FINANCIAL AID (1999–2000)

Grants, loans, research assistantships, scholarships, teaching assistantships, and work study. Aid is available to part-time students. Financial aid application deadline: 3/1. **Financial Aid Contact** Ms. Jeanette Head, Director of Student Financial Services, WTAMU Box 60999, Canyon, TX 79016-0001. **Phone:** 806-651-2055. **Fax:** 806-651-2924.

RESOURCES AND SERVICES

Information about online services, personal computer policies, library resources, international exchange programs, internship programs, and placement services at this institution and others can be found at **www.petersons.com/mba**

International Students

27% of students enrolled are international students.

Services and Facilities Counseling/support services, ESL/language courses, international student housing, visa services. Financial aid is available to international students.

Applying *Required:* TOEFL with recommended score of 550 (paper), proof of health/immunizations.

International Student Contact Program Coordinator, International Student Office, WTAMU Box 60999, Canyon, TX 79016-0001. **Phone:** 806-651-2073. **Fax:** 806-651-2071.

■ APPLICATION

Required GMAT, application form, baccalaureate/first degree, interview, transcripts of college work.

Deadlines and Fees *Deadlines:* 8/24 for fall, 1/15 for spring, 6/2 for summer, 8/24 for fall (international), 1/15 for spring (international), 6/2 for summer (international).

Application Contact Dr. Neil Terry, MBA Coordinator, PO Box 60187, Canyon, TX 79016-0001. **Phone:** 806-651-2512. **Fax:** 806-651-2514.

UTAH

Brigham Young University

Provo, Utah

MARRIOTT SCHOOL OF MANAGEMENT

Graduate Business Faculty

Full-time: 118   Part-time: 10

Student Body

Total: 842
Full-time: 722   Average Age: 28
Part-time: 120   Women: 23%

Admissions

Applications: 476   Average GMAT: 642
Admitted: 200   Average GPA: 3.53
Enrolled: 137

Costs (1999–2000)

Full-time tuition: $5390 per academic year
Part-time tuition: $296 per credit hour

After Graduation (Class of 1998–99)

Employed within 3 months of graduation: 91.5%
Average starting salary: $63,652

Accreditation

AACSB—The International Association for Management Education

DEGREES JD/MBA • JD/MOB • JD/MPA • M Acc • MBA • MBA/MA • MBA/MS • MISM • MOB • MOB/MA • MPA

JD/MBA—Juris Doctor/Master of Business Administration Full-time. At least 126 total credits required. 48 to 60 months to complete program. *Concentrations:* entrepreneurship, finance, human resources, information management, international business, management, management information systems, marketing, operations management, organizational behavior/development, production management, quantitative analysis, strategic management.

JD/MOB—Juris Doctor/Master of Organizational Behavior Full-time. At least 113 total credits required. 48 to 60 months to complete program.

JD/MPA—Juris Doctor/Master of Public Administration Full-time. At least 126 total credits required. 32 to 60 months to complete program.

M Acc—Master of Accountancy Full-time. At least 82 total credits required. Minimum of 18 months to complete program. *Concentrations:* accounting, taxation.

MBA—Executive Master of Business Administration Part-time. At least 53 total credits required. 20 months to complete program. *Concentrations:* banking, business law, entrepreneurship, European business studies, finance, financial management/planning, international business, international finance, management information systems, marketing, operations management, organizational behavior/development, production management, quantitative analysis, strategic management.

MBA—Master of Business Administration Full-time. At least 66 total credits required. 20 to 60 months to complete program. *Concentrations:* entrepreneurship, finance, human resources, information management, international business, management, management information systems, marketing, operations management, organizational behavior/development, production management, quantitative analysis, strategic management.

MBA/MA—International Relations MBA Full-time. At least 89 total credits required. 28 to 60 months to complete program. *Concentrations:* entrepreneurship, finance, human resources, information management, international business, management, management information systems, marketing, operations management, organizational behavior/development, production management, quantitative analysis, strategic management.

MBA/MS—Master of Business Administration/Master of Science Full-time. At least 87 total credits required. 36 to 60 months to complete program. *Concentrations:* entrepreneurship, finance, human resources, information management, international business, management, management information systems, marketing, operations management, organizational behavior/development, production management, quantitative analysis, strategic management.

MISM—Master of Information Systems Management Full-time. At least 79 total credits required. 36 to 60 months to complete program. *Concentrations:* accounting, information management, management consulting, management information systems, system management, technology management.

MOB—Master of Organizational Behavior Full-time and part-time. At least 53 total credits required. 20 to 60 months to complete program. *Concentrations:* human resources, organizational behavior/development, strategic management.

MOB/MA—International Development MOB Full-time. At least 72 total credits required. 28 to 60 months to complete program. *Concentrations:* human resources, organizational behavior/development, strategic management.

MPA—Executive Master of Public Administration Part-time. At least 44 total credits required. 12 to 60 months to complete program.

MPA—Master of Public Administration Full-time. At least 64 total credits required. 20 to 60 months to complete program. *Concentrations:* city/urban administration, financial management/planning, human resources, information management, management information systems, public policy and administration.

COSTS

Tuition *Full-time:* $5330. *Part-time:* $296 per credit hour. **Required fees:** *Full-time* $60. Tuition and fees vary by academic program. **Graduate housing:** Room and board costs vary by number of occupants, type of accommodation, and type of board plan. *Typical cost:* $6100 (including board).

FINANCIAL AID (1999–2000)

470 students received aid, including grants, loans, research assistantships, scholarships, and teaching assistantships. Financial aid application deadline: 3/1. **Financial Aid Contact** Ms. Rixa Oman, Assistant to the Dean, 730 TNRB, Provo, UT 84602-3184. **Phone:** 801-378-6824. **Fax:** 801-378-4501. **E-mail:** rixa_oman@byu.edu.

RESOURCES AND SERVICES

Information about online services, personal computer policies, library resources, international exchange programs, internship programs, and placement services at this institution and others can be found at **www.petersons.com/mba**

International Students

9% of students enrolled are international students.

Services and Facilities Counseling/support services, ESL/language courses, housing location assistance, international student housing, international student organization, orientation, international student scholarship program. Financial aid is available to international students.

Applying *Required:* TOEFL with recommended score of 230 (computer) or 570 (paper), proof of adequate funds, proof of health/immunizations.
International Student Contact Ms. Terri Hagler, Managing Director, Center for International Business, 650 TNRB, Marriott School of Management, Provo, UT 84602-3184. **Phone:** 801-378-9305. **Fax:** 801-378-2411. **E-mail:** terri_hagler@byu.edu.

■ **APPLICATION**

Required GMAT, application form, baccalaureate/first degree, essay, interview, 3 letters of recommendation, personal statement, resume/curriculum vitae, transcripts of college work. **Recommended** 2 years of work experience.
Deadlines and Fees *Deadlines:* 3/1 for fall, 1/15 for fall (international). *Application fee:* $30, $30 (international).
Application Contact Ms. Debbie Ruse, Program Administrator, 640 Tanner Building, Marriott School of Management, Provo, UT 84602-3184. **Phone:** 801-378-3500. **Fax:** 801-378-4808. **E-mail:** mba@byu.edu.

See full description on page 580.

Southern Utah University
Cedar City, Utah

SCHOOL OF BUSINESS

Graduate Business Faculty
Full-time: 6

Student Body
Total: 29
Full-time: 22
Part-time: 7
Average Age: 25
Women: 28%

Admissions
Applications: 39
Admitted: 34
Enrolled: 32
Average GMAT: 500
Average GPA: 3.2

Costs (1999–2000)
Full-time tuition: $2066 per academic year (resident), $6438 per academic year (nonresident)
Part-time tuition: $100 per credit (resident), $300 per credit (nonresident)

After Graduation (Class of 1998–99)
Employed within 3 months of graduation: 100%
Average starting salary: $36,800

Accreditation
ACBSP—The American Council of Business Schools and Programs

DEGREE M Acc

M Acc—Master of Accountancy Full-time and part-time. At least 30 total credits required. 9 to 36 months to complete program. *Concentrations:* accounting.

COSTS

Tuition, state resident: *Full-time* $1612. *Part-time* $100 per credit. **Tuition, nonresident:** *Full-time* $5984. *Part-time* $300 per credit. **Required fees:** *Full-time* $454. Tuition and fees vary by number of courses or credits taken. **Graduate housing:** Room and board costs vary by number of occupants, type of accommodation, and type of board plan. *Typical cost:* $2432 (including board), $1220 (room only).

FINANCIAL AID (1999–2000)

Loans, scholarships, and work study. Aid is available to part-time students. **Financial Aid Contact** Mr. Rex Michie, Director of Financial Aid, 357 West Center Street, Cedar City, UT 84720. **Phone:** 435-586-7735. **Fax:** 435-586-7736. **E-mail:** michie@suu.edu.

RESOURCES AND SERVICES

Information about online services, personal computer policies, library resources, international exchange programs, internship programs, and placement services at this institution and others can be found at **www.petersons.com/mba**

International Students

Services and Facilities Counseling/support services, ESL/language courses, visa services. Financial aid is not available to international students.
Applying *Required:* TOEFL with recommended score of 500 (paper), proof of adequate funds, proof of health/immunizations.
International Student Contact Ms. Lynne J. Brown, Director of International and Multicultural Services, Sharwan Smith Student Center, 351 West Center Street,

Cedar City, UT 84720. **Phone:** 435-586-7771. **Fax:** 435-586-8235. **E-mail:** brown_lj@suu.edu.

■ **APPLICATION**

Required Application form, baccalaureate/first degree, 3 letters of recommendation, personal statement, transcripts of college work. School will accept GMAT.
Deadlines and Fees Applications for domestic and international students are processed on a rolling basis. *Application fee:* $30, $30 (international).
Application Contact Ms. Laurie Harris, Office Manager, Business Department, Cedar City, UT 84720. **Phone:** 435-586-5462. **Fax:** 435-586-5493. **E-mail:** harris@suu.edu.

University of Utah
Salt Lake City, Utah

GRADUATE SCHOOL OF BUSINESS

Graduate Business Faculty
Full-time: 56
Part-time: 24

Student Body
Total: 402
Full-time: 191
Part-time: 211
Average Age: 30
Women: 34%

Admissions
Applications: 430
Admitted: 255
Enrolled: 179
Average GMAT: 601
Average GPA: 3.4

Costs (1999–2000)
Full-time tuition: $3752 per academic year (resident), $10,954 per academic year (nonresident)
Part-time tuition: N/R

After Graduation (Class of 1998–99)
Employed within 3 months of graduation: 95%
Average starting salary: $52,400

Accreditation
AACSB—The International Association for Management Education

DEGREES JD/MBA • M Pr A • M Stat • MBA • MBA/M Arch • MSF

JD/MBA—Juris Doctor/Master of Business Administration Full-time. 120 to 140 total credits required. 36 to 72 months to complete program.

M Pr A—Master of Professional Accountancy Full-time and part-time. Bachelors degree in Accounting from a US institution required. At least 30 total credits required. 9 to 48 months to complete program. *Concentrations:* taxation.

M Stat—Master of Statistics Full-time and part-time. 34 to 51 total credits required. 12 to 48 months to complete program. *Concentrations:* management. Master of Statistics Full-time and part-time. 34 to 51 total credits required. 12 to 48 months to complete program. *Concentrations:* management.

MBA—Evening MBA Part-time. At least 48 total credits required. 27 to 72 months to complete program.

MBA—Executive MBA Part-time. 5 years of full-time work experience required. At least 48 total credits required. 21 months to complete program.

MBA—Two-year program Full-time and part-time. 64 to 72 total credits required. 18 to 72 months to complete program. *Concentrations:* accounting, health care, international business, management information systems, taxation.

MBA/M Arch—Master of Business Administration/Master of Architecture Full-time. 141 to 149 total credits required. 36 to 72 months to complete program.

MSF—Master of Science in Finance Full-time and part-time. 32 to 64 total credits required. 12 to 48 months to complete program.

COSTS

Tuition, state resident: *Full-time* $3752. **Tuition, nonresident:** *Full-time* $10,954. Tuition varies by number of courses or credits taken and local reciprocity agreements. **Graduate housing:** Room and board costs vary by number of occupants, type of accommodation, and type of board plan. *Typical cost:* $5400 (including board), $3000 (room only).

FINANCIAL AID (1999–2000)

Fellowships and scholarships. Aid is available to part-time students. Financial aid application deadline: 1/15. **Financial Aid Contact** Ms. Carrie Radmall, Admissions and Scholarship Coordinator, 1645 East Campus Center Drive Room 101, Salt Lake City, UT 84112-9301. **Phone:** 801-581-7785. **Fax:** 801-581-3666. **E-mail:** masters@business.utah.edu.

University of Utah (continued)

RESOURCES AND SERVICES
Information about online services, personal computer policies, library resources, international exchange programs, internship programs, and placement services at this institution and others can be found at www. petersons.com/mba

International Students
10% of students enrolled are international students.

Services and Facilities Counseling/support services, ESL/language courses, international student housing, international student organization, orientation, visa services. Financial aid is available to international students.
Applying *Required:* TOEFL with recommended score of 250 (computer) or 600 (paper), TSE with recommended score of 45, proof of adequate funds, proof of health/immunizations.
International Student Contact Ms. Carrie Radmall, Admissions and Scholarship Coordinator, 1645 East Campus Center Drive, Room 101, Salt Lake City, UT 84112-9301. **Phone:** 801-581-7785. **Fax:** 801-581-3666. **E-mail:** masters@ business.utah.edu.

■ APPLICATION
Required Application form, baccalaureate/first degree, essay, 2 letters of recommendation, resume/curriculum vitae, transcripts of college work. School will accept GMAT. **Recommended** 2 years of work experience.
Deadlines and Fees *Deadlines:* 3/15 for fall, 1/15 for summer, 3/15 for fall (international), 1/15 for summer (international). *Application fee:* $40, $60 (international).
Application Contact Ms. Carrie Radmall, Admissions and Scholarship Coordinator, 1645 East Campus Center Drive, Room 101, Salt Lake City, UT 84112-9301. **Phone:** 801-581-7785. **Fax:** 801-581-3666. **E-mail:** masters@business. utah.edu.

See full description on page 984.

Utah State University

Logan, Utah

COLLEGE OF BUSINESS

Accreditation
AACSB—The International Association for Management Education

DEGREES M Acc • MBA • MS • MSS

M Acc—Master of Accountancy Full-time and part-time. At least 30 total credits required. 9 to 72 months to complete program. *Concentrations:* taxation.
MBA—Master of Business Administration Full-time and part-time. *Distance learning option.* At least 30 total credits required. 9 to 72 months to complete program. *Concentrations:* accounting, business information science, entrepreneurship, international economics, management science, manufacturing management, quantitative analysis.
MS—Master of Science in Business Information Systems and Education Full-time and part-time. *Distance learning option.* At least 33 total credits required. 12 to 72 months to complete program. *Concentrations:* business education, business information science, information management.
MS—Master of Science in Economics Full-time and part-time. At least 30 total credits required. 9 to 72 months to complete program. *Concentrations:* agricultural economics, developmental economics, managerial economics.
MSS—Master of Social Science in Human Resource Management Full-time and part-time. *Distance learning option.* At least 36 total credits required. 12 to 72 months to complete program.

RESOURCES AND SERVICES
Information about online services, personal computer policies, library resources, international exchange programs, internship programs, and placement services at this institution and others can be found at www. petersons.com/mba

International Students
Services and Facilities Counseling/support services, ESL/language courses. Financial aid is available to international students.
International Student Contact Mrs. Afton Tew, Director, International Students/Scholars, Logan, UT 84322-0140. **Phone:** 435-797-1124. **Fax:** 435-797-3522. **E-mail:** global@cc.usu.edu.

■ APPLICATION
Application Contact School of Graduate Studies, University Hill, Logan, UT 84322-0900. **Phone:** 435-797-1189.

Weber State University

Ogden, Utah

JOHN B. GODDARD SCHOOL OF BUSINESS AND ECONOMICS

Graduate Business Faculty
Full-time: 5   Part-time: 1

Student Body
Total: 56   Average Age: 28
Full-time: 22   Women: 36%
Part-time: 34

Admissions
Applications: 38   Average GMAT: 590
Admitted: 32   Average GPA: 3.45
Enrolled: 27

Costs (1999–2000)
Full-time tuition: $2202 per academic year (resident), $6620 per academic year (nonresident)
Part-time tuition: N/R

After Graduation (Class of 1998–99)
Employed within 3 months of graduation: 86%
Average starting salary: $31,300

Accreditation
AACSB—The International Association for Management Education

DEGREES MBA • MS

MBA—Master of Business Administration Full-time and part-time. *Distance learning option.* At least 36 total credits required. 12 to 60 months to complete program.
MS—Master of Professional Accountancy Full-time and part-time. *Distance learning option.* At least 30 total credits required. 12 to 60 months to complete program. *Concentrations:* accounting, financial management/planning, taxation.

COSTS
Tuition, state resident: *Full-time* $1766. **Tuition, nonresident:** *Full-time* $6184. **Tuition, international:** *Full-time* $6184. **Required fees:** *Full-time* $436. Tuition and fees vary by number of courses or credits taken. **Graduate housing:** Room and board costs vary by number of occupants and type of accommodation. *Typical cost:* $3196 (including board), $1680 (room only).

FINANCIAL AID (1999–2000)
Research assistantships and scholarships. Aid is available to part-time students. Financial aid application deadline: 2/1. **Financial Aid Contact** Dr. Michael Vaughan, Dean of the John B. Goddard School of Business and Economics, 3801 University Circle, Ogden, UT 84408-3801. **Phone:** 801-626-7308. **Fax:** 801-626-7423. **E-mail:** mvaughan@weber.edu.

RESOURCES AND SERVICES
Information about online services, personal computer policies, library resources, international exchange programs, internship programs, and placement services at this institution and others can be found at www. petersons.com/mba

International Students
2% of students enrolled are international students.

Services and Facilities Counseling/support services, ESL/language courses, housing location assistance, international student housing, international student organization, language tutoring, orientation, visa services. Financial aid is available to international students.
Applying *Required:* TOEFL with recommended score of 550 (paper), proof of adequate funds, proof of health/immunizations.
International Student Contact Ms. Diann Stewart, Director of Services for International Students, 1130 University Circle, Ogden, UT 84408-1130. **Phone:** 801-626-6853. **Fax:** 801-626-7963. **E-mail:** dstewart@weber.edu.

■ APPLICATION
Required GMAT, application form, baccalaureate/first degree, 3 letters of recommendation, transcripts of college work. **Recommended** Interview, work experience.
Deadlines and Fees *Deadlines:* 7/1 for fall, 10/1 for spring, 3/1 for summer, 7/1 for fall (international), 10/1 for spring (international), 3/1 for summer (international). *Application fee:* $30, $35 (international).
Application Contact Dr. Michael Vaughan, Dean of the John B. Goddard School of Business and Economics, 3810 University Circle, Ogden, UT 84408-3801. **Phone:** 801-626-7308. **Fax:** 801-626-7423. **E-mail:** mvaughan@weber.edu.

Westminster College

Salt Lake City, Utah

THE BILL AND VIEVE GORE SCHOOL OF BUSINESS

Graduate Business Faculty
Full-time: 17   Part-time: 9

Student Body
Total: 387   Average Age: 32
Full-time: 109   Women: 33%
Part-time: 278

Admissions
Applications: 156   Average GMAT: 520
Admitted: 139   Average GPA: 3.21
Enrolled: 90

Costs (1999–2000)
Full-time tuition: N/R
Part-time tuition: $492 per credit

After Graduation (Class of 1998–99)
Employed within 3 months of graduation: 95%
Average starting salary: $51,000

Accreditation
ACBSP—The American Council of Business Schools and Programs

DEGREE MBA

MBA—Master of Business Administration Full-time and part-time. At least 42 total credits required. Maximum of 72 months to complete program. *Concentrations:* accounting, economics, finance, health care, human resources, information management, international business, marketing, organizational behavior/development, resources management.

COSTS

Tuition *Part-time:* $492 per credit. **Required fees:** *Full-time* $100. Fees vary by number of courses or credits taken.

FINANCIAL AID (1999–2000)
162 students received aid. Aid is available to part-time students. **Financial Aid Contact** Ms. Ruth Henneman, Director of Financial Aid, 1840 South 1300 East, Salt Lake City, UT 84105-3697. **Phone:** 801-832-2500. **Fax:** 801-485-1989. **E-mail:** faidpub@wcslc.edu.

RESOURCES AND SERVICES
Information about online services, personal computer policies, library resources, international exchange programs, internship programs, and placement services at this institution and others can be found at www.petersons.com/mba

International Students
2% of students enrolled are international students.
Services and Facilities Counseling/support services. Financial aid is not available to international students.
Applying *Required:* TOEFL with recommended score of 213 (computer) or 550 (paper), proof of adequate funds.
International Student Contact Ms. Victoria Stirling, Graduate Admissions Counselor, 1840 South 1300 East, Salt Lake City, UT 84105-3697. **Phone:** 801-832-2200. **Fax:** 801-484-3252. **E-mail:** admispub@wcslc.edu.

■ APPLICATION

Required GMAT, application form, baccalaureate/first degree, resume/curriculum vitae, transcripts of college work. School will accept GRE. **Recommended** 3 years of work experience.

Deadlines and Fees Applications for domestic students are processed on a rolling basis. *Deadlines:* 7/1 for fall (international), 10/1 for spring (international), 3/1 for summer (international). *Application fee:* $25, $25 (international).

Application Contact Ms. Victoria Stirling, Graduate Admissions Counselor, 1840 South 1300 East, Salt Lake City, UT 84105-3697. **Phone:** 801-832-2200. **Toll-free Phone:** 800-748-4753. **Fax:** 801-484-3252. **E-mail:** admispub@wcslc.edu.

VERMONT

Saint Michael's College

Colchester, Vermont

PROGRAM IN ADMINISTRATION AND MANAGEMENT

Graduate Business Faculty
Full-time: 1   Part-time: 37

Student Body
Total: 199   Part-time: 191
Full-time: 8   Women: 62%

Admissions
Applications: 59   Enrolled: 54
Admitted: 56   Average GPA: 3.02

Costs (1999–2000)
Full-time tuition: N/R
Part-time tuition: $305 per credit hour

DEGREE MSA

MSA—Master of Science in Administration Full-time and part-time. 37 to 43 total credits required. 24 to 84 months to complete program. *Concentrations:* business policy/strategy, human resources, international management, management, management information systems, marketing, nonprofit management, organizational behavior/development, organizational management.

COSTS

Tuition *Part-time:* $305 per credit hour. Tuition varies by class time.

FINANCIAL AID (1999–2000)
15 students received aid, including loans and scholarships. Aid is available to part-time students. **Financial Aid Contact** Daniel Couture, Financial Aid Officer, One Winooski Park, Box 4, Financial Aid Office, VT. **Phone:** 802-654-3243. **Fax:** 802-654-2591. **E-mail:** dcouture@smcvt.edu.

RESOURCES AND SERVICES
Information about online services, personal computer policies, library resources, international exchange programs, internship programs, and placement services at this institution and others can be found at www.petersons.com/mba

International Students

Services and Facilities ESL/language courses, visa services. Financial aid is available to international students.
Applying *Required:* TOEFL with recommended score of 550 (paper).
International Student Contact Paul Olsen, Assistant Director, MSA Programs, One Winooski Park, Colchester, VT 05439. **E-mail:** polsen@smcvt.edu.

■ APPLICATION

Required Application form, baccalaureate/first degree, essay, 2 letters of recommendation, resume/curriculum vitae, transcripts of college work, 3 years of work experience.

Deadlines and Fees Applications for domestic and international students are processed on a rolling basis. *Application fee:* $25, $25 (international).

Application Contact Dr. Robert Letovsky, Director, Graduate Programs in Administration, One Winooski Park, Box 273, Colchester, VT 05439. **Phone:** 802-654-2100. **E-mail:** rletovsky@smcvt.edu.

School for International Training

Brattleboro, Vermont

MASTER'S PROGRAMS IN INTERCULTURAL MANAGEMENT, LEADERSHIP, AND SERVICE

Graduate Business Faculty
Full-time: 11   Part-time: 10

Student Body
Total: 213   Average Age: 32
Full-time: 157   Women: 72%
Part-time: 56

Admissions
Applications: 418   Enrolled: 156
Admitted: 334

School for International Training (continued)

Costs (1999–2000)
Full-time tuition: $20,805 per academic year
Part-time tuition: N/R

After Graduation (Class of 1998–99)
Employed within 3 months of graduation: 100%

DEGREE MS

MS—Master's Programs in Intercultural Management, Leadership and Service
Full-time. At least 40 total credits required. 21 to 60 months to complete program. *Concentrations:* international development management, international management, management, nonprofit management.

COSTS
Tuition *Full-time:* $19,340. **Required fees:** *Full-time* $1465. Tuition and fees vary by academic program. **Graduate housing:** Room and board costs vary by number of occupants, type of accommodation, and type of board plan. *Typical cost:* $2941 (including board), $1275 (room only).

FINANCIAL AID (1999–2000)
80 students received aid, including grants, loans, scholarships, and work study. Financial aid application deadline: 4/1. **Financial Aid Contact** Mr. Michael Ireland, Financial Aid Officer, PO Box 676, Kipling Road, Brattleboro, VT 05302-0676. **Phone:** 800-336-1616 Ext. 3280. **Fax:** 802-258-3500. **E-mail:** finaid@sit.edu.

RESOURCES AND SERVICES
Information about online services, personal computer policies, library resources, international exchange programs, internship programs, and placement services at this institution and others can be found at **www.petersons.com/mba**

International Students
25% of students enrolled are international students.

Services and Facilities Counseling/support services, ESL/language courses, orientation, visa services. Financial aid is available to international students.
Applying *Required:* TOEFL with recommended score of 213 (computer) or 550 (paper), proof of adequate funds, proof of health/immunizations.

International Student Contact Ms. Janet Hulnick, International Student Advisor, Kipling Road, PO Box 676, Brattleboro, VT 05302. **Phone:** 802-258-3364. **Fax:** 802-258-8248. **E-mail:** janet.hulnick@sit.edu.

■ APPLICATION

Required Application form, baccalaureate/first degree, essay, 4 letters of recommendation, personal statement, resume/curriculum vitae, transcripts of college work, 1 year of work experience. **Recommended** Interview.

Deadlines and Fees Applications for domestic and international students are processed on a rolling basis. *Application fee:* $45, $45 (international).

Application Contact Ms. Kim Noble, Admission Assistant, Kipling Road, PO Box 676, Brattleboro, VT 05302. **Phone:** 800-336-1616 Ext. 3267. **Fax:** 802-258-3500. **E-mail:** admissions@sit.edu.

University of Vermont
Burlington, Vermont

SCHOOL OF BUSINESS ADMINISTRATION

Graduate Business Faculty
Full-time: 21

Student Body
Total: 91	Average Age: 27
Full-time: 21	Women: 33%
Part-time: 70	

Admissions
Applications: 76	Average GMAT: 568
Admitted: 39	Average GPA: 3.2
Enrolled: 23	

Costs (1999–2000)
Full-time tuition: $7032 per academic year (resident), $17,580 per academic year (nonresident)
Part-time tuition: $293 per credit (resident), $733 per credit (nonresident)

Accreditation
AACSB—The International Association for Management Education

DEGREE MBA

MBA—Master of Business Administration Full-time and part-time. At least 48 total credits required. 12 to 60 months to complete program.

The School of Business at the University of Vermont is distinguished by its continuing ability to provide a superior educational experience for its students. The M.B.A. program prepares a select group of high-quality students for effective management practice in businesses, public-sector agencies, and not-for-profit institutions. Courses emphasize the understanding and critical evaluation of conceptual and theoretical principles relevant to the decision-making process. The program, which is accredited by AACSB-The International Association for Management Education, builds a foundation of enduring business knowledge that helps students solve problems and adapt to changing environments. Students receive individualized guidance from a world-class faculty in applying knowledge to develop practical strategies for implementing change in actual organizations.

The University prides itself on maintaining a small, high-quality program. With approximately 85 enrolled students, the School is able to maintain a high level of personalization and integrity in the educational process. The average class size is 17 students. Classes in the School of Business are not taught by graduate students. Rather, classroom teachers are faculty members who possess doctoral degrees and who conduct significant scholarly research in their respective fields.

The University is located in Burlington, a community of approximately 110,000 nestled between the Green Mountains and Lake Champlain.

COSTS
Tuition, state resident: *Full-time* $7032. *Part-time* $293 per credit. **Tuition, nonresident:** *Full-time* $17,580. *Part-time* $733 per credit. Tuition varies by number of courses or credits taken.

FINANCIAL AID (1999–2000)
8 students received aid, including research assistantships and teaching assistantships. Financial aid application deadline: 3/1. **Financial Aid Contact** Mr. Don Honeman, Director of Financial Aid, 330 Waterman Building, Burlington, VT 05405. **Phone:** 802-656-3156. **Fax:** 802-656-4076.

RESOURCES AND SERVICES
Information about online services, personal computer policies, library resources, international exchange programs, internship programs, and placement services at this institution and others can be found at **www.petersons.com/mba**

International Students
11% of students enrolled are international students.

Services and Facilities Counseling/support services, ESL/language courses, housing location assistance, international student organization, orientation, visa services. Financial aid is not available to international students.
Applying *Required:* TOEFL with recommended score of 550 (paper).

International Student Contact Ms. Marisha Kazeniac, International Student Advisor, B161 Living/Learning Center, Faculty Box 8, Burlington, VT 05405. **Phone:** 802-656-4296. **Fax:** 802-656-8553.

■ APPLICATION

Required Application form, baccalaureate/first degree, 3 letters of recommendation, personal statement, transcripts of college work. School will accept GMAT.

Deadlines and Fees *Deadlines:* 7/1 for fall, 11/15 for spring, 7/1 for fall (international), 11/15 for spring (international). *Application fee:* $25, $25 (international).

Application Contact Ms. Terry Winton, MBA Program Administrator, 218 Kalkin Hall, School of Business Administration, Burlington, VT 05405. **Phone:** 802-656-4015. **Fax:** 802-656-8279. **E-mail:** mba@bsadpo.emba.uvm.edu.

VIRGINIA

Averett College

Danville, Virginia

PROGRAM IN BUSINESS ADMINISTRATION

Graduate Business Faculty
Full-time: 11   Part-time: 79

Student Body
Total: 657   Average Age: 38
Full-time: 304   Women: 51%
Part-time: 353

Admissions
Applications: 350   Enrolled: 117
Admitted: 285

Costs (1999–2000)
Full-time tuition: $6932 per academic year
Part-time tuition: $320 per credit hour

DEGREE MBA

MBA—Graduate and Professional Studies Full-time. *Distance learning option.* At least 36 total credits required. Maximum of 24 months to complete program. *Concentrations:* management.

COSTS

Tuition *Full-time:* $6632. *Part-time:* $320 per credit hour. Tuition varies by class time, number of courses or credits taken, campus location, and academic program. **Required fees:** *Full-time* $300.

FINANCIAL AID (1999–2000)

Loans. Aid is available to part-time students. **Financial Aid Contact** Ms. Pam Harris, Financial Aid Coordinator, PO Office Box 2670, Danville, VA 24541. **Phone:** 804-791-5849. **Fax:** 804-791-5850.

RESOURCES AND SERVICES

Information about online services, personal computer policies, library resources, international exchange programs, internship programs, and placement services at this institution and others can be found at **www.petersons.com/mba**

International Students

Services and Facilities Financial aid is available to international students. **Applying** *Required:* TOEFL with recommended score of 500 (paper).

International Student Contact Stephanie Mullins, Admissions Counselor, 420 West Main Street, Danville, VA 24541. **E-mail:** smullins@averett.edu.

■ APPLICATION

Required Application form, baccalaureate/first degree, 3 letters of recommendation, personal statement, resume/curriculum vitae, transcripts of college work, 3 years of work experience.

Deadlines and Fees Applications for domestic and international students are processed on a rolling basis. *Application fee:* $20, $20 (international).

Application Contact Ms. Katherine Pappas-Smith, Marketing Manager, PO Box 2670, Danville, VA 24541. **Phone:** 804-791-5851. **Toll-free Phone:** 800-791-5851. **Fax:** 804-791-5850. **E-mail:** kapappas@averett.edu.

The College of William and Mary

Williamsburg, Virginia

SCHOOL OF BUSINESS

Graduate Business Faculty
Full-time: 48   Part-time: 5

Student Body
Total: 398   Average Age: 29
Full-time: 228   Women: 31%
Part-time: 170

Admissions
Applications: 450   Enrolled: 108
Admitted: 165   Average GMAT: 630

Average GPA: 3.2

Costs (1999–2000)
Full-time tuition: $6820 per academic year (resident), $16,500 per academic year (nonresident)
Part-time tuition: $240 per credit hour (resident), $525 per credit hour (nonresident)

After Graduation (Class of 1998–99)
Employed within 3 months of graduation: 100%
Average starting salary: $73,000

Accreditation
AACSB—The International Association for Management Education

DEGREES MBA

MBA—Evening MBA Part-time. At least 48 total credits required. 36 to 72 months to complete program. *Concentrations:* accounting, finance, information management, management, marketing, operations management.

MBA—Executive MBA Part-time. At least 45 total credits required. 20 months to complete program. *Concentrations:* accounting, finance, information management, management, marketing, operations management.

MBA—Full-time MBA Full-time. At least 65 total credits required. 24 months to complete program. *Concentrations:* accounting, finance, information management, management, marketing, operations management.

COSTS

Tuition, state resident: *Full-time* $6820. *Part-time* $240 per credit hour. **Tuition, nonresident:** *Full-time* $16,500. *Part-time* $525 per credit hour. **Graduate housing:** Room and board costs vary by number of occupants, type of accommodation, and type of board plan. *Typical cost:* $8330 (including board).

FINANCIAL AID (1999–2000)

290 students received aid, including fellowships, loans, research assistantships, scholarships, and work study. Financial aid application deadline: 3/1. **Financial Aid Contact** Ms. Susan Rivera, Director of MBA Admissions/Student Services, PO Box 8795, Williamsburg, VA 23187-8795. **Phone:** 757-221-2898. **Fax:** 757-221-2958. **E-mail:** susan.rivera@business.wm.edu.

RESOURCES AND SERVICES

Information about online services, personal computer policies, library resources, international exchange programs, internship programs, and placement services at this institution and others can be found at **www.petersons.com/mba**

International Students

19% of students enrolled are international students.

Services and Facilities Counseling/support services, housing location assistance, international student housing, international student organization, language tutoring, orientation, visa services. Financial aid is not available to international students.

Applying *Required:* TOEFL with recommended score of 600 (paper), proof of adequate funds, proof of health/immunizations.

International Student Contact Ms. Susan Rivera, Director of MBA Admissions/Student Services, PO Box 8795, Williamsburg, VA 23187. **Phone:** 757-221-2898. **Fax:** 757-221-2958. **E-mail:** susan.rivera@business.wm.edu.

■ APPLICATION

Required Application form, baccalaureate/first degree, essay, interview, 2 letters of recommendation, personal statement, resume/curriculum vitae, transcripts of college work, 2 years of work experience. School will accept GMAT.

Deadlines and Fees *Deadlines:* 10/1 for fall, 2/1 for winter, 3/1 for spring, 10/1 for fall (international), 2/1 for winter (international), 3/1 for spring (international). *Application fee:* $50, $50 (international).

Application Contact Ms. Susan Rivera, Director of MBA Admissions/Student Services, PO Box 8795, Williamsburg, VA 23187-8795. **Phone:** 757-221-2898. **Toll-free Phone:** 888-203-6994. **Fax:** 757-221-2958. **E-mail:** susan.rivera@business.wm.edu.

See full description on page 606.

George Mason University

Fairfax, Virginia

SCHOOL OF MANAGEMENT

Graduate Business Faculty
Full-time: 62   Part-time: 23

George Mason University (continued)

Student Body
Total: 385
Full-time: 59
Part-time: 326

Average Age: 31
Women: 35%

Admissions
Applications: 136
Admitted: 73
Enrolled: 52

Average GMAT: 620
Average GPA: 3.25

Costs (1999–2000)
Full-time tuition: N/R
Part-time tuition: $258 per credit hour (resident), $522 per credit hour (nonresident)

Accreditation
AACSB—The International Association for Management Education

DEGREES EMBA • MBA • MS

EMBA—Executive MBA Part-time. At least 55 total credits required. Maximum of 22 months to complete program.

MBA—Master of Business Administration Part-time. 2 year full-time professional work experience. 51 total credits required. 33 months to complete program. *Concentrations:* entrepreneurship, finance, management information systems, marketing.

MS—Master of Science in Technology Management Part-time. At least 36 total credits required. 18 months to complete program.

COSTS

Tuition, state resident: *Part-time* $258 per credit hour. **Tuition, nonresident:** *Part-time* $522 per credit hour. Tuition varies by number of courses or credits taken and academic program.

FINANCIAL AID (1999–2000)
150 students received aid, including loans. Aid is available to part-time students. Financial aid application deadline: 3/1. **Financial Aid Contact** Ms. Jennifer Douglas, Director, Financial Aid, 4400 University Drive, Mail Stop 3B5, Fairfax, VA 22030. **Phone:** 703-993-2353. **Fax:** 703-993-2350.

RESOURCES AND SERVICES
Information about online services, personal computer policies, library resources, international exchange programs, internship programs, and placement services at this institution and others can be found at **www.petersons.com/mba**

International Students
3% of students enrolled are international students.

Services and Facilities Counseling/support services, ESL/language courses. Financial aid is not available to international students.
Applying *Required:* TOEFL with recommended score of 600 (paper), proof of adequate funds, proof of health/immunizations.
International Student Contact Ms. Julia Friedheim, Director, International Programs and Services, 4400 University Drive, Mail Stop 4C3, Fairfax, VA 22030. **Phone:** 703-993-2970. **Fax:** 703-993-2966. **E-mail:** oips@gmu.edu.

■ APPLICATION
Required GMAT, application form, baccalaureate/first degree, essay, 2 letters of recommendation, personal statement, resume/curriculum vitae, transcripts of college work, 2 years of work experience. **Recommended** Interview.

Deadlines and Fees *Deadlines:* 4/1 for fall, 11/1 for spring, 3/1 for fall (international), 9/1 for spring (international). *Application fee:* $50, $50 (international).

Application Contact Mr. David Toomer, Coordinator, Admissions, School of Management, 4400 University Drive, Mail Stop 5A2, Fairfax, VA 22030. **Phone:** 703-993-2136. **Fax:** 703-993-1886. **E-mail:** masonbiz@som.gmu.edu.

See full description on page 662.

Hampton University

Hampton, Virginia

SCHOOL OF BUSINESS

Graduate Business Faculty
Full-time: 8

Student Body
Total: 26
Full-time: 5

Part-time: 21
Average Age: 30

Women: 54%

Admissions
Applications: 37
Admitted: 35
Enrolled: 12

Average GMAT: 410
Average GPA: 2.9

Costs (1999–2000)
Full-time tuition: $4075 per academic year
Part-time tuition: $225 per credit hour

After Graduation (Class of 1998–99)
Employed within 3 months of graduation: 95%
Average starting salary: $38,000

DEGREE MBA

MBA—Master of Business Administration Full-time and part-time. 36 to 60 total credits required. 16 to 84 months to complete program.

COSTS
Tuition *Full-time:* $4075. *Part-time:* $225 per credit hour.

FINANCIAL AID (1999–2000)
5 students received aid, including grants, research assistantships, and work study. Aid is available to part-time students. Financial aid application deadline: 4/15. **Financial Aid Contact** Financial Aid Office, Hampton, VA 23668. **Phone:** 757-727-5332.

RESOURCES AND SERVICES
Information about online services, personal computer policies, library resources, international exchange programs, internship programs, and placement services at this institution and others can be found at **www.petersons.com/mba**

International Students
15% of students enrolled are international students.

Services and Facilities Counseling/support services, housing location assistance. Financial aid is not available to international students.
Applying *Required:* TOEFL, proof of adequate funds, proof of health/immunizations.
International Student Contact Mrs. Martha Hall, Assistant to the Provost, Office of the Provost, Hampton, VA 23668-0001. **Phone:** 757-727-5080.

■ APPLICATION
Required GMAT, application form, baccalaureate/first degree, 2 letters of recommendation, transcripts of college work.

Deadlines and Fees Applications for domestic and international students are processed on a rolling basis. *Application fee:* $25, $25 (international).

Application Contact Dr. Edward Pyatt, Director, MBA Program, School of Business, Hampton, VA 23668-0001. **Phone:** 757-727-5205. **Fax:** 757-727-5048.

James Madison University

Harrisonburg, Virginia

COLLEGE OF BUSINESS

Accreditation
AACSB—The International Association for Management Education

DEGREES MBA

MBA—Master of Business Administration in Information Security Part-time. *Distance learning option.* At least 39 total credits required. 23 months to complete program.

MBA—Master of Business Administration Full-time and part-time. *Distance learning option.* At least 36 total credits required. 15 to 72 months to complete program. *Concentrations:* entrepreneurship, health care, technology management.

RESOURCES AND SERVICES
Information about online services, personal computer policies, library resources, international exchange programs, internship programs, and placement services at this institution and others can be found at **www.petersons.com/mba**

International Students
Services and Facilities Counseling/support services, visa services.
International Student Contact Ms. Cindy Allen, Graduate School, MSC 2602, Harrisonburg, VA 22807. **Phone:** 540-568-6131. **Fax:** 540-568-6266. **E-mail:** allenci@jmu.edu.

■ APPLICATION

Application Contact Ms. Deborah Mach, MBA Program Office, James Madison University, Harrisonburg, VA 22807. **Phone:** 540-568-3253. **Fax:** 540-568-3275. **E-mail:** machda@jmu.edu.

Lynchburg College

Lynchburg, Virginia

SCHOOL OF BUSINESS AND ECONOMICS

Graduate Business Faculty

Full-time: 16	Part-time: 3

Student Body

Total: 90	Part-time: 84
Full-time: 6	Average Age: 28

Admissions

Applications: 43	Average GMAT: 520
Admitted: 41	Average GPA: 3.06
Enrolled: 25	

Costs (1999–2000)
Full-time tuition: N/R
Part-time tuition: $280 per credit

After Graduation (Class of 1998–99)
Employed within 3 months of graduation: 100%

DEGREES MBA

MBA—One-year MBA Full-time and part-time. Must have undergraduate business degree. At least 30 total credits required. 12 to 60 months to complete program.

MBA—Two-year MBA Full-time and part-time. At least 48 total credits required. 24 to 60 months to complete program.

COSTS

Tuition *Part-time:* $280 per credit. Tuition varies by number of courses or credits taken. **Graduate housing:** Room and board costs vary by campus location, number of occupants, type of accommodation, and type of board plan. *Typical cost:* $5000 (including board).

FINANCIAL AID (1999–2000)

14 students received aid, including grants, loans, research assistantships, and teaching assistantships. Aid is available to part-time students. Financial aid application deadline: 5/1. **Financial Aid Contact** Ms. Michelle Davis, Director of Financial Aid, 1501 Lakeside Drive, Lynchburg, VA 24501. **Phone:** 804-544-8228. **Fax:** 804-544-8653. **E-mail:** davis_m@lynchburg.edu.

RESOURCES AND SERVICES

Information about online services, personal computer policies, library resources, international exchange programs, internship programs, and placement services at this institution and others can be found at **www.petersons.com/mba**

International Students

Services and Facilities Counseling/support services, international student housing, visa services. Financial aid is not available to international students.
Applying *Required:* TOEFL with recommended score of 550 (paper), proof of adequate funds. *Recommended:* TWE, proof of health/immunizations.

International Student Contact Ms. Annette Stadtherr, Enrollment Counselor, Enrollment Services, 150 Lakeside Drive, Lynchburg, VA 24501. **Phone:** 800-426-8101. **Fax:** 804-544-8653. **E-mail:** stadtherr@lynchburg.edu.

■ APPLICATION

Required GMAT, application form, baccalaureate/first degree, 3 letters of recommendation, personal statement, transcripts of college work. **Recommended** Interview, work experience.

Deadlines and Fees *Deadlines:* 6/1 for fall, 6/1 for fall (international). *Application fee:* $30, $30 (international).

Application Contact Dr. David Behrs, Vice President of Enrollment, 1501 Lakeside Drive, Lynchburg, VA 24501-3199. **Phone:** 804-544-8300. **Toll-free Phone:** 800-426-8101. **Fax:** 804-544-8653. **E-mail:** behrs@lynchburg.edu.

Marymount University

Arlington, Virginia

SCHOOL OF BUSINESS ADMINISTRATION

Graduate Business Faculty

Full-time: 34	Part-time: 37

Student Body

Total: 820	Average Age: 35
Full-time: 102	Women: 62%
Part-time: 718	

Admissions

Applications: 333	Average GMAT: 500
Admitted: 314	Average GPA: 3
Enrolled: 224	

Costs (1999–2000)
Full-time tuition: N/R
Part-time tuition: $480 per credit

Accreditation
ACBSP—The American Council of Business Schools and Programs

DEGREES MA • MBA • MS

MA—Master of Arts in Human Performance Systems Full-time and part-time. At least 36 total credits required. 12 to 60 months to complete program. *Concentrations:* human resources.

MA—Master of Arts in Human Resource Management Full-time and part-time. At least 36 total credits required. 12 to 60 months to complete program. *Concentrations:* human resources.

MA—Master of Arts in Legal Administration Full-time and part-time. At least 36 total credits required. 12 to 60 months to complete program. *Concentrations:* legal administration.

MA—Master of Arts in Organization Development Full-time and part-time. At least 36 total credits required. 12 to 60 months to complete program. *Concentrations:* organizational behavior/development.

MBA—Master of Business Administration Full-time and part-time. 36 to 63 total credits required. 12 to 60 months to complete program. *Concentrations:* management.

MS—Master of Science in Health Care Management Full-time and part-time. At least 36 total credits required. 12 to 60 months to complete program. *Concentrations:* health care.

MS—Master of Science in Information Management Full-time and part-time. At least 36 total credits required. 12 to 60 months to complete program. *Concentrations:* information management.

MS—Master of Science in Organizational Leadership and Innovation Full-time and part-time. At least 36 total credits required. 12 to 60 months to complete program. *Concentrations:* leadership.

COSTS

Tuition *Part-time:* $480 per credit. **Required fees:** Tuition and fees vary by number of courses or credits taken. **Graduate housing:** Room and board costs vary by number of occupants. *Typical cost:* $6160 (including board).

FINANCIAL AID (1999–2000)

136 students received aid, including fellowships, grants, and loans. Aid is available to part-time students. **Financial Aid Contact** Ms. Debbie Raines, Director of Financial Aid, 2807 North Glebe Road, Arlington, VA 22207-4299. **Phone:** 703-284-1530. **Fax:** 703-516-4771. **E-mail:** draines@marymount.edu.

RESOURCES AND SERVICES

Information about online services, personal computer policies, library resources, international exchange programs, internship programs, and placement services at this institution and others can be found at **www.petersons.com/mba**

International Students

5% of students enrolled are international students.

Services and Facilities Counseling/support services, ESL/language courses, international student housing. Financial aid is not available to international students.
Applying *Required:* TOEFL with recommended score of 600 (paper), proof of health/immunizations.

International Student Contact Sr. Irene Cody, International Admissions Counselor, 2807 North Glebe Road, Arlington, VA 22207-4299. **Phone:** 703-284-1500. **Fax:** 703-522-0349. **E-mail:** admissions@marymount.edu.

Marymount University (continued)

■ APPLICATION

Required Application form, baccalaureate/first degree, 2 letters of recommendation, resume/curriculum vitae, transcripts of college work. School will accept GMAT and GRE. **Recommended** Work experience.

Deadlines and Fees Applications for domestic and international students are processed on a rolling basis. *Application fee:* $35, $35 (international).

Application Contact Mr. Dan Higdon, Coordinator of Graduate Business Admissions, Ballston Campus, School of Business Administration, 2807 North Glebe Road, Arlington, VA 22207-4299. **Phone:** 703-284-5901. **Toll-free Phone:** 800-548-7638. **Fax:** 703-527-3815. **E-mail:** admissions@marymount.edu.

Old Dominion University

Norfolk, Virginia

COLLEGE OF BUSINESS AND PUBLIC ADMINISTRATION

Graduate Business Faculty
Full-time: 68

Student Body
Total: 570
Full-time: 155
Part-time: 415

Average Age: 31
Women: 40%

Admissions
Applications: 300
Admitted: 265

Enrolled: 180

Costs (1999–2000)
Full-time tuition: N/R
Part-time tuition: $196 per credit hour (resident), $520 per credit hour (nonresident)

Accreditation
AACSB—The International Association for Management Education

DEGREES M Tax • MA • MBA • MPA • MSA

M Tax—Master of Taxation Full-time and part-time. *Distance learning option.* GMAT or GRE is required. 30 total credits required. 24 to 72 months to complete program.

MA—Master of Arts in Economics Full-time and part-time. GRE is required if undergraduate GPA falls below a certain level. At least 30 total credits required. 20 to 72 months to complete program. *Concentrations:* economics.

MBA—Master of Business Administration Full-time and part-time. *Distance learning option.* GMAT and essay are required. At least 49 total credits required. Maximum of 72 months to complete program. *Concentrations:* accounting, electronic commerce (e-commerce), finance, financial management/planning, information management, international business, management, management information systems, marketing, port/maritime management, public policy and administration.

MPA—Master of Public Administration Full-time and part-time. Essay required. 39 total credits required. 24 to 72 months to complete program. *Concentrations:* city/urban administration, decision sciences, financial management/planning, health care, human resources, public management, public policy and administration.

MSA—Master of Science in Accounting Full-time and part-time. 30 total credits required. 24 to 72 months to complete program.

COSTS

Tuition, state resident: *Part-time* $196 per credit hour. **Tuition, nonresident:** *Part-time* $520 per credit hour. Tuition varies by campus location. **Required fees:** *Part-time* $50 per semester. Fees vary by number of courses or credits taken.

FINANCIAL AID (1999–2000)

Fellowships, loans, research assistantships, and work study. Aid is available to part-time students. **Financial Aid Contact** Dr. Bruce Rubin, Director, MBA Program, 111 Constant Hall, Norfolk, VA 23529. **Phone:** 757-683-3585. **Fax:** 757-683-5750. **E-mail:** brubin@odu.edu.

RESOURCES AND SERVICES

Information about online services, personal computer policies, library resources, international exchange programs, internship programs, and placement services at this institution and others can be found at **www.petersons.com/mba**

International Students

35% of students enrolled are international students.

Services and Facilities Counseling/support services, ESL/language courses, housing location assistance, international student housing, international student organization, language tutoring, orientation, visa services, airport pick-up. Financial aid is not available to international students.

Applying *Required:* TOEFL with recommended score of 550 (paper), proof of adequate funds, proof of health/immunizations.

International Student Contact Ms. Jan Aycock, Director, International Admissions, Dragas International Center, Norfolk, VA 23529. **Phone:** 757-683-3701. **Fax:** 757-683-5196. **E-mail:** jaycock@odu.edu.

■ APPLICATION

Required GRE, application form, baccalaureate/first degree, letter(s) of recommendation, transcripts of college work. **Recommended** Work experience.

Deadlines and Fees *Deadlines:* 6/15 for fall, 10/15 for spring, 3/15 for summer, 5/15 for fall (international), 9/15 for spring (international), 2/15 for summer (international). *Application fee:* $30, $30 (international).

Application Contact Dr. Bruce Rubin, Director, MBA Program, 111 Constant Hall, Norfolk, VA 23529. **Phone:** 757-683-3585. **Fax:** 757-683-5750. **E-mail:** brubin@odu.edu.

Radford University

Radford, Virginia

COLLEGE OF BUSINESS AND ECONOMICS

Graduate Business Faculty
Full-time: 25

Part-time: 1

Student Body
Total: 128
Full-time: 44
Part-time: 84

Average Age: 28
Women: 47%

Admissions
Applications: 140
Admitted: 61
Enrolled: 33

Average GMAT: 500
Average GPA: 3.15

Costs (1999–2000)
Full-time tuition: $3810 per academic year (resident), $7451 per academic year (nonresident)
Part-time tuition: $159 per credit hour (resident), $310 per credit hour (nonresident)

Accreditation
AACSB—The International Association for Management Education

DEGREES MBA • MS

MBA—Master of Business Administration Full-time and part-time. At least 36 total credits required. 12 to 60 months to complete program. *Concentrations:* accounting, finance, information management, management, marketing.

MS—Master of Science in International Economics Full-time and part-time. At least 30 total credits required. 12 to 60 months to complete program. *Concentrations:* international economics, international finance, international trade.

COSTS

Tuition, state resident: *Full-time* $2489. *Part-time* $159 per credit hour. **Tuition, nonresident:** *Full-time* $6130. *Part-time* $310 per credit hour. **Required fees:** *Full-time* $1321. Tuition and fees vary by number of courses or credits taken. **Graduate housing:** Room and board costs vary by number of occupants and type of board plan. *Typical cost:* $4937 (including board), $2717 (room only).

FINANCIAL AID (1999–2000)

66 students received aid, including fellowships, grants, loans, scholarships, teaching assistantships, and work study. Financial aid application deadline: 4/1. **Financial Aid Contact** Mr. Herbert H. Johnston, Director, Financial Aid, Box 6905, Radford, VA 24142. **Phone:** 540-831-5408. **Fax:** 540-831-5138. **E-mail:** bjohnsto@radford.edu.

RESOURCES AND SERVICES

Information about online services, personal computer policies, library resources, international exchange programs, internship programs, and placement services at this institution and others can be found at **www.petersons.com/mba**

International Students

11% of students enrolled are international students.

Services and Facilities Counseling/support services, ESL/language courses, international student organization, language tutoring, visa services. Financial aid is not available to international students.

Applying *Required:* TOEFL with recommended score of 550 (paper). *Recommended:* Proof of adequate funds.

International Student Contact Ms. Katrina Smith, Coordinator, International Student Services, PO Box 6979, Radford, VA 24142. **Phone:** 540-831-5765. **Fax:** 540-831-5820. **E-mail:** kismith@radford.edu.

■ APPLICATION

Required GMAT, application form, baccalaureate/first degree, 2 letters of recommendation, transcripts of college work. School will accept GRE and MAT. **Recommended** Personal statement, resume/curriculum vitae.

Deadlines and Fees Applications for domestic and international students are processed on a rolling basis. *Application fee:* $25, $25 (international).

Application Contact Dr. Wayne Saubert, Director, MBA Program, Box 6956, Radford, VA 24142. **Phone:** 540-831-5258. **Toll-free Phone:** 800-890-4265. **Fax:** 540-831-6655. **E-mail:** rumba@radford.edu.

Regent University

Virginia Beach, Virginia

SCHOOL OF BUSINESS

Graduate Business Faculty

Full-time: 10	Part-time: 7

Student Body

Total: 238	Average Age: 35
Full-time: 134	Women: 28%
Part-time: 104	

Admissions

Applications: 139	Enrolled: 76
Admitted: 120	Average GPA: 3

Costs (1999–2000)
Full-time tuition: $13,446 per academic year
Part-time tuition: $8964 per degree program

After Graduation (Class of 1998–99)
Employed within 3 months of graduation: 90%
Average starting salary: $40,000

DEGREES MA • MBA

MA—Master of Arts and Management Full-time and part-time. *Distance learning option.* At least 33 total credits required. 12 to 20 months to complete program. *Concentrations:* electronic commerce (e-commerce), human resources.

MBA—Accelerated MBA Full-time and part-time. At least 48 total credits required. 12 to 24 months to complete program. *Concentrations:* electronic commerce (e-commerce), human resources.

MBA—Executive MBA *Distance learning option.* At least 36 total credits required. 12 to 18 months to complete program. *Concentrations:* electronic commerce (e-commerce), human resources.

MBA—Professional Master of Business Administration Full-time and part-time. *Distance learning option.* At least 48 total credits required. 12 to 60 months to complete program. *Concentrations:* electronic commerce (e-commerce), entrepreneurship, financial management/planning, human resources, international business, marketing, nonprofit management.

Today's competitive marketplace demands the strategic and technical education that the Regent Graduate School of Business programs provide. To really compete today, it is essential to understand the primary and most important resource—people. With Regent University's M.B.A., students gain not only first-rate business knowledge and skills but also the vision, values, and people skills they need to lead organizations in the twenty-first century.

From this unique perspective, Regent prepares business leaders who are able to transform the global marketplace. Regent M.B.A. graduates advance in the largest global corporations, found and run entrepreneurial ventures, and lead nonprofit organizations, government agencies, and Church organizations worldwide.

Students can use their God-given talents and abilities not only to advance professionally but to advance themselves personally.

COSTS

Tuition *Full-time:* $13,446. *Part-time:* $8964 per degree program. **Required fees:** Fees vary by academic program.

FINANCIAL AID (1999–2000)

118 students received aid, including grants and scholarships. Aid is available to part-time students. **Financial Aid Contact** Mr. Tom Stansbury,

Director of Management, Recruitment, and Admissions, 1000 Regent University Drive, Virginia Beach, VA 23464-9800. **Phone:** 757-226-4096. **Fax:** 757-226-4823. **E-mail:** tomstan@regent.edu.

RESOURCES AND SERVICES

Information about online services, personal computer policies, library resources, international exchange programs, internship programs, and placement services at this institution and others can be found at **www.petersons.com/mba**

International Students

6% of students enrolled are international students.

Services and Facilities Counseling/support services, ESL/language courses, housing location assistance, international student housing, international student organization, orientation, visa services. Financial aid is available to international students.

Applying *Required:* TOEFL with recommended score of 550 (paper), proof of adequate funds, proof of health/immunizations.

International Student Contact Mrs. Almare Munley, Admissions Representative, 1000 Regent University Drive, Virginia Beach, VA 23464-9800. **Phone:** 757-226-4267. **Fax:** 757-226-4823. **E-mail:** almadon@regent.edu.

■ APPLICATION

Required Application form, baccalaureate/first degree, interview, 2 letters of recommendation, personal statement, resume/curriculum vitae, transcripts of college work.

Deadlines and Fees Applications for domestic students are processed on a rolling basis. *Deadlines:* 6/15 for fall (international), 10/15 for spring (international). *Application fee:* $40, $40 (international).

Application Contact Mr. Tom Stansbury, Director of Marketing, Recruitment and Admissions, 1000 Regent University Drive, Virginia Beach, VA 23464-9800. **Phone:** 757-226-4361. **Toll-free Phone:** 800-477-4823. **E-mail:** tomstan@regent.edu.

See full description on page 780.

Shenandoah University

Winchester, Virginia

BYRD SCHOOL OF BUSINESS

Graduate Business Faculty

Full-time: 12	Part-time: 15

Student Body

Total: 51	Average Age: 33
Full-time: 16	Women: 45%
Part-time: 35	

Admissions

Applications: 50	Average GMAT: 500
Admitted: 45	Average GPA: 3.1
Enrolled: 38	

Costs (1999–2000)
Full-time tuition: $8820 per academic year
Part-time tuition: $490 per credit

After Graduation (Class of 1998–99)
Employed within 3 months of graduation: 85%

DEGREE MBA

MBA—Master of Business Administration Full-time and part-time. At least 36 total credits required. 12 to 24 months to complete program. *Concentrations:* accounting, banking, health care, international business, management, management information systems, marketing, public management.

COSTS

Tuition *Full-time:* $8820. *Part-time:* $490 per credit. **Tuition, international:** *Full-time* $8820. Tuition varies by number of courses or credits taken and academic program. **Graduate housing:** Room and board costs vary by number of occupants, type of accommodation, and type of board plan. *Typical cost:* $6000 (including board).

FINANCIAL AID (1999–2000)

23 students received aid, including fellowships and scholarships. Aid is available to part-time students. Financial aid application deadline: 2/15. **Financial Aid Contact** Ms. Nancy Bragg, Director, Financial Aid, 1460 University Drive, Winchester, VA 22601-5195. **Phone:** 540-665-4538. **Fax:** 540-665-5433. **E-mail:** nbragg@su.edu.

Shenandoah University (continued)

RESOURCES AND SERVICES
Information about online services, personal computer policies, library resources, international exchange programs, internship programs, and placement services at this institution and others can be found at **www.petersons.com/mba**

International Students
22% of students enrolled are international students.

Services and Facilities Counseling/support services, ESL/language courses, housing location assistance, international student organization, orientation. Financial aid is available to international students.

Applying *Required:* TOEFL with recommended score of 550 (paper), proof of adequate funds, proof of health/immunizations.

International Student Contact Dr. William Berghaus, Associate Vice President—Academic Programs, 1460 University Drive, Winchester, VA 22601-5195. **Phone:** 540-665-4520. **Fax:** 540-665-5433. **E-mail:** bberghau@su.edu.

■ APPLICATION
Required GMAT, application form, baccalaureate/first degree, essay, interview, 2 letters of recommendation, personal statement, resume/curriculum vitae, transcripts of college work. School will accept GRE and MAT.

Deadlines and Fees Applications for domestic and international students are processed on a rolling basis. *Application fee:* $30, $30 (international).

Application Contact Mr. Michael Carpenter, Director of Admissions, 1460 University Drive, Winchester, VA 22601-5195. **Phone:** 540-665-4581. **Fax:** 540-665-4627. **E-mail:** mcarpent@su.edu.

University of Richmond

Richmond, University of Richmond, Virginia

RICHARD S. REYNOLDS GRADUATE SCHOOL

Graduate Business Faculty
Full-time: 42   Part-time: 7

Student Body
Total: 229
Full-time: 6   Average Age: 29
Part-time: 223   Women: 33%

Admissions
Applications: 60   Average GMAT: 598
Admitted: 46   Average GPA: 3.02
Enrolled: 37

Costs (1999–2000)
Full-time tuition: $20,240 per academic year
Part-time tuition: $1125 per course

Accreditation
AACSB—The International Association for Management Education

DEGREES JD/MBA • MBA

JD/MBA—Juris Doctor/Master of Business Administration Full-time. 110 to 125 total credits required. 36 to 48 months to complete program.

MBA—Master of Business Administration Full-time and part-time. 2 years work experience. At least 51 total credits required. 10 to 60 months to complete program.

COSTS
Tuition *Full-time:* $20,240. *Part-time:* $1125 per course. **Tuition, international:** *Full-time* $20,240. Tuition varies by number of courses or credits taken and academic program.

FINANCIAL AID (1999–2000)
22 students received aid, including loans and research assistantships. Aid is available to part-time students. Financial aid application deadline: 5/1. **Financial Aid Contact** Ms. Cynthia Bolger, Director, Financial Aid Office, Sarah Brunet Hall, Richmond, VA 23173. **Phone:** 804-289-8438. **Fax:** 804-289-6003. **E-mail:** cbolger@richmond.edu.

RESOURCES AND SERVICES
Information about online services, personal computer policies, library resources, international exchange programs, internship programs, and placement services at this institution and others can be found at **www.petersons.com/mba**

International Students
4% of students enrolled are international students.

Services and Facilities Counseling/support services, visa services. Financial aid is available to international students.

Applying *Required:* TOEFL with recommended score of 250 (computer) or 600 (paper), proof of adequate funds, proof of health/immunizations.

International Student Contact Dr. Robert Phillips, Associate Dean and Director, The Richard S. Reynolds Graduate School, The E. Claiborne Robins School of Business, Richmond, VA 23173. **Phone:** 804-289-8553. **Fax:** 804-287-6544. **E-mail:** mba@richmond.edu.

■ APPLICATION
Required GMAT, application form, baccalaureate/first degree, transcripts of college work, 2 years of work experience.

Deadlines and Fees *Deadlines:* 5/1 for fall, 5/1 for fall (international). *Application fee:* $50, $50 (international).

Application Contact Ms. Arlene Davis, Administrative Assistant, The Richard S. Reynolds Graduate School, The E. Claiborne Robins School of Business, Richmond, VA 23173. **Phone:** 804-289-8553. **Fax:** 804-287-6544. **E-mail:** adavis@richmond.edu.

University of Virginia

Charlottesville, Virginia

COLGATE DARDEN GRADUATE SCHOOL OF BUSINESS ADMINISTRATION

Graduate Business Faculty
Full-time: 53   Part-time: 27

Student Body
Total: 486   Average Age: 28
Full-time: 486   Women: 26%

Admissions
Applications: 2,682   Average GMAT: 676
Admitted: 490   Average GPA: 3.3
Enrolled: 243

Costs (1999–2000)
Full-time tuition: $16,945 per academic year (resident), $22,671 per academic year (nonresident)
Part-time tuition: N/R

After Graduation (Class of 1998–99)
Employed within 3 months of graduation: 98%
Average starting salary: $81,677

Accreditation
AACSB—The International Association for Management Education

DEGREES JD/MBA • MBA • MBA/MA • MBA/MS • ME/MBA • PhD/MBA

JD/MBA—Juris Doctor/Master of Business Administration Full-time. Maximum of 48 months to complete program.

MBA—Master of Business Administration Full-time. At least 78 total credits required. Maximum of 24 months to complete program.

MBA/MA—Master of Business Administration/Master of Arts Full-time. Maximum of 36 months to complete program.

MBA/MS—Master of Business Administration/Master of Science in Nursing Full-time. At least 93 total credits required. Maximum of 36 months to complete program.

ME/MBA—Master of Engineering/Master of Business Administration Full-time. At least 93 total credits required. Maximum of 36 months to complete program.

PhD/MBA—Doctor of Philosophy/Master of Business Administration Full-time. Maximum of 48 months to complete program.

COSTS
Tuition, state resident: *Full-time* $16,945. **Tuition, nonresident:** *Full-time* $22,671. **Graduate housing:** *Typical cost:* $7610 (including board).

FINANCIAL AID (1999–2000)
368 students received aid, including fellowships, loans, and scholarships. **Financial Aid Contact** Mr. Laurence Mueller, PO Box 6550, Charlottesville, VA 22906. **Phone:** 804-924-7559. **Fax:** 804-243-5033. **E-mail:** muellerl@darden.virginia.edu.

RESOURCES AND SERVICES

Information about online services, personal computer policies, library resources, international exchange programs, internship programs, and placement services at this institution and others can be found at **www.petersons.com/mba**

International Students

22% of students enrolled are international students.

Services and Facilities Counseling/support services, housing location assistance, international student organization, orientation, visa services. Financial aid is available to international students.
Applying *Required:* TOEFL, proof of adequate funds, proof of health/immunizations.
International Student Contact Dawna Clarke, Interim Director of Admissions, PO Box 6550, Charlottesville, VA 22906. **Phone:** 804-924-7281. **Fax:** 804-243-5033. **E-mail:** darden@virginia.edu.

■ APPLICATION

Required GMAT, application form, essay, letter(s) of recommendation, personal statement, transcripts of college work, 3 years of work experience. **Recommended** Baccalaureate/first degree, interview.
Deadlines and Fees *Deadlines:* 3/14 for fall, 3/14 for fall (international). *Application fee:* $100, $100 (international).
Application Contact Dawna Clarke, Interim Director of Admissions, PO Box 6550, Charlottesville, VA 22906. **Phone:** 804-924-7281. **Toll-free Phone:** 800-UVA-MBA-1. **Fax:** 804-243-5033. **E-mail:** darden@virginia.edu.

Virginia Commonwealth University

Richmond, Virginia

SCHOOL OF BUSINESS

Graduate Business Faculty
Full-time: 100 — Part-time: 40

Student Body
Total: 483 — Average Age: 32
Full-time: 137 — Women: 42%
Part-time: 346

Admissions
Applications: 290 — Average GMAT: 560
Admitted: 132 — Average GPA: 3
Enrolled: 64

Costs (1999–2000)
Full-time tuition: $5112 per academic year (resident), $13,027 per academic year (nonresident)
Part-time tuition: $264 per credit (resident), $704 per credit (nonresident)

After Graduation (Class of 1998–99)
Employed within 3 months of graduation: 95%
Average starting salary: $30,000

Accreditation
AACSB—The International Association for Management Education

DEGREES M Tax • MA • MBA • MS

M Tax—Master of Taxation Full-time and part-time. At least 30 total credits required. 12 to 60 months to complete program. *Concentrations:* taxation.

MA—Master of Arts in Economics Full-time and part-time. GRE required. At least 30 total credits required. 12 to 60 months to complete program. *Concentrations:* economics, financial economics.

MBA—Fast Track MBA Part-time. At least 39 total credits required. Maximum of 20 months to complete program.

MBA—Master of Business Administration Full-time and part-time. 30 to 54 total credits required. 12 to 60 months to complete program. *Concentrations:* accounting, decision sciences, economics, finance, human resources, management information systems, marketing, real estate, risk management.

MS—Master of Science in Business Full-time and part-time. 30 to 45 total credits required. 12 to 60 months to complete program. *Concentrations:* decision sciences, finance, human resources, management information systems, marketing, real estate.

COSTS

Tuition, state resident: *Full-time* $5112. *Part-time* $264 per credit. **Tuition, nonresident:** *Full-time* $13,027. *Part-time* $704 per credit. Tuition varies by number of courses or credits taken and local reciprocity agreements. **Required fees:** Fees vary by class time, number of courses or credits taken, and academic program. **Graduate housing:** Room and board costs vary by number of occupants, type of accommodation, and type of board plan. *Typical cost:* $3000 (including board).

FINANCIAL AID (1999–2000)

Fellowships, loans, research assistantships, teaching assistantships, and work study. Aid is available to part-time students. Financial aid application deadline: 3/15. **Financial Aid Contact** Ms. Sallie Reese, Program Support Tech, Box 844000, 1015 Floyd Avenue, Richmond, VA 23284-4000. **Phone:** 804-828-1741. **Fax:** 804-828-7174. **E-mail:** sreese@vcu.edu.

RESOURCES AND SERVICES

Information about online services, personal computer policies, library resources, international exchange programs, internship programs, and placement services at this institution and others can be found at **www.petersons.com/mba**

International Students

Services and Facilities Counseling/support services, ESL/language courses. Financial aid is not available to international students.
Applying *Required:* TOEFL with recommended score of 600 (paper), TSE, TWE, proof of adequate funds, proof of health/immunizations.
International Student Contact Ms. Arlene Jackson, Center for International Programs, 916 West Franklin Street, Box 843043, Richmond, VA 23284. **Phone:** 804-828-8471. **Fax:** 804-828-2552. **E-mail:** ajackson@saturn.vcu.edu.

■ APPLICATION

Required GMAT, application form, baccalaureate/first degree, interview, 3 letters of recommendation, personal statement, transcripts of college work. **Recommended** Resume/curriculum vitae, 3 years of work experience.
Deadlines and Fees *Deadlines:* 7/1 for fall, 12/1 for spring, 4/1 for summer, 4/1 for fall (international), 10/1 for spring (international), 2/1 for summer (international). *Application fee:* $30, $30 (international).
Application Contact Ms. Janice Covington, Senior Secretary, Box 844000, 1015 Floyd Avenue, Richmond, VA 23284-4000. **Phone:** 804-828-1741. **Fax:** 804-828-7174. **E-mail:** jcovington@vcu.edu.

See full description on page 996.

Virginia Polytechnic Institute and State University

Blacksburg, Virginia

PAMPLIN COLLEGE OF BUSINESS

Graduate Business Faculty
Full-time: 113 — Part-time: 5

Student Body
Total: 566 — Average Age: 25
Full-time: 180 — Women: 35%
Part-time: 386

Admissions
Applications: 313 — Average GMAT: 582
Admitted: 177 — Average GPA: 3.19
Enrolled: 88

Costs (1999–2000)
Full-time tuition: $4950 per academic year (resident), $7758 per academic year (nonresident)
Part-time tuition: $229 per credit hour (resident), $374 per credit hour (nonresident)

After Graduation (Class of 1998–99)
Employed within 3 months of graduation: 79%
Average starting salary: $54,731

Accreditation
AACSB—The International Association for Management Education

DEGREES M Acc • MBA

M Acc—Master of Accountancy Full-time and part-time. At least 30 total credits required. Maximum of 48 months to complete program.

Virginia Polytechnic Institute and State University (continued)

MBA—Master of Business Administration Full-time and part-time. *Distance learning option.* At least 48 total credits required. 18 to 24 months to complete program. *Concentrations:* electronic commerce (e-commerce), finance, financial management/planning, human resources, information management, international business, leadership, management, management information systems, management science, marketing, technology management.

COSTS

Tuition, state resident: *Full-time* $4122. *Part-time* $229 per credit hour. **Tuition, nonresident:** *Full-time* $6930. *Part-time* $374 per credit hour. Tuition varies by number of courses or credits taken. **Required fees:** *Full-time* $828. **Graduate housing:** Room and board costs vary by number of occupants, type of accommodation, and type of board plan. *Typical cost:* $4114 (including board), $2230 (room only).

FINANCIAL AID (1999–2000)

71 students received aid, including fellowships, loans, scholarships, and teaching assistantships. **Financial Aid Contact** Ms. Susan Vest, Enrollment Services Coordinator, 1044 Pamplin Hall (0209), Blacksburg, VA 24061. **Phone:** 540-231-6152. **Fax:** 540-231-4487. **E-mail:** susanv@vt.edu.

RESOURCES AND SERVICES

Information about online services, personal computer policies, library resources, international exchange programs, internship programs, and placement services at this institution and others can be found at **www.petersons.com/mba**

International Students

15% of students enrolled are international students.

Services and Facilities Counseling/support services, ESL/language courses, international student organization, language tutoring, orientation, visa services. Financial aid is available to international students.
Applying *Required:* TOEFL with recommended score of 213 (computer) or 550 (paper).
International Student Contact Ms. Susan Vest, Enrollment Services Coordinator, 1044 Pamplin Hall (0209), Blacksburg, VA 24061. **Phone:** 540-231-6152. **Fax:** 540-231-4487. **E-mail:** susanv@vt.edu.

■ APPLICATION

Required GMAT, application form, baccalaureate/first degree, 2 letters of recommendation, resume/curriculum vitae, transcripts of college work. **Recommended** Personal statement, 2 years of work experience.
Deadlines and Fees *Deadlines:* 2/1 for fall, 2/1 for fall (international). *Application fee:* $45, $45 (international).
Application Contact Ms. Susan Vest, Enrollment Services Coordinator, 1044 Pamplin Hall (0209), Blacksburg, VA 24061. **Phone:** 540-231-6152. **Fax:** 540-231-4487. **E-mail:** susanv@vt.edu.

See full description on page 998.

Virginia State University
Petersburg, Virginia
SCHOOL OF BUSINESS

Graduate Business Faculty
Full-time: 6

Student Body
Average Age: 25

Costs (1999–2000)
Full-time tuition: $3804 per academic year (resident), $9322 per academic year (nonresident)
Part-time tuition: $135 per credit hour (resident), $375 per credit hour (nonresident)

DEGREE MA

MA—Master of Arts in Economics Full-time and part-time. 30 to 36 total credits required. 18 to 72 months to complete program.

COSTS

Tuition, state resident: *Full-time* $3804. *Part-time* $135 per credit hour. **Tuition, nonresident:** *Full-time* $9322. *Part-time* $375 per credit hour. **Tuition, international:** *Full-time* $9322. **Graduate housing:** *Typical cost:* $5096 (including board), $2898 (room only).

FINANCIAL AID (1999–2000)

Fellowships and work study. Financial aid application deadline: 5/1. **Financial Aid Contact** Mr. Henry DeBose, Financial Aid Office, PO Box 9031, Petersburg, VA 23806. **Phone:** 804-524-5990. **Fax:** 804-524-6818.

RESOURCES AND SERVICES

Information about online services, personal computer policies, library resources, international exchange programs, internship programs, and placement services at this institution and others can be found at **www.petersons.com/mba**

International Students

Services and Facilities Counseling/support services.
Applying *Required:* TOEFL with recommended score of 500 (paper).

■ APPLICATION

Required Application form, baccalaureate/first degree, transcripts of college work. School will accept GRE.
Deadlines and Fees Applications for domestic and international students are processed on a rolling basis. *Application fee:* $25, $25 (international).
Application Contact Dean, School of Graduate Studies, Research, and Outreach, Box 9080, Petersburg, VA 23806-0001. **Phone:** 804-524-5984. **Fax:** 804-524-5401.

WASHINGTON

Antioch University Seattle
Seattle, Washington
PROGRAM IN MANAGEMENT

Graduate Business Faculty
Full-time: 3   Part-time: 4

Student Body
Total: 25
Full-time: 25   Average Age: 39   Women: 68%

Admissions
Applications: 15   Enrolled: 9
Admitted: 11

Costs (1999–2000)
Full-time tuition: $13,500 per academic year
Part-time tuition: $410 per credit

After Graduation (Class of 1998–99)
Employed within 3 months of graduation: 100%

DEGREE MS

MS—Master of Science in Management Full-time. At least 66 total credits required. Maximum of 20 months to complete program. *Concentrations:* business ethics, economics, finance, human resources, international business, leadership, logistics, management, management science, marketing, operations management, organizational behavior/development, organizational management, quality management, strategic management, system management.

COSTS

Tuition *Full-time:* $13,500. *Part-time:* $410 per credit.

FINANCIAL AID (1999–2000)

10 students received aid, including loans, scholarships, and work study. Financial aid application deadline: 7/15. **Financial Aid Contact** Ms. Kathy Battraw, Financial Aid Officer, 2326 Sixth Avenue, Seattle, WA 98121-1814. **Phone:** 206-441-5352 Ext. 5003. **Fax:** 206-441-3307. **E-mail:** kbattraw@antiochsea.edu.

RESOURCES AND SERVICES

Information about online services, personal computer policies, library resources, international exchange programs, internship programs, and placement services at this institution and others can be found at **www.petersons.com/mba**

International Students

16% of students enrolled are international students.

Services and Facilities Financial aid is not available to international students.
Applying *Required:* TOEFL with recommended score of 600 (paper), proof of adequate funds, proof of health/immunizations.

International Student Contact Mr. Mark Hower, Admissions Counselor, 2326 Sixth Avenue, Seattle, WA 98121-1814. **Phone:** 206-441-5352 Ext. 5713. **Fax:** 206-441-3307. **E-mail:** mhower@antiochsea.edu.

■ **APPLICATION**

Required Application form, baccalaureate/first degree, essay, interview, 2 letters of recommendation, personal statement, resume/curriculum vitae, transcripts of college work. **Recommended** Work experience.

Deadlines and Fees *Deadlines:* 8/1 for fall, 8/1 for fall (international). *Application fee:* $50, $50 (international).

Application Contact Mr. Mark Hower, Admissions Counselor, 2326 Sixth Avenue, Seattle, WA 98121-1814. **Phone:** 206-441-5352 Ext. 5713. **Fax:** 206-441-3307. **E-mail:** mhower@antiochsea.edu.

City University

Bellevue, Washington

SCHOOL OF BUSINESS AND MANAGEMENT PROFESSIONS

Graduate Business Faculty

Full-time: 14	Part-time: 689

Student Body

Total: 2,772	Average Age: 37
Full-time: 408	Women: 39%
Part-time: 2,364	

Admissions

Applications: 1,046	Enrolled: 390
Admitted: 1,046	

Costs (1999–2000)
Full-time tuition: $7056 per academic year
Part-time tuition: $294 per credit hour

DEGREES MA • MBA • MBA/MPA • MPA • MS

MA—Master of Arts in Management Full-time and part-time. *Distance learning option.* At least 45 total credits required. *Concentrations:* leadership, management.

MBA—Master of Business Administration Full-time and part-time. *Distance learning option.* At least 45 total credits required. *Concentrations:* financial management/planning, international banking, management, management information systems, marketing.

MBA/MPA—Master of Business Administration/Master of Public Administration Full-time and part-time. *Distance learning option.* At least 60 total credits required. *Concentrations:* legal administration, public policy and administration.

MPA—Master of Public Administration Full-time and part-time. *Distance learning option.* At least 45 total credits required. *Concentrations:* legal administration, public policy and administration.

MS—Master of Science Full-time and part-time. *Distance learning option.* At least 45 total credits required. *Concentrations:* management information systems, project management.

COSTS

Tuition *Full-time:* $7056. *Part-time:* $294 per credit hour.

FINANCIAL AID (1999–2000)

90 students received aid, including loans and scholarships. Aid is available to part-time students. **Financial Aid Contact** Ms. Jean Roberts, Financial Aid Counselor, 335 116th Avenue SE, Bellevue, WA 98004. **Phone:** 425-637-1010. **Fax:** 425-637-9689. **E-mail:** jroberts@cityu.edu.

RESOURCES AND SERVICES

Information about online services, personal computer policies, library resources, international exchange programs, internship programs, and placement services at this institution and others can be found at **www.petersons.com/mba**

International Students

50% of students enrolled are international students.

Services and Facilities Counseling/support services, ESL/language courses, housing location assistance, international student organization. Financial aid is not available to international students.

Applying *Required:* TOEFL with recommended score of 540 (paper), proof of adequate funds.

International Student Contact International Advising Director, 919 SW Grady Way, 2nd Floor, Renton, WA 98055. **Phone:** 425-637-1010 Ext. 3821. **Fax:** 425-204-3929. **E-mail:** info@cityu.edu.

■ **APPLICATION**

Required Application form, baccalaureate/first degree, transcripts of college work.

Deadlines and Fees Applications for domestic and international students are processed on a rolling basis. *Application fee:* $75, $175 (international).

Application Contact Admissions Advisor, 919 SW Grady Way, 2nd Floor, Renton, WA 98055. **Phone:** 425-637-1010. **Fax:** 425-277-2437. **E-mail:** info@cityu.edu.

See full description on page 590.

Eastern Washington University

Cheney, Washington

COLLEGE OF BUSINESS ADMINISTRATION

Graduate Business Faculty

Full-time: 23	Part-time: 14

Student Body

Total: 98	Average Age: 29
Full-time: 36	Women: 40%
Part-time: 62	

Admissions

Applications: 99	Average GMAT: 500
Admitted: 58	Average GPA: 3.56
Enrolled: 31	

Costs (1999–2000)
Full-time tuition: $4626 per academic year (resident), $13,464 per academic year (nonresident)
Part-time tuition: $144 per credit (resident), $428 per credit (nonresident)

After Graduation (Class of 1998–99)
Employed within 3 months of graduation: 80%
Average starting salary: $25,000

Accreditation
AACSB—The International Association for Management Education

DEGREES MBA • MBA/HSAD • MBA/MPA • MPA

MBA—Master of Business Administration Full-time and part-time. At least 49 total credits required. 12 to 72 months to complete program. *Concentrations:* accounting, entrepreneurship, finance, financial management/planning, health care, human resources, information management, international business, management, management information systems, marketing, operations management, resources management.

MBA/HSAD—Master of Business Administration/Health Services Certificate Full-time and part-time. At least 69 total credits required. 18 to 72 months to complete program. *Concentrations:* health care.

MBA/MPA—Master of Business Administration/Master of Public Administration Full-time and part-time. 75 to 85 total credits required. 18 to 72 months to complete program. *Concentrations:* city/urban administration, nonprofit management, nonprofit organization, public policy and administration.

MPA—Master of Public Administration Full-time and part-time. GMAT not required. At least 60 total credits required. 12 to 72 months to complete program.

COSTS

Tuition, state resident: *Full-time* $4326. *Part-time* $144 per credit. **Tuition, nonresident:** *Full-time* $13,164. *Part-time* $428 per credit. Tuition varies by number of courses or credits taken and local reciprocity agreements. **Required fees:** *Full-time* $300. *Part-time* $10 per course. **Graduate housing:** Room and board costs vary by number of occupants and type of board plan. *Typical cost:* $4399 (including board).

FINANCIAL AID (1999–2000)

4 students received aid, including loans, research assistantships, teaching assistantships, and work study. Financial aid application deadline: 2/1. **Financial Aid Contact** Director, Financial Aid and Scholarships, MS 142, 526 5th Street, Cheney, WA 99004-2431. **Phone:** 509-359-2314. **Fax:** 509-359-6153.

RESOURCES AND SERVICES

Information about online services, personal computer policies, library resources, international exchange programs, internship programs, and

Eastern Washington University (continued)

placement services at this institution and others can be found at **www.petersons.com/mba**

International Students

34% of students enrolled are international students.

Services and Facilities Counseling/support services, ESL/language courses, international student organization, language tutoring, visa services. Financial aid is not available to international students.
Applying *Required:* TOEFL with recommended score of 580 (paper), proof of adequate funds. *Recommended:* Proof of health/immunizations.
International Student Contact Ms. Lily Gao, Director, International Student Programs, MS 28, 526 5th Street, Cheney, WA 99004-2431. **Phone:** 509-359-2331. **Fax:** 504-359-4643. **E-mail:** lily.gao@mail.ewu.edu.

■ APPLICATION

Required GMAT, application form, baccalaureate/first degree, transcripts of college work. **Recommended** Interview, 3 letters of recommendation, 3 years of work experience.

Deadlines and Fees Applications for domestic and international students are processed on a rolling basis. *Application fee:* $35, $35 (international).

Application Contact Dr. Lynn Stephens, Director, MBA Program and International Programs, 668 North Riverpoint Boulevard, Suite A, Spokane, WA 99202-1660. **Phone:** 509-358-2270. **Fax:** 509-358-2267. **E-mail:** lynn.stephens@mail.ewu.edu.

Gonzaga University

Spokane, Washington

SCHOOL OF BUSINESS ADMINISTRATION

Graduate Business Faculty
Full-time: 19 | Part-time: 11

Student Body
Total: 142
Full-time: 83 | Average Age: 30
Part-time: 59 | Women: 31%

Admissions
Applications: 125
Admitted: 82 | Average GMAT: 531
Enrolled: 53 | Average GPA: 3.15

Costs (1999–2000)
Full-time tuition: N/R
Part-time tuition: $425 per credit hour

After Graduation (Class of 1998–99)
Employed within 3 months of graduation: 90%
Average starting salary: $50,000

Accreditation
AACSB—The International Association for Management Education

DEGREES JD/M Acc • JD/MBA • M Acc • MBA

JD/M Acc—Juris Doctor/Master of Accountancy Full-time. At least 111 total credits required. 48 to 60 months to complete program. *Concentrations:* accounting.

JD/MBA—Juris Doctor/Master of Business Administration Full-time. At least 114 total credits required. 48 to 60 months to complete program.

M Acc—Master of Accountancy Full-time and part-time. At least 30 total credits required. 12 to 60 months to complete program. *Concentrations:* accounting, management information systems, taxation.

MBA—Master of Business Administration Full-time and part-time. At least 33 total credits required. 12 to 60 months to complete program. *Concentrations:* management information systems.

COSTS

Tuition *Part-time:* $425 per credit hour. **Graduate housing:** Room and board costs vary by number of occupants, type of accommodation, and type of board plan. *Typical cost:* $6110 (including board).

FINANCIAL AID (1999–2000)

35 students received aid, including loans, research assistantships, scholarships, and work study. Aid is available to part-time students. Financial aid application deadline: 2/1. **Financial Aid Contact** Mr. Tim Henning, Associate Director of Financial Aid, PO Box 72, Spokane, WA

99258. **Phone:** 509-328-4220 Ext. 6582. **Fax:** 509-324-5718. **E-mail:** henning@gu.gonzagu.edu.

RESOURCES AND SERVICES

Information about online services, personal computer policies, library resources, international exchange programs, internship programs, and placement services at this institution and others can be found at **www.petersons.com/mba**

International Students

20% of students enrolled are international students.

Services and Facilities Counseling/support services, ESL/language courses, language tutoring. Financial aid is not available to international students.
Applying *Required:* TOEFL with recommended score of 550 (paper), proof of adequate funds, proof of health/immunizations.
International Student Contact Mr. Raymond Fadeley, Director, International Students Program, 311 East Boone Avenue, Spokane, WA 99258. **Phone:** 509-328-4220 Ext. 6284. **Fax:** 509-324-5814. **E-mail:** fadeley@gonzaga.edu.

■ APPLICATION

Required GMAT, application form, baccalaureate/first degree, 2 letters of recommendation, transcripts of college work. **Recommended** Personal statement, resume/curriculum vitae.

Deadlines and Fees Applications for domestic and international students are processed on a rolling basis. *Application fee:* $40, $40 (international).

Application Contact Dr. Larry Lewis, Associate Dean, School of Business Administration, 502 East Boone Avenue—AD Box 9, Spokane, WA 99258. **Phone:** 509-328-4220 Ext. 3430. **Toll-free Phone:** 800-572-9658 (in-state), 800-523-9712 (out-of-state). **Fax:** 509-324-5811. **E-mail:** lewis@jepson.gonzaga.edu.

Pacific Lutheran University

Tacoma, Washington

SCHOOL OF BUSINESS ADMINISTRATION AND MANAGEMENT

Graduate Business Faculty
Full-time: 9 | Part-time: 1

Student Body
Total: 105
Full-time: 64 | Average Age: 32
Part-time: 41 | Women: 34%

Admissions
Applications: 58
Admitted: 53 | Average GMAT: 561
Enrolled: 46 | Average GPA: 3.1

Costs (1999–2000)
Full-time tuition: $12,168 per academic year
Part-time tuition: $507 per credit

Accreditation
AACSB—The International Association for Management Education

DEGREE MBA

MBA—Master of Business Administration Full-time and part-time. Application deadline: 6/1 for Saturday program. 40 to 48 total credits required. 18 to 84 months to complete program. *Concentrations:* technology management.

COSTS

Tuition *Full-time:* $12,168. *Part-time:* $507 per credit. Tuition varies by number of courses or credits taken. **Graduate housing:** Room and board costs vary by number of occupants and type of board plan. *Typical cost:* $5038 (including board).

FINANCIAL AID (1999–2000)

28 students received aid, including fellowships, grants, research assistantships, scholarships, and work study. Aid is available to part-time students. Financial aid application deadline: 3/1. **Financial Aid Contact** Kay Soltis, Director of Financial Aid, Pacific Lutheran University, Tacoma, WA 98447. **Phone:** 253-535-7161. **Fax:** 253-535-8320. **E-mail:** finaid@plu.edu.

RESOURCES AND SERVICES

Information about online services, personal computer policies, library resources, international exchange programs, internship programs, and placement services at this institution and others can be found at **www.petersons.com/mba**

International Students
15% of students enrolled are international students.

Services and Facilities Counseling/support services, ESL/language courses, international student housing, orientation, visa services. Financial aid is available to international students.
Applying *Required:* TOEFL with recommended score of 213 (computer) or 550 (paper), proof of adequate funds, proof of health/immunizations.
International Student Contact David Gerry, Coordinator, International Student Services, Pacific Lutheran University, Tacoma, WA 98447. **Phone:** 253-535-7194. **Fax:** 253-535-8752. **E-mail:** gerrydp@plu.edu.

■ **APPLICATION**

Required GMAT, application form, baccalaureate/first degree, 2 letters of recommendation, personal statement, resume/curriculum vitae, transcripts of college work. **Recommended** 2 years of work experience.
Deadlines and Fees Applications for domestic and international students are processed on a rolling basis. *Application fee:* $35, $35 (international).
Application Contact Ms. Catherine Pratt, Assistant Dean and Director, MBA Program, School of Business, Tacoma, WA 98447. **Phone:** 253-535-7250. **Toll-free Phone:** 800-274-6758. **Fax:** 253-535-8723. **E-mail:** business@plu.edu.

See full description on page 760.

Saint Martin's College

Lacey, Washington

DEPARTMENT OF ECONOMICS AND BUSINESS ADMINISTRATION

DEGREE MBA

MBA—Master of Business Administration Full-time and part-time. At least 33 total credits required. 12 to 84 months to complete program.

RESOURCES AND SERVICES
Information about online services, personal computer policies, library resources, international exchange programs, internship programs, and placement services at this institution and others can be found at **www.petersons.com/mba**

International Students

Services and Facilities Counseling/support services, ESL/language courses, visa services. Financial aid is not available to international students.
International Student Contact Ms. Josephine Yung, Director of International Student Services, 5300 Pacific Avenue, SE, Lacey, WA 98503. **Phone:** 360-438-4375.

■ **APPLICATION**

Application Contact MBA Director, 5300 Pacific Avenue, SE, Lacey, WA 98503. **Phone:** 360-438-4326. **Fax:** 360-438-4522.

Seattle Pacific University

Seattle, Washington

SCHOOL OF BUSINESS AND ECONOMICS

Graduate Business Faculty
Full-time: 19   Part-time: 6
Student Body
Total: 151   Average Age: 32
Full-time: 21   Women: 47%
Part-time: 130
Admissions
Applications: 38   Average GMAT: 530
Admitted: 32   Average GPA: 3.2
Enrolled: 25
Costs (1999–2000)
Full-time tuition: $11,394 per academic year
Part-time tuition: $422 per credit hour
After Graduation (Class of 1998–99)
Employed within 3 months of graduation: 96%
Average starting salary: $63,750
Accreditation
AACSB—The International Association for Management Education

DEGREES MBA • MS

MBA—Master of Business Administration Full-time and part-time. Minimum GMAT score of 460 required. 45 to 72 total credits required. 18 to 72 months to complete program. *Concentrations:* human resources, management, management information systems.
MS—Master of Science in Information Systems Management Full-time and part-time. GRE required. 45 to 60 total credits required. 18 to 72 months to complete program. *Concentrations:* management information systems.

COSTS
Tuition *Full-time:* $11,394. *Part-time:* $422 per credit hour. **Graduate housing:** Room and board costs vary by number of occupants, type of accommodation, and type of board plan. *Typical cost:* $6500 (including board).

FINANCIAL AID (1999–2000)
8 students received aid, including research assistantships. Aid is available to part-time students. **Financial Aid Contact** Office of Financial Aid, 3307 Third Avenue West, Seattle, WA 98119-1997. **Phone:** 206-281-2046.

RESOURCES AND SERVICES
Information about online services, personal computer policies, library resources, international exchange programs, internship programs, and placement services at this institution and others can be found at **www.petersons.com/mba**

International Students
13% of students enrolled are international students.

Services and Facilities Counseling/support services, ESL/language courses. Financial aid is not available to international students.
Applying *Required:* TOEFL with recommended score of 225 (computer) or 565 (paper), proof of adequate funds.
International Student Contact Mr. Kevin McMahan, International Program Coordinator, 3307 Third Avenue West, Seattle, WA 98119. **Phone:** 206-281-2486. **Fax:** 206-281-2730. **E-mail:** kmcmahan@spu.edu.

■ **APPLICATION**

Required GMAT, application form, baccalaureate/first degree, essay, 2 letters of recommendation, resume/curriculum vitae, transcripts of college work, 1 year of work experience.
Deadlines and Fees *Deadlines:* 8/1 for fall, 11/1 for winter, 2/1 for spring, 5/1 for summer, 8/1 for fall (international), 11/1 for winter (international), 2/1 for spring (international), 5/1 for summer (international). *Application fee:* $35, $35 (international).
Application Contact Ms. Debra Wysomierski, Assistant Graduate Director, 3307 Third Avenue West, Seattle, WA 98119. **Phone:** 206-281-2753. **Fax:** 206-281-2733. **E-mail:** djwysom@spu.edu.

See full description on page 818.

Seattle University

Seattle, Washington

ALBERS SCHOOL OF BUSINESS AND ECONOMICS

Graduate Business Faculty
Full-time: 47   Part-time: 18
Student Body
Total: 681   Average Age: 32
Full-time: 132   Women: 39%
Part-time: 549
Admissions
Applications: 239   Average GMAT: 576
Admitted: 179   Average GPA: 3.1
Enrolled: 125
Costs (1999–2000)
Full-time tuition: N/R
Part-time tuition: $465 per quarter hour
Accreditation
AACSB—The International Association for Management Education

DEGREES MAE • MBA • MIB • MP Ac • MSF

MAE—Master of Applied Economics Full-time and part-time. 45 to 63 total credits required. 12 to 72 months to complete program. *Concentrations:* financial economics.

Seattle University (continued)

MBA—Master of Business Administration Full-time and part-time. 55 to 73 total credits required. 12 to 72 months to complete program. *Concentrations:* accounting, business law, economics, finance, human resources, international business, management, management information systems, marketing, operations management.

MIB—Master of International Business Full-time and part-time. 45 to 64 total credits required. 12 to 72 months to complete program. *Concentrations:* international business.

MP Ac—Master of Professional Accountancy Full-time and part-time. 46 to 85 total credits required. 12 to 72 months to complete program. *Concentrations:* accounting.

MSF—Master of Science in Finance Full-time and part-time. 45 to 63 total credits required. 12 to 72 months to complete program. *Concentrations:* finance.

COSTS

Tuition *Part-time:* $465 per quarter hour. Tuition varies by number of courses or credits taken. **Graduate housing:** Room and board costs vary by number of occupants, type of accommodation, and type of board plan. *Typical cost:* $5880 (including board).

FINANCIAL AID (1999–2000)

Loans, scholarships, and work study. Aid is available to part-time students. Financial aid application deadline: 2/1. **Financial Aid Contact** Jim White, Director, Financial Aid and Student Employment, 900 Broadway, Seattle, WA 98122. **Phone:** 206-296-5480. **E-mail:** whitejim@ seattleu.edu.

RESOURCES AND SERVICES

Information about online services, personal computer policies, library resources, international exchange programs, internship programs, and placement services at this institution and others can be found at **www. petersons.com/mba**

International Students

10% of students enrolled are international students.

Services and Facilities Counseling/support services, ESL/language courses, international student organization, orientation, visa services. Financial aid is not available to international students.

Applying *Required:* TOEFL with recommended score of 237 (computer) or 580 (paper), proof of adequate funds.

International Student Contact Faizi Ghodsi, Director, International Student Center, 900 Broadway, Seattle, WA 98122. **Phone:** 206-296-6260. **Fax:** 206-296-6262. **E-mail:** ghodsif@seattleu.edu.

■ APPLICATION

Required GMAT, application form, baccalaureate/first degree, resume/curriculum vitae, transcripts of college work, 1 year of work experience.

Deadlines and Fees *Deadlines:* 8/20 for fall, 11/20 for winter, 2/20 for spring, 5/20 for summer, 6/1 for fall (international), 9/1 for winter (international), 1/1 for spring (international), 3/1 for summer (international). *Application fee:* $60, $60 (international).

Application Contact Michael McKeon, Dean of Admissions, Graduate Admissions, 900 Broadway, Seattle, WA 98122. **Phone:** 206-296-5900. **Toll-free Phone:** 800-542-0833 (in-state), 800-426-7123 (out-of-state). **Fax:** 206-296-5902. **E-mail:** grad-admissions@seattleu.edu.

See full description on page 820.

University of Washington

Seattle, Washington

SCHOOL OF BUSINESS ADMINISTRATION

Graduate Business Faculty
Full-time: 80

Student Body

Total: 440	Average Age: 29
Full-time: 298	Women: 34%
Part-time: 142	

Admissions

Applications: 1,159	Average GMAT: 628
Admitted: 374	Average GPA: 3.2
Enrolled: 157	

Costs (1999–2000)
Full-time tuition: $5745 per academic year (resident), $14,283 per academic year (nonresident)

Part-time tuition: $1642 per quarter (resident), $4081 per quarter (nonresident)

After Graduation (Class of 1998–99)
Employed within 3 months of graduation: 94%
Average starting salary: $59,425

Accreditation
AACSB—The International Association for Management Education

DEGREES JD/MBA • MBA • MBA/MA • MBA/MHA • MBA/MS • MPA

JD/MBA—Juris Doctor/Master of Business Administration Full-time. At least 212 total credits required. 48 to 72 months to complete program. *Concentrations:* business law, legal administration.

MBA—Evening MBA Part-time. At least 66 total credits required. 33 to 45 months to complete program. *Concentrations:* management.

MBA—Executive MBA Part-time. At least 66 total credits required. 24 months to complete program. *Concentrations:* management.

MBA—Master of Business Administration Full-time. At least 96 total credits required. 24 to 72 months to complete program. *Concentrations:* accounting, decision sciences, economics, electronic commerce (e-commerce), entrepreneurship, finance, human resources, information management, international business, management, management information systems, managerial economics, marketing, operations management, organizational behavior/development, quantitative analysis, strategic management, technology management, transportation and logistics.

MBA/MA—Master of Business Administration/Master of Arts in International Studies Full-time. At least 132 total credits required. 36 to 72 months to complete program. *Concentrations:* international and area business studies, international business, international economics, international finance, international logistics, international management, international marketing, international trade.

MBA/MHA—Master of Business Administration/Master of Health Administration Full-time. At least 112 total credits required. 24 to 72 months to complete program. *Concentrations:* management.

MBA/MS—PEMM-Program in Engineering and Manufacturing Management Full-time. At least 166 total credits required. 24 to 72 months to complete program. *Concentrations:* manufacturing management, production management.

MPA—Master of Professional Accounting in Taxation Full-time and part-time. At least 48 total credits required. 12 to 72 months to complete program. *Concentrations:* taxation.

COSTS

Tuition, state resident: *Full-time* $5745. *Part-time* $1642 per quarter. **Tuition, nonresident:** *Full-time* $14,283. *Part-time* $4081 per quarter. Tuition varies by class time and number of courses or credits taken. **Graduate housing:** Room and board costs vary by campus location, number of occupants, type of accommodation, and type of board plan. *Typical cost:* $7845 (including board).

FINANCIAL AID (1999–2000)

181 students received aid, including fellowships, loans, research assistantships, scholarships, teaching assistantships, and work study. Financial aid application deadline: 3/1. **Financial Aid Contact** Mr. Dan Poston, Associate Director, Admissions, Box 353200, Seattle, WA 98195-3200. **Phone:** 206-685-8395. **Fax:** 206-616-7351.

RESOURCES AND SERVICES

Information about online services, personal computer policies, library resources, international exchange programs, internship programs, and placement services at this institution and others can be found at **www. petersons.com/mba**

International Students

16% of students enrolled are international students.

Services and Facilities Counseling/support services, ESL/language courses, international student housing, orientation, visa services. Financial aid is available to international students.

Applying *Required:* TOEFL with recommended score of 600 (paper), proof of adequate funds, proof of health/immunizations. *Recommended:* TSE.

International Student Contact Mr. Dan Poston, Associate Director, Admissions, Box 353200, Seattle, WA 98195-3200. **Phone:** 206-543-4661. **Fax:** 206-616-7351. **E-mail:** dposton@u.washington.edu.

■ APPLICATION

Required GMAT, application form, baccalaureate/first degree, essay, 2 letters of recommendation, personal statement, resume/curriculum vitae, transcripts of college work. **Recommended** Interview, 2 years of work experience.

Deadlines and Fees *Deadlines:* 3/1 for fall, 2/1 for fall (international). *Application fee:* $50, $50 (international).

Application Contact MBA Program Office, Box 353200, 110 Mackenzie Hall, Seattle, WA 98195-3200. **Phone:** 206-543-4661. **Fax:** 206-616-7351. **E-mail:** mba@u.washington.edu.

See full description on page 986.

Washington State University

Pullman, Washington

COLLEGE OF BUSINESS AND ECONOMICS

Graduate Business Faculty
Full-time: 63

Part-time: 2

Student Body
Total: 236
Full-time: 157
Part-time: 79

Average Age: 28
Women: 43%

Admissions
Applications: 334
Admitted: 181
Enrolled: 114

Average GMAT: 560
Average GPA: 3.4

Costs (1999–2000)
Full-time tuition: $5660 per academic year (resident), $13,872 per academic year (nonresident)
Part-time tuition: $268 per credit (resident), $678 per credit (nonresident)

After Graduation (Class of 1998–99)
Employed within 3 months of graduation: 94%
Average starting salary: $47,500

Accreditation
AACSB—The International Association for Management Education

DEGREES M Acc • MBA • MTM

M Acc—Master of Accounting Full-time. At least 34 total credits required. 12 to 24 months to complete program. *Concentrations:* accounting, taxation.

MBA—Master of Business Administration Full-time. 35 to 64 total credits required. 12 to 24 months to complete program. *Concentrations:* accounting, decision sciences, finance, international business, management information systems, marketing, real estate, travel industry/tourism management.

MTM—Master of Technology Management Part-time. 30 to 48 total credits required. 24 to 48 months to complete program. *Concentrations:* technology management.

COSTS

Tuition, state resident: *Full-time* $5660. *Part-time* $268 per credit. **Tuition, nonresident:** *Full-time* $13,872. *Part-time* $678 per credit. **Graduate housing:** Room and board costs vary by campus location, number of occupants, type of accommodation, and type of board plan. *Typical cost:* $7166 (including board).

FINANCIAL AID (1999–2000)

Loans, research assistantships, scholarships, teaching assistantships, and work study. **Financial Aid Contact** Wayne Sparks, Director, Financial Aid Office, Lighty Student Services Building, Room 380, Pullman, WA 99164-1068. **Phone:** 509-335-9711.

RESOURCES AND SERVICES

Information about online services, personal computer policies, library resources, international exchange programs, internship programs, and placement services at this institution and others can be found at www.petersons.com/mba

International Students

35% of students enrolled are international students.

Services and Facilities Counseling/support services, ESL/language courses, international student housing, international student organization, orientation, visa services. Financial aid is available to international students.
Applying *Required:* TOEFL with recommended score of 580 (paper), proof of adequate funds, proof of health/immunizations.
International Student Contact Hutnak Uta, Associate Director, International Programs, Pullman, WA 99164-5110. **Phone:** 509-335-4508. **Fax:** 509-335-2373. **E-mail:** hutnaku@wsu.edu.

■ APPLICATION

Required GMAT, application form, baccalaureate/first degree, 3 letters of recommendation, transcripts of college work. **Recommended** Personal statement, resume/curriculum vitae, work experience.

Deadlines and Fees Applications for domestic students are processed on a rolling basis. *Deadlines:* 3/1 for fall (international), 7/1 for spring (international), 3/1 for summer (international). *Application fee:* $35, $35 (international).
Application Contact Dr. Val Miskin, Director, College of Business and Economics, Pullman, WA 99164-4744. **Phone:** 509-335-7617. **Fax:** 509-335-4735. **E-mail:** mba@wsu.edu.

Western Washington University

Bellingham, Washington

COLLEGE OF BUSINESS AND ECONOMICS

Graduate Business Faculty
Full-time: 31

Part-time: 1

Student Body
Total: 41
Full-time: 27
Part-time: 14

Average Age: 30
Women: 51%

Admissions
Applications: 29
Admitted: 15
Enrolled: 15

Average GMAT: 573
Average GPA: 3.29

Costs (1999–2000)
Full-time tuition: $4647 per academic year (resident), $13,623 per academic year (nonresident)
Part-time tuition: $140 per credit (resident), $426 per credit (nonresident)

Accreditation
AACSB—The International Association for Management Education

DEGREE MBA

MBA—Master of Business Administration Full-time and part-time. At least 60 total credits required. 12 to 27 months to complete program.

COSTS

Tuition, state resident: *Full-time* $4647. *Part-time* $140 per credit. **Tuition, nonresident:** *Full-time* $13,623. *Part-time* $426 per credit. Tuition varies by number of courses or credits taken. **Graduate housing:** Room and board costs vary by campus location, number of occupants, type of accommodation, and type of board plan. *Typical cost:* $5300 (including board), $3650 (room only).

FINANCIAL AID (1999–2000)

Loans, scholarships, teaching assistantships, and work study. Aid is available to part-time students. Financial aid application deadline: 3/31. **Financial Aid Contact** Student Financial Resources, MS 9006, 516 High Street, Bellingham, WA 98225-9900. **Phone:** 360-650-3470. **Fax:** 360-650-7291. **E-mail:** fmd@admsec.wwu.edu.

RESOURCES AND SERVICES

Information about online services, personal computer policies, library resources, international exchange programs, internship programs, and placement services at this institution and others can be found at www.petersons.com/mba

International Students

22% of students enrolled are international students.

Services and Facilities Counseling/support services, visa services. Financial aid is not available to international students.
Applying *Required:* TOEFL with recommended score of 227 (computer) or 565 (paper), proof of adequate funds, proof of health/immunizations.
International Student Contact Multicultural Services Center, Bellingham, WA 98225. **Phone:** 360-650-3843. **Fax:** 360-650-3715.

■ APPLICATION

Required GMAT, application form, baccalaureate/first degree, essay, personal statement, resume/curriculum vitae, transcripts of college work.

Deadlines and Fees *Deadlines:* 5/1 for fall, 5/1 for spring, 5/1 for summer, 1/1 for fall (international), 1/1 for summer (international). *Application fee:* $35, $35 (international).

Application Contact Mrs. Juliet Barnes, Program Coordinator, MBA Program, MS 9072, Bellingham, WA 98225-9072. **Phone:** 360-650-3898. **Fax:** 360-650-4844. **E-mail:** mba@wwu.edu.

Whitworth College

Spokane, Washington

GRADUATE SCHOOL OF INTERNATIONAL MANAGEMENT

Graduate Business Faculty
Full-time: 4 — Part-time: 14

Student Body
Total: 57
Full-time: 50 — Average Age: 33
Part-time: 7 — Women: 37%

Admissions
Applications: 33 — Average GMAT: 550
Admitted: 28 — Average GPA: 3.2

Costs (1999–2000)
Full-time tuition: $7300 per academic year
Part-time tuition: $365 per credit

After Graduation (Class of 1998–99)
Employed within 3 months of graduation: 95%
Average starting salary: $40,000

DEGREE MIM

MIM—Master of International Management Full-time and part-time. At least 37 total credits required. 12 to 72 months to complete program. *Concentrations:* international business, international management, nonprofit management.

COSTS

Tuition *Full-time:* $7300. *Part-time:* $365 per credit. **Tuition, international:** *Full-time* $7300. **Graduate housing:** Room and board costs vary by number of occupants, type of accommodation, and type of board plan. *Typical cost:* $5244 (including board).

FINANCIAL AID (1999–2000)

25 students received aid, including grants, loans, scholarships, and work study. Financial aid application deadline: 3/1. **Financial Aid Contact** Mrs. Wendy Olson, Director of Financial Aid, 300 West Hawthorne Road, MS-0107, Spokane, WA 99251-0001. **Phone:** 509-777-4306. **Fax:** 509-777-3725. **E-mail:** wolson@whitworth.edu.

RESOURCES AND SERVICES

Information about online services, personal computer policies, library resources, international exchange programs, internship programs, and placement services at this institution and others can be found at **www.petersons.com/mba**

International Students

Services and Facilities Counseling/support services, ESL/language courses, international student organization, orientation, visa services. Financial aid is available to international students.
Applying *Required:* TOEFL with recommended score of 550 (paper), proof of adequate funds, proof of health/immunizations. *Recommended:* TWE with recommended score of 4.
International Student Contact Mrs. Loretta M. Wilkening, Program Coordinator/Graduate Education Advisor, 300 West Hawthorne Road, MS-2704, Spokane, WA 99251-0001. **Phone:** 509-777-3742 Ext. 4280. **Fax:** 509-777-3723. **E-mail:** lwilkening@whitworth.edu.

■ APPLICATION

Required Application form, baccalaureate/first degree, essay, 2 letters of recommendation, resume/curriculum vitae, transcripts of college work. School will accept GMAT or GRE. **Recommended** Interview, 5 years of work experience.
Deadlines and Fees *Deadlines:* 4/1 for fall, 11/1 for spring, 4/1 for fall (international), 11/1 for spring (international). *Application fee:* $35, $35 (international).
Application Contact Ms. Loretta M. Wilkening, Program Coordinator/Graduate Education Advisor, 300 West Hawthorne Road, MS—2704, Spokane, WA 99251-0001. **Phone:** 509-777-4280. **Fax:** 509-777-3723. **E-mail:** lwilkening@whitworth.edu.

See full description on page 1012.

WEST VIRGINIA

Marshall University

Huntington, West Virginia

LEWIS COLLEGE OF BUSINESS

Graduate Business Faculty
Full-time: 31

Student Body
Total: 170

Admissions
Applications: 79 — Average GMAT: 530
Admitted: 67 — Average GPA: 3
Enrolled: 60

Costs (1999–2000)
Full-time tuition: N/R
Part-time tuition: $121 per credit hour (resident), $361 per credit hour (nonresident)

Accreditation
AACSB—The International Association for Management Education
ACBSP—The American Council of Business Schools and Programs

DEGREES MBA

MBA—Executive MBA Part-time. 2 years of work experience required. At least 36 total credits required. 18 to 24 months to complete program.

MBA—Master of Business Administration Full-time and part-time. At least 36 total credits required. 12 to 60 months to complete program.

COSTS

Tuition, state resident: *Part-time* $121 per credit hour. **Tuition, nonresident:** *Part-time* $361 per credit hour. **Graduate housing:** Room and board costs vary by number of occupants and type of board plan. *Typical cost:* $4280 (including board).

FINANCIAL AID (1999–2000)

Loans, research assistantships, teaching assistantships, and work study. Aid is available to part-time students. Financial aid application deadline: 6/1. **Financial Aid Contact** Mr. Jack Toney, Director of Financial Aid, 400 Hal Greer Boulevard, Huntington, WV 25755-2020. **Phone:** 304-696-3162. **Fax:** 304-696-3242. **E-mail:** toney@marshall.edu.

RESOURCES AND SERVICES

Information about online services, personal computer policies, library resources, international exchange programs, internship programs, and placement services at this institution and others can be found at **www.petersons.com/mba**

International Students

12% of students enrolled are international students.

Services and Facilities Counseling/support services, ESL/language courses, visa services. Financial aid is not available to international students.
Applying *Required:* TOEFL with recommended score of 525 (paper), proof of adequate funds, proof of health/immunizations.

International Student Contact Mr. Scott Hoppe, International Programs Office, 400 Hal Greer Boulevard, Huntington, WV 25755-2020. **Phone:** 304-696-2379. **Fax:** 304-696-6353. **E-mail:** hoppes@marshall.edu.

■ APPLICATION

Required GMAT, application form, baccalaureate/first degree, transcripts of college work. **Recommended** Interview, letter(s) of recommendation, resume/curriculum vitae.

Deadlines and Fees Applications for domestic and international students are processed on a rolling basis. *Application fee:* $15, $25 (international).

Application Contact Dr. Michael Newsome, Director of Graduate Studies, 400 Hal Greer Boulevard, Corbly Hall 217, Huntington, WV 25755-2305. **Phone:** 304-696-2315. **Fax:** 304-696-3661. **E-mail:** newsome@marshall.edu.

University of Charleston

Charleston, West Virginia

JONES-BENEDUM DIVISION OF BUSINESS

DEGREES MBA • MHRM

MBA—Executive MBA Part-time. Minimum 2 years of management experience required. At least 40 total credits required. 24 months to complete program.

MHRM—Master of Human Resources Management Part-time. Minimum 2 years of business experience required. At least 36 total credits required. 24 to 84 months to complete program.

RESOURCES AND SERVICES

Information about online services, personal computer policies, library resources, international exchange programs, internship programs, and placement services at this institution and others can be found at **www.petersons.com/mba**

International Students

Services and Facilities Counseling/support services, ESL/language courses, visa services. Financial aid is available to international students.
International Student Contact Ms. Janet Schneider, Office of International Student Programs, 2300 MacCorkle Avenue, SE, Charleston, WV 25304-1099. **Phone:** 304-357-4881. **Fax:** 304-357-4769. **E-mail:** jschneider@uchaswv.edu.

■ APPLICATION

Application Contact Dr. Mark L. Wilson, Cecil I. Walker Chair, Jones-Binedum Division of Business, 2300 MacCorkle Avenue SE, Charleston, WV 25304. **Phone:** 304-357-4863. **Fax:** 304-357-4872. **E-mail:** mwilson@uchaswv.edu.

West Virginia University

Morgantown, West Virginia

COLLEGE OF BUSINESS AND ECONOMICS

Graduate Business Faculty
Full-time: 53   Part-time: 4

Student Body
Total: 281
Full-time: 147   Average Age: 28
Part-time: 134   Women: 41%

Admissions
Admitted: 35   Average GMAT: 562
Enrolled: 30

Costs (1999–2000)
Full-time tuition: N/R
Part-time tuition: $173 per credit hour (resident), $479 per credit hour (nonresident)

After Graduation (Class of 1998–99)
Employed within 3 months of graduation: 98%

Accreditation
AACSB—The International Association for Management Education

DEGREES MBA • MPA • MS

MBA—Executive MBA Part-time. *Distance learning option.* 2 years of work experience required. At least 48 total credits required. 30 months to complete program.

MBA—Master of Business Administration Full-time. At least 48 total credits required. 14 months to complete program.

MPA—Master of Professional Accountancy Full-time and part-time. *Distance learning option.* At least 30 total credits required. 12 to 84 months to complete program.

MS—Master of Science in Industrial Relations Full-time and part-time. GMAT or GRE accepted. At least 47 total credits required. 12 to 84 months to complete program.

COSTS

Tuition, state resident: *Part-time* $173 per credit hour. **Tuition, nonresident:** *Part-time* $479 per credit hour. **Required fees:** Tuition and fees vary by number of courses or credits taken. **Graduate housing:** *Typical cost:* $4832 (including board).

FINANCIAL AID (1999–2000)
2 students received aid, including fellowships, loans, research assistantships, teaching assistantships, and work study. Financial aid application deadline: 2/1. **Financial Aid Contact** Financial Aid Office, Morgantown, WV 26506. **Phone:** 304-293-5242.

RESOURCES AND SERVICES
Information about online services, personal computer policies, library resources, international exchange programs, internship programs, and placement services at this institution and others can be found at **www.petersons.com/mba**

International Students
16% of students enrolled are international students.
Applying *Required:* TOEFL with recommended score of 550 (paper).
International Student Contact Don Delgado, Director of International Admissions, PO Box 6009, ddelgado@wvu.edu, Morgantown, WV 26506. **Phone:** 304-293-2121.

■ APPLICATION

Required GMAT, application form, baccalaureate/first degree, 3 letters of recommendation, personal statement, resume/curriculum vitae, transcripts of college work. School will accept GRE. **Recommended** Essay, interview.

Deadlines and Fees Applications for domestic and international students are processed on a rolling basis. *Application fee:* $45, $45 (international).
Application Contact Director, Graduate Programs, PO Box 6025, Morgantown, WV 26506. **Phone:** 304-293-7810. **Fax:** 304-293-2385.

West Virginia Wesleyan College

Buckhannon, West Virginia

FACULTY OF BUSINESS

Graduate Business Faculty
Part-time: 6

Student Body
Total: 48   Average Age: 32
Full-time: 29   Women: 38%
Part-time: 19

Admissions
Applications: 6   Enrolled: 6
Admitted: 6

Costs (1999–2000)
Full-time tuition: N/R
Part-time tuition: $360 per credit hour

DEGREE MBA

MBA—Master of Business Administration Full-time and part-time. At least 42 total credits required. 12 to 84 months to complete program.

COSTS

Tuition *Part-time:* $360 per credit hour.

FINANCIAL AID (1999–2000)
Aid is available to part-time students. **Financial Aid Contact** Lana Golden, Director of Financial Aid, 59 College Avenue, Buckhannon, WV 26201. **Phone:** 304-473-8080.

RESOURCES AND SERVICES
Information about online services, personal computer policies, library resources, international exchange programs, internship programs, and placement services at this institution and others can be found at **www.petersons.com/mba**

International Students
8% of students enrolled are international students.
Applying *Required:* TOEFL with recommended score of 500 (paper).
International Student Contact Alice Leigh, Director of Advising and Career Center and Assistant Dean, 59 College Avenue, Buckhannon, WV 26201. **Phone:** 304-473-8440. **E-mail:** leigh@wvwc.edu.

■ APPLICATION

Required GMAT, application form, baccalaureate/first degree, interview, personal statement, resume/curriculum vitae, transcripts of college work. **Recommended** 2 letters of recommendation.

Deadlines and Fees Applications for domestic and international students are processed on a rolling basis. *Application fee:* $30, $30 (international).

Application Contact Dr. Thomas Cline, Director of MBA Program, 59 College Avenue, Buckhannon, WV 26201. **Phone:** 304-473-8622. **Fax:** 304-473-8479.

Wheeling Jesuit University

Wheeling, West Virginia

DEPARTMENT OF BUSINESS

Graduate Business Faculty

Full-time: 6	Part-time: 2

Student Body

Total: 104	Average Age: 28
Full-time: 20	Women: 42%
Part-time: 84	

Admissions

Applications: 44	Average GMAT: 456
Admitted: 40	Average GPA: 3.02
Enrolled: 30	

Costs (1999–2000)
Full-time tuition: $7100 per academic year
Part-time tuition: $390 per credit hour

DEGREES MBA • MS

MBA—Master of Business Administration Full-time and part-time. 36 to 54 total credits required. 12 to 84 months to complete program.

MS—Master of Science in Accountancy Full-time and part-time. 24 to 36 total credits required. 12 to 84 months to complete program.

COSTS

Tuition *Full-time:* $7020. *Part-time:* $390 per credit hour. **Tuition, international:** *Full-time* $7020. **Required fees:** *Full-time* $80. *Part-time* $135 per year. **Graduate housing:** Room and board costs vary by campus location, number of occupants, and type of accommodation. *Typical cost:* $5200 (including board), $2300 (room only).

FINANCIAL AID (1999–2000)

Loans and research assistantships. Financial aid application deadline: 5/1. **Financial Aid Contact** Ms. Karen Mackay, Director of Student Financial Planning, 316 Washington Avenue, Wheeling, WV 26003-6295. **Phone:** 304-243-2304. **Fax:** 304-243-4397. **E-mail:** kmackay@wju.edu.

RESOURCES AND SERVICES

Information about online services, personal computer policies, library resources, international exchange programs, internship programs, and placement services at this institution and others can be found at **www.petersons.com/mba**

International Students

10% of students enrolled are international students.

Services and Facilities Counseling/support services, ESL/language courses, housing location assistance, international student organization, language tutoring, visa services, international student organization. Financial aid is not available to international students.
Applying *Required:* TOEFL with recommended score of 550 (paper), proof of adequate funds.
International Student Contact Mrs. Eileen Viglietta, International Student Advisor, 316 Washington Avenue, Wheeling, WV 26003-6295. **Phone:** 304-243-2346. **Fax:** 304-243-2397. **E-mail:** eileenv@wju.edu.

■ APPLICATION

Required GMAT, application form, baccalaureate/first degree, 3 letters of recommendation, transcripts of college work. **Recommended** Interview.
Deadlines and Fees Applications for domestic students are processed on a rolling basis. *Deadlines:* 8/1 for fall (international), 12/15 for spring (international), 4/15 for summer (international). *Application fee:* $25, $25 (international).
Application Contact Ms. Becky Forney, Director of Admissions, Graduate and Adult Education, 316 Washington Avenue, Wheeling, WV 26003-6295. **Phone:** 304-243-2250. **Toll-free Phone:** 800-873-7665 (in-state), 800-973-7665 (out-of-state). **Fax:** 304-243-4441. **E-mail:** adulted@wju.edu.

WISCONSIN

Cardinal Stritch University

Milwaukee, Wisconsin

COLLEGE OF BUSINESS AND MANAGEMENT

Graduate Business Faculty

Full-time: 11	Part-time: 450

Student Body

Total: 867	Average Age: 36
Full-time: 867	

Costs (1999–2000)
Full-time tuition: N/R
Part-time tuition: $385 per credit

DEGREES MBA • MBA-H • MS • MSFS

MBA—Master of Business Administration Full-time. *Distance learning option.* 36 total credits required.

MBA-H—Master of Business Administration for Health Care Executives Full-time. 39 total credits required. *Concentrations:* health care.

MS—Master of Science in Management Full-time. 33 total credits required. *Concentrations:* management.

MSFS—Master of Science in Financial Services Full-time. 36 total credits required. *Concentrations:* financial management/planning.

COSTS

Tuition *Part-time:* $385 per credit. Tuition varies by number of courses or credits taken and academic program. **Required fees:** *Part-time* $25 per term.

FINANCIAL AID (1999–2000)

Loans and work study. **Financial Aid Contact** Financial Aid Office, 6801 North Yates Road, Milwaukee, WI 53217-3985. **Phone:** 414-410-4046.

RESOURCES AND SERVICES

Information about online services, personal computer policies, library resources, international exchange programs, internship programs, and placement services at this institution and others can be found at **www.petersons.com/mba**

International Students

Services and Facilities Counseling/support services.
Applying *Required:* TOEFL with recommended score of 600 (paper).
International Student Contact Program Representative, College of Business and Management, 6801 North Yates Road, Milwaukee, WI 53217. **Phone:** 800-347-8822 Ext. 4317. **Fax:** 414-410-4324.

■ APPLICATION

Required GMAT or GRE or MAT, application form, baccalaureate/first degree, resume/curriculum vitae, transcripts of college work, 3 years of work experience.
Deadlines and Fees Applications for domestic and international students are processed on a rolling basis. *Application fee:* $25, $25 (international).
Application Contact Program Representative, College of Business and Management, 6801 North Yates Road, Milwaukee, WI 53217. **Toll-free Phone:** 800-347-8822 Ext. 4317 (in-state), 414-410-4324 (out-of-state). **Fax:** 414-410-4324.

Concordia University Wisconsin

Mequon, Wisconsin

DIVISION OF GRADUATE STUDIES

Graduate Business Faculty
Part-time: 32

Student Body
Total: 150

Admissions
Average GPA: 3.23

Costs (1999–2000)
Full-time tuition: N/R
Part-time tuition: $325 per credit

After Graduation (Class of 1998–99)
Employed within 3 months of graduation: 100%

Accreditation
ACBSP—The American Council of Business Schools and Programs

DEGREE MBA

MBA—Master of Business Administration Full-time and part-time. *Distance learning option.* 39 to 45 total credits required. 12 to 60 months to complete program. *Concentrations:* business education, finance, human resources, international business, management, management information systems, marketing, nonprofit organization, public policy and administration, risk management.

Concordia University Wisconsin (CUW) has a variety of different delivery services to serve students with different academic needs. The on-campus M.B.A. program offers eleven areas of emphasis, including finance, international business, public administration, managerial communication, and MIS. In addition, the program is available in the Chinese language.

For students who are unable to come to the CUW campus, a distance learning program is available. Students anywhere in the world can take classes and complete their degree with only a one-week residency requirement. A variety of videoconference sites are also available around the country, and classes are taught in real time by professors at the main campus. Students who are interested in this option should call the University for site locations and additional information.

In addition to flexibility, Concordia is known for its diversity. More than 15 percent of the students currently in the program are international students. An international office helps in the transition, and students are able to work for American businesses using an internship. Other services available for all students include computer labs, an extensive library collection, technology resources, and career services.

All M.B.A. programs are covered with a guarantee, and students can repeat courses within three years of commencement if they feel the need to do so.

COSTS

Tuition *Part-time:* $325 per credit. **Graduate housing:** *Typical cost:* $3000 (including board).

FINANCIAL AID (1999–2000)

Loans, research assistantships, and work study. Financial aid application deadline: 5/1. **Financial Aid Contact** Mr. Ed Schroeder, Director, Financial Aid, 12800 North Lake Shore Drive, Mequon, WI 53097. **Phone:** 262-243-4347. **E-mail:** eschroeder@cuw.edu.

RESOURCES AND SERVICES

Information about online services, personal computer policies, library resources, international exchange programs, internship programs, and placement services at this institution and others can be found at **www.petersons.com/mba**

International Students

Services and Facilities Counseling/support services, ESL/language courses, international student housing, international student organization, language tutoring, orientation, visa services. Financial aid is not available to international students. **Applying** *Required:* TOEFL with recommended score of 550 (paper), proof of adequate funds.
International Student Contact Ms. Wendy Grapatin, Director of International Center, 12800 North Lake Shore Drive, Mequon, WI 53097. **Phone:** 262-243-4366. **Fax:** 262-243-4459. **E-mail:** wgrapatin@cuw.edu.

■ APPLICATION

Required Application form, baccalaureate/first degree, essay, 2 letters of recommendation, personal statement, resume/curriculum vitae, transcripts of college work. **Recommended** Interview, 2 years of work experience.
Deadlines and Fees Applications for domestic and international students are processed on a rolling basis. *Application fee:* $30, $30 (international).
Application Contact Mr. David Borst, Director, Graduate Business Programs, 12800 North Lake Shore Drive, Mequon, WI 53097-2402. **Phone:** 262-243-4298. **Toll-free Phone:** 800-665-6564. **Fax:** 262-243-4428. **E-mail:** dborst@bach.cuw.edu.

Edgewood College

Madison, Wisconsin

PROGRAM IN BUSINESS

Graduate Business Faculty
Full-time: 19   Part-time: 16
Student Body
Total: 226   Part-time: 202
Full-time: 24   Average Age: 33

Women: 55%

Admissions
Applications: 64   Enrolled: 54
Admitted: 62   Average GPA: 2.75
Costs (1999–2000)
Full-time tuition: N/R
Part-time tuition: $360 per credit

DEGREE MBA

MBA—Master of Business Administration Full-time and part-time. At least 42 total credits required. 36 to 60 months to complete program.

COSTS

Tuition *Part-time:* $360 per credit. **Graduate housing:** Room and board costs vary by number of occupants, type of accommodation, and type of board plan. *Typical cost:* $4380 (including board), $2196 (room only).

FINANCIAL AID (1999–2000)

Loans. Aid is available to part-time students. Financial aid application deadline: 3/15. **Financial Aid Contact** Jan Ocker, Interim Financial Director, 1000 Edgewood College Drive, Madison, WI 53711-1997. **Phone:** 608-663-2206. **Fax:** 608-663-3291. **E-mail:** jocker@edgewood.edu.

RESOURCES AND SERVICES

Information about online services, personal computer policies, library resources, international exchange programs, internship programs, and placement services at this institution and others can be found at **www.petersons.com/mba**

International Students

6% of students enrolled are international students.
Services and Facilities Counseling/support services, visa services. Financial aid is not available to international students.
Applying *Required:* TOEFL with recommended score of 550 (paper), proof of adequate funds.
International Student Contact Helen Jameson, International Student Coordinator, 1000 Edgewood College Drive, Madison, WI 53711-1997. **Phone:** 608-663-2277. **Fax:** 608-663-3291. **E-mail:** hjameson@edgewood.edu.

■ APPLICATION

Required Application form, baccalaureate/first degree, 2 letters of recommendation, personal statement, transcripts of college work, 2 years of work experience. School will accept GMAT.
Deadlines and Fees Applications for domestic and international students are processed on a rolling basis. *Application fee:* $25, $25 (international).
Application Contact Sr. Lucille Marie Frost, Graduate Office, 1000 Edgewood College Drive, Madison, WI 53711-1997. **Phone:** 608-663-2287. **Toll-free Phone:** 800-444-4861. **Fax:** 608-663-3291. **E-mail:** frost@edgewood.edu.

Lakeland College

Sheboygan, Wisconsin

GRADUATE STUDIES DIVISION

DEGREE MBA

MBA—Master of Business Administration Part-time. *Distance learning option.* At least 36 total credits required. 36 to 84 months to complete program. *Concentrations:* accounting, international and area business studies, marketing.

RESOURCES AND SERVICES

Information about online services, personal computer policies, library resources, international exchange programs, internship programs, and placement services at this institution and others can be found at **www.petersons.com/mba**

International Students

Services and Facilities Counseling/support services, ESL/language courses. Financial aid is available to international students.
International Student Contact Mr. Patrick Liu, International Students Advisor, PO Box 359, Sheboygan, WI 53082-0359. **Phone:** 920-565-1502. **Fax:** 920-565-1206. **E-mail:** liup@lakeland.edu.

■ APPLICATION

Application Contact Ms. Rebecca Hagan, Graduate Program Coordinator, PO Box 359, Sheboygan, WI 53082-0359. **Phone:** 920-565-1256. **Toll-free Phone:** 800-569-2166. **Fax:** 920-565-1206. **E-mail:** haganrl@lakeland.edu.

Marian College of Fond du Lac

Fond du Lac, Wisconsin

BUSINESS DIVISION

Graduate Business Faculty
Full-time: 4   Part-time: 8

Student Body
Total: 93   Average Age: 35
Part-time: 93   Women: 52%

Admissions
Applications: 42   Enrolled: 36
Admitted: 36

Costs (1999–2000)
Full-time tuition: N/R
Part-time tuition: $285 per credit

After Graduation (Class of 1998–99)
Employed within 3 months of graduation: 100%
Average starting salary: $40,000

DEGREE MS

MS—Master of Science in Organizational Leadership and Quality Part-time. At least 36 total credits required. 21 to 24 months to complete program. *Concentrations:* leadership, quality management.

COSTS

Tuition *Part-time:* $285 per credit.

FINANCIAL AID (1999–2000)

Work study. Aid is available to part-time students. **Financial Aid Contact** Ms. Debbie McKinney, Director of Financial Aid, 45 South National Avenue, Fond du Lac, WI 54935-4699. **Phone:** 920-923-7614. **Fax:** 920-923-7154. **E-mail:** dmckinney@mariancollege.edu.

RESOURCES AND SERVICES

Information about online services, personal computer policies, library resources, international exchange programs, internship programs, and placement services at this institution and others can be found at **www. petersons.com/mba**

International Students

3% of students enrolled are international students.

Services and Facilities Financial aid is not available to international students.
Applying *Required:* TOEFL.
International Student Contact Dr. Richard Dienesch, Assistant Dean of Evening/Weekend Programs, 45 South National Avenue, Fond du Lac, WI 54935-4699. **Phone:** 920-923-8125. **Fax:** 920-923-7167. **E-mail:** rdienesch@mariancollege.edu.

■ APPLICATION

Required Application form, baccalaureate/first degree, essay, 2 letters of recommendation, personal statement, transcripts of college work, 3 years of work experience. **Recommended** Interview, resume/curriculum vitae.
Deadlines and Fees Applications for domestic and international students are processed on a rolling basis. *Application fee:* $25, $25 (international).
Application Contact Ms. Bev Compton, Program Coordinator, Business Division, 45 South National Avenue, Fond du Lac, WI 54935-4699. **Phone:** 920-923-7651. **Fax:** 920-923-7154. **E-mail:** bcompton@mariancollege.edu.

Marquette University

Milwaukee, Wisconsin

COLLEGE OF BUSINESS ADMINISTRATION

Accreditation
AACSB—The International Association for Management Education

DEGREES EMBA • MBA • MS

EMBA—Executive MBA Full-time and part-time. Minimum of 5 years of managerial experience required. At least 51 total credits required. 17 months to complete program.
MBA—Master of Business Administration Full-time and part-time. 33 to 47 total credits required. 12 to 72 months to complete program. *Concentrations:* accounting, economics, finance, international business, leadership, marketing, quality management.

MS—Master of Science in Accounting Full-time and part-time. 30 to 45 total credits required. 12 to 72 months to complete program.
MS—Master of Science in Applied Economics Full-time and part-time. 30 to 42 total credits required. 12 to 72 months to complete program. *Concentrations:* financial economics, international economics, public policy and administration.
MS—Master of Science in Engineering Management Full-time and part-time. At least 36 total credits required. 12 to 72 months to complete program.
MS—Master of Science in Human Resources Full-time and part-time. 36 to 48 total credits required. 12 to 72 months to complete program.

RESOURCES AND SERVICES

Information about online services, personal computer policies, library resources, international exchange programs, internship programs, and placement services at this institution and others can be found at **www. petersons.com/mba**

International Students

Services and Facilities Counseling/support services, ESL/language courses, visa services. Financial aid is available to international students.
International Student Contact Ms. Cheryl Nelson, Director of Student Services, PO Box 1881, Milwaukee, WI 53201-1881. **Phone:** 414-288-7145. **Fax:** 414-288-1660. **E-mail:** mba@biz.mu.edu.

■ APPLICATION

Application Contact Dr. Jeanne M. Simmons, Assistant Dean for Graduate Programs, PO Box 1881, Milwaukee, WI 53201-1881. **Phone:** 414-288-7145. **Fax:** 414-288-1660. **E-mail:** mba@biz.mu.edu.

Milwaukee School of Engineering

Milwaukee, Wisconsin

ENGINEERING MANAGEMENT PROGRAM

DEGREE MS

MS—Master of Science in Engineering Management Part-time. *Distance learning option.* 48 to 51 total credits required. 36 to 84 months to complete program. *Concentrations:* marketing, operations management, project management, quality management.

RESOURCES AND SERVICES

Information about online services, personal computer policies, library resources, international exchange programs, internship programs, and placement services at this institution and others can be found at **www. petersons.com/mba**

International Students

Services and Facilities Counseling/support services, ESL/language courses.
International Student Contact Patrick Coffey, Dean of Student Life, 1025 North Broadway, Milwaukee, WI 53202-3109. **Phone:** 414-277-7226. **Fax:** 414-277-7248. **E-mail:** coffey@msoe.edu.

■ APPLICATION

Application Contact Ms. Helen Boomsma, Director, Lifelong Learning Institute, 1025 North Broadway, Milwaukee, WI 53202-3109. **Phone:** 414-277-7282. **Toll-free Phone:** 800-332-6763. **Fax:** 414-277-7475. **E-mail:** boomsma@msoe.edu.

Silver Lake College

Manitowoc, Wisconsin

PROGRAM IN MANAGEMENT AND ORGANIZATIONAL BEHAVIOR

Graduate Business Faculty
Part-time: 17

Student Body
Total: 109   Average Age: 36
Full-time: 59   Women: 63%
Part-time: 50

Admissions
Applications: 50   Enrolled: 31
Admitted: 50   Average GPA: 3

Costs (1999–2000)
Full-time tuition: N/R
Part-time tuition: $275 per credit

After Graduation (Class of 1998–99)
Employed within 3 months of graduation: 100%
Average starting salary: $35,000

DEGREE MS

MS—Master of Science in Management and Organizational Behavior Full-time and part-time. At least 40 total credits required. 24 to 84 months to complete program. *Concentrations:* health care, human resources, international business, management.

COSTS

Tuition *Part-time:* $275 per credit.

FINANCIAL AID (1999–2000)

27 students received aid, including grants, loans, and scholarships. **Financial Aid Contact** Sr. Mary Beth Kornely, Director, Student Financial Aid, Manitowoc, WI 54220-9319. **Phone:** 920-686-6127. **Fax:** 920-684-9072. **E-mail:** smbkor@sl.edu.

RESOURCES AND SERVICES

Information about online services, personal computer policies, library resources, international exchange programs, internship programs, and placement services at this institution and others can be found at **www.petersons.com/mba**

■ APPLICATION

Required Application form, baccalaureate/first degree, letter(s) of recommendation, personal statement, resume/curriculum vitae, transcripts of college work.

Deadlines and Fees *Application fee:* $25.

Application Contact Dr. Sandhya Sridhar, Director, Graduate Business Programs, 2406 South Alverno Road, Manitowoc, WI 54220-9319. **Phone:** 920-686-6189. **Fax:** 920-684-9734. **E-mail:** sandhya@silver.sl.edu.

University of Wisconsin–Eau Claire

Eau Claire, Wisconsin

COLLEGE OF BUSINESS

Graduate Business Faculty
Full-time: 24

Student Body
Total: 73
Full-time: 5
Part-time: 68

Average Age: 33
Women: 45%

Admissions
Average GMAT: 530

Average GPA: 3.2

Costs (1999–2000)
Full-time tuition: $2 per academic year (resident)
Part-time tuition: $243 per credit (resident), $708 per credit (nonresident)

After Graduation (Class of 1998–99)
Employed within 3 months of graduation: 100%

Accreditation
AACSB—The International Association for Management Education

DEGREE MBA

MBA—Master of Business Administration Full-time and part-time. *Distance learning option.* 30 to 32 total credits required. 17 to 30 months to complete program. *Concentrations:* accounting, finance, information management, management, marketing.

COSTS

Tuition, state resident: *Full-time* $2. *Part-time* $243 per credit. **Tuition, nonresident:** *Part-time* $708 per credit. Tuition varies by number of courses or credits taken and local reciprocity agreements. **Graduate housing:** Room and board costs vary by number of occupants, type of accommodation, and type of board plan. *Typical cost:* $2850 (including board).

FINANCIAL AID (1999–2000)

Fellowships, grants, loans, research assistantships, scholarships, and work study. Aid is available to part-time students. **Financial Aid Contact** Department of Financial Aid, PO Box 4004, Eau Claire, WI 54702-4004. **Phone:** 715-836-3373. **Fax:** 715-836-3846. **E-mail:** montampa@uwec.edu.

RESOURCES AND SERVICES

Information about online services, personal computer policies, library resources, international exchange programs, internship programs, and placement services at this institution and others can be found at **www.petersons.com/mba**

International Students
7% of students enrolled are international students.

Services and Facilities Counseling/support services, ESL/language courses, housing location assistance, international student housing, international student organization, language tutoring, orientation. Financial aid is available to international students.

Applying *Required:* TOEFL with recommended score of 550 (paper), proof of adequate funds. *Recommended:* Proof of health/immunizations.

International Student Contact Dr. Karl Markgraf, Director of International Education, PO Box 4004, Eau Claire, WI 54702-4004. **Phone:** 715-836-4411. **Fax:** 715-836-4948. **E-mail:** markgraf@uwec.edu.

■ APPLICATION

Required GMAT, application form, baccalaureate/first degree, transcripts of college work. **Recommended** Letter(s) of recommendation, personal statement, resume/curriculum vitae.

Deadlines and Fees Applications for international students are processed on a rolling basis. *Application fee:* $45, $45 (international).

Application Contact Dr. Robert Erffmeyer, MBA Program Director, PO Box 4004, Eau Claire, WI 54702-4004. **Phone:** 715-836-5473. **Fax:** 715-836-2944. **E-mail:** erffmerc@uwec.edu.

University of Wisconsin–Green Bay

Green Bay, Wisconsin

PROGRAM IN ADMINISTRATIVE SCIENCE

Graduate Business Faculty
Full-time: 5

Part-time: 1

Student Body
Total: 32
Full-time: 3
Part-time: 29

Average Age: 35
Women: 63%

Admissions
Enrolled: 10

Costs (1999–2000)
Full-time tuition: $3787 per academic year (resident), $12,145 per academic year (nonresident)
Part-time tuition: $225 per credit (resident), $690 per credit (nonresident)

After Graduation (Class of 1998–99)
Employed within 3 months of graduation: 100%

DEGREE MS

MS—MS in Administrative Science Full-time and part-time. At least 36 total credits required. *Concentrations:* nonprofit management, project management, public management, public policy and administration, quality management.

COSTS

Tuition, state resident: *Full-time* $3510. *Part-time* $195 per credit. **Tuition, nonresident:** *Full-time* $11,868. *Part-time* $660 per credit. Tuition varies by number of courses or credits taken and local reciprocity agreements. **Required fees:** *Full-time* $277. *Part-time* $30 per credit. Tuition and fees vary by number of courses or credits taken. **Graduate housing:** Room and board costs vary by number of occupants, type of accommodation, and type of board plan. *Typical cost:* $3200 (including board), $2200 (room only).

FINANCIAL AID (1999–2000)

Loans, research assistantships, teaching assistantships, and work study. Financial aid application deadline: 4/15. **Financial Aid Contact** Mr. Ron Ronnenberg, Director of Financial Aid, Financial Aid, 2420 Nicolet Drive,

University of Wisconsin–Green Bay (continued)

Green Bay, WI 54311-7001. **Phone:** 920-465-2075. **Fax:** 920-465-5754. **E-mail:** ronnenbr@uwgb.edu.

RESOURCES AND SERVICES
Information about online services, personal computer policies, library resources, international exchange programs, internship programs, and placement services at this institution and others can be found at **www.petersons.com/mba**

International Students
Services and Facilities Counseling/support services, housing location assistance, international student organization. Financial aid is available to international students.
Applying *Required:* Proof of adequate funds, proof of health/immunizations. *Recommended:* TOEFL.
International Student Contact Dr. Cristina Ortiz, Director of International Education, SS1900, 2420 Nicolet Drive, Green Bay, WI 54311-7001. **Phone:** 920-465-2450. **Fax:** 920-465-2949. **E-mail:** ortizc@uwgb.edu.

■ APPLICATION
Required GMAT or GRE, application form, baccalaureate/first degree, essay, 3 letters of recommendation, personal statement, transcripts of college work.
Deadlines and Fees Applications for domestic and international students are processed on a rolling basis. *Application fee:* $45, $45 (international).
Application Contact Dr. David Littig, Coordinator of Administrative Science, RH324, 2420 Nicolet Drive, Green Bay, WI 54311-7001. **Phone:** 920-465-2081. **Fax:** 920-465-2791. **E-mail:** littigd@uwgb.edu.

University of Wisconsin–La Crosse

La Crosse, Wisconsin

COLLEGE OF BUSINESS ADMINISTRATION

Graduate Business Faculty
Full-time: 43

Student Body
Total: 81	Average Age: 29
Full-time: 11	Women: 41%
Part-time: 70	

Admissions
Applications: 35	Average GMAT: 500
Admitted: 32	Average GPA: 3.45
Enrolled: 25	

Costs (1999–2000)
Full-time tuition: $4474 per academic year (resident), $12,832 per academic year (nonresident)
Part-time tuition: $253 per credit (resident), $718 per credit (nonresident)

After Graduation (Class of 1998–99)
Employed within 3 months of graduation: 100%

Accreditation
AACSB—The International Association for Management Education

DEGREE MBA

MBA—Master of Business Administration Full-time and part-time. *Distance learning option.* 30 to 60 total credits required. 18 to 36 months to complete program.

COSTS
Tuition, state resident: *Full-time* $4474. *Part-time* $253 per credit. **Tuition, nonresident:** *Full-time* $12,832. *Part-time* $718 per credit. Tuition varies by local reciprocity agreements. **Graduate housing:** Room and board costs vary by number of occupants, type of accommodation, and type of board plan. *Typical cost:* $3500 (including board).

FINANCIAL AID (1999–2000)
12 students received aid, including grants, loans, research assistantships, and work study. Aid is available to part-time students. Financial aid application deadline: 3/15. **Financial Aid Contact** Mr. A.C. Stadthaus, Director of Financial Aid, 1725 State Street, La Crosse, WI 54601-3742. **Phone:** 608-785-8604. **E-mail:** stadthau@mail.uwlax.edu.

RESOURCES AND SERVICES
Information about online services, personal computer policies, library resources, international exchange programs, internship programs, and placement services at this institution and others can be found at **www.petersons.com/mba**

International Students
6% of students enrolled are international students.
Services and Facilities Counseling/support services, ESL/language courses, international student organization, language tutoring, visa services. Financial aid is available to international students.
Applying *Required:* TOEFL with recommended score of 550 (paper), proof of adequate funds, proof of health/immunizations.
International Student Contact Mr. Jay Lokken, Director, Office of International Education, 1725 State Street, La Crosse, WI 54601-3742. **Phone:** 608-785-8016.

■ APPLICATION
Required GMAT, application form, baccalaureate/first degree, transcripts of college work. **Recommended** Letter(s) of recommendation, 3 years of work experience.
Deadlines and Fees *Deadlines:* 3/15 for fall (international), 9/15 for spring (international). *Application fee:* $45, $45 (international).
Application Contact Ms. Amelia Dittman, Coordinator, MBA Program, 1725 State Street, La Crosse, WI 54601-3742. **Phone:** 608-785-8092. **Fax:** 608-785-6700. **E-mail:** dittman@mail.uwlax.edu.

University of Wisconsin–Madison

Madison, Wisconsin

SCHOOL OF BUSINESS

Graduate Business Faculty
Full-time: 85

Student Body
Total: 513	Average Age: 28
Full-time: 438	Women: 31%
Part-time: 75	

Admissions
Applications: 976	Average GMAT: 616
Admitted: 365	Average GPA: 3.26
Enrolled: 205	

Costs (1999–2000)
Full-time tuition: $6524 per academic year (resident), $18,282 per academic year (nonresident)
Part-time tuition: N/R

After Graduation (Class of 1998–99)
Employed within 3 months of graduation: 93%
Average starting salary: $62,899

Accreditation
AACSB—The International Association for Management Education

DEGREES EMBA • M Acc • MA • MBA • MS

EMBA—Executive MBA Full-time. 8 to 10 years of work experience. 24 months to complete program. *Concentrations:* management.

M Acc—Master of Accountancy Full-time. 30 to 66 total credits required. 12 to 48 months to complete program. *Concentrations:* accounting, taxation.

MA—Master of Arts in Business Full-time. 40 to 46 total credits required. 12 to 48 months to complete program. *Concentrations:* arts administration/management.

MBA—Evening MBA Part-time. At least 55 total credits required. Minimum of 36 months to complete program. *Concentrations:* management.

MBA—Master of Business Administration Full-time. 41 to 54 total credits required. 12 to 36 months to complete program. *Concentrations:* accounting, agribusiness, banking, entrepreneurship, finance, human resources, information management, insurance, international business, management, management information systems, marketing, marketing research, operations management, quality management, real estate, risk management, supply chain management.

MS—Master of Science in Business Full-time and part-time. 30 to 48 total credits required. 12 to 48 months to complete program. *Concentrations:* banking, entrepreneurship, finance, human resources, information management, insurance, international business, management, management information systems, manufacturing management, marketing research, operations management, quality management, real estate, risk management, supply chain management, technology management.

MS—Master of Science in Business Full-time and part-time. GMAT or GRE accepted for actuarial science only. 30 to 49 total credits required. 12 to 18 months to complete program. *Concentrations:* actuarial science.

COSTS

Tuition, state resident: *Full-time* $6524. **Tuition, nonresident:** *Full-time* $18,282. **Tuition, international:** *Full-time* $18,282. Tuition varies by class time, number of courses or credits taken, academic program, and local reciprocity agreements. **Graduate housing:** Room and board costs vary by campus location, number of occupants, type of accommodation, and type of board plan. *Typical cost:* $4543 (room only).

FINANCIAL AID (1999–2000)

158 students received aid, including fellowships, grants, loans, research assistantships, scholarships, teaching assistantships, and work study. Financial aid application deadline: 2/15. **Financial Aid Contact** Graduate Programs Office, 2266 Grainger Hall, 975 University Avenue, Madison, WI 53706-1323. **Phone:** 608-262-1555. **Fax:** 608-265-4192. **E-mail:** uwmadmba@bus.wisc.edu.

RESOURCES AND SERVICES

Information about online services, personal computer policies, library resources, international exchange programs, internship programs, and placement services at this institution and others can be found at **www.petersons.com/mba**

International Students

35% of students enrolled are international students.

Services and Facilities Counseling/support services, ESL/language courses, international student housing, international student organization, orientation, visa services. Financial aid is not available to international students.
Applying *Required:* TOEFL with recommended score of 250 (computer) or 600 (paper), proof of adequate funds, proof of health/immunizations. *Recommended:* TSE, TWE.
International Student Contact Director, International Students and Scholar Services, 975 University Avenue, Madison, WI 53706-1380. **Phone:** 608-262-2044. **Fax:** 608-262-2838. **E-mail:** intstudents@redgym.wisc.edu.

■ APPLICATION

Required GMAT, application form, baccalaureate/first degree, essay, 3 letters of recommendation, resume/curriculum vitae, transcripts of college work, 2 years of work experience. **Recommended** Interview.
Deadlines and Fees *Deadlines:* 4/15 for fall, 4/15 for fall (international). *Application fee:* $45, $45 (international).
Application Contact Graduate Programs Office, 3150 Grainger Hall, 975 University Avenue, Madison, WI 53706. **Phone:** 608-262-4000. **Fax:** 608-265-4192. **E-mail:** uwmadmba@bus.wisc.edu.

See full description on page 990.

University of Wisconsin–Milwaukee

Milwaukee, Wisconsin

SCHOOL OF BUSINESS ADMINISTRATION

Accreditation
AACSB—The International Association for Management Education

DEGREES MBA • MS

MBA—Executive MBA Full-time. At least 32 total credits required. 22 months to complete program.
MBA—Master of Business Administration Full-time and part-time. At least 32 total credits required. 24 to 84 months to complete program.
MS—Master of Science in Management Full-time and part-time. 30 to 32 total credits required. 24 to 84 months to complete program. *Concentrations:* accounting, finance, health care, international business, management information systems, marketing, organizational management, quality management, taxation.

RESOURCES AND SERVICES

Information about online services, personal computer policies, library resources, international exchange programs, internship programs, and placement services at this institution and others can be found at **www.petersons.com/mba**

International Students

Services and Facilities Counseling/support services, ESL/language courses, visa services. Financial aid is not available to international students.
International Student Contact Ms. Sharon Seager, Graduate Evaluator, International Studies and Programs, PO Box 340, Milwaukee, WI 53201. **Phone:** 414-229-4845. **Fax:** 414-229-3750. **E-mail:** sseager@uwm.edu.

■ APPLICATION

Application Contact Ms. Sarah M. Sandin, MBA/MS Program Manager, School of Business Administration, PO Box 742, Milwaukee, WI 53201-0742. **Phone:** 414-229-5403. **Fax:** 414-229-2372. **E-mail:** uwmbusmasters@csd.uwm.edu.

University of Wisconsin–Oshkosh

Oshkosh, Wisconsin

COLLEGE OF BUSINESS ADMINISTRATION

Graduate Business Faculty
Full-time: 45

Student Body

Total: 475	Average Age: 32
Full-time: 20	Women: 35%
Part-time: 455	

Admissions

Applications: 200	Average GMAT: 540
Admitted: 180	Average GPA: 3.1
Enrolled: 90	

Costs (1999–2000)
Full-time tuition: N/R
Part-time tuition: $245 per credit (resident), $710 per credit (nonresident)

After Graduation (Class of 1998–99)
Employed within 3 months of graduation: 98%

Accreditation
AACSB—The International Association for Management Education

DEGREE MBA

MBA—Master of Business Administration Full-time and part-time. 30 to 51 total credits required. 18 to 84 months to complete program. *Concentrations:* finance, human resources, management, management information systems, marketing.

COSTS

Tuition, state resident: *Part-time* $245 per credit. **Tuition, nonresident:** *Part-time* $710 per credit. Tuition varies by local reciprocity agreements. **Graduate housing:** Room and board costs vary by number of occupants and type of board plan. *Typical cost:* $3700 (including board).

FINANCIAL AID (1999–2000)

45 students received aid, including loans, research assistantships, and work study. Aid is available to part-time students. Financial aid application deadline: 3/15. **Financial Aid Contact** Beatriz Contreras, Director of Financial Aid, Financial Aid Office, Oshkosh, WI 54901. **Phone:** 920-424-3377. **Fax:** 920-424-0284.

RESOURCES AND SERVICES

Information about online services, personal computer policies, library resources, international exchange programs, internship programs, and placement services at this institution and others can be found at **www.petersons.com/mba**

International Students

6% of students enrolled are international students.

Services and Facilities Counseling/support services, international student housing, international student organization, orientation. Financial aid is available to international students.
Applying *Required:* TOEFL with recommended score of 213 (computer) or 550 (paper), proof of adequate funds, proof of health/immunizations.
International Student Contact Ms. Judy Jaeger, International Student Advisor, Dean of Students Office, Oshkosh, WI 54901. **Phone:** 920-424-3100. **Fax:** 920-424-7317. **E-mail:** jaeger@uwosh.edu.

University of Wisconsin–Oshkosh (continued)

■ APPLICATION

Required GMAT, application form, baccalaureate/first degree, personal statement, resume/curriculum vitae, transcripts of college work. **Recommended** 3 years of work experience.

Deadlines and Fees *Deadlines:* 7/1 for fall, 12/1 for spring, 4/1 for summer, 1/1 for fall (international), 5/1 for spring (international), 11/1 for summer (international). *Application fee:* $45, $45 (international).

Application Contact Ms. Lynn Grancorbitz, MBA Program Assistant Director and Advisor, 800 Algoma Boulevard, Oshkosh, WI 54901. **Phone:** 920-424-1436. **Fax:** 920-424-7413. **E-mail:** mba@uwosh.edu.

University of Wisconsin–Parkside

Kenosha, Wisconsin

SCHOOL OF BUSINESS AND TECHNOLOGY

Graduate Business Faculty
Full-time: 15

Student Body
Total: 92
Full-time: 7

Part-time: 85
Average Age: 32

Admissions
Applications: 30
Admitted: 27

Average GMAT: 543
Average GPA: 3.32

Costs (1999–2000)
Full-time tuition: N/R
Part-time tuition: $248 per credit (resident), $713 per credit (nonresident)

After Graduation (Class of 1998–99)
Employed within 3 months of graduation: 98%

Accreditation
AACSB—The International Association for Management Education

DEGREE MBA

MBA—Master of Business Administration Part-time. At least 32 total credits required. 30 to 84 months to complete program.

COSTS

Tuition, state resident: *Part-time* $223 per credit. **Tuition, nonresident:** *Part-time* $688 per credit. Tuition varies by class time, number of courses or credits taken, and local reciprocity agreements. **Required fees:** *Full-time* $223. *Part-time* $25 per credit.

FINANCIAL AID (1999–2000)

Financial Aid Contact Ms. Ingrid Austin, Director of Financial Aid, 900 Wood Road, Box 2000, Kenosha, WI 53141-2000. **Phone:** 414-595-2195. **E-mail:** ingrid.austin@uwp.edu.

RESOURCES AND SERVICES

Information about online services, personal computer policies, library resources, international exchange programs, internship programs, and placement services at this institution and others can be found at **www.petersons.com/mba**

International Students

Services and Facilities Counseling/support services, ESL/language courses, international student organization, visa services, international advisor. Financial aid is not available to international students.

Applying *Required:* TOEFL with recommended score of 550 (paper), proof of adequate funds.

International Student Contact Mr. Brad Piazza, Assistant to the Dean, School of Business and Technology, 900 Wood Road, Box 2000, Kenosha, WI 53141-2000. **Phone:** 262-595-2046. **Fax:** 262-595-2680. **E-mail:** bradley.piazza@uwp.edu.

■ APPLICATION

Required GMAT, application form, baccalaureate/first degree, 2 letters of recommendation, personal statement, resume/curriculum vitae, transcripts of college work. **Recommended** Work experience.

Deadlines and Fees *Deadlines:* 8/1 for fall, 12/15 for spring, 4/15 for summer, 8/1 for fall (international), 12/15 for spring (international), 4/15 for summer (international). *Application fee:* $45, $45 (international).

Application Contact Mr. Brad Piazza, Assistant to the Dean, School of Business and Technology, 900 Wood Road, Box 2000, Kenosha, WI 53141-2000. **Phone:** 262-595-2046. **Fax:** 262-595-2680. **E-mail:** bradley.piazza@uwp.edu.

University of Wisconsin–Stout

Menomonie, Wisconsin

PROGRAM IN TRAINING AND DEVELOPMENT

Graduate Business Faculty
Full-time: 20

Part-time: 5

Student Body
Total: 80
Full-time: 35
Part-time: 45

Average Age: 32
Women: 44%

Admissions
Applications: 65
Admitted: 53

Enrolled: 47

Costs (1999–2000)
Full-time tuition: $4194 per academic year (resident), $12,552 per academic year (nonresident)
Part-time tuition: $233 per credit (resident), $697 per credit (nonresident)

After Graduation (Class of 1998–99)
Employed within 3 months of graduation: 98.7%
Average starting salary: $28,000

DEGREES MS

MS—Master of Science in Management Technology Full-time and part-time. 2 years of work experience required. At least 30 total credits required. Maximum of 84 months to complete program. *Concentrations:* arts administration/management, construction management, industrial administration/management, industrial/labor relations, risk management, system management.

MS—Master of Science in Training and Development Full-time and part-time. At least 30 total credits required. Maximum of 84 months to complete program.

COSTS

Tuition, state resident: *Full-time* $4194. *Part-time* $233 per credit. **Tuition, nonresident:** *Full-time* $12,552. *Part-time* $697 per credit. Tuition varies by local reciprocity agreements. **Graduate housing:** Room and board costs vary by number of occupants and type of board plan. *Typical cost:* $3284 (including board).

FINANCIAL AID (1999–2000)

Fellowships, grants, research assistantships, scholarships, teaching assistantships, and work study. Aid is available to part-time students. Financial aid application deadline: 4/1. **Financial Aid Contact** Beth Resech, Director of Financial Aid, Menomonie, WI 54751. **Phone:** 715-232-1363. **Fax:** 715-232-5246. **E-mail:** resechb@uwstout.edu.

RESOURCES AND SERVICES

Information about online services, personal computer policies, library resources, international exchange programs, internship programs, and placement services at this institution and others can be found at **www.petersons.com/mba**

International Students

34% of students enrolled are international students.

Services and Facilities Counseling/support services, international student housing, visa services. Financial aid is available to international students.

Applying *Required:* TOEFL with recommended score of 213 (computer) or 500 (paper), proof of adequate funds.

International Student Contact Vickie Kuester, Administrative Program Specialist, Menomonie, WI 54751. **Phone:** 715-232-2132. **Fax:** 715-232-2500. **E-mail:** kuesterv@uwstout.edu.

■ APPLICATION

Required Application form, baccalaureate/first degree, letter(s) of recommendation, personal statement, transcripts of college work, work experience. **Recommended** Resume/curriculum vitae.

Deadlines and Fees Applications for domestic and international students are processed on a rolling basis. *Application fee:* $45, $45 (international).

Application Contact Richard Lowery, Coordinator for Graduate Studies, Menomonie, WI 54751. **Phone:** 715-232-1666. **Fax:** 715-232-2413. **E-mail:** loweryr@uwstout.edu.

University of Wisconsin–Whitewater

Whitewater, Wisconsin

COLLEGE OF BUSINESS AND ECONOMICS

Accreditation
AACSB—The International Association for Management Education

DEGREES MBA • MPA • MS

MBA—Graduate Business Program Full-time and part-time. *Distance learning option.* GMAT score (minimum 570) required. 36 to 51 total credits required. 24 to 84 months to complete program. *Concentrations:* accounting, decision sciences, finance, health care, international business, management, marketing, production management, technology management.

MPA—Graduate Business program Full-time and part-time. GMAT score (minimum 570) required. At least 30 total credits required. 24 to 84 months to complete program. *Concentrations:* accounting.

MS—Master of Science in Management Computer Systems Part-time. At least 36 total credits required. 36 months to complete program. *Concentrations:* management information systems.

RESOURCES AND SERVICES
Information about online services, personal computer policies, library resources, international exchange programs, internship programs, and placement services at this institution and others can be found at **www.petersons.com/mba**

International Students
Services and Facilities Counseling/support services, ESL/language courses, international student housing. Financial aid is not available to international students.
International Student Contact Mr. Stephen Kazar, Director, International Programs, Roseman Hall, Whitewater, WI 53190. **Phone:** 262-472-4992. **Fax:** 262-472-1515. **E-mail:** kazars@uwwvax.uww.edu.

■ APPLICATION
Application Contact Dr. Donald Zahn, Associate Dean, College of Business and Economics, Carlson Hall, Whitewater, WI 53190. **Phone:** 262-472-1945. **Fax:** 262-472-4863. **E-mail:** zahnd@mail.uww.edu.

WYOMING

University of Wyoming

Laramie, Wyoming

COLLEGE OF BUSINESS

Graduate Business Faculty
Full-time: 29

Student Body
Total: 95
Full-time: 46
Part-time: 49

Average Age: 31
Women: 46%

Admissions
Applications: 72
Admitted: 40
Enrolled: 32

Average GMAT: 538
Average GPA: 3.2

Costs (1999–2000)
Full-time tuition: $2430 per academic year (resident), $7520 per academic year (nonresident)
Part-time tuition: $135 per credit hour (resident), $418 per credit hour (nonresident)

After Graduation (Class of 1998–99)
Employed within 3 months of graduation: 90%
Average starting salary: $42,000

Accreditation
AACSB—The International Association for Management Education

DEGREE MBA

MBA—Master of Business Administration Full-time and part-time. *Distance learning option.* At least 54 total credits required. 11 to 72 months to complete program.

COSTS
Tuition, state resident: *Full-time* $2430. *Part-time* $135 per credit hour. **Tuition, nonresident:** *Full-time* $7520. *Part-time* $418 per credit hour. Tuition varies by class time, number of courses or credits taken, campus location, academic program, and local reciprocity agreements. **Required fees:** Tuition and fees vary by class time, number of courses or credits taken, and local reciprocity agreements. **Graduate housing:** Room and board costs vary by campus location, number of occupants, type of accommodation, and type of board plan. *Typical cost:* $4446 (including board).

FINANCIAL AID (1999–2000)
18 students received aid, including fellowships, loans, research assistantships, scholarships, and work study. Aid is available to part-time students. Financial aid application deadline: 3/1. **Financial Aid Contact** Student Financial Aid, PO Box 3335, Laramie, WY 82070. **Phone:** 307-766-2116. **Fax:** 307-766-3800.

RESOURCES AND SERVICES
Information about online services, personal computer policies, library resources, international exchange programs, internship programs, and placement services at this institution and others can be found at **www.petersons.com/mba**

International Students
12% of students enrolled are international students.

Services and Facilities Counseling/support services, ESL/language courses, housing location assistance, international student organization, language tutoring, orientation, visa services, newsletter, student exchange program. Financial aid is available to international students.
Applying *Required:* TOEFL with recommended score of 207 (computer) or 540 (paper), proof of adequate funds, proof of health/immunizations.
International Student Contact Mr. Dennis Dreher, Director, International Student Services, PO Box 3228, Laramie, WY 82071. **Phone:** 307-766-5193. **Fax:** 307-766-4053. **E-mail:** wecnhelp@uwyo.edu.

■ APPLICATION
Required GMAT, application form, baccalaureate/first degree, essay, 3 letters of recommendation, personal statement, transcripts of college work. **Recommended** Resume/curriculum vitae, 2 years of work experience.
Deadlines and Fees *Deadlines:* 3/31 for fall, 3/31 for fall (international). *Application fee:* $40, $40 (international).
Application Contact Dr. Martin Greller, Director, MBA Program, College of Business, PO Box 3275, Laramie, WY 82071. **Phone:** 307-766-2449. **Fax:** 307-766-4028. **E-mail:** mba@uwyo.edu.

PUERTO RICO

Inter American University of Puerto Rico, San Germán Campus

San Germán, Puerto Rico

DEPARTMENT OF BUSINESS ADMINISTRATION

Graduate Business Faculty
Full-time: 8

Part-time: 13

Student Body
Total: 335

Average Age: 28
Women: 56%
Full-time: 80
Part-time: 255

Admissions
Applications: 307

Enrolled: 200
Average GPA: 2.5
Admitted: 271

Costs (1999–2000)
Full-time tuition: $3156 per academic year
Part-time tuition: $155 per credit

DEGREE MBA

MBA—Master of Business Administration Full-time and part-time. At least 42 total credits required. 30 to 84 months to complete program. *Concentrations:* accounting, business education, finance, human resources, industrial administration/management, management information systems, marketing.

COSTS

Tuition *Full-time:* $2790. *Part-time:* $155 per credit. **Required fees:** *Full-time* $366. *Part-time* $183 per semester. **Graduate housing:** Room and board costs vary by type of accommodation and type of board plan. *Typical cost:* $2200 (including board), $900 (room only).

FINANCIAL AID (1999–2000)

Fellowships, loans, scholarships, teaching assistantships, and work study. Financial aid application deadline: 5/15. **Financial Aid Contact** Ms. Maria Lugo, Director of Financial Aid, PO Box 5100, San German, PR 00683. **Phone:** 787-264-1912 Ext. 7252. **Fax:** 787-892-6350. **E-mail:** milugo@sg.inter.edu.

RESOURCES AND SERVICES

Information about online services, personal computer policies, library resources, international exchange programs, internship programs, and placement services at this institution and others can be found at **www.petersons.com/mba**

International Students

1% of students enrolled are international students.

Services and Facilities Counseling/support services, ESL/language courses. Financial aid is available to international students.

Applying *Required:* Proof of health/immunizations.

International Student Contact Mr. Efrain Anglero, Dean of Students, PO Box 5100, San German, PR 00683. **Phone:** 787-264-1912 Ext. 7298. **Fax:** 787-892-6350.

■ APPLICATION

Required GMAT, application form, baccalaureate/first degree, 2 letters of recommendation, transcripts of college work. **Recommended** Resume/curriculum vitae.

Deadlines and Fees Applications for domestic and international students are processed on a rolling basis. *Application fee:* $31, $31 (international).

Application Contact Mr. Waldemar Velez, Director of Graduate Center, PO Box 5100, San German, PR 00683. **Phone:** 787-264-1912. **Fax:** 787-892-6350. **E-mail:** wvelez@sg.inter.edu.

Pontifical Catholic University of Puerto Rico

Ponce, Puerto Rico

COLLEGE OF BUSINESS ADMINISTRATION

Graduate Business Faculty
Full-time: 4

Part-time: 8

Student Body
Total: 277

Average Age: 29
Women: 58%
Full-time: 53
Part-time: 224

Admissions
Applications: 127

Enrolled: 108
Average GPA: 3
Admitted: 108

Costs (1999–2000)
Full-time tuition: $3287 per academic year
Part-time tuition: N/R

After Graduation (Class of 1998–99)
Employed within 3 months of graduation: 90%

DEGREES JD/MBA • MBA

JD/MBA—Juris Doctor/Master of Business Administration Full-time. At least 122 total credits required. 36 to 96 months to complete program.

MBA—Master of Business Administration Full-time. At least 43 total credits required. 24 to 60 months to complete program. *Concentrations:* accounting, commerce, human resources, management.

COSTS

Tuition *Full-time:* $2520. Tuition varies by academic program. **Required fees:** *Full-time* $767. **Graduate housing:** Room and board costs vary by type of board plan. *Typical cost:* $3967 (including board).

FINANCIAL AID (1999–2000)

277 students received aid, including fellowships, loans, scholarships, and work study. Aid is available to part-time students. Financial aid application deadline: 5/15. **Financial Aid Contact** Mrs. Margaret Alustiza, Student Financial Aid Director, 2250 Las Americas Avenue, Suite 549, Ponce, PR 00717-0777. **Phone:** 787-841-2000 Ext. 1054. **Fax:** 787-840-4295. **E-mail:** malustiza@pucpr.edu.

RESOURCES AND SERVICES

Information about online services, personal computer policies, library resources, international exchange programs, internship programs, and placement services at this institution and others can be found at **www.petersons.com/mba**

International Students

Services and Facilities Counseling/support services, international student organization. Financial aid is available to international students.
Applying *Required:* TOEFL, proof of health/immunizations.

International Student Contact Mrs. Anna Bonilla, Counselor, 2250 Las Americas Avenue, Suite 511, Ponce, PR 00717-0777. **Phone:** 787-841-2000 Ext. 1004. **Fax:** 787-840-4295. **E-mail:** abonilla@pucpr.edu.

■ APPLICATION

Required Application form, baccalaureate/first degree, interview, 2 letters of recommendation, transcripts of college work. **Recommended** Personal statement, resume/curriculum vitae, work experience.

Deadlines and Fees *Deadlines:* 6/15 for fall, 6/15 for fall (international). *Application fee:* $15, $15 (international).

Application Contact Mrs. Ana Bonilla, Director of Admissions, 2250 Las Americas Avenue, Suite 584, Ponce, PR 00717-0777. **Phone:** 787-841-2000 Ext. 1004. **Fax:** 787-840-4295.

University of Puerto Rico, Mayagüez Campus

Mayagüez, Puerto Rico

COLLEGE OF BUSINESS ADMINISTRATION

DEGREES MBA

MBA—Master of Business Administration in Human Resources Full-time and part-time. PAEG—475 required. At least 48 total credits required. Maximum of 60 months to complete program.

MBA—Master of Business Administration in Industrial Management Full-time and part-time. PAEG—475 required. At least 48 total credits required. Maximum of 60 months to complete program.

MBA—Master of Business Administration Full-time and part-time. PAEG—475 required. At least 48 total credits required. Maximum of 60 months to complete program.

RESOURCES AND SERVICES

Information about online services, personal computer policies, library resources, international exchange programs, internship programs, and placement services at this institution and others can be found at www.petersons.com/mba

International Students

Services and Facilities Counseling/support services, ESL/language courses, visa services.
International Student Contact Ms. Norma Guardiola, Director, International Students Office, Mayaguez, PR 00681-5000. **Phone:** 787-265-3861.

■ APPLICATION

Application Contact Prof. Hector Bravo-Vick, Director, Graduate Program of Business Administration, PO Box 9009, Mayaguez, PR 00681-9009. **Phone:** 787-265-3887. **Fax:** 787-832-5320.

University of Puerto Rico, Río Piedras

San Juan, Puerto Rico

GRADUATE SCHOOL OF BUSINESS ADMINISTRATION

Graduate Business Faculty
Full-time: 7 — Part-time: 13

Student Body
Total: 345 — Part-time: 250
Full-time: 95 — Women: 57%

Admissions
Applications: 177 — Average GMAT: 460
Admitted: 118 — Average GPA: 3.4
Enrolled: 92

Costs (1999–2000)
Full-time tuition: N/R
Part-time tuition: $75 per credit (resident)

DEGREES JD/MBA • MBA

JD/MBA—Joint Program MBA/JD Full-time. Up to 122 total credits required. 48 to 60 months to complete program.

MBA—Master of Business Administration Full-time and part-time. At least 52 total credits required. 24 to 72 months to complete program. *Concentrations:* accounting, finance, international business, managerial economics, marketing, operations management, quantitative analysis.

COSTS

Tuition, commonwealth resident: *Part-time* $75 per credit. Tuition varies by number of courses or credits taken.

FINANCIAL AID (1999–2000)

107 students received aid, including fellowships, loans, research assistantships, teaching assistantships, and work study. Financial aid application deadline: 5/31. **Financial Aid Contact** Miss Luz M. Santiago, Director, Financial Aid Programs, PO Box 23336, San Juan, PR 00931-3336. **Phone:** 787-764-0000 Ext. 3055. **Fax:** 787-763-5733.

RESOURCES AND SERVICES

Information about online services, personal computer policies, library resources, international exchange programs, internship programs, and placement services at this institution and others can be found at www.petersons.com/mba

International Students

3% of students enrolled are international students.
Services and Facilities Counseling/support services, language tutoring, visa services. Financial aid is not available to international students.
Applying *Required:* Proof of adequate funds, proof of health/immunizations.

International Student Contact Prof. Manuel Hernandez, Director, PO Box 23336, San Juan, PR 00931-3336. **Phone:** 787-764-0000 Ext. 3055. **Fax:** 787-763-5733.

■ APPLICATION

Required Application form, baccalaureate/first degree, essay, 2 letters of recommendation, transcripts of college work. School will accept GMAT.
Deadlines and Fees *Deadlines:* 2/5 for fall, 9/1 for spring. *Application fee:* $15, $15 (international).
Application Contact Ms. Carmen Gonzalez, Student Affairs Official, PO Box 23325, San Juan, PR 00931-3325. **Phone:** 787-764-0000 Ext. 4128. **Fax:** 787-763-6911.

3 University of the Sacred Heart

San Juan, Puerto Rico

DEPARTMENT OF BUSINESS ADMINISTRATION

Graduate Business Faculty
Full-time: 20 — Part-time: 15

Student Body
Total: 216 — Average Age: 31
Full-time: 10 — Women: 55%
Part-time: 206

Admissions
Applications: 160 — Average GMAT: 500
Admitted: 121 — Average GPA: 2.75
Enrolled: 62

Costs (1999–2000)
Full-time tuition: $3070 per academic year
Part-time tuition: $300 per credit

DEGREES MBA

MBA—Master of Business Administration in Human Resource Management Full-time and part-time. At least 47 total credits required. 36 to 72 months to complete program. *Concentrations:* human resources.

MBA—Master of Business Administration in Management Information Systems Full-time and part-time. At least 48 total credits required. 36 to 72 months to complete program. *Concentrations:* management information systems.

MBA—Master of Business Administration in Marketing Full-time and part-time. At least 47 total credits required. 36 to 72 months to complete program. *Concentrations:* marketing.

MBA—Master of Business Administration in Taxation Full-time and part-time. At least 47 total credits required. 36 to 72 months to complete program. *Concentrations:* taxation.

COSTS

Tuition *Full-time:* $2700. *Part-time:* $150 per credit. Tuition varies by number of courses or credits taken, academic program, and local reciprocity agreements.
Required fees: *Full-time* $370. *Part-time* $150 per credit. Tuition and fees vary by local reciprocity agreements.

FINANCIAL AID (1999–2000)

81 students received aid, including grants, loans, scholarships, and work study. Financial aid application deadline: 5/31. **Financial Aid Contact** Mr. Luis Aquiles, Financial Aid Office Director, PO Box 12383, San Juan, PR 00914-0383. **Phone:** 787-728-1515 Ext. 3605. **Fax:** 787-728-1515 Ext. 3609. **E-mail:** laquiles@sagrado.edu.

RESOURCES AND SERVICES

Information about online services, personal computer policies, library resources, international exchange programs, internship programs, and placement services at this institution and others can be found at www.petersons.com/mba

International Students

Services and Facilities Financial aid is not available to international students.
Applying *Required:* Proof of adequate funds, proof of health/immunizations.
International Student Contact Mrs. Ivette Lugo-Fabre, Co-op and Student Exchange Program Coordinator, PO Box 12383, San Juan, PR 00914-0383. **Phone:** 787-728-1515 Ext. 1218. **Fax:** 787-268-8843. **E-mail:** ilugo@sagrado.edu.

■ APPLICATION

Required GMAT, application form, baccalaureate/first degree, essay, interview, 2 letters of recommendation, resume/curriculum vitae, transcripts of college work.

University of the Sacred Heart (continued)

Deadlines and Fees Applications for domestic and international students are processed on a rolling basis. *Application fee:* $25, $25 (international).

Application Contact Coordinator of Admissions Office, Box 12383, San Juan, PR 00914-0383. **Phone:** 787-728-1515 Ext. 3237. **Fax:** 787-727-5890.

VIRGIN ISLANDS

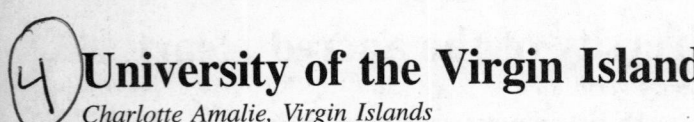

University of the Virgin Islands

Charlotte Amalie, Virgin Islands

DIVISION OF BUSINESS ADMINISTRATION

Graduate Business Faculty
Full-time: 5   Part-time: 1

Student Body
Total: 41   Average Age: 30
Full-time: 10   Women: 85%
Part-time: 31

Admissions
Average GPA: 2.1

Costs (1999–2000)
Full-time tuition: N/R
Part-time tuition: $228 per credit (resident), $456 per credit (nonresident)

DEGREE MBA

MBA—Master of Business Administration Full-time and part-time. At least 36 total credits required. 24 to 60 months to complete program.

COSTS

Tuition, state resident: *Part-time* $228 per credit. **Tuition, nonresident:** *Part-time* $456 per credit. Tuition varies by number of courses or credits taken.

FINANCIAL AID (1999–2000)

Aid is available to part-time students. Financial aid application deadline: 6/1. **Financial Aid Contact** Mrs. Ardrina Scott-Elliott, Financial Aid Supervisor, 2 John Brewers Bay, Charlotte Amalie, St. Thomas, VI 00802-9990. **Phone:** 340-693-1090. **Fax:** 340-693-1405. **E-mail:** ascott@uvi.edu.

RESOURCES AND SERVICES

Information about online services, personal computer policies, library resources, international exchange programs, internship programs, and placement services at this institution and others can be found at **www.petersons.com/mba**

International Students

2% of students enrolled are international students.

Services and Facilities Counseling/support services. Financial aid is not available to international students.

Applying *Recommended:* TOEFL.

International Student Contact Ms. Carolyn Cook, Director of Admissions and New Student Services, 2 John Brewers Bay, Charlotte Amalie St. Thomas, VI 00802-9990. **Phone:** 340-693-1224. **Fax:** 340-693-1055. **E-mail:** ccook@uvi.edu.

■ APPLICATION

Required GMAT, application form, baccalaureate/first degree, essay, transcripts of college work. School will accept GRE. **Recommended** Letter(s) of recommendation, personal statement, resume/curriculum vitae, work experience.

Deadlines and Fees *Deadlines:* 4/30 for fall, 10/30 for spring. *Application fee:* $20, $20 (international).

Application Contact Ms. Carolyn Cook, Director of Admissions and New Student Services, 2 John Brewers Bay, Charlotte Amalie, St. Thomas, VI 00802-9990. **Phone:** 340-693-1224. **Fax:** 340-693-1055. **E-mail:** ccook@uvi.edu.

AUSTRALIA

Australian National University

Canberra, Australia

AUSTRALIA ASIA MANAGEMENT CENTRE

Graduate Business Faculty
Full-time: 4   Part-time: 25

Student Body
Total: 34   Average Age: 31
Full-time: 34   Women: 44%

Admissions
Applications: 139   Enrolled: 34
Admitted: 118

Costs (1999–2000)
Full-time tuition: N/R
Part-time tuition: N/R

After Graduation (Class of 1998–99)
Employed within 3 months of graduation: 90%

DEGREE MBA

MBA—Master of Business Administration Full-time. At least 28 total credits required. 13 to 15 months to complete program. *Concentrations:* Asian business studies, strategic management.

COSTS

FINANCIAL AID (1999–2000)

12 students received aid, including scholarships. Financial aid application deadline: 3/31. **Financial Aid Contact** Prof. Mark Dodgson, Executive Director, Australia Asia Management Centre, Sir Roland Wilson Building, Canberra, ACT 0200, Australia. **Phone:** 02-6279-9830. **Fax:** 02-6249-4895. **E-mail:** mgr.mba.program@anu.edu.au.

RESOURCES AND SERVICES

Information about online services, personal computer policies, library resources, international exchange programs, internship programs, and placement services at this institution and others can be found at **www.petersons.com/mba**

International Students

88% of students enrolled are international students.

Services and Facilities Counseling/support services, ESL/language courses, international student housing, international student organization, orientation. Financial aid is available to international students.

Applying *Required:* IELT with recommended score of 6.5, TOEFL with recommended score of 570 (paper), TWE with recommended score of 4.5.

International Student Contact Mr. Tim Beckett, Director, Student Recruitment and International Education, Canberra, ACT 0200, Australia. **Phone:** 02-6249-3682. **Fax:** 02-6249-5550.

■ APPLICATION

Required Application form, baccalaureate/first degree, letter(s) of recommendation, personal statement, resume/curriculum vitae, transcripts of college work, 3 years of work experience. School will accept GMAT.

Deadlines and Fees Applications for domestic students are processed on a rolling basis. *Deadline:* 3/31 for winter (international).

Application Contact Prof. Mark Dodgson, Executive Director, Australia Asia Management Centre, Sir Roland Wilson Building, Canberra, ACT 0200, Australia. **Phone:** 02-6279-9830. **Fax:** 02-6249-4895. **E-mail:** mgr.mba.program@anu.edu.au.

Bond University

Gold Coast, Australia

SCHOOL OF BUSINESS

DEGREES M Acc • MBA • MBA/MBL • MBA/MIA • MBA/MIM • MBA/MIT • MBA/MLB • MBA/MLJ • MIB • MIM

M Acc—Master of Accounting Full-time and part-time. At least 12 total credits required. 15 to 84 months to complete program. *Concentrations:* accounting.

MBA—Executive MBA Part-time. At least 12 total credits required. 13 to 91 months to complete program. *Concentrations:* accounting, Asian business studies, entrepreneurship, international business, management, marketing.

MBA—Master of Business Administration Full-time and part-time. At least 12 total credits required. 12 to 84 months to complete program. *Concentrations:* accounting, Asian business studies, business law, business policy/strategy, entrepreneurship, finance, human resources, international business, leadership, management, marketing, new venture management, strategic management, technology management.

MBA/MBL—Master of Business Administration/Master of Law Full-time and part-time. At least 18 total credits required. 20 to 84 months to complete program. *Concentrations:* accounting, business law, entrepreneurship, finance, management, marketing, strategic management.

MBA/MIA—Master of Business Administration/Master of Information Analysis Management Full-time and part-time. At least 18 total credits required. 20 to 84 months to complete program. *Concentrations:* accounting, entrepreneurship, finance, management, marketing, strategic management, technology management.

MBA/MIM—Master of Business Administration/Master of International Management Full-time and part-time. At least 18 total credits required. 20 to 84 months to complete program. *Concentrations:* accounting, entrepreneurship, finance, international business, management, marketing, strategic management.

MBA/MIT—Master of Business Administration/Master of Information Technology Full-time and part-time. At least 18 total credits required. 20 to 84 months to complete program. *Concentrations:* accounting, entrepreneurship, finance, management, marketing, strategic management, technology management.

MBA/MLB—Master of Business Administration/Master of Business Law Full-time and part-time. At least 18 total credits required. 20 to 84 months to complete program. *Concentrations:* accounting, business law, entrepreneurship, finance, management, marketing, strategic management.

MBA/MLJ—Master of Business Administration/Master of Jurisprudence Full-time and part-time. At least 18 total credits required. 20 to 84 months to complete program. *Concentrations:* accounting, business law, entrepreneurship, finance, management, marketing, strategic management.

MIB—Master of International Business Full-time and part-time. At least 12 total credits required. 12 to 84 months to complete program. *Concentrations:* Asian business studies, entrepreneurship, finance, human resources, international business, international management, leadership, manufacturing management, marketing, new venture management.

MIM—Master of International Management Full-time and part-time. At least 12 total credits required. 12 to 84 months to complete program. *Concentrations:* accounting, Asian business studies, entrepreneurship, finance, human resources, international business, international management, leadership, management, marketing, new venture management.

RESOURCES AND SERVICES

Information about online services, personal computer policies, library resources, international exchange programs, internship programs, and placement services at this institution and others can be found at **www.petersons.com/mba**

International Students

Services and Facilities Counseling/support services, ESL/language courses, visa services.
International Student Contact Ms. Jodie Maguire, Student Service Officer, Student Services, Queensland, Australia. **Phone:** 7-5595-4001. **Fax:** 7-5595-1160. **E-mail:** jodie_maguire@bond.edu.au.

■ APPLICATION

Application Contact Mrs. Kathie Parkinson, Manager, Academic Programs, School of Business, University Drive, Queensland, Australia. **Phone:** 7-5595-2254. **Fax:** 7-5595-1160. **E-mail:** kathie_parkinson@bond.edu.au.

Curtin University of Technology

Perth, Australia

GRADUATE SCHOOL OF BUSINESS

DEGREES MBA • MLM

MBA—Master of Business Administration Full-time and part-time. *Distance learning option.* 16 to 36 months to complete program. *Concentrations:* accounting, Asian business studies, banking, business law, business policy/strategy, financial economics, human resources, industrial/labor relations, information management, international business, international management, international marketing, leadership, marketing, organizational behavior/development, project management, quality management, quantitative analysis.

MLM—Master of Leadership Management Full-time and part-time. 18 to 36 months to complete program. *Concentrations:* accounting, decision sciences,

entrepreneurship, human resources, international and area business studies, international development management, leadership, legal administration, management, marketing, operations management, organizational behavior/development, organizational management, quality management, strategic management.

RESOURCES AND SERVICES

Information about online services, personal computer policies, library resources, international exchange programs, internship programs, and placement services at this institution and others can be found at **www.petersons.com/mba**

International Students

Services and Facilities Counseling/support services, ESL/language courses, international student housing. Financial aid is available to international students.
International Student Contact Dr. Sylvester Boudville, Dean of International Programs, International Office, GPO Box U1987, Western Australia, Australia. **Phone:** 8-9266-3064. **Fax:** 8-9266-3960. **E-mail:** international@cc.curtin.edu.au.

■ APPLICATION

Application Contact Enrollment Officer, Graduate School of Business, QVI, 250 St. Georges Terrace, Western Australia, Australia. **Phone:** 8-9266-3460. **Fax:** 8-9266-3368.

Deakin University

Geelong, Australia

FACULTY OF BUSINESS AND LAW

Graduate Business Faculty

Full-time: 30	Part-time: 10

Student Body

Total: 850	
Full-time: 50	Average Age: 30
Part-time: 800	Women: 50%

Admissions

Applications: 400	Enrolled: 200
Admitted: 300	

Costs (1999–2000)
Full-time tuition: 10,400 Australian dollars per academic year
Part-time tuition: 1300 Australian dollars per unit

After Graduation (Class of 1998–99)
Employed within 3 months of graduation: 90%
Average starting salary: 40,000 Australian dollars

DEGREES MBA • MComm • MEC • MIBA

MBA—Master of Business Administration Full-time and part-time. *Distance learning option.* 12 total credits required. 12 to 84 months to complete program. *Concentrations:* electronic commerce (e-commerce), human resources, international business, management, management science, management systems analysis, public management, strategic management.

MComm—Master of Commerce Full-time and part-time. *Distance learning option.* 12 total credits required. 12 to 84 months to complete program. *Concentrations:* commerce, economics, international business, management.

MEC—Master of Electronic Commerce Full-time and part-time. 12 total credits required. 12 to 84 months to complete program. *Concentrations:* electronic commerce (e-commerce).

MIBA—Master of International Business Full-time and part-time. *Distance learning option.* 12 total credits required. 12 to 84 months to complete program. *Concentrations:* international business, international management.

COSTS

Tuition *Full-time:* 10,400 Australian dollars. *Part-time:* 1300 Australian dollars per unit. **Tuition, international:** *Full-time* 12,000 Australian dollars. **Graduate housing:** Room and board costs vary by campus location, number of occupants, type of accommodation, and type of board plan. *Typical cost:* 6200 Australian dollars (room only).

RESOURCES AND SERVICES

Information about online services, personal computer policies, library resources, international exchange programs, internship programs, and placement services at this institution and others can be found at **www.petersons.com/mba**

Deakin University (continued)

International Students
12% of students enrolled are international students.

Services and Facilities Counseling/support services, ESL/language courses, housing location assistance, international student housing, international student organization, language tutoring, orientation, visa services. Financial aid is not available to international students.

Applying *Required:* IELT with recommended score of 6, TOEFL with recommended score of 580 (paper), TWE with recommended score of 5.

International Student Contact Deakin International, 336 Glenferrie Road, Malvern, Victoria, 3144, Australia. **Phone:** 392-445-095. **Fax:** 392-445-094.

■ APPLICATION
Required Application form, baccalaureate/first degree, 2 letters of recommendation, personal statement, resume/curriculum vitae, transcripts of college work, 2 years of work experience.

Deadlines and Fees *Deadlines:* 5/31 for winter, 11/30 for summer, 6/15 for winter (international), 2/15 for summer (international). *Application fee:* 50 Australian dollars, 50 Australian dollars (international).

Application Contact MBA Program Director, Faculty of Business and Law, Geelong, 3217, Australia. **Phone:** 352-272-216. **Fax:** 352-272-655. **E-mail:** mba-enq@deakin.edu.au.

Edith Cowan University
Churchlands, Australia

FACULTY OF BUSINESS AND PUBLIC MANAGEMENT

Graduate Business Faculty
Full-time: 25

Student Body
Total: 473	Part-time: 366
Full-time: 107	Average Age: 30

Admissions
Applications: 430	Enrolled: 228
Admitted: 290	

Costs (1999–2000)
Full-time tuition: 13,600 Australian dollars per academic year (nonresident)
Part-time tuition: N/R

After Graduation (Class of 1998–99)
Employed within 3 months of graduation: 87%
Average starting salary: 54,500 Australian dollars

DEGREES MB • MBA • MEC • MF • MMIS • MPA

MB—Master of Business Full-time and part-time. 24 to 48 months to complete program. *Concentrations:* accounting, economics, finance, human resources, information management, management, marketing.

MBA—Master of Business Administration Full-time and part-time. *Distance learning option.* 18 to 48 months to complete program. *Concentrations:* accounting, finance, health care, human resources, information management, international business, legal administration, management, marketing, marketing research, organizational behavior/development, sports/entertainment management, travel industry/tourism management.

MEC—Master of Electronic Commerce 18 to 48 months to complete program. *Concentrations:* electronic commerce (e-commerce), information management.

MF—Master of Professional Finance 18 to 48 months to complete program. *Concentrations:* finance.

MMIS—Master of Management Information Systems Full-time and part-time. 18 to 48 months to complete program. *Concentrations:* contract management, electronic commerce (e-commerce), information management, management science, operations management, technology management.

MPA—Master of Professional Accounting Full-time and part-time. 18 to 48 months to complete program. *Concentrations:* accounting, taxation.

COSTS
Tuition, nonresident: *Full-time* 13,600 Australian dollars. Tuition varies by number of courses or credits taken.

FINANCIAL AID (1999–2000)
Grants, research assistantships, scholarships, and teaching assistantships. Aid is available to part-time students. Financial aid

application deadline: 10/30. **Financial Aid Contact** Research and Graduate School, Bradford Street, Western Australia, Australia.

RESOURCES AND SERVICES
Information about online services, personal computer policies, library resources, international exchange programs, internship programs, and placement services at this institution and others can be found at **www. petersons.com/mba**

International Students
Services and Facilities Counseling/support services, ESL/language courses, international student housing. Financial aid is not available to international students.
Applying *Required:* IELT with recommended score of 6, TOEFL with recommended score of 600 (paper).
International Student Contact Ms. Geetha Shute, International Students Office, Pearson Street, Western Australia, Australia. **Phone:** 8-9273-8499. **Fax:** 8-9273-8732.

■ APPLICATION
Required Application form, baccalaureate/first degree, letter(s) of recommendation, personal statement, resume/curriculum vitae, transcripts of college work, 2 years of work experience. **Recommended** Interview.

Deadlines and Fees Applications for domestic and international students are processed on a rolling basis.

Application Contact Prof. Dave Allen, Associate Dean, Research and Higher Degrees, Faculty of Business and Public Management, Pearson Street, Western Australia, Australia. **Phone:** 8-9273-8673. **Fax:** 8-9273-8810. **E-mail:** pgrad.business@ecu.edu.au.

La Trobe University
Bundoora, Australia

GRADUATE SCHOOL OF MANAGEMENT

Graduate Business Faculty
Full-time: 16	Part-time: 10

Student Body
Total: 385	Average Age: 33
Full-time: 285	Women: 27%
Part-time: 100	

Costs (1999–2000)
Full-time tuition: 9000 Australian dollars per academic year (resident)
Part-time tuition: 1000 Australian dollars per course (resident)

DEGREES MBA

MBA—Executive MBA Full-time and part-time. Substantial managerial experience. At least 240 total credits required. 12 to 46 months to complete program. *Concentrations:* management.

MBA—Standard MBA Full-time and part-time. 18 to 46 months to complete program. *Concentrations:* management.

COSTS
Tuition, state resident: *Full-time* 9000 Australian dollars. *Part-time* 1000 Australian dollars per course. **Tuition, international:** *Full-time* 12,000 Australian dollars. Tuition varies by academic program. **Graduate housing:** Room and board costs vary by number of occupants, type of accommodation, and type of board plan. *Typical cost:* 9000 Australian dollars (including board), 5720 Australian dollars (room only).

FINANCIAL AID (1999–2000)
Loans. **Financial Aid Contact** Ms. Brooke Young, School Manager, Graduate School of Management, Victoria, Australia. **Phone:** 3-9458 2755. **Fax:** 3-9458 2575. **E-mail:** mba@latrobe.edu.au.

RESOURCES AND SERVICES
Information about online services, personal computer policies, library resources, international exchange programs, internship programs, and placement services at this institution and others can be found at **www. petersons.com/mba**

International Students
74% of students enrolled are international students.

Services and Facilities Counseling/support services, ESL/language courses, housing location assistance, international student housing, international student organization, language tutoring, orientation, visa services, career program. Financial aid is not available to international students.

Applying *Required:* IELT with recommended score of 6.5, TOEFL with recommended score of 575 (paper), TWE with recommended score of 5.

International Student Contact Mr. Stephen Connelly, Marketing Director of International Programs, International Programs Office, La Trobe University, Victoria, Australia. **Phone:** 3-9479 1199. **Fax:** 3-9479 3660. **E-mail:** international@latrobe.edu.au.

■ **APPLICATION**

Required Application form, baccalaureate/first degree, 2 letters of recommendation, personal statement, transcripts of college work. School will accept GMAT. **Recommended** Work experience.

Deadlines and Fees *Deadlines:* 3/29 for fall, 6/16 for winter, 9/13 for spring, 1/4 for summer, 3/1 for fall (international), 5/19 for winter (international), 8/16 for spring (international), 12/7 for summer (international). *Application fee:* 50 Australian dollars, 50 Australian dollars (international).

Application Contact Ms. Jodie Datson, Student Services Officer, Graduate School of Management, Victoria, Australia. **Phone:** 3-9458 2755. **Fax:** 3-9458 2575. **E-mail:** mba@latrobe.edu.au.

Macquarie University

Sydney, Australia

MACQUARIE GRADUATE SCHOOL OF MANAGEMENT

Graduate Business Faculty
Full-time: 36 | Part-time: 46

Student Body
Total: 2,086 | Women: 33%
Average Age: 35

Admissions
Applications: 1,256 | Enrolled: 852
Admitted: 1,035

Costs (1999–2000)
Full-time tuition: N/R
Part-time tuition: 1995 Australian dollars per unit (resident), 1995 Australian dollars per unit (nonresident)

After Graduation (Class of 1998–99)
Employed within 3 months of graduation: 100%
Average starting salary: 90,000 Australian dollars

DEGREES M Mgt • MBA

M Mgt—Master of Management Full-time and part-time. 3 to 5 years of work experience required. At least 40 total credits required. 12 to 18 months to complete program. *Concentrations:* environmental economics/management, financial management/planning, human resources, information management, international management, management, management information systems, marketing, operations management, organizational behavior/development, strategic management, technology management, travel industry/tourism management.

MBA—Master of Business Administration Full-time and part-time. Minimum 5 years of work experience required. At least 64 total credits required. 12 to 36 months to complete program. *Concentrations:* economics, financial management/planning, human resources, information management, international management, management, management information systems, marketing, operations management, organizational behavior/development, strategic management, technology management.

COSTS

Tuition, state resident: *Part-time* 1995 Australian dollars per unit. **Tuition, nonresident:** *Part-time* 1995 Australian dollars per unit. Tuition varies by number of courses or credits taken and academic program. **Graduate housing:** Room and board costs vary by number of occupants and type of accommodation. *Typical cost:* 15,000 Australian dollars (including board).

FINANCIAL AID (1999–2000)

Financial Aid Contact Ms. Amy Dickson, Information Officer, International Office, Cottage C1, New South Wales, Australia. **Phone:** 2-9850-7346. **Fax:** 2-9850-7733. **E-mail:** iso@mq.edu.au.

RESOURCES AND SERVICES

Information about online services, personal computer policies, library resources, international exchange programs, internship programs, and placement services at this institution and others can be found at www.petersons.com/mba

International Students
28% of students enrolled are international students.

Services and Facilities Counseling/support services, ESL/language courses, international student housing, visa services, health coverage, social activities, career development. Financial aid is not available to international students.
Applying *Required:* IELT with recommended score of 6.5, TOEFL with recommended score of 600 (paper), TWE with recommended score of 5, proof of health/immunizations.

International Student Contact Ms. Amy Dickson, Information Officer, International Office, Cottage C1, New South Wales, Australia. **Phone:** 2-9850-6320. **Fax:** 2-9850-7733. **E-mail:** iso@mq.edu.au.

■ **APPLICATION**

Required Application form, baccalaureate/first degree, 3 letters of recommendation, personal statement, transcripts of college work, work experience.

Deadlines and Fees *Deadlines:* 10/29 for winter, 5/14 for spring, 5/14 for summer.

Application Contact Ms. Kim Wright, Marketing Executive, MGSM, Macquarie University, New South Wales, Australia. **Phone:** 2-9850-9944. **Fax:** 2-9850-9022. **E-mail:** kim.wright@mq.edu.au.

Monash University

Clayton, Australia

MONASH MT. ELIZA BUSINESS SCHOOL MBA PROGRAMME

Graduate Business Faculty
Full-time: 60 | Part-time: 25

Student Body
Total: 591 | Average Age: 30
Full-time: 215 | Women: 35%
Part-time: 376

Admissions
Applications: 1,176 | Enrolled: 336
Admitted: 355

Costs (1999–2000)
Full-time tuition: N/R
Part-time tuition: 25,280 Australian dollars per degree program

After Graduation (Class of 1998–99)
Employed within 3 months of graduation: 98%
Average starting salary: 70,000 Australian dollars

DEGREES GCBA • GDBA • MBA

GCBA—Graduate Certificate of Business Administration Full-time and part-time. 5 to 16 months to complete program. *Concentrations:* accounting, international business, organizational behavior/development, quantitative analysis.

GDBA—Graduate Diploma of Business Administration Full-time and part-time. 9 to 36 months to complete program. *Concentrations:* accounting, Asian business studies, business ethics, business policy/strategy, economics, finance, human resources, international and area business studies, international business, international management, management, management information systems, marketing, organizational behavior/development, public policy and administration, quality management, quantitative analysis, strategic management.

MBA—Master of Business Administration Full-time and part-time. 16 to 72 months to complete program. *Concentrations:* accounting, Asian business studies, business ethics, business policy/strategy, economics, finance, human resources, international and area business studies, international business, international management, management, management information systems, marketing, organizational behavior/development, public policy and administration, quality management, quantitative analysis, strategic management.

COSTS

Tuition *Part-time:* 25,280 Australian dollars per degree program. **Tuition, international:** *Full-time* 16,800 Australian dollars. Tuition varies by number of courses or credits taken. **Graduate housing:** Room and board costs vary by campus location, number of occupants, type of accommodation, and type of board plan. *Typical cost:* 12,000 Australian dollars (including board).

FINANCIAL AID (1999–2000)
Financial Aid Contact

RESOURCES AND SERVICES
Information about online services, personal computer policies, library resources, international exchange programs, internship programs, and placement services at this institution and others can be found at www.petersons.com/mba

Monash University (continued)

International Students

31% of students enrolled are international students.

Services and Facilities Counseling/support services, ESL/language courses, housing location assistance, international student housing, international student organization, language tutoring, orientation, visa services. Financial aid is not available to international students.

Applying *Required:* IELT with recommended score of 6.5, TOEFL with recommended score of 237 (computer) or 580 (paper), TWE with recommended score of 5, proof of health/immunizations.

International Student Contact Ms. Christine Montgomery, MBA International Liaison, PO Box 2224, Caulfield Junction, Victoria, 3161, Australia. **Phone:** 39-215-1850. **Fax:** 39-215-1821. **E-mail:** genmba@mteliza.edu.au.

■ APPLICATION

Required Application form, baccalaureate/first degree, 2 letters of recommendation, personal statement, transcripts of college work, 2 years of work experience. School will accept GMAT.

Deadlines and Fees *Deadlines:* 4/30 for winter, 11/30 for spring, 11/30 for summer, 4/30 for winter (international), 11/30 for summer (international).

Application Contact Ms. Christine Montgomery, MBA Admissions, PO Box 2224, Caulfield Junction, Victoria, 3161, Australia. **Phone:** 39-215-1850. **Fax:** 39-215-1821. **E-mail:** genmba@mteliza.edu.au.

Murdoch University

Perth, Australia

SCHOOL OF BUSINESS

Graduate Business Faculty

Full-time: 60	Part-time: 20

Student Body

Total: 158	Average Age: 27
Full-time: 95	Women: 20%
Part-time: 63	

Admissions

Applications: 198	Enrolled: 102
Admitted: 125	Average GMAT: 525

Costs (1999–2000)
Full-time tuition: 14,100 Australian dollars per academic year (resident)
Part-time tuition: 4700 Australian dollars per trimester (resident)

After Graduation (Class of 1998–99)
Employed within 3 months of graduation: 97%
Average starting salary: 65,000 Australian dollars

DEGREES M Sc • MBA • MEC • MHRM

M Sc—One-year Master of Science in Telecommunications Management Full-time and part-time. *Distance learning option.* At least 48 total credits required. 12 to 24 months to complete program.

MBA—One-year MBA in International Business: China Full-time and part-time. GMAT plus 2 years of experience and a valid passport and visa for China required. At least 48 total credits required. 12 to 24 months to complete program. *Concentrations:* Asian business studies, international business, manufacturing management, project management, telecommunications management.

MBA—One-year Master of Business Administration Full-time and part-time. GMAT plus 2 years of experience required. At least 48 total credits required. 12 to 36 months to complete program. *Concentrations:* environmental economics/management, international business, management, new venture management.

MEC—One-year Masters in Electronic Commerce Full-time and part-time. *Distance learning option.* At least 48 total credits required. 12 to 24 months to complete program. *Concentrations:* economics, electronic commerce (e-commerce), information management, management information systems, management systems analysis, system management, technology management.

MHRM—One-year Masters of Human Resources Management Full-time and part-time. At least 48 total credits required. 12 to 24 months to complete program. *Concentrations:* human resources, management consulting, management science, managerial economics.

COSTS

Tuition, state resident: *Full-time* 14,100 Australian dollars. *Part-time* 4700 Australian dollars per trimester. **Tuition, international:** *Full-time* 22,000 Australian

dollars. Tuition varies by number of courses or credits taken. **Graduate housing:** *Typical cost:* 9000 Australian dollars (including board).

RESOURCES AND SERVICES

Information about online services, personal computer policies, library resources, international exchange programs, internship programs, and placement services at this institution and others can be found at **www. petersons.com/mba**

International Students

36% of students enrolled are international students.

Services and Facilities Counseling/support services, ESL/language courses, housing location assistance, international student housing, international student organization, language tutoring, orientation, visa services. Financial aid is not available to international students.

Applying *Required:* TOEFL with recommended score of 550 (paper), proof of adequate funds, proof of health/immunizations. *Recommended:* IELT with recommended score of 6.

International Student Contact Mr. Neil Bryan, Postgraduate Admissions Officer, South Street, Western Australia, Australia. **Phone:** 8-9360 6428. **Fax:** 8-9310 5090. **E-mail:** nbryan@central.murdoch.edu.au.

■ APPLICATION

Required Application form, 2 letters of recommendation, personal statement, resume/curriculum vitae, transcripts of college work, 2 years of work experience. School will accept GMAT. **Recommended** Baccalaureate/first degree.

Deadlines and Fees *Deadlines:* 12/14 for fall, 4/30 for winter, 10/31 for fall (international).

Application Contact Mr. John Krasnostein, Programme Chair, MBA, School of Business, South Street, Western Australia, Australia. **Phone:** 8-9360 6039. **Fax:** 8-9360 5004. **E-mail:** j.krasnostein@murdoch.edu.au.

Queensland University of Technology

Brisbane, Australia

BRISBANE GRADUATE SCHOOL OF BUSINESS

Graduate Business Faculty

Full-time: 9	Part-time: 16

Student Body

Total: 2,420	Part-time: 1,173
Full-time: 1,247	Average Age: 35

Admissions

Applications: 788	Enrolled: 331
Admitted: 466	Average GMAT: 593

Costs (1999–2000)
Full-time tuition: N/R
Part-time tuition: N/R

After Graduation (Class of 1998–99)
Employed within 3 months of graduation: 89%
Average starting salary: 56,000 Australian dollars

DEGREES MBA

MBA—Executive MBA Part-time. *Distance learning option.* Minimum five years of work experience with a prior degree or 10 years without a degree. Up to 144 total credits required. Maximum of 16 months to complete program.

MBA—Master of Business Administration Full-time and part-time. At least 144 total credits required. 12 to 60 months to complete program. *Concentrations:* accounting, advertising, business law, economics, electronic commerce (e-commerce), entrepreneurship, finance, human resources, information management, international business, leadership, managerial economics, manufacturing management, marketing, new venture management, operations management, public relations, strategic management.

FINANCIAL AID (1999–2000)

16 students received aid, including scholarships. Aid is available to part-time students. **Financial Aid Contact** Dr. Carol Dalglish, MBA Director, Brisbane Graduate School of Business, GPO Box 2434, Brisbane, QLD 4001, Australia. **Phone:** 7-3864-5302. **Fax:** 7-3864-5302. **E-mail:** c.dalglish@qut.edu.au.

RESOURCES AND SERVICES

Information about online services, personal computer policies, library resources, international exchange programs, internship programs, and placement services at this institution and others can be found at **www.petersons.com/mba**

International Students

Services and Facilities Counseling/support services, ESL/language courses, international student housing, international student organization, language tutoring, orientation, visa services.

Applying *Required:* IELT with recommended score of 6.5, TOEFL with recommended score of 575 (paper), proof of adequate funds, proof of health/immunizations.

International Student Contact Ms. Susan King, Student Services Team Leader, Brisbane Graduate School of Business, GPO Box 2434, Brisbane, QLD 4001, Australia. **Phone:** 7-3864-1473. **Fax:** 7-3864-1055. **E-mail:** sm.king@qut.edu.au.

■ APPLICATION

Required Application form, resume/curriculum vitae, transcripts of college work, 2 years of work experience. School will accept GMAT. **Recommended** 2 letters of recommendation, personal statement.

Deadlines and Fees *Deadlines:* 5/17 for fall, 7/17 for winter, 9/4 for spring, 1/2 for summer, 5/17 for fall (international), 7/17 for winter (international), 9/4 for spring (international), 1/2 for summer (international). *Application fee:* 50 Australian dollars (international).

Application Contact Ms. Susan King, Student Services Team Leader, Brisbane Graduate School of Business, GPO Box 2434, Brisbane, QLD 4001, Australia. **Phone:** 7-3864-1473. **Fax:** 7-3864-1055. **E-mail:** sm.king@qut.edu.au.

Royal Melbourne Institute of Technology

Melbourne, Australia

GRADUATE SCHOOL OF BUSINESS

Graduate Business Faculty
Full-time: 40   Part-time: 60

Student Body
Average Age: 30

Costs (1999–2000)
Full-time tuition: 12,000 Australian dollars per academic year
Part-time tuition: 6000 Australian dollars per year

DEGREES M Tax • MB • MBA • MCL • MF

M Tax—Master of Taxation Part-time. 18 to 60 months to complete program. *Concentrations:* taxation.

MB—Master of Business in Accountancy Full-time and part-time. 18 to 60 months to complete program. *Concentrations:* accounting.

MB—Master of Business in Corporate Governance Part-time. 18 to 60 months to complete program. *Concentrations:* business ethics, business law, business policy/strategy.

MB—Master of Business in Information Technology Full-time and part-time. 12 to 60 months to complete program. *Concentrations:* business information science, technology management.

MB—Master of Business in Integrated Logistics Management Full-time and part-time. *Distance learning option.* 12 to 60 months to complete program. *Concentrations:* international logistics, logistics.

MB—Master of Business in Logistics Management Full-time and part-time. *Distance learning option.* 12 to 60 months to complete program. *Concentrations:* international logistics, logistics.

MB—Master of Business in Property Full-time and part-time. 18 to 60 months to complete program. *Concentrations:* real estate.

MB—Masters of Business in Industrial Relations/Human Resource Management Part-time. 12 to 60 months to complete program. *Concentrations:* human resources, industrial administration/management.

MB—Masters of Business in Municipal Management and Health Administration Part-time. 12 to 60 months to complete program. *Concentrations:* health care, public policy and administration.

MBA—Master of Business Administration in International Management Part-time. 24 to 60 months to complete program. *Concentrations:* international management.

MBA—Master of Business Administration Full-time and part-time. 18 to 36 months to complete program. *Concentrations:* management.

MCL—Master of Corporate Law Full-time and part-time. 18 to 60 months to complete program. *Concentrations:* business law.

MF—Master of Finance Full-time and part-time. 14 to 60 months to complete program. *Concentrations:* economics, finance, international finance.

COSTS

Tuition *Full-time:* 12,000 Australian dollars. *Part-time:* 6000 Australian dollars per year. Tuition varies by academic program.

FINANCIAL AID (1999–2000)

16 students received aid, including scholarships. Aid is available to part-time students. **Financial Aid Contact** International Services Financial Aid Officer, GPO Box 2476V, Victoria, Australia. **Phone:** 39-660-5156. **Fax:** 39-663-6925. **E-mail:** isu@rmit.edu.au.

RESOURCES AND SERVICES

Information about online services, personal computer policies, library resources, international exchange programs, internship programs, and placement services at this institution and others can be found at **www.petersons.com/mba**

International Students

Services and Facilities Counseling/support services, ESL/language courses, housing location assistance, international student housing, international student organization, language tutoring, orientation, visa services. Financial aid is available to international students.

Applying *Required:* IELT with recommended score of 6.5, TOEFL with recommended score of 580 (paper).

International Student Contact Ms. Belinda Ventura, MBA Administration Officer, GPO Box 2476V, Victoria, Australia. **Phone:** 39-925-5585. **Fax:** 39-925-5580. **E-mail:** belinda.ventura@rmit.edu.au.

■ APPLICATION

Required Application form, baccalaureate/first degree, interview, 1 letter of recommendation, personal statement, resume/curriculum vitae, transcripts of college work, work experience.

Deadlines and Fees *Deadlines:* 5/31 for winter, 11/10 for summer, 5/31 for winter (international), 11/10 for summer (international).

Application Contact Mrs. Belinda Ventura, MBA Administration Officer, GPO Box 2476V, Victoria, Australia. **Phone:** 39-925 5585. **Fax:** 39-925 5580. **E-mail:** belinda.ventura@rmit.edu.au.

Swinburne University of Technology

Hawthorne, Australia

SWINBURNE GRADUATE SCHOOL OF MANAGEMENT

Graduate Business Faculty
Full-time: 10   Part-time: 28

Student Body
Total: 837   Part-time: 628
Full-time: 209   Women: 39%

Admissions
Enrolled: 837

Costs (1999–2000)
Full-time tuition: N/R
Part-time tuition: N/R

DEGREES M Mgt • MBA • MEI

M Mgt—Master of Management Full-time and part-time. At least 150 total credits required. 18 to 36 months to complete program. *Concentrations:* management.

MBA—Executive MBA Full-time and part-time. At least 175 total credits required. Minimum of 18 months to complete program. *Concentrations:* strategic management.

MBA—Master of Business Administration Full-time and part-time. 2 years of work experience required. At least 175 total credits required. 18 to 36 months to complete program. *Concentrations:* European business studies, human resources, information management, international management, management, management information systems, manpower administration, marketing.

MEI—Master of Enterprise Innovation Part-time. At least 150 total credits required. 30 to 36 months to complete program. *Concentrations:* entrepreneurship.

Swinburne University of Technology (continued)

COSTS
Tuition varies by number of courses or credits taken and academic program.

FINANCIAL AID (1999–2000)
8 students received aid, including scholarships. **Financial Aid Contact** Ms. Melina Wong, Student Liaison Officer (Ausaid), 473 Bunwood Road, Victoria, Australia. **Phone:** 3-9214 5551. **Fax:** 3-9818 3648. **E-mail:** mwong@swin.edu.au.

RESOURCES AND SERVICES
Information about online services, personal computer policies, library resources, international exchange programs, internship programs, and placement services at this institution and others can be found at **www.petersons.com/mba**

International Students
23% of students enrolled are international students.

Services and Facilities Counseling/support services, ESL/language courses, housing location assistance, international student housing, international student organization, orientation, visa services, health services. Financial aid is available to international students.
Applying *Required:* IELT, TOEFL with recommended score of 580 (paper), TWE with recommended score of 4.
International Student Contact Ms. Malu Ferrer, Admissions Coordinator, International Student Unit, Internal Mail 5, 473 Burwood Road, Victoria, Australia. **Phone:** 3-9214-8647. **Fax:** 3-7818 3648. **E-mail:** mferrer@swin.edu.au.

■ APPLICATION
Required Application form, baccalaureate/first degree, interview, resume/curriculum vitae, transcripts of college work. School will accept GMAT or GRE or MAT. **Recommended** Letter(s) of recommendation, personal statement.
Deadlines and Fees Applications for domestic and international students are processed on a rolling basis.
Application Contact Ms. Yennhi McConnell, MBA Administrator, SGSM, PO Box 218, Victoria, Australia. **Phone:** 3-9214 5335. **Fax:** 3-9214 5336. **E-mail:** sgsm@swin.edu.au.

The University of Adelaide
Adelaide, Australia

GRADUATE SCHOOL OF MANAGEMENT

Graduate Business Faculty

Full-time: 8	Part-time: 47

Student Body

Total: 427	Part-time: 407
Full-time: 20	Average Age: 34

Admissions

Applications: 154	Enrolled: 80
Admitted: 83	Average GMAT: 600

Costs (1999–2000)
Full-time tuition: N/R
Part-time tuition: N/R

After Graduation (Class of 1998–99)
Employed within 3 months of graduation: 99%
Average starting salary: 81,880 Australian dollars

DEGREE MBA

MBA—Master of Business Administration Full-time and part-time. 2 years of relevant work experience required. At least 48 total credits required. 12 to 72 months to complete program. *Concentrations:* Asian business studies, finance, international management, marketing, general MBA.

COSTS
Tuition varies by number of courses or credits taken and academic program. **Required fees:** Tuition and fees vary by number of courses or credits taken. **Graduate housing:** Room and board costs vary by campus location, number of occupants, type of accommodation, and type of board plan. *Typical cost:* 8840 Australian dollars (including board).

FINANCIAL AID (1999–2000)
3 students received aid, including scholarships. **Financial Aid Contact** Ms. Carol McHugh, School Registrar, Graduate School of Management,

South Australia, Australia. **Phone:** 8-8303-4650. **Fax:** 8-8223-4782. **E-mail:** cmchugh@gsm.adelaide.edu.au.

RESOURCES AND SERVICES
Information about online services, personal computer policies, library resources, international exchange programs, internship programs, and placement services at this institution and others can be found at **www.petersons.com/mba**

International Students
4% of students enrolled are international students.

Services and Facilities Counseling/support services, ESL/language courses, housing location assistance, international student housing, international student organization, language tutoring, orientation, visa services. Financial aid is available to international students.
Applying *Required:* IELT with recommended score of 5, TOEFL with recommended score of 575 (paper), TWE with recommended score of 6, proof of adequate funds.
International Student Contact Ms. Carol McHugh, School Registrar, South Australia, Australia. **Phone:** 8-8303-4650. **Fax:** 8-8223-4782. **E-mail:** cmchugh@gsm.adelaide.edu.au.

■ APPLICATION
Required Application form, baccalaureate/first degree, 2 letters of recommendation, personal statement, resume/curriculum vitae, transcripts of college work, 2 years of work experience. School will accept GMAT.
Deadlines and Fees *Deadlines:* 6/15 for fall, 2/15 for winter, 11/15 for spring, 6/15 for fall (international), 2/15 for winter (international), 11/15 for spring (international). *Application fee:* 50 Australian dollars (international).
Application Contact Ms. Carol McHugh, School Registrar, Graduate School of Management, South Australia, Australia. **Phone:** 8-8303-4650. **Fax:** 8-8223-4782. **E-mail:** cmchugh@gsm.adelaide.edu.au.

University of Melbourne
Melbourne, Australia

MELBOURNE BUSINESS SCHOOL

Graduate Business Faculty

Full-time: 31	Part-time: 20

Student Body

Total: 740	Part-time: 486
Full-time: 254	Average Age: 29

Admissions

Applications: 460	Average GMAT: 640
Enrolled: 115	

Costs (1999–2000)
Full-time tuition: N/R
Part-time tuition: N/R

DEGREES MBA • MM • MMT

MBA—Master of Business Administration Full-time and part-time. At least 20 total credits required. 16 to 48 months to complete program. *Concentrations:* finance, international management, management, management information systems, marketing, organizational management.

MM—Master of Marketing Full-time and part-time. At least 12 total credits required. 12 to 36 months to complete program. *Concentrations:* marketing.

MMT—Master of Management Technology Full-time and part-time. At least 16 total credits required. 16 to 48 months to complete program. *Concentrations:* information management, management information systems, operations management, project management.

COSTS
Tuition varies by academic program. **Graduate housing:** Room and board costs vary by number of occupants and type of accommodation. *Typical cost:* 7500 Australian dollars (room only).

FINANCIAL AID (1999–2000)
40 students received aid, including research assistantships, scholarships, and teaching assistantships. Financial aid application deadline: 10/31.
Financial Aid Contact Financial Aid, Ground Floor, Baldwin Spencer Building, Victoria, Australia. **Phone:** 39-344-6053. **Fax:** 39-344-5624.

RESOURCES AND SERVICES
Information about online services, personal computer policies, library resources, international exchange programs, internship programs, and

placement services at this institution and others can be found at **www. petersons.com/mba**

International Students
16% of students enrolled are international students.

Services and Facilities Counseling/support services, ESL/language courses, international student housing, international student organization, orientation, visa services. Financial aid is not available to international students.

Applying *Required:* IELT with recommended score of 6.5, proof of adequate funds, proof of health/immunizations. *Recommended:* TOEFL with recommended score of 253 (computer) or 610 (paper).

International Student Contact Ms. Ann Sankey, Executive Officer, 200 Leicester Street, Victoria, Australia. **Phone:** 39-349-8122. **Fax:** 39-349-8133. **E-mail:** a.sankey@mbs.unimelb.edu.au.

■ APPLICATION

Required GMAT, application form, baccalaureate/first degree, 2 letters of recommendation, personal statement, resume/curriculum vitae, transcripts of college work, 2 years of work experience.

Deadlines and Fees *Deadlines:* 10/31 for winter, 10/31 for winter (international).

Application Contact Ms. Ann Sankey, Executive Officer, 200 Leicester Street, Victoria, Australia. **Phone:** 39-349-8122. **Fax:** 39-349-8133. **E-mail:** a.sankey@mbs.unimelb.edu.au.

University of Newcastle
Callaghan, Australia

GRADUATE SCHOOL OF BUSINESS

Graduate Business Faculty

Full-time: 25 | Part-time: 5

Student Body

Total: 565 | Women: 33%
Average Age: 34 |

Admissions

Applications: 305 | Enrolled: 160
Admitted: 270 | Average GMAT: 550

Costs (1999–2000)
Full-time tuition: 12,311 Australian dollars per academic year (resident)
Part-time tuition: 1000 Australian dollars per course (resident)

After Graduation (Class of 1998–99)
Employed within 3 months of graduation: 95%
Average starting salary: 63,000 Australian dollars

DEGREES M Stat • MAF • MBA • MHRMIR • MIT • MM • MMktg • MTD

M Stat—Master of Statistics Full-time and part-time. *Distance learning option.* At least 12 total credits required. 18 to 36 months to complete program. *Concentrations:* quality management, quantitative analysis.

MAF—Master of Applied Finance Full-time and part-time. At least 8 total credits required. 12 to 24 months to complete program. *Concentrations:* banking, finance.

MBA—Master of Business Administration Full-time and part-time. At least 12 total credits required. 18 to 36 months to complete program. *Concentrations:* accounting, commerce, economics, financial economics, human resources, management information systems, marketing, quantitative analysis.

MHRMIR—Master of Human Resource Management and Industrial Relations Full-time and part-time. At least 8 total credits required. 12 to 24 months to complete program. *Concentrations:* human resources, industrial/labor relations, organizational behavior/development.

MIT—Master of Information Technology Full-time and part-time. At least 12 total credits required. 18 to 36 months to complete program. *Concentrations:* information management, management information systems, quantitative analysis.

MM—Master in Environmental and Business Management Full-time and part-time. *Distance learning option.* 12 to 24 months to complete program. *Concentrations:* environmental economics/management.

MM—Master of Applied Management in Aviation Full-time and part-time. *Distance learning option.* 12 to 24 months to complete program. *Concentrations:* aviation management.

MM—Master of Applied Management in Education Full-time and part-time. *Distance learning option.* 12 to 24 months to complete program. *Concentrations:* training and development.

MM—Master of Applied Management in Health Full-time and part-time. *Distance learning option.* 12 to 24 months to complete program. *Concentrations:* health care.

MMktg—Master of Marketing Full-time and part-time. At least 8 total credits required. 12 to 24 months to complete program. *Concentrations:* entrepreneurship, marketing, marketing research.

COSTS
Tuition, state resident: *Full-time* 12,000 Australian dollars. *Part-time* 1000 Australian dollars per course. **Tuition, international:** *Full-time* 21,000 Australian dollars. Tuition varies by number of courses or credits taken and academic program. **Required fees:** *Full-time* 311 Australian dollars. **Graduate housing:** *Typical cost:* 8320 Australian dollars (including board).

FINANCIAL AID (1999–2000)
20 students received aid, including loans and scholarships. Aid is available to part-time students. Financial aid application deadline: 1/1. **Financial Aid Contact** Student Support Office, University of Newcastle, University Drive, NSW, Australia. **Phone:** 2-4921-6466.

RESOURCES AND SERVICES
Information about online services, personal computer policies, library resources, international exchange programs, internship programs, and placement services at this institution and others can be found at **www. petersons.com/mba**

International Students
Services and Facilities Counseling/support services, ESL/language courses, housing location assistance, international student housing, international student organization, language tutoring, orientation, visa services. Financial aid is not available to international students.

Applying *Required:* IELT with recommended score of 6.5, TOEFL with recommended score of 550 (paper), TWE with recommended score of 4.5. *Recommended:* Proof of adequate funds, proof of health/immunizations.

International Student Contact Ms. Suzanne Ryan, Assistant Director, Graduate School of Business, NSW, Australia. **Phone:** 2-4921-6015. **Fax:** 2-4921-7398. **E-mail:** mgser@cc.newcastle.edu.au.

■ APPLICATION

Required Application form, baccalaureate/first degree, resume/curriculum vitae, transcripts of college work, 3 years of work experience. School will accept GMAT. **Recommended** Personal statement.

Deadlines and Fees Applications for domestic and international students are processed on a rolling basis.

Application Contact Ms. Angela Bennett, Administration Officer, Graduate School of Business, NSW, Australia. **Phone:** 2-4921-8749. **Fax:** 2-4921-7398. **E-mail:** gsbinfo@cc.newcastle.edu.au.

University of New South Wales
Kensington, Australia

AUSTRALIAN GRADUATE SCHOOL OF MANAGEMENT

Graduate Business Faculty

Full-time: 52 | Part-time: 114

Student Body

Total: 353 | Average Age: 29
Full-time: 253 | Women: 24%
Part-time: 100 |

Admissions

Applications: 500 | Average GMAT: 641
Enrolled: 85 |

Costs (1999–2000)
Full-time tuition: 21,000 Australian dollars per academic year (resident)
Part-time tuition: 1750 Australian dollars per course (resident)

After Graduation (Class of 1998–99)
Average starting salary: 88,000 Australian dollars

DEGREES EMBA • MBA

EMBA—Executive Master of Business Administration Part-time. *Distance learning option.* Maximum of 36 months to complete program. *Concentrations:* accounting, actuarial science, economics, finance, international management, management, management systems analysis, marketing, organizational behavior/

University of New South Wales (continued)

development, organizational management, quality management, strategic management.
MBA—Master of Business Administration Full-time and part-time. 18 to 21 months to complete program. *Concentrations:* accounting, economics, entrepreneurship, finance, industrial/labor relations, management, marketing, operations management, organizational behavior/development, quality management, quantitative analysis.

COSTS
Tuition, state resident: *Full-time* 21,000 Australian dollars. *Part-time* 1750 Australian dollars per course. **Tuition, international:** *Full-time* 25,000 Australian dollars. Tuition varies by academic program.

FINANCIAL AID (1999–2000)
Scholarships. Financial aid application deadline: 11/30. **Financial Aid Contact** Ms. Christine Kelly, Admissions Coordinator, New South Wales, Australia. **Phone:** 2-9931 9225. **Fax:** 2-9931 9231.

RESOURCES AND SERVICES
Information about online services, personal computer policies, library resources, international exchange programs, internship programs, and placement services at this institution and others can be found at **www.petersons.com/mba**

International Students
57% of students enrolled are international students.
Services and Facilities Counseling/support services, ESL/language courses, international student housing, visa services. Financial aid is not available to international students.
Applying *Recommended:* IELT.
International Student Contact Mrs. Sue Bernett-Wilken, Associate Director, Full-Time MBA and PhD Programs, Australian Graduate School of Management, New South Wales, Australia. **Phone:** 2-9931-9491. **Fax:** 2-9931-9231. **E-mail:** sueb@agsm.edu.au.

■ APPLICATION
Required Application form, baccalaureate/first degree, essay, 2 letters of recommendation, personal statement, transcripts of college work, 2 years of work experience. School will accept GMAT. **Recommended** Interview, resume/curriculum vitae.
Deadlines and Fees *Deadlines:* 11/30 for spring, 11/30 for summer, 11/30 for summer (international). *Application fee:* 50 Australian dollars, 50 Australian dollars (international).
Application Contact Ms. Christine Kelly, Admissions Coordinator, Australian Graduate School of Management, New South Wales, Australia. **Phone:** 2-9931-9225. **Fax:** 2-9931-9231.

University of South Australia
Adelaide, Australia

INTERNATIONAL GRADUATE SCHOOL OF MANAGEMENT

Graduate Business Faculty
Full-time: 12   Part-time: 30
Student Body
Total: 4,581
Full-time: 2,369   Average Age: 37
Part-time: 2,212   Women: 51%

Costs (1999–2000)
Full-time tuition: 10,218 Australian dollars per academic year
Part-time tuition: N/R

After Graduation (Class of 1998–99)
Employed within 3 months of graduation: 100%

DEGREES IMBA • MBA

IMBA—International Master of Business Administration Full-time. At least 72 total credits required. 12 to 24 months to complete program. *Concentrations:* arts administration/management, electronic commerce (e-commerce), finance, human resources, information management, marketing, public management, public relations.
MBA—Master of Business Administration Full-time and part-time. *Distance learning option.* At least 72 total credits required. 18 to 60 months to complete program. *Concentrations:* arts administration/management, business policy/strategy, electronic commerce (e-commerce), finance, human resources, informa-

tion management, international marketing, leadership, marketing, strategic management.

COSTS
Tuition *Full-time:* 10,000 Australian dollars. **Tuition, international:** *Full-time* 11,500 Australian dollars. **Required fees:** *Full-time* 218 Australian dollars. *Part-time* 218 Australian dollars per year.

FINANCIAL AID (1999–2000)
2 students received aid, including scholarships. Aid is available to part-time students. **Financial Aid Contact** Mr. Murray Olliver, Course Coordinator MBA, GPO Box 2471, Adelaide, 5000, Australia. **Phone:** 8-83020032. **Fax:** 8-83020709. **E-mail:** murray.olliver@unisa.edu.au.

RESOURCES AND SERVICES
Information about online services, personal computer policies, library resources, international exchange programs, internship programs, and placement services at this institution and others can be found at **www.petersons.com/mba**

International Students
Services and Facilities Counseling/support services, ESL/language courses, international student housing, orientation, visa services. Financial aid is available to international students.
Applying *Required:* IELT, TOEFL with recommended score of 550 (paper).
International Student Contact Ms. Janny Maddern, Course Coordinator International MBA, GPO Box 2471, Adelaide, 5000, Australia. **Phone:** 8-83020520. **Fax:** 8-83020709. **E-mail:** janny.maddern@unisa.edu.au.

■ APPLICATION
Required Application form, letter(s) of recommendation, personal statement, resume/curriculum vitae, transcripts of college work, 2 years of work experience. **Recommended** Baccalaureate/first degree.
Deadlines and Fees *Application fee:* $50.
Application Contact Mr. Murray Olliver, Course Coordinator MBA, GPO Box 2471, Adelaide, 5000, Australia. **Phone:** 8-83020032. **Fax:** 8-83020709. **E-mail:** murray.olliver@unisa.edu.au.

University of Southern Queensland
Toowoombu, Australia

FACULTY OF BUSINESS

DEGREES MB • MBA • MIT

MB—Master of Business Full-time and part-time. 48 to 60 months to complete program.
MBA—Distance Learning MBA Part-time. *Distance learning option.* 18 to 48 months to complete program.
MIT—Master of Information Technology Full-time and part-time. *Distance learning option.* 24 to 48 months to complete program.

RESOURCES AND SERVICES
Information about online services, personal computer policies, library resources, international exchange programs, internship programs, and placement services at this institution and others can be found at **www.petersons.com/mba**

International Students
Services and Facilities Counseling/support services, ESL/language courses, international student housing. Financial aid is not available to international students.
International Student Contact International Education Centre, Private Mail Bag #1, PO Darling Heights, Queensland, Australia. **Phone:** 7-46312362. **Fax:** 7-46362211.

■ APPLICATION
Application Contact Administration Officer, Faculty of Business, Queensland, Australia. **Phone:** 7-46311881. **Fax:** 7-46312811. **E-mail:** bizness@usq.edu.au.

The University of Sydney
Sydney, Australia

AUSTRALIAN GRADUATE SCHOOL OF MANAGEMENT

DEGREES M Mgt • MBA

M Mgt—Master of Management Full-time and part-time. At least 36 total credits required. 18 to 30 months to complete program. *Concentrations:* management.

MBA—Master of Business Administration Full-time and part-time. 2 years of full-time work experience and high GMAT score required. At least 48 total credits required. 18 to 21 months to complete program. *Concentrations:* management.

RESOURCES AND SERVICES

Information about online services, personal computer policies, library resources, international exchange programs, internship programs, and placement services at this institution and others can be found at **www. petersons.com/mba**

International Students

Services and Facilities Counseling/support services, ESL/language courses, international student housing, visa services. Financial aid is not available to international students.

International Student Contact Ms. Karina Murray, Operations Manager, Full-Time MBA and PhD Program, New South Wales, Australia. **Phone:** 2-99319227. **Fax:** 2-99319231.

■ APPLICATION

Application Contact Ms. Jenny Woodward, Australian Graduate School of Management, Locked Bag 20, New South Wales, Australia. **Phone:** 2-9931-9220. **Fax:** 2-9931-9231. **E-mail:** jennyw@gsb.usyd.edu.au.

University of Technology, Sydney

Sydney, Australia

GRADUATE SCHOOL OF BUSINESS

Graduate Business Faculty
Full-time: 130	Part-time: 100

Student Body
Total: 2,706	Average Age: 31
Full-time: 963	Women: 35%
Part-time: 1,743	

Admissions
Applications: 1,147	Enrolled: 968
Admitted: 1,090	

Costs (1999–2000)
Full-time tuition: 11,520 Australian dollars per academic year (resident)
Part-time tuition: 5920 Australian dollars per year (resident)

DEGREES MB • MBA • MM

MB—Master of Business Full-time and part-time. At least 72 total credits required. 18 to 54 months to complete program. *Concentrations:* accounting, electronic commerce (e-commerce), finance, industrial/labor relations, insurance, international business, international marketing, marketing, operations management.

MBA—Master of Business Administration Full-time and part-time. Minimum four years work experience. At least 96 total credits required. 18 to 72 months to complete program. *Concentrations:* accounting, arts administration/management, banking, business law, city/urban administration, electronic commerce (e-commerce), finance, human resources, information management, international business, international marketing, management, management information systems, marketing, operations management, organizational behavior/development, organizational management, project management, sports/entertainment management, strategic management, travel industry/tourism management, engineering, facilities management.

MM—Master of Management Full-time and part-time. At least 72 total credits required. 18 to 34 months to complete program. *Concentrations:* arts administration/management, health care, management, nonprofit management, sports/entertainment management, travel industry/tourism management.

COSTS

Tuition, state resident: *Full-time* 11,200 Australian dollars. *Part-time* 5600 Australian dollars per year. **Tuition, international:** *Full-time* 14,000 Australian dollars. Tuition varies by number of courses or credits taken and academic program. **Required fees:** *Full-time* 320 Australian dollars. *Part-time* 320 Australian dollars per year.

FINANCIAL AID (1999–2000)

210 students received aid, including loans. Aid is available to part-time students. Financial aid application deadline: 1/20. **Financial Aid Contact** Student Services, POB 123, Broadway, Sydney, NSW 2007, Australia. **Phone:** 2-9514-1177.

RESOURCES AND SERVICES

Information about online services, personal computer policies, library resources, international exchange programs, internship programs, and placement services at this institution and others can be found at **www. petersons.com/mba**

International Students

40% of students enrolled are international students.

Services and Facilities Counseling/support services, ESL/language courses, international student housing, international student organization, orientation. Financial aid is not available to international students.

Applying *Required:* IELT with recommended score of 6.5, TOEFL with recommended score of 575 (paper), TWE with recommended score of 4.5, proof of adequate funds, proof of health/immunizations.

International Student Contact Ms. Vanessa Joseph, International Admissions Officer, UTS International Programs Office, PO Box 123, New South Wales, Australia. **Phone:** 2-9514-1544. **Fax:** 2-9514-1530. **E-mail:** vanessa.joseph@uts.edu.au.

■ APPLICATION

Required Application form, baccalaureate/first degree, 1 letter of recommendation, resume/curriculum vitae, transcripts of college work, 2 years of work experience. **Recommended** Personal statement.

Deadlines and Fees *Deadlines:* 10/31 for fall, 5/31 for spring, 10/31 for fall (international), 5/31 for spring (international). *Application fee:* 50 Australian dollars (international).

Application Contact Graduate Student Advisor, UTS Graduate School of Business, PO Box 123, New South Wales, Australia. **Phone:** 2-9514-3660. **Fax:** 2-9514-3554. **E-mail:** graduate.business@uts.edu.au.

The University of Western Australia

Nedlands, Australia

GRADUATE SCHOOL OF MANAGEMENT

Graduate Business Faculty
Full-time: 20	Part-time: 10

Student Body
Total: 340	Average Age: 32
Full-time: 102	Women: 39%
Part-time: 238	

Admissions
Applications: 288	Enrolled: 50
Admitted: 71	Average GMAT: 605

Costs (1999–2000)
Full-time tuition: N/R
Part-time tuition: 1300 Australian dollars per unit (resident), 2000 Australian dollars per unit (nonresident)

After Graduation (Class of 1998–99)
Employed within 3 months of graduation: 95%
Average starting salary: 55,000 Australian dollars

DEGREE MBA

MBA—Master of Business Administration Full-time and part-time. 16 to 72 months to complete program. *Concentrations:* finance, human resources, information management, international business, management, marketing, operations management.

COSTS

Tuition, state resident: *Part-time* 1300 Australian dollars per unit. **Tuition, nonresident:** *Part-time* 2000 Australian dollars per unit. **Graduate housing:** *Typical cost:* 14,000 Australian dollars (including board).

FINANCIAL AID (1999–2000)

Financial Aid Contact Ms. Catherine Vogel, Administrative Assistant, Graduate School of Management, Western Australia, Australia. **Phone:** 8-9380 2919. **Fax:** 8-9380 1072. **E-mail:** cvogel@ecel.uwa.edu.au.

RESOURCES AND SERVICES

Information about online services, personal computer policies, library resources, international exchange programs, internship programs, and placement services at this institution and others can be found at **www. petersons.com/mba**

The University of Western Australia (continued)

International Students

14% of students enrolled are international students.

Services and Facilities Counseling/support services, ESL/language courses, international student housing, visa services. Financial aid is not available to international students.

Applying *Required:* IELT with recommended score of 6.5, TOEFL with recommended score of 550 (paper).

International Student Contact Dr. Roger Smith, GSM International Studies Coordinator, Graduate School of Management, Western Australia, Australia. **Phone:** 8-9380 1441. **Fax:** 8-9380 1072. **E-mail:** rsmith@ecel.uwa.edu.au.

■ APPLICATION

Required GMAT, application form, baccalaureate/first degree, 2 letters of recommendation, personal statement, transcripts of college work, 2 years of work experience. **Recommended** Interview, resume/curriculum vitae.

Deadlines and Fees *Deadlines:* 11/30 for fall, 3/31 for winter, 6/30 for spring, 10/31 for fall (international), 6/30 for spring (international).

Application Contact Dr. Roger Smith, GSM International Studies Coordinator, Graduate School of Management, Western Australia, Australia. **Phone:** 8-9380 1441. **Fax:** 8-9380 1072. **E-mail:** rsmith@ecel.uwa.edu.au.

University of Western Sydney, Macarthur

Campbelltown, Australia

FACULTY OF BUSINESS AND TECHNOLOGY

DEGREES MBA • MComm • MIE

MBA—Master of Business Administration in Hotel Management Full-time and part-time. At least 6 total credits required. 12 to 48 months to complete program. *Concentrations:* accounting, economics, entrepreneurship, finance, international business, management, managerial economics, organizational management, quality management, strategic management, travel industry/tourism management.

MBA—Master of Business Administration in International Business Full-time and part-time. At least 16 total credits required. 12 to 48 months to complete program. *Concentrations:* accounting, economics, entrepreneurship, finance, international business, management, managerial economics, marketing, organizational behavior/development, organizational management, quality management, strategic management.

MBA—Master of Business Administration in Tourism Management Full-time and part-time. At least 8 total credits required. 12 to 48 months to complete program. *Concentrations:* accounting, economics, entrepreneurship, finance, international business, management, managerial economics, organizational management, quality management, strategic management, travel industry/tourism management.

MComm—Master of Commerce in Accounting Full-time and part-time. At least 8 total credits required. 12 to 48 months to complete program. *Concentrations:* accounting, organizational behavior/development.

MIE—Master of International Economics Full-time and part-time. At least 8 total credits required. 12 to 48 months to complete program. *Concentrations:* environmental economics/management, finance, international economics, international finance.

RESOURCES AND SERVICES

Information about online services, personal computer policies, library resources, international exchange programs, internship programs, and placement services at this institution and others can be found at **www. petersons.com/mba**

International Students

Services and Facilities Counseling/support services, ESL/language courses, international student housing, visa services. **International Student Contact** Ms. Ingrid Elliston, Executive Officer, Office of International Programs, PO Box 555, New South Wales, Australia. **Phone:** 246-203-313. **Fax:** 246-266-677. **E-mail:** i.elliston@uws.edu.au.

■ APPLICATION

Application Contact Director of International Programs, PO Box 555, New South Wales, Australia. **Phone:** 246-203-313. **Fax:** 246-266-677.

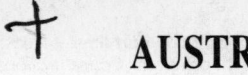

AUSTRIA

Vienna University of Economics and Business Administration

Vienna, Austria

WU WIEN MBA

Graduate Business Faculty

Full-time: 32   Part-time: 5

Student Body

Average Age: 31

Admissions

Applications: 290   Average GMAT: 593
Admitted: 102   Average GPA: 3.3
Enrolled: 70

Costs (1999–2000)

Full-time tuition: $25,000 per academic year (resident), $25,000 per academic year (nonresident)
Part-time tuition: N/R

After Graduation (Class of 1998–99)

Employed within 3 months of graduation: 98%
Average starting salary: $70,000

DEGREES MBA

MBA—International MBA Full-time. 2 years of work experience required. At least 48 total credits required. 15 months to complete program. *Concentrations:* international business, international management.

MBA—Vienna Executive MBA Part-time. Minimum 5 years of work experience and 3 letters of recommendation required. At least 48 total credits required. 14 months to complete program. *Concentrations:* management.

COSTS

Tuition, state resident: *Full-time* $25,000. **Tuition, nonresident:** *Full-time* $25,000. **Tuition, international:** *Full-time* $25,000. Tuition varies by academic program.

FINANCIAL AID (1999–2000)

4 students received aid, including fellowships, loans, scholarships, and teaching assistantships. Financial aid application deadline: 4/1.
Financial Aid Contact Ms. Bridget Blackwell, Financial Aid Officer, Financial Aid Office, University of South Carolina, Columbia, SC 29208. **Phone:** 803-777-8134. **Fax:** 803-777-0941.

RESOURCES AND SERVICES

Information about online services, personal computer policies, library resources, international exchange programs, internship programs, and placement services at this institution and others can be found at **www. petersons.com/mba**

International Students

Services and Facilities Counseling/support services, ESL/language courses, housing location assistance, orientation, visa services, www-based preparation for part-time students. Financial aid is available to international students.
Applying *Required:* TOEFL with recommended score of 600 (paper), proof of adequate funds, proof of health/immunizations.

International Student Contact Ms. Antje De Zwaan, Student Affairs Manager, IMBA Augasse 2-6, Vienna, A-1090, Austria. **Phone:** 1-31336-5312. **Fax:** 1-31336-768. **E-mail:** imba@isis.wu-wien.ac.at.

■ APPLICATION

Required GMAT, application form, baccalaureate/first degree, essay, 2 letters of recommendation, personal statement, resume/curriculum vitae, transcripts of college work, 2 years of work experience. School will accept GMAT or GRE. **Recommended** Interview.

Deadlines and Fees *Deadlines:* 1/1 for spring, 2/1 for summer, 1/1 for spring (international), 2/1 for summer (international). *Application fee:* $35, $35 (international).

Application Contact Ms. Monika Moser, Assistant to Director, WU Wien MBA, IMBA Augasse 2-6 A, Vienna, A-1090, Austria. **Phone:** 1-31336-4027. **Fax:** 1-31336-768. **E-mail:** imba@wu-wien.ac.at.

BANGLADESH

International University of Business Agriculture and Technology (IUBAT)

Dhaka, Bangladesh

COLLEGE OF BUSINESS ADMINISTRATION

DEGREE MBA

MBA—Master of Business Administration Full-time. At least 74 total credits required. Minimum of 20 months to complete program. *Concentrations:* financial management/planning, management, management science, marketing, operations management, production management.

RESOURCES AND SERVICES

Information about online services, personal computer policies, library resources, international exchange programs, internship programs, and placement services at this institution and others can be found at **www. petersons.com/mba**

International Students

Services and Facilities Financial aid is available to international students.

▪ APPLICATION

Application Contact Dr. M. Alimullah Miyah, Vice Chancellor, IUBAT, House 135, Road 9A, Dhanmondi, GPO Box 2857, Dhaka, 1000, Bangladesh. **Phone:** 02-81-60-64. **Fax:** 02-81-04-94.

BELGIUM

27

28

The International Management Institute

Antwerp, Belgium

INTERNATIONAL BUSINESS SCHOOL

Graduate Business Faculty
Full-time: 5   Part-time: 10

Student Body
Total: 50
Full-time: 30   Average Age: 25
Part-time: 20   Women: 30%

Admissions
Applications: 100   Average GMAT: 500
Admitted: 40   Average GPA: 2
Enrolled: 35

Costs (1999–2000)
Full-time tuition: $9000 per academic year
Part-time tuition: N/R

DEGREES MA • MBA • MS • MTL

MA—Master of Arts in Business Communications and Public Relations Full-time and part-time. 12 to 36 months to complete program. *Concentrations:* public relations.

MBA—Master of Business Administration Full-time and part-time. *Distance learning option.* 12 to 36 months to complete program. *Concentrations:* business information science, finance, international business, international marketing, management.

MS—Master of Science in Information Systems Full-time and part-time. 12 to 36 months to complete program. *Concentrations:* management information systems.

MTL—Master of Transportation and Logistics Full-time and part-time. 12 to 36 months to complete program. *Concentrations:* logistics.

COSTS

Tuition *Full-time:* $9000. **Graduate housing:** Room and board costs vary by campus location, number of occupants, and type of accommodation. *Typical cost:* $2400 (room only).

RESOURCES AND SERVICES

Information about online services, personal computer policies, library resources, international exchange programs, internship programs, and placement services at this institution and others can be found at **www. petersons.com/mba**

International Students

80% of students enrolled are international students.

Services and Facilities Counseling/support services, housing location assistance, international student housing, language tutoring, visa services. Financial aid is not available to international students.

Applying *Required:* TOEFL with recommended score of 450 (paper).

International Student Contact Mr. Luc Van Mele, Director of MBA Admissions, Jacob Jordenstraat 77, Antwerp, 2018, Belgium. **Phone:** 03-218-5431. **Fax:** 03-218-5868. **E-mail:** info@timi.edu.

▪ APPLICATION

Required Application form, baccalaureate/first degree, interview, 2 letters of recommendation, personal statement, resume/curriculum vitae, transcripts of college work. School will accept GMAT.

Deadlines and Fees *Deadlines:* 7/1 for fall, 9/1 for winter, 1/1 for spring, 4/1 for summer, 7/1 for fall (international), 9/1 for winter (international), 1/1 for spring (international), 4/1 for summer (international). *Application fee:* $100.

Application Contact Mr. Luc Van Mele, Director of MBA Admissions, Jacob Jordenstraat 77, Antwerp, 2018, Belgium. **Phone:** 03-218-5431. **Fax:** 03-218-5868. **E-mail:** info@timi.edu.

See full description on page 688.

Katholieke Universiteit Leuven

Leuven, Belgium

DEPARTMENT OF APPLIED ECONOMIC SCIENCES

DEGREES MBA • MS

MBA—Master of Business Administration Full-time and part-time. 10 to 22 months to complete program. *Concentrations:* accounting, business information science, European business studies, finance, human resources, international business, international finance, management, marketing, operations management, organizational behavior/development, quantitative analysis, strategic management.

MS—Master in Financial Economics

MS—Master in International Business Economics

MS—Master of Science in Applied Economics Full-time. Minimum of 10 months to complete program.

MS—Master of Science in Marketing Full-time. Minimum of 10 months to complete program.

RESOURCES AND SERVICES

Information about online services, personal computer policies, library resources, international exchange programs, internship programs, and placement services at this institution and others can be found at **www. petersons.com/mba**

International Students

Services and Facilities Counseling/support services, international student housing. Financial aid is not available to international students.

International Student Contact Mrs. Gonda Huybens, Program Coordinator, Naamsestrat 69, Leuven, B-3000, Belgium. **Phone:** 16-326-619. **Fax:** 16-326-620. **E-mail:** gonda.huybens@econ.kuleuven.ac.be.

▪ APPLICATION

Application Contact Mrs. Gonda Huybens, Program Coordinator, Naamsestraat 69, Leuven, B-3000, Belgium. **Phone:** 16-663-219. **Fax:** 16-663-220.

St. Ignatius University Faculty of Antwerp (UFSIA)

Antwerp, Belgium

CENTER FOR BUSINESS ADMINISTRATION

DEGREE MBA

MBA—Master of Business Administration Full-time. At least 60 total credits required. Minimum of 12 months to complete program. *Concentrations:* management.

RESOURCES AND SERVICES
Information about online services, personal computer policies, library resources, international exchange programs, internship programs, and placement services at this institution and others can be found at www.petersons.com/mba

International Students

Services and Facilities Counseling/support services, international student housing. Financial aid is not available to international students.
International Student Contact Ms. Marie-Jeanne Criel, Administrative Coordinator, Prinsstraat 13, Antwerp, B-2000, Belgium. **Phone:** 3-220-4001. **Fax:** 3-220-4079.

■ APPLICATION

Application Contact Ms. Marie-Jeanne Criel, Administrative Coordinator, Prinsstraat 13, Antwerp, B-2000, Belgium. **Phone:** 3-220-4001. **Fax:** 3-220-4079.

dev eua.ac.be

CANADA

Athabasca University

Athabasca, Alberta, Canada

CENTRE FOR INNOVATIVE MANAGEMENT

Graduate Business Faculty
Full-time: 7 — Part-time: 55

Student Body
Total: 1,030 — Average Age: 40
Part-time: 1,030 — Women: 29%

Admissions
Applications: 204 — Enrolled: 136
Admitted: 151

Costs (1999–2000)
Full-time tuition: N/R
Part-time tuition: $25,000 Canadian per degree program (resident), $25,000 Canadian per degree program (nonresident)

After Graduation (Class of 1998–99)
Employed within 3 months of graduation: 100%
Average starting salary: $88,113 Canadian

DEGREES MBA

MBA—Executive MBA Part-time. *Distance learning option.* At least 48 total credits required. 30 to 72 months to complete program.
MBA—MBA in Information Technology Management Part-time. *Distance learning option.* At least 48 total credits required. 30 to 72 months to complete program. *Concentrations:* financial management/planning, management systems analysis, strategic management, system management.

Athabasca University's graduate business programs are conducted through an online distance learning model that enables students to combine their studies with their careers. Because the programs are electronically delivered, students have the ability to complete their studies from the comfort and convenience of home, from work, or while on the road. This allows them to work according to their own schedules, without losing valuable time through commutes and preset classes.

The programs aim to give students the skills they need to succeed in the multifaceted role of modern managers, which includes being a leader, team player, decision maker, and coach. Students focus on key tasks on management—managing strategy, information, people, resources, markets, and operations—from a decision-making perspective. Throughout the program, students apply the theories they are learning to real situations in their own organizations.

The Athabasca graduate business programs utilize Lotus Notes, a groupware product that enables students to access course information and materials, conduct group discussions, complete teamwork projects, and submit course work electronically. Students and faculty and staff members are all connected, creating a rich, interactive learning environment, while giving students the support and services they require to succeed.

Students in the master's programs must complete ten required courses, two electives, two comprehensive exams, and one applied project for a total of 48 credits. In addition, students must attend one weeklong summer school and two weekend schools.

COSTS
Tuition, state resident: *Part-time* $25,000 Canadian per degree program. **Tuition, Canadian resident:** *Part-time* $25,000 Canadian per degree program.

FINANCIAL AID (1999–2000)
Financial Aid Contact

RESOURCES AND SERVICES
Information about online services, personal computer policies, library resources, international exchange programs, internship programs, and placement services at this institution and others can be found at www.petersons.com/mba

International Students
3% of students enrolled are international students.
Services and Facilities Orientation. Financial aid is not available to international students.

■ APPLICATION

Required Application form, baccalaureate/first degree, essay, 3 letters of recommendation, resume/curriculum vitae, transcripts of college work, 3 years of work experience.
Deadlines and Fees *Deadlines:* 6/15 for fall, 10/15 for winter, 2/15 for spring, 6/15 for fall (international), 10/15 for winter (international), 2/15 for spring (international). *Application fee:* $165 Canadian, $165 Canadian (international).
Application Contact Customer Service Representative, 301, 22 Sir Winston Churchill Avenue, St. Albert, AB T8N 1B4, Canada. **Phone:** 780-459-1144. **Toll-free Phone:** 780-459-1144 (in-state), 800-561-4650 (out-of-state). **Fax:** 780-459-2093.

Carleton University

Ottawa, Ontario, Canada

SCHOOL OF BUSINESS

Graduate Business Faculty
Full-time: 21 — Part-time: 10

Student Body
Total: 60 — Average Age: 27
Full-time: 42 — Women: 53%
Part-time: 18

Admissions
Applications: 124 — Average GMAT: 550
Admitted: 61 — Average GPA: 9/12 scale
Enrolled: 30

Costs (1999–2000)
Full-time tuition: N/R
Part-time tuition: N/R

After Graduation (Class of 1998–99)
Employed within 3 months of graduation: 100%
Average starting salary: $40,000 Canadian

DEGREE MMS

MMS—Master of Management Studies Full-time and part-time. 12 to 36 months to complete program. *Concentrations:* business information science, finance, international business, management, marketing, production management, research and development administration.

*T*he School of Business is situated amidst one of the best learning environments in the world. Canada's capital city has one of the largest concentrations of export-oriented high-tech firms in the country, including corporate headquarters, libraries, research centers, embassies, and major Canadian and international government agencies.

Enrolment in the Master of Management Studies (M.M.S.) is limited, so every students benefit from the individual attention and support of faculty members with a wide variety of research interests and experiences. Students also have access to the University's comprehensive computer resources. Eight organized research units offer vital learning support and provide established links with business, government, and academic organizations throughout Canada and the world.

Two options are available in the M.M.S.: a Research Thesis Option, which requires the completion of courses and a research thesis, and a Research Project Option, which requires the completion of courses and a research project. Both M.M.S. programs provide innovative alternatives to traditional M.B.A. programs by focusing on developing specialized applied research and analytical skills for resolving complex business problems in an intensive, personalized education environment. A rigorous curriculum that links management research with modern business practices, together with personalized guidance from faculty members in specific functional areas of interest, allows students to design a custom-tailored curriculum that fits their needs.

COSTS

Tuition, international: *Full-time* $4295 Canadian. Tuition varies by local reciprocity agreements. **Graduate housing:** Room and board costs vary by number of occupants and type of board plan. *Typical cost:* $5700 Canadian (including board).

FINANCIAL AID (1999–2000)

9 students received aid, including research assistantships, scholarships, and teaching assistantships. Financial aid application deadline: 2/1. **Financial Aid Contact** Jean Blair, Graduate Secretary, School of Business, 1125 Colonel By Drive, Ottawa, ON K1S 5B6, Canada. **Phone:** 613-520-2600 Ext. 8077. **Fax:** 613-520-4427. **E-mail:** mms_info@business.carleton.ca.

RESOURCES AND SERVICES

Information about online services, personal computer policies, library resources, international exchange programs, internship programs, and placement services at this institution and others can be found at **www.petersons.com/mba**

International Students

Services and Facilities Counseling/support services, ESL/language courses, international student organization, orientation, visa services. Financial aid is available to international students.
Applying *Required:* TOEFL with recommended score of 550 (paper), proof of adequate funds.
International Student Contact Jean Blair, Graduate Secretary, School of Business, 1125 Colonel By Drive, Ottawa, ON K1S 5B6, Canada. **Phone:** 613-520-2600. **Fax:** 613-520-4427. **E-mail:** mms_info@business.carleton.ca.

■ APPLICATION

Required GMAT, application form, baccalaureate/first degree, 2 letters of recommendation, personal statement, transcripts of college work. **Recommended** Resume/curriculum vitae.
Deadlines and Fees *Deadline:* 2/1 for fall (international). *Application fee:* $35 Canadian.
Application Contact Jean Blair, Graduate Secretary, School of Business, 1125 Colonel By Drive, Ottawa, ON K1S 5B6, Canada. **Phone:** 613-520-2600 Ext. 8077. **Fax:** 613-520-4427. **E-mail:** mms_info@business.carleton.ca.

Concordia University

Montréal, Quebec, Canada

FACULTY OF COMMERCE AND ADMINISTRATION

Graduate Business Faculty

Full-time: 44	Part-time: 7

Student Body

Total: 447	Average Age: 29
Full-time: 277	Women: 42%
Part-time: 170	

Admissions

Applications: 400	Average GMAT: 610
Admitted: 103	Average GPA: 3.3/4.3 scale
Enrolled: 52	

Costs (1999–2000)

Full-time tuition: $1176 Canadian per academic year (resident), $2195 Canadian per academic year (nonresident)
Part-time tuition: $56 Canadian per credit (resident), $124 Canadian per credit (nonresident)

After Graduation (Class of 1998–99)

Employed within 3 months of graduation: 90%
Average starting salary: $64,595 Canadian

Accreditation

AACSB—The International Association for Management Education

DEGREES MBA

MBA—Executive MBA Full-time. At least 54 total credits required. Maximum of 24 months to complete program.
MBA—International Aviation MBA Program Full-time and part-time. At least 57 total credits required. 12 to 24 months to complete program.
MBA—Master of Business Administration Full-time and part-time. At least 63 total credits required. 16 to 84 months to complete program.

COSTS

Tuition, state resident: *Full-time* $834 Canadian. *Part-time* $56 Canadian per credit. **Tuition, Canadian resident:** *Full-time* $1854 Canadian. *Part-time* $124 Canadian per credit. **Tuition, international:** *Full-time* $4134 Canadian. Tuition varies by number of courses or credits taken, academic program, and local reciprocity agreements. **Required fees:** *Full-time* $341 Canadian. *Part-time* $141 Canadian per term. **Graduate housing:** Room and board costs vary by number of occupants. *Typical cost:* $2202 Canadian (room only).

FINANCIAL AID (1999–2000)

2 students received aid, including fellowships, loans, and scholarships. Financial aid application deadline: 4/30. **Financial Aid Contact** Phung Tu, Coordinator, Financial Aid, 1455 de Maisonneuve Boulevard West, LB085-5, Montreal, QC H3G 1M8, Canada. **Phone:** 514-848-3521. **Fax:** 514-848-3508.

RESOURCES AND SERVICES

Information about online services, personal computer policies, library resources, international exchange programs, internship programs, and placement services at this institution and others can be found at **www.petersons.com/mba**

International Students

12% of students enrolled are international students.

Services and Facilities Counseling/support services, ESL/language courses, international student organization, orientation, visa services, health insurance program. Financial aid is not available to international students.
Applying *Required:* TOEFL with recommended score of 600 (paper).
International Student Contact Claudette Fortier, Coordinator, 1455 de Maisonneuve Boulevard West, Montreal, QC H3G 1M8, Canada. **Phone:** 514-848-3514. **Fax:** 514-848-3599. **E-mail:** fortier@topaz.condordia.ca.

■ APPLICATION

Required GMAT, application form, baccalaureate/first degree, essay, 3 letters of recommendation, personal statement, resume/curriculum vitae, transcripts of college work, 2 years of work experience.
Deadlines and Fees *Deadlines:* 6/1 for fall, 10/1 for winter, 2/28 for spring, 2/28 for summer, 2/15 for fall (international), 6/15 for winter (international), 10/15 for summer (international). *Application fee:* $50 Canadian.
Application Contact Rebecca Midgley, Admissions Officer, 1455 de Maisonneuve Boulevard West, Montreal, QC H3G 1M8, Canada. **Phone:** 514-848-2717. **Fax:** 514-848-2816. **E-mail:** profmba@vax2.concordia.ca.

See full description on page 612.

Dalhousie University

Halifax, Nova Scotia, Canada

FACULTY OF MANAGEMENT

Graduate Business Faculty

Full-time: 32	Part-time: 20

Student Body

Total: 106	Average Age: 26
Full-time: 100	Women: 37%
Part-time: 6	

Admissions

Applications: 452	Average GMAT: 560
Admitted: 158	Average GPA: 3.6/4.3 scale
Enrolled: 98	

Dalhousie University (continued)

Costs (1999–2000)
Full-time tuition: $5900 Canadian per academic year (resident), $5900 Canadian per academic year (nonresident)
Part-time tuition: $590 Canadian per course (resident), $590 Canadian per course (nonresident)

After Graduation (Class of 1998–99)
Employed within 3 months of graduation: 85%
Average starting salary: $50,000 Canadian

DEGREES MBA • MBA/LL B

MBA—Accelerated MBA for Business Graduates Full-time and part-time. At least 13 total credits required. 10 to 72 months to complete program. *Concentrations:* accounting, developmental economics, economics, environmental economics/management, finance, health care, human resources, international business, management information systems, management systems analysis, marketing, operations management, public policy and administration, system management.

MBA—Financial Services MBA Full-time and part-time. *Distance learning option.* Must be recommended through employer bank. At least 27 total credits required. Maximum of 60 months to complete program. *Concentrations:* banking.

MBA—Master of Business Administration—Information Technology Part-time. *Distance learning option.* Must be enrolled full-time at Information Technology Institute. At least 10 total credits required. 36 to 72 months to complete program. *Concentrations:* management information systems.

MBA—Master of Business Administration Full-time and part-time. 17 to 20 total credits required. 20 to 72 months to complete program. *Concentrations:* accounting, developmental economics, economics, environmental economics/management, finance, health care, human resources, international business, management information systems, management systems analysis, marketing, operations management, public policy and administration, system management.

MBA/LL B—Master of Business Administration/Bachelor of Laws Full-time. 40 to 50 total credits required. 48 to 72 months to complete program. *Concentrations:* accounting, developmental economics, economics, environmental economics/management, finance, health care, human resources, international business, legal administration, management information systems, management systems analysis, marketing, operations management, public policy and administration, system management.

COSTS
Tuition, state resident: *Full-time* $5900 Canadian. *Part-time* $590 Canadian per course. **Tuition, Canadian resident:** *Full-time* $5900 Canadian. *Part-time* $590 Canadian per course. **Tuition, international:** *Full-time* $8900 Canadian. Tuition varies by number of courses or credits taken and academic program. **Graduate housing:** Room and board costs vary by number of occupants, type of accommodation, and type of board plan. *Typical cost:* $5450 Canadian (including board).

FINANCIAL AID (1999–2000)
26 students received aid, including fellowships, research assistantships, scholarships, and teaching assistantships. Financial aid application deadline: 3/1. **Financial Aid Contact** Ms. Mary Hamblin, MBA Program Coordinator, School of Business Administration, 6152 Coburg Road, Halifax, NS B3H 3J5, Canada. **Phone:** 902-494-1814. **Fax:** 902-494-7154. **E-mail:** mba.admissions@dal.ca.

RESOURCES AND SERVICES
Information about online services, personal computer policies, library resources, international exchange programs, internship programs, and placement services at this institution and others can be found at **www.petersons.com/mba**

International Students
8% of students enrolled are international students.
Services and Facilities Counseling/support services, international student housing. Financial aid is not available to international students.
Applying *Required:* TOEFL with recommended score of 237 (computer) or 580 (paper), proof of adequate funds. *Recommended:* Proof of health/immunizations.
International Student Contact Ms. Suzanne Kolmer, Advisor, International Students, Lester Pearson Institute, 1321 Edward Street, Halifax, NS B3H 3H5, Canada. **Phone:** 902-494-6047. **Fax:** 902-494-1216. **E-mail:** suzanne.kolmer@dal.ca.

■ APPLICATION
Required GMAT, application form, baccalaureate/first degree, 2 letters of recommendation, personal statement, resume/curriculum vitae, transcripts of college work. **Recommended** Work experience.
Deadlines and Fees *Deadlines:* 6/1 for fall, 11/1 for winter, 4/1 for fall (international), 9/1 for winter (international). *Application fee:* $55 Canadian.

Application Contact Ms. Mary Hamblin, MBA Program Coordinator, School of Business Administration, 6152 Coburg Road, Halifax, NS B3H 3J5, Canada. **Phone:** 902-494-1814. **Fax:** 902-494-7154. **E-mail:** mba.admissions@dal.ca.
See full description on page 618.

École des Hautes Études Commerciales
Montréal, Quebec, Canada

PROGRAM IN BUSINESS ADMINISTRATION AND MANAGEMENT

Graduate Business Faculty
Full-time: 166

Student Body
Total: 602
Full-time: 119
Part-time: 483

Average Age: 33
Women: 39%

Admissions
Applications: 455
Admitted: 283

Enrolled: 206

Costs (1999–2000)
Full-time tuition: $3328 Canadian per academic year (resident), $6278 Canadian per academic year (nonresident)
Part-time tuition: $87 Canadian per credit (resident), $146 Canadian per credit (nonresident)

After Graduation (Class of 1998–99)
Employed within 3 months of graduation: 92%
Average starting salary: $61,000 Canadian

DEGREE MBA

MBA—Master of Business Administration Full-time and part-time. At least 50 total credits required. 12 to 36 months to complete program. *Concentrations:* entrepreneurship, financial management/planning, human resources, international management, marketing, technology management.

COSTS
Tuition, state resident: *Full-time* $3088 Canadian. *Part-time* $62 Canadian per credit. **Tuition, Canadian resident:** *Full-time* $6038 Canadian. *Part-time* $121 Canadian per credit. **Tuition, international:** *Full-time* $14,088 Canadian. Tuition varies by academic program and local reciprocity agreements. **Required fees:** *Full-time* $240 Canadian. *Part-time* $25 Canadian per credit. Tuition and fees vary by academic program. **Graduate housing:** *Typical cost:* $8200 Canadian (including board).

FINANCIAL AID (1999–2000)
50 students received aid. **Financial Aid Contact** Mrs. Joann Harvey, Student Services, 3000, Chemin de la Cote-Sainte-Catherine, Montreal, QC H3T 2A7, Canada. **Phone:** 514-340-6168. **Fax:** 514-340-5636. **E-mail:** joann.harvey@hec.ca.

RESOURCES AND SERVICES
Information about online services, personal computer policies, library resources, international exchange programs, internship programs, and placement services at this institution and others can be found at **www.petersons.com/mba**

International Students
14% of students enrolled are international students.
Services and Facilities Counseling/support services, housing location assistance, . Financial aid is not available to international students.
International Student Contact Mrs. Jacqueline Lemay, International Exchange Program Coordinator, 3000, Chemin de la Cote-Sainte-Catherine, Montreal, QC H3T 2A7, Canada. **Phone:** 514-340-6840. **Fax:** 514-340-5636. **E-mail:** jacqueline.lemay@hec.ca.

■ APPLICATION
Required GMAT, application form, baccalaureate/first degree, 3 letters of recommendation, personal statement, resume/curriculum vitae, transcripts of college work, 2 years of work experience.
Deadlines and Fees *Deadlines:* 4/1 for fall, 10/1 for winter, 4/1 for fall (international), 10/1 for winter (international). *Application fee:* $40 Canadian, $40 Canadian (international).

Application Contact Mrs. Diane St.-Pierre, Administrative Director of MBA and Graduate Program, 3000, Chemin de la Cote-Sainte-Catherine, Montreal, QC H3T 2A7, Canada. **Phone:** 514-340-6136. **Fax:** 514-340-6411. **E-mail:** mba@hec.ca.

See full description on page 634.

See full description on page 634.

Laurentian University

Sudbury, Ontario, Canada

SCHOOL OF COMMERCE AND ADMINISTRATION

Student Body

Total: 40
Full-time: 16

Part-time: 24
Women: 35%

Admissions

Applications: 35
Admitted: 15

Enrolled: 8
Average GMAT: 574

Costs (1999–2000)

Full-time tuition: $5640 Canadian per academic year (resident), $11,280 Canadian per academic year (nonresident)
Part-time tuition: $564 Canadian per course (resident), $1128 Canadian per course (nonresident)

After Graduation (Class of 1998–99)

Employed within 3 months of graduation: 100%

DEGREE MBA

MBA—Master of Business Administration Full-time and part-time. *Distance learning option.* At least 60 total credits required. 24 to 96 months to complete program. *Concentrations:* finance, human resources, marketing.

COSTS

Tuition, state resident: *Full-time* $5640 Canadian. *Part-time* $564 Canadian per course. **Tuition, Canadian resident:** *Full-time* $11,280 Canadian. *Part-time* $1128 Canadian per course. Tuition varies by number of courses or credits taken and academic program. **Graduate housing:** Room and board costs vary by number of occupants, type of accommodation, and type of board plan. *Typical cost:* $5700 Canadian (room only).

FINANCIAL AID (1999–2000)

8 students received aid, including teaching assistantships. **Financial Aid Contact** Dr. Tov Assogbavi, Chair, MBA Program, Ramsey Lake Road, Sudbury, ON P3E 2C6, Canada. **Phone:** 705-675-1151 Ext. 2144. **Fax:** 705-673-6518.

RESOURCES AND SERVICES

Information about online services, personal computer policies, library resources, international exchange programs, internship programs, and placement services at this institution and others can be found at **www. petersons.com/mba**

International Students

8% of students enrolled are international students.

Services and Facilities Counseling/support services, ESL/language courses. Financial aid is not available to international students.

Applying *Required:* TOEFL with recommended score of 550 (paper).

International Student Contact Tov Assogbavi, Chair, MBA Program, Ramsey Lake Road, Sudbury, ON P3E 2C6, Canada. **Phone:** 705-675-1151 Ext. 2144. **Fax:** 705-673-6518.

■ APPLICATION

Required GMAT, application form, baccalaureate/first degree, 2 letters of recommendation, personal statement, transcripts of college work, 2 years of work experience.

Deadlines and Fees *Deadlines:* 5/31 for fall, 5/31 for fall (international). *Application fee:* $50 Canadian.

Application Contact Dr. Tov Assogbavi, Chair, MBA Program, Ramsey Lake Road, Sudbury, ON P3E 2C6, Canada. **Phone:** 705-675-1151 Ext. 2144. **Fax:** 705-673-6518.

McGill University

Montréal, Quebec, Canada

FACULTY OF MANAGEMENT

Graduate Business Faculty

Full-time: 40

Part-time: 14

Student Body

Total: 348
Full-time: 348

Average Age: 27
Women: 33%

Admissions

Applications: 771
Admitted: 318
Enrolled: 169

Average GMAT: 637
Average GPA: 3.34

Costs (1999–2000)

Full-time tuition: N/R
Part-time tuition: N/R

After Graduation (Class of 1998–99)

Employed within 3 months of graduation: 94%
Average starting salary: $73,000 Canadian

DEGREES JD/MBA • MBA • MBA/MS • MMM

JD/MBA—Juris Doctor/Master of Business Administration Full-time. At least 138 total credits required. 48 to 60 months to complete program.

MBA—Master of Business Administration Full-time and part-time. 2 years full-time work experience. At least 60 total credits required. 20 months to complete program. *Concentrations:* entrepreneurship, finance, international and area business studies, international business, international development management, international finance, international management, international marketing, management, marketing, operations management, strategic management.

MBA/MS—Agriculture Master of Business Administration Full-time. At least 60 total credits required. 32 months to complete program. *Concentrations:* agribusiness, agricultural economics.

MMM—Master of Manufacturing Management Full-time and part-time. GRE or GMAT. At least 60 total credits required. Minimum of 16 months to complete program. *Concentrations:* logistics, manufacturing management, supply chain management, engineering.

COSTS

Tuition, international: *Full-time* $18,000 Canadian. Tuition varies by number of courses or credits taken and local reciprocity agreements. **Required fees:** *Full-time* $835 Canadian. Tuition and fees vary by number of courses or credits taken.

FINANCIAL AID (1999–2000)

35 students received aid, including fellowships, scholarships, and teaching assistantships. Financial aid application deadline: 3/1. **Financial Aid Contact** MBA Admissions Office, 1001 Sherbrooke Street West, Montreal, QC H3A 1G5, Canada. **Phone:** 514-398-4066. **Fax:** 514-398-2499.

RESOURCES AND SERVICES

Information about online services, personal computer policies, library resources, international exchange programs, internship programs, and placement services at this institution and others can be found at **www. petersons.com/mba**

International Students

53% of students enrolled are international students.

Services and Facilities Counseling/support services, ESL/language courses, housing location assistance, international student organization, orientation. Financial aid is available to international students.

Applying *Required:* TOEFL with recommended score of 250 (computer) or 600 (paper), proof of adequate funds. *Recommended:* Proof of health/immunizations.

International Student Contact International Student Advisor, 3600 MacTaush Suite 3215, Montreal, QC H3A 1V2, Canada. **Phone:** 514-398-4349. **E-mail:** intlad@stuserv.lan.mcgill.ca.

■ APPLICATION

Required GMAT, application form, baccalaureate/first degree, essay, 2 letters of recommendation, personal statement, resume/curriculum vitae, transcripts of college work, 2 years of work experience.

Deadlines and Fees *Deadlines:* 5/1 for fall, 3/1 for fall (international). *Application fee:* $100 Canadian.

Application Contact MBA Admissions Officer, 1001 Sherbrooke Street West, Montreal, QC H3A 1G5, Canada. **Phone:** 514-398-4066. **Fax:** 514-398-2499. **E-mail:** mba@management.mcgill.ca.

See full description on page 722.

McMaster University

Hamilton, Ontario, Canada

MICHAEL G. DEGROOTE SCHOOL OF BUSINESS

Graduate Business Faculty
Full-time: 54   Part-time: 20

Student Body
Total: 630   Average Age: 26
Full-time: 439   Women: 38%
Part-time: 191

Admissions
Applications: 532   Average GMAT: 620
Admitted: 352   Average GPA: 3.5
Enrolled: 235

Costs (1999–2000)
Full-time tuition: $4856 Canadian per academic year (resident), $4856 Canadian per academic year (nonresident)
Part-time tuition: $570 Canadian per course (resident), $570 Canadian per course (nonresident)

After Graduation (Class of 1998–99)
Employed within 3 months of graduation: 98%
Average starting salary: $58,600 Canadian

DEGREE MBA

MBA—Master of Business Administration Full-time and part-time. At least 20 total credits required. 20 to 96 months to complete program. *Concentrations:* accounting, electronic commerce (e-commerce), finance, health care, human resources, management, management information systems, marketing, operations management, technology management.

COSTS

Tuition, state resident: *Full-time* $4560 Canadian. *Part-time* $570 Canadian per course. **Tuition, Canadian resident:** *Full-time* $4560 Canadian. *Part-time* $570 Canadian per course. **Tuition, international:** *Full-time* $12,000 Canadian. **Required fees:** *Full-time* $296 Canadian. *Part-time* $25 Canadian per semester. **Graduate housing:** Room and board costs vary by type of board plan. *Typical cost:* $6400 Canadian (including board).

FINANCIAL AID (1999–2000)

100 students received aid, including loans, scholarships, teaching assistantships, and work study. Financial aid application deadline: 5/1. **Financial Aid Contact** Ms. Lisa Jamani, Manager, Student Financial Aid, Hamilton Hall, Room 404, Hamilton, ON L8S 4L8, Canada. **Phone:** 905-525-9140 Ext. 24319. **Fax:** 905-521-9565.

RESOURCES AND SERVICES

Information about online services, personal computer policies, library resources, international exchange programs, internship programs, and placement services at this institution and others can be found at **www.petersons.com/mba**

International Students

4% of students enrolled are international students.

Services and Facilities Counseling/support services, ESL/language courses, international student organization, language tutoring, visa services. Financial aid is not available to international students.

Applying *Recommended:* TOEFL with recommended score of 230 (computer) or 580 (paper).

International Student Contact Miss Cheryl Jackson, International Students Advisor, Hamilton Hall, Room 405, Hamilton, ON L8S 4L8, Canada. **Phone:** 905-525-9140 Ext. 24748. **Fax:** 905-527-6510. **E-mail:** cjackson@mcmaster.ca.

■ APPLICATION

Required GMAT, application form, baccalaureate/first degree, interview, 2 letters of recommendation, personal statement, resume/curriculum vitae, transcripts of college work. **Recommended** 1 year of work experience.

Deadlines and Fees *Deadlines:* 5/1 for fall, 5/1 for fall (international). *Application fee:* $125 Canadian.

Application Contact Mrs. Denise Anderson, Manager, Recruiting and Admissions, Michael DeGroote Building, Room 104, Hamilton, ON L8S 4M4, Canada. **Phone:** 905-525-9140 Ext. 24433. **Fax:** 905-521-8632. **E-mail:** mbainfo@mcmaster.ca.

See full description on page 724.

Memorial University of Newfoundland

St. John's, Newfoundland, Canada

FACULTY OF BUSINESS ADMINISTRATION

Graduate Business Faculty
Full-time: 28   Part-time: 1

Student Body
Total: 225   Average Age: 31
Full-time: 75   Women: 49%
Part-time: 150

Admissions
Applications: 170   Average GMAT: 580
Admitted: 88   Average GPA: 2.5/3 scale
Enrolled: 64

Costs (1999–2000)
Full-time tuition: $2900 Canadian per academic year (resident), $2900 Canadian per academic year (nonresident)
Part-time tuition: $5800 Canadian per degree program (resident), $5800 Canadian per degree program (nonresident)

After Graduation (Class of 1998–99)
Employed within 3 months of graduation: 95%

DEGREE MBA

MBA—Master of Business Administration in General Management Full-time and part-time. 10 to 20 total credits required. 8 to 84 months to complete program.

COSTS

Tuition, state resident: *Full-time* $2900 Canadian. *Part-time* $5800 Canadian per degree program. **Tuition, Canadian resident:** *Full-time* $2900 Canadian. *Part-time* $5800 Canadian per degree program. **Tuition, international:** *Full-time* $2900 Canadian. **Graduate housing:** Room and board costs vary by number of occupants, type of accommodation, and type of board plan. *Typical cost:* $7920 Canadian (including board).

FINANCIAL AID (1999–2000)

15 students received aid, including fellowships, research assistantships, and scholarships. **Financial Aid Contact** Ms. Lisa Savage, MBA Program Secretary, Faculty of Business Administration, St. John's, NF A1B 3X5, Canada. **Phone:** 709-737-8522. **Fax:** 709-737-2467. **E-mail:** lsavage@mun.ca.

RESOURCES AND SERVICES

Information about online services, personal computer policies, library resources, international exchange programs, internship programs, and placement services at this institution and others can be found at **www.petersons.com/mba**

International Students

4% of students enrolled are international students.

Services and Facilities Counseling/support services, ESL/language courses, international student organization. Financial aid is not available to international students.

Applying *Required:* TOEFL with recommended score of 237 (computer) or 580 (paper).

International Student Contact Ms. Susan Vaughan, Director, Centre for International Business Studies, Faculty of Business Administration, St. John's, NF A1B 3X5, Canada. **Phone:** 709-737-4504. **Fax:** 709-737-7999. **E-mail:** svaughan@mun.ca.

■ APPLICATION

Required Application form, baccalaureate/first degree, 3 letters of recommendation, personal statement, transcripts of college work. School will accept GMAT. **Recommended** Resume/curriculum vitae, work experience.

Deadlines and Fees *Application fee:* $40 Canadian.

Application Contact Ms. Lisa Savage, MBA Program Secretary, Faculty of Business Administration, St. John's, NF A1B 3X5, Canada. **Phone:** 709-737-8522. **Fax:** 709-737-2467. **E-mail:** lsavage@mun.ca.

Queen's University at Kingston

Kingston, Ontario, Canada

SCHOOL OF BUSINESS

Graduate Business Faculty
Full-time: 43   Part-time: 4

Student Body
Total: 60   Average Age: 30
Full-time: 60   Women: 20%

Admissions
Applications: 297   Average GMAT: 672
Admitted: 80   Average GPA: 3.2
Enrolled: 60

Costs (1999–2000)
Full-time tuition: $35,365 Canadian per academic year (resident), $35,365 Canadian per academic year (nonresident)
Part-time tuition: N/R

After Graduation (Class of 1998–99)
Employed within 3 months of graduation: 90%
Average starting salary: $80,500 Canadian

Accreditation
AACSB—The International Association for Management Education

DEGREES EMBA • MBA • NEMBA

EMBA—Executive MBA Part-time. *Distance learning option.* At least 23 total credits required. Minimum of 24 months to complete program.

MBA—MBA for Science and Technology Full-time. At least 23 total credits required. Minimum of 12 months to complete program. *Concentrations:* finance, marketing, operations management, technology management.

NEMBA—National Executive Master of Business Administration Part-time. At least 23 total credits required. Minimum of 24 months to complete program.

COSTS

Tuition, state resident: *Full-time* $35,000 Canadian. **Tuition, Canadian resident:** *Full-time* $35,000 Canadian. **Tuition, international:** *Full-time* $35,000 Canadian. **Required fees:** *Full-time* $365 Canadian. **Graduate housing:** Room and board costs vary by campus location, number of occupants, type of accommodation, and type of board plan. *Typical cost:* $8500 Canadian (including board), $5250 Canadian (room only).

FINANCIAL AID (1999–2000)

55 students received aid, including loans. Financial aid application deadline: 3/1. **Financial Aid Contact** Ms. Diane Cross, Director, MBA for Science and Technology, Mackintosh-Corry Hall, Kingston, ON K7L 3N6, Canada. **Phone:** 613-533-2302. **Fax:** 613-533-6281. **E-mail:** admin@mbast.queensu.ca.

RESOURCES AND SERVICES

Information about online services, personal computer policies, library resources, international exchange programs, internship programs, and placement services at this institution and others can be found at **www.petersons.com/mba**

International Students

5% of students enrolled are international students.

Services and Facilities Counseling/support services, ESL/language courses. Financial aid is not available to international students.

Applying *Required:* TOEFL with recommended score of 250 (computer) or 600 (paper), proof of adequate funds, proof of health/immunizations.

International Student Contact Ms. Susan Anderson, International Student Advisor, International Centre, John Deutsch University Centre, Kingston, ON K7L 3N6, Canada. **Phone:** 613-533-2604. **Fax:** 613-533-6190.

■ APPLICATION

Required GMAT, application form, baccalaureate/first degree, essay, interview, 2 letters of recommendation, personal statement, resume/curriculum vitae, transcripts of college work, 2 years of work experience.

Deadlines and Fees Applications for domestic and international students are processed on a rolling basis. *Application fee:* $100 Canadian.

Application Contact Ms. Diane Cross, Director, MBA for Science and Technology, Mackintosh-Corry Hall, Kingston, ON K7L 3N6, Canada. **Phone:** 613-533-2302. **Fax:** 613-533-6281. **E-mail:** admin@mbast.queensu.ca.

See full description on page 776.

Saint Mary's University

Halifax, Nova Scotia, Canada

FACULTY OF COMMERCE

Graduate Business Faculty
Full-time: 30   Part-time: 17

Student Body
Total: 342   Average Age: 33
Full-time: 217   Women: 42%
Part-time: 125

Admissions
Applications: 308   Average GMAT: 570
Admitted: 220   Average GPA: 3.3
Enrolled: 133

Costs (1999–2000)
Full-time tuition: N/R
Part-time tuition: $827 Canadian per credit (resident), $1555 Canadian per credit (nonresident)

DEGREES MBA

MBA—Executive MBA Part-time. Up to 11 total credits required. Maximum of 24 months to complete program. *Concentrations:* management.

MBA—Master of Business Administration Full-time and part-time. Up to 11 total credits required. 12 to 24 months to complete program. *Concentrations:* entrepreneurship, financial economics, human resources, international management.

COSTS

Tuition, state resident: *Part-time* $827 Canadian per credit. **Tuition, Canadian resident:** *Part-time* $1555 Canadian per credit. Tuition varies by number of courses or credits taken and academic program. **Required fees:** *Full-time* $500 Canadian. Tuition and fees vary by number of courses or credits taken. **Graduate housing:** Room and board costs vary by number of occupants, type of accommodation, and type of board plan. *Typical cost:* $4530 Canadian (including board).

FINANCIAL AID (1999–2000)

Scholarships and teaching assistantships. **Financial Aid Contact** Ms. Jennifer Johnson, Program Manager, Halifax, NS B3H 3C3, Canada. **Phone:** 902-420-5729. **Fax:** 902-420-5119. **E-mail:** jennifer.johnson@stmarys.ca.

RESOURCES AND SERVICES

Information about online services, personal computer policies, library resources, international exchange programs, internship programs, and placement services at this institution and others can be found at **www.petersons.com/mba**

International Students

19% of students enrolled are international students.

Services and Facilities Counseling/support services, ESL/language courses, housing location assistance, international student organization, orientation. Financial aid is available to international students.

Applying *Required:* TOEFL with recommended score of 550 (paper), TWE.

International Student Contact Ms. Alana Robb, International Student Advisor, Student Union Building, Room 300, Halifax, NS B3H 3C3, Canada. **Phone:** 902-420-5436. **Fax:** 902-420-5288. **E-mail:** arobb@shark.stmarys.ca.

■ APPLICATION

Required GMAT, application form, essay, 3 letters of recommendation, personal statement, transcripts of college work. **Recommended** Baccalaureate/first degree, resume/curriculum vitae, work experience.

Deadlines and Fees *Deadlines:* 5/31 for fall, 4/1 for fall (international). *Application fee:* $30 Canadian.

Application Contact Ms. Jennifer Johnson, Program Manager, Halifax, NS B3H 3C3, Canada. **Phone:** 902-420-5729. **Fax:** 902-420-5119. **E-mail:** jennifer.johnson@stmarys.ca.

Simon Fraser University

Burnaby, British Columbia, Canada

FACULTY OF BUSINESS ADMINISTRATION

Graduate Business Faculty
Full-time: 55   Part-time: 23

Student Body
Total: 109   Average Age: 26
Full-time: 109   Women: 43%

Simon Fraser University (continued)

Admissions
Applications: 141
Admitted: 65
Enrolled: 42

Average GMAT: 620
Average GPA: 3.3

Costs (1999–2000)
Full-time tuition: $2729 Canadian per academic year (resident), $2729 Canadian per academic year (nonresident)
Part-time tuition: N/R

After Graduation (Class of 1998–99)
Employed within 3 months of graduation: 95%
Average starting salary: $50,000 Canadian

DEGREE MBA

MBA—Specialist MBA Full-time. Applicants must have completed a four-year undergraduate degree in Business Administration or Commerce. At least 36 total credits required. 12 to 48 months to complete program. *Concentrations:* finance, human resources, international business, management information systems, management science, marketing.

COSTS
Tuition, state resident: *Full-time* $2400 Canadian. **Tuition, Canadian resident:** *Full-time* $2400 Canadian. **Required fees:** *Full-time* $329 Canadian. *Part-time* $110 Canadian per summer. **Graduate housing:** Room and board costs vary by number of occupants and type of accommodation. *Typical cost:* $4731 Canadian (room only).

FINANCIAL AID (1999–2000)
75 students received aid, including fellowships, grants, loans, research assistantships, scholarships, teaching assistantships, and work study. Financial aid application deadline: 3/15. **Financial Aid Contact** Ms. Charlotte French, Director, Financial Assistance, Office of the Registrar, 8888 University Drive, Burnaby, BC V5A 1S6, Canada. **Phone:** 604-291-4356. **Fax:** 604-291-4722. **E-mail:** fiassist@sfu.ca.

RESOURCES AND SERVICES
Information about online services, personal computer policies, library resources, international exchange programs, internship programs, and placement services at this institution and others can be found at **www.petersons.com/mba**

International Students
17% of students enrolled are international students.
Services and Facilities Counseling/support services, visa services. Financial aid is available to international students.
Applying *Required:* TOEFL with recommended score of 230 (computer) or 570 (paper), TWE with recommended score of 5, proof of adequate funds, proof of health/immunizations.
International Student Contact Mr. Randall Martin, Director, International and Exchange Student Services (IESS), Office of the Registrar, 8888 University Drive, Burnaby, BC V5A 1S6, Canada. **Phone:** 604-291-5840. **Fax:** 604-291-5880. **E-mail:** randall_martin@sfu.ca.

■ APPLICATION
Required GMAT, application form, baccalaureate/first degree, 3 letters of recommendation, personal statement, resume/curriculum vitae, transcripts of college work. School will accept MAT. **Recommended** 2 years of work experience.
Deadlines and Fees *Deadlines:* 4/1 for fall, 10/1 for spring, 2/1 for summer, 4/1 for fall (international), 10/1 for spring (international), 2/1 for summer (international). *Application fee:* $55 Canadian.
Application Contact Mrs. Noory Lalji, Coordinator, MBA Program, Faculty of Business Administration, 8888 University Drive, Burnaby, BC V5A 1S6, Canada. **Phone:** 604-291-3639. **Fax:** 604-291-3404. **E-mail:** noory_lalji@sfu.ca.

Université de Moncton

Moncton, New Brunswick, Canada

FACULTY OF ADMINISTRATION

Graduate Business Faculty
Full-time: 12

Part-time: 10

Student Body
Total: 180
Full-time: 60
Part-time: 120

Average Age: 34
Women: 47%

Admissions
Applications: 175
Admitted: 125

Enrolled: 110
Average GPA: 3

Costs (1999–2000)
Full-time tuition: N/R
Part-time tuition: $132 Canadian per credit (resident), $176 Canadian per credit (nonresident)

After Graduation (Class of 1998–99)
Employed within 3 months of graduation: 100%

DEGREES MBA • MBA/LL B

MBA—Multi-media MBA Part-time. *Distance learning option.* At least 45 total credits required. 36 to 60 months to complete program.
MBA—Master of Business Administration Full-time and part-time. At least 45 total credits required. 20 to 28 months to complete program.
MBA/LL B—Master of Business Administration/Bachelor of Laws Full-time. At least 122 total credits required. 48 to 60 months to complete program.

COSTS
Tuition, state resident: *Part-time* $132 Canadian per credit. **Tuition, Canadian resident:** *Part-time* $176 Canadian per credit. **Graduate housing:** *Typical cost:* $4300 Canadian (including board).

FINANCIAL AID (1999–2000)
6 students received aid, including fellowships and scholarships. **Financial Aid Contact** Mrs. Louise McIntyre, Service des Bourses et de L'Aide Financiere, Moncton, NB E1A 3E9, Canada. **Phone:** 506-858-3731. **Fax:** 506-858-4492. **E-mail:** mcintyl@umoncton.ca.

RESOURCES AND SERVICES
Information about online services, personal computer policies, library resources, international exchange programs, internship programs, and placement services at this institution and others can be found at **www.petersons.com/mba**

International Students
11% of students enrolled are international students.
Services and Facilities Counseling/support services. Financial aid is not available to international students.
Applying *Required:* Proof of adequate funds, proof of health/immunizations.
International Student Contact Mr. Hermel Deschenes, Service aux Etudiants Etrangers, Moncton, NB E1A3E9, Canada. **Phone:** 506-858-3713. **Fax:** 506-858-4492. **E-mail:** descheh@umoncton.ca.

■ APPLICATION
Required Application form, baccalaureate/first degree, 2 letters of recommendation, personal statement, resume/curriculum vitae, transcripts of college work. **Recommended** Interview.
Deadlines and Fees *Deadlines:* 6/15 for fall, 2/1 for fall (international). *Application fee:* $50 Canadian.
Application Contact Dr. Nha Nguyen, MBA Program Director, Universite de Moncton, Moncton, NB E1A 3E9, Canada. **Phone:** 506-858-4231. **Fax:** 506-858-4093. **E-mail:** nguyenn@umoncton.ca.

Université de Sherbrooke

Sherbrooke, Quebec, Canada

FACULTY OF ADMINISTRATION

DEGREES MBA • MF • MS

MBA—Master of Business Administration Full-time and part-time. At least 51 total credits required.
MF—Master of Finance At least 45 total credits required.
MS—Master in Administration At least 45 total credits required.

RESOURCES AND SERVICES
Information about online services, personal computer policies, library resources, international exchange programs, internship programs, and placement services at this institution and others can be found at **www.petersons.com/mba**

■ APPLICATION
Application Contact Director of MBA, 2500 University Boulevard, Sherbrooke, QC J1K 2R1, Canada. **Phone:** 819-821-7333. **Fax:** 819-221-7364. **E-mail:** mba@adm.usherb.ca.

Université du Québec à Montréal

Montréal, Quebec, Canada

ECOLE DES SCIENCES DE LA GESTION

Graduate Business Faculty
Full-time: 50

Student Body
Total: 1,200
Full-time: 100
Part-time: 1,100

Average Age: 36
Women: 33%

Admissions
Applications: 300

Average GPA: 3.2/4.3 scale

Costs (1999–2000)
Full-time tuition: $4200 Canadian per academic year (resident), $8000 Canadian per academic year (nonresident)
Part-time tuition: $4200 Canadian per year (resident), $8000 Canadian per year (nonresident)

After Graduation (Class of 1998–99)
Employed within 3 months of graduation: 99%
Average starting salary: $65,000

DEGREES MBA

MBA—Executive MBA 4 years of work experience and BA or 7 years of executive work experience. At least 45 total credits required. Maximum of 48 months to complete program.

MBA—Master of Business Administration Full-time. At least 60 total credits required. 24 months to complete program. *Concentrations:* accounting, banking, finance, human resources, international business, management, management information systems, marketing, operations management, real estate, strategic management.

COSTS

Tuition, state resident: *Full-time* $4200 Canadian. *Part-time* $4200 Canadian per year. **Tuition, Canadian resident:** *Full-time* $8000 Canadian. *Part-time* $8000 Canadian per year. Tuition varies by class time, number of courses or credits taken, campus location, academic program, and local reciprocity agreements.

FINANCIAL AID (1999–2000)

Research assistantships. **Financial Aid Contact** Dr. Leon-Michel Serruya, Director of the MBA Program, CP 6192, Succursale Centre-Ville, Montreal, QC H3C 3P8, Canada. **Phone:** 514-987-4496. **Fax:** 514-987-3084. **E-mail:** serruya.leon-michel@uqam.ca.

RESOURCES AND SERVICES

Information about online services, personal computer policies, library resources, international exchange programs, internship programs, and placement services at this institution and others can be found at **www. petersons.com/mba**

International Students

20% of students enrolled are international students.

Services and Facilities Counseling/support services, international student organization. Financial aid is not available to international students.
International Student Contact Dr. Leon-Michel Serruya, Director of the MBA Program, CP 6192 Succursale Centre-Ville, QC, Canada. **Phone:** 514-987-3000 Ext. 1954. **Fax:** 514-987-3084. **E-mail:** serruya.leon-michel@uqam.ca.

■ APPLICATION

Required Application form, baccalaureate/first degree, 3 letters of recommendation, resume/curriculum vitae, transcripts of college work, 4 years of work experience. **Recommended** Interview.
Deadlines and Fees *Deadlines:* 3/1 for fall, 6/1 for winter, 9/1 for spring, 12/1 for summer, 3/7 for fall (international), 6/1 for winter (international), 9/1 for spring (international), 12/1 for summer (international). *Application fee:* $55 Canadian.
Application Contact Dr. Leon-Michel Serruya, Director of the MBA Program, Universite' du Quebec a Montreal, CP 6192 Succarsale Centre-Ville, Montreal, QC H3C 3PB, Canada. **Phone:** 514-987-4496. **Fax:** 514-987-3084. **E-mail:** serruya.leon-michel@uqam.ca.

Université Laval

Sainte-Foy, Quebec, Canada

FACULTY OF ADMINISTRATIVE SCIENCES

Graduate Business Faculty
Full-time: 60

Part-time: 5

Student Body
Total: 687
Full-time: 360
Part-time: 327

Average Age: 30
Women: 40%

Admissions
Applications: 450
Admitted: 250

Enrolled: 125

Costs (1999–2000)
Full-time tuition: N/R
Part-time tuition: $775 Canadian per semester (resident), $3728 Canadian per semester (nonresident)

After Graduation (Class of 1998–99)
Employed within 3 months of graduation: 95%

Accreditation
AACSB—The International Association for Management Education

DEGREE MBA

MBA—Master of Business Administration Full-time and part-time. At least 45 total credits required. 16 to 48 months to complete program. *Concentrations:* accounting, agribusiness, decision sciences, finance, international business, management, management information systems, marketing, operations management, production management, quantitative analysis.

COSTS

Tuition, state resident: *Part-time* $775 Canadian per semester. **Tuition, Canadian resident:** *Part-time* $3728 Canadian per semester.

FINANCIAL AID (1999–2000)

50 students received aid, including research assistantships. Aid is available to part-time students. **Financial Aid Contact** Service des Bourses L'Aide Financiere, Cite Universitaire, Quebec, QC G1K 7P4, Canada. **Phone:** 418-656-2131 Ext. 3332.

RESOURCES AND SERVICES

Information about online services, personal computer policies, library resources, international exchange programs, internship programs, and placement services at this institution and others can be found at **www. petersons.com/mba**

International Students

16% of students enrolled are international students.

Services and Facilities Language tutoring.
Applying *Required:* Proof of adequate funds, proof of health/immunizations.
International Student Contact Mrs. Marie Lemay, Cite Universitaire, Quebec, QC G1K 7P4, Canada.

■ APPLICATION

Required Application form, baccalaureate/first degree, 3 letters of recommendation, resume/curriculum vitae, transcripts of college work.
Deadlines and Fees *Deadlines:* 8/14 for fall, 11/30 for winter, 8/14 for fall (international), 11/30 for winter (international). *Application fee:* $30 Canadian.
Application Contact Mr. Andre Gascon, Director of the MBA Program, Cite Universitaire, Quebec, QC G1K 7P4, Canada. **Phone:** 418-656-3091. **Fax:** 418-656-2624. **E-mail:** andre.gascon@ulaval.ca.

University of Alberta

Edmonton, Alberta, Canada

FACULTY OF BUSINESS

Accreditation
AACSB—The International Association for Management Education

DEGREES MBA • MBA/LL B • MBA/M Ag • MBA/M Eng • MBA/MF

MBA—Executive MBA Full-time. Up to 54 total credits required. Minimum of 21 months to complete program.

MBA—Master of Business Administration Technology Transfer Full-time and part-time. At least 57 total credits required. 16 to 72 months to complete program. *Concentrations:* technology management.

MBA—Master of Business Administration in International Business At least 57 total credits required. 16 to 72 months to complete program.

MBA—Master of Business Administration in Leisure and Sport Management Full-time and part-time. At least 57 total credits required. 20 to 72 months to complete program.

MBA—Master of Business Administration in Natural Resources and Energy Full-time and part-time. At least 57 total credits required. 20 to 72 months to complete program.

MBA—Master of Business Administration Full-time and part-time. At least 57 total credits required. 16 to 72 months to complete program. *Concentrations:* entrepreneurship, finance, international and area business studies, sports/ entertainment management.

MBA/LL B—Master of Business Administration/Bachelor of Laws At least 120 total credits required. 48 to 72 months to complete program.

MBA/M Ag—Master of Business Administration/Master of Agriculture Full-time and part-time. Undergraduate agriculture degree or equivalent required. At least 63 total credits required. 20 to 72 months to complete program.

MBA/M Eng—Master of Business Administration/Master of Engineering Full-time and part-time. Undergraduate engineering degree or equivalent required. 63 to 69 total credits required. 20 to 72 months to complete program.

MBA/MF—Master of Business Administration/Master of Forestry Full-time and part-time. Undergraduate forestry degree or equivalent required. At least 63 total credits required. 19 to 24 months to complete program.

RESOURCES AND SERVICES
Information about online services, personal computer policies, library resources, international exchange programs, internship programs, and placement services at this institution and others can be found at **www. petersons.com/mba**

International Students
Services and Facilities Counseling/support services, ESL/language courses, international student housing. Financial aid is not available to international students. **International Student Contact** Dr. Kay Devine, Associate Dean, MBA Program, Faculty of Business, Edmonton, AB T6G 2R6, Canada. **Phone:** 780-492-3946. **Fax:** 780-492-7825. **E-mail:** mba.programs@ualberta.ca.

■ APPLICATION
Application Contact Dr. Kay Devine, Associate Dean, MBA Program, Faculty of Business, Edmonton, AB T6G 2R6, Canada. **Phone:** 780-492-3946. **Fax:** 780-492-7825. **E-mail:** mba.programs@ualberta.ca.

University of British Columbia
Vancouver, British Columbia, Canada

FACULTY OF COMMERCE AND BUSINESS ADMINISTRATION

Graduate Business Faculty

Full-time: 85	Part-time: 10

Student Body

Total: 283	Average Age: 30
Full-time: 283	Women: 36%

Admissions

Applications: 684	Average GMAT: 620
Admitted: 180	Average GPA: 3.3
Enrolled: 100	

Costs (1999–2000)
Full-time tuition: $7235 Canadian per academic year (resident), $7235 Canadian per academic year (nonresident)
Part-time tuition: N/R

After Graduation (Class of 1998–99)
Employed within 3 months of graduation: 90%
Average starting salary: $66,500 Canadian

DEGREES MBA • MBA/LL B • MS

MBA—Master of Business Administration Full-time. At least 51 total credits required. 15 months to complete program. *Concentrations:* finance, logistics, management information systems, marketing, operations management, strategic management.

MBA/LL B—Master of Business Administration/Bachelor of Laws Full-time. At least 136 total credits required. 48 to 60 months to complete program. *Concentrations:* finance, logistics, management information systems, marketing, operations management, strategic management.

MS—Master of Science in Business Administration Full-time. At least 30 total credits required. 12 to 36 months to complete program. *Concentrations:* finance, logistics, management information systems, management science, real estate, transportation and logistics.

COSTS
Tuition, state resident: *Full-time* $7000 Canadian. **Tuition, Canadian resident:** *Full-time* $7000 Canadian. **Tuition, international:** *Full-time* $20,000 Canadian. Tuition varies by academic program. **Required fees:** *Full-time* $235 Canadian. **Graduate housing:** Room and board costs vary by number of occupants, type of accommodation, and type of board plan. *Typical cost:* $7950 Canadian (including board), $4050 Canadian (room only).

FINANCIAL AID (1999–2000)
29 students received aid, including fellowships, grants, loans, research assistantships, scholarships, teaching assistantships, and work study. Financial aid application deadline: 1/1. **Financial Aid Contact** Ms. Ethel Davis, Assistant Dean and Director, 102-2053 Main Mall, Vancouver, BC V6T 1Z2, Canada. **Phone:** 604-822-8422. **Fax:** 604-822-9030. **E-mail:** masters.programs@commerce.ubc.ca.

RESOURCES AND SERVICES
Information about online services, personal computer policies, library resources, international exchange programs, internship programs, and placement services at this institution and others can be found at **www. petersons.com/mba**

International Students
16% of students enrolled are international students.

Services and Facilities Counseling/support services, ESL/language courses, international student housing. Financial aid is available to international students. **Applying** *Required:* IELT with recommended score of 6.5, TOEFL with recommended score of 250 (computer) or 600 (paper), proof of adequate funds.

International Student Contact Ms. Winnie Cheung, Director of International Student Services, International House, 1783 West Mall, Vancouver, BC V6T 1Z2, Canada. **Phone:** 604-822-5021. **Fax:** 604-822-5099. **E-mail:** isc@unixg.ubc. ca.

■ APPLICATION
Required GMAT, application form, baccalaureate/first degree, essay, 3 letters of recommendation, personal statement, resume/curriculum vitae, transcripts of college work. School will accept GRE. **Recommended** 2 years of work experience.

Deadlines and Fees *Deadlines:* 4/30 for fall, 2/28 for fall (international). *Application fee:* $125 Canadian.

Application Contact Ms. Ethel Davis, Assistant Dean and Director, 102-2053 Main Mall, Vancouver, BC V6T 1Z2, Canada. **Phone:** 604-822-8422. **Fax:** 604-822-9030. **E-mail:** masters.programs@commerce.ubc.ca.

See full description on page 872.

University of Calgary
Calgary, Alberta, Canada

FACULTY OF MANAGEMENT

Graduate Business Faculty

Full-time: 82	Part-time: 30

Student Body

Total: 431	Average Age: 31
Full-time: 101	Women: 37%
Part-time: 330	

Admissions

Applications: 251	Average GMAT: 610
Admitted: 189	Average GPA: 3.27
Enrolled: 141	

Costs (1999–2000)
Full-time tuition: N/R
Part-time tuition: $510 Canadian per credit (resident), $1020 Canadian per credit (nonresident)

After Graduation (Class of 1998–99)
Employed within 3 months of graduation: 80%
Average starting salary: $60,000 Canadian

Accreditation
AACSB—The International Association for Management Education

DEGREES MBA

MBA—Executive MBA Part-time. At least 20 total credits required. Maximum of 24 months to complete program.

MBA—Master of Business Administration Part-time. At least 20 total credits required. 48 to 72 months to complete program. *Concentrations:* accounting, entrepreneurship, finance, international business, management information systems, marketing, new venture management, operations management, organizational behavior/development, project management.

COSTS

Tuition, state resident: *Part-time* $510 Canadian per credit. **Tuition, Canadian resident:** *Part-time* $1020 Canadian per credit. Tuition varies by class time and academic program. **Required fees:** *Full-time* $300 Canadian. *Part-time* $150 Canadian per year. Tuition and fees vary by academic program.

FINANCIAL AID (1999–2000)
Scholarships. Financial aid application deadline: 2/1. **Financial Aid Contact**

RESOURCES AND SERVICES
Information about online services, personal computer policies, library resources, international exchange programs, internship programs, and placement services at this institution and others can be found at www.petersons.com/mba

International Students
2% of students enrolled are international students.

Services and Facilities Counseling/support services. Financial aid is not available to international students.
Applying *Required:* TOEFL with recommended score of 600 (paper), proof of adequate funds.

International Student Contact Glynn Hunter, Coordinator, International Students, 2500 University Drive, NW, Calgary, AB T2N 1N4, Canada. **Phone:** 403-220-7532.

■ APPLICATION

Required GMAT, application form, baccalaureate/first degree, essay, 3 letters of recommendation, personal statement, resume/curriculum vitae, transcripts of college work, 3 years of work experience.

Deadlines and Fees *Deadlines:* 5/1 for fall, 9/1 for winter, 5/1 for fall (international), 9/1 for winter (international). *Application fee:* $60 Canadian.

Application Contact Ms. Dolores Beeler, MBA Program Office, Faculty of Management, 2500 University Drive, NW, Calgary, AB T2N 1N4, Canada. **Phone:** 403-220-3808. **Fax:** 403-282-0095. **E-mail:** dcbeeler@mgmt.ucalgary.ca.

University of Guelph

Guelph, Ontario, Canada

DEPARTMENT OF AGRICULTURAL ECONOMICS AND BUSINESS

Graduate Business Faculty
Full-time: 13 — Part-time: 2

Student Body
Total: 18 — Part-time: 1
Full-time: 17 — Women: 22%

Admissions
Applications: 34 — Enrolled: 17
Admitted: 23 — Average GPA: 3

Costs (1999–2000)
Full-time tuition: $7500 Canadian per academic year (resident), $7500 Canadian per academic year (nonresident)
Part-time tuition: N/R

After Graduation (Class of 1998–99)
Employed within 3 months of graduation: 100%

DEGREE MBA

MBA—Master of Business Administration in Agribusiness Full-time. 12 to 16 months to complete program. *Concentrations:* agribusiness, agricultural economics.

COSTS

Tuition, state resident: *Full-time* $7500 Canadian. **Tuition, Canadian resident:** *Full-time* $7500 Canadian. **Tuition, international:** *Full-time* $9000 Canadian.
Graduate housing: Room and board costs vary by campus location, number of

occupants, type of accommodation, and type of board plan. *Typical cost:* $9000 Canadian (including board), $4000 Canadian (room only).

FINANCIAL AID (1999–2000)
12 students received aid, including grants, loans, research assistantships, scholarships, and teaching assistantships. Financial aid application deadline: 6/1. **Financial Aid Contact** Dr. Francesco Braga, MBA Coordinator, Department of Agricultural Economics and Business, Guelph, ON N1G 2W1, Canada. **Phone:** 519-824-4120 Ext. 2763. **Fax:** 519-767-1510. **E-mail:** fbraga@agec.uoguelph.ca.

RESOURCES AND SERVICES
Information about online services, personal computer policies, library resources, international exchange programs, internship programs, and placement services at this institution and others can be found at www.petersons.com/mba

International Students
11% of students enrolled are international students.

Services and Facilities Counseling/support services, ESL/language courses, housing location assistance, international student housing, international student organization, language tutoring, orientation, visa services, international student advisor. Financial aid is available to international students.
Applying *Required:* TOEFL with recommended score of 213 (computer) or 550 (paper), proof of adequate funds.

International Student Contact Dr. Francesco Braga, MBA Coordinator, Department of Agricultural Economics and Business, Guelph, ON N1G 2W1, Canada. **Phone:** 519-824-4120 Ext. 2763. **Fax:** 519-767-1510. **E-mail:** fbraga@agec.uoguelph.ca.

■ APPLICATION

Required Application form, baccalaureate/first degree, 2 letters of recommendation, personal statement, resume/curriculum vitae, transcripts of college work. School will accept GMAT. **Recommended** Interview, 2 years of work experience.

Deadlines and Fees Applications for domestic students are processed on a rolling basis. *Deadline:* 6/1 for fall (international). *Application fee:* $60 Canadian, $60 Canadian (international).

Application Contact Dr. Francesco Braga, MBA Coordinator, Department of Agricultural Economics and Business, Guelph, ON N1G 2W1, Canada. **Phone:** 519-824-4120 Ext. 2763. **Fax:** 519-767-1510. **E-mail:** fbraga@agec.uoguelph.ca.

University of Manitoba

Winnipeg, Manitoba, Canada

FACULTY OF MANAGEMENT

Graduate Business Faculty
Full-time: 43 — Part-time: 2

Student Body
Total: 116 — Average Age: 32
Full-time: 18 — Women: 34%
Part-time: 98

Admissions
Applications: 144 — Average GMAT: 576
Admitted: 85 — Average GPA: 3.3
Enrolled: 59

Costs (1999–2000)
Full-time tuition: $25,600 Canadian per academic year (resident)
Part-time tuition: $9500 Canadian per degree program (resident)

After Graduation (Class of 1998–99)
Employed within 3 months of graduation: 100%
Average starting salary: $75,000 Canadian

Accreditation
AACSB—The International Association for Management Education

DEGREES MBA

MBA—Full-time MBA Full-time. At least 66 total credits required. 11 months to complete program. *Concentrations:* management.

MBA—Part-time MBA Part-time. At least 60 total credits required. 36 to 72 months to complete program. *Concentrations:* finance, management, marketing.

COSTS

Tuition, state resident: *Full-time* $17,600 Canadian. *Part-time* $9500 Canadian per degree program. **Tuition, international:** *Full-time* $18,200 Canadian.

University of Manitoba (continued)

Required fees: *Full-time* $8000 Canadian. **Graduate housing:** Room and board costs vary by number of occupants and type of board plan. *Typical cost:* $6500 Canadian (including board).

FINANCIAL AID (1999–2000)
6 students received aid, including fellowships and scholarships. Financial aid application deadline: 1/15. **Financial Aid Contact** Mr. Peter Dueck, Director, Financial Aid and Awards, Room 421, University Centre Building, Winnipeg, MB R3T 2N2, Canada. **Phone:** 204-474-6382. **Fax:** 204-474-7554. **E-mail:** peter_dueck@umanitoba.ca.

RESOURCES AND SERVICES
Information about online services, personal computer policies, library resources, international exchange programs, internship programs, and placement services at this institution and others can be found at **www.petersons.com/mba**

International Students
5% of students enrolled are international students.

Services and Facilities Counseling/support services, ESL/language courses, housing location assistance, international student housing, international student organization, orientation. Financial aid is not available to international students. **Applying** *Required:* TOEFL with recommended score of 213 (computer) or 550 (paper), proof of adequate funds, proof of health/immunizations. **International Student Contact** Sheena Trimble, Director, International Students Center, 541 University Center, Winnipeg, MB R3T 2N2, Canada. **Phone:** 204-474-8501. **Fax:** 204-474-7562. **E-mail:** ics@cc.umanitoba.ca.

■ APPLICATION
Required GMAT, application form, baccalaureate/first degree, interview, 3 letters of recommendation, personal statement, resume/curriculum vitae, transcripts of college work, 3 years of work experience. **Deadlines and Fees** *Deadlines:* 5/1 for fall, 1/15 for fall (international). *Application fee:* $50 Canadian.

Application Contact Ms. Charlene Okell, MBA Program Manager, 268 Drake Centre, Winnipeg, MB R3T 5V4, Canada. **Phone:** 204-474-8448. **Toll-free Phone:** 800-622-6296. **Fax:** 204-474-7529. **E-mail:** cokell@ms.umanitoba.ca.

University of New Brunswick
Fredericton, New Brunswick, Canada

FACULTY OF ADMINISTRATION

Graduate Business Faculty
Full-time: 39	Part-time: 10

Student Body
Total: 98	Part-time: 53
Full-time: 45	Average Age: 27

Admissions
Applications: 60	Average GMAT: 550
Admitted: 35	Average GPA: 3.3
Enrolled: 30	

Costs (1999–2000)
Full-time tuition: $4350 Canadian per academic year (resident)
Part-time tuition: $435 Canadian per course (resident)

DEGREE MBA

MBA—Master of Business Administration Full-time and part-time. Applicants may apply to have GMAT requirements waived if they have 10 years of work experience or a GPA of 3.5 and above. At least 60 total credits required. Maximum of 24 months to complete program.

COSTS
Tuition, state resident: *Full-time* $4350 Canadian. *Part-time* $435 Canadian per course. **Tuition, international:** *Full-time* $6055 Canadian. Tuition varies by number of courses or credits taken. **Graduate housing:** Room and board costs vary by number of occupants, type of accommodation, and type of board plan. *Typical cost:* $5000 Canadian (including board).

FINANCIAL AID (1999–2000)
15 students received aid, including research assistantships, scholarships, and teaching assistantships. Financial aid application deadline: 8/31. **Financial Aid Contact** Karen P. Ivey, MBA Secretary, Tilley Hall 332, Fredricton, NB E3B 5A3, Canada. **Phone:** 506-453-4766. **Fax:** 506-453-3561. **E-mail:** kivey@unb.ca.

RESOURCES AND SERVICES
Information about online services, personal computer policies, library resources, international exchange programs, internship programs, and placement services at this institution and others can be found at **www.petersons.com/mba**

International Students
Services and Facilities Counseling/support services, ESL/language courses, housing location assistance, international student housing, international student organization, language tutoring, orientation. Financial aid is not available to international students. **Applying** *Required:* TOEFL with recommended score of 550 (paper), TWE with recommended score of 4, proof of adequate funds, proof of health/immunizations. **International Student Contact** Ms. Kay Nandlall, Director, International Student Advisor, International Student Advisor's Office, PO Box 4400, NB, Canada. **Phone:** 506-453-4860. **Fax:** 506-453-5005. **E-mail:** nandlall@unb.ca.

■ APPLICATION
Required GMAT, application form, baccalaureate/first degree, 3 letters of recommendation, personal statement, resume/curriculum vitae, transcripts of college work. **Recommended** Work experience. **Deadlines and Fees** *Deadlines:* 5/30 for fall, 5/30 for fall (international). *Application fee:* $25 Canadian.

Application Contact Karen P. Ivey, MBA Secretary, Tilley Hall 332, Fredricton, NB E3B 5A3, Canada. **Phone:** 506-453-4766. **Fax:** 506-453-3561. **E-mail:** kivey@unb.ca.

University of New Brunswick
Saint John, New Brunswick, Canada

FACULTY OF BUSINESS

Graduate Business Faculty
Full-time: 19	Part-time: 10

Student Body
Total: 81	Average Age: 28
Full-time: 41	Women: 43%
Part-time: 40	

Admissions
Applications: 94	Average GMAT: 570
Admitted: 66	Average GPA: 3.3/4.3 scale
Enrolled: 41	

Costs (1999–2000)
Full-time tuition: $21,050 Canadian per academic year (resident), $21,050 Canadian per academic year (nonresident)
Part-time tuition: $435 Canadian per course (resident)

After Graduation (Class of 1998–99)
Employed within 3 months of graduation: 70%
Average starting salary: $58,000 Canadian

DEGREE MBA

MBA—Master of Business Administration Full-time and part-time. Minimum 2 years work experience. 60 to 63 total credits required. 12 to 72 months to complete program. *Concentrations:* international business, telecommunications management.

COSTS
Tuition, state resident: *Full-time* $21,000 Canadian. *Part-time* $435 Canadian per course. **Tuition, Canadian resident:** *Full-time* $21,000 Canadian. **Tuition, international:** *Full-time* $21,000 Canadian. Tuition varies by campus location and academic program. **Required fees:** *Full-time* $50 Canadian. Tuition and fees vary by academic program. **Graduate housing:** Room and board costs vary by campus location, number of occupants, type of accommodation, and type of board plan. *Typical cost:* $5200 Canadian (including board).

FINANCIAL AID (1999–2000)
16 students received aid, including scholarships and work study. Financial aid application deadline: 3/15. **Financial Aid Contact** Ms. Marilyn MacLeod, Graduate Student Inquiries, PO Box 5050, 1 Tucker Park Road, NB, Canada. **Phone:** 506-648-5673. **Fax:** 506-648-5528. **E-mail:** macleodm@unbsj.ca.

RESOURCES AND SERVICES
Information about online services, personal computer policies, library resources, international exchange programs, internship programs, and placement services at this institution and others can be found at **www.petersons.com/mba**

International Students
22% of students enrolled are international students.

Services and Facilities Counseling/support services, ESL/language courses, housing location assistance, international student organization, language tutoring, orientation, visa services. Financial aid is available to international students.
Applying *Required:* TOEFL with recommended score of 213 (computer) or 550 (paper), TWE with recommended score of 4. *Recommended:* TSE.
International Student Contact Mr. Peter Donahue, International Student Advisor, PO Box 5050, 1 Tucker Park Road, NB, Canada. **Phone:** 506-648-5842. **Fax:** 506-648-5528. **E-mail:** donahue@unbsj.ca.

■ APPLICATION
Required GMAT, application form, baccalaureate/first degree, 3 letters of recommendation, personal statement, resume/curriculum vitae, transcripts of college work, 2 years of work experience.
Deadlines and Fees *Deadlines:* 5/15 for spring, 3/15 for winter (international). *Application fee:* $100 Canadian, $100 Canadian (international).
Application Contact Ms. Mary Beth Heighton, MBA Secretary, PO Box 5050, 1 Tucker Park Road, NB, Canada. **Phone:** 506-648-5746. **Toll-free Phone:** 800-50-UNBSJ (in-state), 800-508-6275 (out-of-state). **Fax:** 506-648-5574. **E-mail:** mba@unbsj.ca.

University of Ottawa
Ottawa, Ontario, Canada

FACULTY OF ADMINISTRATION

Graduate Business Faculty
Full-time: 67 — Part-time: 31

Student Body
Total: 444
Full-time: 243 — Average Age: 30 — Women: 45%
Part-time: 201

Admissions
Applications: 462 — Average GMAT: 580
Admitted: 268 — Average GPA: 3
Enrolled: 152

Costs (1999–2000)
Full-time tuition: $2550 Canadian per academic year (resident), $7000 Canadian per academic year (nonresident)
Part-time tuition: $270 Canadian per credit (resident), $750 Canadian per credit (nonresident)

After Graduation (Class of 1998–99)
Employed within 3 months of graduation: 96%
Average starting salary: $66,232 Canadian

DEGREES EMBA • IMBA • MBA

EMBA—Executive Master of Business Administration Full-time. At least 60 total credits required. 24 months to complete program. *Concentrations:* management.
IMBA—International Master of Business Administration Full-time and part-time. At least 30 total credits required. 12 to 72 months to complete program. *Concentrations:* international management.
MBA—Master of Business Administration Full-time and part-time. At least 60 total credits required. 12 to 48 months to complete program. *Concentrations:* finance, international management, management, marketing, public management, technology management.

COSTS
Tuition, state resident: *Full-time* $2550 Canadian. *Part-time* $270 Canadian per credit. **Tuition, Canadian resident:** *Full-time* $7000 Canadian. *Part-time* $750 Canadian per credit. Tuition varies by academic program. **Graduate housing:** Room and board costs vary by number of occupants, type of accommodation, and type of board plan. *Typical cost:* $7600 Canadian (including board), $2372 Canadian (room only).

FINANCIAL AID (1999–2000)
Loans, research assistantships, scholarships, and teaching assistantships.
Financial Aid Contact Mrs. Manon Gauvreau, Administrator, School of Graduate Studies and Research, PO Box 450, Station A, Ottawa, ON K1N 6N5, Canada. **Phone:** 613-562-5800 Ext. 1248. **Fax:** 613-562-5992. **E-mail:** manong@uottawa.ca.

RESOURCES AND SERVICES
Information about online services, personal computer policies, library resources, international exchange programs, internship programs, and

placement services at this institution and others can be found at **www.petersons.com/mba**

International Students
Services and Facilities Counseling/support services, ESL/language courses, international student organization. Financial aid is available to international students.
Applying *Required:* TOEFL with recommended score of 580 (paper), TWE with recommended score of 4.5, proof of adequate funds, proof of health/immunizations. *Recommended:* IELT.
International Student Contact Ms. Sylvie Seguin-Jak, Administrator, IMBA Program, PO Box 450, Station A, Ottawa, ON K1N 6N5, Canada. **Phone:** 613-562-5821. **Fax:** 613-562-5167. **E-mail:** sequin-jak@admin.uottawa.ca.

■ APPLICATION
Required GMAT, application form, baccalaureate/first degree, essay, 2 letters of recommendation, personal statement, resume/curriculum vitae, transcripts of college work, 2 years of work experience. School will accept GRE.
Deadlines and Fees *Deadline:* 3/1 for fall. *Application fee:* $60 Canadian.
Application Contact Ms. Diane Sarrazin, Administrator, PO Box 450, Station A, Ottawa, ON K1N 6N5, Canada. **Phone:** 613-562-5884. **Toll-free Phone:** 800-965-5512. **Fax:** 613-562-5912. **E-mail:** sarrazin@admin.uottawa.ca.

University of Regina
Regina, Saskatchewan, Canada

FACULTY OF ADMINISTRATION

Graduate Business Faculty
Full-time: 17 — Part-time: 2

Student Body
Total: 59
Full-time: 3 — Average Age: 32 — Women: 42%
Part-time: 56

Admissions
Applications: 29 — Average GMAT: 560
Admitted: 21 — Average GPA: 3.2
Enrolled: 21

Costs (1999–2000)
Full-time tuition: N/R
Part-time tuition: $188 Canadian per credit hour (resident), $188 Canadian per credit hour (nonresident)

After Graduation (Class of 1998–99)
Employed within 3 months of graduation: 80%

DEGREES MBA • MHRM • MPA

MBA—Master of Business Administration Full-time and part-time. 15 to 60 total credits required. 30 to 60 months to complete program. *Concentrations:* management.
MHRM—Master of Human Resources Management Full-time and part-time. 15 to 60 total credits required. 30 to 60 months to complete program.
MPA—Master of Public Administration Full-time and part-time. 15 to 60 total credits required. 30 to 60 months to complete program. *Concentrations:* public policy and administration.

COSTS
Tuition, state resident: *Part-time* $188 Canadian per credit hour. **Tuition, Canadian resident:** *Part-time* $188 Canadian per credit hour. Tuition varies by number of courses or credits taken and academic program. **Required fees:** *Full-time* $138 Canadian. *Part-time* $69 Canadian per semester. Tuition and fees vary by academic program. **Graduate housing:** Room and board costs vary by campus location, number of occupants, type of accommodation, and type of board plan. *Typical cost:* $3060 Canadian (room only).

FINANCIAL AID (1999–2000)
2 students received aid, including loans, research assistantships, scholarships, teaching assistantships, and work study. **Financial Aid Contact** Dr. Swaminathan Sankaran, MBA Coordinator, Faculty of Administration, Regina, SK S4S 0A2, Canada. **Phone:** 306-585-4988. **Fax:** 306-585-4805. **E-mail:** sam.sankaran@uregina.ca.

RESOURCES AND SERVICES
Information about online services, personal computer policies, library resources, international exchange programs, internship programs, and placement services at this institution and others can be found at **www.petersons.com/mba**

University of Regina (continued)

International Students

3% of students enrolled are international students.

Services and Facilities Counseling/support services, ESL/language courses, visa services. Financial aid is not available to international students.

Applying *Required:* TOEFL with recommended score of 580 (paper).

International Student Contact Mr. Sel Murray, Manager of Student Affairs/ International Student Services, Regina, SK S4S OA2, Canada. **Phone:** 306-585-4017. **Fax:** 306-585-4957.

■ APPLICATION

Required GMAT, application form, baccalaureate/first degree, interview, 2 letters of recommendation, personal statement, resume/curriculum vitae, transcripts of college work, 2 years of work experience.

Deadlines and Fees *Deadlines:* 7/1 for fall, 11/1 for winter, 2/1 for spring, 2/1 for summer.

Application Contact Dr. Swaminathan Sankaran, MBA Coordinator, Faculty of Administration, Regina, SK S4S 0A2, Canada. **Phone:** 306-585-4988. **Fax:** 306-585-4805. **E-mail:** sam.sankaran@uregina.ca.

University of Saskatchewan

Saskatoon, Saskatchewan, Canada

COLLEGE OF COMMERCE

Graduate Business Faculty
Full-time: 14 — Part-time: 7

Student Body
Total: 125 — Average Age: 33
Full-time: 52 — Women: 41%
Part-time: 73

Admissions
Applications: 98 — Enrolled: 43
Admitted: 82 — Average GMAT: 538

Costs (1999–2000)
Full-time tuition: N/R
Part-time tuition: $382 Canadian per course (resident), $382 Canadian per course (nonresident)

DEGREES M Sc • MBA • MP Acc • MS

M Sc—Master of Science in Accounting (Thesis program) Full-time and part-time. Degree in accounting required. At least 18 total credits required. 8 to 60 months to complete program. *Concentrations:* accounting.

MBA—Master of Business Administration Full-time and part-time. 30 to 60 total credits required. 8 to 60 months to complete program. *Concentrations:* commerce.

MP Acc—Master of Professional Accountancy Full-time. Degree in accounting required. At least 34 total credits required. 12 months to complete program.

MS—Master of Science in Finance Full-time. A degree in finance is preferred. At least 18 total credits required. 16 to 60 months to complete program. *Concentrations:* finance.

COSTS

Tuition, state resident: *Part-time* $382 Canadian per course. **Tuition, Canadian resident:** *Part-time* $382 Canadian per course. **Required fees:** *Full-time* $349 Canadian. *Part-time* $79 Canadian per year. Tuition and fees vary by class time, number of courses or credits taken, and academic program. **Graduate housing:** Room and board costs vary by number of occupants, type of accommodation, and type of board plan. *Typical cost:* $4380 Canadian (including board).

FINANCIAL AID (1999–2000)

12 students received aid, including fellowships, scholarships, and teaching assistantships. Financial aid application deadline: 2/15.

Financial Aid Contact Chandra Kretzer, Administrative Assistant, MBA Program, College of Commerce, 25 Campus Drive, Saskatoon, SK S7N 5A7, Canada. **Phone:** 306-966-8678. **Fax:** 306-966-5408.

RESOURCES AND SERVICES

Information about online services, personal computer policies, library resources, international exchange programs, internship programs, and placement services at this institution and others can be found at **www.petersons.com/mba**

International Students

21% of students enrolled are international students.

Services and Facilities Counseling/support services, ESL/language courses, international student organization, orientation. Financial aid is available to international students.

Applying *Required:* TOEFL with recommended score of 213 (computer) or 550 (paper).

International Student Contact Mr. Kurt Tischler, Advisor, 1 Campus Drive, Room 60, Place Riel, Saskatoon, SK S7N 5A3, Canada. **Phone:** 306-966-4923. **Fax:** 306-966-5081. **E-mail:** tischler@admin.usask.ca.

■ APPLICATION

Required GMAT, application form, baccalaureate/first degree, 3 letters of recommendation, transcripts of college work. **Recommended** Resume/curriculum vitae, 3 years of work experience.

Deadlines and Fees *Deadlines:* 6/15 for fall, 10/15 for winter, 4/15 for fall (international), 8/15 for winter (international). *Application fee:* $50 Canadian.

Application Contact Ms. Chandra Kretzer, Administrative Assistant, College of Commerce, 25 Campus Drive, Saskatoon, SK S7N 5A7, Canada. **Phone:** 306-966-8678. **Fax:** 306-966-5408. **E-mail:** kretzer@commerce.usask.ca.

University of Toronto

Toronto, Ontario, Canada

JOSEPH L. ROTMAN SCHOOL OF MANAGEMENT

Graduate Business Faculty
Full-time: 64 — Part-time: 22

Student Body
Total: 417 — Average Age: 28
Full-time: 252 — Women: 29%
Part-time: 165

Admissions
Applications: 1,085 — Average GMAT: 672
Admitted: 217 — Average GPA: 3.3
Enrolled: 130

Costs (1999–2000)
Full-time tuition: $16,400 Canadian per academic year (resident), $20,500 Canadian per academic year (nonresident)
Part-time tuition: N/R

After Graduation (Class of 1998–99)
Average starting salary: $77,000 Canadian

Accreditation
AACSB—The International Association for Management Education

DEGREES EMBA • MBA • MBA/LL B • MMPA

EMBA—Executive MBA Part-time. At least 60 total credits required. Maximum of 24 months to complete program. *Concentrations:* management.

MBA—Full-time MBA Full-time. At least 60 total credits required. 20 to 42 months to complete program. *Concentrations:* economics, finance, management, marketing, operations management, organizational behavior/development, strategic management.

MBA—Part-time MBA Part-time. At least 60 total credits required. 36 months to complete program. *Concentrations:* economics, finance, management, marketing, operations management, organizational behavior/development, strategic management.

MBA/LL B—Master of Business Administration/Bachelor of Laws Full-time. At least 60 total credits required. 44 months to complete program. *Concentrations:* economics, finance, management, marketing, operations management, organizational behavior/development, research and development administration.

MMPA—Master of Management and Professional Accounting Full-time. At least 70 total credits required. 16 to 27 months to complete program. *Concentrations:* accounting, management.

COSTS

Tuition, state resident: *Full-time* $16,400 Canadian. **Tuition, Canadian resident:** *Full-time* $20,500 Canadian. **Required fees:** Tuition and fees vary by academic program. **Graduate housing:** Room and board costs vary by campus location, number of occupants, type of accommodation, and type of board plan. *Typical cost:* $10,000 Canadian (including board).

FINANCIAL AID (1999–2000)

125 students received aid, including fellowships, grants, loans, research assistantships, scholarships, and teaching assistantships. Financial aid

application deadline: 4/30. **Financial Aid Contact** Ms. Margaret Bauer, MBA Program Assistant, 105 St. George Street, Toronto, ON M5S 3E6, Canada. **Phone:** 416-978-1983. **Fax:** 416-978-5812. **E-mail:** bauer@ mgmt.utoronto.ca.

RESOURCES AND SERVICES
Information about online services, personal computer policies, library resources, international exchange programs, internship programs, and placement services at this institution and others can be found at **www. petersons.com/mba**

International Students
Services and Facilities Counseling/support services, ESL/language courses, housing location assistance, international student organization, language tutoring, orientation, visa services. Financial aid is available to international students.
Applying *Required:* IELT with recommended score of 7, TOEFL with recommended score of 250 (computer) or 600 (paper), TWE with recommended score of 5.
International Student Contact Ms. Grace Raposo, PhD and International Programs Coordinator, 105 St. George Street, Toronto, ON M5S 3E6, Canada. **Phone:** 416-978-4226. **Fax:** 416-978-5812. **E-mail:** raposo@mgmt.utoronto.ca.

■ APPLICATION
Required GMAT, application form, baccalaureate/first degree, essay, 3 letters of recommendation, resume/curriculum vitae, transcripts of college work, 2 years of work experience. **Recommended** Interview.
Deadlines and Fees *Deadlines:* 4/30 for fall, 9/30 for winter, 4/30 for fall (international), 9/30 for winter (international). *Application fee:* $125 Canadian.
Application Contact Ms. Almira Mun, Director, Recruiting and Admissions, MBA Program, 105 St. George Street, Toronto, ON M5S 3E6, Canada. **Phone:** 416-978-3499. **Fax:** 416-978-5812. **E-mail:** mbaprog@mgmt.utoronto.ca.

See full description on page 982.

University of Victoria

Victoria, British Columbia, Canada

FACULTY OF BUSINESS

Graduate Business Faculty
Full-time: 23 — Part-time: 12

Student Body
Total: 150
Full-time: 137 — Average Age: 29
Part-time: 13 — Women: 37%

Admissions
Applications: 280
Admitted: 103 — Average GMAT: 585
Enrolled: 55 — Average GPA: 3.2

Costs (1999–2000)
Full-time tuition: $4267 Canadian per academic year (resident), $4267 Canadian per academic year (nonresident)
Part-time tuition: $7330 Canadian per degree program (resident), $7330 Canadian per degree program (nonresident)

DEGREES MBA • MBA/LL B

MBA—Master of Business Administration Full-time and part-time. At least 52 total credits required. 17 to 60 months to complete program. *Concentrations:* entrepreneurship, international business, management, strategic management.

MBA/LL B—Master of Business Administration/Bachelor of Laws Full-time. At least 131 total credits required. Minimum of 44 months to complete program. *Concentrations:* international business, management.

COSTS
Tuition, state resident: *Full-time* $3665 Canadian. *Part-time* $7330 Canadian per degree program. **Tuition, Canadian resident:** *Full-time* $3665 Canadian. *Part-time* $7330 Canadian per degree program. **Tuition, international:** *Full-time* $3665 Canadian. **Required fees:** *Full-time* $602 Canadian. *Part-time* $118 Canadian per term. **Graduate housing:** Room and board costs vary by campus location, number of occupants, type of accommodation, and type of board plan. *Typical cost:* $5224 Canadian (including board), $2632 Canadian (room only).

FINANCIAL AID (1999–2000)
8 students received aid, including fellowships, research assistantships, scholarships, and teaching assistantships. Financial aid application deadline: 2/15. **Financial Aid Contact** Ms. Leelah Dawson, Assistant Director, MBA Programs, PO Box 1700, STN CSC, Victoria, BC V8W

2Y2, Canada. **Phone:** 250-472-4728. **Fax:** 250-721-7066. **E-mail:** mba@business.uvic.ca.

RESOURCES AND SERVICES
Information about online services, personal computer policies, library resources, international exchange programs, internship programs, and placement services at this institution and others can be found at **www. petersons.com/mba**

International Students
21% of students enrolled are international students.
Services and Facilities Counseling/support services, ESL/language courses, housing location assistance, international student housing, orientation. Financial aid is available to international students.
Applying *Required:* IELT with recommended score of 7, TOEFL with recommended score of 230 (computer) or 575 (paper). *Recommended:* TWE with recommended score of 3.5.
International Student Contact Ms. Leelah Dawson, Assistant Director, MBA Programs, PO Box 1700, STN CSC, Victoria, BC V8W 2Y2, Canada. **Phone:** 250-721-6058. **Fax:** 250-721-7066. **E-mail:** mba@business.uvic.ca.

■ APPLICATION
Required GMAT, application form, baccalaureate/first degree, essay, 2 letters of recommendation, resume/curriculum vitae, transcripts of college work. **Recommended** Interview, 2 years of work experience.
Deadlines and Fees *Deadlines:* 5/31 for fall, 5/31 for fall (international). *Application fee:* $50 Canadian, $50 Canadian (international).
Application Contact Ms. Leelah Dawson, Assistant Director, MBA Programs, PO Box 1700, STN CSC, Victoria, BC V8W 2Y2, Canada. **Phone:** 250-472-4728. **Fax:** 250-721-7066. **E-mail:** mba@business.uvic.ca.

University of Waterloo

Waterloo, Ontario, Canada

GRADUATE STUDIES OFFICE

Graduate Business Faculty
Full-time: 136 — Part-time: 105

Student Body
Total: 537
Full-time: 423 — Part-time: 114
— Women: 48%

Costs (1999–2000)
Full-time tuition: $4848 Canadian per academic year (resident)
Part-time tuition: N/R

DEGREES MA • MAES

MA—Economics Full-time and part-time. Minimum of 12 months to complete program. *Concentrations:* economics, finance, financial economics.

MAES—Local Economic Development Full-time and part-time. Minimum of 12 months to complete program. *Concentrations:* environmental economics/management.

COSTS
Tuition, state resident: *Full-time* $4848 Canadian. **Tuition, international:** *Full-time* $12,240 Canadian. Tuition varies by academic program. **Graduate housing:** Room and board costs vary by number of occupants, type of accommodation, and type of board plan. *Typical cost:* $7780 Canadian (including board), $4330 Canadian (room only).

FINANCIAL AID (1999–2000)
Fellowships, loans, research assistantships, scholarships, teaching assistantships, and work study. **Financial Aid Contact** Ms. Elaine Garner, Graduate Awards Coordinator, Graduate Studies Office, Waterloo, ON N2L 361, Canada. **Phone:** 519-888-4567 Ext. 2841. **Fax:** 519-746-3051.

RESOURCES AND SERVICES
Information about online services, personal computer policies, library resources, international exchange programs, internship programs, and placement services at this institution and others can be found at **www. petersons.com/mba**

International Students
Services and Facilities Counseling/support services, ESL/language courses, housing location assistance, international student organization, language tutoring, orientation. Financial aid is available to international students.
Applying *Required:* IELT, TOEFL with recommended score of 213 (computer) or 550 (paper), TSE, TWE, proof of adequate funds.

University of Waterloo (continued)

International Student Contact Darlene Ryan, International Student Advisor, International Student Office, ON, Canada. **Phone:** 519-888-4567 Ext. 2814. **Fax:** 519-746-2401. **E-mail:** darlene@watserv1.uwaterloo.ca.

■ **APPLICATION**

Required Application form, baccalaureate/first degree, 3 letters of recommendation, transcripts of college work. School will accept GMAT and GRE. **Recommended** Work experience.

Deadlines and Fees Applications for domestic and international students are processed on a rolling basis. *Application fee:* $50 Canadian.

Application Contact Ms. Jeanette Nugent, Recruitment and Admissions Coordinator, 200 University Avenue West, Waterloo, ON N2L 3G1, Canada. **Phone:** 519-888-4567 Ext. 3933. **Fax:** 519-746-3051. **E-mail:** jnugent@uwaterloo.ca.

The University of Western Ontario

London, Ontario, Canada

IVEY BUSINESS SCHOOL

Graduate Business Faculty
Full-time: 80

Student Body
Total: 510	Average Age: 29
Full-time: 510	Women: 25%

Admissions
Applications: 950	Average GMAT: 657
Enrolled: 280	Average GPA: 3

Costs (1999–2000)
Full-time tuition: $16,000 Canadian per academic year (resident), $16,000 Canadian per academic year (nonresident)
Part-time tuition: N/R

After Graduation (Class of 1998–99)
Employed within 3 months of graduation: 93%
Average starting salary: $83,558 Canadian

DEGREE MBA

MBA—Master of Business Administration Full-time. At least 18 total credits required. 20 months to complete program. *Concentrations:* accounting, Asian business studies, banking, business information science, economics, entrepreneurship, European business studies, finance, human resources, international and area business studies, management science, marketing, operations management, organizational behavior/development, production management, strategic management, taxation.

The Ivey Business School has been repeatedly recognized as the best management school in Canada by Canadian Business *and among the best in the world by* Asia Inc., Asian Business, Business Week, U.S. News & World Report, *and* The Journal of International Management. *In 1999 and 2000, Ivey was listed as the best Canadian M.B.A. program by the* Financial Times.

Students are trained by outstanding faculty members in a real-world case-method environment and have the most practical and effective business skills. Students acquire experience solving—as individuals, as team members, and as team leaders—challenges and problems of actual businesses around the world. Ivey faculty members and case writers travel worldwide to research actual enterprises whose situations are unique because of the inherent cultural and political climates.

The program is full-time only and is completed in two years. Using cases, role-playing, simulations, and negotiation exercises, it provides a two-year general management program with a global perspective. Opportunities for international experiences are available through student academic exchanges, overseas projects, and international case competitions. Ivey also offers undergraduate business, Executive M.B.A. (in Canada and Hong Kong), Video-conferencing Executive M.B.A., LL.B./M.B.A., and Ph.D. programs.

COSTS

Tuition, state resident: *Full-time* $16,000 Canadian. **Tuition, Canadian resident:** *Full-time* $16,000 Canadian. **Graduate housing:** Room and board costs vary by campus location, number of occupants, type of accommodation, and type of board plan. *Typical cost:* $6000 Canadian (including board).

FINANCIAL AID (1999–2000)

100 students received aid, including scholarships and work study.
Financial Aid Contact Ms. Ella Strong, Director of Financial Aid, 1151 Richmond Street North, London, ON N6A 3K7, Canada. **Phone:** 519-661-3218. **Fax:** 519-661-3431. **E-mail:** estrong@ivey.uwo.ca.

RESOURCES AND SERVICES

Information about online services, personal computer policies, library resources, international exchange programs, internship programs, and placement services at this institution and others can be found at **www.petersons.com/mba**

International Students

30% of students enrolled are international students.

Services and Facilities Counseling/support services, ESL/language courses, housing location assistance, international student organization, orientation, visa services. Financial aid is available to international students.

Applying *Required:* TOEFL with recommended score of 600 (paper), proof of adequate funds. *Recommended:* Proof of health/immunizations.

International Student Contact Ms. Larysa Gamula, Director, MBA Program Office, Richard Ivey School of Business, 1511 Richmond Street North, London, ON N6A 3K7, Canada. **Phone:** 519-661-3212. **Fax:** 519-661-3431. **E-mail:** lgamula@ivey.uwo.ca.

■ **APPLICATION**

Required Application form, baccalaureate/first degree, essay, personal statement, resume/curriculum vitae, transcripts of college work, 2 years of work experience. School will accept GMAT. **Recommended** Interview, letter(s) of recommendation.

Deadlines and Fees *Deadlines:* 4/1 for fall, 4/1 for fall (international). *Application fee:* $100 Canadian.

Application Contact Ms. Larysa Gamula, Director, MBA Program Office, Richard Ivey School of Business, 1151 Richmond Street North, London, ON N6A 3K7, Canada. **Phone:** 519-661-3212. **Fax:** 519-661-3431. **E-mail:** lgamula@ivey.uwa.ca.

See full description on page 988.

University of Windsor

Windsor, Ontario, Canada

FACULTY OF BUSINESS ADMINISTRATION

Graduate Business Faculty
Full-time: 36

Student Body
Total: 191	Average Age: 25
Full-time: 130	Women: 39%
Part-time: 61	

Admissions
Applications: 550	Average GMAT: 575
Admitted: 350	Average GPA: 3.5
Enrolled: 98	

Costs (1999–2000)
Full-time tuition: $4368 Canadian per academic year (resident), $6195 Canadian per academic year (nonresident)
Part-time tuition: $837 Canadian per semester (resident), $1008 Canadian per semester (nonresident)

After Graduation (Class of 1998–99)
Employed within 3 months of graduation: 95%
Average starting salary: $50,000 Canadian

DEGREES MBA • MBA/LL B

MBA—Master of Business Administration Co-op Full-time. Interview required. 60 to 69 total credits required. 23 months to complete program. *Concentrations:* business policy/strategy, entrepreneurship, finance, human resources, industrial administration/management, industrial/labor relations, international and area business studies, international business, management science, marketing, production management.

MBA—Master of Business Administration Full-time and part-time. 39 to 69 total credits required. 11 to 72 months to complete program. *Concentrations:* business policy/strategy, entrepreneurship, finance, human resources, industrial administration/management, industrial/labor relations, international and area business studies, international business, management science, marketing, production management.

MBA/LL B—Master of Business Administration/Bachelor of Laws Full-time. Must apply separately to Faculty of Business and Faculty of Law. 113 to 119 total credits required. 36 to 48 months to complete program. *Concentrations:* business policy/strategy, entrepreneurship, finance, human resources, industrial administration/management, industrial/labor relations, international and area business studies, international business, management science, marketing, production management.

COSTS

Tuition, state resident: *Full-time* $3873 Canadian. *Part-time* $779 Canadian per semester. **Tuition, Canadian resident:** *Full-time* $5700 Canadian. *Part-time* $950 Canadian per semester. **Tuition, international:** *Full-time* $8453 Canadian. Tuition varies by number of courses or credits taken, academic program, and local reciprocity agreements. **Required fees:** *Full-time* $495 Canadian. *Part-time* $58 Canadian per semester. **Graduate housing:** Room and board costs vary by number of occupants, type of accommodation, and type of board plan. *Typical cost:* $4500 Canadian (including board).

FINANCIAL AID (1999–2000)

Research assistantships, scholarships, teaching assistantships, and work study. Financial aid application deadline: 2/1. **Financial Aid Contact** Ms. Alison Samson, Assistant to the Executive Dean, College of Graduate Studies and Research, 401 Sunset Avenue, Windsor, ON N9B 3P4, Canada. **Phone:** 519-253-3000 Ext. 2112. **Fax:** 519-971-3667. **E-mail:** asamson@uwindsor.ca.

RESOURCES AND SERVICES

Information about online services, personal computer policies, library resources, international exchange programs, internship programs, and placement services at this institution and others can be found at **www.petersons.com/mba**

International Students

8% of students enrolled are international students.

Services and Facilities Counseling/support services, international student housing, visa services. Financial aid is not available to international students.
Applying *Required:* TOEFL with recommended score of 600 (paper), proof of adequate funds, proof of health/immunizations.

International Student Contact Mr. Richard Lanspeary, International Students Advisor, 401 Sunset Avenue, Windsor, ON N9B 3P4, Canada. **Phone:** 519-253-4232 Ext. 3901. **Fax:** 519-973-7046. **E-mail:** lanspea@uwindsor.ca.

■ APPLICATION

Required Application form, baccalaureate/first degree, 1 letter of recommendation, resume/curriculum vitae, transcripts of college work. School will accept GMAT. **Recommended** Essay, interview, work experience.
Deadlines and Fees *Deadlines:* 5/1 for fall, 3/1 for fall (international). *Application fee:* $55 Canadian.
Application Contact Mr. Michael Houston, Assistant to Dean, Faculty of Business Administration, 401 Sunset Avenue, Windsor, ON N9B 3P4, Canada. **Phone:** 519-253-4232 Ext. 3097. **Fax:** 519-973-7073. **E-mail:** mikeh@uwindsor.ca.

Wilfrid Laurier University
Waterloo, Ontario, Canada

SCHOOL OF BUSINESS AND ECONOMICS

Graduate Business Faculty
Full-time: 67 | Part-time: 7

Student Body
Total: 349
Full-time: 87
Part-time: 262
Average Age: 33
Women: 38%

Admissions
Applications: 447
Admitted: 265
Enrolled: 199
Average GMAT: 590
Average GPA: 9/12 scale

Costs (1999–2000)
Full-time tuition: $9118 Canadian per academic year (resident), $14,272 Canadian per academic year (nonresident)
Part-time tuition: $1102 Canadian per term (resident)

After Graduation (Class of 1998–99)
Employed within 3 months of graduation: 90%
Average starting salary: $58,800 Canadian

DEGREES MA • MBA

MA—Master of Arts in Business Economics Full-time. 12 to 18 months to complete program.
MBA—On-Campus MBA Full-time and part-time. Minimum 2 years full-time work experience. At least 20 total credits required. 12 to 60 months to complete program.
MBA—Toronto-Based MBA Part-time. Minimum 2 years full-time work experience. At least 20 total credits required. 39 to 48 months to complete program.
MBA—Master of Business Administration Part-time. Minimum 2 years full-time work experience. At least 20 total credits required. Minimum of 39 months to complete program.

COSTS

Tuition, state resident: *Full-time* $8001 Canadian. *Part-time* $1041 Canadian per term. **Tuition, Canadian resident:** *Full-time* $13,155 Canadian. **Required fees:** *Full-time* $1117 Canadian. *Part-time* $61 Canadian per term. Tuition and fees vary by number of courses or credits taken, campus location, and academic program. **Graduate housing:** Room and board costs vary by number of occupants, type of accommodation, and type of board plan. *Typical cost:* $8100 Canadian (including board).

FINANCIAL AID (1999–2000)

30 students received aid, including fellowships, loans, research assistantships, scholarships, and teaching assistantships. Aid is available to part-time students. Financial aid application deadline: 11/1. **Financial Aid Contact** Pauline Delion, Director of Student Awards, 75 University Avenue West, Waterloo, ON N2L 3C5, Canada. **Phone:** 519-884-0710 Ext. 4256. **E-mail:** pdelion@mach2.wlu.ca.

RESOURCES AND SERVICES

Information about online services, personal computer policies, library resources, international exchange programs, internship programs, and placement services at this institution and others can be found at **www.petersons.com/mba**

International Students

1% of students enrolled are international students.

Services and Facilities Counseling/support services, international student housing, international student organization, visa services. Financial aid is available to international students.
Applying *Required:* TOEFL with recommended score of 550 (paper).
International Student Contact Dr. Al Hecht, Director of Laurier International, 75 University Avenue West, Waterloo, ON N2L 3C5, Canada. **Phone:** 519-884-0710 Ext. 6704. **Fax:** 519-886-4507. **E-mail:** ahecht@wlu.ca.

■ APPLICATION

Required GMAT, application form, baccalaureate/first degree, 3 letters of recommendation, personal statement, resume/curriculum vitae, transcripts of college work, 2 years of work experience. **Recommended** Essay.
Deadlines and Fees *Deadlines:* 5/1 for fall, 5/1 for fall (international). *Application fee:* $100 Canadian.
Application Contact Dianne Hotson, Administrator, 75 University Avenue West, Waterloo, ON N2L 3C5, Canada. **Phone:** 519-884-0710 Ext. 2142. **Fax:** 519-886-6978. **E-mail:** wlumba@wlu.ca.

See full description on page 1016.

York University
Toronto, Ontario, Canada

SCHULICH SCHOOL OF BUSINESS

Graduate Business Faculty
Full-time: 82 | Part-time: 111

Student Body
Total: 1,409
Full-time: 712
Part-time: 697
Average Age: 29.9
Women: 40%

Admissions
Applications: 2,059
Admitted: 965
Enrolled: 630
Average GMAT: 640
Average GPA: 3.3

Costs (1999–2000)
Full-time tuition: $5000 Canadian per academic year (resident)
Part-time tuition: $2000 Canadian per term (resident), $4300 Canadian per term (nonresident)

ty (continued)

After Graduation (Class of 1998–99)
Employed within 3 months of graduation: 94%
Average starting salary: $81,000 Canadian

DEGREES IMBA • MBA • MBA/LL B • MBA/MA • MPA

IMBA—International Master of Business Administration Full-time. International experience, advanced foreign language skills required. At least 72 total credits required. 24 months to complete program. *Concentrations:* accounting, arts administration/management, business ethics, economics, electronic commerce (e-commerce), entrepreneurship, finance, financial management/planning, industrial/labor relations, information management, international business, management information systems, management science, marketing, nonprofit management, operations management, organizational behavior/development, public management, quantitative analysis, real estate, strategic management, financial engineering.

MBA—Master of Business Administration Full-time and part-time. At least 60 total credits required. 8 to 72 months to complete program. *Concentrations:* accounting, arts administration/management, business ethics, economics, electronic commerce (e-commerce), entrepreneurship, finance, financial management/ planning, industrial/labor relations, information management, international business, management information systems, management science, marketing, nonprofit management, operations management, organizational behavior/development, public management, quantitative analysis, real estate, strategic management, financial engineering.

MBA/LL B—Master of Business Administration/Bachelor of Laws Full-time. At least 122 total credits required. 72 months to complete program. *Concentrations:* international business, management information systems, management science, nonprofit management, operations management, organizational behavior/ development, public management, quantitative analysis, real estate, strategic management.

MBA/MA—Master of Business Administration/Master of Arts in Fine Arts Full-time. Four-year undergraduate degree in Fine Arts and relevant work experience in arts/cultural industries required. At least 75 total credits required. Minimum of 36 months to complete program. *Concentrations:* accounting, arts administration/management, business ethics, economics, electronic commerce (e-commerce), entrepreneurship, finance, financial management/planning, industrial/labor relations, information management, international and area business studies, international business, management information systems, management science, marketing, nonprofit management, operations management, organizational behavior/development, public management, quantitative analysis, real estate, strategic management, financial engineering.

MPA—Master of Public Administration Full-time and part-time. At least 60 total credits required. 12 to 72 months to complete program. *Concentrations:* economics, organizational behavior/development, public management, public policy and administration.

COSTS
Tuition, state resident: *Full-time* $5000 Canadian. *Part-time* $2000 Canadian per term. **Tuition, Canadian resident:** *Part-time* $4300 Canadian per term. **Tuition, international:** *Full-time* $10,000 Canadian. **Required fees:** Fees vary by number of courses or credits taken. **Graduate housing:** Room and board costs vary by number of occupants, type of accommodation, and type of board plan. *Typical cost:* $5000 Canadian (room only).

FINANCIAL AID (1999–2000)
Fellowships, grants, loans, research assistantships, scholarships, and teaching assistantships. Financial aid application deadline: 6/1.
Financial Aid Contact Ms. Anne Caulfield, Financial Officer, Schulich School of Business, 4700 Keele Street, Toronto, ON M3J 1P3, Canada. **Phone:** 416-736-2100 Ext. 30515. **Fax:** 416-650-8174. **E-mail:** acaulfield@schulich.yorku.ca.

RESOURCES AND SERVICES
Information about online services, personal computer policies, library resources, international exchange programs, internship programs, and placement services at this institution and others can be found at **www.petersons.com/mba**

International Students
Services and Facilities Counseling/support services, ESL/language courses, international student housing, orientation, visa services. Financial aid is not available to international students.
Applying *Required:* TOEFL with recommended score of 600 (paper). *Recommended:* Proof of adequate funds, proof of health/immunizations.
International Student Contact Ms. Kimberly Paterson, Assistant Director, International Relations, Schulich School of Business, 4700 Keele Street, Toronto, ON M3J 1P3, Canada. **Phone:** 416-736-2100. **Fax:** 416-650-8174. **E-mail:** intladmissions@schulich.yorku.ca.

■ APPLICATION
Required GMAT, application form, baccalaureate/first degree, 2 letters of recommendation, personal statement, resume/curriculum vitae, transcripts of college work. **Recommended** 2 years of work experience.
Deadlines and Fees *Deadlines:* 5/1 for fall, 10/15 for winter, 4/1 for fall (international), 8/15 for winter (international). *Application fee:* $125 Canadian.
Application Contact Ms. Carol Pattenden, Assistant Director, Admissions, Schulich School of Business, 4700 Keele Street, Toronto, ON M3J 1P3, Canada. **Phone:** 416-736-5060. **Fax:** 416-650-8174. **E-mail:** cpattend@schulich.yorku.ca.

See full description on page 1026.

CAYMAN ISLANDS

International College of the Cayman Islands

Newlands, Cayman Islands

GRADUATE PROGRAM IN MANAGEMENT

Graduate Business Faculty
Full-time: 6 — Part-time: 5

Student Body
Total: 35 — Average Age: 36
Full-time: 11 — Women: 77%
Part-time: 24

Costs (1999–2000)
Full-time tuition: $3000 per academic year
Part-time tuition: $100 per credit

DEGREES MBA • MS

MBA—Master of Business Administration Full-time and part-time. At least 60 total credits required. Minimum of 18 months to complete program.

MS—Master of Science in Management Full-time and part-time. At least 60 total credits required. Minimum of 18 months to complete program. *Concentrations:* business education, human resources.

COSTS
Tuition *Full-time:* $3000. *Part-time:* $100 per credit. **Graduate housing:** Room and board costs vary by number of occupants. *Typical cost:* $2438 (room only).

FINANCIAL AID (1999–2000)
Financial Aid Contact Mrs. Diane Levy, Admissions Representative, PO Box 136, Savannah Post Office, Grand Cayman, Cayman Islands. **Phone:** 345-947-1100. **Fax:** 345-947-1210.

RESOURCES AND SERVICES
Information about online services, personal computer policies, library resources, international exchange programs, internship programs, and placement services at this institution and others can be found at **www.petersons.com/mba**

International Students
83% of students enrolled are international students.
Services and Facilities Counseling/support services, ESL/language courses, international student housing.
Applying *Required:* TOEFL with recommended score of 550 (paper).
International Student Contact Mrs. Diane Levy, Admissions Representative, Newlands, Cayman Islands. **Phone:** 345-947-1100. **Fax:** 345-947-1210.

■ APPLICATION
Required Application form, baccalaureate/first degree, essay, 3 letters of recommendation, transcripts of college work. School will accept GMAT. **Recommended** Work experience.
Deadlines and Fees Applications for domestic students are processed on a rolling basis. *Deadlines:* 6/15 for fall (international), 10/1 for winter (international), 1/1 for spring (international), 3/15 for summer (international). *Application fee:* $38.
Application Contact Dr. Eileen Dounce, Director of Graduate Studies, PO Box 136, Savannah Post Office, Grand Cayman, Cayman Islands. **Phone:** 345-947-1100. **Fax:** 345-947-1210.

CHINA

The Chinese University of Hong Kong

Shatin, Hong Kong, China

FACULTY OF BUSINESS ADMINISTRATION

Accreditation
AACSB—The International Association for Management Education

DEGREES EMBA • M Acc • M Phil • M Sc • MBA

EMBA—Executive MBA Part-time. At least 54 total credits required. 24 to 48 months to complete program. *Concentrations:* decision sciences, finance, leadership, management, managerial economics, marketing, strategic management.

M Acc—Master of Accountancy Part-time. At least 30 total credits required. 24 to 36 months to complete program. *Concentrations:* accounting.

M Phil—Master of Philosophy in Business Administration Full-time and part-time. At least 24 total credits required. 24 to 60 months to complete program. *Concentrations:* accounting, decision sciences, finance, international business, management, managerial economics, marketing.

M Sc—Master of Science in Business Economics Program Part-time. 27 to 33 total credits required. Maximum of 19 months to complete program. *Concentrations:* managerial economics.

M Sc—Master of Science in Finance Part-time. At least 30 total credits required. Maximum of 24 months to complete program. *Concentrations:* finance.

M Sc—Master of Science in Information and Technology Management Program Part-time. 27 to 33 total credits required. Maximum of 19 months to complete program. *Concentrations:* management information systems.

M Sc—Master of Science in International Business Program Part-time. At least 30 total credits required. Maximum of 24 months to complete program. *Concentrations:* international business.

MBA—Three-Year MBA Program Part-time. Minimum of 3 years of post-qualification work experience required. At least 54 total credits required. 24 to 60 months to complete program. *Concentrations:* accounting, decision sciences, finance, international business, management, managerial economics, marketing.

MBA—Two-Year MBA Program Full-time. At least 54 total credits required. 20 to 60 months to complete program. *Concentrations:* accounting, decision sciences, finance, international business, management, managerial economics, marketing.

RESOURCES AND SERVICES

Information about online services, personal computer policies, library resources, international exchange programs, internship programs, and placement services at this institution and others can be found at **www. petersons.com/mba**

International Students

Services and Facilities Counseling/support services, international student housing, visa services. Financial aid is not available to international students.
International Student Contact Ms. Lauren Lee, Admissions Coordinator, Shatin, NT, Hong Kong. **Phone:** 2-609-7786. **Fax:** 2-603-6289. **E-mail:** laurenlee@cuhk.edu.hk.

■ APPLICATION

Application Contact Ms. Lauren Lee, Admissions Coordinator, Shatin, NT, Hong Kong. **Phone:** 2-609-7786. **Fax:** 2-603-6289. **E-mail:** laurenlee@cuhk.edu.hk.

City University of Hong Kong

Hong Kong SAR, China

FACULTY OF BUSINESS

Graduate Business Faculty
Full-time: 160

Part-time: 20

Student Body
Total: 3,371
Full-time: 2,551
Part-time: 820

Average Age: 30
Women: 40%

Admissions

Applications: 461
Admitted: 222

Enrolled
Average

Costs (1999–2000)
Full-time tuition: 42,500 Hong Kong dollars
Part-time tuition: 9900 Hong Kong dollars

DEGREES EMBA • MBA

EMBA—Executive Master of Business Administration Part-time. At least credits required. Minimum of 24 months to complete program. *Concentrations:* Chinese business studies.

MBA—Interactive MBA Part-time. *Distance learning option.* At least 43 total credits required. 18 to 72 months to complete program. *Concentrations:* electronic commerce (e-commerce), management.

MBA—MBA Part-time. At least 43 total credits required. Minimum of 24 months to complete program. *Concentrations:* electronic commerce (e-commerce), human resources, management, marketing, real estate.

COSTS

Tuition *Full-time:* 42,500 Hong Kong dollars. *Part-time:* 9900 Hong Kong dollars per course. Tuition varies by number of courses or credits taken and academic program.

RESOURCES AND SERVICES

Information about online services, personal computer policies, library resources, international exchange programs, internship programs, and placement services at this institution and others can be found at **www. petersons.com/mba**

International Students

Services and Facilities Counseling/support services, international student organization, orientation. Financial aid is not available to international students.
Applying *Recommended:* TOEFL with recommended score of 550 (paper).
International Student Contact Ms. Anita Chan, Executive Officer I, 83 Tat Chee Avenue, Kowloon, Hong Kong SAR, China. **Phone:** 852-2788-8332. **Fax:** 852-2788-7182. **E-mail:** fbachan@cityu.edu.hk.

■ APPLICATION

Required GMAT, application form, baccalaureate/first degree, interview, personal statement, 3 years of work experience. **Recommended** Resume/curriculum vitae, transcripts of college work.

Deadlines and Fees *Application fee:* 140 Hong Kong dollars.

Application Contact Ms. Stephanie NG, Executive Officer II, 83 Tat Chee Avenue, Kowloon, Hong Kong SAR, China. **Phone:** 852-2194-2658. **Fax:** 852-2788-7182. **E-mail:** fbsng@cityu.edu.hk.

Fudan University

Shanghai, China

SCHOOL OF MANAGEMENT

DEGREE MBA

MBA—Master of Business Administration

RESOURCES AND SERVICES

Information about online services, personal computer policies, library resources, international exchange programs, internship programs, and placement services at this institution and others can be found at **www. petersons.com/mba**

■ APPLICATION

Hong Kong Baptist University

Kowloon Tong, Hong Kong, China

SCHOOL OF BUSINESS

Graduate Business Faculty
Full-time: 25

Student Body
Total: 85
Part-time: 85

Average Age: 31
Women: 54%

Admissions
Applications: 125
Admitted: 83

Enrolled: 41
Average GMAT: 500

Costs (1999–2000)
Full-time tuition: N/R

business studies, international business, management science, marketing, production management.

MBA/LL B—Master of Business Administration/Bachelor of Laws Full-time. Must apply separately to Faculty of Business and Faculty of Law. 113 to 119 total credits required. 36 to 48 months to complete program. *Concentrations:* business policy/strategy, entrepreneurship, finance, human resources, industrial administration/management, industrial/labor relations, international and area business studies, international business, management science, marketing, production management.

COSTS
Tuition, state resident: *Full-time* $3873 Canadian. *Part-time* $779 Canadian per semester. **Tuition, Canadian resident:** *Full-time* $5700 Canadian. *Part-time* $950 Canadian per semester. **Tuition, international:** *Full-time* $8453 Canadian. Tuition varies by number of courses or credits taken, academic program, and local reciprocity agreements. **Required fees:** *Full-time* $495 Canadian. *Part-time* $58 Canadian per semester. **Graduate housing:** Room and board costs vary by number of occupants, type of accommodation, and type of board plan. *Typical cost:* $4500 Canadian (including board).

FINANCIAL AID (1999–2000)
Research assistantships, scholarships, teaching assistantships, and work study. Financial aid application deadline: 2/1. **Financial Aid Contact** Ms. Alison Samson, Assistant to the Executive Dean, College of Graduate Studies and Research, 401 Sunset Avenue, Windsor, ON N9B 3P4, Canada. **Phone:** 519-253-3000 Ext. 2112. **Fax:** 519-971-3667. **E-mail:** asamson@uwindsor.ca.

RESOURCES AND SERVICES
Information about online services, personal computer policies, library resources, international exchange programs, internship programs, and placement services at this institution and others can be found at **www.petersons.com/mba**

International Students
8% of students enrolled are international students.

Services and Facilities Counseling/support services, international student housing, visa services. Financial aid is not available to international students.
Applying *Required:* TOEFL with recommended score of 600 (paper), proof of adequate funds, proof of health/immunizations.
International Student Contact Mr. Richard Lanspeary, International Students Advisor, 401 Sunset Avenue, Windsor, ON N9B 3P4, Canada. **Phone:** 519-253-4232 Ext. 3901. **Fax:** 519-973-7046. **E-mail:** lanspea@uwindsor.ca.

■ APPLICATION
Required Application form, baccalaureate/first degree, 1 letter of recommendation, resume/curriculum vitae, transcripts of college work. School will accept GMAT. **Recommended** Essay, interview, work experience.
Deadlines and Fees *Deadlines:* 5/1 for fall, 3/1 for fall (international). *Application fee:* $55 Canadian.
Application Contact Mr. Michael Houston, Assistant to Dean, Faculty of Business Administration, 401 Sunset Avenue, Windsor, ON N9B 3P4, Canada. **Phone:** 519-253-4232 Ext. 3097. **Fax:** 519-973-7073. **E-mail:** mikeh@uwindsor.ca.

Wilfrid Laurier University
Waterloo, Ontario, Canada

SCHOOL OF BUSINESS AND ECONOMICS

Graduate Business Faculty

Full-time: 67	Part-time: 7

Student Body

Total: 349	Average Age: 33
Full-time: 87	Women: 38%
Part-time: 262	

Admissions

Applications: 447	Average GMAT: 590
Admitted: 265	Average GPA: 9/12 scale
Enrolled: 199	

Costs (1999–2000)
Full-time tuition: $9118 Canadian per academic year (resident), $14,272 Canadian per academic year (nonresident)
Part-time tuition: $1102 Canadian per term (resident)

After Graduation (Class of 1998–99)
Employed within 3 months of graduation: 90%
Average starting salary: $58,800 Canadian

DEGREES MA • MBA

MA—Master of Arts in Business Economics Full-time. 12 to 18 months to complete program.
MBA—On-Campus MBA Full-time and part-time. Minimum 2 years full-time work experience. At least 20 total credits required. 12 to 60 months to complete program.
MBA—Toronto-Based MBA Part-time. Minimum 2 years full-time work experience. At least 20 total credits required. 39 to 48 months to complete program.
MBA—Master of Business Administration Part-time. Minimum 2 years full-time work experience. At least 20 total credits required. Minimum of 39 months to complete program.

COSTS
Tuition, state resident: *Full-time* $8001 Canadian. *Part-time* $1041 Canadian per term. **Tuition, Canadian resident:** *Full-time* $13,155 Canadian. **Required fees:** *Full-time* $1117 Canadian. *Part-time* $61 Canadian per term. Tuition and fees vary by number of courses or credits taken, campus location, and academic program. **Graduate housing:** Room and board costs vary by number of occupants, type of accommodation, and type of board plan. *Typical cost:* $8100 Canadian (including board).

FINANCIAL AID (1999–2000)
30 students received aid, including fellowships, loans, research assistantships, scholarships, and teaching assistantships. Aid is available to part-time students. Financial aid application deadline: 11/1. **Financial Aid Contact** Pauline Delion, Director of Student Awards, 75 University Avenue West, Waterloo, ON N2L 3C5, Canada. **Phone:** 519-884-0710 Ext. 4256. **E-mail:** pdelion@mach2.wlu.ca.

RESOURCES AND SERVICES
Information about online services, personal computer policies, library resources, international exchange programs, internship programs, and placement services at this institution and others can be found at **www.petersons.com/mba**

International Students
1% of students enrolled are international students.

Services and Facilities Counseling/support services, international student housing, international student organization, visa services. Financial aid is available to international students.
Applying *Required:* TOEFL with recommended score of 550 (paper).
International Student Contact Dr. Al Hecht, Director of Laurier International, 75 University Avenue West, Waterloo, ON N2L 3C5, Canada. **Phone:** 519-884-0710 Ext. 6704. **Fax:** 519-886-4507. **E-mail:** ahecht@wlu.ca.

■ APPLICATION
Required GMAT, application form, baccalaureate/first degree, 3 letters of recommendation, personal statement, resume/curriculum vitae, transcripts of college work, 2 years of work experience. **Recommended** Essay.
Deadlines and Fees *Deadlines:* 5/1 for fall, 5/1 for fall (international). *Application fee:* $100 Canadian.
Application Contact Dianne Hotson, Administrator, 75 University Avenue West, Waterloo, ON N2L 3C5, Canada. **Phone:** 519-884-0710 Ext. 2142. **Fax:** 519-886-6978. **E-mail:** wlumba@wlu.ca.

See full description on page 1016.

York University
Toronto, Ontario, Canada

SCHULICH SCHOOL OF BUSINESS

Graduate Business Faculty

Full-time: 82	Part-time: 111

Student Body

Total: 1,409	Average Age: 29.9
Full-time: 712	Women: 40%
Part-time: 697	

Admissions

Applications: 2,059	Average GMAT: 640
Admitted: 965	Average GPA: 3.3
Enrolled: 630	

Costs (1999–2000)
Full-time tuition: $5000 Canadian per academic year (resident)
Part-time tuition: $2000 Canadian per term (resident), $4300 Canadian per term (nonresident)

York University (continued)

After Graduation (Class of 1998–99)
Employed within 3 months of graduation: 94%
Average starting salary: $81,000 Canadian

DEGREES IMBA • MBA • MBA/LL B • MBA/MA • MPA

IMBA—International Master of Business Administration Full-time. International experience, advanced foreign language skills required. At least 72 total credits required. 24 months to complete program. *Concentrations:* accounting, arts administration/management, business ethics, economics, electronic commerce (e-commerce), entrepreneurship, finance, financial management/planning, industrial/labor relations, information management, international business, management information systems, management science, marketing, nonprofit management, operations management, organizational behavior/development, public management, quantitative analysis, real estate, strategic management, financial engineering.

MBA—Master of Business Administration Full-time and part-time. At least 60 total credits required. 8 to 72 months to complete program. *Concentrations:* accounting, arts administration/management, business ethics, economics, electronic commerce (e-commerce), entrepreneurship, finance, financial management/planning, industrial/labor relations, information management, international business, management information systems, management science, marketing, nonprofit management, operations management, organizational behavior/development, public management, quantitative analysis, real estate, strategic management, financial engineering.

MBA/LL B—Master of Business Administration/Bachelor of Laws Full-time. At least 122 total credits required. 72 months to complete program. *Concentrations:* international business, management information systems, management science, nonprofit management, operations management, organizational behavior/development, public management, quantitative analysis, real estate, strategic management.

MBA/MA—Master of Business Administration/Master of Arts in Fine Arts Full-time. Four-year undergraduate degree in Fine Arts and relevant work experience in arts/cultural industries required. At least 75 total credits required. Minimum of 36 months to complete program. *Concentrations:* accounting, arts administration/management, business ethics, economics, electronic commerce (e-commerce), entrepreneurship, finance, financial management/planning, industrial/labor relations, information management, international and area business studies, international business, management information systems, management science, marketing, nonprofit management, operations management, organizational behavior/development, public management, quantitative analysis, real estate, strategic management, financial engineering.

MPA—Master of Public Administration Full-time and part-time. At least 60 total credits required. 12 to 72 months to complete program. *Concentrations:* economics, organizational behavior/development, public management, public policy and administration.

COSTS

Tuition, state resident: *Full-time* $5000 Canadian. *Part-time* $2000 Canadian per term. **Tuition, Canadian resident:** *Part-time* $4300 Canadian per term. **Tuition, international:** *Full-time* $10,000 Canadian. **Required fees:** Fees vary by number of courses or credits taken. **Graduate housing:** Room and board costs vary by number of occupants, type of accommodation, and type of board plan. *Typical cost:* $5000 Canadian (room only).

FINANCIAL AID (1999–2000)
Fellowships, grants, loans, research assistantships, scholarships, and teaching assistantships. Financial aid application deadline: 6/1.
Financial Aid Contact Ms. Anne Caulfield, Financial Officer, Schulich School of Business, 4700 Keele Street, Toronto, ON M3J 1P3, Canada. **Phone:** 416-736-2100 Ext. 30515. **Fax:** 416-650-8174. **E-mail:** acaulfield@schulich.yorku.ca.

RESOURCES AND SERVICES
Information about online services, personal computer policies, library resources, international exchange programs, internship programs, and placement services at this institution and others can be found at **www.petersons.com/mba**

International Students

Services and Facilities Counseling/support services, ESL/language courses, international student housing, orientation, visa services. Financial aid is not available to international students.
Applying *Required:* TOEFL with recommended score of 600 (paper). *Recommended:* Proof of adequate funds, proof of health/immunizations.
International Student Contact Ms. Kimberly Paterson, Assistant Director, International Relations, Schulich School of Business, 4700 Keele Street, Toronto, ON M3J 1P3, Canada. **Phone:** 416-736-2100. **Fax:** 416-650-8174. **E-mail:** intladmissions@schulich.yorku.ca.

■ **APPLICATION**
Required GMAT, application form, baccalaureate/first degree, 2 letters of recommendation, personal statement, resume/curriculum vitae, transcripts of college work. **Recommended** 2 years of work experience.
Deadlines and Fees *Deadlines:* 5/1 for fall, 10/15 for winter, 4/1 for fall (international), 8/15 for winter (international). *Application fee:* $125 Canadian.
Application Contact Ms. Carol Pattenden, Assistant Director, Admissions, Schulich School of Business, 4700 Keele Street, Toronto, ON M3J 1P3, Canada. **Phone:** 416-736-5060. **Fax:** 416-650-8174. **E-mail:** cpattend@schulich.yorku.ca.

See full description on page 1026.

CAYMAN ISLANDS

International College of the Cayman Islands

Newlands, Cayman Islands

GRADUATE PROGRAM IN MANAGEMENT

Graduate Business Faculty

Full-time: 6	Part-time: 5

Student Body

Total: 35	Average Age: 36
Full-time: 11	Women: 77%
Part-time: 24	

Costs (1999–2000)
Full-time tuition: $3000 per academic year
Part-time tuition: $100 per credit

DEGREES MBA • MS

MBA—Master of Business Administration Full-time and part-time. At least 60 total credits required. Minimum of 18 months to complete program.

MS—Master of Science in Management Full-time and part-time. At least 60 total credits required. Minimum of 18 months to complete program. *Concentrations:* business education, human resources.

COSTS

Tuition *Full-time:* $3000. *Part-time:* $100 per credit. **Graduate housing:** Room and board costs vary by number of occupants. *Typical cost:* $2438 (room only).

FINANCIAL AID (1999–2000)
Financial Aid Contact Mrs. Diane Levy, Admissions Representative, PO Box 136, Savannah Post Office, Grand Cayman, Cayman Islands. **Phone:** 345-947-1100. **Fax:** 345-947-1210.

RESOURCES AND SERVICES
Information about online services, personal computer policies, library resources, international exchange programs, internship programs, and placement services at this institution and others can be found at **www.petersons.com/mba**

International Students
83% of students enrolled are international students.

Services and Facilities Counseling/support services, ESL/language courses, international student housing.
Applying *Required:* TOEFL with recommended score of 550 (paper).
International Student Contact Mrs. Diane Levy, Admissions Representative, Newlands, Cayman Islands. **Phone:** 345-947-1100. **Fax:** 345-947-1210.

■ **APPLICATION**
Required Application form, baccalaureate/first degree, essay, 3 letters of recommendation, transcripts of college work. School will accept GMAT. **Recommended** Work experience.
Deadlines and Fees Applications for domestic students are processed on a rolling basis. *Deadlines:* 6/15 for fall (international), 10/1 for winter (international), 1/1 for spring (international), 3/15 for summer (international). *Application fee:* $38.
Application Contact Dr. Eileen Dounce, Director of Graduate Studies, PO Box 136, Savannah Post Office, Grand Cayman, Cayman Islands. **Phone:** 345-947-1100. **Fax:** 345-947-1210.

CHINA

The Chinese University of Hong Kong

Shatin, Hong Kong, China

FACULTY OF BUSINESS ADMINISTRATION

Accreditation
AACSB—The International Association for Management Education

DEGREES EMBA • M Acc • M Phil • M Sc • MBA

EMBA—Executive MBA Part-time. At least 54 total credits required. 24 to 48 months to complete program. *Concentrations:* decision sciences, finance, leadership, management, managerial economics, marketing, strategic management.

M Acc—Master of Accountancy Part-time. At least 30 total credits required. 24 to 36 months to complete program. *Concentrations:* accounting.

M Phil—Master of Philosophy in Business Administration Full-time and part-time. At least 24 total credits required. 24 to 60 months to complete program. *Concentrations:* accounting, decision sciences, finance, international business, management, managerial economics, marketing.

M Sc—Master of Science in Business Economics Program Part-time. 27 to 33 total credits required. Maximum of 19 months to complete program. *Concentrations:* managerial economics.

M Sc—Master of Science in Finance Part-time. At least 30 total credits required. Maximum of 24 months to complete program. *Concentrations:* finance.

M Sc—Master of Science in Information and Technology Management Program Part-time. 27 to 33 total credits required. Maximum of 19 months to complete program. *Concentrations:* management information systems.

M Sc—Master of Science in International Business Program Part-time. At least 30 total credits required. Maximum of 24 months to complete program. *Concentrations:* international business.

MBA—Three-Year MBA Program Part-time. Minimum of 3 years of post-qualification work experience required. At least 54 total credits required. 24 to 60 months to complete program. *Concentrations:* accounting, decision sciences, finance, international business, management, managerial economics, marketing.

MBA—Two-Year MBA Program Full-time. At least 54 total credits required. 20 to 60 months to complete program. *Concentrations:* accounting, decision sciences, finance, international business, management, managerial economics, marketing.

RESOURCES AND SERVICES
Information about online services, personal computer policies, library resources, international exchange programs, internship programs, and placement services at this institution and others can be found at **www.petersons.com/mba**

International Students
Services and Facilities Counseling/support services, international student housing, visa services. Financial aid is not available to international students.
International Student Contact Ms. Lauren Lee, Admissions Coordinator, Shatin, NT, Hong Kong. **Phone:** 2-609-7786. **Fax:** 2-603-6289. **E-mail:** laurenlee@cuhk.edu.hk.

■ APPLICATION
Application Contact Ms. Lauren Lee, Admissions Coordinator, Shatin, NT, Hong Kong. **Phone:** 2-609-7786. **Fax:** 2-603-6289. **E-mail:** laurenlee@cuhk.edu.hk.

City University of Hong Kong

Hong Kong SAR, China

FACULTY OF BUSINESS

Graduate Business Faculty
Full-time: 160

Part-time: 20

Student Body
Total: 3,371
Full-time: 2,551
Part-time: 820

Average Age: 30
Women: 40%

Admissions

Applications: 461
Admitted: 222

Enrolled: 166
Average GMAT: 570

Costs (1999–2000)
Full-time tuition: 42,500 Hong Kong dollars per academic year
Part-time tuition: 9900 Hong Kong dollars per course

DEGREES EMBA • MBA

EMBA—Executive Master of Business Administration Part-time. At least 44 total credits required. Minimum of 24 months to complete program. *Concentrations:* Chinese business studies.

MBA—Interactive MBA Part-time. *Distance learning option.* At least 43 total credits required. 18 to 72 months to complete program. *Concentrations:* electronic commerce (e-commerce), management.

MBA—MBA Part-time. At least 43 total credits required. Minimum of 24 months to complete program. *Concentrations:* electronic commerce (e-commerce), human resources, management, marketing, real estate.

COSTS
Tuition *Full-time:* 42,500 Hong Kong dollars. *Part-time:* 9900 Hong Kong dollars per course. Tuition varies by number of courses or credits taken and academic program.

RESOURCES AND SERVICES
Information about online services, personal computer policies, library resources, international exchange programs, internship programs, and placement services at this institution and others can be found at **www.petersons.com/mba**

International Students
Services and Facilities Counseling/support services, international student organization, orientation. Financial aid is not available to international students.
Applying *Recommended:* TOEFL with recommended score of 550 (paper).
International Student Contact Ms. Anita Chan, Executive Officer I, 83 Tat Chee Avenue, Kowloon, Hong Kong SAR, China. **Phone:** 852-2788-8332. **Fax:** 852-2788-7182. **E-mail:** fbachan@cityu.edu.hk.

■ APPLICATION
Required GMAT, application form, baccalaureate/first degree, interview, personal statement, 3 years of work experience. **Recommended** Resume/curriculum vitae, transcripts of college work.

Deadlines and Fees *Application fee:* 140 Hong Kong dollars.

Application Contact Ms. Stephanie NG, Executive Officer II, 83 Tat Chee Avenue, Kowloon, Hong Kong SAR, China. **Phone:** 852-2194-2658. **Fax:** 852-2788-7182. **E-mail:** fbsng@cityu.edu.hk.

Fudan University

Shanghai, China

SCHOOL OF MANAGEMENT

DEGREE MBA

MBA—Master of Business Administration

RESOURCES AND SERVICES
Information about online services, personal computer policies, library resources, international exchange programs, internship programs, and placement services at this institution and others can be found at **www.petersons.com/mba**

■ APPLICATION

Hong Kong Baptist University

Kowloon Tong, Hong Kong, China

SCHOOL OF BUSINESS

Graduate Business Faculty
Full-time: 25

Student Body
Total: 85
Part-time: 85

Average Age: 31
Women: 54%

Admissions
Applications: 125
Admitted: 83

Enrolled: 41
Average GMAT: 500

Costs (1999–2000)
Full-time tuition: N/R

Hong Kong Baptist University (continued)

Part-time tuition: 54,000 Hong Kong dollars per year (resident), 54,000 Hong Kong dollars per year (nonresident)

DEGREE MBA

MBA—Master of Business Administration Part-time. At least 37 total credits required. Maximum of 24 months to complete program. *Concentrations:* accounting, business law, Chinese business studies, decision sciences, economics, entrepreneurship, finance, financial management/planning, human resources, international business, management, management information systems, marketing, operations management, organizational behavior/development, quality management, quantitative analysis, strategic management, taxation.

COSTS

Tuition, state resident: *Part-time* 54,000 Hong Kong dollars per year. **Tuition, nonresident:** *Part-time* 54,000 Hong Kong dollars per year.

FINANCIAL AID (1999–2000)

Scholarships. **Financial Aid Contact** Ms. Ice Or, Admissions, Scholarship and Financial Aid Section, Academic Registry, HSC Campus, HKBU, Kowloon Tong, Hong Kong SAR, China. **Phone:** 2339-7942. **Fax:** 2339-7942.

RESOURCES AND SERVICES

Information about online services, personal computer policies, library resources, international exchange programs, internship programs, and placement services at this institution and others can be found at **www.petersons.com/mba**

International Students

1% of students enrolled are international students.

Services and Facilities Counseling/support services, international student housing. Financial aid is not available to international students.
International Student Contact Mr. Benny Petty, Assistant Professor, English Department, International Student Exchange Office, Shaw Campus, HKBU, Kowloon Tong, Hong Kong SAR, China. **Phone:** 2339-5347. **Fax:** 2339-5347. **E-mail:** blpetty@hkbu.edu.hk.

■ APPLICATION

Required GMAT, application form, baccalaureate/first degree, interview, 2 letters of recommendation, resume/curriculum vitae, transcripts of college work, 2 years of work experience.

Deadlines and Fees *Deadlines:* 5/15 for fall, 5/15 for fall (international). *Application fee:* 150 Hong Kong dollars.

Application Contact Ms. Cecilia Tsui, Executive Officer—Research and Postgraduate Studies Section, Academic Registry, Kowloon Tong, Hong Kong SAR, China. **Phone:** 2339-7929. **Fax:** 2339-7929. **E-mail:** postgrad@hkbu.edu.hk.

busd@hkbu.edu.hk

 35

The Hong Kong University of Science and Technology

Kowloon, Hong Kong, China

SCHOOL OF BUSINESS AND MANAGEMENT

DEGREES EMBA • M Phil • MBA • MBA/MS • MS

EMBA—Executive Master of Business Administration Part-time. 10 years of work experience required. At least 32 total credits required. 16 months to complete program.
M Phil—Master of Philosophy Full-time and part-time. At least 18 total credits required. 24 to 60 months to complete program. *Concentrations:* accounting, economics, finance, information management, management, marketing, system management.
MBA—Master of Business Administration Full-time and part-time. One year of work experience for full-time, three years for part-time required. 46 to 56 total credits required. 24 to 60 months to complete program. *Concentrations:* Asian business studies, information management.
MBA/MS—MBA/MS in Information Systems Management Part-time. 3 years of work experience required. At least 60 total credits required. 36 to 60 months to complete program. *Concentrations:* Asian business studies, information management.

MBA/MS—MBA/MS in Investment Management Part-time. 3 years of work experience required. At least 66 total credits required. 36 to 60 months to complete program. *Concentrations:* Asian business studies, information management.
MS—Master of Science in Economics Full-time and part-time. At least 36 total credits required. 18 to 60 months to complete program.
MS—Master of Science in Information Systems Management Part-time. At least 30 total credits required. 24 to 60 months to complete program.
MS—Master of Science in Investment Management Part-time. At least 33 total credits required. 24 to 60 months to complete program.

RESOURCES AND SERVICES

Information about online services, personal computer policies, library resources, international exchange programs, internship programs, and placement services at this institution and others can be found at **www.petersons.com/mba**

International Students

Services and Facilities Counseling/support services, visa services. Financial aid is available to international students.
International Student Contact Ms. Doris Chan, Placement Officer, School of Business and Management, Clear Water Bay, Kowloon, Hong Kong. **Phone:** 2-358-7534. **Fax:** 2-705-9596. **E-mail:** bmsdoris@ust.hk.

■ APPLICATION

Application Contact Ms. Pui Hung Mak, Executive Officer, School of Business and Management, Clear Water Bay, Kowloon, Hong Kong. **Phone:** 2-358-7537. **Fax:** 2-705-9596. **E-mail:** hkustmba@ust.hk.

36

University of Hong Kong

Hong Kong, China

UNIVERSITY OF HONG KONG SCHOOL OF BUSINESS

Graduate Business Faculty

Full-time: 25	Part-time: 6

Student Body

Total: 190	Average Age: 28
Part-time: 190	Women: 24%

Costs (1999–2000)
Full-time tuition: N/R
Part-time tuition: 78,600 Hong Kong dollars per year (resident), 78,600 Hong Kong dollars per year (nonresident)

DEGREE MBA

MBA—Master of Business Administration Part-time. 20 to 48 months to complete program.

COSTS

Tuition, state resident: *Part-time* 78,600 Hong Kong dollars per year. **Tuition, nonresident:** *Part-time* 78,600 Hong Kong dollars per year.

FINANCIAL AID (1999–2000)

Financial Aid Contact Program Director, Pokfulam Road, Hong Kong, China. **Phone:** 2-859-1021. **Fax:** 2-858-5614.

RESOURCES AND SERVICES

Information about online services, personal computer policies, library resources, international exchange programs, internship programs, and placement services at this institution and others can be found at **www.petersons.com/mba**

International Students

Services and Facilities Financial aid is not available to international students.
Applying *Required:* TOEFL with recommended score of 550 (paper).

■ APPLICATION

Required GMAT, application form, baccalaureate/first degree, essay, interview, letter(s) of recommendation, personal statement, transcripts of college work, 3 years of work experience.

Deadlines and Fees *Deadlines:* 4/30 for fall, 4/30 for fall (international). *Application fee:* 150 Hong Kong dollars.

Application Contact Program Director, Pokfulam Road, Hong Kong, China. **Phone:** 2-859-1021. **Fax:** 2-858-5614.

business.hku.hk

27 # COSTA RICA

Instituto Centroamericano de Administración de Empresas

La Garita, Costa Rica

MBA PROGRAM

Graduate Business Faculty
Full-time: 35

Student Body
Total: 306
Full-time: 261
Part-time: 45

Average Age: 29
Women: 24%

Admissions
Applications: 475
Admitted: 298

Enrolled: 261
Average GMAT: 580

Costs (1999–2000)
Full-time tuition: $14,000 per academic year
Part-time tuition: N/R

DEGREES EMBA • MBA

EMBA—Executive MBA Part-time. 10 years managerial experience. Minimum of 16 months to complete program.

MBA—Master of Business Administration Full-time. 2 years work experience. 16 to 21 months to complete program. *Concentrations:* economics, technology management.

COSTS

Tuition *Full-time:* $11,500. Tuition varies by campus location and academic program. **Required fees:** *Full-time* $2500.

FINANCIAL AID (1999–2000)

Grants, loans, and scholarships. **Financial Aid Contact** Dean, Apartado Postal 960-4050, Alajuela, Costa Rica. **Phone:** 6-443-0506.

RESOURCES AND SERVICES

Information about online services, personal computer policies, library resources, international exchange programs, internship programs, and placement services at this institution and others can be found at **www.petersons.com/mba**

International Students

85% of students enrolled are international students.

Services and Facilities Counseling/support services, housing location assistance, orientation, visa services. Financial aid is available to international students.

Applying *Required:* TOEFL, proof of adequate funds, proof of health/immunizations.

International Student Contact Anastasia Mora, Student Affairs Coordinator, Apartado Postal 960-4050, Alajuela, Costa Rica. **Phone:** 506-437-2388. **Fax:** 506-433-9045. **E-mail:** moraa@mail.incae.ac.cr. *← doesn't work*

■ APPLICATION

Required GMAT or GRE, application form, baccalaureate/first degree, essay, interview, 3 letters of recommendation, personal statement, resume/curriculum vitae, transcripts of college work, 2 years of work experience.

Deadlines and Fees Applications for domestic and international students are processed on a rolling basis. *Application fee:* $50, $50 (international).

Application Contact María Enriqueta Stadthagen, MBA Marketing Director, Apartado Postal 960-4050, Alajuela, Costa Rica. **Phone:** 505-265-8141. **Fax:** 505-265-8617.

28 # CZECH REPUBLIC

CMC Graduate School of Business

Celákovice, Czech Republic

BUSINESS PROGRAMS

Graduate Business Faculty
Full-time: 6

Part-time: 15

Student Body
Total: 200
Full-time: 20
Part-time: 180

Average Age: 29
Women: 25%

Admissions
Applications: 80
Admitted: 65

Enrolled: 60
Average GMAT: 544

Costs (1999–2000)
Full-time tuition: N/R
Part-time tuition: $500 per course (resident)

DEGREES IEMBA • MBA

IEMBA—Executive MBA Part-time. 5 years of managerial experience. At least 51 total credits required. Minimum of 15 months to complete program.

MBA—Master of Business Administration Full-time and part-time. 2 years of experience. At least 60 total credits required. 13 to 30 months to complete program. *Concentrations:* finance, international business, international finance, international marketing, marketing.

COSTS

Tuition, state resident: *Part-time* $500 per course. Tuition varies by class time, number of courses or credits taken, and academic program. **Graduate housing:** Room and board costs vary by number of occupants and type of board plan. *Typical cost:* $2700 (including board).

FINANCIAL AID (1999–2000)

1 student received aid, including loans and scholarships. **Financial Aid Contact** Ms. Kristyna Vejtasova, Director of MBA Programs, namesti 5, kvetna 2, Celakovice, 250 88, Czech Republic. **Phone:** 420-202-899 145. **Fax:** 420-202-891 997. **E-mail:** vejtas@cmc.cz.

RESOURCES AND SERVICES

Information about online services, personal computer policies, library resources, international exchange programs, internship programs, and placement services at this institution and others can be found at **www.petersons.com/mba**

International Students

8% of students enrolled are international students.

Services and Facilities Counseling/support services, ESL/language courses, international student housing, visa services. Financial aid is not available to international students.

Applying *Required:* TOEFL with recommended score of 550 (paper).

International Student Contact MBA Office, namesti 5, kvetna 2, Celakovice, 250 88, Czech Republic. **Phone:** 420-202-899 146. **Fax:** 420-202-892 150. **E-mail:** mbaoff@cmc.cz.

■ APPLICATION

Required GMAT, application form, baccalaureate/first degree, essay, interview, 2 letters of recommendation, personal statement, resume/curriculum vitae, transcripts of college work, 2 years of work experience.

Deadlines and Fees Applications for domestic and international students are processed on a rolling basis. *Application fee:* $65, $65 (international).

Application Contact Ms. Jitka Pavlicova, MBA Office, namesti 5, kvetna 2, Celakovice, 250 88, Czech Republic. **Phone:** 420-202-899 146. **Fax:** 420-202-892 150. **E-mail:** mbaoff@cmc.cz.

DENMARK

Copenhagen Business School

Copenhagen N, Denmark

FACULTY OF ECONOMICS AND BUSINESS ADMINISTRATION

Graduate Business Faculty
Full-time: 220   Part-time: 806

Student Body
Total: 5,201   Average Age: 27
Full-time: 3,228   Women: 33%
Part-time: 1,973

Costs (1999–2000)
Full-time tuition: N/R
Part-time tuition: N/R

After Graduation (Class of 1998–99)
Employed within 3 months of graduation: 85%

DEGREES MBA • MS

MBA—Global eCommerce Masters Minimum of 3 years of relevant full-time work experience and proficiency in English required. 16 months to complete program.

MBA—Global eCommerce Masters Minimum of 3 years of relevant full-time work experience and proficiency in English required. 16 months to complete program. *Concentrations:* electronic commerce (e-commerce), organizational behavior/development, organizational management.

MBA—Master of Business Administration in Public Administration Part-time. Minimum of 5 years of relevant full-time work experience and proficiency in Danish and English required. 24 months to complete program. *Concentrations:* economics, management, organizational behavior/development, public management, public policy and administration, strategic management.

MBA—Master of Management Development Minimum of 3 years of relevant full-time work experience and proficiency in Danish and English required. 24 months to complete program. *Concentrations:* management.

MBA—Master of Business Administration Part-time. Minimum of 5 years of relevant full-time work experience and proficiency in Danish and English required. 24 months to complete program. *Concentrations:* finance, international business, international management, logistics, management, marketing, organizational management, strategic management.

MS—Master of Science in Business Administration and Commercial Law Full-time. Proficiency in Danish required. 24 to 70 months to complete program. *Concentrations:* business law, economics, finance, organizational behavior/development, taxation.

MS—Master of Science in Business Administration and Computer Science Full-time. Proficiency in Danish required. 24 to 70 months to complete program. *Concentrations:* economics, information management, management information systems, organizational behavior/development, project management.

MS—Master of Science in Business Administration and Management Science Full-time. Proficiency in Danish required. 24 to 70 months to complete program. *Concentrations:* economics, finance, management science, management systems analysis, marketing research, quantitative analysis.

MS—Master of Science in Business Administration and Modern Language Full-time. Proficiency in English and German or French or Spanish or Russian or Japanese required. 24 to 70 months to complete program. *Concentrations:* developmental economics, international and area business studies, international business, international management.

MS—Master of Science in Business Administration and Philosophy Full-time. Proficiency in Danish required. 24 to 70 months to complete program. *Concentrations:* business ethics, business policy/strategy, economics, management.

MS—Master of Science in Business Economics and Auditing Full-time. Proficiency in Danish required. 24 to 70 months to complete program. *Concentrations:* accounting, business law, taxation.

MS—Master of Science in Economics and Business Administration Full-time. Proficiency in Danish and/or English required. 24 to 70 months to complete program. *Concentrations:* economics, finance, human resources, international business, international economics, international logistics, international management, international marketing, organizational behavior/development, organizational management, strategic management, supply chain management, technology management.

COSTS
Tuition varies by academic program.

RESOURCES AND SERVICES
Information about online services, personal computer policies, library resources, international exchange programs, internship programs, and placement services at this institution and others can be found at www.petersons.com/mba

International Students
10% of students enrolled are international students.

Services and Facilities Counseling/support services, ESL/language courses, housing location assistance, international student housing. Financial aid is not available to international students.

Applying *Required:* TOEFL with recommended score of 230 (computer) or 575 (paper). *Recommended:* IELT with recommended score of 7.

International Student Contact Ms. Robin Jensen, Head of International Office, Dalgas Have 15, Frederiksberg, 2000, Denmark. **Phone:** 45-381-3006. **Fax:** 45-381-3825. **E-mail:** reception.intoff@cbs.dk.

■ APPLICATION
Required Application form, baccalaureate/first degree, resume/curriculum vitae, transcripts of college work. School will accept GRE.

Deadlines and Fees *Deadlines:* 6/1 for fall, 5/15 for fall (international).

Application Contact Student Information, Solbjerg Plads 3, Frederiksberg, 2000, Denmark. **Phone:** 45-381-2710. **Fax:** 45-3815-2777. **E-mail:** cm.oefak@cbs.dk.

EGYPT

American University in Cairo

Cairo, Egypt

SCHOOL OF BUSINESS, ECONOMICS AND COMMUNICATION

DEGREES MA • MBA • MPA

MA—Program in Economics Full-time and part-time. GRE required. At least 27 total credits required. 18 to 84 months to complete program. *Concentrations:* economics, financial economics, international economics, quantitative analysis.

MBA—Master of Business Administration Full-time and part-time. 2 years of work experience and GMAT required. 36 to 54 total credits required. 24 to 84 months to complete program. *Concentrations:* business law, international banking, international trade, management, strategic management.

MPA—Master of Public Administration Full-time and part-time. Up to 3 prerequisite courses required. At least 27 total credits required. 18 to 84 months to complete program. *Concentrations:* city/urban administration, environmental economics/management, international and area business studies, public policy and administration, research and development administration, system management.

RESOURCES AND SERVICES
Information about online services, personal computer policies, library resources, international exchange programs, internship programs, and placement services at this institution and others can be found at www.petersons.com/mba

International Students
Services and Facilities Counseling/support services, international student organization, visa services, international graduate programs office. Financial aid is available to international students.

International Student Contact International Graduate Program Coordinator, Office of Graduate Studies and Research, PO Box 2511, 113 Kasr El Aini Street, Cairo, Egypt. **Phone:** 202-357-5530. **Fax:** 202-355-7565. **E-mail:** aucgrad@aucegypt.edu.

■ APPLICATION
Application Contact International Graduate Program Coordinator, Office of Graduate Studies and Research, PO Box 2511, 113 Kasr El Aini Street, Cairo, Egypt. **Phone:** 202-357-5530. **Fax:** 202-355-7565. **E-mail:** aucgrad@aucegypt.edu.

FINLAND

Helsinki School of Economics and Business Administration

Helsinki, Finland

INTERNATIONAL CENTER

DEGREES EMBA • MBA

EMBA—Executive MBA Part-time. At least 42 total credits required. 12 to 48 months to complete program. *Concentrations:* international business, management.

MBA—International MBA Full-time. At least 75 total credits required. Minimum of 12 months to complete program. *Concentrations:* finance, international business, international management.

MBA—Master of Business Administration—Digital Technology Track Full-time. At least 75 total credits required. 16 to 48 months to complete program. *Concentrations:* finance, international business, international management, technology management.

MBA—Part-time Track/International MBA Part-time. At least 75 total credits required. 24 to 36 months to complete program. *Concentrations:* finance, international business, international management.

RESOURCES AND SERVICES

Information about online services, personal computer policies, library resources, international exchange programs, internship programs, and placement services at this institution and others can be found at **www.petersons.com/mba**

International Students

Services and Facilities Counseling/support services, international student housing, visa services. Financial aid is not available to international students.
International Student Contact Ms. Soile Saloranta, Assistant Director, Foreign Relations (MBA Student Exchange), Runeberginkatu 14-16, Helsinki, 00100, Finland. **Phone:** 9-431-38641. **Fax:** 9-431-36413. **E-mail:** salorant@hkkk.fi.

■ APPLICATION

Application Contact Mariliina Rasanen, External Relations Assistant, Runeberginkatu 14-16, Helsinki, 00100, Finland. **Phone:** 9-4313 8224. **Fax:** 9-4313 8613. **E-mail:** mbafi@hkkk.fi.

FRANCE

40

École de Management

Ecully, Ecully Cedex, France

CESMA MBA

Graduate Business Faculty
Full-time: 80	Part-time: 400

Student Body
Total: 128	Part-time: 71
Full-time: 57	Average Age: 31

Admissions
Applications: 355	Enrolled: 126
Admitted: 132	Average GMAT: 600

Costs (1999–2000)
Full-time tuition: 18,000 euros per academic year
Part-time tuition: N/R

After Graduation (Class of 1998–99)
Employed within 3 months of graduation: 85%

DEGREES MBA • MM • MS

MBA—Cesma MBA Full-time and part-time. 12 to 24 months to complete program. *Concentrations:* management.

MM—ESC Lyon Program Full-time. 24 to 36 months to complete program. *Concentrations:* management.

MS—Master of Science in Corporate Finance Full-time. Minimum of 12 months to complete program. *Concentrations:* finance.

MS—Master of Science in Entrepreneurship Full-time. Minimum of 12 months to complete program.

MS—Master of Science in Food Processing Management Full-time. Minimum of 12 months to complete program. *Concentrations:* agribusiness.

MS—Master of Science in Information and Communication Technology Management Full-time. Minimum of 12 months to complete program.

MS—Master of Science in Internal Corporate Legal Management Full-time and part-time. 12 to 24 months to complete program.

MS—Master of Science in International Business-to-Business Marketing Strategy Full-time. Minimum of 12 months to complete program. *Concentrations:* international marketing, marketing.

MS—Master of Science in International Purchasing Management Full-time. Minimum of 12 months to complete program.

MS—Master of Science in Management of Service Companies Full-time and part-time. 12 to 24 months to complete program. *Concentrations:* management.

MS—Master of Science in Technology Management Full-time. Minimum of 12 months to complete program. *Concentrations:* technology management.

COSTS

Tuition *Full-time:* 18,000 euros. **Graduate housing:** Room and board costs vary by campus location and number of occupants. *Typical cost:* 50,000 euros (including board).

FINANCIAL AID (1999–2000)

11 students received aid, including loans and scholarships. Aid is available to part-time students. Financial aid application deadline: 10/31. **Financial Aid Contact** Ms. Jacqueline DelBello, Programs Promotion Coordinator, 23, Avenue Guy de Collongue, BP 174, Lyon Ecully Cedex, 69132, France. **Phone:** 478-337-865. **Fax:** 478-337-866. **E-mail:** cesmamba@em-lyon.com.

RESOURCES AND SERVICES

Information about online services, personal computer policies, library resources, international exchange programs, internship programs, and placement services at this institution and others can be found at **www.petersons.com/mba**

International Students

Services and Facilities Counseling/support services, ESL/language courses, housing location assistance, language tutoring, visa services. Financial aid is available to international students.
Applying *Required:* TOEFL with recommended score of 250 (computer) or 600 (paper).

International Student Contact Ms. Jacqueline DelBello, Programs Promotion Coordinator, 23, Avenue Guy de Collongue, BP 174, Lyon Ecully Cedex, 69132, France. **Phone:** 478-337-865. **Fax:** 478-337-866. **E-mail:** cesmamba@em-lyon.com.

■ APPLICATION

Required Application form, baccalaureate/first degree, interview, 2 letters of recommendation, resume/curriculum vitae, 2 years of work experience. School will accept GMAT.

Deadlines and Fees *Deadlines:* 6/15 for spring, 6/15 for spring (international). *Application fee:* 110 euros.

Application Contact Ms. Jacqueline DelBello, Programs Promotion Coordinator, 23, Avenue Guy de Collongue, Ecully Cedex, 69130, France. **Phone:** 478-337-865. **Fax:** 478-337-866. **E-mail:** cesmamba@em-lyon.com.

See full description on page 640.

41

École Supérieure des Sciences Économiques et Commerciales

Paris la Defense, France

ESSEC BUSINESS SCHOOL

Graduate Business Faculty
Full-time: 90	Part-time: 300

Student Body
Total: 2,630	Average Age: 21
Full-time: 2,500	Women: 40%
Part-time: 130	

Admissions
Applications: 4,072	Enrolled: 493
Admitted: 982	Average GMAT: 620

École Supérieure des Sciences Économiques et Commerciales (continued)

Costs (1999–2000)
Full-time tuition: N/R
Part-time tuition: 158,000 French francs per degree program

After Graduation (Class of 1998–99)
Average starting salary: 235,000 French francs

DEGREES MBA • MS

MBA—ESSEC MBA Full-time. At least 24 total credits required. Minimum of 15 months to complete program. *Concentrations:* accounting, economics, finance, human resources, international business, management, marketing, operations management.

MBA—Executive MBA Part-time. 5 years of work experience required. At least 60 total credits required. Minimum of 22 months to complete program. *Concentrations:* international business, management.

MBA—MBA in International Agrifood Management Full-time. 3 years of work experience required. Minimum of 11 months to complete program.

MBA—MBA in International Hotel Management Full-time. 1 year of work experience in sector required. At least 34 total credits required. Minimum of 22 months to complete program.

MBA—MBA in International Luxury Brand Management Full-time. 3 years of work experience required. Minimum of 11 months to complete program.

MS—MS in Financial Techniques Full-time. 13 months to complete program. *Concentrations:* international finance.

MS—MS in Food Industry Management Full-time. 13 months to complete program. *Concentrations:* agribusiness, agricultural economics, management.

MS—MS in Insurance Finance Full-time. 13 months to complete program.

MS—MS in International Business Law and Management Full-time. 13 months to complete program. *Concentrations:* business law, legal administration, management.

MS—MS in International Supply Management Full-time. 13 months to complete program. *Concentrations:* industrial administration/management, international logistics, international trade, management, materials management.

MS—MS in Logistics Management and Engineering Full-time. 13 months to complete program.

MS—MS in Management of Information Systems and Telecommunications Networks Part-time. 24 months to complete program. *Concentrations:* management information systems, management systems analysis, system management.

MS—MS in Marketing Management Full-time. 13 months to complete program. *Concentrations:* international marketing.

MS—MS in Strategy and Management of International Business Full-time. 13 months to complete program.

MS—MS in Urban Environmental Services Management Full-time. 13 months to complete program. *Concentrations:* city/urban administration, management, public and private management, public management, public policy and administration.

COSTS
Tuition *Part-time:* 158,000 French francs per degree program. Tuition varies by academic program. **Graduate housing:** Room and board costs vary by number of occupants and type of accommodation. *Typical cost:* 10,000 French francs (including board).

FINANCIAL AID (1999–2000)
Financial Aid Contact Mrs. Cecile Gerard, Head of Student Social Services, BP 230 2 Place de la Defense, Paris la Defense, 92053, France. **Phone:** 1-3443-3107. **Fax:** 1-3443-3001.

RESOURCES AND SERVICES
Information about online services, personal computer policies, library resources, international exchange programs, internship programs, and placement services at this institution and others can be found at **www. petersons.com/mba**

International Students
10% of students enrolled are international students.
Services and Facilities Counseling/support services, ESL/language courses, international student housing, international student organization, visa services. Financial aid is not available to international students.
Applying *Required:* TOEFL with recommended score of 500 (paper), proof of adequate funds, proof of health/immunizations.
International Student Contact Mrs. Michele Pekar-Lempereur, Director of MBA Development, Avenue Bernard Hirsch, BP 105, Cergy-Pontoise, 95021, France. **Phone:** 1-3443-3149. **Fax:** 1-3443-3111. **E-mail:** pekar@essec.fr.

■ APPLICATION
Required Application form, baccalaureate/first degree, essay, interview, 2 letters of recommendation, personal statement, resume/curriculum vitae, transcripts of college work, 5 years of work experience. School will accept GMAT and GRE.
Deadlines and Fees *Deadlines:* 6/5 for fall, 11/25 for winter, 6/5 for fall (international), 11/25 for winter (international). *Application fee:* 980 French francs.
Application Contact Mr. Dominique Xardel, International Relations, Avenue Bernard Hirsch, Cergy-Pontoise, 95021, France. **Phone:** 1-3443-3050. **Fax:** 1-3038-9898.

ESCP-EAP European School of Management
Paris, France

SCHOOL OF MANAGEMENT

Graduate Business Faculty
Full-time: 35 — Part-time: 15

Student Body
Total: 44 — Average Age: 31
Full-time: 44 — Women: 27%

Admissions
Admitted: 45 — Average GMAT: 574
Enrolled: 44

Costs (1999–2000)
Full-time tuition: 125,000 French francs per academic year (resident), 125,000 French francs per academic year (nonresident)
Part-time tuition: N/R

After Graduation (Class of 1998–99)
Employed within 3 months of graduation: 95%
Average starting salary: $110,000

DEGREES MBA

MBA—General Management Full-time. At least 60 total credits required. Minimum of 12 months to complete program. *Concentrations:* management.

MBA—International MBA Full-time. Minimum of 12 months to complete program. *Concentrations:* international management, management.

COSTS
Tuition, state resident: *Full-time* 125,000 French francs. **Tuition, nonresident:** *Full-time* 125,000 French francs.

FINANCIAL AID (1999–2000)
Research assistantships. **Financial Aid Contact**

RESOURCES AND SERVICES
Information about online services, personal computer policies, library resources, international exchange programs, internship programs, and placement services at this institution and others can be found at **www. petersons.com/mba**

International Students
89% of students enrolled are international students.
Services and Facilities Counseling/support services, ESL/language courses. Financial aid is not available to international students.
Applying *Required:* TOEFL with recommended score of 600 (paper).
International Student Contact Daniel Rouach, Dean, MBA Program, 6 avenue de la Porte de Champerret, Paris Cedex 17, 75838, France. **Phone:** 1-4409-3332. **Fax:** 1-4409-3335. **E-mail:** drouach@eap.net.

■ APPLICATION
Required GMAT, application form, baccalaureate/first degree, essay, interview, 2 letters of recommendation, personal statement, resume/curriculum vitae, transcripts of college work, 3 years of work experience.
Deadlines and Fees *Deadlines:* 11/1 for fall, 11/1 for fall (international). *Application fee:* 600 French francs.
Application Contact Ms. Brigitte Blandin, MBA Program Coordinator, 6 avenue de la Porte de Champerret, Paris Cedex 17, 75838, France. **Phone:** 1-4409-3331. **Fax:** 1-4409-3335. **E-mail:** bblandin@eap.net.

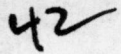

Groupe CERAM

Sophia Antipolis, Sophia Antipolis Cedex, France

CERAM ESC NICE SCHOOL OF MANAGEMENT

DEGREES M Sc • MBA • MSCIB • MSCIF

M Sc—Master of Science in Business Tourism Full-time.

MBA—International MBA Full-time. Minimum 3 years of work experience required. Minimum of 10 months to complete program. *Concentrations:* entrepreneurship, information management, international business, international finance, international management, international marketing, technology management.

MBA—International MBA Part-time. Minimum 3 years of work experience required. At least 54 total credits required. 24 to 36 months to complete program. *Concentrations:* entrepreneurship, information management, international business, international finance, international management, international marketing, technology management.

MSCIB—Master of Science in International Business Full-time. Minimum of 10 months to complete program. *Concentrations:* international business.

MSCIF—Master of Science in International Finance Full-time. Minimum of 10 months to complete program. *Concentrations:* international finance.

RESOURCES AND SERVICES
Information about online services, personal computer policies, library resources, international exchange programs, internship programs, and placement services at this institution and others can be found at **www. petersons.com/mba**

International Students

Services and Facilities Counseling/support services, international student housing, visa services.
International Student Contact Ms. Laurence Descos, Coordinator of International Programs, BP 085, Sophia Antipolis Cedex, 06902, France. **Phone:** 493-954-545. **Fax:** 493-954-524. **E-mail:** laurence.descos@cote-azur.cci.fr.

■ APPLICATION

Application Contact Admissions Office, BP 085, Sophia Antipolis Cedex, 06902, France. **Phone:** 493-9544556. **Fax:** 493-9544529. **E-mail:** mba@ceram.fr.

Groupe ESC Clermont

Clermont-Ferrand, France

CLERMONT GRADUATE SCHOOL OF MANAGEMENT

DEGREE MBA

MBA—Master of Business Administration Full-time. At least 60 total credits required. 27 to 36 months to complete program. *Concentrations:* accounting, entrepreneurship, finance, human resources, international business, management, management information systems, marketing, strategic management.

RESOURCES AND SERVICES
Information about online services, personal computer policies, library resources, international exchange programs, internship programs, and placement services at this institution and others can be found at **www. petersons.com/mba**

International Students

Services and Facilities Financial aid is not available to international students.
International Student Contact Mr. Didier Jourdain, Head of Program, 4 boulevard Trudaine, Clermont-Ferrard, 63037, France. **Phone:** 473-982-424. **Fax:** 473-982-449. **E-mail:** jourdaind@esc-clermont.fr.

■ APPLICATION

Application Contact Michael Bryant, Director of Programs, 4 boulevard Trudaine, Clermont-Ferrard, 63037, France. **Phone:** 473-989-494. **Fax:** 473-982-449. **E-mail:** bryantm@esc-clermont.fr.

Groupe ESC Nantes Atlantique

Nantes, Nantes Cedex 01, France

GROUPE ESC NANTES ATLANTIQUE BUSINESS PROGRAMS

Graduate Business Faculty
Full-time: 44   Part-time: 300

Student Body

Total: 1,279	Average Age: 21
Full-time: 1,210	Women: 50%
Part-time: 69	

Admissions

Applications: 5,936	Enrolled: 506
Admitted: 1,446	

Costs (1999–2000)
Full-time tuition: N/R
Part-time tuition: N/R

After Graduation (Class of 1998–99)
Employed within 3 months of graduation: 94%
Average starting salary: 188,000 French francs

DEGREES MBA • MM

MBA—Euro-MBA *Distance learning option.* At least 18 total credits required. 24 months to complete program.

MBA—MBA in European Management Full-time. English, French and Spanish language fluency required. At least 60 total credits required. 13 months to complete program.

MM—Master of Management Full-time and part-time. At least 120 total credits required. 18 to 24 months to complete program.

RESOURCES AND SERVICES
Information about online services, personal computer policies, library resources, international exchange programs, internship programs, and placement services at this institution and others can be found at **www. petersons.com/mba**

International Students

15% of students enrolled are international students.

Services and Facilities Counseling/support services. Financial aid is not available to international students.
Applying *Required:* Proof of adequate funds. *Recommended:* Proof of health/immunizations.

International Student Contact David Read, Associate Director of International Relations, 8, route de la Joneliere, BP 31222, Nantes Cedex 3, 44312, France. **Phone:** 2-4037-3434. **Fax:** 2-4037-4530. **E-mail:** dread@escna.fr.

■ APPLICATION

Required Application form, baccalaureate/first degree, interview, 2 letters of recommendation, personal statement, resume/curriculum vitae, transcripts of college work. **Recommended** Work experience.

Deadlines and Fees Applications for domestic and international students are processed on a rolling basis. *Application fee:* 700 French francs.

Application Contact David Read, Associate Director of International Relations, 8, route de la Joneliere, BP 31222, Nantes Cedex 3, 44312, France. **Phone:** 2-4037-3434. **Fax:** 2-4037-4530. **E-mail:** dread@escna.fr.

Groupe ESC Toulouse

Toulouse, Toulouse Cedex, France

ESC TOULOUSE GRADUATE SCHOOL OF MANAGEMENT

Graduate Business Faculty
Full-time: 46   Part-time: 70

Student Body

Total: 1,038	Average Age: 24
Full-time: 1,038	Women: 48%

Admissions

Applications: 2,500	Enrolled: 566
Admitted: 629	

Costs (1999–2000)
Full-time tuition: 40,000 French francs per academic year
Part-time tuition: N/R

After Graduation (Class of 1998–99)
Employed within 3 months of graduation: 86%
Average starting salary: 175,000 French francs

DEGREES DESM • MBA • MS

Groupe ESC Toulouse (continued)

DESM—ESC Cycle Superieur Full-time. 24 to 36 months to complete program. *Concentrations:* business law, entrepreneurship, finance, human resources, industrial administration/management, information management, international development management, marketing research, public management.

MBA—Aerospace MBA Full-time and part-time. 3 years of work experience required. 65 to 76 total credits required. 12 to 24 months to complete program. *Concentrations:* management information systems, project management, telecommunications management, travel industry/tourism management, aviation management.

MS—MS Audit Interne et Controle de Gestion Full-time. 12 to 18 months to complete program. *Concentrations:* management systems analysis.

MS—MS Banque et Ingenierie Financiere Full-time. 12 to 18 months to complete program. *Concentrations:* banking, financial management/planning.

MS—MS Gestion de Patrimoine Full-time. 12 to 18 months to complete program. *Concentrations:* developmental economics.

MS—MS Intelligence Economique Full-time. 12 to 18 months to complete program. *Concentrations:* business information science.

MS—MS Logistique et Transport Full-time. 12 to 18 months to complete program. *Concentrations:* transportation and logistics.

MS—MS Management de l'Innovation et de la Technologie Full-time. 12 to 18 months to complete program. *Concentrations:* project management, technology management.

MS—MS Management de la Sante Full-time. 12 to 18 months to complete program. *Concentrations:* health care.

MS—MS Management et Ingenierie des Organisations Full-time. 12 to 18 months to complete program. *Concentrations:* management information systems.

MS—MS Marketing et Communication Commerciale Full-time. 12 to 18 months to complete program. *Concentrations:* marketing, marketing research.

MS—MS Marketing et Technologie Agro-Alimentaires Full-time. 12 to 18 months to complete program. *Concentrations:* agribusiness, technology management.

COSTS

Tuition *Full-time:* 40,000 French francs. **Required fees:** Tuition and fees vary by academic program. **Graduate housing:** Room and board costs vary by number of occupants and type of accommodation. *Typical cost:* 25,000 French francs (room only).

RESOURCES AND SERVICES

Information about online services, personal computer policies, library resources, international exchange programs, internship programs, and placement services at this institution and others can be found at **www. petersons.com/mba**

International Students

16% of students enrolled are international students.

Services and Facilities Counseling/support services, housing location assistance, language tutoring. Financial aid is not available to international students.
Applying *Required:* Proof of adequate funds, proof of health/immunizations.
International Student Contact Mr. William McNulty, Director, International Relations, Toulouse Cedex, 31068, France. **Phone:** 561-294-918. **Fax:** 561-294-994. **E-mail:** w.mcnulty@esc-toulouse.fr.

■ APPLICATION

Required Application form, baccalaureate/first degree, 2 letters of recommendation, personal statement, resume/curriculum vitae, transcripts of college work. **Recommended** Interview, work experience.

Deadlines and Fees *Deadlines:* 7/30 for fall, 6/30 for fall (international).

Application Contact Dr. Andres Atenza, Directeur ESC Toulouse, 20 Boulevard Lascrosses, BP1070, Toulouse Cedex 7, 31068, France. **Phone:** 561-294-992. **Fax:** 561-294-994. **E-mail:** esc@esc-toulouse.fr.

HEC School of Management

Jouy-en-Josas, France

HEC MBA PROGRAM

DEGREE MBA

MBA—Bilingual (English/French) MBA Full-time. At least 70 total credits required. 16 months to complete program. *Concentrations:* accounting, entrepreneurship, European business studies, finance, financial management/planning, human resources, international business, international finance, international management, international marketing, management, management consulting, managerial economics, marketing, organizational behavior/development, production management, public and private management, strategic management.

RESOURCES AND SERVICES

Information about online services, personal computer policies, library resources, international exchange programs, internship programs, and placement services at this institution and others can be found at **www. petersons.com/mba**

International Students

Services and Facilities Counseling/support services, international student housing, visa services. Financial aid is available to international students.
International Student Contact Ms. Pantea Denoyelle, Director of Marketing and Development, 1, rue de la Liberation, Jouy-en-Jasas Cedex, 78351, France. **Phone:** 1-3967-7376. **Fax:** 1-3967-7465. **E-mail:** denoyellep@hec.fr.

■ APPLICATION

Application Contact Ms. Fabienne Lecornay, Admissions Office, 1, rue de la Liberation, Jouy-en-Josas Cedex, 78351, France. **Phone:** 1-3967-7379 Ext. 7382. **Fax:** 1-3967-7465. **E-mail:** isadmission@hec.fr.

INSEAD (The European Institute of Business Administration)

Fontainebleau Cedex, France

MBA DEPARTMENT

Graduate Business Faculty

Full-time: 124	Part-time: 41

Student Body

Total: 679	Average Age: 28.6
Full-time: 679	Women: 23%

Admissions
Average GMAT: 685

Costs (1999–2000)
Full-time tuition: 27,900 euros per academic year
Part-time tuition: N/R

After Graduation (Class of 1998–99)
Employed within 3 months of graduation: 90%
Average starting salary: 82,500 euros

DEGREE MBA

MBA—Master of Business Administration Full-time. Minimum of 11 months to complete program. *Concentrations:* international management, leadership.

COSTS

Tuition *Full-time:* 27,900 euros.

FINANCIAL AID (1999–2000)

74 students received aid, including loans and scholarships. **Financial Aid Contact** MBA Admissions Office, Boulevard de Constance, Fontainebleau Cedex, 77305, France. **Phone:** 1-6072-4000. **Fax:** 1-6074-5535. **E-mail:** mba.candidates@insead.fr.

RESOURCES AND SERVICES

Information about online services, personal computer policies, library resources, international exchange programs, internship programs, and placement services at this institution and others can be found at **www. petersons.com/mba**

International Students

88% of students enrolled are international students.

Services and Facilities Counseling/support services, ESL/language courses, housing location assistance, international student housing, international student organization, orientation, visa services, career management services. Financial aid is available to international students.

Applying *Required:* TOEFL with recommended score of 260 (computer) or 620 (paper), proof of health/immunizations.

International Student Contact MBA Information Office, Boulevard de Constance, Fontainebleau Cedex, 77305, France. **Phone:** 1-6072-4273. **Fax:** 1-6074-5530. **E-mail:** mba.info@insead.fr.

■ APPLICATION

Required GMAT, application form, essay, interview, 2 letters of recommendation, personal statement, resume/curriculum vitae, transcripts of college work, 1 year of work experience. **Recommended** Baccalaureate/first degree.

Deadlines and Fees Applications for domestic and international students are processed on a rolling basis. *Application fee:* 150 euros, 150 euros (international).

Application Contact MBA Information Office, Boulevard de Constance, Fontainebleau Cedex, 77305, France. **Phone:** 1-6072-4273. **Fax:** 1-6074-5530. **E-mail:** mba.info@insead.fr.

See full description on page 686.

Institut Superieur de Gestion

Paris, France

ISG INTERNATIONAL SCHOOL OF BUSINESS

Graduate Business Faculty
Full-time: 12   Part-time: 35

Student Body
Total: 48
Full-time: 19   Average Age: 29
Part-time: 29   Women: 58%

Admissions
Applications: 100   Average GMAT: 570
Admitted: 50   Average GPA: 3.4
Enrolled: 48

Costs (1999–2000)
Full-time tuition: 85,000 French francs per academic year
Part-time tuition: 3000 French francs per course

DEGREES MBA

MBA—Executive MBA Part-time. 21 months to complete program. *Concentrations:* accounting, business ethics, business law, business policy/strategy, economics, European business studies, finance, international and area business studies, logistics, management, managerial economics, marketing, technology management.

MBA—International MBA Full-time. 15 months to complete program. *Concentrations:* accounting, business law, business policy/strategy, economics, European business studies, finance, international and area business studies, international business, international management, international marketing, Japanese business studies, managerial economics, risk management.

COSTS

Tuition *Full-time:* 85,000 French francs. *Part-time:* 3000 French francs per course. Tuition varies by academic program.

RESOURCES AND SERVICES

Information about online services, personal computer policies, library resources, international exchange programs, internship programs, and placement services at this institution and others can be found at **www.petersons.com/mba**

International Students

Services and Facilities Counseling/support services, ESL/language courses, housing location assistance, international student housing, international student organization, orientation, visa services. Financial aid is not available to international students.

Applying *Required:* TOEFL with recommended score of 550 (paper).

International Student Contact Bernadette Naze, Admissions Director/Associate Dean, 8 rue de Lota, Paris, 75116, France. **Phone:** 1-5626 1107. **Fax:** 1-5626 1106. **E-mail:** isb@isg.fr.

■ APPLICATION

Required GMAT, application form, baccalaureate/first degree, essay, interview, 2 letters of recommendation, personal statement, resume/curriculum vitae, transcripts of college work. **Recommended** Work experience.

Deadlines and Fees *Deadlines:* 7/31 for fall, 7/31 for fall (international). *Application fee:* 500 French francs.

Application Contact Bernadette Naze, Admissions Director/Associate Dean, 8 rue de Lota, Paris, 75116, France. **Phone:** 1-5626 1107. **Fax:** 1-5626 1106. **E-mail:** isb@isg.fr.

L'École Nationale des Ponts et Chaussées

Paris, France

ENPC MBA SCHOOL OF INTERNATIONAL MANAGEMENT

Graduate Business Faculty
Full-time: 6   Part-time: 60

Student Body
Total: 56   Average Age: 30
Full-time: 45   Women: 27%
Part-time: 11

Admissions
Applications: 200   Enrolled: 56
Admitted: 76   Average GMAT: 600

Costs (1999–2000)
Full-time tuition: 110,000 French francs per academic year
Part-time tuition: 145,000 French francs per degree program

After Graduation (Class of 1998–99)
Employed within 3 months of graduation: 85%

DEGREE MBA

MBA—International MBA Full-time and part-time. At least 19 total credits required. 13 to 15 months to complete program. *Concentrations:* Asian business studies, business ethics, entrepreneurship, European business studies, financial management/planning, international and area business studies, international business, international economics, international finance, international management, international marketing, Japanese business studies, leadership, logistics, management information systems, marketing, operations management, organizational behavior/development, organizational management, strategic management, technology management.

COSTS

Tuition *Full-time:* 110,000 French francs. *Part-time:* 145,000 French francs per degree program. Tuition varies by academic program.

FINANCIAL AID (1999–2000)

5 students received aid, including grants, scholarships, and work study.
Financial Aid Contact Mrs. Mayalene Crossley, Admissions and Marketing Director, 28, rue des Saints-Peres, Paris Cedex 07, 75343, France. **Phone:** 1-4458-2852. **Fax:** 1-4015-9347. **E-mail:** mayalene.crossley@mail.enpc.fr.

RESOURCES AND SERVICES

Information about online services, personal computer policies, library resources, international exchange programs, internship programs, and placement services at this institution and others can be found at **www.petersons.com/mba**

International Students

82% of students enrolled are international students.

Services and Facilities Counseling/support services, housing location assistance, language tutoring, career development services. Financial aid is available to international students.

Applying *Required:* TOEFL with recommended score of 550 (paper), proof of adequate funds. *Recommended:* Proof of health/immunizations.

International Student Contact Mrs. Mayalene Crossley, Admissions and Marketing Director, Paris Cedex 07, 75343, France. **Phone:** 1-4458-2852. **Fax:** 1-4015-9347. **E-mail:** mayalene. crossley@mail.enpc.fr.

■ APPLICATION

Required GMAT, application form, baccalaureate/first degree, essay, interview, 3 letters of recommendation, personal statement, resume/curriculum vitae, transcripts of college work, work experience.

Deadlines and Fees *Application fee:* 500 French francs.

Application Contact Mrs. Mayalene Crossley, Admissions and Marketing Director, 28, rue des Saints-Peres, Paris Cedex 07, 75343, France. **Phone:** 1-4458-2852. **Fax:** 1-4015-9347. **E-mail:** crossley@paris.enpc.fr.

Schiller International University

Paris, France

MBA PROGRAM

Graduate Business Faculty
Full-time: 4   Part-time: 22

Schiller International University (continued)

Student Body
Total: 40
Full-time: 22
Part-time: 18

Average Age: 26
Women: 63%

Costs (1999–2000)
Full-time tuition: 106,300 French francs per academic year
Part-time tuition: 6900 French francs per course

After Graduation (Class of 1998–99)
Employed within 3 months of graduation: 93%

DEGREES MA • MBA

MA—Master of Arts in International Relations and Diplomacy Full-time and part-time. At least 45 total credits required. 12 to 36 months to complete program.

MBA—Master of Business Administration in International Business Full-time and part-time. At least 45 total credits required. 12 to 36 months to complete program. *Concentrations:* international business.

COSTS
Tuition *Full-time:* 103,500 French francs. *Part-time:* 6900 French francs per course. Tuition varies by number of courses or credits taken and campus location. **Required fees:** *Full-time* 2800 French francs. Tuition and fees vary by campus location.

FINANCIAL AID (1999–2000)
Grants, loans, scholarships, and work study. Financial aid application deadline: 4/1. **Financial Aid Contact** Ms. Teri Reeves, Financial Aid Director, 453 Edgewater Drive, Dunedin, FL 34698. **Phone:** 727-736-5082 Ext. 250. **Fax:** 727-734-0359. **E-mail:** teri_reeves@schiller.edu.

RESOURCES AND SERVICES
Information about online services, personal computer policies, library resources, international exchange programs, internship programs, and placement services at this institution and others can be found at **www.petersons.com/mba**

International Students
Services and Facilities Counseling/support services, ESL/language courses, housing location assistance, international student housing, orientation, visa services. Financial aid is available to international students.
Applying *Required:* Proof of adequate funds. *Recommended:* TOEFL with recommended score of 550 (paper).
International Student Contact Campus Director, 32 Boulevard de Vaugirard, Paris, 75015, France. **Phone:** 1-4538-5601. **Fax:** 1-4538-5430.

▪ APPLICATION
Required GMAT, application form, baccalaureate/first degree, essay, transcripts of college work. **Recommended** Work experience.
Deadlines and Fees Applications for domestic and international students are processed on a rolling basis. *Application fee:* $35, $35 (international).
Application Contact Director of Admissions, 453 Edgewater Drive, Dunedin, FL 34698-7532. **Phone:** 727-736-5082 Ext. 239. **Fax:** 727-734-0359. **E-mail:** admissions@schiller.edu.

See full description on page 816.

Schiller International University

Strasbourg, France

MBA PROGRAM, STRASBOURG, FRANCE CAMPUS

Graduate Business Faculty
Full-time: 1

Part-time: 8

Student Body
Total: 23
Part-time: 23

Average Age: 28
Women: 30%

Costs (1999–2000)
Full-time tuition: N/R
Part-time tuition: 3900 French francs per course

After Graduation (Class of 1998–99)
Employed within 3 months of graduation: 100%

DEGREE MBA

MBA—Master of Business Administration in International Business Part-time. At least 45 total credits required. 12 to 24 months to complete program.

COSTS
Tuition *Part-time:* 3900 French francs per course. Tuition varies by number of courses or credits taken and campus location. **Required fees:** Tuition and fees vary by campus location.

FINANCIAL AID (1999–2000)
Grants, loans, and scholarships. Financial aid application deadline: 4/1. **Financial Aid Contact** Ms. Teri Reeves, Financial Aid Director, 453 Edgewater Drive, Dunedin, FL 34698. **Phone:** 813-736-5082 Ext. 250. **Fax:** 813-727-0359. **E-mail:** teri_reeves@schiller.edu.

RESOURCES AND SERVICES
Information about online services, personal computer policies, library resources, international exchange programs, internship programs, and placement services at this institution and others can be found at **www.petersons.com/mba**

International Students
Services and Facilities Counseling/support services, ESL/language courses, housing location assistance, international student housing, visa services. Financial aid is available to international students.
Applying *Required:* Proof of adequate funds. *Recommended:* TOEFL with recommended score of 550 (paper).
International Student Contact Director of Admissions, Chateau Pourtales, 161 rue Melanie, Strasbourg, 67000, France. **Phone:** 3-8845-8464. **Fax:** 3-8845-8460. **E-mail:** blasiush@aol.com.

▪ APPLICATION
Required GMAT, application form, baccalaureate/first degree, essay, transcripts of college work. **Recommended** Work experience.
Deadlines and Fees Applications for domestic and international students are processed on a rolling basis. *Application fee:* $35, $35 (international).
Application Contact Director of Admissions, 453 Edgewater Drive, Dunedin, FL 34698-7532. **Phone:** 727-736-5082 Ext. 239. **Fax:** 727-727-0359. **E-mail:** admissions@schiller.edu.

See full description on page 816.

Theseus Institute

Sophia Antipolis, Sophia Antipolis Cedex, France

INTERNATIONAL MANAGEMENT INSTITUTE

Graduate Business Faculty
Full-time: 6

Part-time: 40

Student Body
Total: 50
Full-time: 50

Average Age: 32
Women: 34%

Admissions
Applications: 120
Admitted: 60

Enrolled: 50
Average GMAT: 600

Costs (1999–2000)
Full-time tuition: 18,500 euros per academic year
Part-time tuition: N/R

After Graduation (Class of 1998–99)
Employed within 3 months of graduation: 100%
Average starting salary: $80,000

DEGREE MBA

MBA—MBA in High-Tech Management and Entrepreneurship Full-time. 10 months to complete program. *Concentrations:* electronic commerce (e-commerce), entrepreneurship, information management, international business, management information systems, new venture management, strategic management, technology management, telecommunications management.

COSTS
Tuition *Full-time:* 18,500 euros.

FINANCIAL AID (1999–2000)
6 students received aid, including loans and scholarships. Financial aid application deadline: 3/31. **Financial Aid Contact** Mr. Eddy Travia, Admissions Manager, BP 169, Sophia Antipolis Cedex, 06903, France. **Phone:** 4-9294-5107. **Fax:** 4-9365-3837. **E-mail:** admissions@theseus.fr.

RESOURCES AND SERVICES

Information about online services, personal computer policies, library resources, international exchange programs, internship programs, and placement services at this institution and others can be found at **www.petersons.com/mba**

International Students

80% of students enrolled are international students.

Services and Facilities Counseling/support services, ESL/language courses, housing location assistance, international student housing, language tutoring, orientation, visa services. Financial aid is available to international students.
Applying *Recommended:* TOEFL, proof of adequate funds, proof of health/immunizations.
International Student Contact Ms. Joanne Bester, MBA Program Coordinator, BP 169, Rue Albert Einstein, Sophia Antipolis Cedex, 06903, France. **Phone:** 4-9294-5174. **Fax:** 4-9365-3837. **E-mail:** bester@theseus.fr.

■ APPLICATION

Required GMAT, application form, baccalaureate/first degree, essay, interview, 2 letters of recommendation, transcripts of college work, 3 years of work experience. **Recommended** Personal statement, resume/curriculum vitae.
Deadlines and Fees *Deadlines:* 5/15 for fall, 5/15 for fall (international).
Application Contact Mr. Eddy Travia, Admissions Manager, BP 169, Rue Albert Einstein, Sophia Antipolis Cedex, 06903, France. **Phone:** 4-9294-5107. **Fax:** 4-9365-3837. **E-mail:** admissions@theseus.fr.

GERMANY

ESCP-EAP European School of Management

Berlin, Germany

BUSINESS PROGRAMS

DEGREE MBA

MBA—Master of Business Administration Full-time. Minimum of 12 months to complete program.

RESOURCES AND SERVICES

Information about online services, personal computer policies, library resources, international exchange programs, internship programs, and placement services at this institution and others can be found at **www.petersons.com/mba**

European Business School

Oestrich-Winkel, Germany

EUROPEAN BUSINESS SCHOOL GERMANY

Graduate Business Faculty
Full-time: 60 | Part-time: 120

Student Body
Total: 917 | Average Age: 22
Full-time: 917 | Women: 31%

Admissions
Applications: 800 | Enrolled: 220
Admitted: 220

Costs (1999–2000)
Full-time tuition: 9500 euros per academic year
Part-time tuition: N/R

After Graduation (Class of 1998–99)
Employed within 3 months of graduation: 100%
Average starting salary: $45,000

DEGREES Dipl-Kfm

Dipl-Kfm—Diplom-Kaufmann (MBA Equivalent) in Business Administration Full-time. Internship of 6 weeks minimum and 2 foreign languages required. 24 to 30 months to complete program. *Concentrations:* accounting, banking, busi-

ness law, decision sciences, economics, entrepreneurship, finance, human resources, international economics, international management, marketing, real estate, strategic management, taxation, telecommunications management.
Dipl-Kfm—Diplom-Kaufmann (MBA Equivalent) in Business Administration/ Information Systems Full-time. Internship of 6 weeks minimum and 1 foreign language required. 24 to 30 months to complete program. *Concentrations:* accounting, banking, business law, decision sciences, economics, entrepreneurship, finance, human resources, international economics, international management, marketing, real estate, strategic management, taxation, telecommunications management.

COSTS

Tuition *Full-time:* 9500 euros. **Graduate housing:** Room and board costs vary by number of occupants. *Typical cost:* 600 euros (including board).

FINANCIAL AID (1999–2000)

Financial Aid Contact Ms. Heidrun Soehn, Head of Student Office, European Business School, Oestrich-Winkel, 65375, Germany. **Phone:** 67-23690. **Fax:** 67-2369 Ext. 133. **E-mail:** heidrun.soehn@ebs.de.

RESOURCES AND SERVICES

Information about online services, personal computer policies, library resources, international exchange programs, internship programs, and placement services at this institution and others can be found at **www.petersons.com/mba**

International Students

8% of students enrolled are international students.

Services and Facilities Counseling/support services, ESL/language courses, international student organization, orientation, visa services.
Applying *Recommended:* TOEFL with recommended score of 230 (computer) or 570 (paper), proof of adequate funds.
International Student Contact Ms. Angelika Barta, Head of International Program, European Business School, Oestrich-Winkel, 65375, Germany. **Phone:** 67-23690 Ext. 114. **Fax:** 67-2369133. **E-mail:** angelika.barta@ebs.de.

■ APPLICATION

Required Application form, baccalaureate/first degree, interview, personal statement, resume/curriculum vitae, work experience.
Deadlines and Fees *Deadline:* 5/5 for fall. *Application fee:* $125.
Application Contact Ms. Gisela Francis Vogt, Head of Admissions, European Business School, Oestrich-Winkel, 65375, Germany. **Phone:** 67-23690 Ext. 112. **Fax:** 67-23690 Ext. 133. **E-mail:** gisela.vogt@ebs.de.

Schiller International University

Heidelberg, Germany

MBA PROGRAM, HEILDLEBERG, GERMANY

Graduate Business Faculty
Full-time: 6 | Part-time: 30

Student Body
Total: 49 | Average Age: 26
Full-time: 17 | Women: 41%
Part-time: 32

Costs (1999–2000)
Full-time tuition: 27,740 German marks per academic year
Part-time tuition: 1800 German marks per course

After Graduation (Class of 1998–99)
Employed within 3 months of graduation: 95%

DEGREES MBA • MIM

MBA—Master of Business Administration in International Business Full-time and part-time. At least 45 total credits required. 12 to 24 months to complete program.

MIM—Master of International Management in International Business Full-time and part-time. At least 45 total credits required. 12 to 24 months to complete program.

COSTS

Tuition *Full-time:* 27,000 German marks. *Part-time:* 1800 German marks per course. Tuition varies by number of courses or credits taken and campus location.
Required fees: *Full-time* 740 German marks. Tuition and fees vary by campus location.

Schiller International University (continued)

FINANCIAL AID (1999–2000)
Grants, loans, scholarships, and work study. Financial aid application deadline: 4/1. **Financial Aid Contact** Ms. Teri Reeves, Financial Aid Director, 453 Edgewater Drive, Dunedin, FL 34698. **Phone:** 727-736-5082 Ext. 250. **Fax:** 727-734-0359. **E-mail:** teri_reeves@schiller.edu.

RESOURCES AND SERVICES
Information about online services, personal computer policies, library resources, international exchange programs, internship programs, and placement services at this institution and others can be found at **www.petersons.com/mba**

International Students
Services and Facilities Counseling/support services, ESL/language courses, housing location assistance, international student housing, orientation, visa services. Financial aid is available to international students.
Applying *Required:* Proof of adequate funds. *Recommended:* TOEFL with recommended score of 550 (paper).
International Student Contact Campus Director, Bergstrasse 106, Germany. **Phone:** 49-6221-45810. **Fax:** 49-6221-402703. **E-mail:** siu_hd@compuserve.com.

■ APPLICATION
Required GMAT, application form, baccalaureate/first degree, essay, transcripts of college work. **Recommended** Work experience.
Deadlines and Fees Applications for domestic and international students are processed on a rolling basis. *Application fee:* $35, $35 (international).
Application Contact Director of Admissions, 453 Edgewater Drive, Dunedin, FL 34698-7532. **Phone:** 727-736-5082 Ext. 239. **Fax:** 727-734-0359. **E-mail:** admissions@schiller.edu.

See full description on page 816.

University of Applied Sciences Esslingen

Esslingen, Germany

GRADUATE SCHOOL

Graduate Business Faculty
Full-time: 20   Part-time: 30

Student Body
Total: 34
Full-time: 34   Average Age: 28
                                  Women: 53%

Admissions
Applications: 120   Enrolled: 34
Admitted: 48   Average GMAT: 620

Costs (1999–2000)
Full-time tuition: N/R
Part-time tuition: N/R

DEGREE MBA

MBA—MBA in International Industrial Management Full-time. At least 64 total credits required. 12 to 18 months to complete program. *Concentrations:* industrial administration/management, information management, international management.

COSTS
Graduate housing: Room and board costs vary by campus location. *Typical cost:* $300 (room only).

FINANCIAL AID (1999–2000)
15 students received aid, including grants, scholarships, and teaching assistantships. Financial aid application deadline: 5/1. **Financial Aid Contact** Ms. Tudao Luong, Program Manager, MBA, Flaudernstrase 101, BW, Germany. **Phone:** 711-397-4331. **Fax:** 711-397-4333. **E-mail:** mba@fht-esslingen.de.

RESOURCES AND SERVICES
Information about online services, personal computer policies, library resources, international exchange programs, internship programs, and placement services at this institution and others can be found at **www.petersons.com/mba**

International Students
97% of students enrolled are international students.
Services and Facilities Counseling/support services, ESL/language courses, international student housing, visa services, german language courses, cultural program with excursions.
Applying *Required:* TOEFL with recommended score of 550 (paper), proof of adequate funds. *Recommended:* TSE.
International Student Contact Ms. Tudao Luong, Program Manager, MBA, Flaudernstrasse 101, BW, Germany. **Phone:** 711-397 4331. **Fax:** 711-397 4333. **E-mail:** mba@fht-esslingen.de.

■ APPLICATION
Required GMAT, application form, baccalaureate/first degree, essay, letter(s) of recommendation, personal statement, resume/curriculum vitae, transcripts of college work. **Recommended** Interview, work experience.
Deadlines and Fees *Deadlines:* 5/1 for fall, 5/1 for fall (international).
Application Contact Ms. Tudao Luong, Program Manager, MBA, Flandernstrasse 101, BW, Germany. **Phone:** 711-397-4331. **Fax:** 711-397-4333. **E-mail:** mba@fht-esslingen.de.

5X

WHU Koblenz

Vallendar, Germany

OTTO-BEISHEIM GRADUATE SCHOOL OF MANAGEMENT

Graduate Business Faculty
Full-time: 16   Part-time: 30

Student Body
Total: 384   Average Age: 24
Full-time: 273   Women: 17%
Part-time: 111

Admissions
Applications: 499   Enrolled: 77
Admitted: 77   Average GMAT: 649

Costs (1999–2000)
Full-time tuition: N/R
Part-time tuition: 59,000 German marks per degree program

DEGREE MBA

MBA—Executive MBA Part-time. Minimum of 24 months to complete program. *Concentrations:* finance, international finance, marketing, project management, strategic management.

COSTS
Tuition *Part-time:* 59,000 German marks per degree program.

FINANCIAL AID (1999–2000)
70 students received aid, including fellowships, grants, research assistantships, and scholarships. Financial aid application deadline: 7/15. **Financial Aid Contact** Mr. Peter Christ, Admissions Officer, Burgplatz 2, D-56179, Vallendar, Germany. **Phone:** 261-6509510. **Fax:** 261-6509519. **E-mail:** pchrist@whu-koblenz.de.

RESOURCES AND SERVICES
Information about online services, personal computer policies, library resources, international exchange programs, internship programs, and placement services at this institution and others can be found at **www.petersons.com/mba**

International Students
8% of students enrolled are international students.
Services and Facilities Counseling/support services, international student housing, language tutoring, visa services. Financial aid is not available to international students.
Applying *Required:* TOEFL with recommended score of 220 (computer).
International Student Contact Mr. Axel Schumacher-Schroter, Director, International Programmes, Burgplatz 2, D-56179, Vallendar, Germany. **Phone:** 261-6509520. **Fax:** 261-6509529. **E-mail:** ip@whu-koblenz.de.

■ APPLICATION
Required Application form, baccalaureate/first degree, interview, 2 letters of recommendation, resume/curriculum vitae, 3 years of work experience. School will accept GMAT.
Deadlines and Fees *Deadlines:* 5/30 for fall, 5/30 for fall (international).

Application Contact Mr. Peter Christ, Admissions Officer, Burgplatz 2, D-56179, Vallendar, Germany. **Phone:** 261-6509510. **Fax:** 261-6509519. **E-mail:** pchrist@whu-koblenz.de.

INDONESIA

Institut Pengembangan Manajemen Indonesia

Jakarta, Indonesia

BUSINESS PROGRAMS

Graduate Business Faculty
Full-time: 8   Part-time: 20

Student Body
Total: 114   Average Age: 29
Full-time: 26   Women: 18%
Part-time: 88

Admissions
Applications: 192   Enrolled: 114
Admitted: 181   Average GMAT: 518

Costs (1999–2000)
Full-time tuition: N/R
Part-time tuition: N/R

DEGREES MBA

MBA—Executive MBA Full-time and part-time. *Distance learning option.* 5 years work experience. 45 to 50 total credits required. 24 to 30 months to complete program.

MBA—Full-Time Program Full-time. 2 years of work experience required. 36 to 50 total credits required. 12 months to complete program. *Concentrations:* international business.

FINANCIAL AID (1999–2000)

Financial Aid Contact Dr. Hadi Satyagraha, Dean, IMPI Campus, JL Rawajati Timur I/1, Kalibata, Jakarta, 12750, Indonesia. **Phone:** 21-797-0419 Ext. 235. **Fax:** 21-797-0374. **E-mail:** ipmimba@rad.net.id.

RESOURCES AND SERVICES

Information about online services, personal computer policies, library resources, international exchange programs, internship programs, and placement services at this institution and others can be found at **www.petersons.com/mba**

International Students

Services and Facilities Financial aid is not available to international students.
International Student Contact Dr. Hadi Satyagraha, Dean, IPMI Campus, JL Rawajati Timur I/1, Kalibata, Jakarta, 12750, Indonesia. **Phone:** 21-797-0419 Ext. 235. **Fax:** 21-797-0374. **E-mail:** ipmimba@rad.net.id.

■ APPLICATION

Required GMAT, application form, baccalaureate/first degree, essay, interview, 2 letters of recommendation, personal statement, resume/curriculum vitae, transcripts of college work, work experience.

Application Contact Dr. Hadi Satyagraha, Dean, IPMI Campus, Jl. Rawajati Timur I/1, Kalibata, Jakarta, 12750, Indonesia. **Phone:** 21-797-0419 Ext. 235. **Fax:** 21-797-0509. **E-mail:** ipmimba@rad.net.id.

IRELAND

National University of Ireland, Cork

Cork, Ireland

FACULTY OF COMMERCE

Graduate Business Faculty
Full-time: 110   Part-time: 50

Student Body
Total: 500   Average Age: 23

Admissions
Average GMAT: 475

Costs (1999–2000)
Full-time tuition: 5250 Irish punt per academic year (resident), 5250 Irish punt per academic year (nonresident)
Part-time tuition: N/R

DEGREES MBA • MBS • MComm

MBA—Executive MBA Part-time. 24 months to complete program. *Concentrations:* accounting, business ethics, economics, entrepreneurship, financial management/planning, human resources, leadership, management information systems, management systems analysis, managerial economics, marketing, new venture management, operations management, strategic management, system management.

MBS—Master of Business Studies in Business Economics Full-time and part-time. 24 months to complete program.

MBS—Master of Business Studies in Corporate Finance and Accounting Full-time and part-time. 24 months to complete program.

MBS—Master of Business Studies in Entrepreneurialism Full-time and part-time. 24 months to complete program.

MBS—Master of Business Studies in European Accounting Full-time and part-time. 24 months to complete program.

MBS—Master of Business Studies in Managerial Information and Managerial Accounting Systems Full-time and part-time. 24 months to complete program.

MComm—Master of Commerce Part-time. Minimum of 24 months to complete program.

COSTS

Tuition, state resident: *Full-time* 5250 Irish punt. **Tuition, nonresident:** *Full-time* 5250 Irish punt. **Tuition, international:** *Full-time* 10,500 Irish punt. Tuition varies by academic program.

RESOURCES AND SERVICES

Information about online services, personal computer policies, library resources, international exchange programs, internship programs, and placement services at this institution and others can be found at **www.petersons.com/mba**

International Students

Services and Facilities Counseling/support services. Financial aid is not available to international students.
International Student Contact Ms. Marie McSwiney, MBA Programme Administrator, Faculty of Commerce, Alfred O'Rahilly Building, Western Road, Cork, Ireland. **Phone:** 21-4902394. **Fax:** 21-4903251. **E-mail:** commerce@ucc.ie.

■ APPLICATION

Required GMAT, application form, 2 letters of recommendation, transcripts of college work, 2 years of work experience. **Recommended** Baccalaureate/first degree, personal statement, resume/curriculum vitae.
Deadlines and Fees *Deadlines:* 9/11 for fall, 9/11 for fall (international). *Application fee:* 35 Irish punt.
Application Contact Ms. Marie McSwiney, MBA Programmer Administrator, Faculty of Commerce, Alfred O'Rahilly Building, Western Road, Cork, Ireland. **Phone:** 21-4902394. **Fax:** 21-4903251. **E-mail:** commerce@ucc.ie.

60

National University of Ireland, Dublin

Blackrock, Ireland

THE MICHAEL SMURFIT GRADUATE SCHOOL OF BUSINESS

Graduate Business Faculty
Full-time: 79   Part-time: 34

Student Body
Total: 1,071   Part-time: 384
Full-time: 687   Average Age: 29

Admissions
Applications: 164   Enrolled: 82
Admitted: 127   Average GMAT: 585

Costs (1999–2000)
Full-time tuition: 10,500 Irish punt per academic year (resident), 11,000 Irish punt per academic year (nonresident)
Part-time tuition: 5125 Irish punt per semester (resident), 5125 Irish punt per semester (nonresident)

After Graduation (Class of 1998–99)
Employed within 3 months of graduation: 100%
Average starting salary: $67,000

DEGREES EMBA • MBA • MBS • MComm • MMS • MS • MSMP

EMBA—Executive Master of Business Administration Part-time. At least 21 total credits required. Maximum of 24 months to complete program. *Concentrations:* accounting, entrepreneurship, finance, human resources, management information systems, marketing.

MBA—Master of Business Administration Full-time. At least 21 total credits required. Maximum of 12 months to complete program. *Concentrations:* accounting, business law, economics, entrepreneurship, finance, human resources, insurance, international and area business studies, international marketing, management information systems, manufacturing management, marketing, organizational behavior/development, strategic management.

MBS—Master of Business Studies Full-time and part-time. Undergraduate business degree or a degree in a cognate discipline required. 12 to 24 months to complete program. *Concentrations:* actuarial science, finance, human resources, international and area business studies, international business, international marketing, management information systems, manufacturing management, marketing, marketing research, organizational behavior/development, strategic management, travel industry/tourism management.

MComm—Master of Commerce

MMS—Master of Management Science Full-time. Undergraduate business, math, or computing degree required. 12 months to complete program. *Concentrations:* management science.

MS—Master of Science in Disability Management Full-time. Minimum of 12 months to complete program. *Concentrations:* management.

MSMP—Master of Science Marketing Practice Full-time. Undergraduate degree in business marketing required. 12 months to complete program. *Concentrations:* marketing, marketing research.

COSTS

Tuition, state resident: *Full-time* 10,000 Irish punt. *Part-time* 5000 Irish punt per semester. **Tuition, nonresident:** *Full-time* 10,500 Irish punt. *Part-time* 5000 Irish punt per semester. **Required fees:** *Full-time* 500 Irish punt. *Part-time* 125 Irish punt per semester. Tuition and fees vary by class time and academic program. **Graduate housing:** *Typical cost:* 1850 Irish punt (room only).

FINANCIAL AID (1999–2000)

Financial aid application deadline: 3/31.

RESOURCES AND SERVICES

Information about online services, personal computer policies, library resources, international exchange programs, internship programs, and placement services at this institution and others can be found at www.petersons.com/mba

International Students

9% of students enrolled are international students.

Services and Facilities Counseling/support services, international student housing. Financial aid is available to international students.
Applying *Required:* TOEFL.
International Student Contact Mr. Colm Small, International Affairs Officer, Faculty of Commerce, John Henry Newman Building, County Dublin, Ireland. **Phone:** 1-706 8867. **Fax:** 1-283 1911.

■ APPLICATION

Required GRE, application form, baccalaureate/first degree, 2 letters of recommendation, resume/curriculum vitae, transcripts of college work, 3 years of work experience. School will accept GMAT. **Recommended** Interview.
Deadlines and Fees *Deadlines:* 3/31 for fall, 3/31 for fall (international).
Application Contact Ms. Jane O'Mara, MBA Program Manager, Carysfort Avenue, County Dublin, Ireland. **Phone:** 1-706 8860. **Fax:** 1-283 1911. **E-mail:** jane.omara@ucd.ie.

61

National University of Ireland, Galway

Galway, Ireland

FACULTY OF COMMERCE

DEGREE MBA

MBA—Executive MBA Part-time. 12 to 24 months to complete program. *Concentrations:* accounting, business law, economics, entrepreneurship, finance, human resources, management, management information systems, marketing, operations management, organizational behavior/development, quality management, quantitative analysis, strategic management.

RESOURCES AND SERVICES

Information about online services, personal computer policies, library resources, international exchange programs, internship programs, and placement services at this institution and others can be found at www.petersons.com/mba

International Students

Services and Facilities Financial aid is not available to international students.
International Student Contact Mr. Seamus O'Grady, International Affairs Office, University Road, Galway, Ireland. **Phone:** 91-524-411 Ext. 2144. **Fax:** 91-525-051. **E-mail:** intloffice@mis.nuigalway.ie.

■ APPLICATION

Application Contact Dr. Aidau Daly, Master of Business Administration Program, Department of Marketing, Galway, Ireland. **Phone:** 91-524-411 Ext. 2548. **Fax:** 91-524-130. **E-mail:** admissions@mis.nuigalway.ie.

62

University of Limerick

Limerick, Ireland

COLLEGE OF BUSINESS

Graduate Business Faculty
Full-time: 65

Student Body
Total: 259   Average Age: 26
Full-time: 148   Women: 46%
Part-time: 111

Admissions
Applications: 400   Average GMAT: 560
Enrolled: 112

Costs (1999–2000)
Full-time tuition: N/R
Part-time tuition: N/R

DEGREES MBA • MBS • MCG • MPM

MBA—Corporate MBA Part-time. At least 60 total credits required. Maximum of 24 months to complete program. *Concentrations:* entrepreneurship, human resources, international management.

MBA—Executive MBA Part-time. At least 60 total credits required. Maximum of 24 months to complete program. *Concentrations:* entrepreneurship, human resources, international management.

MBS—Master of Business Studies in Entrepreneurial Studies Full-time. At least 60 total credits required. Maximum of 24 months to complete program.

MBS—Master of Business Studies in Human Resources Management Full-time and part-time. At least 60 total credits required. Maximum of 24 months to complete program. *Concentrations:* human resources, industrial/labor relations.

MBS—Master of Business Studies Full-time and part-time. 12 to 24 months to complete program.

MCG—Master's in Corporate Governance Part-time. At least 60 total credits required. Maximum of 24 months to complete program.
MPM—Master of Project Management Part-time. *Distance learning option.* At least 90 total credits required. Maximum of 24 months to complete program. *Concentrations:* organizational behavior/development, project management.

COSTS
Tuition varies by academic program.

FINANCIAL AID (1999–2000)
Grants and scholarships. **Financial Aid Contact** Admissions Office, Limerick, Ireland. **Phone:** 61-202-366. **Fax:** 61-334-859.

RESOURCES AND SERVICES
Information about online services, personal computer policies, library resources, international exchange programs, internship programs, and placement services at this institution and others can be found at **www.petersons.com/mba**

International Students
3% of students enrolled are international students.

Services and Facilities Counseling/support services, ESL/language courses, international student housing. Financial aid is not available to international students. **Applying** *Required:* TOEFL with recommended score of 550 (paper), proof of adequate funds.

International Student Contact Ms. Ann Lyons, Administrative Assistant, Admissions Office, Limerick, Ireland. **Phone:** 61-202-366. **Fax:** 61-334-859. **E-mail:** ann.lyons@ul.ie.

■ APPLICATION
Required Application form, baccalaureate/first degree, interview, personal statement, transcripts of college work, work experience. School will accept GMAT. **Recommended** 2 letters of recommendation, resume/curriculum vitae.

Application Contact Ms. Ann Lyons, Administrative Assistant, Admissions Office, Limerick, Ireland. **Phone:** 61-202-366. **Fax:** 61-334-859. **E-mail:** ann.lyons@ul.ie.

ISRAEL

Bar-Ilan University
Ramat-Gan, Israel

S. DANIEL ABRAHAM CENTER OF ECONOMICS AND BUSINESS, THE GRADUATE SCHOOL OF BUSINESS

Graduate Business Faculty
Full-time: 22

Student Body
Total: 20
Full-time: 20
Average Age: 23
Women: 40%

Costs (1999–2000)
Full-time tuition: $18,000 per academic year
Part-time tuition: N/R

DEGREE MBA

MBA—International MBA Full-time. At least 25 total credits required. Minimum of 14 months to complete program. *Concentrations:* economics, finance, international and area business studies, management, management information systems, marketing.

COSTS
Tuition *Full-time:* $18,000. **Tuition, international:** *Full-time* $18,000.

RESOURCES AND SERVICES
Information about online services, personal computer policies, library resources, international exchange programs, internship programs, and placement services at this institution and others can be found at **www.petersons.com/mba**

International Students
90% of students enrolled are international students.

Services and Facilities Counseling/support services. Financial aid is not available to international students.
Applying *Required:* TOEFL.

International Student Contact Ms. Cindy Sinvani, Coordinator, International MBA, S. Daniel Abraham Center of Economics and Business, The Graduate School of Business, Ramat Gan, 52900, Israel. **Phone:** 3-5317914. **Fax:** 3-5353182. **E-mail:** imba@mail.biu.ac.il.

■ APPLICATION
Required GMAT, application form, baccalaureate/first degree, essay, interview, 2 letters of recommendation, transcripts of college work. **Recommended** Work experience.

Deadlines and Fees Applications for domestic and international students are processed on a rolling basis. *Application fee:* $50, $50 (international).

Application Contact Dr. Jeffrey Kantor, Director, International MBA, S. Daniel Abraham Center of Economics and Business, the Grad. School of Business, Ramat Gan, 52900, Israel. **Phone:** 3-5317914. **Fax:** 3-5317914. **E-mail:** imba@mail.biu.ac.il.

Tel Aviv University
Tel Aviv, Israel

LEON RECANATI GRADUATE SCHOOL OF BUSINESS ADMINISTRATION

Graduate Business Faculty
Full-time: 82
Part-time: 180

Student Body
Total: 2,312
Average Age: 29

Admissions
Applications: 1,761
Admitted: 658
Enrolled: 541
Average GMAT: 600

Costs (1999–2000)
Full-time tuition: $2700 per academic year
Part-time tuition: N/R

DEGREES EMBA • M Sc • MBA • MHA

EMBA—Executive MBA Full-time and part-time. Interview, 3 letters of recommendation, resume/curriculum vitae, and 8 years of work experience required. At least 30 total credits required. 12 to 16 months to complete program.

EMBA—Kellogg-Recanati International Executive MBA Full-time and part-time. Interview, 3 letters of recommendation, resume/curriculum vitae, and 8 years of work experience required. At least 30 total credits required. Minimum of 24 months to complete program.

M Sc—Master of Science in Management Sciences—Decisions and Operations Research Full-time and part-time. Thesis required. At least 22 total credits required. 24 to 60 months to complete program.

M Sc—Master of Science in Management Sciences—Finance and Accounting Full-time and part-time. Thesis required. At least 22 total credits required. 24 to 60 months to complete program. *Concentrations:* accounting, finance.

M Sc—Master of Science in Management Sciences—Organizational Behavior Full-time and part-time. Thesis required. At least 22 total credits required. 24 to 60 months to complete program.

M Sc—Master of Science in Management Sciences—Technology and Information Systems Full-time and part-time. Thesis required. At least 22 total credits required. 24 to 60 months to complete program.

MBA—Master of Business Administration Full-time and part-time. At least 32 total credits required. 24 to 60 months to complete program. *Concentrations:* accounting, decision sciences, entrepreneurship, finance, financial information systems, human resources, information management, management, management information systems, marketing, operations management, organizational behavior/development, project management, strategic management, technology management.

MHA—Master of Health Administration Full-time and part-time. At least 30 total credits required. 24 to 60 months to complete program.

COSTS
Tuition *Full-time:* $2700.

FINANCIAL AID (1999–2000)
Grants, research assistantships, scholarships, and teaching assistantships. Aid is available to part-time students. **Financial Aid Contact** Financial Aid Office, Tel Aviv, 69978, Israel. **Phone:** 3-640-8067.

RESOURCES AND SERVICES
Information about online services, personal computer policies, library resources, international exchange programs, internship programs, and

Peterson's Guide to MBA Programs 2001

491

Tel Aviv University (continued)

placement services at this institution and others can be found at **www.petersons.com/mba**

International Students

Services and Facilities Counseling/support services, housing location assistance, language tutoring, orientation. Financial aid is not available to international students.
International Student Contact Mrs. Gali Berzak, International and Exchange Programs Coordinator, Faculty of Management, Tel Aviv, 69978, Israel. **Phone:** 3-640-8069. **Fax:** 3-640-9560. **E-mail:** galibz@post.tau.ac.il.

■ APPLICATION

Required Application form, baccalaureate/first degree, transcripts of college work. School will accept GMAT.
Deadlines and Fees *Deadlines:* 6/10 for fall, 11/1 for spring, 6/10 for fall (international). *Application fee:* $80.
Application Contact Mrs. Michal Elias, Secretary, Admission Affairs, Faculty of Management, Tel Aviv, 69978, Israel. **Phone:** 3-640-6333. **Fax:** 3-640-9560. **E-mail:** michale@tauex.tau.ac.il.

ITALY

63

Bocconi University

Milan, Italy

SDA BOCCONI

Graduate Business Faculty
Full-time: 73 — Part-time: 83

Student Body
Total: 311
Full-time: 237 — Average Age: 38
Part-time: 74 — Women: 25%

Admissions
Applications: 1,320 — Enrolled: 311
Admitted: 350 — Average GMAT: 630

Costs (1999–2000)
Full-time tuition: 21,500 euros per academic year
Part-time tuition: N/R

After Graduation (Class of 1998–99)
Employed within 3 months of graduation: 95%
Average starting salary: $80,000

DEGREES MBA • MIEM

MBA—Bilingual MBA Full-time. Maximum of 13 months to complete program. *Concentrations:* financial information systems, international and area business studies, international management, management, management information systems, project management.

MIEM—Master of International Economics and Management Full-time. Maximum of 12 months to complete program. *Concentrations:* international economics, international management.

COSTS

Tuition *Full-time:* 21,500 euros.

FINANCIAL AID (1999–2000)

46 students received aid, including scholarships. Financial aid application deadline: 4/30. **Financial Aid Contact** Ms. Rossana Camera, Admissions and Financial Aid Officer, Via Balilla 16/18, Milano, 20136, Italy. **Phone:** 02-5836 3297. **Fax:** 02-5836 3275. **E-mail:** rossana.camera@sda.uni-bocconi.it.

RESOURCES AND SERVICES

Information about online services, personal computer policies, library resources, international exchange programs, internship programs, and placement services at this institution and others can be found at **www.petersons.com/mba**

International Students

33% of students enrolled are international students.

Services and Facilities Counseling/support services, housing location assistance, language tutoring, visa services. Financial aid is available to international students.
Applying *Required:* TOEFL, proof of adequate funds, proof of health/immunizations.
International Student Contact Ms. Barbara Zaccarelli, Student and Internal Relations, Via Balilla 16/18, Milano, 20136, Italy. **Phone:** 02-5836 3273. **Fax:** 02-5836 3275. **E-mail:** barbara.zaccarelli@sda.uni-bocconi.it.

■ APPLICATION

Required GMAT, application form, baccalaureate/first degree, essay, interview, 2 letters of recommendation, personal statement, resume/curriculum vitae, transcripts of college work, 2 years of work experience.
Deadlines and Fees *Deadlines:* 4/30 for fall, 4/30 for fall (international). *Application fee:* 78 euros.
Application Contact Ms. Luisa Negri, Admissions Officer, Via Balilla 16/18, Milano, 20136, Italy. **Phone:** 02-5836 3286. **Fax:** 02-5836 3275. **E-mail:** luisa.negri@sda.uni-bocconi.it.

JAPAN

International University of Japan

64

Minami Uonuma-gu, Japan

GRADUATE SCHOOL OF INTERNATIONAL MANAGEMENT

Graduate Business Faculty
Full-time: 18 — Part-time: 28

Student Body
Total: 115 — Average Age: 28
Full-time: 115 — Women: 19%

Admissions
Applications: 135 — Enrolled: 66
Admitted: 97 — Average GMAT: 580

Costs (1999–2000)
Full-time tuition: 1,900,000 Japanese yen per academic year
Part-time tuition: N/R

DEGREE MBA

MBA—International Management Program Full-time. Interview for domestic applicants required. At least 54 total credits required. 20 to 48 months to complete program. *Concentrations:* accounting, Asian business studies, business law, business policy/strategy, electronic commerce (e-commerce), finance, financial economics, financial management/planning, human resources, information management, international business, international finance, international management, international marketing, Japanese business studies, management, management information systems, marketing, marketing research, operations management, organizational behavior/development, financial engineering.

COSTS

Tuition *Full-time:* 1,900,000 Japanese yen.

FINANCIAL AID (1999–2000)

Research assistantships, scholarships, and teaching assistantships.
Financial Aid Contact Office of Graduate School of International Management (MBA Program Office), 777 Anaji Shinden,Yamato-machi, Niigata, Japan. **Phone:** 257-79-1500. **Fax:** 257-79-4443. **E-mail:** admgsim@iuj.ac.jp.

RESOURCES AND SERVICES

Information about online services, personal computer policies, library resources, international exchange programs, internship programs, and placement services at this institution and others can be found at **www.petersons.com/mba**

International Students

62% of students enrolled are international students.

Services and Facilities Counseling/support services, ESL/language courses, housing location assistance, international student housing, international student organization, language tutoring, orientation, visa services. Financial aid is available to international students.

Applying *Required:* TOEFL with recommended score of 550 (paper), proof of adequate funds, proof of health/immunizations.

International Student Contact Ms. Chikako Hiura, Office of Graduate School of International Management (MBA Program Office), 777 Anaji Shinden, Yamato-machi, Niigata, Japan. **Phone:** 257-79-1500. **Fax:** 257-79-4443. **E-mail:** admgsim@iuj.ac.jp.

■ **APPLICATION**

Required GMAT, application form, baccalaureate/first degree, essay, 2 letters of recommendation, personal statement, transcripts of college work. **Recommended** Resume/curriculum vitae, work experience.

Deadlines and Fees *Deadlines:* 3/25 for fall, 4/1 for fall (international). *Application fee:* 30,000 Japanese yen, 5000 Japanese yen (international).

Application Contact Ms. Kerry Cross, Recruitment Officer and Director of Foreign Public Relations, 777 Anaji Shinden, Yamato-machi, Niigata, Japan. **Phone:** 257-79-1502. **Fax:** 257-79-4443. **E-mail:** admgsim@iuj.ac.jp.

Waseda University

Tokyo, Japan

GRADUATE SCHOOL OF ASIA-PACIFIC STUDIES

Graduate Business Faculty
Full-time: 19   Part-time: 45

Student Body
Total: 312   Average Age: 30
Full-time: 293   Women: 24%
Part-time: 19

Admissions
Applications: 192   Enrolled: 60
Admitted: 62

Costs (1999–2000)
Full-time tuition: 1,706,000 Japanese yen per academic year
Part-time tuition: 65,000 Japanese yen per unit

DEGREE MBA

MBA—Master of Business Administration Full-time and part-time. At least 30 total credits required. 18 to 48 months to complete program. *Concentrations:* accounting, Asian business studies, business information science, business policy/strategy, entrepreneurship, finance, information management, international finance, international management, Japanese business studies, logistics, management systems analysis, marketing, operations management, production management, strategic management, system management.

COSTS

Tuition *Full-time:* 1,706,000 Japanese yen. *Part-time:* 65,000 Japanese yen per unit.

FINANCIAL AID (1999–2000)

Fellowships and scholarships. Financial aid application deadline: 4/23.
Financial Aid Contact Ms. Kazumi Sakamoto, Admissions Officer, Nishi-Waseda Building 7F, 1-21-1 Nishi-Waseda Shinjuku-ku, Tokyo, 169-0051, Japan. **Phone:** 3-5286-3877. **Fax:** 3-5272-4533. **E-mail:** gsaps@list.waseda.ac.jp.

RESOURCES AND SERVICES

Information about online services, personal computer policies, library resources, international exchange programs, internship programs, and placement services at this institution and others can be found at **www.petersons.com/mba**

International Students

47% of students enrolled are international students.
Services and Facilities Counseling/support services, ESL/language courses, international student housing, language tutoring, orientation, visa services. Financial aid is available to international students.
Applying *Required:* TOEFL, proof of adequate funds, proof of health/immunizations.
International Student Contact Ms. Kazumi Sakamoto, Admissions Officer, Nishi-Waseda Building 7F, 1-21-1 Nishi-Waseda Shinjuku-ku, Japan. **Phone:** 3-5286-3877. **Fax:** 3-5272-4533. **E-mail:** gsaps@list.waseda.ac.jp.

■ **APPLICATION**

Required Application form, baccalaureate/first degree, essay, interview, 2 letters of recommendation, personal statement, resume/curriculum vitae, transcripts of college work, 3 years of work experience. School will accept GMAT.

Deadlines and Fees *Deadlines:* 4/23 for fall, 9/14 for spring, 4/23 for fall (international), 9/14 for spring (international). *Application fee:* 36,500 Japanese yen.

Application Contact Ms. Kazumi Sakamoto, Admissions Officer, Nishi-Waseda Building 7F, 1-21-1 Nishi-Waseda, Shinjuku-ku, Tokyo, 169-0051, Japan. **Phone:** 3-5286-3877. **Fax:** 3-5272-4533. **E-mail:** gsaps@list.waseda.ac.jp.

See full description on page 1004.

MEXICO

Duxx Graduate School of Business Leadership

Garza Garcia, Mexico

BUSINESS PROGRAMS

Graduate Business Faculty
Part-time: 39

Student Body
Total: 25   Average Age: 27
Full-time: 25   Women: 8%

Admissions
Applications: 575   Enrolled: 25
Admitted: 31   Average GMAT: 550

Costs (1999–2000)
Full-time tuition: $9500 per academic year
Part-time tuition: N/R

After Graduation (Class of 1998–99)
Employed within 3 months of graduation: 85%
Average starting salary: $67,300

DEGREE MBL

MBL—Master in Business Leadership Full-time. Minimum of 12 months to complete program.

COSTS

Tuition *Full-time:* $9500. **Graduate housing:** *Typical cost:* $9500 (including board).

FINANCIAL AID (1999–2000)

Financial Aid Contact

RESOURCES AND SERVICES

Information about online services, personal computer policies, library resources, international exchange programs, internship programs, and placement services at this institution and others can be found at **www.petersons.com/mba**

International Students

Services and Facilities Counseling/support services, housing location assistance, international student housing, visa services.
Applying *Required:* TOEFL with recommended score of 253 (computer) or 610 (paper). *Recommended:* IELT, TWE.
International Student Contact Admission Office, Calzada del Valle 106, Ote Col. Del Valle, Nuevo Leon, Mexico. **Phone:** 528-153 30 00. **Fax:** 528-153 30 99. **E-mail:** admissio@duxx.mx.

■ **APPLICATION**

Required GMAT, application form, baccalaureate/first degree, essay, interview, 2 letters of recommendation, resume/curriculum vitae, transcripts of college work, 2 years of work experience.

Deadlines and Fees *Deadlines:* 4/30 for fall, 11/14 for spring. *Application fee:* $100, $100 (international).

Application Contact Martha L. Garcia, Admissions, Calzada del Valle 106, Ote Col. Del Valle, Nuevo Leon, Mexico. **Phone:** 528-153 30 00. **Fax:** 528-153 30 99. **E-mail:** admissio@duxx.mx.

Instituto Tecnológico y de Estudios Superiores de Monterrey, Campus Monterrey

Monterrey, Mexico

GRADUATE SCHOOL OF MANAGEMENT AND LEADERSHIP

Graduate Business Faculty
Full-time: 55

Part-time: 72

Student Body
Total: 985
Full-time: 100
Part-time: 885

Average Age: 28
Women: 26%

Admissions
Applications: 290
Admitted: 174

Enrolled: 114
Average GPA: 84/100 scale

Costs (1999–2000)
Full-time tuition: $11,355 per academic year
Part-time tuition: $1300 per course

After Graduation (Class of 1998–99)
Employed within 3 months of graduation: 95%
Average starting salary: $38,400

DEGREES MBA • MS

MBA—Master of Business Administration Full-time and part-time. *Distance learning option.* 45 to 54 total credits required. Minimum of 15 months to complete program. *Concentrations:* business policy/strategy, entrepreneurship, environmental economics/management, finance, marketing, public policy and administration.

MS—Master of International Management for Latin American Managers (MIMLA) Full-time. *Distance learning option.* GMAT. 50 total credits required. 24 months to complete program.

MS—Master of Science in Finance Full-time and part-time. *Distance learning option.* 36 to 48 total credits required. Minimum of 15 months to complete program.

MS—Master of Science in Marketing Full-time and part-time. *Distance learning option.* 36 to 48 total credits required. Minimum of 15 months to complete program. *Concentrations:* advertising.

COSTS

Tuition *Full-time:* $11,100. *Part-time:* $1300 per course. Tuition varies by number of courses or credits taken. **Required fees:** *Full-time* $255. *Part-time* $85 per trimester. **Graduate housing:** Room and board costs vary by campus location and number of occupants. *Typical cost:* $2300 (room only).

FINANCIAL AID (1999–2000)

334 students received aid, including loans, research assistantships, and teaching assistantships. Aid is available to part-time students. **Financial Aid Contact** Ms. Anibel Silvestri, Director of Scholarship Programs, Sucursal de Correos J, Monterrey, Nuevo Leon, 64849, Mexico. **Phone:** 8-358-2000 Ext. 3505. **Fax:** 8-358-2000 Ext. 3505. **E-mail:** asilvest@campus.mty.itesm.mx.

RESOURCES AND SERVICES

Information about online services, personal computer policies, library resources, international exchange programs, internship programs, and placement services at this institution and others can be found at **www.petersons.com/mba**

International Students

6% of students enrolled are international students.

Services and Facilities Counseling/support services, international student housing, visa services. Financial aid is not available to international students.
International Student Contact Ms. Karla Coronado, International Programs Coordinator, Sucursal de Correos J, Monterrey, Nuevo Leon, 64849, Mexico. **Phone:** 8-358-2000 Ext. 6203. **Fax:** 8-358-9802. **E-mail:** kcorona@egade.sistema.itesm.mx.

■ APPLICATION

Required GMAT, application form, baccalaureate/first degree, interview, resume/curriculum vitae, transcripts of college work, 3 years of work experience. **Recommended** 3 letters of recommendation, personal statement.
Deadlines and Fees *Deadlines:* 7/30 for fall, 10/20 for winter, 2/10 for spring, 7/30 for fall (international), 10/20 for winter (international), 2/10 for spring (international). *Application fee:* $92, $92 (international).

Application Contact Ms. Sheyla Horita, Admissions Coordinator, Sucursal de Correos J, Monterrey, Nuevo Leon, 64849, Mexico. **Phone:** 08-358-2000 Ext. 6205. **Fax:** 08-358-9802. **E-mail:** shorita@campus.mty.itesm.mx.

Instituto Tecnológico y de Estudios Superiores de Monterrey, Campus Querétaro

Querétaro, Mexico

POSGRADOS, MBA PROGRAM

Graduate Business Faculty
Full-time: 9

Part-time: 3

Student Body
Total: 172
Full-time: 5
Part-time: 167

Average Age: 35
Women: 32%

Admissions
Applications: 56
Admitted: 47

Enrolled: 28

Costs (1999–2000)
Full-time tuition: N/R
Part-time tuition: $1280 per course

After Graduation (Class of 1998–99)
Employed within 3 months of graduation: 95%

DEGREES MAF • MBA • MMktg

MAF—Master of Applied Finance Part-time. At least 180 total credits required. 15 to 48 months to complete program. *Concentrations:* finance, financial economics, financial information systems, financial management/planning, strategic management, technology management.

MBA—Executive MBA Part-time. At least 180 total credits required. 15 to 48 months to complete program. *Concentrations:* international management, management, strategic management.

MMktg—Master of Marketing Part-time. At least 180 total credits required. 15 to 48 months to complete program. *Concentrations:* advertising, international management, management, marketing, marketing research, strategic management.

COSTS

Tuition *Part-time:* $1280 per course. Tuition varies by number of courses or credits taken. **Required fees:** Fees vary by number of courses or credits taken, campus location, and local reciprocity agreements. **Graduate housing:** Room and board costs vary by campus location, number of occupants, type of accommodation, and type of board plan. *Typical cost:* $3280 (including board).

RESOURCES AND SERVICES

Information about online services, personal computer policies, library resources, international exchange programs, internship programs, and placement services at this institution and others can be found at **www.petersons.com/mba**

International Students

Services and Facilities Counseling/support services, ESL/language courses, housing location assistance, language tutoring, orientation, visa services. Financial aid is not available to international students.
Applying *Required:* TOEFL with recommended score of 570 (paper).

International Student Contact Rachel Bright, International Student Coordinator, International Programs, Av. Epigmenio González No. 500, Fracc. San Pablo, Querétaro, 76130, Mexico. **Phone:** 42-383-287. **Fax:** 42-383-288. **E-mail:** rbright@campus.qro.itesm.mx.

■ APPLICATION

Required Application form, baccalaureate/first degree, 2 letters of recommendation. **Recommended** Interview.
Deadlines and Fees *Deadlines:* 9/11 for fall, 7/17 for summer, 8/18 for fall (international), 6/24 for summer (international).
Application Contact Alejandro Ardila, Dean, MBA Program, Av. Epigmenio González No. 500, Fracc. San Pablo, Querétaro, 76130, Mexico. **Phone:** 42-383-357. **Fax:** 42-383-193. **E-mail:** aardila@campus.qro.itesm.mx.

Universidad de las Américas–Puebla

Cholula, Mexico

SCHOOL OF BUSINESS ADMINISTRATION

Graduate Business Faculty
Full-time: 25   Part-time: 10

Student Body
Total: 196   Average Age: 28
Full-time: 14   Women: 36%
Part-time: 182

Admissions
Applications: 100   Enrolled: 70
Admitted: 75

Costs (1999–2000)
Full-time tuition: N/R
Part-time tuition: N/R

DEGREES M Adm • MBA • MS

M Adm—Master of Administration in Construction Management Full-time and part-time. At least 40 total credits required. 12 to 60 months to complete program. *Concentrations:* construction management.

M Adm—Master of Administration in Finance Full-time and part-time. At least 40 total credits required. 12 to 60 months to complete program. *Concentrations:* finance.

M Adm—Master of Administration in Financial Management and Planning Full-time and part-time. At least 40 total credits required. 12 to 60 months to complete program. *Concentrations:* financial management/planning.

M Adm—Master of Administration in Manufacturing Management Full-time and part-time. At least 40 total credits required. 12 to 60 months to complete program. *Concentrations:* manufacturing management.

MBA—Master of Business Administration Full-time and part-time. At least 40 total credits required. 12 to 60 months to complete program. *Concentrations:* financial management/planning, international business.

MS—Master of Science in Economics Full-time. At least 42 total credits required. 24 to 60 months to complete program. *Concentrations:* economics.

FINANCIAL AID (1999–2000)

Financial Aid Contact Financial Aid Office, Sta Catarina Martir, 72820 Cholula, Mexico. **Phone:** 22-292-013. **E-mail:** infobecas@mail.udlap.mx.

RESOURCES AND SERVICES

Information about online services, personal computer policies, library resources, international exchange programs, internship programs, and placement services at this institution and others can be found at **www.petersons.com/mba**

International Students

3% of students enrolled are international students.

Services and Facilities Counseling/support services, language tutoring, visa services.

Applying *Required:* TOEFL with recommended score of 500 (paper).

International Student Contact Miguel Angel Ruiz, Foreign Students Advisor, International Students Office, Ex-hda Sta. Catgrina Mortir Sln, Cholula, 72820, Mexico. **Phone:** 22-293-166. **Fax:** 22-293-169. **E-mail:** mruiz@mail.udlap.mx.

■ APPLICATION

Required Application form, baccalaureate/first degree, 2 letters of recommendation, personal statement, transcripts of college work. **Recommended** Interview.

Deadlines and Fees *Deadlines:* 7/15 for fall, 6/1 for fall (international).

Application Contact Mr. Mauricio Villegas, Admissions Office Chair, Sta Catarina Martir, Puebla, Mexico. **Phone:** 22-292-017. **Fax:** 22-292-017. **E-mail:** admision@mail.udlap.mx.

MONACO

University of Southern Europe

Monte Carlo, Monaco

MONACO GRADUATE BUSINESS SCHOOL

Graduate Business Faculty
Full-time: 15   Part-time: 25

Student Body
Total: 41   Part-time: 3
Full-time: 38   Average Age: 29

Admissions
Applications: 130   Enrolled: 41
Admitted: 50   Average GMAT: 510

Costs (1999–2000)
Full-time tuition: N/R
Part-time tuition: N/R

DEGREES MBA

MBA—Executive MBA Part-time. At least 60 total credits required. 24 months to complete program.

MBA—MBA in International Management Full-time. At least 60 total credits required. 10 to 20 months to complete program.

MBA—Master of Business Administration Full-time and part-time. At least 60 total credits required. 10 to 20 months to complete program. *Concentrations:* electronic commerce (e-commerce), finance, international marketing.

COSTS

Tuition varies by number of courses or credits taken and academic program.

FINANCIAL AID (1999–2000)

Scholarships and work study. **Financial Aid Contact** Director of Finance, 2, avenue Prince Hereditaire Albert, Monte Carlo, MC 98000, Monaco. **Phone:** 97-986995. **Fax:** 92-052830.

RESOURCES AND SERVICES

Information about online services, personal computer policies, library resources, international exchange programs, internship programs, and placement services at this institution and others can be found at **www.petersons.com/mba**

International Students

Services and Facilities Counseling/support services, ESL/language courses, housing location assistance, international student housing, orientation, visa services. **Applying** *Required:* TOEFL.

International Student Contact Prof. Jean-Pierre Daloz, Executive Vice President, 2, avenue Prince Hereditaire Albert, Monte Carlo, MC 98000, Monaco. **Phone:** 97-986986. **Fax:** 97-986-999.

■ APPLICATION

Required GMAT, application form, baccalaureate/first degree, essay, interview, 2 letters of recommendation, resume/curriculum vitae, transcripts of college work. School will accept GRE. **Recommended** Personal statement, 2 years of work experience.

Deadlines and Fees *Application fee:* 122 euros (international).

NETHERLANDS

Erasmus University Rotterdam

Rotterdam, Netherlands

ROTTERDAM SCHOOL OF MANAGEMENT

Graduate Business Faculty
Full-time: 67   Part-time: 59

Student Body
Total: 240   Average Age: 29
Full-time: 240   Women: 25%

Erasmus University Rotterdam (continued)

Admissions
Applications: 700   Average GMAT: 620
Enrolled: 120

Costs (1999–2000)
Full-time tuition: 27,500 euros per academic year
Part-time tuition: N/R

After Graduation (Class of 1998–99)
Employed within 3 months of graduation: 82%
Average starting salary: 61,250 euros

Accreditation
AACSB—The International Association for Management Education

DEGREES MBA • MBA/MBI

MBA—Full-time International MBA Program Full-time. At least 23 total credits required. 18 months to complete program. *Concentrations:* electronic commerce (e-commerce), entrepreneurship, international business, international finance, international marketing, management information systems, strategic management.

MBA/MBI—Full-time International MBA/Master of Business Informatics Full-time. At least 27 total credits required. 18 months to complete program. *Concentrations:* electronic commerce (e-commerce), entrepreneurship, international business, international finance, international marketing, management information systems, strategic management, technology management.

COSTS
Tuition *Full-time:* 27,500 euros. Tuition varies by academic program. **Graduate housing:** Room and board costs vary by campus location, number of occupants, and type of accommodation. *Typical cost:* 4600 euros (room only).

FINANCIAL AID (1999–2000)
Loans and scholarships. **Financial Aid Contact** Ms. Connie Tai, MBA Admissions Office, Rotterdam School of Management, PO Box 1738, Rotterdam, 3000 DR, Netherlands. **Phone:** 31-10-408-2222. **Fax:** 31-10-452-9509. **E-mail:** rsm@rsm.nl.

RESOURCES AND SERVICES
Information about online services, personal computer policies, library resources, international exchange programs, internship programs, and placement services at this institution and others can be found at **www.petersons.com/mba**

International Students
90% of students enrolled are international students.

Services and Facilities Counseling/support services, ESL/language courses, housing location assistance, international student housing, international student organization, orientation, visa services. Financial aid is not available to international students.

Applying *Recommended:* TOEFL.

International Student Contact Ms. Connie Tai, MBA Admissions Office, Rotterdam School of Management, PO Box 1738, Rotterdam, 3000 DR, Netherlands. **Phone:** 31-10-408-2222. **Fax:** 31-10-452-9509. **E-mail:** rsm@rsm.nl.

■ APPLICATION
Required GMAT, application form, baccalaureate/first degree, essay, interview, 2 letters of recommendation, personal statement, transcripts of college work, 2 years of work experience. **Recommended** Resume/curriculum vitae.

Deadlines and Fees *Deadlines:* 6/15 for fall, 6/15 for fall (international).

Application Contact Ms. Connie Tai, MBA Admissions Director, Rotterdam School of Management, PO Box 1738, Rotterdam, 3000 DR, Netherlands. **Phone:** 31-10408-2222. **Fax:** 31-10452-9509. **E-mail:** rsm@rsm.nl.

See full description on page 646.

Haagse Hogeschool University
The Hague, Netherlands

FACULTY OF ECONOMICS AND MANAGEMENT

DEGREES MBA

MBA—International MBA
MBA—Regular MBA Full-time and part-time. 12 to 30 months to complete program.

RESOURCES AND SERVICES
Information about online services, personal computer policies, library resources, international exchange programs, internship programs, and placement services at this institution and others can be found at **www.petersons.com/mba**

■ APPLICATION
Application Contact Mr. Frank H. Fox, MBA Program Manager, Graduate Studies Center, Room SL 3.01, Johanna Westerdijkplein 75, 2521 EN The Hague, Netherlands. **Phone:** 70-445 8284. **Fax:** 70-445 8194. **E-mail:** fox@sem.hhs.nl.

Maastricht School of Management
Maastricht, Netherlands

BUSINESS PROGRAMS

Graduate Business Faculty
Full-time: 35   Part-time: 35

Student Body
Total: 115   Average Age: 32
Full-time: 85   Women: 35%
Part-time: 30

Admissions
Applications: 450   Enrolled: 113
Admitted: 400

Costs (1999–2000)
Full-time tuition: N/R
Part-time tuition: N/R

After Graduation (Class of 1998–99)
Employed within 3 months of graduation: 100%

DEGREES MBA

MBA—Executive MBA Part-time. 48 total credits required. Minimum of 24 months to complete program. *Concentrations:* management, strategic management.

MBA—Executive MBA in Aviation Management Part-time. 48 total credits required. Minimum of 24 months to complete program. *Concentrations:* management, aviation management.

MBA—Full Time MBA Full-time. 48 total credits required. Minimum of 12 months to complete program. *Concentrations:* accounting, business policy/strategy, electronic commerce (e-commerce), international business, public policy and administration, strategic management, travel industry/tourism management.

COSTS
Tuition varies by number of courses or credits taken. **Graduate housing:** Room and board costs vary by number of occupants and type of accommodation. *Typical cost:* $4000 (room only).

FINANCIAL AID (1999–2000)
18 students received aid, including fellowships. **Financial Aid Contact** Dr. J. L. Huxell, Associate Dean for Masters Programmes, PO Box 1203, Maastricht, 6201 BE, Netherlands. **Phone:** 43-387 0808. **Fax:** 43-307 0800. **E-mail:** huxell@msm.nl.

RESOURCES AND SERVICES
Information about online services, personal computer policies, library resources, international exchange programs, internship programs, and placement services at this institution and others can be found at **www.petersons.com/mba**

International Students
82% of students enrolled are international students.

Services and Facilities Counseling/support services, international student housing, visa services. Financial aid is not available to international students.

Applying *Required:* TOEFL with recommended score of 350 (paper), proof of adequate funds, proof of health/immunizations.

International Student Contact Dr. J. L. Huxell, Associate Dean for Masters Programmes, PO Box 1203, Maastricht, 6201 BE, Netherlands. **Phone:** 43-387 0808. **Fax:** 43-387 0800. **E-mail:** huxell@msm.nl.

■ APPLICATION
Required Application form, baccalaureate/first degree, 3 letters of recommendation, transcripts of college work. **Recommended** 3 years of work experience.

496

Deadlines and Fees *Deadlines:* 5/1 for fall, 5/1 for fall (international). *Application fee:* $100, $100 (international).

Application Contact Dr. J. L. Huxell, Associate Dean for Masters Programmes, PO Box 1203, Maastricht, 6201 BE, Netherlands. **Phone:** 43-387 0808. **Fax:** 43-387 0800. **E-mail:** huxell@msm.nl.

Open University of the Netherlands

Heerlen, Netherlands

BUSINESS PROGRAMS

DEGREE MBA

MBA—Euro*MBA Programme Part-time. *Distance learning option.* 3 years of work experience required, proficiency in English required. Minimum of 24 months to complete program. *Concentrations:* business law, European business studies, human resources, international business, international finance, international management, international marketing, public policy and administration, strategic management, technology management.

RESOURCES AND SERVICES

Information about online services, personal computer policies, library resources, international exchange programs, internship programs, and placement services at this institution and others can be found at **www. petersons.com/mba**

International Students

Services and Facilities Financial aid is not available to international students.
International Student Contact Dr. Ronald S.J. Tuninga, Director, Euro*MBA Programme, Valkenburgerweg 167, PO Box 2960, Heerlen, 6401 DL, Netherlands. **Phone:** 45-5762-507. **Fax:** 45-5762-103. **E-mail:** ron.tuninga@ouh.nl.

■ APPLICATION

Application Contact Dr. Ronald S.J. Tuninga, Director, Euro*MBA Programme, Euro*MBA Desk, Valkenburgerweg 167, Heerlen, 6149 AT, Netherlands. **Phone:** 45-5762-587. **Fax:** 45-5762-103. **E-mail:** euro.mba-desk@ouh.nl.

Univeroiteit Nyenrode

Breukelen, Netherlands

NETHERLANDS BUSINESS SCHOOL

Graduate Business Faculty
Full-time: 52   Part-time: 59

Student Body
Total: 201   Average Age: 32
Full-time: 61   Women: 20%
Part-time: 140

Admissions
Average GMAT: 600   Average GPA: 3.5

Costs (1999–2000)
Full-time tuition: N/R
Part-time tuition: 102,500 Dutch guilders per degree program

DEGREES MBA

MBA—Executive MBA Part-time. At least 65 total credits required. Maximum of 18 months to complete program. *Concentrations:* entrepreneurship, international management, management.

MBA—International MBA Full-time. At least 80 total credits required. Maximum of 13 months to complete program. *Concentrations:* entrepreneurship, international management, management.

MBA—MBA in Financial Services and Insurance Part-time. *Distance learning option.* At least 60 total credits required. Maximum of 18 months to complete program. *Concentrations:* banking, finance, financial economics, financial information systems, financial management/planning, international banking, international finance, management.

MBA—Modular MBA Part-time. *Distance learning option.* At least 69 total credits required. Maximum of 18 months to complete program. *Concentrations:* entrepreneurship, international management, management.

COSTS

Tuition *Part-time:* 102,500 Dutch guilders per degree program.

FINANCIAL AID (1999–2000)

Loans. **Financial Aid Contact** Ms. Olena Miltenburg, MBA Admissions Officer, MBA Office, Straatweg 25, Breukelen, 3621 BG, Netherlands. **Phone:** 346-291-607. **Fax:** 346-250-595. **E-mail:** o.miltenburg@nyenrode.nl.

RESOURCES AND SERVICES

Information about online services, personal computer policies, library resources, international exchange programs, internship programs, and placement services at this institution and others can be found at **www. petersons.com/mba**

International Students

Services and Facilities Counseling/support services, international student housing, international student organization, language tutoring, orientation, visa services. Financial aid is not available to international students.
Applying *Required:* TOEFL with recommended score of 250 (computer) or 600 (paper), proof of adequate funds, proof of health/immunizations.
International Student Contact Ms. Olena Miltenburg, MBA Admissions Officer, MBA Office, Straatweg 25, Breukelen, 3621 BG, Netherlands. **Phone:** 346-291-607. **Fax:** 346-250-295. **E-mail:** o.miltenburg@nyenrode.nl.

■ APPLICATION

Required Application form, baccalaureate/first degree, essay, interview, 2 letters of recommendation, resume/curriculum vitae, transcripts of college work, 2 years of work experience. School will accept GMAT. **Recommended** Personal statement.

Deadlines and Fees *Deadlines:* 5/14 for fall, 5/14 for fall (international). *Application fee:* 150 Dutch guilders.

Application Contact Ms. Olena Miltenburg, MBA Admissions Officer, MBA Office, Straatweg 25, Breukelen, 3621 BG, Netherlands. **Phone:** 346-291-607. **Fax:** 346-250-595. **E-mail:** o.miltenburg@nyenrode.nl.

University of Twente

Enschede, Netherlands

TSM BUSINESS SCHOOL

Graduate Business Faculty
Full-time: 40   Part-time: 70

Student Body
Total: 50   Average Age: 30
Full-time: 26   Women: 14%
Part-time: 24

Admissions
Applications: 140   Enrolled: 47
Admitted: 57   Average GMAT: 550

Costs (1999–2000)
Full-time tuition: N/R
Part-time tuition: N/R

After Graduation (Class of 1998–99)
Employed within 3 months of graduation: 80%

DEGREES MBA

MBA—International Executive MBA Part-time. 21 months to complete program. *Concentrations:* entrepreneurship, leadership, technology management.

MBA—International Full-time MBA Full-time. 18 months to complete program. *Concentrations:* entrepreneurship, leadership, technology management.

COSTS

Tuition varies by class time and academic program. **Graduate housing:** Room and board costs vary by number of occupants and type of accommodation. *Typical cost:* 2750 ECU (room only).

FINANCIAL AID (1999–2000)

4 students received aid, including grants, loans, scholarships, and work study. Financial aid application deadline: 5/1. **Financial Aid Contact** Ms. Anita Steenstra, Programme Manager, TSM Business School, PO Box 217, Enschede, 7500AE, Netherlands. **Phone:** 53-489-8009. **Fax:** 53-489-4848. **E-mail:** mba@tsm.nl.

RESOURCES AND SERVICES

Information about online services, personal computer policies, library resources, international exchange programs, internship programs, and placement services at this institution and others can be found at **www. petersons.com/mba**

University of Twente (continued)

International Students

44% of students enrolled are international students.

Services and Facilities Counseling/support services, ESL/language courses, international student housing, visa services. Financial aid is available to international students.

Applying *Required:* Proof of adequate funds. *Recommended:* TOEFL.

International Student Contact Ms. Anita Steenstra, Programme Manager, TSM Business School, PO Box 217, Enschede, 7500 AE, Netherlands. **Phone:** 53-489-8009. **Fax:** 53-489-4848. **E-mail:** mba@tsm.nl.

■ APPLICATION

Required Application form, baccalaureate/first degree, essay, interview, 2 letters of recommendation, personal statement, resume/curriculum vitae, transcripts of college work, 3 years of work experience. School will accept GMAT.

Deadlines and Fees *Deadlines:* 6/1 for fall, 6/1 for fall (international). *Application fee:* 50 ECU, 50 ECU (international).

Application Contact Ms. Anita Steenstra, Programme Manager, TSM Business School, PO Box 217, Enschede, 7500AE, Netherlands. **Phone:** 53-489-8009. **Fax:** 53-489-4848. **E-mail:** mba@tsm.nl.

NEW ZEALAND

University of Canterbury

Christchurch, New Zealand

DEPARTMENT OF MANAGEMENT

DEGREE MBA

MBA—Master of Business Administration Full-time and part-time. 15 to 30 months to complete program. *Concentrations:* accounting, economics, finance, human resources, management, management information systems, marketing, organizational behavior/development, production management, quantitative analysis, strategic management.

RESOURCES AND SERVICES

Information about online services, personal computer policies, library resources, international exchange programs, internship programs, and placement services at this institution and others can be found at **www.petersons.com/mba**

International Students

Services and Facilities Financial aid is available to international students.
International Student Contact International Student Centre, Private Bag 4800, Christchurch, New Zealand. **Phone:** 3-364 2391. **Fax:** 3-364 2603.

■ APPLICATION

Application Contact MBA Secretary, Private Bag 4800, Christchurch, New Zealand. **Phone:** 3-364-2657. **Fax:** 3-364-2020.

University of Otago

Dunedin, New Zealand

GRADUATE SCHOOL OF BUSINESS

Graduate Business Faculty
Full-time: 21   Part-time: 11
Student Body
Total: 95
Full-time: 23   Average Age: 34
Part-time: 72   Women: 31%
Admissions
Applications: 36   Enrolled: 23
Admitted: 28   Average GMAT: 600
Costs (1999–2000)
Full-time tuition: N/R
Part-time tuition: 25,000 New Zealand dollars per degree program (resident)

After Graduation (Class of 1998–99)
Employed within 3 months of graduation: 90%

DEGREES MBA

MBA—Executive MBA Part-time. 5 years work experience. 24 to 48 months to complete program.
MBA—Master of Business Administration Full-time. 3 years work experience. 16 to 48 months to complete program. *Concentrations:* international business, strategic management.

COSTS

Tuition, state resident: *Part-time* 25,000 New Zealand dollars per degree program. Tuition varies by academic program. **Graduate housing:** Room and board costs vary by campus location, number of occupants, type of accommodation, and type of board plan. *Typical cost:* 8000 New Zealand dollars (including board).

FINANCIAL AID (1999–2000)

Loans. **Financial Aid Contact** MBA Admissions Office, PO Box 56, Dunedin, New Zealand. **Phone:** 3-479-8046. **Fax:** 3-479-8045. **E-mail:** mbainfo@commerce.otago.ac.nz.

RESOURCES AND SERVICES

Information about online services, personal computer policies, library resources, international exchange programs, internship programs, and placement services at this institution and others can be found at **www.petersons.com/mba**

International Students

11% of students enrolled are international students.

Services and Facilities Counseling/support services, ESL/language courses, housing location assistance, international student housing, international student organization, language tutoring, orientation, visa services. Financial aid is available to international students.

Applying *Required:* IELT with recommended score of 6.5, TOEFL with recommended score of 650 (paper).

International Student Contact Glen Munn, Associate Director of Programme, PO Box 56, Dunedin, New Zealand. **Phone:** 3-479-8046. **Fax:** 3-479-8045. **E-mail:** mbainfo@commerce.otago.ac.nz.

■ APPLICATION

Required GMAT, application form, essay, interview, 2 letters of recommendation, personal statement, resume/curriculum vitae, transcripts of college work, work experience. **Recommended** Baccalaureate/first degree.

Deadlines and Fees *Deadline:* 12/1 for winter. *Application fee:* $100, $100 (international).

Application Contact Glen Munn, Associate Director of Programme, PO Box 56, Dunedin, New Zealand. **Phone:** 3-479-8046. **Fax:** 3-479-8045. **E-mail:** gmunn@commerce.otago.ac.nz.

University of Waikato

Hamilton, New Zealand

WAIKATO MANAGEMENT SCHOOL

Graduate Business Faculty
Part-time: 25
Student Body
Total: 200   Average Age: 31
Costs (1999–2000)
Full-time tuition: N/R
Part-time tuition: N/R

DEGREES MBA • MTM

MBA—Executive MBA Part-time. Maximum of 24 months to complete program. *Concentrations:* management.

MBA—International MBA Full-time. Maximum of 14 months to complete program. *Concentrations:* management.

MTM—Master of Technology Management Part-time. Maximum of 24 months to complete program.

FINANCIAL AID (1999–2000)

Scholarships. **Financial Aid Contact** Dr. Ed Weymes, Associate Dean, Executive Education, Private Bag 3105, Hamilton, New Zealand. **Phone:** 7-838-4198. **Fax:** 7-838-4675. **E-mail:** weymesed@waikato.ac.nz.

RESOURCES AND SERVICES

Information about online services, personal computer policies, library resources, international exchange programs, internship programs, and placement services at this institution and others can be found at www.petersons.com/mba

International Students

Services and Facilities Counseling/support services, housing location assistance, international student housing, international student organization, visa services. Financial aid is available to international students.
Applying *Required:* IELT with recommended score of 6.5, TOEFL.
International Student Contact Ms. Lynette Muter, International Manager, Private Bag 3105, Hamilton, New Zealand. **Phone:** 7-838-4727. **Fax:** 7-838-4269. **E-mail:** lynettem@waikato.ac.nz.

■ APPLICATION

Required Application form, baccalaureate/first degree, interview, 3 letters of recommendation, resume/curriculum vitae, transcripts of college work, 3 years of work experience. School will accept GMAT.

Deadlines and Fees Applications for domestic and international students are processed on a rolling basis. *Application fee:* 250 New Zealand dollars, 250 New Zealand dollars (international).

Application Contact Dr. Ed Weymes, Associate Dean, Executive Education, Waikato Management School, Private Bag 3105, Hamilton, New Zealand. **Phone:** 7-838-4198. **Fax:** 7-838-4675. **E-mail:** weymesed@waikato.ac.nz.

Victoria University of Wellington

Wellington, New Zealand

GRADUATE SCHOOL OF BUSINESS AND GOVERNMENT MANAGEMENT

DEGREES M Mgt • MBA • MPM

M Mgt—Master of Management Part-time. 21 to 48 months to complete program.
MBA—Master of Business Administration Full-time and part-time. 16 to 48 months to complete program. *Concentrations:* accounting, international business.
MPM—Master of Public Management Full-time and part-time. 16 to 48 months to complete program.

RESOURCES AND SERVICES

Information about online services, personal computer policies, library resources, international exchange programs, internship programs, and placement services at this institution and others can be found at **www.petersons.com/mba**

International Students

Services and Facilities Counseling/support services, ESL/language courses, international student housing, visa services. Financial aid is not available to international students.
International Student Contact Ms. Eleni Geris, International Liaison Officer, PO Box 600, Wellington, New Zealand. **Phone:** 4-471-5350. **Fax:** 4-495-5056. **E-mail:** international-students@vuw.ac.nz.

■ APPLICATION

Application Contact Ms. Monica Chow, MBA Programme Administrator, PO Box 600, Wellington, New Zealand. **Phone:** 4-471-5367. **Fax:** 4-496-5435. **E-mail:** mba@vuw.ac.nz.

NORWAY

Norwegian School of Management

Sandvika, Norway

GRADUATE SCHOOL

DEGREES MBA • MS

MBA—Full-time MBA Full-time. At least 40 total credits required. 12 months to complete program. *Concentrations:* leadership, strategic management.
MBA—Part-time MBA Part-time. At least 40 total credits required. 24 months to complete program. *Concentrations:* leadership, strategic management.
MS—Master of Science Full-time. At least 40 total credits required. 12 to 36 months to complete program. *Concentrations:* environmental economics/management, financial economics, international business, marketing, strategic management.

RESOURCES AND SERVICES

Information about online services, personal computer policies, library resources, international exchange programs, internship programs, and placement services at this institution and others can be found at **www.petersons.com/mba**

International Students

Services and Facilities Counseling/support services, international student housing, language tutoring, visa services, airport collection service for exchange students. Financial aid is available to international students.
International Student Contact Mrs. Kjersti Stokke, International Coordinator, PO Box 580, Sandvika, N-1301, Norway. **Phone:** 47-67570835. **Fax:** 47-67570541. **E-mail:** kjersti.e.stokke@bi.no.

■ APPLICATION

Application Contact Ms. Gillian Kennedy, Coordinator of MBA Program, PO Box 580, Sandvika, N-1301, Norway. **Phone:** 47-67570559. **Fax:** 47-67570541. **E-mail:** adm95024@bi.no.

PAKISTAN

Lahore University of Management Sciences

Lahore Cantt, Pakistan

GRADUATE SCHOOL OF BUSINESS ADMINISTRATION

Graduate Business Faculty
Full-time: 43 — Part-time: 28

Student Body
Total: 173 — Average Age: 25
Full-time: 173 — Women: 23%

Admissions
Applications: 366 — Enrolled: 72
Admitted: 75 — Average GMAT: 560

Costs (1999–2000)
Full-time tuition: 174,000 Pakistani rupees per academic year
Part-time tuition: N/R

After Graduation (Class of 1998–99)
Employed within 3 months of graduation: 50%
Average starting salary: 240,000 Pakistani rupees

DEGREE MBA

MBA—Master of Business Administration Full-time. 21 to 24 months to complete program. *Concentrations:* finance, management, marketing.

COSTS

Tuition *Full-time:* 174,000 Pakistani rupees. **Graduate housing:** Room and board costs vary by number of occupants. *Typical cost:* 52,200 Pakistani rupees (including board).

FINANCIAL AID (1999–2000)

Loans and scholarships. Financial aid application deadline: 3/1.
Financial Aid Contact Ms. Shazi Malik, Senior Manager, Student Affairs, Opposite Sector U, Phase II LCCHS, Punjab, Pakistan. **Phone:** 42-572 2440 Ext. 2171. **Fax:** 42-572-2591.

RESOURCES AND SERVICES

Information about online services, personal computer policies, library resources, international exchange programs, internship programs, and placement services at this institution and others can be found at **www. petersons.com/mba**

International Students

3% of students enrolled are international students.

Services and Facilities Counseling/support services, ESL/language courses, visa services. Financial aid is available to international students.
International Student Contact Ms. Shazi Malik, Senior Manager, Student Affairs, Opposite Sector U, Phase II LCCHS, Punjab, Pakistan. **Phone:** 42-572-2670. **Fax:** 42-572-2591. **E-mail:** shazi@lums.edu.pk.

■ APPLICATION

Required Application form, baccalaureate/first degree, essay, interview, personal statement, transcripts of college work. School will accept GMAT.
Deadlines and Fees *Deadlines:* 3/1 for fall, 3/1 for fall (international).
Application Contact Ms. Shazi Malik, Senior Manager, Student Affairs, Opposite Sector U, Phase II LCCHS, Punjab, Pakistan. **Phone:** 42-572-2670. **Fax:** 42-572-2592. **E-mail:** admissions@lums.edu.pk.

PERU

Escuela de Administracion de Negocios para Graduados

Lima, Peru

PROGRAMA MAGISTER

Graduate Business Faculty

Full-time: 28	Part-time: 44

Student Body

Total: 254	Part-time: 98
Full-time: 156	Average Age: 30

Admissions

Applications: 987	Enrolled: 254
Admitted: 386	

Costs (1999–2000)
Full-time tuition: $18,500 per academic year
Part-time tuition: N/R

DEGREES MBA

MBA—Magister en Administracion?Programa Magister Full-time Full-time. 2 years of work experience required. Maximum of 14 months to complete program. *Concentrations:* finance, management, management information systems, marketing, operations management, telecommunications management.

MBA—Magister en Administracion?Programa Magister Part-time Part-time. 3 years of work experience required. Minimum of 24 months to complete program. *Concentrations:* finance, management, management information systems, marketing, operations management, telecommunications management.

COSTS

Tuition *Full-time:* $18,500. Tuition varies by academic program.

FINANCIAL AID (1999–2000)

Scholarships. Aid is available to part-time students. **Financial Aid Contact** Mrs. Patricia Reveggino, Head of Admissions, Apdo 1846, Lima, 100,

Peru. **Phone:** 1-345-1267. **Fax:** 1-345-0956. **E-mail:** preveggino@esan. edu.pe.

RESOURCES AND SERVICES

Information about online services, personal computer policies, library resources, international exchange programs, internship programs, and placement services at this institution and others can be found at **www. petersons.com/mba**

International Students

Services and Facilities Counseling/support services, international student housing. Financial aid is not available to international students.
Applying *Required:* Proof of health/immunizations.
International Student Contact Ms. Ana Maria Villanueva, Director of Institutional Relations, Apdo 1846, Lima, 100, Peru. **Phone:** 1-345-1302. **E-mail:** avilla@ esan.edu.pe.

■ APPLICATION

Required Application form, baccalaureate/first degree, interview, personal statement, resume/curriculum vitae, transcripts of college work, work experience. School will accept GMAT.
Deadlines and Fees Applications for domestic and international students are processed on a rolling basis.
Application Contact Mrs. Patricia Reveggino, Head of Admissions, Apdo 1846, Lima, 100, Peru. **Phone:** 1-345-1267. **Fax:** 1-345-0956. **E-mail:** preveggino@ esan.edu.pe.

PORTUGAL

Universidade Nova de Lisboa

Lisbon, Portugal

FACULDADE DE ECONOMIA-GESTAO

DEGREE MBA

MBA—Master of Business Administration Full-time and part-time. At least 37 total credits required. 12 to 24 months to complete program. *Concentrations:* finance, human resources, management, marketing.

RESOURCES AND SERVICES

Information about online services, personal computer policies, library resources, international exchange programs, internship programs, and placement services at this institution and others can be found at **www. petersons.com/mba**

International Students

Services and Facilities Counseling/support services. Financial aid is not available to international students.
International Student Contact Ms. Isabel Paiva, Rua Marquês de Fronteira, 20, Lisbon, 1000, Portugal. **E-mail:** socrates@fe.unl.pt.

■ APPLICATION

Application Contact Manuel Baganha, Program Director, Rua Marques de Fronteira, 20, Lisbon, 1070, Portugal. **Phone:** 1-382-6111. **Fax:** 1-387-3973.

RUSSIAN FEDERATION

The International Management Institute of St. Petersburg

St. Petersburg, Russian Federation

INTERNATIONAL MANAGEMENT INSTITUTE OF ST. PETERSBURG

Graduate Business Faculty
Full-time: 18   Part-time: 14

Student Body
Total: 62   Average Age: 33
Part-time: 62   Women: 48%

Admissions
Applications: 62   Enrolled: 62
Admitted: 62   Average GMAT: 610

Costs (1999–2000)
Full-time tuition: N/R
Part-time tuition: $6000 per degree program

DEGREE MBA

MBA—Executive MBA Part-time. 2 years of working experience. 50 to 70 total credits required. 18 to 22 months to complete program. *Concentrations:* management.

COSTS

Tuition *Part-time:* $6000 per degree program.

FINANCIAL AID (1999–2000)
Financial Aid Contact

RESOURCES AND SERVICES
Information about online services, personal computer policies, library resources, international exchange programs, internship programs, and placement services at this institution and others can be found at **www.petersons.com/mba**

International Students
2% of students enrolled are international students.

Services and Facilities Counseling/support services. Financial aid is not available to international students.
Applying *Required:* TOEFL with recommended score of 500 (paper).
International Student Contact Mr. Fedor Raguine, Director for Development, Entrance 9, Smolny, St. Petersburg, 193060, Russian Federation. **Phone:** 812-271-1968. **Fax:** 812-271-0717. **E-mail:** raguine@imisp.spb.ru.

■ APPLICATION

Required Application form, baccalaureate/first degree, interview, 2 letters of recommendation, 2 years of work experience. School will accept GMAT.

Application Contact Mrs. Tatiana Lvova, MBA Administrator, Entrance 9, Smolny, St. Petersburg, 193060, Russian Federation. **Phone:** 812-271-1968. **Fax:** 812-271-0717. **E-mail:** marketing@imisp.spb.ru.

SINGAPORE

Nanyang Technological University

Singapore, Singapore

NANYANG BUSINESS SCHOOL

Graduate Business Faculty
Full-time: 129   Part-time: 13

Student Body
Total: 208   Part-time: 165
Full-time: 43   Average Age: 31

Women: 30%

Admissions
Applications: 551   Average GMAT: 610
Admitted: 274   Average GPA: 3.2
Enrolled: 209

Costs (1999–2000)
Full-time tuition: 3500 Singapore dollars per academic year (resident)
Part-time tuition: 2500 Singapore dollars per trimester (resident)

After Graduation (Class of 1998–99)
Employed within 3 months of graduation: 95%
Average starting salary: 91,500 Singapore dollars

DEGREES MBA

MBA—Full Time MBA Program Full-time and part-time. At least 54 total credits required. 12 to 20 months to complete program. *Concentrations:* accounting, banking, electronic commerce (e-commerce), finance, international business, marketing, strategic management, technology management.

MBA—Part Time MBA Program Full-time and part-time. At least 54 total credits required. 20 to 48 months to complete program.

COSTS

Tuition, state resident: *Full-time* 3500 Singapore dollars. *Part-time* 2500 Singapore dollars per trimester. **Tuition, international:** *Full-time* 3500 Singapore dollars. **Graduate housing:** Room and board costs vary by number of occupants and type of accommodation. *Typical cost:* 1800 Singapore dollars (room only).

FINANCIAL AID (1999–2000)
5 students received aid, including scholarships. **Financial Aid Contact** Mrs. Lee Lee Ooi, Deputy Director, Nanyang Avenue, Singapore, 639798, Singapore. **Phone:** 65-790-4896 Ext. 4896. **Fax:** 65-790-4896. **E-mail:** alltan@ntu.edu.sg.

RESOURCES AND SERVICES
Information about online services, personal computer policies, library resources, international exchange programs, internship programs, and placement services at this institution and others can be found at **www.petersons.com/mba**

International Students
29% of students enrolled are international students.

Services and Facilities Counseling/support services, ESL/language courses, international student housing, orientation, visa services, optional internship. Financial aid is available to international students.
Applying *Required:* Proof of adequate funds. *Recommended:* TOEFL with recommended score of 600 (paper), proof of health/immunizations.
International Student Contact Mrs. Pearlie Koh Ming Choo, Director, International Exchange Programme, Nanyang Avenue, Singapore, 639798, Singapore. **Phone:** 65-790-6145. **Fax:** 65-790-6145. **E-mail:** amckoh@ntu.edu.sg.

■ APPLICATION

Required GMAT, application form, baccalaureate/first degree, interview, 2 letters of recommendation, personal statement, resume/curriculum vitae, transcripts of college work, 2 years of work experience. School will accept GRE.

Deadlines and Fees *Deadline:* 2/28 for summer. *Application fee:* 50 Singapore dollars, 50 Singapore dollars (international).

Application Contact Mrs. Lee Lee Ooi, Deputy Director, Nanyang Avenue, Singapore, 639798, Singapore. **Phone:** 65-790-4896. **Fax:** 65-790-4896. **E-mail:** alltan@ntu.edu.sg.

See full description on page 734.

National University of Singapore

Singapore, Singapore

GRADUATE SCHOOL OF BUSINESS

DEGREES MBA • MBA/LLM • MS

MBA—Asia Pacific Executive Master of Business Administration Part-time. At least 72 total credits required. 18 to 48 months to complete program. *Concentrations:* business law, business policy/strategy, finance, international business, leadership, logistics, marketing, organizational behavior/development, technology management.

MBA—Master of Business Administration Full-time and part-time. At least 72 total credits required. 12 to 72 months to complete program. *Concentrations:* accounting, banking, finance, international business, management, management information systems, marketing, operations management, organizational behavior/development, strategic management.

National University of Singapore (continued)

MBA/LLM—Master of Business Administration/Master of Laws Full-time and part-time. At least 72 total credits required. 18 to 48 months to complete program. *Concentrations:* accounting, decision sciences, economics, financial management/planning, industrial/labor relations, international business, legal administration, management, management information systems, marketing, operations management, organizational behavior/development, strategic management.

MS—Asia Pacific Master of Science in Human Resource Management Full-time. At least 40 total credits required. 12 to 36 months to complete program. *Concentrations:* accounting, business law, finance, human resources, industrial administration/management, industrial/labor relations, international management, management, organizational management, resources management, strategic management.

MS—Asia Pacific Master of Science in Human Resource Management Part-time. At least 40 total credits required. 18 to 60 months to complete program. *Concentrations:* accounting, business law, finance, human resources, industrial administration/management, industrial/labor relations, international management, management, organizational management, resources management, strategic management.

MS—Master of Science in Applied Finance Part-time. At least 40 total credits required. 18 to 60 months to complete program. *Concentrations:* finance, financial management/planning.

MS—Master of Science in Financial Engineering Part-time. At least 40 total credits required. 18 to 48 months to complete program.

MS—Master of Science in Management of Technology Full-time and part-time. At least 40 total credits required. 9 to 60 months to complete program. *Concentrations:* entrepreneurship, industrial administration/management, management information systems, manufacturing management, new venture management, operations management, production management, quality management, research and development administration, technology management.

MS—Master of Science in Marketing Part-time. At least 40 total credits required. 18 to 48 months to complete program. *Concentrations:* international marketing, marketing, marketing research.

MS—Master of Science in e-Business Full-time and part-time. 12 months of work experience. 12 to 24 months to complete program.

RESOURCES AND SERVICES

Information about online services, personal computer policies, library resources, international exchange programs, internship programs, and placement services at this institution and others can be found at **www.petersons.com/mba**

International Students

Services and Facilities International student housing. Financial aid is available to international students.
International Student Contact Mr. Teck-Kiang Tan, Senior Administrative Officer, 10 Kent Ridge Crescent, Singapore, 0511, Singapore. **Phone:** 874-3427. **Fax:** 874-3427. **E-mail:** gsbtantk@nus.edu.sg.

■ APPLICATION

Application Contact Ms. Hamidah Bte Rabu, MBA Program, The NUS Business School, FBA2, Level 5, Room 06, 17 Law Link, Singapore, 117592, Singapore. **Phone:** 874-2068. **Fax:** 874-2068. **E-mail:** fbagrad@nus.edu.sg.

SLOVENIA

IEDC-Bled School of Management

Bled, Slovenia

SCHOOL OF BUSINESS ADMINISTRATION

Graduate Business Faculty
Full-time: 3   Part-time: 40

Student Body
Total: 50   Average Age: 33
Part-time: 50   Women: 30%

Admissions
Average GMAT: 540

Costs (1999–2000)
Full-time tuition: N/R
Part-time tuition: 15,500 euros per year

DEGREES EMBA • PMBA

EMBA—Executive Master of Business Administration Part-time. 5-10 years of work experience (3 years managerial experience) preferred. 12 months to complete program. *Concentrations:* accounting, business ethics, finance, human resources, international business, international finance, international marketing, leadership, management, marketing, operations management, organizational behavior/development, project management, strategic management, travel industry/tourism management.

PMBA—President's Master of Business Administration Part-time. Must hold top position within company. 12 to 36 months to complete program. *Concentrations:* accounting, business ethics, finance, human resources, international business, international finance, international marketing, leadership, management, marketing, operations management, organizational behavior/development, project management, strategic management, travel industry/tourism management.

COSTS

Tuition *Part-time:* 15,500 euros per year. Tuition varies by academic program. **Graduate housing:** Room and board costs vary by number of occupants, type of accommodation, and type of board plan. *Typical cost:* 5000 euros (including board).

FINANCIAL AID (1999–2000)

Loans and scholarships. Financial aid application deadline: 9/30.
Financial Aid Contact Mr. Andreas Griessler, Head of MBA Office, Brdo Pri Kranju, Bled, 4260, Slovenia. **Phone:** 64 792 500 Ext. 506. **Fax:** 64 792 500. **E-mail:** emba@iedc.si.

RESOURCES AND SERVICES

Information about online services, personal computer policies, library resources, international exchange programs, internship programs, and placement services at this institution and others can be found at **www.petersons.com/mba**

International Students

46% of students enrolled are international students.

Services and Facilities Counseling/support services, international student housing, visa services. Financial aid is available to international students.
International Student Contact Mr. Nenad Filipovic, Deputy Director, Presernova Cesta 33, Bled, 4260, Slovenia. **Phone:** 64 792 500. **Fax:** 64 792 500. **E-mail:** nenad.filipovic@iedc.si.

■ APPLICATION

Required GMAT, application form, baccalaureate/first degree, interview, 2 letters of recommendation, personal statement, resume/curriculum vitae, 3 years of work experience.

Deadlines and Fees *Deadlines:* 9/30 for winter, 9/30 for winter (international).
Application Contact Mr. Andreas Griessler, Head of MBA Office, Presernova Cesta 33, Bled, 4260, Slovenia. **Phone:** 64 792 500 Ext. 506. **Fax:** 64 792 500. **E-mail:** emba@iedc.si.

SOUTH AFRICA

Rhodes University

Grahamstown, South Africa

MANAGEMENT DEPARTMENT

DEGREES M Econ • MComm

M Econ—Master of Economics Full-time. Minimum of 24 months to complete program. *Concentrations:* economics, finance.

MComm—Master of Commerce Full-time. Minimum of 24 months to complete program. *Concentrations:* accounting, economics, information management, management, management information systems.

RESOURCES AND SERVICES

Information about online services, personal computer policies, library resources, international exchange programs, internship programs, and placement services at this institution and others can be found at **www.petersons.com/mba**

International Students

Services and Facilities Counseling/support services, ESL/language courses, international student housing, visa services. Financial aid is not available to international students.

International Student Contact Mrs. Helen Pienaar, International Studies Officer, PO Box 94, Grahamstown, 6140, South Africa. **Phone:** 46-603-8225. **Fax:** 46-622-2845. **E-mail:** adhb@giraffe.ru.ac.za.

■ APPLICATION

Application Contact Dr. Steve Fourie, Registrar, PO Box 94, Grahamstown, 6140, South Africa.

University of Cape Town

Rondebosch, South Africa

GRADUATE SCHOOL OF BUSINESS

Graduate Business Faculty
Full-time: 20 — Part-time: 30

Student Body
Total: 200
Full-time: 110 — Average Age: 30
Part-time: 90 — Women: 23%

Admissions
Applications: 222 — Enrolled: 155
Admitted: 155 — Average GMAT: 580

Costs (1999–2000)
Full-time tuition: 40,000 South African rand per academic year (resident)
Part-time tuition: 24,000 South African rand per year (resident)

After Graduation (Class of 1998–99)
Employed within 3 months of graduation: 90%

DEGREE MBA

MBA—Master of Business Administration Full-time and part-time. GMAT required. 12 to 24 months to complete program. *Concentrations:* accounting, economics, entrepreneurship, finance, human resources, information management, international finance, leadership, manufacturing management, marketing, operations management, organizational management, quantitative analysis, strategic management, taxation.

COSTS

Tuition, state resident: *Full-time* 40,000 South African rand. *Part-time* 24,000 South African rand per year. Tuition varies by campus location. **Graduate housing:** Room and board costs vary by number of occupants. *Typical cost:* 30,000 South African rand (including board).

FINANCIAL AID (1999–2000)

Loans and scholarships. Aid is available to part-time students. Financial aid application deadline: 2/15. **Financial Aid Contact** Mrs. Patricia Boulton, Head of Recruitment and Selection, Private Bag Rondebosch, Cape, South Africa. **Phone:** 21-4061338. **Fax:** 21-4215693. **E-mail:** pboulton@gsb2.uct.ac.za.

RESOURCES AND SERVICES

Information about online services, personal computer policies, library resources, international exchange programs, internship programs, and placement services at this institution and others can be found at **www.petersons.com/mba**

International Students

30% of students enrolled are international students.

Services and Facilities Counseling/support services, orientation. Financial aid is not available to international students.

Applying *Required:* TOEFL with recommended score of 600 (paper).

International Student Contact Mrs. Zubeidah Harris, Head of MBA Administration, The Graduate School of Business, Private Bag Rondebosch, Cape, South Africa. **Phone:** 21-4061450. **Fax:** 21-4215693. **E-mail:** zubeidah@gsb2.uct.ac.za.

■ APPLICATION

Required GMAT, application form, baccalaureate/first degree, interview, 2 letters of recommendation, resume/curriculum vitae, transcripts of college work, 3 years of work experience.

Deadlines and Fees *Deadlines:* 10/30 for fall, 9/30 for fall (international). *Application fee:* 100 South African rand.

Application Contact Ms. Patricia Boulton, Head of Recruitment and Selection, Private Bag Rondebosch, Cape, South Africa. **Phone:** 21-4061339. **Fax:** 21-4215693. **E-mail:** pboulton@gsb2.uct.ac.za.

University of the Witwatersrand

Wits, South Africa

GRADUATE SCHOOL OF BUSINESS ADMINISTRATION

Graduate Business Faculty
Full-time: 23 — Part-time: 10

Student Body
Total: 260
Full-time: 58 — Average Age: 29
Part-time: 202 — Women: 23%

Admissions
Applications: 699 — Enrolled: 180
Admitted: 206 — Average GMAT: 580

Costs (1999–2000)
Full-time tuition: N/R
Part-time tuition: N/R

DEGREE MBA

MBA—Master of Business Administration Full-time and part-time. 12 to 36 months to complete program. *Concentrations:* accounting, economics, entrepreneurship, finance, human resources, industrial/labor relations, international business, international economics, international finance, international management, international marketing, management information systems, marketing, operations management, production management, public and private management, quantitative analysis, strategic management.

FINANCIAL AID (1999–2000)

Loans and scholarships. **Financial Aid Contact** Ms. Liz Fick, Senior Assistant Registrar, Private Bag X3, Wits, Witwatersrand, 2050, South Africa. **Phone:** 11-716-3256.

RESOURCES AND SERVICES

Information about online services, personal computer policies, library resources, international exchange programs, internship programs, and placement services at this institution and others can be found at **www.petersons.com/mba**

International Students

4% of students enrolled are international students.

Services and Facilities International student housing. Financial aid is not available to international students.

Applying *Required:* Proof of adequate funds, proof of health/immunizations. *Recommended:* IELT.

International Student Contact Mrs. Anne Fraser, International Student Coordinator, Box 98, Witwatersrand, 2050, South Africa. **Phone:** 11-717-3627. **Fax:** 11-643-2336. **E-mail:** fraser.a@wbs.wits.ac.za.

University of the Witwatersrand (continued)

■ APPLICATION

Required Application form, baccalaureate/first degree, letter(s) of recommendation, personal statement, transcripts of college work, 4 years of work experience. School will accept GMAT. **Recommended** Essay, resume/curriculum vitae.

Deadlines and Fees *Deadlines:* 7/31 for fall, 2/28 for winter, 8/30 for winter (international), 1/30 for spring (international).

Application Contact Mrs. Lesley Salter, Assistant Registrar, PO Box 98, Witwatersrand, 2050, South Africa. **Phone:** 11-488-5661. **Fax:** 11-643-2336. **E-mail:** 130fbi@witsumb.wits.ac.za.

SPAIN

Escola d'Alta Direcció i Administració (EADA)

Barcelona, Spain

BUSINESS PROGRAMS

DEGREES MBA

MBA—Executive MBA Part-time. 24 months to complete program. *Concentrations:* management.

MBA—Master of Business Administration Full-time. 12 months to complete program. *Concentrations:* management.

RESOURCES AND SERVICES

Information about online services, personal computer policies, library resources, international exchange programs, internship programs, and placement services at this institution and others can be found at **www.petersons.com/mba**

International Students

Services and Facilities Counseling/support services. Financial aid is not available to international students.

International Student Contact Mrs. Brita Hektoen, MBA Director, Arago 204, Barcelona, 08011, Spain. **Phone:** 93-323-1208. **Fax:** 93-323-7317. **E-mail:** eada@cinet.jucs.

■ APPLICATION

Application Contact Mrs. Brita Hektoen, MBA Director, Arago 204, Barcelona, 08011, Spain. **Phone:** 93-323-1208. **Fax:** 93-323-7317.

ESCP-EAP European School of Management

Madrid, Spain

BUSINESS SCHOOL

Graduate Business Faculty
Full-time: 50

Student Body
Total: 122
Full-time: 103

Part-time: 19
Average Age: 29

Costs (1999–2000)
Full-time tuition: N/R
Part-time tuition: N/R

DEGREES EMIM • IEMBA • MBA

EMIM—European Master of International Management Full-time. Proficiency in Spanish and English required. Maximum of 36 months to complete program.

IEMBA—International Executive Master of Business Administration Part-time. Maximum of 16 months to complete program. *Concentrations:* accounting, business information science, finance, human resources, marketing, organizational behavior/development, taxation.

MBA—Full-time MBA Full-time. 7 years of professional work experience required. Maximum of 12 months to complete program. *Concentrations:* accounting, business information science, finance, human resources, marketing, organizational behavior/development, taxation.

COSTS
Tuition varies by class time, number of courses or credits taken, and academic program.

FINANCIAL AID (1999–2000)
Financial Aid Contact Mr. Ramon Rodriquez, Director of External Relations, Arroyofresno Street, 1, Madrid, 28035, Spain. **Phone:** 91-386-2511. **Fax:** 91-373-9229.

RESOURCES AND SERVICES
Information about online services, personal computer policies, library resources, international exchange programs, internship programs, and placement services at this institution and others can be found at **www.petersons.com/mba**

International Students
Applying *Required:* TOEFL with recommended score of 600 (paper), TSE, TWE.

■ APPLICATION

Required Application form, baccalaureate/first degree, interview, resume/curriculum vitae, 4 years of work experience. School will accept GMAT and MAT. **Recommended** Transcripts of college work.

Deadlines and Fees *Deadline:* 9/30 for winter.

Application Contact Mr. Julian Peinador, Director of Business School, Arroyofresno Street, 1, Madrid, 28035, Spain. **Phone:** 91-386-2511. **Fax:** 91-373-9229.

Escuela Superior de Administracion y Direccion de Empresas

Barcelona, Spain

BUSINESS SCHOOL

Graduate Business Faculty
Full-time: 109

Part-time: 218

Student Body
Total: 680
Full-time: 305
Part-time: 375

Average Age: 30
Women: 35%

Admissions
Applications: 1,250
Admitted: 320

Enrolled: 275
Average GMAT: 620

Costs (1999–2000)
Full-time tuition: 14,875 euros per academic year
Part-time tuition: 12,770 euros per year

DEGREES MBA

MBA—Full-time MBA Full-time. 2 years full-time work experience strongly recommended. At least 100 total credits required. Minimum of 21 months to complete program. *Concentrations:* business policy/strategy, finance, health care, human resources, international management, management information systems, marketing, operations management, public management, taxation.

MBA—Part-time MBA Part-time. 3 years full-time work experience required. At least 85 total credits required. Minimum of 21 months to complete program. *Concentrations:* business policy/strategy, entrepreneurship, finance, health care, human resources, insurance, international management, management information systems, marketing, operations management, public management, taxation, travel industry/tourism management.

COSTS
Tuition *Full-time:* 14,875 euros. *Part-time:* 12,770 euros per year.

FINANCIAL AID (1999–2000)
67 students received aid, including loans, scholarships, and work study.
Financial Aid Contact Ms. Núria Guilera, MBA Admissions Director, Avenida de Pedralbes 60-62, Barcelona, 08034, Spain. **Phone:** 93-280-2995. **Fax:** 93-495-2077. **E-mail:** info@esade.es.

RESOURCES AND SERVICES

Information about online services, personal computer policies, library resources, international exchange programs, internship programs, and placement services at this institution and others can be found at **www. petersons.com/mba**

International Students

38% of students enrolled are international students.

Services and Facilities Counseling/support services, ESL/language courses, housing location assistance, international student housing, international student organization, language tutoring, orientation. Financial aid is available to international students.

Applying *Required:* TOEFL with recommended score of 250 (computer) or 600 (paper).

International Student Contact Ms. Antonia Maria Serra, Exchange Coordinator, Avenida de Pedralbes 60-62, Barcelona, 08034, Spain. **Phone:** 93-280-6162 Ext. 241. **Fax:** 93-204-8105. **E-mail:** serram@m.esade.es.

▪ APPLICATION

Required Application form, baccalaureate/first degree, interview, 2 letters of recommendation, personal statement, resume/curriculum vitae, transcripts of college work. School will accept GMAT.

Deadlines and Fees *Deadlines:* 6/30 for fall, 6/30 for fall (international). *Application fee:* $100, $100 (international).

Application Contact Ms. Núria Guilera, MBA Admissions Director, Avenida de Pedralbes 60-62, Barcelona, 08034, Spain. **Phone:** 93-280-2995. **Fax:** 93-495-2077. **E-mail:** info@esade.es.

IADE

Madrid, Spain

INSTITUTO UNIVERSITARIO DE ADMINISTRACION DE EMPRESAS

DEGREES MBA • MBM • MS

MBA—Executive MBA Part-time. At least 65 total credits required. 4 months to complete program. *Concentrations:* financial management/planning, human resources, information management, international economics, international finance, international management, international marketing, new venture management, organizational behavior/development, organizational management, production management, quality management, strategic management.

MBA—Master of Business Administration Full-time. Work experience required. At least 100 total credits required. 9 to 18 months to complete program. *Concentrations:* accounting, business education, business information science, business law, business policy/strategy, decision sciences, economics, finance, financial economics, human resources, industrial/labor relations, international economics, international finance, management information systems, marketing, quality management, quantitative analysis, strategic management.

MBM—Executive Master in Banking Management Part-time. Work experience required. At least 80 total credits required. 6 months to complete program. *Concentrations:* actuarial science, banking, business law, commerce, finance, financial information systems, financial management/planning, human resources, international business, international economics, marketing, organizational management, quality management, strategic management.

MS—Master of Science, Technology and Society Part-time. 11 months to complete program. *Concentrations:* business policy/strategy, developmental economics, management science, organizational behavior/development, public management, public policy and administration, research and development administration, technology management, telecommunications management.

RESOURCES AND SERVICES

Information about online services, personal computer policies, library resources, international exchange programs, internship programs, and placement services at this institution and others can be found at **www. petersons.com/mba**

International Students

Services and Facilities Counseling/support services, international student housing. Financial aid is not available to international students.

International Student Contact Angeles Luque de la Torre, International Affairs, Madrid, 28049, Spain. **Phone:** 91-397-4269. **Fax:** 91-397-4218.

▪ APPLICATION

Application Contact MBA Coordinator, Ciudad Universitaria de Cantablanco, Madrid, 28049, Spain. **Phone:** 91-397-4161. **Fax:** 91-397-4218.

Instituto de Empresa

Madrid, Spain

BUSINESS SCHOOL

Graduate Business Faculty
Full-time: 82 — Part-time: 250

Student Body
Total: 100 — Average Age: 28
Full-time: 100 — Women: 38%

Admissions
Applications: 548 — Enrolled: 100
Admitted: 190 — Average GMAT: 630

Costs (1999–2000)
Full-time tuition: 21,035 ECU per academic year (resident)
Part-time tuition: N/R

After Graduation (Class of 1998–99)
Employed within 3 months of graduation: 98%
Average starting salary: 70,230 ECU

DEGREE IMBA

IMBA—International MBA Full-time. Maximum of 15 months to complete program. *Concentrations:* accounting, advertising, agribusiness, commerce, economics, electronic commerce (e-commerce), entrepreneurship, European business studies, finance, financial economics, financial management/planning, human resources, international and area business studies, international business, international management, leadership, management, management information systems, marketing, operations management, organizational behavior/development, public policy and administration, strategic management, transportation and logistics.

COSTS

Tuition, state resident: *Full-time* 21,035 ECU. Tuition varies by academic program.

FINANCIAL AID (1999–2000)

45 students received aid, including fellowships, grants, loans, research assistantships, scholarships, and teaching assistantships. Aid is available to part-time students. Financial aid application deadline: 6/15. **Financial Aid Contact** Dirk Hopfl, Admissions and Marketing Direction, c/ Maria de Molina 11, 13y 15, Madrid, 28006, Spain. **Phone:** 91-568-9610. **Fax:** 91-411-5503. **E-mail:** admissions@ie.edu.

RESOURCES AND SERVICES

Information about online services, personal computer policies, library resources, international exchange programs, internship programs, and placement services at this institution and others can be found at **www. petersons.com/mba**

International Students

60% of students enrolled are international students.

Services and Facilities Counseling/support services, housing location assistance, language tutoring, orientation. Financial aid is available to international students.

Applying *Required:* TOEFL with recommended score of 260 (computer) or 620 (paper).

International Student Contact Dirk Hopfl, Admissions and Marketing Direction, c/o Maria de Molina 11,13 y 15, Madrid, 28006, Spain. **Phone:** 91-568-9610. **Fax:** 91-411-5803. **E-mail:** admissions@ie.edu.

▪ APPLICATION

Required Application form, baccalaureate/first degree, interview, 3 letters of recommendation, transcripts of college work. School will accept GMAT. **Recommended** 2 years of work experience.

Deadlines and Fees Applications for domestic and international students are processed on a rolling basis.

Application Contact Dirk Hopfl, Admissions and Marketing Direction, c/ Maria de Molina 11, 13y 15, Madrid, 28006, Spain. **Phone:** 91-568-9610. **Fax:** 91-411-5503. **E-mail:** admissions@ie.edu.

Schiller International University

Madrid, Spain

MBA PROGRAM, MADRID, SPAIN CAMPUS

Graduate Business Faculty
Full-time: 6 — Part-time: 26

Schiller International University (continued)

Student Body
Total: 20
Full-time: 15
Part-time: 5

Average Age: 26
Women: 25%

Costs (1999–2000)
Full-time tuition: 1,931,000 Spanish pesetas per academic year
Part-time tuition: 125,000 Spanish pesetas per course

DEGREE MBA

MBA—Master of Business Administration in International Business Full-time and part-time. At least 45 total credits required. 12 to 24 months to complete program.

COSTS
Tuition *Full-time:* 1,875,000 Spanish pesetas. *Part-time:* 125,000 Spanish pesetas per course. Tuition varies by number of courses or credits taken and campus location. **Required fees:** *Full-time* 56,000 Spanish pesetas. Tuition and fees vary by campus location.

FINANCIAL AID (1999–2000)
Grants, loans, scholarships, and work study. Financial aid application deadline: 5/1. **Financial Aid Contact** Ms. Teri Reeves, Financial Aid Director, 453 Edgewater Drive, Dunedin, FL 34698. **Phone:** 727-736-5082 Ext. 250. **Fax:** 727-734-0359. **E-mail:** teri_reeves@schiller.edu.

RESOURCES AND SERVICES
Information about online services, personal computer policies, library resources, international exchange programs, internship programs, and placement services at this institution and others can be found at **www.petersons.com/mba**

International Students
Services and Facilities Counseling/support services, ESL/language courses, housing location assistance, international student housing, orientation, visa services. Financial aid is available to international students.
Applying *Required:* Proof of adequate funds. *Recommended:* TOEFL with recommended score of 550 (paper).
International Student Contact Director of Admissions, San Bernardo 97-99, 1, Spain. **Phone:** 91-448-2488. **Fax:** 91-445-2110. **E-mail:** admissions@schillermadrid.edu.

■ APPLICATION
Required GMAT, application form, baccalaureate/first degree, essay, transcripts of college work. **Recommended** Resume/curriculum vitae, work experience.
Deadlines and Fees Applications for domestic and international students are processed on a rolling basis. *Application fee:* $35, $35 (international).
Application Contact Director of Admissions, 453 Edgewater Drive, Dunedin, FL 34698-7532. **Phone:** 727-736-5082 Ext. 239. **Fax:** 727-734-0359. **E-mail:** admissions@schiller.edu.

See full description on page 816.

University of Navarra

Barcelona, Spain

IESE

Graduate Business Faculty
Full-time: 73

Part-time: 38

Student Body
Total: 211
Full-time: 211

Average Age: 27
Women: 24%

Admissions
Applications: 1,289
Admitted: 281

Enrolled: 211
Average GMAT: 640

Costs (1999–2000)
Full-time tuition: $17,925 per academic year
Part-time tuition: N/R

After Graduation (Class of 1998–99)
Employed within 3 months of graduation: 97%
Average starting salary: $82,470

DEGREE MBA

MBA—Master of Business Administration Full-time. Maximum of 17 months to complete program. *Concentrations:* electronic commerce (e-commerce), entrepreneurship, finance, international management, operations management.

COSTS
Tuition *Full-time:* $17,925. **Graduate housing:** Room and board costs vary by number of occupants and type of accommodation. *Typical cost:* $810 (including board), $360 (room only).

FINANCIAL AID (1999–2000)
29 students received aid, including grants, loans, and scholarships. Financial aid application deadline: 3/31. **Financial Aid Contact** MBA Admissions Department, Avenida Pearson, 21, Barcelona, 08034, Spain. **Phone:** 93-253-4229. **Fax:** 93-253-4343.

RESOURCES AND SERVICES
Information about online services, personal computer policies, library resources, international exchange programs, internship programs, and placement services at this institution and others can be found at **www.petersons.com/mba**

International Students
59% of students enrolled are international students.
Services and Facilities Housing location assistance, language tutoring, orientation. Financial aid is available to international students.
Applying *Required:* TOEFL with recommended score of 600 (paper).
International Student Contact Ms. Teresa Byrne, Avenida Pearson, 21, Barcelona, 08034, Spain. **Phone:** 93-253-4200. **Fax:** 93-258-4343.

■ APPLICATION
Required GMAT, application form, baccalaureate/first degree, essay, interview, 2 letters of recommendation, personal statement, resume/curriculum vitae, transcripts of college work, work experience.
Deadlines and Fees *Deadlines:* 5/1 for fall, 5/1 for fall (international). *Application fee:* 60 ECU.
Application Contact MBA Admissions Department, Avenida Pearson, 21, Barcelona, 08034, Spain. **Phone:** 93-253-4229. **Fax:** 93-253-4343. **E-mail:** mbainfo@iese.edu.

SWEDEN

Stockholm School of Economics

Stockholm, Sweden

DEPARTMENT OF BUSINESS ADMINISTRATION

DEGREES EMBA • MS

EMBA—Executive Master of Business Administration Part-time.
MS—Master of Science in International Economics and Business At least 60 total credits required. Minimum of 18 months to complete program.
MS—Master of Science Full-time. At least 160 total credits required. 24 to 48 months to complete program. *Concentrations:* accounting, economics, financial economics, information management, international business, international economics, logistics, management.

RESOURCES AND SERVICES
Information about online services, personal computer policies, library resources, international exchange programs, internship programs, and placement services at this institution and others can be found at **www.petersons.com/mba**

International Students
Services and Facilities Introduction to swedish language and culture.
International Student Contact Ms. Asa Kjellstrom, Coordinator, Office of International Student Affairs, Stockholm, Sweden. **Phone:** 8-7369744. **Fax:** 8-347540. **E-mail:** admak@hhs.se.

■ APPLICATION
Application Contact International Graduate Program, Box 6501, S-113 83 Stockholm, Sweden. **Phone:** 8-7369520. **Fax:** 8-319927. **E-mail:** iibdo@hhs.se.

SWITZERLAND

American Graduate School of Business

La Tour-de-Peilz, Switzerland

MASTER OF INTERNATIONAL BUSINESS ADMINISTRATION PROGRAM

Graduate Business Faculty
Part-time: 15

Student Body

Total: 33	Average Age: 27
Full-time: 33	Women: 64%

Admissions

Applications: 22	Enrolled: 12
Admitted: 15	Average GMAT: 520

Costs (1999–2000)
Full-time tuition: 26,000 Swiss francs per academic year
Part-time tuition: 2700 Swiss francs per course

After Graduation (Class of 1998–99)
Employed within 3 months of graduation: 85%
Average starting salary: 36,000 Swiss francs

DEGREE MIBA

MIBA—Master of International Business Administration Full-time and part-time. At least 39 total credits required. 12 to 24 months to complete program. *Concentrations:* international business.

COSTS

Tuition *Full-time:* 26,000 Swiss francs. *Part-time:* 2700 Swiss francs per course. Tuition varies by number of courses or credits taken.

FINANCIAL AID (1999–2000)

24 students received aid, including scholarships, teaching assistantships, and work study. Financial aid application deadline: 6/15. **Financial Aid Contact** Mrs. Elizabeth Sluyter-Mathew, Admissions Officer/Registrar, Place des Anciens-Fosses 6, La Tour-de-Peilz, 1814, Switzerland. **Phone:** 21-944-9501. **Fax:** 21-944-9504. **E-mail:** agsb@vtx.ch.

RESOURCES AND SERVICES

Information about online services, personal computer policies, library resources, international exchange programs, internship programs, and placement services at this institution and others can be found at **www.petersons.com/mba**

International Students

100% of students enrolled are international students.

Services and Facilities Counseling/support services, ESL/language courses, international student housing, visa services. Financial aid is available to international students.

Applying *Required:* TOEFL with recommended score of 550 (paper), proof of adequate funds. *Recommended:* TSE with recommended score of 45, proof of health/immunizations.

International Student Contact Mme. Carmen Corchon-Pernet, Director of Student Affairs/President Steering Committee, Place des Anciens Fosses 6, LaTour-de-Peilz, 1814, Switzerland. **Phone:** 21-944-9501. **Fax:** 21-944-9504. **E-mail:** agsb@vtx.ch.

■ APPLICATION

Required GMAT, application form, baccalaureate/first degree, essay, 2 letters of recommendation, personal statement, resume/curriculum vitae, transcripts of college work. School will accept GRE. **Recommended** Work experience.

Deadlines and Fees *Deadlines:* 7/30 for fall, 11/30 for spring, 5/30 for summer, 5/15 for fall (international), 9/15 for spring (international), 3/15 for summer (international). *Application fee:* 100 Swiss francs.

Application Contact Mrs. Elizabeth Sluyter-Mathew, Admissions Officer/Registrar, Place des Anciens-Fosses 6, La Tour-de-Peilz, 1814, Switzerland. **Phone:** 21-944-9501. **Fax:** 21-944-9504. **E-mail:** agsb@vtx.ch.

See full description on page 540.

Graduate School of Business Administration Zurich

Zurich, Switzerland

BUSINESS PROGRAMS

Student Body

Total: 950	Average Age: 36
Part-time: 950	Women: 14%

Admissions
Average GMAT: 560

Costs (1999–2000)
Full-time tuition: 15,000 Swiss francs per academic year
Part-time tuition: 30,000 Swiss francs per degree program

DEGREES M Sc • MA • MBA

M Sc—Master of Science in Finance Part-time. *Distance learning option.* 60 to 100 total credits required. 12 to 24 months to complete program. *Concentrations:* accounting, business law, economics, finance, management, management systems analysis, marketing.

M Sc—Master of Science in Logistics Part-time. *Distance learning option.* 60 to 100 total credits required. 12 to 24 months to complete program. *Concentrations:* accounting, business law, economics, logistics, management, management systems analysis, marketing.

M Sc—Master of Science in Management Information Systems/Information Technology Part-time. *Distance learning option.* 60 to 100 total credits required. 12 to 24 months to complete program. *Concentrations:* accounting, agricultural economics, economics, information management, management, management systems analysis, marketing.

M Sc—Master of Science in Marketing Part-time. *Distance learning option.* 60 to 100 total credits required. 12 to 24 months to complete program. *Concentrations:* accounting, business law, economics, management, management systems analysis, marketing.

MA—Master of Arts in Human Resource Management Part-time. At least 60 total credits required. Maximum of 24 months to complete program. *Concentrations:* accounting, business law, economics, human resources, management, marketing.

MBA—Executive MBA Part-time. *Distance learning option.* 60 to 120 total credits required. 12 to 48 months to complete program. *Concentrations:* accounting, financial management/planning, human resources, international business, international development management, international economics, international finance, international logistics, international management, international marketing, logistics, management information systems, management systems analysis, marketing, operations management, organizational behavior/development, strategic management.

COSTS

Tuition *Full-time:* 15,000 Swiss francs. *Part-time:* 30,000 Swiss francs per degree program.

FINANCIAL AID (1999–2000)

Loans. Aid is available to part-time students. **Financial Aid Contact** Dr. Albert Stahli, Dean, Schutzengasse 4, Postfach 6584, Zurich, 8023, Switzerland. **Phone:** 1-211-6068. **Fax:** 1-221-0984.

RESOURCES AND SERVICES

Information about online services, personal computer policies, library resources, international exchange programs, internship programs, and placement services at this institution and others can be found at **www.petersons.com/mba**

International Students

65% of students enrolled are international students.

Services and Facilities Counseling/support services. Financial aid is not available to international students.

Applying *Required:* TOEFL with recommended score of 500 (paper).

International Student Contact Mr. Heinrich Brugger, Admissions Officer, Schutzengasse 4, Postfach 6584, Zurich, 8023, Switzerland. **Phone:** 1-211-6017. **Fax:** 1-221-0984.

■ APPLICATION

Required GMAT, application form, interview, personal statement, resume/curriculum vitae, 5 years of work experience. **Recommended** Baccalaureate/first degree, letter(s) of recommendation, transcripts of college work.

Deadlines and Fees *Application fee:* 150 Swiss francs.

Graduate School of Business Administration Zurich (continued)

Application Contact Mr. Heinrich Brugger, Admissions Officer, Schutzengasse 4, Postfach 6584, Zurich, 8023, Switzerland. **Phone:** 1-211-6017. **Fax:** 1-221-0984. **E-mail:** gsba@pop.spectraweb.ch.

IMD International Institute for Management Development

Lausanne, Switzerland

BUSINESS PROGRAMS

Graduate Business Faculty
Full-time: 46

Student Body
Total: 85
Full-time: 85

Average Age: 31
Women: 20%

Admissions
Applications: 900

Average GMAT: 650

Costs (1999–2000)
Full-time tuition: 45,000 Swiss francs per academic year
Part-time tuition: N/R

After Graduation (Class of 1998–99)
Employed within 3 months of graduation: 100%

DEGREE MBA

MBA—Master of Business Administration Full-time. Maximum of 11 months to complete program. *Concentrations:* management.

COSTS

Tuition *Full-time:* 45,000 Swiss francs. **Graduate housing:** Room and board costs vary by number of occupants, type of accommodation, and type of board plan. *Typical cost:* 12,500 Swiss francs (room only).

FINANCIAL AID (1999–2000)

18 students received aid, including loans and scholarships. Financial aid application deadline: 8/1. **Financial Aid Contact** Mrs. Marianne Wheeler, MBA Admissions and Information Officer, Chemin de Bellerive 23, PO Box 915, Lausanne, CH-1001, Switzerland. **Phone:** 21-618-0298. **Fax:** 21-618-0615. **E-mail:** mbainfo@imd.ch.

RESOURCES AND SERVICES

Information about online services, personal computer policies, library resources, international exchange programs, internship programs, and placement services at this institution and others can be found at **www.petersons.com/mba**

International Students

95% of students enrolled are international students.

Services and Facilities Counseling/support services, housing location assistance, visa services, partner program, kindergarten. Financial aid is available to international students.
International Student Contact MBA Admissions and Information Officer, Chemin de Bellerive 23, PO Box 915, Lausanne, CH-1001, Switzerland. **Phone:** 21-618-0298. **Fax:** 21-618-0615. **E-mail:** mbainfo@imd.ch.

■ APPLICATION

Required GMAT, application form, baccalaureate/first degree, essay, interview, 3 letters of recommendation, personal statement, resume/curriculum vitae, transcripts of college work, 3 years of work experience.

Deadlines and Fees Applications for domestic and international students are processed on a rolling basis. *Application fee:* 250 Swiss francs, 250 Swiss francs (international).

Application Contact Mrs. Marianne Wheeler, MBA Admissions and Information Officer, Chemin de Bellerive 23, PO Box 915, Lausanne, CH-1001, Switzerland. **Phone:** 21-618-0298. **Fax:** 21-618-0615. **E-mail:** mbainfo@imd.ch.

See full description on page 682.

Schiller International University, American College of Switzerland

Leysin, Switzerland

MBA PROGRAM

Graduate Business Faculty
Full-time: 4

Part-time: 13

Student Body
Total: 18
Full-time: 16
Part-time: 2

Average Age: 23
Women: 72%

Costs (1999–2000)
Full-time tuition: 32,200 Swiss francs per academic year
Part-time tuition: N/R

After Graduation (Class of 1998–99)
Employed within 3 months of graduation: 78%

DEGREE MBA

MBA—MBA in International Business Full-time and part-time. At least 45 total credits required. 12 to 24 months to complete program.

COSTS

Tuition *Full-time:* 25,200 Swiss francs. Tuition varies by number of courses or credits taken and campus location. **Required fees:** *Full-time* 7000 Swiss francs. Tuition and fees vary by campus location. **Graduate housing:** Room and board costs vary by campus location, number of occupants, type of accommodation, and type of board plan. *Typical cost:* 10,780 Swiss francs (including board).

FINANCIAL AID (1999–2000)

Grants, loans, scholarships, and work study. Financial aid application deadline: 4/1. **Financial Aid Contact** Ms. Teri Reeves, Financial Aid Director, 453 Edgewater Drive, Dunedin, FL 34698. **Phone:** 727-736-5082 Ext. 250. **Fax:** 727-734-0359. **E-mail:** teri_reeves@schiller.edu.

RESOURCES AND SERVICES

Information about online services, personal computer policies, library resources, international exchange programs, internship programs, and placement services at this institution and others can be found at **www.petersons.com/mba**

International Students

Services and Facilities Counseling/support services, ESL/language courses, housing location assistance, international student housing, orientation, visa services. Financial aid is available to international students.
Applying *Required:* Proof of adequate funds. *Recommended:* TOEFL with recommended score of 550 (paper).
International Student Contact Ms. Nancy Carroll, Provost, Leysin, CH-1854, Switzerland. **Phone:** 24-494-2223. **Fax:** 24-494-1346. **E-mail:** acs-schiller-regisrtaroffice@bluewin.ch.

■ APPLICATION

Required GMAT, application form, baccalaureate/first degree, essay, transcripts of college work. **Recommended** Work experience.

Deadlines and Fees Applications for domestic and international students are processed on a rolling basis. *Application fee:* $35, $35 (international).

Application Contact Director of Admissions, 453 Edgewater Drive, Dunedin, FL 34698-7532. **Phone:** 727-736-5082 Ext. 239. **Fax:** 727-734-0359. **E-mail:** admissions@schiller.edu.

See full description on page 816.

Université de Lausanne

Lausanne, Switzerland

ECOLE DES HAUTES ETUDES COMMERCIALES

DEGREES MBA • MBF • MBI • MIM • MOT • MS

MBA—Master of Business Administration Full-time and part-time. 12 to 24 months to complete program. *Concentrations:* management.

MBF—Master of Business Finance Full-time and part-time. 12 to 24 months to complete program. *Concentrations:* finance.

MBI—Master in Business Information Systems Full-time and part-time. 12 to 24 months to complete program. *Concentrations:* information management.

MIM—Master of International Management Full-time. Maximum of 15 months to complete program. *Concentrations:* international management.

MOT—Master in Management of Technology Full-time. Maximum of 12 months to complete program. *Concentrations:* technology management.

MS—Master of Science Full-time and part-time. 12 to 24 months to complete program. *Concentrations:* economics.

RESOURCES AND SERVICES

Information about online services, personal computer policies, library resources, international exchange programs, internship programs, and placement services at this institution and others can be found at www. petersons.com/mba

International Students

Services and Facilities Counseling/support services.
International Student Contact Ms. Nicole Farcinade, Program Administrator, BFSH1, Ecole des HEC, MBA Program, Lausanne, CH-1015, Switzerland. **Phone:** 21-692-3390. **Fax:** 21-692-3395. **E-mail:** nicole.farcinade@hec.unil.ch.

■ APPLICATION

Application Contact Program Administrator, BFSH1, Ecole des HEC, MBA Program, Lausanne, CH-1015, Switzerland. **Phone:** 21-692-3390. **Fax:** 21-692-3395.

University of St. Gallen

St. Gallen, Switzerland

BUSINESS SCHOOL

DEGREE EMBA

EMBA—Executive Master of Business Administration Part-time. Maximum of 24 months to complete program. *Concentrations:* banking, finance, international banking, international trade, management.

RESOURCES AND SERVICES

Information about online services, personal computer policies, library resources, international exchange programs, internship programs, and placement services at this institution and others can be found at **www. petersons.com/mba**

International Students

International Student Contact Claudia Rossei, Student Exchange Coordinator, Dufourstr. 50, CH-9000, St. Gallen, Switzerland. **Phone:** 71-224-2339.

■ APPLICATION

Application Contact Program Administrator, Holzweid, St. Gallen, CH-9010, Switzerland. **Phone:** 71-224-2701. **Fax:** 71-224-2700.

THAILAND

Bangkok University

Bangkok, Thailand

GRADUATE SCHOOL

DEGREE MBA

MBA—Master of Business Administration Full-time. At least 48 total credits required. 24 to 60 months to complete program. *Concentrations:* finance, financial management/planning, human resources, international business, management, management information systems, managerial economics, marketing, operations management, quantitative analysis.

RESOURCES AND SERVICES

Information about online services, personal computer policies, library resources, international exchange programs, internship programs, and placement services at this institution and others can be found at **www. petersons.com/mba**

International Students

Services and Facilities Counseling/support services, visa services. Financial aid is available to international students.

International Student Contact Dr. Siriwan Rattanakarn, Director, Bangkok University International College, 40/4 Rama IV Road, Bangkok, 10110, Thailand.

■ APPLICATION

Application Contact Dr. Gloria Vidheecharoen, Director, Graduate School, 40/4 Rama IV Road, Bangkok, 10110, Thailand. **Phone:** 2-671-7507. **Fax:** 2-240-1516. **E-mail:** gloria@lily.bu.ac.th.

Chulalongkorn University

Bangkok, Thailand

SASIN GRADUATE INSTITUTE OF BUSINESS ADMINISTRATION

DEGREES M Mgt • MBA

M Mgt—Executive Master of Management Part-time. At least 72 total credits required. 24 to 48 months to complete program. *Concentrations:* management.

MBA—Master of Business Administration Full-time. At least 75 total credits required. 24 to 48 months to complete program. *Concentrations:* finance, management, marketing, organizational behavior/development.

RESOURCES AND SERVICES

Information about online services, personal computer policies, library resources, international exchange programs, internship programs, and placement services at this institution and others can be found at **www. petersons.com/mba**

International Students

Services and Facilities International student housing, visa services.
International Student Contact Mrs. Oranong Tiradechavataya, Chief of Student Affairs Section, Sasin Graduate Institute of Business Administration, Chulalongkorn University, Sasa Patasala Building, Soi Chula 12 (2) Phyathai, Bangkok, 10330, Thailand. **Phone:** 2-216-8833 Ext. 3862. **Fax:** 2-216-1312. **E-mail:** ssasotr@chula.ac.th.

■ APPLICATION

Application Contact Mrs. Lalida Ruangtrakool, Chief of Admission and Financial Aid Section, Sasa Patasala Building, Soi Chulalongkorn 12, Phyathai Road, Bangkok, 10330, Thailand. **Phone:** 2-216-8833 Ext. 3856. **Fax:** 2-216-1312.

TURKEY

Bilkent University

Bilkent, Turkey

SCHOOL OF BUSINESS ADMINISTRATION

Graduate Business Faculty

Full-time: 20	Part-time: 3

Student Body

Total: 126	Average Age: 26
Full-time: 104	Women: 37%
Part-time: 22	

Admissions

Applications: 164	Average GMAT: 550
Admitted: 64	Average GPA: 2.93
Enrolled: 54	

Costs (1999–2000)
Full-time tuition: $6500 per academic year
Part-time tuition: N/R

DEGREE MBA

MBA—Master of Business Administration Full-time. At least 60 total credits required. 20 to 36 months to complete program. *Concentrations:* finance, international business, management, marketing, organizational behavior/development, quantitative analysis.

COSTS

Tuition *Full-time:* $6500. **Graduate housing:** Room and board costs vary by number of occupants. *Typical cost:* $1400 (room only).

Bilkent University (continued)

FINANCIAL AID (1999–2000)
Scholarships. Financial aid application deadline: 8/16. **Financial Aid Contact** Dr. Erdal Erel, Associate Dean, Ankara, 06533, Turkey. **Phone:** 312-266-4164. **Fax:** 312-266-4950. **E-mail:** fba@bilkent.edu.tr.

RESOURCES AND SERVICES
Information about online services, personal computer policies, library resources, international exchange programs, internship programs, and placement services at this institution and others can be found at **www.petersons.com/mba**

International Students
6% of students enrolled are international students.
Services and Facilities Counseling/support services, ESL/language courses, language tutoring, orientation, turkish language lessons. Financial aid is available to international students.
Applying *Required:* TOEFL with recommended score of 550 (paper).
International Student Contact Ms. Aysegul Basol, Associate Director of Student Affairs, Bilkent University, Ankara, 06533, Turkey. **Phone:** 312-266-4000 Ext. 1240.

■ APPLICATION
Required GMAT, application form, baccalaureate/first degree, interview, 2 letters of recommendation, transcripts of college work.
Deadlines and Fees *Deadlines:* 8/16 for fall, 8/16 for fall (international).
Application Contact Dr. Erdal Erel, Associate Dean, Ankara, 06533, Turkey. **Phone:** 312-266-4164. **Fax:** 312-266-4958. **E-mail:** fba@bilkent.edu.tr.

UNITED ARAB EMIRATES

The American University in Dubai

Dubai, United Arab Emirates

MBA PROGRAM

Graduate Business Faculty
Full-time: 5   Part-time: 2

Student Body
Total: 24
Full-time: 1   Average Age: 28
Part-time: 23   Women: 42%

Admissions
Applications: 23   Enrolled: 9
Admitted: 17   Average GPA: 2.9

Costs (1999–2000)
Full-time tuition: $13,625 per academic year
Part-time tuition: $1365 per quarter

DEGREE MBA

MBA—Master of Business Administration Full-time and part-time. At least 60 total credits required. Minimum of 10 months to complete program. *Concentrations:* international finance, international marketing.

COSTS
Tuition *Full-time:* $13,625. *Part-time:* $1365 per quarter. **Tuition, international:** *Full-time* $13,625. **Graduate housing:** Room and board costs vary by number of occupants. *Typical cost:* $4160 (room only).

FINANCIAL AID (1999–2000)
Financial Aid Contact

RESOURCES AND SERVICES
Information about online services, personal computer policies, library resources, international exchange programs, internship programs, and placement services at this institution and others can be found at **www.petersons.com/mba**

International Students
79% of students enrolled are international students.
Services and Facilities Counseling/support services, ESL/language courses, international student housing, orientation, visa services. Financial aid is not available to international students.
Applying *Required:* TOEFL with recommended score of 213 (computer) or 550 (paper), TWE with recommended score of 4.
International Student Contact Mrs. Carol Maalouf, Admissions Officer, PO Box 28282, Dubai, United Arab Emirates. **Phone:** 4-3999000 Ext. 1090. **Fax:** 4-3998899. **E-mail:** cmaalouf@aud.edu.

■ APPLICATION
Required GMAT, application form, baccalaureate/first degree, 2 letters of recommendation, personal statement, resume/curriculum vitae, transcripts of college work. **Recommended** Interview, 2 years of work experience.
Deadlines and Fees Applications for domestic and international students are processed on a rolling basis. *Application fee:* $35, $35 (international).
Application Contact Dr. Jihad Nader, Dean—Faculty of Business Administration, PO Box 28282, Dubai, United Arab Emirates. **Phone:** 4-3999000 Ext. 3300. **Fax:** 4-3998899. **E-mail:** jnader@aud.edu.

UNITED KINGDOM

American InterContinental University

London, United Kingdom

PROGRAM IN BUSINESS ADMINISTRATION

Graduate Business Faculty
Full-time: 8   Part-time: 19

Student Body
Total: 49   Average Age: 27
Full-time: 39   Women: 57%
Part-time: 10

Admissions
Applications: 72   Enrolled: 17
Admitted: 23   Average GPA: 3.1

Costs (1999–2000)
Full-time tuition: $5407 per academic year
Part-time tuition: N/R

After Graduation (Class of 1998–99)
Employed within 3 months of graduation: 95%

DEGREE MBA

MBA—Master of Business Administration Full-time. At least 60 total credits required. 10 to 24 months to complete program. *Concentrations:* international business.

COSTS
Tuition *Full-time:* $5407. **Required fees:** Tuition and fees vary by number of courses or credits taken and campus location. **Graduate housing:** Room and board costs vary by campus location and number of occupants. *Typical cost:* $2240 (room only).

FINANCIAL AID (1999–2000)
23 students received aid, including loans and scholarships. Aid is available to part-time students. **Financial Aid Contact** Ms. Lillian Rice, Director of Financial Aid, 3330 Peachtree Road, NE, Atlanta, GA 30326-1016. **Phone:** 800-255-6839. **Fax:** 404-965-5701. **E-mail:** lrice@aiuniv.edu.

RESOURCES AND SERVICES
Information about online services, personal computer policies, library resources, international exchange programs, internship programs, and placement services at this institution and others can be found at **www.petersons.com/mba**

International Students
88% of students enrolled are international students.

Services and Facilities Counseling/support services, ESL/language courses, housing location assistance, international student housing, international student organization, language tutoring, orientation, visa services. Financial aid is not available to international students.

Applying *Required:* IELT, TOEFL with recommended score of 550 (paper), proof of adequate funds.

International Student Contact Mr. Geoff Hazell, Director of Admissions and Marketing, 110 Marylebone High Street, London, W1M 3DB, United Kingdom. **Phone:** 207-467-5600. **Fax:** 207-486-0642. **E-mail:** ghazell@aivlondon.ac.uk.

■ **APPLICATION**

Required Application form, baccalaureate/first degree, interview, 2 letters of recommendation, personal statement, resume/curriculum vitae, transcripts of college work. **Recommended** Essay, work experience.

Deadlines and Fees *Application fee:* $35, $35 (international).

Application Contact Mr. Michael Swift, International Programs/Study Abroad, 6600 Peachtree-Dunwoody Road, 500 Embassy Row, Atlanta, GA 30328. **Phone:** 404-965-6500. **Toll-free Phone:** 800-255-6839. **Fax:** 404-965-6501. **E-mail:** mswift@aiuniv.edu.

Ashridge

Berkhamsted, United Kingdom

ASHRIDGE EXECUTIVE MBA PROGRAM

DEGREES MBA

MBA—Ashridge Executive MBA Full-time and part-time. 12 to 24 months to complete program. *Concentrations:* business ethics, finance, human resources, international and area business studies, international finance, international marketing, leadership, logistics, management consulting, marketing, operations management, organizational behavior/development, project management, strategic management, technology management.

MBA—Master of Business Administration Full-time and part-time. 12 to 24 months to complete program. *Concentrations:* accounting, economics, finance, human resources, international business, management, management information systems, marketing, operations management, organizational behavior/development, quantitative analysis.

RESOURCES AND SERVICES

Information about online services, personal computer policies, library resources, international exchange programs, internship programs, and placement services at this institution and others can be found at **www.petersons.com/mba**

International Students

Services and Facilities Language tutoring. Financial aid is not available to international students.

International Student Contact Mrs. Doris Boyle, MBA Administration Manager, Ashridge Management College, Hertfordshire, United Kingdom. **Phone:** 1-442-841-143. **Fax:** 1-442-841-144. **E-mail:** doris.boyle@ashridge.org.uk.

■ **APPLICATION**

Application Contact Mrs. Doris Boyle, MBA Administration Manager, Ashridge Management College, Hertfordshire, United Kingdom. **Phone:** 1-442-841-143. **Fax:** 1-442-841-144. **E-mail:** doris.boyle@ashridge.org.uk.

Aston University

Birmingham, United Kingdom

ASTON BUSINESS SCHOOL

Graduate Business Faculty

Full-time: 40   Part-time: 10

Student Body

Total: 278

Full-time: 175   Average Age: 31

Part-time: 103   Women: 33%

Admissions

Applications: 850   Enrolled: 240

Admitted: 460   Average GMAT: 620

Costs (1999–2000)

Full-time tuition: N/R

Part-time tuition: 10,250 British pounds per course (resident), 12,750 British pounds per course (nonresident)

After Graduation (Class of 1998–99)

Employed within 3 months of graduation: 85%

Average starting salary: 48,000 British pounds

DEGREES M Sc • MBA

M Sc—Master of Science in Business Studies Full-time. Minimum of 10 months to complete program. *Concentrations:* accounting, finance, human resources, management, operations management, strategic management.

M Sc—Master of Science in Business and IT Full-time. Minimum of 10 months to complete program.

M Sc—Master of Science in Financial Management and Control Full-time and part-time. 10 to 24 months to complete program. *Concentrations:* accounting, finance, financial management/planning, management, strategic management.

M Sc—Master of Science in International Business Full-time. Minimum of 10 months to complete program. *Concentrations:* international business, international management, international marketing, management, strategic management.

M Sc—Master of Science in Marketing Management Full-time and part-time. *Distance learning option.* 10 to 24 months to complete program. *Concentrations:* management, marketing, marketing research, strategic management.

M Sc—Master of Science in Personnel Management Full-time. Minimum of 12 months to complete program. *Concentrations:* human resources, industrial/labor relations, management, strategic management.

M Sc—Master of Science in Public Services Management Full-time and part-time. 12 to 60 months to complete program. *Concentrations:* health care, nonprofit management, public management, public policy and administration.

M Sc—Operational Research and Management Studies Full-time. Minimum of 10 months to complete program.

M Sc—Work Psychology and Business Full-time. Minimum of 10 months to complete program.

MBA—MBA in Public Services Management Full-time and part-time. 12 to 60 months to complete program. *Concentrations:* accounting, economics, European business studies, finance, health care, human resources, industrial administration/management, international business, management, marketing, operations management, organizational behavior/development, public policy and administration, quality management, quantitative analysis, strategic management.

MBA—Master of Business Administration Full-time and part-time. *Distance learning option.* 12 to 60 months to complete program. *Concentrations:* health care, nonprofit management, public management, public policy and administration, strategic management.

COSTS

Tuition, state resident: *Part-time* 10,250 British pounds per course. **Tuition, nonresident:** *Part-time* 12,750 British pounds per course. **Graduate housing:** Room and board costs vary by type of accommodation and type of board plan. *Typical cost:* 5000 British pounds (including board).

FINANCIAL AID (1999–2000)

Financial Aid Contact

RESOURCES AND SERVICES

Information about online services, personal computer policies, library resources, international exchange programs, internship programs, and placement services at this institution and others can be found at **www.petersons.com/mba**

International Students

32% of students enrolled are international students.

Services and Facilities Counseling/support services, ESL/language courses, international student housing, international student organization, language tutoring, orientation.

Applying *Required:* IELT with recommended score of 6.5, TOEFL with recommended score of 600 (paper), proof of adequate funds.

International Student Contact Mrs. Jenny Evans, Course Administrator, Postgraduate Office, Aston Business School, Birmingham, B4 7ET, United Kingdom. **Phone:** 121-359-3611 Ext. 4936. **Fax:** 121-333-4731. **E-mail:** j.m.moore@aston.ac.uk.

■ **APPLICATION**

Required Application form, baccalaureate/first degree, 2 letters of recommendation, personal statement, resume/curriculum vitae, transcripts of college work, 3 years of work experience. School will accept GMAT.

Deadlines and Fees *Deadlines:* 7/1 for fall, 11/10 for spring, 7/1 for fall (international), 11/10 for spring (international).

Application Contact Mrs. Jenny Evans, Course Administrator, Postgraduate Office, Aston Business School, Birmingham, B4 7ET, United Kingdom. **Phone:** 121-359-3611 Ext. 4936. **Fax:** 121-333-4731. **E-mail:** j.m.moore@aston.ac.uk.

City University

London, United Kingdom

BUSINESS SCHOOL

Graduate Business Faculty
Full-time: 90   Part-time: 180

Student Body
Total: 1,800   Women: 25%
Average Age: 27

Admissions
Applications: 7,200   Average GMAT: 620
Enrolled: 1,800

Costs (1999–2000)
Full-time tuition: 16,000 British pounds per academic year (resident), 16,000 British pounds per academic year (nonresident)
Part-time tuition: 20,000 British pounds per degree program (resident), 20,000 British pounds per degree program (nonresident)

After Graduation (Class of 1998–99)
Employed within 3 months of graduation: 65%
Average starting salary: 37,000 British pounds

DEGREES MA • MBA • MS

MA—Master of Arts in Property Valuation and Law Full-time and part-time. 12 to 24 months to complete program. *Concentrations:* construction management, real estate.

MBA—Evening MBA Part-time. 2 years of decision-making experience and GMAT score (minimum 550) required. 24 to 68 months to complete program. *Concentrations:* management.

MBA—Full-Time MBA Full-time. 3 years of work experience and GMAT score (minimum 550) required. 12 months to complete program. *Concentrations:* entrepreneurship, finance, human resources, international business, marketing, technology management, telecommunications management.

MS—Master Science in Investment Management Full-time. 12 months to complete program. *Concentrations:* finance, financial management/planning, risk management.

MS—Master of Science in Corporate Property Management Full-time and part-time. 12 to 24 months to complete program. *Concentrations:* construction management, finance, real estate.

MS—Master of Science in Finance Full-time. 12 months to complete program. *Concentrations:* finance.

MS—Master of Science in Insurance and Risk Management Full-time and part-time. 12 to 24 months to complete program. *Concentrations:* insurance, risk management.

MS—Master of Science in Internal Auditing and Management Full-time and part-time. 12 to 24 months to complete program. *Concentrations:* actuarial science, finance, management.

MS—Master of Science in Mathematical Trading and Finance Full-time and part-time. 12 to 24 months to complete program. *Concentrations:* finance, financial economics, international finance, quantitative analysis.

MS—Master of Science in Property Investment Full-time and part-time. 12 to 24 months to complete program. *Concentrations:* construction management, finance, real estate.

MS—Master of Science in Shipping, Trade, and Finance Full-time and part-time. 2 years of work experience required. 12 to 24 months to complete program. *Concentrations:* economics, finance, international trade.

MS—Master of Science in Transport Trade and Finance Full-time and part-time. 2 years of work experience required. 12 to 24 months to complete program. *Concentrations:* economics, finance, international logistics, international trade, logistics.

COSTS

Tuition, state resident: *Full-time* 16,000 British pounds. *Part-time* 20,000 British pounds per degree program. **Tuition, nonresident:** *Full-time* 16,000 British pounds. *Part-time* 20,000 British pounds per degree program. Tuition varies by number of courses or credits taken, academic program, and local reciprocity agreements.

FINANCIAL AID (1999–2000)
Research assistantships and scholarships. Financial aid application deadline: 5/31. **Financial Aid Contact** Ms. Liz Taylor, Post Graduate Admissions Officer, Frobisher Crescent, Barbican Center, London, EC2Y 8HB, United Kingdom. **Phone:** 171-477-8607. **Fax:** 171-477-8898. **E-mail:** cubs-postgrad@city.ac.uk.

RESOURCES AND SERVICES
Information about online services, personal computer policies, library resources, international exchange programs, internship programs, and placement services at this institution and others can be found at **www.petersons.com/mba**

International Students
55% of students enrolled are international students.

Services and Facilities Counseling/support services, ESL/language courses, visa services. Financial aid is available to international students.
Applying *Required:* IELT with recommended score of 7, TOEFL with recommended score of 650 (paper), proof of adequate funds.
International Student Contact Ms. Liz Taylor, Post Graduate Admissions Officer, Frobisher Crescent, Barbican Center, London, EC2Y 8HB, United Kingdom. **Phone:** 171-477-8607. **Fax:** 171-477-8898. **E-mail:** cubs-postgrad@city.ac.uk.

■ APPLICATION

Required Application form, baccalaureate/first degree, 2 letters of recommendation, personal statement. School will accept GMAT. **Recommended** Interview, resume/curriculum vitae, transcripts of college work, work experience.

Deadlines and Fees *Deadlines:* 5/31 for fall, 5/31 for fall (international). *Application fee:* 45 British pounds.

Application Contact Ms. Liz Taylor, Post Graduate Admissions Officer, Frobisher Crescent, Barbican Center, London, EC2Y 8HB, United Kingdom. **Phone:** 171-477-8607. **Fax:** 171-477-8898. **E-mail:** cubs-postgrad@city.ac.uk.

Cranfield University

Cranfield, United Kingdom

CRANFIELD SCHOOL OF MANAGEMENT

Graduate Business Faculty
Full-time: 148   Part-time: 123

Student Body
Total: 367   Average Age: 31
Full-time: 206   Women: 19%
Part-time: 161

Admissions
Applications: 623   Enrolled: 206
Admitted: 318   Average GMAT: 640

Costs (1999–2000)
Full-time tuition: 18,500 British pounds per academic year (resident), 18,500 British pounds per academic year (nonresident)
Part-time tuition: 12,000 British pounds per year (resident), 12,000 British pounds per year (nonresident)

After Graduation (Class of 1998–99)
Employed within 3 months of graduation: 95%

DEGREES M Sc • MBA

M Sc—Master of Science in Project Management Full-time. 4 years of postgraduate work experience. At least 43 total credits required. 12 months to complete program. *Concentrations:* management, project management.

MBA—Executive MBA Part-time. 3 years of postgraduate work experience. At least 44 total credits required. 24 months to complete program. *Concentrations:* finance, management, public management.

MBA—Master of Business Administration Full-time. 3 years of postgraduate work experience. At least 43 total credits required. 12 months to complete program. *Concentrations:* electronic commerce (e-commerce), finance, management, public management.

COSTS
Tuition, state resident: *Full-time* 18,500 British pounds. *Part-time* 12,000 British pounds per year. **Tuition, nonresident:** *Full-time* 18,500 British pounds. *Part-time* 12,000 British pounds per year. **Tuition, international:** *Full-time* 18,500 British pounds. **Graduate housing:** Room and board costs vary by number of occupants, type of accommodation, and type of board plan. *Typical cost:* 4000 British pounds (including board).

FINANCIAL AID (1999–2000)
33 students received aid, including scholarships. Financial aid application deadline: 4/1. **Financial Aid Contact** Mrs. Pat Hayes, Admissions Officer, Cranfield School of Management, Cranfield, Bedford, MK43 OAL, United Kingdom. **Phone:** 1234 754431. **Fax:** 1234 754431. **E-mail:** p.hayes@cranfield.ac.uk.

RESOURCES AND SERVICES

Information about online services, personal computer policies, library resources, international exchange programs, internship programs, and placement services at this institution and others can be found at **www. petersons.com/mba**

International Students

29% of students enrolled are international students.

Services and Facilities Counseling/support services, ESL/language courses, housing location assistance, orientation. Financial aid is available to international students.

Applying *Required:* IELT with recommended score of 7, TOEFL with recommended score of 250 (computer) or 600 (paper), proof of adequate funds.

International Student Contact Mrs. Maureen Williams, Graduate Programmes Marketing Executive, Cranfield School of Management, Cranfield, Bedford, MK43 OAL, United Kingdom. **Phone:** 1234 751122 Ext. 3082. **Fax:** 1234 751122. **E-mail:** m.williams@cranfield.ac.uk.

■ APPLICATION

Required GMAT, application form, baccalaureate/first degree, interview, 2 letters of recommendation, 3 years of work experience.

Deadlines and Fees Applications for domestic and international students are processed on a rolling basis. *Application fee:* 75 British pounds, 75 British pounds (international).

Application Contact Mrs. Pat Hayes, Admissions Officer, Cranfield School of Management, Cranfield, Bedford, MK43 OAL, United Kingdom. **Phone:** 1234 754431. **Fax:** 1234 754431. **E-mail:** p.hayes@cranfield.ac.uk.

See full description on page 616.

De Montfort University

Leicester, United Kingdom

DE MONTFORT UNIVERSITY SCHOOL OF BUSINESS

DEGREES M Sc • MA • MBA

M Sc—Master of Science in Accounting and Finance Full-time. Minimum of 12 months to complete program. *Concentrations:* accounting, finance, financial information systems, taxation.

M Sc—Master of Science in Strategic Marketing Full-time and part-time. 12 to 48 months to complete program. *Concentrations:* international marketing, marketing, marketing research.

MA—Master of Arts in Marketing Administration Full-time and part-time. 12 to 48 months to complete program. *Concentrations:* international marketing, marketing, marketing research.

MA—Master of Arts in Personnel and Development Full-time. Minimum of 12 months to complete program. *Concentrations:* human resources, industrial/labor relations, organizational behavior/development.

MBA—Master of Business Administration Full-time and part-time. *Distance learning option.* At least 16 total credits required. 12 to 24 months to complete program. *Concentrations:* accounting, finance, human resources, international business, management, marketing, operations management, organizational behavior/development, public policy and administration, strategic management.

RESOURCES AND SERVICES

Information about online services, personal computer policies, library resources, international exchange programs, internship programs, and placement services at this institution and others can be found at **www. petersons.com/mba**

International Students

Services and Facilities Counseling/support services, ESL/language courses, international student organization, orientation. Financial aid is available to international students.

International Student Contact Ms. Sue Owen, MBA Program Administrator, The Gateway, Leicester, LE1 9BH, United Kingdom. **Phone:** 116-257-7230. **Fax:** 116-250-6329. **E-mail:** seowen@dmu.ac.uk.

■ APPLICATION

Application Contact Ms. Sally Thomas, MBA Program Administrator, The Gateway, Leicester, LE1 9BH, United Kingdom. **Phone:** 116-257-7230. **Fax:** 116-250-6329. **E-mail:** sthomas@dmu.ac.uk.

ESCP-EAP European School of Management

Oxford, United Kingdom

BUSINESS PROGRAMS

Graduate Business Faculty

Full-time: 45   Part-time: 50

Student Body

Total: 350

Full-time: 320   Average Age: 23

Part-time: 30   Women: 40%

Admissions

Average GMAT: 570

Costs (1999–2000)

Full-time tuition: N/R

Part-time tuition: N/R

After Graduation (Class of 1998–99)

Employed within 3 months of graduation: 90%

Average starting salary: 309,008 French francs

DEGREES EMM • MBA • MEB

EMM—European Master in Management Full-time. European Management Admissions Test (EMAT) and fluency in first two languages of program required. 36 to 48 months to complete program. *Concentrations:* European business studies, international business, international management.

MBA—European MBA in International Business Full-time. GMAT score (minimum 550), TOEFL score (minimum 600), and 3 or more years of relevant work experience required. 12 to 24 months to complete program. *Concentrations:* international business, international management, strategic management.

MEB—Master of European Business Full-time. Proficiency in French, German or Spanish required. 12 to 15 months to complete program. *Concentrations:* European business studies, information management, international management.

COSTS

Tuition varies by academic program.

FINANCIAL AID (1999–2000)

15 students received aid, including scholarships. **Financial Aid Contact** Ms. Isabelle Pochic-Fuerst, University Relations, United Kingdom Admissions, 12 Merton Street, England, United Kingdom. **Phone:** 186-263205. **Fax:** 186-251960.

RESOURCES AND SERVICES

Information about online services, personal computer policies, library resources, international exchange programs, internship programs, and placement services at this institution and others can be found at **www. petersons.com/mba**

International Students

Services and Facilities Counseling/support services, language tutoring. Financial aid is available to international students.

Applying *Required:* Proof of adequate funds. *Recommended:* IELT with recommended score of 6.5, TOEFL with recommended score of 230 (computer) or 600 (paper).

International Student Contact Mr. Kitson Smith, International Dean of Students, 12 Merton Street, England, United Kingdom. **Phone:** 186-26 32 00. **Fax:** 186-2519 60.

■ APPLICATION

Required Application form, baccalaureate/first degree, essay, interview, 2 letters of recommendation, personal statement, resume/curriculum vitae, transcripts of college work.

Deadlines and Fees *Deadlines:* 4/15 for fall, 9/15 for winter. *Application fee:* 45 British pounds, 45 British pounds (international).

Application Contact Ms. Isabelle Pochic-Fuerst, University Relations, United Kingdom Admissions, 12 Merton Street, England, United Kingdom. **Phone:** 186-263205. **Fax:** 186-251960. **E-mail:** ukadmission@eap.net.

Henley Management College

Oxfordshire, United Kingdom

BUSINESS PROGRAMS

Graduate Business Faculty

Full-time: 47   Part-time: 70

Henley Management College (continued)

Student Body
Total: 6,551
Part-time: 6,551

Average Age: 30

Admissions
Applications: 225
Admitted: 159

Enrolled: 116

Costs (1999–2000)
Full-time tuition: N/R
Part-time tuition: 17,000 British pounds per degree program

DEGREES MBA • MBA/MS

MBA—Master of Business Administration Full-time and part-time. *Distance learning option.* 12 to 36 months to complete program. *Concentrations:* management, strategic management.

MBA/MS—Master of Business Administration/Master of Science in Project Management Part-time. *Distance learning option.* 24 to 36 months to complete program. *Concentrations:* project management.

COSTS

Tuition *Part-time:* 17,000 British pounds per degree program. Tuition varies by academic program and local reciprocity agreements. **Required fees:** Tuition and fees vary by academic program. **Graduate housing:** Room and board costs vary by campus location, number of occupants, and type of accommodation. *Typical cost:* 1650 British pounds (including board).

RESOURCES AND SERVICES

Information about online services, personal computer policies, library resources, international exchange programs, internship programs, and placement services at this institution and others can be found at **www. petersons.com/mba**

International Students

Services and Facilities Counseling/support services, ESL/language courses, international student housing. Financial aid is not available to international students. **Applying** *Recommended:* IELT, TOEFL.

International Student Contact Mrs. Lynne Stone, Business Development Director, Greenlands, Oxfordshire, United Kingdom. **Phone:** 149-571-454. **Fax:** 149-410-184.

■ APPLICATION

Required Application form, baccalaureate/first degree, interview, 2 letters of recommendation, work experience.
Application Contact Mrs. Lynne Stone, Business Development Director, Greenlands, Oxfordshire, United Kingdom. **Phone:** 149-571-454. **Fax:** 149-410-184.

Heriot-Watt University

Edinburgh, United Kingdom

EDINBURGH BUSINESS SCHOOL

DEGREES MBA • MS

MBA—Consortium MBA At least 60 total credits required. 27 to 84 months to complete program.
MBA—Master of Business Administration Full-time and part-time. *Distance learning option.* At least 60 total credits required. 12 to 84 months to complete program.
MS—Master of Science in International Accounting and Financial Studies Full-time. 12 months to complete program.
MS—Master of Science in International Banking and Financial Studies Full-time. 12 months to complete program.

RESOURCES AND SERVICES

Information about online services, personal computer policies, library resources, international exchange programs, internship programs, and placement services at this institution and others can be found at **www. petersons.com/mba**

International Students

Services and Facilities Counseling/support services, ESL/language courses, visa services. Financial aid is not available to international students.
International Student Contact Dr. David Boak, Director, International Division, Riccarton, Edinburgh, EH14 4A5, United Kingdom.

■ APPLICATION

Application Contact Ms. Gillian Steele, Director of MBA Programmes, Edinburgh Business School, Edinburgh, EH14 4AS, United Kingdom. **Phone:** 131-451-3479. **Fax:** 131-451-3002. **E-mail:** enquiries@ebs.hw.ac.uk.

Huron University USA in London

London, United Kingdom

MBA PROGRAM

Graduate Business Faculty
Full-time: 15

Student Body
Total: 65

Women: 58%

Average Age: 25

Admissions
Applications: 65
Admitted: 61
Enrolled: 39

Average GMAT: 550
Average GPA: 3

Costs (1999–2000)
Full-time tuition: 9840 British pounds per academic year
Part-time tuition: 795 British pounds per course

DEGREES MA • MBA

MA—International Relations Full-time and part-time. At least 42 total credits required. 12 to 24 months to complete program. *Concentrations:* international business, international development management.

MBA—Master of Business Administration Full-time and part-time. 36 to 63 total credits required. 12 to 24 months to complete program. *Concentrations:* entrepreneurship, international finance, management information systems, marketing.

COSTS

Tuition *Full-time:* 9840 British pounds. *Part-time:* 795 British pounds per course. **Tuition, international:** *Full-time* 9840 British pounds. Tuition varies by number of courses or credits taken. **Graduate housing:** Room and board costs vary by number of occupants and type of accommodation. *Typical cost:* 4000 British pounds (room only).

FINANCIAL AID (1999–2000)

9 students received aid, including scholarships and work study. **Financial Aid Contact** Ms. Alison Rubin, Dean of Students, 58 Princes Gate, Exhibition Road, London, SW7 2PG, United Kingdom. **Phone:** 207-584-9696 Ext. 220. **Fax:** 207-589-9406. **E-mail:** marco@huron.ac.uk.

RESOURCES AND SERVICES

Information about online services, personal computer policies, library resources, international exchange programs, internship programs, and placement services at this institution and others can be found at **www. petersons.com/mba**

International Students

92% of students enrolled are international students.

Services and Facilities Counseling/support services, ESL/language courses, international student housing, visa services. Financial aid is available to international students.
Applying *Required:* IELT with recommended score of 6, TOEFL with recommended score of 213 (computer) or 550 (paper), proof of adequate funds.
International Student Contact Ms. Alison Rubin, Dean of Students, 58 Princes Gate, Exhibition Road, London, SW7 2PG, United Kingdom. **Phone:** 207-581-4899 Ext. 220. **Fax:** 207-589-9406.

■ APPLICATION

Required Application form, baccalaureate/first degree, essay, 2 letters of recommendation, resume/curriculum vitae, transcripts of college work. School will accept GMAT. **Recommended** Interview, personal statement.

Deadlines and Fees Applications for domestic and international students are processed on a rolling basis. *Application fee:* 25 British pounds, 25 British pounds (international).

Application Contact Mr. Marco Gorin, Director of Admissions, 58 Princes Gate, Exhibition Road, London, SW7 2PG, United Kingdom. **Phone:** 207-584-9696 Ext. 203. **Fax:** 207-589-9406. **E-mail:** marco@huron.ac.uk.

Imperial College

London, United Kingdom

MANAGEMENT SCHOOL

DEGREES M Sc • MBA

M Sc—Master of Science in Finance Full-time. 12 months to complete program. *Concentrations:* finance, international finance.

MBA—Full-time MBA Full-time. 2 years of work experience required. 12 months to complete program. *Concentrations:* entrepreneurship, finance, marketing, new venture management, project management, public management.

MBA—Part-time MBA Part-time. 3 years of work experience required. 27 months to complete program. *Concentrations:* entrepreneurship, finance, health care, marketing, new venture management, project management, public management.

RESOURCES AND SERVICES

Information about online services, personal computer policies, library resources, international exchange programs, internship programs, and placement services at this institution and others can be found at **www.petersons.com/mba**

International Students

Services and Facilities Financial aid is not available to international students. **International Student Contact** Mr. Paul Granger, 53 Prince's Gate, Exhibition Road, London, SW7 2PG, United Kingdom. **Phone:** 171-594-9205. **Fax:** 171-823-7685. **E-mail:** m.school@ic.ac.uk.

■ APPLICATION

Application Contact Ms. Debbie Johnson, Marketing and Admissions Administrator, 53 Prince's Gate, London, SW7 2PG, United Kingdom. **Phone:** 171-594-9206. **Fax:** 171-823-7685. **E-mail:** m.school@ic.ac.uk.

Kingston University

Kingston upon Thames, United Kingdom

KINGSTON BUSINESS SCHOOL

Graduate Business Faculty
Full-time: 90   Part-time: 20

Student Body
Average Age: 34

Costs (1999–2000)
Full-time tuition: 5250 British pounds per academic year
Part-time tuition: N/R

DEGREES MA • MBA

MA—Master of Arts in Accounting and Finance Full-time. Minimum of 24 months to complete program.

MA—Master of Arts in Business Management Full-time. 12 to 30 months to complete program.

MA—Master of Arts in Employment Relations and Law Part-time. Minimum of 24 months to complete program.

MA—Master of Arts in Managing Human Resources Part-time. Minimum of 24 months to complete program.

MA—Master of Arts in Marketing Full-time and part-time. 12 to 24 months to complete program.

MA—Master of Arts in Personnel Management Full-time and part-time. 12 to 24 months to complete program.

MA—Master of Arts in Strategic Financial Management Part-time. Minimum of 24 months to complete program.

MBA—Master of Business Administration Part-time. Minimum of 24 months to complete program.

COSTS

Tuition *Full-time:* 5250 British pounds. Tuition varies by academic program and local reciprocity agreements. **Graduate housing:** Room and board costs vary by campus location, type of accommodation, and type of board plan. *Typical cost:* 3000 British pounds (room only).

RESOURCES AND SERVICES

Information about online services, personal computer policies, library resources, international exchange programs, internship programs, and placement services at this institution and others can be found at **www.petersons.com/mba**

International Students

Services and Facilities ESL/language courses. Financial aid is not available to international students.
Applying *Required:* IELT with recommended score of 7.5, TOEFL with recommended score of 600 (paper). *Recommended:* Proof of adequate funds.
International Student Contact International Officer-Students, Millennium House, 21 Eden Street, Kingston upon Thames, KT1 1BL, United Kingdom. **Phone:** 208-547-7755. **Fax:** 208-547-7789.

■ APPLICATION

Required Application form, baccalaureate/first degree, letter(s) of recommendation, personal statement, transcripts of college work, 5 years of work experience. **Recommended** Interview.
Deadlines and Fees *Deadlines:* 8/30 for fall, 8/30 for fall (international). *Application fee:* 25 British pounds.
Application Contact MBA Administrator, Kingston Hill, Kingston upon Thames, KT2 7LB, United Kingdom. **Phone:** 208-547-7200. **E-mail:** mba@kingston.ac.uk.

Lancaster University

Lancaster, United Kingdom

MANAGEMENT SCHOOL

Graduate Business Faculty
Full-time: 90   Part-time: 23

Student Body
Total: 542   Average Age: 25
Full-time: 319   Women: 38%
Part-time: 223

Admissions
Applications: 850   Enrolled: 71
Admitted: 230   Average GMAT: 613

Costs (1999–2000)
Full-time tuition: 15,000 British pounds per academic year (resident),
    15,000 British pounds per academic year (nonresident)
Part-time tuition: 15,000 British pounds per degree program (resident),
    15,000 British pounds per degree program (nonresident)

After Graduation (Class of 1998–99)
Employed within 3 months of graduation: 90%

DEGREES M Phil • MA • MBA • MS

M Phil—Master of Philosophy in Critical Management Part-time. 36 to 42 months to complete program. *Concentrations:* business policy/strategy, information systems, leadership, organizational management, public and private management, strategic management.

MA—Master of Arts in Accounting and Finance Full-time. 12 months to complete program. *Concentrations:* accounting, finance.

MA—Master of Arts in Management Learning Part-time. *Distance learning option.* 24 months to complete program. *Concentrations:* business education, human resources, management, organizational management, training and development.

MA—Master of Arts in Management and Organizational Learning Full-time. 12 months to complete program. *Concentrations:* business education, human resources, international management, management, organizational management, training and development.

MA—Master of Arts in Organizational Analysis and Behavior Full-time and part-time. 12 to 24 months to complete program. *Concentrations:* human resources, industrial/labor relations, management, organizational behavior/development, organizational management, research and development administration.

MBA—Executive Master of Business Administration Part-time. Minimum of 5 years work experience at managerial level. 24 months to complete program. *Concentrations:* accounting, human resources, international management, marketing, operations management, strategic management.

MBA—Master of Business Administration Full-time. 12 to 18 months to complete program. *Concentrations:* accounting, business ethics, commerce, electronic commerce (e-commerce), financial management/planning, human resources, international management, management, project management, quantitative analysis, strategic management.

MS—Master of Science in Finance Full-time. 12 months to complete program. *Concentrations:* finance.

Lancaster University (continued)

MS—Master of Science in Information Management Full-time. 12 months to complete program. *Concentrations:* information management.

MS—Master of Science in International Business Full-time. 12 months to complete program. *Concentrations:* economics, financial economics, international business, international economics, international marketing, international trade.

MS—Master of Science in Management Full-time. 12 months to complete program. *Concentrations:* accounting, entrepreneurship, financial management/planning, management, marketing, organizational management.

MS—Master of Science in Operational Research Full-time. 12 months to complete program. *Concentrations:* logistics, management science, operations management.

COSTS

Tuition, state resident: *Full-time* 15,000 British pounds. *Part-time* 15,000 British pounds per degree program. **Tuition, nonresident:** *Full-time* 15,000 British pounds. *Part-time* 15,000 British pounds per degree program. **Tuition, international:** *Full-time* 15,000 British pounds. **Graduate housing:** Room and board costs vary by number of occupants. *Typical cost:* 3060 British pounds (room only).

FINANCIAL AID (1999–2000)

9 students received aid. **Financial Aid Contact** Ms. Sue Atherton, Programme Manager, The MBA Office, Lancaster University Management School, Lancaster, LA1 4YX, United Kingdom. **Phone:** 1524 594068. **Fax:** 1524 594068. **E-mail:** mba@lancaster.ac.uk.

RESOURCES AND SERVICES

Information about online services, personal computer policies, library resources, international exchange programs, internship programs, and placement services at this institution and others can be found at **www.petersons.com/mba**

International Students

34% of students enrolled are international students.

Services and Facilities Counseling/support services, ESL/language courses, housing location assistance, international student organization, language tutoring, orientation, religious facilities.

Applying *Required:* IELT with recommended score of 7, TOEFL with recommended score of 250 (computer) or 600 (paper), proof of adequate funds.

International Student Contact Sue Hird, International Officer, University House, Lancaster, LA1 4YW, United Kingdom. **Phone:** 1524 594530. **Fax:** 1524 594530. **E-mail:** s.hird@lancaster.ac.uk.

■ APPLICATION

Required GMAT, application form, baccalaureate/first degree, interview, 2 letters of recommendation, personal statement, transcripts of college work, 3 years of work experience. **Recommended** Resume/curriculum vitae.

Deadlines and Fees *Deadlines:* 6/30 for fall, 6/30 for fall (international).

Application Contact Ms. Sue Atherton, Programme Manager, The MBA Office, Lancaster University Management School, Lancaster, LA1 4YX, United Kingdom. **Phone:** 1524 594068. **Fax:** 1524 594068. **E-mail:** mba@lancaster.ac.uk.

London School of Economics and Political Science

London, United Kingdom

THE GRADUATE SCHOOL

Student Body
Total: 928   Full-time: 928

Costs (1999–2000)
Full-time tuition: 9360 British pounds per academic year (resident), 9360 British pounds per academic year (nonresident)
Part-time tuition: 4680 British pounds per year (resident), 4680 British pounds per year (nonresident)

After Graduation (Class of 1998–99)
Employed within 3 months of graduation: 98%

DEGREES M Sc

M Sc—Accounting and Finance Full-time. 9 months to complete program. *Concentrations:* accounting, finance, international finance.

M Sc—Analysis, Design, and Management of Information Systems Full-time. Minimum of 12 months to complete program.

M Sc—Decision Sciences Full-time. Minimum of 12 months to complete program. *Concentrations:* decision sciences.

M Sc—Development Management Full-time. 12 months to complete program.

M Sc—Econometrics and Mathematical Economics Full-time. 9 to 21 months to complete program. *Concentrations:* economics.

M Sc—Economics Full-time. 10 months to complete program. *Concentrations:* economics, international economics, public policy and administration.

M Sc—Finance and Economics Full-time. 10 months to complete program. *Concentrations:* economics, international finance.

M Sc—Global Market Economics Full-time. 22 months to complete program.

M Sc—Industrial Relations and Personnel Management Full-time. 12 months to complete program. *Concentrations:* industrial/labor relations.

M Sc—International Accounting and Finance Full-time. 9 months to complete program. *Concentrations:* accounting, international finance.

M Sc—Management Full-time. 12 months to complete program. *Concentrations:* management, public management.

M Sc—Management (Public Sector) Full-time. 12 months to complete program.

M Sc—Management of Non-Governmental Organizations Full-time. Minimum of 12 months to complete program. *Concentrations:* management, nonprofit management, nonprofit organization.

M Sc—Politics of the World Economy Full-time. Minimum of 9 months to complete program.

M Sc—Public Administration and Public Policy Full-time. Minimum of 12 months to complete program. *Concentrations:* public management, public policy and administration.

M Sc—Risk Full-time. Minimum of 10 months to complete program.

M Sc—Voluntary Sector Organization Full-time. Minimum of 9 months to complete program. *Concentrations:* nonprofit management, nonprofit organization.

COSTS

Tuition, state resident: *Full-time* 9360 British pounds. *Part-time* 4680 British pounds per year. **Tuition, nonresident:** *Full-time* 9360 British pounds. *Part-time* 4680 British pounds per year. **Graduate housing:** Room and board costs vary by campus location, number of occupants, type of accommodation, and type of board plan. *Typical cost:* 5044 British pounds (including board).

FINANCIAL AID (1999–2000)

Grants, loans, and scholarships. **Financial Aid Contact** Graduate Admissions Office, Houghton Street, London, WC2A 2AE, United Kingdom.

RESOURCES AND SERVICES

Information about online services, personal computer policies, library resources, international exchange programs, internship programs, and placement services at this institution and others can be found at **www.petersons.com/mba**

International Students

Services and Facilities ESL/language courses. Financial aid is available to international students.

Applying *Required:* IELT with recommended score of 6.5, TOEFL with recommended score of 600 (paper).

International Student Contact Tim Rogers, Student Recruitment Manager, Houghton Street, London, WC2A 2AE, United Kingdom. **Phone:** 20-7955 6143. **Fax:** 20-7955 7421. **E-mail:** stu.rec@lse.ca.uk.

■ APPLICATION

Required Application form, baccalaureate/first degree, 2 letters of recommendation, personal statement, transcripts of college work. School will accept GMAT and GRE.

Deadlines and Fees *Deadlines:* 3/1 for fall, 3/1 for fall (international). *Application fee:* 25 British pounds.

Application Contact The Graduate Admissions Office, Houghton Street, London, WC2A 2AE, United Kingdom. **Phone:** 20-7955 7160. **Fax:** 20-7955 6137. **E-mail:** graduate-school@lse.ac.uk.

Loughborough University

Loughborough, United Kingdom

THE BUSINESS SCHOOL—POSTGRADUATE OFFICE

Graduate Business Faculty
Full-time: 40

Student Body
Total: 1,326   Part-time: 140
Full-time: 1,186   Average Age: 28

Admissions
Applications: 60   Enrolled: 50
Admitted: 54

Costs (1999–2000)
Full-time tuition: 2700 British pounds per academic year (resident), 2700 British pounds per academic year (nonresident)
Part-time tuition: N/R

DEGREES EMBA • M Sc

EMBA—Executive MBA Part-time. At least 180 total credits required. 36 to 84 months to complete program. *Concentrations:* business ethics, decision sciences, economics, finance, human resources, international business, management, marketing, strategic management.

M Sc—Master of Science in Management Full-time. At least 150 total credits required. Minimum of 12 months to complete program.

COSTS

Tuition, state resident: *Full-time* 2700 British pounds. **Tuition, nonresident:** *Full-time* 2700 British pounds. Tuition varies by number of courses or credits taken and academic program.

FINANCIAL AID (1999–2000)
10 students received aid, including grants. **Financial Aid Contact** Mrs. Ros Fleming, MSc Management Administrator, Leicestershire, United Kingdom. **Phone:** 150-922-3398. **Fax:** 150-922-3960. **E-mail:** mscmanagement@lboro.ac.uk.

RESOURCES AND SERVICES
Information about online services, personal computer policies, library resources, international exchange programs, internship programs, and placement services at this institution and others can be found at **www.petersons.com/mba**

International Students

Services and Facilities Counseling/support services, international student housing. Financial aid is not available to international students.
Applying *Required:* IELT, TOEFL with recommended score of 550 (paper), proof of adequate funds.
International Student Contact Mrs. Ros Fleming, MSc Management Administrator, Loughborough, LE22 3TU, United Kingdom. **Phone:** 150-922-3291. **Fax:** 150-922-3960. **E-mail:** mscmanagement@lboro.ac.uk.

■ APPLICATION

Required Application form, baccalaureate/first degree, 2 letters of recommendation, resume/curriculum vitae, transcripts of college work, 3 years of work experience. School will accept GMAT. **Recommended** Interview, personal statement.
Deadlines and Fees *Deadlines:* 9/25 for fall, 8/25 for fall (international). *Application fee:* 7100 British pounds.
Application Contact Ms. Gabriella Stenson, MBA Administrator, Business School Loughborough University, Leicestershire, United Kingdom. **Phone:** 150-922-3398. **Fax:** 150-922-3960. **E-mail:** mbainfo@lboro.ac.uk.

Manchester Metropolitan University

Manchester, United Kingdom

FACULTY OF MANAGEMENT AND BUSINESS, DEPARTMENT OF MANAGEMENT

Graduate Business Faculty
Full-time: 20   Part-time: 30

Student Body
Total: 110   Average Age: 33
Part-time: 110   Women: 33%

Costs (1999–2000)
Full-time tuition: N/R
Part-time tuition: 9000 British pounds per degree program (resident)

DEGREES MBA

MBA—International MBA Full-time. Minimum of 12 months to complete program. *Concentrations:* international business.

MBA—Master of Business Administration Part-time. 24 to 30 months to complete program.

MBA—Master of Business Administration Part-time. 30 to 60 months to complete program. *Concentrations:* accounting, business ethics, finance, health care, human resources, international business, management, marketing, operations management, organizational behavior/development, public policy and administration, quality management, strategic management.

COSTS

Tuition, state resident: *Part-time* 9000 British pounds per degree program.

FINANCIAL AID (1999–2000)
Scholarships. **Financial Aid Contact** Mrs. Val Downes, MBA Administrator, Aytoun Building, Aytoun Street, Manchester, M1 3GH, United Kingdom. **Phone:** 161-247-3717. **Fax:** 161-247-6319. **E-mail:** v.downes@mmu.ac.uk.

RESOURCES AND SERVICES
Information about online services, personal computer policies, library resources, international exchange programs, internship programs, and placement services at this institution and others can be found at **www.petersons.com/mba**

International Students

Services and Facilities Counseling/support services, international student housing. Financial aid is available to international students.
Applying *Recommended:* IELT, TOEFL.
International Student Contact Mrs. Sheila Aynsley-Smith, Head of Student Services, All Saint's Building, All Saint's, Manchester, M15 6BH, United Kingdom. **Phone:** 161-247-3480.

■ APPLICATION

Required Application form, baccalaureate/first degree, interview, 2 letters of recommendation, resume/curriculum vitae, 5 years of work experience.

Application Contact Mrs. Val Downes, MBA Course Administrator, Aytoun Building, Aytoun Street, Manchester, M1 3GH, United Kingdom. **Phone:** 161-247-3717. **Fax:** 161-247-6319. **E-mail:** mba@mmu.ac.uk.

Middlesex University

London, United Kingdom

BUSINESS SCHOOL

Student Body
Total: 70   Part-time: 35
Full-time: 35   Average Age: 27

Admissions
Enrolled: 75

Costs (1999–2000)
Full-time tuition: 9900 British pounds per academic year (resident), 9900 British pounds per academic year (nonresident)
Part-time tuition: N/R

DEGREE MBA

MBA—Master of Business Administration Full-time and part-time. 12 to 27 months to complete program. *Concentrations:* accounting, finance, human resources, international business, management, marketing, operations management.

COSTS

Tuition, state resident: *Full-time* 9900 British pounds. **Tuition, nonresident:** *Full-time* 9900 British pounds. **Graduate housing:** Room and board costs vary by number of occupants and type of accommodation. *Typical cost:* 3120 British pounds (room only).

FINANCIAL AID (1999–2000)
Financial Aid Contact Ms. Martine Clark, MBA Admissions Administrator, The Burroughs, Hendon, London, NW4 4BT, United Kingdom. **Phone:** 181-362-5986. **Fax:** 181-362-6069. **E-mail:** m.clark@mdx.ac.uk.

RESOURCES AND SERVICES
Information about online services, personal computer policies, library resources, international exchange programs, internship programs, and placement services at this institution and others can be found at **www.petersons.com/mba**

International Students

Services and Facilities Counseling/support services, ESL/language courses, language tutoring. Financial aid is available to international students.
Applying *Required:* IELT with recommended score of 6.5, TOEFL with recommended score of 580 (paper).

Middlesex University (continued)

International Student Contact Mrs. Hema Tank, Academic Operations Supervisor, The Burroughs, Hendon, London, NW4 4BT, United Kingdom. **Phone:** 181-362-5749. **Fax:** 181-362-5749.

■ **APPLICATION**

Required Application form, baccalaureate/first degree, interview, 2 letters of recommendation, personal statement, transcripts of college work, 3 years of work experience. School will accept GMAT.

Deadlines and Fees Applications for domestic and international students are processed on a rolling basis.

Application Contact Ms. Martine Clark, MBA Admissions Administrator, The Burroughs, Hendon, London, NW4 4BT, United Kingdom. **Phone:** 181-362-5090. **Fax:** 181-362-6069. **E-mail:** m.clark@mdx.ac.uk.

Napier University

Edinburgh, United Kingdom

NAPIER BUSINESS SCHOOL

Graduate Business Faculty
Full-time: 130   Part-time: 55

Student Body
Total: 460   Average Age: 35
Part-time: 460   Women: 40%

Costs (1999–2000)
Full-time tuition: 4995 British pounds per academic year (resident), 7200 British pounds per academic year (nonresident)
Part-time tuition: 5775 British pounds per degree program

DEGREES MBA

MBA—Distance Learning MBA Part-time. *Distance learning option.* 36 to 60 months to complete program.

MBA—Full-time MBA Programme Full-time. 12 to 18 months to complete program.

MBA—Open-learning MBA Program Part-time. *Distance learning option.* 2 letters of recommendation required. Minimum of 24 months to complete program.

MBA—Part-time MBA Part-time. 36 to 60 months to complete program.

COSTS

Tuition *Part-time:* 5775 British pounds per degree program. **Tuition, state resident:** *Full-time* 4995 British pounds. **Tuition, nonresident:** *Full-time* 7200 British pounds. **Required fees:** Tuition and fees vary by academic program.

FINANCIAL AID (1999–2000)

Financial Aid Contact

RESOURCES AND SERVICES

Information about online services, personal computer policies, library resources, international exchange programs, internship programs, and placement services at this institution and others can be found at **www. petersons.com/mba**

International Students

Services and Facilities Counseling/support services. Financial aid is not available to international students.

International Student Contact Business School Information Center, Craiglockhart, 219 Colinton Road, Edinburgh, EH14 1DJ, United Kingdom. **Phone:** 131-455-3369. **E-mail:** bsinfo@napier.ac.uk.

■ **APPLICATION**

Required GMAT, GRE, application form, personal statement, resume/curriculum vitae, transcripts of college work. **Recommended** Baccalaureate/first degree, interview, work experience.

Deadlines and Fees Applications for domestic students are processed on a rolling basis. *Deadline:* 8/1 for fall (international).

Application Contact Mrs. Sheila Ferrier, Programme Administrator, South Craig, Craighouse Campus, Craighouse Road, Edinburgh, EH10 5LG, United Kingdom. **Phone:** 131-455-5016. **Fax:** 131-455-5041. **E-mail:** s.ferrier@napier.ac.uk.

Open University

Milton Keynes, United Kingdom

BUSINESS SCHOOL

Graduate Business Faculty
Full-time: 52

Student Body
Total: 6,000   Average Age: 35

Admissions
Applications: 4,500

Costs (1999–2000)
Full-time tuition: N/R
Part-time tuition: 1520 British pounds per course (resident), 1520 British pounds per course (nonresident)

DEGREES MBA • MS

MBA—Masters Program *Distance learning option.* At least 120 total credits required. 36 to 120 months to complete program. *Concentrations:* business education, environmental economics/management, human resources, management, organizational behavior/development, public policy and administration, strategic management.

MS—Masters Program At least 120 total credits required.

COSTS

Tuition, state resident: *Part-time* 1520 British pounds per course. **Tuition, nonresident:** *Part-time* 1520 British pounds per course.

FINANCIAL AID (1999–2000)

Financial Aid Contact Mr. Richard Wheatcroft, Program Director, PO Box 481, Walton Hall, Buckinghaimshire, United Kingdom. **Phone:** 190-655-851.

RESOURCES AND SERVICES

Information about online services, personal computer policies, library resources, international exchange programs, internship programs, and placement services at this institution and others can be found at **www. petersons.com/mba**

International Students

Services and Facilities Financial aid is not available to international students.

■ **APPLICATION**

Required Application form, transcripts of college work, 5 years of work experience.

Deadlines and Fees *Deadlines:* 9/15 for fall, 3/15 for spring, 9/15 for fall (international), 3/15 for spring (international).

Application Contact Ms. Christine McIlroy, Customer Services Department, PO Box 481, Walton Hall, Milton Keynes, MK7 6B7, United Kingdom. **Phone:** 190-652-143. **Fax:** 190-655-898.

Oxford Brookes University

Oxford, United Kingdom

SCHOOL OF BUSINESS

Graduate Business Faculty
Full-time: 25   Part-time: 5

Student Body
Total: 175   Average Age: 29
Full-time: 75   Women: 43%
Part-time: 100

Admissions
Applications: 600   Enrolled: 90
Admitted: 200   Average GMAT: 520

Costs (1999–2000)
Full-time tuition: 8700 British pounds per academic year (resident)
Part-time tuition: N/R

After Graduation (Class of 1998–99)
Employed within 3 months of graduation: 90%

DEGREES MA • MBA • MS

MA—Master of Arts in Human Resource Management Part-time. At least 180 total credits required. 12 months to complete program. *Concentrations:* human resources.

MBA—Master of Business Administration Full-time and part-time. *Distance learning option.* At least 180 total credits required. 12 to 24 months to complete program. *Concentrations:* human resources, management, marketing, operations management, organizational management.

MS—Master of Science in International Management Full-time. At least 180 total credits required. 12 months to complete program. *Concentrations:* human resources, management, marketing, operations management, organizational management.

COSTS

Tuition, state resident: *Full-time* 8700 British pounds. **Tuition, international:** *Full-time* 8700 British pounds. Tuition varies by academic program. **Graduate housing:** Room and board costs vary by number of occupants and type of board plan. *Typical cost:* 9000 British pounds (including board), 6000 British pounds (room only).

FINANCIAL AID (1999–2000)

5 students received aid, including scholarships. Financial aid application deadline: 5/1. **Financial Aid Contact** Mrs. Jackie Carter, MBA Course Administrator, School of Business, Wheatley Campus, Oxfordshire, United Kingdom. **Phone:** 186-548-5920. **Fax:** 186-548-5830. **E-mail:** mba@brookes.ac.uk.

RESOURCES AND SERVICES

Information about online services, personal computer policies, library resources, international exchange programs, internship programs, and placement services at this institution and others can be found at **www.petersons.com/mba**

International Students

31% of students enrolled are international students.

Services and Facilities Counseling/support services, ESL/language courses, housing location assistance, international student housing, international student organization, language tutoring, orientation. Financial aid is available to international students.

Applying *Required:* IELT with recommended score of 6, TOEFL with recommended score of 213 (computer) or 550 (paper), proof of adequate funds, proof of health/immunizations.

International Student Contact Mr. Paul Gilliam, Deputy Head, Marketing, Wheatley Campus, Wheatley, Oxford, OX33 1HX, United Kingdom. **Phone:** 186-548-5922. **Fax:** 186-548-5830. **E-mail:** phgilliam@brookes.ac.uk.

■ APPLICATION

Required Application form, baccalaureate/first degree, 2 letters of recommendation, personal statement, transcripts of college work, 3 years of work experience. School will accept GMAT. **Recommended** Interview, resume/curriculum vitae.

Deadlines and Fees *Deadlines:* 6/30 for fall, 6/30 for fall (international).

Application Contact Mrs. Jackie Carter, MBA Course Administrator, School of Business, Wheatley Campus, Oxfordshire, United Kingdom. **Phone:** 186-548-5920. **Fax:** 186-548-5830. **E-mail:** mba-bus@brookes.ac.uk.

Richmond, The American International University in London

Richmond, United Kingdom

SCHOOL OF BUSINESS

Graduate Business Faculty
Full-time: 11   Part-time: 15

Student Body
Total: 85   Average Age: 28.5
Full-time: 85   Women: 35%

Admissions
Applications: 129   Average GMAT: 540
Admitted: 94   Average GPA: 3.3
Enrolled: 60

Costs (1999–2000)
Full-time tuition: 14,960 British pounds per academic year
Part-time tuition: N/R

After Graduation (Class of 1998–99)
Employed within 3 months of graduation: 100%

DEGREE MBA

MBA—Full-time MBA-Master of Business Administration Full-time. At least 45 total credits required. Minimum of 12 months to complete program. *Concentrations:* international business, international finance, international marketing, management.

COSTS

Tuition *Full-time:* 14,960 British pounds. Tuition varies by number of courses or credits taken and academic program. **Required fees:** Fees vary by class time and academic program. **Graduate housing:** *Typical cost:* 8500 British pounds (including board).

FINANCIAL AID (1999–2000)

9 students received aid, including scholarships. **Financial Aid Contact** Office of Financial Aid, Queens Road, Richmond, Surrey, TW10 6JP, United Kingdom. **Phone:** 020-8332-9000. **Fax:** 020-8332-1596. **E-mail:** enroll@richmond.ac.uk.

RESOURCES AND SERVICES

Information about online services, personal computer policies, library resources, international exchange programs, internship programs, and placement services at this institution and others can be found at **www.petersons.com/mba**

International Students

100% of students enrolled are international students.

Services and Facilities Counseling/support services, ESL/language courses, housing location assistance, international student housing, language tutoring, orientation, visa services. Financial aid is available to international students.

Applying *Required:* TOEFL with recommended score of 240 (computer) or 600 (paper), proof of adequate funds. *Recommended:* Proof of health/immunizations.

International Student Contact Ms. Nancy Barrett, Director of Graduate Admissions, 16 Young Street, London, W8 5EH, United Kingdom. **Phone:** 020-8368-8475. **Fax:** 020-8376-0836. **E-mail:** grad@richmond.ac.uk.

■ APPLICATION

Required Application form, baccalaureate/first degree, essay, 2 letters of recommendation, personal statement, resume/curriculum vitae, transcripts of college work, 2 years of work experience. School will accept GMAT and GRE. **Recommended** Interview.

Deadlines and Fees Applications for domestic and international students are processed on a rolling basis. *Application fee:* 35 British pounds.

Application Contact Ms. Nancy Barrett, Director of Graduate Admissions, 16 Young Street, London, W8 5EH, United Kingdom. **Phone:** 020-7368-8475. **Fax:** 020-7376-0836. **E-mail:** grad@richmond.ac.uk.

See full description on page 786.

Schiller International University

London, United Kingdom

GRADUATE PROGRAMS, LONDON CAMPUS

Graduate Business Faculty
Full-time: 8   Part-time: 38

Student Body
Total: 95   Part-time: 10
Full-time: 85   Women: 56%

Costs (1999–2000)
Full-time tuition: 9600 British pounds per academic year
Part-time tuition: 620 British pounds per course

After Graduation (Class of 1998–99)
Employed within 3 months of graduation: 80%

DEGREES MA • MBA

MA—Master of Arts in International Hotel and Tourism Management Full-time. At least 45 total credits required. 12 to 24 months to complete program.

MA—Master of Arts in International Relations and Diplomacy Full-time and part-time. At least 45 total credits required. 12 to 24 months to complete program.

MBA—Master of Business Administration in International Business Full-time and part-time. *Distance learning option.* At least 45 total credits required. 12 to 24 months to complete program.

MBA—Master of Business Administration in International Hotel and Tourism Management Full-time and part-time. At least 45 total credits required. 12 to 24 months to complete program.

Schiller International University (continued)

COSTS

Tuition *Full-time:* 9300 British pounds. *Part-time:* 620 British pounds per course. Tuition varies by number of courses or credits taken, campus location, and academic program. **Required fees:** *Full-time* 300 British pounds. Tuition and fees vary by campus location and academic program. **Graduate housing:** Room and board costs vary by campus location, number of occupants, type of accommodation, and type of board plan. *Typical cost:* 5160 British pounds (including board).

FINANCIAL AID (1999–2000)

Grants, loans, scholarships, and work study. Financial aid application deadline: 4/1. **Financial Aid Contact** Ms. Teri Reeves, Financial Aid Director, 453 Edgewater Drive, Dunedin, FL 34698. **Phone:** 727-736-5082 Ext. 250. **Fax:** 727-734-0359. **E-mail:** teri_reeves@schiller.edu.

RESOURCES AND SERVICES

Information about online services, personal computer policies, library resources, international exchange programs, internship programs, and placement services at this institution and others can be found at **www. petersons.com/mba**

International Students

98% of students enrolled are international students.

Services and Facilities Counseling/support services, ESL/language courses, housing location assistance, international student housing, orientation, visa services. Financial aid is available to international students.

Applying *Required:* Proof of adequate funds. *Recommended:* TOEFL with recommended score of 550 (paper).

International Student Contact Ms. Jocelyn Everett, Associate Director of Admissions, 51-55 Waterloo Road, London, SE1 8TX, United Kingdom. **Phone:** 207-928-8484. **Fax:** 207-620-1226. **E-mail:** admissions@schillerlondon.ac.uk.

■ APPLICATION

Required GMAT, application form, baccalaureate/first degree, essay, transcripts of college work. **Recommended** Resume/curriculum vitae, work experience.

Deadlines and Fees Applications for domestic and international students are processed on a rolling basis. *Application fee:* $35, $35 (international).

Application Contact Director of Admissions, 453 Edgewater Drive, Dunedin, FL 34698-7532. **Phone:** 727-736-5082 Ext. 239. **Fax:** 727-734-0359. **E-mail:** admissions@schiller.edu.

See full description on page 816.

Sheffield Hallam University

Sheffield, United Kingdom

BUSINESS SCHOOL

Admissions
Average GMAT: 550

Costs (1999–2000)
Full-time tuition: N/R
Part-time tuition: 1300 British pounds per semester (resident), 1300 British pounds per semester (nonresident)

After Graduation (Class of 1998–99)
Employed within 3 months of graduation: 100%

DEGREES MA • MBA • MS

MA—MA in Finance and Banking Part-time. Up to 180 total credits required. 24 to 48 months to complete program. *Concentrations:* accounting, banking, financial management/planning.

MBA—MBA in Consultancy Full-time. Up to 180 total credits required. 36 to 60 months to complete program. *Concentrations:* European business studies, management.

MBA—MBA in Enterprise and Entrepreneurship Full-time and part-time. *Distance learning option.* At least 180 total credits required. 12 to 60 months to complete program. *Concentrations:* insurance, management.

MBA—MBA in European Management Full-time. Up to 100 total credits required. 12 to 36 months to complete program.

MBA—MBA in International Management Full-time and part-time. *Distance learning option.* At least 180 total credits required. 12 to 60 months to complete program. *Concentrations:* international business, management.

MBA—Master of Business Administration in Financial Management Full-time and part-time. *Distance learning option.* Up to 180 total credits required. 12 to 60 months to complete program. *Concentrations:* financial management/planning, international finance, management.

MBA—Master of Business Administration in Financial Services Full-time and part-time. *Distance learning option.* Up to 180 total credits required. 12 to 60 months to complete program. *Concentrations:* banking, insurance, international banking, management.

MBA—Master of Business Administration in Information Technology Management Full-time and part-time. *Distance learning option.* Up to 180 total credits required. 36 to 60 months to complete program. *Concentrations:* information management, management, management information systems, system management.

MBA—Master of Business Administration Full-time and part-time. *Distance learning option.* At least 180 total credits required. 12 to 48 months to complete program. *Concentrations:* management.

MS—MS in Business Process Development *Distance learning option.* Up to 180 total credits required. 24 to 48 months to complete program. *Concentrations:* system management.

MS—MS in Operational Research *Distance learning option.* Up to 180 total credits required. 24 to 48 months to complete program. *Concentrations:* management science.

MS—MS in Operational Research for Health Services *Distance learning option.* At least 180 total credits required. 24 to 48 months to complete program. *Concentrations:* accounting, banking, financial management/planning.

MS—MS in Total Quality Management *Distance learning option.* Up to 180 total credits required. 24 to 48 months to complete program. *Concentrations:* quality management.

MS—Master of Science in E-Business and Marketing Part-time. 24 to 48 months to complete program. *Concentrations:* electronic commerce (e-commerce), marketing.

MS—Master of Science in Human Resource Development Full-time and part-time. At least 180 total credits required. 12 to 36 months to complete program. *Concentrations:* human resources.

MS—Master of Science in Human Resource Management Full-time and part-time. At least 180 total credits required. 12 to 36 months to complete program. *Concentrations:* human resources.

MS—Master of Science in International Business Full-time and part-time. At least 180 total credits required. 12 to 36 months to complete program. *Concentrations:* international business.

MS—Master of Science in International Marketing Full-time and part-time. At least 180 total credits required. 12 to 36 months to complete program. *Concentrations:* international marketing.

MS—Master of Science in Knowledge Management Full-time and part-time. At least 180 total credits required. 12 to 24 months to complete program. *Concentrations:* information management, management.

MS—Master of Science in Management Studies Full-time and part-time. At least 180 total credits required. 12 to 36 months to complete program. *Concentrations:* management.

MS—Master of Science in Organization Development Full-time and part-time. At least 180 total credits required. 12 to 36 months to complete program. *Concentrations:* organizational behavior/development.

MS—Master of Science in Strategic Information Systems Management Full-time and part-time. At least 180 total credits required. 12 to 36 months to complete program. *Concentrations:* management information systems.

MS—Master of Science in Strategic Leadership Part-time. At least 180 total credits required. 24 to 48 months to complete program. *Concentrations:* human resources, leadership.

COSTS

Tuition, state resident: *Part-time* 1300 British pounds per semester. **Tuition, nonresident:** *Part-time* 1300 British pounds per semester. Tuition varies by number of courses or credits taken and local reciprocity agreements. **Graduate housing:** Room and board costs vary by campus location, number of occupants, type of accommodation, and type of board plan. *Typical cost:* 2000 British pounds (including board).

FINANCIAL AID (1999–2000)

Research assistantships. **Financial Aid Contact** Ms. Jayne Barker, Business School Postgraduate Programme Coordinator (MBA), B.I.T.C. Building, Howard Street, Sheffield, S1 1WB, United Kingdom. **Phone:** 114-253-2820. **Fax:** 114-225-5268. **E-mail:** sbs.pgdinfo@shu.ac.uk.

RESOURCES AND SERVICES

Information about online services, personal computer policies, library resources, international exchange programs, internship programs, and placement services at this institution and others can be found at **www. petersons.com/mba**

International Students

Services and Facilities Counseling/support services, ESL/language courses, international student housing, visa services. Financial aid is not available to international students.

Applying *Required:* IELT with recommended score of 5.5, TOEFL with recommended score of 500 (paper). *Recommended:* Proof of adequate funds.

International Student Contact John Kirk, Business Development Officer (International Officer), International Office, Pond Street, Sheffield, S1 1WB, United Kingdom. **Phone:** 114-253-3930. **Fax:** 114-253-2046. **E-mail:** j.kirk@shu.ac.uk.

■ APPLICATION

Required GMAT, application form, baccalaureate/first degree, 2 letters of recommendation, personal statement, resume/curriculum vitae, transcripts of college work, 2 years of work experience.

Deadlines and Fees *Deadlines:* 7/31 for fall, 11/30 for winter.

Application Contact Ms. Joanne Houghton, Business School Postgraduate Programme Admissions Officer, B.I.T.C. Building, Howard Street, Sheffield, S1 1WB, United Kingdom. **Phone:** 114-253-2820. **Fax:** 114-225-5268. **E-mail:** sbs.pgdinfo@shu.ac.uk.

South Bank University

London, United Kingdom

BUSINESS SCHOOL

Student Body

Total: 1,000
Full-time: 300
Part-time: 700

Average Age: 29
Women: 50%

Admissions

Applications: 450
Admitted: 50

Enrolled: 40

Costs (1999–2000)

Full-time tuition: N/R
Part-time tuition: 6250 British pounds per semester (resident)

After Graduation (Class of 1998–99)

Employed within 3 months of graduation: 90%

DEGREES MBA • MS

MBA—European MBA Full-time. Minimum of 12 months to complete program.

MBA—Master of Business Administration in International Management Full-time. Minimum of 12 months to complete program.

MBA—Master of Business Administration Part-time. 18 to 30 months to complete program. *Concentrations:* accounting, business policy/strategy, financial management/planning, human resources, management, marketing, organizational behavior/development, organizational management, strategic management.

MS—Master of Science Full-time and part-time. 18 to 24 months to complete program. *Concentrations:* human resources, international business, public policy and administration, technology management.

COSTS

Tuition, state resident: *Part-time* 6250 British pounds per semester. Tuition varies by campus location. **Graduate housing:** *Typical cost:* 1800 British pounds (room only).

FINANCIAL AID (1999–2000)

Loans and scholarships. **Financial Aid Contact** Mr. Charles Fenech, MBA Program Director, 103 Borough Road, London, SE1 0AA, United Kingdom. **Phone:** 171-815-7783. **Fax:** 171-815-8280.

RESOURCES AND SERVICES

Information about online services, personal computer policies, library resources, international exchange programs, internship programs, and placement services at this institution and others can be found at **www.petersons.com/mba**

International Students

Services and Facilities Counseling/support services, ESL/language courses, housing location assistance, international student housing, international student organization, language tutoring, orientation, visa services. Financial aid is not available to international students.

Applying *Required:* IELT with recommended score of 6, TOEFL with recommended score of 600 (paper).

International Student Contact Ms. Min Liu, International Officer, Student Support Office, 103 Borough Road, London, SE1 0AA, United Kingdom. **Phone:** 171-815-6709.

■ APPLICATION

Required Application form, baccalaureate/first degree, interview, 2 letters of recommendation, personal statement, resume/curriculum vitae, transcripts of college work, 2 years of work experience.

Deadlines and Fees *Deadlines:* 9/15 for fall, 9/15 for fall (international). *Application fee:* 100 British pounds.

Application Contact Mr. Charles Fenech, MBA Program Director, 103 Borough Road, London, SE1 0AA, United Kingdom. **Phone:** 171-815-7783. **Fax:** 171-815-8280.

University of Bath

Bath, United Kingdom

SCHOOL OF MANAGEMENT

Graduate Business Faculty

Full-time: 63

Part-time: 30

Student Body

Total: 662
Full-time: 246
Part-time: 416

Average Age: 33
Women: 36%

Admissions

Applications: 1,796
Admitted: 717

Enrolled: 223
Average GMAT: 580

Costs (1999–2000)

Full-time tuition: 15,750 British pounds per academic year (resident), 15,750 British pounds per academic year (nonresident)
Part-time tuition: 14,000 British pounds per course (resident), 14,000 British pounds per course (nonresident)

After Graduation (Class of 1998–99)

Employed within 3 months of graduation: 80%
Average starting salary: 55,000 British pounds

DEGREES M Sc • MBA • PhD/Mphil

M Sc—Master of Science in Management Full-time. Open only to graduates, with minimum 2nd class honours degree. At least 60 total credits required. 12 to 15 months to complete program. *Concentrations:* management.

M Sc—Master of Science in Management with Finance Full-time. Minimum 2nd class honors degree. At least 60 total credits required. 12 to 15 months to complete program.

M Sc—Master of Science in Management with Human Resource Management Full-time. Minimum 2nd class honors degree. At least 60 total credits required. 12 to 15 months to complete program. *Concentrations:* human resources, management.

M Sc—Master of Science in Management with Marketing Full-time. Minimum 2nd class honors degree. At least 60 total credits required. 12 to 15 months to complete program. *Concentrations:* management, marketing.

M Sc—Master of Science in Management with Operations Management Full-time. Minimum 2nd class honors degree. At least 60 total credits required. 12 to 15 months to complete program. *Concentrations:* management, operations management.

M Sc—Master of Science in Management with Strategic Information Systems Full-time. Minimum 2nd class honours degree required. At least 60 total credits required. 12 to 15 months to complete program. *Concentrations:* management, management information systems.

M Sc—Master of Science in Responsibility and Business Practice Part-time. At least 75 total credits required. 24 to 30 months to complete program. *Concentrations:* business ethics, environmental economics/management.

MBA—Bath-MIM Executive MBA Part-time. Minimum of 5 years of full-time business experience required. At least 75 total credits required. 24 to 30 months to complete program. *Concentrations:* business policy/strategy, international business, management, strategic management.

MBA—Executive MBA Part-time. 3 years of full-time business experience. At least 75 total credits required. 24 to 30 months to complete program. *Concentrations:* business policy/strategy, international business, management, strategic management.

MBA—Full-time MBA Full-time. 3 years of full-time business experience and GMAT score (minimum 550) required. At least 75 total credits required. 12 to 18 months to complete program. *Concentrations:* business policy/strategy, entrepreneurship, management, strategic management.

University of Bath (continued)

MBA—Modular MBA Part-time. Minimum of 3 years of full-time business experience. At least 75 total credits required. 36 to 96 months to complete program. *Concentrations:* business policy/strategy, management, strategic management.

PhD/Mphil—Doctor of Philosophy/Research Master of Philosophy Full-time and part-time. 24 to 60 months to complete program. *Concentrations:* construction management, environmental economics/management, human resources, industrial/labor relations, international business, international marketing, management, management information systems, marketing, materials management, operations management, organizational behavior/development, production management, technology management.

COSTS

Tuition, state resident: *Full-time* 15,750 British pounds. *Part-time* 14,000 British pounds per course. **Tuition, nonresident:** *Full-time* 15,750 British pounds. *Part-time* 14,000 British pounds per course. **Tuition, international:** *Full-time* 15,750 British pounds. Tuition varies by class time, number of courses or credits taken, and academic program. **Graduate housing:** Room and board costs vary by campus location, number of occupants, and type of accommodation. *Typical cost:* 3000 British pounds (room only).

FINANCIAL AID (1999–2000)

10 students received aid, including research assistantships, scholarships, and work study. Financial aid application deadline: 6/30. **Financial Aid Contact** Mrs. Barbara Coward, MBA Admissions Manager, Claverton Down, Bath, BA2 7AY, United Kingdom. **Phone:** 441-225323851. **Fax:** 441-225826210. **E-mail:** mnsbc@bath.ac.uk.

RESOURCES AND SERVICES

Information about online services, personal computer policies, library resources, international exchange programs, internship programs, and placement services at this institution and others can be found at **www.petersons.com/mba**

International Students

38% of students enrolled are international students.

Services and Facilities Counseling/support services, ESL/language courses, international student housing, international student organization. Financial aid is available to international students.

Applying *Required:* IELT with recommended score of 7, TOEFL with recommended score of 250 (computer) or 600 (paper), proof of adequate funds, proof of health/immunizations. *Recommended:* TSE, TWE.

International Student Contact Ms. Carla Dewhurst, Head of International Office, Clavertown Down, Bath, BA2 7AY, United Kingdom. **Phone:** 441-225826832. **Fax:** 441-225826366. **E-mail:** international_office@bath.ac.uk.

■ APPLICATION

Required GMAT, application form, baccalaureate/first degree, essay, 2 letters of recommendation, personal statement, resume/curriculum vitae, transcripts of college work, 3 years of work experience. **Recommended** Interview.

Deadlines and Fees *Deadlines:* 7/31 for fall, 6/30 for fall (international).

Application Contact Mrs. Barbara Coward, MBA Admissions Manager, Claverton Down, Bath, BA2 7AY, United Kingdom. **Phone:** 122-5323432. **Fax:** 122-5826210. **E-mail:** mba-info@management.bath.ac.uk.

University of Birmingham

Birmingham, United Kingdom

BIRMINGHAM BUSINESS SCHOOL

Student Body
Total: 625	Average Age: 31
Full-time: 175	Women: 38%
Part-time: 450	

Admissions
Average GMAT: 590

Costs (1999–2000)
Full-time tuition: 8750 British pounds per academic year (resident), 9750 British pounds per academic year (nonresident)
Part-time tuition: N/R

After Graduation (Class of 1998–99)
Employed within 3 months of graduation: 90%

DEGREES MBA

MBA—Full-time MBA Full-time. 12 to 24 months to complete program. *Concentrations:* international business, strategic management.

MBA—Master of Business Administration Joint Program with ESC Montpellier Full-time and part-time. 12 to 24 months to complete program. *Concentrations:* management.

MBA—Master of Business Administration in International Banking and Finance Full-time. 12 to 24 months to complete program. *Concentrations:* international banking, international business.

MBA—Part-time MBA Part-time. 24 to 48 months to complete program. *Concentrations:* international business, strategic management.

COSTS

Tuition, state resident: *Full-time* 8750 British pounds. **Tuition, nonresident:** *Full-time* 9750 British pounds. **Graduate housing:** Room and board costs vary by campus location, number of occupants, type of accommodation, and type of board plan. *Typical cost:* 4500 British pounds (including board).

FINANCIAL AID (1999–2000)

2 students received aid, including loans and scholarships. Aid is available to part-time students. **Financial Aid Contact** Mr. David Perman, Admission Tutor, Priorsfield 46, Edgbaston Park Road, Birmingham, B15 2RU, United Kingdom. **Phone:** 121-414-6693. **Fax:** 121-414-3553. **E-mail:** mba@bham.ac.uk.

RESOURCES AND SERVICES

Information about online services, personal computer policies, library resources, international exchange programs, internship programs, and placement services at this institution and others can be found at **www.petersons.com/mba**

International Students

100% of students enrolled are international students.

Services and Facilities Counseling/support services, ESL/language courses, international student housing, visa services, career management. Financial aid is available to international students.

Applying *Required:* IELT with recommended score of 6, TOEFL with recommended score of 550 (paper), proof of adequate funds.

International Student Contact Mr. David Perman, Admission Tutor, Priorsfield 46 Edgbaston Park Road, Birmingham, B15 2RU, United Kingdom. **Phone:** 121-414-6693. **Fax:** 121-414-3553. **E-mail:** mba@bham.ac.uk.

■ APPLICATION

Required Application form, 2 letters of recommendation, 5 years of work experience. School will accept GMAT.

Deadlines and Fees Applications for domestic and international students are processed on a rolling basis.

Application Contact Mr. David Perman, Admission Tutor, Priorsfield 46, Edgbaston Park Road, Birmingham, B15 2RU, United Kingdom. **Phone:** 121-414-6693. **Fax:** 121-414-3553. **E-mail:** mba@bham.ac.uk.

University of Brighton

Brighton, United Kingdom

BRIGHTON BUSINESS SCHOOL

Graduate Business Faculty
Full-time: 70

Student Body
Total: 322	Average Age: 27
Full-time: 35	Women: 38%
Part-time: 287	

Admissions
Applications: 205	Enrolled: 110
Admitted: 150	Average GMAT: 550

Costs (1999–2000)
Full-time tuition: 7000 British pounds per academic year (resident), 8000 British pounds per academic year (nonresident)
Part-time tuition: N/R

After Graduation (Class of 1998–99)
Employed within 3 months of graduation: 80%

DEGREES M Sc • MBA

M Sc—International Capital Markets Full-time. Work experience is NOT required. At least 120 total credits required. Minimum of 12 months to complete program. *Concentrations:* financial economics, financial management/planning.

MBA—MBA [European Business] Full-time. At least 160 total credits required. 16 months to complete program. *Concentrations:* accounting, economics, entrepreneurship, European business studies, finance, human resources, international banking, international marketing, management, management consulting, management information systems, marketing research, operations management, organizational behavior/development, public policy and administration, strategic management, technology management, travel industry/tourism management.

MBA—Master of Business Administration Full-time. At least 130 total credits required. Minimum of 12 months to complete program.

MBA—Master of Business Administration Part-time. At least 120 total credits required. 36 to 60 months to complete program. *Concentrations:* accounting, economics, European business studies, finance, human resources, international business, management, management information systems, marketing, operations management, organizational behavior/development, strategic management, travel industry/tourism management.

COSTS

Tuition, state resident: *Full-time* 7000 British pounds. **Tuition, nonresident:** *Full-time* 8000 British pounds. **Tuition, international:** *Full-time* 8000 British pounds. Tuition varies by academic program and local reciprocity agreements. **Graduate housing:** Room and board costs vary by number of occupants. *Typical cost:* 2300 British pounds (room only).

FINANCIAL AID (1999–2000)

3 students received aid, including scholarships. Financial aid application deadline: 6/30. **Financial Aid Contact** Ms. Julie Grahem, Administrator, Academic Registry, Mithras House, Lewes Road, East Sussex, United Kingdom. **Phone:** 127-364-2821. **Fax:** 127-364-2825. **E-mail:** b.l.scherer@brighton.ac.uk.

RESOURCES AND SERVICES

Information about online services, personal computer policies, library resources, international exchange programs, internship programs, and placement services at this institution and others can be found at **www.petersons.com/mba**

International Students

14% of students enrolled are international students.

Services and Facilities Counseling/support services, ESL/language courses, housing location assistance, language tutoring, orientation. Financial aid is available to international students.

Applying *Required:* IELT with recommended score of 7, TOEFL with recommended score of 590 (paper), TWE with recommended score of 5.

International Student Contact Mr. Barry Lee Scherer, Director of International Studies in the Business School, Mithras House, Lewes Road, East Susses, United Kingdom. **Phone:** 127-364-2196. **Fax:** 127-364-2980. **E-mail:** b.l.scherer@brighton.ac.uk.

■ APPLICATION

Required GMAT, application form, baccalaureate/first degree, 2 letters of recommendation, personal statement, resume/curriculum vitae, transcripts of college work, 3 years of work experience.

Deadlines and Fees *Deadlines:* 8/30 for fall, 8/30 for fall (international). *Application fee:* 10 British pounds, 10 British pounds (international).

Application Contact Miss Linda Freston, Senior Program Administrator, MBA Program, Mithras House, Lewes Road, East Sussex, United Kingdom. **Phone:** 127-364-2794. **Fax:** 127-364-2980.

University of Cambridge

Cambridge, United Kingdom

THE JUDGE INSTITUTE OF MANAGEMENT

Graduate Business Faculty

Full-time: 61   Part-time: 34

Student Body

Total: 241   Women: 34%
Full-time: 241

Admissions

Admitted: 118   Enrolled: 82

Costs (1999–2000)

Full-time tuition: $30,400 per academic year (resident), $30,400 per academic year (nonresident)
Part-time tuition: N/R

After Graduation (Class of 1998–99)

Average starting salary: $80,000

DEGREES MBA

MBA—Full-time MBA Full-time. 12 months to complete program. *Concentrations:* international business, international management, management.

MBA—Integrated MBA Part-time. 24 months to complete program. *Concentrations:* international business, international management, management.

MBA—e-MBA *Distance learning option.* 24 months to complete program. *Concentrations:* international business, international management, management.

COSTS

Tuition, state resident: *Full-time* $30,400. **Tuition, nonresident:** *Full-time* $30,400. **Tuition, international:** *Full-time* $30,400. Tuition varies by academic program. **Graduate housing:** Room and board costs vary by campus location and type of accommodation. *Typical cost:* $14,800 (including board), $5800 (room only).

FINANCIAL AID (1999–2000)

5 students received aid, including scholarships. Financial aid application deadline: 3/31. **Financial Aid Contact** Ms. Tessa Payne, Educational Administrator, The Judge Institute, Cambridge University, Trumpington Street, Cambridge, CB2 1AG, United Kingdom. **Phone:** 1-223-339-817. **Fax:** 1-223-339-701. **E-mail:** t.payne@jims.cam.ac.uk.

RESOURCES AND SERVICES

Information about online services, personal computer policies, library resources, international exchange programs, internship programs, and placement services at this institution and others can be found at **www.petersons.com/mba**

International Students

Services and Facilities Counseling/support services, housing location assistance, international student organization, orientation. Financial aid is available to international students.

Applying *Required:* IELT with recommended score of 7, TOEFL with recommended score of 250 (computer) or 600 (paper), TWE with recommended score of 5, proof of adequate funds. *Recommended:* Proof of health/immunizations.

International Student Contact Graduate Office, The Judge Institute, Cambridge University, Trumpington Street, Cambridge, CB2 1AG, United Kingdom. **Phone:** 1-223-337-051. **Fax:** 1-223-339-581. **E-mail:** mba-enquiries@jims.ca.ac.uk.

■ APPLICATION

Required GMAT, application form, baccalaureate/first degree, interview, 3 letters of recommendation, transcripts of college work, 2 years of work experience.

Deadlines and Fees Applications for domestic and international students are processed on a rolling basis.

Application Contact Graduate Office, The Judge Institute, Cambridge University, Trumpington Street, Cambridge, CB2 1AG, United Kingdom. **Phone:** 1-223-337-051. **Fax:** 1-223-339-581. **E-mail:** mba-enquiries@jims.cam.ac.uk.

See full description on page 882.

University of Durham

Durham, United Kingdom

BUSINESS SCHOOL

Graduate Business Faculty

Full-time: 50   Part-time: 20

Student Body

Total: 426   Average Age: 31
Full-time: 138   Women: 30%
Part-time: 288

Admissions

Applications: 800   Enrolled: 250
Admitted: 400

Costs (1999–2000)

Full-time tuition: 12,000 British pounds per academic year (resident)
Part-time tuition: 9750 British pounds per degree program (resident)

After Graduation (Class of 1998–99)

Employed within 3 months of graduation: 95%

DEGREES MA • MBA

MA—MA in Entrepreneurship Part-time. Minimum 2 years of work experience required. Minimum of 24 months to complete program.

MA—MA in Human Resource Management Part-time. Minimum 2 years of relevant work experience required. Minimum of 23 months to complete program.

University of Durham (continued)

MA—MA in Management Full-time. Minimum of 11 months to complete program.

MBA—Master of Business Administration Full-time and part-time. *Distance learning option.* Minimum 2 years of work experience required. 12 to 48 months to complete program.

COSTS

Tuition, state resident: *Full-time* 12,000 British pounds. *Part-time* 9750 British pounds per degree program. **Tuition, international:** *Full-time* 12,500 British pounds. Tuition varies by academic program. **Graduate housing:** Room and board costs vary by campus location, number of occupants, type of accommodation, and type of board plan. *Typical cost:* 6000 British pounds (including board), 2640 British pounds (room only).

FINANCIAL AID (1999–2000)

29 students received aid. **Financial Aid Contact** Miss Anne-Marie Nevin, MBA Program Manager, Business School, Mill Hill Lane, Durham, DH1 3LB, United Kingdom. **Phone:** 191-374-2233. **Fax:** 191-374-3748.

RESOURCES AND SERVICES

Information about online services, personal computer policies, library resources, international exchange programs, internship programs, and placement services at this institution and others can be found at **www.petersons.com/mba**

International Students

18% of students enrolled are international students.

Services and Facilities Counseling/support services, ESL/language courses, international student housing, international student organization, language tutoring, orientation, visa services. Financial aid is not available to international students.
Applying *Required:* IELT with recommended score of 6.5, TOEFL with recommended score of 550 (paper), proof of adequate funds. *Recommended:* TWE with recommended score of 5.

International Student Contact Ms. Rosalind Martin, International Student Coordinator, International Office, Old Shire Hall, Durham, DH1 3HP, United Kingdom. **Phone:** 191-374-7219. **Fax:** 191-374-7216. **E-mail:** international.office@durham.ac.uk.

■ APPLICATION

Required Application form, baccalaureate/first degree, 2 letters of recommendation, personal statement, 2 years of work experience. School will accept GMAT or GRE.

Deadlines and Fees *Deadlines:* 8/30 for fall, 8/30 for fall (international).

Application Contact Miss Jill Robson, Admissions Coordinator, Business School, Mill Hill Lane, Durham, DH1 3LB, United Kingdom. **Phone:** 191-374-2233. **Fax:** 191-374-1230. **E-mail:** pg.bus@durham.ac.uk.

University of Edinburgh

Edinburgh, United Kingdom

EDINBURGH UNIVERSITY MANAGEMENT SCHOOL

Graduate Business Faculty
Full-time: 82   Part-time: 13

Student Body
Total: 365   Part-time: 250
Full-time: 115   Average Age: 31

Admissions
Applications: 690   Enrolled: 108
Admitted: 170   Average GMAT: 600

Costs (1999–2000)
Full-time tuition: N/R
Part-time tuition: N/R

After Graduation (Class of 1998–99)
Employed within 3 months of graduation: 80%
Average starting salary: 42,000 British pounds

DEGREES MBA • MS

MBA—Full-time Master of Business Administration Full-time. 12 months to complete program. *Concentrations:* entrepreneurship, finance, international business, management, marketing, nonprofit management, nonprofit organization, operations management, organizational behavior/development, strategic management.

MBA—Master of Business Administration in International Business Full-time. 15 months to complete program. *Concentrations:* Asian business studies, developmental economics, entrepreneurship, finance, international and area business studies, international business, international economics, international management, international marketing, international trade, management, marketing, operations management, organizational behavior/development, strategic management.

MBA—Part-time Master of Business Administration Part-time. 30 to 36 months to complete program. *Concentrations:* entrepreneurship, finance, international business, management, marketing, nonprofit management, operations management, organizational behavior/development, strategic management, technology management.

MS—Master of Science in Financial Mathematics Full-time. 12 months to complete program. *Concentrations:* banking, finance, financial information systems, risk management.

MS—Master of Science in Logistics Full-time. 12 months to complete program. *Concentrations:* business policy/strategy, international logistics, logistics, technology management.

MS—Master of Science in Management Science and Operations Research Full-time. 12 months to complete program. *Concentrations:* international business, international logistics, logistics, management, management science, quantitative analysis.

T*he Edinburgh M.B.A. can be studied in three modes: the Full-Time M.B.A. (twelve months), the M.B.A. in international business (fifteen months with a work placement), and the Part-Time M.B.A. All M.B.A.'s have general management courses that cover all the main management disciplines and give students the opportunity to choose a concentration. All courses start with a foundation block, and students choose five of fifty optional subjects, with a compulsory core course in strategic management, in the second and third terms. Students in the M.B.A. in international business program go on to study with a partner institution. There is a parallel program of negotiation, communication, and presentation skills and outdoor development opportunities. Students also carry out a team consultancy project for a local company or complete a work placement and a dissertation. All M.B.A. courses are accredited by the Association of M.B.A.'s—few M.B.A. providers in the U.K. have this distinction for all of their M.B.A. courses. The city itself is also a beautiful, safe location, with the most lived-in city center in Britain. More than 80 percent of students live within a 15-minute walk of the management school.*

COSTS

Tuition varies by academic program and local reciprocity agreements.

FINANCIAL AID (1999–2000)

25 students received aid, including scholarships. **Financial Aid Contact** Ms. Patricia Fraser, Full-time MBA Administrator, 7 Bristo Square, Scotland, United Kingdom. **Phone:** 131-650 8066. **Fax:** 131-650 6501. **E-mail:** trishf@ed.ac.uk.

RESOURCES AND SERVICES

Information about online services, personal computer policies, library resources, international exchange programs, internship programs, and placement services at this institution and others can be found at **www.petersons.com/mba**

International Students

26% of students enrolled are international students.

Services and Facilities Counseling/support services, ESL/language courses, housing location assistance, international student housing, international student organization, language tutoring, orientation, visa services. Financial aid is not available to international students.
Applying *Required:* IELT with recommended score of 7, TOEFL with recommended score of 580 (paper), TWE with recommended score of 5, proof of adequate funds, proof of health/immunizations.

International Student Contact Mr. Richard Kerley, Full-time MBA Director, 7 Bristo Square, Scotland, United Kingdom. **Phone:** 131-650 8068. **Fax:** 131-650 8077. **E-mail:** r.kerley@ed.ac.uk.

■ APPLICATION

Required GMAT, application form, essay, 2 letters of recommendation, personal statement, resume/curriculum vitae, transcripts of college work, 2 years of work experience. **Recommended** Baccalaureate/first degree, interview.

Deadlines and Fees Applications for domestic and international students are processed on a rolling basis.

Application Contact Ms. Patricia Fraser, Full-time MBA Administrator, 7 Bristo Square, Scotland, United Kingdom. **Phone:** 131-650 8066. **Fax:** 131-650 6501. **E-mail:** management.school@ed.ac.uk.

See full description on page 898.

University of Glasgow

Glasgow, United Kingdom

UNIVERSITY OF GLASGOW BUSINESS SCHOOL

Graduate Business Faculty
Full-time: 73   Part-time: 9

Student Body
Total: 165   Average Age: 32
Full-time: 22   Women: 42%
Part-time: 143

Admissions
Applications: 300   Enrolled: 60
Admitted: 90   Average GMAT: 600

Costs (1999–2000)
Full-time tuition: 8000 British pounds per academic year (resident),
    11,000 British pounds per academic year (nonresident)
Part-time tuition: 4000 British pounds per year (resident)

After Graduation (Class of 1998–99)
Employed within 3 months of graduation: 90%

DEGREES MBA

MBA—Master of Business Administration Part-time. 24 to 36 months to complete program. *Concentrations:* accounting, economics, entrepreneurship, finance, human resources, information management, international management, leadership, management, marketing, operations management, organizational behavior/development, organizational management, project management, strategic management, technology management.

MBA—Master of Business Administration Full-time. 12 months to complete program. *Concentrations:* accounting, business law, economics, entrepreneurship, European business studies, finance, human resources, information management, international business, international finance, international trade, marketing, operations management, organizational behavior/development, organizational management, strategic management, technology management.

COSTS

Tuition, state resident: *Full-time* 8000 British pounds. *Part-time* 4000 British pounds per year. **Tuition, nonresident:** *Full-time* 11,000 British pounds. Tuition varies by local reciprocity agreements. **Graduate housing:** Room and board costs vary by campus location, number of occupants, type of accommodation, and type of board plan. *Typical cost:* 4000 British pounds (room only).

RESOURCES AND SERVICES

Information about online services, personal computer policies, library resources, international exchange programs, internship programs, and placement services at this institution and others can be found at **www.petersons.com/mba**

International Students

7% of students enrolled are international students.

Services and Facilities Counseling/support services, ESL/language courses, international student housing, international student organization, visa services, learning support services.

Applying *Required:* Proof of adequate funds, proof of health/immunizations. *Recommended:* IELT, TOEFL with recommended score of 570 (paper).

International Student Contact Ms. Hazel Sydeserff, Assistant Director, Postgraduate Recruitment, Student Recruitment and Admissions Service, Scotland, United Kingdom. **Phone:** 141-330-3747. **Fax:** 141-330-4413. **E-mail:** m.ba.admissions@mgt.gla.ac.uk.

■ APPLICATION

Required Transcripts of college work, 2 years of work experience. **Recommended** Personal statement, resume/curriculum vitae.

Deadlines and Fees *Deadlines:* 8/1 for fall, 7/1 for fall (international).

Application Contact Ms. Elaine de Vries, Development Officer, University of Glasgow Business School, Scotland, United Kingdom. **Phone:** 141-330-3993. **Fax:** 141-330-4939. **E-mail:** m.ba.admissions@mgt.gla.ac.uk.

University of Hull

Hull, United Kingdom

SCHOOL OF MANAGEMENT

DEGREES MA • MBA

MA—Master of Arts in Management Systems Full-time. Maximum of 12 months to complete program.

MBA—General MBA Full-time and part-time. 12 to 24 months to complete program.

MBA—Master of Business Administration in Financial Management Full-time. Maximum of 12 months to complete program.

MBA—Master of Business Administration in Information Management Full-time. Maximum of 12 months to complete program.

RESOURCES AND SERVICES

Information about online services, personal computer policies, library resources, international exchange programs, internship programs, and placement services at this institution and others can be found at **www.petersons.com/mba**

International Students

Services and Facilities Counseling/support services, ESL/language courses, international student housing, visa services. Financial aid is available to international students.

International Student Contact Derek Newham, Head, International Office, Cottingham Road, Hull, HU6 7RX, United Kingdom. **Phone:** 142-246-6579.

■ APPLICATION

Application Contact Mr. Louis Fong, Deputy Director, Cottingham Road, East Yorkshire, United Kingdom. **Phone:** 142-246-6650. **Fax:** 142-246-6236. **E-mail:** l.fong@msd.hull.ac.uk.

University of London

London, United Kingdom

LONDON BUSINESS SCHOOL

Graduate Business Faculty
Full-time: 102   Part-time: 15

Student Body
Total: 1,147   Average Age: 29
Full-time: 754   Women: 23%
Part-time: 393

Admissions
Admitted: 406   Average GMAT: 680
Enrolled: 274

Costs (1999–2000)
Full-time tuition: N/R
Part-time tuition: N/R

After Graduation (Class of 1998–99)
Employed within 3 months of graduation: 100%
Average starting salary: 53,000 British pounds

DEGREES MBA • MS

MBA—EMBA- Global Part-time. At least 28 total credits required. Minimum of 20 months to complete program.

MBA—Executive MBA Part-time. At least 28 total credits required. 24 months to complete program.

MBA—Full-time MBA Full-time. At least 30 total credits required. 21 months to complete program.

MS—Master of Science in Finance Full-time and part-time. At least 10 total credits required. 9 to 24 months to complete program.

MS—Master of Science in Management Full-time. At least 13 total credits required. 10 months to complete program.

COSTS

Tuition, international: *Full-time* $24,720. Tuition varies by academic program.

FINANCIAL AID (1999–2000)

40 students received aid, including scholarships. Financial aid application deadline: 3/1. **Financial Aid Contact** Mr. Gareth Howells, Programme Manager, Full-time MBA Programme, Sussex Place, Regent's

University of London (continued)

Park, London, NW1 4SA, United Kingdom. **Phone:** 207-706-6863. **Fax:** 207-724-7875. **E-mail:** ghowells@london.edu.

RESOURCES AND SERVICES

Information about online services, personal computer policies, library resources, international exchange programs, internship programs, and placement services at this institution and others can be found at **www.petersons.com/mba**

International Students

70% of students enrolled are international students.

Services and Facilities Counseling/support services, housing location assistance, orientation. Financial aid is available to international students.

Applying *Recommended:* IELT with recommended score of 7, TOEFL with recommended score of 267 (computer) or 630 (paper), proof of adequate funds.

International Student Contact Ms. Emily Wilkinson, Programme Manager, Full-time MBA Programme, Sussex Place, Regent's Park, London, NW1 4SA, United Kingdom. **Phone:** 207-262-5050 Ext. 3460. **Fax:** 207-262-5050. **E-mail:** ewilkinson@london.edu.

■ **APPLICATION**

Required GMAT, application form, baccalaureate/first degree, essay, interview, 2 letters of recommendation, personal statement, transcripts of college work, 3 years of work experience. **Recommended** Resume/curriculum vitae.

Deadlines and Fees *Deadlines:* 11/24 for fall, 1/14 for winter, 3/1 for spring, 4/12 for summer, 11/24 for fall (international), 1/14 for winter (international), 3/1 for spring (international), 4/12 for summer (international). *Application fee:* $160, $160 (international).

Application Contact MBA Information Officer, MBA Programme Office, Sussex Place, Regent's Park, London, NW1 4SA, United Kingdom. **Phone:** 207-706-6859. **Fax:** 207-724-7875. **E-mail:** mbainfo@london.edu.

The University of Manchester

Manchester, United Kingdom

MANCHESTER BUSINESS SCHOOL

Graduate Business Faculty

Full-time: 50	Part-time: 40

Student Body

Total: 400	Average Age: 29
Full-time: 250	Women: 38%
Part-time: 150	

Admissions

Applications: 443	Enrolled: 142
Admitted: 254	Average GMAT: 603

Costs (1999–2000)

Full-time tuition: 22,000 British pounds per academic year (resident), 22,000 British pounds per academic year (nonresident)
Part-time tuition: N/R

DEGREES MBA

MBA—Executive MBA Part-time. 18 to 60 months to complete program. *Concentrations:* accounting, electronic commerce (e-commerce), entrepreneurship, financial management/planning, management consulting, marketing, organizational behavior/development, strategic management.

MBA—Master of Business Administration Full-time and part-time. *Distance learning option.* 18 to 60 months to complete program. *Concentrations:* accounting, electronic commerce (e-commerce), entrepreneurship, financial management/planning, international business, management consulting, marketing, organizational behavior/development, strategic management.

COSTS

Tuition, state resident: *Full-time* 22,000 British pounds. **Tuition, nonresident:** *Full-time* 22,000 British pounds. **Tuition, international:** *Full-time* 25,000 British pounds. Tuition varies by academic program.

FINANCIAL AID (1999–2000)

Financial Aid Contact Ms. Helen Dowd, Admissions Officer, Booth Street West, Manchester, M15 6PB, United Kingdom. **Phone:** 161-275-6311. **Fax:** 161-275-6489. **E-mail:** hdowd@man.mbs.ac.uk.

RESOURCES AND SERVICES

Information about online services, personal computer policies, library resources, international exchange programs, internship programs, and placement services at this institution and others can be found at **www.petersons.com/mba**

International Students

35% of students enrolled are international students.

Services and Facilities Counseling/support services, ESL/language courses. Financial aid is not available to international students.

Applying *Required:* IELT with recommended score of 6, TOEFL with recommended score of 580 (paper), proof of adequate funds.

International Student Contact Ms. Helen Dowd, Admissions Officer, Booth Street West, Manchester, M15 6PB, United Kingdom. **Phone:** 161-275-6311. **Fax:** 161-275-6489. **E-mail:** hdowd@man.msb.ac.uk.

■ **APPLICATION**

Required GMAT, application form, baccalaureate/first degree, essay, 2 letters of recommendation, transcripts of college work, 3 years of work experience. **Recommended** Interview, resume/curriculum vitae.

Deadlines and Fees *Deadlines:* 6/30 for fall, 6/30 for fall (international). *Application fee:* 50 British pounds, 50 British pounds (international).

Application Contact Ms. Helen Dowd, Admissions Officer, Booth Street West, Manchester, M15 6PB, United Kingdom. **Phone:** 161-275-6311. **Fax:** 161-275-6489. **E-mail:** hdowd@man.mbs.ac.uk.

University of Newcastle upon Tyne

New Castle upon Tyne, United Kingdom

SCHOOL OF MANAGEMENT

Graduate Business Faculty

Full-time: 25

Student Body

Total: 297	Average Age: 27
Full-time: 228	Women: 47%
Part-time: 69	

Admissions

Applications: 1,800	Enrolled: 297
Admitted: 400	Average GMAT: 530

Costs (1999–2000)

Full-time tuition: 7500 British pounds per academic year (resident), 9500 British pounds per academic year (nonresident)
Part-time tuition: 7950 British pounds per degree program (resident)

DEGREES MA • MBA

MA—Human Resource Management Full-time and part-time. 12 to 24 months to complete program.

MA—International Business Management Full-time. 12 months to complete program.

MBA—Master of Business Administration Full-time and part-time. 12 to 30 months to complete program. *Concentrations:* accounting, banking, economics, entrepreneurship, human resources, international marketing, marketing, nonprofit management, operations management, organizational behavior/development.

COSTS

Tuition, state resident: *Full-time* 7500 British pounds. *Part-time* 7950 British pounds per degree program. **Tuition, nonresident:** *Full-time* 9500 British pounds. Tuition varies by local reciprocity agreements.

FINANCIAL AID (1999–2000)

Financial Aid Contact Student Office, Office of Registrar, Kensington Terrace, Newcastle upon Tyne, NE1 7RU, United Kingdom. **Phone:** 191-222-8672.

RESOURCES AND SERVICES

Information about online services, personal computer policies, library resources, international exchange programs, internship programs, and placement services at this institution and others can be found at **www.petersons.com/mba**

International Students

30% of students enrolled are international students.

Services and Facilities Counseling/support services, ESL/language courses, housing location assistance, international student housing, international student organization. Financial aid is not available to international students.

Applying *Required:* IELT with recommended score of 6.5, TOEFL with recommended score of 580 (paper).

International Student Contact Ms. Linda Cowen, Admissions/International Office, Kensington Terrace, Newcastle upon Tyne, NE1 7RU, United Kingdom. **Phone:** 191-222-8672.

■ **APPLICATION**

Required GMAT, application form, baccalaureate/first degree, 2 letters of recommendation, personal statement, transcripts of college work, 3 years of work experience. **Recommended** Interview.

Deadlines and Fees *Deadlines:* 8/1 for fall, 8/1 for fall (international).

Application Contact MBA Administrator, Armstrong Building, Queen Victoria Road, Newcastle upon Tyne, NE1 7RU, United Kingdom. **Phone:** 191-222-5494. **Fax:** 191-222-8131. **E-mail:** school.of.management@nck.ac.uk.

University of Northumbria at Newcastle

Newcastle upon Tyne, United Kingdom

NEWCASTLE BUSINESS SCHOOL

Graduate Business Faculty
Full-time: 140

Student Body
Average Age: 31

Admissions
Enrolled: 26

Costs (1999–2000)
Full-time tuition: N/R
Part-time tuition: N/R

DEGREES MA • MBA

MA—Master of Arts in European Business Administration Full-time. 3 years of work experience required. At least 80 total credits required. Maximum of 12 months to complete program. *Concentrations:* economics, finance, human resources, international banking, international business, international trade, management information systems, marketing, organizational behavior/development, strategic management.

MA—Master of Arts in International Business Administration Full-time and part-time. Work experience not required. At least 80 total credits required. 12 to 36 months to complete program. *Concentrations:* finance, information management, international business, international finance, international marketing, strategic management.

MBA—Master of Business Administration Full-time and part-time. *Distance learning option.* 3 years of work experience required. At least 80 total credits required. 12 to 36 months to complete program. *Concentrations:* finance, management information systems, management science, marketing, organizational behavior/development, strategic management.

COSTS

Tuition varies by academic program. **Graduate housing:** Room and board costs vary by campus location and type of accommodation. *Typical cost:* $1575 (room only).

FINANCIAL AID (1999–2000)

Financial Aid Contact Mr. Paul Croney, Corporate and Executive Programme Director, Newcastle Business School, Longhirst Campus, Northumberland, United Kingdom. **Phone:** 167-795-000. **Fax:** 167-795-021. **E-mail:** paul.croney@unn.ac.uk.

RESOURCES AND SERVICES

Information about online services, personal computer policies, library resources, international exchange programs, internship programs, and placement services at this institution and others can be found at **www.petersons.com/mba**

International Students

Services and Facilities Counseling/support services, ESL/language courses, international student housing, international student organization, language tutoring. Financial aid is not available to international students.

Applying *Required:* IELT with recommended score of 5.5, TOEFL with recommended score of 550 (paper).

International Student Contact Mr. Maurice Dimmock, Head of International Office, Ellison Terrace, Newcastle upon Tyne, NE1 8ST, United Kingdom. **Phone:** 191-227 4438. **Fax:** 191-261 1264. **E-mail:** maurice.dimmock@unn.ac.uk.

■ **APPLICATION**

Required Application form, baccalaureate/first degree, personal statement, transcripts of college work, 3 years of work experience. School will accept GMAT. **Recommended** Interview, 1 letter of recommendation, resume/curriculum vitae.

Deadlines and Fees Applications for domestic and international students are processed on a rolling basis.

Application Contact Mrs. Alison Venis, Senior Administrator, New Castle Business School, Northumberland, United Kingdom. **Phone:** 191-227 4075. **Fax:** 191-227 3893. **E-mail:** alison.venis@unn.ac.uk.

University of Nottingham

Nottingham, United Kingdom

BUSINESS SCHOOL

DEGREES MBA

MBA—Executive MBA Part-time. At least 180 total credits required. 24 to 48 months to complete program. *Concentrations:* business ethics, entrepreneurship, human resources, international business, international management, management, marketing, organizational management, strategic management.

MBA—General MBA Full-time and part-time. At least 180 total credits required. 12 to 48 months to complete program. *Concentrations:* business ethics, entrepreneurship, human resources, international business, international management, management, marketing, organizational management, strategic management.

MBA—Insurance Management MBA Part-time. At least 180 total credits required. 24 to 48 months to complete program. *Concentrations:* finance, insurance, management, strategic management.

MBA—International MBA Full-time. At least 180 total credits required. 12 months to complete program. *Concentrations:* business ethics, entrepreneurship, international business, international management, international marketing, management, public management.

MBA—Local Government MBA Full-time and part-time. At least 180 total credits required. 12 to 48 months to complete program. *Concentrations:* management, nonprofit management, nonprofit organization, public management, public policy and administration, strategic management.

MBA—MBA in Education Full-time and part-time. At least 180 total credits required. 24 to 48 months to complete program. *Concentrations:* management, nonprofit management, nonprofit organization, public management, public policy and administration, strategic management.

MBA—MBA in Financial Studies Full-time and part-time. At least 180 total credits required. 12 to 48 months to complete program. *Concentrations:* accounting, banking, finance, insurance, international finance, management, management information systems, strategic management.

MBA—MBA in Health Full-time and part-time. At least 180 total credits required. 24 to 48 months to complete program. *Concentrations:* management, nonprofit management, nonprofit organization, public management, public policy and administration, strategic management.

MBA—Modular MBA Part-time. At least 180 total credits required. 24 to 48 months to complete program. *Concentrations:* business ethics, entrepreneurship, human resources, international business, international management, management, marketing, profit management, public management, strategic management.

MBA—Risk and Insurance MBA Full-time and part-time. At least 180 total credits required. 12 to 48 months to complete program. *Concentrations:* finance, insurance, management.

RESOURCES AND SERVICES

Information about online services, personal computer policies, library resources, international exchange programs, internship programs, and placement services at this institution and others can be found at **www.petersons.com/mba**

International Students

Services and Facilities Counseling/support services, ESL/language courses, international student housing. Financial aid is available to international students.

International Student Contact Dr. Christine Humphrey, Director, International Office, Portland Building, University of Nottingham, University Park, Nottingham, NG72RD, United Kingdom. **Phone:** 115-951-5243.

■ **APPLICATION**

Application Contact Mr. Ron Hodges, Admissions Director, Business School, University Park, Nottingham, NG7 2RD, United Kingdom. **Phone:** 115-951-5500. **Fax:** 115-951-5503.

University of Oxford

Oxford, United Kingdom

SAÏD BUSINESS SCHOOL

Graduate Business Faculty
Full-time: 16   Part-time: 6

Student Body
Total: 76   Average Age: 29
Full-time: 76   Women: 22%

Admissions
Applications: 394   Enrolled: 76
Admitted: 148   Average GMAT: 664

Costs (1999–2000)
Full-time tuition: 16,000 British pounds per academic year (resident),
    16,000 British pounds per academic year (nonresident)
Part-time tuition: N/R

After Graduation (Class of 1998–99)
Employed within 3 months of graduation: 90%
Average starting salary: 54,000 British pounds

DEGREES MBA • MS

MBA—Master of Business Administration Full-time. Minimum of 12 months to complete program. *Concentrations:* accounting, information management, leadership, marketing, strategic management.

MS—Master of Science in Industrial Relations and Human Resource Management Full-time. Minimum of 12 months to complete program. *Concentrations:* human resources, industrial/labor relations.

MS—Master of Science in Management Research Full-time. Minimum of 12 months to complete program. *Concentrations:* management science.

COSTS

Tuition, state resident: *Full-time* 16,000 British pounds. **Tuition, nonresident:** *Full-time* 16,000 British pounds. **Required fees:** Fees vary by campus location. **Graduate housing:** Room and board costs vary by campus location, number of occupants, type of accommodation, and type of board plan. *Typical cost:* 8000 British pounds (including board).

FINANCIAL AID (1999–2000)

Scholarships. Financial aid application deadline: 1/31. **Financial Aid Contact** International Office, Wellington Square, Oxford, OX1 2JD, United Kingdom. **Phone:** 1865 270105. **Fax:** 1865 270105.

RESOURCES AND SERVICES

Information about online services, personal computer policies, library resources, international exchange programs, internship programs, and placement services at this institution and others can be found at **www.petersons.com/mba**

International Students

79% of students enrolled are international students.

Services and Facilities Counseling/support services, housing location assistance, international student housing. Financial aid is available to international students.

Applying *Required:* TOEFL with recommended score of 250 (computer) or 600 (paper), proof of adequate funds.

International Student Contact Ms. Beverly Potts, International Office, University Offices, Wellington Square, Oxford, OX1 2JD, United Kingdom. **Phone:** 1865 270189.

■ APPLICATION

Required GMAT, application form, baccalaureate/first degree, essay, interview, 3 letters of recommendation, transcripts of college work, 2 years of work experience.

Deadlines and Fees Applications for domestic and international students are processed on a rolling basis. *Application fee:* 60 British pounds, 60 British pounds (international).

Application Contact Mrs. Alison Mills, MBA Manager, The Radcliffe Infirmary, Woodstock Road, Oxford, OX2 6HE, United Kingdom. **Phone:** 018-1865 224371. **Fax:** 1865 224371. **E-mail:** enquiries@sbs.ox.ac.uk.

University of Plymouth

Plymouth, United Kingdom

GRADUATE BUSINESS SCHOOL

Graduate Business Faculty
Full-time: 75

Student Body
Total: 227   Average Age: 27.5
Full-time: 27   Women: 35%
Part-time: 200

Admissions
Applications: 1,215   Enrolled: 227
Admitted: 417

Costs (1999–2000)
Full-time tuition: N/R
Part-time tuition: 2700 British pounds per year (resident), 2700 British pounds per year (nonresident)

DEGREES MBA • MHRM • MIB • MM • MMS • MS

MBA—Master of Business Administration in Finance Full-time and part-time. At least 120 total credits required. 12 to 24 months to complete program. *Concentrations:* finance, management.

MBA—Master of Business Administration Full-time and part-time. At least 120 total credits required. 12 to 36 months to complete program. *Concentrations:* management.

MHRM—Master of Human Resources Management Part-time. At least 120 total credits required. 12 months to complete program. *Concentrations:* human resources, management.

MIB—Master of International Business Full-time. At least 120 total credits required. 12 to 24 months to complete program. *Concentrations:* international development management, international finance, international management, international marketing.

MM—Master of Marketing Full-time and part-time. At least 120 total credits required. 12 months to complete program. *Concentrations:* management, marketing, marketing research.

MMS—Master of Management Studies Full-time and part-time. At least 120 total credits required. 12 to 24 months to complete program. *Concentrations:* management.

MS—Master of Science in Management of Technology Part-time. At least 120 total credits required. 24 to 36 months to complete program. *Concentrations:* manufacturing management, technology management.

COSTS

Tuition, state resident: *Part-time* 2700 British pounds per year. **Tuition, nonresident:** *Part-time* 2700 British pounds per year. Tuition varies by academic program. **Graduate housing:** Room and board costs vary by campus location, number of occupants, and type of accommodation. *Typical cost:* 2700 British pounds (room only).

FINANCIAL AID (1999–2000)

12 students received aid, including grants, loans, and scholarships. Financial aid application deadline: 5/1. **Financial Aid Contact** Mr. Paul Williamson, Graduate Business School Administrator, Drake Circus, Devon, United Kingdom. **Phone:** 175-232859. **Fax:** 175-232497. **E-mail:** gradschool@pbs.plym.ac.uk.

RESOURCES AND SERVICES

Information about online services, personal computer policies, library resources, international exchange programs, internship programs, and placement services at this institution and others can be found at **www.petersons.com/mba**

International Students

23% of students enrolled are international students.

Services and Facilities Counseling/support services, housing location assistance, international student organization, language tutoring, orientation, visa services. Financial aid is available to international students.

Applying *Required:* IELT with recommended score of 6.5, TOEFL with recommended score of 570 (paper).

International Student Contact Ms. Carol Roden, Director, International Office, Drake Circus, Devon, United Kingdom. **Phone:** 175-233345. **Fax:** 175-232014. **E-mail:** intoff@plymouth.ac.uk.

■ APPLICATION

Required Application form, baccalaureate/first degree. School will accept GMAT. **Recommended** Interview, letter(s) of recommendation, personal statement, resume/curriculum vitae, transcripts of college work, work experience.

Deadlines and Fees *Deadlines:* 8/30 for fall, 6/30 for fall (international). *Application fee:* 75 British pounds.

Application Contact Mr. Paul Williamson, Graduate Business School Administrator, Drake Circus, Devon, United Kingdom. **Phone:** 175-232859. **Fax:** 175-232497. **E-mail:** gradschool@pbs.plym.ac.uk.

University of Reading

Reading, United Kingdom

ISMA CENTRE

Graduate Business Faculty

Full-time: 15 | Part-time: 11

Student Body

Total: 200 | Average Age: 25
Full-time: 200 | Women: 33%

Admissions

Applications: 884 | Average GMAT: 615
Admitted: 330 | Average GPA: 3.3
Enrolled: 200

Costs (1999–2000)

Full-time tuition: 9500 British pounds per academic year
Part-time tuition: N/R

After Graduation (Class of 1998–99)

Employed within 3 months of graduation: 70%
Average starting salary: 30,000 British pounds

DEGREES MS

MS—Master of Science in Financial Engineering and Quantitive Analysis Full-time. High level of numeracy required. 12 months to complete program. *Concentrations:* finance, quantitative analysis.

MS—Master of Science in International Securities, Investment, and Banking Full-time. 9 months to complete program. *Concentrations:* finance, international banking.

MS—Master of Science in Risk Management, Operations, and Regulation Full-time. 9 months to complete program. *Concentrations:* finance, risk management.

COSTS

Tuition *Full-time:* 9500 British pounds. **Graduate housing:** Room and board costs vary by campus location, number of occupants, type of accommodation, and type of board plan. *Typical cost:* 2550 British pounds (including board).

FINANCIAL AID (1999–2000)

3 students received aid, including research assistantships, scholarships, and teaching assistantships. Financial aid application deadline: 7/7. **Financial Aid Contact** Ms. Samantha Heslop, Admissions Coordinator, ISMA Centre, Whiteknights, PO Box 242, Reading, RG6 6BA, United Kingdom. **Phone:** 118-931-6675. **Fax:** 118-931-4741. **E-mail:** s.heslop@ismacentre.reading.ac.uk.

RESOURCES AND SERVICES

Information about online services, personal computer policies, library resources, international exchange programs, internship programs, and placement services at this institution and others can be found at **www.petersons.com/mba**

International Students

77% of students enrolled are international students.

Services and Facilities Counseling/support services, ESL/language courses, international student housing, international student organization, language tutoring. Financial aid is available to international students.

Applying *Required:* IELT with recommended score of 7, TOEFL with recommended score of 590 (paper), TWE with recommended score of 4.5, proof of adequate funds.

International Student Contact Ms. Samantha Heslop, Admissions Coordinator, ISMA Centre, Whiteknights, PO Box 242, Reading, RG6 6BA, United Kingdom. **Phone:** 118-931-6675. **Fax:** 118-931-4741. **E-mail:** s.heslop@ismacentre.reading.ac.uk.

■ APPLICATION

Required Application form, baccalaureate/first degree, 2 letters of recommendation, personal statement, transcripts of college work. School will accept GMAT. **Recommended** Resume/curriculum vitae.

Deadlines and Fees Applications for domestic and international students are processed on a rolling basis. *Application fee:* 30 British pounds.

Application Contact Ms. Samantha Heslop, Admissions Coordinator, ISMA Centre, Whiteknights, PO Box 242, Reading, RG6 6BA, United Kingdom. **Phone:** 118-931-6675. **Fax:** 118-931-4741. **E-mail:** sheslop@ismacentre.reading.ac.uk.

See full description on page 948.

University of Salford

Salford, United Kingdom

GRADUATE SCHOOL OF MANAGEMENT

DEGREES MBA • MS

MBA—Master of Business Administration Full-time and part-time. 12 to 60 months to complete program. *Concentrations:* management.

MS—Master of Science Full-time and part-time. 12 to 60 months to complete program. *Concentrations:* developmental economics, finance, human resources, international banking, international business, international trade, logistics, management information systems, marketing, quality management, technology management.

RESOURCES AND SERVICES

Information about online services, personal computer policies, library resources, international exchange programs, internship programs, and placement services at this institution and others can be found at **www.petersons.com/mba**

International Students

Services and Facilities Counseling/support services, international student housing. Financial aid is not available to international students.

International Student Contact Mr. David C. Lavender, Director of Admissions, The Management School, Greater Manchester, United Kingdom. **Phone:** 161-295-5530 Ext. 5071. **Fax:** 161-295-5022. **E-mail:** d.c.lavender@man-sch.salford.ac.uk.

■ APPLICATION

Application Contact Mr. David C. Lavender, Director of Admissions, Graduate School of Management, Greater Manchester, United Kingdom. **Phone:** 161-295-5530 Ext. 5071. **Fax:** 161-295-5022. **E-mail:** d.c.lavender@man-sch.salford.ac.uk.

University of Sheffield

Sheffield, United Kingdom

MANAGEMENT SCHOOL

Graduate Business Faculty

Full-time: 40 | Part-time: 6

Student Body

Total: 80 | Average Age: 29
Full-time: 50 | Women: 25%
Part-time: 30

Admissions

Applications: 540 | Enrolled: 80
Admitted: 170 | Average GMAT: 575

Costs (1999–2000)

Full-time tuition: 7750 British pounds per academic year (resident)
Part-time tuition: N/R

After Graduation (Class of 1998–99)

Employed within 3 months of graduation: 80%

DEGREES MBA

MBA—Executive Master of Business Administration Full-time and part-time. At least 180 total credits required. 12 to 30 months to complete program.

MBA—Master of Business Administration Full-time. At least 180 total credits required. 12 to 15 months to complete program. *Concentrations:* accounting, finance, international business, management, marketing.

COSTS

Tuition, state resident: *Full-time* 7750 British pounds. **Tuition, international:** *Full-time* 9250 British pounds. Tuition varies by academic program.

FINANCIAL AID (1999–2000)

Financial aid application deadline: 9/15. **Financial Aid Contact**

RESOURCES AND SERVICES

Information about online services, personal computer policies, library resources, international exchange programs, internship programs, and placement services at this institution and others can be found at **www.petersons.com/mba**

International Students

71% of students enrolled are international students.

University of Sheffield (continued)

Services and Facilities Counseling/support services, ESL/language courses, housing location assistance, international student housing, international student organization, language tutoring, orientation. Financial aid is not available to international students.

Applying *Required:* IELT with recommended score of 6.5, TOEFL with recommended score of 250 (computer) or 600 (paper), TWE with recommended score of 4.5, proof of adequate funds.

International Student Contact Ms. Debora Green, International Student Officer, Academic Secretary's Office, Firth Court, Western Bank, Sheffield, S10 2TN, United Kingdom. **Phone:** 114-222-1266. **Fax:** 114-276-5496. **E-mail:** debora.green@sheffield.ac.uk.

■ APPLICATION

Required Application form, baccalaureate/first degree, 2 letters of recommendation, transcripts of college work, 3 years of work experience. School will accept GMAT. **Recommended** Personal statement, resume/curriculum vitae.

Deadlines and Fees *Deadlines:* 8/31 for fall, 8/15 for fall (international). *Application fee:* 25 British pounds.

Application Contact Ms. Debra Maxwell, MBA Program Manager, Management School, 9 Mappin Street, Sheffield, S1 4DT, United Kingdom. **Phone:** 114-222-3378. **Fax:** 114-222-3348. **E-mail:** d.maxwell@sheffield.ac.uk.

University of Stirling

Stirling, United Kingdom

FACULTY OF MANAGEMENT

Graduate Business Faculty

Full-time: 28	Part-time: 3

Student Body

Total: 31	
Full-time: 30	Average Age: 27
Part-time: 1	Women: 35%

Admissions

Applications: 318	Enrolled: 31
Admitted: 64	

Costs (1999–2000)
Full-time tuition: N/R
Part-time tuition: N/R

DEGREE MBA

MBA—Master of Business Administration Full-time and part-time. 12 to 27 months to complete program. *Concentrations:* entrepreneurship, finance, human resources, international business, management information systems, marketing.

COSTS

Tuition, international: *Full-time* 8490 British pounds. Tuition varies by local reciprocity agreements. **Graduate housing:** Room and board costs vary by campus location. *Typical cost:* 2400 British pounds (room only).

FINANCIAL AID (1999–2000)

2 students received aid, including scholarships. Financial aid application deadline: 7/31. **Financial Aid Contact** Mrs. June Johnston, MBA Administrator, Faculty of Management, Stirling, FK9 4LA, United Kingdom. **Phone:** 1786 467415. **Fax:** 1786 467415. **E-mail:** mba@stir.ac.uk.

RESOURCES AND SERVICES

Information about online services, personal computer policies, library resources, international exchange programs, internship programs, and placement services at this institution and others can be found at **www.petersons.com/mba**

International Students

48% of students enrolled are international students.

Services and Facilities Counseling/support services, ESL/language courses, housing location assistance, international student organization. Financial aid is available to international students.

Applying *Required:* IELT with recommended score of 6.5, TOEFL with recommended score of 213 (computer) or 550 (paper), proof of adequate funds.

International Student Contact Mrs. June Johnston, MBA Administrator, Faculty of Management, Stirling, FK9 4LA, United Kingdom. **Phone:** 1786 467414. **Fax:** 1786 467414. **E-mail:** mba@stir.ac.uk.

■ APPLICATION

Required Application form, baccalaureate/first degree, 2 letters of recommendation, personal statement, transcripts of college work, 2 years of work experience.

Deadlines and Fees Applications for domestic and international students are processed on a rolling basis.

Application Contact Mrs. June Johnston, MBA Administrator, Faculty of Management, Stirling, FK9 4LA, United Kingdom. **Phone:** 1786 467414. **E-mail:** mba@stir.ac.uk.

University of Strathclyde

Glasgow, United Kingdom

GRADUATE SCHOOL OF BUSINESS

Graduate Business Faculty

Full-time: 175	Part-time: 25

Student Body

Total: 345	
Full-time: 95	Average Age: 31
Part-time: 250	Women: 29%

Admissions

Applications: 750	Enrolled: 520
Admitted: 585	Average GMAT: 590

Costs (1999–2000)
Full-time tuition: N/R
Part-time tuition: 9750 British pounds per degree program (resident), 9750 British pounds per degree program (nonresident)

After Graduation (Class of 1998–99)
Employed within 3 months of graduation: 95%
Average starting salary: 45,000 British pounds

DEGREES IMBA • M Sc • MBA • MBA/MS

IMBA—International Master of Business Administration Part-time. *Distance learning option.* 3 years of work experience required; minimum age requirement: 24. At least 60 total credits required. 30 to 42 months to complete program.

M Sc—Master of Science in Business Information Technical Systems Full-time. At least 60 total credits required. Minimum of 12 months to complete program.

M Sc—Master of Science in Business and Management Full-time. At least 60 total credits required. Minimum of 12 months to complete program.

MBA—Master of Business Administration Full-time and part-time. *Distance learning option.* 3 years of work experience required; minimum age requirement: 24. At least 60 total credits required. 12 to 72 months to complete program. *Concentrations:* strategic management.

MBA/MS—MBA with specialization in Leadership Studies *Distance learning option.* Up to 180 total credits required. Minimum of 36 months to complete program.

COSTS

Tuition, state resident: *Part-time* 9750 British pounds per degree program. **Tuition, nonresident:** *Part-time* 9750 British pounds per degree program. Tuition varies by class time, campus location, and academic program. **Graduate housing:** Room and board costs vary by number of occupants, type of accommodation, and type of board plan. *Typical cost:* 6500 British pounds (including board), 2500 British pounds (room only).

FINANCIAL AID (1999–2000)

Scholarships. **Financial Aid Contact** Ms. Meg Lavery, Admissions Manager, 199 Cathedral Street, Glasgow, G4 0QU, United Kingdom. **Phone:** 141-553-6118. **Fax:** 141-552-8851. **E-mail:** admissions@sgbs.strath.ac.uk.

RESOURCES AND SERVICES

Information about online services, personal computer policies, library resources, international exchange programs, internship programs, and placement services at this institution and others can be found at **www.petersons.com/mba**

International Students

17% of students enrolled are international students.

Services and Facilities Counseling/support services, ESL/language courses, international student organization, orientation, international student advisor . Financial aid is not available to international students.

Applying *Required:* IELT with recommended score of 6.5, TOEFL with recommended score of 250 (computer) or 600 (paper), proof of adequate funds, proof of health/immunizations.

International Student Contact Full-time MBA Program Administrator, 199 Cathedral Street, Glasgow, G4 OQU, United Kingdom. **Phone:** 141-553-6110. **Fax:** 141-552-2501. **E-mail:** m.english@strath.ac.uk.

■ **APPLICATION**

Required GMAT, application form, baccalaureate/first degree, essay, 2 letters of recommendation, personal statement, transcripts of college work, 3 years of work experience. **Recommended** Interview, resume/curriculum vitae.

Deadlines and Fees Applications for domestic and international students are processed on a rolling basis.

Application Contact Ms. Meg Lavery, Admissions Manager, 199 Cathedral Street, Scotland, United Kingdom. **Phone:** 141-553-6056. **Fax:** 141-552-8351. **E-mail:** admissions@sgbs.strath.ac.uk.

University of the West of England, Bristol

Bristol, United Kingdom

BRISTOL BUSINESS SCHOOL

Graduate Business Faculty
Full-time: 28

Student Body
Total: 1,319
Full-time: 104
Part-time: 1,215

Average Age: 34
Women: 51%

Costs (1999–2000)
Full-time tuition: 9487 British pounds per academic year (resident), 9487 British pounds per academic year (nonresident)
Part-time tuition: 8384 British pounds per degree program (resident), 8384 British pounds per degree program (nonresident)

DEGREES MA • MBA

MA—MA in Finance Full-time and part-time. 12 to 30 months to complete program. *Concentrations:* accounting, finance, financial information systems, financial management/planning, international finance, risk management, taxation.

MA—MA in Marketing Full-time and part-time. 12 to 30 months to complete program. *Concentrations:* business education, international marketing, management information systems, marketing, marketing research, strategic management.

MA—MA in Personnel Management Full-time and part-time. Minimum of 12 months to complete program. *Concentrations:* business ethics, business law, human resources, industrial/labor relations, manpower administration.

MBA—Master of Business Administration European Route Full-time. 3 years of management experience required. 12 months to complete program. *Concentrations:* accounting, business policy/strategy, economics, entrepreneurship, European business studies, finance, human resources, international finance, international marketing, management, management information systems, marketing, operations management, organizational behavior/development, project management, public policy and administration, quantitative analysis, strategic management, taxation.

MBA—Master of Business Administration UK Route Full-time. 3 years of management experience required. 12 months to complete program. *Concentrations:* accounting, business policy/strategy, economics, entrepreneurship, finance, human resources, international finance, international marketing, management, management information systems, marketing, operations management, organizational behavior/development, project management, public policy and administration, quantitative analysis, strategic management, taxation.

MBA—Master of Business Administration Part-time. 3 years of management experience required. 18 to 30 months to complete program. *Concentrations:* accounting, business policy/strategy, economics, finance, human resources, management, management information systems, marketing, operations management, organizational behavior/development, public policy and administration, quantitative analysis, strategic management, taxation.

COSTS

Tuition, state resident: *Full-time* 9487 British pounds. *Part-time* 8384 British pounds per degree program. **Tuition, nonresident:** *Full-time* 9487 British pounds. *Part-time* 8384 British pounds per degree program. Tuition varies by campus location and academic program.

FINANCIAL AID (1999–2000)

Financial Aid Contact Centre for Student Affairs, University of the West of England, Frenchay Campus, Bristol, BS16 1QY, United Kingdom. **Phone:** 117-965 6261. **Fax:** 117-976 3851.

RESOURCES AND SERVICES

Information about online services, personal computer policies, library resources, international exchange programs, internship programs, and placement services at this institution and others can be found at **www.petersons.com/mba**

International Students

1% of students enrolled are international students.

Services and Facilities Counseling/support services, ESL/language courses, housing location assistance, international student housing.
Applying *Required:* IELT with recommended score of 6.5, TOEFL with recommended score of 570 (paper).
International Student Contact Ms. Sharon Bohin, MBA Admissions Officer, Bristol Business School, Frenchay Campus, Bristol, BS16 1QY, United Kingdom. **Phone:** 117-344 2857. **Fax:** 117-344 2925. **E-mail:** business@uwe.ac.uk.

■ **APPLICATION**

Required GMAT, application form, baccalaureate/first degree, interview, 3 years of work experience.

Deadlines and Fees Applications for domestic and international students are processed on a rolling basis.

Application Contact Ms. Sharon Bohin, MBA Admissions Officer, Bristol Business School, Frenchay Campus, Bristol, BS16 1QY, United Kingdom. **Phone:** 117-344 2857. **Fax:** 117-344 2925. **E-mail:** business@uwe.ac.uk.

University of Ulster at Jordanstown

Newtown Abbey, United Kingdom

FACULTY OF BUSINESS AND MANAGEMENT

DEGREES M Sc • MBA

M Sc—Executive Programme/MSc in Executive Leadership Part-time. Minimum of 7 years of management experience at a senior level required. 16 to 24 months to complete program. *Concentrations:* business policy/strategy, entrepreneurship, information management, leadership, management, strategic management.

M Sc—Postgraduate Diploma/MSc in Business Improvement Part-time. Minimum of 3 years of work experience in a management position required. 16 to 24 months to complete program. *Concentrations:* business policy/strategy, finance, financial management/planning, leadership, management, risk management, strategic management.

MBA—Master of Business Administration Full-time and part-time. Minimum of 3 years of work experience required. 12 to 36 months to complete program. *Concentrations:* accounting, economics, entrepreneurship, finance, management, management information systems, marketing.

RESOURCES AND SERVICES

Information about online services, personal computer policies, library resources, international exchange programs, internship programs, and placement services at this institution and others can be found at **www.petersons.com/mba**

International Students

Services and Facilities Counseling/support services, housing location assistance, international student housing, international student organization, visa services. Financial aid is not available to international students.
International Student Contact Marjorie Coulter, Room 03G03, Faculty of Business and Management, County Antrim, United Kingdom. **Phone:** 1232 366 805. **Fax:** 1232 366 805. **E-mail:** me.coulter@ulst.ac.uk.

■ **APPLICATION**

Application Contact Dr. Stephen Parkinson, Director of Graduate School of Business and Management, Faculty of Business and Management, Shore Road, County Antrim, United Kingdom. **Phone:** 1232 368 087. **Fax:** 1232 368 087. **E-mail:** s.parkinson@ulst.ac.uk.

University of Wales

Cardiff, United Kingdom

CARDIFF BUSINESS SCHOOL

DEGREES M Sc • MBA

M Sc—Master of Science, Applied Economics Full-time. 12 months to complete program.

University of Wales (continued)

M Sc—Master of Science, Financial Economics Full-time. 12 months to complete program.

M Sc—Master of Science, Human Resource Management Full-time. 12 months to complete program.

M Sc—Master of Science, International Economics, Banking and Finance Full-time. 12 months to complete program.

M Sc—Master of Science, Lean Operations Part-time. 24 to 36 months to complete program.

MBA—Master of Business Administration Full-time and part-time. 12 to 24 months to complete program. *Concentrations:* environmental economics/management, international and area business studies, management, organizational management, public and private management.

RESOURCES AND SERVICES

Information about online services, personal computer policies, library resources, international exchange programs, internship programs, and placement services at this institution and others can be found at **www.petersons.com/mba**

International Students

Services and Facilities Counseling/support services, ESL/language courses, international student housing, visa services. Financial aid is not available to international students.

International Student Contact Dr. Timothy Westlake, Head of International Office, PO Box 921, Wales, United Kingdom. **Phone:** 029-2087-4432. **E-mail:** internat@cardiff.ac.uk.

■ APPLICATION

Application Contact Ms. Rosemarie Dillon, Senior Assistant Registrar, PO Box 495, Wales, United Kingdom. **Phone:** 029-2087-4557. **E-mail:** dillonr@cardiff.ac.uk.

University of Warwick

Coventry, United Kingdom

WARWICK BUSINESS SCHOOL

Graduate Business Faculty
Full-time: 112   Part-time: 2

Student Body
Total: 2,780
Full-time: 320   Average Age: 32
Part-time: 2,460   Women: 33%

Admissions
Applications: 3,100   Enrolled: 760
Admitted: 1,690   Average GMAT: 610

Costs (1999–2000)
Full-time tuition: 19,000 British pounds per academic year (resident), 19,000 British pounds per academic year (nonresident)
Part-time tuition: 9075 British pounds per degree program (resident)

After Graduation (Class of 1998–99)
Employed within 3 months of graduation: 88%
Average starting salary: 44,000 British pounds

Accreditation
AACSB—The International Association for Management Education

DEGREES M Sc • MA • MBA • MPA

M Sc—Master of Science in Economics and Finance Full-time. 12 months to complete program.

M Sc—Master of Science in Financial Mathematics Full-time. 12 months to complete program.

M Sc—Master of Science in Management Science and Operational Research Full-time and part-time. 12 to 24 months to complete program.

MA—Master of Arts in European Industrial Relations Full-time. 12 months to complete program.

MA—Master of Arts in Industrial Relations Full-time and part-time. 12 to 24 months to complete program.

MA—Master of Arts in Organization Studies Full-time and part-time. 12 to 24 months to complete program.

MBA—Distance Learning MBA *Distance learning option.* 4 years of work experience required. 36 to 96 months to complete program.

MBA—Evening MBA Part-time. 4 years of work experience required. 36 months to complete program.

MBA—Full-time MBA Full-time. 3 years of work experience required. 12 months to complete program.

MBA—Modular MBA Part-time. 4 years of work experience required. 36 months to complete program.

MPA—Master of Public Administration Part-time. Current employment at executive level. 36 months to complete program.

COSTS

Tuition, state resident: *Full-time* 19,000 British pounds. *Part-time* 9075 British pounds per degree program. **Tuition, nonresident:** *Full-time* 19,000 British pounds. **Tuition, international:** *Full-time* 19,000 British pounds. Tuition varies by class time and academic program. **Graduate housing:** Room and board costs vary by campus location, number of occupants, type of accommodation, and type of board plan. *Typical cost:* 3000 British pounds (room only).

FINANCIAL AID (1999–2000)

2 students received aid, including scholarships and teaching assistantships. **Financial Aid Contact** Ms. Karen Bull, Programme Secretary, Warwick Business School, Coventry, CV4 7AL, United Kingdom. **Phone:** 24-7652-4485. **Fax:** 24-7652-4643. **E-mail:** fmbain@wbs.warwick.ac.uk.

RESOURCES AND SERVICES

Information about online services, personal computer policies, library resources, international exchange programs, internship programs, and placement services at this institution and others can be found at **www.petersons.com/mba**

International Students

41% of students enrolled are international students.

Services and Facilities Counseling/support services, ESL/language courses, housing location assistance, international student housing, orientation, language center. Financial aid is not available to international students.

Applying *Recommended:* TOEFL with recommended score of 600 (paper), proof of adequate funds, proof of health/immunizations.

International Student Contact Mrs. Diana Holton, Communications Officer, Warwick Business School, Coventry, CV4 7AL, United Kingdom. **Phone:** 24-7625-4306. **Fax:** 24-7652-3719. **E-mail:** inquiries@wbs.warwick.ac.uk.

■ APPLICATION

Required GMAT, application form, baccalaureate/first degree, interview, 2 letters of recommendation, resume/curriculum vitae, 3 years of work experience. **Recommended** Essay, personal statement, transcripts of college work.

Deadlines and Fees Applications for domestic and international students are processed on a rolling basis.

Application Contact Ms. Karen Bull, Programme Secretary, Warwick Business School, Coventry, CV4 7AL, United Kingdom. **Phone:** 24-7652-4485. **Fax:** 24-7652-4643. **E-mail:** fmbain@wbs.warwick.ac.uk.

University of Westminster

London, United Kingdom

HARROW BUSINESS SCHOOL

Graduate Business Faculty
Full-time: 40   Part-time: 10

Student Body
Total: 260   Average Age: 32
Full-time: 70   Women: 48%
Part-time: 190

Costs (1999–2000)
Full-time tuition: 7735 British pounds per academic year
Part-time tuition: N/R

DEGREES MBA

MBA—Master of Business Administration in Design Management Part-time. *Distance learning option.* Minimum age requirement: 25. Maximum of 24 months to complete program.

MBA—Master of Business Administration in Public Service Management Part-time. Minimum age requirement: 25. 18 to 24 months to complete program.

MBA—Master of Business Administration Full-time and part-time. Minimum age requirement: 25. 12 to 24 months to complete program. *Concentrations:* management.

COSTS

Tuition *Full-time:* 7735 British pounds. Tuition varies by academic program. **Graduate housing:** Room and board costs vary by campus location and number of occupants. *Typical cost:* 3162 British pounds (room only).

RESOURCES AND SERVICES

Information about online services, personal computer policies, library resources, international exchange programs, internship programs, and placement services at this institution and others can be found at **www. petersons.com/mba**

International Students

23% of students enrolled are international students.

Services and Facilities International student housing. Financial aid is available to international students.

Applying *Required:* IELT with recommended score of 6.5, TOEFL with recommended score of 600 (paper). *Recommended:* TWE with recommended score of 4.5.

International Student Contact MBA Course Coordinator, 35 Malibone Road, London, NW1 5LS, United Kingdom. **Phone:** 171-911-5000 Ext. 3087.

■ APPLICATION

Required GMAT, application form, baccalaureate/first degree, 2 letters of recommendation, personal statement, resume/curriculum vitae, transcripts of college work, 3 years of work experience. **Recommended** Essay, interview.

Deadlines and Fees Applications for domestic and international students are processed on a rolling basis.

Application Contact MBA Course Coordinator, 35 Malibone Road, London, NW1 5LS, United Kingdom. **Phone:** 171-911-5000 Ext. 3087. **Fax:** 171-911-5059.

In-Depth Descriptions of MBA Programs

The following In-Depth Descriptions were prepared for this book by the dean or director of the MBA program or business school. Each description is designed to give the student a sense of the individuality of the school.

The absence from this section of any institution does not constitute an editorial decision on the part of Peterson's. In essence, this section is an open forum for institutions, on a voluntary basis, to communicate their particular messages to prospective students. The descriptions are arranged alphabetically by the official name of the institution.

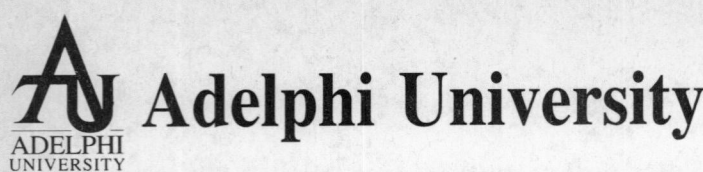

Adelphi University

Garden City, New York

DEVELOPING BUSINESS LEADERS FOR THE TWENTY-FIRST CENTURY

Today, business needs leaders with the analytic sophistication and entrepreneurial judgment to effectively deal with the forces that are transforming our "global village." Rather than attempting to train individuals for jobs that may not even exist two or three years hence, our progressive interdisciplinary approach to management education is designed to produce individuals with a broad education who have the managerial competence, curiosity, and creativity needed for success in the twenty-first century.

In this era of enormous challenges and radical possibilities, we are guided by a firm commitment that ensures our graduates will be thinkers with a broad perspective as well as proficient in the skills necessary for professional excellence and success.

—Russell Boisjoly, Dean

Programs and Curricular Focus

In keeping with Adelphi University's tradition of a liberal education, all of the School's graduate degree programs provide for a general management orientation along with solid training in all the functional areas of business. This general management orientation is achieved through a highly integrated group of professional foundation core courses. Through the foundation core, students acquire the analytic and quantitative decision-making skills needed for success by learning how to view and resolve management problems from all functional perspectives.

The program's breadth component examines twenty-first-century management issues, such as leadership, entrepreneurship, technology management, and total quality management on the global level and is designed to further enrich the students' professional and learning experience.

Themes such as the global perspective, creativity, change and innovation, team building, ethics, and cultural diversity are important components of the programs of study. These are not individual courses but unifying themes that are infused into the entire curricula.

Elective and specialization courses are also integral to the programs, affording students the opportunity to tailor their program of study to their own professional interests and career needs.

In addition to the M.B.A. with its eight areas of specialization, the School

offers an M.B.A./CPA degree program; M.S. degrees in accounting and in finance and banking; and post-master's certificates in banking, human resources management, and management. The number of credits required to earn a degree and the length of time it takes to complete a degree program vary and are dependent upon the student's previous academic background and on whether he or she chooses to study on a full-time or part-time basis.

Students and the M.B.A. Experience

Students come from across the United States and many other countries, bringing with them a wide variety of undergraduate majors and professional backgrounds. They form a dynamic community whose diversity enriches the educational experience. Professional clubs and organizations, such as the Accounting Society, the Marketing and Finance clubs, and the Business Council, bring together students with common interests.

Guest speakers, internship opportunities, and the Distinguished Lecture Series further serve to enhance and enrich the learning environment.

There is a Student Board that serves as an advisory council, and interaction between the faculty, staff, and students is strong, even outside the classroom. Faculty and staff support and participate in events run by students, and students also get the opportunity to network with alumni, advi-

sory board members, and other corporate executives at special events.

Special Features

Course schedules are designed to accommodate the schedules of men and women engaged in full-time careers. In addition to the main Garden City campus, courses are also offered at the Huntington Center, making graduate business education more accessible to those who reside on eastern Long Island. Courses at both locations are scheduled Monday through Thursday evenings and on Saturdays. Each course meets once a week.

A weekend M.B.A. program option is also available at the University's Garden City campus and Huntington Center. Classes meet on Saturdays. Trisemester programming enables qualified business majors to earn an M.B.A. in about eighteen months.

Switching between campuses is a student's option. Students may take courses at Garden City one semester and go to Huntington the next, or they may take courses both campuses during the same semester.

The Faculty

The School's faculty members have strong academic and professional backgrounds. Many have held top-level positions in business, engage in research and publication activities, and have been educated at many of the best academic institutions around the world.

Excellence in, and equal emphasis on, both teaching and research is the hallmark of the School. The faculty's research is considered to be pioneering and on the cutting edge and consistently wins critical acclaim and praise from both the academic and business worlds. The faculty members' wide range of expertise makes them sought after as consultants to major companies, entrepreneurial firms, and not-for-profit agencies.

The students profit from the faculty's academic and professional backgrounds, as well as from their commitment to the advancement of knowledge in their area of specialization. All of the research and consulting the professors do enriches every course they teach, and this, in combination with their dynamic and superb teaching skills, enables them to effectively communicate the principles and practices of management as it is actually conducted.

The Business School Network

An advisory board helps ensure that the programs meet the needs of the corporate community and provide and assist with internships and job placements. The School's advisory board consists of prominent alumni, CEOs, presidents, CFOs, and other senior executives from major corporations.

The College and Environs

Adelphi University is located in Garden City, Long Island, New York, a beautiful suburban community that is approximately 18 miles east of midtown Manhattan. It is the oldest private university on Long Island. Today, a full-time faculty of nearly 200 serves a student body of about 6,000 undergraduate and graduate degree candidates.

The location affords easy access both to the beaches, waters, and quiet living of Long Island and to the commercial and cultural capital of the world, New York City.

Facilities

The average class size in the School of Business is only 20, and many of the classrooms are outfitted with the very latest in multimedia technology.

The library is completely computerized. It houses approximately 470,000 volumes and an ever-growing collection of electronic resources based on CD-ROM and Internet technology.

Adelphi boasts one of the largest mainframe computer installations on Long Island, and, in addition, there are more than 450 IBM and Macintosh personal computers that are available for student use. High-speed access to the Internet databases is also available.

Placement

Placement is coordinated through the University's Center for Career Planning and Placement. More than 200 top corporations, major banks, and international accounting firms recruit on campus.

Experienced counselors take the time to assess the student's interests and skills and to help the student effectively market himself or herself and make the right career decisions whether he or she is a young graduate, an experienced professional seeking a career change, or someone returning to the work force.

Admission

Candidates applying for admission must submit a completed application form with an essay, official transcripts, two letters of recommendation, and their score on the Graduate Management Admission Test (GMAT) to the Office of Graduate Admissions. The GMAT score for students enrolling at Adelphi has recently ranged between 450 and 500. The average undergraduate GPA has been 3.0.

International applicants must also submit a TOEFL score of at least 550, as well as a declaration and certificate of finances.

Finances

For 1999–2000, the tuition rate was $500 per credit plus a $150 nonrefundable University fee. Additional fees and charges may be assessed. Students should consult with the Office of Student Financial Services for the latest tuition rate and fee information, as well as the latest information concerning financial aid.

Graduate assistantships are available to qualified full-time students. Applicants should have high GMAT scores and undergraduate grade point averages, as well as computer and quantitative skills.

Students should consult with the Office of Residential Life and Housing for information about the availability and costs for graduate housing.

Application Facts and Dates

Applicants should file their application and supporting credentials by the following dates: fall semester, August 15; spring semester, December 15; and summer sessions, May 15. For more information, applicants should contact:

Jennifer Spiegel
Associate Director of Graduate
    Admissions
Adelphi University
Garden City, New York 11530
Telephone: 800-ADELPHI (toll-free)
Fax: 516-877-3039
E-mail: admissions@adelphi.edu
World Wide Web: http://www.adelphi.
    edu

Alfred University

Alfred, New York

RESPONDING TO CRITICAL DEMANDS

Alfred University's M.B.A. responds to three critical demands from the market-place. First, it offers an interdisciplinary approach to management education. Second, it is practice oriented, focusing on application and skill development. Third, it is compact and accessible, providing students an efficient opportunity for completing graduate work in a reasonable time period. This work is completed on a personal scale, with small classes and close interaction with faculty members and peers. These features provide an intense and dynamic learning environment.

—Dr. David Szczerbacki, Dean

Programs and Curricular Focus

The Alfred University M.B.A. is a general management degree that emphasizes the development of leadership. The program can be completed in a minimum of 30 semester credit hours or a maximum of 55 semester credit hours. Individuals possessing an undergraduate degree in business or the equivalent are, in most cases, able to complete the program with 30 credit hours. Individuals with little or no business education first complete the foundation classes, then move into the core and electives. This can total a maximum of 55 credits.

The time frame for the M.B.A. is two semesters and one summer session for those requiring 30 credits. Those requiring up to 55 credits may require an additional two semesters. The program is available on a full-time and part-time basis.

Foundation classes are in the functional areas of business: accounting, economics, financial management, information systems, statistics, quantitative methods, organizational behavior, and marketing. This body of knowledge totals 25 semester credit hours. Students complete this sequence before entering the M.B.A. core classes.

The core focuses on leadership development in a global, highly competitive business environment. The work is case-based and involves team analysis and problem solving. The classes are leadership dynamics; financial decision making; legal, political, and social environment of business; global dimensions of management; quality information systems; and a capstone strategic management simulation. This M.B.A. core is 18 semester credit hours.

Elective courses may be selected from the areas of accounting, economics, finance, information systems, management, marketing, and quantitative methods. Students are also able to integrate graduate course work from other colleges within Alfred University. These include ceramic engineering, community services administration, and education. All electives are tailored to meet the career objectives of M.B.A. students.

Students and the M.B.A. Experience

The M.B.A. program enrolls approximately 10 full-time students and 30 part-time students. The average age of full-time students is 25, and they average two to three years of work experience before entering the M.B.A. program. Approximately 25 percent are female, and the majority of the full-time students have a business undergraduate degree. Part-time students average 32 years of age and are equally divided among business, engineering, and liberal arts educational backgrounds.

Classwork in the M.B.A. core is teamwork in nature. This creates a high degree of camaraderie among students, which is enhanced by the fact that full-time students move through these classes as a group.

The Faculty

M.B.A. students benefit from faculty members who have significant practical experiences in their field of interest. They are constantly engaged in research, which enriches the classroom learning process and in which students may participate. All College of Business graduate faculty members hold doctorates in their field. The ratio of faculty members to students is 1:16.

The Business School Network

The M.B.A. program at Alfred University is supported by an advisory board comprising senior managers from companies such as Corning Inc., Dresser-Rand, and GE. These corporate leaders provide significant input as to the relevance of the curriculum and trends in management practice. They also enrich the program by critiquing case presentations and speaking on recent developments in management practice.

The College maintains an Executive in Residence program that brings important corporate and government leaders to campus for extended periods. These executives serve as resources for M.B.A. classes and participate in various seminars and colloquia of the College.

The College and Environs

Alfred University, founded in 1836, comprises the privately endowed Colleges of Business, Engineering and Professional Studies, and Liberal Arts and Sciences as well as the publicly funded New York State College of Ceramics. The oldest coeducational institution in New York State, the University grants degrees at the bachelor's, master's, and doctoral levels. The fifty-eight building, 232-acre hillside campus adjoins the village of Alfred, located in an attractive natural setting between the foothills of the Allegheny Mountains and the Finger Lakes Region of upstate New York.

Alfred University is consistently ranked among the top comprehensive universities in the Northeast.

Facilities

The College of Business is housed in the recently completed F. W. Olin Building. This $5.6-million facility offers outstanding classroom, lecture, conferencing, and laboratory facilities. The M.B.A. program is supported by three networked classrooms as well as an advanced computer laboratory for projects. All computers have Internet access in addition to a

variety of commonly used software and specialized software. Additionally, most of the lecture rooms are equipped for in-class computer utilization.

The University maintains two libraries, Scholes Library of Ceramics, which supports engineering and the College of Ceramics, as well as Herrick Library, which supports liberal arts and sciences, professional studies, and the College of Business. Herrick Library holds more than 320,000 volumes and more than 1,600 periodicals. Library facilities provide workstations for access to the Internet and electronic subscriptions to additional journal titles. The library maintains an online public access catalog.

Placement

The University Career Development Center works closely with M.B.A.

students. All M.B.A. students are required to complete a two-session Career Development Seminar as part of their professional development. This program covers areas such as resume and cover letter writing, electronic job searching, effective interviewing, and how to survive the first year of one's first job.

Admission

Admission to the M.B.A. program is based on undergraduate performance, letters of recommendation, and GMAT scores. Recommendations are typically submitted by a former employer and professor. Using the formula GMAT plus undergraduate GPA times 200, the College requires a minimum total score of 1025.

Finances

Tuition for the 2000–01 academic year is $21,384. Room and board are $7094 per year. The College of Business is able to offer all qualified full-time students a graduate assistantship, which reduces tuition by half. The assistantship requires students to work 7.5 hours per week, typically with a graduate faculty member in their area of interest. These assistantships are renewable.

Financial aid, typically in the form of loans, is available. Information can be obtained from the Office of Student Financial Aid at 607-871-2159.

Application Facts and Dates

Applications are accepted until early June. For more information, students should contact:

Lori Hollenbeck, Director, MBA
    Program
College of Business
Alfred University
Alfred, New York 14802
Telephone: 607-871-2630
Fax: 607-871-2114
E-mail: hollenl@alfred.edu
WWW: http://business.alfred.edu/html/
    mba.html

For applications, students should contact:

Office of Graduate Admissions
Alfred University
Saxon Drive
Alfred, New York 14802-1232
Telephone: 607-871-2141
            800-541-9229 (toll-free)
E-mail: gradinquiry@alfred.edu
WWW: http://www.alfred.edu

American Graduate School of Business

La Tour-de-Peilz, Switzerland

▶ **DEVELOPING BUSINESS LEADERS FOR THE TWENTY-FIRST CENTURY**

AGSB, the American Graduate School of Business, is a nonprofit private institution of higher education, offering the Master of International Business Administration, the specialized M.B.A. AGSB has the unique ability to claim a dedicated and caring faculty, a small but select student body composed of a cultural cross section, and a sound academic program designed to prepare students to lead the world and meet the challenges of the future. By providing a basis for competent and responsible leadership in business and politics, AGSB aims to develop in each student the principles of equality, multilingualism, a broad-based approach to entrepreneurship, and a desire for continued intellectual growth.

—Carmen Corchon Pernet, President, Steering Committee

Programs and Curricular Focus

The Master of International Business Administration (M.I.B.A.) program offered by AGSB is based on a philosophy that the world's future leaders must operate in a multicultural environment and be able to adapt to changing social, political, legal, and economic conditions. The M.I.B.A. is a one-year intensive program for university graduates who hold a bachelor's degree with a major in business administration. For university graduates who do not hold such a degree, the M.I.B.A. is a two-year program, with the first year consisting of business foundation courses.

To earn the M.I.B.A. degree, the student must successfully complete a program consisting of eight internationally oriented core courses (24 semester credit hours), one two-term seminar course (3 semester credit hours), two advanced foreign language courses (6 semester credit hours), and an internship with accompanying thesis project (6 semester credit hours). At least 30 semester credit hours of work (excluding foundation courses) must be completed in residence. For students whose English language competence is below the level required for the M.I.B.A. program, AGSB will arrange for special language courses outside the regular curriculum.

Courses for the M.I.B.A. degree include International Business Economics, International Accounting Practices, The International Legal and Ethical Environment, International Management, International Marketing, Decision Theory, Information Systems Concepts, International Finance, the Special Topics

Seminar, Foreign Language, and, for advanced students, Business Foreign Language.

Among other professional affiliations, the programs offered by AGSB are recognized by the Department of Education of the United States and the Swiss Canton of Vaud and are authorized by the Nonpublic Postsecondary Education Commission of the State of Georgia, U.S.A.

Students and the M.I.B.A. Experience

The student body at AGSB is truly international in scope. The average student at AGSB is 26 years old with roughly five years of work experience. Forty-five percent of the student body are women, and a majority of the students have a previous background in business, engineering, or related technologies.

Special Features

An integral and distinguishing part of the M.I.B.A. program is the three- to six-month internship, in which the student is involved in the normal business operations of an organization. The nature of the internship is defined prior to a student's placement with a company. This internship must be taken under the sponsorship of the M.I.B.A. program and may be carried out in any country. Over the course of the internship, the student submits periodic reports and a final internship project, covering an in-depth company and industry analysis relating to the internship. With the directed internship experience and integrated projects,

the substantial language training provided by the M.I.B.A. program, and the international education given through the academic courses, AGSB's M.I.B.A. graduates are well-equipped to enter the international business arena.

The Faculty

The M.I.B.A. program provides a basis for competent and responsible leadership in international business, government, and nonprofit organizations. The language of instruction is English, with courses taught by dedicated, highly-trained, multilingual faculty members with extensive international experience. Methods of teaching include lectures, case analyses, student presentations, seminars with leaders from business and government, and directed internships with national and international organizations. Moreover, students benefit from the numerous field trips to such internationally recognized establishments as Nestlé, Caterpillar, and the Zurich Stock Exchange, to name a few.

The Business School Network

All of the AGSB programs are designed to develop an understanding of human behavior, cultural sensitivity, and a global perspective in business and politics. AGSB's location in Switzerland helps accomplish these objectives. The Montreux-Vevey region affords easy access to the culturally rich and internationally active cities of Geneva, Zurich, and Bern. Geneva, with its many international organizations such as the United Nations, the World Trade Organization, the International Labor Organization, and the World Health Organization, is an ideal setting for students to observe and become involved in the world of international relations. In addition, the university city of Lausanne is only 20 minutes away by car or rail. Switzerland's central location in Europe makes Paris, Milan, Munich, and other business and political centers quickly and easily accessible by rail, air, or private transportation.

The College and Environs

Located on the shores of Lac Léman (Lake Geneva) in the heart of the Swiss Riviera,

AGSB: Swiss quality, American style.

La Tour-de-Peilz offers a relatively mild climate. Long known for its tourist appeal, the Montreux-Vevey region, of which La Tour-de-Peilz is a part, has also built a cultural reputation through events such as the Montreux Jazz Festival and the renowned International Festival of Classical Music. Annual international conferences and symposiums, in communication and direct marketing for example, indicate the region's vibrancy and commitment to the world of business.

Students may take advantage of many extracurricular activities such as cycling, hiking, sailing, and skiing in the internationally known resorts of the Swiss Alps. The ski areas of Gstaad, Verbier, and Crans-Montana are easily accessible for a day's outing. For an evening's excursion, theaters, museums, and cinemas abound.

Facilities

AGSB is one of the few private schools in Switzerland with modern facilities specially designed to serve the needs of its students. The facilities include modern classrooms, faculty and administrative offices, a computer laboratory, a specially equipped language classroom, a student lounge, and a library reference room. A LAN link to the University of Lausanne Library complex allows for easy reference to more than 1.2 million volumes, and book delivery service affords quick access to any resource within the Swiss library system.

Placement

All of the programs at AGSB emphasize the importance of oral presentations as a means to enrich interpersonal communication skills. In the end, students are well-prepared for the interview process. Students are assisted in their resume writing, often into several languages, by experienced professionals. AGSB works directly with M.I.B.A. candidates in their search for an internship that is both stimulating to the student and beneficial to the corporate sponsor. In many cases, the relationship between the intern and the sponsor is so mutually rewarding that the student is requested to remain with the organization following graduation.

Admission

Applicants for the M.I.B.A. program must possess a bachelor's degree from a recognized college or university and demonstrate an academic record indicating potential for success in the M.I.B.A. program. To apply for admission, students must complete application procedures and submit scores for the Graduate Management Admission Test (GMAT) as well as the Test of English as a Foreign Language (TOEFL) for nonnative English speakers.

Finances

For 2000–01, tuition is Sw Fr 13,000 per semester. Living expenses, including housing, food, and transportation, are estimated at Sw Fr 1000 per month, depending on the living standard to which the student is accustomed. AGSB is one of the few European business schools whose students are eligible for the U.S. Department of Education's Federal Family Education Loan (FFEL) Program. Scholarships, based on merit and financial need, are available to U.S. and international students.

Application Facts and Dates

AGSB has a policy of rolling admissions, with students admitted on a space-available basis. Notification of acceptance or rejection will be made in writing as soon as possible after an applicant has completed admissions procedures. For more information, applicants should contact:

Director of Admissions
The American Graduate School of
    Business (AGSB)
Place des Anciens-Fossés 6
1814 La Tour-de-Peilz (P)
Switzerland
Telephone: 0041-21-944-95–01
Fax: 0041-21-944-95–04
E-mail: agsb@vtx.ch
World Wide Web: http://www.agsb.ch

American International College

School of Business Administration

Springfield, Massachusetts

> ### GRADUATE BUSINESS DEGREES THAT PAY OFF
>
> *Today's business environment is complex, fast paced, and diverse. Those leaders who succeed and thrive possess innovative, practical, and nimble approaches to that dynamic environment. At American International College (AIC), we offer two graduate programs, a traditional M.B.A. and a Master of Science in Accounting and Taxation (M.S.A.T.). Each professionally prepares you for today and tomorrow's ever-changing business world. Both programs focus on current, real-world applications that enhance our students' breadth, as well as their management and technical skills. Learn the rules; better yet, recognize when they should be broken.*
>
> —Michael T. Peterson, Acting Dean

Programs and Curricular Focus

The M.B.A. program consists of 36 credit hours of graduate-level courses. Concentrations can be pursued in accounting, finance, general business, international business, management, marketing, and materials operations management. Full-time students with a business undergraduate degree can complete the program in twelve to eighteen months. Students who lack adequate undergraduate preparation in business may be required to complete some foundation work.

The M.S.A.T. program consists of 30 credit hours of graduate-level courses. Undergraduate accounting foundation courses may be required in addition to business foundation courses.

Each program is flexible, and students may begin in the fall, winter, or summer semesters. The two summer sessions help accelerate degree completion. All courses are offered during late afternoons, evenings, and weekends to accommodate both full-time and part-time students. Class sizes are small and typically have 5–20 students in each.

Students and the M.B.A. Experience

Approximately 100 men and women are enrolled in AIC's graduate business programs. Many have prior work experience, and their educational backgrounds range from music to business. A wide cross section of ages, backgrounds, and training enriches discussions, as students bring their life experiences to the classroom. An increasing number of international students are entering the program, adding yet more perspectives to the study of business administration, accounting, and taxation.

Special Features

AIC is a teaching/learning institution that focuses on the student. Personal, individualized attention is the norm. Frequent contact with faculty members and the Graduate Business Director are the cores of the programs' successes.

The Faculty

Graduate business faculty members bring extensive business, teaching, consulting, and research backgrounds to the classroom. They are credentialed, experienced, and dedicated to teaching.

The Business School Network

Springfield is the major center of economic activity in western Massachusetts. Many AIC alumni are employed by local businesses and major corporations (such as Massachusetts Mutual Life, Friendly Ice Cream, Milton Bradley Company, and United Technologies) with home offices in greater Springfield.

There is ample local opportunity to see business in action. Full-time and part-time students learn extensively from each others' current and past experiences, supplemented by periodic guest speakers.

The College and Environs

A coeducational and small urban college, AIC is attractive to its students, its alumni, and to the greater Springfield community for many reasons. Set in the heart of a bustling, medium-sized city, it is an active and vibrant institution.

AIC is a student-centered college with academic programs that include the traditional major offerings in the liberal arts, various specialties in business administration and teacher training, and career-oriented programs such as nursing, occupational therapy and physical therapy, medical technology, criminal justice studies, and computer-augmented specialties in business, mathematics, the sciences, international business, economics, and management information systems.

AIC is located in Springfield, Massachusetts, a city of 160,000 and the metropolitan center for half a million people. Springfield is also the transportation center of western New England and is easily reached by automobile via Interstate 91 and the Massachusetts Turnpike, by rail via major north-south and east-west lines, and by plane from Bradley International Airport, which is 30 minutes south of AIC and served by all major U.S. carriers. The AIC campus is less than 2 miles from downtown Springfield. Within 25 miles of AIC are a dozen colleges and universities, making the region one of the most important centers for higher education in the nation. Springfield also offers repertory theater, symphony concerts, arts and sciences museums, nationally known guest speakers, and, in the Civic Center, a varied program of cultural, athletic, and entertainment events.

Placement

The primary mission of AIC's Center for Career Development and Placement is to promote, coordinate, and provide services to assist students and alumni with career guidance and current job-search strategies. Services include individual career counseling to assist in exploring and setting career goals, matching the students' interests and qualifications with options for job opportunities, workshops pertaining to job-search issues, assistance with resume writing and cover letters, mock interviews, an on-campus recruiting program, and sponsoring other activities to network students, alumni, and employers.

Admission

Qualified men and women with four-year bachelor's degrees from accredited colleges and universities are considered for admission. Admission is based on an evaluation of undergraduate transcripts, personal references, GMAT score, (optional) and work experience. International applicants must submit TOEFL scores. Remedial English as a second language (ESL) programs are held on campus for those international students who need English language enhancement.

Admissions are considered on a rolling basis, with no fixed application deadlines.

Finances

Tuition for 2000–01 is $420 per credit. Room, medical insurance, and board (September through May) is approximately $7000. Personal expenses, supplies, and books vary from student to student, with most averaging about $3000 (September through May). Typical loan programs and a variety of financial aid packages are available.

International Students

The College has had an international mission since its founding in 1885. International students are an important element of the student body that adds significantly to its richness and diversity. AIC actively recruits international students, and they currently comprise about 20 percent of graduate business students.

The International Student Office provides both necessary immigration information and programs for international students at American International College. Throughout the academic year, the International Student Office provides social events, including the International Social for faculty and staff members and international students; picnics; shopping trips; and trips to special community events. An international student newsletter is published and distributed across campus on a monthly basis, with announcements important to international students, information on American holidays, listings of campus events, and international student birthdays.

The International Club meets bi-monthly and sponsors events such as trips to New York City and Boston, socials, and an International Day in the spring. This club is open to all students to foster interaction and understanding among students of all backgrounds.

Application Facts and Dates

Applications for both part-time and full-time students are accepted year-round, with admission decisions made promptly after receipt of a completed application. For applications or additional information on the programs and the admissions process, students should contact:

Trudy Somers, Ph.D.
Dean
School of Business Administration
American International College
1000 State Street
Springfield, Massachusetts 01109
Telephone: 413-747-6230
Fax: 413-737-2803
E-mail: business@www.aic.edu

 **American University**

Kogod School of Business

Washington, D.C.

KOGOD'S ADVANTAGE IN THE GLOBAL ECONOMY

▶ *As technology continues to dominate new business development, Kogod creates entrepreneurial leaders who can effectively manage the non-tech issues overwhelming business growth. Student leadership and participation are the cornerstones of Kogod tradition and culture. The opportunities offered by our unique location at the technology crossroads on the East Coast affords us the ability to offer innovative business education.*

—Myron J. Roomkin, Dean

Programs and Curricular Focus

Flexible and challenging, the program prepares students to manage global commerce in an environment that is changing due to the explosion of information technology use and tightly integrated international markets. The M.B.A. is a 51-credit-hour program, of which up to 12 credit hours can be waived and 21 credit hours are chosen by the student. The customer-focused approach of the program drives the student-centered experience that defines the Kogod culture. Students are expected to maximize their educational experience by graduating with two areas of concentration and becoming heavily involved in the actual running of the program through student volunteerism. These two exceptional elements of the Kogod M.B.A. program, along with optional field-study experience, offer excellent opportunities for students to develop hard-core managerial skills while pursuing their degree. Expert full-time faculty members play an important role in providing the students with a wealth of research knowledge and experiential learning that can prepare them for any business decision.

The Kogod M.B.A. places particular focus on managerial aspects of information technology and global business practices. Two new and popular concentrations are Management of Global Information Technology (MoGIT) and Marketing Information Technology (Marketing IT). In both cases, corporate involvement plays an important role in defining the curriculum and class content. Such companies as IBM and AOL actually have representatives come into the classroom to be part of the learning process. All course work incorporates the multicultural and international perspective, and the International Business Department of the School is one of the oldest in the nation. The department offers concentrations in international finance, international marketing, and international management. Other exciting concentrations include accounting, economic development, finance, real estate and urban development, marketing, entrepreneurship and management, human resource management, and language and international studies.

Kogod also offers joint-degree programs, including a J.D./M.B.A. and the M.B.A./M.A. in international affairs. Master of Science programs include personnel and human resource management, accounting, taxation, and finance.

Students and the M.B.A. Experience

Students at the University come from all fifty states and 150 countries and represent nearly all age groups and interests. Many business students are already successful executives and bring relevant experience with them into the classroom.

Students in the M.B.A. program have undergraduate degrees from all the disciplines. In a recent entering class, the average age was 26, with five as the average number of years of work experience. Forty-five percent of the class were women, 21 percent were members of minority groups, and 51 percent were international students.

As part of its student-centered philosophy, Kogod considers student participation in the running of the School a vital part of the graduate experience. Students are expected to participate in at least one of seven student-run advisory groups that help steer the direction of their program. Activities include opportunities to be involved in corporate visits, redesigning the academic process, conducting interviews with potential candidates, and offering recommendations on the curriculum.

❖ Global Focus

The Kogod program promotes a global orientation through new, globally focused concentrations; diversity training; links with international institutions; and international exchange programs. In the M.B.A. program, students can work for one of the many international organizations based in Washington or intern abroad with a multinational organization. They can also choose to become exchange students at a distinguished international university.

A global perspective permeates the entire curriculum. More than 50 percent of Kogod graduate students are from one of fifty-five nations. In their classes, students learn to do business with people from Latin America, the Middle East, the Pacific Rim, and Europe by learning about business with them.

The Faculty

Kogod's reputation is distinguished by a faculty of internationally recognized scholars who, like Kogod students, come from every corner of the world. Through their consultancies with all sectors of government and business and their own research, the 55 full-time faculty members have an immense body of knowledge to share with students. Kogod faculty members involve students in developing state-of-the-art solutions to real problems facing industry today.

The Business School Network

Kogod's ties with national and international businesses ensure that students make solid professional contacts and get a thorough grounding in the realities of the global economy. Executives in residence give students insight into day-to-day problem solving in current business practice. Prominent men and women, high-echelon officials from industry, government, and nonprofit organizations, answer students' queries in a leadership speaker series. Executive Working Groups that consist of top executives from such companies as GM,

The home of the Kogod School of Business.

AOL, and IBM provide input in the development of new concentrations and the direction of the School's programs.

Field projects and internships with firms in the thriving private sector of Washington (in communications, biotechnology, and software development, to name a few areas) offer outstanding opportunities for making corporate contacts. Through AU's connections to organizations throughout the world, students expand their professional networks abroad.

The College and Environs

American University is an independent, coeducational university in Washington, D.C., chartered by an Act of Congress in 1893. The Kogod School of Business was the first such school in the nation's capital; its M.B.A. program has been offered since 1949. The University's 76-acre main campus, site of Kogod's offices and classrooms, and an 8-acre satellite campus are located in northwest Washington. In quiet, residential neighborhoods surrounded by embassies and historic buildings, both campuses are minutes from the wealth of historical and cultural resources of the city. Home to political leaders, diplomats, and businesspeople, Washington is vibrant, diverse, and stimulating.

Placement

Kogod's Graduate Business Career Services Office is available exclusively to graduate business students. From orientation through graduation and beyond, this office offers career workshops, one-on-one career advising, resume and cover letter critiquing services, and job and internship postings sent directly to student e-mail accounts. The office also promotes networking with alumni and other professionals through an alumni database, networking receptions, career fairs, and other professional events throughout the year.

Kogod is a founding member of the Capital M.B.A. Consortium, an annual fall event that brings national and international employers to the Washington area to interview M.B.A. students from fifteen accredited graduate business programs. In addition, Kogod's Career Services Office hosts employers in the fall and spring semesters for on-campus interviewing and company information sessions.

Students have full access to the University's Co-op Office, which assists students in finding credit-bearing work experiences during the graduate program. Domestic and international co-ops are available.

Admission

To apply to the Kogod graduate business programs, students must have a baccalaureate degree from a regionally accredited institution, a satisfactory score on the Graduate Management Admission Test (GMAT), and a satisfactory grade point average for the last 60 hours of academic work. If English is not an applicant's native language, he or she must present a satisfactory score on the Test of English as a Foreign Language (TOEFL). The M.B.A. program and the M.S. programs in accounting and finance do not require an undergraduate degree in a particular discipline; the graduate taxation program requires an undergraduate degree in business administration.

The Kogod graduate admissions committee pays close attention to how applicants present themselves in the application's Personal Statements. Interviews, by phone or in person, are required. The committee looks for indications of an applicant's commitment both to graduate study and to his or her particular field of study. Above all, American University seeks graduate students who are committed to excellence. Prior work experience is required.

Finances

Tuition for the Kogod M.B.A. Program is $758 per credit hour for part-time students and $9540 per semester for full-time students. This fee also covers the costs for the orientation and all workshops. The cost of the Master of Science degree programs is $758 per credit hour. Additional costs for full-time students include room and board, books, and other miscellaneous fees and expenses.

Financial awards based on merit are available for full-time students, who are automatically considered for this type of aid when they apply for admission. Need-based financial assistance, in the form of federally or commercially sponsored loans, is available for full- and part-time students. To apply, students need to submit the Free Application for Federal Student Aid by March 1. The loan programs have a variety of qualifications and eligibility requirements, which are maintained in the University's collection of information. Only U.S. citizens and permanent residents are eligible for federal need-based aid.

Notification of financial assistance is March 15 through June.

Application Facts and Dates

Applications are accepted for fall and spring enrollment on a rolling admissions basis. For priority consideration for merit awards, applications should be on file by June 1 for fall enrollment and by November 1 for spring enrollment. For more information, students should contact:

Sondra Smith
Director of Graduate Admissions
Kogod School of Business
American University
4400 Massachusetts Avenue, NW
Washington, D.C. 20016
Telephone: 202-885-1907
          800-AN-AU-MBA
          (toll-free)
Fax: 202-885-1078
E-mail: aumbams@american.edu

ASU Arizona State University

Tempe, Arizona

REALISTIC KNOWLEDGE—THE ASU MBA PROGRAM

These are exciting times for business professionals. Global markets are expanding rapidly and opening new doors. Fast-paced technological advances are rendering established products and services obsolete and changing the way business is conducted. The ASU MBA Program is committed to providing an M.B.A. experience that will prepare students for management positions in this dynamic business climate. The program is characterized by two main features. The first is an emphasis on the carefully selected, critical skills of leadership, teamwork, communications, global and multicultural awareness, and realistic knowledge of business practice. The second is a faculty cognizant of the business knowledge and skills necessary to meet the demands of the twenty-first century.

I am proud to introduce you to this vital, creative, future-oriented institution and its outstanding programs and faculty. I invite you to visit us and meet faculty, staff, and students. See for yourself the campus environment, with its semitropical beauty, outstanding computer facilities, nationally ranked research library, and unparalleled recreational facilities.

—Larry Edward Penley, Dean

Programs and Curricular Focus

The objective of the ASU MBA Program is to provide an enriching educational experience that has lifelong value. The central theme is to build and strengthen students' knowledge, basic skills, and managerial abilities by means of technical, analytical, and case materials associated with the functional areas of business.

The first-year core provides students with a broad exposure to functional areas of business applicable to many types of businesses. Special emphasis is given to team skills, analytical skills, ethical decision-making skills, and written and oral communication. Options for the second year include career tracks in service marketing and management, supply chain management, financial management and markets, and sports business and dual degrees in Master of Accountancy, Taxation, Information Management, Health Services Administration, and Economics. An MIM with Thunderbird (AGSIM) may also be completed in the second year. Other master's programs may be considered for concurrent degrees (e.g., M.S. in engineering).

Dual degrees that take more than two years are the ASU MBA/J.D. and ASU MBA/M.S. in architecture. Application must be made separately to each program for acceptance. The ASU MBA for

Executives program and the Ph.D. degree in business administration and in economics are also available.

Students and the M.B.A. Experience

Students at ASU have diverse academic and geographic backgrounds. In the fall 2000 entering class, the average age was 28, with 4.6 years of work experience. Sixteen percent of the students are ethnic minorities, 20 percent are international students, and more than 26 percent are women. Fifty-three percent of the students are from the Southwest and West, but more students are applying from other parts of the country as ASU rises in national prominence. Business and engineering bachelor's degrees are held by the largest percentage of incoming students.

Students automatically become members of the ASU MBA Association and may participate in community service through the Collegiate Volunteer Council, work on field projects, do summer internships, or join the Graduate Women in Business organization, Hispanic MBA Student Association, Black Student MBA Association, ASU MBAsia, or the Masters Consulting Group.

Arizona State is one of eighteen universities nationwide that participates in the Washington Campus program. This

one-week opportunity is available for credit between the first and second year.

❖ Global Focus

A summer program is available in Toulouse, France. English is the language of instruction for this program and other international summer programs. Other exchange programs include Group ESC Toulouse—Toulouse, France; ESAN, Peru; Universidad Carlos III de Madrid—Madrid, Spain; and ITESM, Mexico City.

The Faculty

The nationally renowned faculty at Arizona State is cognizant of the business knowledge and skills necessary for a changing business environment. All courses are taught by full-time faculty members with established records in business, consulting, leading-edge research, and professional education. The School of Accountancy and Information Management has one of the largest accounting faculties in the United States. The College has 165 full-time faculty members, 62 of whom teach in the ASU MBA Program.

The Business School Network
Corporate Partnerships

The ASU College of Business, one of the largest comprehensive business schools in the nation, is emerging as a leader in management research and education. Contributing to the College's success is its close relationship with the business community through organizations like the Dean's Council of 100. Faculty members and senior managers recently collaborated in the Business Partners program to develop a challenging vision and responsive strategic plan for the College of Business. A key part of that strategy involves increasing relationships with local and international companies.

Most career tracks in the ASU MBA Program offer a practicum or an applied project. These hands-on activities allow students to develop problem-solving skills, enhance communication skills, and gain valuable insight into current issues involving the business community. These projects put students in touch with innovations in technology and practical uses of research.

Prominent Alumni
Distinguished alumni include Craig Weatherup, CEO, PepsiCo; Tom Evans, Chairman and CEO, Official Payments Corporation; Steve Marriott, Vice President of Corporate Marketing, Marriott Hotels; Scott Wald, President, Romar Services, LLC; Wayne Doran, Chairman of the Board, Ford Motor Company; Linda Brock-Nelson, President-Manager, LBN & Associates, LLC; and Jack Furst, Managing Director/Partner, Hicks, Muse, Tate & Furst, Inc.

The College and Environs
ASU, founded in 1885, is the sixth-largest university in the United States, with more than 43,000 students on its 700-acre main campus. Spacious walkways and modern architecture define the picturesque campus setting. ASU's campus evolved into an arboretum of national status in 1990—one of six in Arizona. The sunny and semitropical climate contributes to a Southwestern lifestyle with mild winter temperatures that enable students to enjoy the outdoors year-round.

Facilities
The University's Charles Trumbull Hayden Library is one of the largest research libraries in North America. It contains more than 2.9 million volumes, including many in business and economics, and the specialized Arthur C. Young Tax Collection.

The College of Business is housed in two adjacent buildings that contain an auditorium; lecture halls; seminar rooms; faculty, administrative, and graduate offices; and several computer resource centers. The ASU MBA Program Suite includes the ASU MBA Student Center, the Project Room, conference rooms, student organization offices, and classrooms. A media services center is also located in the College. The College is home to the L. William Seidman Research Institute, whose affiliated centers and programs conduct specialized research on business topics such as entrepreneurship, economics, finance, ethics, and quality.

Technology Environment
ASU has one of the largest and most comprehensive computing facilities of all U.S. universities. The Computing Commons provides access to Macintosh and IBM PCs. All printers are laser printers. A variety of Internet software packages provide students with access to e-mail and Internet news groups and opportunities to browse the Internet. There are numerous other computer sites on campus, including a fully equipped project room in the ASU MBA Suite of the College of Business.

Placement
On average, 95 percent of the ASU MBA graduating class is employed within three months after graduation. The ASU MBA and Graduate Business Career Management Center partner with ASU MBA students and alumni in personal career development at the executive level. The ASU MBA and Graduate Business Career Management Center also partner with more than 100 companies that schedule over 1,800 on-campus interviews annually. In 1999, ASU MBA graduates' average salary was $85,000, with 96 percent placement within three months of graduation. The Director of the ASU MBA and Graduate Business Career Management Center coordinate the efforts of a dedicated staff of 4 full-time Career Consultants, 5 full-time Corporate Relations Representatives, a Business Manager, a full-time Corporate Recruiting Manager, and a Corporate Recruiting Coordinator.

Admission
Application to the ASU MBA Program is open to individuals with at least two years of work experience who hold a bachelor's degree or its equivalent in any discipline from an accredited college or university. During evaluation of candidates, the Admissions Committee looks for well-rounded individuals with strong academic credentials, managerial experience or potential, and the ability to contribute to the diversity of the class. Transcripts, GMAT scores, TOEFL scores (for international students), work history, a personal statement, and letters of recommendation all influence the decision. The entering class of fall 1999 had an average GPA of 3.3 on a 4.0 scale, an average GMAT score of 635, an average TOEFL score of 635 (paper-based)/266 (computer-based), and average postbaccalaureate work experience of four and a half years. Due to the high volume of applications and the limited size of the entering class, students are strongly encouraged to apply as early as possible.

Finances
Estimated tuition costs for 2000–01 are $7344 for Arizona residents and $15,800 for nonresidents. Books and supplies average $1200 per year. Most ASU MBA students live off campus in nearby apartment complexes where the rent ranges from $450 to $600 (one to two bedrooms) per month. On-campus residential facilities are available on a limited basis and cost approximately $7500 (room, board, and personal expenses).

A limited number of tuition scholarships and assistantships are available on a competitive basis. These awards are based strictly on merit and are awarded for one year only. State and federal funds should be pursued through the ASU Financial Assistance Office.

International Students
International diversity is highly valued at ASU, and nearly 20 percent of its M.B.A. students come from outside the U.S., from large countries as well as some of the smallest. During orientation and throughout the year, sponsored activities help international students adjust to the U.S. business and social climate.

Application Facts and Dates
Application deadlines are December 15, March 1, and May 1. Decision letters are usually mailed thirty to forty-five days after each deadline. A file must be complete before it will be evaluated. Annual admission to the full-time and part-time M.B.A. programs is for the fall term only. Graduate college applications are available on the World Wide Web (http://www.asu.edu/gradapp) For more information, students should contact:

Ms. Judith Heilala
Director of ASU MBA Admissions
  and Recruiting
ASU MBA Program
College of Business
Arizona State University
Box 874906
Tempe, Arizona 85287-4906
Telephone: 480-965-3332
Fax: 480-965-8569
E-mail: asu.mba@asu.edu
World Wide Web:
  http://www.cob.asu.edu/mba/ (for
    ASU MBA)
  http://www.cob.asu.edu/acct (for
    School of Accountancy and
    Information Management)
  http://www.cob.asu.edu/hap/index.
    html (for Health Administration)

Armstrong University

Oakland, California

> **TRAINING WORLD BUSINESS LEADERS FOR THE TWENTY-FIRST CENTURY**
>
> *Continuously enhancing what it has done for many years, Armstrong University trains domestic and international students to assume global business management and leadership roles. Our faculty members bring theory and practical experience together to provide students with specific, practical management skills they can use on the job immediately, anywhere in the world. Our curricula were revised recently to increase emphasis on internationalism and leadership. Curricula are built around problem-solving approaches that stress analytical proficiency, creativity, and teamwork, enabling students to work across cultures, manage change, and seize opportunities with entrepreneurial vision.*

Programs and Curricular Focus

All successful organizations—whether public or private, national or international, profit or nonprofit—require mastery of business principles. The Armstrong M.B.A. curriculum relates theories to practices, with the goal of turning students into professionals.

Twelve courses are required for the M.B.A. degree: eight core and four concentration courses. All courses include contemporary computer applications whenever possible. The core courses teach the most indispensable business fundamentals. To develop a sharper focus on specific aspects of business, students take four courses within one of the following concentration areas: finance and accounting, international business, international business law, or marketing management.

Armstrong University's Doctor of Business Administration Program is in process and awaiting approval by the Bureau for Private Post-secondary and Vocational Education.

Since the latest techniques may well be obsolete in a short period, problems are approached with intellectual flexibility, analytical skill, and creativity. Students are prepared to deal with the dynamism of business and not simply locked into techniques that may soon be passé.

Students and the M.B.A. Experience

Business is an international subject whose principles are applicable universally. The student profile supports the M.B.A. program's cross-cultural emphasis. Individuals from thirty-two countries attend Armstrong University. The average student is 26 years old, with approximately two years of work experience in various fields, including engineering, education, and banking. Women comprise 40 percent of the class.

Education at the University is a very personal matter. Student-teacher interaction is encouraged through small classes and easy access to faculty members. Faculty and administrative staff members are eager to help each student achieve his or her academic goals. Peer relationships are also central to the educational experience. Many assignments require students to put theory into practice and model real-world situations by integrating teamwork and case studies into the learning process. Conducting case analyses, research, and presentations in teams is central to the M.B.A. curriculum.

❖ Global Focus

The M.B.A. program focuses on the growing global economy. Realizing the importance of providing students with the necessary tools to excel in today's international marketplace, globalism is a structural part of the program, not merely an intellectual focus. The culturally diverse student body, staff, faculty, and alumni are a reflection of the international community. At Armstrong, students have the opportunity to interact in a multinational environment that equips them with the skills to become responsible business leaders in the emerging interdependent world economy.

The Faculty

The professors at Armstrong University are distinguished academics who have significant experience in business practice and education. Each possesses a doctoral degree or other terminal degree, such as the Master of Business Administration. Classes are small in order to give students high-quality contact with instructors. Faculty members are experienced in working with students from diverse backgrounds.

The Business School Network
Corporate Partnerships

Armstrong's Business Advisory Council helps the University develop and maintain a curriculum that is current, realistic, and relevant to the needs of the business community. In regular meetings with University officials, the council reviews and evaluates the mission, the objectives, and the programs of the University. It also identifies ways in which the external community can support the University. Council members guest lecture in classes and speak to groups of students on topics of current interest. The council includes representatives from banking, consulting, insurance, technology, education, and politics (U.S. and abroad).

Armstrong's Board of Directors includes prominent representatives from the fields of law, finance, international business, politics, publishing, and education who provide leadership and guidance based on their areas of expertise.

Armstrong also hosts a lecture series in which executives and international business experts offer insights and perspectives that enhance the students' learning experience.

The College and Environs

Armstrong is a small, independent university. Its diverse student population reflects that of the city in which it is located. Oakland is noted for its tolerant attitude and cosmopolitan atmosphere.

Opportunities to explore cultural arts are varied and countless. Small, inexpensive restaurants, clubs, and stores abound. The institution's urban setting in the San Francisco Bay Area, a major business center, and its proximity to Silicon Valley, the high-technology center of the United States, make it an ideal place to study business.

Technology Environment

Armstrong University's computer lab houses state-of-the-art personal computers running on the Novell 3.12 network. Microcomputer systems are networked so that they can act as workstations to access a variety of mail, bulletin boards, and a high-speed network connecting universities and research centers world-wide.

The Library has 10,000 volumes and receives about 100 periodical titles. Students have access to several CD-ROM databases that index and abstract business and general subject periodicals. One database provides full-text articles from regional business journals. Students enjoy open-stack privileges at the University of California and public library systems and remote access to those systems via modem. Students are also encouraged to explore the vast research and reference opportunities offered via the Internet.

Placement

Job placement services are available in the Career Management Services (CMS) Department. The CMS Director assists students in their job search both before and after graduation. It maintains current listings of part-time and full-time positions. In addition, the staff members are available to advise students about career planning, job placement, resume preparation, and interview skills.

Admission

Applicants are admitted based on demonstrated academic abilities. Personal qualities, such as maturity and motivation, are also considered. Applicants to the Graduate School must have earned a bachelor's degree from an approved college or university with at least a 2.5 GPA. All applicants are required to submit an application for admission and have official transcripts sent to the Office of Admissions from every college and university attended. TOEFL scores of 500 or above are required of all applicants whose native language is not English and who graduated from an institution where English was not used as the only language of instruction. Students without a TOEFL score may be admitted conditionally contingent upon completion of English Level 4.

Finances

The 1999–2000 tuition and fees were $4200 per semester. Books and supplies are estimated at $350 per academic year. The average cost for room and board is $7500 per academic year.

Application Facts and Dates

Applications for admission are accepted throughout the year, and students may enter in the fall or spring semester or summer session. For more information, students should contact:

Office of Admissions
Armstrong University
1608 Webster Street
Oakland, California 94612
Telephone: 510-835-7900 Ext. 10
      800-222-9297 (toll-free)
Fax: 510-835-8935
E-mail: admin@armstrong-u.edu
World Wide Web: http://www.
    armstrong-u.edu

ARTHUR D. LITTLE
SCHOOL
of MANAGEMENT

Arthur D. Little School of Management

One-Year Master of Science in Management Program

Chestnut Hill and Cambridge, Massachusetts

THE CORPORATE ADVANTAGE

If you are an experienced professional ready to assume greater managerial responsibility and are looking for a minimal disruption of your career and income, the Master of Science in Management (M.S.M.) program at the Arthur D. Little School of Management (ADLSOM) may be for you. Arthur D. Little, Inc. (ADL), a leading international consulting firm, is the only corporation to create an accredited graduate business program. We provide the unequaled opportunity to combine leading academic theory and the best consulting practices, all in an international context.

Arthur D. Little concentrates on helping major economic entities and businesses improve their operations, products, and processes by providing pragmatic solutions and visible involvement in the implementation of those solutions. Similarly, the M.S.M. is designed to provide a practical, experience-based curriculum with an emphasis on global issues, cross-cultural awareness, and team building. Courses are taught by practicing Boston-area business school professors and Arthur D. Little consultants who bring their knowledge to the classroom. We engage our participants in an intensive, year-long dialogue to develop and strengthen their management skills, which allows them to become more effective within their organizations.

We encourage to you to visit our program. We think you will see what makes our program truly unique in the international business school marketplace.

—William G. Makris, Director of Marketing and Chairman,
Admission Committee

Programs and Curricular Focus

The Arthur D. Little School of Management is the first and only accredited graduate business program to be created by a corporation. The School takes a holistic approach to international business education by delivering a curriculum that transcends cultural barriers. At the heart of this approach is a student body and faculty of internationally diverse, experienced professionals.

The one-year Master of Science in Management (M.S.M.) program is an innovative curriculum called "action learning" that emphasizes the interrelation of management theory and practice. The M.S.M. curriculum builds the managerial competence necessary to lead in a dynamic, global business environment. The curriculum delivers competency in the functional knowledge, skills, and abilities of a business, while extending capabilities in critical success factors for industry leadership and career management.

The four modules, Achieving High Performance, Managing the Business as an Integrated System, Sustaining Competitive Advantage, and Creating the Future, reflect the stages of business development and incorporate the managerial competencies

required for success. M.S.M. participants develop an understanding of these managerial competencies through case discussions, team learning, integrated exercises, and simulations.

Unifying the four M.S.M. modules are the three distinctive capabilities of innovation, globalization, and consulting. All reinforce ADLSOM's unique understanding of business, as demonstrated by the association with Arthur D. Little, Inc. Participants complete a four-month consulting assignment with ADL as part of the curriculum. Participants take electives to tailor their program to meet their interests.

The ADLSOM Executive M.B.A./M.S.M. is offered in conjunction with the School's newest alliance partners, in two new ways. An Executive M.B.A./M.S.M. degree is offered in Mexico City in partnership with the Universidad La Salle. This eighteen-month executive program is conducted on alternating Fridays and Saturdays with several intensive residencies, including two in Boston. The program is available beginning January 2001 at a cost of $40,000. ADLSOM's On-Line Executive M.B.A./M.S.M. is available in conjunction with Unexus University, Canada's first on-

line university. This cohort program is conducted completely via the Web over a twenty-one-month period. An option for attending an integration seminar in Boston is also available. The program begins in January, May, and September and costs $28,000. Both programs offer the same educational advantage as ADLSOM's Boston-based program with the added value of the resources of these two excellent facilities.

Students and the M.B.A. Experience

One of the leading attributes of the program is the depth of the professional experience of the class participants. Enrollment in the M.S.M. program represents the diversity of most work environments, bringing together professionals with different educational backgrounds such as finance, law, and engineering. Although the profile of a typical ADLSOM student varies, most participants have between four and eight years of work experience and are in their early or middle thirties. Many are sponsored by their employers or by international agencies and return to their organizations after graduation. ADLSOM students are among the most experienced in the business school marketplace.

❖ Global Focus

The diversity of the class provides a unique opportunity to learn and practice the skills of international business management by working closely with colleagues from approximately twenty-two countries. The students represent a broad diversity of cultures and a wide range of industry and functional expertise. Each year, 65 participants, more than 90 percent of whom are international students, are enrolled in the M.S.M. program. Courses and projects are designed to incorporate teamwork and team building as an approach to developing managerial skills. Class discussions, study groups, and projects completed in teams provide intense cross-cultural experiences and the opportunity to gain a global perspective in nearly every course.

Special Features

Action learning is central to the M.S.M. curriculum. Throughout an intensive year, M.S.M. faculty members reinforce business theory with practical applications with several exercises, including five business simulations and the Management Consulting Project (MCP). The MCP links participant teams with an Arthur D. Little consultant to complete a four-month consulting project for ADL or one of its key clients. These projects cover a wide array of industries, including e-commerce, energy, transportation, pharmaceuticals, and banking.

The ADL Fridays Distinguished Speaker Series is another way for participants to develop an understanding of business practices in and out of Arthur D. Little. The series is held at ADL headquarters in Cambridge on alternate weeks and typically includes presentations by 3 senior executives who discuss strategic business issues across several industries.

The Faculty

The Arthur D. Little School of Management faculty members are professionals—management specialists, economists, scientists, engineers, lawyers, and consultants—who hold advanced degrees and have years of international experience working at the forefront of their fields. Faculty members include senior consultants from Arthur D. Little and other organizations, as well as professors from international business schools. Incorporating their working knowledge into classroom discussions, the ADLSOM faculty focuses on the relevant needs of managers throughout the world.

The Business School Network

As a result of its strategic alliance with Boston College's (BC) Carroll School of Management, the program is housed on BC's 148-acre Chestnut Hill campus and at ADLSOM headquarters in Cambridge. While at Boston College, M.S.M. participants have complete access to all the academic and athletic facilities of Boston College. During the elective portion of the M.S.M., students are able to cross-register for courses with BC's Carroll School of Management graduate offerings.

M.S.M. students also learn about Arthur D. Little through special presentations arranged throughout the year.

The College and Environs

Since 1964, more than 3,300 professionals from more than 115 countries have participated in ADLSOM's programs. Founded as a subsidiary of Arthur D. Little, ADLSOM was chartered in 1971 and received its accreditation in 1976 from the New England Association of Schools and Colleges, Inc.

Arthur D. Little and Boston College are located in the metropolitan Boston area.

Boston is home to more than fifty universities, institutes, and colleges. Boston provides outstanding cultural, social, athletic, and academic resources.

Facilities

ADLSOM participants have access to all of the facilities at Boston College and Arthur D. Little headquarters in Cambridge.

Classes are held in a state-of-the-art classroom within the Wallace E. Carroll School of Management's Fulton Hall. The Carroll School recently received $15 million in renovations and offers students several resources, including team study rooms, a career resources room, and a quiet-study library. The building facilitates interaction among the different student groups in the business school and is a central location on BC's campus for presentations from various members of the business community.

In addition to the space in the Fulton Hall, the School's offices are located at 194 Beacon Street in a beautiful Georgian brick house. The 194 Beacon Street location, a few minutes' walk from the classroom, provides a central meeting place for program participants. It has a student lounge, a communication area for announcements, and a kitchen with a refrigerator and a microwave. All administrative and faculty offices are also in the building.

The Boston College library system provides a wide array of resources for research and learning. The BC collections consist of more than 1.5 million volumes, plus microfilm, serials, government documents, and media. In addition, there is an outstanding computing facility within the library complex. Access to ADLSOM's Global Information Resources and a vast interlibrary loan network is also available.

All facilities are convenient to library, computing, and parking facilities, as well as shuttle bus service to public transportation and residential neighborhoods.

Placement

The School works individually with each participant to develop a career strategy. The Career Management Curriculum (CMC) is a 12-hour course designed to enhance skill development regarding the job-search process. CMC is complemented by workshops to further enhance job-search skills and provide opportunities to practice these new techniques. CMC provides individual career counseling, presentations of industry panels, and access to networking events.

Admission

Applicants for the M.S.M. program are considered on the basis of a qualitative evaluation of the relevance of work experience

and career objectives, the applicant's undergraduate records, strength of recommendations, personal motivation, and analytical ability. Submission of a GMAT score is required of most candidates, and a TOEFL score must be submitted where appropriate. Interviews are recommended and are often required.

Finances

Tuition for the one-year M.S.M. program is $32,000. The fee covers the cost of all instruction and includes transportation for the travel required for the Industry Research Project. Participants should plan to spend $1900 to cover books and instructional materials and $2600 for a laptop computer. There is an additional fee of $2500 for the Summer Preparatory Program. The estimated annual living expenses, including rent, utilities, food, medical insurance, local transportation, and laptop computer, are $20,500. Participants who are U.S. citizens or permanent residents may be eligible for federally insured Stafford loans, which are available through banks and other lending institutions. Limited partial tuition scholarships are also available.

International Students

More than 90 percent of the M.S.M. student body comes from outside the United States. The class of 1999 is represented by twenty-three countries with the following geographic distribution: Asia Minor, 17 percent; Africa, 8 percent; Europe, 12 percent; Latin America, 33 percent; North America, 15 percent; and Pacific Rim, 15 percent.

Application Facts and Dates

The application deadlines for August enrollment are January 15, March 1, April 15, May 15, and June 15. Late applications are reviewed on a space-available basis. Early application is suggested, as enrollment is limited. Correspondence should be directed to:

William G. Makris
Chairman, Admission Committee
Arthur D. Little School of
    Management
194 Beacon Street
Chestnut Hill, Massachusetts 02467-3853
Telephone: 617-552-2877
Fax: 617-552-2051
E-mail: adlsom@adlittle.com
World Wide Web: http://www.adlsom.edu

Auburn University

Auburn University, Alabama

EDUCATION FOR SUCCESS IN THE TWENTY-FIRST CENTURY

Increased competition, reengineering, social responsibilities, and borderless corporations affect American business and American business schools. Business schools must create, through classroom learning, real-life situations, team-building, and leadership exercises, students who are more versatile and globally aware. Students still require the knowledge and analytical skills of the traditional graduate, but also should be more skilled in understanding organizations and the needs of colleagues and employees. Students should be more entrepreneurial, more confident in assuming leadership roles, and more sophisticated in the use of technology. Graduates of the Auburn M.B.A. program will acquire these qualities as well as a firm grounding in the traditional business disciplines.

I urge you to weigh the merits of our program, compare it with others, hold it to the highest of standards. I believe you will agree that the Auburn M.B.A. program offers exceptional value for our students and provides the education necessary to succeed in the business world of the twenty-first century.

—C. Wayne Alderman, Dean

Programs and Curricular Focus

Auburn University's Master of Business Administration program is fully accredited by the AACSB–The International Association for Management Education. The M.B.A. program is designed to prepare students for positions of leadership in public and private enterprise. The program consists of 36 to 42 semester hours of course work. At Auburn, the focus is on the core analytical and communication skills that best prepare students for an uncertain future. The program incorporates a mix of theory with practical applications and supplements traditional lectures with case analyses. While the program keeps abreast of the latest trends, it is not trendy. The curriculum has staying power; it reflects the broad, fundamental knowledge upon which students can build a successful career, while allowing students to specialize and develop further expertise in a particular area of concentration. Students take eight core courses in the program and four electives. Students may choose their electives to earn a concentration in a variety of functional areas, which can include finance, health care, human resource management, marketing, operations management, management information systems, economics, management of technology, agribusiness, and natural resources management. A team case analysis is the capstone requirement for the degree. Classes typically have 50 students in them. Most students can complete the program in three

semesters of full-time work. Students are required to have had undergraduate courses in calculus and statistics prior to entering the program. In addition, students must have an adequate background in the fundamentals of business education, which can be met through successful completion of course work in the following subject areas: accounting, economics, finance, management, and marketing. In lieu of completing undergraduate courses in each of these fields, students can pass a competency examination administered through the M.B.A. office.

Since 1990, the Auburn M.B.A. has also been available off campus through the video-based Graduate Outreach Program. Well over 200 students have completed their degrees through this flexible, innovative program. This program offers professionals the opportunity to continue their education while maintaining full-time employment, wherever they may be located. Video-based M.B.A. students receive the same instruction as on-campus students and complete all class assignments and tests. Students from across the United States in Fortune 500 companies, small firms, and all branches of the military are currently earning an Auburn M.B.A. through the Graduate Outreach Program.

The most recent program additions are the Executive M.B.A. (E.M.B.A.), the Physicians Executive M.B.A. (P.E.M.B.A.), and the Techno E.M.B.A.

degree options. These tracks were designed to give full-time working professionals the opportunity to earn a fully accredited M.B.A. degree in less than two years. Both the E.M.B.A. and the P.E.M.B.A. combine the video-based outreach program with the traditional, on-campus experience. Students receive videotaped and Internet instruction coupled with several residency experiences. These programs offer the innovation and flexibility necessary to create a cohesive learning environment.

Students and the M.B.A. Experience

There are approximately 390 students in Auburn's M.B.A. program, with equal percentages on and off campus. The average GMAT for the entering class in the fall of 1999 was 600, with an average GPA of 3.2. Twenty-eight percent of the students are female, and 5 percent are international students. Degree backgrounds include business (38 percent), engineering (36 percent), and liberal arts (12 percent), with the remainder a mix of other disciplines. While work experience is not a requirement for admission, it is encouraged. Many on-campus students have significant business experience to bring to the classroom. For those students that do not, an internship while in the program is strongly encouraged. While teamwork is a strong focus within the curriculum, individual responsibility and accountability is stressed, as well. There are a number of professional student associations on campus, including an active M.B.A. student association that sponsors many activities.

The Faculty

The M.B.A. faculty members of Auburn University's College of Business excel as instructors and researchers. All faculty members have doctoral degrees and all are actively involved in research and consulting, keeping at the forefront of their disciplines. Good teaching is taken seriously and that is reflected in the quality of classroom instruction. By keeping the classes small, professors can take the time to work with the students individually. By making themselves available outside of the classroom, the faculty members provide a sup-

portive atmosphere for learning, while at the same time they challenge the students to succeed.

The Business School Network

Interactions with the business community, through guest lecturers, company visits, and case analyses, are as important a component of an M.B.A. as the classroom lecture. That interaction strengthens the context in which students develop their understanding of theory. The Auburn program is constantly developing new networks and linkages for the students.

Corporate Partnerships

The Auburn M.B.A. Alumni Advisory Board, comprising 25 prominent business leaders throughout the country, works closely with the M.B.A. program to provide both programmatic advice and financial support. In addition, they actively work to identify and expand placement and internship opportunities, provide guest lecturers for the classroom, recruit companies to host site visits, or participate in team strategic analyses. They also cosponsor social events throughout the year, including football tailgate parties, picnics, and other informal gatherings that give the students a chance to discuss various business issues one-on-one with experienced professionals.

Prominent Alumni

Auburn M.B.A. graduates hold senior positions in local, national, and international companies, including BellSouth, Nationsbank, Chevron, Eastman Chemical, Andersen Consulting, Ernst and Young, IBM, Hewlett-Packard, McDonnell Douglas, Sprint, Southern Company, Michelin,

Texas Instruments, UDS Motorola, and many others. An Auburn M.B.A. was listed in the June 1996 issue of *Entrepreneur* magazine as one of the top 100 new business entrepreneurs in the United States.

The College and Environs

Auburn University, ranked by *U.S. News & World Report* as one of the nation's fifty top public universities in 1998–99, is a land-grant institution dedicated to serving Alabama and the nation through instruction, research, and extension.

Chartered in 1856, the University is located in the friendly, small-town environment of Auburn, Alabama. The University's beautiful 1,900-acre campus is home to 21,775 students (including 3,970 business students), 1,100 faculty members, a library with more than 2.6 million volumes, and more than fifty major academic buildings.

Auburn is approximately a 2-hour drive from the metropolitan areas of Atlanta, Georgia, and Birmingham, Alabama, and a 3½-hour drive from the Gulf Coast beaches.

Facilities

Classes are held in a $15-million facility that is one of the most modern structures of its type in the nation. The building includes curved and tiered classrooms, a conference room designed as a formal reception area to entertain business guests and host small meetings, two video M.B.A. classrooms, and six audiovisual classrooms linked to the Auburn University satellite system. The quality of the educational environment provided by the building is among the finest in the country.

Placement

The Auburn University placement office provides students with personal help on developing interview skills, resume preparation, alumni networking, and access to on-campus corporate recruiting. In addition, placement efforts within the M.B.A. program include direct contacts with businesses and position notifications through an e-mail network. The 1999 average starting salary for on-campus students without significant prior work experience was $47,350, with a 97 percent placement rate within three months of graduation.

Admission

The Auburn M.B.A. program accepts applicants for the on-campus program for fall semester only. Applicants for the distance M.B.A. program are accepted for fall and spring semesters. Applicants must submit transcripts of all previous college work, recent GMAT and TOEFL scores, completed Graduate School and M.B.A. applications, and three letters of recommendation with a $25 application fee ($50 for international students). Prior work experience is a plus, and personal interviews are encouraged.

Finances

Tuition per quarter for the 1999–2000 academic year was $920 for in-state students and $2760 for out-of-state students. Students enrolled in the video-based M.B.A. program pay $225 per credit hour. Most of the M.B.A. classes are 5 credit hours.

Application Facts and Dates

Applications are accepted for fall semester only for the on-campus program. The application deadline for the fall semester is May 1. Applications are accepted for the fall and spring semesters for the distance M.B.A. program. The application deadline for the spring semester is October 1. Students are encouraged to submit completed applications well in advance of these deadlines.

Completed applications are reviewed by the M.B.A. Admission Committee and students are generally informed within two weeks of the receipt of all elements of the application. For more information, students should contact:

M.B.A. Program Admissions
Suite 503
College of Business
Auburn University
Auburn, Alabama 36849
Telephone: 334-844-4060
Fax: 334-844-2964
E-mail: mbainfo@business.auburn.edu
World Wide Web: http://www.mba.
    business.auburn.edu

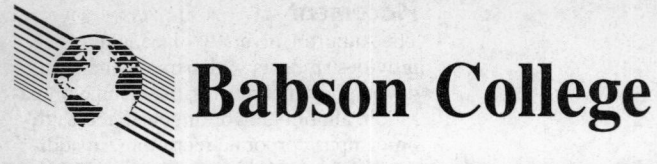

Babson College

F. W. Olin Graduate School of Business

Wellesley, Massachusetts

EDUCATING THE WORLD'S FUTURE ENTREPRENEURIAL LEADERS

▶ *The Franklin W. Olin Graduate School of Business at Babson College is committed to educating entrepreneurial leaders. Entrepreneurial leadership is a way of thinking and acting to create opportunities. Recognized as the world leader in entrepreneurial education and as a leader in integrated curriculum design, Babson is a very special place to study. Students are noted for their creativity, teamwork, and ability to see business problems from a holistic perspective. I know that as you read more about Babson, you will want to become a part of this unique educational community.*

—Thomas Moore, The Murata Dean

Programs and Curricular Focus

All programs emphasize the global aspects of business and the value of the entrepreneurial spirit.

The Two-Year M.B.A. program is a coordinated curriculum based on the theme of entrepreneurial leadership in a changing global environment. First-year discussions and course work trace the business development cycle from the invention of a product or service, through assessing the business opportunity, into creating the marketing and delivery systems, and onto further development of products in the cycle. The highlight of the first year is participation in the mentor program, which assigns student teams to year-long projects with local businesses. Students complete two projects for the mentor company: one that analyzes the company's industry externally and another that evaluates an internal system. Teams provide written reports for both projects and present findings to top management. In the second year of the two-year M.B.A. program, students complete a schedule that is equivalent to ten courses (30 credit hours) and that builds on the first-year experience, which allows students to focus on elective study.

The One-Year M.B.A. is an accelerated program that allows students with an undergraduate business degree to complete their M.B.A. in three full-time semesters. Beginning each May, students enroll in a series of integrated modules over the first semester and then join the second-year M.B.A. students to complete the equivalent of fifteen courses in one calendar year. Candidates who work in the Boston area may complete the

summer modules full-time, return to work in September, and finish the remainder of the program on a part-time basis in two years.

The Evening M.B.A. program, designed for working professionals, begins each fall and spring. The program offers a solid foundation in the functional areas of management and in the behavioral and quantitative sciences, giving students an invaluable understanding of business practice and strategy.

Students and the M.B.A. Experience

Students in the Two-Year M.B.A. program are, on average, 29 years old and have about six years of work experience. GMAT scores range from 520 to 750. Women comprise one third of the class. Students come from such diverse industries as banking and investment institutions to advertising, biotechnology, publishing, telecommunications, and high technology.

❖ Global Focus

Global business perspectives are not new at Babson. An international concentration is available and requires bilinguality, participation in a Global Management Program, and completion of required and elective international courses. The Global Management Program places students in structured field consulting projects with corporations in Asia, Australia, Europe, and South America. International electives combine intensive classroom experience with industry-based projects in thirteen international cities. International internships, electives, and study-abroad opportunities satisfy the Two-Year

M.B.A. program cross-cultural requirement and are open to students in all Babson programs.

Special Features

Babson fosters the entrepreneurial spirit through a variety of activities and opportunities, including electives, endowed chairs in entrepreneurship, induction of innovative business people into the Academy of Distinguished Entrepreneurs on Founder's Day, the Douglass Foundation Entrepreneurial Prizes, and the Babson Entrepreneurial Exchange, a student-run network of current and future entrepreneurs who exchange information about business development and venture opportunities.

The Faculty

Babson's faculty is an internationally and professionally diverse group, representing nations in Asia, Australia, Europe, and North and South America and with backgrounds in pharmaceutical, banking, high-technology, retailing, and other industries. They are practitioners and scholars, executives and teachers, and researchers and consultants who have lived and worked in international settings.

The Business School Network

Corporate Partnerships

Successful business partnerships have always been a major component of Babson's programs. First-year student teams consult with Boston-area organizations through the year-long mentor program. The Management Consulting Field Experience offers a variety of second-year consulting projects, many in e-business.

The Graduate Advisory Board offers feedback on curriculum initiatives and facilitates ongoing relationships with the business community. The international advisory boards draw worldwide membership from senior executives with demonstrated expertise in global management.

The College and Environs

Babson College, founded in 1919 by financier and entrepreneur Roger W. Babson, is located on a 450-acre wooded site in Wellesley, Massachusetts, just 12

Building on the strength of seventy-five years of excellence in management education, Babson College embraces new challenges and opportunities and furthers successes.

miles from Boston. Boston and the surrounding region offer a pleasing and exciting environment with a rich artistic, historic, and intellectual life.

Facilities

The Horn Library houses more than 130,000 volumes, 1,500 periodicals, and a collection of business and financial statements from more than 10,000 corporations. Online search services provide access to more than 250 databases, covering bibliographical and statistical information, thirty-five newspapers, and 100 magazines. Students and faculty members can access 1,000 databases from more than forty different online services, including LEXIS-NEXIS, FirstSearch, Prodigy, Bridge, Dow Jones, DataStar, Investext, Bloomberg, and Datastream. Housed in the Horn Library, the new Cutler Investment Management Center expands student and faculty access to financial resources and information.

Graduate housing offers living units of various sizes in eleven buildings, with surrounding recreation and picnic areas.

Technology Environment

The Horn Computer Center is equipped with 150 computer workstations that run a diversified library of business-oriented programs in a Windows environment. A separate lab houses twenty-five Macintosh

SE computers. The center operates a 24-hour computer lab. Most classrooms are equipped with computer projection hardware. Babson expects that entering students are comfortable with basic spreadsheet and word-processing operations.

Placement

Made up of a staff of 4 professionals, the Center for Career Development offers a career management curriculum that is integrated into the first-year course work and is required for all full-time students; an online professional development survey of work experience and interests, allowing the staff to direct students to internship and employment opportunities; internships offering either stipends or course credit; job fairs; and online alumni and employer databases.

Admission

Students are admitted to the program based on a careful evaluation of academic records, professional qualifications, GMAT scores, and personal attributes. Interviews are required for admission to full-time M.B.A. programs. Current class GMAT scores are in the 520 to 750 range, and the average undergraduate GPA is 3.1. International students must submit TOEFL results and official English translations of all academic documents. All candidates should have

strong mathematics, computer, economics, and business writing skills.

Finances

Nine-month academic year cost estimates for 2000–01 for the Two-Year M.B.A. program are $23,662 for tuition, $1406 for books and supplies, $7488 for housing, and $3106 for food. Tuition for the One-Year M.B.A. program is $34,143. Per-course tuition is $2208. The pre-M.B.A. for international students costs $1000.

Merit programs that award scholarships include Babson Fellows, Olin Fellows, Babson Fellowships for Students of Color, Olin Scholarships, and Babson Scholars.

International Students

International students comprise 30 percent of M.B.A. enrollment. The pre-M.B.A. orientation for international students begins two weeks before Module I classes. This intensive program consists of familiarization with the campus, library, computer center, and other services and workshops. Also, Babson faculty members present a basic introduction to economics, marketing, and the case method. Recreational and social events are scheduled. International students may apply for a U.S. internship and are eligible for the Global Management Program.

Application Facts and Dates

Application deadlines for the Two-Year M.B.A. program are January 5, February 1, March 1, and April 15; for the One-Year M.B.A. program, December 1 and January 5; and for the Evening M.B.A. program, November 1 and December 1 for spring admission and May 15 and June 15 for fall admission. Decisions are mailed four to six weeks after each deadline. For more information, applicants should contact:

Office of Graduate Admission
F. W. Olin Graduate School of
   Business
Babson Park, Massachusetts 02157-
   0310
Telephone: 781-239-4317
        800-488-4512 (toll-free
        within the U.S.)
Fax: 781-239-4194
E-mail: mbaadmission@babson.edu
World Wide Web: http://www.babson.
   edu/mba

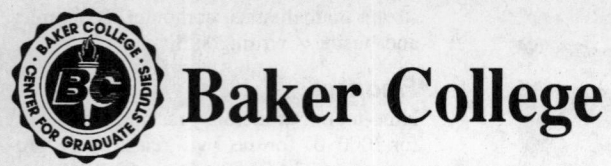

Baker College

DEVELOPING LEADERS FOR THE TWENTY-FIRST CENTURY

"Executives are problem solvers; at best, they are visionaries, developing and implementing strategies for the twenty-first century." I read that definition in someone's catalog in the past year. I thought then that it was a marvelous way of introducing a graduate program in business. I still do! In fact, these words are so important to the accurate description of what we do at Baker College that we have formulated our vision statement along the same lines: "Developing leaders, thinkers, visionaries, and problem solvers who can effectively empower both self and others in a dynamic and global economic environment."

The business programs at Baker College are the product of years of planning. We asked our students, faculty and staff members, and the employers in our communities to tell us what they wanted. Then we set out to make sure we gave them the very best possible programs to support all those constituencies. We've even added a computer component to make the M.B.A. experience a memorable one. Most importantly, we continue to support and implement the marvelous mission and purpose statements of this organization. The M.B.A. programs at Baker College have been specifically designed with your experience, goals, and aspirations in mind.

Whether you are a manager, a professional, or an entrepreneur seeking to improve your business or leadership skills, Baker College offers you adult-oriented, practical, convenient, and efficient programs tailored for your lifestyle and needs.

—Chuck Gurden, Director, Graduate Admissions

Programs and Curricular Focus

Baker College's program seeks to combine the best of conventional academic training with the best of field-based learning. Most typical business disciplines are represented in the curriculum because the College believes that a successful manager must be conversant with different aspects of running any of today's organizations or companies. Thus, the standard curriculum addresses accounting, computers, finance, communications, ethics, marketing, and management. This M.B.A. program is organized into six areas of concentration: communications and information systems, research and analytical support, economic and financial applications, issues within and outside the organization, leadership and the management process, and emphasis in the chosen concentration area. Students may elect to focus their studies in one of the following areas: computer information systems, health-care management, human resource management, industrial management, international business, leadership studies, marketing, accounting, or finance.

The curriculum at Baker College is offered in two different models, which are designed to accommodate the schedules of almost all working adults. The concentration model requires a total of 50 quarter hours, and all students in this program can complete their academic program in eighteen months by enrolling in two concurrent classes each term. Students are expected to produce a portfolio, which is designed as both a research tool during the program and a good reference tool once the student completes the degree.

The corporate model requires a total of 60 quarter hours. There is an extensive research project required in conjunction with this approach. Students in this approach can expect to graduate in two years by enrolling in two courses each quarter.

M.B.A. programs are offered on campuses in Flint, Owosso, Muskegon, Port Huron, Cadillac, Auburn Hills, Mount Clemens, and Jackson, Michigan. The program is also available in corporate facilities and through Baker College On-line.

Students and the M.B.A. Experience

Baker College students bring a wide range of experience and backgrounds to the classroom. Typically, experiences represented are in areas such as business, education, psychology, engineering, and medicine. These diverse backgrounds and experiences are valued highly by Baker and are incorporated into the curriculum of the M.B.A. program.

Fifty-two percent of graduate students at Baker are women, 20 percent are members of minority groups, and about 12 percent are international students.

Special Features

Baker College, a recognized leader in the development of market-worthy educational and training opportunities, stands in the unique position of being able to meet the special needs of working adults. The tradition of quality with flexibility has enabled Baker to establish accredited degree programs in a variety of nontraditional settings.

In meeting with this tradition, courses are offered in three formats: weekend, weeknight, and on line. Students are able to attend courses on campus one weekend a month or one night a week for nine weeks. Students also have the option to take courses on line in six-week sessions with no on-ground classroom requirements.

The Faculty

Baker College faculty members know their business. Faculty members are selected for both their business experience and their academic credentials and bring great breadth and depth to the program. The flexibility of course offerings allows Baker to expose graduate students to instructors from all over the United States. This cadre of professionals, known as Baker's National Faculty, brings experience from their industries and is committed to the best education program possible.

The focus of Baker's faculty is somewhat different from traditional universities. Instead of placing an emphasis on empirical research, Baker values practitioner-oriented education. Faculty members remain continually active in their professions by consulting, conducting seminars, running their own businesses, writing, volunteering in their communities, and even working for other organizations.

The Business School Network

Corporate Partnerships

An advisory board of community leaders is established for every discipline at Baker College. These advisory boards give advice on current and future curricula, program needs or changes, employment opportunities for students, and other general advice on college activities. Students have the ability to interact with community leaders outside the classroom through the Baker College Leadership Institute.

The College and Environs

The Baker College System has evolved from schools that have been providing high-quality and practitioner-oriented degree programs in Michigan for more than a century.

The oldest of the system schools was founded in 1888 by Woodbridge Ferris in Muskegon. In 1911, Eldon Baker established Baker Business University in Flint. These two institutions merged to form the Baker College System in 1986; it is now the largest private not-for-profit independent college in the state of Michigan. Total enrollment figures, including outreach operations, for the system exceeds 17,000 students. The Center for Graduate Studies has approximately 780 students located throughout the system.

Facilities

The Baker College Library System is part of the Flint Area Library Consortium (FALCON), a consortium of libraries based in Flint that supports an online catalog database of more than 500,000 holdings of the Baker College System Libraries, the GMI Engineering and Management Institute, Mott Community College, and the eighteen branches of the Genesee County libraries. Baker also participates in the Online Computer Library Center interlibrary loan subsystem. The library facility also features INFOTRAC periodical indexing databases, the UMI/ProQuest General Periodicals On-Disc and Business Periodicals On-Disc full-article imaging station, and Books-in-Print with Reviews. Fiche and microfilm collections provide additional document retrieval resources.

Technology Environment

Every Baker College student is assigned an e-mail account. Students may also use their accounts to access the World Wide Web. Through the World Wide Web, students are able to communicate with each other and their instructors as well as members of the graduate school staff. There are more than 1,600 microcomputers in student labs available for student use.

Placement

Baker College prides itself on the fact that 99 percent of all graduates are employed. A successfully employed graduate is the result of the College's continuous contact with hundreds of employers throughout the year as well as the annual Job Fair. Approximately seventy employers participate in the Job Fair every year. The employment service of the College is a lifetime arrangement for all graduates.

Admission

To qualify for admission to Baker College's M.B.A. program, a student must have a bachelor's degree from a regionally accredited institution, have a 2.5 or better GPA in their undergraduate work, be able to display appropriate written communication skills, submit three letters of reference, submit a current resume, and have completed no less than three years of full-time work. A TOEFL score is required for all applicants for whom English is not the native language. Once submitted, the applicant's record will be evaluated by an Admissions Committee.

Finances

Tuition for the 1999–2000 school year was approximately $225 per quarter hour. The total program cost was approximately $12,500. The cost of books ranged from $150 to $200 each quarter.

Application Facts and Dates

Baker College uses a rolling admissions process, so there are no deadlines for applications, and students are able to begin at any quarter. Once the Admissions Committee receives an application, applicants usually receive a decision in approximately four weeks.

Chuck Gurden
Director of Graduate Admissions
Center for Graduate Studies
Baker College
1050 West Bristol Road
Flint, Michigan 48507
Telephone: 810-766-4390
          800-469-3165 (toll-free)
Fax: 810-766-4399
E-mail: gurden_c@corpfl.baker.edu

Baldwin-Wallace College

> ### THE M.B.A. THAT PREPARES INTERNATIONAL MANAGERS FOR SUCCESS
>
> *Many of America's most highly respected M.B.A. programs have recently begun to incorporate "new" concepts like teamwork, hands-on experience, and multidisciplinary curricula. At Baldwin-Wallace College, our M.B.A. programs were founded on these fundamental philosophies—in 1972.*
>
> *Every manager knows that corporations have become increasingly global in their operations and that their work forces have become increasingly diverse. To effectively lead these corporations, the ideal executive of the future needs to be global in outlook, able to capitalize on diversity, and a master of teamwork. The Baldwin-Wallace College M.B.A. in International Management program challenges students to foster these qualities.*
>
> —Tom Riemenschneider, Director, International M.B.A. Programs

Programs and Curricular Focus

The M.B.A. in International Management (I.M.B.A.) is offered through both full-time and part-time programs. The full-time program is designed to meet the needs of individuals seeking significant career advancement or the education necessary to become managers in a global setting. It has a sixteen-month sequential format requiring class attendance 9 hours per week during each of three 15-week terms. Students have the opportunity to study with part-time students who, in most cases, are currently employed in international management positions.

The part-time evening program is designed to meet the needs of individuals who are working in such areas as accounting, data processing, engineering, marketing, and management and are seriously seeking significant career advancement as managers in a global corporate setting. The program has a sequential two-year format requiring class attendance 3 hours per evening, two evenings per week.

Students have the opportunity to take foundation courses with other graduate students. These foundation courses make it possible for students with little or no undergraduate business education to successfully participate in the program.

Baldwin-Wallace also offers M.B.A and Executive M.B.A. programs through its Division of Business Administration. These two-year, part-time programs are based on teamwork, hands-on experience, and multidisciplinary curricula. The M.B.A. program is designed for individu-

als with at least two years of business experience. Approximately 270 students are currently enrolled in the evening and weekend classes. The Executive M.B.A. program is designed for individuals with at least seven years of managerial experience. Approximately 100 students are currently enrolled in this program, with classes that meet every other weekend for two years.

Students and the M.B.A. Experience

The M.B.A. in International Management welcomes nearly 50 percent of its students from outside the United States. I.M.B.A. students represent six continents and more than nineteen countries including Argentina, Bolivia, Brazil, China, Germany, Greece, Indonesia, Japan, Peru, Russia, Thailand, and Turkey. Of the more than 100 students enrolled in the program, approximately three fourths have prior work experience, one fourth are women, and one half are enrolled full-time.

❖ Global Focus

Students really learn from each other at Baldwin-Wallace. As they are put into mixed groups, they explore differing logic patterns and approaches to solving problems from their various countries. The Internet is used to link students from several countries. Working together and communicating by computer network, this diverse group analyzes all phases of an actual multinational company. Through

this project, students gain a better understanding of the business, communication, and organizational skills needed to work with international teams.

Special Features

A series of faculty-led management study tours is available to students in the M.B.A. programs. Past tours have visited China, Japan, Nicaragua, and Thailand.

There is an American Language Academy (ALA) program on the Baldwin-Wallace campus. ALA offers English as a foreign language preparation designed specifically for I.M.B.A. applicants and candidates. Many I.M.B.A. students successfully meet the TOEFL requirement while studying at the ALA. In addition, these students receive an orientation to academic life at Baldwin-Wallace as well as to the facilities and resources of the I.M.B.A. program.

The Faculty

Committed to teaching rather than research, the full-time and adjunct faculty share the College's commitment to "Quality Education with a Personal Touch." The faculty members bring a unique combination of educational and professional experiences to their teaching responsibilities. Within the student-centered, teaching-oriented environment, education is the number one priority.

The Business School Network

Through on-site and in-class projects, business partnerships enable students to put their knowledge to work. Field studies, internships, and supervised in-company research projects place students in regional businesses where they work with corporate leaders to identify problems and develop solutions.

The College and Environs

Baldwin-Wallace is a liberal arts college, founded in 1845. The campus features forty buildings on 56 tree-shaded acres. The College serves approximately 5,300 students, of whom 4,800 are undergraduate students and 575 are graduate students.

Gerald Anderson, Ph.D., Indiana; Economist, Federal Reserve Bank of Cleveland. Economics.

Eugene Beem, Ph.D., Pennsylvania. Managerial ethics.

Harry Bury, Ph.D., Case Western Reserve. Management.

Yu Da, Ph.D., Connecticut. Strategic management.

Pierre David, Ph.D., Kent State. International marketing.

Robert Ebert, Buckhorn Professor of Economics; Ph.D., Case Western Reserve.

Ronald Ehresman, M.S., Case Tech. Management information systems and finance.

Douglas Fryett, M.B.A., Northland Open. Marketing.

Tony Khuri, Ph.D., Case Western Reserve. Management.

David Krueger, Spahr Professor of Managerial Ethics; Ph.D., Chicago.

Judy Krutky, Ph.D., Columbia. Managerial ethics and political science.

James McInerney, M.B.A., Case Western Reserve. International finance.

Dennis Miller, Ph.D., Colorado. Economics.

Earl Peck, Ph.D., Colorado. International finance.

Lee Pickler, D.B.A., Nova. Management.

Peter Rea, Ph.D., Akron. Marketing.

Timothy Riggle, Ph.D., Ohio State. Mathematics and computer science.

Malcolm Watson, Director, American Language Academy; M.A., Emory. Intercultural communications.

Ivan Winfield, B.B.A., Pittsburgh. Management.

The campus is located in Berea, a picturesque suburban area 14 miles southwest of Cleveland. It is easily accessible from Cleveland Hopkins International Airport (2 miles) and from interstate highways I-71, I-80, and I-480.

Many cultural and recreational activities are held on the Baldwin-Wallace College campus. Students can attend athletic events, concerts, theater productions, movies, and lectures by speakers who come from throughout the United States to address a variety of topics. For most events, admission is free.

Cleveland is the headquarters city for eighty-three major corporations with annual sales exceeding $100 million, a concentration larger than that of Los Angeles, Boston, or Atlanta. Cleveland is also the twelfth-largest consumer market, the eighth-largest industrial market, and the twelfth-largest retail market in the United States.

The Cleveland area offers a range of cultural, recreational, and entertainment opportunities. Outstanding museums and galleries, professional sports events, exciting nightlife, and a citywide park system are a short distance from campus.

Placement

The College Office of Career Services works aggressively to help students with career placement, career counseling and planning, resume referral to employers, and resume preparation. The Office of Career Services also has a career library and sponsors career fairs.

Admission

Required for admission into the I.M.B.A. program are a bachelor's degree from an accredited institution, two letters of recommendation, a resume, and a satisfactory score on the Graduate Management Admission Test (GMAT). The average GMAT score for entering students is 485.

For students whose native language is not English, a minimum of 500 is required on the Test of English as a Foreign Language (TOEFL). Applicants who have not taken the TOEFL or those with TOEFL scores of less than 500 are eligible for conditional acceptance. Course work in Business English as a Second Language is required of students with a TOEFL score less than 523. International students must present proof of adequate funds to cover the cost of study.

Finances

Tuition for 2000–01 is $1665 for each of the program's twelve courses and $555 for each seminar elective course. In addition to the tuition, a book cost of approximately $85 per course is to be expected.

Off-campus housing is available in the immediate area. The Office of Residential Life maintains a list of off-campus rooms, apartments, and houses that may be rented by students. Apartment rents start at $400 per month. An on-campus board plan is offered at approximately $800 per quarter. On-campus housing is available to graduate students.

Application Facts and Dates

Students may begin the I.M.B.A. program at three times throughout the year: August, January, and May. Students should apply well ahead of the desired starting date, as it takes approximately three months to complete the application process. For more information, students should contact:

International M.B.A. Programs
275 Eastland Road
Berea, Ohio 44017-2088
Telephone: 440-826-2196
Fax: 440-826-3868
E-mail: pshepard@bw.edu
World Wide Web: http://www.bw.edu

Baylor University

Waco, Texas

DISCOVER THE OPPORTUNITIES

Immerse yourself in hands-on applications of classroom theory through direct interaction with an actively functioning company. Each semester, one publicly held company serves as the "focus firm," and its core issues become the center-piece for the M.B.A. curriculum. At the conclusion of sixteen months in Baylor's M.B.A. program, you will have experienced complex issues facing three different focus firms.

Come see for yourself. The best way to learn about Baylor's graduate business programs is to visit our campus, tour the facilities, and sit in on classes. Meet current students and see how you can join the Baylor graduates who are emerging as tomorrow's business leaders.

—Linda Livingstone, Associate Dean for Graduate Programs

Programs and Curricular Focus

The Hankamer School of Business at Baylor offers a variety of graduate degrees designed to meet different career goals. These are the Master of Business Administration (M.B.A.), Master of Business Administration in International Management (M.B.A.-I.M.), Master of Business Administration in Information Systems (M.B.A.-I.S.M.), Master of Science in Information Systems (M.S.I.S.), Master of Taxation (M.Tax.), Master of Accountancy (M.Acc.), and Master of Science in Economics (M.S.Eco.). Two additional degrees offered in cooperation with Baylor School of Law are the Doctor of Jurisprudence/ Master of Business Administration (J.D./M.B.A.) and the Doctor of Jurisprudence/Master of Taxation (J.D./M.Tax.). Baylor also offers a joint degree in business and information systems, the Master of Business Administration/Master of Science in Information Systems (M.B.A./M.S.I.S.).

The M.B.A. is an integrative learning experience in which students solve real-world business problems from several perspectives at once—just as they will on the job. The full-time program requires students to move through the semesters as a unit, creating a team approach to learning and camaraderie among class members. Each semester, one publicly held company volunteers to serve as the M.B.A. "focus firm." The focus firm study teaches students to work cooperatively in teams, resolve conflicts, foster personal relationships, and hone communication skills—all competencies

cited by managers as critical in today's workplace. In addition to the focus firm, corporate executives frequently serve as guest speakers on campus. Professors also arrange on-site visits with many Texas firms in which students apply principles learned in the classroom.

Students and the M.B.A. Experience

Each year, the Hankamer School of Business attracts hundreds of talented graduate students who want to discover the opportunities of graduate education. Their origins are diverse—from back-

grounds in business, engineering, and music and from a variety of states and countries—and at Baylor they come together in a team-centered learning environment. What they find is a high level of excellence and a commitment to high-quality graduate education. Most students complete the Baylor M.B.A. in sixteen to twenty-one months. Students with an undergraduate degree in business can enter the M.B.A. program directly. For those without a business background, there is a unique, one-semester Integrated Management Seminar that satisfies all business prerequisites.

Distance learning and videoconferencing are integral parts of classroom activities. Videoconferencing sessions with corporate executives are held each semester in conjunction with the "focus firm" project. In addition, many classrooms are equipped with the latest innovations in multimedia presentation devices.

The Faculty

As nationally recognized faculty members, Baylor professors are highly motivated and committed to the learning experience of their students. They encourage active discussions and debate both in and out of the classroom. Students evaluate the expertise and accessibility of faculty members as one of the strengths of the Baylor M.B.A. program. Core classes are intentionally limited to an average of 25 students, while electives average approximately 10 students, allowing for a more personalized teaching environment. All graduate courses are taught by faculty members who hold doctoral degrees. Baylor faculty members are well published, serve on corporate advisory boards, and hold leadership positions in professional organizations in order to maintain active ties with the business community.

The College and Environs

Founded in 1845, Baylor University is Texas's oldest institution of higher learning in continuous existence since its founding. The 432-acre campus is located on the banks of the Brazos River in Waco, Texas, a metropolitan area of

200,000 people. Baylor is located just 90 miles south of Dallas, 90 miles north of Austin, and less than 200 miles from Houston and San Antonio. The enrollment at Baylor is slightly less than 13,000 students, of whom approximately 1,700 are graduate students. Enrollment for graduate business programs is limited to approximately 200 students.

Facilities

To advance the separate identity of the graduate business programs, a specific area of the business school's facilities has been converted into a Graduate Center. It houses core faculty offices, graduate administration offices, and a graduate student study area. The Central Libraries, Special Libraries, and Resource Centers of Baylor house more than 1.5 million bound volumes, more than 2 million microforms and government document pieces, and thousands of audiovisual items, maps, charts, and photographs. Information is stored on microfilm, microfiche, CD-ROM, computer disks, videotape, compact discs, and cassette tapes in addition to traditional print books and journals. Students take advantage of the online catalog *Bear Cat* to search and view the libraries' vast holdings.

Technology Environment

The Casey Computer Center contains more than ninety-six IBM computers as well as scanning equipment and color printers. Graduate students have free access to the Internet and e-mail service. Baylor was recently named the twenty-

second "best wired" school by *Yahoo! Internet Life*. All M.B.A. students are required to purchase a laptop computer designated by the School through the fixed-rate expense plan.

Placement

A special resource to currently enrolled students and alumni, Baylor's Career Services Center assists students in formulating and implementing career planning techniques, providing career resource and job listings, and directing resumes to interested companies. The Associate Director of MBA Careers coordinates on- and off-campus interviews with some of the nation's largest firms, government agencies, and other organizations. Within three months of graduation, 98 percent of Baylor M.B.A. graduates are employed. Graduates are routinely sought by larger firms in the Southwest region of the United States. The most graduating class averaged $51,000 in starting salaries.

Admission

Admission is based on an applicant's professional experience, successful academic history, GMAT scores, resume, essays, letters of recommendation, and, for international students, TOEFL scores. For 1999–2000, average GMAT scores were 601 and the average GPA was 3.2 (on a 4.0 scale). For international students, TOEFL scores must be at least 600. Professional work experience is strongly encouraged. Interviews are strongly recommended for all applicants.

Finances

One of the most affordable private institutions in the country, Baylor offers a fixed-rate expense plan for the M.B.A., M.B.A./M.S.I.S., and M.S.I.S. programs. The rate for the M.B.A. program is $26,809. The M.B.A./M.S.I.S. program is $34,800. The M.S.I.S. program is $19,065. The IMS semester is priced separately by the semster hour. Tuition in 2000–01 is $355 per semester hour. Graduate assistantships and fellowships are available on a competitive basis. For more information on these opportunities, students should contact the Graduate Business Office at 254-710-3718. For questions regarding financial aid, students can contact the Student Financial Aid Office at 254-710-2611.

International Students

International students from countries such as the Czech Republic, China, India, Russia, Mexico, Canada, and Pakistan make up about 24 percent of the enrollment in Baylor graduate business programs. International students provide a global perspective, representing a unique component to the programs. For additional questions regarding visa and immigration requirements, students can contact the International Programs Office at 254-710-1461.

Application Facts and Dates

The deadline for applications for admission for fall entrance is July 1; for spring entrance, November 1; and for summer entrance, April 1. Applications are processed on a rolling basis. For international students to be considered for the highly competitive graduate assistantships, they should observe the following application deadlines: for consideration for fall entry, April 1; for spring entry, September 1; and for summer entry, February 1. For more information, students should contact:

Laurie Wilson, Director of Graduate Admissions
Hankamer School of Business
Baylor University
P.O. Box 98013
Waco, Texas 76798-8013
Telephone: 254-710-3718
            800-583-0622 (toll-free)
Fax: 254-710-1066
E-mail: mba@hsb.baylor.edu
World Wide Web: http://hsb.baylor.edu/mba

Bellevue University

Bellevue, Nebraska

ONLINE EDUCATION FOR AN ONLINE WORLD

Our mission is to inspire, enable, and actively engage learners to pursue a high-quality business education, which is critical to succeed in modern business and society. To this end, the College of Business faculty members use active learning that is manifested in team activities, role playing, computer simulations, case analyses, presentations, readings in the current literature, and other activities that require the student to think critically and exchange ideas with other members of the class.

The curriculum stresses performance and application, i.e., students learn to apply business concepts, standards, and information systems to work activities in the community.

—Douglas A. Frost, Ph.D., Dean

Programs and Curricular Focus

The Master of Business Administration (M.B.A.) program, both on-site and online, covers the tools and methods required to run a business. The program requires 36 credit hours of course work. The schedule of course offerings permits an individual working full-time to complete all the requirements for the M.B.A. degree in eighteen months with two classes per term.

Students who do not have an undergraduate degree in business generally take the Foundation (12 credit hours) and the Core (24 credit hours) to complete the degree. Foundation courses include business processes and functions, statistics and methods, accounting and information systems, and the environment of business. Core courses include quantitative methods, financial strategy, applied production and management, advanced organizational behavior, advanced organization and theory, managerial accounting and systems, and marketing strategy. Students with an undergraduate degree in business normally have met all or most of the Foundation requirements and take the Core (24 credit hours) and a concentration of 12 credit hours instead of the Foundation. Concentrations in accounting, cyber law, finance, international management, and management information systems (MIS) are available.

Students and the M.B.A. Experience

Bellevue University serves more than 3,000 students, and its diverse student body includes students from forty countries. Since the majority of students are adult learners, they are invited to bring their work experiences to the classroom. As a result, class members learn about current business practices and problems from each other and gain a better understanding of how principles are applied in both profit and nonprofit environments.

The University is strongly committed to the life and career success of its students, particularly working students who seek advancement by acquiring broader and deeper knowledge, new skills, and academic credentials. A supportive learning environment emphasizes principles of active learning that expose students to both theoretical knowledge and practical application. Traditional teacher-to-learner lectures are replaced by active involvement in the learning using applied workplace projects, library and database research, and supplementary multimedia and through interaction with teachers and other students.

Special Features

The M.B.A. program offers in-class or online options. It has no prerequisite course work, regardless of the student's undergraduate degree, and can be completed in eighteen months. Concentrations in cyber law, MIS, accounting, international business, and finance are available.

The concentration in accounting may fulfill the educational requirements to sit for the CPA exam and for professionals to earn continuing professional education hours. Most states require 150 credit hours to sit for the exam, in addition to the completion of accounting and business courses, which may be met via online courses.

Through Access Plus, it is possible for international students to be admitted directly into the M.B.A. program.

The Faculty

The professors provide fundamental knowledge, practical applications, and a supportive environment that facilitates the learning process. Fifty percent of the faculty members are women, and most faculty members hold terminal degrees.

The Business School Network

Local business leaders help advise the Dean and faculty members on the curriculum and content in the M.B.A. program. Progressive companies recognize the need for employees with a technological aptitude and vision for change. Bellevue University forges strategic alliances for educational and

FACULTY LIST

Douglas A. Frost, Dean; Ph.D.
Linda T. Thomas, Associate Dean; Ph.D.
Pamela Dinville, Chair, M.B.A., CPA, CMA. Accounting.
Monica McElhaney, M.B.A., M.S.M.I.S., CPA, CMA. Accounting.
Cynthia Nye, M.S., CPA, CMA. Accounting.
Douglas L. Brown, D.B.A. Business.
Anthony J. Clarke, Ph.D. candidate. Business.
Steven L. Farner Jr., Ph.D. Business.
Paul Poppler, Ph.D. Business.
Kevin S. Schieuer, Ph.D. Business.
Jena Shafai-Asgarpoor, Ph.D. Business.
Linda T. Thomas, Ph.D. Business.
Raymond A. Carpenter, Ph.D., CCP, CSI. Computer information systems.
Danny J. Creagan, M.S., CNE, MCSE, MCP. Computer information systems.
Susan A. McDaniel, M.S., CNA, MCP. Computer information systems.
Melony Sue Sampson, M.S., CNA. Computer information systems.
Tessa K. White, M.S. Computer information systems.

Bellevue University.

management development with corporate partners, extending its reach with regional and national partnerships, including Lucent Technologies, Boys Town, Army Corps of Engineers, and First National Bank. Internationally, partnerships extend to Thailand, India, and the United Arab Emirates.

The College and Environs

Since 1966, when 409 students began classes in a single campus building, Bellevue University has catered to the nontraditional student by providing both day and evening class schedules and services. The University offers classes and degree programs at several locations in Nebraska and Iowa as well as online.

Bellevue, the state's oldest city, shares its borders with Omaha, the Missouri River, and Offutt Air Force Base. Bellevue is proud of its small-town atmosphere in the state of Nebraska. In addition to its deep-rooted Western heritage, Nebraska also features top-rated attractions, including a world-class zoo and the College World Series.

Facilities

The University strives to provide a high-quality physical learning environment for its students. The Lozier Professional Center, located in northwestern Omaha, was completed in 1998, and most facilities on the main Bellevue campus are new or have been renovated since 1986. Plans call for major renova-

tions of the library, humanities center, gymnasium, and learning center within the next three years.

The library is the primary center for support of academic research and information services. The University library is technologically advanced, with numerous electronic services. Qualified staff members are available to assist students with research and information retrieval.

The collection is available via the Internet through any of the library's workstations and any personal computer. WEBCat, the Bellevue University online library catalog, provides access to all resources held in the Bellevue University Library plus nine other Nebraska libraries.

Placement

Career counseling, job search programs, and numerous resources help students develop and achieve their career goals. Career Service assists in arranging internship opportunities and with job placement for current students and graduates. Students seeking full-time or part-time employment while completing their education find numerous resources and materials to assist with their job searches. Up-to-date job listings, general employment information, and files containing specific company information on many employers are available. Books, periodicals, and handouts address such topics as resumes and cover letters, interviewing, salary negotiations, using the Internet, and other strategies for conducting a successful job search.

Students may complete their M.B.A. online or on campus.

Admission

All students are required to submit an application for admission and a nonrefundable application fee. Candidates must possess an undergraduate degree from a regionally accredited college or university or a U.S. equivalent degree from a nationally or internationally accredited college or university. A GPA of 2.5 or better for the most recent 60 credits of undergraduate course work and a cumulative GPA of 3.0 or better for prior graduate work are required. Applicants must also submit two letters of professional or academic recommendation and essays in response to life experience summary questions.

Finances

On-site tuition is $260 per semester credit hour and online tuition is $280 per semester credit hour. There are a nonrefundable application fee of $50, a general College fee of $35 per term, and a graduation fee of $75.

Financial aid is available from the federal and state government and institutional and private sources, including grants, scholarships, work-study programs, and student loans. Grants and scholarships do not have to be repaid. Student loans must be repaid.

International Students

International students have the same admission requirements as U.S. students. In addition, an Affidavit of Support form with supporting documentation is required. TOEFL results are required for graduate admission, except from English-speaking countries. Access Plus and ESL programs provide international students with a multilevel English language skills and acquisition program.

Application Facts and Dates

Bellevue University has a policy of rolling admission, with students admitted on a space-available basis. Notification of acceptance or rejection is made in writing. For more information, applicants should contact:

Director of Graduate Admissions
Bellevue University
1000 Galvin Road South
Bellevue, Nebraska 68005
Telephone: 402-293-2057
Fax: 402-293-3730
E-mail: bellevue-g@scholars.bellevue. edu
World Wide Web: http://www. bellevue.edu/MBA

Bentley College

McCallum Graduate School of Business

Waltham, Massachusetts

BUSINESS SCHOOL FOR THE INFORMATION AGE

Bentley's innovative approach to business education recognizes that the practice of business in the next century will be predicated upon new principles and behaviors. No longer will expertise in traditional disciplines of finance, management, operations, or marketing be enough. Individuals prepared for the practice of business will have to be knowledgeable of concepts of business process and change management, cyberlaw and e-business, information-age marketing, and global financial analysis. Bentley has successfully taken technology and elevated it from being a tool of business to a foundational property for the conduct of business.

The Information Age, Self-Paced, and One-Year M.B.A. programs, with Thirteen areas of concentration, and nine highly focused Master of Science degrees in business integrate technology as a core requirement for business success.

Bentley is committed to providing the most advanced business education possible.

—Patricia M. Flynn, Dean

Programs and Curricular Focus

Strategically designed to prepare managers for the challenges in the global information age marketplace, Bentley's M.B.A. program integrates information technology with core business fundamentals, creating the most advanced business education possible. The McCallum Graduate School offers the Information Age M.B.A. (a unique 2-year program, the Self-Paced M.B.A. (a flexible part time program with courses that may be taken on a full-time basis) and the One-Year M.B.A. (a fast track program for those awarded full advanced standing credit in nine common body of knowledge courses).

The Information Age M.B.A. program is an intensive, two-year program that gives students an integrated understanding of the business organization. It focuses on building competitive advantage by designing effective business processes and adopting a customer orientation. Key business concepts such as accounting, economics, finance, information technology, marketing, management, and operations are interrelated and build upon each other in a multiperspective format. Elective courses, internships, and field-based learning experiences allow students to customize the program to meet their individual interests and career goals. Second-year electives can be used to create a concentration (such as accounting, change management,

corporate finance, e-business, global financial analysis, management information systems, information age marketing, or to explore different areas of business.

The Self-Paced M.B.A. provides the flexibility and choice that allows each student to create a program that best complements his or her academic background and career interests. The One-Year M.B.A. is designed for those with an undergraduate degree in business. With full advanced standing credit, the program is completed in one year of full-time study. The M.B.A. program allows students to specialize their broad-based management degree by selecting a concentration in one of thirteen areas: accounting systems, business data analysis, business economics, business ethics, change management, e-business, entrepreneurial studies, finance, information-age marketing, international business, management, management information systems, and management of operations and technology. Depth is added to the M.B.A. curriculum by shared electives from Bentley's nine business specialty programs, which include Master of Science degrees in accountancy, accounting information systems, computer information systems, corporate finance, global financial analysis, human factors in information design, personal financial planning, and taxation.

Students and the M.B.A. Experience

Bentley, one of the largest graduate schools of business in New England, brings together approximately 1,500 students representing fifty-four countries. This includes 200 full-time and 1,300 part-time students; 45 percent are women. While work experience is preferred, students with no prior work experience may apply.

❖ Global Focus

A focus on the global economy permeates the Bentley curriculum. Specific subjects and courses that explore international themes in all graduate programs are offered. Students interested in studying abroad can enroll in seven- to ten-day study tour courses to countries that include Australia, Austria, China, Estonia, France, Japan, and the Netherlands. Intermediate business language courses are offered in French, Spanish, and Italian.

The McCallum Graduate School's international perspective is enhanced through collaboration agreements with Groupe ESC Clermont in Clermont, France, and with Export Akademie Baden-Wurtemberg in Reutingen, Germany.

The Faculty

Experience, expertise, and accessibility are the trademarks of Bentley's faculty. Dedicated teaching professionals highly regarded in their respective fields, they are available to students and bring the most current and critical concepts and experiences to the classroom. Consulting keeps them current with business trends and technological advances. As a result, curriculum and course content remain up-to-date and oriented in the real world.

The Business School Network

The business community supports both curriculum design and student networking at Bentley. The Graduate School Advisory Council and MBA Advisory Board, made up of key executives from the Boston area's multinational, national, and regional firms, provides ongoing corporate input for program development. Bentley brings a real-world approach to the educational process through activities that promote interaction among graduate students and business professionals. Students can connect with guest speakers who participate in the Graduate School's Executive Speaker Series, INSIGHTS From Successful Business Women, and events sponsored by student organizations. In addition, Bentley's popular Mentor Program pairs students with business professionals, who serve as resources on job-related issues and concerns.

Through the Alumni Career Exploration (ACE) Network, more than 1,000 alumni are available to meet with students to discuss their career development, share information about work experience, assist with interviewing skills, and connect students with other corporate resource people.

The College and Environs

Founded in 1917, the College is an independent, coeducational institution recognized internationally for its excellence in professional business education. In addition to the students at the Graduate School, more than 3,000 undergraduates are enrolled in business and liberal arts. Bentley is accredited by AACSB–The International Association for Management Education and regionally accredited by the New England Association of Schools and Colleges (NEASC).

Located in Waltham, Massachusetts, in the heart of the region's high-technology sector, the 143-acre suburban campus is minutes from Boston's business, financial, and cultural resources; 30 minutes from Logan International Airport; and a 3-hour drive from New York City.

Facilities

The library houses more than 200,000 volumes, receives more than 1,700 periodicals, and has 155,000 microform titles. Study rooms, computer terminals, and various databases (e.g., LEXIS-NEXIS, Dow Jones News Retrieval Service, and InfoTrac) are available for student use. The media services department provides television facilities, conferencing telephones, video conferencing, and recordings for both instruction and group-work support.

Bentley has a limited number of furnished one- and two-bedroom apartments and single dormitory rooms that are equipped with a personal computer connection to the campus network. Interested applicants should request a housing application.

The Dana Physical Education Center houses an Olympic-size swimming pool, exercise rooms, an indoor track, basketball courts, racquetball courts, and a dance studio.

Technology Environment

Bentley is committed to continually upgrading its technological resources to ensure that graduate students understand how business processes can be enhanced through the strategic application of information technology. It is one of only a handful of academic institutions in the nation to have an on-site financial Trading Room. The multimillion-dollar facility simulates actual stock exchange experience and serves as a practical vehicle for learning across a range of academic disciplines. The Center for Marketing Technologies is a one-of-a-kind educational and research facility that features a wide range of technological tools for marketing in an online world.

The integration of business and technology further supports graduate student study through the school's Graduate Computer Learning Center, CE Lab, on- and off-campus access to individual accounts, e-mail, and various sophisticated database systems that are used for research. Communication and group interaction are enhanced by the use of videoconferencing, course Web sites, faculty and student home pages, and group work.

Placement

The Nathan R. Miller Office of Career Services assists students with networking and provides an impressive array of career planning resources. Workshops help students obtain information, refine job search strategies, develop effective personal marketing materials, and prepare for employment interviews. More than 200 local, national, and international employers visit the campus annually to recruit graduate students. Ninety-seven percent of all 1999 graduates had jobs within six months after commencement.

Admission

Students in the Information Age M.B.A. program begin in September and move through their two-year program together. Students in the M.S. and Self-Paced and One-Year M.B.A. programs begin their studies in the fall, spring, or summer terms.

Applicants should submit a completed application form, a $50 application fee, official transcripts of all academic work beyond high school, GMAT scores, and

two letters of recommendation. An evaluative interview and updated resume are required for Information Age M.B.A. applicants.

Finances

The 2000-2001 academic-year tuition is $2240 per 3-credit course. Tuition for the Information Age M.B.A. is $23,000 per year. Books, supplies, health insurance, living expenses, and personal expenses for a nine-month academic year are approximately $12,551. Summer living expenses are approximately $3800. Costs are subject to change.

Graduate Assistantships (GA) are available for highly qualified applicants and consist of a partial tuition waiver and possibly a stipend in exchange for work as a research assistant.

International Students

Bentley supports international students through a seminar series on the academic, cultural, and social aspects of the U.S. graduate school experience. Individual tutoring in language skills is available. In addition, the Joseph M. Cronin International Center has a full-time information student adviser and staff to meet the social and academic needs of international students. The Nathan R. Miller Office of Career Services also conducts seminars on immigration regulations and U.S. employment and labor certification and provides information on overseas job postings.

Application Facts and Dates

For fall start in September, the preferred deadline for Information Age M.B.A. applicants, GA applicants, international candidates, or those wishing an early decision to ensure options for housing and financial assistance is March 1; the regular application deadline is June 1. For spring start in January, the preferred deadline for GA applicants, international candidates, or those wishing an early decision is October 1; the regular application deadline is November 1. For summer start in May, the regular application deadline is March 1.

For more information, applicants should make inquiries to:

McCallum Graduate School of
  Business
Bentley College
175 Forest Street
Waltham, Massachusetts 02452-4705
Telephone: 781-891-2108
Fax: 781-891-2464
World Wide Web: http://www.bentley.
  edu/graduate

Baruch College of the City University of New York

Zicklin School of Business

New York, New York

> ### AN M.B.A. IN A GLOBAL ENVIRONMENT
>
> *Baruch College is proud of its place in New York City, the world's most dynamic financial and cultural center. We are uniquely positioned to provide students with an excellent education at a very reasonable cost in a global environment. Our outstanding faculty, flexible full- and part-time programs, and convenient location offer students unequaled access to opportunities for both learning and professional advancement.*
>
> —Sidney Lirtzman, Interim President

Programs and Curricular Focus

Zicklin's premier program is the Full-Time M.B.A., a very selective honors format that evolved from the successful Jack Nash Honors M.B.A. program. The M.B.A. is also offered in the FlexTime format for full- or part-time students who need a wider range of options in scheduling their graduate study. Eighteen courses (54 credits) are required. The nine-course core curriculum is designed to provide students with an understanding of the basic principles of both management and the environment in which managerial decisions are made. Courses include accountancy, economics, finance, behavioral sciences, quantitative methods, information systems, production, and marketing.

Supplementing the core are 9 credits of elective courses, including one international elective, one quantitative elective, and one general elective. Beyond the core, students can specialize in accountancy, computer information systems, economics, entrepreneurship, finance and investments, health-care administration, industrial/organizational psychology, international business, management, marketing, operations research, statistics, or taxation.

Those who wish to design their own M.B.A. programs can select unique, cross-disciplinary combinations of courses to fulfill the 18-credit specialization requirement. These combinations are useful for students interested in careers in such fields as marketing in financial institutions or banking operations. A few examples of the many specialization courses available to students are Futures and Forwards Markets, Options Markets, Mergers and Acquisitions, International Trade and Investment Law, International Commodity Trading,

International Corporate Finance, Computer Simulation for Solving Business Problems, Product Planning and Development, and Entrepreneurial Ventures. The Zicklin School also offers a strategic management Executive M.B.A. program as well as an Executive M.S. in finance.

Students and the M.B.A. Experience

Baruch's reputation for excellence extends to all parts of the world, attracting students from New York, neighboring states, and abroad. The cohort-style M.B.A. program offers students the option of full-time or part-time study. Full-time students complete the degree program in two years, part-time students average four. The diverse group of men and women doing graduate work at Baruch hold undergraduate degrees from more than 200 colleges and universities. There are more than 400 international graduate students, who represent approximately fifty countries.

The average graduate student is 28 years old. Although students generally have an average of five years of work experience, applicants with little or no work experience are occasionally admitted. Many M.B.A. students at Baruch have undergraduate degrees in business, but the majority have majored in the liberal arts, the sciences, or engineering. Professional experience varies widely. Forty percent of the students are women, while members of minority groups represent almost 30 percent of the student body. International students make up 50 percent of the full-time M.B.A. student population.

The Faculty

The faculty at Baruch is top-notch, with strong academic credentials and ties to New York's business and financial communities. All share a commitment to teaching. Baruch's retired Harry Markowitz held the Marvin M. Speiser Professorship when he earned the Nobel Prize in Economics in 1990. Other faculty members recognized for outstanding honors include Robert Schwartz, University Distinguished Professor of Finance, an expert on market microstructures; Prakash Sethi, University Distinguished Professor of Management, an expert on business ethics and corporate policy; E. S. Savas, an expert on privatization of public enterprises; and Yoshihiro Tsurumi, an authority on cultural and economic relations between the United States and Japan.

The Business School Network

Prominent Alumni

The Baruch degree is highly valued. Graduates may be found at all levels in business, industry, and public life. Notable graduates include Laura Altschuler, President, New York City League of Women Voters; the Honorable Abraham D. Beame, former Mayor of the City of New York; Lawrence Zicklin, Chairman of the Board, Neuberger Berman Inc.; Matthew Blank, Chairman of the Board and CEO, Showtime Networks; Irving Schneider, Vice Chairman, Helmsley Spear; and Sally Guido, CEO, Lee Myles.

The College and Environs

With a prime location in Manhattan's historic Gramercy Park neighborhood and the leading-edge Flatiron District, Baruch is at the heart of one of the world's most dymanic business and cultural centers—within easy reach of Wall Street, the World Trade Center, "Silicon Alley", and the headquarters of major business and financial firms and nonprofit organizations. This real-world environment adds immeasurably to the value of a Baruch education and offers unparalled internship and career opportunities. The campus extends from East 18th Street to East

One of Baruch College's main buildings, located in the center of activity at 23rd Street and Lexington Avenue in Manhattan.

26th Street and is surrounded by a variety of ethnic restaurants and stores of all kinds. All of New York City's museums, theaters, concert halls, clubs, sports arenas, and beaches are easily accessible by public transportation.

The College is currently building a seventeen-story academic complex that will become the home for the Zicklin School in 2001. The award-winning design will enclose modern, multimedia-equipped classrooms; all faculty members' offices; two large production-level theaters; a fitness center with a gym and a swimming pool; a television studio; and an enhanced Center for Student Life.

Technology Environment

In addition to the seven other buildings comprising Baruch's campus, the Information and Technology Building opened on East 25th Street in 1994. This completely renovated 1890s classic houses The William and Anita Newman Library, the Baruch Computing and Technology Center (which includes 400 computer workstations in an open-access lab), student and administrative offices, and a state-of-the-art multimedia center.

More than three times the size of its predecessor, the 1,450-seat library has local area networks that provide access to a wide variety of electronic information resources. Students and faculty members can access the Internet and hundreds of online databases through the Dow Jones News/Retrieval, LEXIS-NEXIS, and Dialog services, in addition to its traditional holdings. The Baruch community also has access to the 4.5 million

volumes in the CUNY library system and to the collections of the New York Public Library.

Baruch recently opened the Subotnick Financial Services Center/Bert W. and Sandra Wasserman Trading Floor, a unique educational facility for students and the financial community that features a fully-equipped simulated trading environment with continuous live data feeds by Reuters, integrating financial services practice into the M.B.A. curriculum.

Placement

A core curriculum of workshops is offered to all students and covers topics such as job search strategies, resume writing, interviewing techniques, networking strategies, and job search correspondence. Individual career counseling and consultation are also available. On-campus recruiting is held in the fall and spring semesters, and career fairs are held throughout the year. Students have unlimited access to the various full-time and internship position openings that are posted in the office on a daily basis. Special events, such as career seminars, company information sessions, and other networking opportunities, are also held throughout the year.

Admission

Applicants for any M.B.A. program must take the Graduate Management Admission Test (GMAT). The average student entering the program in 1999–2000 had a GMAT score of 585 and an undergraduate grade point average of 3.2. For the honors Full-Time M.B.A. program, the GMAT is 650 and the GPA is 3.4. International students whose native language is not English must take the Test of English as a Foreign Language (TOEFL) and the Test of Written English (TWE). In addition to test scores, applicants must submit application forms, an essay, a resume, official transcripts from every college or university attended, two letters of recommendation, and a nonrefundable application fee of $40.

Finances

Tuition for New York State residents in 2000–01 is $2175 per semester for full-time and $185 per credit for part-time study. For out-of-state residents and international students, tuition is $3800 for full-time and $320 per credit for part-time study. Tuition and fees are subject to change without notice. Average estimated annual cost for books, supplies, transportation, and personal expenses is $12,000 per year.

Financial aid is available and is merit based. Nash Tuition Scholarships of $2000 to $5000 per year are awarded to

20 to 25 of the most qualified students in the Full-Time M.B.A. (honors) program. Graduate assistantships require 15 hours of work for a faculty member or administrative area each week for a $5000 annual stipend. They are awarded primarily to honors students and do not include a tuition waiver. International students are eligible for both Nash Scholarships and graduate assistantships.

In the fall, the Mitsui USA Foundation awards two annual scholarships of $5000 each to newly admitted full-time students pursuing an M.B.A. degree in international business. Applicants for the Mitsui Scholarships must be United States citizens or permanent residents. The Carl Spielvogel Scholarship offers an annual award of $5000 in the fall to newly admitted full-time students pursuing an M.B.A. degree in international marketing.

Financial aid is also available to graduate students through other sources, including various state, federal, and College programs, although international students are not eligible for most of these programs.

Application Facts and Dates

Application deadlines for fall admission are February 28 for Full-Time M.B.A. students (honors program, fall entry only), domestic students, and international students; April 30 for full- or part-time international FlexTime students; and May 31 for domestic students. For spring, the deadlines are October 31 for international students and November 30 for domestic students. Applicants are encouraged to submit their applications as early as possible, particularly if they wish to be considered for a graduate research assistantship or scholarship.

To request application materials, applicants should contact:

Office of Graduate Admissions
Baruch College of the City
   University of New York
17 Lexington Avenue, Box H-0880
New York, New York 10010-5518
Telephone: 212-802-2330
Fax: 212-802-2335
E-mail: graduate_admissions@baruch. cuny.edu
World Wide Web: http://www.zicklin. baruch.cuny.edu

For Executive Programs information, applicants should contact:
Zicklin School Executive Programs
Baruch College of the City
   University of New York
17 Lexington Avenue, Box F-1215
New York, New York 10010-5518
Telephone: 212-802-6700
Fax: 212-802-6705
E-mail: exprog_bus@baruch.cuny.edu
World Wide Web: http://www.zicklin. baruch.cuny.edu

bSu Boise State University

Boise, Idaho

ON THE ROAD TO KNOWLEDGE AND CHANGE

Our program's goal is to equip you, our future leaders, with the skills necessary to manage in the present environment and the learning skills needed to respond to change.

Through the tremendous support of our business advisory council, our program is able to achieve a high level of quality and to provide excellent opportunities for our M.B.A. candidates to interact with businesses as part of their educational experience.

Boise State University is surrounded by an exciting city that offers a variety of social, educational, cultural, and recreational opportunities. This setting will encourage you to discover more about yourself and the world around you.

When you come to Boise State, I can promise you a demanding and academically intellectual environment along with an enjoyable social environment. At Boise State University, you will find traditions of pride, determination, and, above all, academic excellence. It is a road full of challenge, new knowledge, and great change.

—William C. Lathen, Dean

Program and Curricular Focus

The Master of Business Administration degree program at Boise State University is designed to prepare future business leaders to handle the challenges of change in a global economy. Emphasizing the needs of fully employed students, the program strives to provide students with a thorough grounding in each of the functional business areas. Integration of students' knowledge across these functional disciplines is one of the program's key objectives.

The Boise State M.B.A. program provides a general perspective of business management that requires students to consider the social, environmental, and ethical context of managerial actions. It is a high-quality academic program that assists in the development of tomorrow's business leaders. It provides a general management perspective that enables students to target problems, select viable alternatives, and take appropriate action. Boise State makes the international perspective a priority throughout the curriculum.

The Boise State M.B.A. requires a minimum of 33 semester credit hours and a maximum of 54 semester credit hours. The exact number of credits required depends upon the student's prior academic experience. While there is no major available in the M.B.A. program, once students satisfy the functional core

of courses, they emphasize an area of concentration with their elective credits. This specialization can expand beyond business to such areas as public administration or health administration.

Students and the M.B.A. Experience

Students in Boise State University's M.B.A. program bring a wide variety of work experiences and geographic and academic diversity to their M.B.A. experience. Many Boise State M.B.A. students are professional people, continuing their education while working full-time. This mix of backgrounds promotes the beneficial exchange of experience and ideas among peers, a significant factor in the quality and excitement of the program.

A recent student profile shows that the average student is 32 years old, with an average of more than six years of full-time work experience. Women comprise 42 percent of the student population, and students who are members of minority groups make up 15 percent of the M.B.A. student body.

Most Boise State M.B.A. students have undergraduate degrees in business, engineering, science, or social science.

Special Features

Boise State University's M.B.A. program is small enough to enable students to

work in groups on classwork and projects. Many projects are required that develop small group, negotiation, and presentation skills—the same skills demanded of successful managers.

The Faculty

The College of Business and Economics faculty brings a high standard of excellence to Boise State's M.B.A. program. The M.B.A. faculty members hold doctoral degrees from universities across the nation. Most have extensive experience in business, industry, or consulting. This actual business experience enables the faculty to bring a realistic and pragmatic orientation to the classroom.

Boise State University's faculty members are dedicated to excellence in teaching. The faculty consults with, and researches for, top businesses to constantly update materials and to bring the most practical and current business information and problems/solutions into the classroom. This day-to-day contact allows Boise State's faculty members to gain knowledge of the skills businesses find valuable as well as the tools and information students need to allow insight into tomorrow's business needs. The M.B.A. curriculum incorporates these insights to ensure that the program addresses the demands professional managers confront.

The Business School Network
Corporate Partnerships

Boise is the commercial, financial, health-care, and government center of Idaho, allowing students to reach beyond the classroom for experiences not available elsewhere in the state. Boise State University has the advantage of being situated in a city where major firms are headquartered, including Albertson's, Boise Cascade, Idaho Power, Morrison-Knudsen, Simplot, Trus Joist, and the state's leading banks and insurance companies. Major manufacturing locations for Hewlett-Packard and Micron Technology are also located in Boise.

Prominent Alumni

The College of Business and Economics counts among its alumni a number of notable business leaders, including William C. Glynn, CEO of Intermountain Gas; George A. Haneke, CFO of Micron Computer; Douglas G. Hansen, Controller, US Bancorp; Daniel J. Kunz, President and CEO, MK Corp.; Alan J. Moore, Vice President and CFO, MK Corp.; Sony M. Perry, Vice President, Telecommunications, NCI Information Systems, Inc.; Lyle R. Price, Bechtel; Mary J. Schofield, Controller of Hewlett-Packard's Boise Division; Jan B. Packwood, Executive Vice President, Idaho Power; Randy J. Lawrence, CFO, Western Power Sports, Inc.; Allen Lavelle, President, Pacific Property Consultants; Lorelli Hackler, Controller, Micron Technology; Russell Fulcher, National Sales Manager, Micron Technology; Dean A. Froehlich, Financial Vice President, Lewis-Clark State College; Deborah L. Flandro, Manager of Planning, Hewlett-Packard; Christian J. Anton, CEO, St. Alphonsus Regional Medical Center; John Jack Veale, Vice President of Finance and Administration, Spicer Gas/USA Fuel; Ronald D. Sargent, Senior Vice President, Bank of America; and Claudia G. Peterson, CFO, Golden Valley Health Centers.

The College and Environs

Boise State University is located in Boise, Idaho's capital and largest city and one of America's most enjoyable places to live and learn, featuring big city opportunities and small town friendliness. Set against a backdrop of mountains where the Boise River flows out of its lava canyons into a fertile valley, Boise is one of the most appealing metropolitan areas in the West. Named for the Boise River, present-day Boise is a green tribute to the magic of irrigation, with its parks, greenbelt, tree-lined neighborhood streets, golf courses, and University campus. Boise has a pleasant four-season climate; it is one of the premier locations in the country for those who like the outdoors.

Founded in 1932 as a private community college, today Boise State University has the largest enrollment in Idaho with about 17,000 students, more than 200 of whom are in the M.B.A. program.

Students come from all parts of the world and from diverse academic and professional backgrounds.

Technology Environment

Through the Office of Information Technology, Boise State University provides student access to the University's computer resources. Many of Boise State's offices and computer labs are connected to the campus fiber-optic network, allowing users to tap into the Campus-Wide Information System or gain access to the Internet, BITNET, and other networks.

The College of Business and Economics has its own computing facilities, consisting of two microcomputing laboratories with approximately seventy terminals. Facilities are open seven days a week during convenient hours. The College of Business and Economics also houses seven electronic classrooms furnished with the latest multimedia systems.

Placement

Boise State University's Career Center provides career guidance and information through computerized career guidance/information systems and from professional staff members. Information and advice on resume and cover letter writing, application procedures, interviewing, and other job-hunting skills are available. A library of career and employer information is also available. Notification of employment opportunities, participation in on-campus interviews, and optional establishment of a file of professional references are available to M.B.A. students during the academic year in which they complete their degree.

Admission

Applicants must possess a bachelor's degree from an accredited institution. Completed applications must include official transcripts from all institutions previously attended, a GMAT report, two letters of recommendation, a current professional vitae, and an essay. In addition, two years of significant work

experience is required but can be waived based on a superior GMAT score. The average GMAT score of enrolling students is 552; the average undergraduate GPA is 3.2.

A score of at least 587 on the paper-based version or 240 on the computer-based version of the TOEFL is required of all students for whom English is not the native language. International students must also present proof of adequate funding and certified English translations of transcripts.

There are no prerequisite courses for admission, but students must have a basic level of proficiency in college-level algebra and with word processing, database, and spreadsheet programs.

Finances

Tuition and fees for 2000–2001 are $3500 for Idaho residents and $12,500 for nonresidents. On-campus and off-campus housing is available. Most graduate students choose to live off campus in nearby apartments. Many live within walking distance. On-campus room and board are estimated to cost $6000 for the academic year. Off-campus housing and food costs average $12,500 a year.

A number of graduate assistantships are available. To be eligible, students must be admitted to the M.B.A. program and attend as full-time students during the academic year(s) of the awards. The application deadline is February 1.

Application Facts and Dates

Application deadlines are October 1 and February 1.

For more information, students should contact:

Renee Anchustegui
Business Graduate Studies
College of Business and Economics B117
Boise State University
1910 University Drive
Boise, Idaho 83725-1600
Telephone: 208-426-1126
Fax: 208-426-4989
E-mail: ranchust@boisestate.edu

Boston College

The Graduate School of the Wallace E. Carroll School of Management

Chestnut Hill, Massachusetts

AN INVESTMENT IN SUCCESS

A Boston College M.B.A. is an investment in career success. Our alumni are leaders in some of the most prestigious firms in finance and industry. They are particularly prized by companies whose markets are global and executives high performing. Their success is founded on the Boston College M.B.A. program's unique educational philosophy, which stresses executive skill development through consulting, business planning, and global study projects. Our graduates' accomplishments are testimony to the core competencies of the Boston College M.B.A. program: preparing executives for leadership roles in finance and financial services, consulting, electronic commerce, the application of information technology and strategic management. We invite your investment.

—Hassell H. McClellan, Graduate Dean

Programs and Curricular Focus

The M.B.A. program at Boston College's Graduate School of Management (GSOM) provides students with the skills and perspectives necessary for success in today's global and technology-based business environment. In addition to receiving a thorough education in the functional areas of business, students have numerous opportunities to apply their knowledge in real-world settings. Students grapple with actual management problems through innovative classroom exercises, consulting projects, and new venture planning activities. This innovative combination of classroom and applied learning gives Boston College M.B.A. students a distinct career advantage.

The curriculum is designed not only to provide an understanding of the fundamentals of management, but also to offer abundant opportunities to tailor the program to meet specific needs and career goals. After completing the core study, students have many opportunities to explore possible career paths through electives, concentrations, industry-specific programs, independent studies, and other options. These options include concentrations in the traditional functional areas as well as interdisciplinary concentrations in such areas as entrepreneurship, consulting, international management, and the management of financial institutions.

The School also offers a number of joint-degree programs: the M.B.A./J.D.; the M.B.A./M.S.F.; the M.B.A./M.S.W.; the M.B.A./Ph.D. in sociology; the M.B.A./M.A. in mathematics, political science, Slavic studies, French studies, Italian stud-

ies, or Hispanic studies; and the M.B.A./M.S. in biology, geology/geophysics, or nursing. Offered on a full- or part-time (evening) basis, the M.B.A. program at Boston College's Graduate School of Management is part of a portfolio of programs that includes a Master of Science in finance and a Ph.D. in management, with concentrations in finance and organization studies.

Students and the M.B.A. Experience

There are approximately 210 full-time and 625 evening M.B.A. students. Approximately thirty percent of students in the M.B.A. program are women. Full-time M.B.A. students have an average of 4 years of full-time work experience; evening M.B.A. students have an average of 4.4 years.

❖ Global Focus

Boston College's M.B.A. curriculum is global in its outlook. Global management issues are woven throughout the curriculum so that course work across the spectrum of functional areas routinely addresses the international dimensions of business. Moreover, with approximately one third of the entering full-time class typically made up of international students, a global perspective comes naturally to the program. Students develop worldwide perspectives in a kind of learning laboratory that is much like the business environment into which they will graduate.

The Boston College Graduate School of Management maintains an extensive

program of international study opportunities. The International Management Experience (IME) elective allows M.B.A. students to study a region of the world and see first-hand how business is conducted. During the three weeks of travel, students visit corporations, major commercial centers, and government agencies. The IMEs have included Asia, Europe, and Latin America. Global management is the focus of a special dual degree GSOM offers with Strasbourg (France) Graduate School of Management. Other international study opportunities include a number of exchange programs maintained with leading management schools around the world and a semester in China option offered through the Beijing International Management Center.

Special Features

The Boston College M.B.A. program constantly develops new programs to meet emerging managerial challenges. In 1998, the program established a management of information technology concentration to meet the unprecedented demand for executives with IT and management skills. In 1999, the program launched five new "Techno M.B.A." concentrations combining the study of information technology with a complementary field of management. Also new is the joint M.B.A./M.S. in Finance, providing a beneficial fusion of managerial and financial skills. In all, the program offers six interdisciplinary concentrations and fifteen joint degree options that provide students with a distinctive career edge by combining management education with study in another discipline.

The Faculty

The members of the Graduate School of Management faculty represent a vibrant mix of knowledge, experience, and professional dedication. Many of them bring extensive industry backgrounds and contacts directly into the classroom, which adds to the "real-world" aspect of the learning experience. The School seeks faculty members who are able to balance scholarship and teaching excellence.

The Business School Network

Corporate Partnerships

Top executives regularly visit the Graduate School of Management. The M.B.A. Executive Lecture Series and the Women in the Boardroom series are just two examples of programs that give students the chance to interact directly with leaders in the business and nonprofit worlds.

The Board of Advisors, a group of senior executives from leading companies, consults regularly with the Graduate School of Management on program and curricular issues. The School of Management also sponsors the Chief Executives Club of Boston, one of the nation's top business speaking forums.

The Boston College M.B.A. program has developed an Executive Fellows Program in partnership with State Street Global Advisors, the nation's third-largest investment manager, and Liberty Mutual Insurance. Through this program, students participate in internships in investment management research and financial services marketing. The school is committed to expanding these opportunities through partnerships with other leading corporations.

The College and Environs

Located on 185 acres on the Boston line, Boston College is just a short ride by car or subway from downtown Boston, a world-renowned center of culture, learning, and industry.

Boston College is a coeducational, two-campus university with four undergraduate schools and six graduate and professional schools. The University offers fourteen degree programs and two certificate programs and enrolls 8,900 full-time undergraduates and 4,800 graduate students. Established in 1863, Boston College is the largest Jesuit-affiliated university in the country.

Facilities

Fulton Hall, which houses the Graduate School of Management, is a state-of-the-art center for management education. Among Fulton's advantages: many classrooms outfitted with advanced computer and audiovisual technologies, including direct Internet access; abundant space for meetings, study groups, and gatherings, including a dramatic five-story atrium that functions as the School's "town square"; and its location in the heart of Boston College's Chestnut Hill campus, close to the libraries, the recreation complex, and the student union.

Computer facilities are available to M.B.A. students in the graduate computer lab in Fulton Hall and in the O'Neill Computing Facility, which provide access to a wide variety of hardware, software, and peripherals.

The University's libraries offer a wealth of resources to support research, teaching, and learning. The book collections exceed 1.6 million volumes and approximately 20,000 serial titles are currently received. The library holds 2.7 million microforms. In addition, Boston College libraries provide access to more than 500 databases, including many in business and economics.

Graduate housing is not provided on campus; however, the Office of University Housing provides off-campus listings and suggestions for interested students.

Placement

Boston College's Graduate School of Management is committed to helping students achieve the best possible career outcomes. Graduate Management Career Services provides M.B.A. students with the means to achieve their career goals through placement initiatives, career coaching, and other services. The office also serves as a bridge to corporations through its outreach activities and links to Boston College's worldwide alumni network.

Services include extensive on- and off-campus recruiting programs, resume books for first- and second-year students, an online job-posting system, and two career fairs. The office also maintains a database of alumni career advisers and offers career advising, interviewing and resume-writing workshops, information sessions, and a library of career resources. Career strategies courses are offered throughout the year.

Admission

The Graduate School of Management welcomes applications from graduates of accredited colleges and universities. For the M.B.A. program, the Admissions Committee considers applicants with academic backgrounds from virtually all areas of study.

Courses in business administration or management are not required for admission to the Graduate School of Management M.B.A. program. However, students are expected to be proficient in English and mathematics. In addition, all applicants are expected to take the GMAT. International students must have the equivalent of a U.S. bachelor's degree and a minimum score of 600 on the TOEFL exam.

The Admissions Committee looks for evidence of academic and management potential. Work experience and prior academic performance are significant criteria in their evaluation. In general, students enter the program after at least two years of full-time work experience. Leadership and community involvement are also important factors in admissions decisions.

Finances

Tuition for the 2000–01 academic year is $792 per credit hour. Books, fees, and supplies average $1500 per year and medical insurance is $470. Living expenses currently average $5662 per semester.

The Graduate School offers a significant program of graduate assistantships or scholarships to full-time M.B.A. classes. Awardees usually have two or more years of full-time work experience, a score of 630 or above on the GMAT, a grade point average of 3.2 or above, and a strong set of application materials. Graduate assistantships involve research or administrative duties in exchange for tuition remission. A portion of assistantship awards is subject to tax.

In addition to the assistantships and scholarships offered through GSOM, the University Financial Aid Office provides a variety of programs to help students finance their education.

Application Facts and Dates

The evening M.B.A. program admits students in September and January; the full-time M.B.A. program begins only in September. Admission deadlines are April 1 for the full-time M.B.A., November 15 for January admission to the evening program, and June 1 for September admission. International students must submit a complete application and TOEFL score by March 1. Deadlines for assistantships are outlined in the application. Prospective students may apply online through the M.B.A. Web site or at http://www.MBA.CollegeEdge. com. For more information, applicants should contact:

Director of M.B.A. Admissions
The Graduate School of the Wallace
   E. Carroll School of Management
Fulton Hall, Room 315
Boston College
140 Commonwealth Avenue
Chestnut Hill, Massachusetts 02467-3808
Telephone: 617-552-3920
Fax: 617-552-8078
E-mail: bcmba@bc.edu
World Wide Web: http://www.bc.edu/mba

Boston University

THE BOSTON UNIVERSITY M.B.A.: A FOCUS ON THE SYSTEM

The Boston University M.B.A. curriculum is a pioneering program designed to concentrate on management processes instead of functions alone. In this M.B.A. program, you will learn management as a system—a horizontal continuum of interdependent departments or functions. Many graduate schools structure their curriculum to develop general managers. But they tend to take a segmented route, where accounting is isolated from marketing, operations from finance, and so on. In such classes, case studies are usually approached for an accounting (or marketing or operations) solution only. That is not how the real world operates. At Boston University, we develop general managers with a view that extends across multiple departments to encompass the whole organization.

—Louis E. Lataif, Dean and Former President, Ford Europe

Programs and Curricular Focus

Boston University (BU) offers the M.B.A. in general management, with specializations in entrepreneurship, finance, international management, marketing, operations, organizational behavior, and strategy. The University offers the new MS.MBA Program as well as the M.B.A. in health-care management, the M.B.A. in public and non-profit management, the M.S. in investment management, the executive M.B.A., the M.S. in management information systems, and the Doctor of Business Administration.

The M.B.A. program provides graduates with the full range of foundation skills required to be an outstanding and adaptable performer immediately upon graduation, the competencies required for long-term career development, and the perspectives necessary to understand the complex social and ethical dimensions of management. The program provides real-world action learning coupled with a rigorous, research-based conceptual education. A new core curriculum debuts in fall 2001.

The MS.MBA Program is the School's newest offering and represents the ideal preparation for a changing economy and world. Built on the newly revised IT-infused core curriculum, this dual degree option (one of eight available) allows students to earn two degrees, an M.S. in Information Systems and an M.B.A., in just twenty-one months. It allows students to develop the critical capabilities necessary for success in an economy that demands IT skills of all managers, while permitting a functional concentration (e.g. finance, marketing, etc.).

Teamwork is an essential part of today's workplace, and thus it is a major component of the M.B.A. education. In fact, the term Team-Learning is service-marked by Boston University. In most Boston University M.B.A. courses, students work in consistent cohorts, simulating the way actual organizations work. Students join in study teams, project teams, and consulting teams to outside industry. Each of these experiences helps the student learn how to facilitate the teamwork process in every phase of his or her M.B.A. education and career.

Students and the M.B.A. Experience

Boston University has among the most internationally diverse student bodies in the nation (as reported by the Institute of International Education), and this is reflected in the M.B.A. program. Thirty-nine percent of the students are international. The students, who come from six continents and forty-three countries, benefit from a rich and varied interchange of views. The M.B.A. curriculum capitalizes on this diversity in its emphasis on the global business environment. The students are highly intelligent, diverse, ambitious, and determined to make a positive difference in society. Their active participation in the evaluations of the programs and activities ensures a continuing vibrancy and responsiveness in the School.

There are approximately 1,200 students enrolled in full- and part-time graudate business programs. Each year, 220 new full-time MBA students join the program, creating the ideal-sized learning environment. The program is large enough to offer students a broad range of elective courses and extra-curricular activities, but small enough to ensure access to faculty members and the University's many resources. Student life is rich and active with a range of academic, networking, and social events that create a very close-knit student community. Applications are traditionally received from more than sixty-five countries. The average student is 27 years old, has three to five years of work experience, and entered the program with an average TOEFL score of 261 and GMAT score of 631 (anticipated, Fall 2000).

❖ Global Focus

Students can begin their M.B.A. program by joining a ten-week management program in Kobe, Japan. The program draws students from the Pacific Rim and countries around the world for a rich intercultural experience. Courses taught by Boston University professors combine classroom work with field visits and guest lecturers to help students develop an understanding of the social, political, and economic aspects of global business. During their second year, students may live and study abroad through the student exchange programs between Boston University and the University of Manchester, England, or the University of Lyon, France. During the summer, students may choose from a number of two-week overseas programs that take the BU faculty members and students to Europe, Latin America, and Asia. A formal concentration in International Management and the dual M.B.A./M.A. in International Relations provide further opportunity for a globally-focused education. More than a quarter of the School's faculty members are from abroad, with most others having international living, work, consulting, or educational experience.

Special Features

The School of Management has developed a three-week orientation program to help international students adjust to the dynamic atmosphere of the American M.B.A. classroom and to prepare for the rigorous demands of case discussions. This distinctive program provides both English instruction and an introduction to the M.B.A. curriculum. Attendance may be required for students whose native language is not English and whose prior academic work has not been in English or has not fully prepared them for the case study method.

Students have the opportunity to read, analyze, and discuss actual case studies. The orientation program also introduces students to the American economic system, including the operation of private firms and the role the American government plays in the business environment. Students also receive training in preparation for class presentations and an introduction to the M.B.A. classroom culture.

The Faculty

The faculty is the School of Management's major resource. Committed to advancing management knowledge, through both theoretical and applied research, and to improving the quality of teaching and learning, faculty members bring the benefits of their vast professional experience to the classroom. The faculty members have earned worldwide recognition and respect for their applied research. They bring a refreshing approach to teaching within interdisciplinary frameworks and also bring wide-ranging experience with local, national, and global organizations.

The Business School Network

The Boston University School of Management has a wealth of research centers and institutes, each of which addresses issues that extend beyond the boundaries of traditional disciplines. These organizations have become magnets for faculty members from disciplines around Boston University and for top-level managers from around the world, who come together and share their understanding of contemporary management challenges. Among the School's most active centers are the Systems Research Center, the Human Resources Policy Institute, the Entrepreneurial Management Institute, and the Center for Enterprise Leadership.

The research centers and institutes and the School's executive training programs offer significant advantages to students seeking leadership roles in major organizations. Through an industrial network that extends around the globe, faculty members maintain contact and exchange data with colleagues in universities and business firms. This real-world involvement brings exciting results into the classroom—timely and topical material for case studies and a steady stream of high-level managers from a variety of firms.

The Bronner e-Business Center and Hatchery provides a further link between the School and the corporate community. The Center funds up to twelve students or student teams during the business plan development process and then connects them to a network of five top-tier venture capital firms who have first option for investment in the student e-business.

The College and Environs

The fourth-largest private university in the nation, Boston University is consolidated at the 86-acre Charles River Campus and Boston University's Medical Center in the city's South End. The School of Management was established as the College of Business Administration in 1913 and is located on the Charles River Campus. Boston offers a wealth of cultural, educational, sports, and social resources. Combining a proud history with a contemporary lifestyle, it is a cosmopolitan center for the financial and insurance industries, the heart of the high-technology industry, an extensive medical and educational center, and the capital of Massachusetts. As the hub of one of the nation's largest metropolitan areas, Boston offers numerous opportunities for strong practical experience in business, government, health, technology, and public management.

Facilities

The Boston University School of Management opened the nation's most technologically advanced building for management education in 1997. Designed specifically for teaching management as an integrated system, and built to accommodate team learning and team teaching, the building integrates leading-edge technology throughout. The building features classrooms with computer ports and plugs for all students, instructional workstations with Internet access, and advanced audiovisual capabilities for slide, videotape, and computer-generated presentations. In addition, the management library houses more than 90,000 books, periodicals, and journals, as well as the latest technology for information retrieval.

Placement

The School of Management's state-of-the-art Career Center assists students in making informed career and life decisions. Through comprehensive career education programming, job development services, and individualized career counseling, the center collaborates with students in developing and managing careers at both the entry and experienced level. On-campus recruiting has tripled during the last three years and the roster of firms hiring BU M.B.A. graduates is exceptional. McKinsey, BCG, Johnson and Johnson, Dell, Digitas, and J.P. Morgan are among the firms that have hired interns and graduates in 2000. The average salary for 2000 graduates is projected to surpass $70,000, exclusive of non-salary compensation.

Admission

The requirements for applying are a completed application form with a nonrefundable $75 application fee, official transcripts of the academic record from each college or university attended, three letters of evalua-

tion, and results of the Graduate Management Admission Test (GMAT).

International applicants must also submit English translations of transcripts (the undergraduate degree must be equivalent to a U.S. bachelor's degree), results of the Test of English as a Foreign Language (TOEFL) (if the student's native language is English or if the student received an undergraduate degree from an institution where English is the language of instruction, the TOEFL is not required), and the International Student Data Form and financial documents. Since scholarship funds are not generally available to international students, applicants must submit a financial declaration showing adequate funding for both tuition and living expenses for the duration of the M.B.A. program.

Finances

Tuition for the 2000–01 academic year is $24,770, and fees are approximately $330. Single students living off campus should anticipate living costs for twelve months of approximately $15,000; the costs for married students are estimated at $22,300. Most students live in apartments in nearby neighborhoods, easily accessible from the School by public transportation. The School offers scholarships, work-study awards, and endowment funding to full-time students. Awards are made based on academic merit. All students are required to have medical insurance, estimated at $576.

Application Facts and Dates

Students seeking financial aid should apply by March 15. The deadlines for September admission are April 15 for full-time study (domestic students) and June 15 for part-time study. The deadline for January admission is November 15 (part-time study only).

International students are admitted to the M.B.A. program for full-time study in September only. All international applications must be received by the Graduate Admissions Office by March 1.

Applications are reviewed on a rolling basis. Review begins in January for September admission. Students are encouraged to submit applications early to ensure adequate processing time. An online application is available through the Web site. For more information, applicants should contact:

Boston University School of
    Management
Graduate Admissions Office
595 Commonwealth Avenue
Boston, Massachusetts 02215
Telephone: 617-353-2670
Fax: 617-353-7368
E-mail: mba@bu.edu
World Wide Web: http://management.
    bu.edu

Bowling Green State University

Bowling Green, Ohio

THERE IS A DIFFERENCE

M.B.A. programs are as varied as the business schools that offer them. Some are big. We're not. Our incoming class of full-time students consists of only 35 students. This means small class sizes and easy access to our faculty. Some penalize the liberal arts graduate. We don't. Our full-time M.B.A. may be completed in fourteen months with or without an undergraduate business degree. A specialization requires only an additional semester. Some require business experience for admission. We don't. We designed our full-time program for students who will be new to their chosen fields. Most business schools (75 percent) are not accredited by AACSB–The International Association for Management Education. We are. Accreditation is one way to demonstrate how serious we are about what we do. We have created a small-school atmosphere within a major research university. After you review our program, we believe you will see that, at BGSU, "There is a difference."

—Dr. James McFillen, Associate Dean

Programs and Curricular Focus

In order to function effectively in a professional world that is more diverse, team oriented, global, and dynamic than ever before, the Bowling Green State University (BGSU) M.B.A. program is designed to prepare students to know the fundamentals of business, recognize the ethical obligations of leadership, engage problems creatively, continuously learn on their own, work well in teams with diverse memberships, understand change and know how to adapt and succeed in the midst of change, and communicate effectively, both orally and in writing.

The M.B.A. program provides a broad curriculum, organized around three principal components: foundation, core, and capstone courses. The foundation courses cover financial and managerial accounting, economic analysis, statistics, quantitative analysis, and information technology. The core courses include finance, operations management, marketing, and ethics and law in business. The capstone courses cover economic policy, leadership and change, strategy design and implementation, and international business and management. For full-time students, the program includes modules on computer skills, international business principles, and the foundations of ethical leadership. In addition, students take part in a series of cocurricular professional development seminars, dealing with topics such as presentations and report writing, team facilitation, effective

negotiations, career planning, and organizational politics.

Although students may choose to pursue a general M.B.A., they also may pursue a formal specialization in finance, management information systems, marketing, or supply chain management. A student may also pursue the dual-degree option and earn a second master's degree in any of a variety of fields, such as organization development, public health, industrial technology, and public administration.

The M.B.A. degree requires a minimum of 42 semester hours (47 semester hours for full-time students). The general M.B.A. may be completed in fourteen months, regardless of the student's prior undergraduate preparation. An M.B.A. with a specialization requires 12 additional semester hours (one additional semester of full-time study). The full-time M.B.A. program primarily serves students who will be entry-level professionals upon graduation and does not require business experience for admission. The evening M.B.A. program serves students with professional experience and an ongoing career. Neither the full-time nor the evening program requires prior academic preparation in business.

The Executive M.B.A. program is a rigorous program with accelerated courses that may be completed in thirty-one months. The program consists of 36 semester hours delivered during six

2-week sessions. The program serves students with extensive professional experience and is designed to accommodate the demands of professional travel and relocation. The program does not require prior academic preparation in business. Candidates must be nominated by their employer unless they are self-employed.

Students and the M.B.A. Experience

The BGSU M.B.A. program, accredited by AACSB–The International Association for Management Education, is recognized nationally and internationally for the quality of its students and faculty. The incoming class of full-time M.B.A. students is limited to a maximum of 35 students to maintain the small class sizes and faculty accessibility for which the M.B.A. program is known. The program works to foster an esprit de corps among the students. Within each semester, students are part of a cohort that shares a common schedule. This cohort experience is vital to the development of communication and teamwork skills and promotes valuable networking abilities that are critical in any business professional career.

The student body in the M.B.A. program is very diverse, and this diversity enhances the learning environment. The current M.B.A. student population includes students from nineteen countries and fourteen states. In addition, approximately 25 percent of the program's students are international. Across all programs, students range in age from 23 to 50, with an average age of 29. The average work experience of full-time, part-time, and executive students is two, three, and nine years, respectively, but work experience is not required of full-time or part-time students. BGSU's M.B.A. programs do not require undergraduate degrees in business for admission, so participants' academic backgrounds vary.

The Faculty

Because the faculty greatly influences the quality of learning in any formal education program, all graduate faculty members are selected on the basis of superior scholarship in both teaching and research. Many of the faculty members at BGSU are nationally and internationally renowned. Distinguished faculty members include 3 corporation-endowed professors and 3 University Distinguished Teaching Award recipients.

Many members of the faculty are actively involved in consulting in both the public and private sectors and have brought the results of their observations, experiences, and research into the classroom. A high priority for the faculty is to prepare students for the roles of leadership they will assume. Faculty members accomplish this not only by excellent teaching but also by advising students on their business research and consulting projects.

The Business School Network

Students in the M.B.A. program connect with the Ohio business community via field studies, consulting projects, internship opportunities, symposiums, and conferences sponsored by departments in the College. Corporate leaders are featured speakers at the annual student banquet and at the biweekly professional development seminars.

Bowling Green State University also has a corporate M.B.A. partnership with Dana Corporation and recruits extensively at numerous organizations in northwest Ohio for a part-time program of more than 100 students.

The College and Environs

Bowling Green State University was founded in 1910. The 1,338-acre campus houses more than 100 buildings in a small-town setting. BGSU serves approximately 15,000 undergraduate students and 2,700 graduate students. The College of Business Administration serves approximately 2,400 undergraduates and 200 graduate students.

BGSU is located 23 miles south of Toledo, just off Interstate Highway 75. Airport transportation is provided by the Toledo Express Airport or the Detroit Metropolitan Airport, which is approximately an hour's drive north from Bowling Green. Metropolitan areas within comfortable driving distance include Indianapolis, Chicago, Cincinnati, Columbus, Dayton, and Windsor, Ontario.

The largest campus library houses more than 6 million items. Through OhioLINK, BGSU students have access to an additional 17 million volumes held in Ohio's other state university libraries. The comprehensive network of twenty-nine academic computing labs includes both IBM and Apple microcomputers and the Business Administration Computer Labs, which house more than 150 personal computers.

Placement

The Career Services Office provides students with personal help on developing interviewing skills, resume preparation, alumni and professional networking skills and opportunities, and access to on-campus corporate recruiters. These services are provided using state-of-the-art Web-based computer systems that have received national recognition.

BGSU M.B.A. graduates find themselves employed worldwide in a variety of both large and small corporations. A sampling of employers of recent graduates includes such companies as Allied Signal, BP Oil Company, Cap Gemini of America, Honda Manufacturing of America, Intel, the Kellogg Company, Andersen Consulting, Owens-Corning, and Procter & Gamble.

Admission

The Bowling Green Graduate Studies in Business Office welcomes applications from individuals regardless of undergraduate majors. Applicants must submit an application, transcripts of all previous college work, GMAT scores (and TOEFL when applicable), two letters of recommendation, a personal statement, a current resume, and a $30 application fee. Prior work experience is also reviewed when making assistantship decisions. Students may begin the application process by submitting an electronic application (http://www.bgsu.edu/colleges/gradcol/).

Finances

Tuition and fees in 1999–2000 for 12 semester hours (full-time) per semester for Ohio residents were $3181. Nonresidents paid $5955 per semester. Additional costs of books and supplies varied from $400 to $750 for the academic year.

The primary form of financial aid is the graduate assistantship (GA). Highly qualified full-time students may be eligible for a GA position providing a stipend and scholarship covering all tuition and fees for the semesters of the appointment. A student serving the fall and spring semesters also receives a scholarship covering all tuition for the program's three summer sessions. In the 1999–2000 academic year, the stipends ranged from $3550 to $7100. GA positions are available through the College of Business Administration as well as through nonacademic offices such as the Instructional Media Center and the Office of Greek Life.

Application Facts and Dates

The program begins in late June/early July with a one-week orientation program followed by two courses. As a result of the limited admissions and midsummer starting date, completed application materials, including test scores (GMAT and TOEFL), must be received by the following deadlines: international applicants applying for a graduate assistantship award, January 15; international applicants who are not applying for a graduate assistantship award, February 15; domestic applicants who are applying for a graduate assistantship award, February 15; and domestic applicants who are not applying for a graduate assistantship award, March 15. International applications received or completed after the February 15 deadline are unlikely to be processed in time for admitted students to apply for and receive their student visas and begin the program in late June/early July. Domestic applications received or completed after the March 15 deadline are accepted for consideration on a space-available basis.

For more information, applicants should contact:

Carmen Castro-Rivera, Director
Graduate Studies in Business
Bowling Green State University
Bowling Green, Ohio 43403
Telephone: 419-372-2488
          800-BGSU-MBA
Fax: 419-372-2875
E-mail: mba-info@cba.bgsu.edu
World Wide Web: http://www.cba.
  bgsu.edu

Brandeis University

Waltham, Massachusetts

PREPARING PROFESSIONALS FOR THE GLOBAL ECONOMY

The Graduate School of International Economics and Finance is the first school at a major U.S. university to focus on global markets, the best possible preparation for professional careers in the global economy. Our degree programs, with their strong analytical and financial orientations, will equip you with the practical and conceptual skills that are necessary to be successful in doing business across borders. Classes are small—we accept about 55 students per year—but very diverse, as more than forty countries are represented. The internationally known faculty comprises a dynamic teaching and research team that works closely with MBAi students in course work as well as on projects outside the classroom. Our approach is thoroughly international and includes a semester of study overseas with one of our twenty partner exchange schools.

—Peter A. Petri, Carl J. Shapiro Professor of International Finance and Dean

Programs and Curricular Focus

The MBA/International Program (MBAi) is a full-time degree program intended for students with prior work experience and offers a focused practical education in international business administration built upon a strong foundation of analysis and applied technical skills. The program provides excellent preparation for positions in multinational companies, international financial institutions, and government agencies. The program requires completion of sixteen courses over a two-year period, including one semester overseas at one of the School's prestigious partner universities.

For students who are in the early stages of their careers or who have just earned an undergraduate degree, the Graduate School offers the Lemberg M.A. in International Economics and Finance (MAief), which has an interdisciplinary curriculum in international business, finance, or economics and shares many core courses with the MBAi Program. Like the MBAi, the Lemberg Program requires two years of full-time study, including a semester abroad at one of four partner institutions.

Finally, the part-time M.S. in Finance Program is an evening program for working professionals seeking to develop skills in financial theory and analysis with an international focus. The M.S. is offered year-round and requires completion of ten courses: five required courses and five electives. Electives include one-week field studies in major international financial markets. Although the usual progress through the program is two courses per semester, students on a fast track may complete the degree in fifteen months.

Students and the M.B.A. Experience

The MBA/International Program at the Graduate School of International Economics and Finance at Brandeis University develops expertise in doing business across borders. The Graduate School provides a cosmopolitan yet intimate environment that supports students in developing and reaching their goals. Each entering class is limited to 55 master's students (MBAi and MAief), affording every individual the opportunity to get to know and interact with classmates, faculty members, and administrators through a variety of academic and extracurricular activities. The student body is diverse, with about 60 percent of the students from outside the United States; typically, more than forty nations are represented at the School. About 40 percent of the students are women and about 15 percent are members of minority groups.

❖ Global Focus

Since the entire curriculum is focused on developing skills for use in the global marketplace and since the students are from such diverse international backgrounds, each class becomes an international learning experience. Students often work in multicultural teams with a faculty of internationally known experts, and differences in perspectives and cultural norms are actively discussed.

Special Features

The MBAi and Lemberg MAief Programs are the only professional programs in the U.S. that require a semester of graduate study overseas. Students choose to study at one of twenty partner schools and in so doing develop a firsthand understanding of the business and economic systems of a major international country. Many students take course work in the local language, attaining the foreign language proficiency required for graduation. This semester abroad also allows participants to develop friendships and networks that usually intensify and expand after graduation.

The Faculty

The faculty includes several internationally known authorities on business management, exchange rates and trade policy, patents and technology transfer, and Asian economies and business. Other members conduct research with a focus on international finance. In addition, several high-level executives from Boston's business, finance, and legal communities offer their expertise in applied technical areas as adjunct professors.

Many of the faculty members conduct research in the School's Asia Pacific Center for Economics and Business using grant funding provided by prestigious international agencies, such as the Center for Global Partnership, the Luce Foundation, the United Nations, and the World Bank. The Graduate School has also been designated as one of thirteen official Asia Pacific Economic Cooperation (APEC) Study Centers in the U.S. and is the only such center in New England.

The Business School Network

The Graduate School has developed an extensive network of partnerships with financial and multinational corporations and with professionals in the finance and economics professions. Corporate partners include BankAmerica, Citicorp, Coopers

& Lybrand, Imperial Chemical Industries (ICI), Macandrews and Forbes, Revlon, and the Sony Corporation. The multinational Board of Overseers of the School includes executives from Arthur Andersen & Co., the Bank of Tokyo-Mitsubishi Ltd., Erving Industries, Fuji Xerox Co., Goldman Sachs, ICI, Mellon Bank, the Monitor Company, the Ssangyong Business Group of Korea, and the World Bank. Visitors from these companies and many others provide opportunities to address important issues through informal lectures, conferences, and seminars. The School also runs an Executive Education Program in alliance strategy.

The College and Environs

Founded in 1948, Brandeis is one of the leading private research universities in the United States, with approximately 3,000 undergraduates and 1,100 graduate students. The University is situated on a parklike campus 10 miles west of Boston and Cambridge, while the Graduate School is located in a wooded corner of the campus in the Sachar International Center. The University has superb sports and theater facilities and brings a series of distinguished lecturers, artists, and performance groups to campus. Public transportation provides quick access to Boston's cultural and educational amenities and to nearby ocean and New England rural attractions.

Facilities

Master's students frequently participate in faculty research and in seminars and discussions with visiting scholars and practitioners. As an APEC Study Center, there are special opportunities for those interested in Asian economics and business.

The School operates its own IBM-compatible computer network with access to current software, databases, LEXIS-NEXIS, and the World Wide Web.

Students have access to university libraries and to other resources through the Boston Library Consortium and through exchange agreements with other leading colleges and universities in the area.

Placement

Virtually all graduates of the program are employed in positions utilizing their economic, financial, and international training. Leading employers include Citibank, KPMG Peat Marwick, Morgan Stanley, and the U.S. Federal Reserve Banks. Graduates from recent classes have received offers from consulting firms such as the Boston Consulting Group and McKinsey & Co. and from corporations such as Adidas America, AT&T, and Microsoft. Students work closely with the Office of Career Services to learn about career alternatives and to implement an effective career development strategy during their time at Brandeis.

Admission

Applicants for all master's programs are required to have an American bachelor's degree or the equivalent international degree. Prior training in a modern foreign language is highly desirable. All applications should include official copies of transcripts and three letters of recommendations. All international applicants must submit TOEFL scores.

Applicants to the MBAi and M.S. in Finance Programs should have some prior work experience and must submit scores from the GMAT (not the GRE).

For the Lemberg MAief Program, prior course work should include at least two semesters of economics and one semester of international relations or politics. MAief applicants must also submit scores from either the general GRE or the GMAT.

Finances

Tuition charges for full-time students for 2000–01 are $25,392 per year for MBAi

and M.A. students. Tuition rates for the part-time M.S. in Finance program are $2280 per course. Ten-month living expenses in the area are estimated to range from $8500 to $10,000 for a single student. Limited on-campus housing is available; most students live within a short commute of campus.

Candidates may apply for tuition scholarships, assistantships, and loans, which are available to American and international students. Special American Leadership Awards are available to U.S. citizens or permanent resident applicants who exhibit outstanding potential for international careers.

International Students

Approximately 60 percent of the graduate students are international, typically coming from more than forty nations. Well-represented areas include the Far East, Latin America, and Central and Eastern Europe. The University also has a large international population and provides support through the International Students Office and via an active International Student Association.

Application Facts and Dates

Application deadlines are February 15 for an April 1 notification and April 15 for notification in May. Candidates applying for financial aid are urged to meet the February 15 deadline. For further information, students should contact:

Geraldine F. Koch
Assistant Dean for Admissions
Graduate School of International
    Economics and Finance
Brandeis University, MS-032
Waltham, Massachusetts 02454-9110
Telephone: 781-736-2252
Fax: 781-736-2263
E-mail: admissions@lemberg.brandeis.
    edu
World Wide Web: http://www.
    brandeis.edu/global

Brandeis University

A CUTTING-EDGE MANAGEMENT EDUCATION

This is an exciting time in the Heller Graduate School's history. This is because our country is in the midst of a service revolution. The human services—health care, elder services, child, youth, and family services, and so on—all represent fast-growing economic sectors. New trends are affecting the delivery of social services—social patterns are changing, health services needs are intensifying, and the population is aging. These trends are challenging, yet they are creating opportunities for a talented cadre of managers who understand the policy issues that affect the provision of services and who are capable of leading organizations and delivery systems into the future. Few general management M.B.A. programs focus on the policies, programs, and underlying values that drive the human services sector. Heller's unique blend of cutting-edge management education combined with a deeper understanding of the social policy context of health and human services gives our graduates a comparative advantage.

—Jon Chilingerian, Director, Master's Program

Programs and Curricular Focus

Brandeis University's Master of Management (M.M.) and Master of Business Administration (M.B.A.) degrees in health and human services at the Heller Graduate School prepare individuals for leadership positions in the complex and changing environments of public and private for-profit and not-for-profit health and human services organizations. The context-specific curriculum at the core of both degrees is at the intersection of cutting-edge management and policy, educating effective leaders who will take organizations into the twenty-first century. Both degrees promote an awareness of how politics and markets work in the context of social policy. Students acquire a quantitative proficiency that is used in problem finding, modeling, implementation, and evaluation; a mastery of organizational structures and processes; skills in handling and communicating information; a comprehension of and respect for strategy; and a working knowledge of financial and managerial accounting and control, all aspects of which are adapted to meet the goals of the particular degree.

The M.M. degree is designed to meet the needs of individuals planning careers in small, community-based provider organizations; government agencies; think tanks; or foundations and prepare tomorrow's leaders to manage multiple aspects of an organization, from operations to marketing to financial control. The M.B.A. (human services) degree prepares individuals to become managers in large, multisite health and human services corporate structures, developing future leaders who are trained to utilize large information systems and solve complex problems in an increasingly global environment. Master's students can declare management concentrations in health care; child, youth, and family services; or services for the elderly and people with disabilities. Full-time day study is completed in fifteen months, starting in June. There is an evening program for the M.M. degree only. Heller has joint-degree programs with Brandeis's Hornstein Program in Jewish communal services and with Tufts University's School of Medicine and Northeastern University's College of Business Administration for an M.D./M.B.A. in health-care management.

Students and the M.B.A. Experience

Heller students are drawn from many places geographically and professionally. Many have worked in health and human services organizations, while others have decided to change careers. Of the June 1999 master's class, the average student was 28 years old; students' ages ranged from 21 to 45. Twenty-six percent were international, and 70 percent were women. Ninety-one percent were enrolled full-time, and 26 percent were enrolled in the dual-degree program in Jewish communal services with the Hornstein Program. Heller's master's program, composed of both the M.M. and M.B.A. degree programs, will enroll approximately 35–40 full-time students in the upcoming year.

Special Features

In addition to a focus on health and human services, Heller provides its master's students the rich history and offerings of its doctoral program in social policy. Students augment their management training with policy courses in the areas of child, youth, and family services; health care; developmental disabilities; elder services; substance abuse; poverty; workforce and community development; violence; and social change and inequality.

Master's study culminates with a Team Consulting Project, which allows students to apply their management and analytical skills to solve real organizational problems. Teams of 3 to 7 students provide management consulting services to community-based health or human services agencies during a 2½- to 3-month period. By working on a real-world problem with its human resources, technical, financial, strategic, or other management challenges, students are better prepared to function as managers in their chosen health and human services field after they graduate.

The Heller Alumni Network is more than 1,200 strong and spans forty-six states and twenty-four countries. Alumni keep the Heller Graduate School abreast of career trends, job opportunities, and networking leads.

The Faculty

Heller's faculty includes a mix of outstanding scholars and practitioners trained in fundamental management sciences, traditional social science disciplines, and multidisciplinary policy sciences. Of those teaching required courses in the master's program, 82 percent have doctorates. The faculty is committed to integration of social policy and management in the curriculum, as demonstrated, for example, by the health and human services context module that takes place in classroom sessions of management courses during the first summer of the program.

The Business School Network

Since its founding in 1959, the Heller Graduate School has built ties to local, regional, national, and international health and human services organizations. Through the School's Team Consulting Project requirement, many local agencies have worked with Heller School master's students and have high regard for their work. Many Heller alumni—employed by such organizations as Pew Charitable Trusts, U.S. Department of Health and Human Services, Johnson & Johnson, Massachusetts Society for the Prevention of Cruelty to Children, and Harvard Pilgrim Health Care—maintain active interactions with the School. The School's Board of Overseers includes individuals based in diverse organizations such as A-D-S Group/The Multicare Companies, Partners HealthCare Systems, W. K. Kellogg Foundation, and Blue Cross and Blue Shield of Massachusetts.

The College and Environs

Founded in 1948, Brandeis University has become one of the leading small private research universities in the United States, having earned recognition by Phi Beta Kappa only thirteen years after its founding; Brandeis is the youngest institution to be so honored in more than 100 years. In a national review, Brandeis was named the top emerging research institution in the United States.

The University has a student population of 4,405, almost 1,265 of whom are graduate students. Brandeis offers students a broad diversity of events: The University attracts noted speakers and artists, there are weekly classical music concerts, and the Spingold Theater Arts Center stages a varied program of dramatic entertainment. The Rose Art Museum offers a full range of paintings and sculpture by prominent artists. Student groups and clubs exist for a wide variety of academic and leisure activities. The Gosman Sports Center is a facility with an indoor track, multipurpose courts, a swimming pool, and weight/fitness rooms. The Boston Celtics train in the Brandeis facilities.

Minutes from Boston, the Heller Graduate School is on Brandeis's picturesque 235-acre suburban campus in Waltham. Shuttle buses and the commuter train link the campus to the state capital, which is rich in history and offers many attractions and cultural resources, and provide easy access to beaches and mountains.

Facilities

Management students interested in social policy benefit from association with an expert research staff in six policy centers conducting nationally significant projects in a wide range of areas. Heller course offerings reflect the work of the Institute for Health Policy, the Policy Center on Aging, the Center for Human Resources, the Family and Child Policy Center, the Center for Social Change, and the Nathan and Toby Starr Center for Mental Retardation. In addition to the work at the six centers, active research is conducted in mental health, substance abuse, work and inequality, and long-term care.

The School also has a state-of-the-art student computer lab containing Windows NT workstations capable of the word processing, spreadsheet development, statistical analysis, and Internet access required for the academic demands of the master's program and anticipated for future employment.

Placement

The educational goal of the master's program is to develop outstanding leaders who are well-prepared for managerial roles in health and human services organizations and responsible citizenship in the community. To assist students in their transition back into the workforce, the Associate Dean for Academic Services and the Career Services Coordinator at the Heller Graduate School provide counseling to students regarding job searches and networking, coordinate listings of job opportunities, and manage the Heller Career Mentor Program, which involves alumni who have volunteered to be coaches and advisers to students reentering the workforce.

Graduates of the master's program have gone on to hold a variety of challenging positions in the not-for-profit, public, and for-profit sectors. According to a recent survey, 76 percent are in management/administration, and 24 percent are in research/policy analysis.

Admission

Recruitment of students to the Heller Graduate School is focused on those individuals who plan to become managers and leaders in health and human services. M.M. students must have an undergraduate degree and two or more years of work experience, although some applicants who have excellent academic records and evidence of leadership potential are accepted directly from undergraduate programs. M.B.A. students must have an undergraduate degree and two or more years of work experience in health or human services (or two years of work experience in another field and extensive volunteer experience in health or human services). Admission is competitive and based on a completed application, Graduate Management Admission Test (GMAT) scores (GRE scores are acceptable for those applying to the M.M. program), undergraduate academic performance, two letters of recommendation, and a writing sample.

Finances

For 1999–2000, the cost of study for the full-time, fifteen-month program was $6105 per semester (four-semester program). Part-time and evening study was $1940 per course.

The Heller School attempts to assist as many students as possible in securing financial aid. Candidates for admission are expected to explore a variety of outside funding sources, such as private scholarships, G.I. bill benefits, and government loan programs. The School has a limited number of need-based scholarships as well as administrative assistantships. In order to be eligible for financial aid of any kind, a candidate must have both the Free Application for Federal Student Aid (FAFSA) and the CSS PROFILE on file at the School. Forms may be obtained from the Office of Finance and Administration. Aid decisions are made on the combined basis of financial need and academic merit. Evening program students can apply for student loans by filing the FAFSA.

In 1999–2000, the cost of living for a single student was about $1300 a month. University housing at Brandeis University is limited; most students rent nearby apartments. Rents for a studio apartment are $500 to $650 a month; a one-bedroom apartment rents for $600 to $700 a month.

Application Facts and Dates

Application forms and financial aid information can be obtained from the Office of Admissions. M.M. and M.B.A. day program applicants must submit their materials by March 15 to begin the program in June, though review of applications begins in November and early application is encouraged. Applications to the M.M. evening program must be submitted by August 1 for fall admission and December 1 for spring admission. Prospective applicants are invited to attend information sessions.

For more information, students should contact:

Office of Admissions
The Heller Graduate School, MS 035
Brandeis University
Waltham, Massachusetts 02454-9110
Telephone: 781-736-3820
Fax: 781-736-3881
E-mail: hellergs@brandeis.edu
World Wide Web: http://heller.
   brandeis.edu

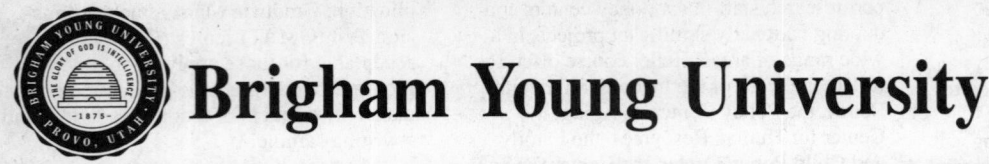

Brigham Young University

Marriott School

Provo, Utah

DEVELOPING LEADERS FOR THE TWENTY-FIRST CENTURY

At the Marriott School, we have long believed that great input leads to great output. That's why one of our major focuses has been attracting outstanding students from across the nation and around the world. Over the past decade, we have seen marked improvements in the qualifications of our entering students.

Input alone doesn't produce great managers. We have adopted a unique approach to business education that is not only rooted in strong management and disciplinary training but is also supported by an emphasis on value- and principle-based leadership.

The combination of this input and our faculty's expertise produces men and women prepared to become outstanding contributors and leaders in organizations throughout the world.

—Ned C. Hill, Dean

Programs and Curricular Focus

The Master of Business Administration (M.B.A.) program is designed to provide a balance between general management training and in-depth functional specialization. Students spend the majority of their first year in a general management core that ensures breadth of understanding. In these core classes, students work in preassigned teams that are designed to ensure diverse backgrounds and cultural viewpoints. Most of the core classes are taught using the case method.

While the core curriculum engenders general management capabilities, the M.B.A. program also creates opportunities for disciplinary specialization. During the first year, students enroll in specialty tracks that run parallel to the core. The formal tracks currently available are finance, marketing, organizational behavior, and information systems management. Students may also choose a self-managed track, which allows them to customize their own curriculum.

The Marriott School's track system is distinctive in the respect that faculty members feel a sense of responsibility for the tracks they supervise. Faculty members are responsible for designing and delivering the track curriculum and are held accountable for the quality of the track's activities, including the placement of students. This system of specialized skill development, combined with a solid management core, produces graduates with leadership skills who can immediately contribute to the bottom line.

Students and the M.B.A. Experience

The M.B.A. program uses a combination of case studies, conferences, lectures, computer simulations, group presentations, and field studies, all designed to develop managerial skills and to assist in the acquisition of knowledge. As a result, a high level of student participation is required. The classroom becomes a forum for considering management problems, testing analytical skill and judgment, exercising oral and written expression, and increasing knowledge. Students work extensively in groups.

Special Features

A Marriott School education is enhanced by several auxiliary centers. The new Rollins Center for eBusiness is preparing students to manage the digital world. It is positioned to become one of the leading e-commerce institutions in the nation. The Center for Entrepreneurship hosts renowned executives for weekly lectures and helps provide research projects, internships, and classes that focus on creativity and new venture management. The Center of International Business Education and Research (CIBER) focuses on an international curriculum (business classes are taught in eight foreign languages), faculty research programs, student scholarships, international conferences, and visiting international faculty.

The Faculty

The Marriott School faculty members are productive scholars with a commitment to students and to teaching. In this role, they become mentors as well as teachers. Marriott School faculty members are willing and able to teach, direct, and inspire students. Many of the faculty members are recognized as leaders in their respective fields. Some currently serve as leaders of professional organizations, such as the American Academy of Management, American Accounting Association, and American Taxation Association. Active involvement in these organizations as well as consulting with leading firms helps faculty members integrate contemporary, practical, and theoretical business principles into the M.B.A. curriculum. Of the 118 full-time faculty members, 99 percent have Ph.D.s.

The Business School Network

One of the Marriott School's greatest strengths is the support it receives from national professional groups, including the Marriott School National Advisory Council, Entrepreneur Founders, Marriott School Alumni Board, and national and international chapters of the Brigham Young University (BYU) Management Society. These select groups of experienced men and women have become leaders in business and government. They return to BYU to help direct and support the Marriott School by meeting regularly with the administration and faculty,

Brigham Young University is nestled in the heart of the beautiful Wasatch Mountains.

Students in the Marriott School enjoy close associations with their colleagues.

mentoring students, and committing their time, skills, and resources to the School.

Prominent Alumni

Prominent alumni and supporters include the Chair of Host Marriott Corporation, Chair of Nationwide Insurance, President and CEO of Black & Decker Corporation, Co-Chair of Franklin Covey, Former Chair of LifeRE Insurance, Former Chair and CEO of Times Mirror Company, Vice Chair of Dell Computers, President and CEO of Madison Square Garden, President and CEO of Salt Lake Organizing Committee for the 2002 Winter Olympics, and CFO of Amazon.com.

The College and Environs

BYU is the largest privately owned, church-sponsored university in the United States. It was established by the Church of Jesus Christ of Latter-day Saints in 1875.

The University is located on a beautiful 600-acre campus at the foot of the Wasatch Mountains in Provo, Utah. The University has excellent cultural programs and is near numerous outdoor recreational areas for skiing (water and snow), hiking, biking, and camping. Salt Lake City, 45 miles north, offers the Utah Symphony, Ballet West, and Pioneer Theater, as well as professional basketball, baseball, and hockey.

BYU has approximately 30,000 full-time students, including 900 who are enrolled in the Marriott School's five graduate programs.

Facilities

The School is housed in the seven-story N. Eldon Tanner Building, which provides computer facilities, research areas, technology-enhanced learning environment classrooms, and special graduate study rooms. The University's Lee Library houses more than 4 million volumes. A new business wing of the library, which opened in 1999, more than tripled the size of the business school's library.

Technology Environment

The Marriott School provides student computer labs as well as Internet connections in the Tanner Building's atrium. The School utilizes technology both in instructional design and in the provision of Web-based student services. Students receive extensive training in the use of business-related computer applications. These technologies are integrated directly with course material.

Placement

Placement, internship, and field studies support are being combined in the Marriott School's new Corporate Development and Career Services Center. The center is scheduled for completion in fall 2000 and will provide more space and enhanced placement and career development assistance for students and recruiters. Located on the fourth floor of the Tanner Building, the center will house an advanced career resource library, twenty interview rooms, a hosting center, and administrative offices. The career resource library is designed to provide students with current information on careers, companies, cost-of-living indexes, and other information to help students make the best employment decisions. The center's interview rooms will be equipped with video interviewing and conferencing capabilities as well as Internet connections. The hosting center will provide a business environment for corporate partners to host company presentations and share information about their firms. The center's professional staff offers career counseling and interview and resume advice as well as helping to facilitate both on- and off-campus recruiting. Students can also include their resumes in the School's searchable, online graduate resume database.

Admission

The M.B.A. admissions committee considers a student's overall GPA, with an emphasis on performance during the last two years of undergraduate education; the GMAT score, paying particular attention to the quantitative score; work experience; and evidence of leadership skills from the letter of intent, the letters of recommendation, and personal essays. Students who have graduated from a university where the primary language is not English must also receive a minimum TOEFL score of 570 on the paper-based test or 230 on the computer-based test. The average GMAT score for the class of 2001 was 642, and the average undergraduate GPA was 3.53.

Finances

Tuition for 2000–01 is $2770 per semester for members of the Church of Jesus Christ of Latter-day Saints and $4160 per semester for nonmembers. Books and supplies average $700 per semester.

The School provides financial assistance to qualified students through scholarship grants, teaching and research assistantships, and loans (including Federal Stafford Student Loans) handled by the University's financial aid office. Approximately 70 percent of M.B.A. students receive some form of financial assistance.

International Students

Approximately 20 percent of the M.B.A. students are international. The University provides numerous support programs through the international services office. Nearly two thirds of the faculty members and more than 80 percent of the students are bilingual. In addition, some 30 percent of the students speak three or more languages. This diversity enhances the education of Marriott School students, helping to instill a global business perspective.

Application Facts and Dates

The priority application deadline is January 15, and the final application deadline is March 1. The international student application deadline is January 15. Students should take the GMAT no later than January of the year in which they are applying. It is recommended that students apply early, as applications are evaluated in the order they are received.

M.B.A. Program Office
Marriott School
640 Tanner Building
Brigham Young University
Provo, Utah 84602
Telephone: 801-378-3500
Fax: 801-378-4808
E-mail: mba@byu.edu
World Wide Web:
    http://marriottschool.byu.edu/mba

Bryant College

Smithfield, Rhode Island

PROFESSIONAL DEVELOPMENT THROUGH A STUDENT-CENTERED PROGRAM

The Graduate School at Bryant College is dedicated to providing students a rich and rewarding professional development experience. All of our efforts, from admission to commencement, are student centered. We aspire, in particular, to ensure that graduate programs and instructional methods are tailored to meet the distinctive needs of the professional population we serve.

I am delighted to invite students to participate in the Bryant M.B.A. I am confident that it will prove to be among the most rewarding experiences of their professional lives.

—Dayle Nattress, Ph.D., Dean

Programs and Curricular Focus

The Bryant M.B.A. program uses a hands-on approach to learning that links theory to real life and prepares business-people to manage change, build and lead cohesive teams, and make sound decisions based upon incisive analysis. M.B.A. students may choose to concentrate in accounting, computer information systems, finance, management, operations management, marketing, or general business. The Bryant M.B.A. program is accredited by the prestigious AACSB–The International Association for Management Education.

Program courses are offered in the evening. Most students complete the program on a part-time basis while working full-time, and earn their degrees in three to six years. Students carrying a full-time course load who have undergraduate degrees in business may achieve their degrees in as little as one year. International students must maintain full-time status.

The M.B.A. program consists of 48 semester hours of courses. Required core courses provide 33 credits of a broad business foundation. The program is completed with 15 credits of electives, most in a chosen field of concentration.

Professionals in the field of accounting may be interested in Bryant's Master of Science in Taxation or Master of Science in Accounting programs. Experienced managers who already have a master's degree but are interested in developing their knowledge in a particular field may be interested in a Certificate of Advanced Graduate Study (C.A.G.S.).

Students and the M.B.A. Experience

Bryant graduate students possess diverse academic and professional backgrounds. Students have completed undergraduate degrees in business, social sciences, and engineering. Entering M.B.A. students are an average age of 29, with seven or more years of professional work experience. Women represent 40 percent of the total graduate student population, and international students comprise approximately 30 percent of full-time graduate enrollment.

The M.B.A. curriculum is infused with the challenges of professional practice. Courses are designed to connect to each other and to relate to the real world, adding relevance, coherence, and immediacy to the curriculum. In all classes, the focus is on active, participative learning, using a variety of methods and media, including in-class exercises, role playing, case studies, debates, group projects, and lecture. Bryant's graduate programs provide rigorous immersion into the nuts and bolts of business in such areas as accounting, finance, marketing, and management. There is also an in-depth examination of the all-important intangibles that can make or break a career. Bryant's programs do not just balance the books; they help students to become balanced professionally by developing skills such as leadership, communication, and team building.

The Faculty

Bryant's graduate faculty members are distinguished authors, researchers, consultants, and professional leaders in national and international business, industry, and government. They are full-time professors recognized for their research contributions published in academic and practitioner journals. In addition, faculty members have experience in the areas of public accounting, private accounting, and consulting. They use their practical experience to illustrate and supplement business theories learned in class. Class size averages 20 students in core courses, allowing for valuable interaction between the students and professor.

The Business School Network

Bryant College is more than a leader in business education, it is also renowned for practicing the principles it teaches. Through the College's outreach efforts, Bryant students, the faculty, and the staff form an important resource for the state's economic growth. Students have opportunities to become involved in international trade, telecommunications, management development, technology transfer, and small-business development.

The College and Environs

Bryant College was founded in Providence in 1863. Today it continues in its mission to educate successful businesspeople.

The campus is located on 387 acres in suburban Smithfield, Rhode Island. Modern facilities include a comprehensive business library, computer center, language/learning laboratory, student center, classrooms, and a fitness/sports complex. Students interested in living on campus may choose between traditional double rooms and suites or award-winning town houses.

Placement

The Career Services Office offers a variety of services, including counseling and assessment of career decision making. Assistance is also available for resume writing, interviewing, and job search strategies. Students can access a resource library to research careers or companies. A weekly publication lists current job openings.

Admission

Because Bryant's program integrates real-world experience with concepts, it is preferred that applicants have a minimum of two years of work experience. Entry requirements include a bachelor's degree from an accredited institution. A strong score on the Graduate Management Admission Test (GMAT) is required. For students for whom English is not their primary language, a satisfactory score on the Test of English as a Foreign Language (TOEFL) is required. Prospective students must also submit an official transcript, one letter of recommendation, and a 500-word statement of objectives.

Finances

Tuition for the 2000–01 academic year is $1170 per 3-credit course. The fee for a single room in the town houses during the 2000–01 school year is $5500; for a double, $5200. A $100 deposit is required to reserve a room. A nineteen-meal-per-week plan costs $3000.

Students may compete for graduate assistantships, working with an academic department related to their concentration area or with the Center for International Business (CIB). Responsibilities may include faculty support, academic research, or preparation of class materials. Up to four courses may be offset with an assistantship, at which a student may work a maximum of 16 hours per week.

International Students

Thirty-two percent of the full-time graduate students come from outside of the United States. The Multicultural Student Services Office provides orientation directed to acclimating international students to American classroom conduct and culture. This office provides ongoing support and counsel.

Application Facts and Dates

Application deadlines are July 15 for the fall semester, November 15 for the spring semester, and April 1 for the summer session. There is a $60 application fee that must be submitted with the completed application form. International students' admission applications and full-time students' graduate assistant applications are due April 1 for the fall term and November 15 for the spring term. March 1 is the deadline for international students who are applying for the summer session. For more information, students should contact:

Graduate Admission
Bryant College
1150 Douglas Pike
Smithfield, Rhode Island 02917
Telephone: 401-232-6230
Fax: 401-232-6494
E-mail: gradprog@bryant.edu

Carnegie Mellon University

Graduate School of Industrial Administration

Pittsburgh, Pennsylvania

> **BUILDING A SUCCESSFUL CAREER TOGETHER**
>
> *What makes Carnegie Mellon University's Graduate School of Industrial Administration (GSIA) savvy enough to always be in touch with the latest dynamic global economy, industries, currencies, and multimedia intelligence? Superb management processes tie the students, faculty, and school to the business community of tomorrow. We recognize that the challenge for our graduates will be to anticipate, adapt, and lead in this dynamic economy. We educate professionals who can analyze data quickly and apply quantitative methods easily. Our students learn to capture the best technology and bring it to markets successfully. Armed with consensus-building skills, our students form lifelong partnerships with our business school—partnerships that help them harness the management technologies of today's new economy.*
>
> —Douglas M. Dunn, Dean

Programs and Curricular Focus

By the terms of its original charter, GSIA offers a two-year full-time Master of Science in Industrial Administration (M.S.I.A.) degree, which is similar to the M.B.A. degree. To fulfill the requirements for the M.S.I.A. degree, students must satisfactorily complete, with a grade of C- or better, all of the required courses, totaling 96 units, and a minimum of 108 units of elective courses. To encourage collaboration and to encourage students to choose courses that challenge them, student grades and class rank are not disclosed. Almost all students leave GSIA at the end of their first year for a summer internship.

GSIA emphasizes interdisciplinary thinking. There are no departments at GSIA, and there are no required majors in the M.S.I.A. program, although students must fulfill certain breadth and depth requirements. A rich collection of electives allows students the flexibility to focus on areas of special interest.

GSIA also offers a three-year M.S.I.A. option, which provides students with a chance to earn a graduate degree while continuing their careers; an early graduation option; an intensive, twelve-month M.S. in Computational Finance (M.S.C.F.) program; a twelve-month M.S. in Electronic Commerce (M.S.E.C.); a twenty-month Master's in Business Management and Software Engineering (M.B.M.S.E.) program; a two-year Master of Science in Civil Engineering and Management (M.S.C.E.M.) program; a two-year Master of Science in Environmental Engineering and Manage-ment program; a fourteen month Master of Science in Information Networking program (M.S.I.N.); a J.D./M.S.I.A. dual-degree program offered in conjunction with the University of Pittsburgh School of Law; and a collaborative program in private and public management and policy in conjunction with Carnegie Mellon's Heinz School of Public Policy and Management.

Students and the M.B.A. Experience

The GSIA student body exhibits diverse backgrounds, with undergraduate degrees split almost evenly between technical and nontechnical majors. All parts of the United States and more than thirty countries are represented in the average entering class, which normally numbers 220. About 99 percent of GSIA students have full-time post-graduate work experience, with an average of five years each. This mix of students invigorates the educational experience at GSIA, where teamwork and student interaction play a larger role than at virtually any other top business school. Because GSIA recognizes that most managers' business lives revolve around critical small group meetings, students work on projects in small groups for many of their courses. GSIA's emphasis on group work encourages the development of interpersonal skills while fostering a cooperative, rather than competitive, educational experience.

❖ Global Focus

M.S.I.A. candidates can spend a semester abroad attending one of GSIA's many partner universities, including Koblenz School of Corporate Management in Germany, Lyon Graduate School of Business in France, Manchester Business School in the United Kingdom, The Wirtschaftsuniversitat Wien in Austria, and the Monterrey Institute of Technology in Mexico. GSIA also has formed numerous alliances with other universities worldwide, including the University of Bradford in the United Kingdom, the Academy of National Economy in Russia, the University of Nancy in France, Universitat Pompeu Fabra in Spain, Hong Kong University of Science and Technology, City Polytechnic of Hong Kong, Aoyama Gakuin University in Japan, and Umea University in Sweden. GSIA is also the home of the Carnegie Bosch Institute for Applied Studies in International Management.

While most courses offer a global perspective, GSIA offers several specific courses in international business, as well as language courses in French, German, Japanese, and Spanish that are specifically tailored for business students.

Special Features

The School's mini-semester system—a GSIA innovation now copied by other top business schools—splits the typical semester in half, creating four mini-semesters per academic year. This enables students to gain exposure to a wide range of topics and unique courses (18 electives in all) such as FAST—the program in Financial Analysis and Security Trading, which gives students access to the latest trading hardware, software, and data feeds—and the Entrepreneurship Project—which teaches students to create and evaluate ideas for new businesses. The most popular elective areas include finance, e-commerce, operations management, infotechnology, and entrepreneurship.

The capstone course, Management Game, taken during the spring of the first year and fall of the second year, uses complex computer simulations of a consumer products industry to engage students in teamwork, decision making, negotiation, and communication. Teams of 5 to 7 students act as senior managers and make strategic decisions involving marketing, financing, production, and research and development. Each team meets with a board of directors, drawn from alumni and major corporations, and works out labor contracts with representatives from local unions. Area bankers arrange financing, and teams seek out legal advice from third-year law students at the University of Pittsburgh Law School.

The Faculty

GSIA faculty members have won worldwide acclaim—as well as three Nobel Prizes—for their groundbreaking research in organizational theory, artificial intelligence, operations research, and corporate finance. Faculty members from various fields work together on projects, as it is GSIA's conviction that important new ideas come from interdisciplinary research. The small size of the student body results in a student-faculty ratio that is among the best of top-tier graduate business programs.

The Business School Network

Students have a multitude of opportunities to interact with business executives while in the program. Project courses allow students to gain hands-on experience solving real-world problems for company clients. Top executives are frequent guests on campus and share their experiences with students both inside and outside the classroom. Career forums, workshops, and the corporate presentation series provide venues for students to explore career issues through the experience of successful professionals. Students also have opportunities to network with participants in the Executive Education programs.

Prominent Alumni

Because of its commitment to progressive, interdisciplinary education, Carnegie Mellon alumni rapidly become leaders. Among its 49,000 alumni, the University counts nearly 3,400 company chairpersons, chief executive officers, presidents, and vice presidents, including Paul A. Allaire (class of 1966), Chairman and CEO, Xerox Corporation; Michael J. Bertasso (class of 1976), Senior Vice President, H.J. Heinz Company; David A. Coulter (class of 1971), former CEO, Bank America Corporation; Dina Dublon (class of 1979), CFO, Chase Manhattan; Cyrus F. Freidheim Jr. (class of 1963), Vice Chairman, Booz•Allen & Hamilton, Inc.; T. Jerome Holleran (class of 1969), President, Precision Medical Products, Inc.; T. Patrick Kelly (class of 1984), CFO, The SABRE Group; James H. Levy (class of 1966), Chairman and CEO, Park Lane Group; Paul W. Lewis (class of 1973), Assistant Treasurer, Ford Motor Company; Therese E. Myers (class of 1968), CEO, Bouquet Multimedia; Anne-Marie Petach (class of 1984),

Assistant Treasurer, Ford Motor Company; J. Thomas Presby (class of 1963), COO, Deloitte and Touche; and Frank A. Risch (class of 1966), Assistant Treasurer, Exxon Corporation.

The College and Environs

Carnegie Mellon is a small university of approximately 7,000 students; more than one third are graduate students. Nearly 560 faculty members hold full-time teaching positions, and another 250 are scientists on research staffs.

Pittsburgh is a big-league city with small-town assets—low crime rates, tree-lined streets, and one of the cleanest and healthiest environments of any major city. Cozy neighborhoods, Fortune 500 headquarters, major league sports teams, and world-class symphony, opera, ballet, and theater all reside in this friendly city. Pittsburgh is one of the top ten largest corporate headquarters cities in the United States, and Pittsburgh International Airport is one of the largest in the nation.

Technology Environment

Many classrooms are equipped with power and network hookups allowing students to plug in required laptop computers, and wireless access to the campus computer network is available throughout the school. There are also satellite downlinks to all classrooms, and the school has installed interactive video equipment to take advantage of videoconferencing, using this technology for job interviews and discussions with corporate project partners. Nearly all GSIA students enroll in voluntary, noncredit training courses in which they learn to use the University's sophisticated computer networks—the backbone of current and future computing.

Placement

The Career Opportunities Center provides excellent resources for every GSIA student's job search. Individual counseling and job search workshops help students plot their job search strategies and polish resume writing, interviewing, and salary negotiation skills. Career forums bring panels of corporate representatives from various fields to campus, and students are encouraged to contact alumni who have succeeded in their area of interest. Recruiting forums provide students with opportunities to talk to firms in various parts of the U.S. and the world. Students have access to numerous other resources including a World Wide Web recruiting system, alumni database, and interactive searches. Alumni are active in providing mock interviews, resume reviews, and mentoring relationships.

Admission

GSIA seeks a diverse student body and welcomes applications from those who have worked and studied in many fields; previous study in business-related areas is not required. Because the M.S.I.A. program is quantitatively and analytically oriented, previous course work and a demonstrated capacity for mathematics are essential for successful performance. Students must possess good interpersonal and communications skills and must be highly motivated, self-directed, energetic, and innovative. GSIA looks at the applicant's entire academic record: grade trends, major areas of study, school of graduation, extracurricular activities, and part-time and full-time work. GMAT scores, letters of recommendation, essays, and a personal interview are also vital to the evaluation process. Above all, GSIA's central concern in admissions is the applicant's academic potential and promise for a productive management career.

Finances

Estimated 2000–01 tuition and fees costs are tuition, $26,750; activity fee, $136; room and board, $9800; and books, $1450. Carnegie Mellon provides a variety of scholarships and financial aid possibilities designed to equalize educational opportunities. Financial aid awards are based on need as determined by filing the U.S. Department of Education's Free Application for Federal Student Aid (FAFSA) and the NEED ACCESS Application. Scholarship awards are based solely on merit. GSIA General Fellowships are awarded to students in good academic standing who demonstrate financial need. Federal Perkins Loans, Federal Stafford Loans, privately insured loans, international student loans, and work-study are also available.

Application Facts and Dates

Students who apply by November 17 are notified by December 18; those who apply by January 31 are notified by February 28; those who apply by March 23 are notified by April 23. After March 23 admissions are on a rolling basis. Interested students should contact:

Graduate School of Industrial Administration
Carnegie Mellon University
Schenley Park
Pittsburgh, Pennsylvania 15213
Telephone: 412-268-2272
              800-850-GSIA (toll-free, U.S. only)
Fax: 412-268-4209
E-mail: gsia-admissions@andrew.cmu.edu
World Wide Web: http://www.gsia.cmu.edu

Case Western Reserve University

> ### THE WEATHERHEAD FOCUS ON MANAGEMENT IN THE DIGITAL ECONOMY
>
> *The Weatherhead School integrates strategic, interdisciplinary, and entrepreneurial approaches in educating management leaders for an environment in which telecommunications and information technology are of increasing importance. Our objective is to enable managers to benefit from opportunities created by a digital economy through the development of business strategies and the application of innovative technologies. We accomplish this by including basic Web page design and implementation in the core curriculum taken by all students. Opportunities for students to study the digital economy in depth include a 9-credit specialization in e-business as part of the M.B.A. degree, or, for more advanced preparation in e-business, M.B.A. students may complete a 15-credit certificate program.*
>
> *—Julia Grant, MBA Faculty Director and Associate Professor of Accountancy*

Programs and Curricular Focus

The Weatherhead M.B.A. curriculum emphasizes the assessment and development of management skills along with knowledge of the functional areas of business and offers a liberalizing experience through exploration of the diverse contexts of management.

The Weatherhead School offers an integrative M.B.A. core curriculum that enhances the potential of each student to create value by drawing from different perspectives to identify, analyze, and resolve complex problems; develop and enhance organizational leadership; make a personal commitment to lifelong learning; add value in a special area of expertise; and contribute to the betterment of communities and society.

Spanning the first year of the M.B.A. program is the Strategic Issues and Applications course, which introduces M.B.A. students to the complexity of issues confronting the manager and the organization.

The Management Assessment and Development course fosters educational partnerships that offer students an active role in developing the shape and character of their learning experience.

Using information gained through individual abilities assessments, M.B.A. students enroll in appropriate Managerial and Career Skills modules. Working in small groups, students learn to master skills in presentation, written and oral communications, group management, team building, negotiation, persuasion,

and collaboration. Second-year M.B.A. students may engage in biweekly dialogues with leaders of regional and multinational organizations in Executive Leadership Dialogues.

The Weatherhead M.B.A. program offers a unique functional core that integrates the management disciplines while also providing students with the tools necessary to identify and analyze issues. The eight core courses are integrated with the Strategic Issues and Applications course to form a solid foundation for management and decision making.

Students complete interdisciplinary thematic electives to examine the ways in which external influences and issues affect organizations and their managers.

The Weatherhead School offers both a four-semester M.B.A. curriculum and an accelerated program for undergraduate business majors beginning in June and ending in May of the following year. Both programs are available on a full-time and part-time basis. Joint-degree programs with the schools of law, nursing, and engineering are available along with master's programs in accountancy and nonprofit organizations, the Master of Science in Management Information Systems, and the Executive Master of Business Administration degree program.

Students and the M.B.A. Experience

The Weatherhead program is composed of highly qualified individuals representing a diversity of academic, professional,

and cultural backgrounds and experiences. The average student is 28 years old, with five years of work experience. Women comprise 32 percent of the class. The campus culture is enriched by international students, who represent 40 percent of the class and forty-eight countries. A typical class represents twenty-five states and twenty countries.

Weatherhead students have undergraduate degrees in a wide variety of disciplines.

❖ Global Focus

M.B.A. students may choose a concentration in international management or complete a joint M.B.A./Master of International Management degree program with the Thunderbird School in Glendale, Arizona. Internship opportunities for M.B.A. students are available in several countries during the summer term. The Weatherhead School participates in third-semester M.B.A. exchange programs with schools of management on four continents. Weatherhead students may participate as Agency for International Development (AID) business advisers in developing countries at the end of their first year in the program and in the M.B.A. Enterprise Corps in one- to two-year post–M.B.A. positions in firms in the former Eastern Bloc nations.

Students can complete their first year of the M.B.A. program at the International Management Center (IMC) in Budapest, Hungary, the most prestigious management school in Central/Eastern Europe.

Special Features

During the first year of the program, the Weatherhead Office of Career Planning and Placement offers a mentoring program and matches students with Cleveland-area executives and managers who help to focus students' academic and career interests. Along with the traditional business concentrations, Weatherhead offers concentrations in the areas of health-care management, e-business, nonprofit management, and entrepreneurial studies.

The Faculty

There are 99 full-time faculty members, all of whom have a doctorate in their

field. Many of the faculty members have earned international reputations for teaching and research. The faculty is housed in seven different departments: accountancy, banking and finance, economics, MIDS, marketing and policy studies, operations research, and organizational behavior. Students benefit from a student-faculty ratio of 14:1.

The Business School Network
The Weatherhead School has forged a strong network of corporate partners in the northeast Ohio area (headquarters of thirty of the Fortune 500 corporations). Students engage in a variety of field projects under the guidance of experienced area executives. The curriculum is enhanced by guest lecturers and speakers from the corporate community.

The Visiting Committee of the Weatherhead School of Management is composed of leaders in the international community who have a continuing concern for the quality of management education. The committee provides counsel and assistance to the School throughout the year.

The College and Environs
The Weatherhead School of Management resides in a parklike campus setting in Cleveland's University Circle. Campus neighbors include Severance Hall, home of the Cleveland Orchestra, and the Cleveland Art and History museums. The Weatherhead campus places students within what is probably the most extensive concentration of educational,

scientific, medical, and cultural institutions in the United States.

Technology Environment
The Weatherhead computer network makes available a wide variety of software, languages, and peripheral equipment. Qualified support personnel are on duty daily, and computer instruction and seminars are offered. Computer-supported conference rooms are available. The School maintains computer-supported classrooms for computer literacy and M.B.A. class instruction. The University computing resources include a unique fiber-optic network linking more than eighty-five campus buildings. Users have access to a range of information resources and networks. Other resources include an integrated online library system and access to off-campus resources, including the Internet.

Placement
The Weatherhead School's Office of Career Planning and Placement provides a placement program for each student. It assists students in focusing career interests and invites recruiters to campus to participate in information sessions, receptions, career forums, seminars, workshops, and mock interviews. A full schedule of placement interviews for both summer and permanent positions is conducted in the fall and spring semesters. In the CareerNet program, alumni from across the country provide advice and placement assistance to students and

graduates. Students can access the entire M.B.A. alumni database through the School computer lab. The Weatherhead School is a founding member of the National M.B.A. Consortium in Chicago, a cooperative corporate interview day for M.B.A. students, with eighty separate corporate schedules.

Admission
Applicants are admitted on the basis of academic and professional accomplishments, performance on the GMAT, individual career goals, written recommendations, and responses to interview and application essay questions. The median GMAT score is 620. The average undergraduate GPA is 3.2. Class size is limited to 150 students.

The Test of English as a Foreign Language is required of all applicants whose native language is not English and who graduated from an educational institution where the language of instruction was not English. A special four-week MBA Language Skills Program is available.

Finances
The 2000–01 tuition and fees are $11,450 per semester. Books and supplies are estimated at $850 per semester. The estimate for room and board is $5500 per semester.

A limited number of merit scholarships are available for individuals with exceptional academic, professional, and life experiences. The School offers an Express Financial Aid Service to expedite determination of the financing options that are available.

International Students
The School offers international students a tuition stabilization plan, internships, and multicultural experiences through the multicultural task force and International Business Club.

Application Facts and Dates
The final application deadline for all applicants is usually in early April. For international candidates living outside the United States, the early decision deadline is usually in mid-March. For more information, students should contact:

Christine Gill
Director of Admissions
The Weatherhead School of
    Management
Case Western Reserve University
Cleveland, Ohio 44106-7235
Telephone: 800-723-0203
Fax: 216-368-5548
E-mail: questions@exchange.som.
    cwru.edu

Chapman University

> ## STRONG FACULTY, PERSONALIZED PROGRAM = STUDENT SUCCESS
>
> *The Argyros School of Business and Economics M.B.A. program benefits from a strong faculty with a commitment to excellent teaching and research. The Argyros School is linked to the entrepreneurial heritage of our Orange County location and is built on the strong analytical framework of our economics faculty.*
>
> *This personalized program offers students close working relationships with a faculty that is committed to student success. The focus on information technology, enhanced by the new Arnold and Mabel Beckman Business and Technology Hall, forms the basis for strategic advantage both now and in the future.*
>
> *We welcome your consideration of our M.B.A. program.*
>
> —Richard McDowell, Dean

Programs and Curricular Focus

The Argyros School of Business and Economics M.B.A. offers students the concepts and tools necessary to formulate sound strategic decisions as well as the leadership skills needed to implement those plans. The program provides rigorous training in the analytical and communication skills needed for success in the contemporary global and entrepreneurial business environment. Specifically, the program is designed to provide a solid economic foundation for making business decisions; develop skills in applying financial, marketing, management, information technology, and statistical techniques to complex management problems; and improve skills in effectively presenting and implementing solutions to business problems.

The M.B.A. curriculum is divided into four groups of courses: 1) cornerstone courses that provide the skills necessary to complete the core courses and are waivable based on demonstrated competence; 2) core courses covering all functional areas of business; 3) capstone courses, which are integrative in nature and; 4) electives through which students may customize the program.

The Argyros School also offers an Executive M.B.A. program for working professionals with organizational experience. The two-year program includes three residentials—one regional, one national, and one international trip designed to provide three important perspectives on business issues and practices.

Students and the M.B.A. Experience

The Argyros School of Business and Economics has a diverse M.B.A. population that totals 175 full- and part-time students and 50 executive M.B.A.'s. The average age at entrance to the M.B.A. program is 27, with four years of work experience. Women comprise 38 percent of the M.B.A. student population, and minority students make up 30 percent. Foreign nationals comprise 19 percent of the student body, with 20 percent coming from Europe, 75 percent from Asia, and the remaining 5 percent from throughout the world.

❖ Global Focus

Chapman's Walter Schmid Center for International Business was founded in 1992. Its goal is to provide facilities and support for students and faculty engaged in international business and economics research. The center also disseminates results of its research to the business community and consults both U.S. and international companies on all data required to make decisions for international trade, i.e. markets, business conditions, and the legal and regulatory environments. The Fletcher Jones Chair in International Business plays a leadership role in the Center and in the integration of an international dimension in the School's research and curriculum.

Special Features

The Ralph W. Leatherby Center for Entrepreneurship and Business Ethics was es-

tablished to promote the study of entrepreneurship within a framework of ethical business practices. The center provides a sequence of entrepreneurial courses, creates opportunities for students to work closely with entrepreneurs, arranges seminars, and provides general reference information relevant to entrepreneurs. The work of this center demonstrates the University's dedication to the nurturing and promotion of entrepreneurialism.

The Faculty

Faculty members at the Argyros School of Business and Economics have as their first priority the enhancement of the learning experience. Chapman has a long tradition of emphasizing outstanding teaching. Faculty members have chosen to teach in a small school, with an emphasis on personalized education. They are accessible and approachable. At the same time, the Chapman faculty members are from major universities, are committed to research and scholarly endeavors, and are well-published in major academic journals.

The Business School Network

The A. Gary Anderson Center for Economic Research provides the cornerstone for Chapman's strong relationship with the southern California business community. The center, with the involvement of students, has developed and continually improves a complex econometric model used to forecast economic trends for southern California. One thousand business leaders participate annually in the Argyros School of Business and Economics' forecast events. The Ralph W. Leatherby Center for Entrepreneurship and Business Ethics sponsors conferences and guest speakers on small business. There are numerous additional opportunities for students to interface with business leaders through guest lectures and speaker series.

The College and Environs

Founded in 1861, Chapman University is situated on approximately 50 acres in Orange, California. The mission of the University is to provide a personalized education of distinction that leads to inquiring, ethical, and productive lives as

global citizens. Chapman is located 35 miles southeast of Los Angeles and 90 miles from San Diego and Mexico. Ocean beaches are less than 10 miles away; mountains and deserts are within an hour's drive. Within minutes are such attractions as Disneyland, Knott's Berry Farm, Orange County Performing Arts Center, Pacific Amphitheater, and Anaheim Stadium.

Facilities

The Arnold and Mabel Beckman Business and Technology Hall, completed in January 1999, provides students with a state-of-the-art learning environment. The building design integrates today's technology into the classroom and prepares the school to take advantage of future innovations. The building creates a synergy between telecommunications, technology, and the business world.

The use of computer technology is an integral part of the M.B.A. program. Beckman Hall has the most up-to-date computer labs, with approximately eighty IBM-based and fifty Macintosh computers and a staff that is available for individual assistance. In addition, workshops are given for those who need to learn or refresh their skills. Each student receives an Internet account and an e-mail address upon enrollment.

Placement

The Career Development Center offers a number of services and programs that assist students with their professional development. The dual focus includes both assisting students in identifying their career goals and preparing them for an effective job search. On-campus recruiting takes place in the fall (for accounting

firms) and spring semesters. National as well as local companies come to the campus to recruit students. Networking is encouraged through alumni mentor programs, alumni career days, and a myriad of business events that are held on campus.

Admission

Admission to the M.B.A. program requires a bachelor's degree from an accredited college or university, a completed application for admission, transcripts of all previous course work, an acceptable score on the GMAT, and two letters of recommendation. International students must submit a TOEFL score of 550 or above and a statement of financial resources.

Finances

The 2000–01 tuition for the M.B.A. program is $605 per credit for either part- or full-time study. Tuition for the Executive M.B.A. is $45,000 for the two-year program. Financial aid opportunities are offered to graduate students through tuition grants, graduate fellowships, and loans. Scholarships are based on performance on the GMAT as well as on undergraduate GPA. The loan programs include the federally sponsored Stafford subsidized and unsubsidized student loans and privately sponsored loans.

International Students

Nineteen percent of Chapman's M.B.A. population comes from outside the United States. The International Students Services office acts as a source of information and assistance, with the goal of making the international experience a comfortable and productive one. The office sponsors an orientation program; counseling on academic, financial and personal matters; assistance in class registration; information on immigration requirements; and information on social and cultural events. Various informational and social events are organized throughout the year.

Application Facts and Dates

Applications for the fall, spring, and summer sessions should be received by June 15, November 15, and April 15, respectively. The deadline for consideration for financial aid is March 2. For information and application materials, students should contact:

Office of Graduate Admissions
Chapman University
333 North Glassell Street
Orange, California 92866
Telephone: 714-997-6786

City University

> ### DEVELOPING BUSINESS LEADERS FOR THE TWENTY-FIRST CENTURY
>
> *Innovation, responsiveness, and commitment to excellence have been City University's standards since our founding in 1973. Our M.B.A. program exemplifies these standards. Well-respected and well-established, the M.B.A. program at City University assists learners in achieving excellence in their chosen field via teaching and learning communities that foster exploration, examination, and extension of professional theory and practice. Students are compelled to reach inward to achieve personal leadership, and reach forward to embrace changes and challenges—today, tomorrow, and in the twenty-first century.*
>
> —Douglas Arnold, Associate Dean

Programs and Curricular Focus

City University's M.B.A. program is oriented toward adult learners who are self-starters, who seek recognition as leaders among their peers, and whose intellectual curiosity takes them beyond the simple finding of solutions to advanced inquiry and the formulation of new questions.

The M.B.A. program offers a strategic systems approach to leading and managing organizations. Specifically, the M.B.A. focuses on those strategic systems that are critical to transforming the way we work. These systems are approached from a conceptual framework that is strategy-driven, stakeholder-oriented, and teamwork-based, supported by data-based decision making, guided by vision and a whole systems organizational design, and enhanced by continuous improvement through organizational learning. Within this framework, students explore established business practices and learn to understand and anticipate future trends as well. They analyze management principles, strategies, and philosophies in regard to the local workplace as well as the global economy.

Students may pursue one of several M.B.A. specializations. The structure of the M.B.A. is simple: a common 33-credit core and (with some exceptions) a 12-credit specialty block.

The common core is a series of eleven courses that build skills essential to the successful completion of a graduate degree program in business. At the same time, they introduce the major sectors of knowledge whose application is important to each of the respective specializations.

To the greatest extent possible, every core course explores the ethical and philosophical issues underlying the subject, affords an opportunity for oral presentation and analytical research, and relates content to leadership, socially conscious, humanitarian, and environmental dimensions.

The specialty block, effectively the major component, aggregates four courses with content particular to each specialization. Regardless of specialty, all M.B.A. students hone skills in general management, leadership, and organizational development and change management.

City University also offers a combined M.B.A./M.P.A. for those students whose career pursuits place them in the arena of both governmental and profit-oriented organizational management.

Students and the M.B.A. Experience

Of the students enrolled in the M.B.A. program, 39 percent are women, 23 percent represent members of minority groups, and 10 percent are international students. The average age of the students is 36 years. Consequently, students who enter City University's M.B.A. program typically have several years of work experience behind them.

Course work combines textbook theory with current, real-world case studies. Research is a significant component in all courses; it is second in emphasis only to in-class discussion. Faculty members encourage discussion, rather than sticking to straight lecture; this is facilitated by the fact that City

University maintains an average class size of 24 students. Students also engage in team projects and student presentations.

❖ Global Focus

City University's M.B.A. program enjoys a global focus for several reasons. Every core M.B.A. course contains an international business slant, thanks to specially selected texts and readings. Cultural exchange also takes place in the classroom when students from different countries travel to pursue their M.B.A. at the University's various sites in North America, Germany, and Switzerland.

As City University makes its M.B.A. program available on-line, education will become truly global. Students from all around the world will gather in "electronic classrooms" to share learning, ideas, and experience.

Special Features

One of the most innovative features of City University's M.B.A. program is the variety of formats in which it is offered. Students are welcome to take classes in the daytime, evening, or on weekends. In addition, the University offers its M.B.A. degree via Distance Learning (DL), which allows students to complete the same course work required for classroom-based courses outside the classroom itself.

City University is especially proud to announce the availability of its M.B.A. program on-line. Using the Internet, students are able to register for and complete courses electronically. Through City University's World Wide Web site, students access live forums featuring special guests; post messages to other students and faculty; participate in live, course-specific study groups; and communicate with students, faculty, and advisers via e-mail. Taking advantage of this exciting technology is another example of City University's commitment to maximizing educational opportunities.

The Faculty

Distinguished practitioners in the fields of business, education, government, health care, and human services; civic and research organizations; and the legal community comprise the City University faculty. They unite strong academic preparation and active professional careers in the fields in which they teach. City University employs 15 full-time faculty members and more than 400 adjunct faculty members to deliver its M.B.A. courses. Of these, 30 percent are women, and 9 percent are members of minority groups.

The Business School Network

City University prides itself on the successful relationships it has established with the corporate community. Corporate representatives are an integral part of the community advisory groups that help the University to update course content, relate courses to current trends in the marketplace, and ensure that programs provide students with skills employers are seeking. In addition, City University is able to offer its M.B.A. program in-house to companies. These have included such industry leaders as Boeing, Weyerhaeuser, and Siemens/Nixdorf Corporation (Germany).

The College and Environs

City University opened its doors in 1973 with one primary purpose: to provide educational opportunities for those segments of the population not being fully served through traditional means. This purpose has guided the University's growth from a single-room facility in Seattle, Washington, to an international leader in education with nearly two dozen locations worldwide. City University's headquarters are located in Bellevue, Washington. It operates instructional sites in other locations in the United States, Canada, Denmark, Germany, Switzerland, and Slovakia.

City University is accredited by the Northwest Association of Schools and Colleges. It offers over eighty programs at the undergraduate and graduate levels. Students who attend one of the University's North American sites will enjoy the temperate climate of the Pacific Northwest, its beautiful landscape, and its clean and cultured cities.

Facilities

City University's library serves students throughout the Seattle area, providing extensive reference resources, indexes and journals, and on-line databases. The library maintains cooperative arrangements with many other libraries. Furthermore, the library conducts searches for students who call in from outlying areas and arranges to send them annotated bibliographies and other information when possible.

Technology Environment

The University requires students to have access to a computer. Students are expected to use computer technology in the development of research papers; certain M.B.A. courses require computerized data manipulation as well. The University has established two computer labs at sites in the Seattle area and small lab facilities at outlying sites.

Placement

City University's Alumni Association operates a Career Resource Center, which provides assistance to graduates and current students in finding professionally satisfying employment. More than 500 employers currently list position openings with the center. In addition, the Alumni Association publishes a networking directory to help alumni maintain important and useful professional contacts. The University does not provide direct placement services for its students.

Admission

Generally, admission to City University graduate programs requires that students hold a baccalaureate degree or equivalent from an accredited or otherwise recognized institution. No specific undergraduate emphasis or major is required for entrance into a particular graduate program.

If available, reported scores on standardized entrance examinations such as the Graduate Record Examinations (GRE), the Miller Analogies Test (MAT), and the Graduate Management Admission Test (GMAT) should be submitted, although they are not required.

Finances

Standard tuition rates for graduate courses for the 2000–01 academic year are $309 per credit, or $927 per 3-credit class. While the number of required texts and other course materials vary with each course, textbooks typically each cost between $80 and $95.

City University does not provide student housing. In the Seattle area, rental expenses for a one-bedroom apartment are approximately $700.

For information about financial assistance, contact the Student Financial Services office at the toll-free number listed below.

International Students

The University's International Student Affairs Office helps international students to adjust to life and study in the United States and Canada, offering assistance with procedures related to the issuance and maintenance of student visas, counseling in academic matters, and student referral to appropriate agencies for health and other services.

Application Facts and Dates

A rolling admissions policy governs most City University programs. That is, the University accepts applications and announces admissions decisions continuously throughout the year. Most degree programs may be commenced in the fall, winter, spring, or summer quarter or at the monthly start of Distance Learning courses. For more information, students should contact:

Office of Admissions
City University
919 Southwest Grady Way
Renton, Washington 98055
Telephone: 206-637-1010
          425-450-4660 (TYY/TDD)
          800-426-5596 (toll-free)
Fax: 206-277-2437
E-mail: info@cityu.edu
World Wide Web: http://www.cityu.edu

Claremont Graduate University

A FUSION OF LEADERSHIP, STRATEGY, AND MANAGEMENT

The Peter F. Drucker Graduate School of Management is committed to delivering an academic program of the highest international standard. Our purpose is to make a difference in the lives of those with whom we learn and in the institutions we serve. To this end, we emphasize the liberal art of management—an integrating discipline of human values and conduct, of social order and intellectual inquiry in the quest for lifelong learning. We seek to equip our students not only for the management realities of today but also for the new realities that await us in the global century of connectivity and relationship. Consistent with this pioneering vision of Peter F. Drucker, our faculty is a team of outstanding scholars and practitioners whose first and primary purpose is to enhance the professional lives of our students and the organizations they lead.

—Peter R. D. Withers, Director, Management Program

Programs and Curricular Focus

The Peter F. Drucker Graduate School of Management has been delivering top-quality executive and management education for more than twenty-five years. From its earliest days, the School has emphasized the importance of outstanding scholarship and its relevance to practicing managers. One of the two degree programs, the Master of Business Administration (the Drucker M.B.A.), is geared toward those students who join the School with two to five years of prior work experience. The Executive Management Program educates managers who work in the upper echelon of their organizations.

The early-career M.B.A. provides leadership and strategy training for the advancement of individuals and organizations, and it is widely recognized for academic rigor, exceptional teaching, and a highly personalized and supportive environment. The Drucker M.B.A. embodies the philosophies of management pioneer Peter F. Drucker, a longtime faculty member and prolific writer and lecturer on management. The program's success is based on several key concepts, including the convergence of theory and practice, aligning core competencies and market needs, and succeeding as an exemplary executive. Students learn to apply cutting-edge theory and the best practices from multiple disciplines, functions, and cultures to pivotal management and leadership challenges to derive and implement innovative solutions that address short-term needs and position the students

and their organizations for long-term success. Students are also trained to integrate the talents of individuals, departments, organizations, industries, societies, and nations to achieve rapid progress. Drucker graduates benefit from course work designed to provide them with vision, critical insight, know-how, skills, and tools to become exemplary strategic leaders.

Students and the M.B.A. Experience

The Drucker M.B.A. comprises 60 academic units (with 4 units allotted to a typical course). The program takes between twenty-four and thirty-six months to complete, depending on whether a student attends full- or part-time and has prior business course work and experience. Classroom experience is enriched through student participation and faculty blending of the theory and practice of strategy, leadership, and management.

The Drucker M.B.A. recognizes that leadership potential comes in a variety of forms. The program provides students with substantial value to complement their unique talents, undergraduate course work, and work experience. The curriculum instills a powerful knowledge base with a minimum number of required courses.

Special Features

The Drucker M.B.A. features internship options, including honors consulting projects and mentoring programs.

The honors consulting projects provide students with the opportunity to master strategic management and consulting. The mentoring program offers students access to a powerful network of senior managers within the Drucker community and younger applicants who need guidance.

Full-time students pursue internships between the spring term of their first year and the fall term of their second with the assistance of Claremont Graduate University's Office of Career Services and Corporate Relations.

The Faculty

Faculty members of the Peter F. Drucker Graduate School of Management study strategically important managerial issues and advance the theory and practice of management through teaching and field-based research. The faculty's emphasis on strategically important issues stresses the strategic dimension of each functional area and the role of executive leadership in outstanding organizational performance.

The Drucker School's faculty members are selected for the high quality of their academic training and research, their knowledge of management and leadership practice, and their superior teaching skills. Most of the full-time faculty members are experienced consultants or have significant managerial experience.

The Business School Network

Through Drucker School institutes, faculty research, and consulting alliances, the Drucker School maintains key relationships in the business community. The School's Board of Visitors includes CEOs and other eminent businesspeople who provide guidance and financial resources to further the Drucker School's programs. The Dean's Executive-in-Residence Program provides small-group and one-on-one interaction between Drucker M.B.A. students and senior executives. In addition, a range of leading corporate partners sponsor research, collaborate with the Drucker School faculty members, and regularly recruit Drucker School M.B.A. interns and graduates.

The new home of the Drucker School at Claremont.

The College and Environs

The Claremont Colleges are a group of small and distinguished liberal arts colleges. Claremont Graduate University, founded in 1925, was the second member of The Claremont Colleges. It provides graduate education in the liberal arts, information technology, and management. The University enrolls approximately 1,600 students, about 225 of them in the Early Career Management Program (Drucker M.B.A.) and another 225 in the Executive Management Program.

The mission of Claremont Graduate University is to prepare a diverse group of outstanding individuals to assume leadership roles in the worldwide community through research, teaching, and practice in selected fields. Claremont Graduate University believes superb instruction, innovative research, and practical experience are the keys to an excellent graduate education; educational institutions have an obligation to become civically engaged in order to enrich and to better serve society; institutions of higher education must be ethically vigilant, consciously exploring normative and moral issues; knowledge consists of more than facts and has more than merely utilitarian ends; knowledge pursues and reflects values; education is immeasurably enriched by the experience and insights of those outside the educational community; human diversity is indispensable for improving the quality and texture of the educational experience; ongoing education is a lifelong responsibility of the global community's leaders; and advanced education is essential for the well-being and future of an increasingly complex society.

Claremont is a beautiful residential community of 34,000 located 35 miles east of Los Angeles, close to skiing, the beach, the desert, and other recreational areas. This pleasant college town with an Ivy League atmosphere is situated in the foothills of the San Gabriel Mountains.

Technology Environment

Claremont Graduate University has an academic computing center reserved for student use. IBM, Apple, and Digital Equipment computers are provided in this area. Most software packages utilized in instruction are Microsoft products, but many other software packages are available.

The Claremont Colleges' Honnold-Mudd Library is advanced in electronic access and CD-ROM capability.

Placement

The Office of Career Services and Corporate Relations helps students and alumni effectively manage their career paths to ensure long-term success in their chosen fields. Career Services and leaders within the Drucker School conduct a consistent marketing and corporate communications program to solicit additional placement opportunities in areas of interest to CGU students and alumni. Career Services maintains an aggressive program of flexible and tailored response to potential employers based on a state-of-the-art resume database. Career Services also offers a variety of services, including one-on-one counseling, resume and cover letter critiquing, networking opportunities, individual job listings, on- and off-campus recruiting, a career resources library, and a number of career skills workshops.

In 1999, 95 percent of Drucker M.B.A. graduates were placed within ninety days. The average starting salary for 1999 graduates was $72,500. These graduates took diverse positions in consulting, general management, marketing, finance, information sciences, and operations.

Admission

Applicants to the Drucker M.B.A. program must submit a completed application, a GMAT score, undergraduate and graduate school transcripts, three letters of reference, a resume, a personal statement, and an application fee to the Admissions Office of Claremont Graduate University.

Finances

Full-time tuition for the 2000–01 academic year is $21,580. Part-time tuition is $940 per unit in the M.B.A. program and $1076 per unit in the Executive Management Program. Living expenses are about $12,360 for on-campus residence and $16,000 for off-campus residence for the academic year.

Approximately 50 percent of Drucker M.B.A. students receive fellowships, assistantships, or other grants, with the average award amounting to about $2500. Institutional aid programs based on both academic merit and financial need are available, as are loans and work-study programs.

International Students

To support a global learning environment in the Drucker School, approximately one half of incoming Drucker M.B.A. students are international. The Claremont Colleges excel in helping these students feel welcome and receive maximum benefit from their degrees. In the intimate and collegial environment, domestic and international students share their experiences and perspectives for a truly global graduate education.

Application Facts and Dates

The Drucker School utilizes a rolling admissions process for fall, spring, and summer admissions. February 15 is the priority deadline for financial aid consideration. Late applications are accepted. Applicants are notified of the admission decision within six weeks of applying.

For further information or to request an application, students should contact:

The Peter F. Drucker Graduate School of Management
Claremont Graduate University
1021 North Dartmouth
Claremont, California 91711-6184
Telephone: 800-944-4312 (toll-free)
Fax: 909-607-9104
E-mail: drucker@cgu.edu
World Wide Web: http://www.drucker.cgu.edu

CLARION UNIVERSITY
Clarion University of Pennsylvania

College of Business Administration

Clarion, Pennsylvania

SUCCESS BEGINS WITH KNOWLEDGE

▶ *The M.B.A. at Clarion University is an ideal blend of theoretical knowledge and practical application that develops managers for responsible positions in business, industry, and government. The faculty members teaching in this program are outstanding national scholars, yet they possess significant managerial experience upon which graduate students may draw. Full accreditation by AACSB– The International Association for Management Education ensures the highest-quality academic program, and Clarion's attractive tuition puts graduate business education within reach for nearly everyone.*

—Dr. James G. Pesek, Interim Dean

Programs and Curricular Focus

The Master of Business Administration (M.B.A.) degree program at Clarion University is fully accredited by the AACSB–The International Association for Management Education, one of higher education's most prestigious and rigorous accrediting bodies, which stresses academic excellence and a commitment to continuous improvement.

The major objective of graduate study in the College of Business Administration is to provide those enrolled with the opportunity to develop a basic core of knowledge concerning the theory, techniques, and practices of administering business activities. In addition to studying the basic core of knowledge, candidates for the M.B.A. degree have the opportunity for in-depth study in a particular area of interest.

The program is designed to accommodate candidates with an undergraduate degree in business administration as well as graduates from other degree programs. Candidates with undergraduate degrees other than business administration must take foundation courses that make up the undergraduate common body of knowledge in business administration. Foundation requirements may be removed by course work at Clarion or other approved institutions.

This nonthesis program leading to the M.B.A. is based on a total requirement of 33 credits beyond the foundation courses, which are determined at the time of admission. Twenty-four of these 33 credits are specifically required courses. All students must take courses in organizational structure and behavior, quantitative analysis for business

decisions, management accounting, managerial economics, financial management, production management, marketing decision making, and a capstone course in business policy. The remaining 9 credits in the program are elective, permitting the student to design the program to particular objectives with the approval of the M.B.A. Director.

The normal length of study for students attending full-time is two years. A three-semester program without summer study is also available, as is an eleven-month accelerated program that includes summer study. Students can also enroll in the program on a part-time basis.

Students and the M.B.A. Experience

Students enrolled in the M.B.A. program have greatly varied experiences. Undergraduate academic backgrounds include not only business administration but also social sciences, engineering, and computer technology. The M.B.A. program brings together students who are recent graduates with others who have as much as twenty years of professional experience. Approximately 20 percent of students are enrolled part-time bringing valuable current perspectives to the classroom. Fourteen percent of those enrolled are international students and 27 percent are women.

Special Features

Clarion's M.B.A. offers special features that enhance student learning. They include exposure to national scholars and editors of major American professional

journals; "live case" business consulting opportunities; opportunity for international study and travel; up-to-date, in-classroom learning technology, opportunity for student/faculty research, and small class size supporting extensive interaction.

Students pursuing the M.B.A. degree may enroll in the professional accountancy course of study. The sequence of 36 semester hours of graduate course work is designed to prepare students for entry into the practice of professional accountancy as prescribed by the American Institute of Certified Public Accountants.

The Faculty

Courses in the M.B.A. program are taught exclusively by terminally qualified faculty members who are active in scholarship and business consultation. Faculty members represent diverse backgrounds academically, professionally, and culturally. Twenty percent of the faculty members are women, 17 percent are international, and 13 percent are from minority groups. Faculty members hold degrees in accounting, economics, finance, law, marketing, administrative sciences, and engineering. Students in the program find that faculty members bring a unique blend of professional, academic, and international perspectives that enhance the classroom experience.

The Business School Network

Having "real-world" experiences that are woven into the fabric of graduate

FACULTY LIST

Department Heads:
Carole Anderson, Interim Chair, Department of Administrative Sciences
Robert S. Balough, Director, M.B.A. Program and Chair, Department of Economics
Soga O. Ewedemi, Chair, Department of Finance
James G. Pesek, Interim Dean, College of Business Administration
Paul Y. Kim, Chair, Department of Marketing
Thomas W. Oliver, Chair, Department of Accountancy
Mary Lou Pae, Assistant Dean

business education assures that an M.B.A. degree provides the kind of educational experience that is highly desired by employers. Clarion brings this perspective to its graduate program through its Business Advisory Council, which is comprised of top-level business executives from corporations across America. M.B.A. course work provides the opportunity for graduate students to work directly with corporations and other organizations in solving real business problems through research, consultation, and participative decision making. Choosing a program like Clarion's, in which business applications are a primary focus, is the first step toward an effective managerial career.

The College and Environs

Clarion University of Pennsylvania was established in 1867. It is one of the fourteen institutions in the state system of higher education of Pennsylvania. The University has an enrollment of approximately 6,000 students, 19 percent of whom are students in the College of Business Administration. In a typical year, approximately 50 students are enrolled in the M.B.A. program, with approximately 35 attending full-time. The University has grown significantly during the past twenty years. Most of the physical plant consists of newer buildings.

Located high on the Allegheny Plateau overlooking the Clarion River, the University is surrounded by some of Pennsylvania's most scenic resort areas. The rolling, wooded countryside affords some of the best hunting, fishing, camping, and hiking in northwestern Pennsylvania. The Clarion River and its tributaries provide an ideal setting for summer boating, swimming, and aquatic sports.

Facilities

The College of Business Administration is located in Still Hall, the newest classroom building on campus. In addition to classrooms and a 225-seat auditorium, this modern facility includes an up-to-date microcomputer lab and reading/study center.

Technology Environment

Students are provided access to the University's Central Alpha VMS Cluster Network. All students receive an account that allows them to access programming languages, the library system, e-mail, and the Internet from the Pentium–III class computers in the Still Hall computer lab.

Many electronic databases are available including WestLaw Tax Library, Citibase macro data tapes, CRSP tapes, IMF trade data, Panel Study of Income Dynamics, Consumer Expenditure Surveys, County Business Patterns, and other databases. Additionally, faculty members have access to and support for computer software such as SAS, SPSS, TSP, Soritec, Statistic-A, Viza, RATS, Compenstat, LINDO, GINO, Markstrat, Epistat, StatAnalyst, and other PC and mainframe packages.

Placement

The University maintains an Office of Placement Services. This office is visited annually by representatives of leading companies. The M.B.A. program has had an excellent job placement record over the past several years.

Admission

Admission to the M.B.A. program is open to qualified graduates of recognized colleges or universities accredited by a regional or general accrediting agency. The Graduate Management Admissions Test (GMAT) score report, official transcripts from all previous colleges and universities attended, and three letters of reference must be submitted. A combination of satisfactory GMAT score and undergraduate GPA is required. International students presenting transcripts from institutions outside the U.S. must submit an official Test of English as a Foreign Language (TOEFL) score of 550 or higher.

Finances

Tuition and fees for in-state students for the 1999–2000 academic year, not including the summer term, were $4775. For out-of-state students, tuition and fees for 1999–2000 were $7590. The total cost for out-of-state students, including tuition and fees, housing, meals, books, and insurance, for 1999–2000 was estimated at $14,102. The total cost for in-state students is lower, reflecting the lower tuition rate. Graduate assistantships are available to qualified students and cover all or part of the basic tuition and fees expenses and provide a stipend. All international students admitted to the M.B.A. program who are not awarded a graduate assistantship automatically qualify for and receive an international assistantship award in the form of tuition reductions of $3000 to $5000.

Application Facts and Dates

Domestic student applications are considered on a continuous basis without application deadline. The international student application deadlines are July 1 for the fall term and November 1 for the spring term. For further information, students should contact:

Director of the M.B.A. Program
Clarion University of Pennsylvania
Clarion, Pennsylvania 16214
Telephone: 814-393-2605
Fax: 814-393-1910
E-mail: mba@clarion.edu
World Wide Web: http://www.clarion.edu/mba/

Clarkson University

Potsdam, New York

ENCOURAGING THE ENTREPRENEURIAL SPIRIT

At the School of Business, it is our privilege to provide a Clarkson education to men and women motivated to engage in the study of business enterprise. A Clarkson education is designed to provide talented and ambitious students with the knowledge and skills necessary to achieve positions of leadership within their chosen profession. We accomplish this by providing a team-intensive learning community in which each of the business disciplines are blended to form a better understanding of how businesses should operate.

The study of business at Clarkson is distinctive. We are committed to developing the student's entrepreneurial, leadership, and communications skills through hands-on learning. Our focus on these and the other skills and attributes that are most in demand by industry today assures that Clarkson business graduates are ready for productive careers. Our students are prepared to assume positions of responsibility upon graduation, not by virtue of their degree but by virtue of the experience we provide within our program.

At Clarkson, we are committed to excellence. All programs of the School of Business are fully accredited by AACSB–The International Association for Management Education and enjoy a strong national reputation. Students should visit our Web site to learn more about Clarkson.

—Timothy F. Sugrue, Dean

Programs and Curricular Focus

Accredited by the AACSB–The International Association for Management Education, Clarkson University offers M.B.A. and Master of Science in management systems (M.S.) degree programs that prepare students for professional positions within an increasingly global and dynamic environment. The focus of the Clarkson M.B.A. is on developing students' leadership and managerial abilities and in developing their abilities to analyze problems and make effective decisions. The ability to work effectively in teams is critically important in today's business environment. Teamwork, effective communication skills, experiential learning, and leadership development are integral to the Clarkson M.B.A. program.

The majority of Clarkson M.B.A. students complete the program requirements in one academic year. The fast-paced and highly integrated curriculum includes 10 core modules and 12 academic credits devoted to the development of functional and experiential learning (see right).

To participate in Clarkson's One-Year M.B.A. program, students must have completed courses deemed equivalent to first-year foundation requirements—accounting, business law, computer applications, economics, finance, management, marketing, production, and statistics—prior to entering

the program. Undergraduate business majors are typically able to complete the M.B.A. in one year. Nonbusiness majors can also receive transfer credit for foundation courses taken during their undergraduate studies and can complete any remaining foundation requirements at Clarkson, prior to entering the One-Year M.B.A. program.

The Master of Science in management systems program can also be completed in one year and allows for the development of highly focused expertise in one of four dynamic areas: information systems, human resources, manufacturing management, and environmental manufacturing.

Students and the M.B.A. Experience

At each year's commencement exercises, students gather to say their good-byes, and, without question, the M.B.A. and M.S. classes produce the loudest cheers and the sincerest tears. This degree of closeness stems from the team emphasis, the co-experiences, and the intensity of the Clarkson M.B.A. and M.S. programs.

This annual outcome is even more significant when one considers the diversity of each class's membership. Typically one third are women and one third represent international students and members of minority groups. Academically, two fifths are from undergraduate programs in engineering, science, or liberal arts. Students returning from industry, who typically account for one quarter of the class, bring professional experience into the class discussions, team activities, and experiential projects. Clarkson attracts energetic individuals who possess the ambition and leadership skills necessary to accept challenges and reach for high achievements.

❖ Global Focus

Modern industries in all countries need managers and business leaders who understand the complexities and opportunities associated with international competition. Clarkson's ties with Canadian industry and its proximity to Montreal and Ottawa allow Clarkson M.B.A. and M.S. students to deal firsthand with international business issues. While Canada is America's largest trading partner, conducting business with Canada still embodies the complexities of international trade.

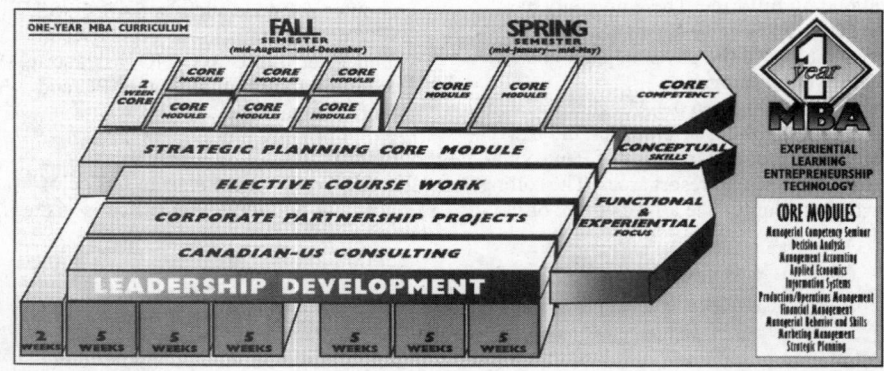

The Center for Canadian-U.S. Business Studies is unique among graduate programs and a major component of the Clarkson M.B.A. and M.S. programs. The Canadian-U.S. Business Consulting Service provides Clarkson students with a unique opportunity to gain practical business experience through the study of cross-border trade and economic opportunities. Professionally staffed and managed by Clarkson M.B.A. and M.S. students, the program provides client engagements that can lead to permanent career opportunities after graduation.

In addition to Clarkson's focus on Canadian-U.S. business issues, a joint program is offered with the Business School of Technology and Intercultural Management in Grenoble and the Reims School of Management, both located in France, and the University of Ottawa, located in Canada. These programs provide firsthand exposure to international business issues.

Special Features

Clarkson's M.B.A. and M.S. Leadership Program begins with a two-week Managerial Competency Seminar starting in mid-August. During this core module, students are individually assessed. From this assessment, individual developmental plans are created. Individualized feedback is received from a professional assessment organization, Clarkson faculty members, and fellow graduate students. Throughout the remainder of their program, students engage in course work and experiential activities to further develop these skills.

The Faculty

More than 90 percent of the faculty members possess a doctorate. Faculty members bring creative ideas and introduce exciting experiential components into their courses. At the same time, faculty members conduct research and publish their findings in top scholarly journals.

The Business School Network

Clarkson's graduate business programs reflect the advisory input from an executive council staffed by such firms as CIGNA, Chase Manhattan Bank, AMS, Xerox, and Anderson Consulting.

In addition, the Shipley Center for Leadership and Entrepreneurship brings corporate executives and other organizational leaders to campus to share the managerial and leadership philosophies of today's business leaders. Prominent alumni, such as John McLennan, former President and CEO of Bell Canada, regularly participate in these activities.

The College and Environs

An intellectual and cultural oasis nestled within a rural setting, Clarkson University enrolls approximately 2,200 undergraduate and 400 graduate students in the disciplines of business, engineering, and science. Business school graduates typically number between 80 and 100. Potsdam, New York (population 10,200), is a short drive from the scenic Adirondack Park; 80 miles from Ottawa, Ontario; and 90 miles from Montreal, Quebec. In addition to Clarkson's 640-acre campus, the region is home to three other institutions: Potsdam College of the State University of New York, St. Lawrence University, and SUNY College of Technology at Canton, all within a 10-mile radius.

This year's class will study in the new building that is being uniquely designed to accommodate the specialized programs, student-led consulting services, and educational partnerships. It will be the home of three centers: the Center for Excellence in Communication, the Shipley Center for Leadership and Entrepreneurship, and the Center for Global Competitiveness.

Technology Environment

Clarkson M.B.A. and M.S. students have a wide range of computer technology available to them. There are more than sixty workstations with full printing and Internet access on Clarkson's local area network. Color scanning and color printing facilities are also available. As a Novell and Microsoft education partner, the School of Business at Clarkson is able to offer industry-recognized networking classes to its M.B.A. and M.S. students.

Placement

In 1999, 80 percent of graduates were employed within three months of graduation, with an average first-year compensation of $52,800. Placement services include online resume referral, alumni referral networks, and a variety of workshops throughout the year. In addition, the career center sponsors an industrial fair and participates in the NYS M.B.A. Consortium, an organization focused on placing M.B.A. students. On-campus interviews by more than 150 organizations round out Clarkson's placement services.

Admission

Admission decisions are based on upper-division GPA, the highest attained GMAT score, and relevant professional experience. The average GPA is 3.3 and the average GMAT score is 560. Students for whom English is not their native language must submit scores of at least 600 on the TOEFL and 50 on the Test of Spoken English (TSE).

Finances

The 2000–01 tuition costs for the M.B.A. program are $21,984; costs are $20,610 for the M.S. Fees are $215. Books, living expenses, and other costs are estimated to be $8615 per year. Each year, roughly three fourths of incoming students receive merit-based tuition remission awards ranging from 20 to 100 percent. All applicants are considered for these awards, which are based on GPA, GMAT scores, references, and work experience.

International Students

Culture nights, diversity festivals, and the International Reading Room are all examples of Clarkson's efforts to enhance the acclimation of international students into Clarkson life. Students needing to improve TOEFL or TSE scores can enroll in intensive English language programs at regional institutions with which Clarkson has close working relationships.

Application Facts and Dates

Clarkson accepts applications on a rolling basis. Students who have been accepted and have received credit for all foundation requirements may begin the One-Year M.B.A. program in mid-August only. Students enrolling for the M.S. or to fulfill foundation requirements may enter in either the fall or spring semester. For more information, students should contact:

Office of Graduate Business Programs
Clarkson University
P.O. Box 5770
Potsdam, New York 13699
Telephone: 315-268-6613
E-mail: gradprog@clarkson.edu
World Wide Web: http://www.clarkson.edu/

Clark University

Worcester, Massachusetts

> ### AN M.B.A. FOR THE GLOBAL ECONOMY
>
> *Clark University combines three features that will make your experience here unique. First, we are small—120 full-time students, 15 full-time faculty. The extraordinary accessibility of our faculty builds a rapport with students that enhances the learning environment. Second, we are internationally focused. Our curriculum reflects a deep commitment to preparing you to manage effectively in the global enterprises of the new millennium. Third, our faculty is research oriented. We share a dedication to staying at the forefront of our disciplines. This means that you will learn best practices and state-of-the-art techniques for today's business world plus how to develop the new best practices needed for tomorrow's world.*
>
> —Ed Ottensmeyer, Dean

Programs and Curricular Focus

Accredited by AACSB–The International Association for Management Education, Clark University's Graduate School of Management offers a personal setting for a multinational management education and attracts students from more than thirty countries.

Clark's integrated M.B.A. curriculum goes far beyond offering the fundamentals. Through projects and internships, the program provides students with rich opportunities to work on multidisciplinary teams with people from all over the world. Students solve complex business problems designed to develop an understanding of global marketplace trends, sharpen leadership skills, and acquire essential practical experience.

Clark's M.B.A. curriculum is designed to provide students with strong analytical foundations and critical management judgment. What sets Clark apart is its emphasis designing courses that reflect the way the world does business: in teams of managers bringing together diverse cultures, skills, and experiences to meet the toughest business challenges.

Other curricular features include a one-year M.B.A. for business undergraduates, an M.B.A. in Health Services, a Master of Science in Finance (M.S.F.) degree program, an expanded accounting concentration that qualifies students to sit for the CPA exam, international management courses in Europe, and the opportunity to audit one course per semester in other divisions of the University.

Students and the M.B.A. Experience

Clark's M.B.A. program attracts a diverse student body. Hailing from many states and countries, students come together to form a microcosm of the contemporary business arena. They work together in teams in many courses, notably the Projects in Management course. This course offers students the opportunity to work as a member of a consulting team on actual management problems facing corporations.

The average full-time student has one to two years of full-time professional work experience, along with a record of strong undergraduate achievement. Fewer than 30 percent of students have an undergraduate business background. Women comprise 46 percent of the class,

and approximately half of the students come from other countries. Because of the program's small size, students readily form lasting friendships with their classmates and professors; friendships that stand them in good stead as they enter the business world in both the U.S. and abroad.

❖ Global Focus

Students' understanding of the world's way of doing business is not limited to just a few courses at Clark. Clark has intentionally created a curriculum that reflects the world's rapidly changing business environment, and international issues are discussed in every class. Students also develop a personal understanding of global topics by getting to know students from all over the world.

The Faculty

The Graduate School of Management emphasizes excellence in both teaching and research. The School's reputation in the United States and abroad is maintained, in large measure, through respect for the intellectual contributions of its faculty members. The School is a community, and it fosters collegiality and close relationships between students and faculty members.

The Business School Network

Faculty consulting and research activities ensure Clark's link to the business

community. Semester after semester, corporations, Fortune 500 firms among them, turn to Clark for assistance in addressing management issues. A visiting committee, comprising prominent CEOs and other top executives, ensures that the M.B.A. curriculum is continually refined to reflect the dynamic nature of business.

The College and Environs

A teaching and research institution founded in 1887, Clark University is the second-oldest graduate institution in the nation. Clark is one of only three New England universities, with Harvard and Yale, to be a founding member of the Association of American Universities. Clark is the only U.S. institution of its size to have its M.B.A., M.S.F., and undergraduate management program nationally accredited. The University's tree-shaded residential campus is located in Worcester, New England's second-largest city and a center of high technology, biotechnology, and financial services industries. Boston is just a short drive away.

Placement

Because of the program's small size, students have unparalleled access to

career-related services for a university of Clark's quality. From the first day of orientation, career services staff members are ready to help students assess their skills, research career options, develop experience, prepare their resumes, and meet employers. Alumni mentoring, individual advising, mock interviews, and on-campus recruiting are just a few of the many career services offerings. The staff members never forget that students' primary motivating factor in seeking an M.B.A. is to improve employment prospects.

Admission

Clark seeks students who will add to the vitality of the interactions between faculty members and students. Applications from men and women with diverse educational and professional backgrounds are encouraged. The average GMAT for the most recently enrolled class was 560 (80 percent of students scored between 480 and 660). A minimum TOEFL score of 213 (computer-based) or 550 (paper-based) is required for international students. In addition to these factors, students' records of undergraduate academic achievement along with letters

of recommendation and a personal statement are considered. Although no formal academic or professional business background is required for admission, a solid preparation in English, mathematics, and economics is beneficial.

Finances

Tuition is calculated on a per course basis, rather than per semester. For the 2000–01 academic year, tuition per course is $2120. Mandatory activity and insurance fees are estimated at $625. Living and personal expenses, including books, are estimated at $9000.

The Graduate School of Management offers scholarship assistance, based exclusively on merit, to both U.S. and international students. Awards range up to 100 percent of tuition. All applicants are considered for these merit-based awards.

International Students

Clark University is an exceptionally hospitable place for international students. With students from more than seventy countries and with an M.B.A. class composed of approximately 50 percent international students, the University prides itself on the range of support services available to these students. The University maintains a department dedicated to the service of students from overseas, assisting them with the social, cultural, and academic adjustments to life at an American University.

Application Facts and Dates

For the fall semester, the admission deadline is June 1, and, for the spring semester, the admission deadline is December 1. For more information, students should contact:

Mr. John Brandon
Director of Admissions
Graduate School of Management
Clark University
950 Main Street
Worcester, Massachusetts 01610-1477
Telephone: 508-793-7406
Fax: 508-793-8822
E-mail: clarkmba@clarku.edu
World Wide Web: http://www.mba.
    clarku.edu

Clemson University

> ## DISTINCTIVE AND DIVERSE OPPORTUNITIES—A CLEMSON TRADITION
>
> *Clemson has a proud history of educating leaders in many fields. Our M.B.A. programs are dedicated to creating leaders in the field of business and preparing them for success in an ever-changing and dynamic global economy. Our M.B.A. programs attract talented, highly motivated young professionals with diverse cultural heritages, academic backgrounds, and business experiences.*
>
> *Since our clientele have such varied backgrounds and interests, we offer two options for our M.B.A. programs. Whether your requirements are supplementary, requiring a flexible evening program located in an urban setting, or expanding, looking for a dedicated, intensive but personal program set in a small, scenic collegiate town, Clemson can offer you a challenging and rewarding experience.*
>
> —Jerry Trapnell, Dean

Programs and Curricular Focus

Clemson University's M.B.A. programs, which are accredited by AACSB–The International Association for Management Education, enable individuals to study advanced, integrated concepts of business, industry, and government. Students include active managers as well as recent graduates interested in expanding their analytical, business, and interpersonal skills.

Full-time participants take a highly intensive and rigorous 62-semester-hour program over two years. The first year (32 semester hours) provides foundation knowledge in core business areas: accounting, business communications, marketing, finance, economics, operations management, statistics, and law. Courses are taught in a condensed seven-week format during the first year. The second year (30 semester hours) is flexible, with either a track in entrepreneurship or technology management or a student-designed area of specialization. These courses are supplemented by a choice of tools courses and free electives that are taught in a semester-long format. Business majors may waive, with replacement, up to 15 semester hours by testing. Diverse learning environments offer approaches that include role playing, simulations, internships, consulting, teamwork, and case studies.

Clemson's part-time, evening program allows business professionals who have at least two years of work experience to pursue a degree in Greenville, South Carolina, at the University Center or in Greenwood, South Carolina, on Lander University's campus. Students with no undergraduate business courses can expect to complete the four core courses and eleven advanced courses, which include three electives, in approximately three years. There are two prerequisites: calculus and computer fundamentals. Course content and delivery are similar to the full-time program but provide more flexibility for the nontraditional student. Students, who are all working professionals, actively enrich class learning by contributing and integrating personal business experiences.

Students and the M.B.A. Experience

Clemson's M.B.A. students are drawn worldwide, providing a rich infusion of cultural and business backgrounds. The average evening student is 29, with seven years of work experience. Full-time students are an average of 25 years old with two years of work experience. Overall, 39 percent have business degrees, 37 percent engineering and pure sciences, and 24 percent social sciences and humanities. Almost 40 percent are women. Approximately 30 percent of the students are international, representing more than ten countries. The domestic students come from the South (60 percent), Northeast (21 percent), Midwest (14 percent), and West (5 percent).

❖ Global Focus

Clemson offers students many opportunities to broaden their international perspectives. Besides international course content and interaction with the large international student population, individuals can also take two or four courses abroad during the summer. In addition, guest lecturers from multinational firms provide unique international perspectives.

The Faculty

Clemson's faculty members all carry a Ph.D. in their teaching discipline. They are highly qualified to bring students outstanding learning opportunities by offering superb teaching skills, applied business research and professional experience, and high-quality student interaction.

The Business School Network

Corporate Partnerships

As part of a land-grant university with strong traditional ties to the business community, the College of Business and Public Affairs maintains dynamic partnerships with area corporate leaders. The College Executive Advisory Board, composed of prominent business executives from South Carolina industry, including NationsBank, ARAMARK Corp., and Wachovia, provides critical business guidance, expertise, and participation for College programs. Internships, hands-on consulting, and executive guest speakers provide additional real-world exposure for the M.B.A. student.

The College and Environs

Clemson is a state-assisted university located in South Carolina's lake and mountain region. The campus itself consists of more than 1,400 wooded acres on the former plantation of John C. Calhoun. Founded in 1889, the University has a student population of approximately 17,000 and offers more than 100 graduate degrees in almost seventy areas.

The town of Clemson is a small college community of 25,000 located on the shores of Lake Hartwell. Large population centers are conveniently located within 20 to 40 minutes of the area.

Technology Environment

Clemson has one of the largest Novell networks in the world; it links all student labs and University departments to each other and the Internet. Student labs, which are strategically located throughout the campus, contain state-of-the-art, networked, Windows-based personal computers. All lab computers have access to laser-quality printers, mainframe applications, e-mail, and a large selection of current software, including Microsoft Office. Both Clemson's Virtual Laptop Environment and Collaborative Learning Environment have won national software awards for innovation, functionality, and quality. The University supports almost 100 "smart classrooms," which offer students and faculty members the latest in learning technologies. The library's more than 1.6 million items, including books, periodicals, online databases, CD-ROMs, and government publications, are accessible for catalog search and checkout via online computer access.

Placement

Seventy-one percent of the full-time M.B.A. students who graduated in 1999 had jobs at graduation. Hiring companies included PriceWaterhouseCoopers, Michelin, Ernst & Young, and Bank of America. Clemson's M.B.A. Career Services Center provides assistance to students in identifying and obtaining professional positions through a range of customized placement services. These include job fairs, active student marketing through resume books and the Web, individualized resume and cover letter writing assistance, personalized placement counseling, and workshops to enhance search and interview skills, networking techniques, and resume preparation. In addition, the center coordinates with the University's Michelin Career Services Center to ensure maximum support services and career opportunities for M.B.A. recipients.

Admission

Acceptance is based on careful appraisal of each candidate's academic record, performance on the Graduate Management Admission Test (GMAT), letters of recommendation, and work experience. The admission process is highly personalized, with emphasis on each applicant's accomplishments. A score of at least 550 on the TOEFL is required for all students whose native language is not English.

Calculus and fundamentals of computers are prerequisites for both the full-time and part-time programs.

Finances

The 1999–2000 tuition and fees for the Clemson campus full-time program were $1840 per semester for South Carolina residents and $4728 per semester for nonresidents. Graduate assistants paid $612 per semester. Books and supplies cost approximately $1200 per year. On-campus housing ranged from $1055 per semester for a residence hall to $1320 for a 4-person apartment. Off-campus apartments typically cost around $400 per month. A limited number of competitive graduate assistantships are available. Awards are based on personal interviews and candidates' qualifications.

Tuition for the evening programs in 1999–2000 was $245 per semester hour for South Carolina residents and $490 per hour for nonresidents.

All tuition and fees are subject to change as conditions warrant.

Application Facts and Dates

Application deadlines for the full-time program are April 15 for international students and June 15 for domestic students. For the part-time program, deadlines are April 15, July 15, and November 30. For more information, students should contact:

Director of Admissions
M.B.A. Programs
Clemson University
124 Sirrine
Box 341315
Clemson, South Carolina 29634-1315
Telephone: 864-656-3975
Fax: 864-656-0947
E-mail: mba@clemson.edu
World Wide Web: http://www.clemson.edu/business/MBA

CSU Cleveland State University

Cleveland, Ohio

NEW CURRICULUM AND FLEXIBLE PROGRAMS

Cleveland State University (CSU) offers the opportunity to earn an M.B.A. degree in the heart of one of America's most exciting cities. The M.B.A. curriculum features full integration of the business disciplines and an expanded emphasis on global business practices, team dynamics, and management of innovation and technology. Programs are scheduled for full-time or part-time students and meet on weekdays or weekends, daytime or evening, on campus and at business locations outside the downtown area. Flexibility of options enables students to tailor a program to meet their specific needs. The new building contains state-of-the-art classroom space, computer labs, faculty offices, conference rooms, and distance learning technology.

—Allan D. Waren, Interim Dean

Programs and Curricular Focus

CSU offers a variety of M.B.A. programs. There are full-time and part-time programs, given both in the daytime and evening. There is also a one-year, accelerated program: classes meet all day Saturday and every other Friday evening, starting in August. The Executive M.B.A. is a twenty-three-month program with classes primarily on Saturdays, featuring international and governmental seminars; the program is limited to candidates with five years of work experience. The M.B.A. in health-care administration is a special program that features an internship and course work with a health-care emphasis. The J.D./M.B.A. is a joint program with the Cleveland Marshall College of Law that permits students to work on both degrees simultaneously.

The College also offers other more specialized degree programs. The Master of Accountancy and Financial Information Systems (M.A.F.I.S.) aims to develop accountants who are knowledgeable in financial information systems and are able to provide and interpret sophisticated financial information. The Master of Computer Information Science (M.C.I.S.) combines an education in computer and information science with its application in business, engineering, and mathematics to qualify students as computer professionals. The Master of Labor Relations and Human Resources (M.L.R.H.R.) offers two tracks: labor relations, which deals with unionized situations, and human resource development, which presents various personnel issues, such as affirmative action, hiring, evaluation, and staff development.

The curriculum exposes students to the full range of business disciplines in both skill-building and integrative courses. It consists of three levels of course work: skill development, basic business knowledge, and core courses.

Skill development courses are offered in spoken and written communications, computer literacy, mathematics, and statistics. These courses may be waived through prior course work or departmental examination.

Basic business knowledge courses are offered in business environment, economics, financial accounting, financial management, management and organizational behavior, marketing, and production management. These courses are prerequisite to the M.B.A. core courses and may be waived through prior course work.

Core courses consist of environment of international business, finance, human resource management and labor relations, management of innovation and technology, managerial accounting, marketing management, and team dynamics. Other program requirements are a capstone seminar focusing on the interrelationships between the major business disciplines and three elective courses, one of which may be either a research project or a business internship. Electives are available in all disciplines as well as in information technology and e-commerce.

Students and the M.B.A. Experience

CSU has a student population of 16,000, drawn from the city of Cleveland, its suburbs, and many countries of Europe, Central and South America, Africa, and Asia. The 1,100 graduate students are drawn from each of these areas, range in age from their early 20s to 50s, and provide a broad racial and cultural mix. Many have established business careers. The classroom experience gives each student a chance to work alongside persons of different backgrounds and heritages.

❖ Global Focus

International trade is one of Cleveland's and northeastern Ohio's most active business segments. The import-export community has provided CSU with a rich resource of materials for building a global emphasis into the core courses of the M.B.A. program and enables CSU to present the course Environment of International Business as part of the M.B.A. core.

The Faculty

Each member of the graduate faculty of the James J. Nance College of Business Administration has an earned doctorate in his or her academic discipline. The total full-time faculty numbers 80, with extensive industry experience and international background.

The Business School Network

CSU's proximity to the central business district affords regular interchange with the rich commercial and industrial activities of the area. Programs emphasize the practical application of business principles, affording students the opportunity to learn from the area's leading practitioners. Members of the College of Business Administration's Visiting Committee represent major corporations in the area, providing students opportunities to interact at the top level of decision making. Frequent guest speakers expose students to a variety of styles and corporate cultures.

Corporate Partnerships

The College of Business Administration collaborates with a number of regional and national firms to enrich the educational experience of its students. Corporate partners include Enterprise Rent-A-Car, KPMG Peat Marwick LLP, the Cleveland Clinic, Keane Inc., and Made2Manage Systems, Inc.

Prominent Alumni

Prominent alumni of the James J. Nance College of Business Administration include Monte Ahuja, Chairman and CEO of Transtar Industries and former CSU Chairman of the Board and Board of Trustees member; June Gibbs Brown, Inspector General of the Department of Health and Human Services; Lloyd G. Trotter, President and CEO of GE Industrial Systems and recent recipient of CSU's Alumni Special Achievement Award; Jose C. Feliciano, President of the Bar Association and partner at Baker & Hostetler; Kenneth J. Semelsberger, Chief Operating Officer of Scott & Fetzer; and Gary C. Suhadolinik, Director of the Ohio Department of Commerce.

The College and Environs

The James J. Nance College of Business Administration is one of seven colleges of Cleveland State University. The campus is located within a short walk of the central business district; Playhouse Square, a major theater and entertainment area; and Gateway, a new major sports complex. Cleveland offers a world-class symphony orchestra, opera and ballet companies, theater companies, three major-league sports teams, and one of the most extensive networks of public parks in the United States. A new building for the College of Business Administration opened in 1998.

Facilities

The resources of CSU's main library and Law Library and those of the Cleveland Public Library system are available to M.B.A. students. The Computer Center provides student access to mainframe computing, several personal computer laboratories, online interactive processing, and use of OhioLINK and Dialog information retrieval systems.

Placement

CSU's Career Services Center offers advice on career direction and the career development process. It operates a placement service to match student skills with job opportunities from more than 500 companies.

Admission

Applicants for M.B.A. programs must possess a baccalaureate degree from an accredited college or university and must take the Graduate Management Admission Test (GMAT). Admission is based on undergraduate grade point average and GMAT score. International applicants must also take the Test of English as a Foreign Language (TOEFL) and achieve a score of at least 525.

Finances

For 1999–2000, graduate tuition was $202 per credit hour for Ohio residents and $404 per credit hour for nonresidents, plus a $2.35 per-credit-hour technology fee. (Costs are subject to change for 2000–01). Books and supplies averaged $60 to $95 per course. Financial aid in the form of tuition grants is available to a limited number of highly qualified first-year graduate students. Dormitory space ranging from $1505 to $2058 per semester (excluding meals) is available on a limited basis. Relatively low-cost rental housing is available in Cleveland and nearby suburbs; monthly rates range from $300 to $500.

International Students

CSU's International Student Services Office provides counseling in matters dealing with visas, housing, and academic affairs and conducts an orientation program prior to a student's initial semester of classes.

The International Student M.B.A. Bridge Program is available to students with three-year bachelor's degrees who meet the regular admission standards. They are required to complete 24 credit hours of bridge courses. Successful completion of the bridge program enables the student to complete the entire M.B.A. program in two years on a full-time basis. Students are evaluated and are given specific course assignments based on their individual backgrounds and preparation.

Application Facts and Dates

Applicants should submit an application at least two months prior to the semester of desired entrance. Official copies of transcripts must be forwarded to CSU directly from all institutions previously attended. Test scores (GMAT and TOEFL) must be reported directly by the Educational Testing Service. Copies of program descriptions and application forms may be obtained from:

James J. Nance College of Business Administration
Cleveland State University
1860 East 18th Street
Cleveland, Ohio 44114
Telephone: 216-687-3730
Fax: 216-687-5311
World Wide Web: http://www.csuohio.edu/mba

The College of Saint Rose

Albany, New York

> ## TOOLS FOR SUCCESS IN THE TWENTY-FIRST CENTURY
>
> *Today's increasingly competitive business environment requires that an M.B.A. program provide students with opportunities to acquire cutting edge knowledge, analytical abilities, and practical application skills to prepare business managers for productive and efficient leadership. The Saint Rose M.B.A. curriculum is designed to meet these requirements. The Saint Rose M.B.A. program includes course work that addresses subjects such as leadership, communication, production and quality management, finance, technology, human resource management, and marketing. The Saint Rose M.B.A curriculum and instruction synthesize contemporary realities with theoretical analyses of those realities.*
>
> *The business world of the twenty-first century will present managers with even more challenges than they face today. Graduates of our M.B.A. program are equipped with the tools they need to meet the demands of tomorrow successfully.*
>
> —Severin Carlson, Dean, School of Business

Programs and Curricular Focus

The College of Saint Rose M.B.A. program, which is accredited by the Association of Collegiate Business Schools and Programs, balances theoretical instruction with case-study simulations. The M.B.A. program's courses are designed to teach students how to lead and communicate on the job and in the community. The educational approach of the Saint Rose School of Business is to emphasize results-oriented management. Faculty members apply a variety of teaching methods, such as group discussion, computer-aided instruction, seminars by members of the business community, and individual and team projects.

The School of Business offers two M.B.A. program options that both share the goal of preparing M.B.A. students to be effective, innovative managers. The part-time M.B.A. option allows students the flexibility of taking one or two courses per semester and completing the program at their own pace. Or, students may take more than two courses per semester, plus summer sessions, to complete the part-time program in two calendar years. The one-year M.B.A. program combines intensive course work with career development opportunities, including a mentorship with a local business executive and a 6-credit internship. All program options require the completion of a minimum of 36 graduate credit hours. Students may transfer up to 12 degree-applicable graduate credits from another accredited institution.

In addition, the Juris Doctor/Master of Business Administration (J.D./M.B.A.) program that Saint Rose offers jointly with Albany Law School can be completed in four years of full-time study. Saint Rose also offers the certificate program in not-for-profit management to provide formal training and credentials for not-for-profit employees who wish to become eligible for a promotion or career change. Upon successful completion of this certificate program, students are eligible to take the Certified Association Executive (CAE) comprehensive examination, sponsored by the American Association of Association Executives (AAAE). In addition, credits earned for the not-for-profit management certificate may be applied toward the M.B.A. program. The College's site in Glens Falls, New York, an hour north of Albany, provides students with a convenient alternative location where they can complete some of the 36 required credits of the M.B.A. program. In addition, the College's noncredit Financial Planning Certificate is offered in the evening at a convenient downtown location.

Students are expected to graduate with the ability to define, analyze, and solve problems; apply legal and ethical considerations in the decision-making process; communicate effectively; and develop efficiency of and effective use of strategic plans that integrate economic optimization, cost of capital, market opportunities, production, technology, and human resources.

Students and the M.B.A. Experience

The M.B.A. program is structured to accommodate the needs of a wide range of students, including those with substantial knowledge of business, those without an undergraduate business degree or previous business experience, and those returning to advanced study after an absence. Classes for the M.B.A. are conveniently scheduled in the evenings and on weekends to fit into the schedules of students who work full-time or have other commitments during the day. Students enrolled in the intensive one-year M.B.A. program attend classes primarily during the day. Class size is kept to an average of 16 students in order to facilitate interaction in the classroom. The average age of M.B.A. students is 33, and the majority live within a 50-mile radius of Saint Rose. Approximately 52 percent of the M.B.A. students are women.

Special Features

Saint Rose offers a one-year M.B.A. program option to students who have successfully completed a set of ten prerequisite, undergraduate, business-related courses. This option provides students with the outstanding opportunities of a mentorship program and a graduate internship. When students enter the program, they are paired with business executives in their fields of interest who help them explore career options and network in the local business community throughout the academic year. The one-year option culminates with a 6-credit internship that places students as interns in business organizations. Several businesses have offered M.B.A. interns full-time employment as a result of their outstanding work.

The Faculty

Graduate business faculty members are professionals with significant experience who have built strong relationships with members of the business community and remain involved with private companies, nonprofit organizations, and government agencies in a variety of capacities. All M.B.A. courses are taught by full-time faculty members or experts from the local business community. Eighty-two percent of the faculty members in the School of Business hold a doctorate or the highest degree in their area of expertise, and 50 percent of the faculty members are women.

The Business School Network

Corporate Partnerships

The College of Saint Rose Peter M. Tully Endowed Lecture on Financial Services and Economic Development strengthens ties with Capital Region businesses and provides a forum to explore financial sector developments. The institute's Advisory Board includes members from Key Corp; AT&T; Chase Manhattan Bank, NA; Fleet Bank; ALBANK; Independent Bankers Association of New York State; and the New York State Department of Economic Development.

Prominent Alumni

Prominent alumni of the School of Business include Betty Barnette, Treasurer of the City of Albany; Josephine Farinella, a partner in the firm Farinella Construction Co. Inc.; Charles A. Reinemann, Vice President of Investments and Financial Consultant for Smith Barney, a member of Travelers Group; and Kelly Mansfield Waechter, former Vice President for Key PrivateBank.

The College and Environs

Founded in 1920 by the Sisters of Saint Joseph of Carondelet, Saint Rose is a private, independent, coeducational institution serving more than 4,000 graduate and undergraduate students. The urban residential campus is nestled in the historic Pine Hills neighborhood of New York's capital city, where a variety of restaurants, shops, museums, and theaters are easily accessible by walking or by bus. The College is just a short ride away from many destinations, including New York City, Boston, and Montreal; the Adirondack and Catskill Mountains of New York; and the Green Mountains of Vermont.

Facilities

The campus of seventy historic and contemporary buildings features the Neil Hellman Library, Science Center, Learning Center, Pauline K. Winkler Speech-Language-Hearing Center, Music Building, Picotte Hall Art Center, Campus Activities Center, athletic facilities, and renovated Victorian homes.

Two classrooms designed to facilitate faculty-student interaction are reserved for use by M.B.A. classes. Both classrooms feature state-of-the-art technology that allows faculty members to utilize computer-based instructional support.

The open-stack Neil Hellman Library contains more than 199,000 volumes, 980 periodical subscriptions, 215,000 titles on microform, and a collection of rare books. The library's resources include an online catalog, CD-ROM databases, librarian-assisted database searching, Internet access, and interlibrary loan services.

On-campus housing for graduate students consists of five residence halls and eleven apartments. Off-campus housing also is readily available in the vicinity of Saint Rose.

Technology Environment

The use of computers is integral to the course work of the Saint Rose M.B.A. program. Many assignments require proficiency with word processing, spreadsheet, and presentation software. Students have access to approximately 220 IBM Pentium computers, featuring the most up-to-date software packages, as well as Internet and World Wide Web service. "Smart" classrooms are equipped with full multimedia capabilities and possess high-quality projection equipment in order to make classroom instruction exciting and to allow students to create and demonstrate professional presentations. User assistance and laser printing are available in all computer labs, and some also offer scanning and color printing capabilities. The College's on-site Document Center can aid students in creating full-color slide presentations and bound proposals.

Placement

The College's Career Development Center provides students and alumni with a resource center consisting of job banks, information about job fairs, career assessment and counseling, a computer-assisted career guidance and job searching system, resume preparation assistance and referral, credential files, on-campus interviews, videotaped mock interviews, and workshops. These services are available to all M.B.A. students and alumni free of charge.

Admission

Admission to any of the three M.B.A. program options is dependent upon the completion of an undergraduate degree program at an accredited college or university. An applicant with a background in any undergraduate major is qualified to apply; however, students must meet M.B.A. program prerequisites prior to beginning their studies.

Applicants must file a completed application form, official transcripts from all colleges and universities attended, a personal essay, and two letters of recommendation for graduate study. There is a nonrefundable application fee of $30. International students should request the international application. Only individuals with an undergraduate GPA of less than 3.0 must submit Graduate Management Admission Test (GMAT) scores. Applicants whose native language is not English must submit TOEFL scores; official English translations of all transcripts, a grading key, and a copy of a diploma.

Finances

Tuition for the 2000–01 academic year is $363 per semester hour of credit. Saint Rose serves graduate students through a comprehensive program of federal, state, and institutional financial aid, which may include Federal Stafford Student Loans (subsidized and unsubsidized), the New York State Tuition Assistance Program (TAP), graduate assistantships, graduate multicultural and international scholarships, or graduate merit scholarships, if the applicant is qualified. Applicants are required to submit the Free Application for Federal Student Aid (FAFSA), the New York State Tuition Assistance application, and signed copies of federal and state income tax documents and W-2 wage statements. To be considered for assistance, students must file for aid by March 1 for the fall and summer semesters and by November 1 for the spring semester.

International Students

The College's Office of International Programs is located in the Center for Cultural Diversity, and the International Student Organization is also located on campus. A full-time adviser coordinates activities and programs for international students studying at Saint Rose, including orientation, immigration and personal advisement, language assessment and assistance, and the coordination of on- and off-campus community programs. In addition, the Learning Center also offers English for speakers of other languages (ESOL) tutorial support.

Application Facts and Dates

Application deadlines are December 1 for the spring semester, April 1 for the summer semester, and July 15 for the fall semester.

M.B.A. Program Director
School of Business
The College of Saint Rose
Albany, New York 12203-1490
Telephone: 518-454-5272
Fax: 518-458-5449
E-mail: mba@mail.strose.edu
World Wide Web: http://www.strose.edu

or

Dean of Graduate, Adult and
    Continuing Education Admissions
The College of Saint Rose
432 Western Avenue
Albany, New York 12203-1490
Telephone: 518-454-5143
Fax: 518-458-5479
E-mail: ace@mail.strose.edu

College of William and Mary

> ### OUR MISSION: REFLECTING WILLIAM AND MARY VALUES
>
> *The mission of the M.B.A. program at the College of William and Mary is to serve the commonwealth, the nation, and the international community by offering high-quality educational programs. Reflecting its tradition of excellence, the M.B.A. program accomplishes this mission by application of five basic principles: (1) reflecting William and Mary values; (2) teamwork and building leadership skills; (3) functional skill building; (4) interaction with the external community; and (5) learning through doing (internships and mandatory field studies).*
>
> —Larry Pulley, Dean

Programs and Curricular Focus

During the first year of the M.B.A. program, students are assigned to teams of 6 people with whom they work very closely. The members of these teams are very diverse in terms of gender, age, academic background, work experience, and areas of interest. The incoming class is made up of approximately 110 new students, divided into two sections of 55. Students take a mixture of courses in financial and managerial accounting, quantitative methods, operations management, organizational behavior, marketing, economics, finance, management communications, information systems, and business policy.

All entering students are required to bring laptop computers with them into the program. They are used consistently throughout their course work.

In the second year, students return from their highly successful internships ready to focus on their areas of concentration (accounting, finance, marketing, operations/information technology, or human resource management). Students also have the option of remaining on a generalist track, taking a combination of electives from different areas. All students participate in a field studies project, providing them with firsthand experience and the opportunity of making immediate contributions to the companies that participate.

Students and the M.B.A. Experience

William and Mary students bring with them a wide range and depth of experiences. Undergraduate majors range from anthropology to engineering, and work experiences extend from architectural engineering to nonprofit management to corporate finance.

About 40 percent of incoming students have liberal arts and science degrees and approximately 15 percent have engineering backgrounds. More than 98 percent of each entering class has at least two years of significant full-time work experience. Of each entering class (approximately 110 new students), 38 percent are women, 10 percent are students of color, and 40 percent are international students.

Special Features

Study-abroad opportunities are available during the first semester of the second year with Norges Handelshoyskole (Norwegian School of Economics), the INCAE M.B.A. program in Costa Rica, and ESCP in Paris. Joint-degree programs are also available with the Marshall Wythe School of Law and the Thomas Jefferson Program in Public Policy.

William and Mary students are strongly encouraged to participate in one of the fifteen active committees within the MBAA (the student government organization).

Every William and Mary student participates in a field studies project during the second year. Students are given the opportunity to work with a team of students at a company (according to their area of interest) and complete a real hands-on project.

The Faculty

With more than 50 full-time faculty members on board, William and Mary offers an outstanding 4:1 ratio of students to professors. Not only do the professors possess a wide range of skills and backgrounds, they are widely known and are noted researchers and outstanding teachers. Students are encouraged to seek out professors for individual counseling and assistance; students are always welcome to discuss issues with their professors.

Graduate research assistants have excellent opportunities to participate in assisting faculty members with their active and diverse research projects during the second year of the program.

The Business School Network

Members of the Advisory Board at William and Mary take an active interest in the students. Twice a year they visit the campus and students give team presentations to them. Members of the Advisory Board and the alumni have ties to all the major industrial centers in the nation as well as those in select international cities.

Prominent Alumni

Prominent alumni are invited to address students and serve as active participants in the annual "Mock Interview Relay," which is always a successful event for

Crim Dell.

Wren Building.

both the students and alumni. They also serve as guest panelists and lecturers throughout the year.

The College and Environs

The College of William and Mary is the second-oldest institution of higher learning in the United States. It was founded in 1693 by King William III and Queen Mary II of England. Its alumni include 4 signers of the Declaration of Independence, 3 U.S. presidents, 4 justices of the Supreme Court, more than 30 U.S. senators, and more than 60 members of the House of Representatives.

Colonial Williamsburg is in proximity to the school. In 1999, it was named one of the top six vacation spots for families in the U.S. Each year, students on field trips from all over the country visit this

historic area. The William and Mary campus is part of the Colonial Williamsburg tour and it boasts the oldest classroom in America (the original classroom from 1693 is still in operation).

Close to Williamsburg are the cities of Richmond, Newport News, Hampton, and Virginia Beach, homes to every type of business from international manufacturing facilities to Fortune 500 corporate headquarters.

Facilities

William and Mary has excellent resources available at Swem Library and has its own Professional Resource Center in Tyler Hall. In Blow Hall (where all William and Mary M.B.A. classes are held) is its computer lab, available for all M.B.A. students to use. All students bring their own laptop computers with them into the program, and computer technology is used widely throughout the curriculum. All students are connected to and utilize the Internet on a constant basis.

Placement

William and Mary's Career and Employer Development Office, which works exclusively for the M.B.A. program, has an active staff of 4 full-time employees who work closely with each individual student in the program. The "Big Seven" of placement activities available within the M.B.A. program include The M.B.A. Connection; M.B.A. Career Coaches and Mentors; M.B.A. Career Conversations; M.B.A. Career Seminars; M.B.A. Mock Interview Relay; M.B.A. networking events in Washington, D.C., New York, and Richmond; and M.B.A. internships.

All M.B.A. students take part in a summer internship program. At the time of graduation (early May each year), 85 percent of the class has been placed. Within three months of graduation, approximately

95 percent are placed. The average starting salary for 2000 graduates was approximately $75,000.

Admission

Requirements for admission include a minimum of two years of work experience, GMAT scores (the range of scores is usually 580–740, and a minimum of 600 is recommended), official transcripts from all colleges and universities attended, current resumes, and personal interviews (students unable to visit the campus personally due to time/distance constraints may arrange a telephone interview with the Director of Admissions). International students must also submit TOEFL scores (minimum recommended score 600). Admissions are made on a rolling basis beginning October 1 each year and ending May 1. Decisions are made within 2 weeks of a file being completed, and students are notified immediately of their status.

Finances

Tuition for Virginia residents for 2000–01 is $7301; for out-of-state students it is $16,647. Average living expenses are estimated at approximately $5000 per year.

Application Facts and Dates

For application materials, students should contact:

Director of M.B.A. Program and of
    M.B.A. Admissions and Student
    Services
College of William and Mary
P.O. Box 8795
Williamsburg, Virginia 23187-8795
Telephone: 757-221-2900
        888-203-6994 (toll-free)
Fax: 757-221-2958
E-mail: admissions@business.wm.edu
World Wide Web: http://business.wm.
    edu

Colorado State University

Fort Collins, Colorado

TRADITION, TECHNOLOGY, TRANSFORMATION

These words are at the heart of the College of Business at Colorado State University. Here a tradition of academic excellence merges with a contemporary focus on technology to bring transformation to students and businesses. The College is leading the way in the push to graduate decision makers who have the managerial knowledge and functional skills necessary for success in a technology-driven, global business environment.

—Daniel E. Costello, Dean

Programs and Curricular Focus

Diversity is a key word in the College of Business—diversity in programs as well as the student body. The College, accredited by AACSB–The International Association for Management Education, employs a full range of programs to address the needs of the entire spectrum of students: domestic and international, part-time and full-time, on-campus and off-campus distance learning. Students can obtain a general M.B.A. degree or an M.S. degree in business administration with a specific concentration. Students may complete the M.B.A. degree in one of four different programs: an accelerated eleven-month program, an Evening M.B.A. program, a Distance M.B.A. program, or an Executive M.B.A. program (Denver). The content of each program is integrative and has a strong emphasis on information technology, global issues, and teamwork.

The Accelerated M.B.A. program provides an opportunity to quickly supplement an undergraduate degree with a graduate business degree. This 36-credit program requires a full-time commitment and meets during the day, Monday through Friday.

The Evening M.B.A. program is designed to serve the needs of working professionals. This 36-credit program takes twenty-two months to complete, including one summer session. All classes meet in the evening, Monday through Thursday.

The College is very proud to be a nationally recognized leader in distance M.B.A. education. *Forbes* magazine ranks Colorado State University's Network for Learning (CSUN) program among the nation's top twenty distance degree programs. Through the CSUN program, the classroom is brought directly to the student via the Internet and videotape. The CSUN Distance M.B.A. program is designed to serve work-

ing professionals who need flexibility in schedule and location. There is no on-campus requirement; course work is completed entirely at a distance. This 36-credit program takes two or four years to complete and includes some summer classes.

The Executive M.B.A. program is an accelerated program designed for students who wish to complete their M.B.A. degree in twenty-one months. The schedule is sensitive to the needs of working professionals. The executive site is in Colorado State University's Denver Center, located in downtown Denver, Colorado. The facility, including a computer center with multimedia instructional equipment, is specifically designed to support a state-of-the-art M.B.A. curriculum.

Students and the M.B.A. Experience

Diversity and balance characterize the on-campus graduate student body, resulting in an interactive, stimulating learning environment. More than half of Colorado State's M.B.A. students establish their careers be-

fore enrolling in graduate school. The College admits a select number of highly qualified international students each year to maintain the international enrollment at approximately 30 percent of its graduate population.

The Faculty

Research conducted by the College of Business faculty has led to published articles in respected journals such as *The Journal of Marketing, The Academy of Management Review,* and *The Journal of Retailing.* Equally impressive is the extensive applied business experience of the faculty members. More than 50 percent have significant business experience in their professional portfolios. Faculty members integrate their applied business experience and their research experience to bring a balanced approach to classroom instruction, creating a learning environment that exemplifies the best in modern management education.

The Business School Network

The College of Business Advisory Council is a vital element in maintaining a productive relationship between the College of Business and the business and professional community. Membership includes upper-level managers from public and private institutions, government, and international firms. In a typical year, College of Business students have frequent opportunities to interact with corporate executives from major firms in all areas of business.

Rockwell Hall

The College and Environs

Colorado State University, located at the foot of the picturesque Rocky Mountains, is recognized worldwide for its contributions to technology and science, quality of instruction, and discoveries that improve the world's quality of life, health, environment, and economy. A Carnegie Foundation Class I research university, Colorado State represents the best of the land-grant traditions—education, research, and service. The College of Business contributes to the University's growth, prestige, and national acclaim through its emphasis on excellence in instruction and research.

The city of Fort Collins offers a relaxed lifestyle and an abundance of cultural and social activities. Skiing, hiking, backpacking, and water sports areas are all adjacent to Fort Collins. More than 53 miles of bikeways wind along the Cache la Poudre River. Fort Collins has a clear, dry climate with more than 300 days of sunshine and a generally pleasant temperature throughout the year.

Technology Environment

The future of business is inextricably linked to technology. The underlying philosophy at the College of Business is an integration of technology into the academic program. This integration prepares students for the future in two ways: first, by providing them with a tool bag that includes the ability to use technology in their chosen fields, and second, by helping them gain an understanding of the way technology will affect them and the business world in the future. Every graduate course is held in the College's new technology wing. Each state-of-the-art classroom in the new wing has an instruction station equipped with a computer with Internet access and the latest computerized presentation equipment. The College of Business supports two fully accessible computer labs for the exclusive use of business students. The Hewlett-Packard Student Computer Laboratory is equipped with seventy-four Pentium-class computers, including Windows 95–based PCs and Macintoshes, seven networked laser printers, two color printers, a scanner, and more than sixty soft-

ware packages. The computer teaching lab houses another thirty-three computers.

Placement

The University Career Center and the College of Business career counselors work closely with faculty members to offer a wide range of placement opportunities to master's candidates in business. Many local, national, and international firms have developed a recruiting relationship with Colorado State University. For example, Hewlett-Packard Company considers the College of Business one of their top ten recruiting schools. In 1997, Hewlett-Packard hired more graduates from Colorado State's College of Business than from any other business school in the country. In addition, the College of Business participates in the Rocky Mountain M.B.A. Consortium.

Admission

An applicant for admission must have earned a bachelor's degree in any field from an accredited college or university. Admission is dependent primarily on an integrated analysis of an applicant's undergraduate grade point average, score on the Graduate Management Admission Test (GMAT), and letters of recommendation. The Evening M.B.A. and CSUN Distance M.B.A. programs require a minimum of four years of work experience. The Denver Executive M.B.A. program requires a minimum of eight years of work experience.

If the applicant's native language is not English, the Test of English as a Foreign Language (TOEFL), with a minimum score of 565, is also required. International students are required to submit proof of adequate funding for support for the length of time necessary to obtain their degree, and they must have health insurance.

To request an information packet, students should visit the College on the World Wide Web at the address below or contact the College admissions office (telephone: 970-491-6471).

Finances

The College offers several teaching and research assistantships in every business

discipline. In addition, tuition scholarships may be awarded. An application for a teaching or research assistantship is included in the application packet. Assistantships are not available for distance education students.

In 1999–2000, tuition for a Colorado resident for the eleven-month Accelerated M.B.A. program was $1708 per semester, plus $521 for the summer session. Nonresident tuition for the Accelerated M.B.A. program was $5591 per semester, plus $1785 for the summer session. Resident tuition for the Evening M.B.A. program was $1561 per semester, plus $521 for the summer session. Nonresident tuition for the Evening M.B.A. program was $5009 per semester, plus $1785 for the summer session. Tuition for the CSUN distance education program is assessed per credit hour and is noted as a student credit hour (SCH). Tuition includes delivery of the tapes to the student. The current rate is $416 per SCH. These figures are based on the current published schedules and are subject to change without notice.

Prices for housing vary, depending on the type of housing, amenities, and proximity to campus. For detailed information on current housing costs and availability, students should contact the Office of Housing and Food Services (telephone: 970-491-6511).

Application Facts and Dates

Colorado State admits students to the Accelerated M.B.A. and Evening M.B.A. programs for the fall semester only. For information on application deadlines, students should visit the College's Web site at the address listed below. For information on the application deadlines for the Executive M.B.A. program, students should contact the EMBA Director at 303-534-3194. There is a limited number of seats available for each M.B.A. program, so students are encouraged to apply early. The graduate admission application requires a nonrefundable fee of $30. For further information, students should contact:

Dr. Ajay Menon, Associate Dean
College of Business
Colorado State University
Fort Collins, Colorado 80523-1270
Telephone: 970-491-6471
Fax: 970-491-0596

Distance Education Center
College of Business
Colorado State University
Fort Collins, Colorado 80523-1270
Telephone: 800-491-4MBA (4622)
    Ext. 1 (toll-free)
Fax: 970-491-2348
World Wide Web: http://www.biz.colostate.edu

Columbia University

Columbia Business School

New York, New York

THE GLOBAL M.B.A.

Given the constant changes in the global business environment, today's M.B.A. must equip students with practical, adaptable skills that give them a competitive edge and prepare them to be leaders in the international marketplace. Columbia Business School meets this challenge by combining an outstanding faculty with the unmatched resources of an Ivy League university in a living laboratory—New York City.

The School's location and strong relationships enable it to draw more than 300 business leaders to campus every year—as teachers, speakers, adjunct lecturers, and advisers. Whether they are headquartered in New York or just passing through, the opportunity to learn from those who have made an impact on the global business community adds to the School's unique academic and hands-on atmosphere.

The Columbia M.B.A. provides students with unparalleled opportunities and options for mobility across fields and industries in leadership roles and meeting the demands of the dynamic, international marketplace of the twenty-first century.

—Professor Meyer Feldberg, Dean

Programs and Curricular Focus

Hailed as one of the most innovative M.B.A. curricula, Columbia Business School's structure and course offerings prepare students to take leadership roles in tomorrow's fastest-growing industries, from media and entertainment to real estate finance, while giving them fundamental skills across all disciplines. Virtually every course, seminar, and conference approaches business as a global undertaking.

The first two terms of study consist of the core curriculum. Addressing four main themes—globalization, total quality management, ethics, and human resource management—the core is taught in clusters of approximately 60 students, which not only fosters cooperative and teamwork skills but also provides students with the opportunity to learn from the striking diversity of their peers and to form lasting bonds.

More than 200 elective courses in twelve fields of concentration provide opportunities for second-year M.B.A. students to focus their studies. Combining strong offerings in the disciplines of accounting, finance, marketing, and management with cutting-edge concentrations such as entrepreneurship; media, entertainment, and communications; public and nonprofit management; and real estate, students graduate with a breadth of basic skills and a depth of knowledge in their chosen field.

Students may opt to pursue one of the thirteen dual-degree programs offered jointly by the Business School and other schools at Columbia University or may select electives at any of those schools. The Executive M.B.A. program allows executives, who are sponsored by their employers, to earn M.B.A.s without interrupting their careers in a flexible degree program that meets on Friday or every other Friday and Saturday. In addition, in an unprecedented collaboration between two of the world's top business schools, London Business School and Columbia Business School join forces to offer the EMBA-Global. The EMBA-Global will provide graduates with an M.B.A. degree from both institutions as well as access to two distinguished faculties and alumni and student networks.

Students and the M.B.A. Experience

Diversity and individuality are the hallmarks of the Columbia Business School student body. Approximately 36 percent of the students are women, and more than a fifth are members of minority groups, making the School consistently the most diverse of the nation's top business schools. The School's global reputation and location in New York City attract large numbers of students from different cultures and backgrounds. A typical class includes lawyers, physicians, consultants, musicians, writers, professional athletes, and entrepreneurs. Their diverse interests are reflected in the more than ninety professional, social, and academic student-run organizations at the School. These clubs often sponsor programs and lectures that enhance classroom work and contribute to the community.

❖ Global Focus

Students, faculty, and members of the Columbia Business School community come from all parts of the nation and the globe, creating a vibrant international community. Hailing from more than sixty countries, forty states, and 140 undergraduate institutions, the student body is highly talented and culturally diverse. One out of every 3 students was born outside of the U.S., and more than half of the students from the U.S. have lived or worked outside of the country. The majority of Columbia Business School students speak at least two languages fluently.

The Jerome A. Chazen Institute of International Business is the focal point for international programs at the School. The Institute sponsors overseas study tours to six continents, lecture series, conferences, and student-exchange programs in addition to business-oriented language programs.

The Faculty

Columbia Business School has a full-time faculty of 117. The faculty members combine excellence in teaching with rigorous research that adds to the core of academic scholarship and addresses issues of practical importance to the businessplace. Their pioneering research, widespread consultation, and commitment to the creation of new knowledge produce an energy that carries into the classroom. More than 80 adjunct faculty members, professionals culled from the Fortune 500, bring their expertise and experience into the classroom in areas ranging from investment banking to new media and from venture capital to real estate. An outstanding resource, the faculty prepares students to solve real problems by blending theory with practice.

The Business School Network

Corporate Partnerships

The Business School's location and relationships with New York's largest firms and industry leaders create unique opportunities for students. During a typical day, students

Professor Rajeev Kohli's class.

can attend a lecture featuring guest speakers from AT&T, Xerox, Avis, J. P. Morgan, the National Basketball Association, or Donaldson, Lufkin & Jenrette; visit a major corporation's headquarters as part of a group project; or meet on campus with or in the downtown office of a recruiter for a discussion regarding employment opportunities. Many students take advantage of informational interviews with one of the Business School's 13,000 alumni who live in and around New York or of networking opportunities through forty-six alumni clubs around the world.

Contributing to the academic experience, the School draws adjunct professors from their offices to the classroom to add real-world application to course work. Courses such as Inner City Consulting, Initial Public Offerings, and Emerging Financial Markets are developed and co-taught by Business School faculty members and senior managers at selected corporations. A key competitive advantage is that students learn the pace, perspective, and culture of the business community from the inside out and can hit the ground running upon graduation.

Prominent Alumni

Alumni remain actively involved with the School, participating in student-run events, conducting admission interviews, and advising students through the Alumni Counseling Board. Many prominent alumni, including Warren Buffett (M.S. '51), Chairman, Berkshire Hathaway, Inc.; Michael Gould (M.B.A. '68), Chairman and CEO, Bloomingdale's; Henry R. Kravis (M.B.A. '69), founding partner, Kohlberg Kravis Roberts & Company; Rochelle Lazarus (M.B.A. '70), President and CEO, Ogilvy & Mather Worldwide; and Benjamin Rosen (M.B.A. '61), Chairman, Compaq Computer Corporation and Rosen Motors Corporation, contribute demonstrated leadership and management expertise as in-class lecturers, members of the School's governing board, and guest speakers at Business School events.

The College and Environs

Columbia University was founded in 1754 as King's College by a royal charter of King George II of England. It is the oldest institution of higher learning in the state of New York and the fifth oldest in the United States. Columbia University's campus, located on the Upper West Side of Manhattan in a hilly neighborhood called Morningside Heights, is bordered by Riverside Park and Morningside Park. The 36 acres include tree-shaded lawns and brick paths connecting stately buildings and the University's fifteen colleges and graduate schools.

Facilities

The new Business/Law building, which opened in January 1999, provides state-of-the-art multimedia classrooms. The classrooms include videoconferencing capability, allowing the delivery and/or recording of events in one classroom to be broadcast to any other classroom. The amphitheater classroom feature hubs for data and electric connectivity, with every seat wired to the network. The new building also increases the amount of room available for group-study space as well as reception and event space. Eight-story Uris Hall, the Business School's original building, houses classrooms, faculty and administrative offices, the Thomas J. Watson Library of Business and Economics, and a café. As part of an ongoing renovation project, the library in Uris Hall was expanded during the summer of 1999. Classrooms and administrative offices were also renovated as part of this project.

Placement

Columbia Business School maintains one of the strongest corporate recruiting programs, consistently ranking among the top five favorite hunting grounds of corporate recruiters. The School's proximity to Wall Street and to leading firms in all industries provides unparalleled opportunities for students. More than 500 companies recruited

on campus last year, and the School received more than 3,500 job postings from firms worldwide.

The recruiting environment is on line, allowing more than 10,500 first- and second-year interviews to be scheduled annually. The Office of Career Services provides more than sixty workshops, seminars, and panels that cover topics ranging from conducting effective job searches and networking to career changes and from presentation skills to writing cover letters. Students can also take advantage of individualized career counseling and one-on-one resume reviews with Career Services officers.

Admission

Applicants are evaluated in three categories: professional promise, personal characteristics, and academic credentials. The School looks for well-rounded people from diverse economic, social, ethnic, geographic, and professional backgrounds. Ideal applicants have demonstrated leadership, have the ability to work as members of a team, and can contribute to the academic experience of their peers. Admission prerequisites include a bachelor's degree, a minimum of two years of work experience, GMAT scores, and, for international students, TOEFL scores. The School selects those applicants who have the focus and drive to become tomorrow's business leaders.

Finances

The cost of tuition per term for the 2000–01 academic year is $14,580. There are two types of financial aid available: fellowships, which are based on academic excellence, professional promise, and personal merit, and need-based assistance, including scholarships and low-interest loans. Questions may be directed to the Office of Financial Aid, 111 Uris Hall (telephone: 212-854-4057).

Application Facts and Dates

Domestic application deadlines are April 20 for the fall semester and October 1 for the spring semester. International application deadlines are March 1 for the fall semester and October 1 for the spring semester. Decisions are sent out on a rolling basis.

For more information, students should contact:

Office of Admissions
Columbia Business School
Room 216, Uris Hall
Columbia University
3022 Broadway
New York, New York 10027
Telephone: 212-854-1961
Fax: 212-662-6754
World Wide Web: http://www.gsb.
columbia.edu

 # Concordia University

THE CONCORDIA M.B.A. SURPASSES THE BENCHMARK IN BUSINESS LEARNING

Our students excel through the professionalism and challenging curriculum of our program. Our history of excellence, innovation, and leadership is a cause for celebration. We have recruited a stellar faculty and created a dynamic, flexible, and innovative program that destines our graduates for success.

We foster a community that reflects the international and multifaceted reality of the business world. Our faculty works with the spirit of mutual respect with students, combining their business acumen with solid instruction. Our staff maintains a warm and responsive relationship with the students.

Attentive instructors, a high caliber of fellow learners, and a flexible, innovative program all combine to meet the diverse needs of our success-driven participants. We help students envision business not as it was, but how it will be, thus providing our students with the tools to succeed.

—Lea Prevel Katsanis, Ph.D., Director, M.B.A. Program

Program and Curricular Focus

As the nature of business becomes more complex and new technologies speed up the tempo of change, the management of companies and institutions becomes increasingly a task for professionals. It is precisely with this fact in mind that the Concordia M.B.A. Program has been designed. Whether one's interests lie in achieving a high-level management position in industry or government, an entrepreneurial career, or simply extending one's education to increase the scope of opportunities, an M.B.A. from Concordia provides the necessary ingredients. These include an emphasis on teamwork, motivating others, and interpersonal skills in an applied learning environment.

In addition, Concordia University has been confirmed as one of the leading business schools by AACSB–The International Association for Management Education. Out of approximately 1,200 institutions that offer business programs, only 305 U.S. and four Canadian schools have accreditation. This designation is a seal of approval for the high quality of programs offered by Concordia University's Faculty of Commerce and Administration.

The Concordia M.B.A. Program emphasizes an interdisciplinary general management perspective. This orientation provides students with the expertise they need to become effective business professionals. The program focuses on the achievement of managerial success in an increasingly complex and competitive business environment. The objective of the program is to enable students to integrate the knowledge and skills they have acquired in the principal functional areas of business to achieve overall corporate goals; make decisions that reflect sensitivity to the relationships between the firm and the social, ethical, economic, and political environments in which it operates, both locally and internationally; apply the analytical, interpersonal, and communication skills necessary for the effective management of human capital, technical, and information resources; and refine their career goals to develop the confidence to confront an ever-changing business environment.

Students and the M.B.A. Experience

The Concordia M.B.A. student body consists of approximately 350 individuals with varied academic, cultural, and professional backgrounds. This creates a dynamic learning environment in which students learn from each other. On average, students are 30 years of age with six years of full-time work experience. Women comprise approximately 40 percent of the class. The ratio of full-time to part-time students is 60:40.

Concordia takes pride in providing its students with approachable and friendly faculty and staff members who treat them with respect. This makes the learning experience more effective and more enjoyable.

❖ Global Focus

The Concordia University curriculum is designed to take a global focus in all courses. In addition, a multicultural student body and faculty allows for diverse viewpoints and business philosophies. In keeping with this focus, exchange programs are available at Gothenburg School of Economics and Commercial Law in Sweden, the Schiller Institute at the University of Heidelberg in Germany, the Centre d'Enseignement et de Recherche Applique au Management in France, ITAM (Mexico), the University of Groningen (Netherlands), and several other universities throughout Europe and the U.S.

Special Features

The International Case Competition is an annual event that was created and is directed by students at Concordia University. M.B.A. programs from around the world participate in what has grown into a prestigious, highly recognized, five-day, thirty-team competition. The event provides access to industry leaders and excellent opportunities for networking.

Another important feature of the M.B.A. program is the option of taking the practicum or business research paper. The practicum project provides students with an opportunity to carry out an in-depth investigation of an actual business problem within an organization. The business research paper is a one-on-one research project with a professor in a specialized area of interest to the student.

The Faculty

Concordia's faculty is one of the largest and most respected in Canada because of its experience and international background. Many professors are consultants in industry and government, and others are internationally known for their research. Faculty members are selected by a separate committee to be members of the core M.B.A. faculty, and appointments are made every three years. These faculty members have a special interest in the M.B.A. program and are a valuable resource to students. In addition, Concordia has faculty members who have attained special recognition. For example, Professor Michel Laroche is a Fellow of the Royal Society of Canada; Professor Steven Appelbaum was recently selected for the *Financial Post's* Leaders in Management Award; and Associate Professor Bryan Barbieri was selected by the alumni to receive the Alumni Award for Excellence in Teaching.

A real education for the real world.

The Business School Network

Corporate Partnership

The M.B.A. program is closely linked to the pharmaceutical industry in Canada. The Pharmaceutical Management Centre offers a seminar in pharmaceutical marketing, which is open to M.B.A. students. In addition, the University has linkages with the Canadian aviation industry.

Prominent Alumni

Concordia alumni hold many prominent industry positions around the world, and the University is proud to count the following individuals as its M.B.A. graduates: Holger Kluge, President of Personal and Commercial Banking, CIBC; Brian Steck, Chairman and CEO, Nesbitt Burns; Donald Wright, President and COO, Toronto Dominion Securities; Andre Desmarais, President and co-CEO, Power Corporation of Canada; and Robert MacDonald, President, Bell Helicopter Textron.

The College and Environs

Concordia University is an English-language university located in the city of Montreal, the second-largest French-speaking city in the world. Montreal is located on an island in the heart of the St. Lawrence Valley. It dates back to the seventeenth century and is built around a mountain known as Mont-Royal in the centre of the island. The city is within an hour's drive of New York and Vermont in the U.S. and a myriad of lakes and ski resorts in the Laurentian Mountains and the Eastern Townships.

Few cities are as exciting and multidimensional as Montreal. As one of the great cities of the world, it has an Olympic Stadium, a famous hockey team, a National League baseball team, world-class art galleries, an excellent metro system, and some of the finest shops this side of the Atlantic. Montreal is a major financial, business, and industrial centre.

Facilities

The confident, modern stance of Concordia's downtown campus, where all the M.B.A. classes are held, is symbolic of the energy and forward thinking that have made this institution into one of the largest universities in Canada. The University has two campuses: the Sir George Williams Campus in the heart of the city and the Loyola Campus, nestled in a tranquil setting near Montreal West. The two campuses are connected by the door-to-door shuttle bus service operated by the University and by the bus and metro system of the city of Montreal.

Concordia offers a rich university experience to its community of more than 25,000 full- and part-time students. In its faculties—Arts and Science, Commerce and Administration, Engineering and Computer Science, and Fine Arts—there are more than 150 academic programs leading to bachelor's, master's, and doctoral degrees.

The Faculty of Commerce and Administration is located in the Guy Metro Building on the Sir George Williams campus. In addition to lecture halls and seminar rooms, it houses the Webster Library, which contains reference and research material selected to meet the specific needs of commerce and administration graduate students.

Technology Environment

The Faculty has its own computer lab with Pentium computers and a wide variety of business software. Students are connected by e-mail to faculty and staff members and to each other for ease of communication.

Placement

Student job searches are supported by the Faculty of Commerce and Administration Placement Centre, which is instrumental in marketing Concordia graduates to major national and international corporations. Each year, on-campus information and recruiting sessions are held on an ongoing basis.

Admission

Acceptance into the Concordia M.B.A. Program is based on academic qualifications and work experience and is highly competitive. Applicants must have completed a bachelor's degree with high standing at a recognized institution and achieved a satisfactory score on the GMAT. A minimum of two years of full-time work experience is also required.

Finances

Program fees for 2000–01 for a full-time student are based on an eight-term billing structure and amount to Can$585.81 per term for Quebec residents, Can$1028.31 per term for residents of other Canadian provinces, and Can$3168.73 per term for international students. Beyond program costs, students should budget for living expenses of at least Can$11,000 per year. This figure is based on the standard needs of a single person and includes accommodation, groceries, clothing, public transportation, and miscellaneous expenditures.

For U.S. students, the favorable 40 percent exchange rate provides a significant benefit for both tuition and living expenses.

Application Facts and Dates

The program provides three entry dates per year: September, January, and May. The application deadlines for September entry are June 1 for Canadian residents and February 15 for international students; for January entry, they are October 1 for Canadian residents and June 15 for international students; and for May, February 28 for Canadian residents and October 15 for international students. Applications for full-time study should be submitted to the Faculty of Commerce and Administration at the address below, along with a Can$50 application fee. International students are eligible for full-time study only.

M.B.A. Program
Faculty of Commerce and
    Administration
Concordia University
1455 de Maisonneuve Boulevard
    West, GM-710
Montreal, Quebec H3G 1M8
Canada
Telephone: 514-848-2727
E-mail: profmba@vax2.concordia.ca
World Wide Web: http://www-
    commerce.concordia.ca/mba.htm

Cornell University

Ithaca, New York

> ### SMALL . . . RIGOROUS . . . INNOVATIVE . . .AGILE . . . INTERNATIONAL . . . CAREER RELEVANT
>
> *At Cornell's Johnson School, we have turned our classrooms into high-speed, interactive environments that are every bit as intense as life in the business world. The curriculum is built around career-relevant learning: real-time data analysis, live cases, immersion learning, and specialized leadership development. Our relatively small size encourages greater interaction among students than is typically found in larger schools. Our faculty members pride themselves on their accessibility as well as their superior teaching; their office doors—and frequently, their homes—are open to students. Our diverse international community ensures that developing a global perspective becomes a personal process rather than an academic exercise. Together, it adds up to a simultaneously challenging and supportive environment that is conducive to building the foundation for personal and professional success.*
>
> —Robert J. Swieringa, Dean

Program and Curricular Focus

The Johnson School program combines rigor and flexibility. A first-year core includes integration between functional areas and a heavy emphasis on case analysis, strategy, and leadership, team-building, and communication skills.

Core courses are scheduled so that students may take electives during their first year and gain advanced training prior to the summer internship. Many students participate in the acclaimed immersion courses (currently offered in e-commerce, marketing, manufacturing management, managerial finance, and investment banking). Immersion courses offer an integrated, real-world focus, which has made them vastly popular with students and recruiters alike.

The Parker Center's Wall Street–quality trading room (equipped with $1.5 million of live data feeds analyst software) and a $2 million student-run investment fund offer hands-on experience in securities analysis and asset management.

The popular entrepreneurship program focuses on high-growth businesses and enables students to interact closely with successful entrepreneurs and to work as consultants for start-up and small businesses. The venture capital fund and incubator are opportunities for students to evaluate, fund, and support new businesses. Falling under the umbrella of the Center for Leadership in Dynamic Organizations, the leadership program is one of the few to combine self-assessment, academic theory, and leadership projects to ensure the broadest impact.

Johnson students are also encouraged to make full use of Cornell's other internationally renowned programs, such as industrial and labor relations, biotechnology, law, engineering, health-care management, public policy, international development, hotel administration, languages, and advanced computing. One quarter of the M.B.A. program may be fulfilled with any graduate-level course at Cornell.

Students and the M.B.A. Experience

The Johnson School tradition of both working and socializing together leads to an unusually strong sense of community and collegiality. The average age of students is 29, and the average work experience is five years. Women comprise 28 percent of the class; members of minority groups, 21 percent; and international students, 30 percent. About one third of the students are married.

❖ Global Focus

Exchange programs with eighteen overseas universities, intersession study tours (recent destinations include Brazil, China, India, Japan, Romania, and Venezuela), and internships through the School's Central and Eastern European Development (CEED) Program allow students to experience international business firsthand. On campus, international business concerns are fully integrated into the curriculum. The joint M.B.A./M.A. in Asian studies and Cornell's varied offerings in regional and language studies supplement the Johnson School program. The large number of students from outside the U.S. ensures a global perspective and forms the foundation for a future international business network. The Johnson School is one of the only business schools to allow academic credit for foreign language study.

Special Features

The highly competitive two-year, full-tuition-plus-stipend Park Leadership Fellowships, open only to U.S. citizens, are awarded to 30 entering M.B.A. students each year. Park Fellows receive enriched leadership opportunities and are expected to complete a leadership project.

The Twelve-Month M.B.A. Option allows individuals with graduate degrees in scientific or technical fields to complete an accelerated core curriculum during the summer (June to August) and join the second-year class in the fall.

Joint-degree programs exist in human resources management, engineering, law, and Asian studies. An Executive Option to the M.B.A. program, with classes on alternating weekends, is taught in the New York City metropolitan area to accommodate students' career and family responsibilities. This intensive, year-round program, which is taught by Cornell faculty members, allows students to meet the Johnson School M.B.A. requirements in less than two years. Upon completion of the program, graduates are awarded the same M.B.A. degree as full-time Johnson School students. Students must have substantial management experience and be sponsored by their companies. For more information about the E.M.B.A. option, students should send e-mail to emba@cornell.edu or call 607-255-4251.

The Faculty

Johnson School faculty members consistently receive high marks for the quality of their teaching and research. Because of their links with the business world, they are also a good resource for sound career advice.

The renovation of Sage Hall, the Johnson School's home, has turned one of Cornell's most dramatic buildings into one of the most technologically advanced management education centers in the world.

The Business School Network

Corporate Partnerships

The Visiting Executives Program, immersion courses, the Park Leadership Fellows Program, the Leadership Skills Program, and the Johnson Mentor Program, as well as the large number of conferences, symposia, and networking events organized by the student professional organizations, provide a wide variety of formal and informal opportunities to interact with successful business leaders. Recent visitors have included Jay Walker, Craig Barrett, Thomas Jones, and Abby Joseph Cohen. Corporate advisory boards, and often corporate sponsorship, exist for a number of programs, including the Parker Center, the entrepreneurship program, and the immersion courses. Corporate leaders also sit on the Johnson School Advisory Board.

The College and Environs

Cornell is an Ivy League university, and its 19,000 students hail from more than 100 countries. Ithaca, with its combination of cosmopolitan sophistication and small-town accessibility, offers residents the best of both worlds—diverse cultural offerings and recreational activities in a beautiful setting of lakes, waterfalls, forests, and countryside. Students with families find it a hospitable place for balancing family and career; the public school system is excellent.

Facilities

Sage Hall, the Johnson School's new home, is located in the center of the Cornell campus. The $38.2-million historic renovation project, completed in 1998, has turned one of Cornell's original and most dramatic buildings into one of the most technologically advanced management education centers in the world.

Technology Environment

Sage Hall's state-of-the-art technology infrastructure includes fiber-optic cable throughout the building, 1,400 computer ports, distance learning and teleconferencing capabilities, three student computing labs, a multimedia lab, and access to live electronic data feeds from the top financial information services, including Bridge, Bloomberg, and First Call. The Parker Center's "trading room" is equipped with more than $1.5 million of the most sophisticated analyst software. Students are required to own a laptop computer.

Placement

More than 175 companies recruit on campus, and students average eleven on-campus interviews for permanent jobs. Through Career Network, 700 alumni in the U.S. and overseas offer information and mock interviews, resume critiques, and job search advice. Individual counseling sessions support targeted job searches.

The Johnson Mentor Program matches M.B.A. students with successful Cornell alumni for advice and support in their fields of interest. In addition to School-sponsored networking programs, the School participates in a variety of career forums and corporate recruiting events worldwide. A special fund supplements salaries for summer internships at small entrepreneurial and midsize companies. The School also offers a variety of lifetime career services for alumni.

Admission

The Admissions Committee considers an applicant's prior academic performance, GMAT scores, breadth and depth of work experience, demonstrated leadership, interpersonal and communication skills, extracurricular and community involvement, career aspirations, recommendations, and previous achievements. For the class of 2002, the average GMAT score was 679; the average undergraduate GPA, 3.35; and the average TOEFL score, 644 (paper-based)/275 (computer-based). Interviews are set at the discretion of the Office of Admissions, and staff member, student, and alumni interviews are given equal weight. All applicants are encouraged to visit the campus; the Office of Admissions arranges for a student host.

Finances

In 2000–01, tuition is $27,600. Books and the computer cost $3400, and housing and food costs approximately $7500 (based on the cost of sharing a moderately priced apartment). The School awards more than $1.5 million in merit-based scholarships each year in addition to need-based loans and work-study funds. International applicants receive similar consideration as U.S. citizens for merit-based awards.

Application Facts and Dates

Application deadlines for the two-year program are November 15, January 15, and March 15. The application deadline for the Twelve-Month M.B.A. Option are November 15, December 15, and January 15. For more information, students should contact:

Office of Admissions
111 Sage Hall
Cornell University
Ithaca, New York 14853-6201

Telephone: 607-255-4526
　　　　　800-847-2082 (toll-free in
　　　　　　　the U.S. and Canada)
Fax: 607-255-0065
E-mail: mba@cornell.edu
World Wide Web: http://www.johnson.
　　cornell.edu/

Cranfield University

Cranfield, Bedford, England

E-BUSINESS OPPORTUNITIES WITHIN THE CRANFIELD M.B.A. PROGRAM

▶ *Consistent with its reputation for innovation, Cranfield School of Management is the first European business school to actively assist students in setting up Internet businesses during their M.B.A. program. Business incubator CranfieldCreates.com provides a full range of services for students launching Internet and technology-enabled businesses. The venture has the backing of the faculty, alumni, and a number of eminent business partners. CranfieldCreates.com also facilitates introductions to venture capitalists. More detail can be found on its Web site (http://www.CranfieldCreates.com). This venture typifies the ongoing development of Cranfield's M.B.A. program to equip students for success in the new economy.*

—Professor Leo Murray, Director of the School

Programs and Curricular Focus

Central to the Cranfield learning process are the emphasis on personal development that runs through the whole program, the sharing of experience and skills through the learning teams, and the practical case study approach.

At Cranfield, participants learn in the context of a stimulating environment and a mature and diverse student body. Faculty members have management experience and maintain strong links with organizations from the private and public sectors.

The content of the program is both practical and international. It is constantly updated and reviewed to ensure that what is learned at Cranfield enables participants to cope with the speed of change and meet the challenges of a dynamic, global business environment.

The one-year program is very intensive, covering much of the same ground in the four taught terms as the traditional two-year American programs. During the first two terms, participants increase their knowledge of the basic elements of business management. The course structure stresses the integral nature of key functional areas and the interrelationships between them. Terms three and four provide the opportunity to customize the program by selecting a group of courses from more than ninety electives, including European languages.

Cranfield also offers a two-year, part-time Executive M.B.A. program, enabling participants to remain in full-time employment. They attend Cranfield on sixteen weekends (all day Friday and Saturday) and for four 1-week residential periods each year. A modular M.B.A. program is due to be introduced in 2001.

Students and the M.B.A. Experience

With an age range from 25 to 45 (average age 31) and approximately eight years of work experience behind them, participants come from a wide variety of industry backgrounds and job functions: from all aspects of business, the professions, the armed forces, and the public sector. The Cranfield approach to learning, with its emphasis on learning teams and the use of case studies, draws on the experience and skills of these participants. The student body is becoming increasingly international, with 40 percent of the current students coming from overseas, representing thirty countries. Women make up about 24 percent of the total. The annual intake of 200 students is divided into four streams, ensuring class sizes of approximately 50. The program is large enough to provide a diversity of experience, and yet small enough for all the students to get to know each other, creating a cooperative but dynamic environment for study.

❖ Global Focus

Exchange programs exist with schools in the Far East, the U.S.A., South Africa, and continental Europe, and there is a double-degree program with EM Lyon in France. Increasingly, however, students

Professor Malcolm McDonald, author of the best-seller *Marketing Plans,* introduces his marketing elective.

The sharing of experience and skills through the learning teams is central to the Cranfield process.

are undertaking overseas, short consultancy-type projects as an alternative to spending a whole term abroad.

Special Features

A four-week preprogram English language and business culture course is offered to students speaking English as a second language and may be a condition of the offer of placement in the program. The course prepares students for the intensive workload and participative style of teaching at Cranfield by means of interactive lectures, group discussions, individual presentations, mini-projects, role play, and report writing.

The Faculty

The program is taught by people who understand the problems of putting theory into practice. The majority of Cranfield faculty members have managerial experience, a strength reinforced by close links with outside organizations through consultancy, sponsored research, and teaching on executive development programs with practicing managers. Most of the faculty members are preeminent in their field, with a significant number of books, publications, and articles to their names. With some 90 members in the full-time teaching staff, 18 visiting professors, and 36 research staff members, the School of Management faculty is one of the largest in Europe.

The Business School Network

In addition to the permanent faculty, Cranfield has more than 40 visiting fellows, including a number of high-profile leaders of industry.

Several of the core and elective courses involve students in working on projects with outside organizations. These include a business check-up course, during which teams of students carry out a complete business audit.

M.B.A. participants also have structured access to the 6,000 senior managers who attend the School's executive development programs each year.

The College and Environs

Founded in 1967, the School is a faculty of Cranfield University, and the campus is entirely postgraduate, serving some 1,500 master's and doctoral students. Set in a peaceful area of the Bedfordshire countryside, Cranfield is midway between Oxford and Cambridge, only an hour's drive from London and a similar distance from Stratford-upon-Avon, birthplace of William Shakespeare.

Facilities

The School has its own television studio that is used for project presentations and the exploration of interpersonal situations during the compulsory communications skills courses.

Each M.B.A. student is provided with a "Cranfield-ready" laptop PC for the duration of the program. This provides students with access to teaching material through the School's Intranet system, which also makes online tutorial support available.

There is a good range of on-campus accommodations for single students, couples, and families. Cranfield offers a peaceful, safe, and healthy environment, and the cost of living is lower than in the cities in the United Kingdom.

Placement

The School has its own Career Development Office dedicated to the unsponsored M.B.A. students. Services include personal planning and stocktaking workshops; lectures on various aspects of job searching; individual career counseling sessions; seminars with alumni on networking, careers, and CV writing; advice and assistance on interview techniques and researching companies; and corporate presentations. A "liftoff" elective course at the end of the program prepares students for integration back into the workforce. The School's alumni association also operates an Executive Recruitment Service.

Admission

Entry requirements include a good degree from a U.K. university or its equivalent from a similar overseas institution, at least three years of post-qualification work experience, and a good GMAT score. An IELTS or TOEFL score is required from candidates for whom English is a second language.

Finances

Tuition fees for all students for the 2000–01 academic year are £20,000 sterling. Candidates should allow approximately £8000 sterling for accommodation, living costs, and books for the one-year program. Fees for the 2001–02 part-time M.B.A. program will be £13,000 per annum. Fees include provision of a laptop PC for the duration of the program.

Application Facts and Dates

Places are offered on a continuing basis from January onward. Although there is no cutoff date, early application is strongly recommended. Processing applications and arranging interviews for overseas candidates takes about four weeks, and a decision can normally be expected within a week of the interview. The application forms can be found on the School's Web address (http://www.cranfield.ac.uk/som/applicfo.htm) and downloaded onto a PC for completion.

Mrs. Pat Hayes
Admissions Officer
Cranfield School of Management
Cranfield, Bedford MK43 0AL
England
Telephone: 44(0)1234 754431
Fax: 44(0)1234 752439
E-mail: p.hayes@cranfield.ac.uk
World Wide Web: http://www.cranfield.ac.uk/som/mba

Dalhousie University

Halifax, Nova Scotia, Canada

PREPARING STUDENTS FOR A COMPLEX SOCIETY

We provide students with an excellent general management education, a true appreciation of effective people skills, and a high level of technical abilities. The M.B.A. degree is designed to meet the needs of active professionals from the private, public, and nonprofit sectors. Students work closely together and with faculty members in a small urban environment that provides for excellent quality of life. The program assists students in developing and enhancing the critical values and talents necessary to solve the problems of a complex society, gives them an edge in a highly competitive job market, and better prepares them for life in a rapidly changing, technological society.

—Abolhassan Jalilvand, Ph.D., Dean, Faculty of Management

Programs and Curricular Focus

The Dalhousie University M.B.A. Program brings together intelligent and highly motivated men and women from Canada and other nations. They are involved in a demanding, globally focused curriculum by an internationally respected faculty. The program makes frequent use of the Atlantic Canadian business community to enrich the M.B.A. learning experience through practical application of skills and abilities.

The Dalhousie M.B.A. degree is recognized internationally for its excellence. Top Canadian firms actively recruit Dalhousie M.B.A. graduates, who are supported in their job search by the Career Resource Centre. Whether a student wants to work for a multinational corporation, a small start-up company, or start one of his or her own, the curriculum provides the knowledge, skills, and abilities to succeed. Highly motivated classmates significantly enhance the learning environment and provide a lifetime international network of friends.

Dalhousie's Faculty of Management offers two options for graduate business education: the Two-Year M.B.A. Program, which is twenty months (two 8-month academic periods) or an Accelerated Ten-Month M.B.A. Program for applicants with an undergraduate degree in business. These programs are offered both full-time and part-time and are usually completed within one to six years.

The M.B.A./LL.B. Program is a four-year joint-degree program offered by the Faculty of Management and Dalhousie Law School. It begins only in September and requires full-time attendance.

Students and the M.B.A. Experience

Dalhousie's culture encourages students in teamwork and networking. About 50 percent of the students in each class are native to central and western Canada. The international and domestic students come from varied ethnic and socioeconomic backgrounds. International students represent more than 10 percent of the student body. Women constitute about one third of each class. Seventy-five percent of the students have worked two years or more before enrollment, with an average of 4½ years of work experience. Students average 28 years of age. The students come from diverse academic backgrounds ranging from the arts to the sciences.

❖ Global Focus

The Dalhousie M.B.A. Program emphasizes international content throughout the M.B.A. curriculum. Students are continually exposed to a global perspective of management through the first-year curriculum. Students gain additional exposure and experience through the Centre for International Business Studies. The Centre offers a variety of second-year elective courses focused specifically on international business, the Foreign Study Mission, and international internships.

Dalhousie M.B.A. students can also participate in exchange programs with a number of top business schools in Europe, Latin America, and Asia. Exchanges add an even greater international dimension to the M.B.A. education. Students can elect to study abroad for one term after completion of the first year of the M.B.A. Program.

However, arrangements must be made during the first year in order to do so. The School's Centre for International Business Studies, in addition to developing the international business curriculum, coordinates an annual Foreign Study Mission and international internships.

Special Features

Dalhousie offers students a unique experience among Canadian M.B.A. programs because of its small size of fewer than 200 students. The size allows more academic and social involvement between faculty members and students and among students themselves. It allows faculty members to maintain an open-door policy and administer more team projects and directed studies, including a major consulting project for business clients in the second year. In these projects, student teams work with local businesses on key issues and problems, presenting solutions to the clients at year's end.

A variety of teaching approaches are used, including lectures/discussions, case studies, team projects, simulation exercises, and independent study. With a student-faculty ratio of 8:1, each student is ensured individual attention.

The Faculty

Professors and researchers include nationally and internationally renowned experts in core business areas and in information sciences, international business, finance, and marketing. Together they provide an open, supportive, and balanced approach, enabling the student to bring theory and real-world experience together.

The Business School Network

Corporate Partnerships

Dalhousie's M.B.A. Program, located in downtown Halifax, takes full advantage of its proximity by drawing on Atlantic Canadian business leaders as instructors in classrooms and as speakers at numerous special events. Group projects in the M.B.A. program use local businesses as the focal point for their activities. The School's Advisory Board comprises the top business leaders in Canada, who regularly meet at the school to offer their advice and assistance.

Prominent Alumni

Dalhousie's M.B.A. Program has produced more than 2,000 graduates who occupy significant leadership positions in business and organizations throughout Canada and internationally. They comprise part of the growing Dalhousie University alumni network of business contacts and friends, which includes graduates of the University of Toronto Bachelor of Commerce Program and other management programs.

The College and Environs

Dalhousie University is set in a picturesque urban campus with appealing ivy-covered schools, libraries, resource centres, recreational facilities, and dormitories. The University is centrally located in historic Halifax, Nova Scotia's capital city and Atlantic Canada's premier centre for business, international trade, the arts, and entertainment.

In addition to being the regional center for finance, government, health care, and education, the city enjoys an entrepreneurial spirit and an information technology community growing in international success and reputation. Greater Halifax has a population of about 350,000, which makes it big enough to have many of the good things of a larger city—such as cultural activities, sports, nightlife, public transportation, and an international airport—as well as many of the best aspects of a smaller city.

Technology Environment

Students have access to some of the best communication technology available on university campuses today. They communicate with each other, with outside businesses, and with the world's research resources at the touch of a button. State-of-the-art multimedia stations, color printers, presentation and layout software, and ana-

lytical programs are just a few of the technology resources readily available in the School's computer facilities.

Placement

The M.B.A. Career Resource Centre actively helps students prepare themselves for the job search and recruitment process. The Career Resource Centre provides a job-listing service, an on-campus recruiting program, and assistance to the M.B.A. alumni. Last year, more than seventy companies were in contact with the Career Resource Centre to recruit Dalhousie M.B.A. graduates. Dalhousie's Career and Counseling Centre helps students prepare and manage their careers. The Career and Counseling Centre offers individual career counseling, resume clinics, mock interview sessions, and a career resource library.

Admission

Candidates for admission are evaluated on a total portfolio of previous performance, personal characteristics, life experiences, and professional and academic references. Candidates must have a recognized undergraduate degree with a minimum B average in their final two years of study (73 percent, a 3.0 GPA, or Second Class Standing with Honours); GMAT results (scores above 500 preferred); demonstrated evidence of leadership, initiative, and a superior capacity for high-level work productivity; and two professional or academic reference letters. For the one-year M.B.A., an undergraduate business degree is required with a minimum B+ average (77 percent) and a GMAT score of at least 550. A very good command of both written and spoken English is essential for all incoming graduate students. International students must submit results of the TOEFL exam (normally 580 or greater on

the paper-based version and 237 or greater on the computer-based version).

Finances

Tuition for the 2000–01 academic year is approximately Can$6000 for Canadian full-time M.B.A. students and Can$3000 for part-time students. International students pay approximately Can$9000 for the full-time program and Can$6000 for the part-time program. These figures are based upon a per course fee of $590 and the average two-year M.B.A. student taking twenty ½-credit courses for the degree. In addition to tuition fees, a full-time student spends approximately Can$1500 per year on other fees, books, case materials, and supplies. Living expenses, food, lodging, and personal expenses are minimally estimated to be Can$8000 for the academic year. Some financial assistance is available to qualified applicants.

International Students

Diversity in Dalhousie's M.B.A. Program includes a rich mix of cultural and ethnic backgrounds of students. The M.B.A. Program enrolls about 15 percent of each class from many different countries outside of Canada, including Japan, Bosnia, Russia, China, Sweden, and the United States.

Application Facts and Dates

Applicants to the full-time program are usually admitted only in September of each year. Canadian applicants must forward complete application documents by June 1. International students must complete their application process by April 1 at the latest. The deadline for the People's Republic of China is January 31. In special circumstances, applicants with a prior business degree from a recognized program may qualify for January admission, but only with consultation and approval by the M.B.A. Admissions Committee. In such cases, all application materials must be received by November 1. International applicants pursuing this option are strongly encouraged to send application materials to be received by October 1.

Ms. Mary Hamblin
M.B.A. Program Director
School of Business Administration
Dalhousie University
6152 Coburg Road
Halifax, Nova Scotia
Canada B3H 3J5
Telephone: 902-494-1814
          888-432-5622 (toll-free)
Fax: 902-494-7154
E-mail: mba.admissions@dal.ca
World Wide Web: http://www.mgmt.
    dal.ca/

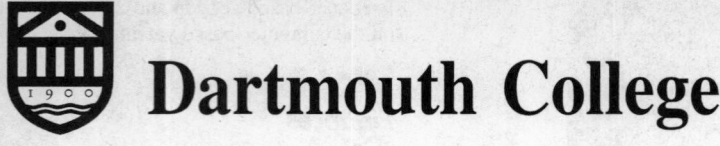

Dartmouth College

Hanover, New Hampshire

> ## A CHALLENGE YOU FACE TOGETHER
>
> *A student once said that when you graduate from Tuck, you've gained your education, your diploma, and friends for life. That statement captures something very special about Tuck that goes beyond statistics. Without a doubt, Tuck is one of the most selective and academically challenging M.B.A. programs. We provide students with an excellent general management education, a true appreciation of effective people skills, and a high level of technical abilities. Although the Tuck experience is rigorous, it is also supportive. Students work closely together, and with faculty, in a small-town, New England environment that provides for excellent quality of life. If you are interested in Tuck, I suggest that you contact some of our alumni. They are the best evidence of the value of the Tuck M.B.A..*
>
> —Paul Danos, Dean

Programs and Curricular Focus

Founded in 1900, Tuck was the first graduate school of management in the world, and it is the only top U.S. business school that offers the M.B.A. degree exclusively.

The core curriculum is a key element in the two-year, general management M.B.A. program. The first year is organized into four terms, and the second year is divided into three terms. A new curriculum retains Tuck's in-depth coverage of such areas as accounting, economics, finance, interpersonal behavior, marketing, operations, quantitative analysis, and strategy while emphasizing teamwork. By allowing students to select two of their courses during the first year and to choose the topic for their integrative team project, the new core program provides students with unique opportunities to shape their own learning paths.

The Tuck Forum, a key addition to the first year, focuses on developing critical general management knowledge and skills best taught using nontraditional methodologies. There are three segments that make up the Tuck Forum: course work designed to integrate material taught in the core courses from the perspective of a general manager or entrepreneur, a major project involving the development of a business plan for a new enterprise or business, and a series of seminars and tutorials organized by industry or career.

Tuck stands out, as it has for a century, as a school that combines the traditional values of great teaching, thought leadership, and personal scale with today's need to be innovative,

global, and technological. To advance the best business practices through global scholarship and education, Tuck has established new research centers focusing on Asia and the Emerging Economies, Private Equity, Corporate Governance, Digital Strategy, and Global Leadership.

New exchange programs are available with HEC in France; Templeton at Oxford, England; and IMD in Switzerland. Tuck also offers exchanges with the London School of Business; the Instituto de Estudios Superiores in Barcelona, Spain; the Institut Superieur des Affaires in France; WHU in Germany; and the International University of Japan. Joint-degree programs are available in international affairs (with Tufts' Fletcher School of Law and Diplomacy), medicine (with Dartmouth Medical School), engineering (with Dartmouth's Thayer School of Engineering), environmental law (with Vermont Law School), and public administration (with Harvard's Kennedy School).

Students and the M.B.A. Experience

Tuck's culture encourages students to work and grow with their peers. International students make up 32 percent of Tuck's overall student population. Members of minority groups represent more than 14 percent of the student body. Women make up 32 percent of each class. The average student has five years of work experience and is 28 years old.

Special Features

Tuck is distinctive among M.B.A. programs because its student-faculty ratio of 9:1 allows for ample interaction and individual attention. During the first term, faculty members advise team consulting projects for local businesses. Following the first year, most students work in a summer internship, and upon completion, they can participate in the Field Study in International Business program, consulting for a major corporation in Asia or South America. Critical Insight, one of the School's innovative projects, is a student-created Web site that tracks, streamlines, and reviews cutting-edge business topics such as e-commerce, database marketing, and current business practices in China. Tuck students have mastered the ability to work hard and have fun, epitomized by TYCOON, a computerized simulation game in which teams of students compete to launch a project.

The Faculty

Tuck faculty members are renowned for their teaching, research, and scholarly excellence. With generous research budgets, Tuck faculty members have access to the latest technology and research assistance. Faculty members utilize a variety of teaching methods including case studies, lecture/discussions, team projects, simulation exercises, and independent studies.

The Business School Network
Corporate Partnerships

Dartmouth College and the Tuck School of Business offer an extensive network of corporate partnerships. Tuck's Visiting Executive Program is the major avenue of exchange between real-world executives and Tuck students and faculty members. Executives give lectures; sit in on classes and seminars; lend their expertise to the subject at hand; contribute to student projects, presentations, and career forums; dine with students; and meet informally with small groups. Recent visiting executives represent companies such as Procter & Gamble, General Mills Inc., McKinsey & Co., Integral Capital Partners, Time Warner Cable, and America Online.

Tuck Hall—the first building on campus.

Prominent Alumni

The expertise of its graduates is a vital element of the Tuck M.B.A. program. Alumni consulting has been integrated into the new curriculum, and their support is essential to the admissions process. Among the best known of Tuck's graduates are L. William Seidman, Chief Commentator, CNBC (Class of 1944); Andrew C. Sigler, Retired Chairman, Champion International (Class of 1956); Didier Pineau-Valencienne, Honorary Chairman, Groupe Schneider, Paris (Class of 1957); Frank C. Herringer, Chairman, Transamerica Corporation (Class of 1965); Paul Clark, President and CEO, ICOS Corporation (Class of 1971); Noreen Doyle, Deputy Vice President, European Bank for Reconstruction and Development (Class of 1974); Alexander Cutler, President and CEO, Eaton Corporation (Class of 1975); Charles Schetter, Managing Director, McKinsey & Co. (Class of 1976); Konrad Kruger, Co-CEO, NatWest Markets (Class of 1977); Edson Mitchell, Head of Global Markets, Deutsche Bank Group (Class of 1978); Judy Fearing, Senior Vice President of Marketing, Walt Disney Co, GO.com division (Class of 1980); Susan Friedlander, Chief Administrative Officer, Bloomberg Financial Markets (Class of 1980); and Peter Neupert, CEO, drugstore.com (Class of 1980).

The College and Environs

Tuck is located on the Dartmouth College campus in Hanover, New Hampshire, on the banks of the beautiful Connecticut River. Hanover is the quintessential New England college town, from the brick-facade shops lining Main Street to the Colonial homes of the residential areas. All Dartmouth facilities are open to Tuck students, including a centralized computer network, nine-library system, art museum, creative and performing arts center, ski area, and indoor sports center. A variety of outdoor activities are available, including hiking in the White Mountains, canoeing on the Connecticut River, and cross-country and downhill skiing. Hanover is off Interstate 91 and near I-89. Driving distance is 2 hours from Boston; 3 hours from Montreal, Canada; and 4 hours from New York City.

Technology Environment

Dartmouth College and the Tuck School have always been at the forefront of new technology. The recent renovation of the student computer laboratory and the addition of the Whittemore Wing for Information Technology have ushered Tuck into the twenty-first century. The new facility offers the latest in desktop and mobile computing along with videoconferencing, multimedia production, data visualization, and group collaboration. All classrooms and study rooms at Tuck are equipped with computers and network jacks, which provide access to library databases, online information services, the World Wide Web, electronic mail and bulletin boards, file service, and high-speed laser printers. Network jacks in dormitory rooms and dial-up support for students off campus guarantee that all services can be accessed from student computers as well.

Placement

Tuck has powerful connections to international, national, and regional business communities, giving its students unparalleled access to leading companies. A comprehensive recruiting program for both first-year and second-year students draws more than 180 company representatives to interview students and more than 130 companies to interview for summer interns. More than 700 companies provide job listings each year, offering opportunities in a wide variety of geographic areas and industries. Placement rates are over 99 percent at the time of graduation.

Admission

The application consists of a personal application form, essay questions, official transcripts from every college or university ever attended, at least two letters of recommendation, scores from the GMAT taken within five years, and a nonrefundable application fee of $150. Applicants for whom English is not their native language or who have not attended an undergraduate institution in which English is the language of instruction must take the Test of English as a Foreign Language (TOEFL). Interviews are not required for admission but are encouraged. Off-campus interviewing is often available.

Finances

Tuition for the 1999–2000 school year was $27,150. This charge covered instruction, instructional facilities, and infirmary care services. For tuition, food, room, books and supplies, and personal expenses, a single student should budget approximately $43,500; a married student, approximately $4000 to $4500 more. The School provides financial assistance to qualified applicants through deferred-payment loans and a limited number of scholarships and fellowships.

International Students

Tuck welcomes international students and embraces the global perspectives that they bring. In the classes of 1999 and 2000, students represented twenty-eight countries from around the world.

Application Facts and Dates

A rolling decision process is used, so applicants are urged to complete their applications as early as possible. Students whose applications are received by mid-December are notified by mid-January, mid-January by mid-February, mid-February by mid-March, and mid-April by mid-May. For more information, students should contact:

Ms. Sally O. Jaeger
Director of Admissions
The Tuck School of Business
100 Tuck Hall
Dartmouth College
Hanover, New Hampshire 03755
Telephone: 603-646-3162
Fax: 603-646-1308

Dominican University

Graduate School of Business

River Forest, Illinois

SHAPING THE FUTURE TAKES A VISION

Dominican University provides its students with a vision of what their careers can be and the means to turn that vision into reality. Our new programs focus on changing technology and global business operation. The faculty of the Graduate School of Business looks beyond short-term issues to forecast the needs of tomorrow's business community in accordance with our goal of preparing students to meet those needs. As a result, Dominican University alumni currently hold high-ranking positions in many of America's largest corporations, as well as mid-size entrepreneurial ventures and financial institutions.

Shaping your future takes a vision. Your professional development depends upon obtaining superior business skills, not just acquiring a credential. That's why top-level professionals continue to choose our programs. I encourage you to discover how Dominican University's accredited programs can help you achieve personal and professional success.

—Dr. Molly Burke, Dean, School of Business

Programs and Curricular Focus

The primary goals of the Graduate School of Business are to achieve excellence in teaching and to promote excellence in learning. The course of study is intended for students who are either entering the business and management professions or who are preparing for advancement within their professions. The program also serves the continuing education needs of practicing managers through its Center for Effective Organizations.

A candidate for the M.B.A. normally needs seventeen courses to complete the degree. The seventeen-course curriculum consists of seven foundation courses, five core courses, and five electives. Depending upon the candidate's undergraduate preparation and official GMAT scores, one to all of the foundation courses may be waived. A minimum of ten courses is required for the degree. The M.B.A. program offers a choice of nine areas of concentration: accounting, entrepreneurship, finance, general management, health-care administration, management information systems, marketing, human resource management, and international business. Dominican University also offers master's degrees in computer information systems (M.S./C.I.S.), management information systems (M.S./M.I.S.), accounting (M.S.A.), and organization management (M.S.O.M.).

In order to serve the needs of students whose professional commitments require extensive travel, the Graduate School of Business offers a weekend M.B.A. program. Depending upon the candidate's academic background, a part-time student can complete this program in two calendar years, including one summer session. The Graduate School of Business also offers several joint-degree programs. The M.B.A./J.D. program is awarded in cooperation with The John Marshall Law School of Chicago. The M.B.A./M.S.L.I.S. is awarded in cooperation with the Dominican University Graduate School of Library and Information Science. The five-year B.A./M.B.A. is offered to qualified Dominican University juniors and seniors.

Students and the M.B.A. Experience

Students enrolled in the Graduate School of Business bring a wide range of professional and academic experiences into the classroom. The graduate business program is 48 percent men and 52 percent women, with an average age of 29. Students entering the M.B.A. program have approximately seven years of work experience. Cultural diversity enriches the Graduate School of Business. International students represent 17 percent of the graduate business student body and come from more than twenty countries.

Special Features

Student interaction with the faculty at Dominican University is not limited to the classroom. Traditionally, Dominican University offers a variety of activities designed to develop and enhance student-faculty relationships. Incoming students are given the opportunity to meet one another, current students, alumni, and faculty members through new-student orientation.

The Graduate School of Business offers an international business course for those students with an interest in studying abroad. The European business program is an extensive two-week course offered to graduate business students every other summer.

Graduate business students looking to pursue their personal interests closer to home are encouraged to become involved with the Graduate School of Business Student Government Association. This organization sponsors a host of social and networking events for graduate business students throughout the year. Eligible students are also encouraged to join Dominican University's chapter of Sigma Iota Epsilon (SIE), the National Honor Society of the Academy of Management. SIE sponsors several career development, networking, and social activities throughout the year. Scholarship support is also available through the chapter and the national office.

The Faculty

Dominican University has a commitment to excellence in teaching and the Graduate School of Business faculty is made up of highly experienced practitioners in their respective fields. Faculty interests are diverse. Some faculty members are involved in topical research projects and are widely published, while other faculty members are called upon by many of Chicago's top businesses for consultation. More than 75 percent of the courses are taught by professors who have completed their doctorate. Part-time faculty members are selectively chosen based upon their education, specialized skills, and accomplishments within the business community. Together, these full- and part-time faculty members offer Dominican students a rich and diverse business education that integrates theory and research into practical experience.

The Business School Network
Corporate Partnerships

The majority of Dominican's alumni live within the greater Chicago area. Consequently, students have access to an enor-

mous network of business professionals working in diverse fields. The GSB Alumni Association and the Alumni Career Network offer a variety of events designed to keep students in constant contact with Dominican alumni from all around Chicago and beyond.

The Graduate School of Business serves the needs of local, national, and international businesses through the Center for Effective Organizations (CEO). The CEO provides practical training for working managers in a variety of industries and fields.

Prominent Alumni

The Graduate School of Business is proud to count among its distinguished alumni senior executives from America's largest corporations, such as Ameritech, Motorola, and Zenith, as well as business leaders from some of Chicago's most well-known mid-size companies. Alumni are particularly prominent in the field of banking, where many Graduate School of Business graduates are senior executives at such organizations as First Chicago NBD, Citibank, Harris Bank, and LaSalle National.

The College and Environs

Dominican University traces its origin to the charter granted in 1848 by the state of Wisconsin to St. Clara Academy. The academy was formally incorporated as St. Clara College in 1901. In 1918, the school was moved to River Forest, incorporated in Illinois, and renamed Rosary College. In 1997, Rosary College became Dominican University.

Dominican University is home to more than 2,200 graduate and undergraduate students. It is conveniently located just 20 minutes west of downtown Chicago. Dominican offers its students an excellent opportunity to take advantage of all the Chi-

cago business community has to offer while also enjoying Dominican's lovely, quiet River Forest campus. The Graduate School of Business also offers classes at several sites throughout Chicago, including Northbrook, which is conveniently located just 25 minutes north of downtown Chicago.

Technology Environment

Dominican offers four computer laboratories and four computer classrooms for students' use. In these facilities, students can use Dominican's software, send and receive e-mail, and search the Internet. All students are entitled to receive a network account that permits use of the Internet free of charge. Students also have access to a collection of more than 210,000 volumes, 1,100 current periodical and newspaper titles, CD-ROMs, and 100,000 federal documents in the Rebecca Crown Library. For students involved in large research projects, Crown's professional librarians are available to assist students with a variety of tasks, including Dialog database searches.

Placement

Working closely with Dominican University's Placement Office, the Graduate School of Business provides students with a number of opportunities and services designed to facilitate a productive job search. Because the majority of Dominican's alumni live and work in the greater Chicago area, graduating students have an enormous network of business professionals in many fields who are willing to assist with the job placement process. The Graduate School of Business Career Consortium also posts career opportunities in the School of Business office on a weekly basis.

Admission

Admission to the Graduate School of Business is open to those who hold a bachelor's

degree in any field from an accredited institution. No prior business courses are required. The Committee on Graduate Admissions bases its decision on the applicant's total academic record, satisfactory scores on the Graduate Management Admission Test, three letters of reference from the applicant's professors and/or supervisors, and pertinent information from the student's application. Students may enter the program at the beginning of the fall, spring, or summer terms.

The Graduate School of Business welcomes applications from international students. For those who were educated outside the United States and/or require an F-1 visa and an I-20 form, an official TOEFL score (minimum 550, paper-based; 213, computer-based) is also required. All international students are required to show proof of financial support for one year.

Finances

Tuition for the 2000–01 year is $1500 per 3-credit-hour course. Room and board for the 2000–01 year range from $5030 to $6080, depending on the meal plan chosen. Books and supplies are approximately $75 per course, and there is a student fee of $10 per course.

International Students

The classroom experience is strengthened by a strong international student community. An international student adviser assists all international students with the application and admission process.

Application Facts and Dates

Applications are accepted on a rolling basis. While there is no application deadline, it is recommended that all application materials be submitted to the Graduate School of Business at least one month before the beginning of the semester in which the student desires admission. Applicants may also apply on line at the Web site listed below. For additional information, students should contact:

Roberta McMahon
Assistant Dean for Graduate Business
    Programs
Dominican University
Graduate School of Business
7900 West Division Street
River Forest, Illinois 60305-1066
Telephone: 708-524-6507
Fax: 708-524-6939
E-mail: gradbus@email.dom.edu
World Wide Web: http://www.dom.edu

Dominican University of California

School of Business and International Studies

San Rafael, California

FACULTY LIST

> ### THE M.B.A. IN THE GLOBAL ECONOMY
>
> *Today, more than ever before, a graduate degree is a sign of accomplishment in business education. But at the same time, it is not enough to just master the core business competencies that make up a traditional graduate business degree. Management science has grown profusely and is now focused on questions surrounding how U.S. firms must adapt to a fiercely competitive global market. The rebuilding of the economies of Japan and Western Europe after World War II, as well as the emergence of the newly industrialized economies in East Asia, have given rise to a global market, with levels of competition unrivaled in the past. At the same time, revolutionary advances in information technology have transformed our understanding of the business enterprise. I invite you to learn more about our exciting program and how it addresses today's global business realities.*
>
> —Wesley Young, Director

Fernando Arias, Lecturer; M.B.A., Golden Gate. International finance.

Liz Capener, Instructor; B.A., Berkeley; CPA. Accounting.

Asayehgn Desta, Professor; Ph.D., Stanford. International development and sustainable development.

Arnon Hadar, Professor; Ph.D., NYU. International economics.

Laurie Ribble Libove, Instructor; M.S., Rutgers. Finance, human resources management.

Ann Mannheimer, Instructor; M.B.A., Harvard. International marketing and management.

Alister Milroy, Assistant Professor; M.A., Oxford. Finance, international management.

Boris Porkovich, Associate Professor and Dean, School of Business and International Studies; Ed.D., Boston University. International marketing.

Alfred Siu, Instructor; D.B.A., Golden Gate. International accounting.

Edmond Temple, Instructor; Ph.D., New Hampshire. Marketing research.

Wesley Young, Associate Professor and Director of Graduate Business; Ph.D., Berkeley. International political economy of East Asia.

Edward Zabrycki, Instructor; M.B.A., Ohio State. Economics.

Programs and Curricular Focus

The Graduate Program in Pacific Basin Studies at Dominican University of California offers an M.B.A. degree in international business, Pacific Basin, and an M.A. in international economic and political assessment, Pacific Basin. Degrees are more than just an international concentration within a traditional graduate degree; each course is designed around an international focus. The curriculum includes courses dedicated to giving students the necessary background in the politics, economics, and culture of the Asia-Pacific region. Cross-cultural and multidisciplinary perspectives are integrated throughout the curriculum.

Students are given the skills and knowledge that are most important in today's business environment. The business faculty includes working professionals who bring the latest in business thinking and techniques into the classroom. Students translate theory into practice through a semester-long, project-based internship while building a professional network of contacts.

The program emphasizes socially responsible business practices and decision making. The program trains business leaders who understand the importance of environmental sustainability in the context of competitive business practices by drawing connections between business decisions and environmental outcomes.

Students and the M.B.A. Experience

Dominican's M.B.A. students are academically, professionally, and ethnically diverse. Students have an average of 4½ years of work experience, and their average age is 31. The student profile is diverse; 51 percent are international students from Asia, Europe, Latin America, the Middle East, and Australia. Women comprise 44 percent of the student body. The diversity of the student body has a positive impact on students' experiences, as what happens inside and outside of the classroom is an accurate reflection of modern business realities.

Fifty-two percent of students have an undergraduate degree in the social sciences and the humanities, 35 percent have an undergraduate degree in business and economics, and 13 percent have undergraduate degrees in the sciences.

Collaborative work is emphasized, and students frequently work together in teams and study groups. Given the diverse student body, class interaction and group work are daily, real-life exercises in cross-cultural communication.

Special Features

Students are placed in a semester-long project-based internship either in Asia or in the San Francisco Bay Area, depending on the student's area of interest and skill level. Internships are available at various companies worldwide and are often an important factor in securing employment after graduation.

Professional Development Seminars are held throughout the academic year. Top-level business and nonprofit executives meet with students to discuss current business topics.

The Faculty

The distinguished multinational faculty, headed by Dr. Wesley Young, is continually active in the international arena, bringing fresh concepts and network contacts to the program. Beyond their contributions as Dominican College lecturers and facilitators, faculty members are business owners and executives, management consultants, political and economic rights advocates, and members of major corporate and civic boards.

The Business School Network

The Pacific Basin Advisory Board assists in the development and promotion of the graduate program, ensuring the program's quality and relevance while developing job placement and internship opportunities for students. Its members, who represent international business, nonprofit organizations, and government, provide strong links to those sectors throughout the world.

The University and Environs

Dominican's 80-acre campus is located in a residential neighborhood in San Rafael, Marin County, just 11 miles (about 18 kilometers) north of San Francisco. The buildings are surrounded by trees and meadows, where students find a safe and quiet environment. Nearby are Berkeley and the Silicon Valley, open space and hills, Muir Woods, Pacific beaches, and the wine country. Within a few hours' drive are the spectacular Sierra Nevada Mountains and Yosemite National Park. Public transportation is available to San Francisco and throughout Marin County.

Facilities

Archbishop Alemany Library contains about 100,000 volumes in open stacks, almost 3,000 reels of microfilm, subscriptions to nearly 500 periodicals in print, and another 1,200 periodicals in full text online. The library also houses the Fletcher Jones Computer Laboratory, an art gallery, a listening room, and a fireplace corner. The University recently opened its Conlan Recreation Center, featuring fitness rooms, basketball and volleyball courts, an outdoor swimming pool, tennis courts, and a soccer field.

A limited number of residence hall rooms are available for single graduate students. Housing for single and married students is available in the immediate area at varying costs.

Placement

Students receive individualized placement assistance from faculty members. Alumni have been hired or made offers by such organizations as Andersen Consulting Group, Autodesk, Bechtel Group, Beringer Wine Estates, Berlitz, Charles Schwab, Chubb & Sons, Ciba-Geigy, Creative Artists Agency, Ernst & Young, The Gap, Hewlett Packard, Hitachi Ltd., Host Marriott, Institute of Southeast Asian Studies, Johnson & Johnson, Levi Strauss & Co., Merrill Lynch, Montgomery Securities, Oracle Corporation, Pacific Gas & Electric, Republic National Bank, Sprint, United Airlines, U.S. Department of Energy, University of Maryland, Warner Brothers, and Westdeutsches Landesbank.

Admission

To be admitted to the M.B.A. program, the applicant must have a bachelor's degree or the equivalent and submit official transcripts from each university attended, a resume, three letters of recommendation, a statement of purpose, and recent GRE test results. International students are required to take the TOEFL examination. It is recommended that students already have completed undergraduate course work in microeconomics and macroeconomics, managerial finance, managerial accounting, and either marketing research or business statistics. Students without these foundation courses need to take additional course work in the first two semesters of graduate study.

Finances

Graduate tuition for full-time study in the 2000–01 academic year is $14,040, and the estimated total expenses for the same year are $24,500. This amount includes tuition, fees, books, supplies, room, board, transportation, and personal expenses.

A limited number of departmental fellowships are awarded each year. Students may apply for federal and state financial aid, including loans from the Federal Stafford Student Loan Program.

International Students

Forty-nine percent of the student body is American; 36 percent are from Asia, with the balance coming from Europe, the Middle East, and Latin America. Orientations for international students are held each August to acclimate students to the U.S. and the San Francisco Bay Area.

Application Facts and Dates

Priority deadlines are March 2 for fall and December 1 for spring. Qualified candidates will be considered as long as vacancies exist. For complete information, students should contact:

School of Business and International Studies
Dominican University of California
50 Acacia Avenue
San Rafael, California 94901
Telephone: 415-257-1359
Fax: 415-459-3206
E-mail: pbsadm@dominican.edu
World Wide Web: http://www.dominican.edu/pbs

Drexel University

Philadelphia, Pennsylvania

AN INTEGRATED, HOLISTIC APPROACH

▶ *Drexel stands at the forefront of a national movement to revitalize the M.B.A. degree. An integrative, holistic approach lies at the core of the Drexel curriculum. This approach responds to the demands of the business world that M.B.A. graduates have a "big picture" view. The educational objective of the Drexel M.B.A. is to prepare each student for lifelong professional development. The experience encompasses not only specific professional skills, but also a general intellectual framework for approaching business opportunities. This framework provides the M.B.A. graduate with the ability to respond creatively to future trends.*

—Tom Hindelang, Associate Dean

Programs and Curricular Focus

The M.B.A. program at Drexel is designed to meet a wide range of student needs. It can provide a broad, balanced curriculum or one that's more focused. The M.B.A. program offers the conceptual tools to back up previously acquired experience, or it can provide professional experience as part of the M.B.A. studies. In fact, the program can be tailored to match a wide variety of student preferences. Many of the courses have been enhanced through an added emphasis on people skills, pragmatic exercises, communication skills, global perspectives, technology, and ethical dimensions of business.

The M.B.A. program has concentrations in fifteen areas and may be pursued on a full-time or part-time basis, day or evening. There is also a general M.B.A. program. Drexel's academic calendar of four 10-week terms gives students the option to enter most of the College's programs at any time of the year.

The M.B.A. degree program requires completion of 72 credits, consisting of eight 3-credit foundation courses and sixteen 3-credit advanced courses. It is organized as a two-year program, but the actual time required to complete the degree depends on the number of credits that a student transfers into the program and the number of courses he or she chooses to register for each term.

The foundation courses represent the basic knowledge required by AACSB–The International Association for Management Education, which has fully accredited the College's M.B.A. program. In general, the foundation courses should be completed before the advanced courses are undertaken. Some or all foundation courses can be waived if a student has completed equivalent courses as an undergraduate.

The advanced level includes five required core courses, five professional electives (one course from each of five business disciplines), four courses in the student's field of concentration, and two business electives.

Students and the M.B.A. Experience

Drexel's M.B.A. program enrolls approximately 1,000 students, one fourth of whom are enrolled full-time. These students represent widely diverse backgrounds: those entering directly from undergraduate programs and businesspeople with years of experience; those who completed undergraduate degrees at Drexel as well as alumni of universities throughout the United States, Europe and Asia; and those with degrees in business subjects along with engineers, scientists, physicians, liberal arts graduates, and military officers. Not only is Drexel's program flexible enough to accommodate these many individuals, it is also enriched by the variety of their perspectives. Approximately 60 percent of the full-time students are international.

Special Features

The Drexel Career Integrated Education option (CIE) provides a wealth of real-world hands-on career experience. The CIE option allows students to enrich their master's studies in business by earning credit for supervised employment experience related to their academic and career goals. This option provides an outstanding opportunity for recent college graduates to begin building their base of experience as well as their resumes, for international students to gain experience in the American workplace and Americans to gain international experience working

abroad, and for established professionals to prepare for a transition from one career field to another. For those students seeking to gain global experience, Drexel's M.B.A. program offers the opportunity to take some courses at L'Ecole Supérieure de Commerce de Paris (ESCP). Drexel students and French students take many of their courses abroad, and both can earn their M.B.A. degrees from Drexel.

Drexel's LeBow College of Business is one of a prestigious group of U.S. business schools selected by SAP America to integrate R/3 in their curricula and to become a full SAP academic partner. Drexel was the first university in the region to join the SAP America, Inc. University Alliance Program. Three faculty members have received over 600 hours of SAP training to prepare them to use SAP R/3 as a teaching tool in their classes. Drexel uses the software to prepare M.B.A. students for jobs in the information technology arena. The College's 1999 curriculum proposal to SAP defining a model curriculum was ranked first nationally by SAP's international panel of judges, while its 1998 research proposal was ranked second. Drexel sought a limited number of high-caliber corporate partners to assist in developing an SAP-based curriculum. Under this arrangement, corporate partners assist with Drexel's SAP infrastructure and curriculum development while building relationships with the increasing numbers of students taking R/3-based courses. Currently, Bristol-Myers Squibb, Andersen Consulting, Unisys, CSC, and Lockheed Martin are Drexel's SAP corporate partners.

Drexel's Safeguard Center for E-Commerce Management was a recent gift from Safeguard Scientifics, with Microsoft as the center's first corporate partner. Drexel will offer an e-commerce management field of concentration for the M.B.A. program.

The Faculty

Drexel's Bennett S. LeBow College of Business has an outstanding faculty. More than 95 percent hold the doctoral degree, and they have earned distinction for their published research as well as for the many journals and textbooks they have edited or authored. In keeping with the College's practical orientation, faculty members also enjoy strong ties with the business community, dramatically enhancing the educational environment at

the College. Drexel faculty members have served as consultants for a range of corporations, government agencies, and other organizations. Corporate and entrepreneurial leaders augment the full-time faculty by coming to campus as guest lecturers or part-time teachers.

The Business School Network

Drexel's Bennett S. LeBow College of Business maintains extensive relationships with the business community through an advisory board consisting of senior executives from major corporations and nonprofit organizations. The advisory board meets with the dean and faculty on a regular basis to provide input for curriculum and program revision and development.

The College's relationship with the local business community is further enhanced by the prestigious Business Leader of the Year Award, which grew out of one student's suggestion that the College cite a business leader as an example of success, service, citizenship, and leadership. The student who made that suggestion, George M. Ross, Class of '55, is now a resident partner with Goldman, Sachs, and Co. and a past Business Leader of the Year Award recipient.

The College and Environs

Philadelphia is an appealing place to earn a graduate degree. As a leading center for commerce, industry, government, and the arts, the city also offers museums, libraries, and other resources that support learning. The metropolitan area provides ample employment opportunities for students and graduates alike, in such growing fields as banking, finance, pharmaceuticals, insurance, and telecommunications.

Philadelphia features countless opportunities for cultural and recreational activities, as well. Historic sites, such as Independence Hall and the Liberty Bell; major league

teams in baseball, basketball, football, and ice hockey; the world-famous Philadelphia Orchestra; and the Philadelphia Museum of Art are only a few of the attractions that students enjoy. Fairmount Park, the nation's largest city park; the Philadelphia Zoo; and Penn's Landing, the city's riverfront development, provide additional options for spare-time activities. Ethnically diverse Philadelphia is often called "the city of neighborhoods," with such colorful communities to visit as Chinatown and South Philadelphia's Italian Market.

Drexel is ideally located for students to take advantage of public transportation. Just two blocks away is 30th Street Station—Philadelphia's major railroad station and a stop for Amtrak trains from New York City and Washington, D.C., local commuter trains, and a shuttle to the airport. New Jersey's beaches and Pennsylvania's Pocono Mountains are each within a 2-hour drive of the city. The University also provides ample parking.

Facilities

The Bennett S. LeBow College of Business is housed in two buildings on campus. The buildings contain modern lecture halls, conference rooms, and the Center for Executive Education. University computer facilities include several mainframes and the campus is networked. Students have access to the Internet with their own account. In addition, the University microcomputer support facility contains more than 500 microcomputers and supports a full range of consulting and training workshop services. Business students also have access to the College's own IBM PC and Macintosh Power PC computer labs.

Placement

Placement services are provided through the Career Services Center (CSC) free of charge up to one year past date of graduation. Graduates can also obtain job listings and use other resources at any time. For those students who wish to refine their interviewing skills, Drexel offers the General Electric Video Interview Program (GEVIP). This service allows students to practice their interviewing skills on videotape to learn where they can make improvements. Drexel's CSC has its own Career Library. It contains extensive files and videotapes of general career and specific employer information from which students can develop a list of potential employers. Drexel offers an on-campus interview program. Each fall, winter, and spring, employer representatives visit campus to interview the current graduating class for upcoming employment opportunities. Candidates are selected for interviews by the employer organizations.

Admission

All applicants must have received a four-year bachelor's degree from an accredited

college or university. Degrees earned abroad must be deemed equivalent. The College's admissions committee reviews applicants based on undergraduate accomplishments, performance on the GMAT, previous professional accomplishments, career goals, references, and the personal essay.

Students whose native language is not English and who do not hold degrees from U.S. institutions are required to submit a score on the Test of English as a Foreign Language (TOEFL).

Finances

Tuition for master's courses is billed by the credit hour. As of the 2000–01 academic year, the cost is $534 per credit hour; all graduate business courses are 3 credits. Tuition is the same for full-time and part-time students.

Graduate assistantships are available to full-time master's business students. An assistantship requires the student to work for 20 hours per week for a department or professor in return for tuition remission for three courses per term plus a monthly stipend. Applications for assistantships are available in the Graduate Business Office. Federal Stafford Student Loans and other loans are available for part-time and full-time students through the University's Financial Aid Office.

International Students

International students are an important component of Drexel's graduate student body and are actively recruited. International students come from all over the world and more than forty countries, including Asia, the Pacific Rim, Europe, South America, and Canada. The International Students Office conducts an orientation program to assist international students in becoming acclimated to the American social and educational culture.

Application Facts and Dates

Drexel's Bennett S. LeBow College of Business admits students for each of its four quarters. For the fall quarter, the final application deadline is August 31 for U.S. citizens and June 20 for non–U.S. citizens. For the winter quarter, the deadline is November 30 for U.S. citizens and September 25 for noncitizens. For the spring quarter, it is March 1 for citizens and January 3 for noncitizens, and for the summer, it is May 31 for citizens and March 31 for noncitizens. For more information, students should contact:

Office of Graduate Admissions
Drexel University, Box P
Philadelphia, Pennsylvania 19104
Telephone: 800-2-DREXEL (toll-free)
E-mail: admissions-grad@
     post.drexel.edu

Duquesne University

John F. Donahue Graduate School of Business

Pittsburgh, Pennsylvania

PREPARING FOR THE TWENTY-FIRST CENTURY

Graduate schools of business have a special obligation to help prepare their students for the challenges and opportunities of the twenty-first century. We at Duquesne are especially mindful of that obligation to all of our stakeholders—our students, our supporters, the business community, and the greater society of which we are a part. The John F. Donahue Graduate School of Business at Duquesne University is committed to excellence in a dynamic environment of change and continuous improvement. We hope the information that we provide below helps you to make an informed decision about your future education— and, of course, we hope that you select our Graduate School of Business.

—James C. Stalder, Dean

Programs and Curricular Focus

Fully accredited by AACSB–The International Association for Management Education, Duquesne University's Donahue Graduate School of Business provides a program of study that is consistent with its mission of "preparing leaders who appreciate the importance of blending technical competence with a broad-based education that positions them to add value in a highly competitive global business environment." The curriculum is structured to provide fundamental skills in quantitative and qualitative analysis, a solid foundation in key functional areas of business, and an opportunity for students to apply their skills and knowledge to real-world business problems. Students also have an opportunity to choose a specialization in several disciplines, including accounting, environmental management, ethics, finance, human resource management, health-care management, international business, information systems management, marketing, and taxation. The School also offers Master of Science degrees in information systems management and taxation. A dual M.B.A./M.S. in information systems management is also available.

The M.B.A. curriculum stresses the relationships among business disciplines. A three-course business problems sequence provides students with the opportunity to integrate their knowledge of functional disciplines and develop recommendations for dealing with real business problems presented by the faculty, business practitioners, and the executive faculty.

The contemporary business issues of globalization, ethics, total quality, and the management of technology are integrated in all core courses as is a reading program that is designed to relate the specific disciplines to the world at large.

Based on the belief that students are best able to position themselves competitively if they can present samples of work completed in their graduate studies and professional positions, students are required to organize a portfolio of substantive, professionally presented work accomplished during their program of study.

Students and the M.B.A. Experience

The student body of approximately 650 students is diverse. Full-time students, who make up approximately 25 percent of the enrollment, get an enriching experience by sharing classes with full-time business professionals who are working toward their degrees on a part-time basis. Part-time students bring an average of five years of professional work experience to the classroom, providing a rich source of real-world issues that add value to the educational experience.

The student body also represents countries from around the world, including those in Africa, Asia, Europe, and Latin America, who bring an important international dimension to the program.

Special Features

The Donahue Graduate School of Business believes that it makes good sense for a university to leverage its resources for the maximum benefit of its students. Therefore, it has developed important partnerships with other schools on the campus to offer dual-degree programs. The M.B.A. degree and degrees in environmental science and management, health management systems, industrial pharmacy, liberal studies, law, and nursing are offered. In addition and upon prior approval, students may also take up to 6 elective credits in other graduate programs on campus.

The Faculty

The faculty members of the Donahue Graduate School of Business are committed to teaching excellence, scholarship that focuses on real business problems, and developing creative academic-business partnerships. The academic and professional experiences of the faculty members are complemented by the executive faculty who, teamed with the full-time faculty, regularly address classes in their areas of expertise, directly relating their daily experiences to the material covered in the courses. Graduate students benefit from the exposure to a roster of executives, including chief executive officers, presidents, vice-presidents, and top administrators.

The Business School Network

The School has built a significant network with the business community that helps to promote its commitment to business-academic partnerships. Approximately 150 business professionals are members of the School's ten advisory boards. They offer their expertise and guidance on curricular matters and internship and professional placement opportunities to the students.

The College and Environs

Duquesne University first opened its doors as the Pittsburgh Catholic College of the Holy Ghost in October 1878. With its beautifully self-contained 39-acre campus of tree-lined walks, fountains, and a blend of modern and historic buildings, Duquesne provides a hilltop vista overlooking one of the nation's most attractive cities for its 9,000 students.

Long noted as one of the world's great business centers, Pittsburgh combines the features of big-city living with many of the charms and personal characteristics of a much smaller town. Pittsburgh is one of the largest corporate headquarters centers in the United States and has developed a strong civic identity and sense of pride in its rebirth as a modern urban community. Students from Duquesne and other colleges and universities in the city can choose from a wide variety of cultural, social, and sporting events and programs.

Facilities

The Donahue Graduate School of Business is located in Rockwell Hall, at the downtown Pittsburgh edge of the University's campus. Facilities in the building include special seminar and conference rooms, a lecture hall/theater complex, and the University's Communications and Information Technology Center, which features two Digital Equipment Corporation mainframe computers and a new computer resource center for student use.

The School operates three computer laboratories dedicated to personal computers and their use across the business curriculum, online access to software and applications associated with the University's mainframe system, and multimedia development.

The School offers a state-of-the-art investment center with twenty computers networked to the Bridge Information System. The center provides students and faculty members with the opportunity to do sophisticated financial analysis on thousands of companies with up-to-the-minute data. Duquesne's Graduate School of Business is one of only a dozen schools equipped with the capabilities provided by the Bridge Information System.

The University's Gumberg Library houses nearly 500,000 volumes, more than 3,700 journal titles, and an extensive micro-print and audiovisual center. Other library facilities include an online card catalog and a CD-ROM center that permits users to access the library's data files. The CD-ROM system gives students access to hundreds of additional periodicals not physically housed in the library.

Placement

Career planning and placement services are provided through the University's Office of Career Services. In addition, the M.B.A. Office of Career Development, located in the Donahue Graduate School of Business, works closely with the University's Office of Career Services to develop placement opportunities for its students. Workshops on resume writing, mock interview sessions, and career fairs that attract major employers to campus are some of the services available to students. Students may also take advantage of the Duquesne University Career Advisory Network, an organization made up of alumni of the Graduate School of Business to provide professional networking opportunities for students and alumni.

Admission

Candidates who have earned an undergraduate degree from an accredited four-year college or university (or its equivalent in another country) are eligible for admission. Admissions criteria include the undergraduate grade point average; the quality of undergraduate course work completed; scores on the Graduate Management Admissions Test; at least two letters of recommendation from those who can make reasonable judgments on the candidate's potential for graduate study, including professors and/or business associates; a personal essay; and the quality and duration of work experience. International students are required to provide proof of adequate financial support and, if their native language is not English, take the Test of English as a Foreign Language (TOEFL).

Finances

Tuition for the 2000–01 academic year is $535 per credit. There is also a $53 University fee charged for each credit. Room and board are $3157 per semester, based on double occupancy. Housing is also available off campus. The University's Office of Residence Life can assist students in locating off-campus housing. A limited number of graduate assistantships, which provide up to 9 credits of tuition remission each semester and a monthly cash stipend, are available to students. The application fee is $40.

International Students

Students come to Duquesne University's campus from ninety countries throughout the world. Approximately 11 percent of the M.B.A. students come from countries in Africa, Asia, Europe, and Latin America. The University offers substantial support for international students through its International Affairs Office. ESL programs are available to help students improve their skills in English. An active International Student Organization provides networking support and social and educational activities for international students.

Application Facts and Dates

Application deadlines are June 1 for fall admission, November 1 for spring admission, and March 1 for summer admission. Students applying for the fall who are scheduled to take the GMAT in June should submit the completed application by June 1 indicating that they are taking the GMAT in June. The review process for their applications will be completed after GMAT scores are received. For more information, students should contact:

The Graduate School of Business
704 Rockwell Hall
Duquesne University
Pittsburgh, Pennsylvania 15282
Telephone: 412-396-6276
Fax: 412-396-5304
E-mail: grad-bus@duq.edu
World Wide Web: http://www.bus.duq.edu/GRAD/

East Carolina University

Greenville, North Carolina

AN M.B.A. WITH ADVANTAGES

In today's competitive environment, it pays to investigate all of your M.B.A. options. At East Carolina University (ECU), we offer an M.B.A. program with four distinct advantages: professional preparation, recognized quality, program flexibility, and exceptional value.

—Ernest B. Uhr, Dean

Programs and Curricular Focus

The M.B.A. program at East Carolina University is one of approximately 300 graduate business programs accredited by the AACSB–The International Association for Management Education and was the second program accredited in North Carolina. It is one of approximately 130 M.B.A. programs that belong to the Graduate Management Admissions Council.

The goal of the M.B.A. program is to prepare men and women for managerial leadership in profit and nonprofit organizations. Required and elective courses are taught from the managerial perspective. A blend of teaching methods, including lectures, discussions, computer simulations, team projects, cases, and independent study, is used to develop critical thinking and human relations skills. The average class size is twenty-five.

The ECU M.B.A. program is flexible and can be individually tailored to the student's background and needs. For example, students who have previously taken business administration courses at the undergraduate level and received high grades may be exempted from some or all of the first-year M.B.A. classes. Such waivers could reduce the program to a minimum of 30 semester hours, or one year full-time. The maximum program length is 60 semester hours or two years.

Students may begin the M.B.A. program in any term—fall, spring, or summer. Spring or summer entrance presents no scheduling problems, since courses required of new students are offered in all terms. The availability of two terms each summer allows students to accelerate the completion of the program.

Students working full-time can complete the M.B.A. by taking evening classes, since all courses have an evening section. Part-time students set their own pace, depending on their work requirements, and most finish in two to five years.

An M.B.A. with a concentration in management information systems (MIS) may be obtained by choosing four electives in MIS.

The ECU Schools of Medicine and Business offer joint M.D./M.B.A. dual-degree programs, which take five years to complete. The M.D./M.B.A. is also available to students who are accepted to or enrolled in another accredited medical school. Medical residents whose training program allows one year away from clinical responsibilities may enroll in the M.D./M.B.A. program. Students enter in late June and complete the M.B.A. program twelve months later. The GMAT requirement is waived for applicants with M.D. degrees or students from accredited medical schools.

The ECU School of Business offers two Master of Science in Accounting (M.S.A.) programs to prepare students for careers in public and management accounting. One program is for students with an undergraduate degree in accounting and is 30–60 semester hours, depending on undergraduate courses and grades. The other M.S.A. program is for students with a degree in fields other than accounting and is 60 semester hours. Enrollment in the M.S.A. programs is approximately 65 students. A concentration in tax is also available.

Students and the M.B.A. Experience

East Carolina's M.B.A. students are drawn from a wide variety of educational and business backgrounds. Approximately 190 attend full-time, and 120 work full-time and attend part-time. The typical student is 28 years old and has six years of work experience. The 1999–2000 student body included 43 percent women and 13 percent minorities. Approximately 48 percent have undergraduate business degrees and about 20 percent studied engineering or science. The social sciences and health professions were also strongly represented, including 8 M.D.'s. Approximately 110 different undergraduate institutions were represented in the student body.

Special Features

In addition to elective courses in the traditional business subjects, East Carolina's M.B.A. program offers six options in related fields. About 20 percent of the students take their electives in another ECU professional school and receive a certificate from that school. Options are available in health-care management, hospitality management, apparel and textile management, development and environmental planning, school business management, and international management. There is an additional application for the international management option, as fluency in a second language and international experience are required.

The Faculty

ECU is committed to high-quality teaching. Faculty members' backgrounds are diverse and cosmopolitan and include extensive business, consulting, teaching, and research experience. The School of Business faculty members hold graduate degrees from institutions such as Chicago, Duke, Georgetown, Harvard, Indiana, North Carolina, Virginia, Wharton, Arizona State, Florida, Georgia, Illinois, Michigan State, Tennessee, Texas, Texas A&M, and Wisconsin. Professors are dedicated to providing meaningful, challenging experiences for ECU's M.B.A. students and are readily available for discussion and assistance outside the classroom.

The Business School Network

Many M.B.A.'s work full-time for major organizations and attend graduate school

Home of the ECU School of Business.

part-time. Full- and part-time students are in class together and work on projects that enhance learning and networking opportunities. Eastern North Carolina is home to scores of major corporations, including Abbott Laboratories, Black & Decker, DuPont, Firestone, Frigidaire, NACCO, Sara Lee, TRW, and Weyerhaeuser.

Through the Small Business Institute, students can get hands-on experience consulting with local developing businesses.

The School of Business is served by a distinguished Business Advisory Council of 35 senior executives who advise the dean on a broad range of issues. These executives participate as guest lecturers in many courses each year.

The College and Environs

East Carolina University, founded in 1907, is the third-largest campus of the University of North Carolina. Enrollment is about 18,500 students, which includes 2,900 graduate students and 300 medical students. The ECU School of Medicine is one of the top producers of primary-care physicians in the nation.

Quality of life during the M.B.A. experience is an important consideration. Greenville is a comfortable city of 56,000 with a reasonable cost of living, a temperate climate, and a relaxed outdoor lifestyle. It is an educational, commercial, industrial, medical, and cultural center. The North Carolina beaches are 90 minutes away, and it's a half-day drive to the mountains and skiing. Greenville is a 1-hour drive from I-95 and is served by regional airports.

Facilities

The M.B.A. program is housed in a modern facility, completed in 1988,
which includes a large, comfortable M.B.A. lounge and study area. ECU's Joyner Library holds 1.2 million bound volumes plus microforms and periodicals.

Technology Environment

M.B.A. computing is available in labs with ninety-six Windows-based computers that are connected to a 155-Mbps campus network with a 10-Mbps link to the Internet. A variety of software packages and databases are available.

Placement

East Carolina University Career Services provides career and placement services to M.B.A. students and recent alumni. Resume preparation and interviewing skills workshops and computerized databases are part of the services offered to M.B.A.'s. A career fair and on-campus recruiting are augmented by business contacts through the School of Business as well as Career Services.

The Office of Cooperative Education assists M.B.A. students in preparing for and securing career-related temporary employment, usually of a semester's duration. This is particularly valuable for students who do not have extensive full-time work experience. With ECU's flexible M.B.A. program, co-op jobs do not create scheduling problems because students can easily interrupt and then resume their programs.

Admission

The ECU M.B.A. program is open to applicants with baccalaureate degrees from accredited institutions in business and nonbusiness fields. Work experience is recommended but not required. Ability is evaluated on the basis of the applicant's prior undergraduate record and
performance on the Graduate Management Admission Test (GMAT). The average GMAT score is above 500. A GMAT review course is available twice a year through the School of Business's Division of Professional Programs.

Applications from non-English-speaking countries must submit results of the Test of English as a Foreign Language (TOEFL). The minimum acceptable TOEFL score is 550 for the paper test or 213 for the computer-based test.

Finances

Value is a function of quality and cost. East Carolina provides a substantial accredited M.B.A. program at a reasonable cost. Full-time tuition and fees are $2000 per academic year for North Carolina residents and $9600 per year for nonresidents, with additional charges for optional summer sessions. Tuition and fees for part-time students are lower.

Waivers of business core classes may provide additional value by eliminating one or more semester's tuition, fees, and living expenses.

Off-campus housing, estimated at $6000 per year, is readily available and is used by most graduate students. University housing is also available.

The School of Business offers approximately eighty-five graduate assistantships awarded on academic merit. Students may earn between $3250 and $6500 per year working 10 to 20 hours each week assisting professors in research or working with undergraduates in the computer labs.

International Students

The ECU M.B.A. program welcomes international students. During 1999–2000, there were students from Argentina, Armenia, Belize, China, France, Germany, Honduras, Hungary, India, Japan, Kazakhstan, Morocco, Norway, Pakistan, Panama, Sierra Leone, Sweden, Taiwan, Ukraine, the United Kingdom, and Uzbekistan.

Application Facts and Dates

Applications are accepted for any term. Early applications are strongly encouraged because of the rolling admission process. For more information and an application, students should contact:

Frederick Niswander
Assistant Dean for Graduate Programs
School of Business
East Carolina University
Greenville, North Carolina 27858-4353
Telephone: 252-328-6970
Fax: 252-328-2106
E-mail: gradbus@mail.ecu.edu
World Wide Web: http://www.business.ecu.edu/grad/

Eastern College

DEVELOPING BUSINESS LEADERS FOR THE TWENTY-FIRST CENTURY

Eastern's programs are responsive to the specialized needs of students, offering a variety of concentrations (nonprofit management, health administration, economic development, and accounting), timeframes for completion of the degree (evening M.B.A. and fast-track M.B.A.), and featuring in-class use of laptop computer technology by students and faculty members.

—Vivian Nix-Early, Dean

Programs and Curricular Focus

The new Global M.B.A. program reflects the established international focus of the Graduate School and emphasizes the interactive nature of the world economy and increasing cultural diversity. The program deepens the broad base of teaching business leadership.

In its current configuration, the Global M.B.A. is distinctive for three reasons. First, a specific emphasis is placed on international business and the necessity to understand the global marketplace. Secondly, the Global M.B.A. has a strong ethical focus. Eastern College has regarded ethics as an indispensable key to understanding successful business. The aim of this program is to provide a strong foundation for leaders to make sound ethical choices in a business world that requires rapid-fire decision making. Finally, the structure is designed to be convenient. Unlike some other M.B.A. programs, professional experience is not a prerequisite.

The Global M.B.A. consists of a core curriculum (27 credit hours) plus electives (9 credit hours), for 36 total graduate credit hours. The core curriculum focuses on accounting, economics, finance, organizational behavior, marketing, management, and business ethics. If foundation courses have been satisfied in undergraduate programs or continuing education programs, they may be waived. Also, there is an Accelerated Qualifying Option that allows high-performing students to waive two core courses. This reduces the completion time of the Global M.B.A. There is an Honors Mentoring Program that allows qualified honors students direct access to, observation of, and coaching by a key business leader in the Philadelphia area.

The Graduate School also offers the M.B.A. and M.S. in economic development and the M.B.A. and M.S. in nonprofit management. The innovative concentration in nonprofit organization includes courses in fund-raising, legal mandates, public relations, strategic planning, and management of volunteers. To earn an M.S. in economic development or nonprofit management, 33 credit hours need to be completed successfully.

Eastern College offers three dual degree programs with Eastern Theological Baptist Seminary. The joint degrees of 116 total credit hours are an M.Div./M.S. in economic development, an M.Div./M.B.A. in economic development, and an M.Div./Global M.B.A.

Students and the M.B.A. Experience

Students at Eastern College bring diverse resumes as well as culturally varied backgrounds to their M.B.A. experience. The average student is a 30-year-old with seven years of work experience. Women comprise one third of the student population, and minority students make up 16 percent.

The Northeast sends 65 percent of Eastern College M.B.A. students, while 5 percent come from the Midwest. Six percent come from the West Coast, and international students make up the final 24 percent.

Eastern College students not only learn from the professors, they learn from each other. The diverse cultural and business backgrounds of the professors and students offer each student the opportunity to explore other countries and careers without leaving the classroom.

Special Features

The economic development program offers many opportunities to develop a broader understanding of cross-cultural issues. The capstones to this program involve Two-Thirds World summer field courses in an international setting, as well as a two-semester internship in a community development center located in the city of Philadelphia. The internship enables the student to develop professional experience in an urban setting. The primary emphasis is placed on the creation and growth of microscale and small-scale enterprises.

More than half of the total courses, including all the foundation courses of the M.B.A. program, are available on video distance learning. At least two thirds of economic development students receive financial aid. Internships are available in the nonprofit management and economic development programs.

The Faculty

The business programs have attracted and employed the talents of an experienced and dynamic faculty. Faculty members have researched, visited, lived, and performed professionally all over the world. They have established and managed businesses and development organizations. They have also served as consultants to international and urban organizations.

The Business School Network

Since the inception of the M.B.A. program, there have been strong partnerships with corporations and organizations in the Philadelphia metro and suburban areas. Students in the nonprofit M.B.A. program have the opportunity to introduce fundraising strategic plans to foundations for professional review and critique. This as well as other networking experiences are available in the business program.

The College and Environs

In 1982, Eastern College launched the first Master of Business Administration program in the western suburbs of Philadelphia. Located in St. Davids on the main

Lin Geiger, Ph.D., Distinguished Professor of International Economics and Chair, Business Department.

Jack Bower, Ph.D., Associate Professor of Accounting.

Kerk Burbank, Ph.D., Templeton Chair in Christian Service through Entrepreneurship.

Tony Campolo, Ph.D., Professor of Sociology and Founder of Evangelical Association for Promotion Education.

Jim Engel, Ph.D., Professor of Business and Distinguished Professor of Marketing.

J. Samuel Escobar, Ph.D., Professor of Business.

Eloise Meneses, Ph.D., Professor of Cultural Anthropology.

Cynthia Moultrie, M.A., Director of Economic Development Programs.

Ronald Sider, Ph.D., Executive Director of Evangelicals for Social Action.

John Stapleford, Ph.D., Associate Professor of Economics.

Van Weigel, Ph.D., Professor of Economic Development and Ethics.

line of Philadelphia, Eastern College is a beautiful suburban campus within 3 miles of Interstate 476. Only 20 minutes by train or car from the city, the heart of the campus is the Charles S. Walton estate, built in 1913. Eastern has grown beyond the original estate to include twenty-six buildings and more than 100 acres of woods, ponds, creeks, and lawns. The total population at Eastern College has grown to more than 2,600 students.

Technology Environment

Eastern College has its own computing lab facilities, consisting of more than fifty terminals. There is a separate computer lab for graduate students. The computer lab is open from 9 a.m. to 11 p.m., Monday through Friday. It is also open on the weekends. The Warner Library is an attractive and comfortable facility housing more than 13,000 volumes. The library is a part of the OCLC information network, opening 22 million volumes to students as resources.

Placement

The career center at Eastern College enables graduate students the opportunity to develop networks in the Philadelphia area. The career center has contacts with many of the national and international companies based in the eastern Pennsylvania region.

Admission

Admission to an M.B.A. or an M.S. program is open to all qualified college graduates, regardless of field of undergraduate study. Those wishing to apply for admissions to any of the M.B.A. or M.S. programs should submit the following: a complete application form; a nonrefundable application fee of $35; official undergraduate transcripts indicating a minimum undergraduate GPA of 2.5; two letters of professional recommendation; official results of the GMAT (not required for the M.S. programs); and for international students, the official results of the TOEFL, with a minimum total score of 550 on the paper-based test or 213 on the computer-based test. Students who wish to take a limited number of courses at the graduate level may enroll as nondegree, provisional students.

Finances

Tuition for graduate courses is $410 per semester credit hour, and for foundation courses, the tuition is $410 per semester credit hour. Estimated fees for the 2000–01 year are $650 for all students. Books and miscellaneous expenses are approximately $3200 per year. Estimated living expenses for a single student are approximately $4400 for housing and $2700 for food per year. Married couples typically spend $6900 for housing and $3400 for food.

Assistantships and scholarships are available for certain M.B.A. programs. Students must apply for assistance to be eligible for either an assistantship or for a scholarship.

International Students

One fourth of the graduate students at Eastern College come from outside the United States. The on-campus international student adviser provides international students assistance in becoming acclimated to their new environment as well as to American culture and practices.

Application Facts and Dates

Once an application is complete, it is evaluated, and a response is given in a timely manner. Eastern's commitment is to keep students well informed through all stages of this process. Admissions are handled on a rolling basis, and there is no application deadline. However, students are urged to apply well in advance of the semester they plan to enter. For more information, students should contact:

Leonard N. Jamison
Director of Graduate Admissions
Tia B. McCoun
Graduate Admissions Representative
Eastern College
Graduate Admissions
1300 Eagle Road
St. Davids, Pennsylvania 19087
Telephone: 610-341-5972
Fax: 610-341-1466
E-mail: gradm@eastern.edu

École des Hautes Études Commerciales

Master of Business Administration Program

Montreal, Canada

> ### THE WORLD IS CHANGING—OUR M.B.A. AS WELL
>
> *Completely redesigned, our M.B.A. program has undergone major changes that enables it to remain one of the front-runners in business education, as it has for thirty years. Implemented in the fall of 1996 and now offered in English, the program has been extremely well received by students and businesspeople alike. This endorsement confirms the École des HEC's ability to understand the needs of the market and take appropriate action.*
>
> —Jean-Marie Toulouse, Director

Program and Curricular Focus

Since its creation thirty years ago, the HEC M.B.A. has undergone a variety of adjustments designed to keep the program constantly a step ahead. The curriculum structure, teaching approach, and course content ensure that the HEC M.B.A. accurately reflects the cross-functionality of management. Teaching is multidisciplinary, so that students develop a broad and accurate vision of managerial roles as well as strong problem-solving skills.

For full-time students, the intensive M.B.A. extends over fifty-four weeks. A part-time option is also available for students who want to remain "in action" at their places of work.

The HEC M.B.A. degree program is composed of four phases. During the first phase, students learn about business fundamentals, the skills required in today's business world, and the inherent complexity of management. In the second phase, they learn to master the basic techniques of the management trade and gain insight into how various functions interrelate.

With its exceptional range of more than 100 courses, the third phase—the core of the program—allows students to tailor the program to fit their needs by building their own personalized major or opt for one of the proposed majors: corporate finance, international business, investment and portfolio management, and marketing. As an alternative, students can choose among minors such as entrepreneurship, general management, human resources management, information technologies, and supply chain management.

The fourth and final phase focuses on managing all aspects of change: new technologies, human resources management, personal attitudes, and corporate environment. In addition to the courses in change management, students take part in a supervised field project in an organization, within a small team, under the supervision of professors.

Students and the M.B.A. Experience

Although all of them have met the same criteria, candidates admitted to the HEC M.B.A. program are nevertheless an extremely diverse group. In nearly 70 percent of cases, they have a bachelor's degree in a field other than business administration. They have acquired their work experience in a wide variety of economic sectors. Their ranks include engineers, lawyers, psychologists, biologists, communications consultants, accountants, information system specialists, and administrators, each of whom brings his or her own wealth of knowledge and experience to the program. The School expects to increase its intake of international M.B.A. students, who now represent nearly 30 percent.

The average student is 32 years old, with eight years of full-time work experience. Thirty-eight percent of the student population is female.

❖ Global Focus

"We would like our graduates to be open-minded managers and agents of change with a strong sense of responsibility. To that purpose, students throughout our program are exposed to the larger socioeconomic issues, local and international, facing the business world today. Our program also emphasizes the acquisition and development of qualities such as curiosity, inventiveness, flexibility, team spirit, and openness to foreign languages and cultures."

—Ruth Dupré, Director, M.B.A. program

More than ever, HEC's M.B.A. provides a strong international perspective throughout its curriculum as well as through its major in international management. During the third phase of the program, honor students can even add an international experience to their education by traveling to another country as part of the School's exchange program. Beginning in fall 2000, the HEC M.B.A. is offered in English, if there is sufficient demand. Moreover, in the third phase (specialization), some courses may be taught in Spanish.

A new major in energy management, where the participants form a cohort of their own and where the teaching is offered in English, allows the maintenance of a specific learning environment and industry-tailored contents for the oil, gas, and electricity group.

The Faculty

École des Hautes Études Commerciales is renowned for its qualified and multidisciplinary teaching staff, the largest business administration faculty in Canada. It includes 175 career professors, all graduates of major universities in North America and Europe, supported by 225 lecturers who are also full-time managers.

HEC professors are experts in their fields who are much in demand as consultants to companies. A great many of them have backgrounds in management or as corporate executives. Several sit on the boards of large and medium-sized businesses, professional associations, or community organizations.

The Business School Network

Businesspeople are aware that their career advancement—and even the success of some of their projects—depends partly on the quality of their networks. HEC M.B.A. alumni form just such a network. The close ties they formed with their fellow students during their years of study continue to bear fruit throughout their professional careers. The HEC M.B.A. network includes some 3,600 managers who have graduated from the program since its creation thirty years ago.

The M.B.A. program counts among its alumni a number of notable leaders, in-

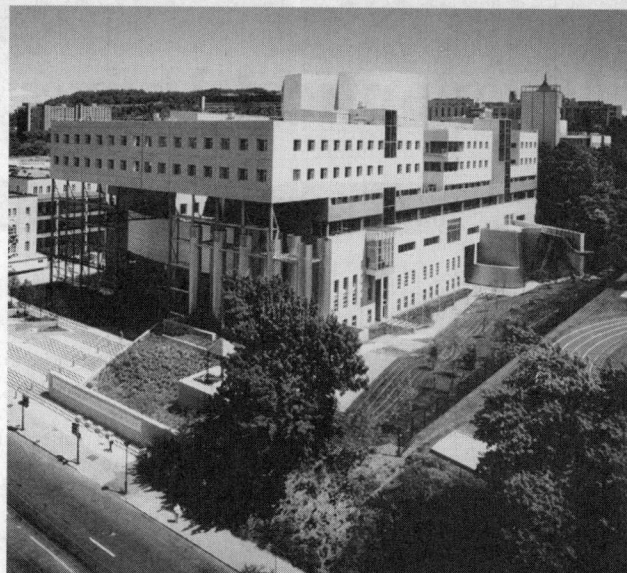

HEC's ultramodern facilities provide students with an exceptional environment for living and learning.

cluding Guy Bisaillon, First Vice President, Quebec, Scotia Bank; François Legault, Minister, Education, Government of Quebec; Serge Bragdon, President and CEO, Uniboard Canada; Denis Côté, Vice President, Worldwide Marketing and Sales, Harris Corporation, Farinon Division (U.S.A.); and Daisy Aubry-Golaz, President, Georg Fischer Disa Group International (Switzerland).

The College and Environs

Montreal's unique blend of intellectual, economic, and cultural characteristics makes it a popular destination for international students.

In Montreal, students find a harmonious blend of North American efficiency and European refinement.

Greater Montreal began assuming a technological vocation several years ago, and today, half of Canada's pharmaceutical companies are clustered there. Nearly one third of Canada's industrial research is conducted in the city. Several Montreal companies are world leaders in high-technology sectors, including telecommunications, aeronautics, aerospace, and biotechnology.

Situated on Mount Royal, an immense park in the heart of Montreal, HEC is just minutes from the downtown core and is served by several bus lines and by a subway station.

Facilities

Since the fall of 1996, HEC has been housed in a brand-new building on Côte-Sainte-Catherine Road, on the edge of the Université de Montréal campus. With multimedia rooms, study carrels, and comfortable lounges, the School's open and spacious new facilities provide students with an exceptional environment for living and learning.

HEC's library is recognized as one of the world's largest business administration libraries. People come from far and wide to consult its unique collection of 325,000 documents, including 6,000 periodicals from a variety of countries, covering all management-related fields. Research is facilitated by the library's computerized reference system.

The library has an imposing collection of annual reports from large and medium-sized businesses, an essential source of information for preparing field studies and corporate projects. Also available are several Canadian, American, and European databanks on CD-ROM. Students also have access to major business and general information newspapers and magazines, including several years of back issues available on microfilm.

Technology Environment

Equipped with state-of-the-art computer and telecommunications facilities, the new HEC building enables students and staff members to make the most of advanced information technologies. New M.B.A. students are required to purchase a portable computer, which will give them the opportunity to hone their computer skills as well as gain access to greater resources.

Placement

The School's Placement Office provides valuable long-term support to HEC M.B.A. graduates.

The department provides a wide variety of counseling services to assist students in their search for employment and attainment of their career goals; these services include individual career profile evaluations, proactive job-search techniques, job interview simulations, curriculum vitae writing techniques, descriptions of trends in the job market, and information on companies and career planning.

Montreal is the first North American university to earn the prestigious European Quality Improvement System (EQUIS) accreditation from the European Foundation for Management Development. The quality of research and development, the caliber of the students and professors, and the national and international reach are among the criteria evaluated.

Admission

Every application for admission to the HEC M.B.A. program is carefully evaluated by a committee composed of professors and members of the program administration. The requirements for admission are a bachelor's degree with a minimum average grade of 70; at least two years of relevant work experience; satisfactory results on the HEC M.B.A. admission tests or in the GMAT (Graduate Management Admission Test), which must be written within prescribed time limits; and a good knowledge of the language of study (French or English).

Finances

For the 2000–01 school year, tuition fees for international students are Can$15,551 for the entire fifty-four-week, intensive M.B.A. program. However, students from certain countries and those whose status meets certain criteria are exempted from these tuition fees and pay the same amount as Quebec residents, which is Can$3671 for the entire intensive M.B.A. in 2000–01.

Application Facts and Dates

Candidates who wish to be admitted for a specific term must submit their applications before the following deadlines: fall term, April 1, and winter term, October 1.

For more information on procedures for applying for residency in Canada, tuition fees, or admission to the HEC M.B.A. program, applicants should contact:

Registrar's Office
École des Hautes Études Commerciales
3000, Chemin de la Côte-Sainte-Catherine
Montréal, Québec H3T 2A7
Canada
Telephone: 514-340-6151
Fax: 514-340-5640
E-mail: mba@hec.ca
World Wide Web: http://www.hec.ca

Embry-Riddle Aeronautical University

Daytona Beach, Florida

AN M.B.A. AIMED AT THE FUTURE

Business graduate programs that best prepare a student for a successful career are those that supply a broad-based foundation in the basics and then provide special training and experience in a particular area. The M.B.A. program at Embry-Riddle Aeronautical University (ERAU) follows this model, with a special emphasis on aviation. The program is particularly relevant today because aviation promises a future of exciting growth.

There are some industries that have always required a truly global approach, many of which change at high speed due to rapidly advancing technology and many that are unusually capital dependent. But of all the industries in the world, it is difficult to imagine one that embodies all of these characteristics to the same extent as the aviation/aerospace industry.

The Business Department and its programs are set up to specifically target all the unique characteristics of this industry and provide its participants exceptional knowledge and skills for management.

—Andres Zellweger, Associate Provost, Graduate Programs and Research

Programs and Curricular Focus

The Master of Business Administration (M.B.A.) degree program is designed to develop aviation managers who can apply the concepts of modern management techniques to the challenges of the aviation industry. There are two M.B.A. options: the Master of Business Administration in Aviation (M.B.A./A.) and the Executive Master of Business Administration (Executive M.B.A.). The M.B.A./A. is offered as a full-time resident program on the Daytona Beach campus and as a classroom program at more than 100 resident centers throughout the United States and in Europe through the Extended Campus' College of Career Education. The Executive Master of Business Administration requires a part-time residency on the Daytona Beach campus. The M.B.A. curriculum combines a strong traditional business core with specialization electives in aerospace production and operations management, international management and aviation policy, airline operations and management, airport operations and management, aviation law and insurance, aviation labor relations, and aviation economics. The development of versatility and analytical resourcefulness are two of the key aims of the M.B.A. program. The program is fashioned to stress pragmatic solutions to the managerial, technical, and operational problems likely to arise in the aviation industry as a result of the frequent and sweeping changes that occur in technology as well as in the domestic and international regulations with which the industry must abide.

M.B.A./A. candidates must complete a minimum of 39 credit hours of course work consisting of 27 hours of core curriculum, thesis or graduate research project options, and specified electives. The M.B.A./A. degree program can usually be completed in fourteen months.

Executive M.B.A. candidates are generally sponsored by their employer. The program is delivered over eighteen months in a series of six 2-week residency sessions, approximately one session every two-and-a-half months, with assigned work between the residency sessions. The capstone activity, the Executive Project, is designed to benefit both the participant and the sponsoring organization by giving the participant the opportunity to apply the knowledge and diagnostic competencies learned throughout the program to a specific business issue of the sponsor.

Students and the M.B.A. Experience

ERAU's graduate programs currently enroll approximately 250 graduate students on the Daytona Beach campus. The College of Career Education enrolls about 3,000 students in graduate degree programs off campus at more than 100 locations throughout the United States and Europe. Of the graduate students on the Daytona campus, 40 percent are from other countries, 41 percent are women, and 42 percent are members of minority groups. Approximately 12 percent of the campus-based graduate students are employed full-time; many hold professional positions in the aviation industry. In the M.B.A. degree program, students with diverse academic backgrounds but with common scholastic abilities enrich the program. The majority of incoming students have business degrees. The average age of incoming students is 28, and 25 percent are women.

The Faculty

The business administration faculty takes pride in bringing relevant, real-world problems, issues, and experiences into the classrooms. A high priority for the faculty is to prepare students for the roles of leadership they will assume. Faculty members accomplish this not only by excellent teaching but also by advising students on their business research and consulting projects. Many members of the faculty serve as consultants to a variety of industries. The diverse backgrounds of the faculty members provide a multicultural teaching field, with an emphasis on global standards and practices.

The Business School Network

The Embry-Riddle Business Program Advisory Committee (Daytona Beach campus) provides key input to the M.B.A. program by helping to develop the program curricula on a continuous basis to meet the current demands of the industry. Through this process, Embry-Riddle is able to shape the curriculum as necessary to provide students with the skills and educational background that suit the current needs of the aviation/aerospace industry. The Embry-Riddle Business Program Advisory Committee, which is composed of various distinguished representatives from throughout the industry, participates directly with the M.B.A./A. program by providing key guest speakers and lecturers for industry colloquiums and specialized classroom lectures. Through these events, students are able to further nurture their talents and develop contacts within the industry itself.

The College and Environs

The University comprises the eastern campus at Daytona Beach; a western campus in Prescott, Arizona; and the Extended Campus, with off-campus programs. Within the field of aviation, Embry-Riddle Aeronautical University has built a reputation for high-quality instruction in its programs since its founding in 1926.

The Daytona Beach campus is located next to the Daytona Beach International Airport and 10 minutes from the Daytona beaches. Within an hour's drive are Disney World and EPCOT, Kennedy Space Center, SeaWorld, Universal Studios, and St. Augustine. The Extended Campus resident centers are located in thirty-seven states and seven other nations. (See http://www.ec.erau.edu for a location map.)

Technology Environment

A cluster of mainframes (UNIX and IBM) and PCs supported by a telecommunications network provide the faculty and students with the latest advances in information management and computing facilities. These are augmented by academic student labs, the Airway Science Simulation Lab, and the Aviation Human Factors Research Lab. Extensive modern computer facilities and Internet access are available to all students.

Placement

In addition to contacts gained from internships, the M.B.A./A. degree program conducts placement activities for its graduates. Years of research and consulting have allowed the faculty to cultivate contacts within the aviation industry, and its network provides job opportunities for graduates. The Career Services Office sponsors an annual industry Career Expo, which attracts more than 100 major companies such as Boeing, Federal Express, Delta, and United Airlines. In addition, the Career Resource Center offers corporate profiles, job postings, and development information. The office also assists with resume development and interview preparation.

Admission

The desired minimum undergraduate cumulative GPA is 2.5 on a 4.0 scale, with a minimum 3.0 in the junior and senior years. The GMAT is a requirement of the M.B.A./A. program. Extensive work experience, some at the management/supervisory level, is required of Executive M.B.A. candidates.

Finances

In 2000–01, tuition costs are $685 per semester hour on the Daytona Beach campus and $238 per semester hour at the Extended Campus resident centers. The cost of books and supplies are estimated at $300 per semester. Some on-campus housing is available to graduate students on the Daytona Beach campus. A standard double-occupancy room is $1450 per semester. Single students sharing rental and utility expenses can expect yearly off-campus room and board expenses of $4000. Scholarship aid and graduate assistantships are available but limited. Students may apply for financial aid by calling 800-943-6279 (toll-free). All graduate programs are approved for Veterans Administration education benefits. The fee for the Executive M.B.A. option is $45,000, which includes University tuition, activity fees, all books, class materials, and lodging.

Application Facts and Dates

Applications are accepted on a revolving basis and should be completed thirty days prior to the start of a semester for U.S. citizens and resident aliens and ninety days prior for international students.

Applicants should contact the admissions office that corresponds to their preferred mode of study:

Graduate Admissions
Daytona Beach Campus
Telephone: 904-226-6115
          800-388-3728 (toll-free)
Fax: 904-226-7111
E-mail: gradadm@db.erau.edu
World Wide Web: http://www.db.erau.edu

Business Administration Office
Executive Management Institute
Telephone: 904-225-7946
Fax: 904-226-7984
E-mail: emi@db.erau.edu

College of Career Education
Admissions, Records and Registration
Extended Campus
Telephone: 904-226-6910
Fax: 904-226-6984
World Wide Web: http://www.ec.erau.edu

The mailing address is the same for all of the above:
Embry-Riddle Aeronautical University
600 S. Clyde Morris Boulevard
Daytona Beach, Florida 32114-3900

FACULTY LIST

The following are faculty members at the Daytona Beach campus:

Massoud Bazargan, Ph.D., New South Wales (Australia).
Bruce Chadbourne, Ed.D., Florida Atlantic.
David S. Kiker, Ph.D., South Carolina.
Abe Harraf, Ph.D., Utah.
Saad Laraqui, Ph.D., I.S.G. Institut Superieure de Gestion.
Pamela Marett, Ph.D., Michigan State.
Robert McGrath, Ph.D., LSU.
Easwar Nyshadham, Ph.D., Mississippi.
Vadhindran Rao, Ph.D., Mississippi.
Dawna Rhodes, Ph.D., Houston.
Thomas Tacker, Ph.D., North Carolina.
Bijan Vasigh, Ph.D., NYU.
Blaise Waguespack, Ph.D., North Texas.
Seth Young, Ph.D., Berkeley.

The following are faculty members at the Extended Campus:

Paul Bankit, Ph.D., Michigan State.
Thomas S. Barker, Ph.D., North Texas.
Francis L. Barrett, M.S., Golden Gate.
Robert P. Bateman, Ph.D., Texas A&M.
Alan R. Bender, Ph.D., Berkeley.
Thomas Brown, M.A.M., Embry-Riddle.
Richard P. Buchtmann, M.A.M., Embry-Riddle.
Gene E. Burton, Ph.D., North Texas State.
Larry S. Carlton, M.S., Golden Gate.
Ronald E. Clark, Ed.D., Nova.
Chester Crosby, Ph.D., Saint Louis.
Paul K. Dygert, Ph.D., Michigan.
Robert C. Freewald, M.A., Webster.
Aaron Givan, Ph.D., Union (Ohio).
Frank Glazier, M.A., Western Kentucky.
Wayne R. Harsha, Ed.D., Montana State.
Wade R. Helm, Ph.D., South Dakota.
William F. Herlehy, Ph.D., Kent State.

Kent J. Horne, Ph.D., North Dakota.
Daniel E. Johnson, Ed.D., USC.
William H. Kraus, M.S., USC.
Mary E. Landers, Ed.D., East Texas.
William L. March, Ed.D., Indiana.
David A. Miramonti, Ed.D., Western Michigan.
Vance F. Mitchell, Ph.D., California.
Thomas Moe, J.D., North Dakota.
Gerald P. Nicoletta, M.A., Alabama.
Stephen B. O'Brien, Ed.D., Auburn.
Robert W. Reed, Ph.D., Michigan.
David B. Reese, M.A., Webster.
Martin J. Rielage, M.A., Lewis.
Artemio Rosado, D.P.A., La Verne.
Franz G. Rosenhammer, D.B.A., Tennessee.
Bruce A. Rothwell, D.P.A., Alabama.
James T. Schultz, Ed.D., USC.
Larry W. Shadow, Ph.D., US International.
Guy Smith, Ed.D., Montana State.
Bernard S. Stern, Ph.D., Pennsylvania.
Gene Townsend, M.S., M.B.A., FIT.
Sidney Earl Wheeler, Ph.D., Florida.
Mary K. Whitmire, M.B.A., Corpus Christi State.

Emerson College

PIONEERING BUSINESS EDUCATION THROUGH COMMUNICATION

All business functions are fundamentally activities of communication. Establishing an image for a corporation, positioning goods and services in the marketplace, responding to external circumstances such as legislative regulations and environmental disasters, and organizing and leading the members of a work team all require knowledge of the communication process. The study of communication within the business context concerns the strategic design, deployment, and assessment of messages and message campaigns.

Through two of its master's programs, Integrated Marketing Communication and Global Marketing Communication and Advertising, Emerson College has pioneered business education with a communication focus. Our distinguished faculty of academics and professionals prepares students for careers in marketing communication, advertising, management, and public relations for both domestic and global industries.

—Stuart Sigman, Dean

Programs and Curricular Focus

Emerson College offers programs of study leading to the M.A. in Integrated Marketing Communication and the M.A. in Global Marketing Communication and Advertising.

A newly defined professional degree program, the M.A. in Integrated Marketing Communication at Emerson unites the marketing functions of advertising, public relations, direct marketing, sales promotion, and interactive marketing under a comprehensive strategic umbrella. Emerson's programs provide degree candidates with a big-picture perspective, unifying all marketing functions toward a single goal: Better enabling businesses, not-for-profits, social causes, and individuals—such as politicians, actors, and athletes—to communicate with customers and publics. This focus gives students a wider breadth of course offerings across the marketing function as well as depth within specialty areas, such as marketing for the arts and entertainment industries.

The M.A. in Global Marketing Communication and Advertising is an intensive one-year, full-time program that prepares students to meet the diverse requirements of a rapidly growing global economy. Through courses such as Cultural Foundations of Buyer Behavior and New Technologies in Global Markets, the program prepares global marketers who understand the distinctive challenges

of targeting multicultural audiences. Each course offers a cutting-edge approach that blends theory with hands-on application. The program's tightly integrated academic structure includes internships in a broad range of enterprises both in the United States and abroad. Graduates go on to positions in international brand management, account management at international ad agencies, marketing management at international firms or U.S. firms seeking expansion, and international consulting, among others.

Students and the Program Experience

Emerson draws full-time communication students from more than thirty-eight countries, with backgrounds in law, business, and the liberal arts and sciences. With more than a 20 percent international population, the classroom experience offers the global perspective necessary for educating future business leaders. Emerson's part-time students consist of working professionals from Boston's advertising and corporate community. Students' ages have ranged from 22 to 42 years, with an average age of 27.

❖ Global Focus

Past international internships have included the World Wildlife Fund, Grey Advertising, CNN, the Foreign Trade Academy, McCann-Erickson Worldwide,

Honeywell, Hungarian Tourist Bureau, and ITT. Domestic internships have included Hill Holliday, Ogilvy & Mather, Dreamworks, and Anderson Consulting.

Special Features

EmComm, Emerson's in-house advertising agency, is dedicated to providing a training ground for tomorrow's marketing communication professionals. EmComm gives students practical experience in strategic marketing and advertising with both on- and off-campus accounts. Students work with real clients, professional graphic production companies, and sound studios, equipping them with valuable hands-on experience.

Graduate students in the School of Communication, Management and Public Policy may also spend a semester at Emerson's Los Angeles campus. The L.A. program is a fast-paced semester in which students work at internships by day and take classes with Emerson professors and industry professionals in the late afternoon and evening. Furnished housing is adjacent to the Los Angeles Center and just minutes from Universal Studios, Warner Brothers, and NBC Studios.

The Faculty

The School of Communication, Management and Public Policy faculty members are well-respected scholars and professionals drawn from all over the world. Through an integrated approach to business education, Emerson faculty members commit themselves to a curriculum of both theory and hands-on experience and foster a friendly openness with students both in and out of the classroom.

The Business School Network

With more than 16,000 Emerson alumni working worldwide, Emerson's vast network of alumni professionals provides a great resource for guidance on seeking leadership in a particular career field. Alumni members of the Emerson Career Connection are available for informational interviews and may be contacted through the Office of Career Services. Recent employers of graduates include

Arnold Communication, Bell Atlantic, The Gillette Company, Hill Holiday Atschiller, Norwegian Cruise Line, Prudential Securities, and Reebok.

The College and Environs

Emerson College is an independent, privately supported, coeducational, specialized college. Founded in Boston in 1880, it is the only college in the nation entirely devoted to the communication arts and sciences. It has been a pioneer in all aspects of communication from oral presentations to the latest digital technologies. The increasingly vital role of communication in today's world gives added relevance and significance to an Emerson education.

Located in the heart of Boston near Beacon Hill and the Boston Common, Emerson College lies in the midst of one of the nation's largest media and publishing markets and corporate centers. Culturally, Boston is a cosmopolitan city at the highest level. It is home to an active theater district, the world-famous Boston Symphony Orchestra, the legendary Celtics and Red Sox, and the Museum of Fine Arts, open without charge to Emerson students. Emerson's urban campus, itself a Boston landmark, is within walking distance of eclectic neighborhood bistros, the Public Garden, Newbury Street's shopping district, the Charles River Esplanade, and the Freedom Trail, along which are some of the most important landmarks in U.S. history.

Facilities

The Emerson College Library houses more than 185,000 print and nonprint items that focus on the communication arts and sciences. Through membership in the Fenway Consortium, graduate students have access to more than 2 million volumes. Computer-assisted reference services provide bibliographic databases through Dialog, BRS, and other online services. The On-line Computer Library Center is used for student research support. Other facilities include a focus group interview room complete with observation room and two-way mirror, computers equipped with SPSS for Windows, and Web design software.

Placement

The Career Services Office provides internship and job placement as well as lifetime career assistance. Listing more than 1,500 positions in Boston, the United States, and Europe, Emerson's internship program is the largest of its kind. Internships are available in every variety of media, corporate, nonprofit, theatrical, medical, and political organization.

Admission

Admission to the graduate programs is based on a combination of factors, including academic performance, GRE or GMAT scores, letters of recommendation, personal and professional experience, portfolios, and potential contributions to the proposed major field of study.

An application and fee must be submitted along with official transcripts and three letters of recommendation. International students must submit results of the Test of English as a Foreign Language (TOEFL).

Emerson College encourages applications from graduating college seniors and from individuals who wish to reenter the labor market, seek a career change, or strengthen their credentials. Part-time evening degree programs are available in several of the major program areas.

Finances

Tuition for the 2000–01 academic year is $610 per credit. Though Emerson does not offer on-campus housing to graduate students, the College's Office of Off-Campus Student Services assists graduate students in arranging for private accommodations in the Boston area. Costs of living in Boston are comparable to those in any large metropolitan city.

Several types of financial aid are available to graduate students, including need-based loans and awards based on academic merit. Merit awards consist of teaching, research, and administrative assistantships. The deadline for applicants interested in merit-based awards is March 1.

International Students

Emerson College offers a unique six-week intensive language program for international graduate students. This preparatory program is designed to strengthen and develop necessary communication skills in order to succeed both in and out of the classroom. In a supportive environment, the program integrates academic work, English language preparation, and social and cultural activities. There is an additional fee for the program.

Application Facts and Dates

July 15 is the application deadline for fall enrollment; December 1, for spring. For further information, students should contact:

Office of Graduate Admission
Emerson College
100 Beacon Street
Boston, Massachusetts 02116
Telephone: 617-824-8610
Fax: 617-824-8614
E-mail: gradapp@emerson.edu
World Wide Web: http://www.emerson.edu/gradopp

E. M. Lyon

Cesma M.B.A.

Lyon-Ecully, France

ENHANCING YOUR MANAGEMENT CAREER WITH AN INNOVATIVE M.B.A.

For more than twenty-five years, E. M. Lyon has provided excellence in management education through its entire range of graduate and executive development programs. At Cesma M.B.A., we dedicate ourselves to providing you with the tools and opportunities you need to meet the challenges of today's international business environment. Our pedagogy encourages you to share your experience while learning from your classmates and our renowned faculty. Even before you graduate, the esprit de corps of the Cesma M.B.A. alumni and our placement service will help you to develop a new career dynamic. We look forward to welcoming you to Cesma M.B.A. and to helping you acquire that winning edge.
—Bernard Belletante, Vice President

Programs and Curricular Focus

The Cesma program is a bilingual, European-style M.B.A., accredited by AMBA (Association of M.B.A.'s) and is ranked among the leading M.B.A. programs in Europe. E. M. Lyon itself is one of the first European management schools to be accredited EQUIS by the European Foundation for Management Development (EFMD).

Since 1997, a single program has been offered in two different versions: a one-year full-time format that is taught in English or a two-year part-time format for executives that is taught in English and French.

Three interrelated themes characterize the Cesma M.B.A. program: the development of personal managerial competencies, entrepreneurship, and international management issues.

Via core courses and a choice of more specialised gateway courses that focus on international strategic management, services management, business-to-business marketing, and corporate restructuring; electives; personal development workshops; and a series of interdisciplinary seminars, participants are encouraged to learn, starting from concrete cases and from their own personal and professional experience. There is a strong emphasis on group work, which, given the diversity of the Cesma M.B.A. year-group, provides a rich laboratory of intercultural exchanges. In addition to company placements, a range of independent projects is proposed—both in France and elsewhere—to enable participants to develop their

capacity to analyze situations, imagine solutions, make recommendations, and then take responsibility for action.

Students and the M.B.A. Experience

Around one third of the participants are from countries other than France. The average age is 30 years for full-time students and 33 for the part-time executive M.B.A. Ninety percent are practicing managers with an average of seven years of experience. The remaining 10 percent are recent graduates.

In terms of academic background, approximately 40 percent are engineers, 25 percent are scientists, and 35 percent have arts, languages, social sciences, or other types of degrees.

The diversity of the year-group is one of the real strengths of the Cesma M.B.A. As in any project team, participants find themselves constantly confronted with the challenges of working in intercultural and interprofessional groups. They are encouraged to support and to learn as much from each other as they do from the taught classes.

❖ Global Focus

International and comparative management issues are at the heart of the Cesma M.B.A. curriculum and are inescapably present in the work of the different tutorial and study groups. All of the core courses are international in content. There is also a field of specialisation offered in interna-

tional business, backed up by a wide range of electives, many of which are taught by visiting professors.

Specific missions, normally conducted in small groups, give participants an opportunity to work on the creation of business start-up plans, consulting projects, or other types of action research in companies. There are also opportunities for shorter or longer periods of exchange with Cesma's partner schools. They include Cranfield School of Management in the U.K. and Belgrano University in Buenos Aires, Argentina (with whom there are double-degree arrangements); the Management School at Lancaster University, U.K.; ESADE in Barcelona, Spain; Carnegie Mellon in Pittsburgh, U.S.A.; HEC in Montreal, Canada; Waseda University in Tokyo, Japan; Monash MT Eliza University in Australia; Foundation Getulio Vargos, Brasil; and Pontificia Universidad Catolica in Chile.

In order to react to the challenges of globalisation, five top management schools from each of the principal economic regions in the world have devised a unique and original strategic alliance: AEA Alliance–The Cross-Regional Business School.

By pooling professional and technological resources, the mission of AEA Alliance is to provide tailor-made management programs for companies, students, and alumni who need transnational knowledge and skills to develop activities and career opportunities in other countries.

The five founding members of AEA Alliance are: for Europe, E. M. Lyon (France) and a leading British business school whose name will be revealed shortly; for NAFTA, HEC–Montreal (Canada); for Mercosur, Belgrano University (Argentina); and for Asia-Pacific, Lingnan (University) College–ZSU (China).

The Faculty

Eighty permanent members make up the teaching and research faculty at E. M. Lyon They are recruited not only on the basis of academic qualifications but also on the basis of their business experience and international exposure.

Numerous visiting international professors and experts participate in the Cesma M.B.A. program every year. By encouraging research and collaboration with institutions in other countries, developing a new global alliance, as well as consulting in companies, E. M. Lyon has allowed its faculty members to attain high degrees of competence and to produce numerous publications.

The Business School Network

The traditionally close links with the Lyon Chamber of Commerce and Industry and the funding of educational and research projects as well as international scholarships by companies have made E. M. Lyon exceptionally responsive to the needs of business.

Cesma M.B.A. offers operational training based on pragmatism and encourages participants to develop their polyvalence, team spirit, and abilities to anticipate and adapt to change.

Representatives and professionals from various sectors and functions in companies often participate in the seminars that punctuate the program. Company representatives and managers take part in numerous events organized to provide the most favorable conditions for in-depth exchange between students and companies. More than 100 European firms and European subsidiaries of international companies visit E. M. Lyon each year to give presentations and to prospect for potential employees.

The College and Environs

E. M. Lyon was created in 1872. Initially established in Lyon, the school experi-

enced strong growth, which in 1972 led it to move to an ultramodern campus in Ecully, a residential suburb minutes from the centre of Lyon. The campus is spread within a teaching and research zone that includes higher educational institutions, a small-business incubator, and a number of high-tech firms.

It is located near Lyon's city centre, the third-largest city in France. Lyon has an unrivalled geographical situation, and it takes only a 2- to 3-hour drive to get to Alpine skiing resorts or to the beaches of the French Riviera.

Facilities

Educational resources include a documentation centre (17,600 titles, 321 periodicals, CD-ROMs), a database and computer center, audiovisual facilities (television studios), and language laboratory facilities. A gymnasium and several tennis courts complete the infrastructure of the school. The campus offers Cesma M.B.A. participants accommodations and restaurant facilities (two residence complexes, a cafeteria, and a restaurant).

Placement

Counsellors from the E. M. Lyon Careers and Orientation Department offer individualized support and advice to participants in planning their career and development opportunities.

Cesma M.B.A. graduates have responsibilities all over the world, mainly in medium-sized companies owned by large multinationals. One third work as managing directors or directors of subsidiaries and 44 percent work in

commercial or marketing functions. The most represented sector is industry. The remainder work in finance or as consultants. In the last twenty-five years, 20 percent of graduates have created their own companies.

Admission

Applicants are at least 24 years of age, highly motivated, have strong intellectual ability, and are committed. Ideal applicants are managers holding a first degree and possessing significant work experience. The admission process is in two stages.

First, the completed application form must be submitted and, if approved, the applicant is then invited to the second stage—the admission tests and selection interview. GMAT or TAGE-MAGE (French equivalent of GMAT) as well as the TOEFL or the Cesma M.B.A. French test scores are required. It is possible to arrange to take the admission tests and to participate in a selection interview in specific countries other than in France.

Finances

For 2000–01, the application fee is €110 (Fr 722), the tuition fee for the full-time program is €18,000 (Fr 118,072) for self-sponsored applicants and €20,000 (Fr 131,191) for company-sponsored applicants (payable in installments). Living expenses are estimated to be approximately €7,700 (Fr 50,509).

International Students

Typically, one third of Cesma M.B.A. participants are from countries other than France, with around fifteen nationalities being represented in the year group. Ninety percent are from Europe, 1.5 percent are from Central America, 7 percent are from North America, and 1.5 percent are from other areas.

Application Facts and Dates

There is only one intake per year, in September, and applications must be submitted by June 15. Interested students should contact:

Cesma M.B.A.
E. M. Lyon
23, Avenue Guy de Collongue
BP 174
69132 Lyon Ecully Cedex
France
Telephone: 33-4-78-33-78-65
Fax: 33-4-78-33-77-55
E-mail: mba13@em-lyon.com
WWW: http://www.em-lyon.com

EMORY Emory University

Roberto C. Goizueta Business School

Atlanta, Georgia

BUILDING MOMENTUM AT A WORLD-CLASS INSTITUTION

Since coming to Goizueta Business School as Dean in 1998, several remarkable events have charged the School with renewed momentum. Recent gifts of $50 million enabled the School to expand its recruitment of world-class faculty members and to increase student fellowships and scholarships. We are proud that 10 new faculty members have joined the School and that students are enjoying the success of the Career Management Center. With these resources as well as a new state-of-the-art building, cutting-edge technology, and an innovative curriculum, the School is quickly moving forward in its progress toward preeminence.

—Thomas S. Robertson, Dean

Programs and Curricular Focus

The Goizueta Business School M.B.A. program offers students the opportunity to pursue an M.B.A. in a flexible, innovative environment. Students are encouraged to work closely with professors, to individualize a course of study, and to customize career goals. The core curriculum includes the "flex core," which allows students to take electives earlier in the program. In addition, Lead Week, a weeklong introduction to each semester, consists of a simulation game in the fall term, and in the spring, a focus module addressing contemporary industry or region-specific issues is taught. Faculty members use teaching methods best suited to the course material, including cases, lectures, class discussions, student presentations, team and field projects, and computer simulations with a balanced emphasis on quantitative and qualitative approaches.

Beginning in fall 2000, Goizueta Plus, a new Goizueta offering, begins during Lead Week and spans the entire program. It is a coordinated program for developing the essential competencies of entrepreneurial leadership. The yearlong program enables students to build skills in complex decision making, communication, and leadership.

During the first year, students complete a core curriculum that stresses the fundamental building blocks of business and the basic principles in each of the primary functional areas. During the second year, students have the opportunity to develop an area of concentration in areas that include finance, marketing, management, accounting, or decision and information analysis.

In addition to the full-time, two-year M.B.A. program, other programs leading to the M.B.A. degree are offered. Graduates of undergraduate business schools accredited by AACSB–The International Association for Management Education may start the program in May and complete the program in one calendar year. Goizueta Business School offers a part-time, three-year Evening M.B.A. program for working professionals and a sixteen-month Executive M.B.A. program for candidates with significant managerial experience. Joint-degree programs are available with the law school, J.D./M.B.A. (four years); the School of Public Health, M.P.H./M.B.A. (five semesters); and the Candler School of Theology, M.B.A./M.Div. (four years).

Students and the M.B.A. Experience

The Goizueta Business School consists of 360 full-time and 170 part-time M.B.A. students, who come from a wide variety of academic disciplines, geographic regions, and professions. For the full-time program, the average length of postgraduate work is five years, with 100 percent of the students having at least one year of work experience. More than 30 percent of the students are women, and one third are international students who represent forty-five countries. The range of GMAT scores is 600–740 for the middle 80 percent.

❖ Global Focus

Students at the Goizueta Business School experience global issues on many levels within the M.B.A. program. The Global Perspectives course, which is the first part of a two-class sequence and is taught in the second semester, serves as an introduction using a multidisciplinary, integrated approach. By bringing all the functional disciplines together, the course helps students learn to operate in a global environment and develop political, cultural, ethical, and geographic perspectives. There are also international course electives in finance, accounting, management, marketing, and e-business.

Students have the opportunity to study abroad in exchange programs currently offered with more than twenty universities in such countries as China, Costa Rica, England, Finland, France, Germany, Italy, Mexico, Singapore, and Venezuela. Specialized programs with Soviet, Post-Soviet, and East European Studies and Latin American Area Studies at Emory University enable students to gain further experience in a geographic area.

Special Features

Students at the Goizueta Business School are very involved in the Atlanta community. A case competition organized by the Goizueta Marketing Association gives students the opportunity to apply marketing research and strategy development skills to real business challenges for such companies as the Coca-Cola Company, the Ritz-Carlton Hotel, the American Red Cross, Georgia-Pacific Corporation, UPS, and BellSouth. Community involvement also occurs with such projects as volunteer days and fund-raising events for Atlanta's underprivileged residents.

The Faculty

Emory places teaching first among equals with respect to scholarly research and service to the business community. Faculty members have joined the Business School from such institutions as Chicago, Harvard, Michigan, MIT, Northwestern, Pennsylvania (Wharton), Stanford, and Yale.

The Business School Network
Corporate Partnerships
The Customer Business Development Track involves such companies as Procter & Gamble, Coca-Cola, IBM, and Chubb in a program that incorporates integration of classroom learning and internship experiences for students and encourages the entrepreneurial spirit.

The College and Environs
The city of Atlanta is the business, cultural, and international center of the southeastern United States and, according to *Fortune* magazine, is considered by business leaders to be one of the top five cities in which to do business. It is the sixteenth-largest metropolitan area in the nation and the largest in the Southeast. The moderate climate and reasonable cost of living, in addition to an impressive array of cultural and recreational offerings, attract people from all over the world. More than 450 of the Fortune 500 companies have headquarters or offices in Atlanta.

Emory University is located 6 miles from downtown Atlanta on the northeast side of the city. The campus consists of 550 heavily wooded acres in a nice residential neighborhood. Emory offers students access to the resources of a cosmopolitan university community with more than 11,000 students. The diverse learning environment is enhanced by specialized centers and affiliates such as the Carter Center, the Yerkes Primate Center, the Law and Economics Center, Scholars Press, and the Centers for Disease Control and Prevention (CDC).

Facilities
The Goizueta Business School moved into its current home on Emory's campus in July 1997. The building is 119,000 square feet, with state-of-the-art technology throughout the facility. The five-story structure has a strategic design that facilitates an interactive teaching and research environment.

Technology Environment
Information technology at the Goizueta Business School is comprehensive with modern facilities, a professional staff, and extensive documentation. Extensive library resources are available to students with online databases such as ABI Inform business magazine index, LEXIS-NEXIS, and Dow Jones News/Retrieval Service.

Placement
The mission of the Career Management Center is centered on assisting students in pragmatically focusing particular abilities, experiences, and interests toward a career goal and helping the student develop an individual strategy for marketing himself or herself in order to conduct an effective job search. Workshops, speakers, internships, mentors, interview coaching, and alumni are some of the resources available to students.

The average starting salary for the class of 2000 was more than $78,000. Consulting, finance, marketing, entrepreneurship, and e-commerce were the most popular career fields for Goizueta graduates.

Admission
Admission to the M.B.A. program is highly selective. Each candidate is evaluated on the basis of his or her ability to perform in an academically rigorous environment as well as contribute to classroom discussions based on work and/or life experiences. Diversity and international perspectives are valued in the admission process. To apply to the Goizueta Business School, a student must submit the results of the Graduate Management Admission Test (GMAT); official transcripts from all previous undergraduate, graduate, and professional work; two letters of recommendation; and the completed application form including statistical data, work history, and essays. Applicants from non-English-speaking countries also must submit scores from the Test of English as a Foreign Language (TOEFL) and a statement of financial resources. A personal interview is highly recommended.

Finances
Tuition for the 2000–01 academic year at Goizueta Business School is $26,200. The estimated annual living expenses and fees for a student living off campus total $15,000. Students who complete an application by February 15 are automatically considered for merit-based scholarships. Need-based aid in the form of loans is available to M.B.A. students. Applicants should file the FAFSA and Financial Aid PROFILE for loan consideration. To contact Emory University's Financial Aid Office, students should call 404-727-1141 or write to Financial Aid Office, Emory University, Atlanta, Georgia 30322.

International Students
International students are encouraged to apply. Good communication skills are essential to the program. Applicants whose native language is not English must score a minimum of 600 on the TOEFL (250 on the computer-based test). A limited amount of merit-based financial assistance is available for international students.

Application Facts and Dates
The deadline for applying to the two-year, full-time M.B.A. program is March 31. For full scholarship consideration, the application deadline is February 15. Applications for the one-year M.B.A. program are due February 15; for the Evening M.B.A. program, March 1; and for the Executive M.B.A. program, October 1, 2000. Access to online applications is available via the School's Web site (address below). Students may also obtain applications and admissions information from:

Julie R. Barefoot
Assistant Dean of Admissions and
  Career Services
Goizueta Business School
Emory University
Atlanta, Georgia 30322-2712
Telephone: 404-727-6311
Fax: 404-727-4612
World Wide Web: http://www.emory.edu/BUS/

Emporia State University

Emporia, Kansas

PREPARING STUDENTS FOR TOMORROW

Emporia State University's (ESU) School of Business prepares students to excel in an increasingly global business environment. We are small enough to practice a truly student-oriented philosophy but large enough to provide a high-quality educational experience.

Our M.B.A. faculty members maintain close relations with business practitioners and integrate business experiences into classroom presentations. The School of Business Council of Advisors, comprised of prominent business and government leaders, represents a key link in keeping abreast of current and emerging trends.

We care about our students and focus our efforts on providing a meaningful educational experience to prepare them for tomorrow's business world.

—*S. A. Hashmi, Dean*

Programs and Curricular Focus

The standard M.B.A. program is a sequence of courses (36 credit hours) designed to assure competency in the functional areas of business and also to enable a student to acquire content breadth by choosing elective courses. Required courses include study in the areas of accounting, finance, management, information systems for management, managerial economics, marketing, and quantitative methods. Elective courses may be taken in a wide range of subject-matter areas. Increasingly, many students choose elective courses in electronic commerce, global financial markets, global information systems, and knowledge management.

The School also offers a specialized M.B.A. degree (36 credit hours), with a concentration in accounting. This curriculum prepares students for high-level accounting positions and enables them to meet requirements for admission to the uniform CPA examination. In addition to taking required courses in areas such as finance, marketing, and management, students must take a required accounting course and choose two additional elective courses in accounting.

In both M.B.A. curriculums, completion of a core of undergraduate prerequisite business courses is necessary before full admission status is granted. These courses may have been taken to fulfill undergraduate degree requirements or may be taken at Emporia State University. The reason for requiring prerequisite study is to provide a basic understanding

of business that can be further developed by study at the graduate level.

Students and the M.B.A. Experience

M.B.A. students have diverse academic and experiential backgrounds. While some have a limited amount of work experience, others have extensive experience in various managerial positions. A typical M.B.A. student is 30 years old, has four or five years of work experience, and completes degree requirements primarily for professional career development. Seventy percent of the students are men, and between 30 and 35 percent are students who come to the United States to pursue an M.B.A. degree.

As part of their instructional methodology, many professors stress teamwork. Also, students have opportunities to work in cooperation with a professor to complete independent study covering a specialized topic of mutual interest. Although the majority of students have completed undergraduate business degrees, an undergraduate major in business is not a requirement for admission.

The Faculty

Professors who teach M.B.A. courses are members of the graduate faculty. Approximately one fifth of the faculty are women. In addition to instructional responsibilities, many faculty members work as consultants to businesses,

government agencies, and educational organizations. They conduct research, publish papers, and are leaders in professional organizations. Several faculty members have authored or coauthored textbooks printed by major publishing companies. These professional activities bring a high level of intellectual excitement and realism to the classroom.

The Business School Network
Corporate Partnerships

The School maintains strong relationships with business and industry. Some professors work directly with companies to involve students in real-world projects as a component of the classroom educational experience. The business community serves as an important resource to provide valuable expertise and guidance. Each year, the M.B.A. Student Association sponsors educational programs and hosts business leaders who give lectures and participate in seminars.

Prominent Alumni

Numerous alumni have made noteworthy accomplishments during their professional careers. These graduates include Dennis Casarona, president of Graphic Promotions; Kay Gerdes, vice president of operations for Farm Credit Services; Salief Keita, director of agencies for Banque Malienne de Credit et de Depots (Mali); Ken Lerman, a widely known business consultant who formerly served as marketing director for Pizza Hut and Taco Tico; and Yasunori Watanabe, country general manager for TNT Worldwide (Japan).

The College and Environs

"A place where people care about you" is how students describe Emporia State University. With an enrollment of approximately 5,500 students, ESU offers twenty-three graduate degree programs. The University is small enough for students to develop friendships, yet large enough to offer a variety of educational programs.

With a population of nearly 27,000, Emporia is an educational, industrial, trade, and medical center serving east-central Kansas. It is situated on the

The School of Business is housed in Cremer Hall, a modern five-story building.

eastern edge of the Bluestem region of the Flint Hills and is surrounded by numerous lakes and recreational facilities. The city is located on the Kansas Turnpike, Interstate 35, and the Santa Fe Railroad. Three major metropolitan areas of Kansas (Topeka, Kansas City, and Wichita) can easily be reached from Emporia.

Placement
The Office of Career Development, Cooperative Education, and Placement Services coordinates arrangements for corporate recruiters to visit the campus. Students and alumni have access to weekly listings of position vacancies. Each year, the School sponsors a career fair, which gives students opportunities to become acquainted with potential employers. The M.B.A. Student Association encourages networking with corporate executives and sponsors programs to help develop effective interviewing skills.

Admission
Applicants need a minimum grade point average of at least 2.5 (A=4.0) or not less than 2.5 for the last 60 credit hours of undergraduate study. In addition, an acceptable score on the Graduate Management Admission Test (GMAT) is required for unconditional admission. The score on the GMAT and the academic transcript are used to determine admission status.

Finances
For the 2000–01 academic year, estimated fees for a full course load are $3286 per semester for nonresidents. For the 2000 summer session, nonresident fees were $266 per credit hour. Fees are established by the Kansas Board of Regents and are subject to change. Estimated cost of room and board is $3804 per academic year. The cost of books and supplies is approximately $270 per semester. The University Housing Office maintains a list of off-campus rooms, apartments, and houses that may be rented by students. Also, housing is available at the University-owned Emporia State Apartments.

Each year, the School offers a number of graduate assistantships to qualified students. Graduate assistants also may be eligible for reduced fees.

International Students
International students represent approximately one third of the M.B.A. enrollment. The majority of these students come from African, Asian, and South American countries. The University sponsors a number of activities and organizations to accommodate the needs of international students. Also, specialized intensive English language training is available on campus.

Application Facts and Dates
Students are admitted for terms beginning in August, January, and June, with corresponding deadlines of June 1, November 1, and April 1. Applications are processed on a continuous basis. For additional information concerning the application process, admission requirements, or graduate assistantships, students should contact:

Dr. Donald S. Miller
Director, M.B.A. Program
School of Business
Campus Box 4059
Emporia State University
Emporia, Kansas 66801-5087
Telephone: 316-341-5456
Fax: 316-341-6346
E-mail: millerdo@emporia.edu
World Wide Web: http://www.emporia.edu/business

Active interaction between students and professors characterizes classroom sessions.

RSM *Erasmus*

Erasmus University Rotterdam

> **BUILDING UPON SUCCESS**
>
> *The ability to innovate and to remain at the leading edge of developments in management theory and practice are critical for the success of M.B.A. participants and of M.B.A. programs. The Rotterdam School of Management continuously strives to build upon the success we have achieved through a continuous focus on issues of international business, information technology, and soft management skills. These features complement an in-depth, integrated M.B.A. curriculum aimed at creating managers capable of leading global companies.*
>
> —Kai Peters, Dean

Programs and Curricular Focus

The Rotterdam School of Management (RSM) offers two full-time M.B.A. programs: the International M.B.A. Program in General Management and the International M.B.A./M.B.I. (Master of Business Administration/Master of Business Informatics) Program. These eighteen-month programs start each September and are taught entirely in English.

The curriculum of the International M.B.A. Program in General Management covers all major aspects of general management. The first year consists of mandatory courses in management basics and functional areas and includes communication workshops.

The International M.B.A./M.B.I. program is designed for students who, in addition to a general management education, wish to receive theoretical and practical training in the managerial aspects of information technology (IT). M.B.A./M.B.I. graduates help bridge the gap between specialists in information technology and managers who are the main users of information systems. It is clearly not a technical program, but a management program. The M.B.A./M.B.I. program is largely identical to the M.B.A. program but includes M.B.I.-exclusive class blocks later in the program.

The first-year course period for both M.B.A. and M.B.A./M.B.I. students ends with a project management and consulting workshop. During the summer, students are required to undertake an in-company project. M.B.A./M.B.I. students take a required M.B.I. block of courses before performing an IT in-company project.

The second year allows students to tailor their studies to areas of their interest. Through electives and mini-courses, they can focus on areas such as corporate finance, marketing, or IT. Students also have the opportunity to participate in an exchange program with top business schools worldwide in their second year.

Students and the M.B.A. Experience

The Rotterdam School of Management is a business school that attracts students from all over the world. About forty different nationalities are represented in the current student population of 200 (100 students per year). Only 15 percent of the students are Dutch; the remaining 85 percent are international. Students come from a wide variety of academic backgrounds. An average breakdown is 30 percent engineering, 30 percent business, 15 percent science and medicine, 10 percent economics, 10 percent humanities and social sciences, and 5 percent law. The average age of students is 29, and the average number of years of work experience is four.

Working in groups is an essential element of the M.B.A. programs. The emphasis on teamwork provides a realistic model for the way in which management issues are handled in the business world. Students learn the vital significance of teamwork and the value of cooperation when they are confronted with a wide range of approaches to a single problem. By forming teams of students with different cultural and educational backgrounds, various problem-solving techniques are recognized and appreciated. This enriches the learning experience of all students.

Special Features

The Rotterdam School of Management is consistently ranked as one of Europe's top business schools. *The Economist*'s "Which M.B.A.?" describes the School as innovative, interesting, friendly, and representing excellent value.

In addition to the functionally based courses, the M.B.A. programs include extensive workshops, seminars, and mini-courses aimed at building practical skills. Furthermore, students undertake consultancy projects for companies and nonprofit organizations.

In the third semester of the M.B.A. programs, students can apply to go on exchange to a business school in the U.S. (e.g., Wharton, Kellogg, Chicago, Columbia, Berkeley), Europe (e.g., Bocconi-Italy, IESE-Spain, MBS-U.K.), South Africa, Japan, or Mexico.

The Faculty

The academic faculty represents a mix of professors from the Rotterdam School of Management and Erasmus University, visiting faculty members of prestigious international universities, and consultants and managers active in different industries. Faculty members are international professionals who bring up-to-date management techniques and practices into the classroom. They are committed to a wide range of teaching methods such as lectures, case studies, field trips, group work, management games, and real-life projects.

The Business School Network

The Rotterdam School of Management was founded with the support of major Dutch multinationals and has since developed close ties with the international business community. Companies such as Citibank, Arthur D. Little, and ABN AMRO Bank actively take part in the curriculum of the M.B.A. program.

The RSM Alumni Association is a very international network of all RSM graduates. Alumni are closely involved in the School's activities and are always

pleased to meet potential students and discuss their experiences at the RSM with them.

The College and Environs

The Rotterdam School of Management is a foundation of Erasmus University Rotterdam, which is renowned for its business orientation. The University was founded in 1913 by Rotterdam entrepreneurs and named after Erasmus Desiderius Roterodamus. Erasmus was born in Rotterdam in the late fifteenth century. He was a leader of the liberal reform movement in Europe and dreamed of democracy of the intellect and correct use of free will. It is this humanist tradition that still lives on in the University, which today has more than 16,000 students, of whom some 1,600 are enrolled in postgraduate studies.

Facilities

The Rotterdam School of Management is located on the Woudestein Campus of the Erasmus University. The University campus is situated close to the center of Rotterdam. The RSM offers housing services for all international students near the University campus. The language laboratory at Erasmus University is available to RSM students. The RSM has a school restaurant/bar. The Business Library provides business information and supports M.B.A. students' and alumni's

search for information on management and business. The resources of the library are specifically selected to support the M.B.A. and M.B.A./M.B.I. curricula. Students can also make use of the sports center, the main library, and information services from Erasmus University.

Technology Environment

The RSM has excellent computer facilities with dedicated computer labs. The PC network from Novell contains a wide range of software packages, such as database programs, presentation graphics, spreadsheets, statistics, word processing, online information services, and others. RSM students can also make use of e-mail worldwide and Internet access.

Placement

The Career Management Center is dedicated fully to the career development needs of all M.B.A. students while serving the recruitment necessities of companies internationally. The Career Management Center organizes workshops in resume and cover letter writing, self-assessment, and interviewing techniques. The resume (curriculum vitae) book provides a valuable database for both on- and off-campus recruiters. Students are encouraged to include their resumes on the Internet pages of the RSM.

For many RSM students, the yearly on-campus company presentations and

selection interviews turn out to be the starting point of their careers. The RSM is a target school for recruitment among leading national and international companies.

Admission

The RSM welcomes applications from outstanding men and women whose intellectual ability, management potential, and personal qualities indicate that they will benefit from and contribute to the learning environment. Eligibility requirements include a recognized university degree, GMAT scores, two letters of recommendation (academic and/or professional), work experience, proficiency in English, and a personal interview with one of RSM's alumni in the applicant's country of residence.

Finances

If you start in either September 2000 or September 2001, tuition fees for the following programs are $39,000 €27,500 for the entire M.B.A. program and $42,500 €30,000 for the entire M.B.A./M.B.I. program.

Other expenses, such as room rent, books, and living expenses, are estimated to be around €17,625 for the entire program duration of eighteen months.

International Students

All RSM activities are international by definition, as the student body represents so many nationalities. Students can receive assistance with applications for visa and housing matters.

Application Facts and Dates

The application deadline is June 15. Applications are processed on a continuous basis in order of receipt. Late applicants will be placed on a waiting list. Applicants should contact:

Ms. Connie Tai, M.B.A.
Associate Director, Admissions
Rotterdam School of Management
Erasmus Graduate School of Business
P.O. Box 1738
3000 DR Rotterdam
The Netherlands
Telephone: 31-10-4081936/2768
Fax: 31-10-4529509
E-mail: rsm@rsm.nl
World Wide Web: http://www.rsm.nl

Fairfield University

Fairfield, Connecticut

CREATING A COMPETITIVE ADVANTAGE

The Fairfield University School of Business is in the heart of one of the most exciting business learning environments in the world. Only 50 miles northeast of New York City, we are surrounded by more than 100 Fortune 500 headquarters, and Fairfield County alone hosts the largest concentration of U.S. headquarters of foreign multinationals. We enjoy close partnerships with these great companies—organizations that also employ our M.B.A. students and enhance our learning laboratory.

The Fairfield M.B.A. is also distinctive because our business school is a leader in business curriculum innovation, and we capitalize on our faculty members' expertise and their business experience. Our M.B.A. is accredited by AACSB– The International Association for Management Education.

If you want to be prepared for emerging new-economy challenges, come study with us. The Fairfield M.B.A. creates a competitive advantage.

—Walter G. Ryba Jr., Dean

Programs and Curricular Focus

An M.B.A. program is meant to be a generalist degree that covers all the relevant topical areas and gives a student the opportunity to specialize, but not major, in a functional area of business. The M.B.A. program has three components: core courses, breadth courses, and specialization or concentration courses.

The core courses are designed to provide fundamental tools and functional area competencies for students who either did not major in a business specialty as undergraduates, did not perform well academically as undergraduates, or took only a portion of the functional and tool courses that comprise the M.B.A. core.

Most students admitted to the program are able to waive selected core courses on the basis of previous course work or based on relevant work experience when combined with related course work, qualifying examinations, program of graduate study, and other factors.

All students are expected to demonstrate and/or attain proficiency in the use of microcomputers and the mainframe computer during their program of study. Computer use is integrated throughout the curriculum, and it is expected in each course. The School provides fully equipped microcomputer labs for student use, and each student may obtain a computer account for access to the University's mainframe systems.

The specialization options include courses in accounting, finance, health-care management, human resource management, information systems and operations management, international business, and marketing.

The Fairfield M.B.A. allows students to build on their previous education while avoiding repetition of course work mastered elsewhere. With consideration of the individual's prior academic performance, each student's program of study is designed from core and breadth courses and an attractive selection of electives. A minimum of 36 graduate credit hours must be completed in the M.B.A. program. On average, the program of study is made up of 48 credits with the waiver of courses.

Students and the M.B.A. Experience

Students in Fairfield's M.B.A. program have a wide variety of academic and work experience. Although some students in the program are recent college graduates, the average age of students is 27 years, with four years of full-time work experience.

❖ Global Focus

Fairfield's M.B.A. program emphasizes the recognition that business is international by nature. One of the key specialization areas for students is in international business. In addition, virtually all courses discuss international implications of their discipline. The student body represents many nations, with connections to many major international corporations. Student exchange opportunities are available in several countries.

Special Features

The revised curriculum includes practical applications of critical business skills, including negotiation and dispute resolution and market valuation and analysis. Many courses emphasize the role of technology in the competitive position of the firm in a global economy.

The Faculty

The Fairfield faculty have always emphasized outstanding teaching. Ninety percent of the 39 full-time graduate faculty members have extensive experience in the business world, and all have their appropriate doctoral degrees. There is great diversity among the members of the faculty.

The Business School Network
Corporate Partnerships

The School has been the recipient of several major corporate grants for support of curriculum and faculty development. A close relationship exists with dozens of major corporations in Fairfield County, which is the third-largest center of corporate headquarters in the nation. The School also has an outstanding Advisory Council of business leaders from the nation's largest corporations. Corporate executives participate extensively as guests and lecturers in many courses every semester.

The College and Environs

Fairfield University is a coeducational institution of higher learning founded by the Society of Jesus in 1942 and proudly aspires to the Jesuit tradition of developing the whole intellectual potential of its students and creating the true sense of ethical and social responsibility within them. Fairfield partners with Jesuit universities throughout the U.S. to facilitate the transfer of courses and degree completion should graduate students be required to relocate to another geographic area.

The 200-acre campus is among the most beautiful in the country. The School of Business includes modern classrooms, team workrooms, and state-of-the-art technology that make it a model teaching and learning environment.

Fairfield University is situated in a suburban area on the Connecticut shore of Long Island Sound about 1 hour from New

York City and 3 hours from Boston. The University is in America's academic corridor, along with many cultural, recreational, and intellectual activities.

Facilities

The Nyselius Library contains some 300,000 volumes, 772,000 microforms, and 1,800 journals and newspapers, with extensive business collections, including World Wide Web subscription databases such as Disclosure Global Access, IAC's Business & Company ASAP, RIA Checkpoint, Westlaw, LEXIS-NEXIS, and Encyclopedia Britannica Online. ABI-Inform on CD-ROM is also available. Access to library facilities throughout the area is available as well. In spring 2001, the library is scheduled to complete a major expansion and renovation project, doubling its size and including a 24-hour computer lab and increased group study space. The computer center includes a DEC Alpha 2100, with terminals throughout the campus; buildings on the campus are equipped with fiber optics, and a campuswide network of microcomputers is in place.

Placement

The University offers a placement office with a full-time professional staff, including an M.B.A. career coach, to assist students. There are on-campus recruiting visits by representatives of the top corporations in the nation.

Admission

The criteria for admission to the M.B.A. and the M.S. programs are a strong undergraduate grade point average and an appropriate score on the Graduate Management Admission Test (GMAT). A formula score of at least 1100, derived by multiplying the grade point average by 200 and adding the GMAT score, is usually required for admission. Complete official transcripts of all undergraduate and graduate work, two letters of recommendation, and a letter of self-evaluation or an enumeration of work experience must all be submitted. Students from non-English-speaking countries are required to submit a Test of English as a Foreign Language (TOEFL) score of 550 or better. Applicants to the certificate program are not required to submit GMAT scores.

Finances

In 2000–01, tuition is $480 per credit hour for part-time students and $9000 per semester for full-time students. The registration fee is $25 per semester.

The large majority of graduate students live off campus in the surrounding communities. Housing costs in the area vary widely.

Scholarship aid is limited. Most students are employed and receive substantial financial support from their employers. Graduate research assistantships are also available in limited supply. Students may apply for financial assistance after having been accepted into a program. Assistance is usually limited to U.S. citizens.

International Students

The International Programs and Student Services Offices offer special services for international students. International students must attend on a full-time basis and fulfill visa eligibility requirements, including evidence of full financial support. A TOEFL score of 550 or higher is also required. Scholarship and assistantship monies typically are reserved for domestic students.

Application Facts and Dates

Applications are accepted on a revolving basis and should be completed prior to August 15 for those who wish to begin in the fall semester, prior to December 15 to begin in the spring semester, and prior to May 15 to begin in the summer semester. International students should apply by June 15 for fall admission and November 15 for spring admission. The application fee is $50.

Students should address all questions or requests for information and application materials to:

Graduate Admissions
School of Business
Fairfield University
Fairfield, Connecticut 06430
Telephone: 203-254-4180
Fax: 203-254-4029
E-mail: mba@fair1.fairfield.edu
World Wide Web: http://www.fairfield.edu

FACULTY LIST

Jeffrey B. Arthur, Assistant Professor of Management; Ph.D., Cornell.
Gregory Bachand, Visiting Assistant Professor of Marketing; J.D., Connecticut.
Bharat B. Bhalla, Associate Professor of Finance; Ph.D., Cornell.
Mousumi Bhattachara, Assistant Professor of Management; Ph.D., Syracuse.
Bruce Bradford, Associate Professor of Accounting; Ph.D., Virginia Tech; D.B.A., Memphis; CPA.
Gerald Campbell, Associate Professor of Information Systems and Operations Management; Ph.D., Indiana.
Paul Caster, Associate Professor of Accounting; Ph.D., North Texas; CPA.
Gerald O. Cavallo, Associate Professor of Marketing; Ph.D., CUNY Graduate Center.
J. Michael Cavanaugh, Associate Professor of Management; Ph.D., Massachusetts.
Arjun Chaudhuri, Associate Professor of Marketing; Ph.D., Connecticut.
Elia V. Chepaitis, Associate Professor of Information Systems; Ph.D., Connecticut.
Thomas E. Conine Jr., Professor of Finance; Ph.D., NYU.
Sandra J. Ducoffe, Associate Professor of Marketing; Ph.D., Michigan State.

James He, Associate Professor of Information Systems and Operations Management; Ph.D., Penn State.
Walter F. Hlawitschka, Associate Professor of Finance; Ph.D., Virginia.
Christopher L. Huntley, Assistant Professor of Information Systems; Ph.D., Virginia.
Lucy V. Katz, Professor of Business Law; J.D., NYU.
Gregory D. Koutmos, Professor of Finance; Ph.D., CUNY Graduate Center.
Philip J. Lane, Associate Professor of Economics; Ph.D., Tufts.
Mark S. LeClair, Associate Professor of Economics; Ph.D., Rutgers.
Patrick S. Lee, Associate Professor of Operations and Information Systems Management; Ph.D., Carnegie Mellon.
Mark Ligas, Assistant Professor of Marketing; Ph.D., Connecticut.
Lisa A. Mainiero, Professor of Management; Ph.D., Yale.
Anna D. Martin, Assistant Professor of Finance; Ph.D., Florida Atlantic University.
R. Keith Martin, Professor of Information Systems; Ph.D., Washington (Seattle); CDP, CSP.
Dawn W. Massey, Assistant Professor of Accounting; Ph.D., Connecticut; CPA.

Sharlene A. McEvoy, Professor of Business Law; J.D., Connecticut; Ph.D., UCLA.
Krishna Mohan, Associate Professor of Marketing; Ph.D., Wisconsin–Madison.
Milo W. Peck Jr., Assistant Professor of Accounting; LL.M., Boston University; CPA.
Patricia M. Poli, Assistant Professor of Accounting; Ph.D., NYU; CPA.
Ipshita Ray, Assistant Professor of Marketing; Ph.D. candidate, Connecticut.
Walter G. Ryba Jr., Professor of Business Law and Dean; J.D., Connecticut.
Carl A. Scheraga, Associate Professor of Business Strategy and Technology Management; Ph.D., Connecticut.
David P. Schmidt, Associate Professor of Ethics; Ph.D., Chicago.
Michael Schumer, Associate Professor of Information Systems and Operations Management; Ph.D., Princeton.
Winston Tellis, Assistant Professor of Information Systems; Ph.D., Nova Southeastern.
Cheryl L. Tromley, Associate Professor of Management; Ph.D., Yale.
Michael T. Tucker, Professor of Finance; D.B.A., Boston University.
Joan L. Van Hise, Assistant Professor of Accounting; Ph.D., NYU.

Fairleigh Dickinson University

Silberman College of Business

Florham–Madison, New Jersey ❖ *Teaneck–Hackensack, New Jersey*

THE M.B.A. AND THE INDIVIDUAL

The Silberman M.B.A. has been crafted to recognize the new reality of a career in business. Today's business school graduate cannot look to organizations for career security but rather must look to his or her own employability. Whether an individual is employed by a large organization or in his or her own business, he or she must think like an entrepreneur, constantly searching for new opportunities. The Silberman M.B.A. provides students with the skills to identify and capitalize on these opportunities. The work of the faculty in developing a curriculum that meets the needs of the individual who has chosen business as a career received national attention in Success magazine, which twice named Silberman College among the twenty-five best business schools in the nation for entrepreneurs.

The College has a high-quality teaching faculty using an innovative curriculum developed for the contemporary business environment. This combination is designed to give each Silberman M.B.A. graduate the competitive edge necessary to maintain his or her employability and to succeed in a global business community that is characterized by rapid technological and social change.

—Paul Lerman, Dean

Programs and Curricular Focus

The Silberman College of Business has been dedicated to providing high-quality innovative programs for more than forty years. The College strives to develop graduates who are prepared to compete in a rapidly changing business environment. The Master of Business Administration curriculum reflects the integrated, cross-functional manner in which contemporary business operates and focuses on linking theory and practice through innovation.

The program is designed to address the complex demands placed on organizations and the individuals who manage them. Global perspectives and ethical concerns of business are integrated into all courses. The development and refinement of student communication skills is an important component of the integrative courses that form the program core. Topics critical to the value creation process, such as entrepreneurship, creativity, and strategic thinking, are introduced early in the program. The influences of politics, the law, the environment, technology, society, and demographic diversity are integrated throughout the program.

Program requirements include successful completion of between 34½

and 60 credits, depending on waiver of core courses. Core courses comprise four tiers: The External and Internal Environment of Business, The Manager's Skill Set, Functional Areas and Technical Core, and Capstone. Students major in one of eleven fields of study and complete breadth courses outside of the field of specialization. Students may choose to fulfill their breadth requirements with courses outside of the College in areas such as corporate communication or foreign language and culture.

Other program offerings include an Executive M.B.A., an Executive M.B.A. in health systems management, an M.S. in taxation, and a one-year, full-time M.B.A. in global management. The College also offers a five-course post-M.B.A. certificate program in eleven subject areas for individuals already holding an M.B.A.

Students and the M.B.A. Experience

❖ Global Focus

In addition to international business courses offered on the New Jersey campuses, M.B.A. students have the opportunity to attend a two-week summer seminar at the University's historic Wroxton College campus in Oxfordshire,

England. During the seminar, students meet with key academic, business, and political leaders and tour major corporate locations. This program immerses students in British culture and invites them to view international business from a different perspective.

Special Features

In addition to traditional majors, the College offers an M.B.A. in pharmaceutical-chemical studies, the only one of its kind in the nation. The program is conducted on the campuses as well as at corporate locations of Bristol-Myers Squibb, Johnson & Johnson, and Bayer. CEOs and other top executives of industry companies meet with students on a weekly basis during each semester. The College's Executive M.B.A. in health systems management, launched in September 1998, is New Jersey's only executive-level program focusing on the management of health systems.

All students enrolled in the College's graduate business programs participate in at least one course on entrepreneurship offered by the Center for Entrepreneurial Studies. Students may choose to select a sequence of courses in this area. Internship opportunities with new ventures are available.

The Faculty

The College's faculty brings a combination of industry experience and academic training to the classroom. The faculty is committed to excellence in teaching. Faculty research interests concentrate on application of theory to business practice and are supported by research centers that include the Center for Human Resource Management, the Center for Entrepreneurship, and the Center for Pharmaceutical-Chemical Studies.

The Business School Network

Corporate Partnerships

Each of the academic departments is guided by a corporate advisory board that works with the faculty in developing the curriculum. Members of the advisory boards are often guest lecturers.

Prominent Alumni

The College counts among its alumni a number of leading corporate executives, including Patrick Zenner, President and CEO, Hoffman-LaRoche, Inc.; Stephen Sudovar, Senior Vice President, Pharmaceuticals Division, Hoffman-LaRoche, Inc.; Ron Dorfler, Senior Vice President and Chief Financial Officer, Capital Cities/ABC Inc.; Dennis Strigl, President and Chief Executive Officer, Bell Atlantic NYNEX Mobile; Richard Swift, Chairman, President, and Chief Executive Officer, Foster Wheeler Corp.; and Ronald Brill, Executive Vice President and Chief Administrative Officer, Home Depot.

The College and Environs

The 115-acre Teaneck–Hackensack Campus stretches along the east and west banks of the Hackensack River. Robison Hall, the Weiner Library, and Alumni Hall sit on the river's east edge, while the College of Business Administration, located in Dickinson Hall, sits on the west edge. The Florham–Madison Campus is a beautifully landscaped park of 187 acres. Its Georgian-style buildings have been adapted to the educational needs of the University. Both Fairleigh Dickinson University (FDU) campuses are located in attractive residential suburbs close to local theaters, restaurants, and sports arenas. Students can easily reach the business, cultural, and social offerings of New York City by private or public transportation.

Wroxton College, the overseas campus of the University, was originally built as an abbey and later became the home of Lord North in the 1700s. It is centrally located in England between Oxford and Stratford-upon-Avon.

Facilities

In recent years, the University has made extensive renovations to its facilities. On the Teaneck–Hackensack Campus, the College resides in a building that underwent a $12-million renovation. College facilities include executive classrooms, three computer laboratories, and a comprehensive business reference library, which includes general and international business reference volumes, annual reports, subject CD-ROMs, business indexes, and online search services.

On the Florham–Madison Campus, the College occupies a major part of a 100-room mansion designed by Stanford White, as well as of the campus' new academic building, which opened in January 1998, where every classroom is hardwired for computers and Internet access.

Technology Environment

Graduate students have access to a Prime 5370, VAX 4000/5000, Sun 490, and DEC Alpha Sable 2100 and a wide variety of software for use independent of campus or location. There are several PC laboratories on each campus. All PCs are connected to a central file server through a local area network with access to the University-wide network and the worldwide Internet.

Placement

The Career Management Center offers career and employment services to all M.B.A. students and alumni. On-campus recruiting programs and career fairs are augmented by a large network of corporate contacts. Computerized databases and resume and interviewing workshops are a regular part of the services offered to M.B.A. students.

Admission

The College considers each candidate's academic record, GMAT score, and professional experience in the admission process. International students whose native language is not English are required to submit a TOEFL score. It is recommended that students have a basic knowledge of statistics; computer usage, including spreadsheets and word processing; and mathematics, including calculus.

Finances

Tuition for most graduate programs in 2000–01 is $597 per credit hour. Books and supplies are approximately $1200 per year. Approximately twenty-five graduate assistantships are available to qualified candidates, offering tuition remission and a stipend.

International Students

International students from twenty-one countries represent 9 percent of the M.B.A. students. Extensive English language preparation and assistance programs are available.

Application Facts and Dates

Applications are accepted on a rolling basis for fall, spring, and summer sessions. For additional information, students should contact:

Office of Graduate Admissions
Fairleigh Dickinson University
1000 River Road–T170A
Teaneck, New Jersey 07666
Telephone: 800-FDU-8803 (toll-free)
E-mail: global education@fdu.edu
World Wide Web: http://www.fdu.edu

FERRIS STATE UNIVERSITY

Ferris State University

College of Business

Big Rapids, Michigan

▶ PREPARING FOR A BRIGHT BUSINESS FUTURE

The mission of the Information Systems Management (ISM) program at Ferris State University (FSU) is to provide high-quality graduate instruction in current technologies and continuous improvement management philosophies in an innovative, stimulating, and globally diverse learning environment. Our ISM program is a superb choice for the manager who wants to understand how complex systems are integrated toward resolution of specific business problems. Learning is continuous in a campus environment that blends leading-edge technology, an experienced faculty, and a globally diverse graduate student body. The ISM program graduates professionals with the skills and understanding to excel into the next century.

—Dr. James Maas, Interim Dean

Programs and Curricular Focus

The Master of Science in information systems management (M.S. ISM) in the College of Business at Ferris State University is a multidiscipline, applied management program that focuses on technical, human, operational, strategic, and information resource management. The M.S. ISM is composed of a core sequence of four courses (13 semester credit hours); a 12-credit-hour, four-course discipline-specific emphasis; and a thesis, a capstone project, or a three-course option (6–9 credit hours).

The core sequence focuses on management issues and techniques in an information-age organization. The program aims to enhance students' abilities to analyze, plan, design, and implement project-focused activities in a competitive business environment by exploring new and emerging technologies. There are many different electives that can be tailored into the following tracks: information system management, networking, and quality. There is a new course track that is designed to introduce applied e-commerce concepts and techniques. The thesis, capstone project, or three-course option is required of all M.S. ISM candidates for completion of the program.

M.S. ISM courses are specially designed to facilitate flexible scheduling of weekend, evening, and Internet options. It is possible for full-time students to graduate in twelve months.

Students and the M.S. Experience

The program consists of both part-time working professionals and full-time students. There are approximately 135 students in the program. The classes vary in size, from one-on-one independent study with an instructor to a more classical classroom environment with about 20 students.

The program has been termed a technical M.B.A. or applied M.B.A. because of its blend of business management issues relating to information systems.

Ferris State University has an agreement with the Hogeschool Enschede in the Netherlands, which allows the M.S. ISM program to be offered partly in Europe, offering students the opportunity to gain international experience.

Special Features

Courses are offered through several course formats, including on-campus (at Big Rapids, Michigan), off-campus (at Grand Rapids and Flint, Michigan), and Internet options. It is possible to complete the program entirely on weekends and through the Internet option. The program allows for the transfer of two graduate classes that are equivalent to the required classes in the program from recognized, accredited colleges, schools, and universities. Students also have the flexibility of being able to join the program at the start of any semester.

The Faculty

Ferris State University has a full-time faculty of nearly 500 instructors teaching in nearly 100 programs. The ISM program is led by senior faculty members of the College of Business who specialize in the following areas: e-commerce, virtual communities, networking and databases, continuous quality improvement, and the use of telecommunications in current businesses.

The Business School Network

The University has been a pioneer in information systems education since 1987. The extensive business experience of the faculty, a close working relationship with an advisory committee of people in industry, and Ferris' long experience in career-related education make this a top option for students looking to pursue the M.S. ISM.

The College and Environs

Founded in 1884, Ferris State University is Michigan's foremost professional and technical university and is located on a 600-acre campus on the banks of the Muskegon River in Mecosta County, midway between Grand Rapids and Cadillac and the northern and southern ends of Michigan's Lower Peninsula. Big Rapids, with a population of 12,600, is in an area rich in recreational activity, with 100 lakes; thousands of acres of open, rolling terrain; woodlands; creeks; and rivers in the vicinity. Nearly 10,000 students are enrolled in the University.

Technology Environment

The program has some of the most up-to-date technologies, including a dynamic Web server, an effective messaging server, an interconnect to Hogeschool Enschede in the Netherlands, and a distance learning server, that make learning through the Internet viable. Classrooms are equipped with network connections that provide easy Web access. Current hardware and software packages are used for the courses taught. Both e-mail addresses and Web pages are provided by the program. While University labs are widely available to ISM students, it is advisable for students to have notebook computers to facilitate classroom learning and project work.

The Abigail S. Timme Library serves as a gateway to a variety of information resources available both on-site and remotely in print and digital formats. Through licensed access to remote Internet sites, library users may view and print full-text articles from more than 1,400 magazine and journal titles. Article abstracts are available for more than 2,000 additional titles. An on-site collection of more than twenty networked CD-ROMs provides further specialization information for library users. Electronic document delivery and interlibrary loan services significantly supplement the library's array of knowledge resources.

Placement

Through the responses of a placement survey, the average placement rate was 99 percent over the past five years in both the United States and international job markets. The University's students have experienced high job placement rates because its programs are tailored to the needs of employers.

Admission

Entrance requirements for the M.S. ISM program are a baccalaureate degree, a minimum GPA of 2.75, and a minimum GPA of 3.0 in prerequisite courses (statistics, management, accounting or finance, computer literacy, and contract law). The applicants' preparatory background is reviewed to ensure that each individual has the education or experience to succeed in emphasis studies. All applicants must also submit official undergraduate and graduate course transcripts, a one-page typed essay explaining the reason for seeking admission, a resume, and three letters of reference. Candidates interested in enrolling in selected M.S. ISM courses may be granted guest admission. Guest application information is available in the graduate program department office (telephone: 231-591-2168). Students whose native language is not English must have a minimum TOEFL score of 500.

Finances

Students should contact the M.S. ISM program office for information regarding graduate assistantships. For information concerning loans and work-study awards, students should contact the FSU Office of Financial Aid, 420 Oak Street, Big Rapids, Michigan 49307-2020 (telephone: 231-591-2110).

International Students

The program is composed of approximately 50 percent international students. Those students who need more information on international affairs can contact the Office of International Affairs at 303 Bishop Hall, 1349 Cramer Circle, Big Rapids, Michigan 49307-2737 (telephone: 231-591-2405; fax: 231-591-2400).

Application Facts and Dates

Applications for M.S. ISM admission should be received by August 1 for the fall semester, December 1 for the winter semester, and April 1 for the summer semester.

For more information, students should contact:

Coordinator M.S. ISM
S-C 101
1420 Knollview Drive
Big Rapids, Michigan 49307-2289
Telephone: 231-591-2168
Fax: 231-591-2973
E-mail: contact@ism.ferris.edu
World Wide Web: http://ism.ferris.edu

Florida International University

Miami, Florida

GLOBAL BUSINESS LEADERSHIP FOR THE TWENTY-FIRST CENTURY

The College of Business Administration (CBA) at Florida International University (FIU) is south Florida's most important resource for global business education, technology, and research, and is especially noted for its unique expertise in Latin American commerce and in information technology. Its distinctive and successful M.B.A. programs offer integrated, international, multicultural, and technology-supported curricula tailored to address the needs of the specific student groups each is designed to serve.

Regardless of the specific M.B.A. program, however, students emerge with a broad and deep understanding of global strategic management and of enterprise-wide, process-oriented, and customer-driven organizations. Graduates become effective members of such enterprises, able to blend pragmatism and creativity in solving increasingly complex business problems. In short, they are ready to exercise global business leadership today and in the twenty-first century.

—Joyce J. Elam, Dean

Programs and Curricular Focus

The College offers academic programs leading to the Master of Accounting (M.Acc.), the Master of Business Administration (M.B.A.), the Master of Science in Finance (M.S.F.), the Master of Science in Taxation (M.S.T.), the Master of Science in Information Systems (M.S.M.S.), and the Master of Science in e-business. It offers an Executive Master of Science in Taxation (E.M.S.T.) and programs that lead to the Doctor of Philosophy (Ph.D.) degree in business administration, with concentrations in information systems and in marketing. All of its degree programs are accredited by the AACSB–The International Association for Management Education.

Options for students interested in pursuing an M.B.A. degree include the International M.B.A. (I.M.B.A.), the Executive M.B.A. (E.M.B.A.), the Evening M.B.A. (EVE.M.B.A.), and the Global e-M.B.A. for managers in the Americas (Web E.M.B.A.). All require 42 to 43 credit hours of graduate course work.

The I.M.B.A., the College's only full-time master's program, is an intensive, twelve-month lock-step program with daytime classes held during six-week and three-week terms. It features international study and internship components and is especially designed for recent college graduates or international

students interested in pursuing full-time study to further their international business careers.

The E.M.B.A., tailored to the mid-level executive with five to eight years of professional experience, is a twenty-one-month, lock-step program that meets four times a month—primarily on Saturdays. The Global e-M.B.A. is a combined residential and Web-based action-oriented program for mid to senior-level executives in enterprises operating in the Americas.

The EVE.M.B.A. program, which serves working professionals in the south Florida community, offers nightly classes (Monday through Thursday), with each course meeting once a week. It is a part-time program. Students taking six courses per year can complete their degrees in about three years.

Through its five academic departments and seven top-notch research and service centers, the College also provides a broad

range of graduate, professional, and executive education; customized training and certificate programs; seminars, short courses, and conferences; and study-abroad and global programs.

Students and the M.B.A. Experience

The College's student body reflects the demographics of south Florida: Hispanic American, 59 percent; African American, 11 percent; Caucasian, 17 percent; international, 9 percent; and other minorities, 4 percent. It is evenly divided between men and women. The average age of the beginning graduate student is 27. Many international students are from Latin America and the Caribbean region.

Students in the full-time I.M.B.A. program include recent college graduates from south Florida, from Latin America, and from throughout the U.S., as well as those who have been in the international workforce for a time and are returning to pursue an advanced degree full-time. This blend of personal and business backgrounds enriches the learning experience for all students.

Most of the students in the part-time EVE.M.B.A. program are from south Florida, are bilingual, and have personal and business ties with one or more Latin American countries. Their academic work is augmented by their active involvement in the M.B.A. Society, which, in addition to social and seminar activities, maintains close contact with alumni and the business community.

The E.M.B.A. program includes managers from large multinational corporations, entrepreneurs, and officers of small firms. Because they represent a variety of industries and professional expertise, they draw and build upon one another's skills and experiences. The Global e-M.B.A. offers executives in the Americas hands-on experience in applying concepts to increase the value of their respective companies.

All M.B.A. programs combine classroom lecture and discussion with case analyses, field work, computer modeling and analysis, e-business technologies, group research projects, computer simulations, role-playing, and

both written and oral presentations. They also incorporate professional development sessions on teamwork, managing diversity, leadership, and communication.

The Faculty

A dynamic force for excellence, the College's faculty of more than 80 scholars, business leaders, and teachers represent more than ten nationalities, as well as 5 Eminent Scholars, 5 Endowed Professors, and internationally known experts in information systems, e-commerce, operations research, knowledge management, financial derivatives, international trade, consumer research, multinational corporations, international management, and corporate responsibility.

The Business School Network

All students benefit from the international character of the College's many partners and alumni in Miami's business community. Because the city links the two Americas with the rest of the global economy, it serves as regional headquarters for hundreds of multinational companies. A major center for international trade, finance, banking, and real estate, the area also supports a healthy travel and tourism industry, a substantial number of entrepreneurial technology firms, and a growing cable television and entertainment industry. If not already working in this environment, students can participate in it through internships, special research projects, field trips, lectures by top executives, and international business forums.

The College is one of only twenty-six business schools to have received a Department of Education grant to support its Center for International Business, Education and Research (CIBER). Its other research and service centers—such as the Center for Banking and Financial Institutions, the Knight Ridder Center for Excellence in Management, the Jerome Bain Real Estate Institute, and the Ryder

Center for Logistics—also give students opportunities for involvement in industry and professional associations.

The College and Environs

The College is the second largest of Florida International University's sixteen schools and colleges, enrolling about 3,600 undergraduate and more than 850 graduate students each year and serving another approximately 400 members of the business community through its executive education programs. The University, a member of the State University System of Florida, is a comprehensive, urban research institution founded in 1972 and has 31,000 students, 1,300 faculty members, and 84,000 alumni from around the world. It offers more than 180 academic degree programs and is the largest university in south Florida.

The College is headquartered in University Park, a 344-acre tract located about 10 miles west of downtown Miami. It also offers programs at its north campus, located on a natural mangrove reserve near Biscayne Bay in North Miami.

Technology Environment

The College's sizeable investments in its Technology Center, computer labs, Knowledge Management Lab, and wireless multimedia case classrooms provide state-of-the-art IT support for students. Laptop computers are required of all M.B.A. students. As a member of the SAP University Alliance, the College has received more than $1 million in software, training, and technical support to integrate a business process perspective using SAP R/3 into its curriculum.

Placement

The University Career Services' automated systems provide employers and students who are not already employed with placement services and networking

opportunities beyond those provided through the College itself. Career Services also sponsors the M.B.A. Forum, which enables M.B.A. students to hear employers describe career opportunities in their respective organizations and industries.

Admission

Applicants who are considered for admission to the M.B.A. programs must submit a formal application and application fee and must have, at a minimum, a bachelor's degree from a regionally accredited college or university; high promise of success in graduate studies, as determined by the faculty; official transcripts from every college or university attended; and a minimum combination of the Graduate Management Admission Test (GMAT) or Graduate Record Examinations (GRE) score and upper division grade point average (GPA). Exceptions may be made for E.M.B.A. and Global e-M.B.A. applicants. Students whose native language is not English must also obtain a minimum score of 500 on the TOEFL (173 computer-based), or an equivalent score on a comparable exam. Additional criteria vary and reflect the nature of the specific program.

Finances

Different tuition and fee structures apply to each program. For the part-time EVE.M.B.A. program, summer 2000 tuition per credit hour was $144.96 for Florida residents and $505.69 for nonresidents, with additional charges for student fees. These figures are subject to change without notice. Tuition and fees for the other M.B.A. programs vary depending on the program. Financial aid is available for qualified students in some programs.

Application Facts and Dates

For program and application information and materials, interested students should contact the relevant program office:

College of Business Administration
Ryder Business Building
Florida International University
University Park
Miami, Florida 33199
Telephone: 305-348-2754
TDD via FRS: 800-955-8771 (toll-free)
World Wide Web: http://www.fiu.edu/~mba

Florida State University

College of Business

Tallahassee, Florida

GROWTH, INTEGRITY, AND SUCCESS

Florida State University (FSU) has an international reputation as one of the nation's top graduate institutions. The College of Business at Florida State University is committed to preparing M.B.A. students to respond to rapidly changing technologies and the turbulent global marketplace. The M.B.A. program focuses on meeting these challenges through teaching excellence, opportunities for leadership roles, and interactions with top-level executives. The nationally and internationally recognized M.B.A. faculty represents a core of individuals who are committed to the growth, integrity, and success of each M.B.A. student. As you develop personally and in your professional career, I encourage you to explore the challenges of Florida State University's M.B.A. program.

—Pamela L. Perrewé, Jim Moran Professor of Management and Associate Dean for Graduate Programs

Programs and Curricular Focus

As the twentieth century evolves into the twenty-first, the world of business is evolving as well. More than at any other time in history, technology is advancing so rapidly that this new world of business needs new leaders who can respond quickly and adapt creatively to incredible new challenges and opportunities. The Florida State University College of Business provides an accelerated and concentrated M.B.A. program to help students prepare to enter and excel in the global marketplace.

In one year (three semesters), full-time students can receive an M.B.A. with a specific concentration (e.g., finance or entrepreneurship). Students may also receive a general M.B.A. by selecting electives from different areas. Progressing with the same group of students all year, they develop lifelong relationships in a program that emphasizes team building and camaraderie. An outstanding faculty with diverse backgrounds and excellent relationships with the business world guides student teams.

The College of Business offers a 43-hour M.B.A. program for applicants with prior undergraduate business degrees or equivalent course work. The program is also offered on a part-time evening basis in Tallahassee and Panama City, Florida. In conjunction with the College of Law, there is a four-year program leading to the J.D./M.B.A.

Students and the M.B.A. Experience

M.B.A. students at Florida State University bring diverse academic, professional, and personal backgrounds to the M.B.A. programs. The 2000 full-time program had an entering class of more than 50 M.B.A. students. The part-time M.B.A. programs bring the total enrollment up to approximately 150 students. Women comprise approximately 35 percent of the class, and minority and international students comprise approximately 20 percent. The 2000 M.B.A. class represented six countries outside the United States. The average age of the M.B.A. students is 28.5, and the average full-time work experience is 5.5 years.

The small class sizes encourage teamwork, participation, and individual attention. The typical teaching methods in the M.B.A. classes include group projects, case analyses, lectures, and student presentations.

The Faculty

The College of Business faculty members have strong academic and professional backgrounds. Many have held positions in business or government and have been educated at many of the best academic institutions in the world. Faculty members concentrate on both research and teaching. Florida State University emphasizes small classes and strong student-faculty interaction. Faculty members work closely with students on corporate research projects, professional presentations, and career decision making.

The Business School Network

The Florida State University College of Business has strong relationships with corporate leaders and alumni. The College hosts the Charles A. Bruning Distinguished Speaker Series, which brings esteemed business leaders to the campus. These lecturers include executives of major corporations, entrepreneurs, and national and international figures in the business world. Students have the opportunity to organize and attend roundtable discussions with each speaker.

The College of Business is served by three distinguished centers: The DeSantis Center for Executive Education, the Jim Moran Institute for Global Entrepreneurship, and the Center for Human Resource Management. These centers conduct research into the latest developments in business and industry, provide professional support to businesses, and advise the deans and faculty members on trends and issues in the business world. The M.B.A. program also has its own alumni association that is guided by the MBA Advisory Council, a group of involved alumni who provide assistance in resource development, career opportunities for students, admissions, and curriculum. Florida State has also recently formed a prestigious M.B.A. Regional Directors group, which provides assistance for their M.B.A. program through their corporate connections within their respective regions in the United States.

The College and Environs

A city of great Southern charm and beauty, Tallahassee is home to Florida State University. With a population approaching 200,000, the city is nestled in rolling hills and deep verdant forests. Florida State University is less than an hour's drive from the Gulf of Mexico, which claims some of the most beautiful beaches in the world. For cultural pursuits, Tallahassee residents enjoy the world-class music, arts, and film programs at FSU. Tallahassee also serves as the capital of Florida, which brings a flurry of political activity every year during the legislative season.

Facilities

M.B.A. students have access to the Florida State University Library system that consists of a main library, the Robert Manning Strozier Library, four branch libraries, and a law library. Strozier Library and its branch libraries include more than 2 million volumes of books and periodicals for researcher use. It is a member of the Center for Research Libraries. The College of Business has recently opened its Technology Center, which occupies 10,000 square feet of space in the Rovetta Business Building. The facility houses 170 computer systems laboratories and two computer classrooms. M.B.A. students also have access to the Graduate Computer Lab. Classrooms are also equipped with the latest in multimedia equipment.

Placement

Florida State University's M.B.A. program is committed to helping students make contacts in the business world and develop successful career strategies. Through the MBA Career Placement Office, students receive personalized assistance with job searches and in resume preparation. Students can improve their interviewing skills through videotaped mock interviews. Other opportunities available to students are on-campus interviewing, Seminole Futures, a daylong career exposition, and consortia.

Admission

The program's admission policy is intended to ensure that incoming classes are composed of highly qualified students who represent diverse backgrounds in undergraduate institutions, work experience, and accomplishments. Admission to the program requires an undergraduate degree in business or equivalent foundation course work, with an excellent academic record and GMAT score and a minimum of two years of full-time work experience in a professional or supervisory role. Students with undergraduate degrees in a nonbusiness field must complete a core of business foundation courses before acceptance into the program is granted. International students must take the TOEFL.

Finances

Tuition, books, and fees for the full-time one-year program for Florida residents are approximately $10,000. Non-Florida residents pay approximately $25,000. These fees do not include living expenses in the Tallahassee area. The College of Business offers a limited number of assistantships to full-time students. These awards, which are based on academic excellence, include a stipend of approximately $1450 per term, plus tuition waivers for 9 semester hours each term. The University also offers several fellowship and assistantship opportunities.

International Students

The International Student and Scholar Center at Florida State University coordinates international activities on campus, provides advising about immigration requirements, and assists students and their families with cultural adjustment, employment matters, and personal issues. For additional information, students should write to International Student and Scholar Center, Florida State University, 107 South Wildwood Street, Tallahassee, Florida 32306-4240.

Application Facts and Dates

Admission to the full-time program is for the summer semester only. The part-time program begins each spring. The final deadline to apply for the full-time program is March 1 and is October 1 for the part-time programs. Full-time students seeking assistantships and financial aid are encouraged to have their completed application submitted by January 15. For additional information, students should contact:

Graduate Office
College of Business
Florida State University
Tallahassee, Florida 32306-1110
Telephone: 850-644-6458
Fax: 850-644-0915
E-mail: gradprog@cob.fsu.edu
World Wide Web: http://www.cob.fsu.edu/grad/

Fordham University

> ### URBI ET ORBI—FOR THE CITY AND THE WORLD
>
> *This headline is one of the first tangible examples of the total redesign of our school. We are committed to making Fordham's Graduate School of Business Administration (GBA) a leading, world-class business school and are moving toward that goal.*
>
> *Our close ties to New York companies help position us as New York City's business ambassador to the world.*
>
> *As for our students, we know each of them, care about each one's future, and are devoted to doing all we can to insure their success in business, at every level, in any country of the world.*
>
> —Ernest J. Scalberg, Dean

Programs and Curricular Focus

Concern for quality drives Fordham's M.B.A. program. Through the required courses of the program, students acquire the knowledge and basic skills necessary to become leaders in business. In the classroom, faculty members teach fundamental theory and current research tied to pragmatic solutions, so students master both abstract and applied methods of thinking.

Students also develop expertise in a specific field by taking a concentration in one of six areas: accounting, communications and media management, finance, information and communications systems, management systems, and marketing. An International Business Designation is also available as a complement to a student's selected area of concentration. Fordham's course of study is organized on a trimester system (three terms per year) commencing in September, January, and April. Each student can decide how quickly he or she earns the Fordham M.B.A. A full-time student may complete the program in fifteen to eighteen months.

The 60-credit M.B.A. degree program has eight courses (24 credits) in the core business curriculum, including fundamentals of accounting, financial environment, information systems, business law, marketing management, operations management, and business policy. Upper-level courses in a student's selected concentration, together with electives both in and out of that concentration, fill out the M.B.A. program.

Fordham offers an eighteen-month Deming Scholars M.B.A. Program in Quality Management, a joint J.D./M.B.A. program with Fordham Law School, and an M.S. in taxation. A 90-credit M.B.A. in

Taxation and Accounting combines the M.B.A. in accounting with the M.S. in taxation to prepare students to be taxation professionals.

The 2000–01 academic year heralds the fifth year of Fordham's Global Professional Master of Business Administration (GP-MBA). Enrollment in the GP-MBA has tripled since its inception, attesting to the program's success. This 69-credit program is designed for individuals planning a career in international business and responds to the growing demand for M.B.A.'s in the global marketplace.

An exciting new executive-style program that Fordham offers is geared toward advanced professionals and managers. The Transnational M.B.A. (T.M.B.A.) is for students who either have five or more years of business experience or are on a fast track to upper-level managerial positions. This program features forms of distance learning, with classes held one weekend per month at a New York–area executive retreat setting.

With the Beijing M.B.A., Fordham's Graduate School of Business Administration is serving as the lead school in a consortium of twenty-six U.S. Jesuit universities that offer an M.B.A. program in Beijing, China. Fordham is the degree-granting institution in this program.

Fordham GBA and the American Graduate School of International Management (Thunderbird) have forged a partnership in order to offer a dual-degree program, the M.B.A. and the Master in International Management (M.I.M.).

Students and the M.B.A. Experience

The total student population of Fordham's graduate business school is approximately 1,500, with 300 attending on a full-time basis and 1,200 attending on a part-time basis. The average age is 28; 38 percent are women. Students representing more than thirty countries comprise nearly 30 percent of the full-time student body.

On average, Fordham business students have had six years of work experience. As a consequence, many classroom discussions are enriched by students contributing their own on-the-job experiences.

The Faculty

Fordham has 90 full-time faculty members, 96 percent of whom hold a Ph.D. or a similar terminal degree. Women comprise 27 percent of the group. Approximately one third of the faculty members have origins in Western Europe, South America, and Asia. The adjunct faculty pool totals 87, with approximately 50 teaching in a given trimester.

Many members of the faculty serve as consultants to a variety of industries as well as to international governments and institutions. The diverse backgrounds of the faculty members provide a multicultural teaching field, with an emphasis on global standards and practices.

The Business School Network

Because of Fordham's graduate business school's location in New York City, which many consider the business capital of the world, students have easy access to a "who's who" of corporate leaders and Wall Street executives who visit the campus regularly.

Corporate Partnerships

In addition to guest speakers in classes, at seminars, and in panel discussions, students are able to take advantage of several formal programs that provide business contacts: the Mentoring Program, which sponsors one-on-one relationships between individual students and executives; the Field Study Program, in which teams of students solve problems for real corporate assignments; the Master in Taxation and Accounting (M.T.A.) program, funded largely by the accounting and tax industries that then hire

Fordham at Lincoln Center, looking south to the World Trade Center.

the program's graduates; and the Global Fellowship program, which provides fellowships where students work for international companies in developing nations on a pro-bono basis.

Prominent Alumni

Standard and Poor's most recent Executive/College Survey ranked Fordham in the top forty U.S. colleges and universities and number one in Jesuit institutions with the largest alumni representation in leading executive positions. *U.S. News & World Report*'s 1998 overall rankings placed Fordham's Graduate School of Business Administration among the top 20 percent in the country and ranked Fordham GBA's part-time program fourteenth nationally.

The College and Environs

Fordham's Graduate School of Business Administration was established in 1969 and

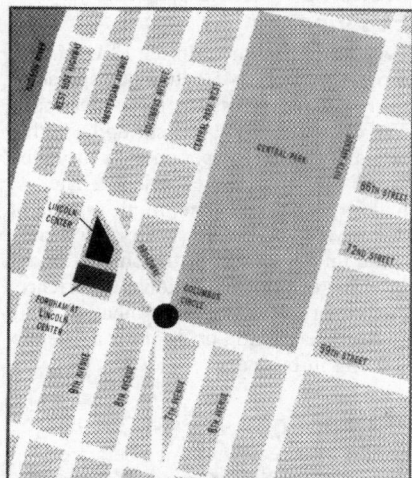
Fordham at Lincoln Center, with Columbus Circle and Central Park.

is founded on the Jesuit tradition of high-quality education. Fordham's business school is located at Lincoln Center on a 7-acre green campus that marks the southern border of the cultural heart of New York City.

The Lincoln Center campus consists of the academic building, the residence hall, and the School of Law, all of which are connected by a central plaza that serves as an island of calm in a city of skyscrapers. It is one block from Central Park and Columbus Circle, a major transportation hub in midtown Manhattan.

Placement

Fordham's Career Services Office offers individual counseling, workshops, and mock interview sessions to guide students in the subtleties of networking, information gathering, and interviewing.

Panel discussions by industry representatives provide the chance to learn about career opportunities and trends in particular areas of academic concentration. In the Mentor Program, students talk to top business executives, one-on-one, to obtain career advice and guidance.

Admission

The principal elements that define a Fordham student are academic and professional accomplishments, clearly defined career objectives, motivation, and personal integrity. Each candidate must possess the U.S. equivalent of a four-year baccalaureate degree and must have taken the Graduate Management Admission Test (GMAT). The candidate's academic record, GMAT scores, personal statements, professional recommendations, and work experience are considered in the admission process. The average GMAT score of those admitted in 2000 was 600.

Applicants from non-English-speaking countries must submit the results of the Test of English as a Foreign Language (TOEFL). The minimum TOEFL score accepted is 250.

Finances

The annual tuition for a full-time student in 2000–01 is $28,125 for 45 credit hours of study. The average part-time student completes 18 credits per year, which costs $11,160 in 2000–01. The estimated cost of fees, insurance, books, and supplies is $1550 per year. Off-campus housing, although greatly varied, is estimated to cost $14,400.

Fordham uses the Free Application for Federal Student Aid (FAFSA) to determine the need of each student for any scholarship, graduate assistantship, or loan, thus the FAFSA should be filed as soon as possible. Deadlines and requirements differ based on the specific aid program.

International Students

Forty percent of Fordham's full-time M.B.A. student population comes from other countries; more than thirty countries are represented in the School. The International Student Society, which is self-governing, hosts multicultural events and takes advantage of New York City's international character for its many social and business activities.

Application Facts and Dates

Application deadlines are June 1 for the September trimester, November 1 for the January trimester, and March 1 for the April trimester for part-time applicants only. Decisions are made on a rolling basis. Notification is usually within one month after application is completed.

International students are asked to submit their application one month prior to the regular deadlines, and they must also provide documentation that they have the resources to pay for their studies prior to receiving their visa. For more information, students should contact:

Dean of Admissions
Graduate School of Business
    Administration
Fordham University
33 West 60th Street, 4th Floor
New York, New York 10023
Telephone: 212-636-6200
Fax: 212-636-7076
E-mail: admissionsgb@fordham.edu
World Wide Web: http://www.bnet.
    fordham.edu

Frostburg State University

LEARNING TO DEAL WITH CHANGE

Noted psychologist B. F. Skinner observed that "education is what survives when what has been learned has been forgotten." Learned facts constitute transitory knowledge that dissipates over time. In today's world, business textbooks are hardly published before they seem quaint and dated. Learning how to deal with change and, in fact, how to be a change agent are lessons that will stand the managers of the twenty-first century in good stead. Frostburg State University's M.B.A. program focuses on the development of a change perspective, utilizing a generalist foundation with a behavioral emphasis. Personal growth and development are emphasized in the belief that good management is founded on an awareness of self and the ability to work with others. FSU's M.B.A. program is the right choice for those who see people as an organization's most valuable asset and effective process as the key to success.

—Steven P. Wilkinson, Dean, School of Business

Programs and Curricular Focus

The Frostburg State University M.B.A. program focuses on a learning process that entails identification and analysis of the pertinent issues facing today's managers, development of a sensitivity to the environmental factors that influence the prospect of implementation, and recognition of the criticality of being able to effectively communicate one's findings and perspective. All of this occurs within the context of change as a given—that one must possess the capacity to deal with uncertainty, working with change to enhance the prospect of success. The program acknowledges that students do, and will, work in a variety of organizational environments, including the public sector, not-for-profits, and private enterprises extending from the entrepreneurial to the large corporate setting.

To that end, students are introduced to a broad-based, generalist understanding of the organizational environment. Concurrently, the program focuses on skill development, particularly in terms of creative problem solving; self awareness and interpersonal capabilities; and the capacity to communicate effectively. Students are challenged to appreciate the desirability of diversity and the reality that there is seldom, if ever, a single right answer. Extensive use of the case study method assists in providing a practitioner perspective as well as the recognition of the complexity of situations with which students are regularly confronted. The goal is to enable students to develop

competencies that will enhance their effectiveness across a range of organizational settings.

The program of study consists of sixteen 3-credit courses organized into a unified and coherent body of knowledge, skills, and processes. Flexible sequencing gives the student some control over scheduling while providing the greatest benefit through the potential to build upon prior knowledge and experience. The final two courses are integrative in nature: one, case-based; the other, a real-world application in a consulting mode. They provide the student different opportunities to synthesize and apply the body of knowledge and developed skills acquired in the previous fourteen courses.

The program assumes that incoming students have no prior academic training in business fields; hence, all courses are required. However, in the event that a student has prior relevant course work, it is possible to transfer up to 9 hours of graduate credit as well as to prove proficiency through testing in up to 12 hours of course work. Joint-degree programs are offered in nursing and accounting.

The courses in the program provide a balanced offering of functional content and behavioral considerations. Overarching themes include an appreciation of the need to analyze, synthesize, and integrate information effectively; the importance of individual participation; the necessity of being able to perform as an effective team member; and the capacity to think

in terms of processes. Students are assessed on their ability to identify and solve problems logically, coherently, and creatively; their use of technology; their ability to convey thoughts both orally and in written form; and their capacity to work productively with others.

FSU's M.B.A. program offers the student an intimate environment in which to pursue his or her educational goals. The average class size of 14 permits extensive interaction, not only between the professor and the class, but also among the students themselves, providing a participative learning environment that facilitates the gaining of knowledge. Furthermore, reflecting the program's commitment to fostering the learning process, professors pride themselves on their availability to students whenever assistance is needed (not constrained to "office hours").

To ease planning, all of the courses in the program are offered every semester (fall, spring, and summer) in three locations (Frostburg, Hagerstown, and Frederick, Maryland). The program has done so for more than twenty-five years. Classes meet once a week in the evening (Monday through Thursday) and are scheduled so it is possible to take two classes an evening.

Students and the M.B.A. Experience

Typically, enrollment in the FSU M.B.A. program is about 450 students, spread fairly equally across the three locations. The diversity of the student body, both in terms of age and experience, contributes to the vitality of the experience. The majority work full-time, in all aspects of the private and public sectors. Women make up 42 percent of the student body. In terms of prior educational experience, three quarters of the department's students have little or no prior academic training in business.

The Faculty

FSU's M.B.A. faculty members are distinguished by the extent of their real-world experience. In addition to their academic training, all have held managerial positions and worked outside of the

university community. The program is committed to this form of credentialing because of the positive impact it has on the learning environment. By having faculty members who are not only knowledgeable but also adept at merging theory and practice, relevance and the prospect of effective application of skills and concepts are enhanced. The diversity of the students is mirrored by the faculty, with almost half being women, and the breadth of experience extending to the public, private, and not-for-profit sectors.

The Business School Network
Given the practical orientation of the M.B.A. program, interaction with the local business and organizational communities is essential. Advisory boards, made up of local executives, provide valuable perspectives regarding what the program emphasis should be to best prepare managers. The program orientation is, in part, a product of that

input. The requirement that students focus on the problems and opportunities faced by real organizations constitutes a significant portion of the overall curriculum. The final course in the program engages the student in consultative work for a local firm or organization. Students may also draw upon the program's linkage with the Small Business Development Institute as an opportunity for connections as well as applied knowledge. The program is committed to the fact that, as this is a professional degree, it must be practiced, not simply conceptualized.

The College and Environs
Founded in 1898, Frostburg State University currently offers degrees in thirty-four fields, serving approximately 4,600 undergraduates and 900 graduate students.

The main campus of Frostburg State University is nestled in the beautiful mountains of western Maryland. Leisure time tends to be spent in the great outdoors, with skiing, white-water rafting, golfing, fishing, boating, and hiking all easily accessible. Western Maryland is the home of Deep Creek Resort and hosts a major country western festival each year. Baltimore; Washington, D.C.; and Pittsburgh are all within 2½ hours' drive.

The Frederick site is located 45 minutes from major entertainment, cultural, and social events taking place in Washington, D.C., and Baltimore, Maryland. The Hagerstown campus is located between Frostburg and Frederick, about 1½ hours outside the nation's capital. Frostburg State University is situated in an area rich in historical significance, with major Revolutionary and Civil War sites located throughout the region.

Placement
The Office of Career Services is available to both graduate and undergraduate students to help with employment issues.

Admission
Students admitted to the M.B.A. program must have an undergraduate degree from a regionally accredited institution and a 2.5 GPA (those with less than a 2.5 GPA may request conditional admission). Students whose native language is not English must demonstrate competence in English through the TOEFL. The GMAT is not required for admission. At least two years of full-time work experience is highly recommended.

Finances
Graduate fees for the main campus are $214 an hour for in-state and $242 an hour for out-of-state students. Fees for the satellite campuses in Hagerstown and Frederick are $180 an hour for in-state and $208 an hour for out-of-state students. An application fee of $30 applies to all incoming students. Room and board for on-campus living in Frostburg are approximately $1730 per semester. These prices apply for the 2000–01 academic year.

Application Facts and Dates
Students may enter the M.B.A. program in any semester: fall, spring, or summer. More specific information about registration fees and deadlines can be obtained by contacting:

Dave Nicol, Department Chair
The M.B.A. Department
College of Business
Frostburg State University
Frostburg, Maryland 21532-1099
Telephone: 301-687-4375
Fax: 301-687-4486
E-mail: mba@frostburg.edu

George Mason University

Fairfax, Virginia

A UNIVERSITY FOR TOMORROW

Our programs provide a solid business core curriculum with strong emphasis on communication and information technologies, entrepreneurial thinking, and the social and cultural aspects of global business.

—Dr. Teresa Domzal, Dean

Programs and Curricular Focus

Students in the M.B.A. program at George Mason University's School of Management are challenged to develop the strategic thinking skills necessary to take advantage of the opportunities created by information technology and an increasingly global marketplace. The M.B.A. program stresses creativity, analytical proficiency, and effective communication combined with a team-oriented learning environment to prepare graduates for today's dynamic business community. The experience is enhanced through alliances GMU has forged with one of the nation's most prosperous and fastest growing economic regions.

The 51-credit-hour curriculum includes eleven core courses designed to solidify students' understanding of a broad range of business principles and practices. These courses cover the spectrum of business functions, from accounting, finance, and operations through marketing, organizational behavior, and strategy. From this foundation, students move on to master an area of interest through six elective courses. Specializations are offered in the areas of enterprise management, financial management, information systems management, and market and business development. Students also have the opportunity to take courses on other topics, such as entrepreneurship, small business consulting, and international business.

Second-year George Mason M.B.A. students participate in a weeklong international residency for academic credit. The international residency, led by a School of Management faculty member, provides students an in-depth look at the impact of the multinational corporation on the current business climate.

Interwoven throughout every course is an emphasis on the impact of information technology, global sensitivity, and entrepreneurial spirit. A cohort class structure promotes interaction between students and faculty members. No single teaching style dominates. Professors use instructional techniques best suited to the subject matter and needs of the students. Typical classes use small groups and cases to support theoretical learning.

Students complete the program in three years on a part-time basis.

Students and the M.B.A. Experience

Approximately 250 M.B.A. students bring strong academic and professional backgrounds to the GMU M.B.A. program. Students have undergraduate degrees in a broad range of disciplines. Typical classes have consisted of majors in humanities and social science (22 percent), business (25 percent), engineering and science (25 percent), and other (28 percent). The typical student is 31 years old and has more than seven years of professional work experience. The program's diversity and team-oriented environment provide for a dynamic learning experience.

The Faculty

The location and entrepreneurial philosophy of George Mason University have attracted a diverse and accomplished business faculty. The men and women are active researchers and stimulating teachers who are eager to share their knowledge and professional accomplishments with students. Easy access to professors is the norm in the M.B.A. program.

The College and Environs

George Mason University's serene, 677-acre wooded campus is located 16 miles west of Washington D.C., in the booming high-technology suburbs of northern Virginia. Washington, D.C. is only a 20-minute drive away and provides students with a multitude of cultural, social, culinary, and entertainment options. Northern Virginia is home to a booming business and technology center and is only a short drive to many points of interest. The history and physical beauty of the state of Virginia are readily accessible. Major cities such as New York and Philadelphia are within a few hours of the campus. The beautiful coastal communities of Maryland and North Carolina are close by, as are the mountains and ski resorts of West Virginia and Pennsylvania. For other destinations, GMU is only 20 minutes away from Washington's two major airports.

A glass atrium links two sections of Enterprise Hall, which houses the School of Management.

The $30-million Johnson Learning Center combines state-of-the-art open space library with retail, recreational, and food service space.

George Mason University enrolls almost 24,000 students in 104 degree programs. The University has emerged as one of the most innovative and visionary institutions in the state and the nation.

Technology Environment

The University's modern and multiple computer facilities are augmented by the School of Management's exclusive LAN. This network links students with the University, faculty members, each other, and the outside world through the Internet. Students use Lotus Notes for e-mail and for creating databases for classes and group projects. Most students use the network to complete large portions of class projects on line, improving the efficiency of collaborative group projects. The School's virtual environment extends into the classroom, with many professors setting up databases to post class notes, current articles, and readings. These databases are also used to continue classroom discussions in between sessions.

Students also have access to proprietary databases such as Compustat PC Plus, Bloomberg, and LEXIS-NEXIS. The University and the School of Management use the Microsoft Office Suite, including Word, Excel, Access, and PowerPoint.

Placement

The Career Services Office (CSO) is a proactive partner in a graduate student's career development. The CSO provides information sessions, resume critiques, individual career counseling, a resource room/video library, and an array of career workshops. Twice a year, the CSO coordinates on-campus recruiting, which includes mock interviews, corporate briefing sessions, and on-campus interviews. Graduate students also have access to an online jobs/internships database, an online Resume Referral Service, a regional employer symposium, a fifteen-university M.B.A. recruiting consortium, and ongoing internship opportunities with local companies.

Admission

The program seeks applicants with diverse academic, professional, ethnic, and national backgrounds. The academic record, GMAT/TOEFL scores, communication skills, and work experience are evaluated for admission to the program. The mean GMAT and TOEFL scores of enrolled students are 620 and 635, respectively. Applicants must hold a degree equivalent to an American bachelor's degree that requires at least four years of study at the university level. Applicants whose native language is not English must submit a TOEFL score. Detailed instructions for international applicants are found in the application.

Finances

Tuition for the 1999–2000 academic year was $257 per credit hour for Virginia residents and $521 per credit hour for nonresidents. Books and software cost approximately $600 per year. Off-campus housing, estimated at $8000 per year, is abundant and a popular choice of graduate business students. Assistance in finding housing is available.

Application Facts and Dates

Early applications are strongly encouraged due to the rolling nature of the admissions process. The application deadline is April 1 for fall and November 1 for spring. For more information, students should contact:

School of Management Admissions
Mailstop 5A2
George Mason University
Fairfax, Virginia 22030-4444
Telephone: 703-993-2136
Fax: 703-993-1886
E-mail: masonbiz@som.gmu.edu
World Wide Web: http://www.som.gmu.edu

Georgetown University

THE M.B.A. FOR THE GLOBAL MARKETPLACE

▶ *Business seeks leaders who have the tools to perform critical analysis, the vision to plan and implement strategically, and the global awareness to compete in tomorrow's marketplace. The new Georgetown M.B.A. curriculum meets the needs of business and prepares students for professional success. The Georgetown Program provides a rigorous education for the future, a future in which every industry is international, every economic issue is global, and every major corporation is multinational. Through four team-based, integrative experiences; thread courses in international business as well as technology and knowledge management; an extensive selection of six-week and twelve-week elective courses; and a "Global Experience" that combines one week of international field-based learning with twelve weeks of related course work, Georgetown delivers an M.B.A. for the global marketplace.*

Programs and Curricular Focus

The Georgetown M.B.A. Program is a 60-credit, full-time program. Students complete all requirements for the degree in two academic years. Required courses are taught during the first year to give Georgetown M.B.A. students the best academic preparation for their summer internships. Electives are offered as six-week module courses or twelve-week semester courses. Almost half of the program is made up of elective course work. The Georgetown M.B.A. focuses on business knowledge applied in an international context through its integrative experiences, the non-U.S. field-based learning exercise, the international business course, the Washington, D.C., location, and the diversity of both its students and faculty.

In addition to electives offered by the School of Business, students often enroll in other University courses that focus on international or business issues. To enhance opportunities to pursue regional interests in global business, qualified M.B.A. students are able to receive graduate elective credit for courses offered in various area studies programs or in the International Business Diplomacy Certificate Program. Opportunities to study abroad during the summer or semester are sponsored by the School.

In conjunction with the Georgetown University Law Center and the School of Foreign Service, there are a four-year program leading to the J.D./M.B.A. degree and a three-year program leading

to the M.B.A./M.S.F.S. degree, respectively. A three-year M.B.A./M.P.P. degree and a five-year M.D./M.B.A. are also offered. The International Executive M.B.A. Program is an eighteen-month M.B.A. program for students with a minimum of eight years of work experience. The Georgetown M.B.A. Program is accredited by AACSB–The International Association for Management Education.

Students and the M.B.A. Experience

Georgetown M.B.A. students bring diverse academic, professional, and personal backgrounds to the program. The fall 1999 entering class numbered 257 and represented every region of the U.S. as well as thirty-six countries. Forty percent of the students are non-U.S. citizens, and 87 percent have nonnative language proficiency and/or have lived or studied abroad. Women comprise 36 percent of the class, and minorities represent 11 percent. The average age of the students is 28, and 97 percent of the class has had one year or more of professional, full-time, postbaccalaureate experience, averaging 4.9 years. The diverse backgrounds of Georgetown M.B.A. students contribute greatly to the curricular and cocurricular aspects of the program through class participation, group work, and student activities.

Small class sizes encourage student participation and interaction. Teaching methodology includes case study and

lecture style. Group projects are an integral part of the curriculum.

The Faculty

The School of Business faculty members have strong academic and professional backgrounds. Many have held positions in business or government; lived, worked, or studied abroad; and been educated at many of the best academic institutions around the world. Faculty members concentrate on both research and teaching.

Georgetown University traditionally emphasizes strong student-faculty interaction. School of Business faculty members are available to students, working together with them on research projects and career decision making. Faculty members also serve as advisers to student clubs in the M.B.A. program, where their expertise in functional areas serves as a great resource for students planning events of professional interest.

The Business School Network

The Georgetown School of Business has developed strong ties with local, national, and international business leaders. The School's location in Washington, D.C., is an asset for the M.B.A. program. The program's relationship with business and government provides students with opportunities for on-site projects, internships, and guest speakers.

The School of Business is served by three distinguished boards: the Board of Visitors, the Graduate Advisory Board, and the Parents Council. The boards advise the Dean on a broad range of issues related to strategy, program enhancement, faculty, curriculum, resource development, and student career opportunities.

The Center for Business-Government Relations, the Center for International Business, the Connelly Program in Business Ethics, the Credit Research Center, the *Journal of International Business Studies*, and the Global Entrepreneurship Program also serve as research and program arms of the business school.

The College and Environs

Georgetown's main campus is located in the heart of the historic Georgetown area of Washington, D.C., alongside the Potomac River. The home of the School of Business, Old North, was constructed in 1795 and is the oldest surviving University building. It is a designated historic landmark. The new Graduate Center in the historic Car Barn adds four state-of-the-art case rooms as well as a new student lounge and MBA computer center.

Washington is a world crossroads for political and corporate leaders. As the seat of the federal government, Washington is the headquarters of many international organizations and major corporations. It provides an ideal laboratory for the study of global management issues and business-government relations.

Facilities

The Washington, D.C., area offers excellent research facilities, including the Library of Congress, trade and professional organizations, agencies and departments of the federal government, foreign embassies, and many businesses. Georgetown M.B.A. students have access to six University libraries, including the Lauinger Library, which houses the School of Business collection. Lauinger has more than 2 million volumes, 2.6 million microforms, 435,400 government documents, 26,000 current serials, and seats 1,350. The School of Business Technology Center contains the Boland Information Systems Laboratory (BISL) and the Decision Support Center (DSC). These computer labs are for use by the students and faculty members of the business school and have approximately 100 IBM-compatible computers. Every unit is connected to a local area network with a broad range of application software and access to the University's minicomputer and mainframe. Internet access and other external information services such as Dow Jones News/Retrieval Service, LEXIS-NEXIS, and Bloomberg are also available. Students can also access the School network by laptop computer in the case-study classrooms and the M.B.A. lounge.

Placement

M.B.A. career management professionals are available to assist and advise students in developing and attaining their career goals. Through individual and group sessions as well as special programs and events, first- and second-year M.B.A. students develop the skills needed to make sound career decisions and conduct effective job searches. Career management services available to M.B.A. students include consortium events, the alumni database, career advising, career information, workshops, on-campus recruiting, the Hoya-Link electronic resume database, the M.B.A. Career Extravaganza, resume books, and summer internships.

Ninety-three percent of the 2000 Georgetown M.B.A. graduates had employment offers by graduation. The median annual salary, exclusive of sign-on bonuses, commissions, and other benefits, was $81,000 for the class of 2000. More than 110 companies recruited on campus during 1999–2000.

While career services are available to all students, international students should be aware that job opportunities in the United States are limited by the type of visa they hold.

Admission

Men and women holding baccalaureate degrees from accredited colleges or universities are eligible for consideration for admission. Georgetown seeks a diverse student body and encourages applications from students with a wide variety of academic backgrounds including the liberal arts and sciences and business.

Academic qualifications are determined by the previous higher education record as indicated by transcripts, letters of recommendation, and results of the Graduate Management Admission Test (GMAT). In addition, international applicants are required to submit results from the TOEFL unless they have obtained an academic degree from a university in a country where English is the native language.

Selection also depends upon an applicant's distinctive achievements, ideas, talents, and motivation for graduate business education. Professional experience, while not required, strengthens an application. International experience, foreign languages, writing ability, interpersonal skills, leadership ability, and entrepreneurship are some favored qualifications. The Admissions Committee seeks to admit students representing various geographic, economic, racial, religious, and minority groups.

Finances

Tuition, fees, books, supplies, transportation, and living expenses for the 2000–01 academic year are approximately $42,000.

The School of Business awards scholarships on the basis of merit. All applicants who are offered admission are considered for scholarship awards; no additional application materials are necessary. Both U.S. citizens and international students are considered for scholarships.

The Georgetown University Office of Student Financial Services attempts to assist financially eligible applicants who are U.S. citizens and permanent residents of the U.S. to meet their educational and living costs. Financial eligibility is met by a combination of loans and employment and is awarded on the basis of financial need.

International Students

Services and organizations available to international students include the Office of International Programs, English as a foreign language classes, Off-Campus Housing Office, and the Graduate Business Programs Office. The M.B.A. program office sponsors an Orientation Residency and preparatory workshops prior to the start of the program for all students.

The fall 1999 M.B.A. entering class included students from the following countries: Argentina; Brazil; Cameroon; China (PRC); Colombia; Costa Rica; El Salvador; Estonia; France; Germany; Ghana; Greece; India; Israel; Jamaica; Japan; Lithuania; Madagascar; Mexico; the Netherlands; Paraguay; Peru; Philippines; Russia; Singapore; South Korea; Spain; Switzerland; Taiwan; Thailand; Tunisia; Turkey; Uganda; United Kingdom; United States; and Venezuela.

Application Facts and Dates

Admission is for the fall semester only; there are no midyear admissions. Applications are considered on a rolling basis. The final deadline for submission of application materials is April 15. International students, students seeking financial assistance, and joint-degree candidates are encouraged to apply before February 1.

For additional information and questions about the Georgetown M.B.A. Program, students should contact:

Georgetown M.B.A. Admissions
    Office
School of Business
3520 Prospect Street, NW
Box 571148
Georgetown University
Washington, D.C. 20057-1221
Telephone: 202-687-4200
Fax: 202-687-7809
E-mail: mba@msb.edu
World Wide Web: http://www.msb.edu

The George Washington University

AN M.B.A. BUILT ON STRENGTHS

It has been aptly referred to as "permanent whitewater"—today's business climate of rapid change, obstacles, and opportunities. With business flowing ever more freely across international boundaries, the times call for a new way of educating leaders. At The George Washington University (GW) we've responded by redesigning our M.B.A.: strengthening the core curriculum, adding the option of taking all first-year courses with the same group of students, building more flexibility into concentration options, and putting an even greater emphasis on the quality of teaching.

Fortunately, the strengths we had to build on were formidable. Our diverse and accomplished faculty has far more practical business experience than most, and Washington is the ideal learning laboratory for exploring international business and the interface between the private and public sectors.

Now we have created initiatives that enable our students to have even more enriching experiences. For instance, through the Greater Washington Board of Trade, our international students work with global businesses headquartered here. We are also creating a center for dealing with economic development problems, and to help students develop entrepreneurial skills, we have established the Center for the Advancement of Small Business.

We expect students to be able to find information, analyze it effectively, communicate their ideas convincingly, and work both in teams and independently to find innovative solutions as they become true professionals who can navigate the course of business successfully, with grace and integrity.

—Robert F. Dyer, Associate Dean, Graduate Programs

Programs and Curricular Focus

The George Washington University Master of Business Administration is designed to deliver a strong general management education through core and integrative courses while maintaining an array of options and opportunities that can be packaged differently for each student.

The full-time M.B.A. program (50–54 credit hours) is designed with a first-year cohort experience structured to promote teamwork; it provides opportunities to approach problems and issues across the curriculum and is enhanced by a series of cocurricular activities that are constructed to support and expand upon classroom concepts. A practicum and a capstone course, designed to integrate the M.B.A. courses, are also required. Students may pursue any of sixteen concentrations (accounting; finance and investments; health services administration; environmental policy and management; human resources management; information systems management; international business; logistics, operations, and materials management; management decision making; management of science,

technology, and innovation; marketing; organizational behavior and development; real estate and urban development; small business and entrepreneurship; strategic management and public policy; and tourism and hospitality management) or craft an individualized concentration. Electives provide flexibility and opportunities for additional depth and breadth.

There are a number of options for students whose lives do not permit full-time study. The accelerated M.B.A. program provides a fast-paced cohort option for employed students. Students attend this 40–48 credit program on a year-round basis, and this option includes residencies as well as applied and integrated projects. The self-paced M.B.A. program (also 40–48 credits) is the most flexible, permitting enrollment in any combination of semesters and at any credit load, as long as the program is completed in five years. Because working professionals have a myriad of needs, a concentration is not required. Electives, which constitute half of the program, help students position themselves for immediate and long-range opportunities. The

Executive M.B.A. program, currently a 60-hour, two-year cohort program, is designed for middle- and senior-level managers who seek an intensive program to enhance their career development. The program consists of courses taught on alternate Fridays and Saturdays, plus four residencies, including one multi-city international experience. It emphasizes management of technology and innovation, management of a culturally diverse work force, and international business.

Through a special credit-hour transfer arrangement between the School of Business and Public Management and GW's School of Law, students can complete both the M.B.A. and J.D. degrees within four years. (Part-time students must do it in five.) Also, students may pursue degrees in the School of Business and Public Management and GW's Elliott School of International Affairs simultaneously, receiving the M.B.A. and M.A. in two to three years.

In addition to the MBA degree, the GW School of Business and Public Management offers the Master of Accountancy, the Master of Public Administration, the Master of Public Policy, the Master of Science in acquisition management, finance, information systems management, or project management, and the Master of Tourism Administration. The Ph.D. is offered in accountancy, business administration, health services administration, human resources management, information and decision systems, management and organization, and public administration.

Students and the M.B.A. Experience

GW M.B.A. students are intellectually mature people who have exhibited a strong potential for management and leadership. The average student is 27 years old. Thirty-eight percent of M.B.A. students are women, and 13 percent are members of U.S. minority groups. International students comprise 42 percent of the student body.

More than 90 percent of GW M.B.A. students possess substantial business experience before beginning their graduate work. They come from domestic and foreign corporations, family-owned companies, nonprofit organizations, private practices, and the arts. Many work on Capitol Hill or in one of the businesses headquartered in the Washington area.

❖ Global Focus

With students from sixty-nine countries, GW offers a culturally diverse environment for learning about life and business around the world. In addition to the core course, The World Economy, students are required to take at least one additional elective that adds international background. For students who choose to study abroad, exchange programs have been established in Europe, Asia, and South America.

The School of Business and Public Management is located within a few blocks of the World Bank, the International Monetary Fund, and embassies from around the world, offering GW M.B.A. students a unique opportunity to gain a global perspective. In addition to internships with international agencies in the Washington area, students may develop opportunities for internships in other countries. For example, a student recently interned at an advertising agency in Ecuador and another in South Africa with USAID in small business and economic development.

The Faculty

The program faculty members form a diverse group of highly respected experts, many of whom have achieved national and international prominence for their research, writing, and professional accomplishments. These experienced executives, managers, and consultants bring an incisive knowledge of current issues to the classroom. In addition to working closely with students, faculty members work together to address themes that cut across all aspects of business, such as management communication, business ethics, cross-cultural management, and career development. This collaborative effort makes it easier for students to integrate their knowledge.

The Business School Network

Students of the School of Business and Public Management develop an extraordinary loyalty to their alma mater, as evidenced by more than 30,000 alumni in the fifty states and seventy countries. This extensive network is the key to helping graduating students establish contacts in the area in which they plan to settle. Through the mentor program, alumni offer guidance in their various areas of expertise, serve on panels to help students make intelligent career decisions, and evaluate students' performance in workshops and case studies.

The Dean's Associates Council includes leaders from both the private and public sectors. These partnerships provide direction for the School of Business and Public Management and opportunities for students to meet and learn from today's business leaders.

The College and Environs

Unquestionably one of the most exciting cities in the world, Washington, D.C., is a global center of power and influence. Courses and faculty members provide opportunities for access to, and the development of, insider perspectives. Living in Washington means enjoying the beauty of four glorious seasons and being in the midst of a region filled with historic sites and natural beauty. Attracting interesting people from all over the world, Washington boasts the highest percentage of college graduates of any metropolitan area in the country. In addition to a wide array of Fortune 500 companies and technology-based industries, the area provides a wealth of cultural and recreational attractions that few cities can match.

Located five blocks from the White House in the historic Foggy Bottom area of northwest Washington, The George Washington University is an integral part of the city. Modern and efficient public transportation makes it easy to participate in the exciting life of the capital city.

Placement

Career services are available to GW M.B.A. students from a variety of resources. The School's Graduate Career Center offers comprehensive career planning and placement services. The M.B.A. Association and the Alumni Association regularly sponsor networking activities and career panels. Cooperative education opportunities and internships become an excellent network for future career opportunities. M.B.A. students find faculty members ready and willing to provide career advice and networking opportunities. These resources allow each student to develop an aggressive strategy for finding the best opportunities after graduation.

Admission

The School of Business and Public Management seeks candidates who have demonstrated potential for management and who have the intellectual ability, maturity, initiative, and creativity to fully participate in the challenging interdisciplinary environment. Applicants must have a bachelor's degree from a regionally accredited college or university. Selection is based upon the applicant's academic record, work experience, statement of purpose, recommendations, and scores on

the required Graduate Management Admission Test (GMAT).

Applications from international students are welcome. Proficiency in reading, writing, and speaking English must be demonstrated by all students from countries where English is not an official language. International students, in addition to the above listed requirements, must submit certified English translations of all academic records of course work corresponding to a bachelor's degree in the United States; scores for the Test of English as a Foreign Language (TOEFL), with a total score of 600 or higher; and a financial certificate, which is required of any applicant who plans to enter or remain in the United States to study and whose immigration status will be either F-1 (student) or J-1 (exchange visitor).

Finances

Tuition for the academic year 2000–01 is $725.50 per credit hour plus a University fee of $34.50 per credit hour. Full-time students normally take 11 to 13 credits per semester. Books, supplies, and health insurance cost approximately $1700 per year. Estimated costs for room, board, and miscellaneous personal expenses total about $10,000 per academic year. The majority of graduate students live off campus.

A number of graduate assistantships and fellowships are available based on academic merit. To be considered, applicants must complete the admissions application process no later than February 1. Additional aid sources are available on the World Wide Web.

Application Facts and Dates

Full consideration for the fall semester is given to applications that are submitted no later than April 1 and for the spring semester by October 1. Applications are considered after the indicated dates on a space-available basis. Students who wish to be considered for fellowships must complete the application process no later than February 1. For more information, students should contact the Office of Graduate Admissions and indicate which M.B.A. options they are interested in.

Office of Graduate Admissions
School of Business and Public
  Management
The George Washington University
710 21st Street, NW
Washington, D.C. 20052
Telephone: 202-994-6584
Fax: 202-994-6382
E-mail: sbpmapp@gwu.edu
World Wide Web: http://www.sbpm.
  gwu.edu

Georgia State University

Atlanta, Georgia

> ## SERIOUS STUDENTS DEMAND SERIOUS TEACHING
>
> *The J. Mack Robinson College of Business has developed nationally recognized specialties in many areas to help our mature and serious students realize their ambitions. Whether your goal is to land a job with an Atlanta-based company, to work abroad, or to better your position within your current company, Georgia State can equip you with the knowledge and tools you need. The College is known not only for the breadth and flexibility of the graduate programs but also for its reputation as an eminent research institution that offers outstanding teaching. Our commitment to excellence earned our part-time M.B.A. program a top 10 ranking for the past five years by U.S. News & World Report.*
>
> —Dr. Sidney Harris, Dean

Programs and Curricular Focus

Business schools are not known for flexibility and allowing students personal choice. However, Georgia State is not like most business schools. The J. Mack Robinson College of Business is not so specialized that students can't find classes to match their interests. At the same time, the College is a recognized leader in such fields as accounting, computer information systems, and risk management.

The College offers the M.B.A. degree in two formats, as well as sixteen specialized master's programs. Students can earn an M.B.A. with a major or concentration in one of sixteen areas. Classes are offered during the daytime and evenings and on Saturdays. Georgia State's part-time M.B.A. program was ranked ninth in *U.S. News & World Report*'s 2000 listing of the nation's best graduate schools.

The Flexible M.B.A. (F.M.B.A.) offers the greatest choice of day, evening, and Saturday courses for both full- and part-time students. Students plan course schedules to fit their needs and can start in any semester. The Executive M.B.A. (E.M.B.A.) is a lockstep, two-year program designed for managers with significant career experience, with classes on alternating Fridays and Saturdays.

Any M.B.A. student can earn a concentration (four courses) or a major (seven courses) in the following areas: accounting, actuarial science, decision sciences, economics, electronic commerce, finance, general business, health administration, hospitality administration, human resource management, information systems, international business, manage-

ment, marketing, personal financial planning, real estate, and risk management and insurance.

While the M.B.A. is a general management degree, the College's specialized master's degrees allow students to focus on one functional business area. The Master of Science is offered with majors in business economics, computer information systems, decision sciences, finance, human resource management, management, marketing, personal financial planning, and risk management and insurance.

Other specialized degrees include the Master of International Business, which requires that students become proficient in another language and intern overseas; Master of Actuarial Science; Master of Professional Accountancy; Master of Science in Health Administration; Master of Science in Real Estate; and Master of Taxation as well as joint programs such as the M.B.A./Master of Health Administration and M.B.A./J.D.

Students and the M.B.A. Experience

Business students at Georgia State learn not only from the faculty but also from each other. That's because the average master's student is 28 years old and has five years of full-time work experience. Students discover that this work experience, and that of their colleagues, is a vital component of the Georgia State program. There are about 1,700 M.B.A. students and 700 specialized master's students. Of all master's students, 37 percent are women, 19 percent are

members of minority groups, and 13 percent are international. The program is large and offers numerous classes in specialized fields not found at other schools. This allows students the opportunity to explore their areas of interest and meet their career goals.

The Faculty

The College's 179 full-time faculty members are teachers, researchers, authors, and leaders. Georgia State business faculty members take pride in bringing relevant, real-world problems, issues, and experiences into the classroom. With degrees from Harvard, MIT, Wharton, and Northwestern, Georgia State faculty members also attract students to one of the largest doctoral programs in the nation.

The Business School Network

As graduates of the largest business program in the Atlanta area, Georgia State's 40,000 business alumni serve as a great network. The College's own Board of Advisors includes more than 40 of the city's top CEOs, presidents, partners, and entrepreneurs, attesting to the College's strong community support.

Prominent Alumni

Some of the nation's top executives are among the College's alumni. They include Bill Dahlberg, CEO of The Southern Co.; Jerry Dempsey, CEO of PPG Industries; Ken Lewis, President of Bank of America, Corp.; Parker Petit, Chairman of Matria Healthcare, Inc.; David Stonecipher, CEO of Jefferson-Pilot Corp.; and James Copeland, CEO of Deloitte & Touche.

The College and Environs

Located in the heart of downtown Atlanta's business and financial district, Georgia State University is home to 30,000 students, making it one of the two largest of the state's universities. The 28-acre main campus includes the Pullen Library, which houses more than 1.5 million volumes. In addition to the main campus, graduate evening and weekend

In the heart of downtown Atlanta, Georgia State University fosters close ties with the business community. Atlanta's role as one of the nation's leaders in job growth, particularly in the high-tech sector, provides ample career opportunities for students.

classes are also offered at the University's Alpharetta Center in North Fulton County.

Facilities

Just across the street from the city's rapid rail hub, the J. Mack Robinson College of Business is located in the historic Citizens and Southern National Bank Building, which was donated to the College by NationsBank (now Bank of America). The building houses all College faculty and administrative offices, including the Office of Academic Assistance and Master's Admissions and the Graduate Business Placement Office.

Placement

The Graduate Business Placement Office offers comprehensive placement services, including an employer library and lists of job and internship opportunities as well as computer terminals for online and database job searches. The office offers workshops to help students in their job search and also hosts the annual Business Career Expo, which attracts more than 125 employers and almost 1,000 students. Career counselors are also available to provide individual assessments of students' career goals and opportunities. More placement information can be found at the College's Web site (http://www.cba.gsu.edu/wwwgpo).

Admission

Admission into the College's graduate programs is competitive, with each applicant being evaluated individually in relation to the current group of candidates. The Master's Admissions Commit-

tee considers previous academic performance and educational background, work experience, and GMAT scores. The College's average GMAT score for all enrolled master's students was 580. The average undergraduate GPA was 3.1. Previous academic work in business is not required.

Finances

Graduate tuition for the 1999–2000 academic year was $390 per 3-hour course for residents and $1554 for nonresidents. Students also paid $236 per semester for student activity, recreation, transportation, health, and athletics fees. Tuition rates are subject to change.

The University awards a limited number of merit and need-based scholarships to eligible students and sponsors various institutional and government loan programs. Full-time students are eligible for research assistantships and a limited number of nonresident fee waivers, which are awarded based on academic performance in graduate course work. For information on scholarship and loan opportunities, students should contact the Office of Student Financial Aid at 404-651-2227. For information on graduate assistantships, students should contact the Office of Academic Assistance and Master's Admissions at the number below.

Application Facts and Dates

Individuals who have earned undergraduate degrees from a regionally accredited institution may apply for graduate admission for any semester (except for the E.M.B.A., which begins only in the fall). For an application and admission information, students should contact:

Office of Academic Assistance and
    Master's Admissions
J. Mack Robinson College of Business
Georgia State University
University Plaza
Atlanta, Georgia 30303-3083
Telephone: 404-651-1913
Fax: 404-651-0219
World Wide Web: http://robinson.gsu.
    edu

Golden Gate University

San Francisco, California

▶ **A REAL-WORLD APPROACH TO EDUCATION**

The Edward S. Ageno School of Business at Golden Gate University offers an exciting environment in which to study. Students come hungry to learn relevant and practical business skills, and our faculty members love to share their knowledge and experience. With small classes energized by the desire of the students and the wealth of knowledge of the professors, students complete each class with an improved ability to meet the challenges of today's business world.
—Barbara Karlin, Dean, Edward S. Ageno School of Business

Programs and Curricular Focus

At Golden Gate University (GGU), students explore the global business environment and launch their futures in the graduate business program. Students are surrounded by motivated and experienced classmates who bring as much richness to the learning environment as the professors. Students apply what they learn before they graduate, and the skills they learn work for them as they pursue their studies.

The M.B.A. program has three parts: the foundation, the advanced program or core courses, and the area of concentration. The foundation and advanced programs focus on the fundamentals of business operation and management techniques, providing a general, but critical, knowledge of business functions. The concentration component of the M.B.A. allows students to select an area of interest from twelve different concentrations or select a general course of study.

The general M.B.A. is also offered as a sixteen-month Executive M.B.A., designed for working managers with at least five years of management experience. This program is a cohort program, which means that a carefully selected group of students begins the program together, takes the same courses, and shares the same experiences.

The M.B.A. degree is broad and inclusive. More specialized options are the Master of Science (M.S.) degrees. The goal of these degrees is to provide the students with a depth of expertise within their particular fields of specialization. These professional degree programs focus on the systems, processes, and administrative concerns relevant to the student's area of specialization. The M.S.

degree is often referred to as a depth degree because all of the courses are in the student's field of study.

Students and the M.B.A. Experience

The students are one of GGU's finest resources. The students accepted into the program are mature and self-directed. They take their education seriously. Working students in the School of Business represent a wide variety of occupations and companies. They are often the nexus of an invaluable network of professional contacts for their classmates.

The School's student population is known for its diversity in culture, ethnicity, age, and work experience. Through working and studying with a variety of different people, students gain an edge in the international business world of today. This makes for an enriching classroom environment, where discussions are challenging and informative on many levels.

❖ Global Focus

At GGU, global perspectives are always emphasized. The curriculum, frequently updated to reflect changing situations in the global marketplace, includes an increasing focus on international business and multinational companies. The University's international reputation brings many faculty members and students from other countries to its campuses.

At the Edward S. Ageno School, students learn to work effectively in the global environment. The laboratory is the student's classroom, where working professionals bring the global strategies they encounter directly into class

discussions. Students learn how to work in culturally diverse teams through team-based class projects. The skills and sensitivity learned in an internationally focused university environment enhance not only the business worldview and acumen but also everyday life.

Special Features

One of the features of the GGU graduate business program is the opportunity to choose from several areas of specialization either in the M.B.A. program or in an M.S. degree program. Students can choose to specialize in accounting, e-commerce, finance, human resource management, information systems, international business, management, marketing, operations management, or telecommunications management. A general course of study is also available.

Another important feature is Cyber-Campus, the University's online program. Students at GGU can choose to complete an entire degree online from anywhere in the world or complement online classes with in-person classes. CyberCampus combines convenience with the academic rigor in a highly interactive learning process.

The Faculty

Integral to the program is the hands-on, practical application of theoretical knowledge. The faculty is composed of teacher-practitioners and full-time professors. All members of the faculty have practiced in their fields and a significant number of adjunct faculty members bring current business trends and information directly from their work environments into the classroom. This creates a dynamic and uncommon teaching partnership.

In the rapidly changing business environment of today and tomorrow, some things will remain constant. Success continues to depend upon students' ability to quickly and accurately analyze the market and respond to the fluctuations. Success equally depends upon their ability to recognize and seize opportunities. Everthing the School teaches is designed to impart to students these critical tools.

The Business School Network

The Edward S. Ageno School of Business curriculum is continuously updated by using feedback from students, alumni, and the business community. Advisory boards that are made up of corporate and industry executives provide valuable input in each management discipline that helps keep the curriculum current.

Since GGU serves primarily working adult students, classrooms become a network of professionals where learning is applied to day-to-day problems encountered in the workplace, and classmates become lifelong career contacts. Faculty members, most of whom come from the business community, also become excellent sources of career advice.

The College and Environs

Golden Gate University traces its origins to the founding of the San Francisco YMCA in 1853, the oldest founding date in the city for an institution of higher learning. It is a fully accredited, nonprofit, and independent university. A pioneer in the case-study method of instruction, Golden Gate is recognized for applied education for the professions. The University provides instruction for more than 7,000 students on several campuses in California, including San Francisco, Silicon Valley, the San Francisco Bay Area, Sacramento, Monterey, and southern California. Programs are also offered in Seattle and Singapore and online via the CyberCampus.

Placement

The skilled staff in the Career Services Center works closely with students and employers. Students benefit from professional career counseling, job-search workshops and programs, computerized skills assessment, placement services, networking opportunities, and annual career fairs that feature on-campus recruiting by major corporations. In addition, students are encouraged to participate in internships as an integral part of their program, which allows for exploration of new career areas and opportunities to see the inside workings of a target company.

Admission

Applicants to the master's program must have a bachelor's degree from a regionally accredited college or university in the United States or the equivalent from a recognized international institution. Students must also satisfy basic mathematics, writing, and computer proficiency requirements.

Applicants to the M.B.A. program must submit an official score report from the Graduate Management Admission Test (GMAT), official transcripts from all schools previously attended, a statement of purpose, and a completed graduate application form along with the appropriate application fee (some applicants are not required to provide a GMAT score). Applicants whose native language is not English are required to meet the English language proficiency requirement by submitting TOEFL scores. University admissions information and online applications can be found at the Web address listed below.

Finances

Golden Gate University is one of the most affordable private universities in northern California. Tuition includes all standard fees and is the same for California residents and nonresidents. Tuition is charged by the course (most courses are 3 units), and costs vary by program. Graduate tuition for 2000–01 is $1500 per course. Books, supplies, and living expenses are additional.

International Students

Approximately 14 percent of Golden Gate University students are from outside the United States. They come from countries in Asia, the Pacific Rim, and elsewhere throughout the world. Many international students bring with them working experience from their countries, creating dynamic global learning environment.

Application Facts and Dates

The University accepts applications on a rolling admissions basis beginning up to one year prior to enrollment, and applications are reviewed as they become complete. International students should apply by the following dates: July 1 for fall trimester, November 1 for spring trimester, and March 1 for summer trimester. For more information, students should contact:

Enrollment Services
Golden Gate University
536 Mission Street
San Francisco, California 94105-2968
Telephone: 415-442-7800 (San Francisco campus)
800-GGU-4YOU (toll-free for any campus)
Fax: 415-442-7807 (San Francisco campus)
E-mail: info@ggu.edu
World Wide Web: http://www.ggu.edu

Haagse Hogeschool University

Faculty of Economics and Management

The Hague, Netherlands

> ### THE HAGUE WAY TO THE M.B.A.
>
> *No one should believe that doing this master's degree is easy. It isn't. Much time and energy will be invested in class hours, assignments, meetings, presentations, discussions, reports, and exams. Thousands of people worldwide opt to invest in the best possible education to improve their quality of life. I hope you accept the challenge.*
>
> —Dr. Leen H. Kroon, Director Graduate, Studies Center

Programs and Curricular Focus

The Haagse Hogeschool M.B.A. program provides a series of graduate management courses in a unified and linked structure, each of which is a balanced, progressive, and cohesive management development experience and related to the other courses in the respective phases.

The management education is vertically and horizontally integrated. Each phase with its suit of modules caters to the needs of managers at different points in their careers. It provides for a logical progression of development experiences. The phases of the curriculum include the Manager as a Team Member, the Manager as a Group Leader, Manager of Strategic Change, and the Business Report/Dissertation.

In addition to the regular M.B.A., the Haagse Hogeschool University and two of its international partners, the University of Luton in the United Kingdom and Central Arkansas State University in Conway, Arkansas, U.S.A., offer an international M.B.A., with study opportunities in all three of them.

The International M.B.A. provides students with an outstanding opportunity to acquire the theoretical and practical skills needed to master the complex international business environment. The participating business schools each offer appropriate experience, academic rigor, and teaching competencies to enable students to fulfill their potential in a demanding international management role.

Both M.B.A.'s are characterized by vocational relevance, close links with industry, and interactive teaching and learning strategies and are well supported by qualified and research/consultancy staff. The programs aim to create critical independent thinkers, team players, and strategic visionaries and to develop personal, transferable skills and attitudes appropriate for senior management responsibility.

Students and the M.B.A. Experience

In July 1998, the school's M.B.A. study became the first English-language course of study in that discipline to be validated by the Dutch (Masters) Validation Council (DVC), receiving a 9 on a 10-point scale. The program was described as providing state-of-the-art M.B.A. graduates. In addition to providing English-speaking students such a study opportunity in Europe, it allows those enrolled to study in one of Europe's diplomatic centers. Of 250 total applicants, 60 were admitted, of which 80 percent are male. The average student age is 34, and twenty-six countries are represented. The University of Louisville (Kentucky) and Texas Tech University have exchange programs, as do the University of Luton and University of Teeside in the United Kingdom and Chulalongkom in Bangkok, Thailand. Both full- and part-time studies are available.

❖ Global Focus

The Haage Hogeschool has always attached great importance to the international dimension. The International Court of Justice and the many embassies, international organizations, and companies within The Hague make for a lively, international, and multicultural environment. Curricula have been adapted to prepare students optimally for the increasingly international context in which careers will unfold.

The Faculty

Of the group of 20 faculty members, 12 are permanent Haagse Hogeschool members, while 8 are guest lecturers. Seven nationalities are represented.

The Business School Network

The program prepares students for management positions with companies and organizations operating internationally.

The College and Environs

The Haagse Hogeschool University is located in The Hague, Netherlands. It is one of approximately 75 "hogescholen/polytechnics" offering higher professional education in the Netherlands. The School dates from 1985 when fourteen smaller, specialized institutions located in the Hague merged. Master's programs began in 1991 with the part-time M.B.A.

In July 1998, the M.B.A. became the first English language M.B.A. to be validated by the Dutch (Masters) Validation Council (DVC).

The University enrolls approximately 15,000 students in the faculties of Economics and Management, Engineering, Health Care, Behavioral and Social Sciences, Information Sciences and Technology, and Education, Sport and Languages.

Facilities

The Haagse Hogeschool Faculty of Economics and Management has been housed in a new building since 1996. The location is ideal, being directly adjacent to the railway station and near the city centre. The entire Hogeschool occupies more than 84,000 square metres and includes a new library, sports hall, auditorium, and restaurant.

Placement

The Hague Masters is the name adopted by the Haagse Hogeschool's M.B.A. graduates for its M.B.A. Alumni Association. The M.B.A. graduates are employed in a wide variety of private and public, profit and nonprofit enterprises and institutions in the Netherlands and abroad. The M.B.A. alumni are employed in every sector of the economy and are located in Belgium, China, Germany, India, Ireland, Indonesia, Italy, the Netherlands, United States of America, United Kingdom, Israel, and South Africa.

Admission

As the program is conducted in English, students must have a good command of this language. Candidates must be at least 21 years old and have a degree from a Netherlands university or polytechnic or its accredited/validated foreign equivalent, including or followed by at least one semester of work experience; or have an equivalent state recognized professional qualification, together with appropriate experience; or be a mature and experienced manager without the requisite academic qualifications, with at least four years in a professional or administrative position and sufficient levels of company training for admission into M.B.A. Phase I. For M.B.A. Phase II, a degree in Business Studies or in a subject with a significant business component from a recognized university or a comparable institution is required. M.B.A. Phase III candidates must have completed the M.B.A. Phase II or its academic equivalent and have at least 1.5 years of appropriate management experience or possess a post-bachelor's-level degree in a management or business study and have a minimum of two years middle-management experience.

Finances

Part-time and full-time tuition, including textbooks, is $12,500 to $15,000, depending on entry level. An M.B.A. foundation course carries a tuition of $2900, with a $400 discount given if the student is proceeding to the M.B.A. curriculum.

Application Facts and Dates

Application deadlines for part-time study are, depending on start date, September 1 and December 1. The deadline for full-time study is August 1.

Frank H. Fox
M.B.A. Program Manager
Haagse Hogeschool University
Faculty of Economics & Management
Graduate Studies Center,
 Room SL3.01
Johanna Westerdijkplein 75
2521 EN The Hague
Netherlands
Telephone: 31-70-445-8162
Fax: 31-70-445-8194
E-mail: fox@sem.hhs.nl/gsc
WWW: http://www.sem.hhs.nl/gsc
    http://www.mba.nl

Hawaii Pacific University

MEETING TODAY'S GLOBAL CHALLENGE

Hawaii Pacific University's (HPU) M.B.A. enhances the career development of today's business professional. The HPU student body is culturally diverse, with representatives from Hawaii, the U.S. mainland, and more than eighty countries. HPU offers the skills, knowledge, and training required in today's highly competitive global business environment.

Academic programs combine practice, theory, and the skills needed in modern career fields. Students learn to implement the latest developments in computer technology, business simulations, communications theory, and strategic planning. Our graduates are well prepared for success in today's rapidly changing marketplace.

—Rodney Romig, Dean of Business Administration

Programs and Curricular Focus

The Hawaii Pacific University M.B.A. program requires 45 semester hours of graduate work (fifteen courses). Core requirements (27 semester hours) include accounting, economics, information systems, finance, law, international business management, human resource management, marketing, and quantitative methods. Elective courses (12 semester hours) may be taken in nine different areas. The last area is the capstone series (6 semester hours), which includes Management Policy and Strategy Formulation and completion of the Professional Paper.

Joint-degree programs (66 semester hours) include the M.B.A./Master of Arts in Human Resource Management, the M.B.A./Master of Arts in Organizational Change, the M.B.A./Master of Arts in Management, the M.B.A./Master of Science in Information Systems (M.S.I.S.), and the M.B.A./Master of Science in Nursing.

Full-time students can complete the program in twelve months. Part-time students can complete the program in eighteen to twenty-four months. Students must complete their professional paper within seven years of initial enrollment in graduate courses and within one year from first enrollment in the Professional Paper course.

Hawaii Pacific University is an independent, not-for-profit, coeducational, nonsectarian, career-oriented postsecondary institution founded in 1965. It is accredited by the Accrediting Commission for Senior Colleges and Universities of the Western Association of Schools and Colleges. The University is a member of the American Assembly of Collegiate Schools of Business. HPU is recognized by the Hawaii Commission of Post-Secondary Education, approved for veteran's benefits, and authorized to issue I-20 documents to international students.

Students and the M.B.A. Experience

The average age of graduate students at Hawaii Pacific University is 26 years of age. Students represent more than eighty countries. Teamwork is an essential ingredient of the M.B.A. program. In various courses throughout the program, students are formed into teams to solve problems collectively and to achieve a better understanding of group dynamics and challenges while producing specific desired results. Hands-on experience is gained through internships with leading Honolulu corporations. For example, students work in accounting, human resource management, and marketing internships, to name but a few.

The Faculty

The M.B.A. program at Hawaii Pacific University permits students to study with some of the most distinguished professors in the Pacific region. Faculty members have contemporary experience with leading corporations, outstanding academic credentials, and a dedication to teaching. The graduate faculty includes 42 (7 women) full-time and 18 (7 women) part-time teachers. Seventy-five percent of the faculty hold the doctorate or its equivalent. Average class size is 24. Two full-time academic advisers are available to assist students.

The Business School Network

The Honolulu business community plays an integral role in the Hawaii Pacific University M.B.A. program. Many of Honolulu's leading corporations sponsor students for internships, many of which eventually result in offers of full-time employment. Senior executives of local investment firms, health-care systems, banks, schools, law firms, and trust companies serve on the University Board of Trustees, providing vision and direction for the future. Other HPU M.B.A. graduates serve on the Alumni Board, helping maintain a base of future employment contacts for new graduates as well as supporting the University. HPU also integrates the business community into the curriculum through the use of guest speakers with individual areas of expertise in appropriate academic disciplines, exposing students to current issues and emerging trends.

The College and Environs

Hawaii Pacific combines the excitement of an urban downtown campus with the serenity of a residential campus set in the foothills of the Koolau mountains. The main campus is located in downtown Honolulu, business and financial center of the Pacific. There are also eight satellite campuses located at Pearl Harbor, Barbers Point, Hickam Air Force Base, Schofield Barracks, Fort Shafter, Tripler Army Medical Center, Kaneohe Marine Corps Air Station, and Camp Smith.

Facilities

Meader Library and two additional on-campus libraries are available to students. Total holdings include 159,000 volumes, 200,000 microforms, and 1,740 current periodical subscriptions. There are thirty-five personal computers in all libraries. CD-ROM players are available for graduate student use. Access is provided to online bibliographic retrieval services.

Rooms and/or apartments are available to single students at an average cost of $8120 per year, including board. The typical monthly cost of living in off-campus housing not owned by the University is $600. For further graduate housing information, students should contact Student Housing at 808-233-3184.

Technology Environment

Computer networks run on DOS Novell, UNIX, and Macintosh. All students have free access to the Internet. Computer labs are available from 8 a.m. to 9 p.m. daily and from 8 a.m. to 5 p.m. weekends.

Placement

Hawaii Pacific University's Career Planning and Placement Center provides, free of charge, two sponsored job fairs per year, job search preparation, seminars, on-campus recruiters, employer visits, workshops, job placement, national computerized resume referral services, a career resource library, internships, and campus employment opportunities. International student advisers are available to provide current information regarding visas, passports, F-1 regulations, work permits, and other concerns critical to international students.

Admission

Admission requirements include a completed application, official transcripts from each postsecondary school attended (sent directly to HPU), a document showing conferral of the bachelor's degree, and two letters of reference. International students should submit certified copies of "A" level (or similar postsecondary) examinations directly to HPU. The Test of English as a Foreign Language (TOEFL) is recommended unless students have completed a bachelor's degree from an accredited American college or university with a grade point average of 2.7 or above.

Hawaii Pacific University seeks students with academic promise, outstanding career potential, and high motivation.

Finances

For the 2000–01 academic year, graduate tuition is $8920, living expenses are $8120, and other expenses (books and insurance) are $1500; the total cost is $18,540. Part-time cost is $372 per credit hour.

Aid is available to part-time students. The University participates in all federal financial aid programs designated for graduate students. These programs provide aid in the form of subsidized (need-based) and unsubsidized (non-need-based) Federal Stafford Student Loans. Through these loans, funds may be available to cover a student's entire cost of education. To apply for aid, students must submit the Free Application for Federal Student Aid (FAFSA) after January 1. Mailing of student award letters usually begins in April. For further financial aid information, students should call 808-544-0253.

International Students

The International Student Office provides a variety of services to international students, including advising on personal, interpersonal, cultural, and academic matters; assisting on immigration matters, especially F-1 requirements, I-20 extensions, and work authorization; advising on money management and housing needs; conducting orientation programs to facilitate academic and social adjustment; and providing medical insurance information. An International Day is held each year to highlight the contributions of HPU's diverse student population. There are fourteen different country-specific organizations on campus.

Application Facts and Dates

Admission decisions for the M.B.A. program are made on a rolling basis, and applicants are notified between one and two weeks after all documents have been submitted. Completed applications should be sent to:

Graduate Admissions
1164 Bishop Street, Suite 911
Honolulu, Hawaii 96813
Telephone: 808-544-0279
          800-669-4724 (toll-free)
Fax: 808-544-0280
E-mail: gradservctr@hpu.edu

Hofstra University

Frank G. Zarb School of Business

Hempstead, New York

THE NEW ZARB M.B.A.

The Zarb School of Business is engaged in a variety of exciting initiatives that directly complement the traditionally strong graduate program offered to students interested in the global dimensions of business and the innumerable advantages of studying within a campus-based program in proximity to New York City. Among the most exciting developments in some time are our new curriculum, implementation of the McGraw-Hill Technology Lab for the use of our students, and the construction of the University's new high-technology building, which will be dedicated primarily to business school use and opens in the fall of 2000.

—Ralph S. Polimeni, Ph.D., Dean

Programs and Curricular Focus

The M.B.A. program at the Zarb School reflects the actual environment in which contemporary managers must make decisions, often under conditions of uncertainty. Course work exposes students to innovative strategies, group interaction, and simulated business situations. The curriculum emphasizes a course-functional approach to teaching. It also provides an experiential learning component within which students engage in business consulting and corporate internships as a means of refining their managerial skills. Students gain hands-on experience with technology, acquire a perspective on international business practices, and study environmental and ethical factors as they pertain to business, government, and not-for-profit organizations.

The M.B.A. program comprises six tiers. The first is residency requirements, which establish facility with computer technology, information resources, and calculus. The second is the core competencies, which establish a basic functional understanding of business. The third is an advanced core, which provides students with a more sophisticated understanding of the functional areas of business and how they are applied across the organization. The fourth component is a cluster of courses called The Contemporary Business Environment, which is a fully interdisciplinary component of the program and includes coverage of communications skills, leadership, and an appreciation for and understanding of a truly diverse and global marketplace. The fifth component of the program enables students to focus on one of seven areas of specialization, including accounting, business computer information systems, banking and finance, marketing, management, international business, or taxation. The sixth and final component is a project-based course, which may take the form of a consulting engagement, internship, research project, or management game.

A one-year, 42-credit program is available for students who hold a baccalaureate degree in business. The regular program is two years and 66 credits. Both part-time and full-time programs are available, as are M.S. programs in business and a J.D./M.B.A. program, which is offered in conjunction with the Hofstra School of Law. An Executive M.B.A. program is also offered, through which full-time administrators who have a minimum of seven years' managerial experience can complete their degree on alternating Fridays and Saturdays over a period of twenty months.

Students and the M.B.A. Experience

Many students entering the Zarb M.B.A. program have at least two years of full-time work experience. Eight states and twenty-five countries are represented among the student body. About 10 percent of the full-time students are members of minority groups, 31 percent are international, and 37 percent are women. Numerous organizations are open to M.B.A. students, including the M.B.A. Association, the Graduate Women in Business Organization, the Minority Student Organization, AIESEC, and the Organization of International Students. One of the most popular student organizations is the Hofstra Business Consulting Group. Membership in this group is by application and "hire" only, and the organization is run similarly to external consulting practices. The Group provides students with hands-on consulting experience and remuneration for their services.

Team projects and the application of technology to conducting business in a dynamically changing world are all critical to the Zarb M.B.A. program, as is the program of internships and study-abroad opportunities. The location of the University on Long Island and within a 40-minute commute from Manhattan provides extraordinary opportunities for employment, internships, and social and cultural activities.

❖ Global Focus

In revising the M.B.A. curriculum, the Zarb School renewed its long-standing commitment to the importance of exposing students to the business of doing business in an international marketplace. The curriculum content focuses heavily on globalization and emphasizes an international focus in virtually every course. These classroom experiences are complemented by the Zarb School's conference series on U.S.-International Trade, by the very diverse faculty, and by the School's Merrill Lynch Center for the Study of International Financial Services and Markets. Each of these provides students with unique opportunities to interact with senior business leaders as well as visiting academicians who are focused on trade and finance issues that affect the U.S. and its trading partners.

Special Features

A full range of services is available for international students enrolled in the Zarb M.B.A. Program. For those requiring course work in the English language, a full program of instruction is available through the English Language Program.

The Faculty

More than 100 faculty members, representing a combination of academicians and business practitioners, teach in the M.B.A. program. It is significant to note that, while many business schools devote senior faculty energies primarily to research, the mission of the Zarb School faculty has always been to be, above all, excellent teachers. This philosophy results in a faculty that possesses both extensive business experience and excellent academic credentials, allowing for a balanced approach to theory and practice in the curriculum, as well as a balance of active scholarship, interaction with students, and involvement in the business community. A complete profile of the faculty is available from the Graduate Programs Office.

The Business School Network

Networking with the local, regional, and international business communities has traditionally been an important part of the Zarb School M.B.A. experience, and that tradition continues. Linkages with these communities are manifested through a variety of means, including the Dean's Executive Council, which is composed of business leaders; an active alumni network, which includes senior officers at a number of multinational corporations; and the Dean's Lecture Series on topics of timely importance to the business community and to students. In addition, Hofstra's Business Development Center, which houses the Merrill Lynch Center for the Study of International Financial Services and Markets, the Family Business Forum, the Long Island Venture Group, the Small Business Institute, and other entities, provides an additional platform for enhanced networking opportunities. A series of conferences that address United States trade issues in the context of other countries throughout the world offers M.B.A. students and alumni access to senior managers and faculty members from a host of organizations. Recent conferences organized to examine American trade relationships were cosponsored by Erasmus/The Rotterdam School of Management (the Netherlands) and SDA Bocconi (Italy).

Distinguished alumni of the School include its namesake, Frank G. Zarb, Chairman, Chief Executive Officer, and President of the National Association of Securities Dealers.

The College and Environs

Hofstra is located on a parklike 240-acre campus in a suburban, residential area of Long Island, New York. The campus has been designated as an arboretum by the American Association of Botanical Gardens and Arboreta. It is within a 40-minute train ride of Manhattan. In addition to the enormous opportunities for cultural, professional, and social activities offered by virtue of Hofstra's location near New York City, the University hosts more than 500 cultural events each year. Athletic facilities include the only indoor Olympic-size pool on Long Island, the fully equipped Physical Fitness and Recreation Centers, and a stadium that seats 15,000.

Facilities

The Axinn Library serves the Zarb School of Business through a fully computerized system featuring LEXICAT, an online listing that includes more than 500,000 records of books, periodicals, microfilms, and media. Other services offered are Business Periodicals on Disk, ABI/Inform, Newspaper Abstracts on Disk, and the Dow Jones News Retrieval Service. Extensive computer lab facilities that support a variety of software applications are available. Microsoft Windows is the operating platform utilized most extensively by the Zarb School. Every M.B.A. student is immediately assigned an e-mail account, which may be utilized for Internet access, upon enrollment. No additional charge is assessed for this service. The McGraw-Hill Technology Laboratory in the Axinn Library consolidates all of McGraw-Hill's proprietary software and databases into one facility available to students and faculty members for research and educational purposes.

The School subscribes to Standard & Poor's Compustat database, which contains company reports and market information for more than 8,000 companies as well as PDE Bank, Full Coverage, and Global Vantage Files. The Center for Research in Security Prices (CRSP) database, which includes daily and monthly price and volume information for more than 8,000 firms, is also available to M.B.A. students.

The main classroom building for the Zarb School is Breslin Hall, which contains rooms equipped for full computer demonstration and instruction. On-campus housing is readily available to M.B.A. students in the form of apartments and dormitories.

Placement

A full complement of career development services is available to M.B.A. students. These services include on- and off-campus recruiting, general job-search information (e.g., interviewing, resume preparation), a comprehensive interview and placement library, videotaping of interview simulations, computerized job banks, career planning seminars, and assistance with internships and part-time employment.

Admission

Admission is selective. Candidates are required to complete the graduate application and all supporting forms and to submit two letters of recommendation, a resume, a statement of professional objectives, official transcripts from every college or university attended, and scores obtained on the Graduate Management Admission Test (GMAT). International students are also required to submit scores obtained on the TOEFL.

For the most recently admitted class, the middle 80 percent range of GMAT scores was from 430 to 610; the average undergraduate grade point average was 3.2 on a 4.0 scale. All credentials submitted in support of the application for admission are carefully considered in making the admission decision.

Finances

Tuition is assessed on a per credit basis and was $475 for each credit in 1999–2000, with courses carrying 3 credits each. Hofstra is a private institution, so tuition is the same for residents and nonresidents of New York State. Room, board, books, and supplies bring the annual cost of a full-time M.B.A. education to approximately $25,000. The cost of tuition for Executive M.B.A. students is approximately $50,000 for the twenty-month program. Financial aid is available in the form of fellowships that provide partial tuition credit and graduate assistantship positions. There is no aid available for international students.

Application Facts and Dates

Hofstra subscribes to a rolling admissions policy, with suggested filing deadlines of May 1 for fall admission and November 1 for spring admission. Students planning to apply for financial aid should file both admissions and financial aid forms no later than March 1 for fall and October 1 for spring. Candidates are generally advised of admission decisions no later than six weeks after the application is completed. Students may obtain additional information and application materials from:

Office of Admissions
100 Hofstra University
Hempstead, New York 11549
Telephone: 516-463-6700
Fax: 516-463-5100
E-mail: hofstra@hofstra.edu
　　　　humba@hofstra.edu

Illinois Institute of Technology

Stuart Graduate School of Business

Chicago, Illinois

> ### BUSINESS EDUCATION FOR A TECHNOLOGICAL WORLD
>
> *As part of a technological university, Stuart's graduate degree programs have always focused on the intersection of business and technology. In e-commerce, for example, Stuart offers not only an M.B.A. concentration but also an M.S. degree program and a concentration in our M.S. in marketing communication program. The M.B.A. program provides depth in specific areas of interest within a holistic, comprehensive business and management perspective, emphasizing the technological and quantitative skills needed in today's business world. The goal of our M.B.A. program is to develop the leaders and managers of tomorrow. I welcome you to join us.*
>
> —M. Zia Hassan, Dean

Programs and Curricular Focus

Stuart Graduate School of Business at Illinois Institute of Technology (IIT) is accredited by AACSB–The International Association for Management Education and offers graduate-level programs exclusively. Stuart offers a wide range of business and management programs that emphasize implementation, a technological orientation, global perspectives, a cross-functional approach, and teamwork. Each program is overseen by an advisory board of industry executives who ensure relevance to current industry needs. Classes are held in a new ten-story building, which features state-of-the-art technological resources and is located in the heart of Chicago's business district.

The Stuart M.B.A. degree program provides a thorough grounding in the functional areas of business, an understanding of the business applications of technology and analytic methods, and ten specialized areas of study, within a holistic, global management perspective.

The curriculum is made up of twenty courses. Eight core courses cover the body of knowledge common to the M.B.A. degree: finance, financial and managerial accounting, international business, marketing, managerial economics, operations management, organizational behavior, and statistical methods. Students also take eleven electives and may choose to specialize in one or two of ten areas: e-commerce, finance, information management, international business, management science, marketing, operations management, organization and management, quality management, and strategic management. All students

complete their degrees by taking Business Policy, a capstone course that integrates the development and implementation of strategy.

Small, interactive classes stimulate students to develop creative solutions, often using case studies. All classes are conducted in English. Classes, many of which are held in the evening, follow a schedule of four 11-week quarters a year. Students take from fourteen to twenty courses, depending on their academic backgrounds. Some full-time students can complete the program in one year.

The Stuart School also offers a Fast-Track M.B.A. at Motorola's Galvin Campus in Schaumburg. This fourteen-course lockstep program is offered on a part-time-only basis to working professionals with at least six years of professional/managerial experience. Other Stuart offerings include an M.S. in e-commerce, an M.S. in environmental management, an M.S. in finance, an M.S. in marketing communication, an M.S. in operations and technology management, and a Ph.D. in management science. Several joint-degree programs are available, including M.B.A./M.S. programs and an M.B.A./J.D. program with IIT's Chicago-Kent College of Law.

Students and the M.B.A. Experience

The M.B.A. student body of approximately 400 individuals comprises eighteen nationalities, with 25 percent international students; people with a wide range of academic, cultural, national, and business backgrounds; ages ranging from

students who have recently received their bachelor's degrees to professionals who have spent years in the workforce; 25 percent full-time students; and students who hold managerial positions in Chicago corporations and elsewhere. Degree backgrounds include economics, science or technology, and law, with the remainder a mix of other disciplines.

At Stuart, students learn from classmates as well as from professors. Typically, students pool their strengths and work in teams to solve problems. Most students and professors possess hands-on experience that they share in class discussion. Classmates include students who hold managerial positions in Chicago corporations and students from other countries. This diversity enables the creation of professional networks to prepare for teamwork in the global economy.

The Faculty

Stuart's faculty includes scholars in the areas of technology management, marketing, information technology, telecommunications standards, organizational design and behavior, quality management, computer modeling, computer-integrated manufacturing, flexible manufacturing systems, demand forecasting, economic forecasting and risk management, and derivatives and foreign exchange. Because its members serve as consultants with corporations, government agencies, and research firms throughout the world, the faculty brings a practical point of view to management issues.

The Business School Network

The Stuart Graduate School Overseers/Student Support Program links students with senior-level executives from a range of industries. These executives hold positions at such companies as Abbott Laboratories; AT&T; Celtic Life Insurance Company; Eastman Kodak Company; Kamco Plastics, Inc.; Motorola, Inc.; and Smith Barney and serve as mentors and career advisers. Students also network with fellow students, many of whom are working professionals, and with Stuart alumni and thousands of other

IIT alumni with contacts in many areas of business, industry, and government.

The College and Environs

Founded in 1890, the Illinois Institute of Technology, a private university with an enrollment of 6,000, is internationally recognized for advanced work in engineering, business, law, architecture, design, and science. The Stuart Graduate School's main campus is located near the financial district in downtown Chicago. Suburban locations are in Wheaton, 45 minutes west of the Chicago loop, and at Motorola's Galvin Center in Schaumburg, 45 minutes northwest. Chicago is home to more Forbes 500 companies than any other city in the U.S., except for New York City. Among the companies headquartered in the Chicago area are McDonald's, Ameritech, Motorola, Archer Daniels Midland, Amoco, United Airlines, Sears, and Baxter International. The city offers many business opportunities for Stuart M.B.A. students, from internships and part-time employment to full-time careers. The city also offers a wealth of recreational and cultural opportunities, ranging from professional sports teams to avant-garde theater, along with beaches and parks. The area's cosmopolitan population offers an interesting and varied choice of cuisines and activities.

Facilities

The Stuart Business Library is located in the Information Center on floors six through ten of the Downtown Campus. The Information Center is an open-stack collection of more than 525,000 volumes, including the business holdings of the Stuart Business Library, the Chicago-Kent Law Library, and the Library of International Relations, which contains international materials in history, economics, political science, and law. The center houses important collections of the European Union, the United Nations, the International Monetary Fund, International Labor Organization, and the World Health Organization.

The Information Center has a seating capacity of more than 600 and contains several computer classrooms, duplicating rooms, microfilm facilities, and small-group study rooms. Seating throughout the center provides access to all of the networked computer facilities, including online research systems both local and remote, such as LEXIS-NEXIS, Business Periodicals Global, and a number of CD-ROM databases.

Stuart students also have access to IIT's full library system, including the Paul V. Galvin Library on the Main Campus, with its collections in engineering, science, social sciences, humanities, and arts.

Technology Environment

Stuart's Downtown Campus is equipped with three computing facilities, including the PC Lab for general use; the Quantitative Research Lab, a state-of-the-art interactive computer teaching lab with industry software, real-time market feeds, and a simulated trading environment that is considered among the nation's best resources for the study of financial markets; and the new e-Lab, which supports e-commerce curricula in the M.B.A. program and in the Master of Science in e-commerce and marketing communication programs.

All of Stuart's computing facilities provide access to a wide range of business tools and resources through a Windows interface. Computers in the lab are linked by a campuswide computer network to the library and other campus computer labs. Software includes the major spreadsheet and word processing programs and database and presentation managers used in business today. CD-ROM databases include Standard & Poor's Corporations, Thomas Register, Knight-Ridder, US Business Reporter, Investexts, and F&S Index.

Placement

Chicago is a dynamic international center of finance, business, and industry whose economic world includes Fortune 500 companies, many midwestern United States major industries, thriving entrepreneurial ventures, and the world's largest futures and options exchanges. The Stuart Career Planning Center, with strong ties to the business community, offers counseling about career planning, goals, and job search strategies, as well as services in developing students' interviewing and resume-writing skills. Companies that have recruited Stuart students include AT&T; Arthur Andersen; Cargill; Chicago Board of Trade; Citicorp; Commonwealth Edison; Ernst & Young; First Chicago; Fuji Securities, Inc.; Lucent; Morgan Stanley & Company; Motorola; Reuters; Shell Oil; and Walgreens.

Admission

Admission to the Stuart M.B.A. program requires submission of a completed application form, two letters of recommendation, official transcripts, a GMAT report, and a summary of work experience. International applicants must also have a TOEFL score of at least 550 (for scores between 550 and 599, a course at the Intensive English Institute is required) and a financial affidavit in the amount of $34,178 for the 2000–01 academic year.

Finances

Tuition for 2000–01 is $1944 per course. Full-time students must register for at least three courses a quarter. International students must enroll for health insurance coverage. Students should anticipate an expense of approximately $100 for books and supplies for each course taken. Room and board on the Main Campus, 3 miles south of the Downtown Center, ranges from $5155 to $8900 for the academic year. An hourly shuttle bus connects the two campuses. Apartment rentals are available within a block of the downtown campus.

The Stuart School administers a number of partial tuition scholarships for full-time students, which are awarded on merit.

International Students

The Stuart Graduate School student body has a diverse makeup of cultures and nationalities, 25 percent of whom are international students. A majority of Stuart's international students have found full- and part-time employment while seeking their degrees through the Curricular Practical Training (CPT) Program, which is administered through Stuart's Career Planning Center. The International Cultural Center at IIT offers a variety of services relating to personal, visa, and immigration concerns; advises students about career planning and internship options; and holds social, cultural, and educational events. IIT also offers counseling and health services, cultural and religious programs, disability resources, and multicultural services.

Application Facts and Dates

Applications are due one month before classes start (two months for international students). Admission decisions typically are sent within three weeks of receipt of all credentials. For more information, students should contact:

Lynn Miller, Ph.D., Assistant Dean of
    Admission and M.B.A. Program
Stuart Graduate School of Business
Illinois Institute of Technology
565 West Adams Street
Chicago, Illinois 60661-3691
Telephone: 312-906-6544
Fax: 312-906-6549
E-mail: lmiller@stuart.iit.edu
World Wide Web: http://www.stuart.iit.
    edu

Illinois State University

Normal, Illinois

THE ILLINOIS STATE M.B.A. PROGRAM—ADDING VALUE TO A DIVERSE STUDENT BODY

At Illinois State, we know our M.B.A. students are investing their most valuable resources—time, energy, and dollars—to earn their advanced degrees. With that in mind, we are committed to adding value to the career of every student pursuing the M.B.A. The Illinois State University College of Business has as its mission providing student-centered lifelong learning and ensuring students the ability to reach their full potential. Our faculty members are accessible and dedicated to making every course an excellent learning experience for M.B.A. students. We have added value by updating the curriculum, and our courses combine serious scholarship with practical approaches. Indeed, in a survey of our graduates, the faculty earned highest praise. Personalized advising also adds value by helping M.B.A. candidates choose the right courses to fulfill their personal and professional goals.

—Dixie Mills, Dean

Programs and Curricular Focus

Illinois State accepts both full- and part-time students. Full-time students typically take three or four classes, and part-time students two, per academic semester. All classes are offered in the evening; thus, full- and part-time students benefit from one another's experiences during class discussions and group activities.

The program curriculum has three interrelated parts: foundation, core, and elective courses. Graduate-level foundation courses are designed for the student with no previous business university course work in order to prepare the student for graduate-level core courses. Students who have earned an undergraduate business degree typically take few, if any, of the seven foundation courses.

The core and elective course requirements for the program consist of 36 semester hours of study (twelve courses). The nine core courses are designed to build analytical, critical thinking, decision-making, team, and communication skills across the functional areas of business, culminating with an integrative capstone course on organizational strategy and planning.

Students may choose to concentrate or diversify the three elective courses in the areas of accounting, finance, marketing, international business, human resources, law, insurance, agribusiness, business communication, information systems, and arts management. Full-time students are encouraged to complete an internship experience as one elective.

The College also offers graduate programs leading to the Master of Science in Accountancy and the Master of Professional Accountancy.

Students and the M.B.A. Experience

Illinois State M.B.A. alumni give the program a 95 percent satisfaction rating. A supportive environment encourages students to reach their potential during and beyond their program. The College is committed to providing the best student-centered education in business, serving the needs of business and society by giving students the time and support needed as they progress toward their degrees and by preparing students for lifelong learning. Concern for students is illustrated by small class sizes (averaging fewer than 25 students), the abundance of elective courses, faculty members who are accessible to students and who challenge them to broaden their business perspectives, and active alumni and student organizations designed to enhance networking and professional skills.

A diverse student body adds to the quality of the M.B.A. experience. More than 200 part-time and full-time students, whose professional and academic backgrounds vary widely, take classes together. Small classes and M.B.A. Association activities allow students to learn from each other as they exchange perspectives reflecting different cultures, professions, and industries.

The M.B.A. Association also allows students to develop leadership and organizational skills through serving as officers or M.B.A. ambassadors. The association sponsors professional, philanthropic, and social activities.

The Faculty

The graduate faculty members hold degrees from major universities throughout the nation. The faculty members combine a strong student-centered orientation with their personal involvement in managerial relevant research. These faculty dimensions foster a stimulating learning environment within which to study contemporary business topics. During exit interviews, graduating M.B.A. students consistently list student-professor relationships, accessibility of professors, and high quality of the courses offered as areas of particular strength for the Illinois State M.B.A. program.

The Business School Network

Corporate Partnerships

A $9.5-million grant provided by State Farm Insurance and matched by the state of Illinois will provide for a new $27-million College of Business building, to be completed in the fall of 2002. In addition, grants from major corporate partners, such as Caterpillar and MassMutual Insurance, have enabled the College to complete major updates in the computer lab and in classroom technology. The M.B.A. program has been offered, on-site, on a contractual basis to employees of the Illinois Power Company, Archer Daniels Midland Company, Bridgestone-Firestone, and Caterpillar, Inc. The College also developed and teaches a two-week overseas study program for the Lloyd's of London APEX Programme. In addition, the College is home to the Katie Insurance School. With funding in excess of $3 million from insurance companies, the Katie Insurance School is devoted to providing the finest undergraduate and graduate insurance programs in the country and sponsors a number of continuing education and professional development programs.

Prominent Alumni
The Illinois State University M.B.A. program counts among its alumni a number of notable business leaders, including Ann Baughan, Assistant Vice President, State Farm Insurance; Robert English, President, English & Associates; John Franklin, Owner, Innotech Communications; Karl Heien, Vice President, Smith Barney Inc.; Phil Maughan, Vice President, The Northern Trust Company; Duane Miller, CEO, Country Companies; Warren Schmidgall, Executive Vice President, Hill's Pet Nutrition Inc.; James C. Tyree, Chairman and CEO, Mesirow Financial Group; and James Van Houten, President/CEO, MSI Insurance.

The College and Environs
Founded in 1857 as the first public institution of higher education in the state, Illinois State has developed into a major university. It prides itself on providing personalized instruction of high quality, developing student potential through superior teaching.

Bloomington-Normal was recognized by *Money* magazine as one of the nation's most livable communities. Five major highways intersect in the Twin Cities, which are in McLean County midway between St. Louis and Chicago. An Amtrak train station is just two blocks from the Illinois State campus, and major airlines serve the local airport.

The community is one of the state's fastest growing, with a population of 95,000. Firms with national headquarters in central Illinois include State Farm Insurance Companies, Caterpillar Inc., Mitsubishi Motor Manufacturing, The Eureka Company, and Country Companies. Other major employers in the Twin Cities include BroMenn Healthcare, St. Joseph Medical Center, Bridgestone/Firestone OTR, and General Electric.

Facilities
Milner Library contains more than 1.8 million items, including in excess of 5,700 journals and 85,000 titles in business and economics. Business publications are located on a single floor in the library. Students can access the library system remotely for online

searching of fifty-two databases in business and economics, full-text databases covering more than 300 journals, the *Business Periodicals Index,* and other indexes on CD-ROM. The Library Computer System online catalog provides access to the collections of forty other university and college libraries in Illinois.

Technology Environment
The College of Business maintains computer labs with hundreds of personal computers with Pentium III processors and featuring the current software programs students are likely to encounter in the business world. Other labs are available 24 hours a day. The computer center offers numerous seminars, open to graduate students, on software packages and current computing topics.

Placement
The University's Counseling and Career Services Center assists students with career decisions, resumes, and finding positions after graduation. A new online placement service becomes fully operational in the fall of 2000. In addition, the M.B.A. office sponsors seminars on using networking to improve job opportunities. M.B.A. Alumni Network members assist students in a variety of ways, including mentoring. Ninety-four percent of Illinois State M.B.A.'s are employed when they complete their degrees, with a majority earning more than $35,000 in those jobs at graduation. Sixty-one percent of graduates now earn $30,000–$60,000; 8 percent earn more than $100,000.

Admission
Admission is limited to holders of baccalaureate degrees who demonstrate high promise of success in graduate business study. All undergraduate majors are acceptable. Criteria considered in the evaluation of applicants are Graduate Management Admission Test (GMAT) score, GPA earned during the last 60 credit hours of undergraduate work, letters of recommendation, and personal essays.

Applicants need to submit an M.B.A. application, essays, a resume, and two letters of recommendation to the M.B.A. office. In addition, official GMAT scores, Test of English as a Foreign Language (TOEFL) scores (if applicable), the

graduate school application, and official transcripts must be submitted to the graduate school.

Recently admitted students have an average GPA of 3.37 and GMAT score of 590 (target minimum 450). A TOEFL score is required of all students whose native language is not English (average minimum: 600, paper-based; 250, computer-based).

Finances
In-state tuition and fees for 2000–01 are $1418 per semester for students taking three courses. Out-of-state tuition is approximately 2½ times the in-state tuition.

Graduate assistantships, tuition waivers, scholarships, student loans, and veterans assistance programs are available. Applications are reviewed in late April for fall graduate assistantship appointments, tuition waivers, and other financial aid and in October for spring semester.

International Students
Twelve percent of current M.B.A.'s are international students, hailing from Africa, Asia, Canada, Europe, Mexico, and South America. The University provides a week-long orientation for international students, an International House dormitory, and married student housing. The Intensive English Language Institute offers programming for family members who are building their language skills.

Application Facts and Dates
Students may begin their programs during any of the three semesters. Full consideration for financial aid and for advance class registration will be given to those submitting completed applications by March 1 for fall admission, October 1 for spring admission, and March 15 for summer admission.

For further information, students should contact:

The M.B.A. Program
College of Business
Campus Box 5500
Illinois State University
Normal, Illinois 61790-5500
Telephone: 309-438-8388
Fax: 309-438-7255
E-mail: isumba@gilbreth.cob.ilstu.edu
World Wide Web: http://gilbreth.cob.
  ilstu.edu/mba

IMD—International Institute for Management Development

M.B.A. Program

Lausanne, Switzerland

IMD—THE LEADER IN INTERNATIONAL MANAGEMENT EDUCATION

The IMD M.B.A. program is designed to enable a very select number of highly qualified young professionals who have demonstrated significant achievement early in their careers to reach responsible positions in international management. Our very intensive program aims at the top end of the spectrum in terms of the caliber of the participants and program rigor. The small class size of 80 participants, representing thirty-five different countries, fosters our belief that world-class business leaders are not mass produced; they are developed with a large degree of personalized attention in a practical, action-oriented environment. This is the only way they can master the craft of leadership in an international arena.

—Dominique Turpin, Director

Programs and Curricular Focus

The IMD general management M.B.A. program is an exclusive eleven-month international program (January through December) designed to develop young managers with solid business experience into global leaders. The combined total of 900 classroom and study-group contact hours are equivalent to a two-year full-time program.

The IMD M.B.A. program transforms business skills into real-world management and leadership competencies. By applying skills to real business situations, graduates leave with hands-on experience in the challenges of modern global business. Each topic covered in the eight program modules is structured from the point of view of the participant as both a manager and a leader. For example, the new module Leading Change and Corporate Renewal is approached from the angle of the manager, who must sometimes take risks, and the leader, who should act as an entrepreneur with the organization. As students progress through the various modules, the emphasis gradually shifts from good management to effective leadership. In addition to the program content, the multinationality of participants and faculty members promotes a truly international perspective. IMD M.B.A. participants come from thirty to thirty-six countries, and the 46 full-time professors come from twenty-one countries. Learning to manage effectively in an international setting, where no single nationality dominates, is an integral part of the IMD experience.

In each module, which averages four to five weeks in length, a number of different, yet complementary, fields of management are combined into a unified learning experience. As a result, participants gain a complete understanding of each field, as well as how they work together. Moreover, the learning process is cumulative; skills learned in one module are reinforced and built upon in subsequent modules. Key topics, such as e-business (including e-commerce and globalization), are included in every learning module, due to their relevance to modern business. The IMD program is inspired more by management practice than academic theory, and learning material is focused on current and emerging issues. Because the faculty members teach in both IMD's Executive Development Programs, which reach more than 4,000 global executives per year, and the M.B.A. program, what they learn through working with leading corporations automatically finds its way into the M.B.A. curriculum. Two years ago, IMD also began an Executive M.B.A. (E.M.B.A.) program for company-sponsored, experienced managers. It can be completed in anywhere from sixteen months to three years. As part of a further innovation, the full range of electives is offered jointly to both E.M.B.A. and M.B.A. participants. This provides students with a valuable opportunity to interact with experienced peers and get another vision of business challenges.

A typical learning activity at IMD is made up of three phases. First, participants study assigned cases individually, identifying issues that require further depth of understanding. They then work in small groups, broadening their outlook by testing their opinions and drawing on the experiences of group members from different cultural and business backgrounds. Participants spend one third of their time working in

teams, ensuring that they tap into the large reservoir of experience among their own classmates and develop their skills in problem solving, communication, and leadership in an international environment. Finally, in the classroom, guided by faculty members, participants explore new concepts, share experiences, and are challenged to present their opinions and solutions.

IMD limits the class size to 85 participants, reinforcing the belief that small class size allows innovation, flexibility, and a personal interplay between students and faculty members that few schools can match.

Students and the M.B.A. Experience

IMD strongly believes that each participant is a key source of learning for other participants in the program. Accordingly, every effort is made to ensure that the right balance occurs among the 85 participants, in terms of work experience, nationality, and academic background, to maximize the learning experience. The students have an average of seven years of work experience, with a range of three to twelve years. Sixty-four percent of the participants have their experience in industry, 14 percent in financial services, 9 percent in consulting, and 13 percent in services and other areas. All participants have shown fast career progression, and most have international work experience. The program has a standard of requiring significant career accomplishments; therefore, the average age of participants is 31, with a range of 26 to 35 years. Typically, more than thirty countries are represented in a single class. The class of 2000 profile is as follows: 51 percent from Europe, 20 percent from Asia, 12 percent from Latin America, 10 percent from the U.S.A. and Canada, 3 percent from Australia, and 4 percent from the Middle East, Africa, and the Caribbean. Educational backgrounds vary as well, with about 60 percent from engineering and business and the balance from finance, economics, natural sciences, and humanities.

Special Features

International Consulting Projects are an integral part of the M.B.A. program. Participants serve as consultants to the top management of client companies and advise them on critical, far-reaching management issues. It is the perfect opportunity for students to apply their classroom learning to developing creative, results-oriented solutions to real management problems. The projects address issues from strategy formulation to operational problems. The International Consulting Projects follow a systematic four-phase approach: the industry analysis phase, the company analysis phase, the issue analysis phase, and the implementation and feedback phase. Participants work in teams of 5 to 6 under the guidance of a faculty adviser. Client companies are located all over the world and include a variety of industries and sectors.

The Team Initiated Enterprise (TIE) projects were developed as a direct response to company comments that M.B.A. graduates are good at analyzing but not very talented at initiating and implementing. The participants are simply told to create an initiative that provides value for someone else and see it through to implementation. The only stipulation is that it be a worthwhile learning experience for the team. The teams are self-selected, and the projects take place during the first half of the program. In the past, participants put a team on top of Mont Blanc; opened a day-care center for students' children; raised $169,000 for a children's hospital in Budapest, Hungary; and taught business education to entrepreneurs in Eastern Europe.

The Faculty

M.B.A. participants receive a high degree of personal attention at IMD with a student-faculty ratio of 2:1. The faculty also reflects IMD's internationality, with almost twenty different nationalities represented. The faculty members are extensively involved in teaching in IMD's executive education programs and, therefore, maintain a close relationship with real-world management issues. The faculty members also serve as advisers for the International Consulting Projects.

The Business School Network

More than 120 companies worldwide have formed a special relationship with IMD through the Partner Program and Business Associate Network. They are IMD's partners in industry and constitute a unique network based on the common goal of improving performance in international management. These companies help ensure that IMD's M.B.A. program addresses the real needs of business via their input on program design and review. M.B.A. participants also have access to hundreds of executives who participate in IMD's executive education program on the same campus. IMD's partner companies include ABB Asea Brown Boveri Ltd.; Baxter International; Bertlesmann AG; British Telecommunications Plc.; Caterpillar, Inc.; Citibank International Plc; Credit Suisse Group; DaimlerChrysler AG; Du Pont de Nemours International; F. Hoffmann-La Roche Ltd.; IBM Europe; Lego Group; Nestlé S.A.; Nokia Corporation; Philips Electronics N.V.; Sony Europe; Tetra Laval Group; Unilever; and UBS AG.

The College and Environs

The history of IMD goes back to 1946 when Alcan created IMI in Geneva, Europe's first business school, and 1957 when Nestlé founded IMEDE, Lausanne, with the active involvement of the Harvard Business School. The merger of the resources and the wide experience of the two institutions gave birth to IMD in 1989. IMD is located in Lausanne, a French-speaking region where there is a strong tradition of international exchange. Lausanne is also home to the International Olympic Committee. The campus is just 40 minutes from Geneva, home to several European corporate headquarters, the United Nations, and several international organizations. The IMD community is small and friendly, allowing participants and faculty members to mix freely on a first-name basis. The atmosphere strikes the right balance between very intensive study and informality. More importantly, IMD's international character brings participants into daily contact with people from many different cultures and traditions.

Placement

IMD M.B.A. graduates are internationally recognized as professionally trained managers, and they are recruited by leading companies to take on challenging global opportunities with high-level responsibility. More than 50 companies come to IMD to recruit each year, but on-campus recruiting is only a small part of the recruiting story. Each year, a large number of job offers are sourced through the IMD network. This network includes executives attending programs on campus, faculty members, Partner and Business Associate companies, International Consulting Project clients, and IMD alumni. For the class of 1999, 97 percent of the participants received at least one job offer by graduation, with an average of three offers per participant. Graduates went around the globe, including 75 percent to Europe, 17 percent to North America, 5 percent to Asia, and 3 percent to Latin America. Sixty-three percent went into industry (in a variety of sectors and functions), 23 percent into consulting, and 14 percent into financial services. The average starting salary was $93,000, and the median starting salary was $91,000 (neither figure includes bonuses).

Admission

An important factor in the success and reputation of the IMD M.B.A. Program is the quality of the people in the class. The admissions committee strives to select only the very best: talented men and women who have demonstrated significant progression in their careers, solid intellectual ability, outstanding potential for leadership, a far-reaching international outlook, and excellent interpersonal skills. Candidates should hold a bachelor's degree or its equivalent from an accredited institution and must complete the GMAT. IMD M.B.A. participants are between 26 and 35 years old, with a minimum of three years and an average of seven years of work experience. Candidates whose applications pass the initial assessment of the admissions committee are invited to interview at IMD. English is the only language of instruction, and participants must have a strong command of both written and spoken English.

Finances

The fees for a self-sponsored participant are set at a subsidized level of SwFr 45,000. Company-sponsored candidates are charged the full cost of their education, SwFr 65,000. Fees cover tuition, use of the library and computer facilities, office supplies, lunches at IMD during the week, and visa and permit costs within Switzerland. Rent and other living expenses vary depending on participants' family situations and personal lifestyles. However, the average yearly rent for an apartment is SwFr 12,500. IMD offers a variety of scholarships and loans to accepted participants.

Application Facts and Dates

Application deadlines are February 1, April 1, June 1, August 1, and September 1 for the following January class start date. Candidates receive notification of the admissions committee's decision approximately six weeks after the deadline date. For more information, students should contact:

M.B.A. Information Officer
International Institute for Management Development
Chemin de Bellerive 23
P.O. Box 915
CH-1001 Lausanne
Switzerland
Telephone: 41-21-618-0298
　　　　　　41-21-618-0111
Fax: 41-21-618-0615
E-mail: mbainfo@imd.ch
World Wide Web: http://www.imd.ch

Indiana University Bloomington

Bloomington, Indiana

EDUCATING FOR THE TWENTY-FIRST CENTURY

Indiana's faculty members are committed to teaching and research—a combination that demands intellect, energy, and a willingness to put some of the best hours of their lives into the classroom. We have created an academic environment in which change occurs as a matter of course—in the curriculum, in ways of teaching and learning, in just about everything. No one should have the slightest doubt that our graduates are technically competent. Years ago, we would have taken that as high praise. Now it is merely an expectation. So we ask ourselves what it is that distinguishes the truly exceptional student. I'd say it is leadership, teamwork, persuasion, communications, and critical thinking. The Indiana graduate with those skills and abilities is the M.B.A. of the twenty-first century.

—Dan Dalton, Dean

Programs and Curricular Focus

The first year of the M.B.A. curriculum is designed to provide students with basic business principles and management tools. Students complete core sequences that include integrative teaching methods, group work, and consideration of the global economy. Critical issues of cultural diversity, ethics, electronic commerce, leadership, and communication are integrated across the curriculum. The second year of the program is flexible. Students usually choose at least one major, but double majors and minors are available, as well as a range of electives and a self-design major option. Majors include economic consulting, e-business, finance, information systems, international management, marketing, new venture and business development, production and operations, strategic human resources, and strategic management consulting.

Students and the M.B.A. Experience

Each year, Indiana enrolls an entering class of approximately 275 students. International students make up 32 percent, women 28 percent, and minority students 15 percent of the student population. The average age for students is 28 years, with an age range of approximately 22 to 40. The average number of years of work experience is five, and students come from a broad range of professional backgrounds. Thirty percent of students are married. Thirty-eight percent of the students are from the

Midwest, 11 percent from the West and Southwest, 12 percent from the Northeast and Mid-Atlantic, and 7 percent from the South. The program puts heavy emphasis on teamwork, community involvement, and an integrated understanding of business functions and issues.

❖ Global Focus

The Indiana M.B.A. program features several study abroad options, foreign language tutoring and instruction, and integrated exposure to international issues. Students may earn a Certificate of Global Achievement through a combination of course work, cultural exposure, and language accomplishments.

The Faculty

M.B.A. faculty members are some of the most accomplished in the Kelley School of Business. Those who volunteer to be part of the core faculty have intensive contact with M.B.A. students in class and outside the classroom, serving as mentors to student teams and participating in orientation activities. Core faculty members work together to prepare an integrated curriculum that eliminates redundancy and emphasizes areas of connection among specific disciplines.

The Business School Network

Corporate Partnerships

Students have access to corporate leaders beginning during orientation, where they meet professionals in a roundtable format to learn about different functions and

industries. Case competitions sponsored by corporations such as Deloitte & Touche and Kraft are a regular feature. Student clubs such as the Finance Guild and Marketing Club regularly sponsor seminars and host speakers from the corporate community.

The College and Environs

Indiana University at Bloomington has 36,000 students on an 1,800-acre campus located in a Midwestern "college town" of about 63,000. The town is set among the rolling hills of southern Indiana, and the campus has been rated among the five most beautiful in the U.S. The University boasts one of the finest music schools in the world. Bloomington and the University have efficient, economical public transportation available, and the city and campus are very safe for students and families.

Facilities

On-campus student housing is available for both single and married students. Indiana University maintains an extensive computer network that provides access to mainframe computers, databases, and the Internet. M.B.A. students routinely use the electronic mail system, the Internet, the Dow Jones News/Retrieval Service, and other electronic resources. The School of Business library has more than 150,000 volumes of research materials. The main library, across the street from the School of Business, is internationally recognized as one of the best university libraries.

Technology Environment

All students are required to own laptop computers and use them to complete their academic work. Computer clusters in the School of Business and around campus provide access to software, electronic services, and printers. Faculty members regularly use computer technology in the classroom.

Placement

The School's nationally recognized Graduate Career Services Office has comprehensive resources and programs to help students secure internships and full-time employment. More than 150 companies visit the campus each year to recruit M.B.A. students for positions around the country. The Graduate Career Services Office also produces resume books and provides students access to an alumni database.

Admission

Indiana University admits M.B.A. students for the fall semester only. A minimum TOEFL score of 580 (237 on the computer-based TOEFL) is required for nonnative English speakers. The average GMAT score is approximately 640. The Indiana M.B.A. Program seeks applicants who are motivated, interested in working in diverse groups, and have a strong professional focus.

Finances

Tuition and fees for the 2000–01 academic year are $9908 for in-state students and $19,258 for out-of-state students. Room and board are $6292, books and supplies $1420, personal expenses $4050, and the computer allowance is $3000, for a total budget of $34,020 for out-of-state students. Approximately 35 percent of Indiana's

M.B.A. students receive financial aid from the Kelley School of Business. Graduate assistantships are available; these provide a partial fee remission and stipend in return for a minimal work obligation with faculty members or within administrative departments in the School of Business. In addition, more than $200,000 in scholarship funds is awarded each year to M.B.A. students. The business school awards are based on merit, not need. The IU Office of Student Financial Assistance administers federal financial aid based on student need. (The cost of a laptop computer is calculated into the student's financial aid budget.) Indiana University participates in the Consortium for Graduate Study in Management, which offers substantial support for candidates from minority groups.

International Students

Thirty-two percent of Indiana's M.B.A. students are non-U.S. citizens. An active International Business Society within the M.B.A. program provides important professional and personal support. The University has a large graduate student and international student population as well. International students enjoy the supportive atmosphere of the M.B.A.

program, and the high level of student services helps them acclimate to their new environment.

Application Facts and Dates

The Indiana University M.B.A. program offers several application deadlines. Application deadlines for domestic students and permanent residents are December 1, January 15, March 1, and April 15. Application deadlines for international students are December 1, February 1, and March 1. Decisions on complete applications can be expected approximately ten weeks from each deadline. Applicants are encouraged to meet the early deadlines. For application materials and information, students should contact:

Kelley School of Business
M.B.A. Program
1309 East Tenth Street, Room 254
Indiana University
Bloomington, Indiana 47405-1701
Telephone: 812-855-8006
 800-994-8622 (toll-free within the U.S.)
Fax: 812-855-9039
E-mail: mbaoffice@indiana.edu
World Wide Web: http://www.kelley. indiana.edu/MBA

INSEAD (The European Institute of Business Administration)

Fontainebleau, France

LEARNING FOR LEADERSHIP—THE GLOBAL EXPERIENCE

▶ *With so many good M.B.A. programmes to choose from, why take ten months for an M.B.A. from INSEAD? INSEAD is the largest and best known of the truly international business schools—the schools with no dominant culture. Since opening a campus in Asia, our programme now enables you to enrich your profile with a global experience from two of the world's largest regions: Europe and Asia.*

There are about 700 of the best and brightest M.B.A.'s at INSEAD from more than fifty different countries. With the workweek regularly reaching 70 hours, INSEAD is not for the fainthearted. A participant described her experience here as "drinking from a fire hydrant." But INSEAD can also be fun, judging from the intense social life that accompanies the intense academics. Finally, students have the full educational benefit, recognition, and career potential of a prestigious M.B.A. degree in less than a year. We look forward to welcoming students who want an intellectually stimulating global management education and who thrive on hard work and intense pressure.

—H. Landis Gabel, Associate Dean

Programs and Curricular Focus

INSEAD's M.B.A. programme ensures a solid general management education while allowing participants to tailor the programme to their individual requirements. To achieve this goal, the programme begins with a series of core courses that cover the fundamentals of business. These ensure that participants obtain a common level of knowledge in the fundamentals of business, irrespective of their backgrounds. The second phase of the programme introduces participants to broader management issues and to the wider economic and political environment that influences both corporate strategies and national industrial policies. The programme's final phase offers the opportunity for participants to select courses to match their career needs and interests. Electives allow participants to focus on a field of particular interest or to further investigate general management issues.

INSEAD's pedagogical approach is pragmatic. It seeks to prepare participants by simulating business reality in a low-risk environment. This means that the M.B.A. programme is based on problem solving in small groups, active participation in class, computer simulations, and individual preparation and research.

There are two 10½-month promotions each year. One promotion starts in Fontainebleau, France, in late August and ends in early July; the other begins in Fountainebleau or in Singapore in January and finishes in December, with a seven-week summer recess. Although always evolving, the two programmes are virtually identical in structure and content. Both programmes are organised into five periods of eight weeks, each period ending with exams followed by a short break. Each period consists of a minimum number of courses for which a participant must register. Students have the opportunity to change campuses for all or part of their elective periods, which run from periods 3 to 5. In order to qualify for the INSEAD M.B.A. degree, participants must obtain credits in at least twenty-two courses. Courses are taught entirely in English.

Students and the M.B.A. Experience

The INSEAD M.B.A. programme is a year of opportunities to make lasting friendships that span the world, to be inspired by professors, and to meet and listen to leading international business figures on campus. Despite the amount of time devoted to studying, INSEAD is a hub of varied activities. The level and intensity of the M.B.A. programme demand highly qualified participants. In an atmosphere of camaraderie and competition, participants are pushed to discover their limits as well as their potential.

The M.B.A. participants represent approximately fifty different nationalities. Not only is the group as a whole international, but each individual has an international outlook, with more than two thirds of INSEAD's M.B.A. participants speaking three or more languages and more than half the class having studied or worked abroad. The average age of participants is 29, and participants have, on average, about five years of professional experience.

Special Features

The INSEAD M.B.A. programme is an intensive one that demands that participants commit themselves from day one. The programme provides a sound generalist management education, broadens horizons, and prepares participants for international careers, without the two-year interruption common to many programmes. The high quality of faculty members and participants, the alumni and corporate network, and a truly international environment have combined to make INSEAD one of the top management schools in the world.

The recent establishment of an Asian campus offers a new global standard in M.B.A. education and a unique opportunity for participants who want to enrich their profile with international experience from two of the world's largest regions: Europe and Asia.

The Faculty

INSEAD prides itself on the many talents of its faculty members and their close ties with both the academic and business communities. The 124 permanent professors, with qualifications from distinguished institutions around the world, represent almost thirty different nationalities. The relevance of their teaching and the innovation in their research are guaranteed by close partnerships with industry, nourished by the constant interaction with about 5,500 business executives who attend programmes at INSEAD each year. INSEAD's faculty members regularly receive international awards for cases, books, and articles and for their contributions to the academic community in management.

The Business School Network

While many of the advantages of an INSEAD M.B.A. degree are obvious during the course of the programme, some become more visible with time. The importance of the International Alumni Association is one. There are almost 20,000 INSEAD alumni worldwide, of whom 10,800 have graduated from the M.B.A. programme and the remainder from executive programmes of at least four weeks in length. In today's global environment, the value of international contacts is increasingly important. The ability to pick up the telephone to question a former classmate is extremely useful in the context of global competition.

A growing network of leading corporations endorses INSEAD's commitment to education in an international context, expressing confidence in INSEAD's teaching and research through generous and highly valued contributions. Through combined research projects, executive education programmes, and M.B.A. and executive alumni, INSEAD has conducted a unique global network of contacts in influential positions. Over time and across distances, the INSEAD network is proving to be a critical tie in bringing successful people and businesses together.

The College and Environs

INSEAD is set on two campuses, one on the edge of the Fontainebleau Forest in the heart of Europe and the other amongst tropical forests in Singapore's education belt, in the heart of Asia. Both provide an ideal study environment, with facilities that include modern, air-conditioned amphitheatres and meeting rooms, coffee bars, and restaurant facilities. The campus in Europe is 65 kilometres southeast of Paris, while the new purpose-built campus in Asia is just a 20 minutes' drive from the city centre of Singapore.

Technology Environment

The campuses are linked electronically, allowing videoconferencing and e-mail exchange. Internet-connected PCs reserved for M.B.A. participants are available on both campuses, and participants also have access to a variety of online CD-ROM databases.

Placement

INSEAD's Career Management Service (CMS) is an advisory and information resource for M.B.A. participants preparing for their careers after graduation. CMS organises a wide range of activities to assist M.B.A. participants in their job searches and career plans, including career counselling, seminars, workshops, and an extensive company resource centre. Special assistance and information sources are available to facilitate independent job search in parallel with on-campus recruitment. A career professional is available on both campuses.

The CMS acts as a liaison between M.B.A. participants and companies, organising the logistics for all on-campus recruitment on both campuses. More than 130 companies recruit at INSEAD twice a year. In 1999, about 500 different companies sought INSEAD M.B.A.'s for career employment, and participants received an average of three different job offers.

Admission

INSEAD aims to attract talented young professionals with high potential for effective leadership in complex international business environments from a wide range of cultural, academic, and professional backgrounds. Sharp intellectual curiosity and a desire to learn and stretch oneself in a rigorous academic programme are expected, as well as personal qualities to contribute meaningfully to the many academic and extracurricular activities at INSEAD.

In addition to completing the application, which includes biographical data, essays, two letters of recommendation, official transcripts of grades, and a job description, applicants must take the GMAT. If preselected, the candidate is invited to attend at least two evaluative interviews. The TOEFL may also be required for nonnative English-speaking candidates.

All candidates must be fluent in English and have a working knowledge of a second language before starting the programme. Upon completion of the programme, all participants must demonstrate knowledge of a third language.

Finances

Tuition for the academic year 2000–01 is €27,900, and it is estimated that a single participant should budget another €16,600 for accommodation and living expenses, books, and insurance.

International Students

The international nature of INSEAD makes it unique. Typically, no single nationality exceeds 15 percent of the student body; it is the INSEAD culture that dominates. Diversity helps ensure that participants see the world through new perspectives and learn how to benefit from both the conflicts and synergies that arise. Ten months spent studying, working, and living among culturally diverse influences means adapting to new approaches, accepting that listening is also learning, and cooperating to achieve results.

Application Facts and Dates

INSEAD has two intakes, one in August (Fountainebleau only) and one in January (Fountainbleau and Singapore). Admission is on a rolling basis, but it is strongly recommended that candidates submit their application as soon as it is complete.

For further information, students should visit INSEAD's Web site at the address listed below. A full brochure and application may be requested via the Web site or by sending an e-mail or a fax to the M.B.A. Information Office. Inquiries should include the student's name, address, telephone number, date of birth, nationality, and e-mail address.

Students may contact:

INSEAD
M.B.A. Information Office
Boulevard de Constance
77305 Fontainebleau Cedex
France
Fax: 33-1-60-74-55-30
E-mail: mba.info@insead.fr
World Wide Web: http://www.insead.
    fr/MBA

IMI International Management Institute

International Business School

Brussels and Antwerp, Belgium

DEDICATED TO CROSS-CULTURAL BUSINESS EDUCATION

Our quality programs are designed to train participants to become well-versed in international business and to speak foreign languages, but most importantly, the objectives are to convey an understanding of other cultures and encourage students to think globally and strategically beyond their own national borders. We form the new generation of managers who must be hands-on, action driven, and inquisitive minded. Development of leadership skills, computer literacy and intercultural aspects of management are the main features of our high-quality career education.

The programs offered by IMI meet the challenges of an ever-changing and complex international business environment.

—Freddy L. Kirschstein, Ph.D., Dean

Programs and Curricular Focus

Through close lecturer-student contact and classes in small groups, the International Management Institute (IMI) provides a professional academic atmosphere to meet students' individual needs. This ensures permanent interaction so that the student will obtain a firm grasp of the material.

To prevent business theory from remaining abstract and inapplicable, syllabi are based on the case-study method. This practical approach to learning involves the study and solving of actual problems as they arise in the business world. Courses and syllabi are developed, monitored, and adapted to the demands of the marketplace with the assistance of an Advisory Council composed of prominent personalities from the business community.

A typical master's program at IMI consists of fifteen courses spread over three terms of ten weeks each. Full-time students may complete their master's program in one academic year; part-time students spread their graduate program over two or three years.

In addition, an educational system allowing students the flexibility of entering in October, January, March, or July is used. Privately taught courses and individual coaching are also available.

IMI encourages students to improve their language skills by choosing elective courses in French, German, Spanish, Italian, English, and Dutch. Besides the Master of Business Administration (M.B.A.) program, IMI offers a Master of Science in Transportation and Logistics, a

Master of Arts in Business Communication and Public Relations, and a Master of Arts in International Hospitality and Tourism Management.

Students and the M.B.A. Experience

Students at IMI are taught in a pragmatic way with the use of simulation techniques and up-to-date case studies. They also learn to think strategically when making decisions, to empathize with their peers, to inspire teamwork and team building, and to contribute to the success of a project. Thinking creatively and independently by questioning, rather than blindly accepting subject material, is strongly encouraged. Throughout the academic year, students are given a number of assignments and tests so that their progress can be assessed.

The average graduate student is 27 years old and is holder of an undergraduate degree in a variety of fields such as engineering, law, social sciences, or economics.

The Faculty

Lecturers are recruited from around the world and bring with them considerable international business experience. Indeed, the majority of lecturers have other occupations in addition to their teaching positions at IMI. This ensures the practical nature of the curricula and makes it possible for students to benefit from the experience these lecturers have accumulated throughout their business careers. In addition, several faculty

members are management consultants who provide services to organizations and companies.

The Business School Network
Corporate Partnerships

Students of the International Management Institute benefit from regularly scheduled lectures from nationally and internationally renowned professionals and academics.

To expose M.B.A. students to a variety of career options, each campus organizes a series of company visits. This allows students to obtain firsthand information on various types of industries. In addition to regularly scheduled classes, IMI organizes seminars directed by professionals with outstanding reputations in the business community at large. These seminars take place on campus or on location and deal with a variety of contemporary business topics.

The College and Environs

The International Management Institute is an independent, privately held, nonprofit organization dedicated to educating and training students and business professionals through a unique cross-cultural approach. IMI's campuses are located in Brussels and Antwerp, Belgium.

In Brussels, the capital of Belgium and Europe, the campus is situated in the heart of the city, offering a wealth of cultural, historical, sports, and social resources. The cosmopolitan capital is the hub for Euro-governmental administration and banking and insurance industries.

Antwerp, the second-largest city of Belgium and renowned for its harbor and diamond industry, offers many amenities. The campus is centrally located and easily accessible by public transportation.

Facilities

Both campuses provide attractive dormitories. However, if students prefer to live off campus in one of the many rooms, studios, or apartments available in the neighborhood, IMI's housing office is happy to assist students in finding appropriate accommodation.

Technology Environment

Realizing the importance of information processing, each campus has its IT center. This center is intended for computer science courses and students' daily use. All students are provided with an e-mail address and utilize the Internet on a regular basis.

Placement

International Management Institute's Placement Office provides consultation and assistance in career services for all graduates. It maintains close contact with numerous companies throughout Europe and provides information on internship and permanent job opportunities. Almost 100 percent of graduates find a satisfactory position soon after graduation.

Admission

When applying for admission to the International Management Institute, applicants must submit a completed application form, hold an undergraduate degree or its equivalent, and submit official GMAT scores. A TOEFL score is required of applicants for whom English is not their native language. Non–European Union applicants must apply for a student visa and must have financial guarantees in the form of letters from sponsors and bank certificates.

Finances

The tuition fee is due at the beginning of each academic term according to the schedule. For the academic year 1999–2000 the tuition fee was €8924 (BEF 360,000). Accommodation and living expenses may be budgeted at €5000 (BEF 200,000) and books and study materials at approximately €400 (BEF 16,000).

International Students

One of the great advantages of the International Management Institute is its diverse, cross-cultural student population. The students represent a wide variety of nationalities from around the globe.

Each campus has its own student associations with officers elected by the student body. The officers are in charge of organizing social, cultural, athletic, and educational events.

Application Facts and Dates

Students may register all year round and start their program in October, January, March, or July. Registration must be completed in accordance with the procedures as determined by the administration. For more information, students should contact:

Mr. Luc Van Mele
Director of Graduate Programs
International Management Institute
Jacob Jordaensstraat 77
2018 Antwerp
Belgium
Telephone: 32-3-218-54-31
Fax: 32-3-218-58-68
E-mail: info@timi.edu
World Wide Web: http://www.timi.edu

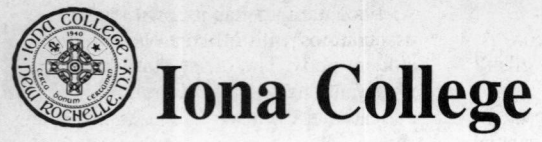

Iona College

New Rochelle, New York

> ## LEADERSHIP—THE HAGAN M.B.A. PROGRAM
>
> *In the face of the swift and complex developments of today's rapidly changing global marketplace, leaders must act quickly and competitively—adding value to their organizations. The most effective leaders will be able to mobilize teams of employees to solve problems creatively.*
>
> —Nicholas J. Beutell, Dean

Programs and Curricular Focus

The goal of the Hagan School of Business M.B.A. program is to produce graduates and future leaders who understand business and its challenges as the twenty-first century approaches. It seeks to graduate women and men who have the skills to work productively in a high-technology society, demonstrate sensitivity to the global and multicultural character of business, provide strategic leadership in a competitive environment, and subscribe to high ethical standards in the practice of their profession.

The new M.B.A. curriculum consists of core courses in the functional areas of business perspectives (an integrated overview), followed by a major concentration allowing for specialized study, advanced electives that provide students an opportunity to custom design the breadth component of the curriculum, and a capstone course.

Computer applications are integrated into the program, as are the development of presentation and communication skills. Case studies, team projects, computer simulation games, experiential exercises, and lectures are the commonly used methods of teaching.

The calendar follows a trimester schedule of twelve weeks each, with two summer sessions, allowing students to earn more credits within the year. Classes meet once a week in the evening, Monday through Thursday from 6:30 to 9:30, with some Saturday morning classes.

The number of credits required for the degree is 57 before waivers and transfer credits are applied. There is a six-year limit to finish the program. A typical M.B.A. student takes 45 credits and completes the program in four years on a part-time basis or two years full-time.

Students and the M.B.A. Experience

Almost all of the students in the program hold full-time jobs at Fortune 500 companies, major brokerage houses, large commercial banks, and insurance companies. Midsize and small companies are also well represented. Many students hold middle-management positions in blue-chip firms such as IBM, Bell Atlantic, Chase Manhattan Bank, Kraft-General Foods, and Lederle Laboratories, to cite a few.

The average age of the students is 30. They have, on the average, about seven years of full-time work experience in various industries. It is this maturity, diverse corporate background, and significant work experience that they bring to the program and contribute to the overall quality of the learning process.

The student body is represented by approximately the same number of women and men. Most come from the tristate area of New York, New Jersey, and Connecticut. International students represent all continents.

❖ Global Focus

The institutional thrust toward global education and the international character of the faculty members strengthen the goal dimension of the M.B.A. curriculum. Students are encouraged to participate in the summer courses offered abroad.

The Faculty

The Hagan School of Business faculty members are dedicated teachers and professionals. As teacher-scholars, they keep current in their fields of expertise, doing research, publishing, and giving presentations at academic conferences. As professionals, they blend theory and practice, drawing upon their own and their students' business experience. Among them are internationally recognized experts in such diverse fields as artificial intelligence, case writing, corporate values, and business ethics.

With very few exceptions, those who teach in the M.B.A. program are full-time, with appropriate terminal degrees earned at America's top universities. Students recognize them for their teaching excellence and seek their advice on career matters.

The Business School Network

Corporate Partnerships

Through the Dean's Business Advisory Council, made up of business executives from corporations that send students to the program, the Hagan School has created a partnership venue with business. Through the council, business has a real opportunity to influence the strategic direction of the School. It is mechanisms of this kind that allow the School to be responsive to the needs of the business community and offer a relevant curriculum. The Hagan Business Forum brings successful alumni as well as prominent local business executives to the campus to give lectures on current issues to the student body. The Hagan Report keeps alumni and students informed.

Prominent Alumni

The Hagan School is proud to count among its distinguished alumni senior executives and business leaders from America's largest and best corporations, such as Philip Morris, Citicorp, IBM, Kraft Foods, Bell Atlantic, and Merrill Lynch.

The College and Environs

Iona College was founded in 1940 by the Congregation of Christian Brothers. Its main campus is located in New Rochelle, a small city on the Long Island Sound in Westchester County, about 20 miles north of the heart of Manhattan. The M.B.A. program is also offered in Rockland County, a few miles west of the Hudson River.

With its strategic locations and proximity to New York City, the Hagan School of Business enables students to

Hagan Hall.

benefit from the rich, diversified environment that is attuned to the advances and innovations of the global market. The New York metropolitan area is the home of many major national and multinational corporations, such as IBM, Texaco, and PepsiCo, as well as many of the nation's largest banks, brokerage houses, and insurance firms.

Technology Environment

The academic programs of the Hagan School are strongly supported by state-of-the-art computer equipment and software. Two multimedia Pentium labs are available in Hagan Hall. More than 500 PCs are available for student use in public facilities, with some of them open around the clock seven days a week. The Helen T. Arrigoni Library and Technology Center houses multimedia systems with access to the Internet and other popular online databases, including ABI/INFORM.

Many course requirements involve the use of computers, and every student is provided with a computer account, an e-mail address, and access to the system. Internet distance learning classes are offered for a number of upper-level M.B.A. classes. Students can access these classes at any time from anywhere.

State-of-the-art interactive video and multimedia systems are available for teaching and student learning. TVs and VCRs with cable access and satellite downlinks are found in Hagan classrooms.

Placement

The Office of Career Services of Iona College provides students with career counseling and job search assistance. It alerts students to job openings and positions in companies and to the organizations that seek graduates of the College. Resume referral, mock inter-

views, and counseling for alumni are among the services available to students.

Admission

Admission is selective and based on an evaluation of the student's academic record, scores on the Graduate Management Admission Test (GMAT), references, and work experience. Applications and credentials should be sent to the Graduate Admissions Office of the Hagan School of Business.

Rolling admissions allow students to begin studies in any trimester: fall, winter, spring, or summer. TOEFL scores are required for all students whose native language is not English. International students must provide evidence of adequate funds to cover all expenses.

Finances

Tuition per credit in 2000–01 is $515. Books and supplies cost approximately $1500 per year. There are no boarding facilities on campus for graduate students. Living expense estimates range from $10,000 to $12,000 for ten months, not including vacation periods.

A limited number of graduate assistantships are available to full-time students.

Tuition scholarships are awarded based on exceptional GMAT scores.

Application Facts and Dates

Rolling admissions allow students to submit their application any time. However, completed applications should be received no later than two weeks prior to the start of the trimester for which the student plans to enroll. For more information, students should contact:

Ms. Carol Shea
Director of M.B.A. Admissions
Hagan School of Business
Iona College
715 North Avenue
New Rochelle, New York 10801-1890
Telephone: 914-633-2288
Fax: 914-633-2012
E-mail: cshea@iona.edu

Iowa State University

Ames, Iowa

EXCELLENCE IN AMERICA'S HEARTLAND

▶ *The Iowa State University (ISU) M.B.A. program is staffed with educators who love what they do. We do it well, attracting students from all over the world. Iowa State works to serve you, the education consumer, by providing a flexible and competitive learning environment.*

Iowa State understands the value you place on your education. Ours is a culture dedicated to excellence in graduate business education and whose faculty is active in research, committed to innovative teaching, and accessible to students.

Students are not just numbers here. Iowa State offers a wide array of educational resources in an environment sensitive to individual student needs. We provide an environment where students can stretch and grow as professionals and as people, making Iowa State a warm and inviting place to be.

—Benjamin J. Allen, Dean

Programs and Curricular Focus

The Iowa State University M.B.A. program offers a friendly, personal environment that emphasizes flexibility and teamwork. As our world gets smaller, and its demographics change, the ability to work effectively with a diverse population is vital to the foundation of global success. First-year M.B.A. students are preassigned to small work groups that are chosen to maximize each member's contribution to diversity, personal strengths, and academic and work backgrounds. Students are then challenged with innovative projects and a curriculum that dovetails with global management issues.

M.B.A. candidates may pursue their course work through a full-time program or, to accommodate employed students, through the part-time Evening M.B.A. and Saturday M.B.A. programs. Evening M.B.A. classes are held in Des Moines, Iowa. The two-year 48-credit-hour M.B.A. program consists of an integrated core curriculum and 24 credit hours of electives. Teamwork is an integral part of the first-year M.B.A. experience. Second-year students tailor their course work to meet individual academic and career goals. By placing a premium on flexibility and accessibility, the program guides candidates through interactive projects that recreate a corporate environment.

M.B.A. students may opt to concentrate their studies in a particular area. Areas of specialization include accounting, agribusiness, finance, human resources, management information systems, manufacturing and quality, and marketing.

Students and the M.B.A. Experience

The 240 graduate business students at Iowa State reflect a diversity of educational, cultural, and professional backgrounds. Drawing upon the University's international stature, the Iowa State M.B.A. program attracts students worldwide, representing twenty countries. Thirty-five percent of the students are women. One third of Iowa State M.B.A. students bring an undergraduate degree in business to their graduate experience, and 25 percent reflect a background in engineering. Science undergraduates make up 20 percent, and social sciences, humanities, and other degrees illustrate the other varying backgrounds of undergraduates who seek the College of Business for graduate work. Iowa State's part-time M.B.A. candidates represent industry sectors throughout the state of Iowa, including agriculture, education, financial services, health and human services, manufacturing, and small business.

Students are encouraged to be active participants in the M.B.A. Association. This organization promotes career development activities, plans social events, and serves as a representative body for M.B.A. students in the College.

❖ Global Focus

To add an international dimension, Iowa State M.B.A. students who wish to study abroad can find many programs and countries to which their graduate program can be tailored. The Study Abroad Center has extensive information on both the ISU Exchange Program and the International Internship Program. The Iowa State College of Business is a member of a university consortium participating in a summer international M.B.A. program in Asolo, Italy. Recent M.B.A. students have pursued summer study in Mexico and internship opportunities in the United Kingdom.

Special Features

M.B.A. students may enhance their educational experience through the College's close association with various academic and outreach centers. The Pappajohn Center for Entrepreneurship offers educational and outreach programs aimed at developing the entrepreneurial interests and capabilities of M.B.A. students. M.B.A. students may be given the opportunity to provide research support and consulting services to Iowa small businesses through the Iowa Small Business Development Center. M.B.A. students interested in transportation and logistics management may select course work offered by the College's Department of Logistics, Operations, and Management Information Systems. Research opportunities are available to M.B.A. students through the Center for Transportation Research and Education. M.B.A. students may participate in an annual conference sponsored by the Murray G. Bacon Center for Ethics in Business.

The Faculty

College of Business faculty members have broad backgrounds in industry and education. They possess doctoral degrees from leading business schools across the nation. Faculty members conduct research that keeps them on the cutting edge of business theory and practice. Many have international experience. College of Business faculty members are accommodating, accessible, and available to advise and help students in achieving their academic and career goals.

The Business School Network
Corporate Partnerships
Iowa State University places immense importance on the exchange of ideas between academic and corporate environments. The College of Business Dean's Advisory Council meets regularly to share its members' expertise and ideas for the M.B.A. program. Speakers from corporations lecture regularly in M.B.A. classrooms. M.B.A. students visit local and regional facilities to observe businesses in action. Through the College's Executive-in-Residence program, M.B.A. students interact with prominent business leaders who visit the Iowa State University campus twice yearly.

Prominent Alumni
Iowa State University counts among its 19,000 business alumni many business leaders, including Bill Adams, Chairman and CEO, Armstrong World Industries (retired); Lynn Vorbrich, President, Midamerican Energy Company (retired); Charles S. Johnson, Executive Vice President, DuPont (retired); Glenn R. Blake, Director, Corporate Personnel, General Mills, Inc.; Cheryl G. Gordon, Chief Executive Officer, Asset Management, Rothschild North America, Inc.; J. Scott Johnson, President/Chief Operating Officer, Norwest Bank Iowa, N.A.; Cara K. Heiden, Executive Vice President, Retail & Direct Client Services, Norwest Mortgage, Inc.; Steve W. Bergstrom, President and Chief Operating Officer, Dynegy, Inc.; C. Richard Stark Jr., President, Iowa Commodities, Ltd.; Craig A. Petermeier, President and CEO, Jacobson Companies; and Kenneth L. Thome, Senior Vice President of Financial Operations, General Mills, Inc.

The College and Environs
The 2,000-acre campus features a quiet lake and a parklike setting. As part of Ames, a community of 50,000, the University is set in the geographic center of the United States, in an area that offers a pleasing mixture of urban and rural life. Founded in 1858, Iowa State is the first land-grant university to have been established under the Morrill Land-Grant Act. The institution was charged with promoting "liberal and practical education . . . in the several pursuits and professions of college life." Today, with more than 25,000 students, Iowa State University is fulfilling that mission: educating students and delivering research discoveries and service to the public.

Facilities
Two state-of-the-art computer labs in the College of Business provide the latest in computer hardware and software technology to M.B.A. students. A distance learning classroom offers instantaneous audiovisual capability to remote sites throughout the state of Iowa. The Durham Computation Center houses 24-hour computer labs and offers related support services for students.

The Parks Library offers a comfortable, friendly environment with a business collection that includes 160,000 bound volumes and 400 periodicals. Also, the library's online information system, SCHOLAR, provides access to the local online catalog.

Technology Environment
Considered one of the nation's "most wired" universities, Iowa State University provides a wide range of computer hardware and software support services, such as e-mail, Internet access, computer consulting, and instructional courses and workshops. Kiosks are located across the campus for students to access personal and University information 24 hours a day. Network connections are available in many classrooms and student residence hall rooms.

Placement
The College of Business offers comprehensive career development and placement programs and services, including job search workshops, career counseling, a career resources center, internship coordination, and campus interviews. A full-time director provides individual career services support to M.B.A. students.

Admission
Each applicant is carefully assessed in terms of his or her intellectual potential, academic achievement, work and professional involvement, interpersonal communication skills, career goals, and motivation. Although it is not required, work experience is strongly preferred for candidacy. Educational records are reviewed from official transcripts, as well as scores from the Graduate Management Admission Test (GMAT) and TOEFL (for international students). Three letters of recommendation, a resume, and the candidate's responses to the essay portion of the application are also required.

Finances
The College of Business and its affiliated centers offer a number of graduate assistantships to qualified M.B.A. students.

Graduate assistants pay resident tuition fees and receive a monthly stipend. Graduate assistants in good academic standing are also awarded a scholarship covering a portion of the resident tuition fee. Scholarship support is also offered to qualified M.B.A. program applicants, including minority and women candidates. Admitted minority M.B.A. students may seek financial assistance through the Graduate Minority Assistantship Program. Outstanding students may be qualified to receive a monetary award through the Premium for Academic Excellence (PACE) program in the Graduate College. PACE recipients generally have an undergraduate GPA of 3.5 or better or a GPA of 3.8 in previous graduate work. The Office of Student Financial Aid offers financial assistance through low-interest loans of various types and employment assistance.

International Students
International Education Services (IES) provides orientation and advising to new international students. IES is a resource through which international students can utilize local community services. It also serves as a liaison with the U.S. Information Agency and the Immigration and Naturalization Service to bring visiting scholars and students to Iowa State University.

Application Facts and Dates
For the M.B.A. program, admission is granted for the fall semester only. Students should submit the Graduate College application form, application fee, official transcripts, and TOEFL scores (if applicable) to the Office of Admissions, 100 Alumni Hall, Iowa State University, Ames, Iowa 50011. Students should submit GMAT scores, letters of reference, a resume, and the personal essays to the Graduate Programs Office at the address below. Although applications are considered after this date, candidates are encouraged to submit application materials by May 1 (March 1 for international students). For more information, students should contact:

Director of Graduate Admissions
College of Business
218 Carver Hall
Iowa State University
Ames, Iowa 50011-2063
Telephone: 515-294-8118
          877-ISU-4MBA (toll-free)
Fax: 515-294-2446
E-mail: busgrad@iastate.edu
World Wide Web: http://www.bus.
   iastate.edu/grad

Johns Hopkins University

School of Professional Studies in Business and Education, Graduate Division of Business and Management

Baltimore, Maryland

► HOPKINS BUSINESS: LEARNING THROUGH LEADERSHIP

At the Johns Hopkins University Graduate Division of Business and Management, students find an academic environment geared to both adult part-time learning and the business marketplace.

The largest part-time graduate business program in the Baltimore-Washington area, the University's programs are expressly designed for adult learning. Small classes feature Hopkins full-time and part-time faculty members, many of whom are leading executives from the region's outstanding corporate, government, and nonprofit sectors. Innovative master's degrees, including the Hopkins M.B.A., and specialized concentrations allow students to tailor programs of study to specific goals and interests. Capstone courses and project-based learning pair students with local companies to address real business challenges. Extensive support services include individual academic advising and career development through the University's extensive Career and Life Planning Center, which assists students in career evaluation and job search strategies.

Hopkins offers business courses at five convenient sites in the Baltimore-Washington region. Evening and weekend classes also help meet the demanding needs of today's working professionals.

The following program description outlines the University's dual mission of providing both a superior academic environment and a lifelong resource for personal and professional growth.

—Ralph Fessler, Dean

Programs and Curricular Focus

Business programs at Hopkins focus on adult students seeking new levels of success as full-time professionals through part-time study. Students choose from a full range of master's and certificate programs, all tailored to provide the business skills and knowledge necessary to compete in an increasingly evolving and competitive marketplace. The curriculum combines practical learning experiences with academic excellence, an outstanding faculty, and flexible formats and scheduling at convenient class locations throughout the Baltimore-Washington metropolitan area.

The Hopkins Master of Business Administration (M.B.A.) is based on a core of cross-disciplinary study. It features a broad-based business education that prepares students for the emerging knowledge economy. In addition, the Hopkins M.B.A. offers students a competitive edge through concentration options in management information systems, electronic business, finance, marketing, management, international business, human resources management, and seniors housing and care.

A central advantage of Hopkins business programs is the number of specialized degrees in addition to the M.B.A. and its concentrations. These programs include the Master of Science in marketing, the Master of Science in real estate (one of the few real estate master's programs in the country), the Master of Science in information and telecommunication systems, and the Master of Science in organization development and human resources. The Police Executive Leadership Program, the first graduate program of its kind in the country, prepares law enforcement executives for the changing role and structure of police departments in the community and region. A specialty M.B.A. in medical services management is offered with the Hopkins School of Medicine. A joint-degree program, the Master of Science in Nursing/M.B.A., is offered with the Hopkins School of Nursing.

While curriculum, sequence, degree requirements, and program length may differ for each program, students usually complete their degree requirements within three to six years.

Hopkins also offers a wide range of certificate programs in business, providing intensive, short-term study in cohort groups. In many instances, credits earned can be transferred to an appropriate master's degree program. Programs include the Graduate Certificate in Investments, graduate and postgraduate certificates in information and telecommunication systems, seniors housing and care, the Skilled Facilitator Certificate, and the Leadership Development Program for Minority Managers. Two certificates, the Business of Medicine (in cooperation with the Hopkins School of Medicine) and the Business of Nursing (offered with the Hopkins School of Nursing), blend business and health-care disciplines.

Students and the Master's Experience

Students enrolled in all master's programs benefit from leadership and learning advantages that are unique to Hopkins. The outstanding faculty comprises some of the region's foremost academicians and business practitioners. Hopkins faculty members involve students in actual business practices through case studies, special projects, and culminating capstone courses, which apply newfound skills and understanding to a diverse range of business challenges currently facing area organizations. Working in teams, students select a regional company, studying all aspects of its business, including market, operations, finance, and distribution. They next prepare strategic plans for their companies, presenting these plans to company officials and other business leaders, who ask students to defend their recommendations. Organizations that have recently engaged capstone students include BGE, Black & Decker, GE Information Systems, Waverly Press, Upper Chesapeake Health System, and Legg Mason, Incorporated.

The Faculty

The Graduate Division of Business and Management blends an experienced full-time faculty with some of the region's foremost business leaders, administrators, and entrepreneurs in the public, private, and nonprofit sectors to create an exciting, innovative teaching dynamic. Hopkins faculty members are not merely experts in their fields; they involve their students in hands-on projects that address current challenges facing real businesses.

Faculty members encourage a partnership approach to learning, which involves students in role playing, debates, case studies, simulations, research, guest speakers, and strategy sessions, among other activities. Capstone courses and special projects focus learning on real business challenges faced by area corporations. Many of these organizations have gone on to adopt the strategies and recommendations of their student "partners."

The Business School Network

Some of the Baltimore-Washington area's most prominent and progressive businesses and institutions are represented on the Hopkins faculty, including Bank of America, AT&T, Honeywell, CSX Intermodal, Bell Atlantic, UNISYS Corporation, the FCC, and the U.S. Department of Commerce.

Local business leaders also serve on a number of the School's academic and community advisory boards.

The College and Environs

Johns Hopkins University was founded in Baltimore in 1876 and was the first American university dedicated to both advanced study and scientific research. There are eight academic divisions within the University, including the School of Professional Studies in Business and Education (SPSBE).

Hopkins began teaching part-time students in 1909. Engineering and business programs were added to the curriculum in 1916. The first graduate degree in business was offered in 1971. In 1999, the school assumed a new name—the School of Professional Studies in Business and Education— that better reflects its expanding graduate business, graduate education, and emerging undergraduate programs.

Fifth in the country in population and strategically located on the mid-Atlantic coast, the Baltimore-Washington metropolitan area offers an unmatched array of business and cultural resources and attractions as well as some of the nation's leading institutions of higher learning.

Facilities

The central Hopkins campus, Homewood, is situated on 140 acres in residential north Baltimore. In this traditional academic atmosphere, SPSBE maintains many of its administrative offices and the offices of its Education and Undergraduate Studies divisions. The Schools of Arts and Sciences and Engineering and the University's administration also are located at Homewood. The renowned Milton S. Eisenhower Library, as well as a full-service bookstore, post office, cafeteria, and extensive computing and distance learning facilities, are available to students at this location.

In addition to Homewood, Hopkins features four satellite campuses in the Baltimore-Washington metropolitan area. The Downtown Center, located in the heart of Baltimore's business district, houses the offices of the Graduate Division of Business and Management. The Columbia Center is centrally located between Baltimore and Washington. The Montgomery County Center is located in Rockville, Maryland, along I-270, just north of the nation's capital. The Washington, D.C., Center is located in the District, near Dupont Circle. All sites feature classrooms, computer labs, conventional and online library resources, a bookstore, academic advising services, and other amenities.

Technology Environment

Hopkins is committed to providing a full-service information technology environment to support its students in pursuit of their educational objectives. SPSBE students are afforded the same access to computing and networking resources as are faculty and staff members. Homewood Information Technology Services (HITS) makes available a wide range of resources, including public-access computing laboratories, central computer systems, and departmental computers. Hopkins also maintains affiliations with regional supercomputing centers. Complementing these resources are extensive communications and networking services allowing access to all campus centers and outside research and academic networks. Remote access to e-mail, Internet applications, compilers, word processors, database managers, spreadsheets, graphics and math/statistical packages, utility programs, and library catalogs and databases is available through dial-up modems or through the University's high-speed PPP service, JHU-Connect.

Placement

Professional career counselors in the SPSBE Career and Life Planning Center guide students through the career decision-making process and assist them in the job search. Students have access to services such as career planning workshops and panel presentations, a multimedia resource library, job search consultations, an online job bank, virtual job fairs, a placement file service, and a resume referral service. Students can also be matched with other SPSBE students and alumni for information interviews.

Admission

To be considered for admission to any degree or certificate program, individuals must submit a formal application (including an essay), official transcripts from all postsecondary institutions attended, a professional resume, and an application fee. Because specific admission requirements vary by program, applicants should contact the admission office or appropriate academic division to determine specific admission criteria, suitability of prior degrees, or certification requirements. Applicants for graduate degrees and certificate programs must hold a bachelor's degree from a regionally accredited college or university. Beginning in summer 2001, M.B.A. applicants will be required to submit an official GMAT score.

Finances

Tuition varies from program to program, and within programs themselves, depending upon individual course costs and other specific expenses. Students should contact the admission office for full information on program and course fees and other costs, including application and registration fees. All tuition and fees must be paid in full at the time of registration; registrations cannot be processed unless accompanied by appropriate payment. Students with employer tuition remission benefits must provide appropriate documentation at the time of registration.

Application Facts and Dates

SPSBE has a rolling admission policy, meaning there is no application deadline except for cohort group programs. However, students are encouraged to submit a complete application by May 1 for fall admission, October 1 for spring admission, and January 15 for summer admission. Individuals should allow from six to eight weeks for completion of the entire admission process (from submission of the application to admission decision).

Students should address all correspondence to:

Office of Admission
School of Professional Studies in
   Business and Education
Johns Hopkins University
6740 Alexander Bell Drive
Columbia, Maryland 21046
Telephone: 410-309-1270
Fax: 410-290-1512
E-mail: spsbeinfo@jhu.edu
World Wide Web: http://www.spsbe.jhu.
   edu

Johnson & Wales University

Alan Shawn Feinstein Graduate School

Providence, Rhode Island

CHALLENGES OF THE YEAR 2000 AND BEYOND

The Alan Shawn Feinstein Graduate School's commitment to a high-quality advanced career education is the central theme of our vision for the twenty-first century at Johnson & Wales University. It is the forefront of our ongoing investment of time and energy in maintaining the highest standards for our faculty members and curricula in a students-come-first environment.

—Clif Boyle, Dean

Programs and Curricular Focus

The M.B.A. in Global Business Program of the Alan Shawn Feinstein Graduate School is driven by the theme "learning that gets results worldwide." Graduates apply the knowledge attained from the M.B.A. programs to their workplaces and throughout their careers. Core courses provide students with the fundamental concepts, analytical tools, and professional skills that industry requires in M.B.A. graduates.

In addition to achieving solid mastery of the basic knowledge and skills needed to be leaders in today's enterprises, all M.B.A. in Global Business students are given the opportunity to develop a special area of expertise in one of the following areas of concentration: marketing, financial management, international trade, organizational leadership, and accounting. Each concentration is designed in partnership with industry to ensure that graduates develop the specific advanced skills that employers are seeking in M.B.A. graduates.

The M.B.A. in Hospitality Administration Program provides students with a similar core of management concepts. Added to this is a focus of hospitality-specific courses that are aimed at assisting managers in maximizing yield, refining strategies in the industry, and strengthening their skills as creative problem solvers and agents of change.

The Feinstein Graduate School also offers an M.A. degree in teacher education in the areas of business and food service and an Ed.D. in educational leadership.

Students and the M.B.A. Experience

The international reputation of the M.B.A. programs enables the Graduate School to recruit and carefully select a distinctly global student body. The graduate students at Johnson & Wales represent diverse cultural, professional, and academic backgrounds. The average student is 27 years old, with four years of work-related experience. The enrollment mix includes students from fifty-seven countries, with women representing 43 percent of the enrollment population. The majority of American students come from the Northeast (52 percent). Another 41 percent of the graduate enrollment are international students. Most of the students have undergraduate degrees in business, with many others having backgrounds in education or liberal arts. Employers provide tuition reimbursement for 21 percent of American students, and 68 percent of American students are working while pursuing their graduate degrees.

Special Features

There are convenient day and evening classes to accommodate any schedule; accelerated programs that allow a student to graduate in twelve months; and three terms instead of semesters, allowing the student to complete more courses in less time. There is a diverse student population, representing fifty-seven countries; a student-focused faculty with esteemed academic and professional experience; creative tuition-payment arrangements; specialized programs with career opportunities; and an outstanding career-placement department that offers lifetime placement services.

The Faculty

The Feinstein Graduate School faculty consists of individuals with excellent teaching skills who focus on professional development and provide a learning environment that encourages student participation. The faculty members are selected based on their academic achievements and professional experiences. They are devoted to preparing students for success in the workplace and go through extensive training on working with a diverse student population and staying informed on the latest technology. The graduate faculty members either hold terminal or professional degrees or are working toward these degrees.

The Business School Network

Corporate Partnerships

Johnson & Wales University is continuously expanding its relationship with corporate America. As University guests, local business leaders meet with students to discuss current business trends and developments. Brainstorming and problem-solving skills are sharpened as real-life situations are addressed. As the alumni base grows, many return and discuss how their course work applies to their daily routine.

Prominent Alumni

Johnson & Wales University prides itself on preparing men and women for leadership roles, often as entrepreneurs in business, industry, and education. Alumni hold top positions in a variety of businesses that range from finance to food. Some prominent alumni are Ira Kaplan, President, Servolift Eastern Corporation; Leonard Pinault, President, Foxboro National Bank; Joseph Damore, President, Food Systems IDBA, Inc.; Tracey Trosko, President, First National Network, Inc.; and William Francis, President, Marbil Enterprises, Inc.

The College and Environs

Johnson & Wales University's main campus is located in Providence, Rhode Island. Providence is New England's second-largest city, but it retains its historic charm in combination with the resources of a cultural, business, and industrial center. An hour from the city of Boston, Massachusetts, and less than 4 hours from New York City, Providence is also within easy reach of such well-

known vacation spots as Newport, Rhode Island, and Cape Cod, Massachusetts.

A true city campus, Johnson & Wales's facilities are located throughout Providence, a city that provides students with a wide variety of cultural, educational, recreational, and social activities. Students enjoy the local restaurants and shops and are able to take advantage of a myriad of theater, music, and performance opportunities. From museums to sports events and Broadway shows to shopping, the city offers something for everyone.

Interstate buses and trains are near Johnson & Wales's downtown campus, and the T. F. Green Airport, served by most major U.S. airlines, is adjacent to the J&W's Radisson Airport Hotel in nearby Warwick, Rhode Island.

Technology Environment
Johnson & Wales University's three computer centers feature IBM-compatible computers. In addition, translation software is available to convert Macintosh-based files for printing in the labs. All computers feature the MS Office suite and offer black-and-white and color printing.

Placement
The Career Development Office (CDO) of Johnson & Wales University provides assistance to graduate students as soon as

they enroll. The CDO sponsors workshops on resume writing, company research, and interviewing, as well as guest speakers. A job hotline also provides postings of full- and part-time jobs on and off campus. Ninety-eight percent of Johnson & Wales students find work after college in their chosen field. Global companies such as Walt Disney; hotel chains such as Four Seasons, Marriott, and Hyatt; resorts such as Canyon Ranch; casinos such as Caesars Palace; and well-known companies such as Abraham & Straus have all hired Johnson & Wales students.

Admission
All applicants must submit a signed application, official college transcripts, and three letters of recommendation to the Feinstein Graduate Admissions Office. In addition, all international students must submit a TOEFL score (unless they wish to be placed in the University's ESL program), a declaration of financial support, and a financial statement that supports the information given in the declaration of financial support.

Finances
Tuition for 2000–01 is $212 per quarter credit hour ($954 per course). All master's programs are 54 to 76.5 quarter credits; each course is 4.5 quarter credits (3 semes-

ter credits are equal to 4.5 quarter credits). Books and supplies cost approximately $800 per year.

Although most graduate students choose to live in independent housing near the campus, room and board are available for graduate students at the University. The University estimates that living expenses for an academic year for a student living off campus are $7500. For more information about room and board, students should contact the Office of Residential Life (401-598-1132). For assistance and information regarding independent housing, students should contact the Feinstein Graduate Admissions Office (401-598-1015).

International Students
The uniqueness of Johnson & Wales's Feinstein Graduate School attracts professionals and students from across the country and around the globe. Forty-one percent of the students attending the Graduate School are international students, representing fifty-seven countries. The University offers international students courses in English as a second language, academic counseling, advice on Immigration and Naturalization Service rules, and assistance with off-campus housing. In addition, the University organizes an international ambassador program and supports international associations.

Application Facts and Dates
Applications are reviewed on a rolling admission basis. Once all application requirements are met, the Feinstein Graduate Admissions staff takes pride in processing the application materials in a timely manner. Enrollment is very limited, and applicants are encouraged to submit required documents as early as possible for each of the fall, winter, spring, and summer terms. All twelve-month programs start in the fall term only. For more information, students should contact:

Allan G. Freedman
Director, Feinstein Graduate
    Admissions
8 Abbott Park Place
Providence, Rhode Island 02903
Telephone: 401-598-1015
Fax: 401-598-4773
E-mail: gradadm@jwu.edu
World Wide Web: http://www.jwu.edu

Jones International University

Englewood, Colorado

ONLINE EDUCATION FOR AN ONLINE WORLD

Jones International University™, Ltd. (JIU), the first fully online accredited university, is committed to making learning more accessible and convenient for adult learners. We seek to reduce barriers of time and distance to serve a diverse group of students located anywhere in the world. Instead of attending a physical classroom at a fixed time and place, students use the Internet and World Wide Web for interacting with faculty members and other classmates. Our M.B.A. program is an important educational option if you want to advance your career and expand your opportunities.

—Pamela S. Pease, Ph.D., President

Programs and Curricular Focus

Jones International University's courses occur entirely on the Internet and take advantage of emerging technologies to foster international communication, learning, and skill acquisition. Through JIU's Master of Business Administration Program, students gain a solid grounding in the fundamentals of conducting business across the globe. A unique combination of academic learning and practical skills allows students to tailor their M.B.A. degrees to fit their career and learning goals and transform business theory into action steps for their professional success. In addition, students master one of seven high-demand specializations:

In Global Enterprise Management students focus on the skills and knowledge necessary to manage effectively in a global, diverse business environment.

In e-commerce students master the Internet as a marketing tool, a medium of business-to-business transaction, and a strategy for gaining competitive advantage by exploring the unique challenges of managing a global digital enterprise.

in Health-Care Management students examine economic issues that make health care a unique business environment and learn to master the communication techniques and health-care technology needed to manage specific business issues which are critical to developing and managing global markets.

Entrepreneurship prepares students to design plans to implement strategies for technology, growth, and human resources for entrepreneurial enterprises.

In Information Technology Management students develop the skills needed to

manage technological innovation and globalization. Students learn techniques for anticipating future technological advances that are critical to business success.

Negotiation and Conflict Management prepares students to respond to the rising demand of corporations for leadership through ethical negotiation and conflict resolution by learning key principles of negotiation decision making and conflict management.

Project Management teaches students to master project management knowledge and techniques necessary for business management of project-based work teams. This work environment increases the demand for credentialed project managers.

Students and the M.B.A. Experience

Information technology is the driving force in today's marketplace. JIU uses this technology to help M.B.A. candidates build their knowledge and skills for conducting business in the global marketplace. Online learning makes it easier for students to balance personal and professional responsibilities.

Through a unique combination of academic understanding and practical, applicable strategies, discussions, interactions, assignments, and lectures can all be reviewed online whenever and wherever it is convenient. The level of instruction and interaction among students from around the world is exceptional.

JIU serves a diverse group of students from more than forty-two countries. The average M.B.A. student is 32 years old and has five to seven years of professional experience.

The Faculty

JIU's learning model represents a true best practice for online education. The content-rich, highly focused curriculum is designed by recognized content experts from prestigious institutions across the globe.

Faculty members are real-life practitioners with advanced degrees who are executives in their area of specialization and are also seasoned instructors. They bring their practical experience and theoretical knowledge to the JIU learning experience.

JIU has 4 full-time and 150 part-time faculty members. Seventy-five percent of the faculty members hold doctorates and 25 percent have master's degrees.

The Business School Network

Through interactions such as group projects and chat forums, students in more than forty countries develop networks that allow them to share knowledge and personal experiences with classmates and instructors worldwide.

Students have access to a network of corporations through JIU's corporate partnership program. JIU's business relationships create opportunities for students to interact with, and learn from, firms around the world.

FACULTY LIST

Pamela S. Pease, President, Jones International University; Ph.D., USC.

Richard B. Kettner-Polley, Academic Chair of the M.B.A. Program, Jones International University; Ph.D., Harvard.

Marcia Bankirer, Academic Vice President, Jones International University; Ph.D., Wyoming.

James C. Brancheau, Associate Professor of Information Systems, University of Colorado, Boulder; Ph.D., Minnesota.

John Daly, Ph.D., Purdue.

Ernest Eugster, Ph.D., Geneva (Switzerland).

Beata Krupa, Academic Chair of the Business Communications Programs, Jones International University; Ph.D., NYU.

Kent E. Menzel, Assistant Professor of Communications Arts and Sciences, DePauw University; Ph.D., Denver.

Paula Noonan, Ph.D., Denver.

Faculty advisers, comprised of business executives and education professionals, assist students in assessing goals and formulating individualized degree plans. In addition to educational planning, these advisers offer a professional network that provides students with business contacts.

The College and Environs

All JIU M.B.A. course offerings take full advantage of the power of the Internet to foster communication, collaboration, and skill acquisition. Students from around the world work collaboratively with instructors and classmates and immediately put what they learn online to use in business. This international community of learners is a highly interactive way to exchange ideas and learn. Using computers and Internet connectivity, students can learn at home, at work, or when traveling.

Facilities

JIU students purchase textbooks through the online bookstore and use the e-global Library™, a Web-based library, to access reference resources through the Internet and World Wide Web. The Student Advising Center offers academic goals, degree planning, and career advising services. JIU offers technical assistance for issues relating to the JIU Web site and online courses 24 hours a day, seven days a week.

For more information about the JIU bookstore, students should visit http://direct.mbsbooks.com/jiu.htm.
Placement

JIU's Web-based Student Advising Center offers interactive services to students. By facilitating forums and discussions, offering specific academic advice, and reviewing postgraduation career options, the center increases students' networking opportunities. In addition, the center enhances job and career services searches through the Internet Guide, a guide for new "surfers" on how to get the most from the Internet.

Admission

For admission into the M.B.A. program, students must provide proof of a bachelor's degree from a regionally accredited college or university, as well as transcripts from all colleges or universities previously attended. A minimum cumulative grade point average of 2.5 for all college-level course work is required.

Application to the program also requires at least one year of professional work experience, three letters of reference from professional or academic associates, a current resume, and a statement of managerial achievements and professional goals.

Finances

Tuition is $725 per 3-credit course. An application fee, a one-time registration fee, and a per-course technology fee also apply.

JIU students can apply for student loans from Sallie Mae or PLATO. Both loan options are available to individuals who are U.S. citizens, U.S. nationals, or U.S. permanent residents.

Students may be qualified for financial assistance under the G.I. bill, the Dependents' Educational Assistance Program, or the Veterans Educational Assistance Program.

International Students

International students must have their transcripts evaluated as an equivalent to a U.S. baccalaureate degree. JIU works with the Office of International Education Services, American Association of Collegiate Registrar and Admission Officers (AACRAO), to provide this service.

Students whose primary language is not English must score at least 550 on the TOEFL.

Application Facts and Dates

JIU courses begin every month. Students may enroll in individual courses or apply to the M.B.A. program at any time. For more information, students can contact:

Enrollment Center
Jones International University
9697 East Mineral Avenue
Englewood, Colorado 80112
Telephone: 303-784-8045
            800-811-5663 (toll-free)
E-mail: info@international.edu.
World Wide Web: http://www.
    jonesinternational.edu

Keller Graduate School of Management

Oakbrook Terrace, Illinois

DEVELOPING BUSINESS LEADERS FOR THE TWENTY-FIRST CENTURY

In today's rapidly changing business environment, a manager's responsibilities are becoming increasingly complex. Technological advances, increasing demographic diversity, and global competition have prompted an ever-growing need for professionally trained managers in all fields.

A Keller M.B.A. equips you with everything you need to meet those business challenges, including dynamic instruction by a faculty of professionals with proven success in the business world. A national leader in graduate education designed for working professionals, Keller teaches you to apply management theories and concepts to the realities of everyday business operations. The result? Better managers and more profitable businesses.

—Timothy H. Ricordati, Dean

Programs and Curricular Focus

Geared toward working adults, Keller teaches students to master the special skills and concepts businesses demand from today's management professionals. Keller graduates are able to blend management theory with real-world applications in a multitude of business settings.

Each Keller student receives a solid background in every important business discipline. Keller also builds flexibility into that sturdy foundation by offering a wide range of electives. That way, students can customize their degrees to suit personal and professional interests.

The Keller M.B.A. program requires students to complete sixteen courses of 4 quarter credit hours each. There are five management core courses, five program-specific courses, and a Business Planning Seminar. Finally, students may choose from six electives in any functional area, including accounting, human resources management, finance, information systems, general management, marketing, health services management, telecommunications management, and project management.

Keller also offers the Master of Accounting and Financial Management, the Master of Human Resource Management, the Master of Project Management, the Master of Information Systems Management, and the Master of Telecommunications Management degrees.

Class hours are designed to accommodate work and family responsibilities. Keller offers five 10-week terms each year. Classes meet once a week for 3½ hours, either on weekday evenings or Saturdays.

Keller's thirty-seven nationwide locations enable students to continue their education after job transfers, temporary assignments, or other relocations with the least possible disruption to their academic schedules.

For students who wish to complete their M.B.A. degree in less than 1½ years without disrupting their work week, Keller offers its M.B.A. program in an accelerated format on Saturdays. The curriculum requires successful completion of sixteen prescribed courses, which provide a solid business management foundation in critical areas, such as leadership, information technology, project and change management, and new product development.

Students who prefer the Internet can complete degree programs through Keller's On-Line Center (http://on-line.keller.edu). Students receive a solid education enhanced by the latest in interactive information technology (computer-mediated e-mail and threaded conversations, videotapes, and the Internet) that enables them to send and receive feedback from instructors as well as to participate in various group and team activities with fellow online students.

Distance learning courses demand the same dedicated student efforts as traditional classroom-based courses. Online students read course materials, write papers, conduct applied research, and take exams. Students have access to the same full range of support services as they would receive at traditional Keller centers.

Students and the M.B.A. Experience

Keller students are working adults who bring their diverse experiences to the classroom. They want, and insist on, useful and relevant instruction. At Keller, knowledge is meant to be practiced in real-world situations, and that "practitioner orientation" colors everything that is done at the School. Whatever their ultimate career goals, students come to Keller for flexible, personalized instruction that equips them for the challenges of a complex, competitive, and rapidly changing working environment.

Nearly 7,000 professionals nationwide have turned to Keller for their advanced business education. A bachelor's degree in business is not required to enter the program; more than half of all Keller students hold undergraduate degrees in nonbusiness fields.

The Faculty

Keller faculty members practice what they teach. They are working professionals who deal with cutting-edge business and management issues both inside and outside the classroom. They bring their expertise to the classroom, emphasizing theories, practices, and issues that most benefit students in the working world. At Keller, it is believed that when students learn from instructors who work in the field in which they teach, they get as close to real-world learning as possible.

The Business School Network

Keller's faculty consists of practicing business professionals—leaders in the corporate community as well as in the classroom. These professionals bring business contacts as well as hands-on knowledge and experience to Keller's students.

Keller's faculty includes both part- and full-time instructors who are effective communicators, coaches, and mentors as well as practitioners with extensive

management experience. Those who teach full-time commit most of their working hours to teaching and curricula development while remaining actively involved in business as consultants and participants in professional organizations. Part-time instructors are full-time managers whose teaching provides adult students with vital professional enrichment and perspectives. All faculty members have developed contacts and relationships with a variety of academic and professional fields and geographic locations. The relationships students develop with these instructors often lead to mentoring arrangements, professional contacts, and even job offers.

The College and Environs

Keller was founded in 1973 on the idea that the most important components of management education are effective teaching and student mastery of practical management skills. Keller's thirty-seven educational centers in eleven states are home to a diverse faculty and student body with a variety of backgrounds and experience. Because of students' multiple real-world demands, Keller centers are in major metropolitan areas and near accessible transportation routes, keeping commuting time to a minimum. These centers' locations include Mesa, Phoenix, and Scottsdale, Arizona; Fremont, Irvine, Long Beach, San Diego, West Hills, and

Pomona, California; Orlando, Miami, and Tampa, Florida; Alpharetta, Atlanta, Buckhead, and Decatur, Georgia; Chicago Loop, Lisle, Orland Park, Schaumburg, Elgin, Lincolnshire, and Oakbrook in Illinois; Merrillville, Indiana; Kansas City downtown, Kansas City south, St. Louis west, and St. Louis downtown in Missouri; Milwaukee and Waukesha, Wisconsin; Bethesda, Maryland; Denver, Colorado; and Tysons Corner and Crystal City, Virginia. Distance learning is available at the previously listed Web site.

Facilities

Keller's multiple locations offer a variety of accommodations, and all provide comfortable areas in which to study, relax, and learn. Most centers include spacious classrooms in handy locations, vending areas, student lounges, and convenient hours for computer labs and information centers. The information centers offer Internet access to 300 databases, alternative texts, student study guides, career service materials, and periodicals.

Placement

Keller Career Services Department helps management-level students and graduates find jobs in accounting, finance, general management, health services, human

resources, information systems, manufacturing, marketing, project management, and sales.

Admission

For regular admission, applicants must hold a baccalaureate degree from a U.S. institution accredited by, or in candidacy status with, a regional accrediting agency recognized by the U.S. Department of Education (international applicants must hold a degree equivalent to a U.S. baccalaureate degree); pass the Graduate Management Admission Test or the Graduate Record Examinations or Keller's alternative admission test; complete a personal interview with an admissions representative; and complete a written application.

Applicants with postbaccalaureate degrees from accredited graduate schools must complete an application and an interview as well as document their degree. However, they do not need to take an admissions test.

Keller's application process is streamlined, so students learn quickly whether they've been accepted.

Finances

Tuition per course (4 quarter credit hours) differs by state, ranging from $1065 to $1440. After acceptance into Keller, new students pay a $100 tuition deposit, which is credited toward the first term's tuition. Tuition is payable in full at registration or in installments of two or three payments (with small handling fees for the latter two choices). Books and materials average $75 per course.

Application Facts and Dates

Keller holds five 10-week terms each year. They begin in September, November, February, April, and June. Students may begin their program with any term. There is no application fee. For more information, students should contact:

Keller Graduate School of
  Management
One Tower Lane, 9th Floor
Oakbrook Terrace, Illinois 60181
Telephone: 630-571-1818
World Wide Web: http://www.keller.
  edu

Kennesaw State University

Kennesaw, Georgia

MAXIMIZE THE RETURN ON YOUR INVESTMENT

Obtaining an M.B.A. that is accredited by AACSB–The International Association for Management Education is a challenging, invigorating, and rewarding endeavor. People who invest their time and money to attend such programs are increasingly asking about "bottom-line benefits." "What am I going to gain by attending this program?" Sponsoring companies are asking similar questions. "What are the benefits of sending someone to such a program?" At Kennesaw State University (KSU) we have directed our efforts toward ensuring that associates in the M.B.A. program maximize the return on their investment.

The Coles College M.B.A. is an innovative, interactive, integrated program that incorporates real-life experiences into every component. Our Atlanta, Georgia, location provides an ideal international business environment. The program is process-oriented rather than functionally oriented and taught in a team environment that simulates the workplace. Individuals completing the program become complete managers and leaders with new ideas, broad perspectives, international business savvy, technology awareness, and an expanded international business network.

We look forward to sharing a learning experience with you and to helping you prepare for an ever-changing, global, competitive future.

—Timothy S. Mescon, Dean

Programs and Curricular Focus

Participants in the Coles College M.B.A. Program don't expect results, they demand them. That's why many have chosen to attend this program. They are looking for fresh new ideas and the opportunity to build skills that can be applied directly to their organizations. Kennesaw State meets these demands by structuring its program to facilitate and encourage the exchange of ideas and problem-solving techniques—real-world, real-business, real-results. Participants leave every class, every meeting, and every function with information, insights, and abilities they can use to make a difference in their own—and their companies'—performance. In this rapidly changing global environment, those using old techniques and old ways will be left behind. Only fresh new approaches and ideas can provide the power and leverage needed to meet the challenges facing businesses today.

Teamwork is a vital component of the learning process at the Coles College of Business. Indeed, one challenge that the College accepts is to most closely emulate the challenges and opportunities that students face in the world of work in the private and public sectors. To this end, it has structured a highly concentrated 36-semester-hour, twelve-course program that enables students to master the core body of graduate business education as well as to select from one of ten leading-edge program concentrations.

The core competency sequence includes course work in managerial accounting, managerial economics, financial analysis and decision making, operations management, management and organizational behavior, marketing management, and corporate strategy. In addition, all students select at least one international core course from a number that are available.

In the latter half of the program, students select a major concentration from one of ten areas. Students immerse themselves in one of these majors by completing four courses, 12 semester hours, in a disciplined area of study. M.B.A. major options available to Coles College students include accounting, business administration, business economics, information systems, entrepreneurship, finance, human resources management and development, and marketing. A range of just-in-time course options are available to provide Coles College students with the latest theory and practice in all of the aforementioned optional courses of study.

The Coles College M.B.A. program is offered in the evenings and on weekends; therefore, it particularly appeals to working professionals or full-time students committed to utilizing their days for internships or research and study. All graduate and undergraduate business programs at the Coles College of Business are fully accredited by AACSB–The International Association for Management Education.

Students and the M.B.A. Experience

The approximately 1,100 graduate students at the Coles College bring a variety of backgrounds and experiences, and academic and cultural diversity, to the M.B.A. program. The average student is a 30-year-old with six years of full-time professional work experience. Women comprise approximately one half of the graduate student population, and members of minority groups represent about 10 percent. Approximately 60 percent of Coles College M.B.A. students have baccalaureate degrees in business, but a number have completed undergraduate studies in engineering, liberal arts, and the sciences. About 10 percent of KSU's students are international, coming from more than 102 nations.

❖ Global Focus

The faculty members in the Coles College of Business are committed to internationalizing the curriculum through ongoing research, development, and travel. In the past few years alone, faculty members have served as guest lecturers or conducted sophisticated research projects in Australia, Belgium, Canada, China, Finland, India, Korea, Mexico, Russia, and South Africa. In addition, students always have the option to complete up to three courses for credit at international universities or term-long exchange or travel programs.

Special Features

The Tetley Distinguished Leader Lecture Series brings an array of chief executive officers to campus throughout the academic year. During their visit to the Coles College, these leaders and entrepreneurs

formally address students and the faculty and then interact with students in a more casual setting. Endowed by Tetley Tea, this series has attracted distinguished leaders from business, industry, and the nonprofit sector, including, among others, Bernard Marcus and Arthur Blank, cofounders of The Home Depot; Jerry Dempsey, Chairman, PPG Industries; Thomas Wheeler, President and CEO, Mass Mutual; and A. D. Correll, Chairman, Georgia-Pacific.

The Faculty

The Coles College of Business is proud of the fact that its 85 full-time, tenure-track faculty members are committed to a balance of teaching, scholarship, and service. Across each of the Coles College's five academic departments, the faculty members represent a unique blend of gifted instructors who successfully meld issues in the world of work with leading-edge theory and practice. The College has been cited for its commitment to diversity and has a distinctive number of faculty members across all disciplines, providing a truly global focus. Women represent more than 30 percent of the faculty in the Coles College of Business.

The College and Environs

Kennesaw State University is nestled on 200 acres in suburban Atlanta, just 25 minutes north of downtown. Because access to the campus is directly off Interstate 75 north, students have the opportunity to live in a variety of convenient locations throughout the Atlanta area. The University is part of the University System of Georgia and was founded in 1963. With a student population in excess of 13,000,

KSU offers instruction through five colleges and schools in more than fifty fields.

The metropolitan Atlanta area is headquarters to a number of Fortune 500 companies and is North American and regional headquarters to a number of other leading multinational organizations.

Facilities

The Coles College is housed in the 110,000-square-foot state-of-the-art A. L. Burruss Building, with tiered lecture halls, networked computer labs, and all faculty and administrative offices. The College's Sturgis Library is considered by many to be among the finest in the nation for online access to periodicals, databases, and network services. A charter member of SOLINET and a member of the Online Computer Library Center, Sturgis Library is part of an international network of libraries. Faculty members and students have access to Galileo, a Web-based system that ensures access to a core of research materials. Sturgis Library houses 550,000 volumes of books and government documents, 3,400 serial publications, and 1 million pieces of microform.

Technology Environment

The Coles College faculty is committed to leveraging technology. To this end, students find numerous computer applications utilized throughout the curriculum. In addition, networked labs are available in the College for M.B.A. student use. In collaboration with the Sturgis Library, students have online access to LEXIS-NEXIS and NAARS as well as dozens of other online services.

Placement

Kennesaw State and the Coles College of Business are proud of the services offered through Career Services, which works diligently to secure strong linkages with on-campus recruiters and to assist students in developing other professional contacts and resources. Career Services regularly secures interview schedules with leading local, regional, national, and multinational employers. Regular seminars and workshops are offered to students to refine interviewing and presentation skills. Career Services is a national leader in the utilization of technology to assist M.B.A. students in recognizing their career goals. A few technology-based programs that are available to M.B.A. students include Resume Expert (Career Connections); JOB-TRAK, a job networking system of positions specifically available to Kennesaw State students; Georgia Hire, a listing of jobs available in the state of Georgia; and National Employment Wire Service, NEWS, which lists current job opportunities and positions throughout the United States.

Admission

To be admitted unconditionally to the M.B.A. program, an applicant must satisfy standards involving the following predictors of success: the adjusted GPA, GMAT score, and work experience. An applicant is required to have an adjusted undergraduate GPA (UGPA) of at least 2.8 on a 4.0 scale plus a total score of at least 475 on the GMAT. Also, the applicant should have a minimum of two years of work experience for unconditional admission to the M.B.A. program. In reviewing the academic work of applicants, the Admissions Committee evaluates the junior/senior adjusted GPA for all applicants. In cases where the applicant has done additional accredited undergraduate work beyond the bachelor's degree or has done accredited graduate work, the most recent two-year adjusted GPA is used in the admissions consideration. A score of at least 550 on the TOEFL is required for all students for whom English is not the native language.

Finances

In 2000–01, tuition and fees for students taking fewer than 12 credit hours are $91 per credit hour for Georgia residents and $272 per credit hour for nonresidents. Georgia residents who take more than 12 hours pay $1334 in tuition and fees per semester; nonresidents, $4589 per semester. There are two semesters during the standard academic year and a third, summer session.

Loans and scholarships are available on both a merit- and a need-based analysis through the Office of Financial Aid. Various alternatives are available to international students as well.

Application Facts and Dates

The Coles College of Business admits qualified students to the M.B.A. program for study in the fall, spring, or summer terms. Approximate application deadlines are July 16, November 19, and April 14, respectively, in any given year. For more information, students should contact:

Michael J. Coles College of Business
Graduate Business Programs
Kennesaw State University
1000 Chastain Road
Kennesaw, Georgia 30144-5591
Telephone: 770-423-6050
Fax: 770-423-6141
E-mail: gselden@ksumail.kennesaw.edu
World Wide Web: http://coles.kennesaw.edu

Lake Forest
Graduate School Of Management

Lake Forest Graduate School of Management

Master's in Business Administration Program

Chicago, Lake Forest, and Schaumburg, Illinois

WHAT DO YOU MAKE?

Make an impact. Make a difference. Make a contribution. At the Lake Forest Graduate School of Management (LFGSM), we make a difference in your career opportunities by delivering a dynamic, contemporary business management education that you can apply immediately for direct impact now.

Our faculty of successful executives and corporate leaders bring their business experience and acumen to your M.B.A. program. In our collaborative, interactive classes, you share ideas and exchange insights with both peers and faculty members. From the first class, and for the rest of your life, you'll enjoy networking opportunities that can be beneficial professionally, financially, and personally.

We know how. We created the "practical" education model in 1946 and have been leading the "practical" revolution for more than fifty years. Bring these years of experience to your business portfolio.

—John N. Popoli, Executive Vice President, Degree Programs

Students in the International Management— An Asia-Pacific Perspective program pose before the Temple of the Emerald Buddha at the Emperor's Grand Palace in Bangkok, Thailand.

Programs and Curricular Focus

The Lake Forest Graduate School of Management is accredited by the North Central Association of Colleges and Schools at the graduate level and is authorized to grant master's degrees by the Illinois Board of Higher Education. Courses in the M.B.A. program have been approved by the State of Illinois Department of Professional Regulation for Illinois public accountants' continuing professional education credit.

The Lake Forest Graduate School of Management is a member of the AACSB EMBA Council.

Students and the M.B.A. Experience

LFGSM students are a diverse group of experienced, working professionals in functional disciplines, many with advanced degrees, who have made career advancement a priority. Averaging eleven years in business, more years than any similar program, they bring a wealth of experiences and current business challenges to LFGSM's interactive, creative, and motivational "practice field" for success. Students share an exciting collaborative learning environment with personal access to experienced business professionals delivering compelling, contemporary content.

❖ Global Focus

The LFGSM curriculum assumes every manager needs a broad knowledge of

international management issues to succeed. The core course International Management is a requirement for all students and addresses the impact of cultural, economic, political, and other variables on global and domestic businesses.

In addition, each year current students and alumni have the opportunity for an in-depth look at international management practices and international cultures through the elective study-abroad courses. Students gain insight into the challenges facing international business and develop a different perspective on business in the United States. Each study-abroad course features group assignments that examine issues particular to the region.

The venues include Eastern and Western Europe, Southeast Asia, and Latin America.

The Faculty

Faculty members are dynamic business leaders who bring their daily experience's and acumen to the classroom. At LFGSM, professionals teach professionals. Students experience a microcosm of the business world in every class. The faculty members create a practice field environment that gives students the opportunity to work with new ideas and skills under conditions that provoke thought and experimentation.

Many of the faculty members hold or have held titles of CEO, President, CFO,

Vice President, Partner, Treasurer, Controller, or General Counsel in their companies. Others are successful directors, business consultants, and functional specialists. Each has a minimum of a master's degree and fifteen years of professional work experience.

The Business School Network

LFGSM was founded in 1946 as a partnership between business and education and has maintained close ties with the business community. More than 4,500 alumni, 700 students, and 150 faculty members work for some of Chicago's finest companies, such as Abbott Laboratories; Motorola, Inc.; W. W. Grainger, Inc.; Baxter International; Fel-Pro, Inc.; Kraft Foods, Inc.; and many others. An active board of directors comprising 21 Chicago-area executives actively spearheads new programs and development in addition to strategic planning and policy making.

LFGSM, through its Corporate Education arm, creates practical business solutions for companies like McDonalds, Hewlett-Packard, I-JAM Multimedia, and Quaker Oats.

John N. Popoli, Executive Vice President, Degree Programs.

The College and Environs

LFGSM offers full programs at three campuses: the Chicago campus in the Federal Reserve Bank Building, located in the loop; the Lake Forest campus; and the Schaumburg campus in the Galvin Center at Motorola, Inc.

Placement

LFGSM students are actively employed at the time of acceptance. The School offers a placement network only for students and alumni who become unemployed. This network helps students and alumni write resumes and work on interviewing skills and acts as a support group.

Admission

Applicants are considered for admission for the August and January terms.

LFGSM requires a bachelor's degree and undergraduate transcripts, GMAT or GRE scores, two letters of recommendation, and an interview with an admissions counselor.

While undergraduate grades and entrance exam scores are a factor, LFGSM places an even greater emphasis on the student's current achievements and future prospects. Applicants must demonstrate communication and leadership skills and the ability to work productively in an organization and in a team environment, in addition to having at least four years of work experience.

Applicants holding the minimum of a bachelor's degree from a U.S. or English-speaking college or university are required to either take the GMAT with writing section or produce an equivalent writing sample privately proctored at LFGSM. The GMAT requirement is waived for applicants with advanced degrees.

Finances

Tuition for the 2000–01 academic year is $1850 per course, which includes books and software. A majority of LFGSM students receive tuition reimbursement from their employers.

LFGSM provides some private scholarship assistance to qualified individuals. LFGSM is also a participant in the Federal Family Educational Loan Program, which provides students with subsidized and unsubsidized Federal Stafford Student Loans. The School is approved for educational aid to veterans who are certified as eligible by the state-approved agency. Details about scholarships and other educational loan programs are available from the Financial Aid Coordinator (847-234-5005).

Application Facts and Dates

The application deadline for Term I is July 13, 2000. The kickoff is August 12, 2000, and classes begin August 19, 2000. The deadline for Term III is December 21, 2000. Kickoff is January 20, 2001, and classes begin January 22, 2001. Applications received after this date are considered on a space-available basis. For further information about the M.B.A. program, students should contact:

Chicago Campus
Federal Reserve Bank
1st Floor
176 West Jackson
Chicago, Illinois 60604
Telephone: 312-425-5330
Fax: 312-425-5333

Lake Forest Campus
280 North Sheridan Road
Lake Forest, Illinois 60045
Telephone: 847-234-5080
Fax: 847-295-3656

Schaumburg Campus
1295 East Algonquin Road
Schaumburg, Illinois 60196
Telephone: 847-576-1212
Fax: 847-576-1213
E-mail: admiss@lfgsm.edu
World Wide Web: http://www.lfgsm.edu

Lawrence Technological University

> ▶ **DEVELOPING TOMORROW'S LEADERS TODAY**
>
> *Our mission is to provide innovative programs and instruction that develop the leadership and managerial skills of our students. We do this by aligning our people and programs around the needs of our students and their employers. We are driven by three fundamental core values—customer confidence and loyalty, program leadership, and operational excellence. We are proud to report that our students ranked the Graduate College of Management in the top 5 percent of the country in a nationwide student satisfaction survey.*
>
> —Louis A. DeGennaro, Dean

Programs and Curricular Focus

Melding theory and practice with the creation of real-world workshops is the primary focus of the college's graduate programs. Its accredited graduate programs were developed with input from industry advisory boards to provide students with the pragmatic tools needed in a competitive environment, and they are offered in the evenings and on Saturday mornings.

Information technology is here to stay, and it is a key enabler in the widespread re-engineering of organizations taking place today throughout the world. The Master of Science in Information Systems (M.S.I.S.) program is designed to provide three essential skill sets. First, students acquire a core set of business skills in two courses: Fundamentals of Business and Fundamentals of Management. Second, in a set of four courses, students acquire a core set of technical skills in the major areas of information technology: database, telecommunications and networks, systems analysis, and project management. Third, students take three courses to specialize in one of two tracks—technical or organizational. Each of these tracks has a capstone course in which students integrate their learning from prior course work. The M.S.I.S. program is an evening program requiring 30 hours for graduation and advancement in, or into, the information systems field.

Nothing is more exciting in a career than to work in a fast-paced, competitive manufacturing environment. The University and American manufacturing literally grew up next door to each other. From its beginnings in 1932 next to Henry Ford's first assembly line, the University has forged a strong interactive relationship with national and international business. In Lawrence Tech's Master of Science in Industrial Operations (M.S.I.O.) program, students join a small, select group of people who represent the future of business and technology.

Students concentrate on real-life industrial problems and applications. Successful completion of eight core courses plus two additional electives from any graduate program (30 hours) is required for graduation. The program can be completed in two years of evening study.

A weekend program is planned for January 2001. Students can complete their structured course work in twelve months by attending class on Saturdays.

The Career-Integrated Master of Business Administration (CI*MBA) exemplifies the Graduate College's mission to provide innovative programs and instruction. The CI*MBA program integrates basic core business subjects into modular components and themes designed to develop the interpersonal, managerial, and leadership skills of a student in a conference setting. CI*MBA is a customized weekend program that begins in the fall of each year and meets twice a month with a distance learning component. The course work incorporates lectures, seminars, cases, simulation activities, and workshops delivered by a team of faculty members, executives, and guest speakers. CI*MBA is a two-year cohort program.

Lawrence Tech's 36-credit Master of Business Administration (M.B.A.) program consists of nine core classes and three electives. Students can select one of six areas of concentration to help expand their experiences and meet future goals:

operations management, information technology, human resources, international business, project management, and e-commerce (under development). The Lawrence Tech M.B.A. can be obtained in as few as two years of evening study.

Students and the M.B.A. Experience

More than 700 graduate students attend the Graduate College of Management. The average length of work experience is more than seven years. Approximately 35 percent are women. More than 200 international students attend the College. The College offers graduate degree programs in Vancouver, Toronto, and Taipei. University housing (apartment-style living) can accommodate up to 400 students.

The Faculty

Lawrence Tech faculty members are dedicated to providing students with a high-quality education and practical career preparation. Their emphasis is on what works and what's around the corner. All of Lawrence Tech's full-time graduate faculty members (and most of the adjunct faculty) have doctoral degrees in specialized areas. In addition to academic preparation from leading universities throughout the world, faculty members have managerial and executive experience. Many have received recognition for research, publishing, and consulting. Most importantly, the faculty members understand what works in practice as well as in theory. Small classes assure close interaction with them and with other students.

For individualized attention, each student has a personal faculty adviser to help make curriculum decisions and troubleshoot any problems.

The Business School Network

The University is situated in proximity to some of the world's leading industrial, technological, business, and scientific enterprises. More than 200 Fortune 500 corporations have their headquarters or major operations within a ½ hour of the campus. the American Society of

Employers ranks Lawrence Tech first in its class as a preferred provider of graduates to southeast Michigan. Standard & Poors also ranks Lawrence Tech in the top one-third of all colleges and universities providing the leaders of America's most successful businesses.

The College and Environs

The College of Management is headquartered in the Wayne H. Buell Management building. Convenient for students due to its location at the heart of campus, this building includes classrooms, faculty and departmental offices, computer classrooms, the University library, dining commons, and bookstore. Abundant free parking in paved, lighted, and patrolled campus lots is easily accessible from major freeways. Lawrence Tech's modern, 110-acre campus is at the intersection of West Ten Mile Road and the Lodge Freeway (M-10), less than a half mile south of I-696.

Facilities

Course work relies heavily on computer hardware and software. Students have ready access to PCs and the University's mainframe system for simulations and to the Graduate College's state-of-the-art computer lab. Many students find it convenient to work on campus (the University's new 80,000-square-foot technological and learning center opens in fall 2001) or log on via modem from their home or work place.

Placement

More than 60 percent of graduate students hold a full-time job while attending school. The Career Services Office facilitates the job search process by assisting students and alumni in their search for employment. Services include on-campus interviews and job postings through the electronic job board. In addition, counseling is available for a variety of career development needs, including job search strategies and interviewing skills. An online resume service is provided for students who choose to register with the office.

Admission

Students can start their degree programs in August, January, or May. Applicants to graduate degree programs are expected to be working or to have work experience. Lawrence Tech requires transcripts sent directly from all colleges attended, and applicants must have a baccalaureate degree or equivalent. Lawrence Tech also requires one of the following: a GPA of 3.0 or higher, satisfactory employer endorsement and significant work experience, an acceptable GMAT score (the most recent GMAT score should be sent to Lawrence Tech), or an earned master's degree from a regionally accredited institution.

Satisfactory completion of courses fundamental to the selected graduate degree program may also be required. Complete information on admission procedures is available from the University's Graduate Admissions Office (telephone: 800-CALL-LTU, Ext. 1, toll-free)

Students may also transfer into the program from another accredited program. If previous graduate course work is similar in content to that offered at Lawrence Tech, up to 12 semester hours of graduate credit may transfer.

Finances

The current tuition rate for a graduate business course is $440 per credit hour. The registration fee for each term is $100. Students interested in financial aid should contact the financial aid office at 248-204-2120.

Application Facts and Dates

The application deadlines are August 15 for fall, January 5 for spring, and May 1 for summer. For more information, students should contact:

Graduate College of Management
Lawrence Technical University
21,000 West Ten Mile Road
Southfield, Michigan 48075
Telephone: 248-204-3055
          800-CALL-LTU (toll-free)
E-mail: management@ltu.edu
World Wide Web: http://www.ltugcom. org

Lehigh University

Bethlehem, Pennsylvania

PARTNERING WITH THE BEST

These are exciting times to begin pursuing your M.B.A. at Lehigh University. With the fervent belief that no man is an island, our innovative M.B.A. core is team taught from an interdisciplinary, cross-functional perspective by faculty members who are committed to excellence. Classes are designed to focus on business problems and opportunities from the perspective of the firm as a whole. Classroom partnerships give you the benefit of shared interaction with some of the most highly experienced students from top national and international companies.

The impact of business on other disciplines is critical for success. Our newest joint degrees reflect a commitment to enhancing our program. Beginning in fall 2000, a joint M.B.A./engineering degree will be offered. Under exploration are the M.B.A./master's in educational leadership and the M.B.A./master's of bioscience degrees. All offer timely application to changing industries as we begin our journey into the next century.

Well-placed graduates, employed on the East Coast's major financial hubs as well as abroad, provide outstanding networking opportunities. Based on the October 1998 Standard and Poors Corporate Register, our graduates rank eighth among private research institutions in the percentage of undergraduate and graduate alumni who hold executive positions.

Our innovative MBAPlus solidifies the commitment to lifelong learning opportunities for graduates seeking professional development or the acquisition of new skills. Gain a distinct competitive advantage with MBAPlus.

The Lehigh M.B.A.—partner with the best faculty members, students, and alumni who can make a difference in your life.

—Richard M. Durand, Dean

Programs and Curricular Focus

Lehigh's M.B.A. Program focuses on the impact of business problems and solutions on all areas of the company. Business issues are viewed and taught from the perspective of the firm as a whole rather than along departmental lines, and each course is team taught by faculty members from several different disciplines. The 36-credit-hour M.B.A. Program begins with a two-day weekend orientation. The core consists of four interdisciplinary modules and ends with a capstone industry project. Students are encouraged to design industry projects within their own firms or with a corporate partner. This approach provides the opportunity to apply the body of knowledge acquired in the core and provides added exposure for the students within their own firms, possibly in business areas outside their current positions.

Due to the compact and integrated core, students have increased flexibility to tailor the program to their individual needs. For a deeper breadth and depth of study in a particular field of study, students may select a concentration in finance, international business, management, management of technology, or marketing or pursue a broader experience by selecting courses from a variety of disciplines.

New for fall 2000 is a joint-degree offering, the M.B.A./master's in engineering. Lehigh's widely reputed undergraduate and graduate engineering programs now offer the perfect complement to the M.B.A. with this joint degree. Requiring a bachelor's degree in engineering or applied science, the 45-credit program merges the disciplines, providing a practicum designed to prepare graduates for real-world applications.

Lehigh students bring a rich depth of experience in a variety of industries and disciplines into the classroom. Students have an average of eight years of work experience, and 20 percent have master's degrees or doctorates in areas other than business. Class discussions encourage students to share these experiences, which broadens their knowledge base by exposure to a variety of practices within business and industry.

Lehigh's M.B.A. Program has been accredited by AACSB–The International Association for Management Education for more than thirty years and provides the cornerstone for career advancement.

Students and the M.B.A. Experience

Lehigh's 375 M.B.A. students come from a variety of academic and professional backgrounds, have achieved distinction academically and/or professionally, are highly committed, and bring a wide range of qualities to the program.

Thirty-five percent of M.B.A. students come from undergraduate backgrounds in business and economics, 55 percent from engineering and applied science, and 10 percent from liberal arts. Women comprise about 30 percent of the M.B.A. population.

Eighty-five percent of Lehigh M.B.A. students attend classes part-time and are an important part of the learning environment. Their business experience and sense of purpose enhance the educational experience of all students.

Special Features

The MBA*Plus* program gives Lehigh's M.B.A. graduates the opportunity to enroll in current courses at less than one third of the regular cost. Graduates gain ongoing, cost-effective access to courses that can enhance their professional development and advance their careers; they are able to keep current in their fields and acquire new skills.

The Faculty

Excellent teaching is a hallmark of business education at Lehigh; 98 percent of the College of Business and Economics' 57 full-time faculty members hold doctoral degrees. Faculty members play an important role in the educational and research activities of interdisciplinary centers and institutes both inside and outside of Lehigh, ensuring that students receive exposure to the latest information. Students are also exposed to the applications experience of carefully chosen business practitioners.

The Iacocca Institute and the College's six centers complement the activities of its academic departments. They host conferences and visiting experts, sponsor faculty and student

Rauch Business Center.

research, and provide services to business firms and the educational community.

The Business School Network
Corporate Partnership
Lehigh maintains extensive relationships with the corporate community. The Business Advisory Council consists of highly accomplished business leaders who are active in committees on curriculum, alumni relations, and distance learning. The Council provides a direct link between the College of Business and Economics and the business world. Members are among the visiting executives who interact with students in conferences, major lectures, classroom sessions, and informal discussions.

Lehigh's distance learning initiative enables employees of its partners to complete a Lehigh M.B.A. while taking their classes at the corporate site. These students interact with the class on campus through voice communication, a computer message center, fax, and interactive white boards.

The Small Business Development Center (SBDC) provides opportunities for students to serve as business analysts, providing consulting services for small and medium-sized businesses in northeast Pennsylvania. M.B.A. students also may complete field projects with SBDC's clients and the International Trade Development Program.

The College and Environs
Lehigh University, founded in 1865, consists of three distinctive, contiguous areas totaling over 1,600 acres. Located 90 miles southwest of New York City and 50 miles north of Philadelphia, the Lehigh Valley is Pennsylvania's fourth-largest metropolitan area. Bethlehem, one of three principal cities of the Lehigh

Valley, is a center of industry, high technology, culture, and education.

Facilities
The Rauch Business Center, headquarters of the College of Business and Economics, is a modern, dynamic, professional environment for learning and teaching. There are forty well-equipped classrooms, computer labs, an auditorium, and conference rooms with advanced computing and audiovisual capabilities. The Clayton Conference Center wing has excellent facilities for executive education programs, conferences, seminars, and other special programs.

Technology Environment
Along with books and journals, Lehigh's library system includes electronic data bases and microfilm, computer software, and media collections. Via the campus-wide integrated voice and data communication network, users can access the Internet, the World Wide Web, the libraries' online catalog, and hundreds of national and international electronic databases and can submit reference inquiries, place orders, request media services, and request delivery of documents electronically.

The campus network provides access to mainframe computers, the Integrated Library System, and other computers on campus. The Computing Center houses several mainframes and maintains hundreds of microcomputers in sites across campus.

Placement
Lehigh has a long tradition of producing successful business leaders and supports an active recruiting effort. A wide variety of corporations and government agencies recruit M.B.A.'s through on-campus interviews, which are conducted in the fall and spring. Career prospects for

graduates of Lehigh's graduate management programs are excellent. The Office of Career Services offers a full range of services to support students' career search efforts. Professional career counselors are available to help students define career goals and initiate the job search process.

Admission
Candidates must have completed an undergraduate program at an accredited U.S. college or university and have at least two years of full-time, professional work experience. International students must have sixteen years of formal education, including four years at the university level. A TOEFL score is required of all applicants for whom English is not the native language. The credentials evaluated by the faculty admission committee include the candidate's undergraduate background, GMAT scores, personal essay, letters of recommendation, and relevant professional work experience.

Finances
Tuition charges for the 2000–01 academic year are $610 per credit hour. Apartment costs range from $365 per month for an efficiency apartment to $500 per month for a three-bedroom apartment.

Several types of financial aid are available, including M.B.A. Scholarships, teaching assistantships (which cover tuition and pay a stipend of $10,000 for the academic year), and business analyst posts in the Small Business Development Center and in Competitive Technologies. Those wishing to be considered for financial aid should submit all application materials, including GMAT scores, by January 15 for aid the next year.

Application Facts and Dates
Lehigh evaluates applications on a rolling basis and usually notifies applicants of admission decisions within three weeks of receiving a completed application. Deadlines for regular students are July 15 for fall semester, December 1 for spring semester, April 30 for summer session I, and June 15 for summer session II. Associate students may apply up to two weeks before classes begin in any semester or summer session. For more information, students should contact:

Kathleen A. Trexler
Associate Dean and Director–M.B.A.
　　Program
Lehigh University
College of Business and Economics
621 Taylor Street
Bethlehem, Pennsylvania 18015
Telephone: 610-758-5280
Fax: 610-758-5283
E-mail: kat3@lehigh.edu
WWW: http://www.lehigh.edu

Lesley College

Cambridge, Massachusetts

► MANAGING IN A CHANGING WORLD

Today more than ever, managers require a strong set of skills to successfully lead complex and changing organizations. At Lesley College, our programs are designed to give managers these skills. Our degree programs address the functional skill areas of management in finance, economics, marketing, and operations and the requisite needs of managers in the skill areas of leadership, communications, teamwork, and strategic thinking. We believe these skills are essential to managers in a multicultural, international economy. The unique aspects of Lesley's School of Management are our commitment to adult learning, continuous improvement of the curriculum, and the integration of theory and practice. Our approach to the learning environment allows students to apply classroom experiences to their workplace.

—Dean, School of Management

Programs and Curricular Focus

The School of Management offers outcome-oriented programs that are designed to develop the competencies necessary for proficient professional managers. To that end, classes are small and are organized around teamwork and small groups. Courses include a range of pedagogies, such as case method, simulations, and fieldwork. In addition, the curriculum grounds students in the international, technological, and ethical dimensions of the workplace.

The School of Management offers management degree programs at both the undergraduate and graduate levels to working adults, who are served by a variety of delivery systems at on-campus, regional, and national sites. The Master of Science in Management program emphasizes broad management competencies, operations, strategy, marketing, and finance as well as leadership and ethics themes.

The overall aim of the management program is to provide a thorough grounding in all aspects of management functions. The School of Management encourages the sharing of experience in the learning process throughout the programs while providing a sound theoretical base and adherence to high academic standards.

The following fully accredited degree programs are offered through the School of Management: the Master of Science in Management degree (with specializations in general management, human resources management, health services manage-

ment, information technology, and fund-raising management) and the Master of Science degree in training and development.

The School of Management also offers certificate programs in change management, institutional development and fund-raising management, information technology, and strategic leadership in health services.

Students and the Program Experience

The School of Management attracts students nationally and internationally because of its special focus on the union of practice and theory and because of the opportunity to accelerate their program of study. Students in the management programs have a wide array of options. They may study on the Cambridge campus or at any of more than forty current sites throughout Massachusetts. Students can choose an accelerated cohort model or a semester-based program, and they may specialize in a focused area of management or study the foundational qualities and competencies of great management.

Special Features

At Lesley College, the student's learning environment is composed of more than textbooks and papers; peers, teacher/practitioners, and the student's own work environment all inform and enrich the student's experience. Students learn by

doing and by passing their own knowledge on to others through peer work groups, special projects, and practicums.

The Faculty

Faculty members of the School of Management possess degrees from some of the world's most prestigious institutions of higher learning. The composition of the faculty, both full-time and adjunct, reflects the commitment of the School to tying theory to practice and is a combination of scholars and practitioners who are drawn from the rich pool of professionals in the greater Boston area. Faculty members understand the needs of students from both sides of the fence and bring many years of practical leadership and management experience to their students.

The Business School Network

One of the strongest aspects of the Lesley College School of Management is its connection to the business communities of New England. For more than twenty years, the School of Management has been offering specialized training and degree programs on site for local companies and organizations and has established important and long-term business relationships that benefit the School's alumni. Because of Lesley's role as a strategic partner and learning consultant within the business community, 67 percent of the graduates improve their career position within one year of graduating from a Lesley management degree program.

The College and Environs

Lesley College is located on an intimate campus of landmark Victorian buildings adjacent to vibrant Harvard Square in Cambridge, Massachusetts, and includes regional, national, and international sites. Students thus have access to Boston's distinguished cultural and educational institutions and to the city's leading businesses and industries in fields such as biotechnology, financial services, information technology, and health care. The School of Management serves more than 1,000 students from all over New England and forty-six countries.

Placement

The Career Resources Center provides career development and job search services to Lesley College degree candidates and alumni. Services include career counseling, workshops, panels, the career resource library, on-campus recruiting, and job fairs. The Career Resource Center also publishes both a job bulletin and a monthly newsletter to assist with career planning and development.

Admission

Applicants to the School of Management must hold a bachelor's degree from an accredited college or university. Applicants to all Master of Science in Management programs must provide documentation of three years of full-time work experience and must have a minimum cumulative grade point average (GPA) of 2.5 in courses previously taken at a regionally accredited college or university. A working knowledge and mastery of college-level mathematics is strongly recommended as preparation for entrance into a program. An interview with the director of a specific program specialization is required for many programs.

Finances

Students in the School of Management pay tuition per course. Tuition charges are $490 per credit for accelerated programs and $475 per credit on campus; most courses are 3 credits. Candidates may apply for financial aid in the form of state and federal loans, employer-sponsored tuition reimbursement programs, and other forms of private funding.

Application Facts and Dates

Admission is on a rolling basis; applications are accepted year-round and decisions are made within approximately six weeks following the submission of a completed application. Prospective students are invited to attend information sessions, open houses, and other special events offered by the School of Management throughout the year. For more information, students may contact:

Office of Graduate and Adult
  Baccalaureate Admissions
Lesley College
29 Everett Street
Cambridge, Massachusetts 02138-2790
Telephone: 617-349-8300
        800-999-1959 Ext. 8300
        (toll-free)
Fax: 617-349-8313
E-mail: info@mail.lesley.edu
World Wide Web: www.lesley.edu/
  som.html

Loyola College

Baltimore, Maryland

DEVELOPING BUSINESS LEADERS FOR THE TWENTY-FIRST CENTURY

Loyola College is first and foremost a Jesuit institution. Our small, caring environment and Ignatian traditions prepare our students for the workplace, where they are integrative thinkers, creative problem solvers, active team players, and, especially, leaders aware of their impact on coworkers, the organization, the community, and the world.

There is a Jesuit philosophy at Loyola that affects every student's experience, and that is personal care—care of the person. We are proud of the way our faculty, staff, and administration make Loyola students their greatest priority, helping them to graduate better businesspeople and individuals.

—Peter Lorenzi, Dean

Programs and Curricular Focus

The Sellinger School M.B.A. program challenges the student to acquire a practical and highly integrated understanding of today's business organizations. Separate functional area courses will be replaced by an advanced, integrated course set called The Value-Added Organization, which reflects the dynamic nature of today's business organizations. Students study the essential components of the modern business enterprise: the operations, marketing, and finance functions that are common to any entity, be it a service provider or manufacturer.

In The Value-Added Organization, a set of cases will be repeated in each course within the set, but from a different functional perspective. The student gains a cross-functional understanding and an ability to see the impact of decision making at different levels within an organization.

The Sellinger School M.B.A. program totals 51 credits and is open to business and nonbusiness undergraduates. The program includes 21 credits of core courses that are waiveable for recent undergraduates of business and business-related disciplines and 30 credits of advanced course work (or ten courses). Of the ten advanced courses, all students must take six required courses; the remaining four courses are electives. The six required courses feature The Value-Added Organization (four courses), a leadership and social responsibility course, and a final course that serves as a capstone, transforming functional

expertise into mission and strategy. The four elective courses may include a concentration—up to three courses in one functional area.

Also available are two Executive M.B.A. programs and a Master of Science in Finance program.

Students and the M.B.A. Experience

Students at the Sellinger School come from a wide variety of professional and academic backgrounds. The average student is 29 years old, works full-time, resides in the state of Maryland, and attends classes part-time in the evening. Full-time students comprise 5 percent of the traditional evening M.B.A. program. Women comprise 40 percent of the student population, and members of minority groups make up 5 percent. There are international students attending the Sellinger School from such countries as France, Germany, Holland, Indonesia, and Thailand.

The majority of Sellinger School M.B.A. candidates have undergraduate degrees in business administration or the social sciences, with 18 percent coming from an engineering or science background.

The Faculty

The Sellinger School faculty numbers 47 full-time teachers, with 96 percent holding doctoral-level degrees. Only a small portion of an M.B.A. student's experience includes adjunct faculty, due to the Sellinger School's commitment to a professional teaching environment.

A large majority of the faculty worked at high levels within their area of expertise before they became teachers, and many continue to practice in their field through work in corporations, their own companies, or consulting.

Many professors had distinguished careers running business operations in the United States, Europe, and the Orient, adding to their effectiveness in the classroom.

The Business School Network

Corporate Partnerships

The Sellinger School promotes the belief that the M.B.A. student is only one of the program's customers; the other is the student's employer. It is part of the School's mission to train new leaders for today's changing organizations, and there is no better way for a school to impart the knowledge of leadership than by asking its corporate customers what is needed in M.B.A. graduates to make them effective leaders in their respective organizations.

To that end, there are several active advisory boards made up of local and regional business leaders and graduates of Sellinger programs who regularly meet to counsel and advise the faculty on curricular issues and needed skill sets. Some companies with whom Sellinger has particularly close relationships occasionally provide live situations for students to use as case studies in their M.B.A. program, a feature that students find particularly stimulating.

The College and Environs

Loyola College in Maryland is located in a beautiful residential section of northern Baltimore city. The 86-acre campus is known as Evergreen campus, a testament to the many green lawns, evergreen trees, flower-lined walkways, and floral gardens that dot the campus.

Founded in 1852, Loyola College is a small, private, Catholic, Jesuit liberal arts college that enrolls approximately 3,000 full-time undergraduates in thirty-three majors and 3,000 graduate students studying nine professional disciplines.

The city of Baltimore is located within an hour's drive of Washington, D.C., and within an easy train ride of many East Coast cities, including New York City and Philadelphia.

Facilities

The main campus in Baltimore holds five classroom buildings, a 300,000-volume library, a college center housing state-of-the-art athletic and fine arts facilities, tennis courts, athletic fields, and a beautifully restored Tudor mansion, Evergreen's centerpiece. Undergraduate residence halls and apartments are located on the eastern and western sides of the main campus.

Classes for traditional M.B.A. students are also held at two state-of-the-art graduate centers in Timonium and Columbia, Maryland.

Computer labs are located in virtually all buildings on the main and satellite campuses, and students have access 24 hours a day.

Technology Environment

The College has a computer and telephone network that connects classroom facilities, offices, the library, and laboratories to a digital and video network of global and local data and communication systems. The Sellinger

School has an excellent MIS laboratory, and the College has IBM, Macintosh, and DEC midframe computing laboratories.

Placement

Loyola College's Career Development and Placement Center provides a variety of services to students seeking employment. Once an applicant to the Sellinger School, a student has immediate access to workshops, testing, and private counseling services designed to assist students in such endeavors as career selection, resume writing, and interviewing skills.

A year-round, on-campus recruitment program hosts more than 200 companies, which interview graduating students for positions. Of those, more than 120 companies seek graduating M.B.A. students for jobs. The center also maintains active job referral and alumni advisory networks, which provide leads to graduating students and alumni.

Admission

Admission is based on undergraduate performance (GPA), scores on the Graduate Management Admission Test (GMAT), and career progress. Each program puts a different emphasis on these criteria. International students must also have transcripts evaluated by a recognized service and must submit

TOEFL scores if their degree is from a non-English-speaking university. Traditional programs admit students for each term, and the Executive M.B.A. programs admit only for the fall.

The average enrolled M.B.A. student holds a GMAT score of 530, an undergraduate GPA of 3.2, and has been working professionally for four to five years. International students who are required to take the TOEFL are expected to achieve a minimum score of 550.

Finances

M.B.A. program tuition is charged on a per-credit basis and is $400 per credit in 2000–01. Most classes are 3 credits each. There is a $25 registration fee every semester in which a student takes courses, and books are purchased separately. M.B.A. students may attend classes year-round on a full-time (9 credits) or part-time (3–6 credits) basis. Students in the Executive M.B.A. programs pay a flat tuition charge per academic year, with the summers off.

Assistance is available through the Federal Stafford Student Loan programs to qualified students.

International Students

The Sellinger School embraces a diverse student population and therefore welcomes applications from students outside the United States. International students should have a command of the English language and some work experience. Due to limited institutional assistance, proof is required of sufficient financial resources to fully meet educational costs while attending Loyola College.

Application Facts and Dates

Application deadlines for the M.B.A. program are July 20 for the fall term (May 15 for international students), November 20 for the spring term (August 15 for international students), and April 20 for the summer term (January 15 for international students). Once an application file is complete with all required and official documents, a student is usually notified in writing within two weeks. For more information, applicants should contact:

Director of Graduate Business
    Programs
Loyola College
4501 North Charles Street
Baltimore, Maryland 21210-2699
Telephone: 410-617-5067
E-mail: mba@loyola.edu
World Wide Web: http://www.loyola.
    edu

Loyola Marymount University

College of Business Administration

Los Angeles, California

THE M.B.A. IN YOUR FUTURE

The life cycle of change is approaching zero. What was advanced technology yesterday is passé today, or certainly by tomorrow. M.B.A. education is changing as well, turning into a growth process that challenges every participant to grasp and resolve the defining organizational, global, economic, cultural, and human issues. The real value of an M.B.A. is not in classes or credit hours, but is found by determining what the program demands of its participants.

Faculty members are demanding, taking students beyond the traditional to the new, the exciting, and the changing. The availability of data demands new levels of involvement and in-depth case analysis beyond anyone's expectations a few years ago. We will press the ethical issues, which, when handled poorly, have been the downfall of many business executives.

If you want to be an important element of the learning equation by demanding more of yourself than you ever expected, I invite you to join the LMU M.B.A. Program. The value awaits your participation.

—John T. Wholihan, Dean

Programs and Curricular Focus

The Loyola Marymount M.B.A. Program develops ethical leaders who possess the knowledge and skills to effectively manage organizations in a diverse and global economy. Students are taught how to create value, handle risk, and manage change.

The core curriculum consists of nine courses, some or all of which may be waived by students with recent bachelor's degrees in business. Competence may also be determined by examination.

Upon completion of the core, students select domestic or international electives to gain breadth of knowledge as well as expertise in a particular area. The domestic track requires three courses in an area of emphasis as well as five additional courses from other areas. Students elect either comparative management systems, strategy courses, or an integrative project to complete the program.

Students selecting the international track receive the M.B.A. degree plus a Graduate Certificate in International Business after completing the same number of courses as are required for the domestic track. In addition to international breadth courses, participation in comparative management systems is required. This provides the opportunity to study the area of emphasis within a given industry outside the United States.

Comparative management systems is also available to domestic-track students.

Depending on waivers and the integrative option selected, ten to twenty courses are required. Full-time students with undergraduate degrees in business often complete the M.B.A. program within one year.

Loyola Marymount students who are relocated or transferred can often complete their degrees at other AACSB-accredited Jesuit universities. Loyola Marymount offers a J.D./M.B.A. program, enabling a student to earn both degrees in four years.

Students and the M.B.A. Experience

Eighty percent of students in the Loyola Marymount M.B.A. Program are fully employed professionals from a wide variety of industries in southern California. Twenty-five percent of the students attend on a full-time basis. While some students enter the program directly after undergraduate school, most do have work experience. The average student is 28 years old, with 3½ years of work experience. Women account for 44 percent of the student body, and 24 percent are members of minority groups.

Thirteen percent of the population are international students from all over the world. International students often provide alternative analyses of the global dimension of business problems, which are extremely valuable in the classroom.

More than half of the students have undergraduate degrees in business, 27 percent in the social sciences, and 18 percent in engineering.

❖ Global Focus

The M.B.A. program offers a wide variety of courses that examine the global nature of business. In addition, students have the opportunity to participate in an exchange program in France.

For eighteen years, the M.B.A. program has sponsored comparative management systems, a two-semester international-strategy sequence. Students form groups and spend a year analyzing various topics about business in a particular regional area. At the conclusion of the year, students spend three weeks meeting with industry executives in the region selected for study. Most recently, the course focused on Finland, Sweden, Denmark, Norway, and the United Kingdom

M.B.A. students can also gain international experience by participating in an exchange program in France for a semester; a two-week seminar on the environment of business in the European Union held in Bonn, Germany; or the Jesuit BiMBA Program in Beijing, China. In addition, students can take courses outside the U.S. offered through other Jesuit universities.

The Faculty

Loyola Marymount's faculty members are exceptional teachers who actively participate in research in their fields. Approximately 94 percent of all courses are taught by faculty members who have doctoral degrees. Classes are intentionally small, to provide faculty members with opportunities to interact with individual students on a regular basis.

Women comprise 18 percent of the faculty, and 13 percent of the faculty are members of minority groups. Loyola Marymount's strong international emphasis is supported by faculty members from India, Korea, Ghana, Hong Kong, Great Britain, and Russia.

The Business School Network

The Business Advisory Council, comprising corporate leaders from a variety of industries, is actively involved in the M.B.A. program. Some of the members serve as speakers for M.B.A. classes or conferences. Others are involved in the recruiting and placement efforts of the M.B.A. program.

The College and Environs

Loyola University, a Jesuit institution incorporated in 1928, merged with Marymount College in 1973 to form Loyola Marymount University. The M.B.A. program was instituted in 1974. The Westchester campus has a student population of more than 5,800. The Loyola Law School is located in downtown Los Angeles.

Loyola Marymount University is located in a lovely residential neighborhood on a bluff offering magnificent views of Marina del Rey and the Pacific Ocean. Excellent weather plus proximity to local beaches provides the perfect setting for outdoor sports. Los Angeles offers an extraordinary variety of theaters, museums, and professional sports teams, all a short distance from the University.

Technology Environment

M.B.A. students have access via networks to an attractive array of computer and related technologies. Word processing, spreadsheets, and Web access are available through the campuswide network. Specific applications, such as simulation and statistical packages, are accessible via departmental networks.

The Conrad N. Hilton Center for Business is intended to provide access to a new generation of technologies. In addition to video projection and Web access, which can be utilized by faculty members in all classrooms, two hands-on computer classrooms are available in the Hilton Building. Videoconferencing will permit students and faculty members to particpate in classes from remote locations.

Placement

Loyola Marymount's Career Development and Placement Office provides a variety of services. Students get advice on resume preparation and interviewing skills. Online databases, career fairs, and on-campus interviews are also available. The M.B.A. Office provides additional placement services, including the distribution of resume books to local employers each semester as well as daily maintenance of a list of jobs and internship opportunities.

Admission

Each applicant's undergraduate record, GMAT scores, and recommendation letters form the basis for evaluation. Although not required, relevant work experience is considered. Applicants must earn a minimum GMAT score of 400 for consideration; the average score is approximately 570. The average undergraduate GPA is 3.2.

International students must achieve a TOEFL score of at least 600 (paper-based test) or 250 (computer-based test) and a minimum score of 550 on the GMAT. Proof of sufficient funds to cover tuition and living expenses for the full period of study is also required.

All entering students are assumed to be proficient in English composition, business mathematics, and computer applications.

Finances

Tuition for 2000–01 is $680 per unit. Each course is 3 units. Annual fees for full-time students are estimated to be $424. Fees for part-time students are estimated to be $188. In addition, all students must have health insurance. The cost of books and supplies varies from approximately $60 to $100 per course.

Merit-based research assistantships are available, as are need-based grants. In addition, the Financial Aid Office can provide information on loan programs available to M.B.A. students.

Application Facts and Dates

Applications are accepted for the fall, spring, and summer semesters. There are no specific deadlines; the M.B.A. Office has a policy of rolling admissions. Once the University has received all application materials, the application package is reviewed and the applicant notified within two weeks. For more information, students should contact:

Ms. Charisse Woods, Coordinator
M.B.A. Office
Loyola Marymount University
Los Angeles, California 90045–8387
Telephone: 310-338-2848
Fax: 310-338-2899
E-mail: cwoods@lmumail.lmu.edu

Loyola University Chicago

Chicago, Illinois

A SUPERB LEARNING ENVIRONMENT

At Loyola, we provide an excellent faculty, a diversity of students, the resources of a great university, and individualized attention to create a superb learning environment. By studying with us you will enhance your ability to think critically, solve problems, work in a team environment, think strategically about technology, and effectively communicate your ideas. Consistent with 450 years of Jesuit education, we emphasize the foundation necessary to make ethical decisions in today's complex business environment.

—Henry Venta, Dean

Programs and Curricular Focus

The Loyola M.B.A. program ranges from fourteen to eighteen courses, depending on the student's undergraduate background. This includes between two and ten required courses and eight to twelve electives. Electives can be used to earn fields of specialization in fifteen areas, such as e-commerce, finance, health-care administration, financial derivatives, or international business.

All classes contain a mix of part-time and full-time students. It is the belief at Loyola that this design is intellectually healthy since it permits all M.B.A. students to interact in the same classroom setting.

The Graduate School of Business offers students the opportunity to pursue M.B.A., M.S.I.M.C. (Integrated Marketing Communications), M.S.I.S.M. (Information Systems Management), or M.S. in accountancy degrees. Several dual-degree programs are also available, including M.B.A./J.D., M.B.A./M.S.N., M.B.A./M.S.I.M.C., M.B.A./M.S.I.S.M., and M.B.A./M.S. in pharmacology. Each of the dual-degree programs allows the student to earn the degrees in a shorter period of time than if they were pursued independently. In addition, Loyola offers graduate certificate programs in e-commerce, data warehousing, and business ethics.

Students and the M.B.A. Experience

The students have undergraduate degrees from more than 200 universities across the globe. The typical Loyola University Chicago M.B.A. student is 27 years old, with five years of full-time work experience; 44 percent of the students are women, 10 percent are members of minority groups, and 16 percent are international. Approximately half of Loyola's students earned their undergraduate degree in business, 30 percent in arts and science, and 10 percent each in economics and engineering.

❖ Global Focus

Loyola helps prepare students for the international demands of business by routinely including international considerations in all of the courses and by offering courses that focus solely on the international dimensions of a topic. All M.B.A. students must take at least one international course. A student can also earn an international specialization as part of the overall M.B.A. by building three to four international courses into his or her program.

Students whose career goals demand an intensive grounding in international business can take advantage of innovative programs in Athens, Bangkok, and Istanbul and at Loyola's Rome campus. Intensive two-week summer courses are offered that focus on topical international issues and are taught by the best of Loyola's Chicago faculty. Since each session is compressed into a two-week block, both part-time and full-time students have the opportunity to attend. Past courses have focused on such issues as strategic marketing in Europe, global operations, international management, the European Union, and emerging markets.

Special Features

The Graduate School of Business blends the theoretical with the practical by linking real-world business with ongoing research. Research is conducted by centers at Loyola. The two most prominent are the Center for Information Management and Technology (CIMT) and the Family Business Center (FBC). The CIMT, which offers graduate certificates in e-commerce, data warehousing, and computer science, acts as a bridge between the University and the community by sharing knowledge, ideas, and innovations in the utilization of information technology. The FBC is an internationally recognized leader in family business development and research. It is a resource to family businesses everywhere and has a library containing one of the nation's largest collections on family business.

The Faculty

The Loyola University Chicago faculty is strongly committed to teaching as well as research. Because 85 percent of the faculty members are full-time and 95 percent of those have a Ph.D. or equivalent degree, classes are taught by experienced, highly trained leaders in their fields. Part-time faculty members are used on a very selective basis and only when they offer specialized skills. Class size is purposely kept small in order to ensure that the faculty is accessible to students—both inside and outside the classroom.

As leaders in their fields, most faculty members have important industry and community ties in such areas as family business, total quality management, and financial and policy studies. So, in teaching, they offer a scholarly approach gained through research as well as practical business experience.

The faculty's dedication to research invigorates the M.B.A. experience by developing new ideas that can be applied in the classroom. The faculty is involved in an impressive range of research projects in all major areas of business and is also widely published.

The Business School Network
Corporate Partnerships
Seventy-five percent of Loyola's alumni live within the greater Chicago area.

Already established and successful in the business world, these alumni provide significant networking opportunities for students. As a result, major businesses in the Chicago area and from around the country are frequently on campus to speak to students and alumni, to advise faculty and administrators on current management education issues, and to recruit Loyola's graduates.

Prominent Alumni

Among Loyola's prominent M.B.A. alumni are Michael Quinlan, Chairman of the Board, McDonald's Corporation; Philip Dion, Chairman of the Board and CEO, Dell Webb Corporation; John Menzer, President and CEO, Wal-Mart International; Robert Parkinson, President and COO, Abbott Labs, Inc.; Joseph Scully, Chairman of the Board and CEO, St. Paul Federal Bank for Savings; Carl Koenemann, Executive Vice President and CFO, Motorola, Inc.; and James R. Daniel, Executive Vice President–Support and CFO, MicroAge, Inc.

The College and Environs

The Graduate School of Business campus is located adjacent to Chicago's Magnificent Mile. LaSalle Street is home to the Chicago Board of Trade, Chicago Board Options Exchange, and Chicago Mercantile Exchange, making the city one of the largest financial trading centers in the world. Many national and multinational companies in a broad range of industries are headquartered in Chicago. As a result, job opportunities at major firms abound throughout the Chicago area, in fields as diverse as manufacturing, retailing, health care, and consulting.

Technology Environment

The Graduate School of Business is housed in the new Graduate Business Center. Loyola's students have state-of-the-art computers and software for instructional and individual use. The Loyola library system offers numerous computerized resources including the Internet, LEXIS-NEXIS, Legal Index, FirstSearch, and LUIS (the Loyola library computerized catalog). Databases on CD-ROM include Business Periodicals on Disc, General Business File, and others.

Placement

The Graduate School of Business (GSB) Placement Service advisers are available to help students with resumes, cover letters, career counseling and planning, and job search strategies. In addition, training workshops on the nuts and bolts of job hunting (such as resume writing, interviewing techniques, targeting potential employers, salary negotiation, and networking) are scheduled throughout the year.

In addition to the many on-campus recruiting opportunities with an array of employers, Loyola sponsors the Midwest M.B.A. Consortium with several other universities. In addition, GSB Placement Services is involved in the annual M.B.A./M.S. International Consortium, which specifically targets the employment needs of GSB's international students. Opportunities for networking and skill building are also provided through Loyola's Career Consultants Network, the M.B.A./Graduate School of Business alumni organization dedicated to assisting students in their job search activities. Students can also join alumni and employers in the Chicago area several times each year when they meet on campus for professional and social networking events.

Admission

Students are admitted into the GSB programs on the basis of interest, aptitude, and capacity for business study as indicated by their previous academic record; achievement scores on the Graduate Management Admission Test (GMAT); recommendations from 3 faculty members or employers; and pertinent information from their applications.

The average student's undergraduate GPA is 3.0, with a range from 2.5 to 4.0. The average GMAT score is 530, with a range from 400 to 720. Average work experience of the entering students is 5 years.

Loyola welcomes applications from international students who have completed a four-year bachelor's degree or its equivalent. A minimum TOEFL score of 550 and proof of financial support for one year are required.

Finances

Tuition for 2000–01 is $2186 per course for both full- and part-time students. A wide variety of housing is available both on and off campus. Many full-time students live in the Gold Coast area of Chicago, which is within walking distance of the Graduate School of Business. Other graduate students choose to live in graduate housing facilities that are located 10 miles north of the Water Tower Campus at Loyola's Lake Shore Campus. The estimated cost of room and board for twelve months is between $8000 and $12,000. The Graduate Business Scholars Program provides more than twenty merit-based assistantships per year to full-time students.

International Students

Loyola's M.B.A. program is greatly enhanced by more than 170 international students from more than forty different countries. Several countries represented include Brazil, Canada, China, Colombia, Denmark, France, Germany, Greece, India, Indonesia, Italy, Japan, Korea, Mexico, the Philippines, Spain, Taiwan, Thailand, Turkey, and Venezuela. Loyola's Students of the World chapter provides an immediate link for international students, while the Office of International Services and Programs helps international students adjust to living and studying in the United States. Chicago's ethnic and culinary diversity make this "city of neighborhoods" a comfortable and exciting home for citizens from around the world.

Application Facts and Dates

A student may enter the program at the beginning of any of the four quarters. To ensure admission in the quarter of choice, the student should apply well in advance. Loyola functions on a rolling admission basis, however, applications are accepted until these deadlines: for the fall quarter, July 1; the winter quarter, September 1; the spring quarter, December 1; and the summer quarter, March 1. For additional information, students should contact:

Admissions Director
Graduate School of Business
Loyola University Chicago
820 North Michigan Avenue
Chicago, Illinois 60611
Telephone: 312-915-6120
Fax: 312-915-7207
E-mail: mba-loyola@luc.edu
World Wide Web:
    http://www.gsb.luc.edu

Manhattan College

A LEARNING COMMUNITY FOR WORKING PROFESSIONALS

Our M.B.A. students are working professionals who attend classes Saturday mornings and weekday evenings. We work hard to provide a sense of community. Our students know each other, the faculty members, and administrators even though they are part-time students. Classes are small—the average size is 17 students—so student involvement is expected. Our policies and procedures are streamlined to fit the needs of working people. We are responsive to individual needs.

—Alfred R. Manduley, Professor and Director of M.B.A. Program

Programs and Curricular Focus

The M.B.A. Program is 39 graduate credits (thirteen courses) plus six foundation prerequisite areas in accounting, economics, computer systems, corporate finance, marketing, and statistics. The prerequisite areas can be waived for some students. There are nine required graduate core courses. The remaining four graduate courses can be used to concentrate in accounting, finance, international business, management, management information systems, and marketing. Students may customize their own set of courses for a concentration with the approval of the director.

Courses are offered year-round. There are courses offered during the fall and spring semesters as well as an intensive three-week January session and two 6-week summer sessions. Students complete the program in about two years by taking one or two courses per term.

Students and the M.B.A. Experience

The Manhattan College M.B.A. students reflect New York's diversity. More than 95 percent of the 200 students have full-time jobs and are residents of the metropolitan area. The average age is 27 years old. Almost 40 percent of students are women. About 25 percent of students are members of minority groups. Students have a wide variety of undergraduate majors in addition to business, including engineering, history, psychology, languages, and literature. International students make up about 5 percent of the student body.

Students frequently work together on team projects. The elective experiential

leadership and team-building course is very popular. Students and faculty members frequently communicate through e-mail.

The Faculty

Nearly 100 percent of full-time faculty members have Ph.D. degrees, but several specialized courses each term are instructed by adjunct professors from industry. Many of the full-time faculty members have industry experience.

The Business School Network

Manhattan College alumni are well represented in prominent positions of managerial success in organizations such as Chase Manhattan, Citibank, Con Ed,

Depository Trust, IBM, J. Walter Thompson, Morgan Guaranty Trust, NYNEX, and many more. The College's location, about 10 miles from midtown Manhattan, facilitates networking. In addition to an active Board of Advisors, the network is enhanced through activities of the M.B.A. Program. The major part

of one Saturday each fall and each spring is devoted to a lunch and discussion forum for an important business issue. Manhattan College alumni attend the forums and are frequently presenters and discussants.

The College and Environs

Manhattan College overlooks Van Cortlandt Park in the Riverdale section of the Bronx. The immediate neighborhood is bounded by the beautiful Fieldston residential neighborhood on the west and a small business district to the east. Access is easy via the Henry Hudson Parkway and the New York Thruway (I-87) for automobiles and the IRT 1/9 subway line, a short 5-minute walk from campus. Parking is free during the evenings and on Saturdays and is just a few steps from class.

Technology Environment

All M.B.A. students have accounts on the Manhattan College computer network. The network provides Internet access and a wide range of application software. There are two computer labs in DeLa-Salle Hall, where the School of Business is located. M.B.A. students also have access to the Learning and Resource Center on the lower campus for additional computers and technical assistance. It is highly recommended that students have access to their own computer and Internet service if they cannot easily use campus facilities. Many courses utilize computer exercises and research, and the computer information system is a primary means of communication.

Placement

The Career Services Center at Manhattan College serves both the graduate and undergraduate programs. In addition to providing students opportunities to interview with companies, the Career Services Center offers career counseling services and various workshops in resume writing and interviewing. There are also a limited number of internship opportunities available to M.B.A. students.

Admission

Undergraduate grade index, Graduate Management Admission Test (GMAT) scores, reference letters, and personal and business experience are all considered in the selection process. The average undergraduate grade index is about 3.0. Work experience and demonstrated career achievements of applicants are significant selection factors. A minimum of three years' work experience is recommended. Applicants are evaluated on a rolling basis so they may begin taking courses soon after acceptance.

Finances

Tuition for 1999–2000 for the M.B.A. Program was $450 per credit, or $1350 per 3-credit course. The application fee was $50, and there was a charge of $50 for registration each term. The estimated total for tuition and fees for the 39-credit graduate program was $17,560 over about two years. There is a tuition deferral program for approved employers, and students may pay through an installment program. Financial aid is limited to loans for qualified students.

Application Facts and Dates

Completed applications must be received by August 10 for fall semester and January 7 for spring semester. Prospective students are welcome to visit with M.B.A. students and faculty members on Saturday mornings. Students should call the M.B.A. office for visiting information.

For information students should contact:

Professor Alfred R. Manduley,
　　Director of the M.B.A. Program
School of Business
Manhattan College
Riverdale, New York 10471
Telephone: 718-862-7222 or 7290
Fax: 718-862-8023
E-mail: amandule@manhattan.edu

Marylhurst University

Marylhurst, Oregon

A SANCTUARY FOR THE CONFIDENT INTELLECT

Students choose to study for their M.B.A. at Marylhurst because they seek the excitement and collaboration that can only happen in small classes taught by teachers who are business veterans. They know they will gain the skills necessary to succeed in their current jobs, obtain that promotion, or start their own company. But more than just gaining business knowledge, students will learn to explore their goals and modes of thinking—and to discover imaginative ways of posing problems and finding solutions.

—Dan Spangler, Academic Chair

Programs and Curricular Focus

The graduate business management program at Marylhurst University is designed for mature learners who are seeking personal growth, career enhancement, and solutions to challenging management issues in the personal, business, and community environments. The program emphasizes applied skills in problem solving, critical thinking, and decision making in today's complex management environment. The curriculum focuses on teamwork, presentation skills, innovation and creativity, cultural development, and holistic thinking in addition to technical business skills. Classes are conveniently scheduled on weekends and evenings and are also offered online.

Marylhurst's M.B.A. is a competency-based degree. At the beginning of the program, at the midpoint, and at the end, students' work is assessed by departmental staff and faculty members and outside evaluators. The purpose is to give students opportunities to demonstrate what they can do in actual business situations.

Incoming students undergo an assessment of their proficiency in basic business concepts. After completing 18 credits in the core business disciplines, students take a course entitled Strategy and Business Planning, which serves as a midpoint assessment. Students prepare business plans, which are assessed by fellow students, the instructor, and at least 1 other professional. They also take 9 credits of perspective classes designed to help them develop critical-thinking skills while they explore both global and personal issues. Students then take 9 to 12 credits in a concentration of their choice and prepare for their final project.

Students and the M.B.A. Experience

Marylhurst's M.B.A. students bring rich and diverse professional backgrounds to the classroom. They are predominantly working adults with the experience and wisdom to create an outstanding learning environment on campus. Many students come with undergraduate degrees in the liberal arts, science, and engineering.

The Marylhurst program attracts an even percentage of women and men from a wide variety of industries, such as financial institutions and high-technology, medical, nonprofit, and entrepreneurial ventures. The University attracts a significant body of international students as well.

The Graduate Department of Management goes beyond the "how" and focuses on the "why," allowing students to explore a wide variety of learning options and to study, research, and reflect on the many facets of an increasingly complex business world.

Special Features

The M.B.A. program allows students to gain a specialization in one of five concentration areas: organizational effectiveness, finance, marketing, international management, and information and knowledge management. Because all core and concentration classes are offered both on-site (evenings and weekends) and online, students can design a schedule that best fits their needs. It is possible to take the entire M.B.A. curriculum online.

The Faculty

Marylhurst University faculty members are predominately working professionals at some of the area's top companies. These adjunct faculty members interact with Marylhurst's permanent faculty members to push the graduate curriculum to a higher level of excellence. The adjunct faculty members, many of whom hold doctorates, work in the public, private, and government sectors and have significant responsibilities at their workplaces and backgrounds in high-technology marketing, organizational development and change strategies, international marketing, and mergers and acquisitions of major entities.

The Business School Network

Marylhurst's graduate department has strong ties to the corporate community, and many faculty members are successful members of the area's leading businesses. Students are encouraged to focus their studies on subjects appropriate to their professional lives and interests, and during the course of their studies, many find themselves making valuable suggestions and greater contributions to their workplace through classroom assignments. For alumni who wish to continue and expand their connections to the University community, the M.B.A. Alumni Association offers study programs and special seminars.

The College and Environs

The oldest Catholic liberal arts university in Oregon, Marylhurst was established in 1893 by the Sisters of the Holy Names of Jesus and Mary. Marylhurst is located just 20 minutes from downtown Portland, Oregon, along the banks of the Willamette River. Situated among large trees, rolling hills, and open fields, the compact and friendly campus features free parking, wooded walking paths, and beautiful views of Mount Hood on clear days. Portland's city life offers an endless variety of cultural and social activities, including parks, museums, botanical gardens, theaters, concert halls, restaurants, and pubs.

The B. P. John Administration Building on the Marylhurst University campus.

Facilities

Shoen Library has a collection of approximately 100,000 books, 475 print journal subscriptions, and 3,000 online full-text journal subscriptions as well as CDs, videos, and access to electronic and Internet databases. Marylhurst's popular art gallery, the Art Gym, is known for displaying some of the Pacific Northwest's finest contemporary artists. Single, private rooms are available in a newly renovated residence hall, which features a community room, a fitness facility, computer network connections, local phone service, and complete meal plans.

Technology Environment

Marylhurst is a regional leader in Web-based learning. The entire M.B.A. degree program is available online. In addition, the University's Web site (listed below) allows students to apply for admission, select and register for classes, and research the institution's facilities, programs, and activities.

Placement

The opportunity to build a network of corporate contacts is an intrinsic part of Marylhurst's M.B.A. program. Students are strongly encouraged to center their course work and projects on companies and fields that are of interest to them. In addition, students may choose to do a practicum at a local business or organization as their final project.

Admission

The goal of Marylhurst's admission process is to select students who have demonstrated potential to become motivated, high-caliber managers and leaders. No specific undergraduate degree is required for admission, but previous course work in finance, marketing, information systems, and human resource management is recommended. Applicants must hold a bachelor's degree from an accredited institution (a business degree is not required) and have strong professional references and substantial work experience.

Finances

Graduate tuition is $293 per credit hour (on-site and online). Supplemental fees include a technology fee of $4 per credit hour (up to 12 credit hours of enrollment) and a student services fee of $17 per term.

All students at Marylhurst are eligible for the standard range of federal aid programs. Additional opportunities for aid are available through state-sponsored programs and University and private scholarships. Sixty-five percent of Marylhurst students receive financial aid of some kind.

International Students

International students make up a growing percentage of Marylhurst's student body. In the 1999–2000 academic year, approximately 6 percent of the University's students came from outside the U.S., representing seventeen countries from around the world.

Application Facts and Dates

Prospective students may apply at any time during the year. Applications are accepted on an ongoing basis and are evaluated in order of their receipt and completion. For more information, students may contact:

Office of Enrollment Management
Marylhurst University
17600 Pacific Highway (Highway 43)
P.O. Box 261
Marylhurst, Oregon 97036
Telephone: 503-699-6268
       800-634-9982 (toll-free)
Fax: 503-635-6585
E-mail: mba@marylhurst.edu
World Wide Web: http://www.
   marylhurst.edu

McGill University

M.B.A. Program

Montreal, Quebec, Canada

OPENING DOORS AROUND THE WORLD

A truly global business education can open doors. The McGill M.B.A. provides a unique, internationally grounded curriculum that not only teaches the fundamentals of business but also provides students with the intangible skills sought by employers today—strategic thinking, sound decision making, leadership and team skills, and the ability to adapt to changing situations. Equally important, the program provides immediate value that is essential for tomorrow's managers— professional and social contact and networking opportunities in a dynamic, multicultural, urban business setting.

—Alfred Jaeger, Associate Dean, Master's Programs

Programs and Curricular Focus

The McGill M.B.A. is an internationally renowned graduate business program designed to provide students with a comprehensive understanding of the concepts of business, specialized knowledge in their chosen field, and the international perspective needed to meet the challenges of today's complex business environment.

Building on traditional strengths in functional areas, the McGill M.B.A. program takes the learning experience one step further. Not only are students provided with a strong grounding in the basic business disciplines, they are also provided with the intangible skills explicitly sought by employers today— the ability to apply their knowledge for the greatest benefit to the organization, to make effective decisions, to both work in teams and lead others, and to adapt to nonstructured situations.

The McGill M.B.A. program is a twenty-month program. In the core year, students follow a sequence of courses taught in three separate nine-week modules. The second year is free of required courses. Students tailor their studies to meet their specific career goals

and interests. Choosing from more than fifty elective courses, students pursue in-depth study in one of the following fields: entrepreneurship, finance, international business, management for developing economies, marketing, operations management, or strategic management. If they prefer, students can create their own general management concentration.

Students may also complete the program on a part-time basis. An advanced option is available for undergraduate majors in business.

Students and the M.B.A. Experience

Students typically hail from every corner of the globe, come from a wide variety of cultures and backgrounds, and possess highly diversified educational and work-related experience. Students also share a number of common characteristics—intelligence, inquisitiveness, an openness to learning and embracing new ideas, and a high degree of motivation.

Of the 170 full-time students in the 1999–2000 class, the ratio of women to men was 1:3, the average age was 28, and they represented twenty-five countries; 33 percent spoke English, 12

percent spoke French, and 54 percent spoke both languages. They came from a cross section of universities: 7 percent American, 49 percent other international, 24 percent Canadian outside Quebec, and the balance from Quebec; 29 percent held a B.A., 25 percent a B.Sc., 11 percent a B.Eng., 26 percent a B.Com./B.B.A., and 9 percent a law or other graduate degree.

A number of M.B.A. activities, such as the weekly Speakers Series and the M.B.A. Business Luncheon, put students in direct contact with leading business-people. For those who enjoy the thrill of competition, Case Competitions are held, which match McGill's case-analysis skills against those of other M.B.A. programs. Students can also participate in the annual M.B.A. Games and the Investment Fund Game.

Special Features

McGill is world renowned as a leader in international management education. All students acquire an inherent understanding of international commerce and an appreciation for other cultures in McGill's multicultural learning environment, and those interested in international business enjoy exceptional opportunities to network and acquire experience.

McGill M.B.A. students can further expand on the international experiences provided through the program by participating in the Faculty's international student exchange program. Students earn academic credit while studying at one of twenty-one world-class universities located in Europe, North America, Latin America, or the Far East.

Through the many cross-disciplinary and joint-degree programs offered with the M.B.A. program, students not only

M.B.A. I: THE BASICS OF MANAGEMENT

MODULE I:	MODULE II:	MODULE III:
Financial Accounting	Finance or Elements of Modern Finance I	Information Systems
Organizational Behaviour	Marketing	International Environment
Managerial Economics	Operations Management	Organizational Strategy
Management Statistics	Human Resource Management	Management Accounting or
Integrative Core Course	Research, Development and Engineering	Elements of Modern Finance II
(full-year course)		

have the opportunity to gain specialized knowledge in today's leading fields, they also benefit greatly from the contact and interaction with the unique students attracted to these programs. Programs offered include the Master in Manufacturing Management (M.M.M.), medicine and management (M.D.–M.B.A.), management and law (M.B.A./Law), M.Sc. (agricultural economics)/M.B.A., and a dentistry and management degree (M.D.R./M.B.A.)

The Faculty

McGill Management is composed of an eclectic team of faculty members who enjoy the challenges that the M.B.A. program affords them, particularly the core year's integrative course, which they jointly plan, teach, and grade.

They represent fifteen nationalities and have all lived, studied, and worked in countries around the world. They bring direct experience of business practices in other countries to the classroom, and many have proven themselves to be in the forefront of research in cross-cultural and multinational business issues. Two faculty-supported initiatives are the McGill Business Consulting Group and its international counterpart, the McGill International Consulting Group (MICG), which offer students professional opportunities.

The Business School Network

Corporate Partnerships

McGill's learning environment includes involvement with businesses of every size in every industry sector, as well as government agencies and departments.

Through various projects, events, and a range of faculty and student initiatives, students interact with CEOs, entrepreneurs, consultants, managers, government officials, conference delegates, and visiting faculty from around the world. They benefit from exceptional opportunities to learn, contribute, network, and explore career directions.

The Faculty continually benefits from valuable counsel from its Faculty of Management International Advisory Board, composed of 11 prominent businesspeople.

The College and Environs

McGill is recognized around the world for its high standards in teaching and research, and it has achieved international

renown for its Faculties of Agriculture, Dentistry, Engineering, Law, Management, and Medicine.

Founded in 1821, the University now comprises fifty institutional buildings for eleven faculties on 75 acres in downtown Montreal. Montreal, North America's most multicultural business center and one of its leading centers for high-tech RD&E, is considered to be one of its most cultured and cosmopolitan cities.

McGill has an undergraduate enrollment of more than 17,000 and a graduate enrollment of 5,500.

Facilities

McGill Management occupies a building specifically designed for its needs. Classrooms have been refurbished with built-in, state-of-the-art computers; video cameras; and 3M data display units that allow professors to select from a variety of teaching mediums. Each classroom features laptop computer connections and is wired for Internet access. Facilities available to M.B.A. students include a lounge and study area, the Acer M.B.A. Computer Lab, and an impressive library featuring electronic database searching services and a number of networked databases. Students also have access to more than 3 million volumes housed in the University's comprehensive system of libraries and specialized collections.

Students enjoy excellent sports facilities, efficient housing services, a graduate house, and a health service.

Placement

Placement starts in Orientation Week when the Management Career Centre holds the first of many networking occasions. Students seeking both permanent and summer employment benefit from workshops, videotaped mock interviews, one-on-one career counselling, a resource library, and an alumni reference database.

The center provides job listings; holds an annual M.B.A. Career Day; publishes a graduating class book, which is distributed to prospective employers in Canada and abroad; and follows up on interviews with both students and employers.

Continual interaction with companies has made McGill's Management Career Centre a valued resource for employers and students alike.

Admission

Admission is competitive. Decisions are based on many factors: solid academic

credentials (minimum 3.0 CGPA, average 3.3); a strong GMAT score (minimum 570, average 635); a TOEFL score of 600 (computer-based, 250) if English was not the language of university education; a minimum of two years of relevant work experience; professional and extracurricular achievements; and letters of reference.

Finances

Tuition fees for the 2000–01 academic year are Can$1668 for Quebec residents, Can$3168 for other Canadian citizens, and Can$20,000 for international students. There are also student service and society fees of Can$761 and a health insurance fee of Can$588 for international students. Bilateral agreements exist with several nations to obtain an international fee waiver.

All accepted candidates are automatically considered for financial aid and fellowships.

A minimal figure for living expenses per academic year is Can$8000 for single students and Can$10,000 for married students.

International Students

International students are warmly received and supported in the Faculty's multicultural environment. Fifty-four percent of incoming students are interational. In addition, the University runs a combined Student Aid/International Advisor's office to handle all nonacademic matters of concern, such as visa status, immigration procedures, health insurance requirements, and cost estimates for Foreign Exchange boards.

Application Facts and Dates

Applications for the full-time program are accepted for September only. Application deadlines are April 1 for Canadian students and March 1 for international students. The application fee is Can$100.

For more information, applicants should contact:

The McGill M.B.A.
Faculty of Management
McGill University
1001 Sherbrooke Street West
Montreal, Quebec H3A 1G5
Canada
Telephone: 514-398-4066
Fax: 514-398-2499
E-mail: mba@management.mcgill.ca
World Wide Web: http://www.
    management.mcgill.ca

McMaster University

Michael G. DeGroote School of Business

Hamilton, Ontario, Canada

THE DEGROOTE M.B.A.: HIT YOUR CAREER PATH RUNNING

The M.B.A. program at the Michael G. DeGroote School of Business offers students outstanding opportunities in specific areas of excellence: management of innovation and new technology, where we are the international focal point for research on intellectual capital; finance, with the first Educational Trading Centre in Canada outside of Quebec; and health services management, the only program of its kind in Canada. In addition, we offer other specializations in areas such as operations management and human resources, plus a new stream in electronic commerce.

As Canada's largest co-op M.B.A. school, our experiential learning philosophy provides all of our M.B.A. students with a competitive advantage through hands-on experience via co-op work terms, internships, and significant work assignments. Bottom line: we had a 100 percent placement rate of co-op graduates upon graduation for the past three years.

—Vishwanath Baba, Dean

Programs and Curricular Focus

A wide range of programs and options are offered enabling M.B.A. students to acquire a business education that is appropriate for their needs. While the Michael G. DeGroote School of Business is Canada's "MBA Co-op School," students may also study full-time or part-time. Most part-time students are already employed. Full-time students must have a minimum of one year's professional experience before entering the program. The co-op option offers students an excellent opportunity to gain real-world experience and investigate up to three career options before graduation.

Several streams of specialization are offered, including the management of innovation and new technology, health services management, finance, accounting, information systems (including electronic commerce), human resources, operations management, and strategic marketing as well as a general M.B.A. Electives in a variety of fields are also available.

Self-directed learning is an essential element of the M.B.A. program, as it enables students to develop a sense of vision and personal responsibility for outcomes. This self-directed learning is carried out in groups in which students work in teams to develop and achieve a common vision. In addition, courses offer opportunities to learn about business strategy in global, national, industry, and firm contexts. Teaching methods include lectures, case studies, seminars, field projects, group problem-solving sessions, and class discussions.

Students and the M.B.A. Experience

Students in the M.B.A. program are one of the program's best resources and one of the reasons for its high acclaim. The 200 students in each entering class have an average GMAT score of more than 620; backgrounds in the social sciences, physical sciences, engineering, humanities, and business; and work experience in a variety of sectors. They come from across Canada and a dozen other countries.

The Faculty

Faculty members are selected for their teaching skills and their ability to generate new business knowledge. Their connections in the business community help to provide students with the openings they need to pursue the practical side of their business education and to facilitate their postgraduate activities. In addition, 40 percent of the professors have at least one degree from outside of North America, and a number have extensive overseas consulting and teaching experience.

The Business School Network

More than 4,000 M.B.A. alumni provide national and international connections to the School. Dedicated alumni encourage their firms to recruit from McMaster— many sending McMaster graduates to conduct interviews. Others serve as mentors or advisers on the National Advisory Board that is comprised of graduates in senior positions in a variety of industries across Canada. The Business Advisory Council, comprised of local business leaders, provides a similar function. Alumni activities are planned on a regular basis to provide networking opportunities.

Prominent Alumni

Many graduates have achieved outstanding success in their chosen fields, such as Wayne Fox (M.B.A., 1973), Vice Chairman, CIBC, and Quentin Broad (M.B.A., 1988), Banks and Insurance Analyst, National Bank Financial.

The College and Environs

McMaster University is located in the business heartland of Canada on a beautiful 300-acre parklike campus beside the renowned Royal Botanical Gardens in Hamilton, Ontario, one of Canada's major centres. Approximately 60 minutes from both downtown Toronto and the U.S. border, Hamilton provides a safe environment and adds to the quality of life for McMaster students with an excellent Art Gallery, Convention Centre, Hamilton Place Theatre Auditorium, and Copps Coliseum.

Facilities

A unique feature of the Michael G. DeGroote School of Business is the Educational Trading Centre, which is designed to simulate major trading rooms. Real-time data is supplied by Reuters (Canada), with links to major Canadian and foreign exchanges. A new state-of-the-art computer classroom is dedicated to e-commerce studies.

Placement

The Business Career Services Office facilitates the career development of

Canada's first Education Trading Centre outside of Quebec offers students real-life, real-time exposure to the trading environment.

co-op, full-time, and part-time M.B.A. students through a variety of activities, such as workshops and small group sessions focusing on career issues, resume writing, and interview and job search techniques. Career services staff members work closely with the student associations to bring together business employers, in-course students, and alumni to share their expertise and provide a better understanding of the employment market prior to graduation. Excellent facilities are available for interviews with employers, information sessions, videotape mock interviews, and other career management activities.

Admission

The ideal candidate for admission has an ability to succeed in a rigorous and demanding academic program, as evidenced by prior academic achievement and GMAT results, as well as proven potential for leadership, as evidenced by work experience, extracurricular activities, and/or community involvement.

Each year, a small number of applicants who do not have an undergraduate university degree are accepted into the program. Such applicants must have very extensive work experience and

a GMAT score of at least 600 to be considered for admission.

Full-time applicants must have a minimum of one year's managerial, professional, or technical work experience.

Finances

A limited number of scholarships are available to qualified students. These are automatically assessed as applications are accepted for the M.B.A. program. Financial assistance is available to students in the form of teaching assistantships, scholarships, bursaries, and loans. Preference is given to advanced level students in awarding teaching assistantships, while the majority of scholarship offers are made to entering students.

Application Facts and Dates

One entering class is admitted each year at the beginning of September. Application may be made online via the School's Web site, or contact:

Michael G. DeGroote School of
  Business
Academic Programs Office
MGD 104
McMaster University
Hamilton, Ontario L8S 4M4
Canada
Telephone: 905-525-9140, Ext. 24433
E-mail: mbainfo@mcmaster.ca
World Wide Web: http://www.
  business.mcmaster.ca

Michigan State University

A DYNAMIC "REAL-WORLD" M.B.A. PROGRAM

This is an exciting time to come to the Eli Broad Graduate School of Management. Our dynamic curriculum, aimed at developing the executives of the twenty-first century, is designed to give future leaders exposure to real-life corporate case analysis, to facilitate teamwork skills development, and to integrate new technologies in the classroom. The core curriculum focuses on the strategic positioning of the firm and using its value chain to build competitive advantage in the global marketplace. We emphasize understanding basic business skills while asking our M.B.A.'s to see the bigger managerial picture—the strategic perspective.

The Broad School's strategic plan puts the M.B.A. program at the center of our efforts to bring greater achievement and recognition and to move us into the top twenty business schools. We emphasize relevance and innovation in courses and teaching, integration of technology into all activities, faculty awards for educational effectiveness, and increased interaction between students and faculty members. In addition, our executive alumni act as liaisons to provide real-world and live case examples. Thus, the Broad M.B.A. is both challenging and rewarding and innovatively designed for those of you who are looking toward a bright future in the business world.

—James Henry, Dean

Programs and Curricular Focus

The Broad M.B.A. is a two-year full-time program designed to prepare students for professional managerial careers. Students study at least one of four primary concentration areas in finance, human resource management, supply chain management, and marketing technology. The design of the program allows students, if they so choose, to pursue dual concentrations. Thus, students can study two primary concentration areas as their focus of study or pick a secondary concentration in addition to their selected primary concentration. The secondary concentrations are in the areas of corporate accounting, business information systems, general management, hospitality business, and international business. The pursuit of dual concentrations allows students to develop a more diverse set of skills and gives the candidates greater post-M.B.A. career flexibility.

The Broad School's curriculum is designed to keep the M.B.A. program on the leading edge of graduate business education. The core curriculum begins with strategic positioning of the firm in the global environment and flows through the firm's value chain. A joint J.D./M.B.A. program is also offered in conjunction with the Michigan State University-Detroit College of Law.

Two other M.B.A. programs are also available. The Program in Integrative Management (PIM) is a seventeen-month M.B.A.

program. It is designed for working professionals with five or more years of work experience. The Executive M.B.A. Program (EMBA) is designed for full-time working executives with ten or more years of work experience. This is a two-year program that is offered at MSU's Management Education Center in Troy, Michigan.

Students and the M.B.A. Experience

The watchword of the Broad M.B.A. student experience is teamwork. The entering class is divided into groups of approximately 40 students called cohorts. The cohort group takes the same series of core courses together during the first two semesters of study. The cohort is further broken into assigned study teams of 5 or 6 students who work together on assignments and case analyses. Teamwork, cooperation, and conflict resolution are learned firsthand through this experience.

With a total student body of approximately 300 students, Broad M.B.A. students are an outstanding and diverse group of men and women from around the world. In the entering class of fall 1999, 41 percent were Michigan residents, 25 percent were residents of other states, 34 percent were international students, 12 percent were members of minority groups, and 31 percent of the student body were women. The average age of the class is 27, with more than four years

of full-time work experience. Most students have had at least two years of full-time work experience.

❖ Global Focus

The Broad School is making a deliberate effort to incorporate the international and cross-cultural dimensions of business into its teaching, research, and outreach. As part of their core program, students are required to take a course on international, comparative, and cross-cultural business. Integration of international components is presented throughout the curriculum. Student teams give students the opportunity to interact with individuals from different countries and cultures.

Each year, an international study trip is an elective option for students. Students can also opt to pursue a secondary concentration in international business. The Broad School has formalized exchange programs with the International University of Japan, ITESM–Monterrey (Mexico), and the Norwegian School of Management BI. Recently, the Broad School announced an association with the Thunderbird School that allows students to receive both the M.B.A. and the Master of International Management. Upon graduation, a select few students choose to participate in the M.B.A. Enterprise Corps, a program that gives M.B.A. graduates the opportunity to act as management consultants for private enterprises in transforming and emerging global economies.

The Faculty

The reputation of the Broad School is solidly built on its distinguished faculty. The faculty is a diverse group of prominent educators who are recognized international authorities, talented teachers, and prominent researchers and consultants in the global business community. Due to the small size of the program, faculty members regularly meet with students outside of classes (including weekly coffee hours) and are dedicated to helping the M.B.A. students learn and develop as professionals.

The Business School Network

The strategic plan of the M.B.A. program is to reach higher levels of excellence by utilizing resources from the college, alumni, and industry. With more than 8,000 graduates of the M.B.A. program, Michigan State Univer-

sity alumni are well represented in corporate boardrooms throughout the world. Some M.B.A. alumni participate in the Broad M.B.A. Alumni Ambassador Program (MAAP), a group of alumni available to provide information and advice to current and admitted M.B.A. students. Other alumni work with the Placement and Career Center to support recruitment efforts and with faculty members to discuss current business issues, which are then incorporated into the classroom.

Corporate Partnerships

One of the primary goals of the Broad M.B.A. curriculum is to give students ample exposure to real-life corporate business cases. In the innovative Leadership Alliance Program (LAP), each M.B.A. study team is linked to a corporate adviser for the first semester of the core curriculum, working with the adviser to focus and present on a strategic issue facing the firm.

In the second semester of the program, a speaker series brings leading business executives and Broad School alumni into the M.B.A. classroom. In the third semester, student teams participate in the Integrative Case Experience (ICE), where they compete against each other in the analysis of a single, live corporate case. The winning teams then present their case analysis to the executives of the corporation studied.

Students also gain corporate exposure through extracurricular endeavors. The Spartan Business Consulting Group is a student-run organization that provides consulting services for small and large companies. The numerous M.B.A. student organizations frequently bring in special-topic corporate speakers and also coordinate corporate networking activities, such as football tailgates and golf outings.

The College and Environs

Founded in 1855, Michigan State University is the country's pioneer land-grant university and is devoted to combining education and research with public service. Located in East Lansing, Michigan, it offers the advantages of a large university in a small-town environment. The East Lansing area offers an excel-

lent variety of cultural, professional, and recreational facilities. MSU's 5,300-acre campus, including the 2,100-acre main campus, is essentially an arboretum park. More than 40,000 students are enrolled in more than 200 programs in fourteen colleges. In addition, the University facilities include a planetarium, a museum, an art center, an international student center, three intramural athletic facilities, two 18-hole public golf courses, and a student events center.

Technology Environment

The Broad School operates three computer laboratories, including a new lab solely dedicated to Broad M.B.A.'s, containing IBM-compatible microcomputers. The computers access the University's mainframe computers and the University library and intranet. All M.B.A. students are required to have laptop computers with Ethernet connections. Four high-technology classrooms are used to teach M.B.A. courses. These classrooms are equipped with interactive software and Ethernet connection ports so students and faculty members can work on live classroom technology demonstrations and cases during class sessions. A fully integrated Web system has been developed for the M.B.A. program, which gives students access to homework assignments, cases, and syllabi on line. All MSU students receive free e-mail and Internet access as part of their tuition.

Placement

The M.B.A. Placement and Career Center (PCC) is dedicated solely to working with full-time M.B.A. students to develop a customized job search campaign. All M.B.A.'s have access to BroadNet, the exclusive Web-based career management system. The PCC also provides services to enhance the M.B.A.'s interviewing and negotiation skills, including career planning, resume review, company contacting strategies, and mock interviews. Major recruiters of Broad M.B.A.'s include Ford Motor Company, Apple Computer, Ernst & Young, General Motors, Honeywell International, PriceWaterhouseCoopers, Procter & Gamble, Intel, US Bank, and Guidant Corporation. Eighty-

five corporations visited the M.B.A. PCC last year to recruit M.B.A.'s for internship and full-time opportunities.

Admission

Admission to the program requires a four-year bachelor's degree (or equivalent) from an accredited educational institution and a minimum of two years of full-time work experience. The admission decision is based on the undergraduate academic record, GMAT scores, TOEFL scores (for appropriate international students), letters of recommendation, essays, work experience, maturity, motivation, and ability to work well with others. Candidates who meet preliminary admission requirements are required to participate in an evaluative interview. For more detailed information on the admissions requirements and application deadlines, students should visit the Web site listed below.

Finances

The Broad M.B.A. program follows a block tuition structure that allows students to register for up to 17 credits per semester. The structure gives students the option to pursue additional business electives or electives in other fields of interest without having to pay for extra credits. The Broad M.B.A. program offers more than $1 million in competitive scholarships and graduate assistantships each year, based on the strategic goals of the M.B.A. program. All applicants to the program are automatically considered for financial aid. Applicants should apply early in the admissions year to be competitive for the financial aid opportunities. For more detailed tuition, living expense, and financial aid information, students should visit the Web site listed below.

Application Facts and Dates

The preferred application deadline for the fall 2001 incoming class is March 30, 2001. The M.B.A. office evaluates applications in order of their receipt and completion and usually can make a final decision within one month. Students who contact the program are asked to mention *Peterson's M.B.A. Programs* as the place where they read about the program. To apply to the M.B.A. program or to receive additional information, students should visit the Web site at http://mba.bus. msu.edu/ptr00.asp.

Students with no Internet access should contact:

The M.B.A. Program
The Eli Broad Graduate School of
Management
215 Eppley Center
Michigan State University
East Lansing, Michigan 48824-1121
Telephone: 517-355-7604
800-4MSU-MBA (toll-free)
Fax: 517-353-1649
E-mail: mba@msu.edu

Millsaps College

REAL APPLICATIONS FOR CRITICAL-THINKING SKILLS

The Else School is committed to providing a student-centered, participative learning environment. The faculty and administration are also committed to maintaining and expanding partnerships between the College and the business community. This combination allows the School to offer students the opportunity to polish their critical-thinking skills through company projects, internships, and residence programs. The School takes a personal interest in each student's development and placement. The School's commitment to quality is exemplified by its unique position as the only School to be accredited by AACSB–The International Association for Management Education at both the undergraduate and graduate levels, coupled with a Phi Beta Kappa chapter.

—W. Randy Boxx, Dean

Programs and Curricular Focus

The educational objective of the M.B.A. program is to provide to the student the base of knowledge, managerial skills, and the broad perspective needed to assume leadership positions in organizations that compete in a dynamic, global environment. Through a comprehensive and advanced management curriculum, the M.B.A. program strives to prepare students to recognize organizational problems and opportunities, to determine a socially responsible course of action, and to implement a strategy that seizes both internal and external opportunities.

The M.B.A. degree requires the equivalent of 48 hours of graduate study. Students with an undergraduate major or who have completed specified business courses may be eligible to waive up to 18 hours of foundation course work. There are four required core courses that provide a general management unit of study designed to provide a comprehensive perspective from which to create and implement decisions and strategies.

The M.B.A. student may use the six elective classes to concentrate part of their curriculum in a particular area of study. Six focus areas are available to the student: accounting for managers, decision making, finance, general management, health-care management, and marketing.

The Else School also offers a Master of Accountancy (M.Acc.) degree. This degree is designed for students who intend to pursue professional careers in public accounting, business, and the government/nonprofit sector. The M.Acc.

program fulfills the educational requirements to sit for the CPA exam in states that have adopted the AICPA's 150-hour requirement. Paid residencies and internships are an important part of the M.Acc. program.

Students and the M.B.A. Experience

Most companies are not homogeneous in makeup. Neither is the School's student body, which comprises people with diverse educational backgrounds, ages, and work experiences. The program is designed to successfully combine those with little or no work experience with those who have extensive work experience, including mid-level and senior managers. The team project orientation of the classroom often combines people with varied backgrounds, requiring students to complete projects in a realistic environment.

Approximately 37 percent of the students have undergraduate degrees in business, 40 percent in the humanities and social sciences, and 23 percent in engineering or science. Two thirds of last year's entering class had prior work experience. The average age of the entering class was 26, and the ages ranged from 23 to 60. Approximately 15 percent of the student body comprises members of minority groups and international students. Women comprise 36 percent of the current student body.

❖ Global Focus

The Else School's European Program offers students an intense firsthand look

at the global business environment through two 3-week terms in Europe. Conducted each summer as an optional course of study, the program synthesizes the instruction of international business topics with practical field trips to Europe's leading industries, businesses, and political institutions. As part of the learning process, students visit the various industries, such as the European Patent Office; Saatchi & Saatchi Advertising; Prague Stock Exchange; the Bank of England; Deutsche Bundesbank; Siemens, Inc.; and British Aerospace. The entire European continent is their classroom in this popular program. Classes meet four days a week in London, Munich, and either Prague or Florence. Weekends are free to venture to any European destination, such as Paris, Edinburgh, Dublin, or Amsterdam. There is no better way for students to develop a global perspective than to immerse themselves in this six-week program in Europe.

Special Features

The Else School offers large-school opportunities complemented by small-school attention. One of the distinctive opportunities provided to students is the General Louis Wilson Fund. This fund was established in 1989 to allow students the real-world experience of managing a stock portfolio. By comanaging the portfolio, students experience the same challenges that they will soon face in their jobs. Students defend their recommendations before the Louis Wilson Fund Investment Policy Board, a group of professional investors who oversee the fund and provide feedback to students.

The Faculty

The Else School faculty members are knowledgeable, have real-world experience, and are accessible to students. They take advantage of the small liberal arts atmosphere of the College to interact with students. Faculty members complement their teaching skills with numerous national publications in their fields of expertise. In addition, they continue with real-world connections by serving on executive boards and consulting with top local and national companies. Ninety-six percent of the faculty members hold a Ph.D. or similar terminal degree in their field. The faculty comprises 27 percent women and 5 percent foreign nationals.

The Business School Network

The Else School Advisory Board is composed of many local and statewide corporate CEOs who actively provide input into the focus of the M.B.A. program. Because of the School's relationship with the corporate community, the School has a strong history of offering a variety of internships, residencies, and opportunities for career placement. The Else School also uses special projects for local companies as part of the practical application of academic study. A problem or area of study is first identified by the company and brought to the School as a proposed undertaking for the students. A team is then formed from current students along with appropriate faculty supervisors to address this project as if it were a consulting job. These intensive projects offer students an opportunity to earn academic credit in a way that is rarely available in traditional M.B.A. programs.

The College and Environs

Founded in 1890, Millsaps College has a strong tradition in the liberal arts and prides itself on the fact that it has consistently prepared students to be contributors in a dynamic society. In 1979, the Else School of Management was established as a complement to the undergraduate liberal arts curriculum.

Located on approximately 100 acres in downtown Jackson, Mississippi, Millsaps offers the intimacy of a liberal arts education in the dynamic atmosphere of a downtown location. Millsaps is nestled between one of the oldest neighborhoods in Jackson and the Jackson Medical and Business Districts.

Placement

The Millsaps Career Center, in cooperation with the Else School, offers workshops and professional development seminars. These workshops are taught by Career Center professionals and alumni who know how to market students effectively. Millsaps also offers on-campus recruiting along with job and career fairs. In addition to the services offered by the Career Center, the faculty and alumni are a tremendous resource for job searches and potential careers. Students are also encouraged to take advantage of internships and residence programs. The M.Acc. program boasts a 100 percent placement rate for its graduates.

Admission

To be considered for admission, students must submit an official undergraduate transcript, GMAT scores, two recommendation letters, and three personal essays. An interview with the Director of Graduate Business Admissions is encouraged. The average GMAT score is 560. A minimum TOEFL score of 550 is required of all students for whom English is not the native language. Students are expected to have completed college

algebra and statistics. Proficiency in computer software packages is assumed.

The admissions committee encourages candidates with degrees in all major fields of study, extensive professional experience, and academic excellence as well as international students.

Finances

For the 2000–01 academic year, tuition is $1740 per class, including a $30 student fee. Books are estimated at $575 per year for a full-time student. Living expenses are approximately $7400 per year. Graduate assistantship are available for all full-time students. Academic scholarships are awarded based on merit. International students are eligible for both graduate assistantships and merit scholarships.

Application Facts and Dates

The Else School has a rolling admission deadline, with most students beginning in the fall. The deadline for fall admission is July 1. The deadline for financial aid is July 15. For additional information, students should contact:

Anne L. McDonald
Director of Graduate Business Admissions
Millsaps College
1701 North State Street
Jackson, Mississippi 39210-0001
Telephone: 800-352-1050 Ext. 1253 (toll-free)
Fax: 601-974-1260
E-mail: mbamacc@millsaps.edu
World Wide Web: http://www.millsaps.edu/esom/index.html

Mississippi State University

Starkville, Mississippi

THE OPPORTUNITY TO LEARN

The mission of the College of Business and Industry is to develop knowledge and critical skills in students and foster economic and professional development through teaching, research, and service. The business world is rapidly changing—today's companies need employees who not only excel in the traditional areas of business but also understand and are prepared to be successful in a world marked by increased globalization, a greater reliance on technology to improve organizational activities, and shorter time periods to respond to opportunities. In addition to having such business knowledge and skills when they graduate, our M.B.A. students learn to apply their knowledge and skills through projects, research, and interaction with businesses and nonprofit organizations. They are also building a solid foundation so that they are prepared to learn how to learn as the business world changes throughout their careers. This same focus on practical application and sensitivity to change underlies the College's research and service activities and contributes to the ongoing development of the M.B.A. curriculum.

—Sara M. Freedman, Dean

Programs and Curricular Focus

The objective of the M.B.A. program is to provide a broad background for business leadership through an emphasis on practical administrative problems. Candidates for the M.B.A. program must complete 30 hours of course work at the graduate level, including a core of 24 hours in the areas of accounting, economics, finance, management, marketing, and statistics, plus a capstone course in business strategy. The remaining 6 hours of graduate courses are elective and may be selected from either within or outside of business.

For M.B.A. candidates who do not hold undergraduate degrees in business, a set of prerequisite courses must be completed. These include courses in accounting, business information systems, economics, finance, legal environment of business, management, marketing, and statistics.

Full-time students with an undergraduate business degree can complete the M.B.A. program in three semesters or one year, and part-time students with an undergraduate business degree can complete the program in five semesters or slightly less than two years. In the absence of previous academic training in business, full-time students can complete the program within two years, and part-time students can usually complete the program within four. The maximum time frame within which the degree may be completed is six years.

Students and the M.B.A. Experience

While ages may range from early twenties to late forties, the average age of students in the M.B.A. program at Mississippi State University (MSU) is 27. The average amount of full-time work experience, since receiving their undergraduate degree, is between two and three years. The student body is generally composed of approximately 60 percent men and 40 percent women. African-American students constitute approximately 10 percent and international students approximately 20 percent of the student body. While undergraduate backgrounds vary from animal husbandry to zoology, the majority of the students hold undergraduate degrees in business, with engineering being the second most prevalent undergraduate background.

The Faculty

The graduate faculty in the College of Business and Industry, a subset of the general faculty, consists of approximately 55 members. Members are reviewed every five years for reappointment to the graduate faculty. Members of the graduate faculty all hold advanced degrees in their respective areas of expertise. Approximately 15 percent of the faculty members are women. Foreign nationals compose about 20 percent of the faculty.

The Business School Network

The corporate community cooperates with the University in several ways to provide students with opportunities for hands-on business contact. The annual M.B.A. Welcome and Orientation Program allows students to interact with corporate leaders and ask questions in a casual atmosphere. Brown bag lunches are frequently held, highlighting corporate executives who discuss their company policies and opportunities for employment.

The College and Environs

The College of Business and Industry is located in McCool Hall at the center of MSU's campus. The University forms a part of a cohesive town-university community with the growing agricultural-commercial-industrial town of Starkville. Located in the eastern part of north-central Mississippi, it is 125 miles northeast of Jackson and 23 miles west of Columbus. Away from urban complexities, the community enjoys many intellectual, cultural, and recreational advantages: the MSU–Starkville Civic Symphony and Chorus; the Starkville Community Theater; the University Lyceum series, which presents performances by popular musical groups of regional and national celebrity; frequent intercollegiate athletic events in modern facilities; and a variety of recreational opportunities on playing fields, courts, lakes, and the nearby Tennessee-Tombigbee Waterway.

Technology Environment

The College of Business and Industry has installed and made available for faculty and student use a large-scale local area network. This network contains more than 200 PC stations and is MS-DOS based using Sperry/Novell Netware. Four student labs with state-of-the-art software applications are available for College of Business and Industry student assignments. There is also an electronic classroom that provides interactive instruction opportunities for faculty members and students to deal with more sophisticated data and analytical techniques. Assistance is available to provide students with computer-assisted instruc-

McCool Hall.

tion topics as well as personal problem solving. A Sun 4/280 UNIX system allows access to UNIX software packages as well as to the Internet.

Placement

Assisting its graduates in finding jobs is a primary concern of Mississippi State University. In order to give its students the best possible opportunities, the University operates the Career Services Center and the Cooperative Education Program.

The Career Services Center (CSC) brings approximately eighty-five businesses to campus each semester to interview students for full-time jobs and professional-level summer employment. In preparation for these interviews, the CSC offers resume critiques and seminars that focus on writing effective resumes, honing interviewing skills, and looking for jobs.

The CSC also maintains an alumni career network and critiques videotaped

mock interviews. In addition, the CSC sponsors Career Day, a program that brings more than 150 businesses to campus each September to let students make future job contacts and gain more information on potential career paths.

Admission

An applicant for admission to graduate study should hold a bachelor's degree, have an undergraduate GPA of at least 3.0 in the last 60 hours of baccalaureate work, and have a minimum GMAT score of 500. A student whose GPA or GMAT is insufficient may be considered for admission if he or she exceeds the minimum required in the other criterion and has a well-written statement of purpose and strong reference letters.

An international applicant who does not hold an undergraduate degree from a U.S. institution must submit a TOEFL report reflecting a score of 575 or higher,

with the application. Students who score below 575 will not be considered for admission into the program.

Finances

For students taking 9 to 13 graduate credit hours in the fall or spring term, estimated tuition and fees are $1508 for Mississippi residents and $3059 for nonresidents. Students enrolling in more than 13 hours must pay according to the rate established per credit hour, which is currently $167.50 per credit hour for residents and $339.75 per credit hour for nonresidents. Residence halls cost approximately $800; books and supplies cost approximately $240; meals, $915; and personal expenses, $740. Fees are subject to change without notice.

A number of assistantships are awarded to students working toward their master's degree. These awards, which include a monthly stipend, also include tuition waivers. The awards are based on the student's GMAT score and GPA, with consideration of the student's skills and the needs of the College. Students must be enrolled full-time to be eligible for an assistantship.

Application Facts and Dates

To ensure full consideration for admission to the M.B.A. program, all application materials must be received according to the following deadlines: fall semester, July 1; spring semester, November 1; first summer term, April 1; and second summer term, May 1. For an application and additional information on the M.B.A. program, or on other graduate programs of study in the College of Business and Industry, students should call or write:

Graduate Studies in Business
College of Business and Industry
Mississippi State University
P.O. Drawer 5288
Mississippi State, Mississippi 39762
Telephone: 601-325-1891
Fax: 601-325-2410
E-mail: gsb@cobilan.msstate.edu

Monterey Institute of International Studies

Fisher Graduate School of International Business

Monterey, California

▶ GOING GLOBAL WITH THE MONTEREY M.B.A.

The M.B.A. program at the Monterey Institute provides a passport to entrepreneurship in international business. M.B.A. students find they can "meet the world in Monterey." Up to 50 percent of M.B.A. students come from outside the United States. Most students have studied or worked abroad, and all students can communicate in at least one language in addition to English. The emphasis on multicultural teamwork further enhances the atmosphere of a global village.

The Monterey M.B.A. combines this international orientation with an entrepreneurial focus. Our goal is to educate innovative leaders who can function effectively in many cultural environments and in global business. At Monterey, students complement their course work with active learning in real-life business settings. We believe these abilities underlie success in international management. To foster their growth, we have created an intimate, collegial M.B.A. program where students and faculty work together in a supportive learning environment.

—William R. Pendergast, Dean

Programs and Curricular Focus

The Monterey M.B.A. prepares students for leadership in international business by developing competence in basic business disciplines, communication skills in at least one foreign language, and interpersonal skills including problem solving and cross-cultural teamwork. The Monterey Institute offers a two-year M.B.A. program and a one-year advanced-entry M.B.A. program. It also offers a Master's International M.B.A. program as a joint venture with the Peace Corps.

The two-year M.B.A. program enrolls students with prior study in diverse academic fields, work experience, and a minimum of two years of university-level foreign language courses. Students enter this program in August or January.

The one-year advanced-entry program enrolls students with previous formal undergraduate business education, significant work experience, and a minimum of three years of university-level foreign language courses. Students enter this program in August or January.

Concentrations within both M.B.A. programs are offered in international trade management, entrepreneurial management, international marketing, international economics and finance, regional business environments, international human resources management, and global business.

Students and the M.B.A. Experience

The Monterey M.B.A. emphasizes the development of skills for effective teamwork in multicultural settings, both in individual courses and particularly in the International Business Plan (IBP).

The IBP integrates the functional disciplines of management through the development of a detailed international business plan for a sponsoring company. It exposes students to the unique aspects of international business environments, hones communication and presentation skills, and develops a strong entrepreneurial orientation. Plans are accomplished in close consultation with a team of experienced faculty members. Students also develop strong relationships with experienced executives at sponsoring companies.

Fifty percent of the M.B.A. students are citizens of countries outside the United States. Fifty percent of the students are women, and approximately 11 percent of American students are members of minority groups.

❖ Global Focus

The Monterey M.B.A. has a distinctive emphasis on cross-cultural communication and effectiveness. During the M.B.A. program, students combine business courses with language study in Chinese, English, French, German, Japanese, Russian, or Spanish. Although fluency in English is required of all students, one of the Institute's unique opportunities is the availability of business courses taught in languages other than English.

Special Features

Students discover numerous extracurricular opportunities, including the annual International Business Conference. Internships and participation in international market research and case studies are available through the Business and Economic Development Center, the Small Business Institute, and the International Trade Research Center. Internships and advanced language study are also available through the Institute's summer programs in France, Mexico, China, and Germany.

The Faculty

Teaching is the paramount mission of the M.B.A. faculty, who are not distracted by the demands of undergraduates or of a research-oriented doctoral program. The small size of the Monterey M.B.A. program creates a sense of intimacy and cohesion between students and faculty members, who encourage lively classroom interaction. The faculty members maintain an active intellectual and professional agenda and a close involvement with corporate contacts.

The Business School Network

Corporate Partnerships

Dynamic, innovative companies form partnerships with the Monterey Institute to manage expansion, explore foreign markets, and experiment with new business concepts. Corporate partnerships include business plan sponsorship, internships, job placement, and guest speakers. Students, in consultation with faculty, also conduct research through the business assistance centers. Business executives provide feedback that is part of the continuous improvement of the Monterey M.B.A.

Prominent Alumni

Monterey M.B.A. alumni live and work around the world. They provide a network that is available for business and social contacts. Alumni often return to Monterey and maintain supportive relationships with faculty and administration. Access to this alumni network is an enduring asset for Monterey graduates.

The College and Environs

The Monterey Institute of International Studies has been a leader since 1955 in integrating advanced foreign language education into professional graduate programs in international business, international policy studies, and international public administration. The Monterey Institute also offers M.A. degrees in teaching English to speakers of other languages (TESOL), teaching foreign language, and in translation and interpretation. About half of the 750 students represent more than fifty countries outside the United States. Students share a multidisciplinary experience in course work and social activities.

The Monterey Institute is situated in one of the most spectacular natural environments in the world. The Monterey Peninsula is 120 miles south of San Francisco on California's central coast, surrounded by ocean and mountains; it has a population of 100,000. Students benefit from exposure to the nearby high-tech companies of the Silicon Valley, hospitality industries, and a concentration of agribusiness enterprises.

Facilities

The Monterey Institute's specialized international library has a collection of 70,000 carefully selected volumes and 550 periodical titles, about one third in languages other than English. Its state-of-the-art integrated computer system handles all major library functions. In addition, the CD-ROM workstations offer indexing, abstracts, or full text of periodical articles. Online database access to a vast array of information is also available through reference services.

Technology Environment

All M.B.A. candidates are expected to achieve literacy in the use of the standard computer software used in today's business environments. Windows-based and Macintosh microcomputer laboratories are available for course-related computing in accounting, finance, quantitative methods, and decision sciences. They also offer workshops, individual assistance, and free Internet access. Computer instruction is further integrated in the preparation of the International Business Plans.

Placement

The School's programs and counseling facilitate job and internship searches, both in the United States and abroad. It provides career counseling, workshops and videotapes on job search skills, coaching for job and internship searches, and a library of internationally oriented career information. Students have access to databases on internship opportunities and to the Institute's 1,400 M.B.A. alumni, who are available to discuss students' career interests and job hunting in their fields and geographic areas.

Admission

Applicants to the M.B.A. programs must have a bachelor's degree from an approved college or university in the United States or the equivalent, with a minimum grade point average of 3.0 on a 4.0 scale. All M.B.A. applicants must submit the GMAT score report and demonstrate foreign language proficiency, or else extend their program with summer language study. Nonnative English speakers must submit a minimum TOEFL score of 550 for the two-year program and a minimum score of 600 for the advanced-entry program. Preference is given to applicants with prior business experience.

Finances

The 2000–01 tuition and fees are $19,500. Personal expenses for housing, food, books and supplies, and other incidentals are estimated at an additional $7500 per year.

Competitive half-tuition scholarships are available to students who combine academic merit with international experience. Scholarship applicants must meet eligibility requirements and complete their admission and scholarship application procedures by the date specified on the scholarship application form.

In addition, some forms of need-based financial aid, available only to U.S. citizens and eligible noncitizens, have application deadlines.

International Students

In recent years, the largest numbers of international M.B.A. students have come from Norway, Japan, France, China, Germany, Belgium, Finland, Denmark, and Austria.

Nonnative speakers of English must use English as their language of study to fulfill the language component. Students who demonstrate exceptionally high levels of written and oral English may take other elective courses in English or study a third language if they qualify at the appropriate level.

In addition to the required orientation for all new students, there is a supplementary orientation for international students and other workshops during the academic year.

Application Facts and Dates

Application may be made at any time, provided it is received at least one month prior to the applicant's proposed semester of enrollment or three months in advance for international students residing in their home countries. Applicants are notified of their admission status within four weeks after the application file is complete.

To request literature about the Monterey M.B.A. or if there are questions regarding application procedures, students should contact:

Monterey Institute of International
    Studies
Admissions Office
425 Van Buren Street
Monterey, California 93940
Telephone: 831-647-4123
Fax: 831-647-6405
E-mail: admit@miis.edu
World Wide Web: http://www.miis.edu

Nanyang Technological University

WHY THE NANYANG M.B.A.?

The Nanyang M.B.A. Programme, a highlight of the Nanyang Business School, continues its tradition of excellence by maintaining high standards, while adapting its programmes so that it remains at the cutting edge of the current business environment. Beginning with the new academic year in July 2000, the Nanyang M.B.A. includes e-business concepts and strategies in all core courses. In addition, a new specialization in e-commerce is offered.

The Nanyang M.B.A. offers a specialized programme with a global perspective focusing on Asia. Courses are taught by highly qualified international faculty members who have outstanding business and professional experience with research publications in reputable local and international scholarly journals. The Nanyang Business School has earned worldwide recognition for its academic excellence and is widely regarded as a premier business school in the region.

—Professor Neo Boon Siong, Dean

Program and Curricular Focus

The M.B.A. Programme aims to inculcate a global perspective with an Asian focus, develop an in-depth knowledge and understanding in a particular area of specialization, prepare leaders for the ever-emerging needs of a global marketplace, and produce graduates who are e-business savvy.

The Nanyang M.B.A. teaches students to have a focused understanding of business, social, and global environments coupled with a strong integration of skills, knowledge, and professional competence. A team approach to learning is encouraged to enhance each student's cognitive, problem-solving, and communication skills. Nanyang's programme emphasizes industry orientation with ample opportunities for interacting and networking with entrepreneurs, professionals, and business leaders both in and out of the classroom.

A unique feature of the Nanyang M.B.A. is that all students must choose an area of specialization. This provides additional strength and marketability for each graduating participant to be able to manage and lead in different aspects of business and industry. In order to maintain high standards, the intake for each specialization is kept to a small number, which creates a cooperative and dynamic environment for study.

The Nanyang M.B.A. specializations are accounting, banking and finance, e-commerce, international business, management of technology, marketing, and strategic management.

Students and the M.B.A. Experience

The average M.B.A. student is 31 years old with seven years of working experience. The profile from the 1999–2000 enrollment is comprised of 20 percent full-time and 80 percent part-time students. Students come from diverse backgrounds. Forty-two percent have engineering degrees, 25 percent have science degrees, 20 percent have commerce degrees, and the remaining 13 percent have degrees from other disciplines. On average, 20 percent of the students are drawn from countries in North America, Africa, Australia, New Zealand, Europe, and Asia. Students have extensive opportunity to interact with each other and increase communication skills through group projects, class participation, and class presentations.

❖ Global Focus

The Nanyang M.B.A. provides participants with an opportunity to obtain a globally focused education and experience. In addition to an international faculty and student body, the programme offers an international exchange programme with twenty-three academic institutions worldwide. Participants also have an opportunity to participate in the Business Study Mission (BSM), which provides firsthand observations of business practices in different cultural environments.

Special Features

Nanyang Technological University (NTU) collaborates with the University of St. Gallen, Switzerland, for a double master's degree, which provides opportunities for students in the M.B.A. in international business to acquire an in-depth knowledge of the best business strategies and concepts utilized in the East and West. Students who successfully complete all formal requirements of both programmes are awarded two master's degrees: an M.B.A. in international business from Nanyang Technological University and a master's degree in international management from the University of St. Gallen, Switzerland.

Beginning in July 2000, the Nanyang M.B.A. includes e-business concepts and strategies in all core courses, in addition to offering a new specialization in e-commerce.

The Faculty

The School has 250 highly qualified faculty members with sound professional and managerial experience. Faculty members are encouraged to undertake consulting work of a specialized nature in order to keep abreast of developments in business and industry. To ensure the relevance of courses to industry and corporations, leading businessmen and managers are invited to participate in the School's academic and research programmes.

The Business School Network

The corporate community plays a role in the M.B.A. students' educational experience by providing guidance from advisory committee members and business contacts. The Nanyang M.B.A. Advisory Committee members include a partner of PriceWaterhouseCoopers; the Chairman and Managing Director of Keppel FELS Ltd.; the Executive Director of Singapore International Chamber of Commerce; the President and CEO of Haw Par Corporation Ltd.; the

President of the Singapore Federation Chamber of Commerce and Industry; the Chief Executive of Singapore Productivity and Standards Board; the Senior Vice President of Asia Pacific SPG Operations, Seagate Technology International; the Managing Director and Deputy CEO of SemCorp Industrial Ltd.; a managing partner of Allen & Gledhill; and the President of Pan Pacific Hotels & Resorts, Ptd., Ltd.

The Nanyang Business School Advisory Committee members include the managing partner of Ernst & Young; the Regional Marketing Director of DHL Air Express Center; the Chairman of the Association of Banks in Singapore; the Vice President of Personnel, SIA Engineering Company; a managing partner of Andersen Consulting; the Senior Executive Director, Economics, Monetary Authority of Singapore; a partner at Wong Partnership; the CEO of Infocomm Development Authority of Singapore; the President, Singapore Exchange Ltd.; the Executive Chairman, PriceWaterhouseCoopers; and the President, Institute of Certified Public Accountants of Singapore.

The College and Environs

Nanyang Technological University is situated in southwestern Singapore and is approximately 25 kilometers from the city centre. The campus, which covers 200 hectares, is modern, with up-to-date teaching and research facilities, conveniently located residences, and a range of recreational amenities for staff and students. Members of the University community work, study, and interact in state-of-the-art and well-equipped laboratories, lecture theatres, libraries, and tutorial rooms.

Facilities

There is a wide range of facilities and services available at NTU, including a library with a collection of approximately 600,000 books and bound periodicals as well as 4,500 current periodicals. Access to a variety of information resources is available through the library's Gateway to Electronic Media Services (GEMS), which provides access to resources such as online databases, CD-ROM databases, electronic journals and books, multimedia CD-ROMs, and audio, visual, and Internet resources. Students and staff can connect to the Internet from anywhere on campus, including on-campus housing sites. In addition, there is a Computer Centre with more than 6,000 network PCs and workstations, a comprehensive sports complex that offers indoor and outdoor recreational facilities, a children's

The Nanyang Technological University campus.

learning centre, a bank, and medical centre, all conveniently located on campus. On-campus housing is available to faculty members and students.

Technology Environment

The new financial trading rooms are equipped with state-of-the-art hardware and software technology, including a videoconferencing facility, which supports teaching and research activities in financial engineering and other areas of high-technology finance. The rooms include live market-data feed from Reuters, historical financial databases, financial trading software, C++, MAT-LAB, e-commerce, and other programming and application software. One of the financial trading rooms also serves as an e-commerce lab for teaching and research in electronic commerce.

Placement

The Career Development Service (CDS) provides advice and assistance to M.B.A. students in their career search. Seminars and workshops on various topics are organized throughout the year in addition to individualized career counseling. Information on companies is also available to students at the M.B.A. career library. The CDS office maintains close contact with businesses and industry and serves as a liaison for career development. An optional internship programme is also available for students (especially international students) for valuable industry exposure and experience.

Admission

Candidates must have a bachelor's degree, a minimum of two years of management or professional experience,

and a minimum GMAT score of 630. For applicants whose language of instruction is not English, an acceptable score in the Test of English as a Foreign Language (TOEFL) is required. The average acceptable TOEFL score is 620.

Finances

Tuition and fees for full- and part-time students are $10,500 and $7,500, respectively, for each academic year. Available scholarships and financial aid include APEC, ASEAN, and NTU M.B.A. scholarships and bursaries. For information on financial aid, students should access the University Web site at http://www.ntu.edu.sg/registrar/postgraduate/coursework.

International Students

Prior to the start of the programme, an orientation and enrichment programme is provided for full-time students. In 1999–2000, the international student body was comprised of students from Africa (1.4 percent), Asia (89.2 percent), Australia and New Zealand (0.7 percent), Europe (7 percent), and North America (3.7 percent).

Application Facts and Dates

For more information, students should contact:

The M.B.A. Office
Nanyang Business School
Nanyang Technological University
Nanyang Avenue
Singapore 639798
Telephone: 65-790-6183 or 6055
Fax: 65-791-3561
E-mail: nbsmba@ntu.edu.sg
World Wide Web: http://www.
    nanyangmba.ntu.edu.sg

National University

La Jolla, California

AN M.B.A. PROGRAM THAT ENCOMPASSES THEORETICAL CONCEPTS AND PRACTICAL APPLICATIONS

The Master of Business Administration (M.B.A.) program provides adult learners with a comprehensive foundation for business decision making and prepares them to be more effective leaders in a rapidly changing business environment. As businesses cope with a changing global environment, new technologies, and more complex government regulations, the need becomes more critical for leaders who possess the knowledge and skills that ensure future success.

National University has been educating business leaders for twenty-eight years, and its rigorous business programs clearly mark the path to success. We are pleased to help applicants determine how our programs might contribute to their future success.

—Dr. S. M. Azordegan, Dean

Programs and Curricular Focus

The M.B.A. programs at National University have several areas of curricular focus. National offers a general M.B.A. as well as areas of specialization in electronic commerce, technology management, international business, public administration, marketing, environmental management, financial management, human resources management, health-care administration, and telecommunications systems management.

Core requirements consist of ten courses designed to provide a solid academic foundation for adult students preparing themselves for the business environment. Courses include accounting and financial management, business research, global management, human resources, international marketing, and strategic planning. The curriculum culminates to help students in a final M.B.A. project.

Students who do not have an undergraduate business degree must satisfactorily complete foundation courses. Successful completion of a foundation skills aptitude exam will exempt students from individual foundation courses. Foundation courses include accounting, algebra, finance, macroeconomics, microeconomics, and statistics.

Students and the M.B.A. Experience

National's School of Business and Technology programs encompass both theoretical concepts and practical

applications. They place special emphasis on the role of management in the formulation and administration of policy and strategic plans.

More than 1,800 students are currently enrolled in graduate business programs at National. The average age of enrolled students is 34, and about half are women. Most students are employed full-time as middle- or upper-level management professionals in business, technology, or government. Class discussions in graduate seminars are enhanced by the maturity, motivation, and varied backgrounds and work experiences of the students.

National draws transfer students from more than 200 universities, with varied interests in careers in accounting, environmental management, finance, health care, human resources, international business, and telecommunications systems.

❖ Global Focus

The M.B.A. degree program culminates in an original, comprehensive project based on a current problem at a deliberately selected site. After completion of statistics and business research methodology and 30 additional quarter units, students are enrolled in the "M.B.A. Project." Students are formed into teams of three or four students who have a common interest or area of specialization and whose schedules enable them to work together. Teams and individuals present their completed project to the University community; the subject organization, if applicable; or at a scheduled presentation event.

Special Features

The Master of Business Administration provides adult learners with a comprehensive foundation for business decision making that prepares them to lead effectively in a rapidly changing business environment. The program enables graduates to manage the challenges of today, including globalization, diversity, social and ethical responsibility, and technology, and to anticipate and adapt to the challenges of tomorrow. The degree encompasses the theoretical concepts and practical applications for business practitioners. Special emphasis is placed on the role of management in the formulation and administration of corporate policy and strategic plans. Six of the courses are also available on CD-ROM as part of the Global M.B.A. Program.

The Faculty

The professors selected to teach in National University's M.B.A. program are among the finest in their chosen fields. They combine academic expertise with real-life experience in the professional world. All faculty members are personally committed to students in the program and are readily available to discuss the course work and any other questions to ensure greater student understanding and success.

All faculty members not only hold advanced degrees in their areas of expertise but are respected professionals with many years of career experience. Learning is facilitated through lectures, outside reading, class discussions, case studies, and research projects relating to problems within the students' interests. The expansive knowledge of the students and the diversity of their backgrounds add richness to the group learning experience.

The Business School Network

Alumni, leaders in business, technology, and military play an integral part in National's statewide business school network. The University draws on the expertise and knowledge from local advisory boards, professors in the field in which they teach, and representatives from local industries who often volunteer to speak in the classroom. On-site programs in business and government entities also serve as a key networking component

The College and Environs

Chartered in 1971, National University is a nonprofit, nonsectarian, independent institution accredited by the Western Association of Schools and Colleges. The University's academic goal is to provide educational opportunities in a meaningful format that prepares students for leadership roles while increasing their competence in specific academic areas. Students are encouraged to register only once for an entire degree program, taking courses in one-month modules of intensive study. A wide variety of core, specialization, and elective courses are offered each month. Both day and evening classes are available.

Facilities

National University's library has been developed with attention to the overall educational purpose of serving career-oriented adults. The University's library includes more than 160,000 volumes and about 2,700 periodicals. Students have free access to the Library Resources Online System (LIBROS), which is on an IBM-platform computer and is available at more than 850 mainframe terminals throughout the University. In addition, students can access the Online Public Access Catalog (OPAC), which contains the bibliographic records for all materials owned by the library.

Writing Across the Curriculum is a University-wide program that enriches students in all areas of learning through the development of writing skills and critical thinking. The University is dedicated to providing students and faculty members with the full range of conceptual, material, and instructional resources and support systems necessary to meet the goals of making writing and research the primary vehicle of education at the University and to distinguish graduates of National University in the eyes of employers and the general public.

Classes are offered at twenty centers in metropolitan areas throughout California, providing increased flexibility. The University also has computer labs, which are open seven days a week to allow students access to the technology required for the programs.

Placement

National has a strong network of more than 60,000 alumni who are employed in business, industry, or government careers. Students who are seeking employment in their career can meet individually with faculty members for career guidance.

Admission

Applicants for master's programs must hold a bachelor's degree or higher from an accredited college or university and have a minimum GPA of 2.5. Under certain conditions, admission on probation may be granted to applicants whose average is 2.0–2.49. All applicants must file a University application, pay a nonrefundable $60 application fee, ($100 for international applicants), and have official transcripts sent to the records office from every college or university previously attended. The University sets no deadlines for receipt of applications for admission and operates under a continuous admission policy. Students may begin their studies any month of the year and pursue their program without delay, following the special one-course-per-month format.

Finances

Many students receive tuition assistance from their employers in the United States or abroad. Students may be eligible for various types of financial assistance such as grants, loans, work-study opportunities, and scholarships, as provided by federal, state, and University programs. Application forms are available in the financial aid office. The University is approved for the training of veterans and maintains a full-service veterans' affairs office.

International Students

National University has students from more than 75 countries enrolled in business programs. Approximately 20 percent of the students in the M.B.A. program are international. Students must provide academic transcripts, a statement of finances, and a TOEFL score of at least 550 or proof of English proficiency.

Application Facts and Dates

For more information, students should contact:

M.B.A. Program
National University
11255 North Torrey Pines Road
La Jolla, California 92037
Telephone: 800-NAT-UNIV
        (628-8648, toll-free)
Fax: 619-642-8709
E-mail: advising@nu.edu
World Wide Web: http://www.nu.edu
                http://online.nu.edu
                (online programs)

For international inquiries, students should contact:

M.B.A. Program
National University
4121 Camino del Rio South
San Diego, California 92108
Telephone: 619-563-7200

New Hampshire College

Manchester, New Hampshire

REAL-WORLD MANAGEMENT—THE M.B.A. AT NEW HAMPSHIRE COLLEGE

The M.B.A. degree at New Hampshire College has always been strongly linked to real-world management. From the very beginning we developed a degree with a practical orientation to the business world. And our focus is far more than business in the region or in the United States: we have as well an international orientation to the business world.

Our multinational culture at the Graduate School and our international programs that students may combine with the M.B.A. have long established us as an environment of choice for students directed toward careers in international business.

The response we receive from business leaders, from those who hire and employ our students, is that we are sending them the kind of leader that today's world demands.

—Paul Schneiderman, Dean

Programs and Curricular Focus

The New Hampshire College M.B.A. program offers students a range of program options and learning experiences to accommodate the needs of the diverse student body. Both full-time and part-time options are available. Full-time study requires between twelve and eighteen months of work, depending upon both prerequisite work and the pace at which the student chooses to move through the program. Part-time students are generally able to complete the program within 2½ to 3½ years.

New Hampshire College is accredited by the Association of Collegiate Business Schools and Programs (ACBSP). The emphasis of the College is on excellence in teaching, reflected in the combined academic and professional application approach of the M.B.A. program. The case-study method, teamwork, lecture, and practical experience are combined to prepare students for the expectations of complex business environments.

The M.B.A. program is also offered via distance learning. Using the Internet, students have the option of completing M.B.A. courses electronically.

All students are required to take twelve core courses. Students thereafter have the option of pursuing a choice of more than eighty electives either to satisfy their M.B.A. electives or by combining the M.B.A. with one or more of fourteen certificate programs and seven M.S. programs.

The certificate programs include the disciplines of accounting, artificial intelligence, computer information systems, database management, finance, health administration, human relations management, international business, marketing, operations management, school business administration, taxation, telecommunications and networking, and training and development.

Combined-degree programs are available with the M.S. degree in international business, finance, computer information systems, business education, accounting, hospitality management, or community economic development.

Students and the M.B.A. Experience

The Graduate School's diverse student body creates a dynamic atmosphere for learning. While some of the students enter the program directly out of college, most have two or more years of work experience to share in the classroom. The College realizes the need for students to gain a world view of business and has been successful in recruiting students from more than twenty-five countries.

Students range in age from 21 to 55 and represent a broad spectrum of academic backgrounds and disciplines. Women comprise 40 percent of the graduate enrollment, and international students represent 12 percent.

Forty percent of students have undergraduate degrees in business administration. Other academic backgrounds include engineering, social sciences, education, and the humanities.

❖ Global Focus

New Hampshire College's M.B.A. program includes students from around the world—Canada, Colombia, Egypt, India, Japan, Kenya, Mexico, Russia, South Africa, South Korea, Spain, Sweden, Taiwan, and Turkey are among the countries represented in the program.

In small-class settings, students are exposed to one another's cultural backgrounds and business practices, significantly enhancing their M.B.A. experience.

The M.B.A. curriculum is developed to incorporate the program's international perspective. Case studies and practical applications in required course work provide students with a critical understanding of global business issues.

In addition, elective options in such topics as multinational finance, international negotiations, and international trade and competitiveness can be taken with the M.B.A. degree.

Students wishing to develop a more intensive focus may pursue a certificate in international business or the M.S. in international business in combination with the M.B.A. degree.

New Hampshire College now offers its M.B.A. program in Dubai, United Arab Emirates, and in Athens, Greece. The program is taught primarily by graduate school faculty members who travel from Manchester, New Hampshire, to Dubai or Athens for a one-term teaching assignment.

The Faculty

New Hampshire College's faculty members are strongly oriented toward interactive teaching approaches. The focus is on direct involvement in the realities of business management. In addition to their superior academic credentials, the faculty members have extensive experience in business—many of them in international settings.

The Business School Network

Corporate Partnerships

Since its inception, New Hampshire Graduate School has developed extensive links to local, regional, national, and international corporate settings. Advisory boards comprised of corporate leaders consistently assist the Graduate School in developing programs that match the needs of the business community.

A variety of regional corporations have collaborated with New Hampshire College Graduate School to offer on-site M.B.A. studies and internship opportunities to current students. An international alumni network that is linked to many of the world's leading corporations provides students with contacts who assist them throughout their working careers.

The College and Environs

New Hampshire College offers uncrowded, attractive surroundings and easy access to the cultural and other advantages of metropolitan centers. The campus is an hour's drive from Boston and within easy traveling distance of the state's seacoast, lakes, and mountain areas.

Facilities

The Graduate School of Business recently moved to a new state-of-the-art facility on the main campus in Manchester. The building contains modern lecture halls, classrooms, and seminar and conference rooms. The building houses a computer center, classroom PCs are networked, and students have access to the Internet with their own accounts.

Technology Environment

New Hampshire College's computing resource center supports a variety of business programming languages. Statistical and analytical packages such as SPSS and simulation and modeling software, including Arena, are also accessible, along with specialized programs in marketing, production, accounting, artificial intelligence/expert systems, and other disciplines. PROLOG and SQL are used in certain courses, and personal computer software used in courses includes EXSYS/ReSolver, Office 97/2000, System Architect, and other Windows-based application software. The Graduate School is the headquarters of the *Journal of Educational Computing Research.*

Placement

New Hampshire College's Career Development Center provides extensive on-campus recruitment opportunities. In addition, internships for credit are available to full-time degree candidates approved by the faculty. Additional services include career advising and assistance in resume preparation.

Admission

Students with bachelor's degrees from accredited institutions are invited to apply to New Hampshire College's M.B.A. program. Although many applicants have work experience in business or other professional settings, students who are just completing their undergraduate careers are also encouraged to apply.

Unconditional admission to the M.B.A. program requires that the student have previously completed specific business-related courses. Students lacking the courses may be required to take Graduate School of Business foundation courses. International students whose native language is not English must submit TOEFL results.

Finances

Tuition for 2000–01 for full-time students is $1188 per course, with additional fees of approximately $540. Books and supplies are about $1000 to $1500 a year.

Application Facts and Dates

Admissions decisions are made on a rolling basis, with a letter normally sent to an applicant within two weeks after the file is complete. International students may obtain applications from the Center for International Education at New Hampshire College (telephone: 603-645-9629, fax: 603-645-9603). For more information, students should contact:

Dean, Graduate School of Business
New Hampshire College
2500 North River Road
Manchester, New Hampshire
    03106-1044
Telephone: 603-644-3102
Fax: 603-644-3144
E-mail: gradad@nhc.edu
World Wide Web: http://www.nhc.edu

New School University

New York, New York

INNOVATIVE, PRACTICAL COMMITTED

▶ *If you want to change your organization, your community, or the world, come to Milano. The Milano Graduate School offers the M.S. degree in the professional areas of: Health Services Management and Policy, Human Resources Management, Nonprofit Management, Organizational Change Management, Urban Policy Analysis and Management, and a Ph.D. in Public and Urban Policy with concentrations in a wide array of management and policy areas. Students may concentrate in topics such as health systems management, community and economic development, compensation, strategic and venture management, social policy and grants management, and international NGO management.*

—Edward J. Blakely, Dean

Programs and Curricular Focus

The Milano Graduate School programs appreciate the interdependence of the private, public, and nonprofit sectors and are structured to meet the management and analytical needs of professionals employed in a variety of institutional settings and industries. Milano offers flexible delivery of courses for busy professionals through evening, weekend, accelerated, and online courses, as well as a number of field experiences to enhance the practical training.

To round out their master's degree requirements, students complete five elective courses chosen from the array of electives in their specific program or from appropriate courses offered elsewhere in the Milaano Graduate School or elsewhere in the university. Students have the option of generalizing their elective course selections, specializing by clustering their electives in a concentration or certificate area within their professional displine, or focusing their electives on management functions across programs

Attempted on a full-time basis, the curriculum typically takes two years to complete; on a part-time basis, the typical length of time to complete the program is three years. Full-time students are strongly encouraged to undertake a summer internship between their first and second years of study. These internships, in appropriate agencies and organizations, enable students to become involved in actual work settings with professionals and the issues they confront, which helps students enhance the knowledge and skills developed in the classroom.

Students and the M.S. Experience

To insure that students receive an education that matches the changing world, the School requires that every student take part in a comparative international field trip that is part of a course or go on an international workshop of up to three weeks. International field trips are part of a course and are conducted in a one-week format to provide the student with a wider view of management and policy problems beyond the American perspective. In 2001, students will be able to travel to London and, in 2002, to Berlin as part of comparative policy and management courses. In addition, the School offers two- and three-week workshop experiences in South Africa, Poland, and Argentina for students who can take advantage of longer projects in a developing nation context. Student lab fees and donations help underwrite these courses. Students attending any of these courses will pay only out-of-pocket costs for land travel and meals other than those planned in the program.

One of the major strengths of the Milano Graduate School is the diversity of its faculty members, students, and administrators. Students come from across the United States and a number of other countries. More than one third of the student body is African American, Latino, and Asian American, and more than half are women. Entering students' ages range from 21 to 50, and the range in years of work experience is comparable. This diversity in ethnicity, age, experience, and geography enhances the quality of discourse in the classroom and provides students with a global outlook.

Special Features

In addition to the five master's degree programs, the Milano Graduate School offers advanced certificates in organizational development, training and development, and career planning and development. Complementing its degree programs, the Milano Graduate School provides additional practical training grounds through three different centers of research and policy analysis, each uniquely committed to providing special service and research projects relevant to issues in its communities and organizations, and related to the missions of the degree programs. Finally, Milano offers the M.S. in health services management and policy and human resources management at branch sites throughout the state of New York.

The J. M. Kaplan Center for New York City Affairs is a public policy education center focusing primarily on New York City issues. The center has been enhancing the public's understanding of the city for more than thirty years with special training, service, and research projects.

The Faculty

The Milano Graduate School's faculty represents a diverse cross-section in terms of ethnicity and fields of interest. Approximately one third of the full-time faculty members are female; approximately one quarter of the full-time faculty members are members of historically underrepresented groups. Supplementing the full-time faculty is the adjunct faculty pool. Adjunct faculty members include corporation executives, current and former government officials, and executives of nonprofit enterprises. Most are currently practicing their professions and are able to bring to their teaching firsthand experience and insights that make theory come alive.

The Business School Network

The Milano Graduate School provides numerous opportunities for students to

Edward Blakely, Dean; Ed.D., UCLA.

Rikki Abzug, Visiting Assistant Professor; Ph.D., Yale.

Warren Balinsky, Associate Professor; Ph.D., Case Western Reserve.

Robert A. Beauregard, Professor; Ph.D., Cornell.

Howard S. Berliner, Associate Professor and Program Chair, Health Services Management; Sc.D., Johns Hopkins.

Anne-Emmanuelle Birn, Assistant Professor; Sc.D., Johns Hopkins.

David W. Brown, Professor of Professional Practice; J.D., Harvard.

Hector R. Cordero-Guzmán, Assistant Professor; Ph.D., Chicago.

Dennis A. Derryck, Professor of Professional Practice; Ph.D., Fordham.

Tim Ettenheim, Acting Program Chair and Instructor, Health Services Management and Policy; M.P.H., Yale, M.B.A., NYU.

Marianne (Mimi) Fahs, Associate Professor and Director, Health Policy Research Center; Ph.D., Michigan.

Joan Fitzgerald, Visting Associate Professor; Ph.D., Penn State.

Alec I. Gershberg, Assistant Professor; Ph.D., Pennsylvania.

Karla Hanson, Assistant Professor; Ph.D., NYU.

David R. Howell, Associate Professor and Program Chair, Urban Policy Analysis and Management; Ph.D., New School.

Mark Lipton, Associate Professor, Acting Dean of Curriculum, and Program Chair, Human Resources Management; Ph.D., Massachusetts.

Edwin Melendez, Professor and Director of the Community Development Research Center; Ph.D., Massachusetts Amherst.

Aida Rodriguez, Associate Professor and Program Chair, Nonprofit Management; Ph.D., Massachusetts.

Mary Bryna Sanger, Professor; Ph.D., Brandeis.

Alex F. Schwartz, Assistant Professor; Ph.D., Rutgers.

Kian Tajbakhsh, Assistant Professor; Ph.D., Columbia.

network with members of the business and professional communities. The adjunct faculty members provide a real link to the professional world and are adept at merging theory with practice. Through internships, students are placed in real-world situations and are confronted with developing solutions to the types of problems professionals face on a regular basis. Each of the School's five programs has an advisory board, comprising practitioners who provide insights on curricular issues. Mentoring opportunities are developed in conjunction with the Office of Career Development and Placement.

Prominent Alumni

Examples of positions attained by graduates of the master's degree programs include Director of Human Resources, Central New Jersey Medical Group; Research Associate, Human Resource/Organizational Effectiveness, The Conference Board; Vice President, Citibank; Supervisor, Pension, Health and Unemployment, New York City Department of Environmental Protection; Director, Personnel Operations, Coopers & Lybrand; Program Officer, Housing and Economic Development, Ford Foundation; Chief Financial Officer, Bellevue Hospital; Associate Commissioner for Administration, NYC Department of Probation; National Director of Major and Planned Gifts, AmFAR; Executive Director of College Advancement, Concordia College; Director of Project Management, Vera Institute of Justice; Program Officer, New York City Department for the Aging; and Chief Operating Officer, Promesa, Inc.

The College and Environs

Established in 1919, the New School University has exemplified a rare tradition of educational innovation. It offers a variety of day, evening, and weekend programs of undergraduate, graduate, and adult education. The University, located in Greenwich Village, is readily accessible from all parts of New York City. Students in the Robert J. Milano Graduate School of Management and Urban Policy are welcome to participate in the many courses and cultural events sponsored by the Graduate Faculty of Political and Social Science and by the Adult Division of New School University.

An incomparable educational environment, New York City affords graduate students unmatched opportunities to engage in specialized research, to secure internships, and to find employment.

Placement

The Office of Career Development and Placement assists students in locating internships and provides a full range of counseling and referral services.

Admission

Admission requirements for the M.S. program include the completed application form, official transcripts from each postsecondary institution attended, two letters of reference, a 300-word essay, and an interview with a member of the program staff.

Finances

Tuition in 1999–2000 for the Robert J. Milano Graduate School of Management and Urban Policy is $690 per credit, payable at registration. A list of fees is included in the brochure describing the various programs. The Milano Graduate School participates in all federal financial aid programs, including the Federal Work-Study program and the Federal Perkins Loan program. Fellowships, assistantships, merit scholarships, and need-based tuition remission are also available.

Application Facts and Dates

The admission decisions are made on a rolling basis after a careful examination of transcripts and letters of recommendation. There is no formal application deadline, but applicants requesting financial aid should apply by April 15 for the fall semester. Ph.D. candidates must apply by May 1.

Office of Admissions and Financial Aid
Robert J. Milano Graduate School of Management and Urban Policy
72 Fifth Avenue
New York, New York 10011
Telephone: 212-229-5462
Fax: 212-229-8935
E-mail: mgsinfo@newschool.edu
World Wide Web: http://www. newschool.edu/milano

New York Institute of Technology

Old Westbury, New York

PROVIDING AN EDGE TO SUCCESSFULLY COMPETE IN THE WORLD OF BUSINESS

New York Institute of Technology (NYIT) has been in the forefront of career education for four decades, facilitating contemporary challenging careers for thousands of men and women from all walks of life. The graduate business schools's offerings in particular have been designed to enhance personal and professional growth of men and women who are already in business or plan to enter the business world. A responsive faculty of gifted men and women who have distinguished themselves in teaching, research, and the business world bring their unique expertise to NYIT students through curriculum offerings that focus on today's increasingly global and technological orientation. As a result, the graduate offerings provide an edge to our student body to compete successfully in the world of business.

—Dr. J.-C. Spender, Dean

Programs and Curricular Focus

The M.B.A. program at NYIT is designed to provide the student with a working knowledge of the world of business. This includes the ability to analyze and forecast environmental trends, formulate business strategies, and manage functional programs; utilize modern theoretical frameworks in the solution of practical business problems; and synchronize the diversity of the workplace with the requirements of ever-changing markets and societal constituencies.

The curriculum consists of nine core courses aimed to equip the student with a managerial "toolkit" in the basic functional areas of business. The core curriculum culminates in an integrative, multidisciplinary business policy seminar.

Further concentration is available in the areas of accounting, energy management, finance, general management, health-care administration, international business, management of information systems, marketing, human resources management, and labor relations.

To complete the M.B.A. degree, candidates in either the 36-credit general management concentration or in any of the other 42-credit concentrations are required to select from among a master thesis project, an oral examination, or completion of additional course work.

Candidates without prior satisfactory business course work are required to complete up to four additional prerequisite courses in addition to the other degree requirements. Therefore, depending upon the need for prerequisites and selected concen-

tration, total credit requirements vary from thirty-six to fifty-four.

A joint M.B.A./D.O. degree is offered in conjunction with the New York College of Osteopathic Medicine (NYCOM) of NYIT.

Students and the M.B.A. Experience

The student body is diverse in terms of ethnicity, gender, socioeconomic characteristics, and professional status, allowing for synergistic educational interactions. The educational process is further enhanced by small class size, interactions with professors, and student-oriented administration.

NYIT students generally fall into one or more of three categories. Many are practicing professionals in such fields as engineering, police and security, accounting, marketing, and research and are preparing to become managers in their specialized areas. A second group, already in management positions at a variety of levels, are in the process of improving administrative skills in order to achieve better performance in their present jobs or gain promotions. The final category is composed of students who enroll directly after completing college.

The great majority of the M.B.A. students are pursuing their degrees on a part-time basis while maintaining full-time employment. In order to accommodate the scheduling needs of this group of students, classes are offered on evenings and weekends on the three New York campuses (Manhattan; Old West-

bury, Long Island; and Islip, Long Island) and in a Saturday-only format at the Boca Raton, Florida, site.

In addition, the M.B.A. program is also offered on line to provide all students, regardless of location or time constraints, an opportunity to complete their degree. Students should see NYIT's Web site (http://www.nyit.edu/olc) for more information about the online program.

❖ Global Focus

Recognizing that today's successful business leader requires a global perspective, all courses incorporate global content. Furthermore, NYIT's M.B.A. program offers an international business concentration that provides students with an opportunity to enroll in courses covering such areas as international finance, international marketing, cross-cultural promotion, import-export operations, and comparative economic systems. In addition, M.B.A. students benefit from the opportunity to study and communicate with students from other countries, who comprise approximately 30 percent of the total annual enrollment, as well as faculty members who have international backgrounds and roots.

The Faculty

All courses are taught and administered by faculty members. No teaching assistants are used for any facet of the educational experience. Full-time faculty members hold terminal degrees from leading U.S. and international institutions. Furthermore, they represent a broad spectrum of business and consulting experience. Adjunct faculty members are utilized to supplement the program's needs in the areas of their unique experience. All in all, faculty members are selected for their academic background, practical experience, and their love for teaching.

The Business School Network

NYIT's Graduate School of Management maintains ongoing relationships with local tri-state business communities through its more than 3,500 alumni and an Advisory Council, whose members represent such well-known organizations as Olsten Corporation; Chemical/Chase Banking Corporation; Harrows, Inc.; and Coopers & Ly-

brand. In addition, several successful on-site M.B.A. programs have been designed and offered to corporate employees.

The College and Environs

Few states offer students more in the way of culture, history, entertainment, or opportunity than New York. The New York Stock Exchange, major financial institutions, broadcast and communication firms, and clothing designers and manufacturers represent just a sampling of the industry that makes New York so dynamic.

NYIT's Manhattan campus is ideally located in the heart of New York City. On Broadway and 61st Street, the campus is adjacent to Lincoln Center and only a short walk from the world-renowned Carnegie Hall. Major museums such as the American Museum of Natural History and the Metropolitan Museum of Art are easily accessible, as are the many other museums located throughout the five boroughs.

With a choice from more than 200 museums and historic sites, students attending either the Old Westbury or Islip campus also find many interesting things to do and places to visit. Long Island is also known worldwide for its beaches and waterways, including the Hamptons and Montauk Point.

International students find a visit to the United Nations of special interest and sports fans find it difficult to choose from among the many professional and collegiate basketball, hockey, soccer, football, and baseball games that are available throughout the year.

Facilities

NYIT libraries are maintained at all campuses, and all students have access to total collections through intralibrary loan service. As a member of the Long Island Resources Council and the New York Metropolitan Reference and Research Library Agency, NYIT provides access to holdings of other academic libraries in the area. Bibliographic searches on computer databases are available through the Wisser Library on the Old Westbury Campus.

Computer lab facilities are available on each campus. All three New York campuses are connected via an interactive state-of-the-art system of distance learning laboratory rooms, which permits a course to be simultaneously taught to students at two or more sites. This feature provides students with an opportunity to gain valuable experience in using the latest technology being used by many corporations for meetings and other forms of communication.

Placement

NYIT maintains a Career Development and Placement Office with a full-time professional staff who assists graduate students in making informed choices. Career counseling, including job search, resume preparation, and interviewing techniques, is provided. On-campus recruiting visits are scheduled with many of the nation's top corporations. The active Business School alumni also provide mentoring and networking opportunities.

Admission

All applicants are required to hold a bachelor's degree or its equivalent from an accredited college or university and must submit the completed application form, application fee, official transcript from each institution previously attended, and scores obtained on the Graduate Management Admissions Test (GMAT). Each application and accompanying materials receive a personal review from the M.B.A. director or M.B.A. administrator. Admission is predicated on the achievement of a satisfactory composite score, as established by the M.B.A. faculty. The composite score consists of a weighted combination of the applicant's undergraduate quality point average and the score achieved on the GMAT. Applicants may be admitted to either fully or provisionally matriculated status, depending on the composite score.

Finances

Tuition for 2000–01 is $525 per graduate credit, along with a one-time application fee of $50. Tuition charges are the same for both residents and nonresidents of New York State. Most students live off-campus in adjacent residential communities. However, NYIT does provide graduate housing on the Islip campus. Costs for on-campus housing for 1999–2000 ranged from $1600 to $1800 per semester, and meal plan costs ranged from $1400 to $1550 per semester. Limited financial aid in the form of tuition credit is available through graduate assistantships and graduate student aide positions. Candidates may also qualify for one of three types of graduate scholarships, which will reduce tuition by one third. The Office of Financial Aid assists applicants who are seeking loans or other available forms of assistance.

International Students

New York Institute of Technology has a long, rich tradition of enrolling qualified graduate students who have completed undergraduate degrees in other countries. International candidates to the M.B.A. program must meet all conditions previously listed and submit a TOEFL of at least 500 for consideration. Prospective international students should note that NYIT tests applicants with less than a 550 on TOEFL. Those students may be required to enroll in additional English courses.

The M.B.A. department also considers applications from students who have successfully completed three- or four-year postsecondary programs at accredited international institutions that are equivalent to at least three years of undergraduate study in the United States. If accepted, such students enroll in a special "bridge" program, which, among other conditions, requires completion of an additional 30 credits of undergraduate/graduate course work.

Application Facts and Dates

NYIT maintains a policy of rolling admissions without cut-off dates but recommends submission of application materials by June for the fall semester and by October for the spring semester. Typically, applicants receive an admissions decision within four to six weeks after receipt of application.

Requests for application materials or additional information should be addressed to:

Executive Director of Admissions
New York Institute of Technology
P.O. Box 8000
Old Westbury, New York 11568-8000
Telephone: 516-686-7520
            800-345-NYIT (toll-free)
Fax: 516-626-0419
E-mail: adolitsk@nyit.edu

North Carolina State University

College of Management

Raleigh, North Carolina

> ### USING TECHNOLOGY FOR COMPETITIVE ADVANTAGE
>
> *North Carolina State University (NC State), the flagship science and engineering campus of the University of North Carolina system, is committed to being a leader in the emerging field of electronic commerce. The M.S.M. concentration in electronic commerce (EC) provides students with an innovative and cutting-edge education that responds to the needs of the emerging digital economy. No matter what your career interest—finance, marketing, operations, engineering, computer science, design, or communication—the EC program will stay ahead of the curve where networking technology and new business models are transforming all organizations.*
>
> —Michael Rappa, Alan T. Dickson Distinguished University Professor of Technology Management

Programs and Curricular Focus

The Master of Science in Management (M.S.M.) is a specialized degree that emphasizes the management of technology. The curriculum was revised in fall 1999 to give all students the ability to take more electives and to allow part-time students to finish the program in less than three years. A new concentration in electronic commerce is being launched. Course offerings in information technology management and supply chain management are being expanded. All students will start in the fall and follow a set course sequence for the first half of the program. A core faculty team has been created to ensure integration of course content and emphasis on technology.

Students begin the program by taking seven required courses in strategy, economics, accounting, marketing, finance, operations, and managing people. Students then begin a concentration, selecting from information technology management, electronic commerce, financial management, operations and supply chain management, technology commercialization, and new product development. Full-time students can complete the program in three or four semesters; part-time students finish in two years and nine months.

The technology focus of the program comes from three sources. First, all students take courses related to technology, including strategy, operations management, information technology management, and managing people in a high-technology environment. Even

courses in traditional management subjects, such as marketing and finance, have a technology slant through the choice of cases and projects used in the course. Second, all students complete a concentration in management of technology. In most of these degree tracks, students can take courses in technical fields, such as industrial engineering and computer science. Students also have the option to take advanced courses in engineering or science through the flexible science and technology concentration. Third, M.S.M. students have a strong technology background and seek careers in high-technology companies. Most M.S.M. courses also include students from other graduate programs at NC State who are working toward a minor in management.

Students and the M.S.M. Experience

Almost all M.S.M. students have professional work experience, many with high-technology industries such as telecommunications or software and others in industries such as health care or financial services, where technology is the key to competitive advantage. A technical background is not essential for the M.S.M., but all students must be willing to learn about technology and the management challenges it creates. More than 60 percent of M.S.M. students have undergraduate degrees in science, computer science, or engineering. Another 24 percent were business majors. The rest come from a variety of fields, including the social sciences and humanities.

The average M.S.M. student has 6 years of work experience. The age range of students is between 22 and 50. Women comprise approximately 45 percent of each entering class; members of minority groups, approximately 8 percent; and international students, 15 percent.

Special Features

The curriculum in electronic commerce is projected to encompass four 3-unit courses: Introduction to the Digital Economy, EC Business Models, EC Network Infrastructure and Software Tools, and EC Practicum, a project-based course that focuses on the practical aspects of creating and running an e-commerce enterprise. Students work with local businesses and community organizations to examine how electronic commerce can best be put to practice.

The Technology, Education, and Commercialization (TEC) program within the M.S.M. is designed to promote both educational and technology transfer objectives. Supported by the National Science Foundation, graduate students and faculty members in the College of Management work closely in teams with their counterparts in the science and engineering disciplines to identify, evaluate, and commercialize promising technologies.

The Faculty

The M.S.M. graduate faculty is composed of outstanding teachers and researchers. Faculty members have been selected for the University of North Carolina (UNC) Board of Governors' Award, alumni distinguished professorships, and the NC State Academy of Outstanding Teachers. The faculty is internationally renowned for research. Faculty members serve on the editorial boards of journals in accounting, finance, production management, industrial relations, and project development. They have been ranked in the top twenty nationally for publishing in the top economics and finance journals.

Two distinguished University professors have been added to the faculty in the last year. Michael Rappa is the Alan T. Dickson Distinguished University

Professor of Technology Management and teaches courses on assessing emerging technologies and electronic commerce. Prior to joining NC State, he was a member of the faculty at MIT for nine years. He is a frequent consultant for industry and government—most recently, to the Presidential Information Technology Advisory Committee in Washington, D.C.

Robert Handfield is the Bank of America Distinguished University Professor of Management and teaches courses in supply chain, operations, and quality management. Handfield comes from Michigan State University, where he had been a faculty member since 1992.

The Business School Network

Business leaders regularly come to the College of Management to give guest lectures in classes and participate in the Wachovia Executive Lecture Series. The College of Management's Advisory Board is taking an active role in the College's affairs and includes executives from IBM, Nortel, Ericsson, Cisco Systems, Andersen Consulting, Wachovia, SAS Institute, Ernst & Young, and KPMG Peat Marwick.

M.S.M. students have multiple opportunities to network with businesses. Students in the TEC program interact extensively with venture capitalists, entrepreneurs, and lawyers to learn how to launch a high-technology enterprise. All TEC projects involve technologies under consideration at local companies. Based on his experience with TEC, Jeffrey Glass, Director of Research and Development at Kobe Steel USA in Research Triangle Park, said, "I think the concept is fantastic. There is a real void in teaching product development in high-tech. So I think this program will be great for industry."

Outside of the classroom, many full-time students help finance their graduate study and gain valuable work experience in co-op positions at the leading companies in the Research Triangle area, such as IBM, Northern Telecom, Glaxo Wellcome, and Ericsson. These positions can be obtained either through the University or by networking with classmates.

The College and Environs

NC State was founded in 1889 as a land-grant institution that, within 100

years, has become one of the nation's leading research universities. Located in the Research Triangle, a world-renowned center of research, industry, technology, and education, the College of Management is housed on the 623-acre main campus of NC State, which lies just west of downtown Raleigh, the state capital. NC State comprises eleven colleges and schools serving a total student population of 27,000. More than 5,000 of those students are in graduate programs.

Facilities

The College of Management is headquartered in Nelson Hall, which houses classrooms, computer labs, and the offices of the faculty members and students. Classrooms have been completely remodeled with tiered seating, laptop connections, and complete multimedia facilities. The College of Management's computer lab houses 100 microcomputers connected to a campuswide network. Students have access to a wide range of spreadsheet, word processing, database, statistical, and econometric software along with several large databases. D. H. Hill Library, located near the center of campus, offers access to millions of volumes of books and journals and an extensive and growing collection of CD-ROM and electronic databases. Graduate students also have borrowing privileges at Duke, UNC–Chapel Hill, and NC Central.

Placement

An M.S.M. degree gives students skills that are highly valued by employers. The College's students have access to a wide range of programs and services to enhance their marketability. Self-assessment exercises are built into the courses, and professional career counseling is available at the University Career Center (UCC). UCC provides workshops on resume writing and cover letters, interviewing skills, and job search strategies. In addition to on-campus recruiting for permanent jobs and internships, UCC maintains an online resume referral service, job listing notebooks, job fairs, and a library of information about career opportunities with specific companies. In addition, students may post their resumes on the M.S.M. home page on the World Wide Web.

Admission

M.S.M. students must have a baccalaureate degree from an accredited college or university and are strongly encouraged to have had courses in calculus, statistics, and economics. Admissions decisions are based on previous academic performance, GMAT scores (600 average), an essay, letters of reference, and previous work and volunteer experience. Applicants whose native language is other than English, regardless of citizenship, must also submit TOEFL scores of at least 250 (computer-based test). Interviews are not required.

Finances

The 1999–2000 budget for M.S.M. students depended on the number of credit hours the student took and the student's residency status. For full-time students who were North Carolina residents, the tuition and fees cost $1235 per semester; the estimated total for living expenses, including tuition and fees, books, medical insurance, housing, food, clothing, transportation, and other miscellaneous items, was $6500 per semester. Tuition and fees for full-time nonresidents were $5818 per semester, with estimated total living expenses at $11,000 per semester. Part-time students who were North Carolina residents paid $886 per semester for tuition and fees only; nonresidents paid $4323. Graduate assistantships are available to full-time students through the College of Management. Grants and loan programs are available through the Graduate School and the University's Financial Aid Office.

Application Facts and Dates

The NC State M.S.M. program accepts applications for the fall semester, with an application deadline of April 1. Once an application has been received and is complete, it is reviewed for admission. This rolling admission process allows an applicant to receive an admission decision within two weeks of receipt of a completed application.

Ms. Pam Bostic
Assistant Director
M.S.M. Program
North Carolina State University
Box 7229
Raleigh, North Carolina 27695
Telephone: 919-515-5584
Fax: 919-515-5073
E-mail: msm@ncsu.edu

Northeastern University

Boston, Massachusetts

▶ **A REAL-WORLD EDUCATION THAT INTEGRATES STUDY AND WORK**

For nearly fifty years, students at Northeastern University's Graduate School of Business Administration have experienced what many feel is the best practice-oriented business curriculum in the nation. The Cooperative M.B.A. Program for full-time students pioneered the concept of integrating classroom learning with professional, paid, on-the-job business experience. The Working Professionals Program offers nationally recognized programs for students who work full-time while attending school: the High-Tech M.B.A., the Part-Time M.B.A., the Executive M.B.A., and the Master of Science in Finance. All degree programs are designed to fit individual objectives and accelerate careers.

—Therese M. Hofmann, Associate Dean

Programs and Curricular Focus

Rich in the tradition of experience-based education, the Graduate School of Business Administration is known for excellence in application and integration of theory and practice. The twenty-one-month Cooperative Education (Co-op) M.B.A. Program combines nine months of integrative course work with a six-month paid professional business experience. A final six months in the classroom allows students to pull together all the concepts they mastered earlier. This integration is specifically needed in the strategic management course and the field consulting courses. In addition, most electives are taken on campus in this final period, allowing students to either continue the general management thrust of the program or specialize in a particular area of interest.

Students begin the Co-op M.B.A. Program in either September or March. In the program, students master a general management curriculum and choose from a broad range of elective courses. These electives allow students to tailor their degrees to match their own needs and interests. Electives may also be taken within any of Northeastern's nine graduate and professional schools. Independent study projects can be designed for in-depth pursuit of a subject of special interest.

The Graduate School of Professional Accounting (GSPA) offers a unique fifteen-month joint M.S./M.B.A. program in accounting that is specifically designed for students with a background in the arts and sciences who are interested in a business career, especially in the area of public accounting. The program is comprehensive and condensed and includes a paid internship.

A joint M.S. Nursing/M.B.A. degree is offered with the School of Nursing, and a J.D./M.B.A. degree program is offered with the School of Law. Both schools involved must admit students for these programs.

Students and the M.B.A. Experience

Students stay connected to the workforce through relationships with their executive mentors, tailored electives, co-op jobs, independent study, and a large number of executives who serve as guest speakers in various courses. A typical entering class consists of students from a myriad of professional, cultural, and academic backgrounds. Career goals are similarly diverse.

Each year, the Graduate School of Professional Accounting begins a class of 60 full-time students. The program draws students nationwide, but 80 percent come from prestigious and competitive arts and sciences programs in the Northeast. The majority of the students have little or no professional experience.

More than 16,000 students call Northeastern University home, representing a wide range of academic, professional, geographic, and cultural backgrounds.

The Faculty

Almost 100 full-time professors, organized in six groups and eighteen functional areas, teach M.B.A. students in the Graduate School of Business Administration. Their credentials, experience, research interests, and publications are profiled in a booklet that is mailed on request. The School actively seeks faculty members who have been mid- to upper-level executives in various for-profit and not-for-profit organizations so that they can relate theory to the practice-oriented curriculum and student body. Many faculty members are active as consultants to businesses around the world. All are accustomed to being challenged on the practical applications of their research.

The faculty of the Graduate School of Professional Accounting is drawn from the College of Business Administration and also includes faculty members from other business colleges around the country who are attracted to this unique program. Pragmatic, practice-oriented faculty members are favored to bring reality into the classroom.

Placement

M.B.A. students at Northeastern have their own dedicated Career Center next to their classrooms and lounges. Placement ser-

vices are provided for co-op and after-graduation employment. Recognizing the challenging nature of the workforce, Northeastern actively trains students in a broad range of skills for job search and career advancement. Workshops are tailored each year to student and industry needs. The M.B.A. Career Center serves employers by matching resumes for employment openings, and it provides students with advanced technology for targeting job search campaigns. Panels of graduates and mentors provide stimulus and support. Alumni are welcome to use the M.B.A. Career Center to refresh their skills.

Almost all graduates of the Graduate School of Professional Accounting join major accounting firms, and 95 percent of them accept positions with firms at which they did their internships.

Admission

Successful applicants demonstrate academic competence through their undergraduate records and GMAT scores. Motivation and maturity are demonstrated through essays and recommendations, and employability is demonstrated through professional work history after the undergraduate degree. Personal interviews may be required. Prospective students are encouraged to visit the campus and meet with current students who conduct tours, arrange class visits, and answer questions.

All applicants to the Graduate School of Professional Accounting must furnish original transcripts from their undergraduate institution, showing ability to succeed in graduate school; three recommendations; and GMAT scores. Applicants must

be interviewed by the Director and at least one member of the Advisory Council whose firms underwrite the internships. All factors are considered in concert, with no single factor disproportionately weighted. Because of the internship, students with no experience are encouraged to apply.

Finances

Total tuition costs for the Co-op M.B.A. Program are $42,000 ($550 per credit in the 80-credit program). Students currently average $20,000 in earnings for the six-month co-op working period, which helps to defray program expenses. Tuition rates, fees, rules, regulations, and curricula are subject to revision by the President and the Board of Trustees at any time.

In the Graduate School of Professional Accounting, tuition for the academic year beginning June 2000 is $8225 per quarter, or $32,900 for the entire program. There is a nominal fee to cover use of library, computer, and athletic facilities. The application fee is $50, and students are required to pay a $200 tuition deposit upon acceptance. However, the three-month internship (generally with an international or regional public accounting firm) is paid, and students have earned between $10,000 and $13,000 in the January to April work period. In addition, all students are eligible for merit-based scholarships, awarded by the program to the top quartile of the class each quarter. These awards range from $500 to $1000 per quarter. Graduate assistantships are also available on a merit basis, which provide partial tuition

remission and require a maximum of 10 hours of work per week.

International Students

International students are encouraged to apply for the Co-op M.B.A. Program. Since virtually all business is global, having students from around the world in the classroom helps create a real-world atmosphere that is vital to the complete discussion of all dimensions of business problems and opportunities.

The University's International Student Office helps with the issues associated with living in a foreign country. It offers counseling on immigration regulations as well as academic, financial, and personal concerns. The office also acts as a liaison between the departments, colleges, and agencies concerned with foreign nationals in the academic community. Moreover, it provides a welcoming haven for students who are far from home, and it stages many events, such as dinners and festivals, to help all students at the University understand and value the diversity that international students bring to the campus.

Application Facts and Dates

The application deadline for the Co-op M.B.A. Program starting in September is June 15 (February 15 for consideration for an assistantship award). The deadline for the program starting in March is December 15 (August 31 to be considered for an assistantship award). Students are admitted on a rolling basis.

The M.S./M.B.A. Program in the GSPA operates on a rolling admissions basis; action follows immediately upon receipt of a completed file. Applications are due no later than May 1 for the program that begins in June.

For more information, students can refer to the School's Web site or contact:

Graduate School of Business
350 Dodge Hall
Northeastern University
Boston, Massachusetts 02115
Telephone: 617-373-5992
Fax: 617-373-8564
E-mail: gsba@cba.neu.edu
World Wide Web: http://www.cba.neu.edu/gsba
Graduate School of Professional Accounting
412 Dodge Hall
Northeastern University
Boston, Massachusetts 02115
Telephone: 617-373-3244
Fax: 617-373-8890
E-mail: gspa@neu.edu
World Wide Web: http://www.cba.neu.edu/gspa

Northern Illinois University

DeKalb, Illinois

PREPARING FOR THE CHALLENGES OF THE NEXT MILLENNIUM

▶ *In keeping with Northern Illinois University's (NIU) commitment to nontraditional, place-bound working students, the College of Business offers a high-quality, cost-effective M.B.A. program at NIU's conveniently located regional education centers, which are national models for programmatic delivery.*

NIU's M.B.A. curriculum provides students with greater opportunities than ever before to hone their communication and technical skills as they prepare for the twenty-first century. We at NIU are dedicated to making the College of Business the "School of Choice" in our region, as our nation and world face the daunting academic and professional challenges of the new millennium.

—David K. Graf, Dean

Programs and Curricular Focus

The M.B.A. program provides challenging opportunities for the mastery of traditional, current, and emerging business knowledge and produces high-quality graduates with the competencies and abilities necessary to participate effectively in a rapidly changing, increasingly diverse, global business environment. Throughout the program, students integrate the themes of a global view of business, leadership, ethics, and communication into term papers, case and group presentations, and classroom discussions. Along with information systems support and elective courses, program objectives are achieved through a required communications block, sequencing of business functions, and an integrative capstone experience.

NIU's programs are accredited by AACSB–The International Association for Management Education. They include the Evening M.B.A. program, which is offered at NIU's Hoffman Estates, Naperville, and Rockford campuses; an Executive M.B.A. program in an eighteen-month format that is delivered on Saturdays at the Hoffman Estates campus; the Master of Accounting Science (M.A.S.) program at the Hoffman Estates and DeKalb campuses; and the Master of Science in management information systems (M.S.) program at the DeKalb campus. Along with these programs, the College of Business also offers the Master of Science in Taxation (M.S.T.) program at the Hoffman Estates and DeKalb campuses. The total graduate enrollment in the College of Business is approximately 750.

For those students with nonbusiness undergraduate degrees, the 18-hour/nine-course Phase One Foundations block includes the functional business courses that are requisite to success in the M.B.A. program. At the time of application to the Evening M.B.A. program, credentials analysis determines those Foundations courses required by each candidate. Depending upon that review, students may be waived from all, some, or none of these requirements.

Once beyond the Foundations block, all students follow the communications-business functions-integrative capstone track. Electives and information support systems fill out the 31-hour/eleven-course M.B.A. program (excluding the Phase One Foundations block). Topics not routinely covered under traditional business curricula, such as emerging technologies, are addressed through an innovative Executive Lecture/Colloquium Series, and interested students can pursue areas of study in the fields of cost management systems, finance, international business, management information systems, marketing, operations management, strategic management, or Southeast Asian studies, in lieu of the general area of study.

Students and the M.B.A. Experience

The Chicago area is a major center for technological, financial, retail, and manufacturing organizations, and NIU's students reflect the diversity of their workplaces. As a result, discussions, team projects, and papers are enriched by the students' business experience. The typical student entering

NIU's program in 1999 had a GMAT score of 539 and an undergraduate GPA of 3.13 on a 4.0 scale and was 32 years old with nine years of work experience. Ninety-five percent of the 1999 entering class were employed full-time while enrolled in the M.B.A. program. The Evening M.B.A. format allows part-time students to select the pace at which they progress through the program.

The Faculty

The *Public Accounting Report*'s survey has ranked NIU's Department of Accountancy among the top ten undergraduate accounting programs nationwide in six of the last eight years and twenty-fifth among graduate accounting science programs nationwide. The National Association of State Boards of Accountancy reports that NIU is ranked fourth nationally for being listed the most number of times in the top ten schools having the highest passing rates on all four parts of the CPA exam. In October 1999, *ComputerWorld* magazine ranked NIU's M.S. in management information systems program nineteenth among the top twenty-five "Techno MBAs" in the nation. In December 1995, the *Journal of Finance* placed NIU's Department of Finance among the top 30 percent of all schools nationally in terms of total articles published in the top sixteen finance journals. In addition to research endeavors, finance faculty members engage broadly in corporate relationships and have extensive, real-world business professional designations, such as Chartered Financial Analyst, Certified Cash Manager, Certified Managerial Accountant, and Certified in Financial Management. *Sales & Marketing Management* has recommended the marketing department's sales program, taught by award-winning faculty members, as one of six programs nationwide from which to recruit new salespeople; it is one of only eight programs in direct marketing offered at four-year universities in the U.S.

The Business School Network
Corporate Partnerships
The College of Business learning experience is enhanced a great deal by strategic

alliances with businesses. These relationships range from a collegewide partnership with Motorola to a partnership between the Department of Operations Management and Information Systems and Wallace Computing. The Board of Executive Advisors, composed of business and community leaders, provides a forum for partnership and dialogue between the College and the business community. The Executive Club, a group of prominent business alumni, assists the College in the implementation of its strategic plan to become the "School of Choice" and collaborates with the M.B.A. program on the Executive Lecture/Colloquium Series. Internship programs, continuous program improvement, strategic planning, public speaking forums, and many opportunities for interaction with executives are some of the initiatives provided by these partnerships.

Prominent Alumni

The College of Business is proud of the large number of senior executive alumni who are major players in the corporate community in a wide variety of industries. Some prominent NIU alumni include Barry Cordeiro, Group Vice President and CIO, CNA Insurance; Michael Corrao, President and CEO of Gingiss Formalwear; David Fatina, President, Financial Network Alliances, Household International; Edward Glanz, Treasurer, Abbott Labs; Kathleen Halloran, Vice President, Nicor Gas; Robert Keith, President and CEO, ServiceMaster; Eileen Kowalski, Vice President, Operations, North Region, Jewel/Osco; Andrew Patti, President and CEO, Belae Brands, Inc. (former CEO, Dial Corporation and former Executive Vice President, Ameritech); Dennis Sester Sr., Vice President and Director of Worldwide Supply Chain and Director of Quality, Motorola Corporation; and Chester (Chet) Young, Division Vice President, Walgreen Company.

The College and Environs

Northern Illinois University is a comprehensive university that was established in 1895 by an act of the Illinois General Assembly. In fulfilling its mission to the northern Illinois region by recognizing the changing demands of the nontraditional student, NIU has operated education centers in Hoffman Estates and Rockford for the past several years and will open its new Naperville Education Center in fall 2000. All three centers provide services or access to services comparable to those found on the main campus. The total student population at the University is about 22,850.

The students engaged in M.B.A. course work at the Hoffman Estates and Naperville campuses live and work almost exclusively in the Chicago and suburban areas—one of the most dynamic regions in the world for commerce and industry. Both communities are within a 40-mile radius of Chicago's

"Loop." Students at the Rockford and De-Kalb campuses live and work primarily in those locales. DeKalb is a quiet, semirural town that is located 65 miles west of Chicago, while Rockford is the second-largest city in the state of Illinois and well known for its industrial manufacturing base.

Facilities

The University libraries contain nearly 1.6 million volumes, 15,000 periodical subscriptions, 3.2 million microform units (including microform, maps, recordings, and audiovisual materials), and more than 1.2 million government publications and hold membership in the Center for Research Libraries and the Illinet Online (IO) System.

Technology Environment

All graduate business students are required to have access to a computer with general purpose software and World Wide Web and e-mail capability. The M.B.A. programs at the Hoffman Estates, Naperville, and Rockford Education Centers offer modern computer labs for teaching and individual student use. All computers are networked and linked to NIU's main communication backbone in DeKalb. Classrooms are also wired so instructors can demonstrate software and utilize the World Wide Web and for similar applications. Students have access to a wide variety of general-purpose software and specialized business applications and databases, and faculty members and students have send/receive capability via e-mail as well as full access to the Internet. Students may also access the campus mainframe and minicomputers remotely from home through high-speed communication servers. Every business student is given unlimited access to the College of Business's computer resources and may use the computing facilities at the site at which their courses are offered and the main DeKalb campus. In addition, the NIU computer lab at the Multi-University Center in Oak Brook, which is within a 20-minute commute of Naperville, is available to students in this region.

Placement

Since students usually are already employed on a full-time basis when they enter the M.B.A. program, graduates generally are managers and directors at many of the Fortune 500 companies whose offices are located in the Chicago area and around the world. The average salary for NIU's recent M.B.A. graduates was $80,849 within one year of graduation.

Admission

Admission is competitive and limited to those candidates who can demonstrate high promise of success. The College of

Business considers several indicators of potential, including undergraduate GPA, GMAT score, work experience, leadership and communication skills (as described in the goals statement and resume), and two letters of recommendation. A minimum TOEFL score of 213 (computer-based test) or 550 (paper-based test) is required for all applicants whose native language is not English. Candidates may also be asked to come in for an interview or to submit additional materials deemed important in assessing their potential for success in the M.B.A. program.

Finances

Hoffman Estates, Rockford, and Naperville M.B.A. course charges are approximately $305 per semester hour. The 3-semester-hour M.S.T. course charge at Hoffman Estates is $1200. Tuition and fees for DeKalb courses are about $175 per semester hour. These amounts are subject to revision without notice.

A limited number of partial scholarships are available for M.B.A. students. Need-based financial aid is administered by the University's Financial Aid Office. Full-time students are eligible to apply for graduate assistantships.

Students in the M.B.A. program commonly live in the Chicago suburban areas or in Rockford. For on-campus students, the University offers several residence hall options.

Application Facts and Dates

Application materials may be obtained from the Director, Graduate Studies in Business and Research, at the address below. There is a $30 nonrefundable application fee payable to NIU by money order or check drawn on a U.S. bank. For U.S. citizens, the completed application form, goals statement, and fee must be received by the graduate school by June 1 for fall semester, November 1 for spring semester, or April 1 for summer session. All remaining application materials must be received by August 1 for fall semester, January 1 for spring semester, or June 1 for summer session. International students must submit all application materials prior to May 1 for consideration for admission for fall semester or by October 1 for spring semester. For more information, students should contact:

Director, Graduate Studies in Business
   and Research
College of Business
Northern Illinois University
DeKalb, Illinois 60115-2897
Telephone: 815-753-1245
       800-323-8714 (toll-free in
       Illinois)
E-mail: cobgrads@niu.edu
World Wide Web: http://www.cob.niu.
   edu/grad/grad.html

NORTH PARK UNIVERSITY North Park University

The Center for Management Education

Chicago, Illinois

> ### ETHICAL ISSUES IN BUSINESS
>
> *The course work in the Center for Management Education is reflective of what you would expect in any good graduate business program. One notable difference at North Park, however, is the unusually high degree of attention given to ethical issues. Becoming acquainted with and being committed to bringing into one's management practice ethical perspectives does not happen easily. The necessity and importance of doing so, however, is essential, as much of what our students face on a daily basis is dependent upon moral and ethical behavior. Our faculty are experienced in discussing ethical issues and are committed to helping our students acquire a strong ethical framework for decision making.*
>
> —Dean A. Lundgren, Director

Programs and Curricular Focus

The M.B.A. program at North Park University is designed primarily to meet the advanced educational needs of business professionals and to respond to the preferences expressed by the corporate community for management personnel who possess the ability to write and speak effectively, have a capacity for critical and quantitative analysis, and the ability to function as a member of a team and provide leadership within an organization. Consistent with North Park's Christian heritage, the M.B.A. program seeks to instill in its students a sense of moral responsibility that is expressed in personal integrity and social concern and is responsive to the ethical dimensions of decision making.

The North Park University M.B.A. program offers students the ultimate in scheduling flexibility and convenience. As a part-time program, the M.B.A. program offers classes on weeknights and Saturdays and students may complete the degree entirely on Saturdays if they desire. The academic year consists of five 8-week quads commencing in September, October, January, March, and June. The M.B.A. requires from sixteen to twenty courses, depending upon a student's undergraduate preparation. Full-time students take two courses per quad and can complete the degree in two years (summer classes may or may not be required). Part-time students take one course per quad. Students with appropriate liberal arts backgrounds may complete the M.B.A. program in one calendar year, taking three courses per term for four quarters. The North Park M.B.A. is a general management degree, and students do have

the option of specializing in areas such as entrepreneurship, finance, health-care management, human resource management, international business, marketing of services, nonprofit management, and organizational development.

The Center for Management Education and the North Park Seminary offer two joint-degree programs that allow students to obtain an M.B.A./M.Div. or M.B.A./M.A.T.S. For health-care professionals, the Center for Management Education and North Park's School of Nursing offer an M.B.A./M.S. with a major in nursing.

Students and the M.B.A. Experience

North Park M.B.A. students come from a range of cultural, academic, and managerial backgrounds. Forty percent of incoming students have undergraduate business degrees and their average age at entrance is 33. There are currently 250 students in the M.B.A. program, of whom 55 percent are women and 25 percent are minorities. M.B.A. students come from a variety of work environments, with large representations from the service, health-care, and nonprofit sectors.

Special Features

Consistent with North Park's commitment to the individual, each M.B.A. student has a faculty member as their program and career adviser. Such an arrangement demonstrates the personal nature of the M.B.A. program and gives students an opportunity to interact with faculty members outside the classroom setting. International students find North Park an excellent place to

pursue their graduate education. Its location in the city provides numerous opportunities for part-time internships.

The Faculty

North Park faculty members come from rich and diverse academic and management backgrounds. With professional degrees from institutions such as Harvard, Stanford, and the University of Chicago, North Park faculty members are uniquely qualified for management instruction.

The Business School Network

The Center for Management Education regularly hosts corporate and community leaders to the classroom. In addition, appearances by corporate recruiters and trainers help assist students with career planning and placement.

The College and Environs

Founded in 1891, North Park is a private university that has a more than 100-year tradition of educating students for service and leadership. North Park is located in a park-like campus setting on the northwest side of Chicago, just minutes from downtown Chicago and easily accessible from most expressways and public transportation. Repeatedly selected by *U.S. News & World Report* as one of the top ten Midwest regional liberal arts colleges, North Park enjoys a wide reputation for academic excellence. With a current enrollment of more than 2,300 students, North Park offers a full compliment of academic programs at the undergraduate level and currently offers programs in business, community development, education, nursing, occupational therapy, and theology at the graduate level.

Facilities

North Park's Wallgren and Mellander libraries have access to more than 3 million books, periodicals, and microfilms. In addition, students have access to the University's three computing centers.

Technology Environment

Computing facilities for M.B.A. students includes more than 300 microcomputers in three student labs. In addition, the

University computing network is accessible by modem.

Placement

As a part-time program, nearly all M.B.A. students currently hold full-time positions. The Center for Management Education does offer, in conjunction with the University, career placement services for students.

Admission

Admission to the M.B.A. program requires an undergraduate degree (or its international equivalent) from an accredited institution; GMAT, GRE, or MAT score (no minimum required); completion of the M.B.A. application; and two letters of recommendation. A minimum TOEFL score of 600 is required of all applicants for whom English is not their native language.

Finances

Tuition for the North Park M.B.A. program is $1100 per course for the 2000–01 academic year. Tuition includes all fees and user costs, including parking. It does not include costs for books and materials. The M.B.A. program offers two scholarships for both full- and part-time students. Students with an undergraduate GPA of 3.65 (based on a 4.0 scale) or above or a GMAT score of 600 or above automatically receive a Presidential Scholarship, which covers 30 percent of tuition costs. Students with an undergraduate GPA of 3.35 to 3.64 (based upon a 4.0 scale) or GMAT score of 550 or above automatically receive a Dean's Scholarship, which covers 15 percent of tuition costs. Loans are available through the Federal Stafford Student Loan Program and several other loan programs.

International Students

Campus housing for international students is not provided. In addition, the Center for Management Education does not provide assistantships of any kind for international students.

Application Facts and Dates

The Center for Management Education accepts applications on a rolling admissions process for any of the five academic quads. Prospective applicants are encouraged to apply well in advance of the quad in which they plan to enter. Upon receipt of all materials, applicants will be notified of the admission decision within four weeks. For application materials, students should contact:

Christopher Nicholson
Director of Admission, Graduate and
    Adult Programs
The Center for Management Education
North Park University
3225 West Foster Avenue
Chicago, Illinois 60625
Telephone: 773-244-5518
    800-888-6728 (toll-free)
Fax: 773-244-4953
E-mail: cnicholson@northpark.edu

 # Northwood University

Richard DeVos Graduate School of Management

Midland, Michigan

DISCOVER MANAGEMENT

Understanding the art of management is difficult. Mastery is impossible. Business success often is fleeting, more a function of the circumstances than the skill of the executive. Sustained corporate success, thus sustained management excellence, is rare. Yet, business schools continue to promise, "if you would just get our M.B.A., you too will be prepared to achieve management excellence." Unfortunately, it is just not that easy. If the practice of management is difficult, the learning and acquiring of the necessary skills so too must be difficult and a lifelong undertaking.

At the DeVos Graduate School of Management, we have designed our programs to provide the opportunity for students to begin the acquisition of skills. Our approach is grounded in the following five guidelines: management is about finding and fixing problems, not as an individual doing tasks, but through others as part of an organization; management is about thinking and reasoning, not buzzwords, fads, formulas, panaceas, beliefs, or simplistic answers. The only right answer is "it depends." Management actions must be based on reality, not just the application of answers. No answer works under all situations, thus management must understand the circumstances; management must deal not only with the "what" that needs to be accomplished, but also the "how" of leading an organization to change; management education must deal with not only intellectual development but also attitudinal and emotional development; and experiential learning (case method, simulation) is more effective and lasting than cognitive learning.

In summary, the acquisition of management skills becomes about change in you—understanding your limiting factors and working to eliminate them.

—Dr. William T. Busby

Programs and Curricular Focus

The Richard DeVos Graduate School of Management offers the M.B.A. in three distinct formats: the Executive M.B.A., the Managerial M.B.A., and the Full-Time M.B.A.

Rather than functional concentrations or majors, the focus of the DeVos M.B.A. program centers on developing students' leadership and problem-solving skills. Students receive their degrees in integrated management.

The fifteen-month, Full-Time M.B.A. program is designed for students from any undergraduate major who have little or no work experience. Small cohort sections of approximately 30 students participate in weekday, daytime courses beginning in late September and continuing year-round for fifteen months.

"Learning by doing" is the cornerstone of this innovative program. The curriculum is highly experiential and immerses students in an atmosphere of continually practicing, assessing, and refining their management skills in dynamic, realistic environments. These interactions occur through a combination of cognitive learning (thinking, reasoning, and acquiring knowledge) and experiential training through case analysis, role play exercises, business and management simulations, and other interactive experiences.

The Executive M.B.A. (EMBA) program is designed to significantly enhance the performance capability and executive potential of experienced business professionals. The program focuses on enhancing skills by engaging the intellectual, attitudinal, and emotional development required for students to reach their full executive potential. The EMBA is conducted one night a week for a thirty-month period. The curriculum is organized to ensure maximum development, team building, and support for the aspiring executive.

The Managerial M.B.A. is designed for students with at least three years of work experience who are currently employed in an entry-level management position or who desire to enter a management career track. Students are admitted early in their career and are provided with the prerequisite, analytical, and functional skills that will be required of managers in the new millennium.

Students and the M.B.A. Experience

The success of the students' experience is a result of assuming an active "partner" role in their education rather than remaining the passive "consumer." Coming from a wide variety of undergraduate majors, students have demonstrated an ability to excel in the classroom and a strong drive to develop their managerial potential.

All three M.B.A. programs compel students to recognize and eliminate their limiting factors, to honestly face change, and to build upon their strengths and experiences as they strive to learn together.

DeVos M.B.A. students come from diverse educational training and backgrounds. Their individual experiences bring reality and breadth to the classroom. The focus of the program moves beyond the functional problems and perspectives and into enduring, performance-enhancing action for the organization as a whole.

❖ Global Focus

As there is no longer a distinction between global and domestic business, the DeVos curriculum is designed to develop the cosmopolitan manager. All courses and activities are designed with a global perspective, and the students hail from around the globe. In addition, the University offers English as a second language programs and foreign language classes year-round.

The Faculty

The faculty members of the DeVos Graduate School of Management aspire to the highest standards of personal and professional growth for their students. They combine academic credentials with significant business experience to bring a mix of reality and practicality to the classroom. The University, a professional school of management, is a teaching institution committed to providing its students with the skills required for graduates to add immediate value to the firms in which they are hired and to the global business community.

The Business School Network
Corporate Partnerships
Outstanding business leaders, professors with executive experience, and M.B.A. alumni assist in the development and implementation of the M.B.A. curriculum. The Full-Time M.B.A. program also utilizes the unique Pathways, Leadership, Unity, and Service (PLUS) program to enhance students' career development. The PLUS program is comprised of a series of career-assistance modules throughout the entire fifteen-month period. Modules cover such subjects as professional attire, etiquette, and networking and includes the Executive Lecture Series.

The College and Environs
Nestled in a natural woodland setting, the campus was designed by Alden B. Dow and stands as a tribute to its founders, who were concerned with endowing others with freedom and an obligation to think carefully of the future. Set on 268 acres, the University hosts an impressive array of facilities, from an interactive classroom with video conferencing technology to a well-equipped sports complex with an indoor swimming pool, a weight room, and basketball and tennis courts.

The city of Midland is located in the "palm of the mitten-shaped lower peninsula of Michigan." A diverse, dynamic, and culturally rich community, Midland is home to the corporate headquarters of the Dow Chemical Company and the Dow Corning Corporation. The city is on the cutting edge of scientific research and development and draws residents from around the globe.

Facilities
The Richard DeVos Graduate School of Management at Northwood University is housed in a state-of-the-art facility on the Midland, Michigan campus. This complex contains multimedia classroom facilities, break-out rooms, computer facilities, a career resource library, and faculty and administrative offices designed specifically to suit the interactive nature of the M.B.A. programs.

Placement
The Graduate School and Office of Career Assistance and Job Placement are committed to helping students prepare for the challenges of the M.B.A. program and to enhancing their job skills. Preparation starts on the very first day of orientation and continues throughout the program.

Orientation enables students to interact with members of their study groups and participate in team-building events, campus activities, and academic exercises. Students participate in a comprehensive individual assessment (CIA) that inventories their skills, strengths, weaknesses, and career objectives and allows them to pinpoint the skills they need to develop for their personal and managerial growth. Students periodically revisit their CIAs with staff members throughout the fifteen months.

Career assistance staff members also provide guidance on resume writing and persuasive job search correspondence and videotape students in mock interview situations.

A variety of corporate and alumni contact databases are available to assist students in individual job search strategies. The resources of the Office of Career Assistance and Job Placement are available to alumni at any time during their careers.

Admission
The Richard DeVos Graduate School of Management offers challenging and rigorous academic programs. Admission is selective and is based on academic acumen and a high motivation to attain challenging personal, professional, and educational goals.

To be eligible for admission, a student must have earned the equivalent of a four-year baccalaureate degree from an accredited institution. No specific undergraduate major is considered preferable; however, nonbusiness degree recipients must fulfill the four prerequisite courses of principles of accounting, principles of microeconomics, principles of macroeconomics, and college algebra or calculus.

GMAT results are considered along with all other application materials, but there is no score that precludes a candidate from receiving consideration by the Graduate Admission Committee and there is no score that guarantees admission. Applicants for whom English is not their native language are required to submit a TOEFL score.

Executive M.B.A. candidates are required to have an evaluative personal interview.

Finances
Total program costs for 2000–01 for the Full-Time M.B.A. are $18,000. This amount covers all tuition, fees, and books for the fifteen-month program. Total program costs for 2000–01 for the Executive M.B.A. are $20,000. This amount covers all tuition, fees, and books for the thirty-month program. The cost for the 35 to 45 credit Managerial M.B.A. is $500 per credit hour. This amount covers all tuition, fees, and books for the program (graduate fees are extra).

Off-campus living expenses for a single individual are estimated at approximately $600 per month. Financial assistance is available in the form of fellowships, scholarships, various government-supported aid and loan programs, and the M.B.A. loan program.

International Students
The Graduate School welcomes applications from qualified international students. All international students are expected to carry a normal course load and to complete the program in the allotted time period.

Application Facts and Dates
Applications for admission are accepted on a rolling basis throughout the year. The Graduate School Admission Committee begins reviewing applications by mid-fall. Applicants are notified of committee decisions within six weeks of receipt of all application materials and supporting documents. For more information, students should contact:

Richard DeVos Graduate School of
   Management
Northwood University
4000 Whiting Drive
Midland, Michigan 48640
Telephone: 517-837-4488
            800-MBA-9000 (toll-free)
Fax: 517-837-4800
E-mail: mba@northwood.edu
World Wide Web: http://www.
   northwood.edu/mba

Nova Southeastern University

Wayne Huizenga Graduate School of Business and Entrepreneurship

Fort Lauderdale, Florida

EMPHASIZING A REAL-WORLD EXPERIENCE

The Huizenga School's carefully designed and sequenced full-time M.B.A. emphasizes application of business concepts to the real world. The program's curriculum provides students with a solid foundation in functional areas of business and equips them with the necessary leadership and managerial skills.

—Dr. Randolph A. Pohlman, Dean

Programs and Curricular Focus

Nova Southeastern University's (NSU) Wayne Huizenga Graduate School of Business and Entrepreneurship offers an innovative and highly flexible full-time Master of Business Administration (M.B.A.) program designed for students with an undergraduate degree who have little or no work experience. The format and schedule enable students to enroll full-time and complete all degree requirements in one calendar year. The program format consists of four terms per year, commencing in January, April, July, and October. Students may enter the program in the October or January terms and enroll in classes scheduled on Monday through Thursday. Although not recommended, students may also choose to enroll for classes in the weekend program. The weekend classes include adult, postentry professional students who are pursuing graduate degrees on a part-time basis.

The Huizenga School also offers a joint program leading to a simultaneous awarding of the J.D. and the M.B.A. degree. Students admitted to the joint program must complete the first-year program at the law center (28 hours). They are not permitted to enroll in courses at the Huizenga School during that period.

Students and the M.B.A. Experience

The typical student enrolled in the full-time M.B.A. program is 23 years of age, with less than two years of full-time work experience. Fifty-four percent of the students are men, and members of minority groups make up 28 percent of the population. Fifty-three percent of the Huizenga School students come from

Southeastern states, while 31.5 percent of the student body comes from Northeastern states.

Special Features

Full-time M.B.A. students have the option to fulfill the internship requirement before graduation. The internship consists of 240 work hours in a private or public institution. The ultimate goal of the internship requirement is to help the student gain further insight into the practical nature of business. Blockbuster Video, the Florida Marlins, Smith-Barney-Shearson, and Holy Cross Hospital are but a few of the high-quality organizations that have trained and supported NSU's M.B.A. students.

Another special feature is the ability to complete undergraduate prerequisite and core M.B.A. courses on line.

The Faculty

All full-time faculty members at the Huizenga School have earned doctorates in their respective fields and have either owned their own business or worked in business or are engaged in consulting. A national core of adjunct faculty members complements NSU's full-time professional staff. The diverse backgrounds and years of experience of the faculty members facilitate in-depth discussion across a broad spectrum. A special effort is made to integrate practical with theoretical points of view.

The College and Environs

Nova Southeastern University is located on 232 acres in the town of Fort Lauderdale, Florida. While the students enjoy a quiet, safe, suburban campus, NSU is easy to reach by public and private transportation. The Huizenga School is

located on a separate 10-acre campus near downtown Fort Lauderdale.

The area is a principal coastal region in south Florida. The climate is subtropical and has an average year-round temperature of 75 degrees. The nearby cities of Fort Lauderdale and Miami offer many activities, including the Fort Lauderdale Museum of Art, the Museum of Science and Discovery, the Center for Performing Arts, the Miami Dolphins training camp, Bayside Marketplace, and Cocowalk.

Facilities

To provide a high-quality educational experience, the School has invested time and resources to improve the students' technological and research training. One of the University's major computer resources, the MicroLab, offers hardware and software resources for course work and workshops based on applied microcomputer technology. The lab has the most popular microcomputers—IBM, Zenith, Gateway, and Apple—and online facilities are available for access to the UNIX operating system.

The Albert and Birdie Einstein Library houses the University's major collection of books and journals in the humanities and sciences. Its more than 75,000 volumes can be searched through the library's computer catalog. In addition, more than twenty specialized indexes in CD-ROM format are available, as is dial-up access to the online catalog.

Placement

The purpose of NSU's Career Resource Center is to assist students in all aspects of the decision-making, planning, and placement process. Its mission is to support students and alumni and enhance their development through a variety of career-related services. The center strongly encourages active participation in students' development throughout their college years and beyond.

Admission

Admission to NSU's full-time M.B.A. program is competitive and is based on a number of important factors, including a student's undergraduate GPA or Graduate Management Admission Test scores.

Finances

Financial support is usually provided in the form of loans, with eligibility based on financial need. Individuals who wish to apply for financial assistance must fill out the NSU financial aid application and a Free Application for Federal Student Aid (FAFSA) form. Financial aid transcripts must be submitted from each institution that the student previously attended, regardless of whether or not financial aid was received. Estimated costs for the one-year M.B.A. degree, including room and board, range from $26,000 to $28,000. Students who have questions about financial assistance are encouraged to contact the Office of Student Financial Aid at 800-522-3243 (toll-free).

International Students

International applicants must submit a TOEFL score of 550 or higher, accompanied by a copy of their undergraduate transcripts printed in or translated to English. Transcripts must show specific subjects taken and the grade earned in each. If grades are expressed other than in an American system, a statement from the school must accompany the transcript showing conversion to an American scale. Diplomas, certificates, or general letters indicating attendance at a school do not substitute for transcripts. In addition, all international student applicants must submit transcripts and documents from international institutions to World Education Services, Inc., for a multipurpose evaluation of the undergraduate degree earned and the institution granting it.

Application deadlines are March 1, May 31, August 30, and November 30. For more information, students should contact:

Mr. Dan Schuckers, Program
  Representative
Wayne Huizenga Graduate School of
  Business and Entrepreneurship
Nova Southeastern University
3100 Southwest Ninth Avenue
Fort Lauderdale, Florida 33315
Telephone: 800-672-7223 Ext. 5100
  (toll-free)
Fax: 954-262-3822

Ohio University

Athens, Ohio

EXPERIENCE THE DIFFERENCE

Our mission in the College of Business at Ohio University is to provide a learning environment that enables individuals to develop the knowledge, skills, and capabilities needed for success in the complex, global business community of the twenty-first century.

—Glenn Corlett, Dean

Programs and Curricular Focus

An intense twelve-month learning experience, the full-time M.B.A. program uses an action-learning format that places the learner into exactly the type of projects and work situations that he or she will face as a leader of information-age organizations in the twenty-first century. The students learn basic business concepts but learn them in the context of their use, maximizing the students' ability to both recall and apply those concepts as they move back into the work world. The students develop the skills (communication, collaboration, teamwork) and the personal characteristics (initiative, creativity, personal responsibility) that are becoming so necessary to succeed. The understanding of the complexities of international business is enhanced through participation in the Joint Student Study Project Abroad. Comfort with information technology increases dramatically as the students regularly access information through the resources of the Internet, collaborate electronically over time and space, and develop and make professional-level computer-driven presentations.

Ohio University's full-time M.B.A. program is a lock step, intensive learning program that requires 72 credit hours over four academic quarters. The program begins on September 1 and ends the following August. Students who join the program without an undergraduate background in business must begin their M.B.A. study in mid-June with an intensive ten-week prerequisite program. Twelve of the 72 credit hours are focused in a specific discipline (finance, management information systems, or marketing), or students may design their own area of concentration through independent study projects.

High-potential, working individuals with a minimum of two to four years'

experience may benefit from Ohio University's part-time program. Combining a series of short, high-intensity residencies with online education based on the OUMBA Intranet, a virtual learning community, the program effectively integrates work and learning. Detailed information is available via the World Wide Web (http://mbawb.cob. ohiou.edu).

The M.B.A. programs are accredited by the AACSB–The International Association for Management Education.

Students and the M.B.A. Experience

There are 50 to 60 students in the full-time M.B.A. program; all parts of the United States and many other countries are represented. About half of the students have liberal arts or technical backgrounds. Diversity of class makeup is a priority. The typical class is about 30 percent women; age ranges from 21 to 45, experience ranges from summer internships to twenty years, members of minority groups range from 5 to 10 percent, and about 40 percent of the student body is international (from such countries as Belgium, China, France, Germany, Ghana, Hong Kong, Hungary, India, Malaysia, Taiwan, and Thailand). There are a number of graduate student associations on campus, including an active M.B.A. student association that sponsors many activities.

❖ Global Focus

In addition to an overall global perspective, there is a mandatory requirement for each student to participate in the Joint Student Consulting Project. This project is a two-week experience in which students are placed in teams with students from the host country; each team is

assigned to one company, analyzes a problem of the company's choosing, and then presents the results to management.

The Faculty

Program modules are delivered by faculty members who hold doctoral degrees and have relevant experience. Six faculty members are assigned to the class; as an integrated team they are responsible for the selection of projects and the modules to be delivered. The team relies on other faculty members within the College to deliver modules depending on the expertise needed for the problem at hand. Typically, the core team is composed of men and women faculty members with domestic and international experience and provides expertise in accounting, business law, finance, human resource management, management, management information systems, marketing, operations, and quantitative business analysis.

The Business School Network

Corporate Partnerships

Corporate leaders from Athens and other communities are asked to be part of continuous improvement teams that reside within the College of Business. These continuous improvement teams deal with student development and curriculum development, among other things.

The Executive Advisory Board and the Society of Alumni and Friends are composed of business managers who provide advice and direction to the program. Often members of these organizations become mentors to students; meetings are formally set up in fall and spring quarters to introduce these businesspeople to M.B.A. students.

The College and Environs

Founded in 1804, Ohio University has grown from a single building to 108 principal buildings covering 623 acres. Full-time enrollment was about 19,000 in 1998–99, including about 3,000 in the Graduate College, University-wide. Student facilities include the aquatic center, an indoor ice-skating rink, a golf course, and basketball, tennis, and racquetball courts.

Facilities

Ohio University's Alden Library, a modern seven-story air-conditioned building, has well more than a million bound volumes, including more than 50,000 documents on business topics. Alden is a repository for U.S. government documents.

Technology Environment

The College of Business is wired for information technology well into the twenty-first century. The physical and technological environments are designed to support the team-oriented, project-based nature of the learning process.

The College of Business Administration maintains four microcomputer labs containing a mixture of Macintosh and IBM-compatible computers. Numerous word processing, spreadsheet, database, graphics, and statistical software packages are available in these labs. In addition, the College of Business maintains a Digital Equipment Corporation VAX 6210 connected to an instructional terminal lab. All facilities are fully networked together and to the Ohio University wide-area network, which includes IBM mainframes, online library systems, electronic mail, and Internet access.

Placement

There are two major recruiting fairs at Ohio University for meeting employers, as well as a constant flow of campus visits by recruiting organizations. A listing of companies who wish to interview is posted weekly on the campuswide electronic network, and students are encouraged to sign up for interviews with companies of their choice.

Admission

Factors considered for admission include undergraduate grade point average, scores on the GMAT (Graduate Management Admission Test), work experience, a personal essay, and recommendations. Successful applicants typically have at least a 3.0 undergraduate cumulative average (on a 4.0 scale) and a score of 500 or better on the GMAT. In addition, international applicants typically have a TOEFL score of 600 or better. All applicants for admission must submit two official transcripts of undergraduate work and three letters of recommendation.

Finances

For 2000–01, the comprehensive fee for a normal quarter's load (9 to 18 credit hours inclusive) is $1542 for Ohio residents and $3309 for nonresidents. The fee for the Joint Student Consulting Project is estimated at $3500. In addition, there is a general fee of $376 per quarter. Scholarships with tuition waivers and stipends up to $9000 are available to qualified applicants based on merit. A number of scholarships have been designated for members of qualified minority groups. Awards of aid are generally announced in April.

Both University and private housing are available for single and married students. Housing costs vary from $400 to $600 per month, depending upon accommodations and furnishings. Room and board costs in University housing were $1500 per quarter in 1999–2000.

International Students

About 40 percent of the candidates are international students who represent such countries as Belgium, China, France, Germany, Ghana, Hong Kong, Hungary, India, Malaysia, Taiwan, and Thailand, among others.

Application Facts and Dates

Applications, with a $30 fee and all supporting credentials, must be received no later than March 1. Students are encouraged to forward application materials well in advance of the deadline. Students are notified no later than May 1 about acceptance into the program. For additional information, students should contact:

M.B.A. Program
Copeland Hall 514
College of Business
Ohio University
Athens, Ohio 45701
Telephone: 614-593-2007
World Wide Web: http://www.cob.
ohiou.edu/www/grad/

FACULTY LIST

School of Accountancy
Yining Chen, Ph.D., Assistant Professor.
James Cox, Ph.D., Associate Professor.
Carol Anne Hilton, Ph.D., Assistant Professor.
Leon Hoshower, Ph.D., Associate Professor.
David Kirch, Ph.D., Associate Professor.
E. James Meddaugh, Ph.D., Professor.
David Senteney, Ph.D., Assistant Professor.
Florence Sharp, Ph.D., O'Bleness Professor of Accounting.
Ray Stephens, Ph.D., Director.

Department of Finance
Natalie Chieffe, Ph.D., Assistant Professor.
Jeffrey A. Manzi, Ph.D., Assistant Professor.
Azmi Mikhail, Ph.D., Professor.
Ganas K. Rakes, Ph.D., O'Bleness Professor of Banking and Chair.
Nanda Rangan, Ph.D., Professor.
John Reynolds, M.B.A., Lecturer.

Department of Management Systems
Frank Barone, Ph.D., Associate Professor.
Thomas W. Bolland, Ph.D., Professor of Quantitative Business Analysis.

David S. Chappell, Ph.D., Assistant Professor.
Garth Coombs, Ph.D., Assistant Professor.
Kenneth Cutright, Ph.D., Associate Professor.
C. Michael Gray, J.D., Lecturer in Law.
Patricia C. Gunn, J.D., Associate Professor of Law.
John Keifer, Ph.D. candidate, Lecturer.
Mary Carter Keifer, J.D., Associate Professor of Law and Chair.
Manjulika Koshal, Ph.D., Professor of Business Administration.
Arthur Marinelli, Ph.D., Professor of Law.
Clarence Martin, Ph.D., Associate Professor.
Peggy Miller, Ph.D., Lecturer.
Richard Milter, Ph.D., Associate Professor.
Valerie Perotti, Ph.D., Professor.
Bonnie Roach, Ph.D., Associate Professor of Human Resource Management.
Jessie C. Roberson Jr., J.D., Associate Professor of Law.
Richard C. Scamehorn, M.B.A., Executive in Residence.
John Schermerhorn, Ph.D., O'Bleness Professor of Management.

Hugh Sherman, Ph.D., Assistant Professor.
Lucian Spataro, Ph.D., Professor.
Rebecca Thacker, Ph.D., Assistant Professor of Human Resource Management.
Ed Yost, Ph.D., Associate Professor.

Department of Marketing
Catherine N. Axinn, Ph.D., Associate Professor.
Elizabeth Blair, Ph.D., Associate Professor.
Barbara Dyer, Ph.D., Assistant Professor.
Ashok Gupta, Ph.D., Professor.
Timothy P. Hartman, Ph.D., Associate Professor.
Daniel Innis, Ph.D., Assistant Professor.
Kahandas Nandola, Ph.D., Professor.
Jane Sojka, Ph.D., Assistant Professor.

Department of Management Information Systems
Ted Compton, Ph.D., Professor.
John Day, Ph.D., Professor and Chair.
Ellsworth Holden, M.A., Assistant Professor.
Hao Lou, Ph.D., Assistant Professor.
Thomas G. Luce, Ph.D., Professor.
James Perotti, Ph.D., Professor.
David Sutherland, Ph.D., Assistant Professor.

Pace University

A DYNAMIC M.B.A.—DEVELOPING GLOBAL MANAGERS FOR THE TWENTY-FIRST CENTURY

In a rapidly changing business environment, major corporations depend on Pace University's Lubin School of Business to provide global business managers to lead them into the twenty-first century. Lubin's M.B.A. program, recently revised and continually being improved, carefully integrates theory and practical applications and offers exciting opportunities for experiential and team learning. Our campus locations, in downtown New York City, minutes away from Wall Street, and at the White Plains Graduate Center, convenient to the headquarters of Fortune 500 companies, provide particularly vibrant environments for professional development. Importantly, Lubin's distinguished faculty members are committed to excellence in teaching and are dedicated to producing successful graduates. Attesting to that success, Lubin alumni are and will continue to be leaders in all fields of business.

—Arthur L. Centonze, Dean

Programs and Curricular Focus

The M.B.A. degree program at the Lubin School of Business is characterized by a curriculum that stresses professional skills while offering students the opportunity to specialize in accounting, business economics, financial management, health systems management, information systems, international business, management, management science, marketing, operations analysis and planning, or taxation. M.B.A. courses reflect the integrated, cross-functional way business operates. Global considerations appear in all appropriate courses, as do critical issues such as technology, ethics, workforce diversity, quality management, and entrepreneurship. Depending upon prior academic course work, between 36 and 61 degree credits are required for most specializations. All Lubin students must demonstrate proficiency in computing, business writing, and quantitative methods.

A core of foundation courses covers fundamental managerial and analytical skills. At the next level, the integrative core builds on the foundation courses to provide the managerial breadth of the curriculum. Cohort classes for the managerial skills courses place the same students together during their first year of study, creating a platform for mastering teamwork and setting up opportunities for networking throughout the M.B.A. experience and beyond. The critical business skills developed translate into greater job success and new opportunities long before graduation.

Lubin also offers a number of special programs for students seeking advanced professional business education. The One-Year M.B.A. in Financial Management program offers qualified business professionals and recent college graduates an accelerated M.B.A. program. The twenty-one-month Executive M.B.A. program affords middle- and upper-level managers the opportunity to enhance and sharpen their business knowledge and skills. Also available are the J.D./M.B.A. program (in conjunction with the Pace University School of Law); Master of Science degree programs in accounting, economics, investment management, operations analysis and planning, and taxation; post-master's Advanced Professional Certificate programs; and a doctoral program in business.

Students and the M.B.A. Experience

Lubin students are busy, highly motivated individuals who seek graduate business education to advance their careers or to enter the business world. The average M.B.A. student at Pace University has seven years of work experience and is 29 years old. Women comprise nearly 48 percent of the current enrollment, minority students 20 percent, and international students 20 percent. Approximately 75 percent of the student population is from the northeast region of the United States.

Students enter the Lubin M.B.A. program with a broad range of academic and professional backgrounds, including business, engineering and technology, humanities, social sciences, physical sciences, mathematics, nursing, and education.

❖ Global Focus

Lubin's strong international focus and reputation for excellence attract many international students to its New York City and Westchester County campuses. These students' diverse cultural perspectives and backgrounds contribute significantly to the global focus and flavor of business education at Lubin. The Lubin School participates in a variety of student and faculty relationships with universities and business schools around the world. Since 1989, the School has been engaged in an exchange of faculty members and students with Tokyo Keizai University, including joint research projects in marketing and advertising. It has an exchange program with Heidelberg University in Heidelberg, Germany and various business schools in Paris and Grenoble, France.

Special Features

New Lubin M.B.A. students participate in a special orientation program that includes a series of workshops and presentations designed to familiarize them with the curriculum, faculty, and student services. Full-time and part-time students take the same courses, taught by the same faculty members, throughout the M.B.A. program. During the first year of study, cohort groups of students participate in a 6-credit managerial theory and skills course. The faculty facilitates classwork through experiential and interactive team exercises, enabling students to increase their cognitive and effective capacity to build constructive relationships with individuals and groups.

The Faculty

Virtually all full-time faculty members are doctorally prepared, and 75 percent of the part-time faculty members hold doctoral degrees. The faculty members of the Lubin School are committed to excellence in teaching and the professional growth of students. Classes are small (average class size is 22 students), and professors are firmly committed to being accessible to students. Outside of the classroom, opportunities are provided for students to conduct research with faculty members, publish findings jointly, and take active roles in coordinating conferences and special programs.

The Business School Network
Corporate Partnerships
Top executives from major corporations participate in Lubin's Executive-in-Residence Program every year, providing opportunities for Lubin graduate students to interact with prominent business leaders from around the world. In addition, an advisory board of business executives and the School's extensive corporate network ensure that the curriculum reflects the changing needs of business.

The College and Environs
Founded in 1906, Pace University is a comprehensive, diversified, coeducational institution with campuses in New York City and Westchester County. Degrees are offered through the Dyson College of Arts and Sciences, the School of Computer Science and Information Systems, the Lubin School of Business, the School of Education, the Lienhard School of Nursing, and the School of Law. Pace University is chartered by the Regents of the State of New York and accredited by the Middle States Association of Colleges and Schools. The Lubin School of Business is accredited by the AACSB–The International Association for Management Education. The M.B.A. program may be pursued at the New York City Campus, which is a self-contained educational complex in lower Manhattan serving the adjacent Wall Street financial community, or the Lubin Graduate Center in White Plains, Westchester County, New York. The Graduate Center is located in the heart of the White Plains business district. Both locations provide easy access to the nation's most significant cultural resources, including major theaters, museums, and concert halls.

Facilities
Pace University's completely integrated online library system holds approximately 825,000 volumes and subscribes to nearly 4,000 serial publications. Electronic access to internal and external information and knowledge sources, including locally mounted CD-ROM databases, online retrieval systems, and the Internet is available. The Pace libraries annually contract with DIALOG, BRS, LEXIS/NEXIS, and Dow Jones/News Retrieval to access statistical, bibliographic, directory, and full-text databases that cover all major subjects. The University computing network provides access to a range of both mainframe and microcomputing hardware and

software. More than 250 computers are currently located in academic computing facilities. Pace University's wide-area network (Pace Net) can be accessed from labs, dormitory rooms, and offices. Computing facilities housed in the Chase Computer Center are for the exclusive use of Lubin students and faculty members. The Lubin School of Business's Center for Applied Research, Center for Global Financial Markets, Center for International Business Studies, and Center for Innovation and Entrepreneurship offer students diverse research opportunities.

Placement
The University Career Development and Placement Services help graduate business students make informed choices. Pace's Cooperative Education Program places Lubin graduate students in paid, career-related working experiences while they pursue their degrees. Because of its close ties to business, the Pace Cooperative Education Program is one of the largest in the United States. Career counseling, which includes job search preparation, resume writing, and interviewing skills, is provided. Leading corporations, banks, accounting firms, insurance companies, retailers, brokerage houses and nonprofit and government organizations regularly recruit Pace M.B.A. students and utilize Pace's Resume Referral Program. The Alumni Mentor Program gives students an opportunity to speak with Pace alumni about their individual occupations, and the Pace Network offers a medium through which to obtain career information and develop personal contacts with Lubin graduates and other students.

Admission
Admission is open to qualified recipients of bachelor's degrees in any field from accredited undergraduate institutions. All applicants for the M.B.A., M.S., and doctoral programs are required to submit official Graduate Management Admission Test score reports. The Lubin School of Business welcomes applications from graduates of colleges and universities in other countries. International students are expected to have sufficient finances available to cover all expenses for the entire period of graduate study. Applicants whose native language is not English are required to submit official TOEFL scores. The evaluation of applicants is based upon capacity for scholarship as indicated by the undergraduate record, GMAT scores, class rank, previous graduate study (if any), letters of reference, career objectives, and other available information.

Finances
Tuition in 2000–01 is $600 per credit. A variety of loan and deferred-payment options are available.

A number of graduate scholarships and assistantships are offered. Scholarships are awarded on the basis of outstanding academic performance as indicated by the applicant's previous college record and standardized test scores. Assistantships are available for full- and part-time students. Graduate assistants received stipends of up to $5100 per year for 1999–2000 and tuition remission for up to 24 credits. Students interested in applying for a graduate assistantship are advised to apply early because in-person interviews are required.

Room and board in 2000–01 cost approximately $7500 for the academic year. Books, supplies, health insurance, and personal expenses are estimated to cost an additional $5500. Students planning to pursue summer study should anticipate an additional cost of approximately $3000, excluding tuition and fees.

International Students
International students at the Lubin School make up about 20 percent of the enrollment. Home countries include, among others, Canada, China, Columbia, France, Germany, India, Japan, Mexico, Pakistan, Russia, Taiwan, and Turkey.

Pace University and the Lubin School of Business are dedicated to providing a supportive environment for international students. Special services are provided through the International Student and Scholars Offices and the English Language Institute.

Application Facts and Dates
The application fee is $65. Preferred application deadlines are August 1 for fall, December 1 for spring, and May 1 for summer session I and summer session II. International applicants are requested to submit credentials approximately one month earlier than the aforementioned dates. For more information, students should contact:

New York City Campus:
Office of Graduate Admission
Pace University
1 Pace Plaza
New York, New York 10038-1598
Telephone: 212-346-1531
Fax: 212-346-1585
E-mail: gradny@pace.edu

White Plains Campus:
Office of Graduate Admission
Pace University
1 Martine Avenue
White Plains, New York 10606-1909
Telephone: 914-422-4283
Fax: 914-422-4287
E-mail: gradwp@pace.edu

Pacific Lutheran University

Tacoma, Washington

INNOVATIVE, HIGH-QUALITY, STUDENT-CENTERED, AND PERSONAL

These are some of the words that define the M.B.A. program at Pacific Lutheran University (PLU). The educational environment here is personal in scale, supportive in nature, and responsive to individual and student needs and provides opportunities for students and faculty members to be partners in learning. Our M.B.A. program is widely respected in the region for its high quality and has been professionally accredited by AACSB–The International Association for Management Education for more than twenty years. Our technology and innovation management (TIM) concentration places the curriculum at the cutting edge of preparation for the new millennium. The breadth of our electives responds directly to student-expressed needs. PLU's M.B.A. program brings the relevant topics for today's and tomorrow's realities to students in creative ways.

—Donald R. Bell, Dean

Programs and Curricular Focus

The M.B.A. program is renowned for its strong business training that engages innovative concepts of course integration with interactive teaching and a focus on relevance. It reinforces strong values, ethics, and service and acknowledges the multicultural influences driving today's market. Students learn sound management through exposure to functional areas of business. Theory and practice are balanced through classroom lectures, case studies, and projects.

Pacific Lutheran University offers two options for completing an M.B.A. degree. Students may choose between an M.B.A. degree and an M.B.A. degree with a concentration in technology and innovation management. The M.B.A. program focuses on the development of critical skills in teamwork, communication, technology, problem solving, leadership, multicultural management, and change management. The M.B.A. with a TIM concentration incorporates these critical skills with a focus on technical management issues and is more relevant to the careers of individuals who work in technology-oriented companies and industries.

Either program option consists of 48 semester credit hours. Students in the M.B.A. program take a core of 34 credit hours and 14 credit hours of electives. Students in the M.B.A. program with a TIM concentration take a core of 30 credit hours and 18 credit hours in technology and innovation management.

Courses are taught in the evening to accommodate both working professionals and full-time students. The M.B.A. program with a TIM concentration is also offered in a two-year, Saturday-only format.

Students and the M.B.A. Experience

Students in the M.B.A. program benefit from small class sizes (average 16 students), which allow for a dynamic and personalized M.B.A. program. The students enrolled in the M.B.A. program in 1999–2000 averaged age 32 and had an average of nine years' work experience at entrance. Forty-four percent had undergraduate degrees in business, and 24 percent had degrees in science/engineering. Thirty-seven percent of the students were women. International students comprised 14 percent of the students. Their average GMAT score was 561, and the average entering GPA was 3.1.

Students are from varied academic and professional backgrounds. Ninety-five percent of M.B.A. students have work experience before entering the M.B.A. program, and the majority of M.B.A. students earn a degree while continuing their careers. Students who are not employed full-time have the option of participating in internships or graduate assistantships concurrent with their M.B.A. studies. Through membership in PLUS Business, the student-alumni association, M.B.A. students may

participate in the Career Mentorship Program. This program links students with business alumni in the professional community to investigate different careers and receive personal guidance in exploring career options. Students also enjoy the benefits of participating in alumni networking events, where they can interact with business alumni in an informal setting.

The Faculty

PLU's M.B.A. faculty members bring both academic credentials and private-sector experience to the classroom. They teach business fundamentals as well as the most current issues and trends. The faculty members are dedicated to teaching, research, and community service; are active members of professional associations; and are recipients of numerous awards and other forms of recognition. Twelve full-time and part-time faculty members currently teach in the M.B.A. program.

The Business School Network
Corporate Partnerships

More than 25 leaders from private, public, and not-for-profit organizations are represented on the School's Executive Advisory Board—from Andersen Consulting and MassMutual to the Frank Russell Company and Moss Adams. The School supports an active alumni network for students and a corporate mentoring network for students. Several recent partnerships with companies such as Boeing and the Frank Russell Company have been formed to serve Russian, Chinese, Korean, and Saudi executives.

The College and Environs

Pacific Lutheran University is an independent university with enrollment of 3,600 students. Its beautiful tree-lined campus is located on 126 acres immediately adjacent to the city of Tacoma (population 186,000). The campus is 40 miles south of Seattle and 20 miles south of Sea-Tac International Airport. Located in the midst of the Puget Sound region, the campus is within a short drive of a wide variety of natural attractions, including Mt. Rainier, the Olympic and Cascade mountain ranges, Puget Sound, the Pacific Ocean, and numerous lakes and rivers.

Facilities
M.B.A. students have access to a full range of University services and resources. The Robert Mortvedt Library, serving the University community with more than 550,000 books, periodicals, and microfilm and audiovisual materials, receives more than 2,200 current magazines, journals, and newspapers and offers online information access technologies. The University Center offers the convenience of a coffee shop, computer user room, bookstore, and commuter lounge. Athletic facilities include a swimming pool, golf course, fitness center, racquetball courts, tennis courts, basketball courts, track, and gymnasium. On-campus housing includes apartment style living in South Hall, and single-room housing in Kreidler Hall, a facility dedicated to serving graduate students.

Technology Environment
M.B.A. course work is closely linked to technology throughout the program. M.B.A. students need access to a PC with compatible software. University computer user rooms provide students with access to the latest in information technology. The School of Business also manages a computer laboratory equipped with high-speed computers, CD-ROM drives, and a computer projection system. All students are provided access to the Internet through their individual PLU accounts.

Placement
M.B.A. students may take advantage of the many career development resources offered by Pacific Lutheran University

and the School of Business. The Center for Careers and Employment serves the campus community and provides counseling, workshops, and a complete library of employment opportunities. Students benefit from School of Business career-oriented programs, including the career mentorship program, which links students with business alumni in the professional community, networking events, and internships.

Admission
Students who hold a bachelor's degree (in any field) from an accredited college or university, and who have demonstrated their ability or potential to do high quality academic work on a consistent basis, are encouraged to apply for admission.

Criteria used to evaluate students are a 2.75 or higher GPA, a 470 or higher GMAT score, and a 1050 formula score (GPA × 200 + GMAT). A minimum 550 (or 213 computerized) TOEFL score is required of applicants whose native language is not English. Applicants are evaluated individually based on evidence of managerial and professional potential, statement of goals, recommendations, prior experience, and overall presentation of factors indicating an equivalence to admission standards, potential for success in the graduate school, and other contributing factors. To apply, submit a complete Application for Graduate Study, a $35 fee, two letters of recommendation, state of goals, a current resume, official transcripts of all prior academic work, an official GMAT score, and a TOEFL score (if applicable).

Finances
Tuition for the 2000–01 academic year is $525 per semester hour. Full-time students can expect to take up to 24 semester hours in one year ($12,168).

Estimated yearly expenses for full-time students include room and board ($5038), books and supplies ($800), and personal expenses ($2100). Part-time students should expect expenses of $125 per 4 semester-hour course for books and supplies.

Financial aid for M.B.A. students is available in the form of Federal Perkins Loans, Federal Stafford Student Loans, graduate assistantships (up to $5000), and scholarships. The priority deadline for assistantship and scholarship applications is April 1. The University also offers scholarships in the amount of $2000 to eligible international students.

Application Facts and Dates
The evening M.B.A. program and the evening M.B.A. TIM program offer year-round admission, so students may apply at any time. Applications for these programs are evaluated as soon as they are complete, and students may enroll in September, January, February, late May, or July. Applicants receive notification approximately one to two weeks after the completed application is received. The two-year Saturday M.B.A. TIM program begins each fall semester, and the priority application deadline is June 1. Applications received after the June 1 deadline are evaluated, and qualified applicants may be admitted on a space-available basis. For more information or an application, students should contact:

Catherine Pratt
Assistant Dean and Director, M.B.A. Programs
School of Business
Pacific Lutheran University
Tacoma, Washington 98447
Telephone: 253-535-7250
E-mail: business@plu.edu
World Wide Web: http://www.plu.edu/ ~busa/mba

The Pennsylvania State University

The Smeal College of Business Administration

University Park, Pennsylvania

THE SMEAL COLLEGE ADVANTAGE

The Smeal M.B.A. at Penn State University reflects the convergence of the "new and old" economies and provides knowledge and training that positions our graduates to excel in the rapidly changing global, networked economy. The Smeal M.B.A. is known worldwide for its Communications Program, the coordinated core curriculum, and for its distinguished faculty members who are among the most quoted thought leaders in their fields. In addition, the Smeal graduate is especially prepared to exploit new market opportunities in areas such as supply chain, e-commerce, new venture creation, and global strategy, reflecting the intersection of the core functions of business with the tools of information technologies. As a student, you will have unparalleled access to the world class benefits of the Penn State campus and the tremendous network of Penn State alumni who are actively engaged in advancing the learning, internship, and placement opportunities for our students. I invite you to take a serious look at the new M.B.A. in the Smeal College.

—Judy D. Olian, Dean

Programs and Curricular Focus

The Smeal College M.B.A. program challenges the student with a comprehensive selection of integrated core and elective courses designed to foster a theoretical and practical grounding, enabling career success. Faculty members use a mix of case discussions, action-learning projects, lectures, and online resources to build conceptual and strategic decision-making skills. Traditionally-structured classes can be combined with shorter weekend workshops to build content expertise and leadership competencies.

This full-time program consists of a coordinated core that is coupled with elective coursework combinations in supply chain, e-commerce, new venture creation, and global strategy. Students may also take graduate courses outside the Smeal College of Business. A number of formal combined degree program options are also available including health care, manufacturing management, hotel and restaurant management, and law. Highly motivated students may also be interested in designing concurrent graduate programs in information science and technology, engineering, and biotechnology.

Students and the M.B.A. Experience

Penn State M.B.A. students bring rich and diverse academic and cultural backgrounds to the program, creating a dynamic and exciting learning environment. A typical entering class numbers 140 students of which 30 percent are women, 15 percent are members of minority groups, and 25 percent are international students representing more than twenty-five nations on six continents. The average student is 28 years of age with five years professional business experience.

Limited class size and an emphasis on group projects encourage a team spirit, a respect for human values, and a strong work ethic. Teaching methodologies include lectures, case studies, problems, readings, management simulations, games, and role playing.

❖ Global Focus

Smeal's M.B.A. students learn to conduct business in an interrelated global environment. In each of the M.B.A. core classes, students not only will view business from this global perspective, but also share experiences with students from any of twenty-five nations. To expand this concept of a global classroom, The Smeal College also has assembled a wide network of exchange programs with institutions abroad. Currently, students may pursue studies at graduate institutions in Australia, Belgium, Denmark, England, Finland, France, Germany, Mexico, New Zealand, Norway, Singapore, and Spain.

Special Features

The Smeal M.B.A. program has been committed to excellence in business communications for more than twenty years. The first of its kind in the country, this year-long course builds a portfolio of individual and team skills that help students lead, manage, coach, and mentor in a variety of business settings. A significant portion of the classroom experience is framed around the application of modern technology in the workplace. Alumni unequivocally state that the Smeal communications course builds skills, confidence, and poise, allowing them to use formal and informal communication effectively.

The Faculty

The Smeal College M.B.A. faculty members offer world-class education by striking a balance between consulting, teaching, and groundbreaking research. Ten research centers help provide a wide variety of experiences for Smeal MBAs including team based decision making, classroom interactions, and research and teaching assistantships.

All 100 members of the graduate faculty hold doctoral degrees and those selected to instruct in the M.B.A. program are known for their experience and skill in enhancing the learning environment. The M.B.A. faculty members interact with students both inside and outside of the classroom, providing a personal educational experience unique to a small M.B.A. program.

The Business School Network

Penn State enjoys one of the largest and most active alumni networks in the world. By fostering strong corporate and alumni relations, the M.B.A. program taps into and continues to build a diverse and vibrant set of opportunities for its students. From the emerging ranks of new economy entrepreneurs to the well-respected leaders of the old guard, Executive Interactions afford Smeal M.B.A.'s exposure and knowledge for developing their career strategies. Student associations in each interest group expand the reach of the College and University by seeking partnerships with other professional organizations and educational institutions. A series of alumni-student-

faculty member interactions promote an ongoing exchange of ideas and fosters lifelong learning.

Technology Environment

The Smeal College offers computer laboratories with the latest technology. Laptop ports and flexible wall structures allow the labs to accommodate experiential learning exercises. Laptops are required for all entering students.

An aggressive effort is underway to bring together core functions of business with the tools of information technology. Students will develop a strong appreciation and understanding for how they can use technology to alter business practice and for creating opportunities for growth. In addition, the incorporation of technology in core and elective courses will enhance students' communication, time management, and learning capabilities.

Placement

The Smeal College M.B.A. program's professional development staff works aggressively to help students chart a clear career strategy that keeps pace with the changing world of work. By accessing and managing corporate and alumni contacts, students can build individualized networks. Career

management services begin before arriving on campus and extend through a graduate's career. Students may participate in consortium events, seminars and workshops, alumni networking and recruiting events, and summer internships. Approximately 85 percent of Smeal M.B.A. students are placed in relevant internships, which often result in offers of full-time employment. While Smeal graduates 150 M.B.A. students per year, more than 200 companies, including small and large and/or local and international, actively recruit and compete to hire M.B.A. graduates.

Admission

Penn State seeks a diverse student body and encourages applications from students with a wide variety of academic backgrounds. Men and women with baccalaureate degrees from accredited colleges or universities are eligible for consideration.

Previous academic records, test scores, previous work experience, recommendations, leadership experiences, and other evidence of maturity and motivation are considered in the admission process. The Graduate Management Admission Test (GMAT) is required and competitive TOEFL scores are required of applicants

from non-English-speaking countries. Personal interviews are required and conducted at the request of the Admissions Committee.

Finances

Tuition for the 2000–01 year is $4211 per semester for in-state residents and $8043 per semester for nonresidents. Books and supplies cost approximately $1200 per year. University housing is available for students with families and single students for approximately $1200–$1800 per semester. Off-campus living expenses are estimated at $650 per month for single students. Meal plans are offered to all students.

Merit-based fellowships, scholarships, and graduate assistantships are awarded to qualified students. Need-based grants, loans, and work-study programs may be pursued through the University's Office of Student Aid.

International Students

International students arrive one week prior to M.B.A. orientation to engage in a week of activities designed to get them settled into the University environment. A student-run committee provides a valuable link for international students, who want to get the most out of their time at the University by hosting a wide variety of events designed to help all students share their cultural heritage.

Application Facts and Dates

Admissions are conducted on a rolling basis. The deadline for receipt of applications is March 1 for international students and June 1 for U.S. students. Application materials may be submitted via paper or through downloadable or electronic options. For more information, students should contact:

M.B.A. Program
The Smeal College of Business Administration
The Pennsylvania State University
106 Business Administration Building
University Park, Pennsylvania 16802-3000
Telephone: 814-863-0474
Fax: 814-863-8072
E-mail: smealmba@psu.edu
World Wide Web: http://www.smeal. psu.edu/mba/

Pepperdine University

Malibu, California

LEADERSHIP FOR THE GLOBAL MARKETPLACE

The Graziadio School is ideally suited to prepare you for a leadership role in this rapidly expanding global marketplace. We understand the reality of the internationalization of business and have established business linkages around the world. The ability to understand the role of constantly advancing technology in business decisions is a primary objective of the programs we teach. The Pepperdine experience is different in another way—our strong commitment to values. In the business world, ethical conduct starts with individuals, not with government or corporations. Preparing you to pursue a career founded on ethical values is a fundamental mission of Pepperdine.

—Dr. Otis W. Baskin, Dean

Programs and Curricular Focus

Designed to prepare students for managerial leadership roles, the Master of Business Administration (M.B.A.) and Master of International Business (M.I.B.) degrees are offered in an environment that fosters an understanding of the behavioral aspects of management. The program organizes faculty and students to interact in a learning community. The curriculum emphasizes a global perspective of international business, ethics, communication, and strategic decision-making skills.

The M.B.A. provides students with a working knowledge of business administration and strategic management. The accelerated one-year, 48-unit program is geared toward students who have completed the necessary business prerequisites and have a minimum of three years of professional work experience. For those with significant professional experience (three or more years), the fifteen-month "fast-track" M.B.A. (60 units), with early graduation, is an option. The two-year, 64-unit program includes an opportunity for a summer internship, which is strongly encouraged, and the option to study abroad for a trimester. Both M.B.A. programs offer concentrations in marketing, finance, global business, alternative dispute resolution, and technology (with an emphasis in e-commerce). Joint J.D./M.B.A. and M.B.A./M.P.P. (public policy) programs are also offered in conjunction with the law and public policy schools.

Students in the M.I.B. program enter either the French, German, or Spanish track. The M.I.B. degree equips students with the management tools, cultural and global understanding, and language skills necessary for a successful international business career. The first year consists of an M.B.A. curriculum with intensive foreign language study at the Malibu campus. During the second year, students travel to Europe (Germany, France, Austria, or Switzerland) or Latin America (Mexico or Chile) to complete their course work and an internship. An intermediate-level language proficiency is preferred at the start of the program. Students also have the flexibility to complete their full-time internship in any French-, German-, or Spanish-speaking country.

Students and the M.B.A. Experience

The business school students represent a diverse range of professional and educational backgrounds. Such diversity contributes to a culture of collaboration. This culture enhances the practical, hands-on learning process. New students are quickly initiated into the M.B.A. program through the communication workshop. The three-day event develops the trust and camaraderie that characterize the entire program. The School values teamwork as an integral part of business education. Professors structure a collaborative learning environment in every class, which helps cultivate well-balanced personal and professional development in each student. The small class sizes (approximately 20 students in a class) foster community-type relationships between faculty members and students.

❖ Global Focus

The two-year M.B.A. programs offer an excellent opportunity to literally expand one's horizons and obtain a broader global perspective, while gaining an appreciation and general background in international business. Students may choose to study abroad for a trimester during their second year. Students apply for this study-abroad program based on the academic performance of their first trimester. This unique experience is offered at partner institutions located in one of the following countries: Belgium, Chile, China, England, France, Germany, Hong Kong, Mexico, the Netherlands, Spain, and Thailand.

Special Features

Pepperdine is distinguished by programs designed to enhance the student's practical learning experience. During the first semester, students participate in the Service Leadership Program, a nonprofit consulting project, which is an excellent opportunity for students to observe organizations and to recommend changes while supporting the community.

Ethical and legal issues are also reinforced through the Seminar in Business Ethics at the Nellis Federal Prison Camp outside Las Vegas. Students interview a panel of white-collar criminals about the potential impact of business decisions.

The Faculty

All faculty members are selected for their vast range of research and management experience in the business world as well as their strong academic qualifications and values-centered focus in teaching. More than 90 percent of the faculty members hold Ph.D. degrees and continue to remain very active in the business community, including consulting relationships and involvement with advisory boards. Students appreciate the accessibility of their professors, the individual attention they receive, and the personal faculty-student relationships that are built as a direct result of these.

The Business School Network

With more than 24,000 graduates, the Graziadio School has one of the largest business school alumni networks in the United States.

The Graziadio School is located on the main campus of Pepperdine University in the coastal community of Malibu, amid a beautiful mountain landscape overlooking the Pacific Ocean.

Corporate Partnerships

The business school is active in the community, with close ties to corporations and industry through its professional and executive programs. The full-time M.B.A. and M.I.B. programs in Malibu benefit from the School's vast network of alumni and corporate relationships. Students have the opportunity to complete a practicum with an executive, to perform executive interviews, to provide consulting to nonprofit organizations, and to apply to the executive mentorship program.

Prominent Alumni

The Graziadio School has many top executives of major corporations and leaders in the community as part of its alumni network. The Presidential/Key Executive M.B.A. program alone has a long list of impressive names in the business community representing such industries as aerospace, biotechnology, entertainment, health care, and manufacturing. The close-knit alumni association, Management Partners, brings together graduates from all programs through professional and social activities to help develop individual networks and interaction with alumni from various industries and companies throughout the world.

The College and Environs

Founded in 1937, Pepperdine University presents a unique combination of academic excellence and a strong commitment to values. The University is an independent institution that enrolls about 9,500 students in five colleges. The Malibu campus is located about 35 miles from downtown Los Angeles.

The School of Business and Management was established in 1969 and was a pioneer in executive M.B.A. education, developing its hallmark by its practical approach to teaching students ethical business concepts that are applicable in the real world. While the full-time programs only enroll about 200 students, the School is still one of the largest in the country, including all of its programs. It was endowed as The George L. Graziadio School of Business and Management in 1996.

Facilities

The 830-acre campus includes athletic facilities such as an Olympic-size swimming pool; gymnasium; baseball, track, and soccer fields; a fitness center; and tennis courts.

Research facilities that are easily accessible to business students include the Payson Library and the School of Law library. Each classroom has wireless Internet access. The School's expanded Intranet capabilities enable students to access online course materials, download software and class assignments, and participate in group projects and virtual office hours with faculty members from remote locations. Students use the School's multimedia development hardware and software, digital cameras, and scanners to develop their own Web sites and digitized professional portfolios as a way to showcase their accomplishments in the M.B.A. program and their prior work experience.

Placement

Recognizing the complexity of the career-planning process and the variety of options available to Pepperdine graduates, the Career Development Center (CDC) provides extensive services to meet the professional development needs of the students. The center partners with students in the process of career management, from self-assessment to placement in a career that meets individual goals. The following are among the many services offered: career consultations, seminars, mentorship programs, online job postings, internship support, student resume Web pages, a resource library, alumni and career networking events, industry forums, and on- and off-campus interview events. As a result, graduates from these Pepperdine programs are sought by a variety of domestic and international firms.

Admission

Consideration is based on many factors in the application process. The average GPA is 3.2, and the average GMAT score is 630. While work experience is not required for the two-year M.B.A. and the M.I.B. pro-grams, it is preferred and can greatly enhance an individual's application as well as his or her learning experience. The one-year and the fifteen-month M.B.A. programs require a minimum of three years of professional experience. Students' work experience averages six to seven years prior to entering the program. Demonstrated leadership qualities and personal characteristics are considered along with the written essays and recommendations. The admission committee seeks individuals who display academic strength and show promise to make a positive contribution to the small-group and interactive classroom environment.

Finances

Tuition is $12,000 per trimester for the 2000–01 academic year. The one-year M.B.A. program consists of a total of three consecutive trimesters, and the fifteen-month M.B.A. consists of a total of four consecutive trimesters. Both the two-year M.B.A. and M.I.B. programs consist of two trimesters per year; the M.I.B. also includes a minitrimester at the end of the first year.

Merit-based scholarships and graduate assistantships are available to full-time students. The admission packet contains the information necessary to apply for a scholarship.

On-campus graduate housing is available for $2500 to $3600 per trimester. Typically, 4 students share a two-bedroom apartment. Many students choose to live off campus, with costs averaging $600 per month.

International Students

International students represent about 40 percent of the enrollment in the full-time programs. The Office of International Student Services provides credential evaluations, language tutoring, visa services, and ESL courses.

A minimum TOEFL score of 550 is required for students whose native language is not English.

Application Facts and Dates

The application deadline is May 1 for fall. The late application deadline is June 15, but applications are reviewed on a space-available basis. There is a $45 application fee. For more information, students should contact:

Office of Admissions
The Graziadio School
Pepperdine University
24255 Pacific Coast Highway
Malibu, California 90263-4858
Telephone: 800-726-9283 (toll-free)
　　　　　310-456-4858 (outside the
　　　　　U.S.)
Fax: 310-456-4876
E-mail: gsbmadm@pepperdine.edu
World Wide Web: http://bschool.
　　pepperdine.edu

Philadelphia University

GRADUATE STUDY—AN ECLECTIC APPROACH

The culture of our small, coeducational campus is such that significant faculty-student interaction is a virtual certainty. While ongoing research is critical for our faculty members, their primary focus remains teaching. The curriculum and all learning experiences are directed toward developing the skills and contacts needed to succeed in modern global commerce.

We are very proud of our faculty members, students, and alumni. We invite you to participate in our exploration of the dynamic forces which will shape the coming decades in entrepreneurial endeavors, trade, banking, finance, and corporate management.

—Elmore Alexander, Dean

Programs and Curricular Focus

The M.B.A. program at Philadelphia University is designed to provide students with the skills and abilities that employers are looking for to lead corporate America into this new century—a global perspective, competence in leading-edge technology, and innovative and entrepreneurial thinking. The curriculum responds to the global and managerial skills needed to be successful in the years to come. Students analyze important and challenging issues in an action-learning and team-building environment, while sharpening decision-making, managerial, and entrepreneurial skills. Furthermore, students develop the ability to interact and communicate with diverse groups, so that they can function effectively in a competitive business environment.

The program comprises eight core courses (22 credits), three option area courses (9 credits), a capstone course in strategic planning (3 credits), and one free elective (3 credits) that may be selected from the M.B.A. program or other graduate program. The eight core courses include Management Communications, the Art of Negotiations, and Managing in the 21st Century, along with courses in the functional areas of business. Students may select from one of the seven option areas: accounting, business administration, finance, health-care management, international business, marketing, or taxation. It is also possible to construct a custom option based on special interests and goals. All students are required to fulfill foundation requirements that may be waived based on undergraduate curriculum and/or work experience.

Other opportunities at Philadelphia University include a full-time, one-year day program and joint-degree programs. The joint degrees offered are an M.B.A./M.S. in Taxation (55 credits) and an M.B.A./M.S. in instructional technology (55 credits). In addition, the University offers a Master of Science in Taxation.

Students and the M.B.A. Experience

Students come from the Northeast region of the country and abroad to study in the M.B.A. program at Philadelphia University. The average student is 27 years old and has five years of work experience. More than half of the students are women, and approximately 13 percent are international students.

❖ Global Focus

International dimensions are incorporated into all courses. In addition, students have the opportunity to participate in an overseas trip that exposes them to a number of international cultures and businesses. Over the last six years, the class has traveled to France, Belgium, and England, where students met with business leaders, labor leaders, and political leaders in the European Union.

The Faculty

Philadelphia University is a teaching institution where the primary focus is the students. Classes are small (average size is 15), which allows for extensive faculty-student interaction. The M.B.A. faculty combines both full-time professors and business leaders from the Philadelphia area. This unique combination provides an interesting mix of real-world experiences and applied research in the classroom.

The College and Environs

Founded in 1884, Philadelphia University is an independent, career-oriented institution that offers both graduate and undergraduate programs of study. Currently, Philadelphia University offers twelve professionally oriented graduate programs, each providing a blend of academic theory and real-world applications.

On a small, coeducational college campus, Philadelphia University fosters close relationships between faculty members and students and enrolls a student body that is academically and culturally diverse. The University is primarily a teaching institution that also encourages research as a service to industry and as a vehicle for faculty and student development. The 100-acre campus is situated 15 minutes from Center City Philadelphia, the fifth-largest city in the nation.

Facilities

The Paul J. Gutman Library is a state-of-the-art facility. A fully computerized book catalog allows access via computer both in the library and from remote locations. The main book collection consists of more than 88,000 volumes, with special emphasis in the areas of architecture, business, design, science and health, and textile arts. Networked electronic databases provide access to more than 2,000 journals, publications, and newspapers, including Infotrac, General Business Index, and SEC 10K Filings. The library has more than 600 journal titles available in full-text retrieval format.

Placement

Graduates of Philadelphia University are guaranteed lifetime assistance with career counseling. Last year, more than 200 companies visited the campus, well above the national average of 23 recruiters per year. Full-time graduate students may take advantage of the extensive on-campus recruiting schedule. Evening hours are also available twice a week, and workshops in resume writing, interview skills, and job search tips are scheduled regularly throughout the semester.

Admission

Candidates who seek admission are reviewed based on the merit of their academic record, work experience, and the required Graduate Management Admission Test (GMAT). Depending on the applicant's academic background, foundation courses may be required.

International students may begin in either the spring or fall semester. A minimum TOEFL score of 550 is required for students for whom English is not their native language. International students must provide proof of adequate funds to cover the cost of tuition, room and board, and expenses.

Finances

The estimated cost for full-time enrollment in 2000–01 is $5688 per semester ($474 per credit). Books and supplies cost approximately $500.

International Students

Thirteen percent of M.B.A. students at Philadelphia University come from outside the United States. International students must take the English language placement exam prior to registering for classes. The International Society is one of the largest groups on campus. It provides students with a network of support for problem solving, social activities, and general advising.

Application Facts and Dates

Applications are accepted for fall, spring, and summer semesters and are reviewed on a rolling basis. International applicants should send completed applications by June 1 for fall semester and October 1 for spring semester. For more information, applicants should contact:

William H. Firman Jr.
Director of Graduate Admissions
Philadelphia University
School House Lane and Henry Avenue
Philadelphia, Pennsylvania 19144
Telephone: 215-951-2943
Fax: 215-951-2907
E-mail: gradadm@philau.edu

Plymouth State College

Plymouth, New Hampshire

LEARN WITH WORKING PROFESSIONALS

The Plymouth State College (PSC) M.B.A. program is an evening program designed to meet the needs of working professionals as well as full-time students. Our classes are taught by full-time PSC faculty members, most of whom have their doctorates and extensive experience in business or government. Faculty members remain at the leading edge of their fields through continuing study and publishing in their areas of expertise. M.B.A. students have the opportunity to help New Hampshire small businesses and gain consulting experience through participation in a Small Business Institute (SBI) team. Over the twenty-two years of the SBI's existence, student teams working under the guidance of faculty members have made important contributions to more than 300 client companies while earning thirty-one state, regional, and/or national awards. Come to the beautiful Lakes Region at the foothills of the White Mountains of New Hampshire and learn with working professionals.

—Colleen C. Brickley, Director, Graduate Studies in Business

Programs and Curricular Focus

Plymouth State College is nationally accredited by the Association of Collegiate Business Schools and Programs (ACBSP). As a regional state college of the University System of New Hampshire, Plymouth State College is dedicated to bringing high-quality business education to regional and international students who join the journey to excellence. A major goal is to provide this educational experience at an extremely attractive cost to the student.

Because the students come from the most diverse of academic backgrounds, PSC has adopted a distinctive two-part curriculum. The first part consists of taking undergraduate courses or demonstrating competence in financial accounting, macroeconomics, microeconomics, statistics, psychology, and computers. Students with a bachelor's degree in business would, ordinarily, have fulfilled these undergraduate requirements before beginning their graduate courses at PSC. Those students who have not already taken these undergraduate courses may complete them at any accredited college or university of their choice before coming to PSC or may complete this first part of the curriculum at PSC. Alternatively, the student may satisfy these first-part undergraduate requirements by examination, i.e., the College Level Entrance Proficiency (CLEP) or PSC competency examination(s). The PSC competency examinations are prepared, administered, and evaluated by PSC.

The second part of the curriculum consists of ten core and two elective graduate courses, for a total of twelve courses of 3 credits each (36 graduate credits). As an option, the student may complete a Master's Research Project (MRP) of 6 credits in lieu of the two electives. The MRP can vary from traditional research to examination of a contemporary business problem. Also, there is the opportunity for individual enrollments and/or independent studies. The faculty has been quite eager to work with students on such projects. The ten core courses are modeled after the strongest academic curricula. These courses are the Legal Environment of Business, Accounting for Managers, Marketing Techniques, Quantitative Analysis, Managing Organizational Behavior, Managerial Economics, Financial Analysis and Decision Making, Information Technology in Organizations, Operations Management, and Seminar in Executive Management.

As a benefit of the two-part curriculum approach, students who have completed the program's undergraduate competency requirements before their arrival at PSC can complete the M.B.A. program in nine months by taking four M.B.A. courses in each of three 12-week terms. This scheduling approach has the dual benefit of dramatic reductions in both tuition costs and the time to earn the M.B.A. degree.

The schedule allows for completion in different time periods as well. Many full-time students complete the program in anywhere from twelve to twenty-one months or more, depending on the number of course requirements that must be satisfied at the start of their program. Flexibility is a keynote of the program.

Students and the M.B.A. Experience

Students average 35 years of age, with more than ten years of work experience. They come from banking, medical, retailing, manufacturing, government, and educational organizations, to name only a few. About 45 percent are women, 8 percent are members of minority groups, and 92 percent are from New Hampshire, Maine, Massachusetts, and Vermont. Each year, there are between 5 and 12 international students.

Students work in teams, develop joint papers, and make team presentations. The program averages between 15 and 20 full-time students and more than 500 part-time working professionals, which enables the full-time students to gain much from the interaction with their working colleagues. As a result, many of the full-time students gain employment in the organizations of their part-time colleagues. This symbiotic relationship has flourished over the twenty-three-year history of the program.

Special Features

Because international students have diverse interests and come from many different countries, the faculty generously devotes time to individual enrollments and independent studies. These opportunities help the international student explore topics of interest. Typical topics are comparative studies in economics and/or law, marketing issues, and organizational behavior.

For international students desiring postgraduate training, the program has been successful in finding suitable placement. About one third of the international students take advantage of this postgraduate training.

The Faculty

The Department of Business at PSC has 22 full-time faculty members, all of whom teach in both the graduate and undergraduate programs. Three of the faculty members are women, and 3 are members of minority groups. More than half have extensive experience in business or management. Teaching and advising are strong components of the faculty culture and a great source of satisfaction to the faculty.

The Business School Network

The Board of Trustees of the University System includes several prominent business leaders who develop guidance for the M.B.A. program. In addition, the Small Business Institute program places the faculty in continual contact with regional business leaders who give advice and valuable feedback to the program.

Prominent Alumni

Some prominent graduates of the M.B.A. program are Jane Babin, Assistant Professor, PSC; Stanley Arnold, Director of Revenue, State of New Hampshire; Christina Ferris, Associate Professor, Johnson State College, Johnson, VT; Jeffrey Coombs, President, Ossipee Mountain Land Company, Tamworth, NH; Frank Johns, Vice President of Operations, Locktite Luminescent Systems, Lebanon, NH; Nancy Stewart, President, North Country Management Systems, North Conway, NH; Dr. Gary Hagens, Oral Surgeon; and Linda Normandin, Vice President, Laconia Savings Bank, Laconia, NH.

The College and Environs

Plymouth State College is a unit of the University System of New Hampshire. Founded in 1871, the College has undergone many changes and has shifted its role from that of a normal school, and later (1970) a state teachers college, to that of a multipurpose institution. It offers the Master of Education and the Master of Business Administration, as well as associate and bachelor's degrees.

Plymouth is situated in the Lakes and White Mountain region of New Hampshire. The scenic beauty of the area is breathtaking, and the surrounding countryside is a center for extensive recreational activities, available year-round. Students have access to skiing, boating, fishing opportunities, and lovely camps with a wealth of amenities. The town of Plymouth has a year-round population of 6,000, with a seasonal increase of twice that number. Plymouth is approximately 2 hours from both Boston, Massachusetts, and Portland, Maine. Hartford, Connecticut, is 3½ hours away. The capital city of Concord is only 40 minutes south on Interstate 93. A jetport is located in Manchester, about 1 hour south on Interstate 93.

Facilities

Classes are taught in Hyde Hall, which also contains the Department of Business

computer cluster with more than forty computers. There are several other clusters about the campus shared by all students.

On-campus apartments are available for full-time students, and there are also apartments available in the town of Plymouth. These apartments are all within walking distance of the academic buildings on campus.

Research in the field of business management is facilitated by the rapidly expanding holdings of the Lamson Library. In addition to 250,000 volumes and 475,000 units of filmed and recorded materials, the library houses a remote-access system for retrieval of appropriate audiovisual programs. Formal library support services are supplemented by a Department of Business collection and by interlibrary agreements with other institutions. Computer resources available allow communication with other institutions throughout the country. In addition, there are computers, which include IBM and Macintosh PCs, available in public clusters.

Technology Environment

PSC uses computers for both administrative and academic computing. There are more than 100 terminals distributed throughout the campus and dormitories, as well as more than twenty port selectors for students who live off campus and have their own computers. Services include e-mail and access to the Internet. Although students are encouraged to bring a computer to PSC, there are seven computer clusters in addition to the terminals.

Placement

The Career Development Office serves both undergraduate and graduate students. Because many of the graduate students are working professionals, the services are utilized most frequently by full-time students. The office has been highly successful in helping international students find opportunities for postgraduate training. Internships are also arranged when appropriate.

Admission

Applicants must submit proof of a bachelor's degree (official transcripts), a GPA of 2.5 or higher, three letters of recommendation (on the forms provided), and acceptable GMAT scores. International applicants must also submit acceptable TOEFL scores and notarized certification of financial resources to cover the costs of education and living expenses.

The admissions board considers the total aspect of the application; therefore, there are no cut-off scores, except for a desired minimum TOEFL score of 550.

The average GMAT score is about 490, with a range of 400 to 760. The average undergraduate GPA is about 3.1 on a 4.0 scale. The GPA of the student is often more reliable as a predictor than the GMAT score, so more weight is given to the GPA of the applicant. About 50 percent of the students have bachelor's degrees in fields other than business.

Finances

The 1999–2000 tuition rate was $867 per three-credit course for state residents and $951 per three-credit course for all others. Therefore, the 36-credit graduate program costs were $10,404 for state residents and $11,412 for all others. All fees were included in the above rates, including graduation fees.

In addition to tuition, books may cost between $75 and $160 per course, for a total of about $1700. An additional $5000 for other living expenses should be anticipated.

Graduate students may live in nontraditional housing. The costs for room and board for the 1999–2000 year were $5000 per year. Apartments for married and single students are available on campus. Off-campus living arrangements can also be made; these vary greatly in cost.

International Students

International students have a unique opportunity to learn with working professionals in a small regional state college environment. The academic experience includes current practice in real business organizations as learned from fellow students.

Application Facts and Dates

The application deadline for fall or winter admission is May 15; for spring or summer admission the deadline is October 15. For more information, applicants should contact:

Karen Hammond, Assistant to the Director
Graduate Studies in Business
Plymouth State College
Plymouth, New Hampshire 03264
Telephone: 603-535-2835
        800-367-4723 (toll-free in the continental U.S. (except Florida), Canada, and Hawaii)
Fax: 603-535-2648
E-mail: mba@mail.plymouth.edu
World Wide Web:
        http://mba.plymouth.edu

Polytechnic University

Brooklyn, New York

COMMIT YOURSELF TO INNOVATION, TECHNOLOGY, AND E-BUSINESS MANAGEMENT—GO BEYOND THE GENERIC M.B.A.

Prowess in broadly defined technology, innovation, information management, and e-business increasingly determines success in business today. The Department of Management at Polytechnic University is an acknowledged pacesetter in the New York City/Tri-State region in these increasingly critical arenas. Our focus is on the areas of greatest growth and opportunity in the emerging economy. In doing so, we serve a diverse and broad range of professionals, and our faculty members and students comprise a highly sought-after and forward-thinking research and learning community.

—Mel Horwitch, Chair, Department of Management

Programs and Curricular Focus

Founded in 1854 and still known fondly as Brooklyn Poly, Polytechnic University is home to more than 4,000 graduate and undergraduate students in science, technology, and management. More important than being the nation's second oldest science and technology university, Polytechnic is the acknowledged major technology-based higher education institution in the New York City/Tri-State region. It is committed to high-level and advanced development, research, and diverse learning programs that deal with technology management and e-business on a broad front.

The Department of Management's overriding mission is to be the major educational gateway and premier learning, research, and development hub, explicitly devoted to innovation, information, and technology management and electronic business. All its carefully tailored learning programs and the intellectual capital produced enable the department to provide valuable and distinctive learning opportunities. The department also continuously upgrades and revises its learning programs and courses to meet the fast-changing demands of a dynamic, technology-driven, competitive environment.

The Department of Management offers five graduate degrees: the Master of Science in Management (M.S.M.), the Master of Science in Financial Engineering (F.E.), and the Master of Science in Organizational Behavior (M.S.O.B.) and two executive programs that meet Fridays and Saturdays or Thursday evenings and Saturdays on alternating weekends: the Master of Science in Management of Technology (M.O.T.)—including an e-business track, a MOTIR Re-

tailing Track, and a MOTIFS Financial Services Track—and the Master of Science in Telecommunications and Information Management (T.I.M.)—including an e-business track. The M.S.M., M.S.O.B., and F.E. programs may be pursued either part-time or full-time, with an evening schedule. Emphasizing technology and innovation management, Polytechnic's M.S.M. (along with the M.B.A.) is recognized by the Graduate Management Admissions Council as a graduate professional management degree.

The M.S.M., M.S.O.B., and F.E. programs offer a group of core courses and choices of concentrations and electives that allow students to focus on areas of professional importance. Concentrations for the M.S.M. include entrepreneurship, electronic business, technology management, human resource management, information management, telecommunications management, operations management, and construction management. The M.S.O.B. concentrations include training and development, human resource management, and management of change. F.E. students choose a Capital Markets or a Financial Technology Track. All master's programs offered by the department require 36 credits (an equivalent of twelve full courses).

The department also offers graduate-level certificates for the M.S.M., M.S.O.B., and F.E. programs that consist of selected courses to obtain advanced special knowledge.

Students and the Program Experience

In 1999–2000, more than 600 students were enrolled, including more than 180 in the

M.O.T. and T.I.M. Executive Programs. About 90 percent of these students attended part-time. Industries represented included financial services, information technology, electronic business, telecommunications, chemicals, pharmaceuticals, energy, utilities, media, entertainment, defense, aerospace, retailing, health, government, transportation, and construction.

Reflecting the current exciting atmosphere of a burgeoning international and high-technology New York City, the department's programs offer an unparalleled international and multicultural learning experience that enhances a real-world understanding of global technology and e-business management issues.

New York City provides graduates with access to leading companies in such booming sectors as new media and e-business. Start-ups and established firms fiercely compete for managerial talents that are emphasized and nurtured in the department's programs.

A technology background is not required. The undergraduate experience represented is extremely diverse, including engineering, science, social science, and liberal arts. A desire to understand how technology and innovation affect decision making and value creation in the modern economy is required. All graduates should have acquired the ability to integrate technology and innovation in business practices in an effective, sophisticated, and pragmatic fashion.

All classes in the department's programs are extremely interactive. Easy access to faculty members, individual attention, and animated class participation are acknowledged and special strengths that are not often found in larger institutions.

The Faculty

The department's faculty members are highly respected scholars in innovation, operations, information technology, electronic business, entrepreneurship, marketing, human resources, organizational behavior, finance, and technology strategy. Adjunct professors also contribute expertise and vast experience, blending theory and practice.

As leaders in technology and innovation management education, the faculty stands at the cutting edge by helping managers in today's knowledge-based business environment. It produces important print- and Web-

Mel Horwich, Professor; Chair, Department of Management; and Co-Director, M.O.T.-T.I.M. Programs; M.B.A., D.B.A., Harvard. Innovation, technology management, e-business.

Yair Berson, Assistant Professor; Ph.D., SUNY at Binghamton. Organizational behavior, leadership in technology environments.

Barry S. Blecherman, Assistant Professor and Academic Director, M.S.M. Program; Ph.D., Pennsylvania (Wharton). Decision theory, business negotiations.

Seymour A. Kaplan, Associate Professor Emeritus; Ph.D., NYU. Financial modeling, business quantitative methods, corporate finance.

Harold G. Kaufman, Professor and Academic Director, M.S.O.B. Program; Ph.D., NYU. Managing professional and technical workers, career management, obsolescence, research methods.

Frank Leiber, Industry Associate Professor and Academic Director, MOTIFS Track, M.O.T. Program; Ph.D., HEI Geneva. Econometrics of financial markets, financial risk management, e-business, quantitative managerial analysis.

Jonathan D. Linton, Assistant Professor; Ph.D., York (Toronto). Operations management and environmental management.

Daniel A. Nathanson, Adjunct Associate Professor; Ph.D., Pennsylvania (Wharton). Entrepreneurship and early-stage venturing.

Frederick Novomestky, Industry Associate Professor and Academic Director, Financial Engineering Program; Ph.D., Polytechnic. Multimedia object development, computational algorithms for business optimization, quantitative investment strategy.

Mihir Parikh, Assistant Professor; M.B.A., Ph.D., Georgia State. Decision support systems, artificial intelligence, information management, knowledge management, hypermedia, intelligent decisional guidance and business training systems.

Bharat Rao, Assistant Professor; Ph.D., Georgia. Collaborative product development, supply chain management, Internet marketing and e-business.

A. George Schillinger, Professor Emeritus; Sc.D., Columbia. Technology and innovation management, science and technology policy.

Nina D. Ziv, Industry Associate Professor and Co-Director, M.O.T.-T.I.M. Programs; Ph.D., NYU. Technology organization and business unit strategic coordination, global technology and entrepreneurial strategies in new sectors.

based learning material on significant technology, innovation, and e-business issues. Such wise incorporation of technology greatly enriches learning.

The Management Department Network

With its unique New York City location, the department draws support from leaders in critical industries. Its Corporate Advisory Board includes the CIO and Senior VP of Wit Capital, the head of the high-technology practice with the Boston Consulting Group, the founder of a leading-edge intelligent agent firm, the Chief Knowledge Officer at Monitor Company, a senior partner in consulting services for PriceWaterhouseCoopers, a Director of Information Strategy, and several high-technology entrepreneurs.

Alumni are found around the world. They comprise senior executives and entrepreneurs wherever technology, innovation, and now e-business are important, spanning all sectors of the economy.

The University and Environs

The M.S.M. Program is offered at Polytechnic's main campus in Brooklyn's Metro-Tech, near Brooklyn Heights, and at the University's Long Island and Westchester County campuses. The M.S.O.B. Program is offered on the Brooklyn campus. The F.E. Program and the M.O.T. and T.I.M. Executive Programs are held in the Global Community Digital Sandbox at 55 Broad Street, in the heart of Manhattan's Silicon Alley and Wall Street. The department's Institute for Technology and Enterprise, which develops significant learning content, is also at 55 Broad Street.

Facilities

The Bern Dibner Library of Science and Technology in Brooklyn contains more than 200,000 volumes and has extensive database, multimedia, and Internet capabilities. Other campuses host smaller libraries. The University maintains large computer facilities with Internet/Web and modem access and a distance learning facility. The home of the F.E., M.O.T., and T.I.M. programs, 55 Broad Street, houses a completely wired learning space. The New York City Public Library's new Library of Science, Industry, and Business is also available.

Placement

While nearly all Department of Management students are employed, the University provides career placement specialists for those interested in new opportunities. Recruiters visit regularly because of Polytechnic's reputation. In addition, informal networks exist between students and between students, alumni, and faculty members, which frequently open unrivaled corporate and entrepreneurial doors. There is an enormous demand for the students in the current high-tech economy.

Admission

Admission requires a bachelor's degree with at least a B average from an accredited college or university and demonstrated evidence of motivation, maturity, and ability to benefit from and contribute to professional programs related to technology, innovation, and information management and e-business. Applicants not meeting all criteria for the M.S.M., M.S.O.B., and F.E. programs may be admitted as nondegree students (with a subsequent opportunity to become a degree candidate). Satisfactory scores on the Graduate Management Admission Test (GMAT) or an acceptable equivalent test, such as the Graduate Record Exam (GRE), may be used and/or requested as support for admission.

Finances

Evening program tuition for the 2000–01 academic year is $695 per credit. Full-semester graduate management courses are 3 credits (and 1.5 credits for half-semester courses). The application fee is $50. (Students may take up to three courses as special students with no application fee.) Applications are also available on line. Credit for special students is applied toward the degree requirements upon matriculation. The University fee is $300 per semester full-time and $135 per semester part-time. Tuition for the M.O.T. and T.I.M. programs is $9300 per semester.

Application Facts and Dates

Applications are accepted at any time. Students may begin evening programs in the spring, summer, or fall semesters. The M.O.T and T.I.M. programs begin in September or January. For application information, students should contact:

Department of Management
Polytechnic University
6 MetroTech Center
Brooklyn, New York 11201
Telephone: 718-260-3760
Fax: 718-260-3874
E-mail: mgt-dept@poly.edu
        mot-tim@poly.edu (Executive Programs)
World Wide Web: http://www.managementdept.poly.edu
http://www.mot-tim.poly.edu (Executive Programs)

Portland State University

Portland, Oregon

EXPLORING BUSINESS IN AN URBAN ENVIRONMENT

At Portland State University's (PSU) School of Business Administration, we are setting a pace for the twenty-first century by moving above and beyond the boundaries of conventional business education. Our graduate programs combine academic integrity with an applied, practical orientation, including involvement with business partners, to produce leaders and professionals to meet the challenges of the global marketplace.

The urban setting of Portland State University provides the best possible learning environment to prepare our graduates for the increasingly competitive world of business. We are committed to providing an outstanding learning experience that prepares our graduates to enter the workplace with needed knowledge, skills, understanding, and drive to be successful for themselves and their employers.

—Roger S. Ahlbrandt, Dean

Programs and Curricular Focus

In the M.B.A. curriculum, emphasis is given to an integrated and systemic perspective of how business competitiveness is achieved. The themes of decision making, problem solving, managing innovation and change, quality management practices, and global competitiveness cut across the program. Careful attention is given to communication, leadership, teamwork skills, and close involvement with the business community. The two-year, 72-quarter-credit M.B.A. program is composed of five distinct elements designed to produce a systematic and integrated understanding of business operations. These elements are business perspective and foundation skills, business disciplines, integrated applications, a business project, and a specialization. Learning is facilitated by use of team and project-based learning, information and information technology, and continued exposure to the thinking and practices of world-class business firms and their leaders. The Master of International Management (M.I.M.) is an innovative twelve-month full-time program (six 8-week terms) or a two-year part-time program that is specifically tailored to address the business challenges created by the world's shifting political, economic, and technological developments. The curriculum (16 core courses; 65 mandatory quarter-credit hours) combines an in-depth exploration of innovative business practices and their relationship to contemporary world affairs

and includes mandatory language study, executive seminars, corporate visits and a three-week field study trip to China and Japan. The School of Business Administration participates in the systems science Ph.D. program, which combines the study of systems with the study of business. Students work closely with faculty members to design an individualized program of study that gives each student the needed foundation in systems, research, and two fields of business.

Students and the M.B.A. Experience

Students in the PSU graduate business programs are a major resource for enhancing the total learning experience. More than 75 percent of the M.B.A. students are employed at the time of admission, with an average of six years of business experience. The average age is 30, and 37 percent are women. Approximately 16 percent are minority and international students. The classroom environment, which includes teams and active student interaction, is rich in diversity of experience, gender, and culture. Sharing and learning from each other is a hallmark of PSU graduate business education. Students in the M.I.M. program have approximately seven years of work and international experience. The average age of the students in the M.I.M. program is 32. The academic experience is augmented by the cultural diversity represented in a student body in which international students represent 51 percent of the total enrollment.

❖ Global Focus

In addition to the M.B.A. program's focus on competing in a global environment, the School of Business offers the M.I.M. degree. This program concentrates on application-oriented knowledge and practical skills that can be applied globally. The M.I.M. emphasizes the essentials of international business and includes a focus on the evolving cultural mores, transforming social systems, and new politics that impact international business daily. The M.I.M. program prepares the talented and highly motivated professional to meet the future of a competitive global business environment.

Special Features

Students in the M.B.A. program are members of a cohort group and complete two 8-hour integrated courses, with each team taught by several faculty members. Students also participate, individually or in teams, in an applied business project. Additional activities are available to help in career planning and development of computer skills. For the M.I.M. program, there is a pre-M.I.M. program designed to ensure academic success for students who have a limited academic business background. The eight-week program begins in late June and covers the fundamentals of business statistics, financial accounting, business finance, microeconomics, and macroeconomics. M.I.M. students also study a second language and participate in a field study trip to Japan and China.

The Faculty

The faculty is a significant strength of the School of Business Administration, bringing to the classroom a strong educational foundation, practical business experience, and dedication to student learning. Faculty members have traveled and taught in the Pacific Rim, the Middle East, Europe, Russia, and the Commonwealth of Independent States. In addition, the best talents within the business community are brought to the classroom as lecturers and guest speakers. A unique feature of the M.I.M. program is that the faculty is drawn from the internationally oriented faculty members at Portland State University, the University of Oregon, and Oregon State University. Furthermore, the M.I.M. program

Students can enjoy Portland's beautiful waterfront.

invites internationally recognized professors and business and government leaders from around the world to participate as faculty members.

The Business School Network

Corporate Partnerships

The School of Business Administration has forged close ties with the business community of the Pacific Northwest and the Pacific Rim. Partnership relationships are used to facilitate applied research, student projects, internships, faculty development, classroom participation by business executives and for networking opportunities for employment for graduates. The M.I.M. program utilizes international business executives to lead executive seminars. In addition, students travel to corporations to interact with business executives to gain firsthand knowledge about doing business internationally.

The College and Environs

Portland State University is ideally situated only 90 minutes from beaches and mountain slopes. As Oregon's economic and population center and a gateway to the Pacific Rim, Portland offers unique opportunities for business, industry, government, and the University to enhance partnerships that promote economic, social, cultural, and international development. Founded in 1946, the campus of nearly 15,000 students occupies forty buildings in a 36-acre area. The University is built around the Park Blocks, a greenway area reserved for pedestrians and bicyclists.

Facilities

The School of Business is located just a few minutes' walk from the downtown Portland business district. Students have access to the University's main library, which houses nearly 1 million volumes, including approximately 10,000 serial publications, a growing number of CD-ROM and online computer databases, and an extensive collection of government documents. Portland State University has numerous housing facilities and options in providing desirable and affordable housing to students of the University.

Technology Environment

The School of Business Administration has a special computer lab for graduate students, equipped with high-speed laser printers and more than twenty-five workstations. From here, students have access to the University's main computer, the Portland Area Library System (PORTALS), the Internet, and numerous other databases. The M.I.M. program provides a new, state-of-the-art language lab. Students can do their language study or computer work in one of many workstations.

Placement

Career development and networking opportunities, coordinated through Corporate, Student, and Alumni Relations, are provided through seminars, workshops, and information meetings. Other resources include an internship program, the Portland State University Career Center, the PSU Business Association (PSUBA), and the M.I.M. Student Association (MIMSA).

Admission

Each candidate's academic record, scores on the required Graduate Management Admission Test (GMAT), and work experience are considered in the M.B.A. admission process. The averages for recently admitted students are a GMAT score of 602 and an undergraduate GPA of 3.2. Students may elect to participate in the full-time day program (fall admittance only) or in the evening program (fall and winter admittance). The evening program is primarily for part-time students. The M.I.M. program prefers students who have at least two years of professional work experience, a GMAT score of at least 470 or an acceptable GRE score, and outstanding letters of recommendation and personal essay. Students who have no or a limited academic business background are required to participate in the eight-week summer pre-M.I.M. program. International students whose native language is not English must score at least 550 on the written TOEFL or 213 on the computerized TOEFL and must present proof of their financial resources.

Finances

Full-time tuition for the M.B.A. program in 1999–00 was $6293 per year for in-state residents and $10,765 per year for nonresidents. A limited number of scholarships and graduate assistantships are available. Tuition for students enrolling in the 1999–2000 Master of International Management program was $18,500 plus a $3500 travel fee for the field study to China and Japan. Students enrolled in the pre-M.I.M. program pay an additional fee based on the number of pre-M.I.M. courses required.

International Students

A number of international students from countries in South America, Asia, and Europe participate in the graduate programs at Portland State University. The M.I.M. program has a 51 percent international student population.

Application Facts and Dates

Application deadlines for the M.B.A. program for international students are March 1 for fall admission and July 1 for winter admission; for domestic students, the dates are April 1 for fall admission and August 1 for winter admission. The Master of International Management program has an April 30 deadline for both international and domestic students. For more information, applicants should contact:

Director of Student Services
School of Business Administration
Portland State University
P.O. Box 751
Portland, Oregon 97207-0751
Telephone: 503-725-3712
Fax: 503-725-5850
E-mail: info@sba.pdx.edu

For the M.I.M. program, contact:

M.I.M. Program
School of Business Administration
Portland State University
P.O. Box 751
Portland, Oregon 97207
Telephone: 503-725-2275
          800-879-5088 (toll-free)
E-mail: mim@sba.pdx.edu
World Wide Web: www.sba.pdx.edu/
mim

Purdue University

Krannert Graduate School of Management

West Lafayette, Indiana

> ### THE SCIENCE AND THE ART OF MANAGEMENT
>
> *The design of our programs encourages the development of technical, interpersonal, and conceptual management skills — skills that will help you practice the science and the art of management. Exposure to outstanding teachers, effective business leaders, and motivated peers combine to provide one of the most outstanding values among top-ranked business programs.*
> —Richard A. Cosier, Dean and Leeds Professor of Management

Programs and Curricular Focus

The Master of Science in Management (M. S.M.) is a two-year residential program. Students select from options in accounting, finance, human resource management, management information systems, marketing, operations, strategic management, and three interdisciplinary options: general, international, or manufacturing management. The Master of Science in Human Resource Management (M.S.H.R.M.) is a two-year residential program that combines the best of human resource management with a strong business focus. The Master of Science in Industrial Administration (M.S.I.A.) is an eleven-month residential program that allows students to earn a management degree in a condensed time span. Krannert participates in a unique partnership with the German International School of Management and Administration (GISMA) in Hannover, Germany, through which the Krannert M.S.I.A. program is offered on a full-time basis. Krannert and GISMA students may participate in eight-week exchange programs at the respective schools. Krannert also offers an Executive M.S. in Management (E.M.S.). The E.M.S. is a 22-month program offered in an innovative format combining on-campus study with distance learning.

The programs emphasize fundamental management theory, case studies, teamwork, and experiential learning opportunities, including computer simulations and consulting projects. The small program size (fewer than 500 students) allows frequent interaction with and personal attention from faculty members. Students also learn from each other in diverse, cross-disciplinary study teams. Complementing course work, student-run organizations provide leadership opportunities, networking with executives and recruiters, and personal and professional development.

Students and the Program Experience

Krannert is an intimate learning environment, in which approximately 200 students are enrolled in the three programs each year. Students come from a wide range of undergraduate disciplines with engineering, science, and mathematics well represented. The average age at enrollment is 27. Twenty-five percent of students are women, 14 percent are members of minority groups, and 35 percent are international. Entering students' GMAT scores typically range from 560 to 750. Their average GPA is 3.3. Students have an average of more than four years of work experience but motivated students with less experience are also encouraged to apply. Krannert attracts a geographically diverse student population with twenty-six countries and twenty-nine states represented.

Special Features

Krannert uses specialized labs, computer simulations, and off-campus projects to enhance the study of specific management issues such as globalization and the information technology revolution. As an SAP Partner School, Krannert offers many advantages. The Enterprise Integration Lab, for example, runs SAP R/3 software using real company data. Several "kaizen" projects in the U.S. and South America are sponsored each year by the Dauch Center for the Management of Manufacturing Enterprises. Krannert students can also participate in a unique study abroad exchange with our sister school, GISMA, in Hannover, Germany. The International Multidisciplinary Management Project sends students abroad for a consulting project with an international company. The Student Managed Investment Fund gives students a hands-on opportunity to learn asset management and security analysis through investing real financial capital.

The Faculty

Krannert has 80 full-time management and economics faculty members. Due to the small program size, students view Krannert faculty members as professional peers as well as professors. Faculty members are responsive to student input concerning everything from course topics and speakers to class administration. Faculty evaluations are published each module to ensure high-quality teaching. Courses are reviewed regularly, often with input from alumni and recruiters, to reflect the changing business world. Purdue's reputation as a research university means Krannert faculty members make a point to include relevant, current applications of cutting-edge research in their courses.

The Business School Network

Krannert alumni and the corporations they work for are important contributors to the master's programs. Corporations and their representatives fund graduate awards, sponsor students, provide computer hardware and software, make presentations in courses and at special events, host interns, and actively recruit on and off campus. Some of the School's major corporate partners include Caterpillar, Eastman Kodak, Eli Lilly, Ernst

Information technology, such as SAP R/3 enterprise integration software, is a key component of Krannert's curricula.

Krannert graduates are sought by top corporations, especially in the consulting, computer, and automotive industries.

& Young, Ford, General Motors, Hewlett-Packard, Ingersoll-Rand, GE, GTE, Pricewaterhouse Coopers, Procter & Gamble, Shell Oil Company, and United Technologies. Students meet and interact with top executives through the Krannert Executive Forum presentation series, the Dean's Advisory Council, and the Krannert School Alumni Association Board. The Alumni Mentor Program links first-year students with active alumni as a source of advice about management studies and careers.

The College and Environs

Purdue University, a world-class research and teaching institution, has 37,000 students and 2,200 faculty members at West Lafayette, Indiana. In addition to management, Purdue is known for its strengths in engineering, computer science, and agriculture. Krannert takes pride in its affiliation with these University programs as well as its corporate partnerships in providing nationally ranked and accredited master's in management programs.

Krannert is located in a friendly college town in the midst of America's thriving heartland. The area economy is strong, and there are many job opportunities for spouses. Local schools are top-rated, and neighborhoods are safe and pleasant. Summers are warm and sunny, with some snow in winter. Chicago and Indianapolis are easily accessible by Interstate 65 for day trips, professional sporting events, and big-city culture.

Technology Environment

Students benefit from Krannert's exceptional information technology infrastructure. The computer laboratories have been developed in conjunction with corporate partners such as Ameritech, AT&T, Hewlett-Packard, IBM, Microsoft, PictureTel, and SAP America. The Krannert Library, with extensive online

resources, is conveniently located in the same complex students attend for classes. Students and faculty members are fully wired with Internet access and e-mail, which encourages them to communicate, exchange data, and conduct research.

Krannert has recently invested in the development of a wireless network throughout the Krannert complex. Wireless hubs and network cards enable students to access the Krannert network and Internet from virtually anywhere within Krannert — without having to "plug in."

Placement

Graduates of Krannert's three master's programs are sought by recruiters in the fields of corporate finance, operations, consulting, information systems, human resource management, and marketing. Major recruiters include Agilent Technologies, Andersen Consulting, Cap Gemini/Ernst & Young, Ford, Hewlett-Packard, IBM, Ingersoll-Rand, Intel, Merrill Lynch, Owens Corning, Pricewaterhouse Coopers, Procter & Gamble, Sun Microsystems, and United Technologies. Operations, finance, consulting, MIS, and marketing are the top functions; computers, consulting, and automotive are the top industries. Typically about 40 percent of placements are in the Midwest, with significant numbers of graduates placed on both coasts and internationally. Preliminary results for the class of 2000 include an average starting base salary of $76,500 and an average signing bonus of $12,500. In recent years, at least ninety-five percent of students have received job offers by graduation.

Admission

Test scores, grade point averages, work experience, and leadership potential are assessed during the admissions process. Ap-

plicants must submit academic records, GMAT scores, essays, recommendations, and resumes. Campus interviews are available after applications are submitted. TOEFL scores are required of applicants from non-English speaking countries. Admissions are conducted on a rolling basis. Prospective students should contact the admissions office about spring preview weekend or tour arrangements throughout the year. Purdue University is an equal access/equal opportunity university.

Finances

Krannert is consistently ranked as one of the best values in management education by publications such as *Business Week*, *Financial Times*, and *Forbes*. Estimated 2000–01 tuition for the M.S.M. and M.S.H.R.M. programs is $8772 for Indiana residents and $17,892 for non-residents. Estimated 2000–01 tuition for the eleven-month M.S. I.A. program is $12,379 for Indiana residents and $24,044 for non-residents.

Krannert grants several cash awards based on academic merit and other criteria. Awards typically range from $2000 to $10,000 for one or two years. Graduate awards are generally restricted to U.S. citizens and permanent residents. Many Krannert students receive assistantships or residence-hall counselorships each year. Assistantships provide a partial remission of tuition and a monthly stipend and range in value from $8500 to more than $28,000 per year, depending on residency and duties. Residence-hall counselorships provide room and board, a stipend for books, and a partial tuition waiver. All students are eligible to apply for assistantships and counselorships. U.S. citizens and eligible non-citizens may also apply for Federal Stafford Student Loans.

Application Facts and Dates

Students should apply by November 1 to receive a decision by December 15. The international application deadline is February 1. Late applications may be accepted through May.

For more information, students should contact:

Ward Snearly, Director of Admissions
1310 Krannert Center, Room 104
Krannert Graduate School of
    Management
Purdue University
West Lafayette, Indiana 47907-1310
Telephone: 765-494-4365
              765-494-7700 (for E.M.S.
              program)
Fax: 765-494-9841
E-mail: krannert_ms@mgmt.purdue.
    edu
    keepinfo@mgmt.purdue.edu
    (for E.M.S. program)
World Wide Web: http://www.mgmt.
    purdue.edu

Queen's University at Kingston

M.B.A. for Science & Technology

Kingston, Ontario, Canada

MAKING A DIFFERENCE

The decision to pursue an M.B.A. says a great deal about you. It says you want to achieve career success. It says you want to develop the knowledge, skills, and perspectives required to be an effective manager. It says you are prepared to make a major investment in your future. Above all, it says you want to make a difference in this world.

The Queen's M.B.A. for Science & Technology will prepare you to make that difference. The program augments traditional M.B.A. programming with a special emphasis on the distinctive challenges facing technology-rich organizations and the professional needs of those who lead them. The result is a one-year, comprehensive program that develops industry leaders of the future.

—Professor John Gordon, Chair

Program and Curricular Focus

The twelve-month Queen's M.B.A. for Science & Technology curriculum gives students the knowledge, management skills, and perspective they need to succeed in today's globally oriented, technology-rich organizations. It takes full advantage of the strong science and technology backgrounds of its students, leveraging their abilities into sophisticated applications.

The curriculum, which begins in May of each year, has four progressive stages. Students first develop a solid base in the disciplines and core concepts of management (stage one), then progress to the key functional fields of business—marketing, finance, and operations/information technology (stage two). With this strong foundation, they are ready to integrate knowledge from a variety of different areas and examine business problems from a strategic perspective (stage three). Students conclude the program with an intensive period of study in their chosen area of concentration—finance, marketing, or technology management. This is followed by a four-week, offsite field project that gives them hands-on experience in business management (stage four). In addition, the academic curriculum is complemented by several week-long career advantage modules that provide students with an array of special skills to enhance their managerial effectiveness.

Students and the M.B.A. Experience

Students enrolled in the Queen's M.B.A. for Science & Technology have undergraduate degrees in engineering, science, computer science, health sciences, or mathematics. They bring a wide variety of work experiences and geographic diversity. The average age is 30, and students have an average of six years' work experience.

Teaching methods include lectures, case studies, teamwork, negotiation and computer simulations, guest presentations, seminars, and field studies. Students are part of a 6-person learning team for the duration of the program. The team draws on the diverse skills and knowledge of all individuals in order to achieve exceptional results. Each team has a professional facilitator whose role is to promote team effectiveness, encourage an environment of mutual respect and cooperation, and mediate problems.

Special Features

One special feature of the Queen's M.B.A. for Science & Technology is its focus on science and technology. The professors, students, textbooks, and cases are all focused on understanding, analyzing, and overcoming the unique managerial challenges faced by technology driven organizations.

Students gain special skills through the program's career advantage modules along with the core elements of a conventional M.B.A. Students are immersed in high-performance team

training, career development seminars, and presentation skills workshops. Weekly interaction with top executives from biotechnology, financial services, high technology, management consulting, and advanced manufacturing provide a new perspective into the business world.

The Faculty

Faculty members for the M.B.A. for Science Technology program are hand-picked from more than 50 full-time faculty members in the School of Business. The faculty members are rich in business experience and offer excellence in teaching, research, and consulting.

The faculty at Queen's has long prided itself on accessibility to students and commitment to teaching excellence. Beyond the classroom, Queen's faculty has a history of widespread involvement in student programs.

Faculty members from other universities also participate in the M.B.A. program through videoconferencing or as visiting lecturers. Guest speakers from industry and government participate actively in classes and in the career advantage program.

The College and Environs

Since its first day of classes in 1842, Queen's University has embodied a standard of excellence in education that makes it one of Canada's leading universities. Queen's distinctiveness is illustrated in the "Queen's Spirit," which has developed from the combination of a close-knit campus community, educational excellence, and beautiful surroundings. Queen's University has approximately 11,000 undergraduate and 4,000 graduate and professional students.

Kingston, Ontario, Canada, with a population of 120,000, is situated on the shores of Lake Ontario and the St. Lawrence River. Kingston enjoys an abundance of cultural and recreational activities. Kingston also provides easy access to major centers of business, technology development, and government, as it is situated within easy reach of Ottawa, Toronto, Montreal, and Syracuse.

Facilities

The M.B.A. for Science & Technology program has a world-class facility built specifically to accommodate and facilitate the curriculum and learning process. It provides participants with exclusive use of a state-of-the-art teaching theatre, seminar rooms, and student and administrative offices. The facility exemplifies the program's philosophy of using technology to enhance efficiency and effectiveness.

Beyond the dedicated facility, students have access to Queen's wide array of athletic, academic, and student service facilities. These include the $43-million Stauffer Library and Electronic Information Centre, a $25-million Bioscience Complex, and the $20-million Walter Light Technology Centre.

Technology Environment

An extensive collection of audiovisual and information technologies extends the boundaries and capabilities of the physical facility. To maximize individual productivity, all students receive a notebook computer on a lease program. When coupled with the computer groupware and other communication tools that connect every room and office, the result is a "virtual facility" that electronically links the program to the world.

Placement

Advancing students' careers is a top priority at Queen's. While most schools help with job placement, the University offers comprehensive career management through the full-time M.B.A. Career Manager. Students learn to focus their goals and receive the best professional communications and presentation training. Students receive advice on resume-writing skills, developing strategies for success on job interviews, and presentation and networking skills. Students have opportunities to attend trade shows, job fairs, and industry conferences where they can find information and contacts that are essential in building a successful career.

Admission

The Queen's M.B.A. for Science & Technology is designed for graduates in the science and engineering fields who have significant professional experience and the potential for continued career growth in management. Engineers, scientists, computer specialists, healthcare professionals, and entrepreneurs, among others, represent the professions of candidates chosen to participate.

Candidates for admission are required to have at least two years of full-time work experience; an undergraduate degree in health sciences, science, engineering, mathematics, or computer science; a minimum score of 600 on the Graduate Management Admission Test (GMAT); two personal evaluations; and a willingness and desire to actively participate in highly intensive interactive classes. After an initial review of all materials, an interview with an officer of the program is scheduled. A final evaluation is made by the admissions committee based on a wide range of criteria, including the candidate's experience and performance and potential to contribute to the group learning experience.

Finances

Proposed fees for the 2001–02 year are Can$37,500. This fee covers the full twelve months of the program and includes tuition, books, case materials, and all other instructional supplies that students need. In order to ensure broad access to this program, Queen's and the Royal Bank of Canada offer a tuition loan plan for individuals who are Canadian citizens or landed immigrants. The plan allows qualified students to borrow their full tuition fee and an extra Can$10,000 for living expenses. Queen's University covers the interest costs on the entire loan while the student is in the program and the interest on the tuition portion for up to six months after graduation or the student receives a job offer of at least Can$50,000 per year.

Application Facts and Dates

Applicants are encouraged to apply early, as enrollment is limited to a maximum of 60. Applications are reviewed on a rolling admissions basis. The deadline for submitting applications is December 1, 2000, for the session beginning in May 2001. For more information, students should contact:

M.B.A. for Science & Technology
School of Business
Queen's University
Kingston, Ontario K7L 3N6
Canada
Telephone: 613-533-2302
Fax: 613-533-6281
E-mail: admin@mbast.queensu.ca
World Wide Web: http://business.
queensu.ca/MBAst

QUINNIPIAC UNIVERSITY **Quinnipiac University**

School of Business

Hamden, Connecticut

INNOVATIVE BUSINESS EDUCATION

The challenges that face business today are to remain viable and competitive in a global economy. This is no simple task since we are all dealing with evolving technology and increasing diversification in the workforce. To meet these challenges one must be able to plan strategic management effectively and adapt efficiently in a changing business environment. The Quinnipiac University Master of Business Administration program will provide you with the tools required for successful business leadership in the twenty-first century.

The Master of Business Administration program at Quinnipiac University provides an innovative business education. Doctorally and professionally qualified faculty members interact with students in small classes and through student team projects. This educational process is provided in our state-of-the-art Lender School of Business Center.

The Quinnipiac M.B.A. program provides a superior learning opportunity through its responsive faculty members, talented students, and a dynamic state-of-the-art learning facility adjacent to a vital business community.

—Phillip B. Frese, Dean

Programs and Curricular Focus

The Master of Business Administration program at Quinnipiac University is designed to give students a practical, useful education that helps them achieve success in the business world. Students gain insight into business systems and theory and develop skills in independent thinking and problem solving. The ethics of business, strategic planning, policy development, and interpersonal communications are part of a student's curriculum. Graduates of Quinnipiac's M.B.A. program are equipped with the skills necessary to be action-oriented, hands-on managers in the twenty-first century.

All M.B.A. students must complete a 30-hour core curriculum that includes such classes as financial management, organizational theory, and quantitative decision analysis. A capstone course, the Integrative Management Seminar, is also part of the core. Students who enter the program without formal business training or academic experience may need to complete a series of introductory courses that provide the basic business educational foundation needed to complete the M.B.A. core curriculum.

Following completion of the core curriculum, students may opt for a 6-credit thesis program, involving research with a faculty adviser. This option requires 36 credits for graduation. Those pursuing thesis research develop a concentration in accounting/taxation, computer information systems, economics, finance, health ad-

ministration, international business, management, or marketing.

In lieu of a thesis, students may choose to take three additional courses that build on core subjects. These courses may focus on a specific concentration or cover multiple disciplines. This option requires 39 credit hours for graduation.

Students may apply for acceptance to both the Law School and the M.B.A. program and, upon completion of both programs, receive a J.D./M.B.A. degree. This specialized joint program shortens the length of time necessary to receive the degrees. There is an 18-credit overlap—9 credits in each program—that counts toward both degrees. M.B.A. students have a concentration in law. A thesis option is not available to participants in the joint program.

Qualified Quinnipiac undergraduate students planning to continue with graduate study immediately after completing their undergraduate studies are eligible to apply for a five-year B.S./M.B.A. This program is designed for outstanding undergraduates with an overall GPA of at least 3.0 who are majoring in business administration.

Part-time students can complete the M.B.A. program in three years, depending on the number of classes taken each semester and the length of the thesis project. A full-time degree program can be completed in as little as fifteen months.

Students and the M.B.A. Experience

Quinnipiac's diverse full- and part-time student body represents a rich mix of background and experience, ranging from mid- and top-level managers, beginning and veteran entrepreneurs, family and small-business owner-operators, and accomplished professionals seeking to develop business leadership competencies to recent baccalaureate recipients preparing to enter the business world. There are approximately 200 students enrolled in the M.B.A. program; 40 percent are women. The average age of students is 30 years. A small but significant number of international students are enrolled in the M.B.A. program, and the University has made a firm commitment to increase the diversity of the student body.

❖ Global Focus

Every curriculum area addresses the problems and challenges of doing business globally. An optional three-week summer session has taken M.B.A. students to Europe, Latin America, and Asia. This intensive experience includes seminars, comprehensive studies, lectures from corporate executives, and meetings with government officials.

The Faculty

Guiding Quinnipiac's M.B.A. program is a faculty with exceptional academic credentials and proven business experience. The University's 46 instructors hold doctorates or equivalent degrees from such prestigious institutions as Berkeley, Brown, Columbia, Harvard, New York University, Yale, and other leading institutions. Many have professional as well as academic backgrounds.

Although their first commitment is to teaching, Quinnipiac's faculty members are also active professionals, knowledgeable about the latest developments in their fields through consulting, leading executive seminars, research, publication, and attendance at conferences and workshops. Among their many areas of expertise are information systems, entrepreneurship, organizational development, fiscal policy, marketing, and competitive strategy.

The Business School Network

Quinnipiac University's School of Business has been one of the traditional strengths of the University for more than sixty years and has strong relationships with businesses and industry throughout the Northeast. Through Quinnipiac's professors and internship programs, the University maintains its network of connections with the business world. The School of Business has studied new markets in Japan for Connecticut companies and the economic impact of a regional airport, and consulted on health management programs in Central America and the Caribbean. The M.B.A. program also features a lecture series, which brings in prominent corporate executives who shape today's business issues.

Prominent Alumni

The 8,000 alumni of the School of Business have made their mark in a wide range of businesses. Graduates of Quinnipiac include Murray Lender, H. Lender & Sons Restaurants and M&M Investments; Paula Tomasetti, Vice President of Goldman Sachs & Company; Robert J. Hauser, CEO of Commonwealth Land Title Company; and Gabriel Ferrucci, President and CEO of Keystone Engineering Company.

The University and Environs

Founded in 1929, Quinnipiac is a private, nonsectarian, coeducational institution located in Hamden, Connecticut. The University offers a full range of undergraduate and graduate programs through the School of Health Sciences, the University for Adults, the School of Business, the School of Liberal Arts, and the School of Law. Quinnipiac College became Quinnipiac University as of July 1, 2000.

The mission of Quinnipiac University is the integration of liberal and professional studies. Quinnipiac guides its students toward the acquisition of knowledge both in the classroom and in all areas of student life, emphasizing critical and creative thinking, effective communication skills, and the ability to make informed value judgments. The special mission of the graduate programs is to provide professionals with the advanced competencies needed to assume leadership positions in their chosen fields.

Quinnipiac University's beautiful, safe central location in southern Connecticut, between New Haven and Hartford, is convenient to New York and Boston. It gives students access to numerous major corporations and science, health-care, and research facilities in the area. The campus itself—180 acres—features thirty-two modern buildings and eighteen impressive residence halls. Adjoining the campus is Sleeping Giant Mountain and State Park, with 20 miles of scenic hiking trails.

Facilities

The heart and home of the M.B.A. program is Quinnipiac's Lender School of Business Center, designed to accommodate the particular needs of graduate students. Local area network classrooms include monitors and keyboards at each desk plus line-of-sight contact with the discussion leader. Case rooms allow groups to work on business problems in lecture-discussions. Team study rooms provide a technologically advanced, learning-conducive environment in which to develop problem-solving strategies with classmates. A reading room features periodicals, access to databases, and CD-ROM stations.

Technology Environment

The Research Library provides M.B.A. students with access to such databases as ABI/INFORM, LEXIS-NEXIS, and the Business Periodicals Index on CD-ROM. A large library of the latest versions of software used by business and industry is available for student use. Online access to the Dialog database, as well as a comprehensive collection of business holdings in hard copy, is also available for all students.

Placement

Quinnipiac M.B.A. graduates currently hold top positions in such companies as United Technologies, Bayer Corporation, Aetna, and General Electric. On-campus recruiters visit Quinnipiac each year in search of prospective employees. Recruiters include four of the "big six" accounting firms, a division of NBC in New York, Pratt & Whitney, and other regional manufacturing firms, insurance companies, banks, pharmaceutical companies, health-care organizations, and state and federal government agencies. The University arranges job interviews for students, assists with preparation of resumes, and maintains an alumni network of potential job contacts for graduate students. Other placement services and resources available to students include career counseling/planning, career fairs on campus, and a career library. Most School of Business graduates find positions in their fields within three months of graduation.

Admission

Admission to the M.B.A. program at Quinnipiac University is competitive. Students seeking admission must have earned a baccalaureate degree in either a business or a nonbusiness field, have a minimum GPA of 2.5, and submit Graduate Management Admission Test (GMAT) scores to the University. Candidates who wish to interview prior to admission may arrange for an appointment with the director of the M.B.A. program.

The University utilizes a formula-based admission system as a primary application screening tool. This system, called "1000-combined," is helps admissions counselors determine a candidate's eligibility by multiplying a candidate's GPA by 200 and adding total GMAT scores to this sum to reach a minimum acceptable score of 1000. For example, a candidate with a 2.5 GPA would need a minimum GMAT score of 500 to be considered qualified for admission. The M.B.A. admissions committee does not consider GMAT scores of less than 400 acceptable for admission to the program. It should be noted that meeting these minimum standards does not guarantee admission. Work experience and recommendations are also strongly considered in the process.

Finances

For 2000–01, the tuition rate for all M.B.A. students is $430 per credit hour. Part-time students pay a $20 registration fee each semester. Full-time students are charged a student fee of $195 for access to the student health center and athletic facilities.

The University offers several types of financial aid to help both full- and part-time students fund their education. Most are supplementary to personal resources and include savings, employer tuition benefits, and other forms of assistance. Graduate assistantships are available on a limited basis to both full- and part-time students. M.B.A. candidates are eligible to apply for subsidized and unsubsidized Federal Stafford Student Loans. Students may also apply for privately sponsored commercial loan programs such as GradEXCEL, TERI, or Family Educational Loan Program (FELP).

Application Facts and Dates

Applications for the M.B.A. program are accepted throughout the year for both full- and part-time study. Candidates are encouraged to submit applications as early as possible to ensure consideration for the semester desired. A complete application consists of the following: an application form, a $45 application fee, GMAT scores, two recommendations, a recent resume, and transcripts of all undergraduate and graduate work completed. For more information, applicants should contact:

Mr. Scott Farber
Director of Graduate Admissions
Quinnipiac University
275 Mount Carmel Avenue
Hamden, Connecticut 06518-9936
Telephone: 203-582-8795
Fax: 203-582-3443
E-mail: graduate@quinnipiac.edu

Regent University

Virginia Beach, Virginia

CREATE, DESIGN, AND LEAD

Today's competitive marketplace demands the strategic and technical education that M.B.A. programs provide. But to really compete on the cutting edge, you must gain an understanding of people. With Regent University's M.B.A., you will gain not only first-rate business knowledge and skills, but also the vision, values, and people skills you need to lead organizations in the 21st century.

Regent is preparing Christian leaders to transform the global marketplace. Regent M.B.A. graduates are advancing in the largest global corporations; founding and running entrepreneurial ventures; and leading nonprofit organizations, government agencies, and church and para-church ministries worldwide.

We believe that God wants each of us to develop and use the gifts and abilities He has given us to make a difference in this world. That is why we have built our programs on three watchwords: **Create**: *create ideas that result in life-improving products and services,* **Design**: *design organizations that will thrive in the 21st century global marketplace, and* **Lead**: *lead people to perform at their peak and achieve results that have eternal value.*

—John Mulford, Ph.D., Dean

Programs and Curricular Focus

The School of Business offers three Master of Business Administration (M.B.A.) programs—the Executive M.B.A. (EMBA), the Professional M.B.A. (PMBA), the accelerated M.B.A. (AMBA, a full-time program), and the M.A. in management. Business students may earn their degrees on the main campus in Virginia Beach; at the Regent Graduate Center in Alexandria, Virginia; through distance learning; or through a combination of online/on-campus learning.

The curriculum integrates the functional areas of business: leadership, marketing, management, finance, human resources, accounting, and technology. Entrepreneurial by design, courses are team taught by experienced faculty members with a Christian perspective on leadership and management. Prospective students from all undergraduate disciplines are encouraged to apply.

The Executive M.B.A. (EMBA) is a twenty-month, 36-semester-credit program offered predominantly online. It is designed for fast-track executives with at least seven years of focused, professional experience.

The Professional M.B.A. (PMBA) is a twenty-eight-month, 48-semester-credit program offered online and on both campuses. It is designed for working business professionals with at least five years of experience.

The Accelerated M.B.A. (AMBA) is a full-time, 48-credit-hour program offered on the main campus (Virginia Beach) that can be completed in 20 months. This rigorous program combines classroom instruction, internships, and mentoring opportunities that give the recent undergraduate every advantage for launching a successful career.

M.B.A. tracks of specialization include e-business, organizational change and development, human resources management, entrepreneurship, financial planning, international business management, finance, management, marketing, and nonprofit management.

The M.A. in management allows students to individualize their course of study or choose one of the career specialization tracks offered in conjunction with the M.B.A. program. The 33-hour program takes twenty months to complete and is available at both campuses and online.

Students and the M.B.A. Experience

The approximately 350 Regent business students are diverse in religious, national, and ethnic origins. Thirty percent are women and 20 percent are members of minority groups. The average student age is 35. Approximately 62 percent of applicants are accepted.

Special Features

The Graduate School of Business provides its students with a "circle of service," which means that from the time they enroll, students will benefit from advocates and advisers, alumni mentors, and colleagues.

Individual career specializations can be crafted by selecting courses from Regent's seven other professional schools, which include law, communication, government, education, divinity, organizational leadership, and psychology. Joint degrees are also available, which enable a student to receive degrees from the Graduate School of Business and another Regent school in a reduced amount of time. Some frequently pursued joint degrees include the Juris Doctor (J.D.), Master of Education (M.Ed.), Master of Divinity (M.Div.), and Master of Arts in communication.

In addition to academic degree programs, the Graduate School of Business also offers Executive Education and Certification Programs. These programs are offered on campus and online in the nine M.B.A./M.A. career specializations and in areas that may be customized.

The Faculty

Challenging instruction is delivered by top-ranking faculty members with years of real-world experience. In addition to relevant theory, students will learn to incorporate Judeo-Christian values that have withstood the test of time. This integration underpins formal grounding in proven business practices.

The Business School Network

Regent University's Graduate School of Business hosts conferences that feature nationally and internationally known business leaders who are proponents of "servant leadership" in their business operations. Dynamic guests have included such notables as Zig Ziglar, Philip B. Crosby, Ken Melrose, Foster Friess, Bob Snelling, and Truett Cathy. Students are afforded opportunities to interact directly with these individuals in order to gain firsthand business information. There is also an Alumni Connection that networks students and alumni in key cities across the U.S. for placement and support.

Prominent Alumni

Prominent alumni work in key companies such as AG Edwards & Sons, Inc.; Allen Memorial Hospital; American Health Assistance Foundation; Andersen Consulting; Blue Cross and Blue Shield; Boeing Air-

craft; Chesapeake Fire Department; Christian Broadcasting Network; Christian Coalition; Coca-Cola, Poland; Compass Bank; Dominion Energy; E21, Inc.; Eastern Virginia Medical School; Enfield Care, Inc.; Fairmont General Hospital; First American National Bank; First National Supermarkets; Founders Inn and Conference Center; Franciscan University of Steubenville; Freedom Ford; General Electric Company; General Motors Corporation; GM Delphi Automotive Systems; Goodyear; Hudson Salvage; Inspirational Network; London Bridge Trading Company; Long and Foster Real Estate; Lyondell Petrochemical Company; Master Builder Association; Mercedes Benz Club of America; Metropolitan Life Insurance Co.; MidAmerican Energy Foundation; Nations Bank; Navy Acquisition Management; Norfolk State University; Palm Beach County Literacy Coalition; Penn State Heisinger Health Systems; Ron Blue Corporation; Salvation Army; Sandoz Pharmaceuticals; Sentara Healthcare; Smith, Barney and Shearson, Inc.; Southwestern Bell Wireless; Texaco; the Heritage Foundation; Turner Broadcasting Systems; United States Air Force; United States Army; University of Arizona; University of Indiana; University of Louisville; University of Virginia Law School; US Air Force; Virginia Natural Gas; Wendy's International; World Vision International.

The College and Environs

The main campus of Regent University is located in the resort city of Virginia Beach, Virginia, which has more than 20 miles of beaches. The campus is about 13 miles from the oceanfront. By car, Regent is about 1 hour from historic Williamsburg and 3½ hours from the nation's capitol. Regent University is a graduate institution offering twenty-five master's and doctoral

degrees from a Judeo-Christian worldview. Regent University's eight colleges and schools include business, communication, counseling, divinity, education, government, law, and organizational leadership. Seventeen graduate programs are offered through the Regent University Distance Education Program known as the Worldwide Campus.

The University Library maintains one of the most extensive and highly regarded electronic database systems in higher education. These databases are available to distance students as well as on-campus students.

Regent has a current enrollment of more than 2,200 students representing the fifty states and more than sixty countries. The University is accredited by the Southern Association of Colleges and Schools (SACS) Commission on Colleges (CC) (1866 Southern Lane, Decatur, Georgia 30033-4097; telephone: 800-248-7701 (toll-free)) to award the master's and doctoral degrees. The Regent University School of Law is fully accredited by the American Bar Association (A.B.A.).

Facilities

Located on a 700-acre complex in Virginia Beach, the Regent University campus is a fascinating study of Georgian architecture accented with arched windows and hand-hewn brick. Inside these walls, Regent University offers its students a technologically advanced educational environment. Regent is a pioneer in distance and online education, offering seventeen degree programs via the Internet, including the M.B.A. and the M.A. in management.

Placement

A Career Services Coordinator personally assists each student in his or her networking

and career development. Both national and international corporations interview M.B.A./ M.A. candidates on the Regent campus. The Graduate School of Business also maintains the Alumni Connection, which supports the career search efforts of Regent University students. In addition, the mentoring nature of the School provides individualized placement assistance and counseling throughout the student's program.

Admission

Admission to Regent University requires a bachelor's degree from a state and regionally accredited postsecondary institution. Applicants possessing earned degrees from nonaccredited institutions are considered on an individual basis.

All students are required to be computer literate and to have access to online services.

While each Regent school maintains specific admissions criteria, the following are considered universal: a cumulative undergraduate GPA of at least 2.75, maturity in spiritual and/or character qualities, and personal goals consistent with the mission and goals of Regent University. Beyond the GPA, consideration is given to the amount and type of business or military experience the applicant has attained since completing undergraduate studies. The GMAT is not required for admission but may be used for financial aid. Students seeking scholarships are encouraged to take the GMAT.

Finances

Tuition for the Executive M.B.A. is $24,900, the Professional M.B.A. tuition is $23,900, the Accelerated M.B.A. is $23,900, and the M.A. in management is $16,500. Students accepted for enrollment may apply for Federal Stafford Student Loans and a variety of school-specific scholarships and grants. DANTES and veteran's benefits also apply. Scholarships for military personnel are also available.

Application Facts and Dates

Application deadlines are eight weeks before the start of any given term. There is a $40 application fee. Forms may be downloaded from the Web site or obtained by mail. For more information, students should contact:
Regent University Graduate School
    of Business
1000 Regent University Drive
Virginia Beach, Virginia 23464-9800
Telephone: 800-373-5504 (toll-free)
Fax: 757-226-4381
E-mail: admissions@regent.edu
World Wide Web: http://www.regent.edu/
    business

Rensselaer Polytechnic Institute

Troy, New York

MANAGEMENT AND TECHNOLOGY M.B.A. AT RENSSELAER

The Lally School's mission is to educate technically sophisticated business leaders who are prepared to guide their organizations in the integration of technology for new products, new businesses, and new systems. The students apply the best classic and new economy business practices to bring technologies to market and to integrate technology in their business strategies.

—Joseph G. Ecker, Dean

Programs and Curricular Focus

The Lally School of Management and Technology offers degree programs that focus on the complexities of integrating technology into business strategies. Lally's programs prepare students to bring innovative technology to market through careers in e-business, MIS, technical entrepreneurship, finance, production and operations management, new product development and management, environmental management and policy, and manufacturing systems.

The Lally M.B.A. program is ideal for those who want a comprehensive business education with an eye on the strategic role of technology. It is a 20 course/60 credit sequence. A typical M.B.A. student's first year consists of ten required courses. All M.B.A. students start with a unique, year-long product development course in their first year entitled design, manufacturing and marketing. This multifunctional, team-based project results in the inception, design, and marketing of a new product or service.

Other first-year courses include information systems, organizational behavior, statistics and operations management, business economics, and financial management and valuation of firms. Many require team projects, consulting type-assignments from corporate partners, and experiential learning experiences.

The second year of the M.B.A. program is composed of 4 required and 6 elective courses. The required courses include a strategy sequence, business ethics, and an international option. Electives are tailored to the student's interests and career goals through courses at Lally or other Rensselaer departments.

The Lally School Master of Science in Management is a 10-course/30-credit focused, yet highly flexible, program. It

is well suited for those who have prior business experience and wish to build depth in a specific function.

The M.S. program requires 4 core management courses and 6 electives. The electives are chosen from Lally courses or other Rensselaer departments.

Entrepreneurship, in both small and large organizations, is a mainstream activity of Lally. *US News and World Report* consistently ranks the Lally Entrepreneurship program among the top 25 programs nationally. The Severino '69 Center for Technological Entrepreneurship, housed in the Lally School, offers an impressive array of programs including the Renssalaer Entrepreneur Internship Program, the Lucent Technologies Business Plan Competition, the Entrepreneur Club, and the Venture Bplan Series.

Management Information Systems remains one of the Lally School's strengths. This M.B.A. focus program integrates Lally's historical strengths in operations research and statistics with Rensselaer's technological preeminence in IT and computer science.

A new course concentration in e-business evaluates the impact of new technologies on business models, supply chain management, customer relationship management, and marketing.

Many Lally students pursue elective courses in other departments or even select a dual degree program, combining an M.S. in biology or computer science or an M.S. in engineering discipline with an M.B.A. This allows the students to assess business opportunities in emerging technologies, such as smart materials or biotechnology, while building their technical expertise in that area.

Students and the M.B.A. Experience

Small classes provide personal attention in a highly interactive exchange between students, faculty members, and guest speakers.

Lally's diverse student population brings a wide variety of educational and business perspectives. The program has approximately 40 percent international students, working professionals who are studying part-time, and Executive M.B.A.'s. The Graduate Management Student Association is active in social, career, and recreational activities, including Network International, intramural sports, and community service.

During the academic year, many students undertake projects with small companies on campus at The Rensselaer Incubator Center, or at nearby local firms.

Each year, several student teams enter projects in The Severino Center's Business Plan Competition, hoping for the chance to win seed stage capital, plus the opportunity to present to venture capitalists in Boston, New York, and/or California.

The Faculty

Lally's faculty members include experts in finance, computer applications, artificial intelligence, manufacturing, statistics, policy and strategy, international business, organizational design, product development, and marketing. Most full-time faculty members have substantial managerial experience in business or government.

The Business School Network

Lally's corporate partners provide curriculum feedback and connections through The Lally Advisory Board and Rensselaer's Key Executive Program and informally through many relationships with faculty and staff members. Students also access the alumni for mentoring relationships and career advice. Classes feature guest speakers and the Executive-in-Resident Program. The people and companies of Rensselaer's Incubator Program and the associated Technology Park, as well as the Capital Region Software Alliance, also tie into the Lally network.

The College and Environs

Rensselaer Polytechnic Institute is located in Troy, New York on a 260-acre hilltop campus overlooking the Hudson River. In the midst of a culturally rich population center surrounded by the Adirondack, Catskill, Berkshire, and Green mountains, the Rensselaer campus is only a few hours by car from Boston, New York City, and Montreal. The area is a major center for government, industrial, research, and academic activity.

A second campus in Hartford, Connecticut, also offers the M.S. Management and M.B.A. degrees.

Technology Environment

The Lally School is housed in the Pittsburgh Building on the Troy campus. It is fully wired for Internet access and has state-of-the-art computer and distance learning facilities. Bloomberg Data, Wharton Research Data Services, and Zachs Investment Research are all available.

Yahoo Internet Life has consistently ranked Rensselaer as one of the top ten most wired campuses in the U.S. Campus-wide, Rensselaer has more than 1,100 laptop connections, plus more than 375 PCs and UNIX based workstations. Students are encouraged to participate in activities in other schools and research centers on campus.

Placement

The Lally Career Resources Office provides a full range of services for full-time and summer positions. Students receive assistance with individualized job search strategies, interview skills, and marketing materials. First-year M.B.A. students are required to take The Craig '68 Leadership Skills Seminar to develop career and communication techniques.

Students also work with Rensselaer's central Career Development Center for on-campus interviews, corporate career days, and other services. Additional career related programs are offered through Rensselaer's award winning Archer Leadership Center.

Admission

The Lally School of Management and Technology places a high priority on building an intellectually and culturally diverse program. The School is committed to the professional development of women and minorities, and it seeks to maintain the strong international character of the student body. Applicants should have a degree in science or engineering, humanities, the arts, or business; possess quantitative skills; a strong interest in technology; and significant work experience, though each year a small number of outstanding recent college graduates from programs in science and engineering are considered for admission.

Applicants must take the Graduate Management Admissions Test (GMAT). Applicants whose native language is not English must also receive a minimum score of 600 on the TOEFL.

Finances

The Lally School and Rensselaer Polytechnic Institute makes every effort to assist qualified students in funding the costs related to seeking an advanced degree through merit based and other assistance (if applicable). The value of the Lally M.B.A program has proven to be a valuable and worthwhile investment made in education.

Tuition for 2000-01 is $700 per credit hour. Each graduate management course is three credits. Living expenses are estimated at $9500 per year.

Approximately 20 percent of full-time M.B.A. students receive a partial merit-based tuition scholarship. A limited number of Teaching Assistantship (TA) positions are available on a competitive basis during the second year of the M.B.A. program.

International students should contact Graduate Admissions, Rensselaer Admissions Office, 110 8th Street, Troy, New York 12180, (518) 276-6216, regarding financial support requirements and I-20 related issues.

Application Facts and Dates

Applications are accepted on a competitive, continual basis. Early submission is strongly encouraged. Full-time MBA students must begin their program in the fall semester while part-time M.B.A. students may begin in the fall, spring (mid-January), or summer (mid-May). M.S. students are encouraged to begin in a fall semester due to course sequencing.

The academic year for the full-time M.B.A. program begins in late August and ends in mid-May of the following year. Most students complete the full-time program in two years. A selection of courses is also offered in the summer for students who wish to accelerate, or who prefer to take fewer courses during the academic year. The schedule for the part-time program is flexible and can be tailored to the student's needs.

For best merit-based aid consideration, full-time M.B.A. students interested in scholarships and fellowships should submit their application, including all supporting credentials, by February 1. Part-time applicants should submit their application at least 2-4 weeks prior to matriculation.

An online application is available through Embark.com. To request an informational brochure and application, students should contact:

Director, M&T M.B.A. Program
Lally School of Management and Technology
Rensselaer Polytechnic Institute
Troy, New York 12180-3590
Telephone: 518-276-6586
Fax: 518-276-2665
E-mail: management@rpi.edu
World Wide Web: http://lallyschool.rpi.edu

Rice University

Houston, Texas

RICE M.B.A.: TURNING KNOWLEDGE INTO ACTION TO CREATE LEADERS

There was a time when earning an M.B.A. meant you had mastered the theories of finance and accounting. Today, classroom learning is only one aspect of a complete business education, and the scope of subjects has broadened immensely. In the era of rapid globalization, change is the only constant, and companies want more than good managers; they want great leaders who can resolve issues with a multidisciplinary approach.

At the Jones School, we have always considered judgment, leadership, and communication skills as important as leading-edge knowledge. But now, we are taking the learning experience one step further. After seeking input from faculty, students, and industry leaders—including top management at major corporations to determine which skills they consider most valuable—we have developed an innovative curriculum that builds on theory with an experiential learning process we call Action Learning. At Rice, you'll cultivate the tools you need to excel regardless of your chosen specialty, graduating with knowledge and confidence. We hope you'll join us!

—Gilbert R. Whitaker Jr., Dean

Programs and Curricular Focus

The Jones Graduate School has implemented an Action Learning Curriculum that is one of the few programs of its kind in the nation. The M.B.A. program combines three essential elements: a comprehensive and challenging core curriculum providing students with a solid foundation of basic business disciplines; a required Action Learning Project, a summer internship, and numerous field project–oriented electives offering ample opportunities for real-world practice; and a host of specialized electives allowing students to further integrate their knowledge and empower them to achieve their career objectives. All courses in the two-year full-time program are streamlined into flexible modules of five, ten, or fifteen weeks each. Managerial communication is integrated across the curriculum, with instruction in strategic communications and both team and individual coaching in oral and written communication.

Depending on the subject matter, faculty members utilize multiple instructional methods to enhance the learning process— case-method study, analytical and quantitative approaches, lectures and discussions, oral and written reports, theoretical studies, management simulation games, individual study, and teamwork.

The first-year core courses address a wide range of management subjects, including finance, accounting, data analysis, marketing, the global business environment, information technology, and organizational behavior. A sequence of modules on leadership and managerial skills includes influence tactics, navigating the political landscape, negotiating effectively, building partnerships, communicating with hostile audiences, when to partner, and when to compete.

Early in the spring semester, students complement their core courses with an elective designed to help them develop a specialty. During the final ten weeks, teams of students integrate the business disciplines they have studied into an Action Learning Project for a host company.

The second year includes core courses in entrepreneurship and strategy formulation and implementation. Students customize the remainder of their schedule with 25 credit hours of specialized electives from the Jones School's course offerings and/or upper-level courses from other Rice University departments.

The School offers two joint-degree options: an M.B.A./Master of Engineering with the Brown School of Engineering and an M.B.A./M.D. with Baylor College of Medicine.

Students and the M.B.A. Experience

A total of 291 M.B.A. students from all regions of the United States and twenty-three other countries were enrolled in 1999–2000. Thirty-eight percent had engineering or science backgrounds; 45 percent majored in business or economics. The mid-50 percent of the students had between 2½ and 7 years of work experience before entering the program. The average age was 28. Women comprise 30 percent of the student body; international students, 20 percent; and members of minority groups, 15 percent.

Courses are sectioned to keep the class size to no more than 50 students, thus promoting greater classroom participation and contact with faculty members.

The Faculty

The faculty maintains an important balance between teaching and research, believing that current industry knowledge is as critical as textbooks to education. All of the School's instructors are either academics with significant business or consulting experience or business executives with significant classroom experience who teach specialized elective courses. With a student-faculty ratio of 9:1, students have opportunities to work closely with their instructors. Faculty members are interested in the students' career goals as well as their academic abilities and are willing to spend extra time helping students develop knowledge and skills.

The Business School Network

The Jones School maintains close ties with the business community through its Council of Overseers, a group of distinguished executives who advise the School on its focus and direction, and the Dean's Lecture series, in which business leaders discuss topics of their choice with students. All students spend the last five weeks of their first year working full-time on site to solve a specific problem for a Houston-area company. Many elective courses also include field projects that give students real-world experience with area businesses. In addition, alumni return to the School to advise students on career choices, serve on stand-

Lovett Hall, Rice University's administration building and one of its original structures.

ing committees, and recruit students for summer internships and permanent positions.

The College and Environs

Rice University, a private, nonsectarian, coeducational institution, admitted its first students in 1912. The Jones School is one of seven academic units offering undergraduate and graduate studies in management, architecture, natural science, engineering, social science, music, and humanities. Rice, which has the tenth-largest endowment of any university in the country, deliberately keeps its enrollment relatively small; the student body of 4,100 includes 1,400 graduate students. The low student-faculty ratio ensures that students receive individual attention from their professors.

The University is situated on a beautiful 300-acre tree-lined campus in one of Houston's finest residential districts yet is only 3 miles from the city center and is adjacent to the world-renowned Texas Medical Center. The nation's fourth-largest city, Houston has the third-largest concentration of Fortune 500 corporate headquarters and is also an operating center for more than half of the world's largest non-U.S.-based corporations. Among the growth industries in the city's well-diversified economy are finance, high technology, engineering/ design services, energy, and health-care services. Houston's symphony, ballet, grand opera, and repertory theater are nationally known performing arts organizations. Sports fans enjoy a variety of professional and collegiate teams.

Facilities

The Business Information Center has online capabilities and subscribes to various compact-disc services that provide financial and bibliographic information. Students also have access to the University research and depository library, which contains 1.9 million volumes, 2.4 million microforms, 12,000 current serials and periodicals, and 83,000 titles on audio and video tapes and compact discs. Students can access the Internet, exchange files, and send and receive e-mail from home or from various locations within the School. Several classrooms contain state-of-the-art projection systems equipped with personal computers and VCRs.

Placement

The Career Planning Center provides instruction in resume and cover letter writing, job interviewing techniques, and use of the School's online, compact disc, and paper sources of company and industry information. Alumni help students sharpen their skills by participating in mock interviews and career panels. Students are actively assisted in finding summer internships between the first and second years. In addition to a full schedule of on-campus recruiting, graduating students also have access to companies that attend the M.B.A. Consortium event in Atlanta and, for international students, similar events in Miami and Orlando. An additional source of contacts for summer internships is the New York M.B.A. Consortium event, which attracts students interested in finance and consulting.

Admission

Admitted for the fall semester only, applicants must submit essays, three recommendations, and transcripts from all universities attended. GMAT scores are required of all M.B.A. applicants, and TOEFL scores are required of applicants whose native language is not English unless an applicant received an undergraduate degree from a U.S. university. Applicants to the joint M.B.A./Master of Engineering program must submit scores from the GRE rather than the GMAT; applicants to the joint M.B.A./M.D. program must submit scores from the MCAT. Candidates are evaluated on their academic records, leadership potential, motivation to succeed, and professional work experience. Personal interviews are strongly recommended.

Finances

Annual tuition for 2000–01 is $19,700. Other estimated annual costs include living expenses, $10,000 (single); books, $1100; fees, $550; and health insurance, about $600. A laptop computer is given to each incoming student. A limited number of scholarships (partial remission of tuition) are available; loan funds are available to those who demonstrate need. Only U.S. citizens are eligible for scholarships and loans. The deadline for loan applications is June 1.

Application Facts and Dates

The deadlines for completed applications are December 1, February 1, and April 16; prospective students are advised to submit their applications by February 1 at the latest, since most admissions decisions are made in the first two rounds. Admissions decisions are mailed within the six weeks following each deadline. For further information, students should contact:

Mr. Peter Vevuki
Executive Director of Admissions
   Career Planning
Jesse H. Jones Graduate School of
   Management - MS 531
Rice University
6100 Main Street
Houston, Texas 77005-1892
Telephone: 888-844-4773 (toll-free)
Fax: 713-348-6147
E-mail: enterjgs@rice.edu
World Wide Web: http://www.rice.edu/
   jgs

Richmond, The American International University in London

London, United Kingdom

> ## THE RICHMOND M.B.A. PROGRAM EXPERIENCE
>
> *In the Richmond M.B.A. Program, you will exchange ideas and experience a lively community with colleagues from many countries. Discussions and case studies will build upon this natural laboratory of experience and ideas. You will also have the opportunity to use up-to-date information technology to analyze complex problems and communicate effectively. Students make use of the remarkable business and cultural resources of London, one of the most exciting cities in the world.*
>
> *Completing the Richmond M.B.A. will make you a better manager. The most distinctive feature of our program that ensures this result is our faculty, representing academic excellence and business experience. Both faculty members and students are drawn from an international background, with our 100 students representing more than thirty-five countries in a balanced mix of cultures, creating a highly interactive environment.*
>
> *Welcome to the most formative period in your business life.*
>
> —Dr. Jean LeFebvre, Dean

The Kensington campus.

Programs and Curricular Focus

The Richmond M.B.A. program is an intensive twelve-month program designed to develop strong management skills for international practitioners. Richmond is the oldest and largest American university in Britain and provides a broad American-style university education. The curriculum is based on the modular approach of individual courses and workshops taken over four quarters. There are two points of entry per year: January and September.

The Richmond M.B.A. has all the hallmarks of best practice in management education: experiential learning, modularity, credit for prior achievement, and a truly international focus across the curriculum. Students may specialize in general management, international finance, or international marketing. In addition, students are given specialized, practical training in skills that increase a manager's effectiveness, such as business software applications, business plan development, report writing, oral presentations, and time management.

Students and the M.B.A. Experience

Richmond strongly believes that each participant is a key source of learning for other participants in the program. The student body consists of approximately 100 students, with an average age of 26, who represent more than thirty-five countries. Each student brings a unique

perspective and background to the program with their work experience in accounting, business, commerce, economics, engineering, humanities, law, mathematics, and science.

Special Features

The Richmond M.B.A. features a Field Experience Program to help students practice what they learn throughout their course of study. Some students work as project managers in an internship program; others work with a company to develop business expansion plans. These projects are relevant to the student's interests and are usually located in London.

Richmond has built strong relationships with companies over the years. Field Experience partners include the American Chamber of Commerce in London, Bank of America, British Airways, Citibank, Coopers & Lybrand, Data General, the European Office of Trade and Investment, Glaxo Wellcome, John Laing Construction, Merrill Lynch, Radisson Edwardian Hotels, the Sony Corporation, and Visa International.

The Faculty

M.B.A. participants receive a high degree of personal attention at Richmond, with an average class size of 20. To teach culturally diverse students with a new and ever-changing management perspective, Richmond has recruited an internationally

oriented, multicultural, and highly qualified faculty. Students benefit from the experience of senior practicing managers with full-time and visiting fellows from Africa, Asia, Europe, and North America. The faculty members encourage students through the application of extensive case study analysis, proactive discussions, and constant group and teamwork activities.

The Business School Network

Local and international business leaders also take part in this network as University guests to discuss current business trends and developments with students. In training new leaders for today's changing organizations, Richmond feels there is no better way for a school to impart the knowledge of leadership than by asking corporate customers what they look for in M.B.A. graduates that will make them effective leaders.

The College and Environs

One of the management, financial, and marketing centers of the world, London is clearly the right place to be. Richmond is a center of academic excellence that provides postgraduate and undergraduate studies in a broad range of disciplines to more than 1,000 students. Richmond's two campuses are located in Richmond and the central London area of Kensington. The M.B.A. program, housed at the Kensington site, combines a metropolitan location with its library and computer

The Richmond Hill campus.

laboratories, as well as student and faculty facilities, to provide an excellent base for M.B.A. studies.

Students' leisure time is enriched by activities of local theater, shared athletic facilities, and the entertainment opportunities provided by one of the world's leading cities. Kensington is within easy walking distance of the Royal Albert Hall, Hyde Park, the Royal Colleges of Music and Art, the Victoria and Albert Museum, Imperial College of Science and Technology, the Museum of Natural History, and many theaters, restaurants, and department stores.

Placement

The Internship Office provides assistance to students in clarifying their career goals for appropriate placement for the internship and seeks to match students' skills with company needs for the internship placement. Richmond M.B.A. graduates are internationally recognized

as a select group of professional managers, and they are recruited by leading companies to take on challenging roles on a global level.

Admission

Each application is evaluated based on the individual merits of the student. The Graduate Admissions Committee looks for a balance among the following criteria: management potential, intellectual ability, academic and professional references, and work experience. In addition, students whose native language is not English must demonstrate, from examination results and written statements, full command of spoken and written English. Candidates are required to have a bachelor's degree or equivalent from a university or polytechnic or similar institute of higher learning and a grade average of at least a B or its equivalent. The GMAT is highly recommended for all applicants with little work experience and those who need to strengthen their academic qualifications.

Nonnative speakers of English must achieve high scores on standard English exams, such as the TOEFL or IELTS.

Finances

Fees for the year beginning in September 2000 and ending August 2001 are £14,960. These charges include all tuition and fees, including participation in the Field Experience program. The University provides housing for graduate students in single rooms on a limited, first-come, first-served basis. From September 15, the cost is £6375 for fifty-one weeks, excluding meals.

Application Facts and Dates

Richmond has a rolling admissions policy, but applications should be received no later than December 15 for January admission or August 20 for September admission. Candidates receive notification of the Admission Committee's decision approximately three weeks after the submission of a full application package. For more information, applicants should contact:

Office of Graduate Admissions
Richmond, The American International
University in London
16 Young Street
London W8 5EH
England
Telephone: 44-0-20-7368-8475
Fax: 44-0-20-7376-0836
E-mail: grad@richmond.ac.uk
World Wide Web: http://www.
richmond.ac.uk

Applicants in the United States or
Canada may contact the Boston
Admissions Office:

U.S.A. Office of Admissions
Richmond, The American International
University in London
19 Bay State Road
Boston, Massachusetts 02215
Telephone: 617-954-9942
Fax: 617-236-4703
World Wide Web: http://www.
richmond.ac.uk

Robert Morris College

Moon Township, Pennsylvania

AN INVITATION FROM THE DEAN

Contemporary, exciting, connected, personal education is the hallmark of the Robert Morris College (RMC) M.B.A. Building on relationships with the business and not-for-profit communities, RMC's high-quality faculty members partner with students to develop real-time solutions to actual management problems. The value of our approach is demonstrated by an extensive alumni network and very high placement rates. Designed to meet the needs of the working adult, our program facilitates time to completion and flexibility through customized study plans. Emphasizing continuous improvement, the faculty members of RMC actively interact with organizations throughout the region to learn about and develop cutting-edge experiential education. We welcome your interest in Robert Morris College and invite you to our state-of-the-art facilities for a personal visit with our attentive faculty and staff members.

—Richard Stolz, Dean, School of Business

Programs and Curricular Focus

The School of Business at Robert Morris College offers a highly respected M.B.A. program that is one of the most sought after and flexible degree programs in the region. This intensive part-time program provides value-added education primarily to mid-level, mid-career managers who are seeking professional advancement. The 36-unit, twelve-course M.B.A. program is designed to challenge and stimulate the working professional through a curriculum that stresses continuous professional improvement based in current best practices, thereby providing employers with knowledgeable workers capable of moving the organization forward.

Courses, scheduled one night a week, are delivered in intensive eight-week sessions. This format allows students to complete two 3-unit courses during the fall and spring semesters and one 3-unit course during the summer semester, for a total of five courses per year. At this pace, a student can complete the M.B.A. program in twenty-eight months. Students may also select to accelerate or decelerate their pace through the program as workload and personal life needs change. A Saturday option is also offered.

The Robert Morris College M.B.A. model is divided into three phases. These phases provide foundational course material in phase I, examine the specific internal needs of organizations in phase II, and promote the customization of the students' programs to support specialty

areas in phase III. To provide the students with maximum opportunities to customize their programs to meet their professional needs, phase III has three options for completion. Option 3 is the General M.B.A., in which the student may mix three graduate-level courses from accounting, finance, marketing, sport management, and computer information systems. Option 2 is the M.B.A. with a specialization. The student may take three courses in one discipline; that is, three courses in accounting or finance or marketing or sport management or computer information systems. Option 1, the M.B.A. with the experiential learning experience, is a contractually based partnership between a student, employer, and faculty member. It requires identification of a researchable problem; the development of a proposal, including a methodology to guide the investigation; and the implementation of the proposal, complete with a report and presentation to the faculty, peers, and the employer.

Students and the M.B.A. Experience

Students who enroll in the Robert Morris College M.B.A. program are, typically, proven middle-level professionals who desire to make a larger impact on their company or organization. This program does not preclude senior-level professionals from enrolling and gaining additional insight in a specific specialization program, and it is ideal for students who

do not have undergraduate degrees in business and who seek to advance in management-level positions.

Because of the flexible format, students come from Pennsylvania, Ohio, West Virginia, and Maryland to participate in the program. With the College's commitment to online education, this program could become available through distance learning for students throughout the world.

Students learn in a very contemporary, interactive style. Professors rely on their professional experience and encourage team projects throughout the program. This style of learning, coupled with the diversity of the students, makes this a very attractive and distinctive M.B.A. program.

There are a total of 651 students in the program; all are part-time. The average age of an M.B.A. student is 32. Most of the students have a minimum of five years of professional experience, and women comprise nearly half of the student body. In fall 1998, the average GPA of entering students was 3.09, and the average GMAT score was 462.

Professionally, students come from diverse professional backgrounds. Accountants, bankers, computer and information specialists, communicators, educators, lawyers, and marketers are common professionals in the Robert Morris College M.B.A. program.

The Faculty

Each faculty member brings expertise in teaching and in the chosen field of study. This experience brings a great measure of wisdom into each course, giving the students a clearer and rewarding experience. The M.B.A. faculty has experience in multiple disciplines, including banking, consulting, management, and marketing.

The Business School Network

At the heart of the Robert Morris College M.B.A. program are the close-knit ties to the business and corporate communities throughout the northeast region of the United States. Robert Morris College brings a real-world approach to the educational process through gifted faculty members, a strong curriculum, and an

intense and rewarding internship program for all M.B.A. candidates.

The College hosts an annual career fair for its students, which has been embraced by many national business leaders who come to the Moon Township campus to recruit both undergraduate and graduate students. In addition, nearly 20,000 college alumni work and live throughout the western Pennsylvania region, giving each graduate a valuable resource to network. The College also has a very active career development office that has had a placement rate of nearly 98 percent over the past decade.

The College and Environs

Robert Morris College, founded in 1921, is a four-year private institution offering more than thirty-five undergraduate degrees, ten master's programs, and doctor of science degree in information systems and communication. The College has two strategic campuses to meet the needs of its student body. The main campus rests upon 230 acres in suburban Moon Township, 17 miles from downtown Pittsburgh and just a 5-minute drive from Pittsburgh International Airport. The second campus is located in the heart of Pittsburgh's golden triangle and the city's metropolitan area, the site of the nation's eleventh-largest concentration of Fortune 500 corporate headquarters. Satellite locations throughout the Pittsburgh region also host the M.B.A. program.

Facilities

State-of-the-art computer facilities are available for students at both campus locations. The Moon Township campus is the home of the Learning Resource Center, which provides a variety of learning facilities, including the traditional library with more than 130,000 bound volumes, 330,000 items on microfilm, and 950 current periodical subscriptions. The library also houses an extensive tax library and specializes in business information and materials.

Students also find plenty of residential living opportunities around both campuses. The Moon Township campus presently has nine residence halls that house approximately 1,000 students, and development is currently under way for the construction of a new town-house complex. There are adequate residential housing options in Pittsburgh for students who desire to take their M.B.A. course work in downtown Pittsburgh Center.

Placement

The Office of Career Services provides career advising, a comprehensive on-campus recruiting program, resume referral service, and resources to support the job search. More than 200 local, national, and international employers visit Robert Morris College annually to recruit students. Over the past decade, approximately 98 percent of Robert Morris College graduates have gained employment following graduation.

Admission

Students who are interested in studying in the Robert Morris College M.B.A. program must submit official undergraduate transcripts, two letters of recommendation, and an official GMAT score to the office of enrollment services.

Finances

Tuition is $387 per credit, with a $17 college fee per credit, for the 2000–01 academic year. Financial aid is available in the forms of student loans and graduate assistantships. A limited number of graduate assistantships are available for highly qualified applicants. These assistantships consist of a partial tuition waiver and, possibly, a stipend in exchange for work in a variety of College office settings. Financial aid is not available for international students.

International Students

The College has a growing international student community at the undergraduate and graduate levels. Two percent of Robert Morris College students are international students. Robert Morris College's International Student Organization exists to assist international students with their personal and academic adjustments, and the College also offers counseling and support services for each international student.

Application Facts and Dates

With a rolling admission structure, students are encouraged to submit their application and $35 application fee as early as possible. Consideration for entrance into the M.B.A. program is given to each student until the start of the academic year. Students may also enter the program at midterm in the fall and spring semesters if all entrance requirements are met.

International students must have a minimum TOEFL score of 500 and proof of adequate funds to apply.

For additional information and requirements for application, students should contact:

Kellie Laurenzi, Director of
  Enrollment Services
Robert Morris College
881 Narrows Run Road
Moon Township, Pennsylvania 15108
Telephone: 412-262-8235
  800-762-0097 (toll-free)
Fax: 412-299-2425
E-mail: laurenzi@robert-morris.edu
World Wide Web: http://www.robert-morris.edu

R·I·T Rochester Institute of Technology

Rochester, New York

LEADERSHIP IN MANAGEMENT EDUCATION

Today's business environment requires leaders and managers attuned to rapid changes in technology and vigorous global competition. RIT College of Business students are educated to excel in this exhilarating, yet demanding, new environment.

You'll notice a real difference in our classrooms. The classrooms are small and diverse, allowing for personalized attention to students as they learn business theory and how it applies to pragmatic business decision making. Students acquire a solid grounding in all the functional areas of business, with emphasis on an international perspective, quality management, and an in-depth understanding of the latest technologies.

The Rochester Institute of Technology College of Business has earned a national reputation for its commitment to innovative learning programs. Join us. I believe it will be the first in a lifelong series of strategically sound business decisions.

—Dr. Thomas D. Hopkins, Dean

Programs and Curricular Focus

The Master of Business Administration (M.B.A.) program provides students with a rigorous, interdisciplinary education preparing them for the challenges of the global environment. An emphasis on technology, a commitment to quality, and a global perspective are the foundations upon which the program is built.

Industry leaders look for employees with comprehensive backgrounds who can integrate an area of specialization with other functional areas of business. Rochester Institute of Technology (RIT) emphasizes that approach. The curriculum begins with a solid, mainstream grounding in all the functional areas of business and combines that foundation with the flexibility that allows students to specialize in one or two areas of expertise. In the classroom, students find a balanced approach between the theoretical and the applied, with an emphasis on concepts, skills, and techniques that are immediately applicable to the workplace.

The M.B.A. curriculum consists of eighteen courses, with eight devoted to core functional areas and ten available for concentration areas and electives. All courses carry 4 credit hours. The academic year is divided into four quarters of eleven weeks each. Students create a concentration field of study by selecting a four-course sequence in a particular area. Students have the option

of a second field of concentration, leaving two open electives.

Traditional business concentrations include public and corporate accounting, finance, health systems administration, human resource management, international business, management and leadership, marketing and sales management, marketing research, and quality and organizational improvement.

A major benefit of earning an M.B.A. at RIT is the number of resources and courses in highly specialized technologies. Technical concentrations include management information systems, manufacturing management, quality and applied statistics, technology management, computer-integrated technology, engineering management, quantitative decision making, software development, and telecommunications.

The College of Business also offers two other master's degree programs. The M.S. in finance degree program is designed to create financial professionals who can adapt to the dynamic changes and growth in financial industry. The M.S. in manufacturing management and leadership is a degree program offered jointly by the Colleges of Business and Engineering. The program is designed to educate graduates to lead manufacturing teams and organizations in a global economy. The College of Business is accredited by AACSB–The International Association for Management Education.

Students and the M.B.A. Experience

Students in the College of Business come from diverse backgrounds and a variety of work experiences. The average student is 29 years old with four years of full-time professional work experience. Students without work experience are encouraged to participate in RIT's cooperative education program. International students comprise one quarter of the student population, and women make up 40 percent of the M.B.A population.

Approximately one third of RIT's M.B.A students have technical undergraduate degrees, 40 percent have degrees in business administration, and the remaining have degrees in social science, the arts, and humanities.

❖ Global Focus

Succeeding in the global marketplace demands a keen understanding of the cultures and business practices of other countries. The College of Business curriculum combines international business theory and practice, using academic courses and corporate research projects. Through interactions with RIT faculty members, enrollment in courses at the Prague campus, or completion of courses in international business at the College of Business, M.B.A. students are able to fully understand the demands of leading and managing in a dynamic global environment.

In 1989, RIT established the U.S. Business School in Prague. Every year RIT grants M.B.A. degrees to 30 students from the Czech Republic and other Eastern European countries.

The Faculty

The College of Business faculty members have integrated a high-quality approach to education, combining business theory with hands-on application in the classroom. The faculty members are totally committed to scholarship, teaching, and service to the community. They continually update their knowledge of the business environment by outside consulting for multinational corporations and government agencies, bringing a unique

The Max Lowenthal Building houses the College of Business.

perspective into the classroom. More than 95 percent have doctoral degrees in their field of study.

The Business School Network

The College of Business maintains extensive relationships with industry. In additional to faculty business and government consulting, the College sponsors the Council on the College of Business, which is composed of prominent industry leaders from around the country who advise the College on strategic issues. The College of Business was among a few elite schools chosen to receive the Motorola University Challenge Award and the IBM Total Quality Management Competition, receiving a $1.28-million grant to integrate quality into the curriculum.

The College and Environs

Founded in 1829, RIT is a privately endowed university situated on 1,400 acres of beautiful rolling suburban land. RIT enrolls more than 13,000 students in its seven colleges. The College of Business has been serving the community for more than seventy years and currently has 14,500 alumni located in all fifty states and in thirty-eight countries throughout the world.

Rochester, New York, is a stimulating and inventive metropolitan community of more than 1 million people. The community is known as "The World's Image Centre" ® due to its unique imaging history and the vast number of businesses engaged in some aspect of imaging technology, service, or products.

Located on Lake Ontario, Rochester offers numerous employment, cultural, and recreational resources for RIT graduate business students and their families. Home to professional hockey,

soccer, and baseball teams, the city also has attractive parks, exciting museums, and an array of institutions for the performing arts.

Technology Environment

RIT is a national leader in incorporating computer and network technology into the classroom. Students have access to extensive computer resources in the College of Business and throughout the campus. RIT is committed to providing students with access to the latest computer technology and to the same business and productivity software used at leading multinational companies worldwide.

The College of Business has recently established the Technology Management Center. The center has initially defined three areas of focus: information technology management, new product development, and science and technology policy. Applied research and outreach projects will be the hallmark of the center. The center is also in the process of developing affiliate programs and sponsorship of seminars and focused conferences, launching a dedicated Web site, and mentoring various student-centered activities.

Placement

Professional career counselors in the Office of Cooperative Education and Career Services offer an array of services for graduate business students, including resume preparation, interviewing techniques, job-search strategies, and individual counseling. They provide critical job leads in addition to coordinating the campus recruiting visits of hundreds of employers each year.

RIT's educational philosophy emphasizes both theory and the practical

application of theories. This dual emphasis is prized by employers and offers graduates upward career mobility and the flexibility for changes in career direction.

Admission

Admission to the M.B.A. program is granted to promising graduates of accredited baccalaureate degree programs. Transcripts, a Graduate Management Admission Test (GMAT) score, relevant professional experience, a personal statement, and recommendations are evaluated by the Graduate Admissions Committee. International applicants must submit the results of the Test of English as a Foreign Language (TOEFL) as part of the application process. The TOEFL requirement is waived for native speakers of English and for those submitting transcripts and diplomas from American undergraduate schools.

Finances

Tuition and fees for the 2000–01 academic year are $20,102 plus $153 for the student activity fee. Books and supplies cost approximately $1500 per year.

Scholarships and assistantships are available. These awards are based on academic merit.

International Students

Twenty-four percent of the graduate students are international, coming from countries in Asia, the Pacific Rim, Eastern and Western Europe, Africa, and Central and South America. These students bring a unique perspective to the classroom, thereby enhancing the understanding of various worldwide cultures.

Application Facts and Dates

Operating on the quarter system, RIT utilizes a rolling admission process. Students are accepted for entry into the M.B.A. program in the fall, winter, spring, and summer. Application for admission should be on file at least five weeks prior to the start of the quarter. For more information, students should contact:

Graduate Business Programs Office
College of Business
Rochester Institute of Technology
105 Lomb Memorial Drive
Rochester, New York 14623-5608
Telephone: 716-475-6221
E-mail: gradbus@rit.edu
World Wide Web: http://www.cob.rit.edu

Rollins College

Winter Park/Orlando, Florida

TAKING THE LEAD

▶ *Students seek an M.B.A. not only to increase their base of knowledge but also to enhance their career opportunities. By pursuing an M.B.A. degree, they are taking the lead in managing their own futures. Similarly, the Crummer School has taken the lead in graduate management study by developing its curriculum into four M.B.A. programs that meet the needs of today's students. Depending on your academic and professional background, the Crummer School has an M.B.A. program that suits you, and I encourage you to learn more about these innovative opportunities.*

—Edward A. Moses, Dean and Barnett Banks Professor of Finance

Programs and Curricular Focus

The Crummer School offers four M.B.A. programs. Each is designed to provide a general management education with the opportunity to earn a concentration in a chosen business discipline through selection of the elective courses.

The Accelerated M.B.A. (AMBA) Program is a full-time, one-year program for students with at least three years of significant work experience. It is an intensive 54-credit-hour curriculum that includes an international study trip.

The Early Advantage M.B.A. (EAMBA) Program is a traditional full-time, two-year program for recent college graduates. This 62-credit-hour program places special emphasis on career development and includes an international study trip.

The Professional M.B.A. (PMBA) Program is a thirty-two-month evening program designed for working professionals. The 50-credit-hour lock-step curriculum offers two classes each week.

The Executive M.B.A. (EMBA) Program is a nineteen-month program for experienced managers. Classes meet on alternating Fridays and Saturdays, all day, and the 50-credit-hour curriculum includes an international study trip.

Students and the M.B.A. Experience

The Crummer School enrolls 50 AMBA students, 60 EAMBA students, 70 PMBA students, and 30 EMBA students each year. As a result of the lock-step format, more than 90 percent of the matriculated students graduate each year.

Crummer classes average 25 percent international students (full-time only) and 35 percent women. Approximately one third of Crummer students have business undergraduate degrees; other disciplines include engineering, humanities, computer science, and the social sciences.

❖ Global Focus

Each Crummer student completes a required international business course as part of the core curriculum. In addition, all EAMBA, AMBA, and EMBA students complete an international study trip as part of their core sequence.

The Crummer School offers all students the opportunity to choose a Global Business Practicum elective. Students work with an actual company with operations overseas to solve a business problem. After conducting research on campus, students travel overseas to meet with business executives and employees to study the problem in person. The students then present their analyses, recommendations, and suggestions for implementation to the company and the professor.

Special Features

The Crummer School provides each student with a notebook computer upon enrollment. The computer is used extensively both in and out of the classroom for spreadsheet and database development, presentation graphics, and online research. Students also use the Internet extensively for research and communication via e-mail.

In addition, the Crummer School is one of only twenty-seven schools accredited by the AACSB–The International Association for Management

Education at the graduate level only. This means that all of the School's facilities, career development services, and faculty members are devoted exclusively to M.B.A. students.

The Faculty

The Crummer School hires only experienced faculty members with proven track records and doctorate degrees. Because of the integrative nature of the Crummer curriculum, faculty members work closely together to ensure that each class builds upon the others, thereby avoiding a redundancy of material and creating an interdisciplinary approach to education.

Class sizes are kept intentionally small so that faculty-student interaction is high. Because all faculty member offices are located in the Crummer building and are readily accessible by e-mail, communication with them is convenient and frequent.

In addition to their teaching experience, faculty members maintain close ties with the business community through consulting work and research. This brings the theoretical material to life in the classroom and encourages immediate application of the course material.

The Business School Network

Corporate Partnerships

Because of its location in one of the nation's fastest-growing business communities, the Crummer School has forged ties with business leaders from a variety of industries. These relationships result not only in financial support in the form of scholarships and resources but also provide Crummer students with role models in the Crummer Mentor Program and in the career development process. These relationships also provide members of the Crummer faculty and administration with crucial insight into the skills that companies seek from M.B.A. graduates.

Prominent Alumni

Crummer alumni have risen to the top in a variety of industries throughout the world. Companies such as Johnson & Johnson, Walt Disney World, and BellSouth have Crummer graduates at the helm.

The College and Environs

As the oldest university in the state of Florida, Rollins College carries a long history of providing excellent liberal arts education. Located in the charming city of Winter Park, the small, private college is just 5 miles from downtown Orlando, a booming business community. In addition to the well-known theme park attractions, the Orlando area is home to many international headquarters, including Harris Corporation, AAA, Tupperware, and Lockheed Martin.

Facilities

Crummer Hall houses all Crummer classrooms as well as all faculty and administrative offices. The executive-style classrooms feature state-of-the-art projection equipment and LAN access. The career development area is an elegant location for recruiters to interview Crummer students. The building also features a student lounge, study rooms, and a computer lab.

Technology Environment

The Crummer School's focus on state-of-the-art technology has positioned it to launch its latest concentration in electronic commerce. MBA students can take courses in electronic commerce, Internet marketing, ERP for accounting systems or supply chain systems, telecommunications, database decision making, Internet languages, and cyberspace law.

Placement

The career development services at the Crummer School are devoted exclusively to graduate students. All full-time students complete a career development course as part of their curriculum. In addition, one-on-one counseling, business seminars, corporate information sessions, videotaped mock interviews, and extensive on- and off-campus interviewing schedules are available.

As a founding member of the M.B.A. Consortium of fifteen top business schools, the Crummer School offers students the opportunity to travel to New York and Atlanta each year to interview with numerous corporate recruiters.

Admission

The Crummer School evaluates each candidate on an individual basis, seeking a balance among the various application criteria. Each applicant to the Crummer School is required to submit a formal application, an application fee, a score on the Graduate Management Admission Test (GMAT), all undergraduate and graduate transcripts, and two to three letters of recommendation. Work experience is evaluated for all but the EAMBA Program.

The average full-time student enters the program with a 3.2 undergraduate GPA and a 595 on the GMAT. Average work experience for the AMBA Program is seven years.

The Crummer School invites international applicants with a completed bachelor's degree, a score on the TOEFL, and proof of financial support.

Finances

Total tuition is $33,600 ($11,200 a term) for the Accelerated M.B.A. Program; $42,000 ($10,500 a term) for the Early Advantage M.B.A. Program; $32,800 ($4100 a term) for the Professional M.B.A. Program; and $41,700 ($5212 a term) for the Executive M.B.A. Program. All tuition costs include the notebook computer, and tuition for the EAMBA, AMBA, and EMBA Programs includes an international study trip. Not included are living expenses or books (except for EMBA students).

There is no on-campus housing for M.B.A. students, but apartments near the school are abundant and reasonably priced. The estimated cost of living for one year is $13,500 for full-time students.

Merit-based scholarships and graduate assistantships are available to full-time students. Each application is automatically reviewed for these awards.

Application Facts and Dates

Admission is granted on a rolling basis for each program, and early application is encouraged. The AMBA Program starts each June, the EAMBA and EMBA Programs start each August, and the PMBA Program starts in both September and January. For additional information, please direct correspondence to the appropriate program director at the following address:

Director of Admission
Crummer Graduate School of Business
Rollins College
1000 Holt Avenue–2722
Winter Park, Florida 32789-4499
Telephone: 407-646-2405
        800-866-2405 (toll-free)
Fax: 407-646-2402
World Wide Web: http://www.
   crummer.rollins.edu

Roosevelt University

Chicago, Illinois

> ### AN M.B.A. PROGRAM FOR BUSINESS PROFESSIONALS
>
> *Roosevelt University's M.B.A. has been designed for the working business professional—so you really learn from your classmates as much as your professors. We have a healthy respect for the experiences our students bring into the classroom, and we provide flexible options and a commitment to student service. In the fall of 1998, we began offering an innovative M.B.A. in arts management at our downtown Chicago campus.*
>
> —James Cicarelli, Dean

Programs and Curricular Focus

The faculty members at Roosevelt University believe they are offering the most innovative M.B.A. in the Chicago area. Roosevelt's M.B.A. represents a complete rethinking of what is taught and how it is taught. The focus of the learning process is the shared responsibility of the student and the instructor. Classes are small, the contact personal. Teamwork and group projects are stressed, with many case analyses that include written and oral presentations. Above all, each student is expected to contribute to the education of his or her colleagues, because adult learners have considerable expertise to share with classmates.

The emphasis of the program is to integrate business core competencies with specialized education to create genuine expertise in one of the functional areas of business or in a concentration from other graduate programs within the University. Some of these areas include hospitality management, integrated marketing communications, and training and development.

Students entering the M.B.A. program with a liberal arts or other nonbusiness baccalaureate degree are encouraged to take, free of charge, classes in the College's M.B.A. "boot camp," which provides just-in-time learning in accounting, finance, and quantitative methods on an as-needed basis. Thereafter, all students take eight core courses. Each course is a self-contained analysis of the stated topic; no prior exposure to the topic is required beyond the boot camp. Students whose academic preparation or work experience has given them a high degree of expertise in a specific subject may petition to take a more advanced

course in lieu of the required course. In addition to the core classes, each M.B.A. student completes a concentration of three courses and one elective for a total of twelve courses (36 credits) to complete their degree.

Students and the M.B.A. Experience

Approximately 725 graduate business students attend classes in the Heller College, where they study for the M.B.A. as well as the Master of Science in accounting, in information systems, and in international business. Students of varied backgrounds and ages, from many states and more than fifty countries, pursue graduate studies at the University. Most work part- or full-time and find evening and weekend classes well suited to their schedules.

Special Features

Roosevelt University is among the few universities to offer an M.B.A. in arts and entertainment management. With reduced government support and shifting corporate foundation priorities, the need is greater than ever for skilled business-trained pro-

fessional and arts administrators. In addition to the core courses, students also take cultural, managerial, and economic environment of the arts; marketing and development of the arts; labor-management relations in the arts; and legal environment of the arts.

The Faculty

Roosevelt University has a diverse faculty representing the culture and the vibrancy of the city. The business faculty includes 28 full-time and more than 50 part-time members.

The Business School Network
Corporate Partnerships

Roosevelt University's corporate clients include an impressive roster of Chicago-area businesses and corporations. By inviting Roosevelt to bring its academic programs to their work sites, they have helped open new doors for their employees and made a strong investment in human potential. Through the Partners in Corporate Education (PCE) program, Roosevelt currently offers graduate classes and degree programs on-site at more than thirty companies and organizations, including AT&T, Kemper, Motorola, Sears, and Northern Trust Bank.

The College and Environs

From its founding as a private university in 1945, Roosevelt pioneered the education of adults and nontraditional students, creating a diverse learning environment for all students. Today, its educational programs are recognized nationwide, and students throughout

metropolitan Chicago and from around the world pursue degrees at its two campuses. Roosevelt's characteristics provide a number of graduate educational benefits: small classes that encourage an open exchange of ideas, an outstanding faculty, excellent academic programs, scheduling flexibility to accommodate working students, and counseling and career planning services.

Facilities

The University offers academic support services and academic computer facilities at both campuses. Student labs feature IBM-compatible PCs and Macintosh equipment, all with the latest software. Research materials are available from just about anywhere in the world, due to interlibrary loans, online computer networks, and electronic databases. Chicago's Murray-Green Library houses more than 300,000 volumes, a music collection with more than 40,000 books and scores, and more than 10,000 sound recordings. Featuring similar services, the Schaumburg Campus Library is also a link between students and the Murray-Green Library. Books and copies of articles are delivered daily from the Chicago campus to the Schaumburg campus.

Placement

Roosevelt University maintains an active placement service for graduates of all of its professional programs. In addition to the fact that business firms from all over the country recruit at Roosevelt, placement opportunities for graduates are enhanced by the University's location in Chicago, where employment opportunities are many and varied.

The Career Counseling and Placement Office assists students in finding part-time, full-time, and second-career positions. Its services remain available to Roosevelt graduates, who may take advantage of a full range of career counseling, planning, and placement opportunities.

Admission

Admission to the M.B.A. program depends on previous academic success and work experience. Domestic students have three options. If they have a bachelor's degree from a regionally accredited college or university and have a grade point average of 3.25 or higher (4.0 scale) or a graduate degree in any discipline, they are granted direct admission. Applicants whose grade point average is 2.8 to 3.24 must submit a detailed work history, a letter of career objectives and goals, or the results of the Graduate Management Admission Test (GMAT). Admission is determined after review of the submitted documents. The third option is for applicants whose grade point average is below 2.8. They must submit a work history, a letter of career objectives and goals, and a GMAT score. Admission is determined after review of these documents.

International students seeking admission to the M.B.A. program must submit a transcript of college-level work, a GMAT score, and results of both the Test of English as a Foreign Language (TOEFL) and the Test of Written English (TWE). Visa services, TOEFL scores of at least 550, and a TWE of 3.5 or higher are required for application. Admission is based on a weighted combination of these measures of ability and aptitude.

Finances

Tuition for 1999–2000 was $8514 per year for full-time students and $473 per credit for part-time students. There was a mandatory fee of $100 (per term) for all students. Scholarships are available that provide grants to cover a partial cost of tuition. Some graduate assistantships are offered by the University that cover tuition and provide a stipend in the range of $5000 for the academic year. Applications for scholarships and assistantships should be submitted by February 15 for priority consideration. The University has limited loan funds. Federal Perkins Loans (formerly National Direct Student Loan Program) are also available. A number of business firms in the Chicago area have employee tuition-reimbursement programs, and many of Roosevelt University's students matriculate under these arrangements.

International Students

International students constitute 7 percent of the student body. Support services include an office/center that provides language tutoring in ESL courses.

Application Facts and Dates

Students should write to the Office of Admissions indicating their field of interest. The deadlines for admission are August 1 for the fall semester, December 1 for the spring semester, and April 15 for the summer terms. The application fee is $25. International students pay an application fee of $35. For more information, students should contact:

Chicago Campus
Roosevelt University
430 South Michigan Avenue
Chicago, Illinois 60605
Telephone: 312-341-3515
Fax: 312-341-3523

Schaumburg Campus
Albert A. Robin Campus
Roosevelt University
1400 North Roosevelt Parkway
Schaumburg, Illinois 60173
Telephone: 847-619-8600
Fax: 847-619-8636
E-mail: mbadvise@roosevelt.edu
World Wide Web: http://www.roosevelt.edu

Rutgers, The State University of New Jersey

Newark and New Brunswick, New Jersey

THE FUTURE AT WORK

The future of business promises to be increasingly global in scope and more changeable, fast-paced, and complex than ever before. It is imperative that those individuals who aspire to be company executives be critical thinkers and problem solvers.

At Rutgers, our goal is to provide you the training, incentive, and experiences necessary to make significant on-the-job contributions from the onset of your career. Rutgers' Graduate School of Management students receive a solid foundation in business theories and principles as well as the sophisticated tools necessary to compete in complicated environments. We have an internationally recognized faculty that brings cutting-edge information, theory, and skills into the classroom. Close connections with the business community here and abroad, a diverse student body, and opportunities for real-world practice set the Rutgers M.B.A. Program apart from the pack.

—Howard P. Tuckman, Dean

Programs and Curricular Focus

Rutgers gives its M.B.A. students the business knowledge and skills required to achieve excellence in their careers. Students are exposed to an array of decision-making and problem-solving tools that have broad applicability in business situations.

The M.B.A. curriculum is offered on a full- and part-time basis at the School's two main campuses—Newark and New Brunswick, New Jersey. In addition, students may begin the program at two convenient off campus locations— Princeton and Morristown, New Jersey. The M.B.A. degree requires completion of no less than 60 credit hours distributed over these categories: proficiency requirements; a 32-credit core, including 3 integrative course credits; an interfunctional team consulting course requirement; and 24 credits of elective courses.

Concentrations are available in a wide variety of disciplines, including finance, marketing, electronic commerce, entrepreneurship, human resources management, international business, management accounting, computers and information systems, and strategic management.

Through a partnership with seven of the nation's leading drug manufacturers, the School also offers an exclusive M.B.A. in pharmaceutical management. Up to 20 students are selected each year for the prestigious Industry Scholars Program. These students receive tuition scholarships, a paid summer internship in the industry, and the opportunity to learn from senior pharmaceutical executives.

The School also offers a twenty-month Executive M.B.A. program, two International Executive M.B.A. programs (in Beijing and Singapore), a fourteen-month M.B.A. program in professional accounting, and a variety of innovative dual degrees, including a J.D./M.B.A., an M.D./M.B.A., an M.P.H./M.B.A., and an M.B.S./M.B.A.

Students and the M.B.A. Experience

Current Rutgers M.B.A. students come from nearly 100 different United States colleges and universities and more than sixty schools in twenty-nine countries. Their average age is 28, and the average student arrives at Rutgers with five years of work experience. The diversity of the student body is enhanced by the number of part-time students who bring to the classroom the issues and situations that they face in their jobs on a daily basis.

The size of the program at Rutgers is deliberately kept small. This enables students to forge lasting friendships and to gain an appreciation of different cultures and business practices from their fellow classmates.

The M.B.A. curriculum stresses teamwork and an integrated, cross-functional view of business. An example of this is the two-term interfunctional team consulting assignment that all students must complete. The program gives students the opportunity to work on a consulting assignment for corporate clients while allowing them to synthesize the concepts and tools that they have learned in the classroom. Students interact with senior management to define the scope of the assignment, work as a team to find an appropriate solution, and are given a real solution in which to hone their oral and written presentation skills.

Rutgers also supplements its classroom lessons with experiential learning, typically with internship opportunities, case study competitions, and guest lectures by corporate executives.

The Faculty

The quality of what an M.B.A. student takes from the classroom is reflected in what the faculty members bring to it. The professors at the Graduate School of Management are internationally renowned scholars, editors of prestigious academic journals, award-winning teachers, and top consultants to industry and government. They have tremendous skill at integrating hands-on management experience with intellectual inquiry and are actively involved in research that will shape management practices for decades to come. By pushing the frontiers of business knowledge, their goal is to enable students to think beyond traditional functional boundaries and ignite in them the confidence needed to meet any business challenge.

The Business School Network

The Rutgers M.B.A. program brings the world of business to the classroom by capitalizing on the fact that the School is located in the midst of the largest concentration of corporate headquarters in the United States.

Each year, a number of CEOs and prominent executives participate in a variety of forums, providing students with the opportunity to engage high-level business leaders in an open exchange. In addition, through its Executives-in-Residence program, the School brings a number of these individuals onto its faculty. Each contributes a significant amount of time and energy to the program, offering a wealth of experience and wisdom to M.B.A. students through

The Management Education Center is the Newark home of the Graduate School of Management.

classroom lectures, mentoring, and career counseling sessions. They also work to arrange internships and play a leadership role in forging links between the University and the business community.

The School also has an active Board of Advisers, comprising 50 distinguished area executives. Advisers provide critical input into the programs of the School, generate internship and placement opportunities for students, and find ways to improve the resources for promoting and enhancing learning.

The College and Environs
Rutgers University was chartered in 1766. From its roots as a colonial college and land-grant institution, it has developed into one of America's leading public research universities. New Jersey's state university fulfills its three-part mission of instruction, research, and service by educating a diverse student body of almost 49,000 on its three campuses, by creating new knowledge, and by contributing to the economic and cultural vitality of the state. Rutgers continues to strengthen its tradition of teaching and research excellence as one of the select members of the prestigious Association of American Universities. The Rutgers Graduate School of Management has been accredited for more than fifty years by AACSB–The International Association for Management Education.

Both of the School's main campuses are accessible by bus, train, or car and are convenient to Newark International Airport. Northern New Jersey is home to five professional sports franchises and a variety of cultural and recreational resources. In addition, midtown Manhattan and Wall Street are both short train rides away from the Newark campus. Midtown is an hour by train from New Brunswick.

Placement
Through the aggressive effort of its full-time professional staff, Rutgers M.B.A. Career Services not only reaches out to recruiters but also actively supports students in every phase of their job search. From the moment M.B.A. students enroll at Rutgers, they participate in a comprehensive career planning program that carries them through graduation and beyond. In a typical term, Rutgers sponsors numerous seminars and workshops designed to help students explore, develop, evaluate, and attain their career goals. Beginning students are immersed in career planning workshops and exposed to the basics of resume writing, cover letter preparation, and interview survival. Students nearing the completion of their degree learn the more technical aspects of career planning, the job search process, and salary negotiation. A special seminar series in the last term before graduation prepares students for the transition from business school to the corporate world. More than 200 corporations, small businesses, and nonprofit organizations recruit Rutgers M.B.A. students. The School's annual M.B.A. resume book is distributed to more than 350 corporate subscribers nationwide.

Admission
The Graduate School of Management admits those students who show promise of succeeding in the program. Primary consideration is given to the applicant's scholastic record, including the distribution and quality of work as well as the GMAT score and work experience. Other considerations include civic leadership, progressively responsible work experience, and clearly defined goals. The Test of English as a Foreign Language (TOEFL) is required of students whose native language is not English. The average GMAT score for the class entering in fall 1999 was 591. The average undergraduate GPA was 3.14.

Finances
Tuition for the 2000–01 academic year is $4932 for full-time in-state students, $7354 for full-time out-of-state students, $408.25 per credit hour for part-time in-state students, and $610 per credit hour for part-time out-of-state students. Fees are $997.50 for full-time students and $334 to $428 for part-time students, depending on the number of credit hours.

International Students
Thirty-eight percent of the School's M.B.A. students are international, representing more than thirty countries. The Rutgers–Newark campus, which has been rated the most diverse of any university campus in America, holds this distinction, in part, because of the large number of international students studying there. The proximity of Newark International Airport and Manhattan make the School's location particularly attractive to international students.

Application Facts and Dates
The application deadline for admission to the full- or part-time program is June 1 for classes starting the following fall. International students must apply by March 15. Students wishing to complete the program on a part-time basis may also apply by November 15 for classes starting the following spring. Candidates may apply online through the Graduate Admissions Web site or through http://www.embark.com. For more information, prospective students may contact:

Graduate School of Management
Office of Admissions
190 University Avenue
Newark, New Jersey 07102-1813
Telephone: 973-353-1234
E-mail: admit@business.rutgers.edu
World Wide Web: http://business.rutgers.edu

Sacred Heart University

College of Business

Fairfield, Connecticut

THE M.B.A. EXPERIENCE AT SACRED HEART UNIVERSITY

Sacred Heart University's business programs are uniquely positioned to enable graduates to face the challenges of the new millennium. Our faculty members are globally experienced and published, and our campuses in Connecticut and Luxembourg allow students to truly globalize their educational experience. The flexibility of course offerings, combined with diverse scheduling options, makes attending courses and working into a positive experience. An internationalized M.B.A. curriculum, coupled with a meaningful work experience, gives future business professionals a competitive advantage.

—Theresa Madonna, Director, Graduate Business Programs

Programs and Curricular Focus

The graduate programs offered through the Sacred Heart University College of Business are designed to prepare future managers and leaders for business, nonprofit, and government agencies. Both theory and application are examined extensively as part of the business school experience, with an emphasis on teamwork, management skills, technology usage, ethics, and global awareness.

The breadth of the graduate business curriculum incorporates a variety of contemporary management topics, such as international management and financial markets, electronic commerce, entrepreneurship, economics and management in health care, investments, mergers, and acquisitions. Combined with a set of core courses that teach fundamental business and leadership skills, students are prepared for the enormous challenges of management in both large and small organizations.

In developing a plan of study, students have the option to choose one of eight concentrations: accounting, economics, finance, health care, human resource management, international business, marketing, and management of technology. Completion of the degree requires 48 credit hours of study in core courses and electives. Four degree program tracks are available: a one-year accelerated M.B.A. program; a two-year full-time M.B.A. program; a part-time M.B.A. program, which can be completed in two to three years; and a five-year B.S./M.B.A. program for Sacred Heart University undergraduate students. Students specifically interested in health-care management may wish to

pursue the 39-credit-hour master's degree program in health systems management, which is also offered through the College of Business. A dual M.S.N./M.B.A. program is available for nurses who seek administrative positions in health-care settings.

The academic calendar for the M.B.A. program is divided into three 12-week sessions as well as a six-week summer session. Class sizes are relatively small, with an average of 18 students, which allows for substantial interaction with faculty members. All courses in the College of Business are offered on the University's main campus in Fairfield. Additional course offerings for part-time students are located in Danbury, Shelton, and Stamford. The University also offers courses in the Grand Duchy of Luxembourg throughout the calendar year.

Students and the M.B.A. Experience

There are more than 600 graduate students in the College of Business at Sacred Heart University. The average student is 30 years old and has approximately five years of work experience. Nearly half of the graduate enrollment in business are women, and 14 percent represent minority groups. Academically, approximately 60 percent of the graduate students in the College hold a baccalaureate degree in a business-related field, with the remainder holding degrees in the liberal arts, science, or engineering.

Students are expected to actively involve themselves in both the academic and professional development aspects of the program. In the classroom, business

students are engaged in team projects, simulations, and case studies. Program faculty members work closely with students to approach complex business problems with creative solutions and new ideas.

A number of social and professional development programs are sponsored through the M.B.A. Student Council. Students are encouraged to participate in the publication of *The New England Journal of Entrepreneurship,* which is focused on topics of interest to academics and business owners conducting research in entrepreneurial studies. Each year, students compete with other business schools in the region. In 1998, Sacred Heart University won the first-ever Connecticut Venture Group Business Plan Competition, surpassing teams throughout the state, including those from Yale University and Rensselaer Polytechnic Institute in Hartford.

❖ Global Focus

Students have the unique opportunity to study at the Sacred Heart University campus located in the Grand Duchy of Luxembourg. It is the only academically accredited M.B.A. program in Luxembourg. Courses are taught in English in six-week modules throughout the year. Students from virtually every European country have participated in studies there. Special two-week seminars are offered in Luxembourg for U.S. students wishing to take a course in Europe. In addition, some classes are held through videoconferencing between Luxembourg and the United States to add an international dimension to the program. Luxembourg serves as a financial center for Western Europe, where more than 200 banks and 6,000 holding companies are registered.

The Faculty

The faculty members bring a wealth of business experience and academic credentials to the classroom. A number of them hold degrees from prestigious institutions, including UCLA, Yale, Columbia, Northwestern, and the Wharton School of Business at the University of Pennsylvania. Professionally, they have held positions in companies such as Bear Stearns & Company and Pitney Bowes. Their primary focus is teaching. In addition, they serve as consultants to a number of major corporations, government agencies, and nonprofit groups, such as the International Monetary Fund, International Paper, and the U.S. Department of Commerce.

The Business School Network

An advisory committee composed of program alumni and corporate leaders assists the faculty in updating the course offerings to meet today's business needs. In addition, executives often serve as guest lecturers and make presentations on developing trends to students. The College has established partnerships with several companies, such as General Electric, American Skandia, and Uno Restaurant Corporation.

The College and Environs

Sacred Heart University is a coeducational, independent, comprehensive institution of higher learning in the Catholic intellectual tradition. The Fairfield Campus is located on 56 acres adjacent to the Merritt Parkway. In recent years, the University has achieved phenomenal growth in enrollment, faculty, and facilities. Current enrollment exceeds 5,600 undergraduate and graduate students, which makes it the third-largest Catholic university in New England. There are more than 1,400 students in the College of Business.

Fairfield is an attractive suburban community located 55 miles northeast of New York City. Established in 1639, the community and the surrounding area have grown to become one of the nation's most dynamic business regions and the home of numerous Fortune 500 companies. This environment is ideal for those who wish to engage themselves in professional development programs and internships while completing their degree.

Placement

The University's Career Development office is available to assist students to plan and organize extracurricular activities for students in the program. They also arrange for interviews with companies visiting the campus to recruit students throughout the year. Employment opportunities and internships are readily available and are advertised through this office or through the M.B.A. program office.

Admission

A bachelor's degree or its equivalent is required for admission, along with a minimum grade point average of 3.0 (on a 4.0 scale) and a GMAT score of at least 450. International students are required to submit a minimum TOEFL score of 550 (paper-based) or 213 to 220 (computer-based). The most important factors regarding admission include maturity, work experience, motivation, and quality of undergraduate work. An interview is not required, but it is strongly recommended.

Finances

Tuition for the M.B.A. programs for the 1999–2000 academic year was $405 per credit for part-time students and approximately $9720 for full-time students. A limited number of graduate assistantships are available on a competitive basis.

Grad-EXCEL Loans, Federal Student Loan Programs, and deferred payment plans are available through the Office of Financial Assistance. University housing is available to graduate students on a space-available basis at approximately $3433 per semester. Off-campus housing costs in neighboring communities range from $400 to $800 per month for rent.

International Students

Sacred Heart University has made a strong commitment to increasing the number of international graduate students. Currently there are more than 100 undergraduate and graduate international students enrolled in full-time study at the University, representing more than sixty countries.

Application Facts and Dates

Applicants must submit an application with a nonrefundable application fee of $45 ($100 for international applicants), official transcripts from all prior college-level course work, GMAT test scores, and a resume. International applicants are also required to demonstrate their ability to finance their education in order to be eligible for an F-1 visa. Applications are considered on a rolling basis, and applicants are notified as soon as possible of any decisions regarding applications.

Office of Graduate Admissions
Sacred Heart University
5151 Park Avenue
Fairfield, Connecticut 06432-1000
Telephone: 203-371-7619
Fax: 203-365-4732
E-mail: gradstudies@sacredheart.edu
World Wide Web: http://www.
    sacredheart.edu

St. Ambrose University

DEVELOPING VISIONARY LEADERS FOR A GLOBAL BUSINESS COMMUNITY

We invite you to join our dynamic students from around the world committed to achieving a Master of Business Administration (M.B.A.) degree in the St. Ambrose University H.L. McLaughlin One-Year M.B.A. Program. The program is dedicated to building well-rounded leaders for an increasingly competitive global economy by enhancing managerial skills and professional competency. Since 1977, our part-time M.B.A. program has prepared working individuals for advancement in private, public, and nonprofit sectors of the business world. Now our visionary, nationally accredited one-year program offers students a superior, accelerated opportunity to increase their earning potential and advance their careers. You'll receive a world-class education while experiencing the heartland of America, where people are friendly, down to earth, and have the finest work ethic in the country. We pride ourselves on educational excellence, family values, and safe living conditions in our beautiful community on the Mississippi River.

—Dr. John W. Collis, Dean

Programs and Curricular Focus

This twelve-month, full-time M.B.A. program is open to those holding a bachelor's degree in any major. Classes are taught during the day, or students may choose a combination of day, night, or Saturday course offerings.

The academic year is August 7, 2000–August 4, 2001. Degree requirements include fifteen 3-credit courses for a total of 45 semester hours of credit. Students are encouraged to keep outside employment to a minimum, given the rigorous schedule.

The program is nationally accredited by the Association of Collegiate Business Schools and Programs.

Courses include case studies, lectures, discussions, and projects, with emphasis on group work, team orientation, and practical application.

Two weeks of pre-semester courses focus on leadership building and labor/management skills.

Fall semester courses each meet once a week, 3 hours a day for twelve weeks. Fall courses focus on statistical methods for decision making, financial accounting, macroeconomics, and organizational theory, behavior, and communication.

During a two-week winter interim, students study business ethics for nine days, 6 hours each day.

Spring semester courses meet once a week, 3 hours a day for twelve weeks. Spring courses examine managerial accounting, managerial economics, the legal and social environment of business, and human resource management.

During the summer, two courses meet once a week, 3 hours a day for twelve weeks, and two courses are split into six-week sessions, each meeting twice a week for 3 hours a day.

Students scoring below the 35th percentile on the quantitative portion of the GMAT are required to take mathematics for management and economics during the third week of August.

A part-time M.B.A. program is also available. Course work and requirements are identical to the one-year program. Classes are offered evenings in seven locations and also on Saturdays on campus.

An M.B.A. in health care is also offered. Course work provides graduate-level training in business, plus advanced studies in health-care administration.

Students and the M.B.A. Experience

The St. Ambrose One-Year M.B.A. Program currently draws 89 percent of its students from the United States and 11 percent from other countries. Students range in age from 23 to 55; the median age is 32. Sixty percent hold bachelor's degrees in business or economics, 20 percent have degrees in science or technology, and 20 percent hold a variety of other bachelor's degrees. The ratio of men to women is 3:2. Forty-eight percent of students enter the program with more than five years of work experience, while eight percent have less than one year of experience.

Students gain a real-world learning experience that combines hands-on industry knowledge with academics. The diversity of the St. Ambrose One-Year M.B.A. student body enriches the learning experience.

Special Features

Small classes (30 maximum) allow excellent opportunities to share knowledge and ideas with classmates and faculty members. The university draws on rich community resources, and students participate in projects at area businesses focusing on local, national, and international issues. Opportunities for course work abroad are also available.

The Faculty

The University's faculty members bring extensive industrial and academic knowledge into the classroom. More than 80 percent of St. Ambrose M.B.A. professors hold doctorates and all have master's degrees. Students enjoy significant access and interaction with faculty members. The faculty places emphasis on case studies of real-world situations. This blend of academic credentials with practical experience enhances the application of an M.B.A. education in the workplace.

The Business School Network

Answering the needs of area companies who wanted stronger, more competent leaders, St. Ambrose University created a contemporary approach to its M.B.A. program. The University is located within a region of eastern Iowa/western Illinois that is home to many internationally known organizations such as Alcoa, Blue Cross/Blue Shield, Deere and Company, General Electric, Goodyear Tire and Rubber, Hon Industries, Motorola, and Rockwell International. Today, many of these corporations partner with the university in the professional develop-

In the heart of the Midwest, on the great Mississippi River, lies Davenport, Iowa, home of St. Ambrose University.

ment of employees. Company representatives serve as adjunct faculty members and guest speakers and provide tours, internships, and employment opportunities.

The College and Environs

Founded in 1882, St. Ambrose University is a progressive, private university campus. Studies provide world-class education through undergraduate and graduate studies. Nestled among beautiful oak trees in the center of the community, St. Ambrose provides convenient and modern campus resources close to restaurants, stores, and activities. More than 2,800 students, including undergraduates, M.B.A. students, and other graduate-program students, provide a diverse mix of culture, interests, and personalities. Davenport, Iowa, is the largest of fifteen Iowa and Illinois communities that make up the Quad Cities area. Together, the area's population exceeds 400,000. Flowing right through the middle of the communities is the mighty Mississippi River, one of this country's grandest landmarks.

Facilities

A state-of-the-art library offers the latest computer technology and serves as the campus hub for technological communication with the world. Other facilities offer a full range of academic and career

counseling, health care, athletics, culture, and extracurricular opportunities. On- and off-campus living accommodations can be arranged by the Office of Student Services.

Technology Environment

Campus labs are equipped with personal computer and Macintosh formats. Students have access to the Internet and the most recent software on the market.

Placement

The University's Academic Support Center and Career Counseling Center offer educational and career assistance. Programs, job fairs, and campus recruiting help students identify career areas, develop job search strategies, hone interviewing skills, and find competitive employment opportunities.

Admission

Ideal candidates for the St. Ambrose University One-Year M.B.A. Program include recent college graduates electing to complete an M.B.A. before starting their careers, professionals granted a one-year sabbatical or leave of absence to seek an M.B.A., and professionals in career transition. Prerequisites for admission include submission of official undergraduate degree transcripts and GMAT scores, and completion of an

application for admission. Applicants are evaluated based on their undergraduate GPA and GMAT score. A minimum TOEFL score of 550 (paper-based) or 213 (computer-based) is required for international students whose native language or undergraduate experience is not in English. A comprehensive orientation program, academic advising, and numerous support services are available to international students.

Finances

The program costs $432 per credit hour. This rate is subject to change each spring semester. The total cost to complete 45 credit hours and receive an M.B.A. degree is approximately $19,500. Additional costs include a $25 application fee and $10 first registration fee. Typical off-campus housing costs between $4800 and $7200 per year. On-campus housing is $995 per semester. Meal plans are optional.

Low-interest government loans and some research assistantships are available for U.S. citizens. Many domestic students participate in tuition-reimbursement programs with their employers.

St. Ambrose does not provide financial aid to international students. A three-course tuition deposit of $3888 is required of international students one month prior to the beginning of the first semester.

Application Facts and Dates

The application deadline is April 15 for students wishing to begin classes on August 7. However, applicants will be considered up to the start of M.B.A. Orientation. Students receive acceptance notices approximately two weeks after receipt of the completed application. For more information, students should contact:

John W. Collis, Ph.D.
Director, H.L. McLaughlin M.B.A. Program and Dean, College of Business
St. Ambrose University
518 W. Locust Street
Davenport, Iowa 52803
Telephone: 319-333-6270
　　　　888-MBA-1-SAU (toll-free within the U.S.)
Fax: 319-333-6268
E-mail: mba@saunix.sau.edu
World Wide Web: http://www.sau.edu

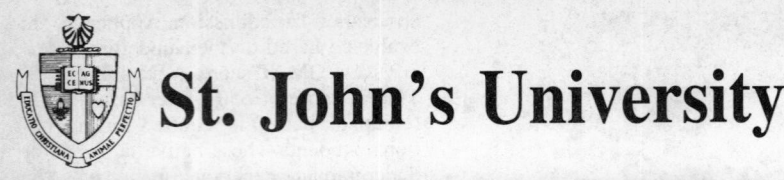

St. John's University

Jamaica, New York

GLOBAL PERSPECTIVE TO BUSINESS: THE ST. JOHN'S M.B.A. ADVANTAGE

St. John's objective is to produce M.B.A. graduates who will be successful in business. We strive to give our students a long-term advantage by enabling them to acquire a broad base of skills in the major business disciplines to adapt to changing job requirements.

The program is fully accredited by AACSB—The International Association for Management Education and emphasizes critical thinking in analytical decision making. Students are prepared for an entrepreneurial future in a global economy, while receiving a strong indoctrination in ethical values. It is these elements of the M.B.A. program that enable our graduates to successfully exercise their leadership skills in business.

—Peter J. Tobin, Dean

Programs and Curricular Focus

The Peter J. Tobin College of Business blends contemporary courses and progressive technology with a tradition of academic excellence, preparing students for rewarding and successful careers.

The Tobin College of Business has the distinction of being professionally accredited by the AACSB–The International Association for Management Education. Fewer than one third of the business programs in the U.S. and Canada have earned AACSB accreditation. The Tobin College of Business has maintained this distinction for 30 years. The Tobin College of Business offers programs of study leading to the M.B.A. degree, with concentrations in accounting, taxation, decision science, economics, executive management, finance, financial services, international business, international finance, marketing management, and computer information systems for managers. The program requires the completion of a minimum of 36 credits taken on either a part-time or full-time basis. These credits are divided into three parts: the M.B.A. curriculum (seven courses), the field of specialization (three courses), and the electives (two courses). In addition, a student who has not taken undergraduate business and economics courses may be required to complete additional credits in the core area, which is determined on an individual basis. The master's thesis option provides the opportunity to plan and execute research study while responding creatively to an intellectual challenge determined by the student's own interests.

For students who are interested in pursuing an M.S. degree, the Tobin College of Business offers degree programs with concentrations in forecasting and planning, purchasing and supply leadership, and taxation.

The Tobin College of Business also offers the Advanced Professional Certificate Program (APC). The APC program enables M.B.A. graduates to gain additional knowledge in a new field, providing the competitive edge necessary to move forward in the new millennium. The APC is earned by successfully completing a minimum of 18 credits in a chosen major field.

Students and the M.B.A. Experience

St. John's student population is comprised of a large number of individuals with diverse work experience. Most are employed full-time in career-track jobs while pursuing their graduate degree.

Students are exposed to the dynamics of group interaction by simulated business situations. They learn negotiation and persuasion skills, how to motivate people, and how to excel in a team environment.

Classes focus on the application of business theory to real-world situations. Students learn to analyze information and make informed decisions in a variety of realistic business situations.

The graduate program is international in scope to provide the student with knowledge of international operations and corporations. The graduate center in Rome, Italy is St. John's University's first graduate program overseas.

The areas of concentration that are available on the Rome campus are international finance and marketing. The Rome campus was established to offer students from all parts of the world a rewarding international educational experience that would prepare them to perform successfully in the global marketplace. Students registered at each campus may take courses at the other campuses of St. John's.

Special Features

The Executive-in-Residence Program provides practical exposure to the business world for a select group of M.B.A. students. Students enrolled in the program have the opportunity to meet with high-level corporate executives who candidly discuss the nature of their firms, the challenges of business, and how those challenges may be addressed. The program is designed to help students understand corporate life and react effectively to the complexities of organizational decision making. The program provides students with the opportunity to develop strategies and business plans for the participating firms, which are discussed with and evaluated by the executive participants. Participating CEO's, CFO's, Senior Partners, and Managers come from such companies as PricewaterhouseCoopers, Sony, American Arbitration Association, and McCann Erickson Advertising.

The Faculty

Tobin College of Business faculty members have attained the highest competence in their areas of expertise. Ninety percent of the full-time faculty hold doctoral degrees. Four faculty members are internationally-recognized Fulbright Scholars. They are passionate about their profession and eager to share their knowledge and real-world experience with students.

The Business School Network

The College forges a strong partnership with corporations and focuses on the issues that are of concern in today's global economy. The annual Business Conference headlines distinguished guest speakers, including CEOs and other senior executives of major corporations. In addition, the Henry George Lecture Series is a semiannual event that features a prominent expert in the field of economics who speaks to the students on current topics.

The Tobin College of Business promotes research in the field of business administration and publishes the *Review of Business,* a refereed publication with a national review board consisting of distinguished business leaders.

Alumni also attest to the quality of a St. John's education and are a valuable network resource for students.

The College and Environs
The Queens and Staten Island campuses provide easy access to the vast resources of the world's foremost metropolis. The Queens campus has 95 acres in residential Hillcrest, with broad lawns, modern buildings, and a spectacular view of the New York skyline. It is a mere 10 miles from midtown Manhattan, providing easy access to all boroughs of New York City and Long Island.

The Staten Island campus is on 16.5 acres on Grimes Hill, overlooking New York Harbor. It offers the full facilities, activities, and resources of the University in a "small college" setting, while being easily accessible from Brooklyn and New Jersey.

The Rome campus location is in the heart of the Eternal City, just behind the Vatican City State.

Facilities
The Main Library of the University is in St. Augustine Hall, located on the Queens Campus. Together with the collections of the Loretto Memorial Library on the Staten Island Campus, the Law School Library, the Oakdale Campus Library, and the Rome Campus Library, the total University Library collection numbers 1.7 million volumes and includes more than 6,000 periodic subscriptions. These materials support course offerings as well as students' cultural and recreational interests. The collection includes government documents and audiovisual materials.

Specific support for the study of business is provided by a collection of more than 63,422 book titles and 648 business periodicals subscriptions. There is also an extensive collection of indexes, abstracts, and full-text databases; these include ABI/INFORM available through UMI/Proquest, LEXIS-NEXIS, and

OCLC First Search. The library houses specialized services, both in print and electronic formats, from Commerce Clearing House, Research Institute of America, Standard & Poor's, Dun & Bradstreet, and Value Line.

Technology Environment
St. John's University is committed to preparing its students with the technological skills necessary to meet the challenges of the twenty-first century marketplace. Students have access to four newly upgraded microcomputer laboratories, more than 100 multimedia classrooms, microcomputer classrooms, library patron computers, and a newly added cyber lounge for resident students. Deployment of desktop computers to these facilities now total more than 825 Intel-based workstations and more than 125 high-end Macintosh computers.

The University's state-of-the-art network enables each microcomputer to access a wide range of software, electronic mail, and the Internet through World Wide Web. A variety of educational, business, statistical and other electronic information resources are accessible through the University's high speed 310 Mbps ATM backbone, with 100 Mbps switched Ethernet to each desktop computer. Internet connectivity is provided through a fractional T3 3 MB link to NYSERNET. Remote 56K dial-in access for Internet connectivity is available as well. In addition, Distance Learning, using interactive video conferencing technology as well as Web based course support tools (e.g. Web CT and Virtual University), is available for use at all three campuses.

Placement
The Career Center's professional placement programs offer a wide variety of services designed to give each graduate student and alumnus the competitive edge. Services and resources include career advisement, on-campus interviews, full-time and part-time employment opportunities, a career resource library, resume preparation and interview techniques, a videotape library, and mock interview sessions.

Admission
All applicants must possess a baccalaureate degree from an accredited undergraduate institution. The candidate should submit, in addition to the $40 nonrefundable application fee, official transcripts from all undergraduate, graduate, and professional schools attended and the results of the GMAT. Applicants whose

native language is not English must submit the results of the TOEFL. In addition, an English as a second language placement test is administered to all international students holding an F-1 or J-1 visa.

Finances
Tuition in 2000–01 is $630 per credit. An additional $75 general fee per term is due at the time of registration. A limited number of graduate assistantships are awarded, based on academic merit.

Living expenses in the New York metropolitan area vary widely, depending on housing and lifestyle. St. John's offers students a variety of housing opportunities. Through the Office of Residence Life, graduate students can secure on-campus housing (subject to availability). To be considered for on-campus housing, students should submit their request in writing to the Office of Admission. Through the University's Housing Service, students can find comfortable and convenient off-campus housing in surrounding neighborhoods. All inquiries concerning off-campus housing should be directed to the Office of Student Life at (718) 990-6257.

Application Facts and Dates
For applications and addtional information, students should contact:

Ms. Sheila Russell
Assistant Director of M.B.A.
   Admissions
Queens Campus
The Peter J. Tobin College of
   Business
St. John's University
8000 Utopia Parkway
Jamaica, New York 11439
Telephone: 718-990-1345
Fax: 718-990-5242

Mr. John Rooney
Director of Admssions
Staten Island Campus
The Peter J. Tobin College of
   Business
St. John's University
300 Howard Avenue
Staten Island, New York 10301
Telephone: 718-390-4500
Fax: 718-390-4298

Mr. Massimiliano Tomassini
Director of Rome Campus
St. John's University
Rome Campus
Via Santa Maria Mediatrice, 24
Rome 00165
Italy
Telephone: 396-636-937
Fax: 396-636-901
E-mail: tomassim@stjohns.edu

Saint Joseph's University

Erivan K. Haub School of Business

Philadelphia, Pennsylvania

EXCELLENCE IN GRADUATE BUSINESS EDUCATION

The M.B.A. program at Saint Joseph's University has a rich history of providing excellent graduate business education. We continuously strive to offer a dynamic combination of cutting-edge theory and practice to those who will be the business leaders of the twenty-first century. Our experienced faculty members are active partners in the learning process. Through their ongoing involvement and research in their respective business disciplines, the faculty creates stimulating environments whereby students can develop the knowledge, skills, and leadership capabilities needed to prosper in highly competitive global business environments.

—Gregory G. Dell'Omo, Dean

DEPARTMENT CHAIRS

Accounting: Joseph M. Ragan, Associate Professor; M.B.A.; CPA.
Finance: Christopher Coyne, Assistant Professor; Ph.D.
Management & Information Systems: William McDevitt, Associate Professor; J.D.
Marketing: Martin Meloche, Associate Professor; Ph.D.
Pharmaceutical Marketing: William Trombetta, Professor; Ph.D., J.D.

Program and Curricular Focus

Saint Joseph's M.B.A. is a program designed for working professionals. It is fully accredited by AACSB-The International Association for Management Education. This part-time evening and Saturday program provides a practical, real-world-based curriculum. It has been developed to give every student the breadth of knowledge necessary in all areas of business as well as the depth of knowledge needed to focus on one particular area of study. This integrated, team-taught curriculum provides Saint Joseph's M.B.A. students with the appropriate knowledge to succeed in their chosen fields. The M.B.A. curriculum consists of 30 credits. An additional 18 credits in foundation courses have been developed for students who do not have an undergraduate degree in business. Students who establish competency through work experience or in-house training may receive a waiver of a foundation course by passing a challenge examination for the applicable course. Within the 30-credit curriculum, students are required to take two courses in an elective track. These courses allow the development of expertise in a specific area of interest. The tracks offered at Saint Joseph's University include e-business, finance, health and medical services administration, international business, marketing, and a general M.B.A. Saint Joseph's M.B.A. program culminates in the ultimate team project: the required Global Business Strategy. This cross-functional, team-taught course utilizes all of the knowledge gained in the program to develop a business plan.

Integral to success in this course are the skills to work in the "team" framework, which are developed throughout the program.

Students and the M.B.A. Experience

One of the measures of an effective M.B.A. program is the number of students who choose that particular program because it meets their needs and professional goals. Today, about 1,000 working professionals from 400 corporate and not-for-profit organizations pursue their M.B.A. at Saint Joseph's University. Students are employed as managers, engineers, programmers, accountants, lawyers, and other professionals who contribute to Saint Joseph's unique M.B.A. environment. The student mix provides a challenging forum where principles are discussed in light of practical applications and real contexts. This setting also furnishes an atmosphere where students can develop leadership qualities and learn dynamics for team presentations.

Students specializing in finance, international business, international marketing, or marketing may participate in the study tours. These study tours allow students to meet with top corporate executives while exploring another part of the world.

The Faculty

In Saint Joseph's M.B.A. program, students are taught by well-qualified full- and part-time professors whose combination of academic credentials and business experience provides for dynamic classroom interaction. Program professors hold doctoral degrees from well-known universities. Just as important, they possess hands-on business expertise coupled with a commitment to work with students on creative solutions to tough business problems.

The Business School Network

Corporate Partnerships

Saint Joseph's M.B.A. program strives to establish partnerships with area corporations by affording these corporations the opportunity to develop their employees professionally by supporting their bid for graduate studies in the evening. Working students contribute greatly to dynamic classroom interaction and in return can apply these new business principles to their current workplace.

The College and Environs

Founded in 1851, Saint Joseph's University is one of twenty-eight Jesuit colleges and universities in the United States. The total University enrollment is 7,050 students, about 1,000 of whom are M.B.A. students. The University is conveniently located on the western boundary of the city of Philadelphia on wooded and landscaped grounds and combines urban accessibility with the traditional charm of the city's well-known Main Line. The environment provides an aura of seclusion, yet the educational, cultural, and entertainment resources of metropolitan Philadelphia are easily accessible.

An off-campus site at Ursinus College in Collegeville, Pennsylvania, is available for Saint Joseph's M.B.A. students residing or employed in the northern part of the Greater Delaware Valley.

Mandeville Hall.

Facilities

Saint Joseph's University opened its newest building, Mandeville Hall, in 1998. This technologically advanced $25-million building is a three-story, 89,000-square-foot facility that houses the Erivan K. Haub School of Business, the Center for Food Marketing Research, and the Academy of Food Marketing. Included in the building are new classrooms, a lecture hall, seminar rooms, research facilities, computer labs, a 180-seat teletorium equipped for teleconferencing and with a translation booth for international presentations, faculty and administrative offices, and informational gathering spaces. Many of the teaching areas are highly innovative in concept and are equipped with interactive communication multimedia technology, which greatly enhances pedagogical possibilities.

One of the most innovative concepts consists of a suite of classrooms that includes two moot board rooms, a preparation seminar room, a video room, and meeting break-out rooms. These rooms are modeled after the moot court concept in law schools. They accommodate the teachings of real-world situations through dramatizations and analysis of interactive business negotiations. They are equipped with stepped, semicircular seating that surrounds a board room table. Video cameras are available to record sessions for later replay or for simultaneous projection to the teletorium or off-site locations around the globe.

The Francis A. Drexel Library contains a business collection of approximately 344,000 bound volumes, 1,850 periodical subscriptions, 750,000 microforms, more than 2,750 videos, and Fortune 500 annual reports. The business print collection also contains a high percentage of the Harvard Core, a list of more than 3,500 books recommended by the Harvard Business School, and it serves as a selective depository for U.S. government documents. The library has an online public access catalog for searching its holdings and the holdings of other university libraries. The catalog is accessible from remote locations via the University's academic computer. There are 100 computer terminals available to Saint Joseph's students, and many online services are available to M.B.A. students. The Instructional Media Center (IMC) at Saint Joseph's University offers students assistance with presentation materials. The IMC has more than 900 videotapes, which can be viewed in the center or signed out if needed as part of a presentation.

Placement

Services at the Career Services Center include individual career counseling, job search advising, access to alumni contact lists, and the career resource library, which contains occupational information, employer literature/directories, and current employment listings. Workshops are offered on resume writing, interviewing, and job search techniques. Graduating students can also participate in on-campus recruiting. In addition, job search assistance is available in the form of a resume referral program.

Admission

Applicants for admission must possess a baccalaureate degree from an accredited college or university. The applicant must submit the following documentation: a completed application form accompanied by the application fee and an essay, official transcripts indicating receipt of a baccalaureate degree, official scores on the Graduate Management Admission Test (GMAT), two letters of recommendation, and an updated resume. International applicants whose native language is not English are required to take the Test of English as a Foreign Language (TOEFL) and submit proof of adequate financial resources. The decision for accepting applicants into the program is made by the admissions committee after it has reviewed the completed application package.

Finances

Tuition and fees for the 2000–01 academic year are $535 per credit hour. On-campus housing for graduate students is available, subject to space limitations. Since the majority of the graduate students are fully employed, they live in the local geographic area. Living costs in the greater Delaware Valley area are reasonable when compared to costs in other large urban centers. Additionally, a limited number of graduate assistantships are available for full-time graduate students.

Application Facts and Dates

Students are admitted for enrollment in September, January, or May of each year. Application should be submitted as far in advance as possible for the following deadlines: July 15 for the fall semester; November 15 for the spring semester; and April 15 for the summer semester. For more information, applicants should contact:

Ms. Adele C. Foley
Associate Dean/Director, M.B.A.
  Programs
Saint Joseph's University
5600 City Avenue
Philadelphia, Pennsylvania 19131-
  1395
Telephone: 610-660-1690
Fax: 610-660-1599
E-mail: sjumba@sju.edu
World Wide Web: http://www.sju.edu/
  mba

Saint Mary's College of California

> ### INTEGRITY—A NECESSITY FOR SUCCESS
>
> *We seek to educate mature adults for challenging and productive management careers in the dynamic global marketplace of the twenty-first century. The programs are designed to prepare students who have a strong knowledge base, analytical skills, intellectual openness and flexibility, a capacity for life-long learning, and an instinct for inquiry; will operate creatively, with vision and imagination, in a complex domestic and international business environment; can apply theory-based knowledge and analytical approaches to diverse, "real-life" management problems; and understand that business management is a profession and not simply a vocation. The School's highly regarded faculty includes teacher/scholars with earned doctorates from leading universities and substantial professional experience, as well as senior-level business practitioners. An underlying premise of education at Saint Mary's is that integrity is not a nicety but a necessity for a successful and satisfying life. Accordingly, a consideration of the ethical implications of business policies and operations is an integral aspect of our curricula.*
>
> —Edwin M. Epstein, Dean

Programs and Curricular Focus

Graduate study in business administration began at Saint Mary's in 1975 with the establishment of the well-respected executive M.B.A. program. It was followed by the evening M.B.A. program in 1984. Most graduate business students at Saint Mary's College are working business professionals who have chosen to earn their M.B.A. degrees on a part-time basis.

The executive M.B.A. program is offered in three formats, weeknight, alternate weekends, or Saturday, for twenty-one months. The flexibility of the evening M.B.A. program allows students to enroll in one, two, or three courses per quarter. Most students complete this program in 2½ years.

The executive M.B.A. program offers a general management perspective. Classes are scheduled in a lock-step pattern, with two classes per quarter, including two electives. The evening M.B.A. program comprises foundation courses, core courses, and electives in finance, marketing, and international business. Class times are determined two years in advance, so students may plan their own schedules when they begin the program.

Students and the M.B.A. Experience

Students in the graduate business programs have earned undergraduate degrees in engineering, science, and the liberal arts, as well as in business and economics. This diversity of backgrounds contributes to the learning that takes place in study groups, an integral part of the curriculum. Students represent virtually all industries, including telecommunications, financial services, engineering, health care, scientific research, consumer product sales, and nonprofit organizations. A strength of the graduate business programs most often cited by students is the professors' emphasis on practical, everyday application of the theory taught in the classroom. Students in the executive M.B.A. program have worked an average of fifteen years before beginning their studies, while students in the evening M.B.A. program have worked approximately five years. The average age of students in the executive M.B.A. program is 38, while in the evening M.B.A. program, the average age is 28. Students in the evening M.B.A. and the executive M.B.A. programs live and work in counties surrounding San Francisco and Oakland.

Special Features

Short-term study-abroad opportunities are available to M.B.A. students. Manage-ment development seminars are offered on a quarterly basis to students in the evening M.B.A. program. These seminars cover practical aspects of business, such as negotiation, time management, and career development. Evening M.B.A. students must participate in four seminars to complete graduation requirements.

The Faculty

The graduate business faculty includes both Ph.D.-trained scholars and experienced business professionals, a combination that reinforces the balance between theory and practice and is a distinguishing characteristic of M.B.A. education at Saint Mary's. Both groups of teachers share a deep commitment to provide academically sound training for professional managers. Because the College places emphasis on teaching rather than research, the primary measure of faculty success is teaching effectiveness, with student evaluation of professors' performance taken very seriously. Professor accessibility is a key element of student satisfaction with the graduate business programs.

The Business School Network

The ties between the San Francisco Bay corporate community and the graduate business programs are varied. Professors invite local business leaders to be guest lecturers. Students interact with local firms, developing strategic business plans that serve as final class projects for the students and as future direction for the companies. Local employers, who believe that a Saint Mary's M.B.A. education adds value to their organizations, sponsor students in the graduate business programs. Alumni association members serve as resources for graduate business students seeking new professional opportunities.

The College and Environs

Saint Mary's College, established in 1863, is one of the oldest institutions of higher learning in California. It is owned and directed by the Christian Brothers, a Catholic teaching congregation. The student population totals about 4,000. The 420-acre campus in Moraga, 20 miles east of San Francisco, lies in a valley surrounded by the hills of a former ranch, which is now parkland open to recreation. It is considered one of the most beautiful and safest colleges in California. The College possesses a rural serenity yet is located in Contra Costa County, a rapidly developing commercial center specializing in financial services, telecommunications, manufacturing, and retail operations.

Placement

The Career Development Center at Saint Mary's College offers self-assessment and career counseling services to graduate students and alumni. A career newsletter with job postings is circulated to all M.B.A. students. The Graduate Business Program facilitates student and graduate networking with the alumni association.

Admission

Applicants with an undergraduate degree in any area are welcome. For students applying to the evening M.B.A. program, the undergraduate GPA, score on the required Graduate Management Admission Test (GMAT), and two letters of recommendation are considered. Applicants to the executive M.B.A. program must currently be employed and have a minimum of five years of business experience, as well as a baccalaureate degree and two recommendations. These candidates are interviewed once their applications are complete; the extent of management experience is given special consideration. The GMAT is not required of executive M.B.A. applicants. A TOEFL score of 550 is required of all candidates whose undergraduate study was not in English.

Students are admitted to the executive M.B.A. program in October, January, and April; to the evening M.B.A. program in October, January, April, and July.

International applicants must show proof of sufficient funds to cover tuition, fees, and living expenses for the duration of the entire program to which they are applying.

Finances

Tuition for the evening M.B.A. program is calculated per course and was $1548 for the 1999–2000 academic year. Each M.B.A. course is worth 4 quarter units. In the evening M.B.A. program, there are eighteen courses. Executive M.B.A. students are guaranteed a fixed quarterly fee for the duration of the program. In 1999–2000, this was approximately $3699–$4425. Living and personal expenses vary according to where students live in the community; on-campus housing is not available for graduate students. Books and supplies average $200 per quarter. Financial aid for graduate study at Saint Mary's is limited to student loans. No teaching fellowships are available.

Application Facts and Dates

There are no application deadlines; it is recommended that applicants send admission materials eight weeks prior to the quarter in which they wish to begin M.B.A. studies. Admission is made on a rolling basis, and decision letters are mailed within two weeks of the date applicants' files are complete. For more information, applicants should contact:

Director of Admissions
Graduate Business Programs
Saint Mary's College
P.O. Box 4240
Moraga, California 94575-4240
Telephone: 925-631-4500
Fax: 925-376-6521
E-mail: smcmba@stmarys-ca.edu

Saint Peter's College

M.B.A. Programs

Jersey City, New Jersey

THIS WORLD IS GOING DIGITAL. BUSINESS IS GOING GLOBAL. WHERE ARE YOU GOING?

With an M.B.A. from Saint Peter's College, you can go anywhere you choose. A recent Standard & Poor's survey of 56,000 business leaders ranked Saint Peter's College in the top twenty liberal arts colleges graduating America's leading corporate officers.

Our 48-credit M.B.A. is taught on a flexible trimester schedule, which means you can complete the program faster than students on a traditional semester calendar. By taking summer session courses, you can earn your degree in two years.

—Dr. Neal Hitzig, Director of M.B.A. Program

Program and Curricular Focus

The M.B.A. program at Saint Peter's College offers five concentrations: finance, management, management information systems, marketing, and international business. The M.B.A. is a 48-credit program, including a common core of 24 credits. The finance concentration emphasizes corporate and international finance as well as advanced topics in financial markets and analysis. The international business concentration focuses on the strategies needed for taking a worldwide perspective of business and the various aspects of globalization, an integral part of the mission of many organizations. The concentration in management examines organizational structure and management control to create flexible, adaptive, and efficient organizations. The concentration in management information systems provides a comprehensive overview of components, technologies, services, current issues, and problem-solving techniques present in every business organization. The marketing concentration focuses on marketing planning strategy and research, consumer behavior, and international aspects of marketing.

Saint Peter's College utilizes the trimester calendar so students can earn their degrees quickly. This unique scheduling pattern offers students three 10-week sessions in one academic year—fall, winter, and spring. The M.B.A. program can be completed strictly in the evenings or on the weekends. Students can also mix and match their class schedule by taking evening and weekend courses.

Students and the M.B.A. Experience

Total enrollment at Saint Peter's is 3,280. Of this number, 251 are graduate business students. Ninety percent of the students enrolled in graduate business programs attend part-time; 46 percent are women; 5 percent are international students; and 36 percent are members of minority groups. The average age of students in the business program is 33.

The Faculty

In addition to being dedicated teachers, the faculty members at Saint Peter's College hold Ph.D.'s from leading universities and are scholars and researchers in their fields. The faculty utilizes a variety of teaching approaches, including lectures, classroom discussions, case studies, team projects, simulation exercises, and independent study.

The College and Environs

Saint Peter's College, founded in 1872, is a Jesuit, Catholic, coeducational, liberal arts college in an urban setting that seeks to develop the whole person in preparation for a lifetime of learning, leadership, and service in a diverse and global society. Committed to academic excellence and individual attention, Saint Peter's College provides education informed by values.

Saint Peter's College offers two campuses with convenient locations. The main campus has long been a landmark on Kennedy Boulevard in Jersey City, New Jersey. The College's atmosphere, architecture, and activity reflect a dynamic, vital, urban institution that offers important intellectual resources to the community. The New York City skyline, visible from Jersey City, is a constant reminder of the College's proximity to a major cultural and financial center. The branch campus at Englewood Cliffs in Bergen County, New Jersey, was established as a college for adults. The campus is perched on a bluff overlooking northern Manhattan and the Hudson River, located on the Palisades, one mile north of the George Washington Bridge. An off-site location at the Jersey City Waterfront affords graduate students the opportunity to take business courses at a location close to their place of work in downtown Jersey City. The site is conveniently located close to PATH and ferry transportation.

Facilities

The libraries of Saint Peter's College provide extensive services and research facilities to the College community at both campuses. The Theresa and Edward O'Toole Library in Jersey City is fully automated, and the catalog is accessible via the campus network. The Jersey City and Englewood Cliffs libraries hold more

than 300,000 volumes. Both libraries provide access to databases in business, nursing, and the humanities. The O'Toole Library also provides a computer lab for word processing and Internet access. The College's computer facilities offer a unique opportunity for students to have hands-on access to several state-of-the-art computer systems as well as a variety of microcomputers. The center has an open-door policy, which means that all students are granted access to the computer facilities. The College's computers are linked to worldwide computer networks such as the Internet and Usenet. The networks provide a method for students to communicate with other students and researchers. All students, upon registration, have free access to these networks.

Placement

Saint Peter's College guides students toward a successful career, a career change, or advancement in their current professions. Services range from career counseling and resume review to current job listings.

A Standard & Poor's survey of 56,000 business leaders ranked Saint Peter's College in the top twenty liberal arts colleges that have graduated America's leading corporate officers. Saint Peter's College has an alumni network of 20,000 active members across the country and abroad.

Admission

A complete graduate admission application to the M.B.A. program includes the

$20 application fee, official undergraduate transcripts, official graduate transcripts, official GMAT score report, and three completed recommendation forms from professional or academic references. International applicants need to submit all of the above plus an official, course-by-course, international credential evaluation of undergraduate and graduate degrees and official TOEFL scores. An initial review of the complete application for admission is conducted by the Office of Graduate Admission. The file is then forwarded to the M.B.A. Program Director for an admission decision. All correspondence should be conducted with the Office of Graduate Admission.

Finances

To make financing an education possible, Saint Peter's financial aid advisers help students explore the best means of affording their degree. Options include tuition deferment and installment plans, employer-sponsored tuition reimbursement plans, and student loans. Interested students should call a financial aid adviser at 201-915-9308.

The cost of tuition for graduate study in 2000–01 is $558 per credit.

Application Facts and Dates

For more information, students should contact:

Office of Graduate Admissions
Saint Peter's College
2641 Kennedy Boulevard
Jersey City, New Jersey 07306
Telephone: 201-915-9216
Fax: 201-432-5860
E-mail: admissions@spcvxa.spc.edu
World Wide Web: http://www.spc.edu

St. Thomas University

▶ ### FOSTERING MORAL AND ETHICAL VALUES

A small university with a personal interest in every student, St. Thomas University has evolved from its humble beginnings as Biscayne College, enrolling some 35 students, to our present enrollment of 2,400 students, representing twenty-five states and forty-seven different countries. While our growth has been dramatic, we have not lost sight of our focal point—the individual student. As a Catholic university welcoming students from all faiths, we remain dedicated to fostering moral and ethical values in the Judeo-Christian tradition. Our students graduate with a sound base from which to build successful careers and productive lives. Our undergraduate programs, graduate programs, and school of law combine to create an educational environment providing students with sound academic preparation for the twenty-first century. The multicultural makeup of our student body offers students a community rich in diversity, preparing them well for their part in the ever changing global community in which we live. The catalogue will provide you with information you will need to shape an academic program for your years ahead. However, there is another aspect of St. Thomas the catalogue cannot express—the personal side of the education experience. Quite simply, we are a small university with a personal interest in every student.

—Rev. Monsignor Franklyn M. Casale, President

Programs and Curricular Focus

The St. Thomas University Master of Business Administration degree is designed for students who are currently in, or plan to enter, responsible positions in management, health management, international business, or sports management as well as professional positions in accounting. The M.B.A. program provides a balance between the quantitative and qualitative aspects of management and focuses on the needs of part time students who may have special concerns because of their employment responsibilities. The M.B.A. also provides an opportunity for full-time students to complete the degree program in four semesters.

The M.B.A. curriculum provides a basic knowledge in the primary core areas of business (24 semester hours) and intensive preparation in one of the five specializations (18 semester hours), except for the accounting specialization, which requires 21 hours of business core and 21 hours of accounting, and is only available to students with an undergraduate degree in accounting or its equivalent. A series of three preparatory courses (9 credits total) provide the needed base skills for those students who have not majored in business or related areas in their undergraduate degree. Concepts and

theory are combined with application. The program's objective is to develop potential managers who not only have the knowledge necessary for today's rapidly changing business environment, but have the skills to apply and utilize this knowledge on an appropriate basis.

St. Thomas University is accredited by the Commission on Colleges of the Southern Association of Colleges and Schools to award bachelor's, master's, and Juris Doctor degrees. The Law School received full accreditation from the American Bar Association in 1994.

Students and the M.B.A. Experience

The total enrollment for the 1999–2000 academic year was approximately 2,400 students. The graduate student population is approximately 500. St. Thomas University provides a learning environment that is intellectually challenging, yet supportive. Classes are kept small to foster maximum interaction between students and faculty members. Many students are working professionals who, along with faculty members, help place theoretical approaches in the context of real-life practical experience. All M.B.A. courses are during nonbusiness hours.

The Faculty

The St. Thomas University Master of Business Administration program has full-time and adjunct faculty members representing a broad background in management, health management, international business, sports administration, and accounting. The graduate faculty has a working relationship with a variety of governmental agencies and businesses, which in turn provide graduate professionals from business, industry, government, education, counseling centers, law enforcement, health care, professional sport management, and the ministry to serve as adjunct faculty members or guest lecturers. The dynamic mixture of academicians and practitioners provides an exciting learning environment.

The College and Environs

St. Thomas University is a small, private, coeducational institution of higher learning sponsored by the Roman Catholic Archdiocese of Miami. St. Thomas offers undergraduate, graduate, professional, and continuing-education programs joining a rich liberal arts curriculum with practical skills that create and enhance career opportunities. Its community of scholars welcomes men and women of all ages, races, nationalities, religious traditions, and beliefs. The University is located midway between Fort Lauderdale and downtown Miami. The University was founded by the Order of Augustinian Friars in 1961 as Biscayne College. It traces its roots to the Universidad de Santo Tomas de Villanueva in Havana, Cuba. In recognition of expanding graduate programs and the founding of the Law School, University status was attained in 1984. Sponsorship was passed to the Archdiocese of Miami in 1988.

South Florida is an international business center. As a major metropolitan center and focus of international business, south Florida offers a wide range of employment opportunities, professional development activities, and cultural leisure events. The general south Florida area offers an unlimited number of attractions and activities which have helped to add to its growth and continuing appeal to tourists. The climate allows for enjoyment of year-round activities that are not possible in many other parts of the United States. St. Thomas' 140-acre campus provides the setting for a variety of sports and leisure activities.

Technology Environment

The main library and law library contain more than 330,000 volumes and volume equivalences. In addition, the main library is a federal depository library and thus has many federal documents available for study. The libraries subscribe to almost 1,000 periodicals and microfilms. The library is a member of Southeast Florida Library Information Network (SEFLIN), which provides for the sharing of resources among south Florida libraries. Online computer searching systems and media center are also available for student use. Moreover, three microcomputer centers are available to supplement the University data processing center. Media facilities include two large screening rooms, a language laboratory, an instructional television recording studio, a film and videotape collection room, and a radio station.

Placement

The Career Center specializes in combining one-on-one advising with the latest in career technology, including an electronic resume writing package/database, a 24-hour Jobline, and a computerized career planning program. Workshops are offered on resume writing, interviewing skills, and business etiquette. Semiannual Career Expos host nearly seventy-five employers who converge on campus to offer full-time professional opportunities, internships, and part-time jobs. On-campus interviews include opportunities with Fortune 500 and small companies and government and service agencies. Students have access to career library holdings and an up-to-date computer lab connected to the Internet.

Admission

Prospective M.B.A. students must have a bachelor's degree from an accredited college or university with at least a 3.0 grade point average. If not, students must submit GRE or GMAT scores. International students must demonstrate adequate proficiency in English by submitting scores from the Test of English as a Foreign Language (TOEFL), with the Test of Written English (TWE).

Finances

Tuition for M.B.A. students during the 1999–2000 academic year was $434 per credit. Financial assistance is available to M.B.A. students in the form of graduate assistantships and federal aid programs. Time payment plans are also available. Some students receive some type of tuition reimbursement for approved job-related M.B.A. courses. Individuals employed in the south Florida area, or by a national or statewide firm based in the area, should contact their human resources department to determine eligibility.

On-campus room and board are available to M.B.A. students through the Office of Student Life. Costs start at $5670 per year. Housing applications should be submitted by July 1. Family housing is not available on campus, but rental apartments abound in the surrounding area. Reasonably priced meals and sandwiches are available on campus.

Application Facts and Dates

St. Thomas University has a rolling admissions policy for students interested in receiving an early decision status letter. Other applicants are encouraged to adhere to the following application deadlines: for applicants to the sports administration program, May 1 for the fall semester, October 1 for the spring semester, and March 1 for the summer term; for domestic applicants to all other programs, June 15 for the fall semester, November 15 for the spring semester, and March 15 for the summer term; and for international applicants, March 1 for the fall semester, September 1 for the spring semester, and January 1 for the summer term.

All requests for information and application forms or admission status should be directed to:

Office of Graduate Admissions
St. Thomas University
16400 NW 32nd Avenue
Miami, Florida 33054

Telephone: 305-628-6614
            305-628-6546
800-367-9006 (toll-free in Florida)
800-367-9010 (toll-free outside
    Florida)
Fax: 305-628-6591
E-mail: signup@stu.edu (applications)
World Wide Web: http://www.stu.edu

Salve Regina University

THE DEAN'S MESSAGE

The M.B.A. program at Salve Regina University gives students an opportunity to pursue specialization in management, accounting, information systems, or finance. Each specialization accommodates both full- and part-time students who demand an education that provides technical know-how based on sound ethical principles. If you are looking for small classes that are student centered and value oriented, where you are a person and not a number, and where you learn skills necessary to be competitive in today's global economy, the M.B.A. program at Salve Regina University is the right place for you.

—A. Frankel, Ph.D., Associate Dean of Graduate Studies

Programs and Curricular Focus

The Master of Business Administration program is designed to prepare graduates for professional careers in organizations that operate in a rapidly changing environment. Acknowledging marketplace globalization, increased emphasis on environmental matters, and concern for the ethical issues confronting today's businessperson, the curriculum provides the technical knowledge and skills to appreciate and address these contemporary issues. The program is directed toward developing managers and focuses on finance, economics, accounting, ethics, organizational behavior, and strategic management. Social purpose and workplace humanization are underlying program values aligned with the University's mission. Students may concentrate in one of the following areas: accounting, finance, information systems science, or management.

Combining academic theory with their own professional practice, the faculty assists students in the development of the maturity and imagination that will guide them in their careers and the wisdom that will help them to select their organization's objectives and goals, and to inspire its people to achieve them.

The M.B.A. program is heavily committed to the practicing manager. In addition to the on-campus M.B.A. program, which enrolls more than 75 students, the University's M.B.A. program includes a Graduate Extension Study (GES) version (M.B.A./management) that provides an alternative to traditional classroom learning for students whose personal and professional circumstances make regular on-campus study

difficult. Graduate Extension Study enables learners to establish their own times and places for study by using faculty-prepared guides for structured, step-by-step graduate-level courses and degree programs. Students engage in one-on-one relationships with faculty members through written exchanges, telephone, e-mail, and the Internet.

Students and the M.B.A. Experience

As faculty members blend academic theory with their own professional practice in the teaching of each course, so the curriculum complements theoretical courses with those that apply the theory to practice. Courses in the first part of the M.B.A. curriculum present the opportunity to learn the theory behind the practice of management. Later course work allows students to continue learning relevant theory while increasingly applying it to practice.

Prerequisite and core courses familiarize students with the managerial processes that link theory and practice. Early requirements teach the language and methods of management to students from diverse global educational and professional backgrounds. Later, courses in strategic management enable students to apply these concepts and methods to the design and implementation of an organization's strategies. Through this, students have the opportunity to develop both their analytical and interpersonal skills. They increase their sensitivity to ethical issues in management and to human values and needs. They are taught to visualize how the various elements and

processes of an organization relate to one another and to the wider global environment.

Students may decide to specialize in a functional area, to declare no specialty at all, or to design an individualized course of study suited to their career requirements. Many students with limited work experience choose to concentrate in one of four functional areas, including accounting, finance, marketing, or management. Currently employed students with an already determined career path within their companies often follow no specialty but choose to take those individual elective courses most suited to their plan. Counseling is available to help students with unique skills and backgrounds choose courses from many programs at the University and create a plan of study suited to their special needs.

To many, the ultimate learning environment is the small liberal arts university, where students can get to know their peers and faculty members. In today's world of high-quality business schools, such environments are rare. The opportunity to study with an impressive faculty in an intimate environment is a great advantage for students at the University. Currently, there are 79 students in the M.B.A. program. This includes both full-time and part-time students. Average class size is 8 to 12 students.

The Faculty

The faculty is the program's most valuable resource. Faculty members are chosen for the quality of their academic training and research, for their knowledge of managerial practice, and for their superior teaching skills. As graduates of leading doctoral, M.B.A., and law programs, they bring a wide variety of backgrounds and perspectives to the classroom. The faculty members all have extensive managerial, legal, or consulting experience, and as such they are on top of current developments and instrumental in guiding policy. The breadth of their experience allows them to teach from a cross-functional, interdisciplinary perspective. This ensures instruction of superior relevance. Professors choose the teaching methods that best fit their individual styles and the needs of their classes. Teaching methods consist of discussions, case studies, individual and group projects, lectures, simulation, and decision-support work utilizing computer technology.

The Business School Network

The University has strong ties with business and industry. Many of the University's graduates have applied their numerous talents to founding, growing, and leading successful small businesses and entrepreneurial ventures. Numerous opportunities exist for students to pursue internships with established corporations, entrepreneurial ventures, small businesses, and governmental agencies.

The College and Environs

The University is located on the Cliff Walk, overlooking the Atlantic Ocean in historic Newport, Rhode Island. Its scenic campus, which combines gardens and horticultural attractions with both historic and modern architecture, is within walking distance from downtown Newport. The surrounding area is a center for government, industrial, research, and academic activity.

The T. F. Green Airport in Warwick is less than an hour away, while Logan Airport in Boston is a 90-minute drive from Newport. The University is easily accessible by interstate highways from Providence, Boston, New York, and Cape Cod.

Technology Environment

The University's purpose is to create a learning environment that showcases and utilizes the highest level of technology and provides an environment where M.B.A. students and faculty can come together and create "Technology Education." A wide variety of high-end computing facilities are located throughout the campus, including a network of 10/100 base workstations and several PC, Macintosh, and multimedia labs. The campus is fully wired for Internet access and has many state-of-the-art computer classrooms and facilities.

Placement

The University has a reputable track record for graduate placement. Students are provided with assistance in their job search efforts by the Career Development and Placement Office. Graduates have found employment in such fields as aerospace, utilities, computer services, financial services, pharmaceuticals, manufacturing, education, and health services.

Companies that have hired the University's M.B.A. graduates include Fleet National Bank, Textron, Raytheon, Navy Federal Credit Union, American Power Conversion, Reebok, and Fidelity Investments.

Admission

Men and women with bachelor's degrees from accredited institutions of higher learning, considered to have the ability to pursue graduate study and who show a desire for personal development, are admitted without regard to age, race, sex, creed, national or ethnic origin, or disability. Applicants must submit test scores from the Miller Analogies Test (MAT), Graduate Record Examinations (GRE), Graduate Management Aptitude Test (GMAT) (CAT), Law School Admission Test (LSAT), or the Medical College Admission Test (MCAT). Scores must be no more than five years old. Applicants whose native language is not English must also achieve a minimum score of 550 on the TOEFL or a Bond Score of 6.5 or above on the International English Language Testing System (IELTS).

The University offers specifically designed prerequisite courses for M.B.A. candidates through Graduate Extension Study. These may not be applied to the Salve Regina degree. Prerequisites may also be taken as undergraduate courses at the University or at another institution of higher education. The Program Director certifies acceptability of all such courses and may permit students to begin graduate-level work before their completion. These courses include accounting I and II (6 credits or PRE 561), economic principles (6 credits or PRE 518), and quantitative analysis or calculus (6 credits or PRE 510). All credentials (official transcripts, test score reports, etc.) must be submitted directly to the Graduate Admissions Office.

Finances

Tuition is $300 per credit hour for regular graduate courses and $350 per credit for Graduate Extension Study. On-campus living accommodations are not available.

Approximately 14 percent of entering full-time M.B.A. students receive financial aid. A variety of loans are available to assist students with tuition, cost of living, and other educational expenses. Work-study positions are generally available for students who qualify under terms of federally supported work-study programs. Information on government loans and other financial programs is available through the Financial Aid Office (telephone: 401-341-2901; fax: 401-341-2928).

Students who receive complete or partial tuition support from their employers may defer payment until a course is completed. These students must provide the Financial Aid Office with a copy of their employer's tuition reimbursement policy and a letter from their employer confirming their eligibility.

Application Facts and Dates

Students may apply at any time. The standard academic year for the full-time M.B.A. program begins in late August and concludes in mid-May of the following year. The schedule for full-time and part-time programs is flexible and can be tailored to meet the students' needs. Matriculation can begin after acceptance to the graduate program. There are two summer sessions (May–June and July–August) for students who wish to accelerate or who prefer to take fewer courses during the academic year. Graduate Extension Study also has a continuous application process, and courses may be taken at any point during the calendar year. The general financial aid application deadline is March 1.

Early submission of application materials is strongly encouraged. Admission is competitive. The admissions committee strives to evaluate the applicant's ability, aptitude, and promise by examining the whole person as revealed in the application materials. To request an informational brochure and application, students should contact:

Graduate Admissions Office
Salve Regina University
100 Ochre Point Avenue
Newport, Rhode Island 02840-4192
Telephone: 401-341-2908
       888-467-2583 (toll-free)
Fax: 401-848-2823
E-mail: perryl@salve.edu
World Wide Web: http://www.salve.edu

Santa Clara University

Santa Clara, California

SANTA CLARA—THE PREMIER M.B.A. PROGRAM

Santa Clara University's M.B.A. program is the premier business program in Silicon Valley. It has been ranked among the nation's top part-time programs. Our extraordinarily beautiful campus is located in the midst of the world's greatest concentration of technological and scientific talent and most dynamic economic marketplaces. This environment inspires our student body, resonates within our faculty, permeates our curriculum, shapes our graduates, and underscores our commitment to quality instruction, rigorous inquiry, and high-performance expectations.

Santa Clara is proud to be a Jesuit business school. It means we take seriously the education of the whole person. Beyond building competence, at Santa Clara we foster conscience and compassion so that students have the ability to consider what is right rather than just doing things right and can appreciate the creation of purpose as well as capital. Still, ours is a practical approach to educating future business leaders, as embodied within these words of St. Ignatius: "To know and not to do, is not to know."

Santa Clara's faculty members do original research and contribute firsthand to knowledge generation, as opposed to merely reporting about the research of others. They also write for thinking managers and executives in a wide variety of practitioner-oriented publications. Their impressive accomplishments in scholarship, impacting both theory and practice, are balanced by a strong commitment to continuous improvement in teaching and service to students.

We look for applicants who seek challenge and stimulation and who love to learn; those with enthusiasm, zest, and an aspiration to make a difference in the lives of others.

—Barry Z. Posner, Dean and Professor of Leadership

Programs and Curricular Focus

Santa Clara University's M.B.A. program was in the original group of programs accredited by AACSB–The International Association for Management Education in 1961. Reaccredited in 1996, the program has consistently met the AACSB's high standards on applicant admissions, curriculum design and content, faculty scholarship, and instructional acumen. The curriculum blends instruction in theory with practical applications, enriched by faculty members engaged in state-of-the-art research and students who deal daily with real-life organizational concerns. The program is ideally suited for people who want to pursue their education while continuing in their current job positions. However, many students attend on a full-time basis, taking advantage of the flexible evening class scheduling and the opportunity to meet and study with employees from more than 500 Silicon Valley companies.

The course of study at Santa Clara University takes a generalist perspective, preparing students to be decision makers across the various functional fields. A full range of electives does, however, allow in-depth concentration in selected areas. Students may choose to follow one of the suggested study plans leading to a concentration in finance, information systems, international business, managing technology and innovation, quantitative approaches to business problems, marketing management, market research, operations, accounting, entrepreneurship, e-commerce, or leading people and organizations.

Depending on prior academic background, students take between fifteen and twenty-four courses to obtain their degrees. Two courses bracket the program: Managerial Competencies and Team Effectiveness, and the capstone course, Business Policy. Beginning in 1999, the Executive M.B.A. program offers an accelerated path for experienced managers. The program is organized around cross-functional themes that focus on contemporary business challenges specifically related to technology companies. The program is completed in sixteen months on a biweekly weekend schedule

with a rigorous curriculum that meets the requirements of AACSB–The International Association for Management Education.

The Leavey School of Business also offers a joint J.D./M.B.A. program with the School of Law. This combined-degree program allows students to obtain both the J.D. and the M.B.A. degree in less time than if the degrees were earned independently. Students must meet the admissions requirements of both the School of Law and the School of Business.

The Food and Agribusiness Institute at Santa Clara University, in conjunction with the Leavey School of Business, offers an M.B.A. in food and agribusiness. The Institute, founded in 1973, is an internationally recognized center for agribusiness management education. The curriculum incorporates both general management courses and agribusiness management courses, and many students complement their course work by participating in the institute's internship, mentor, and site visit programs.

Scheduled for introduction in 2001, the weekend M.B.A. program is designed for working professionals who are unable to attend evening classes. The program is an accelerated cohort model. Admission requirements include three or more years of professional work experience.

Students and the M.B.A. Experience

More than 80 percent of the 1,000 M.B.A. students at Santa Clara study part-time as they pursue their careers. Attending part-time, students generally take three and a half years to complete the program, while full-time students complete the program in two years. The average student is 27 years old upon entering the program and has more than six years of work experience. Thirty-two percent of M.B.A. students are women, and 7 percent of the student body is composed of international students.

Current M.B.A. students come from more than 400 undergraduate colleges and universities across the United States, as well as from international institutions. Undergraduate majors represented are humanities and social sciences, including economics (25 percent); engineering (45 percent); business (25 percent); and other disciplines (5 percent). Twenty percent of entering students already hold an advanced degree. This

blend of academic backgrounds and work experience provides opportunities for enhanced learning inside and outside of the classroom.

The Faculty
The faculty of the Leavey School possesses national stature in each of its six major departments—Economics, Organizational Analysis and Management, Marketing, Finance, Operations Management and Information Systems, and Accounting as well as the Food and Agribusiness Institute. In each department, faculty members play leading roles in their professional associations and in editorial capacities for the top scholarly journals in their fields. This excellence in scholarship is balanced by a strong commitment to teaching and continuous improvement in service to students. The faculty also represents the global world of business today, representing twelve different countries.

The Business School Network
Alumni of the M.B.A. program at Santa Clara University hold executive positions in more than 800 innovative and rapidly growing businesses. The M.B.A. Alumni Association plays an active role in supporting personal and career development of both alumni and current students. As a vital link between the business school and its alumni, the association sponsors a series of educational programs and alumni networking opportunities.

Corporate Partnerships
The Leavey School of Business Advisory Board consists of 48 distinguished CEOs and business leaders. This active board provides a vehicle for the business community to provide input and communicate concerns directly to top administrators and faculty members at Santa Clara. The composition of this board and the willingness of top executives to serve on it reflect and reinforce awareness of the Leavey School and its M.B.A. program at the highest levels in local and national organizations. The high regard for the Santa Clara M.B.A. is also demonstrated by the number of companies that provide tuition reimbursement plans to

encourage their employees to continue their professional development at Santa Clara.

Prominent Alumni
Since 1961, more than 9,000 men and women have received their M.B.A. degrees and have achieved eminence in one of the country's most dynamic regions. Among the University alumni are 435 company presidents and 625 senior corporate executives. In addition, many alumni have started successful entrepreneurial ventures.

The College and Environs
Santa Clara University, founded in 1851, was the first institution of higher learning on the West Coast. The University was established on the Mission Santa Clara de Asis, and the Mission remains at the center of the University. Santa Clara University enrolls more than 7,500 students in its graduate and undergraduate programs.

Santa Clara is located 46 miles south of San Francisco, in Silicon Valley, an area rich in opportunities. The cultural and entertainment center of San Francisco and the magnificent vistas of Marin County are within 1 hour's travel. Also close by are the beaches of Santa Cruz and the Napa Valley wine country, and even closer are the cultural and sports opportunities available in San Jose.

Placement
Career Services offers complete career services for students and alumni, including counseling, on-campus recruiting, seminars, and workshops. Recruiting is ongoing due to Santa Clara's year-round admission and graduation schedule for M.B.A. students. Workshops help students focus on self-assessment, resume writing, and job-search strategies. Career Services maintains the M.B.A. Alumni Network, a database of more than 500 alumni who provide informational interviews. An M.B.A.-dedicated Career Services staff member is housed in the business school to meet the specific needs of the M.B.A. students and alumni.

Admission
Applicants are required to submit their GMAT results, transcripts from all schools previously attended, two essays, two recommendations, and the Santa Clara application form and fee. All of these factors are taken into account by the Admissions Committee when evaluating an application. The average GMAT score of entering M.B.A. students is 640, and the average GPA is 3.22. Although there is no academic business background required before entering the program, applicants must be proficient in algebra and possess basic computer skills. Professional work experience is not a requirement for admission but is strongly recommended.

For any applicant whose first language is not English, the TOEFL and TWE are also required. The minimum acceptable TOEFL score is 600 on the paper-based version or 250 on the computer-based version, and the minimum TWE score is 4.0.

Finances
Tuition for 2000–01 is $539 per quarter unit, and most classes are 3 units. Tuition for the Food and Agribusiness Institute is $564 per quarter unit. Each quarter, there is a $12 registration fee. Books and supplies cost approximately $100 per course.

Financial assistance is generally available to M.B.A. students who have good academic records and can show financial need. Most financial aid covers partial tuition only and is in the form of M.B.A. Project Assistantships, which require working on administrative and/or research tasks. The Food and Agribusiness Institute offers separate grants and awards for students enrolled in their program. Limited resources do not allow the School to offer financial aid to international students. The deadlines to apply for financial aid are one month after the application deadline for each quarter.

Application Facts and Dates
Application deadlines are March 1 for fall quarter early decision, June 1 for fall quarter, September 1 for winter quarter, and December 1 for spring quarter. Decision letters are mailed out six to eight weeks after the application deadline. For more information, contact:

Ms. Elizabeth Ford, Assistant Dean
Graduate Business Programs
Leavey School of Business
Santa Clara University
500 El Camino Real
Santa Clara, California 95053
Telephone: 408-554-4500
Fax: 408-554-2332
E-mail: mbaadmissions@scu.edu
World Wide Web: http://business.scu.edu

Schiller International University

Dunedin, Florida ❖ *London, United Kingdom* ❖ *Paris, France* ❖ *Strasbourg, France* ❖
Engelberg, Switzerland ❖ *Leysin, Switzerland* ❖ *Heidelberg, Germany* ❖ *Madrid, Spain* ❖

▶ **BUILDING THE INTERNATIONAL THEME AT SIU**

The Schiller (SIU) M.B.A. is more than the sum of its component courses. The M.B.A. in international business builds upon the student's previous studies in international marketing, management, finance, and economics and relates these studies to real-world international management situations via case studies, business games, computer simulations, research projects, and class discussion of current global issues. The international business theme is inherent in every facet of the program; the international focus on curriculum, the multinational background of the faculty and the students, and the nature of the projects.

—Dr. Walter Leibrecht, President

Programs and Curricular Focus

Program courses involve theoretical and practical applications, strategic decision-making, teamwork and group mobilization, understanding diverse interdependent environmental forces, and incorporating ethical standards into business decisions.

The 45-semester-credit program may be completed during two semesters and a summer session on a full-time basis, or in two years on a part-time basis. Students must complete fifteen M.B.A. courses including seven core courses; one of each in the areas of advanced accounting, finance, information technology, international management, international marketing, managerial statistics, and methods of research and analysis. The remaining course requirements include eight electives from approved M.B.A. courses and a final comprehensive examination. The overall GPA for all graduate courses completed must be at least 3.0.

The M.B.A. in International Hotel and Tourism Management is directed to students in the fields of business, hotel/restaurant management, and tourism and related areas who wish to earn an advanced business degree. The course work, comprising five international hotel and tourism management courses, in addition to ten M.B.A. courses, provides the credentials to enter the industry at management level. The degree is offered at the London-Waterloo campus and also at the Florida Campus of SIU. It can be completed in two semesters and a summer session of full-time study, and working professionals can earn this degree on a part-time basis in two to four years. The program consists of fifteen

3-credit courses, plus a final comprehensive examination. The overall GPA must be at least 3.0.

M.B.A. programs are offered at SIU's Dunedin, Florida; London, England; Paris, France; Madrid, Spain; and Heidelberg, Germany campuses.

Students and the M.B.A. Experience

Schiller is a university where each student counts, is taken seriously, and where faculty members know students by name. The close attention paid to each individual student is one of the hallmarks of an SIU education.

The Schiller philosophy is based on the conviction that the give and take between students and their teachers is the very essence of education and can never be replaced, not even by the best technical equipment. It is from this personal relationship that students receive inspiration.

The Faculty

The real assets of Schiller are the high quality of its students and their dedication to serious study, as well as the excellence of its instructors. Schiller faculty members are carefully selected not only for the quality of their educational background but also for their practical experience in their fields of expertise.

The educational process puts particular emphasis on developing international and cross-cultural competencies through foreign language skills, facility, intercampus transfer, and other international

academic opportunities, as well as an intense interaction among people with diverse backgrounds.

The Business School Network

The Office of Alumni Affairs coordinates the University's relationships with former SIU students around the world. Using a computerized list, which is continuously updated, the Alumni Affairs Office issues a University Newsletter to all former students and organizes an alumni network to assist potential SIU students. This office is also responsible for collecting evaluations of its own effectiveness. SIU maintains Alumni Affairs staff in the United States to help students and parents in assessing and selecting study abroad opportunities as well as assisting alumni in maintaining their sharing and alumni networking options. An alumni directory is available at each campus.

The College and Environs

Schiller International University was established in 1964, laying the foundation of what was to become a small, independent university offering its students an education of high quality. During the 1960s, when many large universities emerged as mass institutions in which the individual student often felt lost in a crowd, the founding of Schiller was a conscious departure from the growing anonymity of such institutions. With alumni from more than 130 countries and with men and women from more than 100 nations currently enrolled, SIU offers students the unique opportunity to gain an American education in an international setting. English is the language of instruction at all of SIU's ten campuses in six countries where students are prepared for careers in academic institutions, business and management, governmental agencies, multinational organizations, and social services or for further education in their chosen field. Through enrollment in both practical and theoretical courses and through discussions in small classes with instructors and classmates of multicultural backgrounds, students gain firsthand knowledge of business and cultural relations among the peoples of the world. SIU students have the unique opportunity to transfer among SIU's campuses without losing any credits while continuing their chosen program of study. SIU's campuses are in Dunedin, Florida, U.S.; central London, England; Paris and Strasbourg, France; Heidelberg, Germany; Engelberg and Leysin, Switzerland; and Madrid, Spain.

Admission

Admissions requirements include completion of a bachelor's degree with a business specialization (i.e., accounting, economics, finance and management, law, marketing, statistics) or a bachelor's degree in a nonbusiness field followed by business studies at diploma-level or a preparatory program. The average GPA for all graduate courses completed must be at least 3.0, and all students must submit GMAT scores.

Finances

Schiller International University is an independent institution with limited funds for financial aid. Students are encouraged to seek assistance through private or governmental loans and scholarship programs before applying to the University.

Students wishing to apply for financial assistance from SIU should request a scholarship application form when applying for admission.

Graduate fees for the one-year program (two semesters and the summer session) of fifteen courses are $15,750, the activity fee is $390, and the liability deposit is $130 (the liability deposit is refundable).

International Students

From its founding, the University has dedicated itself to the encouragement and active development of international understanding. Schiller study programs have a distinct international focus. Its student body, which is presently from more than 100 nations, has the invaluable experience of studying together with students from many different national and cultural backgrounds and the opportunity to form lifelong relationships. Personal initiative is encouraged throughout. The development of an entrepreneurial spirit is another hallmark of a Schiller education.

Application Facts and Dates

Applications are processed on a rolling basis. For further information, students should contact:

Sonia Ross
Director of International Admissions
Schiller International University
453 Edgewater Drive
Dunedin, Florida 34698-7532
Telephone: 727-736-5082
800-336-4133 (toll-free in the U.S.)
Fax: 727-734-0359
E-mail: schiller_admissions@yahoo.com
World Wide Web: http://www.schiller.edu/

Seattle Pacific University

Seattle, Washington

SERVICE AND LEADERSHIP IN BUSINESS AND SOCIETY

We take pride in the fact that our M.B.A. degree offers the highest quality management education informed by Christian faith and values. We seek students who want to make a positive difference in their workplaces and in their communities. We are a learning community focused on a commitment to Christian faith, applied learning, and a collaborative learning environment. Our M.B.A. graduates are prepared to provide values-based leadership in any organization, think and act strategically, manage knowledge-based organizations that emphasize the intellectual capital of their members, and apply in-depth knowledge in an emphasis area.

—Alexander D. Hill, Dean

Programs and Curricular Focus

The M.B.A. program at Seattle Pacific University (SPU) offers the highest quality graduate management education informed by Christian faith and values and is accredited by the AACSB: The International Association for Management Education. Beyond the advanced instruction in management covered by all students, the degree can be tailored by one's choice of electives to provide depth in specific areas. Current areas of emphasis include general management, human resource management, and information systems management. A separate Master of Science in Information Systems Management (M.S.I.S.M.) degree is also offered.

The M.B.A. curriculum consists of twenty-four courses divided among nine pre-M.B.A. foundations, ten advanced, and five elective subjects. The nine foundations courses are waivable based upon prior college course work. Each course meets for one evening each week for one 3-hour session.

The related M.S.I.S.M. degree consists of a total of twenty courses. This more specialized degree may be pursued individually or can be earned by completing 27 credits (nine courses) beyond the M.B.A.

Students and the M.B.A. Experience

The program primarily serves part-time students, but full-time students are also welcome. With an average age of 32, Seattle Pacific graduate students bring a wealth of experiences with them to the classroom. Small classes allow dynamic interaction between professors and students, individually or in teams. Students come with diverse employment backgrounds ranging from manufacturing and high-technology industries, for which the Puget Sound region is noted, to service and small-business sectors.

International students comprise about 15 percent of the M.B.A. student body; women account for about 47 percent of the students. Three-quarters of the M.B.A. students are employed full-time.

Special Features

Students may choose to develop their own business plans or conduct independent research in the Practice of Business course. Electives may be chosen from a variety of disciplines. Popular electives have included such courses as Advanced Negotiations, Entrepreneurial Management, Pacific-Rim Enterprise, and Telecommunications and Networking.

The Faculty

The faculty is known for its high quality of instruction and broad experience in the marketplace. Additional faculty members in the M.S.I.S.M. program are drawn from industry. An executive-in-residence and a small number of adjunct instructors complete the teaching faculty.

The Business School Network

Composed of more than 30 senior executives from Puget Sound–area companies, SPU's Executive Advisory Council (EAC) is a valuable networking resource for the School of Business and Economics. Through example and professional guidance, these executives interact with faculty members and students to assist in providing a high-quality M.B.A. program based on Christian ethical principles. EAC members meet with faculty members at quarterly luncheons to discuss academic programs and the needs of the Pacific Northwest business community. Many of these executives also participate in a special mentor program in which M.B.A. students also participate.

The College and Environs

Founded in 1891 as an outreach of the Free Methodist Church of North America, Seattle Pacific University has served the Seattle community through Christian higher education for more than 100 years. On-campus enrollment includes 2,400 undergraduate students and 1,200 graduate students, of whom approximately 200 are pursuing M.B.A. or M.S.I.S.M. degrees. The School of Business and Economics is one of three professional schools that, along with the College of Arts and Sciences, administer the academic programs of the University.

Seattle Pacific University is located on the north side of Queen Anne Hill, just north of downtown Seattle, Washington. The attractive campus borders the Lake Washington Ship Canal, which joins Lake Union with Puget Sound. Seattle is the premier business and trade center of the Pacific Northwest and is the U.S. gateway to the Pacific Rim. Bounded by the Cascade Mountains to the east, by the Olympic Mountains and Puget Sound to the west, and by Mount Rainier to the south, the region is a haven for all forms of outdoor recreation. The city and region also have a wide variety of cultural and sporting attractions.

Facilities

The School of Business and Economics is housed in McKenna Hall, built in 1981. Second-floor faculty and administrative offices and conference rooms, together with first-floor classrooms and a computer lab, provide a convenient, safe, and attractive educational setting.

Seattle Pacific University has served the Pacific Northwest through Christian higher education for more than 100 years.

student loans are available for U.S. students taking at least two courses each term. Tuition for the 2000–01 academic year is $435 per quarter credit hour ($1305 per course). One-time application ($35) and matriculation ($50) fees are charged. Typical textbook and miscellaneous costs average $110 per course. Room and board costs for three quarters of study range from approximately $5500 in campus residence halls or University-owned, nontraditional housing up to $7000 for off-campus residence.

International Students

Seattle Pacific welcomes the enrollment of international students. Special educational and social programs are designed to enhance students' cross-cultural experiences. Counseling assistance is also provided for academic achievement, cultural adaptations, and financial and legal concerns at the Center for Special Populations.

The campus library, a state-of-the-art facility, offers online access to a wide range of publications and research materials, as well as traditional periodical and text sources. High-technology classroom learning environments are used. Three networked computer labs are available for student use.

Placement

Career services and resources are available from the University's Career Development Center. These include job openings (for full-time jobs), internships, career library (career, job search, and company information), career workshops, and career fairs.

Admission

Admission to the M.B.A. program requires successful completion of the GMAT; the GRE is required for admission to the M.S.I.S.M. program. A minimum TOEFL score of 565 is required of all applicants whose native language is not English. An essay and two recommendations are also required for admission. Significant work experience and clearly expressed career goals are very important factors in the admission decision process. Applications are encouraged from students holding accredited bachelor's degrees from all disciplines. M.S.I.S.M. applicants should also be able to document experience with at least two programming languages.

Finances

A limited number of graduate assistantship positions are offered each year, and

Applications are accepted for all quarters, including summer. Admission deadlines generally precede the quarter of admission by two months. Applicants should contact the graduate program coordinator for additional information and an admission packet.

Ms. Debra Wysomierski
Assistant Graduate Director
School of Business and Economics
Seattle Pacific University
3307 Third Avenue West
Seattle, Washington 98119
Telephone: 206-281-2753
Fax: 206-281-2733
E-mail: djwysom@spu.edu
World Wide Web: http://www.spu.edu/
    depts/sbe

Seattle University

Seattle, Washington

> ### DEVELOPING CRITICAL SKILLS FOR SUCCESSFUL CAREERS
>
> *This is an exciting time to pursue a graduate degree in business, especially in a commercial center as vibrant as Seattle. In the Albers School M.B.A. program, you will acquire more than just the relevant tools to cope with the rapid pace of change in the business environment. You will develop the critical thinking, learning, and communication skills necessary to create and manage your own successful career. But beyond those critical elements of management education, an Albers program will advance your potential to improve organizations that depend upon your leadership. Consistent with the 500-year tradition of Jesuit education, the program inspires you to serve your community by advancing your understanding of your role as a manager in a global society.*
>
> *—Dean*

Programs and Curricular Focus

Seattle University's graduate business programs offer a winning combination of two distinctive competencies—top-quality academic programs in business and economics and exceptional flexibility and accessibility for both part-time and full-time students. Students enjoy the environment and service of a small private school and the benefits of a large graduate student population.

The Albers School's niche has been, and will continue to be, educating managers from around the world to be leaders in their industries and in their communities. The goals are to stimulate students with the latest global business practices, provoke analytical thinking and discussion among the best and the brightest, and develop an ethical foundation for sound business decisions. The curriculum immerses students in the latest business practices, helps them integrate different functions within the firm, teaches them how to work more effectively in teams, and develops their understanding of what it takes to be a leader in these rapidly changing times.

The M.B.A. program has three components. First, there are six fundamental business preparatory classes. These courses give students the basic foundation on which to build advanced studies. Students who have completed comparable course work with a grade of B (3.0) or better have the option of waiving these classes based on self-assessment materials. Students without previous course work are required to take these classes. The next ten courses are

core courses and are required for all students. These courses are the heart of the M.B.A. program. Most are case based and require considerable integration and application to the business world. Electives are the third component. Students choose eight electives that meet their needs and interests. Students can choose from more than ten areas of concentration, including finance, marketing, and management as well as the newest concentrations in entrepreneurship and e-commerce. Students may also choose one elective from other graduate programs at Seattle University, such as the Master of Public Administration or Master of Software Engineering. Joint degrees with the School of Law are also offered.

All of the graduate classes in business and economics are offered Monday through Thursday in the late afternoon and evening as well as on Saturday mornings and afternoons. Students pick and choose convenient class times, quarter to quarter. Most classes meet once a week for approximately 3 hours. Most part-time students take two classes per quarter and attend four quarters per year. Full-time students generally take three or four classes each quarter. Students can move between part-time and full-time status and, if needed, step out for a quarter or two and easily return to continue the degree.

Seattle University belongs to a consortium of Jesuit M.B.A. programs across the country that allow nearly full transfer of credit between programs. For students concerned about a possible

relocation during their M.B.A. program, this agreement can protect their investment.

Students and the M.B.A. Experience

The Albers School of Business and Economics serves approximately 675 graduate students from across the U.S. and North America, Asia, Europe, Latin America, and Africa. The reputation for rigorous and challenging academics, teaching excellence, and emphasis on integrity in business draws some of the best students in the world. Students work and learn with others from large corporate backgrounds as well as small entrepreneurial organizations. Students come from leading technology and aerospace firms, premier financial institutions, manufacturing and health-care organizations, and multinational corporations in a multitude of industries. Students have the chance to build relationships with students from around the world, some of whom will someday manage companies that play a dominant role in world commerce and economics.

The Albers School is very proud of its exceptional and diverse student body. Eighty percent of the graduate students attend part-time and work for many large and small organizations in the region. It also has a number of full-time students, many of whom are international. The international students bring their unique cultures and perspectives to the classroom. Students have the opportunity to work with others from North American countries as well as from Asia, Europe, and South America.

Approximately 35 percent of the students have an undergraduate major in engineering or science, 42 percent have a Bachelor of Arts in business degree, and the remaining students have degrees in fields ranging from economics to the humanities. The Albers School looks for students who are bright, motivated, and capable of succeeding in a challenging academic program and who bring their own unique experience to the classroom.

❖ Global Focus

Albers School graduate students may choose to take classes abroad in the very

popular international study tours. Seattle University faculty members take small groups of students to Europe, Asia, and Latin America to experience global business practices firsthand. These international trips last from nine days to two weeks, accommodating the part-time as well as the full-time students. They are excellent opportunities to learn about international business with faculty members who know the ropes.

Special Features
Seattle University recognizes the significance of e-business and globalization in today's world and has established Centers for E-Commerce and Information Systems and International E-Commerce & Innovation. Students in the M.B.A. program may select an informal concentration in e-commerce and information systems, and students in the master's in professional accounting (MPAC) program may choose the accounting information systems track. The Albers School created a program, equipped a lab, and recruited faculty members to respond to the changing marketplace and to help students master the practical tools of technology and prepare them to maneuver in the new world.

The Entrepreneurship Center champions the entrepreneurial spirit and talents of the students and local emerging businesses through free consulting and outreach as part of the Small Business Institute. Under the direction of faculty and/or industry mentors, teams of students have provided assistance to more than 1,500 businesses, targeting low-income and inner-city individuals starting up new ventures, as well as participated in a yearly Business Plan Competition.

The Faculty
Jesuit schools are well known for excellence in teaching. The Albers School recruits and rewards faculty members who love to teach and are good at it. Faculty members are at the leading edge of their fields through their research and publishing but are also exceptionally capable of integrating business disci-

plines, communicating knowledge to students, and applying what is learned in the classroom to the real world. Above all, the faculty members care. They are accessible, knowledgeable, and interested in the students' success.

The Business School Network
Corporate Partnerships
A mentor program—one of the first implemented for an evening program and now in its tenth year—helps students network with senior executives as well as get a clearer perspective on their careers. The M.B.A. program relies heavily on the guidance of business leaders from companies that lead the region and the world in their industries.

The College and Environs
Seattle University was founded in 1891 and is one of the twenty-eight Jesuit Schools. Now serving 6,000 undergraduate, graduate, and law students representing forty-two states and territories and seventy-one nations as well as a plethora of religious and ideological viewpoints, the University has a diverse and culturally rich learning environment. The Albers School, established in 1945, has grown significantly over the past few decades and now has the largest M.B.A. program in the Northwest accredited by AACSB–The International Association for Management Education. The proximity to the Pacific Rim, along with local thriving technology, manufacturing, and aerospace industries, creates an ideal environment for learning about the global realities and practices of business.

Facilities
Completely renovated in 1995, the Pigott Building is home to the Albers School. Its welcoming atrium serves as a meeting place for students and a site for special events, such as the Executive Mentor kick-off each fall. First-floor classrooms are designed for case method courses, with tiered comfortable seating and multimedia capabilities. The building also houses computer labs, Albers faculty and staff offices, and, of course, an espresso stand.

Placement
The Albers graduate population is diverse in its experience base and career needs. In response, the Albers Placement Center services are highly individualized and available to working professionals with busy schedules. The center offers a number of services and programs: Graduate Career Management Program,

Career Expo, Internships, Executive Mentorship Program, Executives in Residence, and weekly job listings.

All the students and alumni now have access to e-Recruiting, a Web-based recruiting tool that is accessible to them 24 hours a day. Students can electronically post their resumes and cover letters as well as search for positions based on their interests and skills. Employers can post positions; search for students based on their major, skills, and experience; and set up interviews over the same Web site.

Admission
Prerequisites for admission include completion of an undergraduate degree in any subject at an accredited U.S. college or its equivalent in another country, a GMAT test score above 500, a minimum of one year of work experience, and completion of an Albers School graduate application.

Applicants from non-English-speaking countries must also submit TOEFL scores of 237 or above on the computer-based test. Students who score below the minimum are required to complete Seattle University's Culture and Language Bridge Program, offered in the fall. International students must also submit a Seattle University international application, which includes official financial statements.

Finances
Tuition in 2000–01 is $491 per credit hour. There is also a tuition application fee of $60 and a matriculation fee of $75.

Graduate students must be enrolled at least part-time (3 credits) to be considered for financial assistance. There are three financial aid options available—student loans, scholarships, and graduate assistantships.

Application Facts and Dates
Students may apply for any quarter. Once admitted, a student can begin the M.B.A. program in fall, winter, spring, summer, or intersession (mid-August to mid-September). Applicants receive a decision approximately four weeks after receipt of completed application materials. For further information, students should contact:

Graduate Admissions
Seattle University
900 Broadway
Seattle, Washington 98122
Telephone: 206-296-5900
E-mail: grad-admissions@seattleu.edu
World Wide Web: http://www.seattleu.edu/asbe

Seton Hall University

South Orange, New Jersey

GRADUATE EDUCATION FOCUSED ON BUSINESS INNOVATION

► *Program highlights include a new 42-credit M.B.A. program that can be completed in as few as eighteen months for full-time students and a full schedule of evening classes to accommodate working professionals. The M.B.A. program at Seton Hall allows students to choose from nine different areas of specialization, including financial institutions, environmental affairs, sports management, and pharmaceutical operations. Unique joint-degree programs are available with Seton Hall School of Law (J.D./M.B.A.), School of Diplomacy and International Relations (M.S. in international relations/M.A. in diplomacy and international relations), College of Nursing (M.B.A./M.S. in Nursing) and the Institute for International Business (M.S. in international business/M.B.A.).*

—Dolores Tremewan Martin, Dean

Programs and Curricular Focus

The Stillman School of Business at Seton Hall University offers graduate education geared toward the needs of business leaders in a rapidly changing environment. The Master of Business Administration (M.B.A.) program provides the management skills necessary to manage the effects of technology and globalization. The Master of Science (M.S.) programs offered by the Stillman School focus on specific fields requiring the support of "retooled" managers with updated skills and knowledge in their respective areas.

The focus of the Stillman School is on developing in its students the business skills necessary to identify problems, research relevant information, and determine and evaluate alternative courses of action. Its framework incorporates the role of the latest technology in making and implementing decisions. As the business school of the only Catholic university in New Jersey, the Stillman School curriculum also stresses the importance of ethical and socially responsible decision making.

Developed by corporate partners and Stillman faculty members, students, and alumni, the newly revised M.B.A. program enables a select group of students to engage in an intensive study of the critical aspects of business and participate in original research. The curriculum provides a foundation in accounting, finance, economics, and the behavioral and quantitative sciences, as well as the functional areas of business.

The first three levels of the program form the basis from which students choose one of nine areas of specialization: accounting, finance, financial institutions, marketing, management, information systems, sports management, or pharmaceutical operations. Classes are often team-taught by Stillman faculty members, who are chosen for their strong academic credentials and practical business knowledge and experience.

Students and the M.B.A. Experience

The Seton Hall M.B.A. experience is best described as an amalgamation of program development and delivery system innovations and the strong foundation upon which the School has built its name. Its reputation earned national recognition when the School became the first private business school in the state to be accredited by AACSB–The International Association for Management Education and has gained momentum with the implementation of its M.B.A. program.

❖ Global Focus

The globalization of business was integrated into the School's graduate business education even before it became fashionable. Through the Institute for International Business, established in 1964, the School has cooperative agreements with sister institutions in China, the Dominican Republic, France, and Russia; sponsored academic scholars; implemented Master of Science, joint

M.B.A./M.S., and certificate programs in international business; and expanded M.B.A. electives. In 1994, the Institute received a $1-million endowment grant from the W. Paul Stillman Terminating Trust.

The Faculty

The Stillman School's 57 faculty members facilitate professional business education through a variety of teaching methods, including lecture, seminars, "live" and simulated business cases, and the integration of technology. The School's low faculty-student ratio and small class size encourage opportunities for one-on-one interaction. Its faculty members have expertise in all areas of business and are published in nationally and internationally recognized business journals.

The Business School Network

Seton Hall's network of corporate partners and alumni is extensive and active. Examples of industry relationships include IBM's Mobile Computing Initiative, AT&T's off-campus program, and the Arthur Andersen Planning Skills Center. Alumni commitment is ongoing through active participation in School of Business Alumni Council–sponsored networking and social events such as periodic "Meet the Dean" receptions and golf and tennis outings. When the School has needed the input of business leaders in program development, alumni have contributed their time and shared their expertise in such initiatives as the M.B.A. Reengineering Team, which met for hundreds of hours this past year.

The College and Environs

Seton Hall's heritage has provided the School with the foundation for its success. Founded in 1856, SHU is the largest and oldest diocesan university in the nation and maintains regional accreditation through the Middle States Association of Colleges and Schools. Located on 58 acres in the suburban village of South Orange, New Jersey, it is 14 miles from New York City and less than ½ mile from the Midtown Direct

The Stillman School of Business is housed in the University's newest academic facility, Kozlowski Hall.

train. The Stillman School of Business, founded in 1950, was the first private school in New Jersey to earn accreditation by AACSB–The International Association for Management Education. With approximately 850 graduate students, close to 50 percent of the School's enrollment, the University's commitment to graduate study in business is evident.

Facilities

The state-of-the-art Kozlowski Hall, which houses the Stillman School, has corporate-style breakout and multimedia rooms, a student lounge, a computer lab, and an amphitheater.

Another facility that confirms Seton Hall's commitment to innovation is the Walsh Library. Opened in 1994, the 155,000-square-foot Walsh Library seats more than 1,100 students. Technology available includes CD-ROM databases (both index and full-text), multimedia computer labs, audiovisual installations, an electronic visual aid (scanner-reader), and Setoncat, the online catalog of holdings accessible both on site and via the campus network.

Technology Environment

In addition to University-wide computer and information services, the Stillman School of Business's Andersen Planning

Skills Center provides technical support services solely to business students. The Stillman School of Business is committed to its long-range strategic plan for computing and information technology.

Placement

The University's Career Center provides a team of professionals designated to work with School of Business students. A comprehensive program of career development, cooperative education, employment recruiting, and training is offered. The Career Center has strong partnerships with employers in the New York metropolitan area and throughout the country who recruit students online and participate in campus career events during the academic year, including networking forums and job fairs. More than 300 employers participate in these events each year, recruiting students for co-op placements and internships, as well as full-time positions.

Admission

Admission is selective, and applicants must hold a baccalaureate degree from an accredited college. The Stillman School welcomes applicants from business and nonbusiness undergraduate disciplines. Although each application is considered on individual merit, a minimum GPA of 3.0, a minimum GMAT score of 500, or a

minimum score of 550 on the TOEFL (for international students) are generally required. Decisions are based on relevant professional and academic potential, including work experience and credentials, personal statement, grade point average, letters of academic and professional recommendation, an official transcript from colleges or universities attended, and scores on the GMAT and TOEFL. International students and members of minority groups are encouraged to apply.

Finances

Tuition for the 2000–01 academic year is $622 per credit. There is a fall and spring registration fee of $85 for part-time students and $105 for full-time students per semester ($45 per summer and winter). For information on School-funded aid, which is in the form of graduate assistantships for selected full-time students, admitted students should contact the Office of Graduate Admissions at 973-761-9262. For federal financial aid and loan information, students should contact the University Financial Aid Office by mail or at 973-761-9350.

International Students

Applications from international students interested in full-time studies are encouraged. The University's Office of International Programs provides and organizes a wide variety of supportive services.

The Stillman School of Business's Institute for International Business works closely with visiting dignitaries and scholars.

Application Facts and Dates

Graduate applications are considered year-round on a rolling basis. For further information, students should contact:

Office of Graduate Admissions
Stillman School of Business
Seton Hall University
400 South Orange Avenue
South Orange, New Jersey 07079-2692
Telephone: 973-761-9220
Fax: 973-761-9208
E-mail: busgrad@shu.edu
World Wide Web: http://business.shu.edu

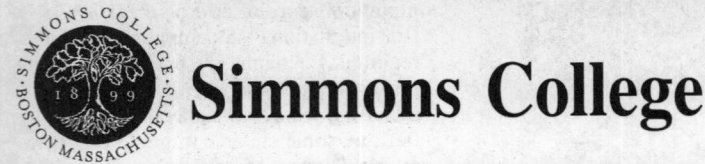

Simmons College

EDUCATING WOMEN FOR POSITIONS OF POWER AND LEADERSHIP

▶ *A quarter of a century ago, the Simmons Graduate School of Management (GSM) was among the first to educate women for positions of power and leadership. Today, we remain the only business school in the world designed exclusively for women. Our challenge is the same: to help women succeed in business and to move from middle management into the most senior positions in organizations of every kind. Wherever senior managers meet, Simmons is determined to position skilled and confident women among them, competing equally, with insight and a real understanding of the business environment.*

—Dr. Patricia O'Brien, Dean

Programs and Curricular Focus

In its emphasis on functional knowledge and quantitative skills, the Simmons M.B.A. program is identical to those offered at other business schools. What sets Simmons apart is its distinctive behavioral focus. This is available nowhere else, and it is available to full-time and part-time students alike.

Simmons offers three M.B.A. program options. The full-time option provides the content of a traditional two-year, four-semester M.B.A. curriculum in an intensive one-year or eighteen-month program. Women who want to parallel work and earnings with education can earn their M.B.A. part-time in either a two-year or a three-year sequence.

The M.B.A. curriculum is a structured sequence of courses, carefully integrated to build upon and reinforce one another. Students take courses in economics, quantitative analysis, accounting, finance, marketing, operations, and strategic planning with a special focus on national and international markets and competition; in the management of organizations—with courses in team strategies, organizational structure, human resources management, communication, and negotiations; and in individual career development. There are electives in advanced accounting, entrepreneurship, corporate and international finance, healthcare management, and leadership. Students may also elect to pursue an internship or a market research project.

Students and the M.B.A. Experience

With work experience averaging eight to ten years, students come to Simmons knowing a great deal about themselves and what they want from their education. They include women in the process of career change, women who have reached a career plateau, and women with substantial management experience who want to move up.

In the current class, minority enrollment is 10 percent and international enrollment is 20 percent. Forty-six percent of the students majored in the humanities or social sciences, while 54 percent majored in math, economics, or the sciences.

Study groups and structured group projects encourage team development, as leaders and as followers.

The Faculty

Twenty faculty members teach in the M.B.A. program; 15 are women. They are graduates of leading doctoral and M.B.A. programs.

The Business School Network

Corporate Partnerships

Simmons students connect with the New England business community through semester-long consulting projects and internships. Corporate leaders are frequent guest lecturers, and the School partners with corporations.

The College and Environs

The School is centrally located in Boston's vibrant academic and cultural community just across the Charles River from Cambridge and is within walking distance of the world-renowned Boston Symphony Orchestra and the Museum of Fine Arts.

Relatively compact among major cities, Boston is a walkable city with an old seaport that is now a completely revitalized waterfront with marinas, shops, theaters, island ferries, seafood restaurants, miniparks, and walkways.

Facilities

The School is housed in a historic complex of turn-of-the-century townhouses. Classrooms, administrative and faculty offices, the computer laboratory, and the library are situated within one city block.

The GSM library contains the latest volumes and periodicals in business and business-related fields as well as a media center with videotaping facilities. Students also have access to the Simmons College main campus library as well as several major libraries in the immediate area, including the famous Kirstein Business Library in Boston's financial district.

The College's new Sports Center offers a running track, swimming pool, squash and racquetball court, and exercise equipment.

The Simmons Graduate School of Management.

M.B.A. students prepare for class.

All the facilities of Simmons College, including the new sports center, are available to GSM students at the main campus, a short distance away.

Technology Environment

The School is equipped with its own microcomputer lab. The computer lab also offers terminals exclusively for work on the Internet and e-mail. Additional microcomputing terminals are available in the undergraduate computing facility.

Through the library's online computer terminals, students can access more than fifty Boston-area university and public library catalogs and forty subject-divided databases, including the Business Periodical Index, Business News Abstracts, Wilson Business Abstracts, and Paperchase (medical information). ABI/Inform, Business Dateline, Morningstar Mutual Funds, SEC/Disclosure, and the National Trade Data Bank are all available on CD-ROM computer workstations. Simmons is a member of the Fenway Library Consortium.

Placement

The Office of Career Services, dedicated to the M.B.A. program, provides personalized and comprehensive career planning and placement services. Advice on appropriate career direction, resume writing, interview preparation, and salary negotiation is integrated with a required Career Strategies course. The office provides students with access to job opportunities through its on-campus recruiting program, functions and industry panels, correspondence recruiting services, job bank, and job fairs that are attended by a wide range of companies.

Admission

Admission is competitive. The Admissions Committee measures potential for both academic success in the program and professional success thereafter. The committee looks closely at the candidate's preparation for a highly quantitative course of study. It does not follow a formula in making its decisions; rather it evaluates the candidate's ability, aptitude, and promise by examining the whole as revealed in the application materials. An applicant must have at least two years of full-time work experience.

The following materials are needed to fulfill application requirements: a completed application form, an application fee, three letters of recommendation, official transcripts of all academic study beyond high school, and a score report from the GMAT. International students whose native language is not English must submit a TOEFL score. Interviews are strongly encouraged.

Finances

The cost of tuition for the 2000–01 academic year is $647 per credit hour.

Forty-five credits are required for the degree. The estimated cost for fees, books, and supplies is $3000.

Financial assistance consists of scholarships, graduate assistantships, grants, and federal loans, which may be offered separately or in combination. Deans' Scholarships are available and candidates applying to the program are automatically considered. These awards are based on merit. The priority deadline for scholarship consideration is March 30.

To be considered for federal aid, a student should file the necessary aid forms by March 1, if possible.

International Students

Twenty percent of Simmons' full-time M.B.A. students come from outside the United States, with representation this year from Europe, Asia, Africa, and the Caribbean.

Alumnae and current students assist international students on their arrival in the United States, and alumnae have often hosted students until they secure permanent housing. On a limited basis, the School offers temporary suite housing for new students until they secure housing.

Application Facts and Dates

The School has a rolling admission policy designed to let students choose their admission decision date. Students are admitted for part-time study in both the fall and spring. Deadlines for part-time study are June 30 for the fall and November 15 for spring. The deadline for full-time study is April 30. For more information, students should contact:

Admission Office
Simmons Graduate School of
    Management
409 Commonwealth Avenue
Boston, Massachusetts 02215
Telephone: 617-521-3840
            800-597-1622 (toll-free)
Fax: 617-521-3880
E-mail: gsmadm@simmons.edu

SIU Southern Illinois University at Carbondale

College of Business and Administration

Carbondale, Illinois

> ### DEVELOPING BUSINESS LEADERS FOR THE 21ST CENTURY
>
> *The focus of the M.B.A. program at Southern Illinois University at Carbondale (SIUC) is toward preparing students for managerial positions in business and government. To facilitate the learning process, the faculty uses a variety of teaching methods, including case discussions, lectures, guest speakers, computer simulations, and student consulting projects with area businesses. In today's global marketplace, it is important that students learn how to conduct business with people from all parts of the world. At SIUC, students have the opportunity to do that while completing the requirements for the SIUC M.B.A. degree. We are proud that our program attracts international students from a wide variety of countries. It is my pleasure to invite you to consider the M.B.A. program at SIUC.*
>
> *—Siva Balasubramanian, Acting Dean*

Programs and Curricular Focus

The M.B.A. program at Southern Illinois University at Carbondale is a 33-credit nonthesis program oriented toward preparing students for managerial positions in business and government. Students in the M.B.A. program may choose to specialize in a wide variety of areas within the College, including international business, management of information (M.O.I.), finance, management, and marketing, or outside the College, including agribusiness economics, industrial technology, workforce education, and computer science. The M.B.A. curriculum consists of 33 credit hours of core course work, with additional foundation course requirements for students with nonbusiness undergraduate degrees. The revised M.B.A. program has expanded the elective options, allowing students greater latitude in customizing their learning experience. Students are encouraged to take advantage of the accessibility of graduate faculty members to complete an independent study or thesis in their chosen area of concentration. The M.B.A. program is accredited by AACSB–The International Association for Management Education.

The College of Business and Administration offers three concurrent degree programs. The School of Law (M.B.A./J.D.), the School of Mass Communication (M.B.A./M.A. in telecommunications), and the School of Agribusiness Economics (M.B.A./M.S. in agribusiness economics) work with the College to provide these unique educational choices. The College offers students the opportunity to study in France through exchange agreements with GROUP ESC Grenoble and GROUPE Sup de Co Montpellier.

SIUC also offers Executive M.B.A. programs in Singapore, Hong Kong, and Lake County (north Chicago), Illinois.

Students and the M.B.A. Experience

The M.B.A. program enrolls approximately 120 students. Nearly 50 percent of the students are international and represent approximately twenty different countries. There is nearly an equal number of men and women. Most students have had previous work experience and attend the program full-time. Small class sizes encourage student participation and interaction. Teaching methodology includes case-study and lecture style. Group projects are an integral part of the curriculum.

The Faculty

The M.B.A. faculty, consisting of members of the School of Accountancy and the Departments of Finance, Management, and Marketing, has a true perspective of business. Many faculty members have both traveled extensively and taught in Asia and Europe. Students benefit from studying under professors who have current knowledge about what is happening in the business world. Many of the M.B.A. faculty members have worked in business and continue to be active as consultants to business firms.

The Business School Network

Top executives from businesses across the nation serve on the College of Business External Advisory Board. The board, which meets twice a year, serves as a group of consultants and advisers to the Dean. The board provides an effective link between business education within the College and business practice within the community. It also serves as a sounding board for programs and activities of the College in areas such as curriculum development, strategic planning, long-range development, and international management.

Many members of the External Advisory Board are alumni of the College of Business and Administration as well as members of the College's Hall of Fame. These senior-level executives represent companies such as Ameritech; A. T. Kearney, Inc.; Caterpillar, Inc.; Cisco Systems; Coopers & Lybrand; Hyatt Corporation; John Deere Foundation; KeyCorp; Northwestern Mutual Life; Peabody Holding Company; The Toro Company; Toshiba; and World Color Press.

The College and Environs

The University is located in Carbondale, Illinois, approximately 100 miles southeast of St. Louis, Missouri. Immediately south of Carbondale are the Illinois Ozarks, some of the most beautiful and rugged terrain in the state. Within 10 miles of campus are two state parks, four recreational lakes, and the 240,000-acre Shawnee National Forest. Camping, caving, rock climbing, boating, hunting, and fishing are just a few of the diversions that are easily accessible. The University was chartered in 1869 and is fully accredited by the North Central Association of Colleges and Schools. There are approximately 22,000 students enrolled.

Facilities

Morris Library, located in the center of the campus and near the College of Business, contains some 2.2 million volumes, more than 3.2 million units of microforms, and about 12,500 current serial subscriptions. Library users have access to nearly 900 electronic data files and CD-ROM products via multiple workstations located throughout the building and through the Internet (World Wide Web). Up-to-date information about library services is available via the Library Information Networks (LINKS) component of the campuswide computer network or through the library's Web page (http://www.lib.SIU.edu).

Students have access to the University's computing facilities. Network-based resources are provided to desktops by UNIX-based RISC servers and an IBM mainframe (ES/9021-500, with vector processor) and four Computer Learning Centers, with computer classrooms and general access areas equipped with a variety of microcomputers. Housed in the same building as the College is a computer laboratory with IBM-compatible PCs and linkage to the University's computer facilities.

Placement

Career development and placement services are provided by University Career Services and the College's H. Scott Hines Placement Center. Recent graduates have accepted positions with companies such as A. G. Edwards, ABN-AMRO, Allstate, Arthur Andersen Consulting, Caterpillar, Deloitte and Touche LP, KPMG Peat Marwick, McNeill Pharmaceuticals, Pacific Bell Mobile Services, and Southwestern Bell Mobile Systems. Some graduates choose to continue their education toward doctoral as well as other degrees, such as the J.D.

Admission

To be eligible for admissions, applicants must hold a baccalaureate degree from an accredited college or university. Applicants with backgrounds that include the liberal arts and sciences are encouraged to apply. Admission to the program is based on the applicant's undergraduate record, a satisfactory score on the Graduate Management Admission Test (GMAT), and other evidence pertaining to ability to perform well in graduate work in business administration. Special circumstances and work experience may be considered if presented. No minimum GMAT score is required. All applicants

whose primary spoken language is not English must obtain a minimum score of 550 on the paper-based version or 220 on the computer-based version of the Test of English as a Foreign Language (TOEFL). The TOEFL must have been taken twenty-four months prior to the semester for which the applicant is seeking admission. If an international applicant has completed at least 100 semester hours of graded course work at an accredited institution in the U.S., the applicant is given the same consideration for admission to the M.B.A. program as a U.S. citizen in regard to the use of English as a foreign language.

Finances

Tuition and fees are established by the Board of Trustees and are subject to change without prior notification. In 2000–01, the per-semester tuition and fees for a student enrolled for 12 credit hours are $2001 (Illinois resident) and $3454 (nonresident). This includes $232 per semester for student medical benefits, which can be waived for students carrying comparable coverage. Southern Illinois University at Carbondale offers residence hall double- and single-occupancy housing for graduate students on a first-come, first-served basis. Efficiency apartments for single graduate students are also available. Family housing is available at two apartment complexes operated by SIUC. Many off-campus rental units are available within walking distance of the campus, including apartments, boarding houses, and mobile homes. Costs for these lodgings vary. In 2000–01, residence hall rates are $2060 for double occupancy and $2657 for single occupancy per semester, including room and board. University apartments rent for $353 per month for an efficiency and $382 per month for a one-bedroom, utilities included.

Graduate assistantships and fellowships provide a monthly salary plus a tuition waiver (fees are not waived). Approximately 25 percent of students receive graduate assistantships through the College. Many more obtain tuition scholarships or find assistantships elsewhere on campus once they are enrolled. Low-interest, federally backed loans are available through the SIUC

Financial Aid Office. Fellowships are awarded on a competitive basis. There are few sources of assistance available to entering international students at the master's level. International students are required to show that they have made satisfactory arrangements to meet their financial obligations at SIUC before admission.

International Students

The International Students and Scholars Office provides a wide range of services and programs for international students. The office is located at Northwest Annex, 860 Lincoln Drive, Building 5, Mail Code 6514, Southern Illinois University at Carbondale, Carbondale, Illinois 62901 (telephone: 618-453-5774; e-mail: iss@siuc.edu). The office may be contacted about housing, financial, and other general questions. Campuswide, international students and scholars total nearly 2,300 and represent 110 countries.

Application Facts and Dates

Admission is permitted for the fall (August), spring (January) and summer (May/June) terms. A nonrefundable application fee of $20 is required. Applications are considered on a rolling basis. The suggested application deadlines are as follows: assistantship applicants, March 15 (fall), September 15 (spring), and February 15 (summer); fellowship applicants, November 15 of the year prior to attendance (fall awards only); other U.S. applicants, June 15 (fall), November 15 (spring), and April 15 (summer); and other international applicants, April 15 (fall), September 15 (spring), and February 15 (summer).

For additional information and questions about the SIUC M.B.A. program, students should contact:

Graduate Programs Office
College of Business and
    Administration
Rehn Hall 133
Mail Code 4625
Southern Illinois University at
    Carbondale
Carbondale, Illinois 62901-4625
Telephone: 618-453-3030
Fax: 618-453-7961
E-mail: mbagp@cba.siu.edu

SᴵU Southern Illinois University at Edwardsville

Edwardsville, Illinois

THE SIUE M.B.A.: MANAGEMENT EDUCATION FOR THE 21ST CENTURY

▶ *The strength of the SIUE program is the total experience that students recieve. This experience includes excellent students, outstanding faculty members, a relevant curriculum, and modern facilities.*

The M.B.A. program prepares students for careers in the technology -focused global business environment. The curriculum is constantly being updated to ensure what it is current and relevant in today's changing business environment.

The faculty is noted for teaching what is current with respect to theory and practice. Because the faculty maintains ties with businesses, instruction is enhanced by "real world" applications.

—M. Robert Carver Jr., Dean

Programs and Curricular Focus

The M.B.A. curriculum aims at preparing individuals for managerial careers leading to advancement through middle- and upper-level positions in business and not-for-profit organizations.

The M.B.A. degree requires a minimum of 30 hours of graduate-level course work consisting of four required courses (12 hours) plus six elective courses (18 hours). The number of hours to be taken in core and pre-entry courses is determined after an analysis of the candidate's previous academic background. Students complete four required courses: MBA 531, External Environment of Business; MBA 532, International Business Environment; MBA 533, Leadership, Influence, and Managerial Effectiveness; and MBA 534, Strategic Management.

Elective courses provide the opportunity for concentration in one or more of the business disciplines.

Students can earn an MBA and specialize in Management Information Systems (MIS), which combines management skills with the study of information systems and design. In addition, graduate students may also earn an MBA with an e-Business specialization, which prepares individuals to work effectively in a unique e-Business environment.

The M.B.A. program has been accredited by AACSB–The International Association for Management Education since 1975.

Students and the M.B.A. Experience

The typical M.B.A. student is employed on a full-time basis while working on the degree. As such, most students have significant business experience. The average student is 31 years old with eight years of full-time work experience. Women represent 35 percent of the student population.

More than two thirds of the students are professionals such as architects, engineers, lawyers, nurses, or doctors or have management positions as accountants, management analysts, education administrators, financial managers, or marketing managers.

❖ Global Focus

The School of Business has developed student and faculty exchange programs with business schools and universities in France, Great Britain, Mexico, and the Netherlands.

Special Features

In addition to graduate fellowships and department-based graduate assistantships, the program provides students with the possibility of corporate-sponsored assistantships/internships.

The Faculty

The faculty of the School of Business is dedicated to providing high-quality instruction and to the personal and professional development of the students enrolled in the M.B.A. program. The skills and backgrounds of the faculty span nearly the entire range of the research-practical experience continuum.

The Business School Network

Corporate Partnerships

The School's Advisory Board includes business executives from a wide range of fields, and students have several opportunities to meet with these corporate leaders.

Prominent Alumni

Notable business leaders who are alumni of the School of Business include Robert Baer, President and Chief Executive Officer, United Van Lines; Wilton Heylinger, Dean, School of Business, Morris Brown College; Ralph Korte, President, Korte Construction Company; Mitch Meyers, President, Zipatoni Company; and James Milligan, President (retired), Spaulding Sports Centers.

The College and Environs

The Edwardsville campus of Southern Illinois University is located on 2,600 acres of gently rolling hills and timberland near the Mississippi River, 17 miles northeast of St. Louis, Missouri. Current enrollment is approximately 11,877 students, of whom nearly 2,564 are graduate students. Master's-level programs are offered in more than thirty fields.

Facilities

The Elijah P. Lovejoy Library is a member of ILLNET Online, a statewide automated resource-sharing network. Through it, 20 million items at thirty-five academic libraries as well as 800 other Illinois libraries can be identified and borrowed. The library also belongs to the Online Computer Library Center (OCLC), which provides access to collections at more than 13,000 libraries in the United States and forty-five other countries. Special arrangements also permit graduate students access to many of the academic, special, and public libraries in the metropolitan St. Louis area.

Technology Environment

The School of Business has its own microcomputer laboratory with about forty computers for student use. In addition, there are two computerized classrooms with a total of more than sixty microcomputers that are networked to a video-projection system and to the campus backbone fiber-optic network.

Placement

Top international companies regularly conduct on-campus interviews at the Career Development Center. The office also presents numerous workshops covering such topics as job search strategies, interviewing, resume writing, and goal setting. In addition, the office works closely with students to formulate specific career plans.

Admission

The following formula is used by the School of Business to evaluate applicants for the M.B.A. degree program: admission score equals 200 times the undergraduate grade point average (A = 4.0), plus the GMAT score. For unconditional admission, unless otherwise noted, applicants must have a minimum admission score of 950, using the four-year cumulative undergraduate grade-point average. Applicants must earn a minimum total score of 400 on the GMAT, with raw scores of at least 20 on both the verbal and quantitative portions of the test, and an Analytical Writing Score of at least 4.0. International students must also earn a score of 550 (or 213 computer based) on the TOEFL examination.

Finances

Tuition and fees in 1999–2000 for 9 semester hours (three courses) were $1,201 for Illinois residents and $2,161 for nonresidents. Part-time tuition (6 hours) was $881 for Illinois and St. Louis residents and $1521 for nonresidents. The additional cost of books and supplies varies from $500 to $1000 per year.

Single-student living expenses at the campus Cougar Village apartments are $1,333 per semester (including utilities), and there is an optional meal plan that costs $100–$500. Family housing is approximately $700 per semester. Housing at the Residence Hall is $1,333 per semester plus a required meal plan that costs $665. Off-campus housing is estimated to cost $2000 per semester.

International Students

Special exchange programs are available with schools in England and Mexico. The St. Louis area has many opportunities for international business interests, and the M.B.A. program offers an array of international business courses.

Application Facts and Dates

Application files must be completed at least four weeks preceding the first day of the term. International application files must be complete at least eight weeks preceding the first day of the term. For more information, applicants should contact:

Office of Business Student Services
School of Business
Box 1186
Southern Illinois University at
    Edwardsville
Edwardsville, Illinois 62026-1186
Telephone: 618-650-3840
Fax: 618-650-3979

FACULTY LIST

Accounting
M. Robert Carver Jr., Professor and Dean; Ph.D. Financial accounting, taxation.
Michael Costigan, Associate Professor and Chairperson; Ph.D. Managerial accounting.
Thomas E. King, Professor; Ph.D. Financial accounting, theory.
Linda Lovata, Associate Professor; Ph.D. Accounting systems, managerial accounting.
Alan K. Ortegren, Associate Professor; Ph.D. Financial accounting, theory.
Marsha Puro, Associate Professor; Ph.D. Financial accounting.
Brad Reed, Assistant Professor; Ph.D. Financial accounting, auditing.

Computer Management and Information Systems
Jon Beard, Associate Professor; Ph.D. e-Business and Technology Management.
Douglas Bock, Professor and Chairperson; Ph.D. Management information systems and design.
Margaret J. Erthal, Instructor; Ph.D. Business education.
Robert W. Klepper, Professor; Ph.D. Management information systems.
Jo Ellen Moore, Assistant Professor; Ph.D. Decision support systems.
Anne Powell, Assistant Professor; Ph.D. Decision Support Systems.
John F. Schrage, Associate Professor; Ph.D. Management information systems theory and design.
Mary R. Sumner, Professor; Ed.D. Educational administration, end-user computing, information systems for business-structured systems analysis and design, CASEtools, decision support systems.

Susan Yager; Assistant Professor; Ph.D. Technology Project Management.
David J. Werner, Professor and Chancellor; Ph.D. Management information systems theory and design, simulation.

Economics and Finance
David E. Ault, Professor; Ph.D. International economics, labor economics.
Rakesh Bharati, Associate Professor; Ph.D. Investment, information economics.
Susan Crain, Assistant Professor; Ph.D. Corporate finance.
Radcliffe G. Edmonds Jr., Associate Professor; Ph.D. Econometrics, international economics.
Donald S. Elliott Jr., Professor and Chairperson; Ph.D. State and local finance.
Rik W. Hafer, Professor; Ph.D. Monetary theory and policy, macroeconomics.
Garett Jones, Assistant Professor; Ph.D. Macroeconomics and Money.
Ali Kutan, Associate Professor; Ph.D. International economics, macroeconomics.
Stanford L. Levin, Professor; Ph.D. Public utility regulation, industrial organization.
An-Yhi Lin, Professor; Ph.D. Econometrics, mathematical economics, economic development.
John B. Meisel, Professor; Ph.D. Industrial organization, antitrust policy.
John C. Navin, Associate Professor; Ph.D. Public finance, labor economics.
Jacky C. So, Professor and Chairperson; Ph.D. International and corporate finance.
Ken Stanton, Assistant Professor; Ph.D. Financial institutions.

Timothy S. Sullivan, Instructor; Ph.D. Social economics.

Management and Marketing
Ralph W. Giacobbe, Associate Professor; Ph.D. Marketing research, consumer behavior, personal selling, services marketing, product marketing.
Janice R. Joplin, Professor; Ph.D. Organizational behavior.
Jack Kaikati, Professor and Chairperson; D.B.A. International marketing, marketing management.
James M. Lynch, Associate Professor; J.D., Ph.D. Advertising and promotion, marketing research.
Kathryn Martell, Associate Professor and Associate Dean; Ph.D. Strategy, international.
Joseph F. Michlitsch, Associate Professor; Ph.D. Organizational theory, strategy, and policy.
Gertrude Pannirselvam, Assistant Professor; Ph.D. Production and operations management.
Timothy S. Schoenecker, Associate Professor; Ph.D. Strategy.
Madhav Segal, Professor; Ph.D. Marketing research and information management, product/services marketing management.
Donald E. Strickland, Professor and Chairperson; Ph.D. Organizational behavior.
George M. Sullivan, Professor; J.D. Regulation, business law, organizational design, business and society.
Laura Swanson, Assistant Professor; Ph.D., candidate. Production and operations management.
John M. Virgo, Professor; Ph.D. Manpower planning, business and society.

SMU ⬚ COX **Southern Methodist University**

Edwin L. Cox School of Business

Dallas, Texas

REAL BUSINESS EDUCATION FOR THE TWENTY-FIRST CENTURY

In the new economy of the twenty-first century, the M.B.A. Program at the Cox School of Business in Dallas, Texas, is positioned to provide you with all of the benefits of an exciting and rewarding business career. Through our unique combination of programs and extensive connections to the business community, the Cox School will prepare you to be a leader in this rapidly changing and globally oriented economy. The American Airlines Global Leadership Program will provide you with a hands-on experience in one of the three major business regions of the world—Asia, Latin America, and Europe. Our e-Business Initiative at Cox (ebi@cox) supplements traditional business training with a curriculum focused on the role of emerging technologies. Cox's unique Business Leadership Center hones your leadership and management skills, and our Executive Mentor Program matches you with a senior-level business executive who can act as a career coach and role model. Only the M.B.A. Program at the Cox School offers these programs to enhance your career, provide hands-on business learning, and enrich your personal experience.

—Albert W. Niemi Jr., Dean

Programs and Curricular Focus

The Cox M.B.A. Program provides an integrated curriculum that helps students establish a solid foundation for success in business. The small class size encourages students to work closely with the faculty and individualize their M.B.A. experience. Located in Dallas, a national and international business center, the Cox School M.B.A. Program offers nationally recognized faculty members, a global focus, and close ties with the business community. At Cox, M.B.A.'s gain much more than a business education—they gain a personalized business experience.

The new, two-year M.B.A. curriculum begins in fall 2000. Composed of 56 credit hours that include a global experience and a modular curriculum, the Cox School's new program builds a strong portfolio of diverse international perspectives and course offerings for the Cox M.B.A. student who is graduating in the twenty-first century. Also new this fall is the e-Business Initiative at Cox (ebi@cox). In partnership with industry, the Cox School has established this program to better prepare its M.B.A. students for the digital economy. ebi@cox offers a leading-edge curriculum to educate existing and future business leaders and provide real-time education through internships and on-site projects that enhance the experience of M.B.A. students. Such courses include

e-Commerce, Internet Marketing, Internet Entrepreneurship, and Venture Capital in the Internet Economy.

First-year students complete nine core courses, the Global Leadership Program (GLP), and a business elective course. Students commence their summer internships after they return from the GLP travel-abroad experience. Second-year students take courses from the new modular curriculum and one core course that builds upon the GLP experience. The new modular curriculum allows students to take up to eighteen modules, which are 6½-week short courses. Some of these courses are closely integrated, while others are short, stand-alone courses. This design provides students with greater curriculum flexibility, which allows students to build depth in an area of emphasis or create breadth for a broader perspective of business. M.B.A.'s can choose from such areas as e-business, finance, business policy, marketing, entrepreneurship, accounting, organizational behavior, business administration, information science and operations management, and real estate.

Cox's distinguished Business Leadership Center (BLC) complements the classroom curriculum throughout the two-year period. The BLC's innovative program is designed to help students develop effective management skills through seminars that center on interpersonal and communication

skills, team building, and negotiation skills. Courses are organized by business leaders and taught by outside consultants from some of today's most progressive corporations.

In addition to the full-time two-year M.B.A. program, Cox offers a part-time, three-year professional M.B.A. program developed for working professionals and a twenty-one-month executive M.B.A. program for candidates with significant managerial experience.

Joint-degree programs are offered in conjunction with the law school for a Juris Doctor/M.B.A. (4½ years) and with the Meadows School of Arts for a Master of Arts in administration/M.B.A. (six semesters).

Students and the M.B.A. Experience

Cox students come from all regions of the United States and the world. The M.B.A. program consists of more than 230 full-time students, with 27 percent hailing from countries other than the U.S. Students have a wide variety of academic disciplines and professional experiences. The average amount of work experience prior to entering the M.B.A. program is slightly more than four years, and the average age is approximately 27. Women comprise more than 30 percent of the population, and minorities account for 14 percent of the student body.

Cox's small size not only promotes collaboration among students, it also creates a close and supportive environment for students, the faculty, and the staff. The small size also gives students significant opportunities to assume leadership roles in M.B.A. student organizations, such as the Finance Club, the Investment Club, the Marketing Club, the Consulting Club, Women in Business, and the Hi Tech Club.

❖ Global Focus

Today's business leaders must be global thinkers. At Cox, global thinking is incorporated into the M.B.A. curriculum. The Global Leadership Program is a mandatory, three-week, travel-abroad course. All first-year students travel to one of three regions of the world—Asia, Europe, or Latin America—to meet with business and government leaders. The goal is to allow students to experience how business is conducted globally. In addition, the School's location at the gateway to NAFTA and Latin America is well positioned for enhancing international perspectives.

An international exchange program allows select students to experience their international business education firsthand by studying abroad. Cox has relationships with schools in Australia, Belgium, Brazil, Denmark, England, France, Hungary, Japan, Mexico, Singapore, Spain, and Venezuela.

Special Features

Like the Business Leadership Center, Cox institutes provide a forum for students, faculty members, and the business community to participate in interactive programs and research. The Caruth Institute of Owner-Managed Business focuses on entrepreneurship, the Maguire Oil & Gas Institute promotes the study of oil and gas industry issues, and the SMU Finance Institute promotes interaction between financial practitioners and the SMU finance community.

The Faculty

Cox students benefit from a nationally recognized faculty that is approachable and accessible and is as dedicated to teaching as it is to research. Classes are taught using a variety of teaching methods that are best suited for the course material, including cases, lectures, class discussions, student presentations, team and field projects, and

computer simulations. The Cox M.B.A. curriculum is developed to equally emphasize quantitative and qualitative skills.

The Business School Network
Corporate Partnerships

At Cox, interaction with the business community is encouraged and formalized for students. The School established the Associate Board Executive Mentor Program with nearly 200 top business executives who actively serve as mentors to Cox M.B.A. students.

In addition to being a valuable source of business contacts, a mentor relationship provides students with insightful career advice, an inside track on current business trends, and a valuable perspective from an experienced business person.

Prominent Alumni

Prominent Cox alumni include Howard M. Dean, CEO and Director, Dean Foods; Martin Flanagan, Senior Vice President and CFO, Franklin Resources; Charles Hansen Jr., Chairman and CEO, Pillowtex Corporation; James MacNaughton, Managing Director, Salomon Smith Barney; Megan Pryor, Vice President of Sales, Pepsi Cola; John J. Murphy, former Chairman, President, and CEO, Dresser Industries; William O'Neill, Chairman, Investor's Business Daily; and John Tolleson, former Chairman and CEO, First USA.

The College and Environs

SMU, established in 1911, has six different schools and graduate programs in addition to its undergraduate program. The total undergraduate and graduate population is 10,361 students.

The University's location in one of the world's major centers of commerce gives students an excellent advantage. The city of Dallas ranks third in the United States as a site of major corporate headquarters and sixth in the world for multinational corporate headquarters. Dallas offers a wide variety of cultural events and opportunities, from national league sports to the nationally renowned Myerson Symphony Center and the Dallas Museum of Art.

Technology Environment

From state-of-the-art classrooms to the newly renovated Business Information Center, the Cox School offers the latest in business technologies. Beginning in fall 2000, the Cox School will offer 802.11b Wireless Networking. This technology allows a student to use his or her own laptop computer on the network from a classroom. After class, students can walk from a classroom to a study room and continue to use the Internet from their computer on the network. Students utilize an in-house network (accessible from home) to communicate with other students and faculty members, connect with the Internet to conduct class-

room assignments, and access numerous business databases and research tools.

Placement

The M.B.A. Career Management Office (CMO) partners with students to help develop and implement successful career strategies. Students participate in the Career Management Training Program and receive individualized career counseling sessions year-round. In 1999, internship placement reached 100 percent, and graduates increased their salaries by 10 percent over 1998 graduates, which reflects the strength of the student body.

Admission

Admission to the M.B.A. programs at the Edwin L. Cox School of Business is highly selective. The Admissions Committee seeks to admit students who represent various geographic, economic, religious, and ethnic groups and have a diverse set of work experiences.

Successful applicants are well-rounded individuals who have clearly demonstrated academic achievement in addition to a commitment and capacity for leadership in today's dynamic business world.

Finances

The cost of tuition and fees for 2000–01 is estimated at $25,085; books and supplies are approximately $1200. Off-campus housing generally costs between $600 and $1200 per month. Scholarships are available and are awarded strictly on merit.

Application Facts and Dates

Students enter the full-time program in the fall semester only (orientation is held mid-August). Application deadlines for all applicants to the full-time M.B.A. program are as follows: November 30, January 8, February 12, March 30, and May 14. To be considered for scholarships, students should apply by February 12. International students should apply by March 30. After May 14, admission decisions are made on a space-available basis.

Students enter the part-time program in the fall (orientation is held in August) and spring (orientation is held in January). The application deadline for fall admission is May 30; for spring admission, November 1.

Director of M.B.A. Admissions
Edwin L. Cox School of Business
Southern Methodist University
P.O. Box 750333
Dallas, Texas 75275-0333
Telephone: 214-768-2630
            800-472-3622 (toll-free)
Fax: 214-768-3956
E-mail: M.B.A.info@mail.cox.smu.edu
World Wide Web: http://www.cox.smu.edu

State University of New York at Binghamton

Binghamton, New York

EDUCATING MEN AND WOMEN FOR LEADERSHIP POSITIONS

The School of Management's programs reflect our commitment to educating men and women for leadership positions in a variety of career fields. Our graduates are leaders in entrepreneurship, university teaching and research, and management of small businesses, major corporations, and government and social agencies. Underlying each of our programs is the conviction that a well-developed sense of social responsibility and an ethical approach are essential characteristics of leadership in all fields of endeavor. We make a serious commitment to those students selected for our programs, and the relationship between the School and every student lasts the whole of each one's career. As a Binghamton University graduate, you will become one of the outstanding individuals who have earned and are expanding the international reputation for excellence enjoyed by the University and the School of Management.

—Glenn A. Pitman, Dean

Programs and Curricular Focus

The School of Management has designed a curriculum to prepare students with the essential skill set needed to be competitive in today's rapidly changing corporate, nonprofit, or public sectors. The next generation of leaders will be expected to combine technical competence with a keen sense of the skills necessary for effective persuasion and negotiation. Consequently, Binghamton instills a generalist's perspective, integrating business fundamentals to bring about creative solutions that are new, different, and better.

The Four Semester program is designed for students who wish to combine their liberal arts, fine arts, science, or engineering background with business to create a dynamic career track. While no prerequisite business course work is required, a working knowledge of calculus and well-developed English and computer skills are expected. Only fall admission is available for full-time study. The first year consists of core courses that provide the base for more individualized study in the second year. In addition, the first year emphasizes the role of managers in today's society by integrating social responsibility, leadership, and cultural sensitivity. The second year includes advanced course work in each field while offering an opportunity to focus on a career specialization. Faculty members work as teams in the classroom,

integrating selected course material to illustrate the links across disciplines.

The Fast Track program offers an accelerated nine-month M.B.A. for students carefully selected based upon their solid foundation in business essentials. Only students who have graduated within five years from a school accredited by AACSB–The International Association for Management Education or the equivalent are accepted. Courses basically consist of the third and fourth semester of the Four Semester program. Only fall admission is available.

Students and the M.B.A. Experience

A growing number of students come to the University with several years of varied work experience. Most are from the northeastern United States, but, increasingly, students are drawn from other parts of the country and from abroad. This diversity enriches the fabric of life at the School of Management. About 40 percent of incoming students have a liberal arts and sciences degree, and 10 percent have training in engineering. Approximately 50 percent of incoming students are women, and the average age is 27 years. Fifteen percent are members of minority groups, and 40 percent are international students from more than eighteen countries.

The Faculty

The School of Management's 54 faculty members bring expertise in a wide range of theoretical, cultural, and practical perspectives. Faculty members come from top universities throughout the world and have published articles and books in the most prestigious journals in their respective fields. Teaching is highly valued; several faculty members have been honored with the University's top teaching awards.

The Business School Network

Binghamton encourages all students to participate in an internship as part of their M.B.A. experience. The Corporate Associates Program provides one such opportunity by allowing students to intern with top-level managers at local companies, such as Lockheed-Martin and New York State Electric and Gas. Top-level managers from throughout the country are also invited to Binghamton to meet with students in the Executive-in-Residence program.

The School has also developed a mentor program to sharpen student skills through working one-on-one with a business professional. Students meet with their mentors several times over the course of the year to discuss how to apply classroom learning to real business situations.

The College and Environs

Binghamton's campus is compactly designed, well maintained, and noted for its scenic setting on a wooded hillside near the Susquehanna River. The University has a 1.5-million volume multibranch research library, a state-of-the-art computer center, and exceptional facilities for the fine and performing arts, including several theaters, music listening and practice rooms, and dance, art, sculpture, and graphics studios. Exhibitions and performances by University groups and internationally known artists add to the cultural richness of the campus. Extensive recreational and physical education facilities are also available. The Nature Preserve, a

117-acre forest and wetland area with a 6-acre pond, forms the southern boundary of the campus.

Placement

Students benefit from the many services and resources offered by the Career Development Office. The office staff assists students with meeting immediate career goals as well as with lifelong career planning. Specially trained counselors are available to work with students one-on-one as requested; however, the vast resources of the office make it easy to self-direct a job search. Services offered by the Binghamton Career Development Office include resume development, a candidate referral system, campus interviews, a job hotline, individual counseling, career workshops,

a career resource library, an alumni career network, and a career development Web page.

Admission

General requirements are a baccalaureate degree from a college or university of recognized standing, two official transcripts of all previous college work, two letters of recommendation from persons acquainted with the applicant's academic achievements (for recent graduates) or with work-related performance (for those currently employed), official Graduate Management Admission Test (GMAT) scores, and a personal statement. Careful consideration is given to each of these items during the admission process. The Test of English as a Foreign Language (TOEFL) is required of most applicants

whose native language is not English; a minimum score of 570 is generally required for admission.

Finances

Estimated costs for full-time study for the 2000–01 academic year are as follows: annual tuition and fees for state residents, $5752, and, for nonresidents, $9130; housing and meals, $6666; and health insurance (twelve months), $341. These costs are subject to change and vary with a student's standard of living and costs for books, supplies, travel, and miscellaneous items. Preterm fees apply only in the first year and vary depending on the program.

Application Facts and Dates

Admission to the full-time Four-Semester and Fast Track program is for the fall semester only. Applications for part-time study are accepted for fall and spring for the regular (Four-Semester) M.B.A. program. (The Fast Track Program is not available for part-time study.) Applications are reviewed on a rolling basis and should be submitted no later than sixty days before the start of the semester in which a student plans to enroll. Applicants receive a decision within one month from the time that the completed application is received.

Graduate Admissions
School of Management
Binghamton University
P.O. Box 6015
Binghamton, New York 13902-6015
Telephone: 607-777-2316
E-mail: mba@binghamton.edu
World Wide Web:
    http://som.binghamton.edu

State University of New York at Buffalo

Buffalo, New York

QUALITY, VALUE, AND STATURE: OUR MBA DEFINED

These are exciting times for the University at Buffalo School of Management. Business Week has ranked the school as one of the nation's best and has cited our M.B.A. program as one of the "best values" in the country. These impressive endorsements are a testament to the career achievements of our students and to the effectiveness of recent innovations within our M.B.A. program. For instance, we are pioneering a core-competency program that has been praised by corporate recruiters and the Wall Street Journal. Our career placement office has received national and statewide awards citing the creative ways it prepares students for career success. We have launched a historic M.B.A. program in China that is infusing our domestic M.B.A. program with a unique global focus. We have equipped our classrooms with Internet access so that students can perform real-time business research during class instruction. These innovations are helping our students to launch rewarding careers, and they will fuel the worldwide reputation of our M.B.A. program in the new millennium.

—Lewis Mandell, Dean

Programs and Curricular Focus

The School of Management is one of the best business schools in the country, according to *Business Week,* and its M.B.A. program has been rated as one of the nation's best values. At the heart of the school's M.B.A. program is a challenging curriculum that develops expertise in fundamental business practices while emphasizing how to strategically apply those concepts in a global business environment. A major aspect of this M.B.A. philosophy is a commitment to team-based learning, designed to prepare students for success in the twenty-first century workplace, where they will be expected to lead and interact with colleagues from diverse social, political, and functional backgrounds.

The two-year, 60-credit, full-time M.B.A. program is built around a 30-hour core and flex-core curriculum that require students to complete nine courses in their first year as preparation for selection of one of the nine major options offered. Upon completion of the core, students begin to target their career direction and customize their program by choosing electives within the major options. Students are also required to participate in the School's highly regarded internship program, considered to be one of the largest and best in the country according to national statistics and student satisfaction surveys. The School of Management

receives more than 1,000 requests for interns per year from businesses, so students can select opportunities most valuable to their career goals. Upon completion of the curriculum, students have developed the critical-thinking, problem-solving, and career skills necessary for success in any business environment in the world.

Dual degree programs are available in law (J.D./M.B.A.), medicine (M.D./M.B.A.), pharmacy (Pharm.D./M.B.A.), architecture (M. Arch./M.B.A.), and geography (M.A./M.B.A.). The School of Management also offers joint undergraduate/M.B.A. degree programs in computer science, economics, engineering, geography, management, and sociology, which generally allow for completion of both degrees in five years instead of six. A three-year, part-time Professional M.B.A. program, a twenty-two–month Executive M.B.A. program, a Ph.D. in management program, and a one-year Master of Science in Accounting program are also offered.

Students and the M.B.A. Experience

The full-time student population of the M.B.A. program is composed of 300 talented individuals who come from a variety of backgrounds and possess a variety of prior work experiences. Many students receive tuition stipends through

assistantship and fellowship programs. The average age of students is 26 years. Thirty percent of the M.B.A. student population is international, and 40 percent are women. Students readily become acquainted with each other and draw from one another's experiences and expertise as a result of the program's team structure.

❖ Global Focus

A pioneer in the development of international business programs, the School of Management is uniquely positioned to prepare students for career success in a business world no longer defined by geographic or political boundaries. The School's history of innovation abroad includes operation of the first U.S.-accredited M.B.A. programs in China and Singapore. These international ventures lend a compelling global backdrop to all courses within the domestic M.B.A. program. Students who want to study the international world of business are offered exciting opportunities through the School's international internship program. The School also has student-exchange programs with institutions in Finland, France, Germany, Korea, Mexico, the Netherlands, and Singapore.

Special Features

The M.B.A. Advantage program greatly enhances the educational experience of its students by providing them with opportunities to develop professional and personal skills that give them a competitive edge in the job market. During a series of fun and informative activities and seminars, which begin during student orientation and continue throughout students' M.B.A. careers, students receive valuable instruction in team skills, problem solving, networking, and even business etiquette. Students who want to develop additional expertise in these areas can participate in the School's Personal Achievement through Competency Evaluation (PACE) program.

The Faculty

The M.B.A. faculty includes internationally renowned scholars in the fields of

University at Buffalo M.B.A. students regularly meet with corporate executives to discuss job opportunities and trends in various business fields.

accounting, finance, management science and systems, marketing, and human resources. Many faculty members have had articles published in top-tier academic journals, and their expertise is often cited by national business media. Six faculty members have received the prestigious SUNY Chancellor's Award for Excellence in Teaching.

The Business School Network

Buffalo is home to several Fortune 500 companies and numerous successful small and midsize businesses. CEOs and managers from these companies often lend their expertise to the M.B.A. program by serving as guest lecturers, case competition mentors and judges, M.B.A. Advantage program facilitators, and volunteer career counselors.

Prominent alumni of the School of Management include Mickey Drexler, CEO of The Gap; Linda Wachner, CEO of Warnaco; Jeremy Jacobs, owner of the Boston Bruins; Robert Rich Sr., chairman and founder of Rich Products; and David Gasiewicz, general manager of worldwide infrastructure operations for Microsoft.

The College and Environs

The University at Buffalo is New York's premier public center for graduate and professional education and the state's largest and most comprehensive public university. As the only public member of the prestigious Association of American Universities in New York and New England, the University at Buffalo ranks first among the nation's leading universities.

The second-largest city in New York State, Buffalo offers big-city attractions and convenience, while still being safe, livable, and easygoing. Buffalo has a first-rate orchestra; one of the leading modern art collections in the world, located in the Albright-Knox Art Gallery; a thriving theater district; professional sports teams; and a lively nightlife.

Technology Environment

The University at Buffalo is one of the nation's "most wired" campuses, according to *Yahoo! Internet Life* magazine. All incoming students must own or have access to a personal computer that meets the minimum standards of the University. The School of Management's computer lab is available daily to students. Since several School of Management classrooms provide computer interactivity at every seat, students may find it useful to have a notebook computer with an Ethernet card that they can bring to class. While ownership of a notebook computer is not required, it is especially recommended for students who major in accounting, finance, and management information systems.

Placement

Average starting salaries of the School's M.B.A. graduates have risen precipitously over the past few years due in large part to the expertise and creativity of the School's award-winning Career Resource Center. Each year, the center arranges nearly 1,000 on- and off-campus interviews for students with more than 200

companies. Students' career opportunities are also boosted by annual invitations to national M.B.A. consortia in Washington, D.C., and Chicago, exclusive corporate interviewing events for M.B.A. students from the nation's top business schools.

Admission

Individuals holding a bachelor's degree or an equivalent degree from an accredited college or university are welcome to apply to the M.B.A. program. Submission of a GMAT score is required. International students must submit a minimum score of 550 (paper-based) or 213 (computer-based) on the TOEFL and provide proof of adequate funds.

Average GMAT scores for accepted students typically range from 550 to 640, and full-time students possess an average of 3.2 years of prior work experience. Prospective students' undergraduate GPA and major, nature and length of prior work experience, and leadership attributes also factor into the admission process.

Finances

Tuition for 2000–01 is $5100 per year for in-state students and $8416 per year for out-of-state students. Many assistantships, fellowships, and scholarships for qualified students are offered. Prospective students should plan to take the GMAT as early as possible and should ideally complete their application by March 1 to be eligible for financial support. In general, graduate assistants receive a full or partial tuition waiver and stipend in return for a specified amount of work for a professor or administrator. Scholarships can take the form of one-time cash awards or ongoing financial assistance.

Application Facts and Dates

The application deadline for the full-time M.B.A. program is July 1. Students are admitted for the fall semester only. Once an application file is complete with all required official documents, a prospective student is usually notified within one month. For more information, applicants should contact:

Katherine Gerstle Ferguson
Assistant Dean and Administrative
   Director of the M.B.A. Program
State University of New York at
   Buffalo
206 Jacobs Management Center
Buffalo, New York 14260-4000
Telephone: 716-645-3204
      877-Bflo-MBA (toll-free)
Fax: 716-645-2341
E-mail: som-mba@buffalo.edu
World Wide Web: http://www.mgt.
   buffalo.edu

State University of New York at Stony Brook

W. Averell Harriman School for Management and Policy

Stony Brook, New York

MANAGING IN THE TWENTY-FIRST CENTURY

▶ *Businesses now operate penitentiaries and school districts. Nonprofit organizations compete with businesses in health-care delivery. Governments both regulate and encourage trade. One lesson is clear: business managers need to understand and be prepared to deal with nonprofit organizations and government agencies.*

At Harriman, we take this to heart. Our curriculum integrates knowledge about the three sectors into almost every course. Our Internship Program and Group Project course provide students with hands-on experience in all three sectors. Our faculty members perform research on the questions that arise as the sectors relate with one another.

This is how the Harriman School stands out among its peers. Come join the excitement!

—Dr. Thomas R. Sexton, Director

Programs and Curricular Focus

The W. Averell Harriman School for Management and Policy offers programs of study leading to the Master of Science degree in management and policy and the Master of Science degree in technology management. The curriculum for the M.S. in management and policy consists of eighteen courses totaling 60 credits, of which thirteen courses constitute the core. The remaining courses are electives that can be packaged to provide specialization in areas such as health-care management, human resource management, and information systems management. The master's degree elective options lead to New York State Advanced Certificates in human resource management, health-care management, and information systems management.

The M.S. degrees from the Harriman School are virtually identical to the M.B.A. degree. The School's curriculum devotes the same attention to managerial functions, such as accounting, finance, human resources, marketing, and operations, as do standard M.B.A. programs. Similarly, the Harriman School program, like leading M.B.A. programs, includes course work in economics, information systems, decision models, statistics, and strategy. Yet, the Harriman School program goes beyond most M.B.A. programs by exploring ways in which business, government, and nonprofit organizations interact. This is in keeping with the School's philosophy that

managers in the twenty-first century must be well versed in all three sectors to be truly effective.

For students interested in government, the Harriman School M.S. in management and policy is similar to an M.P.A. (Master of Public Administration). The principal difference is that the Harriman School program places more emphasis on computer information systems, quantitative decision analysis, and the interactions of government with business and nonprofit organizations. These are the areas that make the difference between a Harriman School graduate and one from a typical M.P.A. program. For students interested in nonprofit management, the Harriman program provides a rare educational experience. Students who are exposed to broad management issues are especially well prepared for careers in nonprofit management.

The Harriman School offers an additional program to students who qualify. The Advanced Credit Program is designed to supplement previous graduate education with management and policy analysis. The program consists of ten courses and an internship. The program normally leads to the M.S. in management and policy in one year.

Students and the Program Experience

Harriman's master's students are a diverse group. Students from all over the world bring their unique personal and

career-related experiences to the program. Many students come to Harriman following their undergraduate work, while others are established members of the business community seeking to broaden their career opportunities. The Harriman program exposes all students to theoretical and practical aspects of management.

Students gain practical experience through participation in the eight- to twelve-week paid internship program. Full-time students typically complete the internship requirement during the summer between their first and second years. Students benefit from the program by gaining career-related experience. Students also establish contacts in business, government, or nonprofit organizations, depending on their interests.

Harriman students gain additional experience through participation in a group project course in which students, in conjunction with faculty members, serve as consultants to clients who request assistance for various projects. Students acquire hands-on experience and provide a valuable service to business, government, and nonprofit organizations.

The Faculty

Faculty members of the Harriman School are strongly committed to teaching and fostering working relationships with students inside and outside the classroom, while maintaining their involvement in research. In their research, Harriman professors examine complex issues and problems confronting today's managers and decision makers in high-technology businesses, nonprofit organizations, and government agencies. They analyze businesses and other institutions as well as the economic, regulatory, and technological forces underlying decision-making processes and ongoing changes within these organizations. They keep close contact not only with other researchers in the United States and abroad, but also with regional, national, and international businesses by conducting applied research projects and working as consultants.

Harriman School students benefit from this high-caliber research in several ways. Faculty members often revise and develop new course materials to incorporate current research into their teaching and instruction. They believe strongly that exposing students to the latest knowledge and management skills best prepares them for future challenges while making the classroom experience dynamic and stimulating. Harriman students work closely with professors, and all students are invited to participate in seminars conducted by the School's researchers.

The Business School Network

The location of the Harriman School within the College of Engineering and Applied Sciences provides the Harriman School with a unique link to regional industry. The Harriman School participates in the Strategic Partnership for Industrial Resurgence (SPIR), which provides funds from New York State to promote relationships between the School and the business community. Students are encouraged to work with faculty members on SPIR projects. The Harriman School also invites business leaders to speak in an executive lecture series, allowing students the opportunity to interact with individuals who are shaping the managerial environment of tomorrow.

The College and Environs

SUNY at Stony Brook is located on the North Shore of Long Island, 50 miles east of New York City, with easy access to the unparalleled resources of the metropolitan area. For those seeking alternatives to the urban scene, the area surrounding the University and points east offer several public beaches, thousands of acres of national forest, quaint villages, wineries, numerous historical sites, the Hamptons, and ferries to southern New England.

Technology Environment

The Harriman School maintains a thoroughly modern computing facility for its students. PCs equipped with the latest software are linked to the library, faculty members, the Internet, and the World Wide Web. The campus's computer complex consists of an IBM system with hundreds of remote devices on the campus. The Frank Melville Jr. Memorial Library houses more than 2 million volumes bound and in microformat and receives more than 14,000 serial publications annually.

Placement

The University Career Placement Center helps students explore their career objectives, identify career opportunities, and conduct successful job searches. Placement services include individual consulting sessions, workshops on essential job search skills, and coordination of internship and job interviews.

Admission

The Harriman School invites applications from individuals regardless of undergraduate major. Students who excel in the program typically have previous experience, academic or otherwise, with computers and quantitative methods. Prior to admission, students are required to have completed at least one semester of calculus with a grade of C or better and to submit a completed application for admission form with official transcripts from all universities and colleges attended, recent GMAT or GRE scores, three letters of reference, and a nonrefundable $50 application fee. International students whose native language is not English must submit a TOEFL score of 550 or above. Almost all admitted students have a GPA of 3.0 or better.

Finances

Tuition for the 2000–01 academic year is $2550 per semester for residents of New York and $4208 per semester for nonresidents. Part-time tuition costs are $213 per credit hour for residents and $351 per credit hour for nonresidents. Books and fees can be expected to add another $500 to $700 to the cost of study. Applicants are encouraged to apply for financial support, which the department awards based on merit. Need-based financial aid programs are also available and include New York State and federally guaranteed student loans as well as the Federal Work-Study Program.

University apartments range in cost from approximately $245 per month to approximately $1200 per month, depending on the size of the unit. Resident meal plans range from $1100 to $1400 per semester for a full meal plan. A budget plan for commuter students, based on a declining balance, is also available. Off-campus housing options include furnished rooms to rent, and houses and/or apartments to share that can be rented for $350 to $550 per month.

Application Facts and Dates

Completed applications for students seeking financial aid must be received no later than March 1 for admission in the fall. For those students not seeking financial aid, the deadline is April 15. Spring admission is possible; the application deadline is November 1. Financial awards are made in early April for the following academic year. For an application package, students should contact:

Office of Student Services
W. Averell Harriman School for
  Management and Policy
University at Stony Brook
Stony Brook, New York 11794-3775
Telephone: 516-632-7296
              516-632-7171
Fax: 516-632-8181
E-mail: oss@notes.cc.sunysb.edu
World Wide Web: http://www.sunysb.
  edu/harriman/home.htm

The State University of New York
Empire State College

Saratoga Springs, New York

THE COMPETENCY-BASED M.B.A. PROGRAM

As a leader in the field of adult, nontraditional higher education, Empire State College (ESC) has created a competency-based M.B.A. program designed for experienced managers. The program combines several weekend residencies, guided independent study, Web technology, and assessment of functional and managerial competencies to provide busy professionals with the opportunity to earn the degree they need to succeed in today's competitive business environment.

—Meredith Brown, Acting Director of Graduate Studies

Program and Curricular Focus

Empire State College's competency-based M.B.A. responds to the needs of today's managers by offering greater flexibility in study and recognition of learning acquired in the workplace. The program is designed for experienced managers who have the motivation and self-discipline to succeed in a Web-based, guided independent study program. The program consists of six course blocks that include Scanning the Business Environment (4), The Functional Core (24), Human Systems and Behavior (4), Managerial Effectiveness (12), Electives (12), and Business Strategy Practicum (4), for a total of 60 credits.

An essential element of the program is the utilization of the competing values management framework as an organizing method for assessing, developing, and applying competencies associated with eight primary managerial leadership roles. In addition, the M.B.A. program curriculum integrates three themes: ethics, globalization, and organizational effectiveness. Another feature of the program is the option to earn credit by demonstrating functional knowledge of business or managerial competency through a Web-based assessment process.

Students and the M.B.A. Experience

Empire State College M.B.A. students come to the program with three to five years of management experience and a wide range of undergraduate disciplines, including marketing, engineering, accounting, and management information systems. Seventy-six percent are men, 24 percent are women, and 20 percent of the enrolled students represent minority populations.

Students are expected to function independently in both managing many practical aspects of their education and completing the required course work. Yet, many of the courses emphasize team-based or interactive group activities carried out on the Internet, which creates a level of interdependence that ensures that the course work is properly addressed and completed. The initial residency experience for a course enables the instructor to establish a framework and common understanding about the topic being studied and the ways in which students can individually, and jointly, pursue that topic.

Special Features

Participants in ESC's competency-based M.B.A. program have the option of participating in an assessment process that gives them the opportunity to test out of up to 28 credits of M.B.A.-level courses based on knowledge and competence acquired at work or through self-study. In addition to the credits earned through these assessments, students may request transfer of up to 12 credits for courses taken in other accredited graduate programs, as long as those credits are less than seven years old and the grade earned was B or better. In most cases, transfer credits are applied to program electives. Transfer credit for functional core courses is possible if the student demonstrates that the course taken elsewhere was substantially comparable to its counterpart in the competency-based M.B.A. program.

The Faculty

Faculty members who teach in the M.B.A. program are employed either full- or part-time at Empire State College and also include some adjunct instructors. They bring with them a combination of industry experience and a broad range of academic expertise.

The Business School Network

Corporate Partnerships

Corporate leaders were involved in providing feedback and support for the M.B.A. program proposal developed by Empire State College, which resulted in its approval by the State University of New York and the New York State Education Department.

Students applying to the M.B.A. program must submit evidence documenting substantial support for their admission to the program from an employer or professional organization or, in the case of persons who are self-employed, as an individual business expense. Empire State College M.B.A. students are employed by corporations and organizations such as Bell Atlantic, Carrier, Daimler-Chrysler, United States Postal Service, Citizens Communications, and Duracell.

The College and Environs

The Office of Graduate Studies is located at the Empire State College Coordinating Center in historic Saratoga Springs, New York. The M.B.A. program is taught at a distance, with several weekend residencies held at conference centers in Saratoga Springs or Albany, New York.

Facilities

Empire State College students may use many public and private libraries' collections. The College, as part of the State University system, participates in the SUNY Open Access Program. Through this arrangement, students can borrow books from, and use the research facilities of, all State University four-year colleges and many of the community colleges. Local libraries and several statewide cooperative arrangements greatly extend the range of library resources available to all state residents.

The College also has a virtual library that is accessible through its Web page. For information, students can contact the ESC Center for Learning and Technology at 518-587-2100, ext. 422, or at 800-468-6372 (toll-free).

Placement

Empire State College M.B.A. students are actively employed at the time of acceptance. The Office of Alumni and Student Relations maintains links to Career Opportunities on their Web page at http://www.esc.edu/Alumni.

Admission

Admission to the Empire State College M.B.A. program is selective and competitive. The following academic prerequi-

sites are required: a bachelor's degree from a regionally accredited university or college; 3 credits of accounting, 6 credits of economics (micro and macro), and 3 credits of statistics; and computer and Internet literacy. GMAT scores are not required.

In order to be considered for admission, international students must have a minimum TOEFL score of 600 (paper-based) or 250 (computer-based), and undergraduate transcripts must be submitted to WES (World Education Services) for evaluation.

Finances

The Empire State College M.B.A. program charges a comprehensive fee of $5000 for 10 to 12 credits per twenty-four-week term or $3500 for 6 to 9 credits per twenty-four-week term. The comprehensive fee includes the cost of course instruction at weekend residencies, course instruction through Web-based courses, assessment of learning gained through work experience, review of applicable graduate transfer credit, and all mandatory college fees. Financial aid and fellowship information is available on the College's Web site, listed below.

Application Facts and Dates

The application deadlines are August 15 for fall term and January 15 for spring term. An online application is available at http://www.esc.edu/MBA.

For additional information, students should contact:

Office of Graduate Studies
Empire State College
28 Union Avenue
Saratoga Springs, New York 12866-4390
Telephone: 877-YOUR MBA (toll-free)
E-mail: mbainfo@esc.edu
World Wide Web: http://www.esc.edu/GRAD

FACULTY LIST

Alan Belasen, Ph.D., SUNY at Albany. Managerial competencies, leadership roles and effectiveness, organizational communication, corporate downsizing, change and development, TQM, organization theory and design.

Bidhan Chandra, Ph.D., SUNY at Buffalo. International management, multinational corporations, cross-cultural management, information technology, managerial finance, technology management.

Andrew DiNitto, Ph.D., SUNY at Albany. Western European politics, elite theory, political ideologies.

Charles Finn, Ph.D., Strathclyde, Scotland. Strategic planning, stakeholder analysis management, public and nonprofit organizations, banking regulations.

Michael Fortunato, Ph.D., Harvard. Decision analysis, corporate-competitive strategy, economies in transition.

Nancy Frank, Ph.D., SUNY at Albany. Organizational studies; social, political and legal environments of business; strategic management.

James Ghent, J.D., SUNY at Buffalo. Labor-management relations, employment law, antitrust and global competitiveness, human resource management, affirmative action—equal employment opportunity and comparable worth.

Carolyn Jarmon, Ph.D., Cornell. Corporate finance, marketing research, consumer decision making and behavior, distributed and individualized learning environments.

Otolorin Jones, Ph.D., Ohio. Micro- and macroeconomics, economic development, managerial economics, management, economics—public policy.

Kristine Kelly, Ph.D., SUNY at Albany. Organizational behavior, public management.

Jane Oppenlander, Ph.D., Union. Managerial decision making, management information systems.

Lokesh Rastogi, D.B.A., Nova. Accounting, strategic management, marketing, TQM, production control management, international business, human resource management.

Rosalyn Rufer, Ph.D., Rensselaer. Marketing, market analysis, strategic business planning.

Arnold Steigman, Ph.D., NYU. Planning and control in public-sector organizations, public personnel management, public budgeting and financial management systems.

Jeff Weiss, Ph.D., Harvard. Economics, health systems, leadership, international studies, public policy.

Suffolk University

Frank Sawyer School of Management

Boston, Massachusetts

IT ALL COMES DOWN TO TEACHING

At Suffolk University, students are our most important customers. We provide you with an exceptionally qualified faculty, a flexible, carefully crafted curriculum that prepares you to anticipate—not merely respond to—the political, social, and economic transformations of the coming decades. You graduate as a skilled, ethical manager—a leader as well as a team player—who blends theoretical and technical expertise with practical work experience in your field.

But we do not stop there. Every professor we hire must care passionately about teaching. I am proud of the faculty we have built: they are teachers who incorporate considerable scholarly research and professional experience into the classroom. Many are nationally and internationally known for their work and must juggle lecture, consulting, and research demands, but nothing interferes with their teaching and office hour schedules. Students are the highest priority.

Thousands of success stories have emerged from our classrooms. Come join us at Suffolk University Frank Sawyer School of Management. Let us help you create your own success story.

—John F. Brennan, Dean

Programs and Curricular Focus

The Suffolk University Sawyer School of Management enrolls 2,300 students, of whom 1,250 are graduate students. All degree programs are offered on a full- or part-time basis so that students can complete their graduate programs while still working in their chosen professions. The School offers fifteen degree programs, which include an executive program, degrees in public management (M.P.A.), and joint programs with the Law School. Class schedules are flexible, with courses offered in the daytime, late afternoon, and evenings and Saturdays so that students can keep full- or part-time positions or begin an internship or co-op job as part of a full-time course of study.

Suffolk's full-time faculty members have excellent academic training and credentials. Everything a student learns is grounded in the realities of professional experience. One professor might be a former vice president of Gillette, another a senior executive from a Big Six accounting firm or a consultant to a government or international agency. Students might include a portfolio manager from a brokerage firm or a nurse manager from a local hospital.

The M.B.A. program consists of eleven to sixteen courses, nine of which are electives. The five integrative core courses cover the major functional areas of management as they are applied within the business world. With strong undergraduate preparation in business, a student can waive core courses and complete the program in as few as eleven courses in ten months of full-time study or as few as sixteen months of part-time study. Courses are waived through equivalent academic work taken at the undergraduate or graduate level. Within the nine electives, students have the opportunity to specialize in more than a dozen areas, including finance, international business, CIS, accounting, marketing, and entrepreneurial studies. An eleven-course Accelerated M.B.A. for Attorneys program and an Accelerated M.B.A. for CPAs are also available.

The Sawyer School offers graduate degree programs in specialty areas, as well as several joint-degree programs. The Master of Science in Accounting (M.S.A.), Master of Science in Taxation (M.S.T.), Master of Science in Finance (M.S.F.), Master of Science in Financial Services/Banking (M.S.F.S.B.), and Master of Science in Entrepreneurial Studies (M.S.E.S.) are offered. There are also several health-related programs. These include an M.B.A. with a concentration in health administration; an M.P.A. with a concentration in health administration; an M.P.A. with a concentration in disability studies; and a Master of Health Administration. Joint degrees include the M.B.A./J.D., M.S.F./J.D., M.P.A./J.D.,

and a Master of Science in International Economics (M.S.I.E.)/J.D. in the College of Liberal Arts and Sciences. There are Executive M.B.A. and accelerated M.P.A. programs, with classes taught only on Saturdays. A combined M.B.A./G.D.P.A. (Graduate Diploma in Professional Accounting) and a combined M.P.A./M.S. in mental health counseling are also available.

Students and the M.B.A. Experience

Diversity and flexibility are the keys to the M.B.A. programs at Suffolk University. Students in the M.B.A. degree programs have an average of three to five years of work experience, while students in the Executive M.B.A. program may have ten or more years of experience. Full-time M.B.A. students are not required to have work experience. Last year the average work experience for full-time students was 3.8 years. The average age is 27 in the M.B.A. programs and 34 in the Executive M.B.A. program. Women comprise approximately 40 percent of each program. Approximately 12 percent of the graduate students are international students from more than twenty countries. In the full-time M.B.A. program, at least one third of the students are international.

❖ Global Focus

Each year more than 350 international students from sixty-two countries come to Boston to attend Suffolk University. A global perspective is an integral part of the Sawyer School at every level—curriculum, faculty, student body, and linkages to the international business community. In addition, the Sawyer School offers a selection of international business courses, including short seminars and site visits to businesses, universities, and government agencies in China, the Czech Republic, England, France, Ireland, Italy, and Spain. Not all sites are visited every year.

The University also maintains the Center for International Education, which supports the English Language for Internationals (ELI) program, sponsors short-term executive programs for internationals, and provides full-time assistance to international students for immigration advising, housing placement, and travel purposes. The center also sponsors orientation and other short-term cultural programs for international students.

The Faculty

Suffolk faculty members are well known for their expertise in such diverse fields as international management, investment analysis and financial policy, direct marketing, personal selling, buyer behavior, health-care marketing, public accounting, total quality management, and professional ethics. There are more than 60 full-time faculty members, 93 percent of whom hold Ph.D. degrees, giving the Sawyer School one of the highest faculty-Ph.D. ratios in the country.

The Business School Network

Corporate Partnerships

Suffolk's Sawyer School of Management maintains close ties with senior managers in both the public and private sectors through active advisory boards that meet regularly with the faculty of each department. Advisory board members include representatives from the Big Six accounting firms, banks, and insurance companies, in addition to executives from large and small businesses, health administrators, government officials, and managers in not-for-profit organizations. Students in the full-time M.B.A. program have an opportunity to complete internships or co-op experiences with such firms as Gillette, Polaroid, Fidelity, John Hancock, and the Federal Reserve Bank in Boston.

Prominent Alumni

The Sawyer School of Management is proud of its more than 6,000 graduate alumni. Among these are Edward McDonnell, former President of Seagram International, and Richard Rosenberg, former CEO of Bank of America. Both have been actively involved in speaking with the alumni and with current students.

The College and Environs

Boston, a dynamic center of education, culture, and commerce for centuries and a truly liveable city, is home to the Sawyer School. Located on historic Beacon Hill in the heart of Boston, Suffolk University was founded in 1937 and comprises the Sawyer School of Management, the College of Liberal Arts and Sciences, and the Law School, with a total enrollment

of 6,200 students. The Sawyer School is the only school of management in New England to be accredited by both AACSB–The International Association for Management Education and the National Association of Schools of Public Affairs and Administration (NASPAA).

The urban location of the University, next door to the Massachusetts State House, is a special advantage. Students are within walking distance of Boston's financial and world trade districts, the center of government, renowned medical centers, and major cultural institutions. The location and reputation of the School of Management make it possible to draw upon the resources and expertise of these institutions to complement and enrich its approach to global business.

Technology Environment

Students have access to the University's PRIME 6350 superminicomputer seven days a week from computer stations on campus or by phone. Electronic access is available to the worldwide Internet system and the LEXIS–NEXIS service. There are a University-wide electronic mail system and user access to online library services such as ABI/INFORM. Microcomputer resources are centered in a modern computing facility, which includes a large student computer laboratory, two computer laboratory classrooms, computerized case classrooms, and a computer station in the graduate student lounge. A separate facility is dedicated to word processing. Multimedia amphitheater classrooms with videoconferencing capabilities enhance learning.

Placement

Career services available to graduate students include the Alumni/ae Career Resources Network, which is an active association of more than 275 recent graduates in every area of management. Network members serve as an important source of information and contacts for job search strategies and placement.

Other career services include career assessment and individual career counseling; extensive listings of full- and part-time jobs, co-op opportunities, and internships; workshops on resumes and interview and job search strategies; a comprehensive career library; regularly scheduled career fairs and an Executive Speaker Seminar Series; and on- and off-campus recruitment programs.

Admission

The Sawyer School of Management seeks qualified, capable applicants with

distinguished undergraduate degrees from diverse educational and professional backgrounds. To apply, students must submit an application, transcripts of all academic work, GMAT scores, two letters of recommendation, a current resume, and a statement of professional goals. M.P.A. students are not required to submit any test scores. Applicants to the J.D./M.B.A. program and the Accelerated M.B.A. for Attorneys program may substitute the LSAT for the GMAT. CPAs with an undergraduate GPA of 2.7 or above waive the GMAT.

International applicants must submit a TOEFL score of at least 213 and a statement of financial resources.

Finances

The Sawyer School of Management offers several innovative financial aid programs. Last year, graduate management students were awarded more than $3 million in aid in the form of grants, loans, employment programs, fellowships, and assistantships. Tuition varies by program. The annual costs are $18,450 full-time or $1845 per course for the M.B.A., $16,920 full-time or $1692 per course for the M.P.A. and the M.H.A., and $20,160 full-time or $2016 per course for the M.S.F. and the M.S.F.S.B. The annual costs are $18,450 full-time or $1845 per course for the M.S.A., the M.S.T., and the M.S.E.S; $2265 per course for the Executive M.B.A.; and $21,750 per year for the M.B.A./J.D. and the M.P.A./J.D. Additional costs are estimated at $10,000 per year.

Application Facts and Dates

Suffolk University accepts applications for fall (September), spring (January), or summer (May). The M.S.F. and Executive M.B.A. programs admit students in the fall and spring only. Application deadlines are June 15 for fall, November 15 for spring, and April 15 for summer. For the M.S.F. program, application dates are June 15 and November 15. For the Executive M.B.A. program, the deadlines are August 15 and February 15. Students applying for financial aid for the fall semester must submit their admission application by March 15. For more information, students should contact:

Judith L. Reynolds
Director of Graduate Admission
Suffolk University
8 Ashburton Place
Boston, Massachusetts 02108
Telephone: 617-573-8302
Fax: 617-523-0116
E-mail: grad.admission@admin.
suffolk.edu

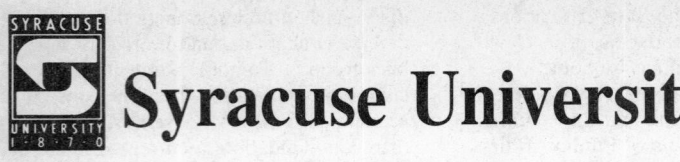

Syracuse University

THE M.B.A. FOR THE ROAD AHEAD

Long before most business schools, we embarked on a journey to redefine the M.B.A. We challenged the assumptions of traditional theory-based programs. We recognized the need to equip our students to compete in the global economy. We investigated opportunities presented by increasing diversity. We examined the role of ethics in business practice and the need for responsible use of natural resources. Our retooled curriculum met with resounding acclaim. Our strategic shift in approach to educating the next generation of leaders set a national trend among other schools. And more than ever, our graduates are achieving remarkable success in an extraordinary range of industries. With a Syracuse M.B.A., you'll be uniquely positioned to take your career across borders and time zones as a key corporate player or global entrepreneur. Wherever you want to go, if you have the drive, you can get there from here.

—George R. Burman, Dean

Programs and Curricular Focus

The M.B.A. curriculum is based on the premise that all managers need broad knowledge and skills, as well as functional expertise. The seven pervasive theme courses are the signature of the new curriculum. The themes—diversity, globalization, quality, ethics, the environment, critical thinking, and paradigms of management—represent the challenges that pervade every function of management today.

The heart of the curriculum is its integrated group of professional core courses that introduce the concepts of the functional areas of business and the relationships that exist among them. Seven elective courses are also integral to the program, offering students the opportunity to tailor the program to their own professional and career interests.

Concentrations are offered in nine areas: accounting, finance, general management, global entrepreneurship, innovation management, management of technology, marketing management, strategic management of human resources, and supply chain management. Elective courses may also be selected from any other graduate program at Syracuse University; engineering, communications, law, computer science, and economics are such examples. Joint-degree programs may also be designed that combine a master's degree in any other graduate program with an M.B.A.

The M.B.A. program includes a 60-credit curriculum that comprises 39 credits of required courses and 21 credits of electives. During the first year, students follow a prescribed sequence that includes pervasive theme courses, personal skills courses, and most professional core courses. During the second year, students complete their required core courses, as well as seven electives. There is an accelerated M.B.A. program for those who hold an undergraduate degree in management and have significant work experience.

Additional graduate degree programs include the Master of Science (M.S.) in accounting, the M.S. in finance, the Juris Doctor (J.D./M.B.A. and J.D./M.S. in accounting) in cooperation with the College of Law, the M.S. in media management offered jointly with the S.I. Newhouse School of Public Communications, and an independent study M.B.A. program.

Students and the M.B.A. Experience

The Syracuse M.B.A. program has a diverse, talented, and interactive student body. More than one third of the 200 full-time M.B.A. students are women, 18 percent are minorities, and 40 percent are from other countries. Approximately 98 percent of the M.B.A. students have worked full-time for at least one year prior to enrolling; the average is more than four years.

Undergraduate majors include such diverse areas as history, engineering, nursing, accounting, and economics. Students are placed in teamwork groups of 4 to 5 individuals of various educational/professional experiences and backgrounds; these groups, in addition to small classes averaging 30 students, help create a feeling of intimacy within a large collegiate environment of 14,000 students and prepare graduates for today's team-oriented organizational environment.

❖ Global Focus

There are both required and elective courses in international business. In the summer, courses are offered in Shangai and internship programs are offered in Hong Kong, London, and Singapore. As a member of the Thunderbird consortium of business schools, students can spend a semester of study at The American Graduate School of International Management in Arizona or at any of their campuses abroad. Another important aspect of the program is that students from other countries contribute to a global classroom experience.

Special Features

New students begin the fall semester with Leadership Week, a five-day orientation program; participants include the faculty and distinguished business leaders. Leadership Week offers new students opportunities for building teams and support groups and an introduction to other personal skills areas, including managing conflict, communication, ethics in management, and teamwork and groups.

The Faculty

The members of the faculty of the Syracuse School of Management are distinguished by their accomplishments in research and consulting, their effectiveness in the classroom, and their genuine concern for students. Teaching methods vary from subject to subject, as appropriate. Methods of instruction include lectures, student presentations, class discussions, case studies, small-group projects, computer and management simulations, and other techniques. Instructional methods take full advantage of the program's small group structure and unique experience base represented by the students in the program.

The Business School Network

"In considering new hires," says Peter M. Sturtevant, a vice president of Xerox Corporation, "one of the qualities we look for is the ability to be a quick study—to get a good understanding of the company quickly."

Syracuse M.B.A. program graduates are quick studies because they can draw on broad exposure to business and business practitioners. Corporate ties are woven throughout the fabric of the program, affording contact with managers in every relevant field and speciality. This explains why graduates find themselves at home in today's complex corporate environment.

The College and Environs

Founded in 1870, Syracuse University—a private, nonsectarian liberal arts institution—is one of the largest and most comprehensive independent universities in the nation. The School of Management, in existence since 1919, has offered graduate programs since 1947. The fiftieth anniversary of the Syracuse M.B.A. was recently celebrated.

Syracuse is a moderately sized, friendly city located in upstate New York. New York City, Boston, Philadelphia, Toronto, and Montreal are all less than a one-half-day drive away. Most importantly, being so close to these major metropolitan centers provides ease of access for graduates to the vast northeastern U.S. M.B.A. job market.

Facilities

The University libraries serve the informational and research needs of the entire Syracuse University community. The library system is one of the largest in the country and ranks in the top 2 percent of university libraries nationally. It contains more than 6 million books, periodicals, and pieces of microform information housed in the main Ernest Stevenson Bird Library and five branch libraries. Also available are sixteen microcomputer clusters of twenty to fifty IBM and Macintosh personal computers, which are found at several campus locations, including two at the School of Management.

Placement

The Career Center provides M.B.A. students with personal help on developing interview skills, resume preparation, alumni networking, and access to on-campus corporate recruiting. In 1999, graduates averaged

$70,000 in starting salary, considerably above the national average for M.B.A. graduates. Employers of the class of 1999 included such diverse organizations as Andersen Consulting, Ford, IBM, LG International, UTC/Carrier, and Xerox.

Admission

Applicants must submit transcripts of all previous college work, their GMAT and TOEFL scores, a completed application for admission, and letters of recommendation, together with a $40 application fee. Prior work experience is strongly preferred, and personal interviews are encouraged. An online application can be found at http://Embark.com.

Finances

Tuition in 2000–01 is $613 per credit ($18,390 for an academic year of 30 credits). Books and other course materials are estimated at $1200 per academic year.

Approximately 30 percent of the M.B.A. students receive merit-based assistance in the form of fellowships, assistantships, or scholarships. Fellowships include full remittance of tuition plus a generous stipend. For 2000–01, scholarships include 10–30 credits of remitted tuition, and assistantships include a stipend of $2000 to $8000. Most assistantships also include a scholarship.

Application Facts and Dates

Applications for admission to the full-time M.B.A. program should be submitted by May 1 for fall admission.

For more information, applicants should contact:

For the master's programs:

Paula A. Charland, Assistant Dean
M.B.A. and Master's Admission and
    Financial Aid Office
Suite 100
School of Management
Syracuse University
Syracuse, New York 13244-2130
Telephone: 315-443-9214
Fax: 315-443-9517
E-mail: MBAinfo@som.syr.edu
World Wide Web: http://www.Embark.
  com

For the Ph.D. program:

Associate Dean S. P. Raj, Director
Ph.D. Program
Suite 200/Dean's Office
School of Management
Syracuse University
Syracuse, New York 13244-2130
Telephone: 315-443-1001
Fax: 315-443-5389
World Wide Web: http://www.som.syr.
  edu

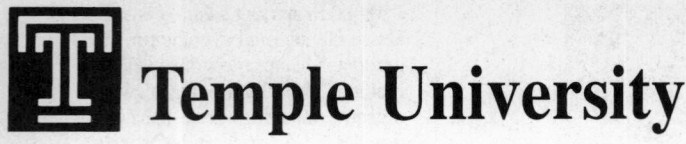

Temple University

DEVELOPING BUSINESS LEADERS FOR THE TWENTY-FIRST CENTURY

▶ *Fox M.B.A. students acquire the knowledge and the analytical, leadership, and communication skills needed for success in top management positions.*
— Linda J. Whelan, Director

Programs and Curricular Focus

The new Fox School M.B.A. curriculum builds upon a tradition of teaching team-based, quality-oriented, and cross-functional models of management. Students develop practical expertise through case analyses and presentations, interaction with business practioners, and team projects. The program has six core and ten advanced courses. Advanced courses include 12 credits of advanced managerial perspectives covering topics such as managing people and organizations; law and ethics in management; information technology perspectives; globalization, managing risk; and valuation of the firm, innovation, and entrepreneurship. This sequence demonstrates how business functions drive organizations and enable students to analyze organizations as a total enterprise. In developing expertise in one area, students may select from ten concentrations, including accounting, business administration, e-business, finance, general and strategic management, health-care management, human resource administration, international business, management information systems, and marketing. The Fox School's capstone sequence gives students a competitive edge in today's marketplace. This two-course sequence addresses industry dynamics and emphasizes the integration of previous course work to provide students with the comprehensive knowledge and understanding of strategic management processes, techniques, concepts, and skills. The sequence takes a problem-solving approach to understanding industry dynamics and the integration of the various functional areas of the firm to the development of managerial strategies. A unique industry focus allows the establishment of sustainable linkages with line and staff executives in an industry sector driving the new economy,

including financial services, health-care, information technology, pharmaceutical technology/biotechnology, and tourism. Evening classes and part- or full-time study at Temple University Center City (1616 Walnut Street) and Temple University Fort Washington (suburban Montgomery County) make the program convenient to the working professionals who comprise 80 percent of the 1,198 M.B.A. students. M.B.A. core courses are currently available online. Graduate students can earn a variety of degrees, including M.B.A., Executive M.B.A., International M.B.A., M.S.B.A., and Ph.D. degrees in business administration; M.A. and Ph.D. degrees in economics; M.S. and Ph.D. degrees in statistics; and an M.S. degree in actuarial science. Dual M.B.A. degrees include the M.B.A./M.S. in health administration/health-care financial management, the M.B.A./M.S. in e-business (full-time only), the M.S. in e-business, the M.B.A./J.D. (with the School of Law), the M.B.A./M.S. in environmental health (with the College of Engineering), and the D.M.D./M.B.A. (with the School of Dentistry). All programs are accredited by AACSB–The International Association for Management Education. The twenty-two-month Executive M.B.A. program prepares managers with ten or more years of experience (including five years in management) for top-level positions. Classes meet on alternate Fridays and Saturdays, allowing participants to complete their studies without interrupting their careers. The eleven-month International M.B.A. program, offered in collaboration with the IGS University in Paris, France, prepares students for management careers in today's global marketplace by requiring students to live and study in Paris, Tokyo, and Philadelphia and by integrating live case studies in global management and entrepreneur-

ship into the curriculum. The full-time, day M.B.A./.M.S. in e-business program educates students for e-business enterprises. This unique program combines advanced knowledge of management strategy with a solid understanding of information systems and e-business concepts and practices. It provides intensive, practical coverage of applicable business and technology topics, an entrepreneurial project for a Web-based start-up business, and an IT industry internship. The program also provides opportunities for interaction with industry practitioners through the School's eBusiness Institute. The Master of Science in Business Administration (M.S.B.A.) programs provide in-depth knowledge of one discipline and comprise ten courses. M.S. programs are offered in accounting, e-business, finance, health-care financial management, human resource administration, management information systems, marketing, risk management and insurance, and statistics. Most students hold an undergraduate business degree; those who don't must complete the business core. The Master of Science (M.S.) in actuarial science and statistics are professional research degrees; each comprises ten courses plus a comprehensive examination. The part-time M.S. in e-business is designed for managers and executives who wish to add a working knowledge of information systems and e-business concepts and practices to their advanced knowledge of management practice. This program is designed for students who already possess a graduate degree in business. Those holding a B.S. degree in business administration may be considered for admission into this program. The doctoral programs in business administration, economics, and statistics equip candidates with the knowledge and skills to attain faculty positions at leading universities or to pursue research careers in the public or private sector. The Ph.D. in business administration program offers a choice of eight fields of study: accounting, finance, general and strategic management, health-care management, human resource administration, international business, marketing, and risk management. Students are expected to have a general

understanding of the management environment before beginning doctoral-level courses and must demonstrate competence in economic analysis, behavioral science, and research methodology. All doctoral candidates must demonstrate the ability to do independent research by completing a dissertation.

Students and the M.B.A. Experience

Eighty percent of Temple M.B.A. students establish their careers before enrolling in graduate school. The average age of the student body is 30; the average amount of work experience is six years. Eighty percent work full-time and attend Temple part-time. Forty percent have undergraduate degrees in business. Most students are from the mid-Atlantic region; 12 percent are international. Enrollment of members of minority groups is approximately 10 percent. A variety of professional development activities — personal career counseling, a resume databank, on- and off-campus recruiting, mentor program, "Executives in the Classroom" program, and workshops — foster career preparation and opportunities. In addition, as part of the curriculum students are encouraged to complete a series of professional development modules. Temple's Fox School of Business and Management is a major supplier of managerial talent to the Philadelphia region, the nation's fifth-largest metropolitan area. Its extensive network includes 40,000 alumni, most of whom live and work in the region. Regional business leaders, including alumni, are actively involved in the M.B.A. program. They sponsor consulting projects and internships, serve as mentors and guest speakers, and offer input on curriculum. The M.B.A. Student Association helps students build a network through guest speakers, professional development programs, and social events. The organization is actively involved in the orientation program and the annual Spring Banquet.

The Faculty

Graduate faculty members challenge students to analyze, anticipate, and innovate. Committed to teaching excellence, many of the 125 full-time graduate faculty members are internationally recognized in their fields. They pursue a wide range of research activities. Faculty contacts with businesses established through research and consulting enhance the learning experience.

The Business School Network

Temple University is a major supplier of managerial talent to the Philadelphia region. Regional business leaders serve as "Executives in the Classroom," sponsor consulting projects and internships, serve as mentors, and offer curriculum input. The Fox School has more than 40,000 graduates, most of whom live and work in the region. Prominent alumni include Dennis Alter, Chairman and CEO, Advanta Corporation; Robert M. Greber, President and CEO, Pacific Stock Exchange; Lacy Hunt, Ph.D., Chief Economist, USA, HSBC Holdings; Wayne Leevy, Vice Chairman, Mitchell & Titus, LLP; Gail F. Lieberman, Vice President–Managing Director and CFO, Moody's Investors Service; Nicholas A. Rago, Senior Vice President, Service Companies, the Dial Corporation; Samuel H. Steinberg, Chief Executive Officer, the Graduate Hospital.

The College and Environs

Founded in 1884, Temple University is a senior comprehensive research institution that awards bachelor's degrees in 100 disciplines, master's degrees in eighty disciplines, and doctoral degrees in sixty. More than 28,000 students are enrolled in the University's sixteen schools and colleges. Philadelphia, the fifth-largest city in the United States, is an international center of commerce, culture, and history. Strategically located in the dynamic industrial region between New York and Washington, D.C., the region is home to thousands of small, midsize, and large businesses.

Facilities

Graduate students have access to state-of-the-art library and computer facilities at the Fort Washington, Center City, and Main campuses. Each campus has an extensive network and a Scholar's Information Center, a network of research databases. Students can borrow books from Paley Library, the University's main research library.

Placement

The M.B.A. and M.S. Placement Office develops job leads for students and alumni. Services include individual career assistance, on- and off-campus recruiting, corporate presentations, a resume databank, workshops, mentoring, and a resume book. During the 1998–99 academic year, more than 100 companies interviewed Temple M.B.A. students.

Admission

Students may start the M.B.A. program in the fall, spring, or summer. The acceptance rate is approximately 50 percent of the number of complete applications received. The average GMAT score is 540 in the evening program, and the average undergraduate grade point average is 3.1. Work experience is encouraged. Full-time M.B.A./M.S. in e-business program candidates have an average GMAT of 600 and a grade point average of 3.2.

Finances

Graduate tuition at Temple University is among the lowest in Pennsylvania. Tuition for the academic year 1999–2000 was $348 per credit hour for Pennsylvania residents and $488 for nonresidents. Most part-time students take 3 to 6 credits per semester. Full-time students take 9 to 15 credits per semester. Students who work full-time may find that their employers have a tuition reimbursement program. Temple offers some assistantships and scholarships for full-time, matriculated M.B.A. students. For more information on financial aid, those interested should contact the Financial Aid Office (Temple University, Conwell Hall, 2nd Floor, Philadelphia, Pennsylvania 19122; telephone: 215-204-1492). Affordable housing is available both on and off campus.

Application Facts and Dates

The application deadlines are April 15 for the fall semester, September 30 for the spring semester, and March 15 for the summer semester. Students should address application inquiries to:

Mr. Natale Butto, Director of Admissions
The Fox School of Business and Management
Speakman Hall, Room 5
Temple University
Philadelphia, Pennsylvania 19122
Telephone: 215-204-7678
Fax: 215-204-8300
E-mail: butto@sbm.temple.edu
World Wide Web: http://www.sbm.temple.edu/mba/

Texas A&M International University

Laredo, Texas

A MICROCOSM OF INTERNATIONAL BUSINESS

We take pride in the tradition of providing specialized graduate business education to our small but very dynamic cadre of students. During the last two decades, we have trained more than 500 M.B.A.'s with specialization in international trade. Recently we have added the M.S. in international banking and the M.S. in international logistics to the list of pioneering programs.

Students in the Graduate School of International Trade and Business Administration have lived and studied in a microcosm of international business. In addition to having gone through an eminently specialized curriculum, they have benefitted from interaction with a highly diversified faculty and student body. The faculty in the College of Business represents ten countries, and the alumni, sixty-three countries and forty states.

—Dr. John Kohl, Dean

Programs and Curricular Focus

In foreseeing the ever-accelerating changes in the global economy and international commerce, the Graduate School of International Trade and Business Administration has pioneered specialized graduate business programs responsive to the world's dynamic business environment. These specialized programs include an M.B.A. in International Trade; M.B.A. in International Banking; and an M.S. in International Logistics. In addition to these specialized programs, a general M.B.A. (taught either in English or Spanish), an M.S. in Information Systems, and a Master of Professional Accountancy (M.P.Acc.) are also offered.

The M.B.A. in International Trade prepares students from a broad spectrum of experiences, cultures, and academic disciplines with the skills necessary to assume leadership roles in the international business community. The M.B.A. in International Banking prepares a cadre of international business leaders with a mastery of the various activities of international banking and a thorough knowledge of different functions performed by international banks. The M.S. in International Logistics prepares students with the skills to assume leadership roles in this vital portion of the international transportation community. This program, although traditional in approach, emphasizes Electronic Data Interchange (EDI) and international transportation. The program introduces students to basic transportation research methods combined with an overview of the traditional logistics disciplines in addition to an introduction to computer science.

All the graduate programs are composed of twelve courses (the M.S. programs have the choice of substituting two courses for a thesis). To ensure that students are prepared to pursue a business curriculum, as many as seven prerequisite business courses may be required. Students having completed prior business courses may apply for course waivers.

Students and the M.B.A. Experience

Students bring to the classroom a wide variety of academic backgrounds, such as international relations, area studies, various business disciplines, foreign languages, and other degree fields. They emanate from all regions of the world. Since 1979, sixty-five countries and forty states have been represented in these specialized international business programs. The average age of the graduate business student is 27.

❖ Global Focus

The strength of the programs is exemplified by a curriculum that consists of forty graduate international business courses; a faculty with extensive practical international business experience; international exposure through study or exchange programs throughout the world; research opportunities and activities that include publication of *The International Trade Journal, Border Business Indicators,* and the *NAFTA Digest;* and an internationally diverse student body.

The geographic location of the University is Laredo, Texas, which is one of the United States's largest inland ports of trade, the second-fastest-growing city in the U.S.,

and the only city on the juncture of Interstate 35 and the Pan American Highway. This provides an ideal "laboratory" to observe international business activities on a daily basis.

The Faculty

The faculty members have a diverse and international background. Approximately 84 percent of the faculty members have extensive international business experience or are foreign nationals. Faculty members collectively possess functional literacy in twenty different languages and have living and/or working experience in Africa, Europe, the Middle East, South and Central America, and Asia.

The College and Environs

Texas A&M International University is one of the newest university campuses in the United States. Founded in 1969 as Texas A&I at Laredo, the University was located on the historic site of old Fort McIntosh. In fall 1995, the University experienced major innovative changes such as becoming a comprehensive University offering a wide variety and level of degrees and majors, many of which have an international component.

Located in south Texas, the city of Laredo is approximately 150 miles from San Antonio, Corpus Christi, and Monterrey, Mexico. Established at an important gateway between the United States and Latin America, Laredo is one of the fastest growing cities in the United States.

Facilities

In fall 1995, Texas A&M International University moved into a brand-new, state-of-the-art campus in northeast Laredo. Phases I and II of construction include a joint library and administration building; business administration, science, arts and humanities, and all-purpose classroom buildings; and a kinesiology convocation building. Phase III, which began in spring 2000, includes the Center for the Study of Western Hemispheric Trade and the Student Development Center. There are also on-campus garden-style apartments, featuring card-access fencing; one-, two-, and four-bedroom units; a small computer lab; a pool; a clubhouse; sand volleyball courts; and laundry facilities.

Technology Environment

There are eight student-access computing laboratories with more than 260 IBM Pentiums and/or Power Macintoshes for instructional purposes. These facilities are open 90 hours per week. In addition, all classrooms have audio/visual capabilities and some have sophisticated multimedia capabilities. There is also a Trans Texas Video Network in place, which provides two-way interactive videoconference capabilities between sixty locations statewide.

Placement

Graduate Student Services and Career Planning and Placement provide a spectrum of services to students and graduates in the areas of career development and professional employment. Professional staff members advise students on all aspects of career preparation and the job search.

Recruiters visit the University each March for annual career fairs. Other services include a career resources library, posting of current job vacancies, a candidate referral service, on-campus recruitment, and student employment.

Admission

Students can enter the University in any semester. Full graduate standing is granted to applicants whose undergraduate GPA in all upper-division course work is at least 3.0 (on a 4.0 scale). Applicants are also required to submit GMAT or GRE scores.

Students who do not have at least one year of full-time academic studies at an accredited U.S. college or university or who come from a country where English is not the official language must earn a minimum score of 550 on the TOEFL. Students who do not have a satisfactory TOEFL score may enroll in Texas A&M International University's International Language Institute, which offers intensive English language courses, TOEFL preparation courses, and an institutional TOEFL. Students must also present proof of adequate funds for educational expenses.

Finances

Tuition and fees for 1999–2000 were $992.70 for a 12-semester-hour load for Texas residents and $3584.70 for non-Texas residents and international students. Full-time students generally take 12 hours per long term, summer being optional. Books and supplies average $85 per class.

All students enrolled in one of the graduate business programs are eligible to apply for fellowships. The fellowships are competitive and awarded according to merit criteria. The fellowship permits out-of-state and international students to pay in-state tuition and gives them a stipend.

International Students

Fifty percent of the full-time students are foreign nationals. In any given semester, 25 percent are from Asia, 25 percent are from Latin America, and 20 percent are from Europe, Africa, and the Middle East, with the remaining 30 percent emanating from both near and far states. Students needing to strengthen their English may do so at the University's International Language Institute.

Application Facts and Dates

Applications are accepted for any semester. Students are encouraged to begin the admissions process as far in advance as possible. For more information, applicants should contact:

Ms. Kriztella I. Lopez-Melendez
Director of Graduate Student Services
Texas A&M International University
5201 University Boulevard
Laredo, Texas 78041-1900
Telephone: 956-326-2270
Fax: 956-326-2769
E-mail: coba@tamiu.edu
World Wide Web: http://www.tamiu.edu/coba/ogss

FACULTY LIST

William Larry Boyd, Professor of Finance, Department of Economics and Finance; Ph.D., Texas A&M.

Willie Newton Cargill, Professor of Accounting and Chair, Department of Accounting and Information Systems; Ph.D., Missouri–Columbia.

Jesus S. Carmona, Instructor of Information Systems, Department of Accounting and Information Systems; M.S., Texas A&M International.

Kamal Fatehi, Professor of Management and Chair, Department of Management and Marketing; Ph.D., LSU.

Oscar R. Flores, Associate Professor of Information Systems, Department of Accounting and Information Systems; Ph.D., North Texas.

James Giermanski, Texas A&M University System Regents Professor, Department of Management and Marketing; D.A., Miami (Florida).

Soongoo Hong, Visiting Assistant Professor of Information Systems, Department of Accounting and Information Systems; M.A.B.A., Nebraska.

Pedro S. Hurtado, Associate Professor of Logistics and Management, Department of Management and Marketing; Ph.D., Maryland.

John P. Kohl, Professor of Management and Dean of the College of Business Administration and the Graduate School of International Trade and Business Administration, Department of Management and Marketing; Ph.D., Penn State.

George Kostopoulos, Professor of Information Systems, Department of Accounting and Information Systems; Ph.D., Arizona State.

Michael Landeck, Professor of Marketing, Department of Management and Marketing; Ph.D., North Texas State.

Stephen Lunce, Associate Professor of Information Systems, Department of Accounting and Information Systems; Ph.D., Texas at Arlington.

Jacqueline Rowley Mayfield, Associate Professor of Management, Department of Management and Marketing; Ph.D., Alabama.

Milton Mayfield, Assistant Professor of Management and Research Methodology, Department of Accounting and Information Systems; Ph.D., Alabama.

Stephen McNett, Associate Professor of Accounting, Department of Accounting and Information Systems; Ph.D., Missouri–Columbia.

Amanda Mukherji, Assistant Professor of Management, Department of Management and Marketing; Ph.D., Memphis.

Jyotsna Mukerjik, Assistant Professor of Marketing, Department of Management and Marketing; Ph.D. candidate, Memphis.

Kamal D. Parhizgar, Professor of Management, Department of Management and Marketing; Ph.D., Northwestern.

J. Michael Patrick, Professor of Economics, Department of Economics and Finance, and Director, TCBEED; Ph.D., Michigan State.

Michael J. Pisani, Instructor of Economics, Department of Economics and Finance; M.A., M.B.A., New Mexico.

F. Eduardo Rivera Porto, Visiting Professor of Information Systems, Department of Accounting and Information Systems; Ph.D., National Polytechnics (France).

Jacqueline Lou Power, Assistant Professor of Accounting, Department of Accounting and Information Systems; Ph.D., Texas A&M.

David Norton Roberts, Assistant Professor of Business Law, Department of Accounting and Information Systems; M.P.Acc., Corpus Christi State; J.D., Texas at Austin.

Antonio J. Rodriguez, Associate Professor of Finance and Chair, Department of Economics and Finance; Ph.D., Alabama.

Betty S. Rogers, Assistant Professor of Business Communications, Department of Management and Marketing; Ph.D., Oklahoma.

Yolanda Ruiz-Vargas, Visiting Assistant Professor, Department of Economics and Finance; M.B.A., Puerto Rico–Mayaguez.

Rolando P. Sanchez, Visiting Assistant Professor, Department of Management and Marketing; Ph.D., Rice.

Henry Smith, Associate Professor of Accounting, Department of Accounting and Information Systems; Ph.D., Virginia Commonwealth.

Stephanie Smith, Associate Professor of Finance, Department of Economics and Finance; Ph.D., Virginia Commonwealth.

Edward N. Willman, Associate Professor of Quantitative Methods, Department of Accounting and Information Systems, and Director of Academic Computing; Ph.D., North Texas State.

David W. Yoskowitz, Assistant Professor, Department of Economics and Finance; Ph.D., Texas Tech.

Texas A&M University–Commerce

Commerce and Dallas, Texas

SERVING TEXANS—SHAPING THE WORLD

Preparing students, both domestic and international, to assume leadership roles in business organizations is the major activity of the College of Business and Technology. In this tradition, the faculty members interact directly with the students in guiding and developing their managerial talent and skills. The curriculum provides tomorrow's managers with the insight, tools, and techniques needed for successfully leading complex organizations into the future. Financial, marketing, human resources, ethical, and environmental concerns are addressed as the student develops and evaluates organizational strategy.

Successful managers are those who are trained to meet today's challenges and who are armed with learning strategies to guide them in the future. In this manner, we prepare tomorrow's managers to "shape the world."

—Robert M. Seay, Director of Graduate Programs in Business

Programs and Curricular Focus

The Master of Business Administration degree offered by the College of Business and Technology (CBT) of Texas A&M University-Commerce prepares the graduate student for advanced management positions which demand analytic and strategic leadership solutions to an interrelated set of economic, ethical, and environmental issues. The curriculum stresses the development and use of analytical skills for both quantitative and qualitative applications which will assist managers in their decision-making and leadership responsibilities. A major focus of the curriculum is placed on developing and evaluating business strategy in a global environment.

Students with a traditional undergraduate degree in business may choose the Fast-Tract M.B.A., a highly focused management curriculum. The 30-hour Fast-Track curriculum consists of a six-course managerial component, a two-course information analysis component, and a two-course elective component.

For those students seeking to declare a minor concentration in an area of study, additional electives are required to constitute at least 12 hours in that particular field of study. These programs vary in length from 33 to 42 semester hours. Minors are available in accounting, economics, finance, human resources, international business, management information systems, marketing, and management of technology.

For those students who do not have a traditional undergraduate degree in business, the 48-hour format is appropriate. Under this curriculum design, 18 hours of background course work in the basic areas of business activity supplement the basic 30-hour format. Minor areas of study are also possible, should the student so choose.

Students and the M.B.A. Experience

The CBT's diverse full- and part-time student body represents a broad mix of educational and cultural backgrounds and work experiences. Our full-time students come from all over the world to enhance their decision-making and leadership skills as they prepare to enter the business world. The part-time student body typically represents working professionals with backgrounds ranging from beginning to veteran business persons, mid- and top-level managers, family and small-business owner-operators, and accomplished professionals seeking to develop their analytic and leadership abilities. Full-time students can complete their program in one year; part-time students, in as little as a year and two semesters.

There are approximately 240 students enrolled in the M.B.A. program, of which 53 percent are female and 32 percent are of international origin. Average age ranges from 26 to 32 years, and average business experience varies from 6 to 8 years. Class sizes average 35 students, although core courses tend to be larger and minor courses are much smaller.

The CBT offers its students live-taught classes in three locations: Dallas, Mesquite, and Commerce. Students from the Dallas-area represent well over half of the 240 students in the M.B.A. program. The CBT also offers its students the option of completing all or part of their degree via distance learning technology. The M.B.A. Online offers students the flexibility of an Internet-delivered program suited to fit their busy schedules.

With tuition costs among the lowest in the area and all programs accredited by the AACSB–The International Association for Management Education, the A&M-Commerce program provides an extremely high educational value to its students and the business community.

❖ Global Focus

The graduate business faculty members believe that all business is global, especially in larger organizational settings. The nature of global business operations is integrated into each course in the management component, although there are specific international business courses available as well. Students also experience the global dimension as they interact in classes with their peers from all over the world. The CBT is also able to accommodate students from all over the globe with the M.B.A. Online program option. The University currently has students from Canada, Nevada, California, and Texas, with inquiries from Taiwan, China, and the United Kingdom. The online learner receives the same one-on-one attention as our live-taught students through the use of global communications technology to successfully interact with their professors, other M.B.A. students, and other program administrators.

The Faculty

Guiding A&M-Commerce's M.B.A. program are faculty members with exceptional academic credentials and proven business experience. The College's graduate faculty members hold doctoral degrees from leading institutions in the United States. Most have professional experience to complement their academic backgrounds. Collectively, the graduate faculty members bring a variety of perspectives and experiences to bear on the issues and topics addressed during the course work.

The faculty members believe that their primary mission of teaching is best advanced by integrating their current scholarly activities and research into the learning experience of the M.B.A. student, whether in a live-taught or online setting.

The Business School Network
Through their research, consulting services, and other participation in professional organizations, the faculty members maintain relationships with key leaders in their respective academic disciplines.

The CBT and its faculty members are also members of the North Texas Commission, whose membership represents the visionary leadership of the greater Dallas-Fort Worth (DFW) business area. The Commission seeks to develop the economic base of the north Texas area by coordinating the needed economic and educational resources available in the region.

The CBT maintains an active liaison with the state and regional banking community through the Bank Operations Institute. Students also can participate in the research activities of the Center for Regional and Economic Development Studies. The CBT's Business Advisory Board also provides leadership to faculty members regarding curriculum design issues.

The College and Environs
Founded in 1889 as East Texas Normal College, Texas A&M University-Commerce developed an initial curriculum that emphasized a liberal arts education. In 1917, the school became a state institution and began to expand its role by adding a number of other academic disciplines to the curriculum. In 1972, the CBT became accredited with the AACSB–The International Association for Management Education. After thirty-one years of growth and service to the north central and east Texas areas, the University joined the Texas A&M University System and became Texas A&M University-Commerce on Sept. 1, 1996, becoming the second largest university in the system.

The mission of the College of Business and Technology at Texas A&M University-Commerce is to provide a variety of high quality academic degree programs and nondegree educational and

consulting services to students and others through faculty and staff members who are dedicated to the improvement of programs, people, and processes. Pursuit of that mission is energized by a commitment from the administration and the faculty members of the CBT to design and deliver degree programs and lifelong learning educational opportunities to business learners.

Facilities
A&M-Commerce's main campus is conveniently located on 2,000 acres in Hunt County in northeast Texas, about a 60-minute drive from Dallas, Texas. The CBT serves three major market segments: Dallas-Mesquite, Commerce, and the international marketplace through the globally delivered M.B.A. Online. The M.B.A. program is delivered at the newly opened and well-equipped Universities Center at Dallas, serving students in the immediate downtown area. Other Dallas area students are served from the recently opened Metroplex Center in Mesquite, an adjoining suburb of Dallas. The M.B.A. Online currently has 134 students taking classes via the Internet.

Technology Environment
Several hundred personal computers are available to students in a number of lab settings throughout the main campus, with on-site labs in the Dallas and Mesquite facilities. On the Commerce campus, business students have priority access to the CBT's sixty-machine, Pentium-class PC Lab. All students are provided Internet access free of charge, even at their home location. The Internet is the gateway to the University's electronic research resource, the Gee Library. There, users gain access to a variety of research tools, databases, and literally tens of thousands of full-text journals, magazines, and newspapers.

Placement
While many of the job search resources and services are available to all who wish to use them, students and alumni can also formally register with the Career Services Office for more direct and active assistance. Services available include assistance with major-related experience through co-op or internship positions; job leads to employers who are currently hiring college graduates; contacts with employers at job fairs and through on-campus interviews; referrals of resumes to employers who contact the Career Services Office, and credential management and mailing services; and

programs to help identify and analyze individuals' career goals and objectives.

Employers from business, industry, and government agencies are invited to attend our Job Fairs, held in both the fall and spring semesters. In previous years, 50 to 60 employers have taken advantage of the opportunity to meet over 400 students and/or alumni from twenty-six different academic majors who have attended the Job Fair. Over half of the candidates are seniors or graduate students, about one quarter are juniors, and nearly one quarter are freshmen or sophomores.

Admission
Admission to the M.B.A. program at A&M-Commerce is based on previous academic achievement and business experience. Students seeking admission must have earned a baccalaureate degree (not necessarily in a business field) and have completed the GMAT examination. The selection process considers the applicant's academic record and their GMAT scores. Details are described on the Web sites listed below.

Finances
The 1999-2000 tuition rates for resident students were $364.50 per course (3 hours) for Texas residents and $1006.50 for nonresidents. The College offers several competitive scholarships ranging from $1,000 to $5,000. Full-time graduate students may apply for Graduate Assistantship (GA) positions. Nonresident recipients of the GA positions or scholarships are eligible for the resident tuition rate.

Application Facts and Dates
Applications for the M.B.A. program are accepted throughout the year for both full- and part-time study. Candidates are encouraged to submit applications as early as possible to ensure consideration for the semester desired. International applicants should apply at least ninety days before the beginning of the semester they wish to begin. For further information contact:

Dr. Robert M. Seay
Director of Graduate Programs in
   Business
Texas A&M University-Commerce
P.O. Box 3011
Commerce, Texas 75429
Telephone: 903-886-5190
Fax: 903-886-5114
E-mail: MBA@tamu-commerce.edu
WWW: http://www.tamu-commerce.
   edu/mba
   http://www.mbaonline.tamu-
   commerce.edu

Texas Christian University

Fort Worth, Texas

> ### THE NEELEY ADVANTAGE
>
> *In the Neeley School, we understand that it takes more than technical expertise to succeed in today's dynamic business environment. Working with our faculty members and corporate partners, we have developed a curriculum that integrates sound business fundamentals with multiple opportunities to round out the academic experience. Communication skills, technology, and hands-on learning are equally emphasized at the Neeley School—both inside and outside of the classroom.*
>
> *The Neeley School is committed to developing ethical leaders who will help shape the economic environment of a rapidly changing future.*
>
> —Bob Lusch, Dean

Programs and Curricular Focus

Because managers seldom face clearly defined problems or opportunities, the Neeley School designed a curriculum to give its graduates a strategic, integrated perspective of business. Eleven required core courses cover a myriad of business principles. Five elective courses allow for more detailed study in one or more areas. The 48-semester-hour program is completed in two academic years by full-time students.

Neeley School faculty members work closely across functional departments to integrate core classes through special case studies and group projects. Faculty members employ a variety of teaching methods in the classroom. The environment is highly interactive and team-oriented.

In addition to a strong conceptual framework, the program emphasizes the development of essential managerial skills, such as effective communication. The Center for Productive Communication provides dedicated professional staff and state-of-the-art facilities as a resource to M.B.A. students.

Students and the M.B.A. Experience

The Neeley School M.B.A. program attracts a diverse group of students. As a private university, Texas Christian University (TCU) does not serve a defined geographic area. The objective is to bring talented students from many countries and regions to share experiences and learn from each other. Approximately one third of the full-time M.B.A. class

comes from outside the United States. Of the remaining students, about half are from Texas and half are from other parts of the United States. Neeley School M.B.A. students also come from a broad range of academic and professional backgrounds. About half hold undergraduate degrees in business. The others have majored in liberal arts, science, technology/engineering, and the fine arts. The majority of full-time students have completed three or more years of professional work experience.

Although diverse, all Neeley School M.B.A. students do share certain characteristics. They are academically talented individuals with demonstrated leadership skills. They are highly motivated and possess a history of success. A typical entering full-time M.B.A. class at TCU includes about 75 students.

❖ Global Focus

Neeley School faculty members bring to the classroom a wealth of international teaching, research, and consulting experience. Students in the second year of the program who have the language capabilities to do so may participate in semester-long exchange programs with universities in Dijon, France; Freiberg, Germany; and Chihuahua or Puebla, Mexico. Additionally, TCU faculty members teach courses based in Germany, France, and Hungary.

Special Features

The Neeley School is home to the second-oldest student-run investment

portfolio. Students in the Educational Investment Fund (EIF) manage more than $1.9 million, and are the ultimate decision-makers. Through the Student Enterprise Program, teams of M.B.A. students are hired as consultants by companies to solve real business problems. The Professional Development Program is designed to develop and enhance the business and social skills necessary to successfully navigate in today's corporate world, including team-building, leadership, ethics, interpersonal skills, and self-management skills. Students in the Summer Internship Program secure professional positions in a variety of industries.

The Faculty

The Neeley School's graduate faculty includes 30 individuals widely recognized as leaders in their academic fields. The dedicated faculty members are respected researchers and frequent consultants to industry. All M.B.A. faculty members hold a Ph.D. or a terminal degree in their field. All classes are taught by faculty members; there are no teaching assistants.

The Business School Network

Corporate Partnerships

The Neeley School works closely with business leaders in developing the M.B.A. curriculum and special programs. The International Board of Visitors, a corporate advisory board of senior-level executives from the U.S. and abroad, serves as a sounding board for the dean and faculty.

The Neeley School's extensive corporate ties directly impact the M.B.A. student's experience. The required Industry-Led Perspective Series of seminars led by seasoned professionals offers students detailed exploration of important issues, such as diversity in the workplace, managing change and technology, and ethical and global issues. The M.B.A. Alumni Association's mentor program matches students with alumni from their chosen career field.

Prominent Alumni

Many TCU alumni have established themselves as business leaders, including Ron Parker, V.P. Field Human Resources, Frito Lay, Inc.; P. D. Shabay, Executive V.P. Administration, Bell Helicopter

Textron, Inc.; Ann Borowiec, Managing Director, J.P. Morgan; and Fehmi Zeko, Managing Director, Salomon Smith Barney.

The College and Environs

Founded in 1873, Texas Christian University is a private university located in Fort Worth, Texas. TCU limits its total undergraduate and graduate enrollment to approximately 7,000 students so that all may benefit from personalized programs and services. TCU has a long-standing reputation for excellence in teaching and research and is accredited by all major accreditation associations.

Although founded by a Christian denomination, TCU is today an independent institution attracting students from many different cultures and faiths. Religious instruction is not a component of the M.B.A. curriculum.

TCU's location provides access to the Dallas–Fort Worth metroplex, a thriving metropolitan area of approximately 5 million people and home to a broad range of industries. Because of the area's central U.S. location, pleasant climate, and relatively low cost of living, many major firms have headquarters or branch offices based in Dallas–Fort Worth. The area is also home to world-class museums, major professional sports, and numerous other recreational opportunities.

Placement

The professional staff of the M.B.A. Career Services Office provides a full range of programs and developmental resources for career activities. The relatively small size of the program allows for an individualized approach to career planning and placement. Student career goals and planning skills are evaluated early in the program. Emphasis is placed on helping students build meaningful professional networks which they can access as students and as graduates.

Admission

The nature of the Neeley School M.B.A. program requires that a holistic approach be used in the admissions process. No single criterion, such as a test score, can determine eligibility for admission. The applicant must demonstrate not only academic ability but also the desire and ability to perform in a highly interactive, team-based environment. The previous academic record, relevant test scores, experience, motivation, maturity, and leadership ability are all considered in the admissions process. Professional work experience is preferred but not required.

Applicants are asked to submit a completed application, personal essays, official transcripts from each university attended, three letters of reference, official GMAT scores, and official TOEFL scores for international applicants (minimum score of 213 required on the computer-based test).

Finances

As a private university, TCU does not charge higher tuition for out-of-state or international students. For full-time M.B.A. students at TCU for the 2000–01 academic year, tuition is $9360 ($390 per semester hour), fees are $2665, and the estimated cost of books and supplies is $800. The cost of an apartment varies depending on the lifestyle of the individual student. The estimated cost for rent, meals, and living expenses for students is estimated at $8000 to $10,000 per academic year.

Through the Neeley School's aggressive scholarship program, approximately half of full-time M.B.A. students receive merit-based awards. Financial assistance based on academic merit is available to students of all nationalities. A number of special corporate-sponsored scholarships include a guaranteed summer internship and a generous living stipend.

International Students

Approximately 35 percent of TCU's full-time M.B.A. students come from outside the United States. Typically, international students come to TCU from Europe, Latin America, South America, and Asia. The Neeley School's small class sizes and emphasis on personal attention can be especially important to students from other cultures. Dedicated faculty members are committed to working closely with students, in and out of the classroom.

Application Facts and Dates

Application deadlines are March 15 for scholarship consideration and April 31 is the general deadline. Following the deadlines, applications are accepted on a space-available basis only. Due to the limited class size, students are encouraged to apply early. Applications are received as early as a year prior to admission.

Admission decisions are made on a rolling basis. Decisions are usually communicated three to four weeks after the completed application is received. For more information, applicants should contact:

Ms. Peggy Conway
Director of M.B.A. Admissions
M. J. Neeley School of Business
Texas Christian University
P.O. Box 298540
Fort Worth, Texas 76129
Telephone: 817-257-7531
      800-828-3764 Ext. 7531
      (toll-free within the U.S.)
Fax: 817-257-6431
E-mail: mbainfo@tcu.edu
World Wide Web: http://www.mba.tcu.edu

Texas Tech University

College of Business Administration

Lubbock, Texas

AN INVITATION FROM THE DEAN

The College of Business Administration at Texas Tech University is an exciting place to be working toward a master's degree in these genuinely challenging times of rapid change. Your experience in college will be the sum of many learning experiences you will have with the faculty and fellow students.

You'll develop leadership and management skills by engaging in skill-building exercises and teamwork. You'll be a part of project teams that will work in the "real world" of businesses, hospitals, community organizations, and government agencies. You'll use the latest information technology tools.

A master's degree in business from Texas Tech will start you on the path of lifelong professional development and learning that will be an integral part of your career.

—Roy D. Howell, Dean

Programs and Curricular Focus

The College offers four fully accredited graduate degree programs. The M.B.A. program is designed to provide a broad background in business complemented by a well-developed managerial perspective and strong analytical skills. Core courses cover the financial, managerial, economical, marketing, and analytical functions of the firm. The Strategic and Global Management course provides a comprehensive overview of all these functions. Concentrations and electives offer the opportunity to develop the specialized knowledge and skills needed for various managerial careers. Concentrations include agribusiness, entrepreneurial studies, finance, foreign language, general business, health organization management (HOM), high-performance management, international business, management information systems (MIS), and marketing.

The Master of Science in business administration (M.S./BA) degree program is designed to produce specialists in one of the following functions of business: banking, business statistics, finance, marketing, management information systems, management information systems/health organization management, production and operations management, and telecommunications.

The Master of Science in Accounting (M.S.A.) degree is offered for students who wish to specialize in the areas of auditing, accounting information systems (assurance), accounting information systems (design control), controllership, HOM/controllership, and taxation.

The M.B.A. and M.S./BA programs may be completed in one to two years, depending on the student's background. The M.S.A. program can take one to 2½ years.

The College of Business Administration also offers joint programs in association with the School of Law, the School of Nursing, the School of Medicine, the College of Architecture, and the College of Arts and Sciences. M.B.A./J.D. and M.S.A./J.D. programs can be completed in three to four years. The M.B.A./M.S.N. program takes 48 to 60 credit hours to complete and is offered jointly with the Texas Tech University Health Sciences Center (TTUHSC) School of Nursing. The M.D./M.B.A. program is offered jointly with the TTUHSC School of Medicine and can be completed in four years. M.B.A./M.A. in architecture and the M.B.A./M.A. in foreign language degree programs allow students to complete two degrees while reducing the duration of each program by 12 hours.

As the newest addition to Texas Tech's global tradition, the TTU/Universidad Anahuac Joint program is a direct response to increasing business transactions between the United States and Mexico. Universidad Anahuac, located in the capital, Mexico City, maintains well-established networks with domestic and worldwide firms and is positioned as a valuable gateway to an exciting international career.

The Ph.D. degree prepares students for careers in teaching, scholarly research, and publication. Doctoral students achieve high levels of expertise in their areas of specialization.

Students and the M.B.A. Experience

The College of Business Administration enrolls about 400 master's and 50 doctoral students. Approximately 75 percent of the students are from the Southwest; the remaining 25 percent come from other areas of the United States and many other countries. They bring to their graduate studies diverse backgrounds in the liberal arts, the sciences, engineering, and business administration. Approximately 70 percent have previous work experience.

The average age of the students in the program is 26. Of the incoming students, 39 percent are women, 7 percent are members of minority groups, and 23 percent are international students representing twenty-four countries.

Students regularly work in teams, take on consulting or marketing research projects from local and regional businesses, do field studies and site visits, and gain firsthand experience through internships and part-time positions. Presentations and group projects build students' confidence and ability to make public speeches.

❖ Global Focus

Students from other countries contribute to the understanding of diverse cultures, traditions, and political frameworks. In addition, a concentration in international business and study-abroad programs in leading business schools in England, Finland, France, Germany, Italy, Mexico, and Spain are available.

Texas Tech is totally committed to globalism, promotes the understanding of global cultures, and enriches the learning environment in and out of the classroom.

The Faculty

With 58 graduate faculty members, Texas Tech has one of the lowest graduate student–faculty ratios among business schools accredited by AACSB–The International Association for Management Education. One of the most talented resource bases in the country, the College's faculty members have a long tradition of successfully integrating teaching and research interests. College of Business Administration faculty members have been recognized for their efforts by industry and academia, receiving numerous awards and grants.

The Business School Network

The relationship between the College and the business community is a strong bond that offers benefits in both directions. The Chief Executives' Roundtable (CER) provides a forum for top professionals in the area that builds a close link between the College, the students, and the local business community. CER members serve as guest lecturers in graduate classes and provide student teams with the opportunity to work on challenging problems or special initiatives in their businesses. In networking with these entrepreneurs and leaders, students gain insights that are invaluable to their career development.

Advisory Councils are made up of members who are drawn from a variety of organizations and firms across the country. In addition, the College of Business Administration has established alliances with leading companies in the nation that are constantly recruiting its graduates. Ernst and Young, Arthur Andersen, Andersen Consulting Co., IBM, Exxon, Bank One, Chase, Compaq, PriceWaterhouseCoopers, Texas Instruments, Covenant Health Systems, Nortel, Deloitte and Touche, and SBC Communications are a few of these corporate partners.

The College and Environs

Founded in 1923, Texas Tech University is a major state-supported coeducational institution with an enrollment of more than 22,000 students. The University complex includes seven colleges; highly regarded schools of law, medicine, and health sciences; and the graduate school. Master's and doctoral/professional degrees are offered in nearly 150 disciplines. Along with accreditation by AACSB–The International Association for Management Education for the College of Business Administration's programs, health organization management master's and certification programs are accredited by the Accrediting Commission on Education for Health Services Administration (ACEHSA).

With a population of 200,000, Lubbock has the amenities of a major metropolitan area, yet it maintains its small-town charm. Lubbock is a principal financial, trade, medical, and industrial center and a growing agricultural, petroleum, and ranching region. The city has a thriving cultural life, featuring a symphony orchestra, three internationally acclaimed wineries, and an annual three-day art festival. In addition, Lubbock has a new hockey team, the Lubbock Cotton Kings. As a member of the Big 12, Texas Tech hosts a variety of intercollegiate sports events.

Facilities

Graduate study in business at Texas Tech is supported by excellent library and computer resources. The University library collections include approximately 2.2 million volumes, 22,827 paper/microform subscriptions, and 4,227 electronic titles. Scholarly and general business articles are readily referenced through the Business Index, a comprehensive, up-to-date microfilm service. An effi-cient interlibrary loan service provides materials not available on campus.

Academic Computing Services (ACS), based in the Advanced Technology Learning Center (ATLC) in the west lower level of the library, provides access to state-of-the-art large systems, servers, and microcomputer equipment and services. Microcomputers available in ATLC labs include Apple Power Macs and Dell PC systems. Terminal Network client access to the Compaq VMS cluster and the IBM system is available in the ATLC and most academic buildings. The OpenVMS systems on the TTUnet, the campus network, serve as the primary academic large-system computing resource for instruction and research. Services on the OpenVMS systems include four instructional and general-use labs, an open-access computing area, a teleconference room, a help desk, and a print dispatch area. ACS also operates a 24-hour computer lab (ATLC West), which is located in the Chitwood/Weymouth complex. More information may be found at http://www.acs.ttu.edu.

Placement

The College supports an active placement effort. Interview rooms in the Graduate Services Center are reserved for employers seeking graduate business students. Students may also utilize the University-wide Career Planning and Placement Center. In addition to Texas Tech's annual career fairs, Marketplace 2000, the College of Business Administration's individualized career fair, is held every spring for graduate students' placement.

The Graduate Services Center provides students with career evaluation and counseling; workshops on resume writing, job search strategies, business correspondence, and interviewing techniques; and a career library. The latest technology in hiring, recruiting, and placement is utilized to assist students with their job search.

Admission

Admission is based upon academic records, GMAT scores, letters of recommendation, a resume, essays, and previous work experience. Acceptable GMAT scores and GPA are required; the spring 2000 averages were 560 on the GMAT and a GPA of 3.4 on a 4.0 scale. International applicants whose native language is not English must also have a minimum TOEFL score of 550 on the paper-based test or 213 on the computer-based test. Applicants to the M.S.A. program must also have a minimum GPA of 3.0 on a 4.0 scale in accounting courses. Personal interviews are encouraged but not required.

Finances

The tuition and fees in 1999–2000 were $1600 per semester for Texas residents and $4100 per semester for non-Texas residents. These fees are based on a 12-credit-hour course load. Books and supplies may cost up to $500 per semester.

Research assistantships are awarded on a competitive basis to students with outstanding academic credentials. They include stipends and a waiver of out-of-state tuition. Additional aid, primarily loan funds, is available through the University Student Financial Aid Office. Dean's Scholarships are awarded to students with high GPAs and GMAT scores. In 1999–2000, these provided a $1000 tuition credit and qualified the student for in-state tuition. Application for the Dean's Scholarship must be made by May 1. In addition, the Chancellor's Fellowship is open to master's and doctoral students university-wide. This is awarded on a highly selective basis, offers $3000 for the academic year for master's students, $3000 for three years for doctoral students, and qualifies each for in-state tuition. Chancellor's Fellowship applications must be made to the Graduate Services Center no later than January 15.

International Students

There is a strong international student presence at Texas Tech. International student groups across the campus host an annual International Week, which includes a variety of activities. The student recreation center hosts the International Olympics. International students may also be matched with a host family in Lubbock to aid in the adaptation to American culture. Twenty-three percent of the students in the College of Business Administration graduate programs are international, representing twenty-four countries.

Application Facts and Dates

The College of Business Administration has a rolling admission policy. Applications may be made for the fall, spring, or summer terms. There are no formal application deadlines for domestic students. International students are advised to complete their applications by April 30 for fall, October 1 for spring, and February 15 for summer. Applicants receive a decision within four to eight weeks of receipt of all the application materials.

Texas Tech University
College of Business Administration
Graduate Services Center
P.O. Box 42101
Lubbock, Texas 79409-2101
Telephone: 806-742-3184
        800-882-6220 (toll-free)
Fax: 806-742-3958
E-mail: grad@coba.ttu.edu
WWW: http://grad.ba.ttu.edu
For more information about the M.D./M.B.A. program, students should contact:

M.D./M.B.A. Program
Office of Admissions—2B116
School of Medicine
Texas Tech University Health Sciences Center
Lubbock, Texas 79430

Thunderbird, The American Graduate School of International Management

Master's Program in International Management

Glendale, Arizona

▶ CITIZENS OF THE WORLD

Our students often tell me that Thunderbird is one of the few places where they have found people who think like they do. These students are truly "Citizens of the World," and theirs is a global perspective. Many of them have traveled in several countries and speak several languages. Others, however, may never have owned a passport. Yet for all of them, it is their global viewpoint that sets them apart. If you are seeking a community of internationalists and you thrive on intellectual challenge, I invite you to be a part of the Thunderbird experience. It will change your life.

—Roy A. Herberger Jr., President

Programs and Curricular Focus

Thunderbird's three-part curriculum provides an interrelated program of instruction in three departments—International Studies, Modern Languages, and World Business—leading to the Master of International Management (M.I.M.) degree. This successful educational concept is based on the proven fact that an ability to understand and adapt to the global business environment is a major reason for executive success in international operations.

The curriculum of the Department of International Studies focuses on the international business environment and is designed to acquaint students with international areas and their cultural management styles. This curriculum also provides the student with a conceptual framework for informed analysis of an international milieu.

The Department of Modern Languages offers courses in nine languages: Arabic, Chinese, French, German, Japanese, Portuguese, Russian, Spanish, and English as a Second Language. The four-level sequence stresses oral proficiency and heavily emphasizes business vocabulary and usage. In addition, many advanced commercial and issues-oriented courses are also offered.

The Department of World Business offers a far wider range of international courses than traditional graduate schools of business. Courses have a strong international practical orientation. There is heavy reliance on group teamwork and the use of computer simulation games.

The School has long enjoyed a reputation for teaching excellence, featuring an approach that is pragmatic and student focused.

Thunderbird has developed dual-degree programs with Arizona State University, the University of Arizona, the University of Colorado Denver, Case Western Reserve University, the University of Florida, Fordham University, Virginia Tech University, Michigan State University, the University of Texas at Arlington, and ESADE in Barcelona, Spain.

Thunderbird also offers a Master of International Management for Latin America (M.I.M.L.A.) and a post-M.B.A./M.I.M degree for individuals who hold an AACSB–The International Association for Management Education-accredited M.B.A.

Students and the M.B.A. Experience

The School's 1,500 students come from every state in the union. By design, 56 percent are from outside the U.S.; usually seventy to eighty countries are represented. The mean student age is 29 years, and approximately 37 percent are women. Students have an average of four years of full-time postbaccalaureate work experience. Diversity is a Thunderbird student trademark. More than 130 undergraduate college majors are represented, from more than 500 undergraduate colleges and universities worldwide.

Thunderbird was established in 1946. More than 31,000 alumni occupy executive offices in multinational enterprises around the world. The bond that unites them is a combination of elements that make up the "Thunderbird Experience." It starts on the Thunderbird campus and extends around the world.

It is a group of alumni living, working, and making business contacts in every state in the United States and nearly 140 countries. It is the "First Tuesday" tradition in New York, Omaha, Paris, Mexico City, Taipei, and 157 other cities around the world where alumni meet to develop social and business relationships. It is strangers who become instant friends when both are T'birds. It is a team spirit that grows from the many challenges of a demanding curriculum. It is the cacophony of students practicing language dialogues in the dining hall. It is an on-campus camaraderie where everyone knows everyone, and lifelong friendships transcend international barriers.

❖ Global Focus

Every year nearly one third of Thunderbird's students study on campuses around the globe in special international programs designed to augment their degree program, improve their language skills, and intensify their exposure to other cultures. Semester and/or summer programs are located in Europe, Asia, and Latin America.

The School has established its own campuses in Japan and in France, near Geneva. In addition, a ten-week session is held each summer in Guadalajara, Mexico.

Students may also avail themselves of exchange opportunities in China, Costa Rica, Finland, Germany, Korea, Norway, and Spain.

Special Features

Each January, Thunderbird presents Winterim, a three-week, on- or off-campus program of seminars that incorporate the newest international business theories along with practical problem-solving tools.

This unique educational opportunity arises from the mutual collaboration of Thunderbird faculty members with distinguished business and government professionals, many of whom are involved in the highest levels of strategic policy planning.

Past Winterim seminars have included Marketing to U.S. Hispanics; International Consumer Marketing Management; Counter Trade/Offset and Barter;

International Banking Symposium; Johnson & Higgins International Insurance and Risk Management Conference; The Corporate Executive Officer; Women Leaders of Today; Competitive Response of U.S. Business; Asia/Pacific Rim Management and Investment; Doing Business in Eastern Europe and Russia; Privatization; Cross-Cultural Communication for International Managers; Opportunity and Risk in the New International Business Order; International Management of Technology; Managing in a Borderless World; and Issues in International Health Care Management.

Winterim courses are also held in numerous international locations, including Austria, Brazil, Central Europe, Chile/Peru, Costa Rica/Nicaragua, Cuba, France, Germany, Kuwait, Mexico, Nepal, Russia, Saudi Arabia, South Africa, Spain/Portugal, and the United Arab Emirates. In the U.S., Thunderbird offers U.S. Foreign Policy and the New Global Environment, which is held in Washington, D.C., and Winterim on Wall Street. Thunderbird also presents a two-week miniterm between summer and fall and between spring and summer for continuing students. Destinations have included Japan/South Korea, Detroit, France, Russia, and Hong Kong.

The Faculty

Thunderbird's faculty combines strong academic credentials with significant international and corporate experience. Among the more than 100 full-time professors are individuals from more than two dozen countries—a truly global representation. The Modern Language faculty features native speakers and scholars. Members of the International Studies Department have spent long periods abroad in diplomatic and economic development assignments. World Business faculty members are involved in international consulting.

The Business School Network

Thunderbird has an unparalleled network of more than 31,000 alumni working internationally in more than 130 countries around the globe. Through the School's exclusive intranet, alumni are able to network with thousands of T-birds, join online discussion groups, and subscribe to lifetime e-mail. The intranet, Alumni My Thunderbird, also hosts a global job connection and provides lifetime learning opportunities.

The College and Environs

Thunderbird is located in the Sun Belt area of the Southwest in a suburb of Phoenix, Arizona, America's sixth-largest city. The Phoenix metropolitan area has numerous cultural resources typical of a major urban center.

Facilities

The International Business Information Center (IBIC) provides a campus facility for study, group meetings, and multimedia presentations. It houses a collection of international and business resources including foreign language materials and remote access to 50 electronic databases, including ProQuest Direct, Ebsco-Host, Business Reference Suite, Bloomberg, Compustat, ISI Emerging Markets, Nikkei Net, Investext, SDC Mergers and Acquisitions, the Economist Intelligence Unit, and LEXIS-NEXIS. IBIC's Web page organizes links to 2,000 Internet sites relevant to the curricular needs of students.

Technology Environment

Thunderbird students have access to 150 public computers, and there are 260 distributed network ports around the campus for laptops. Students also have 24-hour direct access to a state-of-the-art intranet, My Thunderbird, which features online course and research information, personalized home pages, information about campus events, job postings, and direct access to e-mail and the World Wide Web.

Placement

All students begin career preparation during a two-week Foundations course that helps them create a career management action plan. In addition, employers annually provide Thunderbird students with more than 2,000 hiring opportunities for full-time and internship positions. More than 250 of these companies visit the campus to conduct interviews, while many more evaluate Thunderbird candidates at job fairs in the U.S. and Europe. The School hosts a Career Fair each fall and an Internship Fair during the spring trimester. Many of the School's alumni, who work in more than 12,000 organizations in 130 countries, volunteer to help Thunderbird students add focus to their job searches.

Thunderbird developed ProFit, a new Web-based system that allows employers to search a database of student profiles and select resumes of those candidates who best fit the qualifications desired for a specific job, which may include functional interests, industry experience, language proficiencies, and country work eligibility. Several hundred employers are also visited each year by one of the Employer Relations staff members to develop partnerships for mutual success. The aim is to make certain that employers understand the special qualities of the Thunderbird graduate and how to access candidates who meet their hiring needs.

Through the Thunderbird internship program, students are able to participate in internships in Europe, Asia, and Latin America and in corporate centers throughout the United States and Canada. Internships are available throughout the year and may include academic credit.

Admission

A bachelor's degree from an accredited college or university is required for acceptance into the M.I.M. program. Students must submit a minimum GMAT test score of 550 and must have a minimum 3.0 college GPA. International students must submit a TOEFL score of no less than 600. Two to five years of work experience, international travel or living experience, and proficiency in a foreign language are strongly encouraged.

Finances

Tuition and fees for 1999–2000 were approximately $12,000 per trimester. Books and instructional supplies run about $600 per trimester.

The School estimates that living expenses for a single student living in the residence halls are approximately $1320 for lodging and $1455 for board per trimester. Off-campus expenses may be slightly higher. The School requires students to have an IBM or IBM-compatible laptop computer. This cost is additional.

Application Facts and Dates

The deadline for winter and spring entrance is July 31; for fall entrance, January 31; for summer entrance, November 31. For more information, applicants should contact:

Office of Admissions
Thunderbird Campus
American Graduate School of
    International Management
15249 North 59th Avenue
Glendale, Arizona 85306-9903
Telephone: 602-978-7011
         800-848-9084 (toll-free)
         (admissions inquiries only)
Fax: 602-439-5432
E-mail: tbird@t-bird.edu
World Wide Web: http://www.t-bird.
    edu

Truman State University

Division of Business and Accountancy

Kirksville, Missouri

NEW DIRECTIONS FOR THE ACCOUNTING PROFESSION

The passage of the "150-hour" requirement to sit for the Uniform CPA examination by most states is resulting in new directions for entry into the accounting profession. Technology is changing the role of accountants, particularly in the larger public accounting firms. As future accountants assume more professional consulting responsibilities, it is necessary for them to have a broad background in the liberal arts and sciences, in the functional areas of business and economics, and in technical accounting knowledge. The accounting programs at Truman State provide the necessary knowledge and skills to equip students as lifelong learners in a global society.

—Debra Kerby, Head, Division of Business and Accountancy

Program of Study

Truman State University offers instruction at the master's level in the area of accounting. The Master of Accountancy is designed to prepare graduates to enter the fields of public accounting, industrial accounting, government accounting, and accounting education. General objectives of the Master of Accountancy program are to provide students with a well-rounded body of professional knowledge based on a strong liberal arts and sciences undergraduate education; to provide the decision-making tools necessary for handling futuristic problems in a pluralistic and ever-changing society; to build the theoretical foundation necessary for analyzing complex problems in a systematic manner; to promote understanding of an environment that has impacted the evolution of accounting thought and practice; to develop skills in utilizing information databases and in researching the professional accounting and/or tax literature; to develop the leadership skills necessary for making independent and informed professional judgments; to prepare students for admission to and success in a doctoral or other graduate professional program; and to prepare students for successful careers in public, management, and governmental accounting or as accounting educators.

The Master of Accountancy program is structured for qualified individuals with a baccalaureate degree in accounting and business administration but also accommodates those who hold degrees in nonbusiness fields. Total graduate credit hours required for the degree range from 30 to 42, depending on the student's background. A 9-hour tax concentration is also available.

Students who finish the program demonstrate knowledge of the following as measured by a test in the various courses and a rigorous comprehensive examination: accounting theory, familiarity and knowledge of accounting pronouncements, cost and managerial cost with expanded analysis, and a specialty area dependent on the student's focus of study.

The following business and accounting programs offered by the Division of Business and Accountancy are accredited by AACSB–The International Association for Management Education: the Bachelor of Arts and the Bachelor of Science in business administration, the Bachelor of Science in accounting, and the Master of Accountancy. AACSB–The International Association for Management Education is recognized by the Council on Postsecondary Accreditation and the Office of Postsecondary Education, U.S. Department of Education, as a specialized accrediting agency for undergraduate and graduate programs in business administration and accounting.

Student Group

Sixty percent of the students at Truman State have undergraduate degrees in accounting. Other students have degrees in such fields as business, math, English, economics, and sociology. Fifty percent of the students are from the Midwest; others are from states such as Colorado, California, Oklahoma, Kentucky, Michigan, and Washington. One fourth have full-time work experience and 20 percent are international students.

The Faculty

The primary responsibility of every faculty member at Truman State is to become an effective and dedicated classroom teacher. The majority of their efforts are on effective teaching, advising, and student-centered activities. In support of their primary responsibility, each faculty member is expected to continue his/her intellectual and professional growth with scholarly activities and professional service that contributes to the improvement of teaching or the development and dissemination of ideas within his/her academic discipline or professional area of study.

The Business School Network

The Division of Business and Accountancy maintains strong ties with the business community and alumni. Various alumni chapters provide input to the business programs, networking opportunities for job searches, support for classroom speakers, and program sponsors. The Bentele/Mallingckrodt Executive-in-Residence Program is sponsored by the IMCERA Group and Mallinckrodt, Inc. The program provides for two visiting executives to spend two to three days on campus each year. The executives make class presentations and spend time with students in both formal and informal settings.

The College and Environs

Truman State University, formerly Northeast Missouri State University, is the statewide public liberal arts and sciences university for Missouri. Founded in 1867 as a school to educate teachers, Truman State began its historic mission in 1986. Truman State is recognized nationally and internationally for its Value-Added Model of Assessment, a comprehensive testing and surveying program used to monitor student progress and the University's educational success.

The University is situated in Kirksville, which has a population of approxi-

mately 17,000. The city is located 30
miles south of Iowa; 70 miles west of
Quincy, Illinois; and 3 to 4 hours from

Kansas City, St. Louis, and Des Moines,
Iowa. The Kirksville College of Osteopathic Medicine, the birthplace of
osteopathic medicine, is also located in
Kirksville. The Kirksville area features a
3,250-acre state park and a 700-acre lake
for camping, fishing, swimming, sailing,
boating, skiing, and picnicking. Thousand
Hills State Park and Forest Lake are
located within 10 miles of the campus.

Facilities

Pickler Memorial Library has a book
collection of more than 350,000 volumes,
augmented by subscriptions to approximately 1,750 journals and periodicals, 1
million microforms, and both U.S. and
Missouri document depositories. In
addition to an expanding collection of
books, periodicals, and microforms and to
increasing online access to networks and
databases, the library contains several
special collections.

Technology Environment

Pickler Memorial Library is a member of
the On-line Computer Library Center
(OCLC), a worldwide library database,
and has implemented the fully automated
Northwestern Total Integrated Library
System (NOTIS). The Office of Computer Services provides centralized
computing for large-scale research, online
information systems, and online interactive computing capability for all interested students, faculty, and staff.

Placement

The University Career Center (UCC)
offers a full range of job search and
placement services. In addition to
on-campus interviews, the UCC provides
students opportunities for mock interviews, resume reviews, job fairs,
employment bulletin subscriptions, and a
resume referral service.

Admission

Applicants for the Master of Accountancy
program must have a baccalaureate
degree from an accredited institution. The

GMAT must be taken prior to acceptance.
Admission decisions depend heavily on
prior undergraduate work and GMAT
scores.

Finances

In-state tuition was $158 per credit hour,
and out-of-state tuition was $283 per
credit hour for the 1999–2000 academic
year. Living expenses are estimated at
$10,000 per year.

Graduate teaching and research
assistantships are available for a limited
number of students. The assistantships
pay a cash stipend of $5000 per academic
year, and the recipients' tuition is waived
for a maximum of 9 credit hours per
semester. All books and supplies and any
special course fees are the responsibility
of the recipient. Recipients are expected
either to teach one class each semester or
to assist in research for the same number
of hours. To be considered for an
assistantship, the student must have a 3.0
minimum undergraduate grade point
average, a score above the 50th percentile
on the GMAT, enrollment in a minimum
of 15 graduate hours per academic year,
and maintenance of a 3.0 graduate grade
point average. Graduate teaching/research
assistantships are awarded annually and
all applications are due by February 15.
Various grants and loans are also
available.

Application Facts and Dates

Applications are accepted throughout the
year, and students may begin their
program at the start of the fall, spring, or
summer semester.

To request an informational brochure
and application, students should contact:

Dr. Jeffrey Romine
Coordinator of Graduate Studies in
    Accounting
Division of Business and Accountancy
Truman State University
Kirksville, Missouri 63501
Telephone: 816-785-4371
E-mail: jromine@truman.edu
World Wide Web: http//www.truman.
    edu

Tulane University

A. B. Freeman School of Business

New Orleans, Louisiana

> ### FREEMAN: A DYNAMIC M.B.A. EXPERIENCE
>
> *The hallmark of the Freeman School is to develop tomorrow's leaders through innovative education, a team focus, and individual attention. As one of America's oldest and most respected business schools, Freeman offers the opportunity to join a select group of students in a dynamic learning experience.*
> *The M.B.A. program provides a global business perspective in America's most international city. The Freeman M.B.A. will enhance your leadership and management skills. We encourage you to take advantage of this outstanding educational opportunity. It will provide you with the academic tools to assist you in the realization of your goals.*
>
> —James W. McFarland, Dean

Programs and Curricular Focus

The Freeman program is designed to maximize the skills needed to manage in the future. The innovative curriculum begins with a set of intensive seven-week sessions, where student teams complete the majority of the M.B.A. core. More than 30 hours of electives, beginning in the second semester, complete the M.B.A. program in career-focused tracks. The global representation of the student body becomes clear as a student gets to know classmates from around the world. Concurrent with the curriculum, students participate in career development programs, organizational activities, and a range of school and community-sponsored events.

In addition to the full-time M.B.A. program, the Freeman School offers three joint-degree programs and several other degree options. The M.B.A./Juris Doctor allows students to complete both law and business degrees in four years. The M.B.A./Master of Public Health is a three-year program. The M.B.A./Master of Arts in Latin American Studies requires 2½ years of study. A Master of Accounting program, Professional (part-time) M.B.A. Program, Executive M.B.A. Program, and Ph.D. program complete the range of degree options possible at the Freeman School.

Students and the M.B.A. Experience

Freeman students join one of the most diverse and talented peer groups to be found. With 40 percent of the student body made up of international students and 70 percent of the domestic student body multilingual, Freeman students enjoy a truly global perspective.

Professional backgrounds also contribute to the diversity of Freeman students. Students enjoy peers who have worked as consultants for international firms, engineers for multinational corporations, and entrepreneurs, which are among the many careers in private, public, and nonprofit enterprises evident in the Freeman student body.

Special Features

The most striking feature of the Freeman School is its people. Faculty members, renowned in their fields, participate actively in unique class and project settings, and an alumni network of more than 2,000 contacts are ready to lend their expertise in career planning. Freeman students participate in an active and innovative learning experience.

At Freeman, institutes augment the traditional classroom discussion with centers for specific interests. The Goldring Institute focuses on international business, the Levy-Rosenblum Institute focuses on entrepreneurship, and the Burkenroad Institute focuses on the study of leadership and ethics in management. The institutes provide a facility for students, faculty members, and the business community to participate in interactive programs and research. Each year, dozens of business leaders and academics come to the Freeman School to participate in the institute's programs.

The Faculty

The Freeman School faculty designed the innovative curriculum to make the best use of its expertise and the students' own abilities and interests. A combination of teaching styles is used throughout the curriculum, with an emphasis on teamwork. The size of the program is intentionally small. Freeman students have easy access to their professors. The faculty consists of internationally recognized scholars in many business fields.

The Business School Network

Prominent business leaders visit Freeman regularly to address student organizations, to serve as Executives-in-Residence, and to participate in career development and placement programs. The School enjoys tremendous support from its more than 7,000 graduates.

The College and Environs

Tulane is one of the major private research universities in the United States. With its eleven schools and colleges that range from the liberal arts and sciences to a full spectrum of professional schools, Tulane offers a breadth of experience equaled by only six other private universities in the United States. Tulane's history dates back to the Medical College of Louisiana, founded in 1834. Tulane offered the South's first schools of architecture, business, and social work. The University offers a lively academic atmosphere, while each school focuses on the needs and abilities of the individual student.

Tulane is located in a residential, parklike setting in one of America's first great cities, New Orleans. Founded by the French in the early 1700s, New Orleans offers its own unique food, music, architecture, and lifestyle. As the nation's largest port, New Orleans plays a critical role in North America's expanding commerce with Latin America, Europe, and Africa. Annual events such as Mardi Gras, the Jazz and Heritage Festival, and the Sugar Bowl make New Orleans an international tourist destination.

Facilities

The Freeman School is housed in Goldring/Woldenberg Hall, a seven-story complex designed and built for the needs of management education. All business school classes are located in the building, as are an auditorium, group study rooms, faculty offices, and the library. Classrooms are designed to foster an interactive learning environment and include computer ports and presentation equipment. A computer classroom adds to the available technology. The Turchin Library is one of the most modern business libraries in the area. More than a dozen electronic sources complement the 35,000 volumes and more than 700 journals available through the library.

Technology Environment

From state-of-the-art classrooms to a complete television studio, the Freeman School offers the latest in business technologies. The building features its own in-house network (accessible by modem), computer classrooms, and computer labs.

Placement

The School's in-house career development center reviews the abilities of entering students and prepares strategies for future graduates annually. Through seminars and individual counseling, students are provided with the resources to define objectives, explore career options, and identify potential employers. Last year, 97 percent of the class was placed three months after graduation, with salaries ranging between $32,000 and $150,000.

Admission

Diversity among the student body is an integral part of the Freeman experience. The Admissions Committee actively seeks applicants from all over the world and encourages candidates with degrees from accredited institutions in all major fields of study. The committee considers all credentials presented by the candidate. Undergraduate performance and results of the Graduate Management Admission Test (GMAT) are used to assess verbal and quantitative abilities. An essay, a resume, letters of recommendation, and a personal interview provide the committee with further information on candidates' abilities, skills, motivation, and career focus. The Test of English as a Foreign Language (TOEFL) score is required of all applicants for whom English is not the native language or who have graduated from a university in which all or most of the instruction is not in English. Emphasis is given to the breadth of professional experience, academic ability, and fit with Freeman programs in the selection of students.

Finances

For the 2000–01 academic year, tuition is $23,500. University fees are $1600, and there is a health center fee of $320. Estimated costs for books are $800. Estimated housing and living expenses are $10,500.

All full-time applicants are automatically considered for fellowships at the time of admission. Assistantships are held by approximately 40 percent of the first-year students and 60 percent of the

second-year students. Assistantship positions are arranged by students at the beginning of the semester.

International Students

An international flavor permeates New Orleans and the Freeman School. Approximately 40 percent of the entering class come from outside the United States, representing more than twenty-five countries. International programs at the University and within the School highlight the diversity of experiences and cultures within the community. A number of M.B.A. activities and University services focus on the international dimension and the needs of the international business community.

Application Facts and Dates

Admission to the Freeman School is on a rolling basis. Applications are evaluated as early as September of the preceding year. Decisions are issued approximately four weeks after the receipt of completed applications.

Mr. Bill D. Sandefer
Director of Admissions
A. B. Freeman School of Business
Tulane University
7 McAlister Drive, Suite 400
New Orleans, Louisiana 70118
Telephone: 504-865-5410
Fax: 504-865-6770
E-mail: freeman.admissions@tulane.
edu
World Wide Web: http://freeman.
tulane.edu

Union College

ANALYTICAL PROBLEM SOLVING IN MANAGEMENT

The Union College M.B.A. program has dedicated itself to analytical problem solving in management, based on the tradition of a small, select liberal arts and engineering college. The program rests on three pillars. For one, we believe that management is human intervention. Good managers must understand leadership, teamwork, and motivation. Secondly, we believe that management can only achieve its goals when it is based on measurable facts. Finally, we believe that management is interdisciplinary, system-oriented, and global.

Our faculty members dedicate themselves to teaching and supporting students. We seek interaction with and among students. We invite our students to collaborate with us on state-of-the-art research. Our overall aim is to challenge students to achieve individual growth, strong analytical skills, and sharpened global perspectives. We seek to reinforce the intellectual tradition taught in a high-quality college.

—Susan Lehrman, Director

Programs and Curricular Focus

Union College's Graduate Management Institute offers M.B.A. students an opportunity to study in the attractive environment of a liberal arts campus, where students get to know both the faculty and their peers. Union's M.B.A. curriculum blends theory with practice in a well-balanced approach consisting of lectures, case studies, written reports, computer models, and business games. For curricular development, the Institute benefits from the advice of a distinguished council that includes prominent leaders from business, government, and education. Union management students learn problem-solving techniques directly applicable to a progressive decision-making environment.

Union's M.B.A. programs develop the traditional knowledge of accounting, economics, finance, operations, marketing, and organizational behavior. The programs provide a foundation for effective team building, quantitative decision making, creative problem solving, and total quality management process skills. Students are assigned group projects in a number of core courses. These groups are carefully selected to include students with diverse educational and work experiences.

In addition to the M.B.A. degree, Union offers an M.B.A. in health systems administration that includes a paid residency at a health-care institution during the summer between the two years

of the program. This program, fully accredited by the Accrediting Commission on Education for Health Services Administration (ACEHSA), prepares graduates for management positions in health services delivery and related institutions.

Union also offers a combined M.B.A./J.D. program with the Albany Law School of Union University. Students in this program can earn their M.B.A. degree in health systems along with their J.D. degree in four academic years.

Students and the M.B.A. Experience

The Graduate Management Institute includes both full- and part-time students with very diverse backgrounds and work experiences. Full- and part-time students take the same classes. They are offered the flexibility to transfer between full-time and part-time status as personal and professional circumstances dictate. Women comprise approximately 40 percent of the student population, and international and minority students comprise 10 percent of the full-time students.

Approximately 25 percent of the students have undergraduate degrees in business or finance. Another 25 percent come from engineering or technical disciplines, with the remaining 50 percent coming from science, social science,

humanities, and other disciplines. About 10 percent of the students are pursuing a joint degree in law and business.

The Faculty

Faculty ideas and attitudes make one institution different from another. The composition of GMI's faculty attests to Union's concern with providing a comprehensive education that remains relevant in the future. Every full-time member of the faculty is engaged in research, and all publish regularly in national journals. Research allows faculty members to remain current in their fields, and classroom teaching translates this expertise into an educational experience.

The adjunct faculty members are all either researchers in industry or successful in business in their field. They bring practical experience and diversity to all programs.

The Business School Network

GMI's Advisory Council consists of business leaders in industry and in the fields of health and accounting as well as alumni and faculty members. This council functions to advise GMI on the changing needs in the corporate, health, and accounting industries. Council members are also encouraged to visit classes and to meet with students informally.

A series of lectures features prominent business leaders who address Union's graduate students on current business issues. In addition to these lectures, each term a colloquium series is featured. The guests for this series generally address specific functional areas of business. Students are encouraged to attend these functions as part of their educational experience.

The College and Environs

In 1795, Union College became the first college chartered by the Regents of the State of New York. Since its beginnings, Union has been committed to innovative education, offering scientific studies in the early nineteenth century. In 1845, Union became the first liberal arts college to offer engineering. In the 1950s, the College established programs that cut across the barriers separating the traditional academic disciplines. It was in this spirit that the Graduate Management Institute evolved as a center that builds on the values of a broad education.

The Graduate Management Institute offers its programs on the Union College grounds, a campus of some 100 acres located on a hill overlooking Schenectady, a city founded by the Dutch in 1661. The campus, designed by the French architect Joseph Jacques Ramée in 1813, is recognized as a historic landmark in the development of the American college campus.

Technology Environment

Housed in the Stanley G. Peschel Center for Computer Science and Information Systems, Union's computer center is the home of a distributed network that provides access to various computer resources, including seven DEC Alpha servers, a Sun system running UNIX, and three Windows NT servers. There are more that 1,000 personal computers and workstations on campus. The network is the backbone for much of the computing on campus, including academic research and administrative work. The network links classrooms, offices, laboratories, and all College-owned residence hall rooms. The College has several electronic classrooms that are used to enhance the academic program. All students have access to national and international resources of the Internet through the College's membership in the NYSERnet. There is no charge for a student computer account.

Schaffer Library houses more than 500,000 volumes and 1,600 current periodical subscriptions and has a periodicals reading room, faculty studies, and more than 500 individual study spaces. It operates on the open stack plan and offers bibliographic instruction, interlibrary loan services, online bibliographic retrieval services, electronic document delivery, and Internet workstations for access to indexes, abstracts, and full-text journals on line. Automated circulation of books and other library materials as well as the online catalogs are in place. The library has been a

depository for federal government documents since 1901. Professional reference service is offered during nearly all hours that the library is open.

The newly completed Olin Center offers a state-of-the-art high-technology classroom and laboratory building. The building contains a variety of laboratories and classrooms equipped for computer-intensive instruction and a multimedia auditorium, collaborative computer classrooms, and a 16-inch remote-controlled telescope.

Placement

The Career Development Center offers a variety of services for graduate students, including career planning, resume writing, and interviewing skills. On-campus recruiting generally takes place during the fall and winter terms. In addition, the Graduate Management Institute has a strong alumni network to help with placement for its graduates.

Admission

The Graduate Management Institute requires all students to submit official transcripts from all undergraduate and graduate schools, GMAT scores, three letters of recommendation, and an essay. The average GMAT score for enrolling M.B.A. students is 570, with a range of 500 to 700. The average undergraduate GPA is 3.2.

TOEFL results are required for all students for whom English is not the native language. A score of 550 to 600 is required. International students must present proof of adequate funds to cover two full years. International students are considered for assistantships based on academic merit.

There are no specific prerequisite courses. Basic skills in writing and computing are expected. Students who have not taken calculus may take it at the Graduate Management Institute.

Students with appropriate undergraduate backgrounds may waive up to four courses. These students may complete the program in one calendar year.

All students must provide proof of immunization for measles and rubella.

This is a New York State Health Law requirement. Health insurance is available from the College at a very reasonable price.

Finances

Tuition for the 2000–01 academic year is $14,040. Books and fees cost approximately $1500 per year.

There is limited on-campus housing provided for graduate students at Union College, but housing is plentiful within walking distance of the campus. The cost of housing, utilities, and living expenses is estimated to be approximately $7000 per year. Students are not required to purchase a computer, but it is strongly encouraged.

A number of M.B.A. scholarships are available. The awards are based on academic merit and may be awarded to international students.

International Students

Approximately 15 percent of the full-time student population are international students. They are encouraged to attend the orientation held for international students prior to the beginning of classes in September. Graduate international students are also encouraged to participate in the International Club on Union's campus.

Application Facts and Dates

The Graduate Management Institute has a rolling admission process, and students may begin during any of the trimesters or summer sessions. However, most full-time students begin in the fall. For full-time students who wish to be considered for assistantships or fellowships, completed applications must be received no later than March 31. For more information, students should contact:

Rhonda Sheehan
Graduate Management Institute
Union College
Schenectady, New York 12308
Telephone: 518-388-6238
Fax: 518-388-6754
E-mail: sheehan@union.edu
World Wide Web: http://www.mba.
union.edu

The University of Alabama

A COMPLETE BUSINESS EDUCATION

With a long-standing reputation and backed with strong traditions of excellence, the University of Alabama provides students with a unique M.B.A. experience. Our program provides the highest-quality students with a complete business education that emphasizes applied practical learning. The quality of the education, the support of fifty years of loyal alumni, and the satisfaction of spending two years as part of a very special group make the Alabama M.B.A. program what it is. It is distinguished not by its quality alone but also by its relatively low cost and its focus on the education of excellent students. In all of this, the University of Alabama is a unique experience, educating leaders for the twenty-first century.

—J. Barry Mason, Dean, Culverhouse College of Commerce and Business Administration

Programs and Curricular Focus

The Alabama M.B.A. program is a two-year, full-time program developed to give students a broad business and management perspective supported by specialization in fields related to students' goals and interests. At the University of Alabama Manderson Graduate School of Business, continuous improvement and lifelong learning are not just concepts taught in classrooms. They are practiced by faculty members, staff members, and students. Students and faculty members work closely together, building a cooperative environment between students, faculty members, and an active alumni network. At Manderson, continuous improvement and lifelong learning are central to a belief system that is reflected in every step of the program, from the admissions process to orientation to the classroom and beyond.

The first year of the Alabama M.B.A. experience may be thought of as a journey through the operations of an organization. Students learn concepts, explore issues, and define solutions for businesses in the areas of accounting, economics, finance, human resources management, management information systems, marketing, production and operations management, and statistics. During the first year of the M.B.A. experience, students develop and refine skills in these functional areas. This foundation provides the knowledge for each student to build a tool kit to identify and solve cross-functional business problems. Students participate in cross-functional cases that are analyzed and presented by each team to the M.B.A.

faculty. Each student team is called upon to present a solution to a business problem in the presence of 5 or more faculty members representing various disciplines. Thus, the value of teamwork is reinforced, and the importance of cross-functional communication is underscored.

In the second year of the M.B.A., students are eager to begin applying what they have learned during the first year and during their summer internship; thus they begin to focus on their chosen concentration. One faculty member manages each concentration, but the entire faculty team provides academic support, coaching, and counseling.

The M.B.A./J.D. program is a four-year, 108-hour course of study designed for highly qualified students who want to obtain both a Master of Business Administration and a Juris Doctor degree. The program provides a solid foundation for success in corporate law and in a wide range of business fields through study at the nationally recognized University of Alabama School of Law and the Manderson Graduate School of Business. Aspiring corporate attorneys are provided a solid understanding of business processes with a strong foundation for success in virtually any area of business.

Students and the M.B.A. Experience

The hallmark of the Alabama M.B.A. program is teamwork. Students are organized into teams of 4 to 5 students during orientation and work together in and outside of the classroom throughout the first year. Teams are also utilized in the second year within the

concentrations and are often called upon to work on projects for corporations and other organizations. Students also work individually, complementing the team experiences in learning about time and conflict management, leadership skills, ethical decision making, analysis and problem solving, and interpersonal relations.

Each fall, about 60 students begin the M.B.A. program. This small class size provides students with opportunities to form strong bonds with their classmates. Students come to the program with a variety of backgrounds and interests. This diverse student population fosters a sense of mutual respect and responsibility. About 53 percent have undergraduate degrees in business, 25 percent have engineering, science, or other technical degrees, and 22 percent have undergraduate degress in the liberal arts. The Manderson Program is carefully constructed to provide the knowledge and skills, as well as the hands-on opportunities, to prepare students for successful careers in business.

Special Features

The Alabama M.B.A. program begins with a one-week orientation program in which students participate in individual, leadership, and team-building activities. These are designed to foster a sense of corporate leadership and responsibility. From this, a foundation is formed for the remainder of the two-year business education.

Throughout the first year, students are involved in a professional development program for which topics have included art, music, and theater appreciation.

Along with these formal programs, students are involved in many out-of-class activities, including community service, intramural sports, and clubs such as the MBA Association and the Alabama Student Government. Once a year, the students sponsor MBA Week, which includes career development seminars, student/faculty sports competitions, keynote speakers, and an annual MBA Golf Outing that attracts current students, alumni, and prominent corporate executives.

The Faculty

Alabama's faculty is among the best in the business. Those faculty members chosen to work with the M.B.A. program are men and women of widely diverse backgrounds and experience united by a shared love of teaching and an appreciation for the need to have useful knowledge immediately upon entering the workplace. Each is a recognized scholar in his or her chosen field, but, as a cohesive and complementary M.B.A. staff member, each is part of a team dedicated to the future of the Alabama student. Each faculty member is actively engaged in real-world research, consulting, and related activities along with his or her pure academic pursuits.

The Business School Network

M.B.A. alumni are active in all phases of the Alabama M.B.A. experience. From placement opportunities to classroom visits and service on the College's Advisory Boards, Alabama M.B.A. alumni bring a vital practitioner's viewpoint to the operations of the college. Alabama alumni form a deep and dedicated pool of practical knowledge and resources on which the college, its faculty, and ultimately each student depends. Since its establishment in the early 1950s, the University of Alabama's M.B.A. program has graduated more than 1,600 men and women, each of whom is a valuable and loyal member of the Alabama family.

The College and Environs

The University of Alabama is located in Tuscaloosa, Alabama, with a metropolitan statistical area of about 170,000 residents. The University has about 20,000 students, approximately 400 of whom are graduate business students. Tuscaloosa offers its residents and the University of Alabama a blend of small-town and big-city advantages. Located on the Black Warrior River in west Alabama, Tuscaloosa is a thriving center of business, cultural, and educational activity, with easy access to larger urban centers such as Birmingham, Atlanta, Nashville, New Orleans, and Memphis. Tuscaloosa is a nexus of international industry. Mercedes-Benz, JVC, British Steel, Uniroyal Goodrich (an affiliate of Michelin), Phifer Wire, and other international companies have chosen to locate to this community because of the University's involvement in economic expansion and the quality of personal and corporate life available here. UA research facilities serve local businesses in many ways, from technology for improved productivity to international market research. The business community returns the favor by providing internship and employment opportunities to UA students and graduates. Local industry and the University also maintain ties to business and industry in Birmingham, Alabama's largest city; Mobile, an international seaport; Huntsville, home of the U.S. Space and Rocket Center and related technology; and Montgomery, Alabama's capital. Housing is plentiful and relatively inexpensive, and the climate is usually comfortable. Favorite pastimes include outdoor activities, such as water skiing, fishing, camping, biking, and jogging.

Facilities

The College of Commerce and Business Administration is the home of Bidgood Hall, Mary Hewell Alston Hall, and the 65,000-square-foot Angelo Bruno Business Library and Sloan Y. Bashinsky Computer Center. All three buildings house state-of-the-art classrooms and facilities. Alston Hall includes faculty and departmental offices along with the Insurance Hall of Fame. Bidgood houses multimedia classrooms and areas for graduate students, as well as several research centers and the Manderson Graduate School of Business. The Bruno-Bashinsky Library and Computer Center houses more than 200 computer terminals for student use, group study rooms, and computerized library reference systems.

Placement

Finding the right career is a key objective for students pursuing M.B.A. degrees, and the Manderson Graduate School recognizes that career education and options are of the highest importance to the students. The goal of the Manderson Graduate School Placement Office is to provide students with personalized assistance in their approach to career choices. Students are provided with a variety of opportunities and resources to obtain exposure to different career options. For that reason, students are introduced to career counseling even before they begin the program. Information on managing a successful career search continues during orientation and is followed up with workshops and networking opportunities throughout the program. Workshops in areas such as employment search strategies, interviewing skills, resume reviews, and cover letter writing seminars are offered through the M.B.A. Placement Services, as well as the University Career Center Office. Summer internships are strongly encouraged, many of which result in offers of postgraduation employment.

Admission

Application requirements include the completion of an undergraduate degree at an accredited U.S. college or its international equivalent, submission of scores from the General Management Admissions Test (GMAT), and completion of the application materials. Letters of recommendation, transcripts, essays, and an interview are also required and are integral in the admissions decision process. All international students must also submit scores from the TOEFL. Candidates wishing to be considered for admission to the M.B.A./J.D. program must first apply and be accepted, unconditionally, to both the law school and the M.B.A. program. Because of the highly competitive selection process for the joint program, interested students are encouraged to have both their law school and their M.B.A. applications completed by February 15.

Finances

With a growing reputation as a high-quality, cost-effective program, the University of Alabama's M.B.A. program offers opportunities for motivated students to excel in a wide range of career opportunities that make the difference for successful professionals. Full-time tuition per academic year for residents is $2872 and $7722 per academic year for nonresidents, plus an additional $200 fee for each of the ten core courses. This fee totals $2000 over the two-year program. Living expenses may include estimated rent of between $350 and $550 per month for an off-campus apartment. University dorms or apartments are also available.

Each year, more than half of the M.B.A. students receive merit-based financial aid from the Manderson Graduate School of Business in the form of scholarships, fellowships, and graduate assistantships. Individuals who wish to be considered for merit-based financial assistance must first apply to the program by February 15, be unconditionally accepted, and have competitive academic credentials. No additional forms or applications are required in order to be considered for merit-based aid.

Application Facts and Dates

Applicants are encouraged to submit their applications to the University of Alabama as early as possible. The application process begins on October 1 of the year prior to the year applicants wish to start. The final application deadline is May 15. Students who wish to be considered for scholarships, fellowships, or assistantships should apply by February 15. All University of Alabama offices are open between 8 a.m. and 4:45 p.m. Central Standard Time. Students with any questions regarding international applications and requirements should contact:

Mrs. Libby Williams
The University of Alabama Graduate
  School
Box 870118, 102 Rose Administration
  Building
Tuscaloosa, Alabama 35487-0118
Telephone: 205-348-5921

Students may also contact:

Missy Strickland
Coordinator of Graduate Recruiting/
  Admissions
The University of Alabama
Manderson Graduate School of
  Business
Box 870223, 101 Bidgood Hall
Tuscaloosa, Alabama 35487-0223
Telephone: 205-348-6517
  888-863-2622 (toll-free in the
  United States)
E-mail: mba@aslton.cba.ua.edu

The University of Arizona

Tucson, Arizona

INNOVATIVE MANAGEMENT EDUCATION—THE ELLER SCHOOL APPROACH

The goal of the Eller School M.B.A. program is to provide the foundation for a lifetime of development so that each student can maximize his or her potential for success. We accomplish this by providing a curriculum that combines the benefits of education based in the business disciplines with the relevance of dealing with real business problems. When you finish our program, you will be able to identify and formulate business problems, to specify and locate the information needed to solve them, and to develop and implement practical solutions. In short, you will know what questions to ask, where to go for information, and how to use that information to make effective managerial decisions. These are the keys to success in business, and they are the cornerstones of our program. We promise you hard work, a measure of fun, a friendly and supportive learning environment, and the knowledge and skills to be an effective business leader when you graduate. Join us for an unmatched learning experience!

—John C. Buckingham Jr., Associate Dean
and Director of the M.B.A. Program

Programs and Curricular Focus

The Eller School's philosophy is that successful business leaders must have a solid understanding of business concepts and how they are interrelated in the overall business system.

The M.B.A. curriculum is based on two years of full-time study, with an optional internship in industry during the summer between the first and second years. The first year comprises the M.B.A. Core. Nine courses (plus one elective, one career development module, and one consulting project module) are designed to introduce students to crucial concepts and skills for professional managers.

The second-year curriculum offers students the opportunity to pursue their professional interests and goals through a wide selection of electives. Individual majors are not required in the Eller School M.B.A. program. By planning elective choices carefully, students can achieve functional depth and interdisciplinary breadth.

This combination of flexibility and structure lets students customize their individual course of study while ensuring that each student leaves the program with the knowledge and skills required to identify, create, and deliver superior customer value in his or her chosen career. Areas of study and concentration include highly ranked MIS and marketing departments, a nationally recognized entrepreneurship program, and an expanded finance concentration. The final semester of the second year also includes a required business policy course, which serves as the capstone for the program.

Students and the M.B.A. Experience

Communications skills are vital for successful managers. To ensure relevance for business, the Eller School communications component is directly connected to and completely integrated with the first-year core courses. Each oral and written business communications activity has a theoretical and a practical component that relates directly to a corresponding business topic.

Similarly, team building and teamwork are vital aspects of business success. Because these skills are essential to long-term success, M.B.A. students in the Eller School are taught the theoretical underpinnings of good teamwork, and they are coached in the practical methods for achieving it.

The Eller School is deliberately kept small (approximately 100 full-time students are enrolled each year) so that students can grow and develop in a friendly, professional environment. A variety of opportunities for interactions with faculty and staff members in both academic and social settings results in a friendly, supportive atmosphere in which each individual can feel comfortable and confident. Where competition exists, such as in the simulation, it is good-natured and focused on mutual goals of learning and success.

Social life in the M.B.A. program is plentiful and varied. The close-knit, team-oriented nature of the program produces deep and lasting friendships. This past year, students participated in a tour of regional wineries, hiking and camping in the surrounding mountains, intramural sports, and the Eller Cup semiannual golf tournament.

Special Features

Classroom activities alone are not sufficient to prepare students for leadership roles when they finish the program. At the Eller School, we have integrated a consulting project within the first-year curriculum. These projects represent the combination of important initiatives within the M.B.A. program: incorporating real world business experience into the curriculum and allowing business community outreach from the University. The experiences gained in the conduct of these projects create more capable and more marketable business graduates. Two major selection criteria will be used—the academic and experiential value of work to be executed and the likelihood of close interaction between client and student. A student team is selected, which develops an achievable scope and executes a project with an output that is of value to the company or organization. Utlimately, the students must produce a project deliverable that will be evaluated for a grade. Students present their reports with a formal presentation or round-table discussion. When students complete this activity, they leave the program with a level of maturity, competence, and business savvy that is well beyond what is typically learned in a classroom setting. This is one of the highlights of the Eller School M.B.A. program.

The Faculty

Faculty members serve as mentors and coaches to students entering a new realm

of experience. All are highly credentialed scholars who bring their extensive research, consulting, and business backgrounds to the classroom experience. Representing a full range of management disciplines, Eller School faculty members have received national attention for the quality, originality, and leadership of their work. In addition to advancing the state of knowledge in traditional fields, they are pioneering new areas such as judgment and decision making and group decision support systems.

The Business School Network

M.B.A. students find a ready source of mentoring and helpful support in the M.B.A. Student Association (MBASA). One special aspect of the MBASA is the student consulting group. Student consultants work with area businesses to help them solve real business problems. Recent clients include the Tucson Urban League, which retained the MBASA Consulting Group to instruct minority businesspeople in the business planning process.

The College and Environs

The University of Arizona is located in Tucson, a city of more than 650,000 in the southeastern corner of the state. Surrounded by mountains and blessed with an eternally blue sky, the high Sonoran Desert is a delightful place to live and to learn. Housing is readily available and reasonably priced.

Technology Environment

The routine use of the computer is incorporated throughout the curriculum. Students regularly use group collaboration software, e-mail, statistical analysis, word processing, and presentation software packages. Because information technologies are a pervasive component of the M.B.A. program, students should enter with a reasonable comfort with either a Windows or Macintosh computing environment and familiarity with a spreadsheet package (such as Microsoft Excel) and a word processing package (such as Microsoft Word). The Business School Information Technology Service (BITS) offers refresher courses in each of these areas throughout the semester for those students who wish to brush up or expand their skills. BITS also offers courses in the popular statistical packages, so it is not necessary for students to know this material prior to the start of school. Access to computers is available throughout the campus, and graduate student labs are available during the hours when McClelland Hall is open. If individual resources permit, it is recommended that students own a notebook computer with a modem to facilitate 24-hour access to technology.

Placement

The Eller School Graduate Placement Office assists students in developing career plans and job search strategies and actively markets the School and the students to regional and national employers. In addition to on-campus interviews for full-time positions and summer internships, the Eller School participates in the West Coast M.B.A. Consortium, an annual recruiting event held in Irvine, California, and has recently utilized videoconference technology to enable employers to conduct live video interviews with Eller School students. The EllerNet Alumni Network enables students to make contacts with M.B.A. alumni across the country.

Admission

Applicants for admission to the M.B.A. program must submit transcripts from all undergraduate and graduate institutions attended, essays in response to specific questions, a resume, GMAT scores, application forms, and a nonrefundable application fee. International students must submit TOEFL scores (minimum of 600) and evidence of financial resources. Mathematics prerequisites for admission include calculus.

The entering class in the fall of 1999 had an average GMAT score of 645, average GPA of 3.5 (on a 4.0 scale), average age of 28, and an average of six years of work experience.

Finances

The 2000–01 registration fee for full-time in-state students is $7348 per year. Tuition and fees for full-time nonresident students total $15,804 per year. Room and board cost approximately $11,000 per year. Students should budget $1900 for books, software, and photocopying for the first year of study and approximately $1000 for the second year. They should also budget $636 for insurance and $2500 for miscellaneous expenses per year.

Merit-based scholarships are available through the Eller School for full-time students only. This includes waivers of nonresident tuition, graduate assistantships, waivers of registration fees. Loans are available through the Office of Student Financial Aid.

Application Facts and Dates

Applications for fall admission are processed as they are received. Deadlines are March 1 for domestic students (December 1 for first priority) and February 1 for financial aid and for international students. Decision letters are mailed within four to six weeks after receipt of completed applications. For more information, students should contact:

Ms. Susan K. Salinas Wong
Director of Admissions
Eller Graduate School of Management
210 McClelland Hall
P.O. Box 210108
The University of Arizona
Tucson, Arizona 85721-0108
Telephone: 520-621-3915
Fax: 520-621-2606
E-mail: ellernet@bpa.arizona.edu

University of Arkansas

Fayetteville, Arkansas

WINNING IN THE NEXT MILLENNIUM—THE ARKANSAS M.B.A.

Through our new, competency-based M.B.A. program, University of Arkansas (UA) M.B.A. students develop the necessary skills and knowledge to be change agents in the global environment of the twenty-first century. We emphasize an integrated perspective to business problems through our modular core curriculum, concentrations, and Partners in Progress program.

Our program combines the strengths of individuals in numerous team-based, real-world projects. You will find that our students are competitive in nature but cooperative with each other.

From their first exposure to the exceptional beauty of the Ozark Mountains, Arkansas M.B.A. students gain new friendships and experiences that underscore lifelong personal and business success. We will prepare you to manage, lead, and change the business environment for this new millennium.

—Doyle Z. Williams, Dean

Programs and Curricular Focus

The University of Arkansas Master of Business Administration program is designed to produce graduates with a broad view of the issues confronting managers in cutting-edge organizations. In a departure from the traditional collection of 3-hour courses, the Arkansas M.B.A. program is organized around coordinated modules. UA M.B.A. students are involved in classes and projects that ensure graduates possess the following five competencies: the skills, knowledge, and ability to lead change; the ability to approach problems from a managerial perspective; the ability to manage and work in teams; the ability to write and speak persuasively, based upon a comprehensive analysis of situations facing managers; and self-confidence grounded in one's abilities.

Both the full-time and the managerial (part-time) programs comprise five primary blocks: preparatory work, foundations, core modules, a partnering project, and a concentration in one of five areas: strategic retail alliances, finance, entrepreneurship and strategic innovation, global business, or a customized concentration. The customized concentration is designed by the student and can be completed with either business administration courses and/or courses outside of the College. A J.D./M.B.A. program is available.

The UA M.B.A. program is a one-year program for all full-time students,

regardless of their undergraduate degree. Through extensive self-study with preparatory materials, participation in prematriculation workshops, and completion of the foundations module, all students should have sufficient background to pursue the rigorous 38-hour, lock-step curriculum. The managerial program is a two-year (minimum) program. Initial matriculation is approximately July 1 for the full-time program and approximately August 25 for the managerial program.

Students and the M.B.A. Experience

The UA M.B.A. experience is different from the experience found in large M.B.A. programs. Arkansas's small program size allows frequent and substantial contact among students and between students and faculty members. A very active graduate business student association plans and carries out community outreach work, professional development activities, and social functions.

Arkansas M.B.A. students have widely varying backgrounds. More than thirteen states and twenty countries are represented in the M.B.A. student body. Students average 26 years of age and possess, on average, two years of professional work experience prior to joining the program. Approximately 46 percent of students are women, 3 percent are members of minority groups, and 27 percent are international students.

The M.B.A. program is open to any undergraduate degree student. Nearly 20 percent of students possess undergraduate degrees and work experience in chemical, civil, electrical, industrial, or mechanical engineering. Other majors include business, biology, history, liberal arts, political science, psychology, and other social sciences.

Special Features

UA M.B.A. students have the opportunity to participate in numerous international programs and courses. Jointly taught summer classes are offered with the University of Quebec at Montreal and DUXX in Mexico. A dual master's degree program with ESC Toulouse in France allows French-speaking students to complete one year of study at the University of Arkansas and a second year of study in France, with degrees from both institutions being awarded at the completion of the second year. Many M.B.A. students choose to participate in Sam M. Walton College of Business Administration classes in China, Greece, Italy, and Japan.

Future entrepreneurs can participate in the Students Acquiring Knowledge through Enterprise (SAKE) course. SAKE is a retail operation that offers high-quality, unique merchandise for college markets. Profits from the business are used to fund international travel; in the past, students have traveled to Hong Kong, China, and Costa Rica.

The Faculty

Arkansas M.B.A. faculty members possess extensive experience in corporate problem solving for a variety of businesses and government agencies. Twenty-one percent of the graduate faculty are women and members of minority groups. Graduate faculty members have received doctoral degrees from major research institutions, including Carnegie Mellon, Duke, Georgia, Harvard, Indiana, Michigan, Michigan State, North Carolina, Pennsylvania, Purdue, Tennessee, and Texas. Faculty members are active in research and professional publications.

The Business School Network

The Dean's Executive Advisory Board utilizes its experience and expertise to assist

Expectations of excellence; performance to match.

the Sam M. Walton College of Business Administration in defining and realizing its goals. The board consists of 34 corporate leaders, 27 of whom are chairmen, CEOs, presidents, or division presidents of large regional, national, or international corporations, including Wal-Mart Stores, Inc.; Tyson Foods, Inc.; J. B. Hunt Transport, Inc.; Entergy Corporation; ALLTEL Corporation; Beverly Enterprises; Southwestern Bell Telephone; Bank of America; American Freightways; Staffmark, Inc.; and Southwestern Energy Company. These corporate leaders provide valuable insight and contacts and play an integral part of the M.B.A. experience, bridging academic learning with hands-on professional training.

The College also utilizes the services of the Business Alumni Advisory Council members. Council members serve as ambassadors to advance the presence of the College throughout the nation. The council comprises 38 members, all of whom are graduates of the University of Arkansas. Each member is a business leader in his or her field of expertise.

The College and Environs

The University of Arkansas, Fayetteville, serves as the major center of liberal and professional education and as the primary land-grant campus for the state. The University offers graduate education leading to the master's degree in more than eighty-two fields and to the doctoral degree in more than thirty carefully selected areas.

The entire UA population is composed of approximately 15,000 students. The Sam M. Walton College of Business Administration enrolls approximately 2,500 undergraduate students and approximately 200 graduate students.

The University is located in Fayetteville, a community of 60,000 residents. It is situated in the northwestern corner of the state in the heart of the Ozark Mountains at an elevation of 1,400 feet. Fayetteville is a 2-hour drive from Tulsa, a 4-hour drive from Kansas City, and a 5-hour drive from Dallas and St. Louis. A regional airport offering daily flights to Atlanta, Chicago, Dallas, St. Louis, and Memphis services the city.

Facilities

All M.B.A. classes are taught in state-of-the-art, dedicated rooms that allow technology to be fully integrated into classroom discussions. A separate graduate computer lab with the latest computer software is available for M.B.A. students. A graduate lounge is available for student use for team meetings, study, and socializing.

For students' living needs, both on- and off-campus housing (within walking distance of the campus) is available. For on-campus housing, application should be made at least three months prior to the summer enrollment date. A mass transit system is available to all students for transportation in and around the surrounding areas. Transportation fees are nominal and are included as part of the total tuition fee expense.

Placement

The Sam M. Walton College of Business Administration has a full-time placement director dedicated to supporting the career development needs of master's degree students. In addition, the University of Arkansas lends placement support through the Career Planning and Placement Office. Services that are provided include resume preparation, counseling, career workshops, employer information services, and employment search assistance. UA M.B.A. graduates have been successful in finding jobs with partnering firms and with Fortune 500 companies. Eighty-two percent of Arkansas M.B.A. graduates are in career positions or continue additional studies within three months of graduation.

Admission

Admission to the Master of Business Administration program is competitive and limited. Successful applicants are expected to rank in the 80th percentile on the Graduate Management Admission Test (GMAT) and possess a cumulative undergraduate grade point average of 3.4. International applicants must score a minimum of 550 on the Test of English as a Foreign Language (TOEFL), and a TOEFL score of 600 is strongly recommended.

Although work experience is not required for the full-time program, applicants with a minimum of two years of professional work experience are given preference. Applicants to the managerial program must possess two years of full-time work experience prior to graduation. Letters of recommendation from those familiar with the applicant's aptitude for graduate-level work in business and essays from the applicant are weighted heavily in admission decisions.

Finances

Tuition and fees for one semester of the 2000–01 academic year are $3071 for Arkansas residents and $5987 for nonresidents for 12 hours of graduate-level studies. In addition, students enrolled in 6 or more hours are assessed $175 for health, activity, technology, recreation, transportation, and facilities fees. International students must show proof of health insurance and are required to pay a nonimmigrant student service fee of $50 per semester.

Fayetteville consistently has been selected as one of the best cities in which to live in the United States. The area has a relatively low cost of living; students can expect to pay approximately $9200 a year for living expenses, including room, board, books, supplies, and personal expenses.

Students may apply for graduate assistantships, which currently offer a tuition waiver and pay a stipend of $6500 for twelve months. Students who are awarded graduate assistantships are required to work 12 hours per week to support the instructional or research needs of the faculty in the Sam M. Walton College of Business Administration.

Application Facts and Dates

International applicants, all applicants without an undergraduate business degree, and applicants who completed an undergraduate degree in business more than three years ago should submit their completed application materials by November 15. Admission decisions for early applicants are made by December 15, giving the successful applicant sufficient time to complete the preparatory work prior to matriculation in the summer. Preference in admission and financial aid is given to applicants who submit their application prior to February 15. All applications received after February 15 are processed on a space-available basis. In no case is an applicant admitted after May 15.

For additional information, students should contact:

M.B.A. Director
Graduate School of Business
CBA Suite 475
Sam M. Walton College of Business
    Administration
University of Arkansas
Fayetteville, Arkansas 72701
Telephone: 501-575-2851
Fax: 501-575-8721
E-mail: gsb@walton.uark.edu
World Wide Web: http://www.uark.
    edu/depts/mba/public_html/

University of Baltimore

Baltimore, Maryland

MERRICK—FLEXIBILITY TO FIT YOUR LIFE

Sensitive to the time constraints of students with work and family responsibilities, we have created flexible delivery systems for our graduate programs. The Merrick Professional M.B.A. has four tracks that allow students to complete an M.B.A. in as little as one year by studying in ten-week sessions. The Advantage M.B.A. track is a full-time program, the Saturday M.B.A. track offers classes on Saturdays only, the webM.B.A. track allows degree completion entirely via the Internet, and the Custom track allows students to mix and match courses and schedules to best fit their lifestyles. In addition, our more traditional, part-time FLEX M.B.A. offers students the option of attending evening classes on a regular semester schedule. We are proud to offer accredited degree programs on a flexible schedule to fit the lifestyles of busy adult students.

—John D. Hatfield, Dean

Programs and Curricular Focus

The hallmark of the Professional M.B.A. at the Merrick School is flexibility, developing skills applicable to career goals and transferable to future employment opportunities. With an emphasis on teamwork and the case study approach, students learn from real-world business problems and successes. Students may select a personal mentor from the Merrick Advisory Board or the UB Alumni Association. Mentors work with new students, providing access to a vast network of Baltimore business leaders.

The Professional M.B.A. program contains five tracks. They include the FLEX M.B.A. track, a conventional fifteen-week semester evening program; the Advantage M.B.A. track, which is a full-time fast-track option; the Saturday M.B.A. track, a convenient weekend program; and the webM.B.A., which offers courses entirely via the Internet.

Depending on a student's academic background, 30 to 51 credits are required in the FLEX M.B.A. evening program. Preparatory courses covering a basic knowledge of business functions account for up to 21 credits, which can be taken as part of the undergraduate program or in the graduate school. Of the 30 credits in the M.B.A. program, 18 consist of cross-functional areas of business practice. The remaining 12 credits are selected from electives. Students may create their own grouping of elective credits from the following areas: decision technologies, entrepreneurship, finance, health-care management, human resource management, international business, marketing, manage-

ment information systems, and service and manufacturing operations.

The Advantage M.B.A. is a one-year, full-time program. It involves a maximum of 48 credits and is offered on an efficient ten-week module schedule. The courses are scheduled over ten weeks, with a three-week break between sessions. There are four sessions per year. The Advantage M.B.A. involves working together with other fast-track students on both course work and a team project. The project allows opportunities to network with peers and in the business community. It provides valuable contacts and experience.

The two-year Saturday M.B.A. meets exclusively on the weekend, a time of convenience for busy executives and managers. It is offered on the same ten-week schedule as the Advantage M.B.A. Students come from local industry and have the advantage of networking within their groups and by extension with other leaders in the business community.

The webM.B.A. is also offered on the ten-week schedule. It is offered entirely on the Internet, with no requirements for campus visits. The webM.B.A. fits into the schedule of the busiest executive. Even those who travel extensively can complete course requirements online. A built-in course e-mail facility allows asynchronous communication with great interaction. The webM.B.A. can be earned in two years.

The Custom M.B.A. allows students to mix and match courses offered through

the Advantage, Saturday, and webM.B.A. programs on the ten-week schedule.

Students and the M.B.A. Experience

Merrick School students are a mature and diverse population. The average age is 30, and 85 percent have work experience prior to entering the M.B.A. program. Merrick School students are employed at Fortune 500 companies such as Lockheed Martin, Black and Decker, Northrup Grumman, USF&G, AT&T, and BGE as well as regional financial services, government, and business organizations.

In the most recent academic year, women made up 38 percent of the entering M.B.A. class. International students come from such countries as India, China, Israel, Brazil, Turkey, the Ukraine, Kenya, Thailand, France, Greece, and Japan. While some 48 percent completed an undergraduate business degree, others have backgrounds in engineering, science, liberal arts, and the humanities.

The Faculty

The most important resource of any business school is its faculty. Merrick School professors combine a dedication to teaching with significant research, professional, and community service activities. Many Merrick School faculty members have earned national reputations in their fields, both for research and classroom innovations. They are published in leading scholarly journals, including the *Harvard Business Review,* the *Journal of Finance,* and *JAMA* (the *Journal of the American Medical Association*). The faculty includes the founder and president of the international Production and Operations Management Society (POMS) and the former president and current board member of the Consumer Federation of America. At the same time, faculty members have designed new courses for the M.B.A. curriculum that have received recognition from professional groups throughout the region.

Many professors are graduates of prestigious institutions, such as Harvard, MIT, Michigan, and Wharton. As a group, they have nearly 300 years of full-time professional work experience with business, government, and nonprofit organizations. This combination of academic expertise and

real-world experience translates into a unique and rewarding experience for students.

Of the 55 full-time faculty members, 95 percent have terminal degrees, 23 percent are female, and 28 percent are international or members of minority groups.

The Business School Network

The ties between the Merrick School and the region's business leaders are strong. The Merrick Advisory Board is composed of more than 70 senior executives who represent a broad spectrum of companies and industries, both national and international. Faculty members work closely with business leaders to ensure program and course relevance. The School's corporate partners emphasize continuous improvement in academic programs to prepare students for the competitive marketplace. They also support student career development and placement efforts.

Members of the Advisory Board and the UB Alumni Association serve as mentors for all M.B.A. students, providing an opportunity to observe and interact with seasoned professionals, business owners, and entrepreneurs. They meet on a regular basis with the students, arrange for informational interviews with colleagues, and introduce students to the Baltimore business community. In addition, Advantage M.B.A. students work on an intensive one-semester project submitted by local businesses in the Baltimore-Washington area.

Advisory Board members have sponsored internships for Merrick students and serve on panels for student classroom presentations. In addition, they have been active in revising the curriculum, reviewing issues of customer service, and developing systems to track students from inquiry to graduation.

The College and Environs

The University of Baltimore is located in Baltimore, Maryland, a city of 600,000, less than an hour from Washington, D.C., and three hours by car or train from New York. The Baltimore metropolitan area serves as a regional center for the operations of many businesses and nonprofit organizations.

The University is located in the city's revitalized cultural district. Five minutes south of the campus is Baltimore's famous Inner Harbor, which features shopping, restaurants, and entertainment attractions.

The School of Business was named in honor of Robert G. Merrick, a pioneer in the Baltimore financial services industry. The Merrick School is accredited by AACSB–The International Association for Management Education.

Facilities

The Thumel Business Center, home of the Merrick School of Business, includes classrooms, case rooms, seminar rooms, offices, and labs linked together by high-speed digital networks that tie together an array of information technology and facilitate communication within the building, around the campus, and worldwide via the Internet. A Group Decision Support Lab, a Multimedia Lab, and a Microcomputing Lab allow students to work individually or in groups.

The Langsdale Library and School of Law Library house more than 400,000 bound volumes, microform and CD-ROM holdings, government documents, and periodicals. Interlibrary loan programs with area libraries and the thirteen University System of Maryland institutions expand the resources available to UB students. All card catalogs in the system and across the state are accessible from the students' homes via computer and modem.

Placement

The Career Center offers a variety of services to help students and alumni attain their career goals. In individual and group sessions, professional career counselors address such issues as resume writing, job search, and networking. In addition, counselors administer and interpret traditional and computerized self-assessment tools. Job-related services include a job bank and resume referral to employers (both Web-based) and assistance with paid and unpaid internships. Each semester the Career Center sponsors specialized workshops, networking programs for graduating seniors, and career and job fairs.

In support of placement activities, the Merrick School of Business offers students the opportunity to be mentored by a regional business leader and, in addition, sponsors career-related programs specific to academic specializations.

Admission

Students apply by submitting an application, GMAT score, two letters of recommendation, resume, letter of intent explaining reasons for pursuing the master's degree, and official transcripts of undergraduate work. New fall 1999 and spring 2000 registrants had an average GMAT score of 560 and an average GPA of 3.2. Applicants with foreign transcripts should arrange for an evaluation of their academic records and must submit a TOEFL score of at least 550 (213 on the computer-based version).

Finances

Graduate business tuition for the 2000–01 academic year for in-state students is $282 per credit. Tuition for out-of-state students is $420 per credit. The University also applies some flat and some per-credit fees. Thus, a 3-credit course for in-state residents costs $972, while out-of-state charges are $1386. All charges for graduate business courses are on a per-credit basis. No separate scale is used for full-time study.

Merit scholarships are available for all M.B.A. students. Thumel Scholarships provide tuition assistance for Advantage M.B.A. and Saturday M.B.A. students. France and Merrick Scholarships are available for Master of Science and FLEX M.B.A. students.

Graduate students are eligible for graduate assistantships, which cover tuition and include a small stipend.

Applications for scholarships are due by March 1 each year, and applications for financial aid are due by April 1.

International Students

The Merrick School of Business welcomes applicants from outside the U.S. In fall 1998, international students accounted for nearly 12 percent of the graduate enrollment in the Merrick School. The International Services Office provides admission advisement, visa assistance, and orientation services to prospective and enrolled students at the University of Baltimore.

Application Facts and Dates

Applications are accepted for the FLEX M.B.A. program for fall, spring, and summer semesters. The Advantage M.B.A. class enters in July; the Saturday M.B.A. and webM.B.A. classes begin in the summer and in the winter. Applications are processed on a rolling or continuous basis. Early application is recommended for all programs, especially the Advantage and Saturday programs.

Recommended deadlines for the FLEX program are July 15 for the fall semester, December 1 for the spring semester, and April 1 for the summer semester.

Inquiries and requests for application materials should be directed to:

Ms. Lorna Hills
Coordinator of Graduate Admission
University of Baltimore
1420 North Charles Street
Baltimore, Maryland 21201-5779
Telephone: 410-837-4777
         877-ApplyUB (toll-free)
Fax: 410-837-4820
E-mail: admissions@ubmail.ubalt.edu

University of Bridgeport

Bridgeport, Connecticut

ADDRESSING THE GLOBAL PERSPECTIVE

The School of Business offers a master of business administration degree program with concentrations in accounting, global marketing, finance, operations, and management information systems. Degree completion normally requires two years of full-time or three to five years of part-time study. Accelerated study is available for qualified students who have recently completed a business degree from an accredited college. On alternate weekends, a weekend M.B.A. program is available at the University's Stamford campus and can be completed in twelve to eighteen months.

The M.B.A. program begins with a focus on analysis and evaluation of the control of an organization and of the environment for leadership. Courses include accounting, decision theory, economics, the Organization and Management of Finance, production and marketing, and the Socio-Cultural Aspects of People in Organizations. Advanced courses expand and integrate topics explored in introductory courses and provide a strong focus on the global perspective necessary for contemporary management. The School is accredited by the Association of Collegiate Business Schools and Programs (ACBSP).

—Glenn Bassett, Director

Programs and Curricular Focus

The M.B.A. program at the University of Bridgeport (UB) develops effective and responsible leaders for business, industry, and government in the global market. It not only emphasizes traditional management skills but also stresses the technical and cultural preparation necessary to understand the increasingly complex international environment.

The M.B.A. requires between 30 and 54 semester credit hours of study, depending on the student's academic background and level of academic achievement. The curriculum is designed to recognize substantial diversity in preparation and experience for students entering M.B.A. study, as well as different goals and expectations of students.

Core courses provide the management tools for analysis, decision making, and communications; concepts, theory, and current practice in the major functional areas of operation; and the opportunity to study continuing and contemporary problems of management responsibility. The core is central to M.B.A. study, providing a base of knowledge for additional study in electives and a specific professional discipline. The M.B.A. core courses (24 credits) are as follows: Accounting Concepts, Economic Analysis, Financial Management, Organizational Behavior, Operations Management, Marketing Concepts, Management Science and Linear Programming, Management Information Systems, and Statistical Decision Theory.

Listed below are the advanced courses for which the M.B.A. core is only a prerequisite: Accounting for Managers, International Accounting, International Trade and Finance, Advanced Financial Management and Policy, the Financial Management of Financial Institutions, Management Theory, Small Business Entrepreneurship, Advanced Operations Management, Buyer Analysis, Global Market Management and Strategy Planning, Internet Applications and Opportunities, Information Systems Analysis and Design, Business and Society, and Business Policy. The Global Management group of electives comprises International Issues and Languages. The Experiential Learning group comprises Leadership and Organizational Change, Business Games, and internships. Concentrations are offered in accounting, global marketing, finance, operations, and management information systems. Teaching methods include a mix of lecture, case study, experiential learning, and an analysis of international social-political issues.

Students and the M.B.A. Experience

M.B.A. program participants represent fifty nationalities. Five percent are from Europe, 50 percent are from North America, and 45 percent are from other countries. Thirty-five percent of the students have a degree background in sciences/technology, 40 percent in economics, 2 percent in law, and 23 percent in other majors. Student GMAT scores range from 400 to 650; the average is 500. International student TOEFL scores average 550. Women comprise 51 percent of the student population. Student ages range from 22 to 60. The average age is 27. The average length of student work experience for those who are working professionals is eight years.

Special Features

The program features a flexible course of study to meet the convenience of all kinds of students; a strong emphasis on global business to prepare for the twenty-first century business world; experiential learning in a small group setting; a diverse student body composed of domestic and international students; and a systematic understanding of discipline, value, and an ethical code of behavior in business.

The Faculty

The faculty is as diverse as the student body. It is composed of domestic and international members with superb academic qualifications and corporate business experience. Faculty members are active in research, authoring books, journals, and conference papers.

The Business School Network

The University of Bridgeport's 86-acre campus is situated on Long Island Sound. Located in Fairfield County, the area is home to many of the nation's largest multinational corporate headquarters and provides students with excellent opportunities for jobs, internships, and co-op training. Through the Director's Advisory Board, the School interfaces with many executives from corporations, who give advice and direction as well as instruction in the classroom.

The University's Stamford Center is conveniently located in Stamford, Connecticut, and is easily accessible to working professionals from southern Fairfield and Westchester counties, New York, and New Jersey.

Corporate Partnerships

Through the Trefz Center for Venture Management, which is housed in the School of Business, the School sponsors a number of activities that link the School with the business community. Components of Trefz Center of Venture Management include The Business Development

Institute, which assists potential entrepreneurs and small business persons in start-up, business organization, finance, marketing, staffing and management, and evaluating technology and development planning. The Bridgeport Foreign Trade Institute sponsors monthly international business seminars and conferences; develops networks of international business firms; provides consultation services to those individuals and organizations who attempt to enter international business; and assists local governments in promoting local businesses and products made in the state of Connecticut for foreign markets and investors. The Urban Management Institute studies socioeconomic issues in the region and recommends appropriate policy initiatives. The Special Projects Unit promotes activities especially targeted for small businesses.

The College and Environs

Founded in 1927, the University of Bridgeport is a private, nonsectarian, comprehensive, coeducational, urban university located in Bridgeport, Connecticut, just 1 hour (50 miles) from New York City and 3 hours (160 miles) from Boston.

There are approximately 1,400 graduate students enrolled at the University, representing a diverse group of interests, professions, nationalities, and ages. The University maintains an international focus, with 49 percent of its total student body coming from outside the U.S.

Facilities

The University's Wahlstrom Library contains approximately 270,000 bound volumes, including bound journals and indexes, and more than 1 million microforms. It subscribes to more than 1,700 periodicals and other serials. Online databases available from off campus via the library's Internet Web site include more than sixty databases in OCLC's

FirstSearch that cover all subject areas, EBSCOhost's Academic Search Full-TEXT Elite, Bell & Howell's ProQuest Direct ABI Inform Global, Alt-Health Watch, and MANTIS. Links are provided from the library's home page to ERIC and PubMed. Additional online databases available throughout the campus or in the library include LEXIS-NEXIS Academic Universe, STAT-USA, Financial Information Services Online (Moody's), Allied and Alternative Medicine, and the ACM Digital Library. An extension library is maintained at the UB-Stamford campus, with more than 1,000 volumes, more than twenty periodicals, and extensive electronic access. Residence halls are wired for individual computer hookups.

Placement

Many of the University's students are already employed and seek M.B.A. study on a part-time basis. However, because of the University's location in Fairfield county, where sixty-five of Connecticut's Fortune 500 companies are located, students have access to a number of employment opportunities.

Admission

As a professional program, the M.B.A. is designed to build upon undergraduate study in the arts, humanities, science, engineering, or other disciplines. No specific undergraduate curriculum is expected or preferred before entry to M.B.A. study. Admission is based on a bachelor's degree or equivalent in any discipline, scores on the Graduate Management Admission Test (GMAT), and two letters of recommendation. Provisional admission may be granted to a limited number of students, provided that the undergraduate records are exceptionally strong and the applicant has at least three years of management experience. If a student is admitted provisionally, the GMAT must be taken during the first se-

mester. For students whose native language is not English, a TOEFL score of 550 is required.

Finances

For the program, tuition costs $385 per credit (1–12 credits) or $7075 per semester (13 or more credits). Room and board cost $7070 per year, and students should have approximately $1600 allotted for miscellaneous expenses, excluding travel. There is a $40 application fee for domestic students ($35 for international students).

Financial aid is available to U.S. citizens in the form of Federal Stafford Student Loans and graduate assistantships. International students must demonstrate that they have sufficient funds to finance their studies in the United States.

International Students

The focus on a global perspective at the University of Bridgeport offers the international student the opportunity to obtain vital training in a specialized field of study, to enrich his or her life by experiencing another culture, and to gain new perspective on the world and to develop contacts, interpersonal skills, and knowledge necessary to those who work in the international community as technicians, scholars, businessmen, politicians, and scientists.

The University's English Language Institute (ELI) is located on the campus of the University of Bridgeport. ELI offers intensive instruction in English as a second language as well as trips and activities designed to introduce the student to America and its people.

Application Facts and Dates

Applications must be submitted two months prior to the date of intended entry. Electronic applications may be made through the University of Bridgeport's Web site and Polaris. Students may enter in the fall, spring, and summer. For more information, students should contact:

Office of Admissions
University of Bridgeport
126 Park Avenue
Bridgeport, Connecticut 06601
Telephone: 203-576-4552
        800-EXCEL-UB
          (392-3582, toll-free)
Fax: 203-576-4941
E-mail: admit@bridgeport.edu
World Wide Web: http://www.bridgeport.edu

M.B.A. Program
School of Business
University of Bridgeport
230 Park Avenue
Bridgeport, Connecticut 06601
Telephone: 203-576-4363
Fax: 203-576-4388

University of British Columbia

Faculty of Commerce and Business Administration

Vancouver, British Columbia, Canada

UBC'S M.B.A. PROGRAM

Your interest in this reading material indicates that you must be keen in pursuing an M.B.A. experience. You have undoubtedly explored program options and may be contemplating a choice. I, too, experienced a similar situation when considering whether to become Dean of the Faculty of Commerce and Business Administration. However, once I visited UBC, the seemingly difficult career decision was ultimately clear.

UBC Commerce is an outstanding centre of scholarly activity, where the professional staff is committed to ensuring an excellent student environment for career development. The faculty members are dedicated to the creation of new knowledge and the sharing of knowledge in a supportive educational setting. The superb participants, selected from among the best around the globe, are key to the success of the school. We offer an innovative curriculum designed to foster team process and learning, while offering ample opportunities to acquire important international competencies.

UBC was clearly my choice. I welcome and encourage you to make it yours.

—Daniel F. Muzyka, Dean

Programs and Curricular Focus

The M.B.A. program at the University of British Columbia (UBC) is rigorous and challenging, offering both structure and flexibility. Students complete the integrated core, after which they choose the specialization that meets their career objectives. Both the core and the specializations are supported and strengthened through business applications in internships, projects, and a professional development program. UBC offers small classes and a balance of instructional techniques, including lecture, case discussion, simulations, and group projects. The program starts in September, lasts fifteen continuous months, and is offered full-time only.

The program is centred on a four-month integrated core, which provides students with a foundation in finance, marketing, human resources, accounting, statistics, economics, and information systems. The core is a team-taught seminar in which these topics are taught from a multidisciplinary perspective, rather than individual functional areas. This innovative approach has been implemented to emulate more closely the multidimensional problems encountered in business.

Following the core, students select one of the following five specializations: finance, marketing, information technology and management, strategic management, and supply chain management. In addition, international business or

e-business may be offered adjunct to any of the above specializations. Students may also choose from a range of electives, including organizational behaviour, human resources management, logistics, transportation, not-for-profit management, real estate and urban development, and technology management.

Additional opportunities at UBC include a combined M.B.A./LL.B. program. Also offered are a Master of Science in Business Administration (M.Sc.Bus.Admin.) and a Doctor of Philosophy (Ph.D.) in business administration for students wishing to pursue research in business.

Students and the M.B.A. Experience

Students are one of the Faculty's greatest resources. M.B.A. classmates have diverse professional, cultural, and academic backgrounds, which create a unique and dynamic learning environment. On average, students are 30 years of age with six years of full-time work experience. The class is 37 percent women.

❖ Global Focus

UBC is committed to offering students unique international educational experiences. A global perspective is gained through specialized international courses,

interaction with the multicultural student body and faculty, and UBC's extensive exchange program. Exchanges are available with twenty-six leading universities located in twenty countries in Asia, Australia, Europe, the Middle East, Great Britain, and Latin America.

Special Features

Internships and projects are a key part of UBC's M.B.A. program. During the specialization component, students have the opportunity to apply their knowledge in either an internship or an industry-related project directly related to their area of specialization.

Throughout the M.B.A. program, several weeks are devoted to developing professional skills in areas such as communications, teamwork, negotiation, technology, and leadership.

Students are required to have an adequate general knowledge of economics, statistics, accounting, and computers. In addition, students should attend UBC's Pre-core Program, designed to refresh these skills, prior to the start of the M.B.A. program.

The Faculty

UBC is committed to excellence in teaching. The M.B.A. program has a large number of outstanding instructors, some of whom have received national and international recognition for their contributions to teaching. UBC's revised program has a strong focus on teaching innovation and course development.

In addition, the Faculty's reputation for research excellence is unmatched by any other Canadian business school. Exceptional work is ongoing in many areas, such as international business and trade policy, entrepreneurship, nonprofit marketing, decision making and creative problem solving, and strategic thinking in negotiating and bargaining.

The Business School Network

Corporate Partnerships

Strong linkages have been developed between UBC and the corporate community. The Dean's Advisory Board, which assists the Dean in developing and

evaluating commerce initiatives, consists of senior representatives from government, labour, and the private sector.

The corporate community provides opportunities for students to apply their business knowledge through projects, internships, and industry field trips. In addition, M.B.A. students interact directly with prominent business leaders in UBC's distinguished speakers series and by participating in a wide range of professional and social events.

Prominent Alumni

Alumni of the Faculty of Commerce and Business Administration have excelled in business and include individuals in the private and public sectors. UBC alumni have held the titles of President and/or Chief Executive Officer of the Hongkong Bank of Canada, Procter & Gamble, Scotiabank, and the Hudson's Bay Company. They have also been well represented in the major accounting firms in the capacity of senior partners. UBC alumni have used their entrepreneurial skills to develop companies such as the Great Canadian Railtour Company and the Savolite Group. In addition, alumni have led prestigious business schools, including Harvard, Queen's at Kingston, and UBC.

The College and Environs

The University of British Columbia is located in Vancouver, one of the world's most beautiful cities. Vancouver is Canada's third-largest city and is one of the fastest growing. Major economic activities include tourism, forestry, fishing, and mining. Situ-

ated equally between Europe and Asia, Vancouver is ideally located for international business, and its economic potential is extremely promising. In addition, Vancouver offers a wonderful lifestyle in which people can ski, sail, cycle, and stroll along the beach all year round.

UBC is Canada's third-largest university, with more than 35,000 academic students. The campus, a few kilometres from the city centre, is on a 1,000-acre forested peninsula overlooking the Pacific Ocean and the Coastal Mountain range. Students find that the campus offers an exceptional variety of cultural and recreational facilities.

Facilities

At UBC, the Faculty of Commerce and Business Administration is committed to providing the highest quality student services. This is accomplished by the professional staff in the Commerce Masters' Programs Office, the Commerce Career Centre, the Study Abroad and Exchange Office, the David Lam Management Research Library, and the Computer Lab.

Placement

Students' job searches are supported by the Commerce Career Centre, which is instrumental in marketing UBC graduates to major national and international corporations. Each year, on-campus information and recruiting sessions are held for more than 300 companies. Career Centre staff members also organize seminars in resume writing,

interviewing techniques, and job search strategies to assist M.B.A. students in the competitive job market.

Admission

The admissions committee assesses undergraduate performance, GMAT scores, full-time work experience, extracurricular involvement, and demonstrated leadership. Specific minimum academic requirements are outlined in the M.B.A. application. A TOEFL of IELTS score is required from an applicant whose prior degree is from a country other than Canada, the United States, the United Kingdom, Ireland, Australia, New Zealand, Kenya, South Africa, and the English-speaking countries of the West Indies.

Applicants are not required to complete prerequisite courses to be eligible to apply, but a basic level of knowledge in economics, financial accounting, statistics, and computers is required prior to the start of the program.

Finances

Tuition is currently under review. Students may see the Web site listed below for the most recent fee and program information. Annual costs for books and materials are approximately Can$1500. The University estimates room and board for a single student living off campus at Can$900 per month.

All applicants are considered for merit-based awards and fellowships at the time of admission.

Application Facts and Dates

Application deadlines are February 28 for international applicants and April 30 for applicants from the United States and Canada. Application materials are available at UBC's Web site (address below). For additional information, students should contact:

Commerce Masters' Programs Office
102-2053 Main Mall
University of British Columbia
Vancouver, British Columbia V6T 1Z2
Canada
Telephone: 604-822-8422
Fax: 604-822-9030
E-mail: masters.programs@commerce.
   ubc.ca
World Wide Web: http://www.
   commerce.ubc.ca

University of California, Davis

Graduate School of Management

Davis, California

WHAT MAKES A GOOD M.B.A. PROGRAM?

At the Graduate School of Management at UC Davis, we believe that students learn best in a supportive, cooperative learning environment that encourages them to stretch intellectually. To create this environment, we've developed a rigorous program that features small classes, faculty members committed to excellence in teaching, and opportunities to work closely with those faculty members and a select group of bright and energetic students. We then guide you to test your new knowledge and creative thinking in real-world business situations. I invite you to take advantage of an outstanding opportunity to fully develop your managerial potential and leadership skills.

—Robert H. Smiley, Dean

Programs and Curricular Focus

The UC Davis Graduate School of Management has accomplished what many in academic circles felt was impossible for such a small and young M.B.A. program: being ranked among the top fifty in the nation. Conceived just over eighteen years ago, the program is recognized for the high quality of its graduates, its world-class faculty, and the excellence of its overall program.

The UC Davis M.B.A. program cultivates each student's ability to deal successfully with the challenges of a continually changing, increasingly complex global business environment. The program's strengths come from a managerial approach to the basic business disciplines; a student-faculty ratio of 10:1; a curriculum that integrates the technological, social, political, economic, and ethical aspects of business; and a variety of teaching methodologies, including case studies, lectures, class discussions, computer simulations, team projects, and real-world applications.

The program comprises twenty-four classes (72 quarter units). Joint degrees are available in law (M.B.A./J.D.), engineering (M.B.A./M.Eng.), medicine (M.B.A./M.D.), and agricultural management (M.B.A./M.S.). All students spend their first two quarters in core classes mastering the curriculum, which provides a common foundation of fundamental management knowledge and skill. Elective concentrations available in the full-time day program or in the evening M.B.A. Program for Working Professionals are accounting, agricultural management, corporate environmental management, finance, general management, health services management, information

technology, international management, management science, marketing, public-sector management, and technology management. Students can also design a customized concentration. The second-year strategy course, Management Policy and Strategy, places students in teams and gives them an opportunity to apply their decision-making and problem-solving skills by developing a strategic plan for a real client business.

Students and the M.B.A. Experience

UC Davis M.B.A. students bring to the School a wide variety of academic and work experiences, and the School's personalized focus and hands-on teaching approach is augmented by this diversity. While 35 percent of the student body reflects preparation in business and economics, because of its strong emphasis in technology management, the School is also traditionally very attractive to students from engineering and the sciences. More than 21 percent of the 1999 entering class came from undergraduate majors in the humanities and social sciences. The most recently admitted class represents more than forty-three undergraduate institutions.

The average full-time student is 29 years old, with 5 years of full-time work experience. Women make up 38 percent of the student population, and 14 percent are international students. The School sponsors nine international student exchange programs.

Special Features

The School encourages prospective students to take advantage of the

Visitation Program. While visiting the School, prospective students are able to talk one-on-one with current students and professors and can attend one of their classes. To enhance preparation for the job market, the School requires that students participate in a videotaped mock interview with one of several executives from both the public and private sectors. This program gives students a unique chance to meet top executives face to face as well as to dramatically improve interviewing skills. The annual Alumni Day, created to provide current students with the "inside track" on up-to-date industry information and career opportunities from alumni, also provides a valuable networking activity.

The Faculty

Faculty members of the UC Davis Graduate School of Management represent doctoral preparation from many of the most prestigious schools in the country and excel both as teachers and researchers. Their current consulting projects keep them in touch with managerial concerns of leading U.S. corporations as well as federal and state agencies. One of the most distinctive features of this faculty is the close relationships members forge with students. The School recognizes the academic value students receive when given the opportunity to work closely and individually with faculty members and offers many formal and informal chances for them to do so. The student-faculty ratio is 10:1.

The Business School Network

To enhance each student's learning and networking experience, the School has developed close ties with leaders throughout business and government. They are frequent visitors to campus, serving as guest lecturers in classes, as interviewers in the mock interview program, and as speakers at frequent School-sponsored events. Through these important contacts, students gain access to high-profile companies and establish relationships with potential employers.

The Executive-in-Residence program gives students and faculty members alike a unique opportunity to work closely with

a top business leader during the executive's quarter-long visit to the School.

The Dean's Advisory Council, made up of many of California's top business leaders, provides the School with one of its strongest connections to the business community. The School's Business Partnership Program provides an important avenue for top regional organizations to become involved with UC Davis M.B.A. students. Students are invited to network with these corporate executives at breakfast meetings and special lectures.

The College and Environs

In the 2000 rankings by *U.S. News & World Report,* the UC Davis Graduate School of Management was eighteenth in the nation among public M.B.A. programs and forty-second overall, making it the youngest and smallest public M.B.A. program ever to be nationally ranked.

The city of Davis is in a superb location, offering the quintessential college-town environment that encourages learning and enhances the quality of life. Davis is surrounded by some of the most economically vital, naturally magnificent communities in the state of California. Close by, the state capital of Sacramento is home to an expanding high-technology manufacturing industry. A short distance to the west is the cosmopolitan San Francisco Bay Area and the booming Silicon Valley. An hour's drive northwest is the beautiful Napa Valley wine country. Two hours east lies the stunning Lake Tahoe.

Facilities

Academic resources include a library of more than 3.1 million volumes, ranked among the top research libraries in North America. A full-time Business Reference Librarian is available to assist students with the latest information-gathering strategies, including some of the most comprehensive online databases available today. Students also have access to more than 1,000 scholarly and trade journals in business, management, finance, and economics.

Technology Environment

The School maintains a 24-hour computer lab with access to the University's high-speed network, the latest business software, networking to extensive library services, and the Internet and intranet. Each student is issued a University computer account, which includes e-mail.

Placement

From the first week of the program, the Career Services Center begins connecting with each student, offering support and personal guidance. Through workshops, on-campus recruiting, mock interviews, and an emphasis on internships, the Career Services Center provides students with the tools needed to build long-term relationships with the corporate community. In addition to the availability of an online application and job posting system, M.B.A. students participate in on-campus interviewing for career and internship positions, career fairs, company information sessions, and on-site company tours. Approximately 43 percent of UC Davis's M.B.A. students were placed in the high-technology industry, which includes positions in finance, marketing, consulting, and technology management. The School also actively participates in the West Coast M.B.A. Consortium recruiting event to give students an additional avenue for seeking career employment. Over the past few years, an average of 98 percent of the School's M.B.A. graduates have been placed within three months of graduation, with a median total compensation package of $75,000.

Admission

Admission to the UC Davis Graduate School of Management is highly selective. Applicants are evaluated on the basis of demonstrated academic achievement, performance on the Graduate Management Admission Test (GMAT), and interest in professional management. Full-time business experience is considered an asset. No particular area of undergraduate preparation

is required, but the University requires the completion of a bachelor's degree from an accredited college or university. The 1999 entering class had an average GMAT score of 675, an average undergraduate GPA of 3.2, and an average of 5 years of work experience.

Finances

The estimated fees for 2000–01 for full-time study are $10,483 per year for California residents and $19,867 for nonresidents. These fees are subject to change. The 2000–01 cost of the M.B.A. Program for Working Professionals is $1345 per class. Many reasonably priced apartments are within biking distance. Monthly rents range from $550 for a studio to $1400 for a three-bedroom apartment. Student-family housing costs range from $451 for a one-bedroom apartment to $555 per month for a two-bedroom apartment. Need-based grants, loans, and fee offsets are available, as is the merit-based GSM Scholar's Grant.

International Students

The School encourages applications from international students. To be eligible for admission to the program, international students must take the TOEFL and earn a score of 250 or better on the computer-based test or 600 or better on the paper-based test. For visa purposes, international students must provide a statement of finances showing at least $33,000 to cover tuition and fees for their first year.

Application Facts and Dates

Application deadlines are February 1 (full-time program early decision), April 1 (full-time program), and May 15 (Working Professionals evening program) for fall quarter admission. Potential applicants may obtain an application by having the materials mailed or printing the application from the School's Web site (listed below). Applicants may apply electronically by completing a Web-based application through GradAdvantage MBA (http://www.gradadvantage.org) or Embark.com (http://www.embark.com) or purchasing an electronic application from Multi-App (http://www.multi-app.com).

Office of Admissions
School's Admissions and Student
    Services Office
Graduate School of Management
University of California, Davis
One Shields Avenue
Davis, California 95616
Telephone: 530-752-7399
Fax: 530-752-2924
E-mail: gsm@ucdavis.edu
World Wide Web: http://www.gsm.
    ucdavis.edu

University of California, Irvine

Irvine, California

ANSWERS FOR THE FUTURE

▶ *GSM is a school with a sharp focus and an innovative attitude. We are constantly looking for ways to give our students that extra advantage, whether they are in the full-time M.B.A. program or in one of our three degree programs for practicing executives and professionals. This is the nature of our school, and it also is the nature of the dynamic, Tech Coast business community in Orange County and southern California.*

We believe that business will be fundamentally changed by those men and women who have a solid understanding of the constantly changing technology that helps us collect, analyze, disseminate, and use information. Our graduates are recognized for their ability to step into situations where they are using information and technology to bring the customer closer to the supplier, to develop partnerships between vendors and manufacturers, or to create a world-wide network that gives companies the competitive edge. Our graduates are able to develop solutions. No wonder they are in such demand by consulting firms, financial institutions, industrial and customer companies, and others that know that continuous innovation is necessary for success.

GSM is a school that is on the move. What exists now will be changed somewhat tomorrow. Programs will be introduced and revised as appropriate. Our faculty and staff are innovators. We experiment with the new while holding firmly to the rigor and demands of a first-rate M.B.A. program. In other words, we live the change for which we are preparing our students to lead.

—David H. Blake, Dean

Programs and Curricular Focus

The Graduate School of Management (GSM) offers four M.B.A. degree options, three of which are designed for the working professional, and a Ph.D. program. The curriculum for the M.B.A. programs is a broad-based, integrative, and comprehensive one that responds to the needs of the high-tech, international, and global economic environment.

The full-time M.B.A. program takes two years to complete. The first year of study incorporates ten of the twelve core courses; the second year is primarily electives of the student's choosing. Functional areas of study include accounting, marketing, information systems, strategy, operations and decision technologies, health care, public policy, finance, and organizational behavior. Although information technology (IT) is integrated throughout the M.B.A. curriculum, UCI also offers a more specific curriculum in the area of information technology for management (ITM) within the full-time M.B.A. program. This curriculum comprehensively integrates the teaching of information technology, and participants in this curriculum are from all functional areas and represent a variety of backgrounds. These students learn how technology affects organizations and markets and how to use information to create new strategic options and gain a lasting competitive advantage.

The Executive M.B.A. is a two-year program designed for managers and working professionals. The Fully Employed M.B.A. Program is a thirty-three-month program intended for working professionals who require a program conducted entirely outside of regular working hours. The Health Care Executive M.B.A. program is a twenty-four month program designed primarily for health-care professionals. It meets one weekend per month.

The doctoral program prepares individuals for teaching and scholarly positions in academic and other institutions where demonstrated ability to do original research is required. It is neither course- nor unit-based and consists of two separate and distinct phases. It is also a small and highly individualized program and allows students to pursue their own areas of interest.

Students and the M.B.A. Experience

GSM makes a special effort to admit a diverse group of students each year who represent a wide range and variety of academic, cultural, and professional backgrounds. The average age for the class of 2001 is 28, with about five years of work experience. Women comprise approximately 35 percent of the student population, and international students comprise about 25 percent.

Special Features

A highlight of the UCI M.B.A. experience is the Corporate Partners Mentoring Program. This program gives students the opportunity to interact with top-level professionals and the chance to elicit advice about individual skills, career paths, company cultures, and corporate expectations. This program provides an invaluable opportunity for students to get insights and feedback from executives interested in their development and success. Students also have the opportunity to supplement their course work through the International and Intercampus Exchange Programs. A joint M.D./M.B.A. program is also offered with the College of Medicine. Research units associated with the School and its faculty members include the Center for Research on Information Technology and Organizations (CRITO), the only site in the country located in a business school and funded by the National Science Foundation studying the impact of technology on organizations and markets.

The Faculty

The faculty members of the Graduate School of Management at UCI are scholars from some of the most esteemed institutions nationally and internationally. They are a diverse group, and their composition is perhaps one of the most international in all business schools. Due to the smaller size and nature of the program, students also have the opportunity to work closely with faculty members throughout the program.

The Business School Network
Corporate Partnerships

The Corporate Partners program actively brings together GSM students and faculty members with the business community through activities such as the Corporate Partners/M.B.A. Roundtable series, Day-on-the-Job, Executive Speakers Series, and Management Practicum. Companies such as IBM, KPMG Peat Marwick, Hewlett-Packard, Taco Bell Corporation, Western Digital, Monex International, Merrill Lynch, American Airlines, and Manufacturers Bank are just a few represented within the ranks of GSM's Corporate Partners.

The College and Environs

UCI is located midway between Los Angeles and San Diego and is in the center of Orange County, one the nation's fastest-growing regions. It is also one of the most prolific and dynamic seedbeds for entrepreneurial, high-growth, and high-technology companies. The area provides easy access to professional theater, first-run movies, and dance companies, as well as a rich diversity of international cuisine at world-class restaurants. Other advantages include proximity to the mountains and beaches, which offer a variety of recreational opportunities such as water and snow skiing, hang gliding, bicycling, tennis, hiking, sailing, golf, and surfing on a year-round basis.

Technology Environment

The ability to use and manage electronic resources plays a significant role in today's information age. All GSM students are connected to electronic mail and the GSM Intranet, and every seat in GSM's largest classrooms has a network connection, enabling the student to maximize productivity within the classroom setting. Notebook computers are also required of all incoming students.

Placement

The Graduate School of Management provides a full range of placement and career services designed to assist M.B.A. students. Along with the career services director, faculty and staff members work collectively to provide graduates with employment opportunities and contacts with major business and governmental units. Services offered include on-campus recruitment visits, career expo events, resume books, interview skills workshops, and the latest in electronic candidate identification databases. A variety of internship and part-time positions are also available. Graduates receive starting salaries at or above the national average.

Admission

Admission for the M.B.A. and Ph.D. programs is offered each fall and is on a rolling basis. The deadline for the full-time program is May 1; for the Fully Employed M.B.A. program, June 1; for the Executive M.B.A. program, July 1; for the Health Care Executive M.B.A., November 1; and for the Ph.D. program, January 15. Admissions decisions for the M.B.A. programs are based on an overall evaluation of undergraduate GPA, GMAT scores (required), letters of recommendation, statement of purpose, and work experience. A minimum TOEFL score of 600 is required for international applicants whose native language is not English, and proof of adequate funds to cover two years of study is necessary. Introductory courses in calculus and statistics with probability are required prior to beginning the full-time M.B.A. program.

Finances

The 2000–2001 fees for the full-time M.B.A. program are $3833 per quarter for California residents (three academic quarters per year); $10,244 per quarter for non-California residents. Costs for on-campus room and board range from $5801 to $7520; off-campus costs for room and board are approximately $9006. Primary sources of financial aid for the full-time program include loans, grants, and fellowships. The School also has an on-site financial aid director to assist and guide students in this process. To be considered for the full range of financial aid programs, applicants are strongly encouraged to meet the institutional financial aid deadline of March 1.

Ph.D. applicants may also be considered for Regent's, Chancellor's, and tuition fellowships, in addition to teaching and research assistant positions. To be considered for the full range of financial aid programs, applicants are strongly encouraged to meet the institutional financial aid deadline of March 1. Financial aid is awarded only to citizens or permanent residents of the United States.

Application Facts and Dates

The M.B.A. and Ph.D. programs can be contacted directly by telephone: the M.B.A. program (telephone: 949-UCI-4MBA) and the Ph.D. program (telephone: 949-824-8318).

University of California, Irvine
Admissions & Marketing
202 GSM
Irvine, California 92697-3125
E-mail: gsm-mba@uci.edu (M.B.A. program)
gsm-phd@uci.edu (Ph.D. program)
World Wide Web: http://www.gsm.uci.edu

FACULTY LIST

Dennis J. Aigner, Ph.D., Berkeley. Applied econometrics.
Lisa A. Barron, Ph.D., UCLA. Organizational behavior.
Christine M. Beckman, Ph.D., Stanford. Organizational behavior.
David H. Blake, Dean of the Graduate School of Management; Ph.D., Rutgers. International management.
Thomas C. Buchmueller, Ph.D., Wisconsin–Madison. Health care/economics.
Reynold Byers, Ph.D., Rochester. Operations management.
Nai-fu Chen, Ph.D., Berkeley; Ph.D., UCLA. Finance.
Paul Chwelos, Ph.D., British Columbia. Information systems.
Imran S. Currim, Ph.D., Stanford. Marketing.
Marta M. Elvira, Ph.D., Berkeley. Organizational behavior.
Paul J. Feldstein, Ph.D., Chicago. Health care/economics.
Mary Gilly, Ph.D., Houston. Marketing.
Daniel Givoly, Ph.D., NYU. Accounting.

John Graham, Ph.D., Berkeley. Marketing.
Vijay Gurbaxani, Ph.D., Rochester. Management information systems.
Joanna L. Ho, Ph.D., Texas at Austin. Accounting.
Philippe Jorion, Ph.D., Chicago. Finance.
L. Robin Keller, Ph.D., UCLA. Operations and decision technologies.
Bradley L. Killaly, Ph.D., Michigan. Corporate strategy and international business.
John Leslie King, Ph.D., California, Irvine. Management information systems.
Kenneth L. Kraemer, Ph.D., USC. Management information systems.
Barbara A. Lougee, Ph.D., Cornell. Accounting.
Dimitry Lukin, Ph.D., INSEAD. Finance.
Richard B. McKenzie, Ph.D., Virginia Tech. Public policy.
Barrie Nault, Ph.D., British Columbia. Management information systems.
Peter Navarro, Ph.D., Harvard. Public policy.
Jone L. Pearce, Ph.D., Yale. Organizational behavior.
Cornelia Pechmann, Ph.D., Vanderbilt. Marketing.
Lyman W. Porter, Ph.D., Yale. Organizational behavior.

Judy B. Rosener, Ph.D., Claremont. Public policy.
Carlton H. Scott, Ph.D., New South Wales (Australia). Operations and decision technologies.
Claudia B. Schoonhaven, Ph.D., Stanford. Organizational behavior.
Kut C. So, Ph.D., Stanford. Operations and decision technologies.
Jing-Sheng Song, Ph.D., Columbia. Operations and decision technologies.
Neal M. Stoughton, Ph.D., Stanford. Finance.
Eli Talmor, Ph.D., North Carolina at Chapel Hill. Finance.
Robert J. Town, Ph.D., Wisconsin–Madison. Health-care/economics.
Rajeev Tyagi, Ph.D., Pennsylvania (Wharton). Marketing.
Alladi Venkatesh, Ph.D., Syracuse. Marketing.
James S. Wallace, Ph.D., Washington (Seattle). Accounting.
Margarethe F. Wiersema, Ph.D., Michigan. Business strategy.
William F. Wright, Ph.D., Berkeley. Accounting.
Fan Yu, Ph.D., Cornell. Finance/economics.
Kevin Zhu, Ph.D., Stanford. Information systems.

University of California, Los Angeles

Los Angeles, California

THE ANDERSON SCHOOL—CREATING INTELLECTUAL CAPITAL AND ENTREPRENEURIAL LEADERS FOR THE GLOBAL INFORMATION AGE

▶ *The Anderson School at UCLA has long been a leader and innovator in management education. Driven by superior research as well as an astute responsiveness to indicators and trends in the ever-expanding business environment, The Anderson School is preparing the management leaders who will define success in the years to come.*

These leaders will have a strong fundamental grounding in contemporary management and business theory, they will have a thorough knowledge of the role of technology in business, and they will understand the intricacies of global business relations and be skilled in working with people from widely differing personal and professional backgrounds.

If you aspire to the highest levels of managerial success, we invite you to take your place now among the leaders of the future; we invite you to join The Anderson School M.B.A. Program.

—Bruce G. Willison, Dean

Programs and Curricular Focus

The Anderson School M.B.A. Program is designed for highly motivated, exceptional students and is structured to ensure that each graduate leaves with a leadership-level knowledge of all key management disciplines as well as the conceptual and analytical frameworks underlying those disciplines. Consisting of three components—the management core, advanced electives, and the management field study—the curriculum is regularly updated to address the evolving challenges today's business managers must meet.

The Anderson School's M.B.A. program has a general management focus, which enables students to tailor individual discipline-based programs of study rather than declare a major or a concentration. There are nine specialized areas of study and several interdisciplinary studies.

All students are required to take the management core, a set of eight courses that provides the base knowledge for the major functional fields of management. The management core provides the first building blocks on which advanced study in a variety of areas can be developed. The eight core courses are integrated and sequential, so that each successive course builds upon the knowledge gained in prior courses.

Two thirds (fourteen courses) of the M.B.A. curriculum are composed of advanced electives, which are chosen from any of the nine disciplines: accounting, business economics, decision sciences, finance, human resources and organizational behavior, information systems, marketing, operations and technology management, and strategy and organization as well as the interdisciplinary areas of study: entrepreneurial studies, international business and comparative management, and real estate.

The ratio of electives to core courses and the flexibility that students can practice in choosing electives adds breadth to each student's program of study.

The Management Field Study is the capstone requirement of the M.B.A. program and is conducted during the second year of the program. In this project, students integrate and apply their knowledge and skills in a professional setting outside the classroom.

The Anderson School provides two M.B.A. programs for individuals whose professional goals require that they remain employed while completing their M.B.A. degree. The Fully Employed M.B.A. Program is targeted toward emerging managers, typically junior-level professionals averaging 30 years of age and 6 years of work experience. The Executive M.B.A. Program is an intensive twenty-four-month program designed for professionals who have demanding jobs with a high level of responsibility and who seek a high-quality global management education while continuing in their professional roles.

Students and the M.B.A. Experience

The Anderson School at UCLA has a vibrant student body whose extraordinary intellectual, cultural, social, and athletic energies spill out of the classroom into a plethora of nonacademic activities. The average full-time student is 28 years old, with a little more than 4½ years of full-time work experience. Women comprise 29 percent of the student population, members of minority groups make up 23 percent, and international students make up 24 percent.

From day one, The Anderson School teaches students how to work effectively with others to transform ideas into realities. Teamwork is part of everyday life at Anderson. Students work together in study groups or on class assignments or Field Study and other projects.

❖ Global Focus

The Anderson School offers students a wide range of exciting opportunities to increase their international perspectives, from working on group projects with peers from among the forty-five countries represented at Anderson to studying abroad and from enrolling in the International Management Fellows Program to touring a factory in Prague.

The Anderson School encourages students to become involved in academic exchange programs with universities located abroad. Currently, the School participates in more than thirty academic foreign exchange programs.

The Faculty

The renowned Anderson faculty, whose members are widely acclaimed for their expertise and compelling research, teaches advanced management theory and practice in a contemporary and vibrant interactive model of course work and field-based study. The Anderson School has a total of 132 faculty members and twenty-nine endowed chairs, with seventeen chaired professorships.

The Business School Network

Corporate Partnerships

The Anderson School Board of Visitors comprises successful entrepreneurs and business executives from a broad range of national and international industries and professions. Among them are John E. Anderson, the School's namesake and President of Topa Equities, Ltd.; Jeffrey Berg, Chairman and CEO of International Creative Management; B. Kipling Hagopian, founder of venture capitalist firm Brentwood Associates; Lester B. Korn, founder of Korn/Ferry International; and Zuisho Hayashi, President and Chairman of the Board of the Japan-based HUMAX Corporation.

Prominent Alumni

Anderson alumni comprise an eclectic body of talented business leaders and research professionals, from corporate executives to entrepreneurs and from consultants to film producers. Anderson alumni form a valuable management network that spans the globe. This list includes Fred D. Anderson, CFO of Apple Computers and George Montgomery, President and CEO of Taylor Made Golf.

The College and Environs

Strolling to classes through the serene gardens on UCLA's campus, it is easy to forget that The Anderson School is located in the middle of the second-largest city in the United States. For Anderson students, Los Angeles offers the best of many worlds. Beach, mountain, and desert recreation areas are plentiful and easily accessible by car. Los Angeles

museums and theaters offer the world's most acclaimed entertainment. In addition, Westwood Village, which adjoins the UCLA campus to the south, offers shopping, dining, and a wide range of services.

Facilities

The Anderson School's management education complex is a testament to the School's vision of the growing importance of superior management education. Continuing its reputation as a national leader in the use of technology in M.B.A. instruction, the eleven specially designed case study rooms have data ports at each seating station to integrate the instructional program of each faculty member with the School's central computing facility in the Rosenfeld Library.

Placement

Career planning begins before students enter The Anderson School and becomes increasingly focused during the M.B.A. program. Starting with Orientation Week and continuing throughout graduation, Anderson's MBA Career Management Center (CMC) helps students define their career objectives, identify resources, strategize opportunities, hone interviewing skills, and make critical connections. The center's skilled professional staff helps Anderson students attain career goals across a broad span of interests that range from not-for-profit enterprises to Wall Street investment banking. Anderson's class of 1999 had nearly 98 percent placement success. The average salary was $75,000, and signing bonuses averaged $20,000. CMC's many valuable services and resources include

employer briefings and receptions, a campus interview program, videoconferencing interviews, resume books, vacancy listings, counseling and advising, workshops, a career connection program, a career resource center, and online resources.

Admission

The Anderson School admissions policy emphasizes academic ability, leadership, work experience, and breadth of life experiences. Anderson students come from diverse backgrounds yet share important qualities such as superior intelligence, the ability to think broadly and analytically, strong interpersonal skills, and a desire to solve complex problems. The Admissions Committee evaluates applicants' prospects as future leaders and their projected ability to succeed and profit from the M.B.A. program. The committee carefully considers biographical and academic background information, GMAT and TOEFL (for most international applicants) scores, achievements, awards and honors, employment history, letters of recommendation, and college and community involvement, especially where candidates have served in a leadership capacity.

Finances

The cost of attending the UCLA M.B.A. program during the 1999–2000 academic year was $31,185 for California residents and $40,989 for nonresidents. Students can expect 2000–01 costs to increase from 10 percent to 20 percent over 1999–2000 costs. Fellowships and scholarships are available, and, upon admission, students automatically receive a financial aid application packet.

Application Facts and Dates

Applicants may apply for fall 2000 admission from October 4, 2000, through March 27, 2001. The Admissions Committee begins considering applications in December of each year. For more information, students should contact:

Ms. Linda Baldwin
Director of MBA Admissions
The Anderson School at UCLA
110 Westwood Plaza, Suite B201
Box 951481
Los Angeles, California 90095-1481
Telephone: 310-825-6944
Fax: 310-825-8582
E-mail: mba.admissions@anderson.ucla.edu
World Wide Web: http://www.anderson.ucla.edu/

University of California–Riverside

The A. Gary Anderson Graduate School of Management

Riverside, California

BALANCING THE ART AND SCIENCE OF MANAGEMENT

At the A. Gary Anderson Graduate School of Management (AGSM), our M.B.A. curriculum provides a balance of the art and science of management. This recognition of the dual challenges that face today's manager permeates one's educational experience at AGSM. The Anderson School offers an intimate educational environment where classes are small by typical M.B.A. standards, professors are accessible to students, and the business community is very supportive and closely involved with the School's myriad activities.

—Donald H. Dye, Dean

Programs and Curricular Focus

The M.B.A. curriculum balances the art and science of management, with a particular emphasis on managing through information, and recognizes the global context of management. The program stresses the essential interdependencies that exist across functional areas, emphasizing the development of superior management skills as well as theoretical foundations. Great importance is placed on teamwork, relationships, and communication.

The core courses provide the foundation in analytical and managerial skills. The twelve-course core culminates in an integrative case course that synthesizes the various functional area approaches to managerial issues. After a required internship experience, which may be based on current employment, students proceed to study elective topics in greater depth. Most students choose nine elective courses from areas including accounting, corporate environmental management, entrepreneurial management, finance, general management, human resources management/organizational behavior, international management, management information systems, management science, marketing, and production/operations management. Students conclude the twenty-three-course, 92-unit program with a capstone strategic management course and a case project. There is a thesis option for students who wish to do significant research on a special topic.

The program is designed to accommodate the unique requirements of both career professionals and full-time students. Sufficient sections of courses are offered in the evenings to permit career professionals to complete the

M.B.A. on a part-time basis. In this way, full-time and part-time students take classes together, enriching the educational experience of both.

Students and the M.B.A. Experience

Diverse backgrounds and experiences are characteristic of students in the AGSM M.B.A. program. The average age of students is 27, with an age range from 21 to 46. Approximately 40 percent are women, and 21 percent are members of minority groups. Sixty-five percent of the students have an average of three years' work experience in fields ranging from medicine to manufacturing; 35 percent come directly from undergraduate programs. In recent classes, 36 percent of the student body has come from the Western United States, 6 percent from the Northeast and South, and 13 percent from the Midwest. Approximately 45 percent are international students. Forty percent of AGSM's students have undergraduate degrees in business or economics, 30 percent have degrees in science or engineering, and 30 percent have backgrounds in the humanities or social sciences.

❖ Global Focus

Most AGSM required courses include a global perspective, with recognition of the international issues that affect each functional area. In addition, electives in many of the functional areas provide opportunities for in-depth study of international topics. The campus maintains liaison with most of the networks offering international internships, and overseas study options are available in

thirty countries through the University of California Education Abroad Program.

Special Features

The management synthesis course at the end of the first year of study and the required internship are key elements of the AGSM M.B.A. program. The synthesis course is a team-taught, integrative, cross-functional case course that places students in actual managerial decision situations. The required internship enables students to apply their academic background to real-world projects, where they learn to perfect their professional, interpersonal, and communication skills.

The Faculty

The A. Gary Anderson Graduate School of Management has a renowned, multicultural faculty, representing excellence in its respective areas. Faculty members have doctorates from world-class universities and publish research in top journals in their fields. Faculty members also have industry and consulting experience and teach in executive programs and workshops.

The Business School Network

Relationships with the corporate community are an integral part of the AGSM M.B.A. program. The AGSM Advisory Council assists the School with developing and maintaining a relevant curriculum and interacts with M.B.A. students at numerous events. Every year, the School also names two distinguished business leaders as AGSM Fellows. Each Fellow spends one day each quarter speaking to classes and consulting with M.B.A. students. In the spring, a contemporary issues seminar series brings 8 to 10 corporate executives to the School to discuss emerging issues with M.B.A. students. These and other activities ensure that each M.B.A. student has the opportunity to develop a network of business contacts prior to graduation.

The College and Environs

The 1,200-acre Riverside campus of the University of California is conveniently located some 50 miles east of Los Angeles, within easy driving distance of most of the major cultural and recreational offerings in

southern California. Enrollment at UCR is approximately 11,600, nearly 15 percent of whom are graduate students. The campus, with its modern classroom buildings, its beautiful commons, and its 161-foot Carillon Tower, is designed to support the academic and research programs that are part of its assigned mission as a campus in the University of California system.

A city of 250,000, Riverside has several major shopping malls, a symphony orchestra, an opera association, two community theaters, an art center, and many restaurants in proximity to the campus.

Facilities

The University library is the focal point of research and study at UCR. The collection includes more than 1.8 million bound volumes, 13,316 serial subscriptions, and 1.6 million microforms. The collections are arranged and staffed to support programs of instruction and research for faculty and students.

The M.B.A. program is housed in Anderson Hall. M.B.A. students have access to the latest computing equipment, including PC platforms and powerful UNIX workstations.

UCR offers graduate students several affordable housing options both on and off campus. Campus housing includes Bannockburn Village, University Plaza Apartments, and Canyon Crest Married Student Housing.

Technology Environment

The AGSM Microcomputer Facility consists of fifty Intel-based microcomputers. The facility is connected to the campus network and to the Internet. It is centrally located in the A. Gary Anderson Hall, south wing, and is staffed by student lab consultants and a manager.

The facility offers major software packages in the areas of word processing, spreadsheets, presentation graphics, databases, and statistics.

Within the School, the facility is utilized for teaching, class demonstrations, theses, statistical analysis and faculty research projects and as a tool for effective management decision making.

One of AGSM's goals is to graduate students with wide-ranging computer skills that help them become successful in the modern business world.

Placement

A full range of career planning and placement services is offered through the M.B.A. Career Services Center. The center is staffed by professional counselors to address the specific career needs of graduate business students. Services available include on-campus interviews, career seminars and workshops, individual counseling, an alumni career network, a resume directory, and an extensive career library including computerized employment databases. The school participates in the Western M.B.A. Consortium and also sponsors a career night, which provides M.B.A. candidates the opportunity to meet with local and national corporate representatives.

Admission

Admission is open to eligible students from all undergraduate majors. Admission is based on several criteria, including the quality of previous academic work as measured by GPA for the last two years of undergraduate work, scores on the Graduate Management Admission Test (GMAT), letters of recommendation, and potential for success in the program. In recent years, the average GPA for entering students has been approximately 3.4 and the average GMAT score has been 590. Applicants whose first language is not English are required to score a minimum of 550 on the TOEFL.

A course in quantitative methods is a prerequisite to the program. Students may be admitted without this course but must meet this requirement during their first two quarters in residence.

Finances

Tuition and fees for 1999–2000 for full-time students were $4953 for California residents and $14,757 for nonresidents. An additional $5000 per year professional school fee is also assessed. Annual fees for part-time students in 1999–2000 ranged from $5053 to $5913 for California residents, including the professional school fee. Approximate costs for books and supplies are $900 per year. Living expenses, including housing and personal expenses, are estimated to be $6500 to $7500 per year.

Several kinds of financial assistance are available. These include fellowships, teaching assistantships, and research assistantships. Applicants indicate interest in support on the application form. Loans and work study may be applied for through the UCR Financial Aid Office.

International Students

Approximately 50 percent of AGSM's M.B.A. students are international students. The International Services Center provides special assistance to international students and their dependents. An orientation program is held at the beginning of each quarter to help new students adjust to their new environs and the campus. Throughout the year, workshops, excursions, and individual advising sessions are offered. In addition, language workshops tailored to the needs of the international M.B.A. students are available.

Application Facts and Dates

Application deadlines for domestic students are May 1 for fall quarter, September 1 for winter quarter, and December 1 for spring quarter. Deadlines for international students are February 1 for fall, July 1 for winter, and October 1 for spring. Applications are processed on a rolling basis, and decisions are made when files are complete. For further information, applicants should contact:

Gary J. Kuzas
Director of M.B.A. Admissions
The A. Gary Anderson Graduate
    School of Management
University of California
Riverside, California 92521-0203
Telephone: 909-787-4551
Fax: 909-787-3970
E-mail: agsmmba@ucrac1.ucr.edu
World Wide Web: http://www.agsm.
    ucr.edu

University of Cambridge

Cambridge, United Kingdom

> ## CREATIVE THINKING IS THE KEY
>
> *Creative thought is the key to innovative management. It is the distinguishing quality of managers at the top of their profession and the power behind their success. The Cambridge M.B.A. challenges young professionals to rethink management practice and to transform the way they act as leaders throughout their careers. This is neither knowledge dissemination nor simply knowledge delivery. It is knowledge creation.*
>
> *The Cambridge M.B.A.. Join us in global knowledge creation.*
>
> —Chong Ju Choi, M.B.A. Director

Programs and Curricular Focus

The Cambridge M.B.A. is available in two versions that have exactly the same course components but different time structures. Both versions begin in early October, but most students also attend pre-course classes, which begin in late September. The one-year, full-time version finishes the following September. The two-year, integrated version is made up of two 6-month periods of full-time study combined with one 12-month period of full-time employment.

October through March is devoted to a comprehensive core of compulsory course modules, assignments, and practical team projects, including a new venture proposal, working with the young, high-tech firms for which Cambridge is famous, and a major consultancy with multinationals in London or overseas.

April through September allows students to develop their own individual interests through a series of electives and a substantial individual dissertation on a business or management topic of their choice.

Classes are small and interactive, with about 80 students taught in two streams of 40. This is small enough for the teachers to know all the participants individually and to ensure that all those who have something to contribute to a discussion are able to do so. Teaching styles vary to reflect the particular needs of different components, but there is very little traditional lecturing. Most classes take the form of interactive seminars or case-study discussions. Projects and assignments, which make up a large part of the programme, are tutored either individually or in small groups of 4 to 6.

Students and the M.B.A. Experience

The 1999 M.B.A. class of 82 students represents twenty-nine nationalities, from Iceland to Japan, Russia to Argentina. The Sainsbury Bursary for the not-for-profit sector continues to bring managers from the public sector, charities, and international aid programmes. The McKinsey Scholarship scheme attracts those interested in consultancy. The students range in age from 23 to 47, with a median age of 29, and, in work experience, from 2 to 19 years, median 6. Thirty-two percent are women, 22 percent are married, and 10 percent are parents.

The professional and geographic diversity of both students and faculty members (see below) allows every class to take an international approach, including examples and case studies from around the globe. Some electives focus on particular regions for detailed analysis, and some consultancy projects and/or dissertations require overseas field work. The location in Europe allows easy access to a wide range of business

An M.B.A. team celebrates the completion of a project.

cultures, but the focus is firmly global rather than simply European.

Special Features

Cambridge is the focus of a dramatic development of high-tech industry and entrepreneurial activity. The Institute is closely involved in such initiatives as the Cambridge Network (http://www.cambridgenetwork.co.uk), the Cambridge Entrepreneurship Centre (http://www.cec.cam.ac.uk), the Cambridge–MIT Institute (http://www.cmi.cam.ac.uk), and the Cambridge £30k Business Plan Competition (won by an M.B.A. team in 2000).

The Faculty

The Judge Institute has 67 full-time faculty members and 21 senior associates, of whom 34 teach in the M.B.A. program. Twenty-one are women (including the Institute Director), and 22 are from outside the United Kingdom, including nationals of Belgium, Germany, Greece, the U.S., Canada, Mexico, Australia, Korea, India, and Sri Lanka. In addition to this breadth of experience, many electives are taught by specialists from other departments of the University or by external practitioners.

The Business School Network

In larger schools, corporate visitors may have little impact on individual students. The Cambridge M.B.A. class is deliberately small, allowing real interaction with recruiters, staff, and visiting speakers.

M.B.A. speakers last year included the Chairman of Ford of Britain and the Chairman of ARM. Students also attend the Institute's public lectures, most recently meeting the Chief Executive of British Aerospace and the Chief Executive of Pearson.

The M.B.A. includes two live consultancy projects, and the integrated M.B.A. option includes a placement year working in the UK.

The small, interactive Judge community builds close alumni networks. M.B.A. alumni include the Head of Executive Recruitment at Dell, who comes regularly to recruit; the Director in Charge at J. Walter Thompson, who

hosted an M.B.A. project; and the Commercial Director of ICL, who teaches an M.B.A. elective.

The College and Environs

The University is one of the world's foremost centres of academic excellence, set in one of England's loveliest cities.

The Judge Institute provides all management teaching and resources, at the undergraduate, graduate, and executive levels. In addition, every student is a member of one of the Cambridge Colleges, residential communities offering accommodation, meals, social networks, and recreational and sporting facilities. Many colleges are ancient foundations in historic buildings. Some offer special facilities for married students or those with families. All are within 5 kilometers of the Institute.

Cambridge is 1 hour from London and within easy reach of its international airports.

Placement

The Institute's students are outstanding individuals who attract employers from leading-edge businesses. Ninety-one percent of last year's graduates were employed after six months. McKinsey & Co., Dell Computers, Deutsche Bank, and Netdecisions were among the many who held career events at the Institute over the past year.

Career activities include the annual CV book distributed to major employers worldwide, individual career guidance, M.B.A. recruitment presentations, workshops, video-assisted mock interviews, access to resources at the main University Careers Service (http://www.careers.cam.ac.uk), and networking opportunities via senior guest speaker sessions and alumni.

Admission

To be accepted into the Cambridge M.B.A. program, students need to demonstrate a high intellectual ability, including the capacity to think for themselves, practical common sense, and the ability to put ideas into action. They also need to be highly motivated, with a strong desire to learn, to help others to learn, and to make a constructive contribution to society.

Formal requirements include an undergraduate GPA of at least 3.2, GMAT scores, a 7.0 IELTS or 250 (computer-based) TOEFL score for nonnative speakers of English who are not demonstrably fluent, and at least two years' postgraduate work experience.

Finances

An estimated budget includes the University tuition fee of £19,000; college membership fee of £2000; accommodation and meals, £7250; laptop and software, £2000; and textbooks, £750, for a total of £31,000. All figures are approximations only.

The Graduate Office at the Judge Institute can supply a fact sheet of sources of support available specifically to American candidates. Those from other countries should contact their local British Council office for full information or consult the Institute's Web site: http://www.jims.cam.ac.uk.

International Students

The Cambridge M.B.A. has approximately 80 percent overseas students. There are thirty-one different international societies in the University, providing events and social networking. The Students' Union, Graduate Union, and college welfare officers all provide support and advice. Alumni networks span the globe, with Cambridge groups active in seventy-three countries.

Application Facts and Dates

There is no application deadline, but interviews for shortlisted candidates begin in December, and early application is advised. For further information, students should contact:

Graduate Office
The Judge Institute
University of Cambridge
Trumpington Street
Cambridge CB2 1AG
United Kingdom
Telephone: 44-0-1223-33705/2/3
Fax: 44-0-1223-339581
E-mail: mba-enquiries@jims.cam.ac.uk
World Wide Web: http://www.jims.
cam.ac.uk/programmes.html

University of Chicago

Chicago, Illinois

THE CHOICE IS YOURS!

As you plan your business education, I invite you to consider one of the world's premier institutions of general management and business leadership education: the University of Chicago Graduate School of Business (GSB).

Since it was founded in 1898, Chicago has been a focal point of cutting-edge business research as well as innovative educational methods. Our flexible curriculum puts you in charge by allowing you to tailor your business education according to your personal experience, interests, and career plans. The wealth of programs within the School and its integral relationship with the rest of the University offer wide choices from which you can create the course of study most appropriate for you.

—Robert S. Hamada, Dean and Edward Eagle Brown Distinguished Service Professor of Finance

Programs and Curricular Focus

The M.B.A. curriculum is designed to prepare students for significant careers in management. It encompasses both the basic disciplines that underlie management and the operational areas specific to business. The courses are designed to provide the understanding of the components of managerial decision making while furnishing perspective on the role of business as an economic, political, and social institution.

Chicago's curriculum has long emphasized freedom of choice and flexibility, allowing students to develop a program that suits their own needs. Compared to other M.B.A. programs, Chicago has a short list of requirements and a long list of electives. Students have unparalleled flexibility in their choice of courses, professors, and activities.

The curriculum students design for themselves complements their individual backgrounds, interests, and abilities and is targeted to each student's specific career goals. Students are encouraged to build on their previous education and experience rather than repeat work mastered elsewhere. They may take as many as six courses in other University departments and study with some of the world's most renowned scholars in such fields as economics, law, languages, philosophy, or literature. Or they may fashion a joint-degree course of study that combines business with international relations, area studies, law, public policy, or medicine. At Chicago, the ultimate responsibility

for learning and attaining a student's particular educational goals rests with the student.

The Graduate School of Business also includes five alternative programs to meet everyone's needs: the International M.B.A., Evening M.B.A., Weekend M.B.A., Executive M.B.A., and International Executive M.B.A. (Barcelona, Spain, and Singapore).

Students and the M.B.A. Experience

Each of the students plays a critical role in defining the culture, values, and direction of the GSB. The best and the brightest students are chosen from around

the world because they will have an impact on the School and on their chosen profession. From the moment they arrive on campus, the active involvement of all students, both at work and play, is promoted.

The Business Students Association (BSA) and its elected officers coordinate social events, conferences, and professional and special interests groups. Students may participate in a wide variety of organizations and activities that draw people with similar interests and goals.

The Faculty

Intellectual freedom, flexibility, and respect for the individual are hallmarks of Chicago's academic tradition. Faculty members are free, indeed encouraged, to develop innovative ways of presenting and teaching material and to introduce new courses based on cutting-edge research or changing demands from the business community. The result is a wide and lively mix of teaching styles and conceptual frameworks as well as philosophies that add to the richness and diversity of the Chicago experience. Students have the opportunity to study with Nobel Prize winners (Merton Miller, 1990; Robert Fogel, 1993), a former chairman of the President's Council of Economic Advisers, or a senior examiner for the Malcom Baldrige National Quality Award.

The Business School Network

The M.B.A. experience is not restricted to the classroom at Chicago. Although the Graduate School of Business is not a case study institution, a substantial percentage of the course work, depending on the student's choice of classes, consists of various kinds of cases and applied analysis. Because of the School's location in one of the world's major commercial centers, students meet business, economic, labor, and political leaders at the numerous lecture and seminar series held on campus and through alumni and friends in the Chicago business community. A host of companies sponsor numerous laboratory courses at the GSB, including Merrill Lynch & Co., Inc.; A. T. Kearney, Inc.; Kraft General Foods; and the Amoco Corporation.

The College and Environs

Established in 1898, the Graduate School of Business is the second-oldest business school in the United States and one of its most distinguished. The core of the University of Chicago's 175-acre campus, one of the most beautiful urban universities in the country, is a collection of neo-Gothic buildings clustered around quadrangles. Surprises abound. Rockefeller Chapel, the site of graduation and other official events, turns out to be closer in size to a cathedral. Tiny ivy-covered Bond Chapel, barely visible under a canopy of trees, stuns visitors with dazzling stained-glass windows and intricate wood carvings and is a favorite spot for weddings.

Placement

Employers actively seek to hire University of Chicago M.B.A.'s. In 1999–2000, more than 300 employers recruited Graduate School of Business graduates and interns, conducting approximately 13,000 interviews in the School's on-campus recruiting facilities. The Office of Career Services offers individual counseling and career planning resources as well as a quarter-long Career Management Seminar, lecture series, and job search workshops. In addition, student professional interest groups bring corporate speakers to campus to discuss their jobs and their industries.

Admission

Prerequisites for admission include completion of an undergraduate degree from an accredited U.S. institution or the equivalent from another country, the results of the GMAT, and the GSB's application. A TOEFL score is required of all applicants for whom English is not their native language. Interviews are highly recommended but not required. Applicants are evaluated individually based on their professional experience, academic background, and personal qualities.

Finances

The Graduate School of Business is committed to identifying financial resources for students who require assistance in meeting the costs of the M.B.A. program. The School provides loan assistance to students who demonstrate financial need. Scholarship awards are based on academic excellence and demonstrated qualities of leadership. Scholarships are awarded only to students who are entering the campus M.B.A. program.

Application Facts and Dates

The Graduate School of Business has three deadlines for admission for the programs beginning in fall 2001: November 3, 2000; January 5, 2001; and March 9, 2001. Applicants should apply by the January deadline for full scholarship consideration. A decision takes approximately eight weeks from the deadline, but more detailed information is available in the application packet. For more information, students should contact:

Director of Admissions and Financial Aid
Graduate School of Business
University of Chicago
6030 South Ellis Avenue
Chicago, Illinois 60637
Telephone: 773-702-7369
Fax: 773-702-9085
E-mail: admissions@gsb.uchicago.edu
World Wide Web: http://gsb.uchicago.edu

University of Colorado at Boulder

Boulder, Colorado

DEVELOPING THE LEADERS OF TOMORROW

AT CU–Boulder, our M.B.A. program not only provides students with business skills; we educate them for the rapidly changing marketplace of the new millennium. Our strategy in this effort is fourfold. First, by partnering with the region's dynamic business community, we provide students with hands-on experience through internships and course projects. Second, through these industry partnerships, students learn the innovative, technology-focused, entrepreneurial spirit that successfully drives business. Third, with this innovative attitude, students pursue interdisciplinary academic programs that provide a holistic view of business education and industry. Finally, these dynamic, multicurricular strengths enable students to pursue mutual discovery opportunities with our world-renowned professors. These four program components embrace opportunities, challenge students, and develop the leaders of tomorrow.

—Dipankar Chakravarti, Interim Dean

Programs and Curricular Focus

As the premier M.B.A. program in the region, the University of Colorado at Boulder (CU–Boulder) educates its students for success in the marketplace. Partnerships with the local business community; innovative, technology-driven, interdisciplinary educational programs; and mutual discovery opportunities prepare graduates for management roles within the dynamic international economy. In recognition of the need to prepare our students for the volatility of this marketplace, the program recently adopted a market-based curriculum model. All students receive a solid foundation through the core courses covering the functional business areas. The student then has maximun flexibility in structuring the elective component of the curriculum. The faculty members work with the business community, M.B.A. alumni, and current students to ensure that the elective course offerings are providing the necessary skill set to ensure success in today's volatile business economy. By completing course work focusing on entrepreneurship, finance, marketing, operations management, organization management, real estate, technology and innovation management, and e-commerce, students graduate with the background necessary to compete globally. Students are exposed to the latest technological trends in business, and are able to partner with dynamic emerging-growth companies such as netLiberty.com, Requisite Technologies, Fast Ideas/iBelay, Bid-4-

Vacation.com, and Planet Outdoors.com as well as established industry leaders such as Sun Microsystems, IBM, US West, and Level 3 Communications, to acquire the pragmatic experience critical for success in today's technology-intensive environment.

As the marketplace becomes more specialized, a demand for high-technology and legal experience drives the economy. For those interested in telecommunications or law, the college's interdisciplinary program offers the M.B.A./Master of Science in telecommunications and Juris Doctor/M.B.A. joint-degree programs. These programs provide an ideal balance of management expertise and technical focus.

Students and the M.B.A. Experience

Students in the program come from all over the world. Sharing their experiences from countries such as Argentina, China, India, Japan, Korea, Taiwan, and Thailand, students gain from the multi-cultural dialogue that takes place within and beyond the classroom. A typical class is 30 percent women and 70 percent men. The average student is 28 years old and has nearly five years of professional experience. Students bring a wealth of experiences to the program, ranging from consulting to financial services to non-profit management and from engineering to real estate development to biotechnology. About a third of the students have had significant exposure to the high-technology industry.

Special Features

The Colleges of Business and Engineering responded to the country's new venture growth by founding the Robert H. and Beverly A. Deming Center for Entrepreneurship. It features outstanding professors and successful entrepreneurs who teach students to innovatively launch and manage new ventures and practice the risk required to compete. The entrepreneurship program is ranked sixteenth in the nation by *US News and World Report* and emphasizes partnerships with the state's dynamic business community through field projects and lectures.

The CU Real Estate Center, established as a partnership between the College of Business and the CU Real Estate Council, emphasizes an interdisciplinay approach to real estate education. The 150-member council of real estate executives actively participates in curriculum development, mentoring, internships, and job placement. The integrated program encourages students to take courses from the College of Engineering's construction management department and the School of Law.

As a telecommunications hub, Colorado is the headquarters for such industry leaders as Tele-Communications, Inc. (TCI), US West, Level 3 Communications, and Qwest. Responding to the community's high demand for technical strengths, the CU–Boulder Colleges of Business and Engineering created the M.B.A./M.S. telecommunications degree. As one of the few universities in the nation offering this program, students have the opportunity to combine their management expertise with the technical skills necessary to become leaders in this industry.

The Faculty

As leaders in business education, faculty members pursue mutual discovery opportunities with students to provide a comprehensive business education. CU's nationally recognized professors spearhead innovative curriculum, preparing graduates for a challenging and evolving international marketplace. The program's interdisciplinary courses incorporate case studies, group projects, team teaching,

The University of Colorado at Boulder, nestled in the foothills of the Rocky Mountains, offers a beautiful environment in which to pursue a graduate education.

lectures, discussions, simulations, and the Internet. Issues such as ethics, technology, communication, and the global marketplace are integrated throughout the curriculum to enhance students' learning experience.

The Business School Network

By partnering with the business community, this program facilitates critical relationships between students and industry professionals. Advisory boards, comprised of prominent executives, work with students to provide mentoring and support. In addition to the college's Business Advisory Council, each college division (accounting, information systems, finance and economics, management, and marketing), as well as the entrepreneurship and real estate centers, have advisory boards. Members talk to students about new developments in their field, internships, and industry contacts.

In addition to working with board members, M.B.A. students benefit from pursuing their degrees in a booming business region. Students gain pragmatic experience by interacting with regional and international firms. The area's unique business environment provides a setting in which established corporations enjoy success, and entrepreneurial ventures also flourish. The region has business niches in the computer, telecommunications, biotechnology, finance lifestyle and vision, and entrepreneurial fields.

The College and Environs

As the flagship university in the region, CU–Boulder ranks tenth among public

research universities and third among rising research universities in the public sector. The campus is strategically located near the mountains and city, so students can take a 20-mile drive and be atop the Continental Divide or drive 30 miles to Denver. Acres of protected open space surround Boulder, providing beautiful hiking, biking, and riding trails. The city of Boulder hosts cultural and recreational activities, including the Shakespeare Festival, the Colorado Music Festival, and the Bolder Boulder 10K run.

Technology Environment

Technology, a critical dimension of the business world and of an M.B.A. education, is a vital component of CU's academic experience. Students are acquainted with the School's computing environment during the M.B.A. Leadership Forum at the onset of their program, where they are introduced to the College's Web-based information system that maximizes internship and placement opportunities. E-mail accounts and home pages are also established for all M.B.A. students.

The M.B.A. Business Center provides a computing environment for master's students in which they can research course assignments and create presentations using multimedia equipment in an isolated working environment. The College's PepsiCo Case Room is equipped with laptop computer workstations as well as multimedia and distance learning capabilities. The Collaborative Management, Education, and Technology lab also provides computing facilities for

student projects. Classrooms and computer labs use the latest software, state-of-the-art projection systems, and multimedia capabilities.

Placement

By partnering with the business community, the M.B.A. Placement Center helps position students for professional success. Facilitating internships, forums, panel discussions, and executive luncheons, the center establishes networking opportunities that enable students to discuss career and business issues with executives. An online networking directory provides access to alumni for specific career advice and company information. The center enhances students' job search skills and career opportunities through workshops, a career guidebook, videotaped mock interviews, industry forums, resume books, employer briefings, a career resource library, and on-campus recruiting. An online database of student resumes is also available to employers to match their needs with student interests. Students benefit from an online job board that lists internships and job vacancies. In addition to internal resources, the M.B.A. program is a member of the Rocky Mountain M.B.A. Consortium, which hosts national recruiters.

Admission

The M.B.A. program admits high-achieving individuals who demonstrate the ability to lead and manage in today's evolving global marketplace. Ideal candidates demonstrate innovation and initiative in the workplace. Candidates' academic credentials, GMAT scores, work history, and recommendations are all weighed for admission consideration.

Finances

Full-time tuition per semester in 1999–00 was $1924 for residents and $7758 for nonresidents. Students paid semester fees of $326. Half of CU–Boulder's students receive financial aid, which is available to graduate students through fellowships, loans, grants, and work-study.

Application Facts and Dates

For additional information, students should contact:

M.B.A. Program
Campus Box 419
University of Colorado at Boulder
Boulder, Colorado 80309-0419
Telephone: 303-492-1831
Fax: 303-492-1727
E-mail: busgrad@colorado.edu
World Wide Web: http://bus.colorado.edu/

University of Colorado at Denver

College of Business Administration and Graduate School of Business Administration

Denver, Colorado

FLEXIBLE PROGRAMS...BUSINESS PARTNERSHIPS... WORLD-CLASS TEACHING AND RESEARCH

The University of Colorado at Denver (CU-Denver) offers future business leaders a unique combination of flexibility in program schedules, including our new 11-Month M.B.A. and e-Business M.B.A.; faculty committed to excellence in both teaching and research; and close relationships with the Denver business community. This, combined with the vast cultural, recreational, and networking opportunities the thriving downtown Denver environment offers, makes CU-Denver an ideal place for graduate business education. I cordially invite you to learn more about us. Call for further information or consult our home page on the World Wide Web (see the last section of this description).

—Yash Gupta, Dean

Programs and Curricular Focus

The Graduate School of Business Administration at the University of Colorado at Denver is recognized as one of the premier graduate business programs in the Rocky Mountain region. Graduate programs include a number of flexible options for pursuing the Master of Business Administration (M.B.A.) degree: the Individualized M.B.A., the new e-Business M.B.A., the innovative 11-Month Accelerated M.B.A., the Cohort M.B.A., and the M.B.A. with tracks in health administration and human resources. In addition, Master of Science (M.S.) degrees in seven focused fields of study are offered. All management programs are nationally accredited by AACSB–The International Association for Management Education. The Master of Business Administration in Health Administration (M.B.A.H.A.) program is also accredited by the Accrediting Commission on Education for Health Services Administration (ACEHSA).

The sixteen-course, 48-credit-hour M.B.A. program consists of ten core courses that provide an introduction to all functional areas of business management. The emphasis is on integrating the functional area courses through application of theory to real business problems. Skills in both qualitative and quantitative methods of analysis are taught, since both are important for making competitive business decisions. In addition to the functional core, students take elective and special topics courses along with one required international business course.

The new e-Business M.B.A. was designed by CIOs and IT executives in the Rocky Mountain region. Students undertake a rigorous sixteen-course cohort program in eight 10-week terms over two years. Classes are held on alternating Fridays and Saturdays. The program begins each fall and is limited to 40 students.

The innovative 11-Month M.B.A. is an accelerated, full-time program that enables highly motivated students to complete all M.B.A. requirements in five 8-week sessions. The accelerated program allows students to minimize time spent away from work, yet provides students with all of the strategic management skill taught in the Individual and Cohort programs. The program begins in late August, and the degree is completed in mid-July of the following year. Enrollment is limited to approximately 40 students.

For a more specialized business program, students may choose the Master of Science degree in one of seven fields of study: accounting, finance, health services administration, information systems, international business, marketing, or organization and management. Dual-degree programs are available, combining the M.B.A. with any Master of Science degree plan. Selected graduate study in other schools within the University may also be combined with the M.B.A. for a dual degree. In addition, the Graduate School of Business offers a dual Master of Business Administration/Master of International Management (M.B.A./M.I.M.) degree in cooperation with Thunderbird, The American Graduate School of International Management in Glendale, Arizona. Furthermore, the College has added a health administration and human resource

track to the M.B.A. program, and there is an entire M.B.A. available on line.

The University of Colorado Executive M.B.A. program is taught in downtown Denver. The executive program invites business executives to participate in a specialized program of seminars with prominent business faculty members from all three University of Colorado campuses. Classes meet once a week, alternating Fridays and Saturdays, for two academic years.

Students and the M.B.A. Experience

M.B.A. students at CU-Denver are adult learners with an average age of 33; many have five to ten years of work experience. More than half continue to be employed full-time as they complete their degree programs. The Graduate School of Business Administration seeks diversity in the student body. Approximately 12 percent of the students represent more than thirty countries around the world. Denver is a recognized center of international business, and, as an integral part of the greater Denver community, CU-Denver is committed to including international perspectives in all programs. Services to international students, including assistance with arrival, housing, orientation, and immigration concerns, are provided through the Office of International Education. A team of graduate advisers assists all students in the M.B.A. and M.S. programs with degree planning.

The Faculty

M.B.A. and M.S. programs are designed to help students achieve learning and career objectives through interaction with a high-quality, internationally diverse faculty committed to teaching and research. More than 60 full-time faculty members, along with distinguished business professionals, work with students to create a dynamic learning environment. CU-Denver faculty members rank among the top business scholars in the country, conducting leading research directly related to the courses they teach. As a group, the faculty is on the cutting edge of business knowledge, publishing an average of 100 articles a year in scholarly business journals. Several faculty members

have written textbooks used by universities around the world, and many are reviewers or editors for scholarly journals.

CU-Denver's business students also learn from the faculty's extensive managerial and consulting experience. In addition, the faculty members of the graduate school of business rank among the best teachers on campus. Several business faculty members have received the prestigious "Outstanding Teacher of the Year" award from CU-Denver.

The Business School Network

The undergraduate College of Business Administration and the Graduate School of Business Administration are privileged to have the support of a 45-member Board of Advisors, comprising CEOs and senior executives from the greater Denver business community, many of whom are graduates of the program. The board serves in an advisory capacity to the dean and the faculty on matters concerning curriculum; outreach programs, such as mentoring and internships; and the development of strong ties with the local business community.

The College and Environs

The University of Colorado at Denver is in the Auraria Higher Education Consortium. The Auraria campus is safe and vibrant and is located in downtown Denver. The mild climate and the city's proximity to the Rocky Mountains contribute to Denver's status as one of the most beautiful and dynamic cities in the country.

Students in CU-Denver's Graduate School of Business benefit from close ties to Colorado's business community. Through CU-Denver's Executive-in-Residence Program, the CU-in-Class Program, the prestigious Celebration of Success dinner, and the monthly Dean's Business Breakfast lecture series, CU-Denver students stay linked with the business community while they complete their program of study.

Technology Environment

Four computer labs on campus (one reserved exclusively for business students) are equipped with IBM-compatible comput-

ers that are part of a local area network and linked to the Internet. The Auraria Library houses more than 750,000 books, videos, government publications, and media items, with subscriptions to more than 3,500 journals, magazines, and newspapers. Hundreds of periodicals are accessible full-text via the Auraria Online Information System. Within the library, students have access to more than 300 online and CD-ROM commercial databases and the Internet. With a PC, registered students and faculty and staff members may access many of these databases from home. The library is a depository of Colorado and U.S. government publications.

Placement

A full-service career planning and internship advisory office is available on campus to all students at CU-Denver. The Career Center offers information and support to students seeking internships with companies in the greater Denver area; it also provides career counseling and workshops on resume preparation and interview techniques. The Career Center serves as a clearinghouse for employer connections and job vacancy announcements. A computer-assisted resume referral service allows prospective employers to review the qualifications of students and graduates registered with the program and informs students of job openings on the Web.

Admission

The Graduate School of Business Administration admits qualified students for the fall and spring semesters and for the summer session. A two-part application form, optional resume, personal essay, required GMAT score, two original transcripts in sealed envelopes, directly from each institution of higher education attended, and an application fee (M.B.A., $50; M.B.A./M.S. dual degree, $80; and international students, $60) must be submitted by published deadlines. International students whose native language is not English must submit TOEFL scores. Letters of recommendation are required for all international students and M.B.A. in health services administration applicants.

Finances

In 1999–2000, Colorado resident students in business paid $230 per graduate credit hour; nonresidents in business paid $796 per credit hour. Full-time graduate business tuition (covering a tuition "window" of 9 to 15 credit hours) was $1922 for Colorado residents and $6643 for nonresidents. Required student fees totaled approximately $150 per semester. Student health insurance purchased through the University group policy, required for international students, was $710 per calendar year.

Single students should budget approximately $1000 per month for housing, food, books, and moderate entertainment expenses. CU-Denver provides no on-campus housing, but reasonably priced accommodations are available in nearby neighborhoods.

Financial aid may be available to U.S. citizens through the Financial Aid Office. In addition, many graduate scholarships are available to graduate students in business administration through the M.B.A. program or through one of the seven specialized Master of Science programs. Students should request scholarship assistance when they apply for admission. Information about scholarships is available on the Web site listed below.

The Graduate School of Business Administration welcomes applications on an ongoing basis for admission in the fall or spring semester and the summer session. The 11-Month M.B.A. accepts applications for the fall semester only.

Regular application deadlines for admission to a graduate program in business administration are July 1 for the fall semester, November 1 for spring, and April 1 for summer. International applications should be received by March 1 (fall enrollment), July 1 (spring), and December 1 (summer). Completed applications for the 11-Month M.B.A. program must be received by June 15. CU-Denver's programs are competitive; early application is encouraged. Application materials and all program information may be accessed through the World Wide Web. For further information, students should contact:

Graduate School of Business
  Administration
Campus Box 165
University of Colorado at Denver
P.O. Box 173364
Denver, Colorado 80217-3364
Telephone: 303-556-5900
Fax: 303-556-5904
E-mail: gbusiness@maroon.cudenver.edu
World Wide Web: http://business.cudenver.edu

University of Connecticut

Storrs, Connecticut

DEVELOPING LEADERS FOR A TECHNOLOGICAL WORLD

We are the flagship public research institution of the state of Connecticut. Fully accredited since 1959 by AACSB–The International Association for Management Education, our business school has the number one public university M.B.A. program in New England. We excel in information technology, finance, accounting, and health systems. Our curriculum emphasizes the role of technology and globalization as themes across all functional disciplines. Beyond receiving a thorough grounding in graduate business education, you and your classmates capture many opportunities for experiential learning by working on solutions to real-time challenges with our corporate partners. When you complete your M.B.A., you won't have to go very far to continue your career. Connecticut is located in the heartland of Fortune 500 territory and is surrounded by many of the best business organizations in the world—General Electric, Xerox, IBM, United Technologies, Pitney Bowes, Champion, AC Nielsen, Tenneco, US Surgical, Fleet Bank, CitiGroup, Aetna, The Hartford Group, Andersen Consulting, and GE Capital to name a few. These companies recruit at the University of Connecticut.

Our new high-tech, state-of-the-art, $26-million facility (opening in 2000) will contain totally integrated technology capabilities and interconnectivity from virtually any part of the building—from desks in the classrooms to seats in the café. Can you see why taking the next step makes sense? Connect with us via the World Wide Web at http://www.sba.uconn.edu. We look forward to hearing from you.

—Thomas G. Gutteridge, Dean

The University of Connecticut's main campus in Storrs, Connecticut.

Programs and Curricular Focus

UConn's M.B.A. Program emphasizes the role of information technology and globalization across all functional disciplines. The M.B.A. curriculum requires a total of nineteen courses (57 credits) to earn the degree, which typically takes two academic years.

There are three strategic elements of UConn's program that distinguish it from other top-quality M.B.A. programs. UConn's M.B.A. program is one of a handful of programs worldwide that has a laptop computer requirement as a tool of the trade, and the laptop's use is integrated in the classroom. In a lockstep structure, students are assigned to groups and work together throughout their first year as members of cross-functional teams. Spring semester of the first year culminates in a live, real-company integration project that draws upon all formal course instruction as well as the students' work experiences. Presentations are made to faculty members and business leaders, and students are given structured feedback to hone their technical, analytical, and interpersonal skills.

During the second year, students focus on their functional area concentrations, which include more specialized study in information technology, finance, health-care management, management, consulting, and interactive marketing. At this time, students also participate actively in externally directed programs of the School, such as business consulting projects, and work with the School's Career Services to pursue placement opportunities.

Students and the M.B.A. Experience

The type of student a program attracts is an essential ingredient in the quality of the academic experience, and UConn actively recruits the best. The learning environment is also enhanced by the diversity of cultural, geographic, and work backgrounds, creating a microcosm of not only the business world, but also the world of business. Through the many partnerships UConn has with major corporations and smaller entrepreneurial businesses, M.B.A. students augment their experience by obtaining paid internships during the summer between the first and second years.

The Graduate Business Association (GBA) rapidly becomes an integral part of M.B.A. life. Completely organized and governed by the students, the GBA sponsors both professional and social events throughout the year. Through its various committees, the GBA coordinates Career Interview Conferences with prospective employers, an Executive Speaker Series that brings leading executives to campus for up-close and personal discussions, resume workshops, international dinners, and numerous other events.

The Faculty

All of the faculty members who teach in the full-time M.B.A. program have earned their Ph.D. or the equivalent terminal degree in their field. The faculty members have very diverse academic backgrounds, with alma maters that include Harvard, Yale, and Duke. They also have equally interesting and diverse

UConn provides state-of-the-art classrooms and education.

cultural backgrounds, including professors from countries in Africa, South America, and Asia. Students benefit from the latest developments in research and consulting conducted by the faculty.

The Business School Network
Connecticut is located in a major center for financial services, a major manufacturing area with a strong involvement in international trade, and the incredible retail market for the highest per capita income population of any state. This very diverse corporate community provides the context and, ultimately, the resources by which the School of Business maintains its preeminence within the state. Essentially all of the major corporations, as well as many small and medium-size companies in the corporate corridor connecting New York City and Boston, employ the School's alumni. This greatly facilitates both placement and maintenance of a state-of-the-art curriculum.

The College and Environs
Centrally located in the "corporate corridor" between New York and Boston, Connecticut is one of the most commercially diverse states in the country. The University of Connecticut is a large, multifaceted institution with nationally recognized professional schools of business, dentistry, engineering, law, and medicine. The University is one of the nation's major public research universities, with 22,300 students, 140,000 alumni, and 120 major buildings on 3,100 acres at the main campus in Storrs. *U.S. News & World Report* named UConn one of the top public universities in the nation and in New England in its publication *America's Best Colleges, 1999.* UConn's M.B.A. program is ranked in the

top 7 percent in the United States, and it is ranked by *ComputerWorld* as one of the top twenty-five techno-M.B.A. programs in the nation. The UConn M.B.A. program also ranks among the best investment values, according to a survey by *Forbes* magazine in which the top graduate programs in the country were evaluated.

All of the academic, library, computer, social, and cultural opportunities and facilities of a major university are readily available to all M.B.A. students. The immediate area surrounding the main campus is rural, with the bucolic charm of New England. Compared to most major universities, the University campus is a safe and very scenic environment. The cost of living is substantially less than in most metropolitan areas. However, many internship and employment opportunities are available nearby. The capital and metropolitan area of Hartford is a ½-hour, Boston is a 1½-hour, and New York City is a 3-hour drive. One third of the Fortune 500 companies, and hundreds of small and medium-size firms, have their corporate headquarters in this unique corporate corridor.

Placement
For most M.B.A. students, building and developing a challenging and satisfying management career is their primary purpose in attending an M.B.A. program. The University of Connecticut M.B.A. Program provides the education, training, support, and opportunities to advance toward this goal. Activities in career planning begin during orientation and continue throughout the two academic years. Coaching and opportunities to practice specific skills, such as developing effective resumes and cover letters,

interview techniques, arranging interviews, and networking, are available to all M.B.A. students. Mock interviews with supportive but tough alumni executives make a significant difference in preparing students for successful interviews. Many M.B.A. students acquire new and relevant work experience through summer internships or semester co-ops. These experiences augment the academic program and develop skills that make effective managers. Internships can also provide a very important source of financial support.

Admission
The minimum requirements for admission include a 3.0 GPA, out of a possible 4.0, or the equivalent and a total GMAT score of at least 560. However, applicants who do not meet all these requirements may be considered for admission based on strengths in other areas of their application. For international students whose native language is not English, a TOEFL score of at least 575 is required.

Finances
Total costs for students attending the University of Connecticut M.B.A. Program are approximately $17,000 for in-state students and $25,000 for out-of-state students per academic year. Financial aid is available in the form of loans, scholarships, and graduate assistantships. Graduate assistantships normally involve working with faculty members or departments in research or administrative activities. Offers of graduate assistantships are made to those admitted students with the best qualifications in the School's pool as of May 1.

Application Facts and Dates
Admission decisions are made on a rolling basis as completed applications are received, so there is no rigid deadline for submitting an application. However, the size of the entering class is limited, and very few applications from international students submitted after April are approved for admission. Early application is strongly advised. International applicants are encouraged to submit their application prior to taking the GMAT. Admission is available only for the fall semester. For additional information, students should contact:

UConn M.B.A. Program
University of Connecticut
368 Fairfield Road, U-41MBA
Storrs, Connecticut 06269-2041
Telephone: 860-486-2872
Fax: 860-486-5222
E-mail: uconnmba@sba.uconn.edu
World Wide Web: http://www.sba.
  uconn.edu

University of Dallas

Irving, Texas

THE GRADUATE SCHOOL OF MANAGEMENT IN THE GLOBAL ARENA

The Graduate School of Management is a real-world and performance-oriented graduate business school. We believe the best education for business leadership is a high-quality, global, applied, action-oriented, and customer-driven academic curriculum tied to the realities of the world in which we live and work. In that regard, we made a commitment to "internationalize" a significant portion of our academic program long before it became fashionable. We plan to do even more in the global arena in order to be totally prepared for the future.

—Paula Ann Hughes, Dean

Programs and Curricular Focus

The Master of Business Administration programs of the Graduate School of Management (GSM) provide multiple options to suit a variety of career paths. Students seeking a generalist approach may select the M.B.A. in business management, which provides the broadest management education.

Students who wish to develop more specific skills or focus on a particular business environment may select from the following tracks within the M.B.A. program: not-for-profit management, entrepreneurship, franchise management, marketing management, consumer marketing, business-to-business marketing, international marketing, e-commerce, corporate finance, international finance, corporate investment analysis, engineering management, management of technology, industrial management, operations management, quality management, logistics management, purchasing and contract management, financial and estate planning, investment management, health services management, hospital administration, practice management, insurance and managed care, human resource management, international human resource management, organization development, international management, global trade, information technology management, database administration, applications development, sport management, and telecommunications management.

The curriculum for each M.B.A. program includes a set of core courses designed to provide a strong business foundation and a set of specialized courses unique to each concentration.

M.B.A. programs require the completion of 49 credit hours (sixteen courses). This may be reduced to a minimum of 37 credit hours (twelve courses) for students who have courses transferred from another graduate institution or waived on the basis of undergraduate course work. On GSM's thirteen-week trimester system, most full-time M.B.A. students can complete their degree requirements in three or four trimesters.

Students who have already earned an M.B.A. may pursue a second master's degree, the Master of Management. This degree requires the completion of 30 credit hours (ten courses) in the selected area of concentration.

GSM's noncredit Pre-M.B.A. and intensive English programs allow international students to prepare for graduate studies in business while becoming acclimated to life in the United States.

The Pre-M.B.A. program is an intensive, thirteen-week preparatory program that is designed to enhance communication skills, improve GMAT scores, and teach fundamental business concepts. This program is specifically designed to meet the needs of international students who wish to improve their GMAT score or who may not have an undergraduate degree in business.

The full-time intensive English program utilizes the "focal skills" method of instruction, allowing students to progress at their own pace through classes in listening, reading, writing, and immersion, which focuses on all skill areas. Students continuing to GSM may take a business fluency course designed to prepare them for oral presentations and writing research papers.

Students and the M.B.A. Experience

The Graduate School of Management attracts mature students who have substantial professional experience. The average GSM student is 32 years old and has seven years of work experience. The student body includes 40 percent women, 18 percent minorities, and 25 percent international students from more than fifty countries. Nineteen percent of GSM students have engineering degrees, 16 percent were science majors, and 18 percent have various undergraduate degrees, including liberal arts and social sciences. Fourteen percent already hold graduate degrees. This mature, diverse student body is one of the GSM's outstanding educational resources.

❖ Global Focus

The Graduate School of Management has long recognized the importance of global education. The M.B.A. in international management program at GSM is one of the ten largest in the United States and has recently been expanded to include a specialization in global trade. Travel courses, which include faculty-guided study in international business capitals, are offered between trimesters.

Special Features

The Graduate School of Management was the first business school in the region to assign students to real consulting projects for local, national, and international firms. These strategic planning projects allow students to apply the concepts and methods taught in their previous courses to real business problems.

The Faculty

GSM's faculty provides a rare mix of competence in both the theoretical aspects of management and the applied working knowledge of its practical aspects. The faculty is organized into a relatively small resident group and a larger adjunct group. The resident faculty members are full-time instructors with extensive backgrounds in business, teaching, applied research, and consulting. The adjunct faculty consists of practicing

managers, attorneys, accountants, consultants, and other professionals, who teach part-time. GSM students enjoy the best of both the academic and the practical worlds.

The Business School Network

Over the years, GSM has developed significant alliances and corporate partnerships. Each concentration has an advisory board made up of prominent professionals in related fields who assist the program directors in the development of their programs. Through the Management Lecture Series, world business leaders visit the University to lecture to GSM students. In their capstone courses, all GSM students have the opportunity to work on a real project for a corporation.

The College and Environs

The University of Dallas was founded in 1956 as an independent Catholic university dedicated to the pursuit of excellence in its educational programs. The current total enrollment in undergraduate and graduate programs exceeds 3,000 students.

The Graduate School of Management was founded in 1966 as an evening graduate school for individuals who were already employed in business and the professions. Over the years, the school's educational scope has broadened to serve a diverse student population, while its programs have remained focused on the practical realities of managerial life.

The University of Dallas is located in the suburban community of Irving, Texas, a part of the Dallas–Fort Worth metroplex, and is within 10 miles of downtown Dallas and the Dallas–Fort Worth International Airport. The scenic campus, on more than 600 acres of rolling hills, is directly adjacent to Texas Stadium, home of the Dallas Cowboys football team.

The Dallas–Fort Worth metroplex has 3.4 million people and is one of the fastest-growing population centers in the country. Its diversified economy includes important industries in electronics, aerospace, insurance, and banking. The moderate climate and abundance of lakes and parks in the surrounding area offer numerous recreational opportunities. The metroplex also provides rich cultural and entertainment opportunities.

Technology Environment

Faulkner's Communications Infodisk, Computer Select, the National Trade Data Base, Compact Disclosure, and the ABI-Inform full text system are a few of the technical resources available in the University of Dallas Blakley Library. Students also have access to the resources of many other public and university libraries in north Texas.

Computer facilities are available to all students. The on-campus computer center provides access to personal computers and the University's Prime superminicomputer.

Placement

The University of Dallas Career Counseling Center assists M.B.A. students with their job search and offers workshops on resume preparation and interviewing skills. Students participate in job fairs on- and off-campus, and many corporations come to GSM to select students for professional internships.

Admission

Applicants must have a bachelor's degree from an accredited institution. Other admission criteria include an undergraduate GPA of at least 3.0, a satisfactory score on the GMAT, and a work history of professional managerial work experience. International students whose native language is not English must submit satisfactory TOEFL scores; for immigration purposes, these students must show the availability of $23,000 for each year of study.

Finances

Tuition for the Graduate School of Management in 2000–01 is $403 per credit hour. Books and supplies cost approximately $150 per class. Living expenses, including housing, meals, utilities, and miscellaneous expenses, average $850 per month. Mandatory health insurance is $225 each trimester. Students should plan to purchase a car for local transportation.

International Students

International students comprise more than 23 percent of the GSM student body. International students become members of the International Student Association, and many join a regional or country-specific student organization.

Application Facts and Dates

Applications are accepted for the fall, spring, and summer trimesters. Applications from outside the United States should be sent at least eight weeks before the trimester desired. The nonrefundable application fee is $50.

For more information on the University of Dallas Graduate School of Management, applicants should contact:

Office of Admissions
The Graduate School of Management
University of Dallas
1845 East Northgate Drive
Irving, Texas 75062-4799
Telephone: 972-721-5174
Fax: 972-721-4009
E-mail: admiss@gsm.udallas.edu
World Wide Web: http://gsm.udallas.
    edu

The University of Delaware

Newark, Delaware

THE VALUE OF A DELAWARE M.B.A.

Earning an M.B.A. degree is a significant undertaking that requires considerable dedication, energy, and time. We put powerful resources behind our program to make sure students receive a superlative business education. Consequently, at the University of Delaware, you will find an academically accomplished faculty, a demanding and exciting curriculum, and—because of our commitment to admissions quality—highly accomplished classmates. Because we believe that students develop their critical problem-solving and decision-making skills from each other, as well as from the faculty, you will be in a classroom of no more than 35 students, immersing you in a highly concentrated and learning-supportive environment.

—Dean

Programs and Curricular Focus

The College of Business and Economics offers rigorous programs for superior students leading to the M.B.A. and the M.A./M.B.A. degrees. The special combination of academically accomplished faculty, highly qualified students, and ideal location—a small university town in the midst of the large eastern megalopolis—provides the necessary ingredients for an outstanding experience in graduate business education. The Delaware M.B.A. program is accredited by AACSB–The International Association for Management Education.

The Delaware M.B.A. curriculum includes courses that focus on capable leadership, effective team building, group decision making, strategic use of technology, power negotiating, creative problem-solving techniques, international concerns, e-commerce, coordinating an effective total quality management process, and ethical considerations. The new courses complement the traditional courses in accounting, economics, finance, operations, and marketing. Students who wish to pursue more in-depth course work are offered the option of concentrating in accounting, business economics, finance, information technology, international business, leadership and management of museums, management, marketing, operations, or innovation management. Internships are also available to supplement the student's academic program.

The 48-credit M.B.A. program can normally be completed in eighteen to twenty-one months. The program can also be completed on a part-time basis, taking between three and five years. An Executive M.B.A. program allows students with at least five years of professional experience to complete the degree in nineteen months by taking classes Friday evenings and Saturdays. The combination of small class sizes, problem-based learning, and students' practical experiences creates a stimulating environment for the analysis of today's business world and its mastery.

Students and the M.B.A. Experience

For fall 1999, the average length of work experience for entering M.B.A. students was three years, the average age was 26, and the average GMAT score was 608. In 1998–99, approximately 550 students were enrolled in all M.B.A. programs, of whom 37 percent were women, 7 percent were members of minority groups, and 7 percent were international students (20 percent of the full-time student body), including students from China, France, Germany, Iceland, India, Norway, Singapore, and Venezuela. The diversity of the student body adds to the interactive learning environment in the classroom.

Special Features

All Delaware M.B.A. students are given an account on the Internet and are introduced to its many tools during the new student orientation program. The M.B.A. program has its own Usenet news group and Web site that are used for information sharing. Some M.B.A. classes also use news groups and the World Wide Web as additional learning environments. E-mail is the preferred form of communication between students, faculty members, and administrators.

The Faculty

The faculty members who teach M.B.A. classes hold doctoral degrees in their disciplines. Through widely respected research and publishing efforts, they have earned national reputations in their fields of study. M.B.A. faculty members have also enhanced their respective skills through consulting positions with major national and international corporations, a good number of which are headquartered a short distance from the University.

The Business School Network

Because of the excellent reputation of the Delaware M.B.A., positive program relations exist with members of the corporate community, including DuPont, MBNA America, Bank of New York, J. P. Morgan Delaware, ICI America, and Zeneca. These relationships have fostered the development of internship opportunities for Delaware M.B.A. students at these and other firms (e.g., Hewlett-Packard, First USA Bank, Arco, and Cyanamid). The College has also developed an innovative Corporate Associates program that partners with the corporate community to provide a mutually beneficial financial aid package for full-time students.

The College's Visiting Board, composed of high-ranking corporate executives from major corporations, serves as an advisory group to the dean of the College on various matters, including those pertaining to the M.B.A. program.

The activities of an M.B.A. alumni network are supported by the regular publication of the M.B.A. Alumni Resource Directory, which is available to all M.B.A. students and alumni. The directory is a key resource for M.B.A. career planning and placement.

The College and Environs

The University of Delaware, founded in 1743 as a small liberal arts school, now ranks among the finest of the nation's medium-sized universities, with approximately 14,500 undergraduate and 3,000 graduate students. Included in the College of Business and Economics are four departments: accounting, business administration, economics, and finance.

The University of Delaware is located in Newark, a suburban community of approximately 30,000 residents. Newark is situated in the northwest corner of Delaware within 3 miles of the Pennsylvania and Maryland borders. It is located within easy driving distance of Philadelphia (45 miles), Baltimore (50 miles), Washington, D.C. (100 miles), and New York City (130 miles). Newark is also less than 100 miles from the Delaware and New Jersey beaches. Nearby Wilmington is a major center for credit banking and the chemical industry. Eighty percent of all Fortune 500 companies are incorporated in Delaware, which allows the College to maintain strong ties with the corporate sector.

Facilities

The University library is a modern research facility with more than 2 million volumes, is a member of the Association of Research Libraries, and is a depository for U.S. government documents and patents.

Mainframe computer facilities include an extensive array of both hardware and software. Sun Workstations operating under UNIX are used for research, course work, text processing, and communication. The College has a computer laboratory that focuses on business applications, as well as a state-of-the-art local area network.

Placement

In addition to M.B.A. job fairs and on-campus interviews, the Delaware M.B.A. program participates in two M.B.A. Consortia in Philadelphia and Washington, D.C. Along with graduates from other top M.B.A. schools, Delaware's M.B.A. graduates network and arrange interviews with a number of prospective employers. The average annual salary for 1998 graduates of the full-time program was $53,230. Employers of recent full-time graduates include Andersen Consulting, Arthur Andersen, Colgate Palmolive, DuPont, IBM, Lockheed Martin, MBNA America, Stanley Works, and W. L. Gore.

Admission

A student must submit official copies of all undergraduate and graduate transcripts, GMAT scores, and two letters of recommendation. For qualified applicants, a personal interview is also required. Delaware M.B.A. students are a highly accomplished group. For fall 1998, the mean GMAT score of entering students was 605 and the mean undergraduate GPA was 3.1. A score of at least 585 is required on the TOEFL for all students for whom English is not the native language. No prior work experience is required, although it is strongly recommended. Although no prerequisite courses are required, applicants are assumed to possess basic skills in written and oral communication, mathematics, and computer use.

Finances

In 1998–99, the yearly tuition for full-time M.B.A. students was $12,250 ($5360 for Delaware residents). Part-time study was $298 per credit hour for Delaware residents and $681 per credit hour for nonresident students. Rental costs for shared occupancy in a graduate student complex were $350 per month. University and privately owned apartments, furnished and unfurnished, are available at costs ranging from $350 to $900 per month.

Numerous financial aid packages are available to superior full-time M.B.A. students. These include graduate assistantships, corporate assistantships, and tuition grants that are awarded on a competitive basis regardless of nationality or financial need. Awards to first-year students are based on prior experience and academic performance. Awards to second-year students are based on academic performance in the program.

A typical aid package may include a $4000 per year stipend and/or a 50 percent waiver of tuition. These awards are administered by the M.B.A. Programs Office. Information on other possible sources of aid can be obtained by writing to the University's Office of Scholarships and Student Financial Aid.

International Students

More than 30 percent of the full-time student body is international. The Cosmopolitan Club provides activities for international students that help them understand the American culture as well as the cultures of other countries. International students are also oriented to the needs placed on them in a highly interactive M.B.A. classroom. The University of Delaware also offers a Pre-MBA Program for international students via the English Language Institute.

Countries represented by the international students include Colombia, England, Ethiopia, France, Germany, Ghana, Greece, India, Malaysia, the Netherlands, the People's Republic of China, Singapore, South Africa, Sweden, Taiwan, Turkey, and Venezuela.

Application Facts and Dates

Applications for the fall semester must be submitted by May 1. Students seeking financial aid should submit their applications by February 1. For more information, students should contact:

Kathy Kuck, Admissions
M.B.A. Programs
College of Business and Economics
103 MBNA America Hall
University of Delaware
Newark, Delaware 19716
Telephone: 302-831-2221
Fax: 302-831-3329
E-mail: mbaprogram@udel.edu
World Wide Web: http://www.mba.
     udel.edu

University of Denver

PREPARING YOU FOR BUSINESS LEADERSHIP

At the Daniels College of Business, we are committed to your success—as a highly competent professional, a team builder and leader, and a valued member of your community. Founded in 1908, the Daniels College of Business is the nation's eighth-oldest accredited collegiate business school and a leader in management education. With one of the nation's premier M.B.A. programs, we put you at the cutting edge of knowledge, present an educational experience that prepares you for a lifetime of leadership, and provide our commitment to your career placement and development. We do all this in a classic campus setting located in Denver, a wonderful city that symbolizes the dynamic business environment of the Rocky Mountain West.

—James R. Griesemer, Dean

Programs and Curricular Focus

The Daniels College of Business M.B.A. program presents a forward-thinking, integrated curriculum that challenges students through an active learning environment. The core curriculum incorporates experiential elements in leadership, case studies, and group work in addition to traditional methods of learning. Through this exciting experience, students learn technical business knowledge, refine skills that are key to managerial excellence, and gain an appreciation for values-based leadership.

Mirroring the cross-functional involvement of management decision making, the core courses combine the business technical fundamentals and management skills into a more applications-oriented format from which students develop a comprehensive view of business the way it actually operates. Included in the experience are an outdoor leadership and team-building program, opportunities for volunteer participation, and a team field-study project in which students work with Denver-based organizations.

Students move through the core into elective or specialization courses that provide focus to their degree. Specializations in accounting, construction management, electronic commerce, entrepreneurship, finance, information technology, marketing, real estate, and resort and tourism management are available, or students may create their own specializations from courses offered at the University.

A part-time M.B.A. program is available. Other options include an M.B.A./J.D. joint-degree program and a flexible dual-degree program that allows students to combine their M.B.A. degree with programs from other schools and departments within the University of Denver.

The Executive M.B.A. program is an eighteen-month program designed to strengthen the management skills and leadership abilities of middle- and upper-level managers and managing professionals. Intensive course work, creative problem solving, and an international cultural travel seminar provide firsthand knowledge of management, international, and emerging business opportunities.

The Emerging Leaders M.B.A. is an eighteen-month, cutting-edge graduate study program designed for high-potential men and women with at least two years of management experience who want to strengthen technical business skills and enhance leadership abilities.

Students and the M.B.A. Experience

Daniels College of Business students have a wide range of academic and professional backgrounds and represent more than thirty countries around the world. Insights and skills from an average of more than six years of professional experience and undergraduate majors, including business, engineering, international studies, history, and economics, provide diverse perspectives that add to

dynamic classroom environments and group projects. Of the approximately 480 M.B.A. students, 30 percent are working professionals in the evening program, 37 percent are women, and 25 percent are international students.

❖ Global Focus

The Daniels College of Business's M.B.A. program emphasizes international business and a global understanding of cultures and perspectives. A core course focuses on global perspectives, and elective courses include international marketing, comparative management, and multinational finance. In addition, courses in international politics, economics, and policy analysis are available from the University's Graduate School of International Studies.

Special Features

The integrated curriculum helps develop creative critical thinking and decision making through courses that focus on applying business tools in an interrelated format. Exciting core courses have replaced traditional individual function courses to combine tools and skills as students use them.

A three-day outdoor leadership experience provides an arena for students to learn key elements of communication skills, team building, and consensus problem solving. Added to the managerial excellence focus are negotiation skills and Myers-Briggs testing.

The Faculty

The Daniels College of Business's 80 full-time faculty members have a balance of industry experience and academic dedication, providing a classroom environment that is diverse and exciting. They have developed the curriculum with outside business leaders and continue to refine the program as well as maintain their excellence in teaching, research, and consulting. They are recognized worldwide for their industry knowledge and work with educational organizations such as the Fulbright Foundation.

The new Daniels College of Business building opened in 1999.

The Business School Network

Corporate Partnerships

The Daniels College of Business works with corporate advisers in a multitude of program areas. The curriculum continues to be shaped by faculty members and corporate advisers. The Career Placement Center works with executives in operations and panel discussions, and the team field study course, Integrative Challenge, is a partnership with Denver-area corporations and businesses that utilize Daniels students to address management problems. In addition, the Career Placement Center alumni mentor program provides contacts with alumni in a wide range of industries and positions for placement counseling and assistance.

Prominent Alumni

Prominent alumni include James Unruh, Chairman and CEO, Unisys; Peter Coors, CEO, Coors Brewing Company; June Travis, Executive Vice President, National Cable Television Association; Andy Daly, President, Vail Associates; Thomas Marsico, CEO, Marsico Capital Management; and David Bailey, CEO, Wells Fargo Bank West.

The College and Environs

The University of Denver is the largest independent, private university in the Rocky Mountain region, with more than 8,800 students from more than 80 countries. Founded in 1864 by John Evans, the Colorado Territory Governor for Abraham Lincoln, the 125-acre University of Denver campus is located in a quiet neighborhood in Denver, Colorado, providing students an academic atmosphere with access to the cosmopolitan population, activities, and lifestyle of Denver, with the Rocky Mountains nearby.

Facilities

In September 1999, the $22-million Daniels College of Business building opened. One of the nation's most technologically advanced business school facilities, the new building has more than 3,000 data ports for instant access to the Internet. It houses the Advanced Technology Center, a state-of-the-art laboratory with more than $1 million worth of the latest software and hardware.

Computer facilities include labs with 125 networked PCs that support word processing, spreadsheet and visual presentation software, UNIX mainframes that provide statistical packages, and Internet and information research database access.

Placement

The Daniels Career Placement Center helps students assess career choices and develop effective career strategies using a wide range of resources. Workshops and personal counseling are available to help students enhance job search skills, techniques, and knowledge. Career forums, job fairs, alumni networking events, regional consortium events, computerized job and internship listing databases, a research library, and an alumni mentor program provide access to employers from around the nation.

Admission

The Daniels College of Business enrolls students in September and March. Applications are reviewed on a rolling basis through a comprehensive process that evaluates previous academic performance and completion of an undergraduate degree from an accredited college or university, results of the Graduate Management Admission Test (GMAT), professional work experience, responses to essay questions, two letters of recommendation, and a completed application form. International students whose primary language is not English or who graduated from an institution where English is not the primary language of instruction are required to submit TOEFL results. Interviews not always required.

Finances

For the academic year 2000–01, tuition for full-time students attending three quarters is $20,052. Books, supplies, fees, housing, and meal expenses vary, depending on the number of courses taken per quarter and extracurricular activities. Even though Denver is the largest city in the Rocky Mountain region, the cost of living is well below other major U.S. cities.

Application Facts and Dates

Applications are evaluated on a rolling basis as they are received and completed, with a decision response within five weeks of completion. The deadline for September enrollment is May 1, and the deadline for March enrollment is January 1. Applications received after these dates are reviewed on a space-available basis. For inquiries, students should contact:

Office of Student Services
Daniels College of Business
University of Denver
2101 South University Boulevard
Denver, Colorado 80208
Telephone: 303-871-3416
          800-622-4723 (toll-free)
Fax: 303-871-4466
E-mail: dcb@du.edu
World Wide Web: http://www.daniels.
   du.edu

University of Edinburgh

The Management School

Edinburgh, Scotland

A TOP M.B.A. IN SCOTLAND'S CAPITAL

The University of Edinburgh is consistently rated amongst the top three or four universities in the United Kingdom and amongst the top universities in the world. The Edinburgh M.B.A. is therefore obtained at one of the UK's top management schools.

Our students are drawn from all over the world and bring to the course their extensive experience and working knowledge. We add to this our knowledge and experience, gained from being the first Scottish university to introduce the study of business and management, and our current faculty members, who are highly rated for their teaching and research. This powerful combination provides an outstanding learning environment in a school dedicated to postgraduate management education. Our M.B.A. provides a demanding and exciting learning experience, which the hardworking will thrive upon and which will advance their careers.

—Professor David Hatherly, Director, The Management School

Programs and Curricular Focus

The Edinburgh M.B.A. is a general management course that covers all the main management disciplines and provides for specialisation in marketing, finance, operations management, and entrepreneurship.

The full-time course runs for one calendar year, starting in October with a foundation term that covers business policy, economics and quantitative methods, accounting and finance, human behaviour at work, marketing, and operations management. In the second and third terms, students can choose any four of fifty optional subjects to study alongside the core course in strategic management. In addition, there are optional language and outdoor education components to the course, with a parallel programme of communication and presentation skills. The summer term provides for completion of a thesis or project, which can take a number of forms, including a research study, a business plan, or a company-based project. Success in the M.B.A. degree is based on assessment through course work and examinations at the end of the third term and then completion of the M.B.A. thesis or project.

The University also offers a fifteen-month M.B.A. in international business, which requires students to study overseas with a partner school for one trimester and do a practical management placement outside their home country.

Students and the M.B.A. Experience

The student body in each full-time M.B.A. program is genuinely international. The composition of the 1999 class (115 people) included representatives from forty different countries, with 30 percent drawn from the British Isles and no more than 7 or 8 percent from any other single country. The average age is about 30, with the youngest being 24; two students are over 40. The average work experience of the students is around seven years, with most having already held career management positions. In this year, 30 percent of students are women. Students spend a considerable amount of time in the second and third terms working in different syndicate groups, both on class case studies and out-of-school projects.

Special Features

A major element of the course is the requirement in the spring to carry out a team consultancy project for a local company. The project can be based in a small local company, many of which are developing new technologies, or a division of a larger company. Many students base their dissertation on project work with a company, and, in collaboration with the British Council, the University has developed opportunities for overseas students to take up an internship with major Scottish trading companies that have international interests.

The Faculty

There are more than 80 teaching staff members in the Management School, drawn from twelve different countries. Staff members are active in industry-based research and consultancy for both commercial organisations and government. This research work feeds directly into the quality of the teaching to M.B.A. students and also provides opportunities for student dissertations as part of their course.

The Business School Network

The School advisory board includes leading business figures from the city of Edinburgh. In addition, a number of research centres associated with the School involve leading businesspeople. In particular, Connect—a programme that arranges the start-up and growth of high-technology companies—is at the centre of a Scotland-wide network of leading companies, investment organisations, and corporate advisers.

Leading business figures are regular guest speakers at the School, and several, such as Alex Trotman, Chairman and Chief Executive of the Ford Motor Company, are appointed as visiting faculty members. Their teaching and informal contact with students provide a direct insight into current management and business practice.

The College and Environs

The Management School is at the heart of the University campus, in the city centre of the capital of Scotland. Edinburgh is an attractive city, one of the safest in Britain, with the best cultural facilities outside London. The School is opposite the city opera house within a 10-minute walk of the Castle, Holyrood Palace, theatres and concert halls, and the central business district.

Facilities

The School is situated in a city centre building used exclusively by postgraduate

Edinburgh University's campus in the spring.

management students, researchers, and executive course participants. The purpose-built premises have a large computer lab and other specialised facilities for M.B.A. students, all of whom have international e-mail accounts. The building has secure 24-hour access to provide for independent student learning and international Internet contact and the opportunity to work with colleagues at convenient times. It is close to the main University library, one of the best in the country, and to the National Library of Scotland, which has a specialised business information service and where students have automatic membership.

The University has a wide range of accommodation, ranging from full catering to self-contained flats solely for postgraduates. Most students live within the heart of the city in accommodations that are within a few hundred meters of the School.

Technology Environment

The University and the School are part of one of the most powerful area networks in the British university system; there are facilities for videoconferencing and high-speed data transfer. Several elective classes from a number of courses specifically build upon the use of these facilities, and much course work integrates the use of multimedia materials.

Hardware connected to the network is updated each year, and the computer system provides remote student access to personal computers if necessary.

Placement

The induction week for the M.B.A. program starts with a focus on career development, which is fully integrated into all parts of the programme. The Career Management Advisor provides advice and support for careers placement. Many students have gone on to highly successful careers in industry (Mercedes-Benz), consultancy (PA, McKinsey), and finance (First National of Chicago). The University maintains a career book for current and former M.B.A.'s, which is readily accessed by employers through the regularly updated Web site rather than the more traditional printed form.

Admission

Candidates generally are required to have a first degree and good work experience and therefore to be at least 25 years old. All candidates must complete an application statement that explains why they want to pursue an M.B.A. degree and prepare other written work. An interview may be scheduled. A GMAT test score is required. Students are required to have a good command of English (minimum TOEFL score of 580 [6.5 ELTS]); the

University offers preparatory courses in English in the weeks just before the M.B.A. program starts for those who need language support.

Finances

The courses have the highest possible level of accreditation, which ensures that students are able to access loan schemes and grants from their own host country. Some scholarships and grants are available through the School. (Details are sent to all applicants.) Fees for the twelve-month course are £11,400 and £14,500 for the fifteen month M.B.A. in international business. Living costs for students vary according to individual circumstances and may be about £9500 for a full year.

International Students

Welcome sessions are provided for overseas students, and an active M.B.A. student social committee provides entertainment and social events for all students.

Each year there are a number of overseas students funded by their own government agencies and through British scholarships, including Chevening scholarships. These are processed through the local representative of the British Council.

Application Facts and Dates

Applications are dealt with on a rolling basis, although the latest recommended application date is August of each year. The turnaround for applications is within two or three weeks of receiving all documentation.

Course Director
M.B.A. Programme
University of Edinburgh Management
 School
University of Edinburgh
7 Bristo Square
Edinburgh EH8 9AL
Scotland
Telephone: 44-0-131-650-6339
Fax: 44-0-131-650-8077
E-mail: management.school@ed.ac.uk
World Wide Web: http://www.ems.ed.
 ac.uk

University of Florida

Warrington College of Business

Gainesville, Florida

THE FLORIDA M.B.A.: THE NEXT 50 YEARS

For more than fifty years, the University of Florida (UF) has developed successful leaders and managers to meet the challenges of a rapidly changing business environment. We carry that commitment into the next century, with increased emphasis on promoting academic excellence, creating innovative programs, and fostering a collegial environment. Innovative new programs and curricular enhancements provide improved accessibility and greater flexibility for all students. Small class sizes, a low student-faculty ratio, and an expanded program staff ensure that individual needs are met throughout the program. Tremendous value results from the combination of our nationally recognized M.B.A. program, the comparatively low cost of attendance, and Gainesville's high quality of life. We look toward a bright future with renewed focus, ambition, and spirit. We invite you to join the dynamic Florida M.B.A. community.

—John Kraft, Dean

Students attend classes in the heart of the University of Florida's historic campus.

Programs and Curricular Focus

The University of Florida is nationally recognized for the academic excellence of its M.B.A. programs and for the exceptional value that it provides. The M.B.A. experience at Florida is unlike any other in that it empowers students to tailor their educational development according to their individual needs. The University offers seven distinct M.B.A. program options, sixteen academic concentrations, six certificate programs, seven joint-degree programs, and two dual-degree programs.

Florida's full-time traditional program options include the two-year program as well as a one-year program for students with undergraduate degrees in business. Both are packaged in a modular format that is composed of eight-week quarters.

Students can elect to focus their studies in one or more of the following areas of concentration: arts administration, business strategy and public policy, competitive strategy, decision and information sciences, entrepreneurship, finance, general business, global management, international studies, human resource management, Latin American business, management, marketing, real estate, security analysis, and sports administration.

Florida also provides an opportunity for its students to dedicate themselves to a more intensive course of study. The program awards certificates to students who allocate a large majority of their elective hours toward the study of one of the following functional areas: decision and information sciences, electronic commerce, entre-

preneurship and technology management, financial services, global management, and supply chain management.

Busy professionals who want to earn the M.B.A. degree without interrupting a successful career may elect to enroll in one of Florida's programs for working professionals, which provide a broad general management education. Students in the Executive M.B.A. Program and the M.B.A. for Professionals Programs (two-year and one-year options) meet on campus one weekend per month.

Florida also offers its Internet M.B.A. in two-year and one-year options. The Internet M.B.A. utilizes leading-edge interactive technology to deliver a high-caliber graduate degree via distance learning. The program requires only occasional visits to the campus: one weekend for orientation and one weekend at the end of each term.

Seven joint-degree programs enable students to combine their M.B.A. with another UF degree in law, health administration, engineering, exercise and sports sciences, biotechnology, medical sciences, or pharmacy.

Students and the M.B.A. Experience

Florida's programs integrate a distinguished faculty, talented students, a dedicated staff, and successful alumni to form a cooperative and supportive community.

The students enrolled in the Florida M.B.A. programs form a diverse class, with about 29 percent coming from outside the

U.S. and 11 percent from underrepresented ethnic groups; 30 percent are women. Students average approximately five years of work experience and come from a variety of academic backgrounds, ranging from philosophy to engineering. Students also benefit from involvement in various extracurricular activities, including student organizations such as the M.B.A. Association, M.B.A. Ambassadors, the M.B.A. Consulting Club, the Investment Club, Graduate Women In Business, and the International Business Association.

❖ Global Focus

M.B.A. students have the opportunity to study abroad via one of sixteen international exchange programs. In addition, they have the option to pursue a dual degree, the M.B.A./Master of International Management (M.I.M.), offered in conjunction with Thunderbird.

The Faculty

Florida's M.B.A. faculty members possess exceptional credentials and are recognized by industry leaders and their peers for contributions to various areas of expertise. The Departments of Accounting, Marketing, Finance, and Management are consistently ranked among the top twenty-five in the country. Individual faculty members have been honored with national awards for their excellence in research. Members of the fac-

The Florida M.B.A. Programs provide a close-knit, team-oriented community.

ulty serve as editors for major journals of marketing, finance, accounting, management, and business law. They also direct thirteen research centers, which explore emerging trends in a wide array of business disciplines. These faculty members are not just preeminent researchers, they are outstanding teachers as well. The M.B.A. program's 6:1 student-teacher ratio ensures that every student has the opportunity to frequently interact with these accomplished scholars.

The Business School Network

Corporate Partnerships
Corporate leaders are an integral part of Florida's business school community. The program is shaped largely by the contributions of its executive advisory board, corporate recruiters, and alumni.

Prominent business leaders routinely visit the University to speak to students via the Distinguished Speaker Series or by invitation from various professors. Recent speakers include Warren Buffet (Chairman, Berkshire Hathaway), Richard Teerlink (former Chairman of the Board for Harley Davidson), and Mary Alice Taylor (Chairperson and CEO of HomeGrocer.com).

Last year, 287 companies recruited M.B.A. students on campus for full-time employment and internships.

Prominent Alumni
Alumni of Florida's M.B.A. programs include John Dasburg (CEO, Northwest Airlines), Allen Lastinger (former President/COO, Barnett Banks), Judith Rosenblum (Chief Learning Officer, Coca-Cola), and Chris Verlander (President and COO, American Heritage Life).

The College and Environs
The University of Florida is a comprehensive, public research university that was founded in 1853. With more than 42,000 students, it is among the ten largest universities in the nation. A member of the prestigious Association of American Universities, the University of Florida has established a place for itself among the country's elite institutions of higher learning.

Facilities
Florida's business school is located in the northeast corner of campus, in an area known as the "Business Triangle." It is adjacent to the University's administration building and the main library facilities. Bryan Hall contains a computer lab and a study lounge (exclusively for M.B.A. students), along with a student information center and offices for the M.B.A. program staff members. Classrooms, faculty offices, and academic research centers are housed in Stuzin and Matherly Halls, the other two buildings that comprise the Business Triangle. Florida's 2,000-acre campus features athletic facilities that are among the nation's finest—including two state-of-the-art fitness centers and a championship golf course. The campus also has a performing arts center, a wildlife sanctuary, and several museums for students to enjoy.

Technology Environment
The classrooms and study areas utilized by the M.B.A. program are all linked to the business school's computer network. Every M.B.A. student is required to have a notebook computer in order to be able to participate in this interactive learning environment. All M.B.A. students use Microsoft Office software, along with Netscape Navigator and Lotus Notes, to collaboratively complete assignments and communicate with faculty and staff members.

Placement
Florida features a staff of dedicated career services professionals who assist M.B.A. students with their career development. The staff uses a series of skills assessments and other activities to help students develop comprehensive career plans. These tools include workshops for creating effective resumes and improving interview skills. The staff also develops and maintains working relationships with corporate recruiters, coordinates recruiting events, and maintains an extensive list of job postings for positions in major cities. Furthermore, M.B.A. students may utilize the University's Career Resource Center, which is widely regarded as one of the nation's best.

Admission
Candidates are evaluated based upon their demonstrated academic ability, professional experience, community involvement, and personal character. All applicants must have a bachelor's degree from an accredited U.S. institution or an international equivalent. Additional requirements include at least two years of significant work experience, official GMAT scores, official transcripts, two letters of recommendation, four essays, completed application forms, and a personal interview. All one-year program options also require an undergraduate business degree. Official TOEFL scores are usually required for applicants whose native language is not English. Other requirements vary by program. Students should refer to the application packet for details.

Finances
The Florida M.B.A. is consistently rated as one of the best buys in business education. Nationally ranked academic programs, low cost of attendance, and Gainesville's high quality of life combine to provide students with tremendous value. Tuition rates for each program vary based upon the student's residency status. A limited number of M.B.A. fellowships and graduate assistantships are available to help certain students reduce their educational expenses.

Application Facts and Dates

The Traditional M.B.A. Program (two-year option) and the Executive M.B.A. Program begin each August; the M.B.A for Professionals Programs (one-year and two-year options) and the Internet M.B.A. Programs (one-year and two-year options) start in January; and the Traditional M.B.A. Program (one-year option) commences in May. Students should refer to the application packet (or the Florida M.B.A.'s Web site) for specific admissions deadlines, program calendars, and budgets. An online inquiry and application system is available through the Web site as well. Candidates who submit completed applications generally receive a decision within two weeks after the personal interview.

For more information, students should contact:

Florida M.B.A. Programs
Warrington College of Business
University of Florida
134 Bryan Hall
P.O. Box 117152
Gainesville, Florida 32611-7152
Telephone: 877-4-FLA-MBA (877-435-2622, toll-free)
Fax: 352-392-8791
E-mail: floridamba@notes.cba.ufl.edu
World Wide Web: http://www.floridamba.ufl.edu

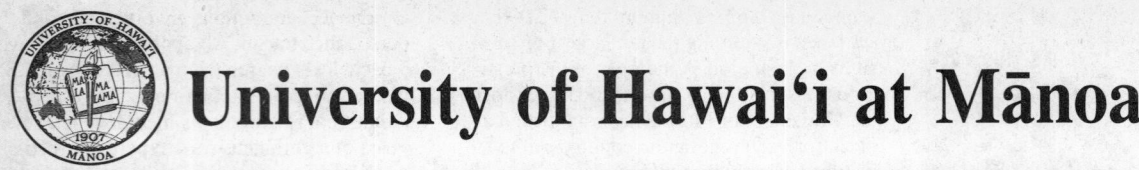

University of Hawai'i at Mānoa

The College of Business Administration

Honolulu, Hawai'i

> **WHAT DO LEADERS NEED TO KNOW TO NAVIGATE IN THE NEW ECONOMY?**
>
> *The College of Business Administration (CBA) at the University of Hawai'i at Mānoa equips its graduates with the ability to learn and to lead throughout their professional lifetime. The curriculum includes state-of-the-art instruction in management, entrepreneurship, and e-business, coupled with language training and cultural diversity that make Hawai'i such a remarkable and unique place to live. Most importantly, you'll be prepared to lead and manage change, the one constant of the new century.*
>
> —David McClain, Dean

Programs and Curricular Focus

The College of Business Administration offers the Master of Business Administration (M.B.A.) and Master of Accounting (M.Acc.) degrees. Both are primarily evening programs and may be pursued on either a full-time or a part-time basis. An Executive M.B.A. program, a Japan-focused M.B.A. program, and a China-focused M.B.A. program are also available.

With its close ties to the Hawai'i community, the College provides internships and study-abroad programs that afford students the opportunity to gain practical experience in solving real business problems. The College provides the only M.B.A., M.Acc., and B.B.A. programs in the state of Hawai'i that are accredited by AACSB–The International Association for Management Education.

The M.B.A. is a 42- to 48-credit-hour program with either a thesis or a nonthesis option. The core consists of four basic modules, followed by six elective courses and the capstone experience, which consists of business policy and strategy and field studies in the enterprise.

The M.Acc. program is a 30-credit-hour program designed to prepare students for careers in professional accounting.

The Japan-focused M.B.A., now in its tenth year, and the companion China-focused M.B.A. are fifteen-month cohort programs that provide intensive study in the language and culture of Japan and China, respectively. As the capstone of these programs, a three-month internship/field study experience with major corporations in Japan or China provides exposure to and practical application of Japanese or Chinese management and allows the student to gain valuable real-world experiences, Asian-style.

The Executive M.B.A. program is a twenty-two-month, accredited, intensive Master of Business Administration degree program. The accelerated format is structured as an intensive one-week residential session held in August prior to the first semester, with the balance of the classes meeting full days on Fridays and Saturdays of alternating weeks.

The CBA also provides access to dual-degree programs with other disciplines within the University, such as law, economics, and public health. The Ph.D. in international management program admitted its first students in 1998. Admission to this program is in the fall only.

Professional development programs and activities are available through the Asia-Pacific Center for Executive Development, the Pacific Asian Management Institute (PAMI), the Pacific Business Center Program, and the Pacific Research Institute for Information Systems and Management. These programs draw participants from major corporations in Hawai'i, the mainland United States, the Pacific Basin, and Asia.

Students and the M.B.A. Experience

Proximity to the United States mainland, Asia, and the Pacific has made Hawai'i, with its population of 1.1 million people on seven major islands, a gateway between the East and West. Reflecting its history as a "gathering place," the city of Honolulu and the University of Hawai'i at Mānoa are among the most multicultural populations in the world. One in every 5 of the 20,000 students studying at the University of Hawai'i at Mānoa is of Japanese ancestry; 1 in 10 is of Chinese ancestry; 1 in every 6 is Filipino, and approximately 12 percent are Hawaiian or part Hawaiian.

Total enrollment in the M.B.A. program is approximately 350; 25–30 students are enrolled in the Japan-focused M.B.A. Half are women, and 60 percent are part-time students, most of whom work full-time. The average M.B.A. student is 28 years old with four years of work experience.

❖ Global Focus

The College believes that no business student should graduate in today's world without a true appreciation and competency in both international business and the utilization of information systems technology. The international business programs at the College have been ranked fifth among graduate programs in the United States. Study-abroad opportunities are also available in Japan and Denmark.

Special Features

PAMI's International Summer Program offers a certificate in international business or management. Students must complete either three PAMI courses or two PAMI courses and one related area studies or language course. Each summer, up to 25 business students have the opportunity to observe firsthand, factories and boardrooms of Asia through the PAMI Asian field study program. CBA offers many study-abroad opportunities in the Asia-Pacific and European regions to broaden, understand, and practice international business procedures.

The Faculty

All full-time M.B.A. faculty members hold doctoral degrees. Students are kept apprised of current business developments as a result of the research and consulting done by the faculty. Many faculty members have completed and/or are currently conducting research on the nations of Asia and the Pacific.

Teaching methods include case analysis, lectures, independent research, and simulation exercises. The interaction of students in group projects is an important part of the M.B.A. experience.

The Business School Network

The College of Business Administration Alumni and Friends, Inc., was formed to broaden career opportunities and support CBA's academic pursuits.

The College and Environs

The University of Hawai'i at Mānoa was founded in 1907. Today's enrollment of approximately 20,000 includes 4,600 graduate students. The College of Business Administration was founded in 1949 and awarded its first M.B.A. degree in 1951. The central campus of the University covers 300 acres in the Mānoa Valley, a residential area close to the heart of Honolulu. Honolulu is an international center with cultural activities that include Pacific Island and Asian festivals as well as symphony concerts, ballet, theater, and opera. Hawai'i and its university are positioned and prepared to play a significant role in the emerging global economy.

Facilities

The University library collections total more than 2 million volumes and more than 35,000 currently received serials. Materials from other libraries in Hawai'i and the mainland are available through interlibrary loan. The Asian Collection in Hamilton Graduate Library has a heavy concentration of materials related to statistics in South and Southeast Asia. Business information on these countries is available in the collection. More than 150 databases can be searched for references.

Technology Environment

Graduate students have access to eighty personal computers in two microcomputer labs at the CBA. An extensive library of software for business applications is available. Use of the IBM ES/9000 is provided by the mainframe lab of the CBA. Mainframe terminals are also available at other locations.

Placement

Career Services offers students and alumni year-round assistance in their career searches. Services include workshops in resume design, letters of application, and interviewing techniques; Dial-a-Job, the University of Hawai'i at Mānoa's automated round-the-clock employment hot line; a career-oriented research library; career fairs and panel discussions; and personal counseling and credential file development.

Admission

The ideal student entering the M.B.A. program at the University of Hawai'i has a record of strong academic performance, high test scores, outstanding motivation, and well-thought-out career goals. Admission to the M.B.A. program is competitive and is based upon a "package" of capabilities indicated by the applicant's grade point average, GMAT scores, work experience, and professional objectives.

For admission into graduate programs, the CBA prefers applicants to have a GMAT score of 500 or above and a grade point average of 3.0 or higher (on a 4.0 scale) in the last two years of undergraduate course work and all past post-baccalaureate work. Applicants from countries where English is not the primary language are required to take the TOEFL. The minimum score is 500. The GRE and IELTS may be substituted in countries where the GMAT and TOEFL are not offered. Work experience is not required but is preferred. A resume and official transcripts are required of all applicants. Translations of transcripts not in English must be certified.

Finances

Full-time graduate tuition per semester in 1999–2000 was $2016 for residents and $4980 for nonresidents. Part-time tuition was $168 per credit hour for residents and $415 for nonresidents. Fees total $50 to $60 per semester. Costs for books and materials are approximately $300.

The 2000–02 Executive M.B.A. program costs $19,400, and the 2000–01 Japan- and China-focused M.B.A. programs cost approximately $29,000. These rates include tuition, fees, and all books and materials.

International Students

There is a strong international student community at the University of Hawai'i College of Business that comprises approximately 22 percent of the M.B.A. student body. The majority of international students come from Asian-Pacific countries. The University's International Student Services Office helps students become acclimated to American university life.

Application Facts and Dates

Application deadlines are May 1 for fall semester and November 1 for spring semester. Application deadlines and admission criteria for the Executive M.B.A. program differ from the M.B.A. and M.Acc. programs. Specifics on these programs can be obtained from the addresses below.

For M.B.A. and M.Acc. programs:

Graduate Programs
Office of Student Academic Services
College of Business Administration
University of Hawai'i at Mānoa
2404 Maile Way
Honolulu, Hawai'i 96822-2282
Telephone: 808-956-8266
Fax: 808-956-2657
World Wide Web: http://www.cba.
hawaii.edu

For the Executive M.B.A. program:

Executive M.B.A. Programs
College of Business Administration
University of Hawai'i at Mānoa
2404 Maile Way, Room C305
Honolulu, Hawai'i 96822-2282
Telephone: 808-956-8266
Fax: 808-956-2657
World Wide Web: http://www.cba.
hawaii.edu/emba/

University of Hawaii at Manoa

Honolulu, Hawaii

DEVELOPING BUSINESS LEADERS FOR ASIA'S NEW ECONOMY

▶ *The University of Hawaii at Manoa's College of Business Administration is recognized for its excellence in international business (top 20 in U.S. News & World Report) and information technology within the Asia-Pacific context. Working with the Japan-American Institute of Management Science (JAIMS), and with scholarship support from Fujitsu, Ltd. and the Asian Development Bank, the College offers two AACSB-accredited fifteen-month programs: the Japan-focused and the China-focused M.B.A. The curricula, which feature the latest in entrepreneurship and e-business, along with a unique language and culture emphasis and a three-month internship in Japan, China, or North America, are ideally suited for those planning to work in or do business with Asia.*

—David McClain, Dean

Programs and Curricular Focus

The fifteen-month M.B.A. curriculum for both the Japan-focused (JEMBA) and China-focused (CHEMBA) M.B.A. programs includes core M.B.A., advanced Japan-focused or China-focused courses in international business and intensive business language courses in Japanese or Mandarin. What makes the programs so unique, however, is the three-month internship at a company or organization in Japan, China, or North America, bringing to the forefront all the business knowledge and language and intercultural skills learned in the preceding twelve months.

The programs consist of four basic core modules—analytical tools for the M.B.A., organizational behavior and the external environment of Asia-Pacific business, finance and managerial accounting, and marketing management and information technologies—followed by a course in business strategy and policy. The advanced international business courses include negotiation and dispute resolution, Japanese/Chinese marketing systems, Japanese/Chinese financial management, and Asian political and legal business environments. The Japanese and Mandarin business language courses—held three mornings per week, with 4 to 6 students per instructor—develop language proficiency and cultural awareness within a business context and prepare students for their internships.

Drawing on Japanese and Chinese business experiences and case studies, the programs give a solid foundation in the principles of management and a working experience in Asia. Both JEMBA and CHEMBA M.B.A. programs are accredited by AACSB–The International Association for Management Education. In addition to the M.B.A. degree, graduates also receive the Japan-focused or China-focused Management Certificate from JAIMS, which reflects the intensive language and culture study and business internship.

Students and the MBA Experience

Students have at least two years of work experience in such industries as education, banking, manufacturing, information technology, and communications. Their ages range from the mid-20s to early 40s, and approximately one third are women. The programs are enriched by the multicultural makeup of the students, as 65 percent of students are from Asia-Pacific countries other than the United States, including Australia, Canada, China and Hong Kong, India, Indonesia, Korea, Malaysia, New Zealand, the Philippines, Singapore, Sri Lanka, Taiwan, and Thailand. This blend of nationalities makes for a dynamic group of individuals already knowledgeable about Asia, and approximately 70 percent of students have had previous Japanese or Mandarin language training. The small program size of 25 to 30 students allows for lively interaction, teamwork, and support, enabling students to establish an international network of contacts, particularly throughout Asia. Faculty members, business leaders, and contacts established through the business internship also extend the global network.

Special Features

The three-month business internship in Japan or China has been a definitive experience for all JEMBA and CHEMBA students. After conferring with students about their goals, JAIMS places them in appropriate internship companies and coordinates housing in Japan and China. As full-time interns, students practice Japanese or Chinese business and communication techniques and learn the rigors of business, Asian style. Internship supervisors oversee additional activities. Internship companies in Japan include Deloitte Touche Tohmatsu, Dentsu, Fidelity Investments, Fujitsu, Levi Strauss, McCann-Erickson, and PricewaterhouseCoopers. In China, CHEMBA students have interned at Citibank China, Portman Ritz-Carlton Shanghai, and TriWorks Computers & Telecommunications Shanghai. An additional internship in North America begins in 2001.

The Faculty

Faculty members at the UH College of Business Administration and JAIMS represent a wide array of expertise on Japan and China. They comprise a diverse group of internationally accomplished researchers and highly recognized teachers, many of whom work in the community and have business or teaching

experience in Asia. Guest lecturers from Asia and premier companies and institutions such as the East-West Center supplement the advanced Japan- and China-focused courses.

The Business School Network

Currently, the JEMBA internship is under the supervision of Ikujiro Nonaka, Dean of the Graduate School of Knowledge Science at the Japan Advanced Institute of Science and Technology. In the People's Republic of China, the CHEMBA internship is under the supervision of the China Europe International Business School in Shanghai.

The University of Hawaii at Manoa College of Business Administration has official student exchange agreements with a number of top business schools: Aarhus School of Business, in Denmark; Chulalongkorn University, in Thailand; Copenhagen Business School, in Denmark; Hong Kong University of Science and Technology, in Hong Kong; Keio University, in Japan; Koblenz University, in Germany; Korea University, in Korea; Reims School of Management, in France; Thammasat University, in Thailand; and Yonsei University, in Korea. In addition, the CBA's Pacific Asian Management Institute is the secretariat for a consortium of twenty-nine business schools that have strong Asia-Pacific programs.

Through a partnership in one of its programs, JAIMS is also associated with Reims School of Management, one of the top business schools in France.

The College and Environs

Hawaii's multicultural environment and its people provide a unique experience for enhancing Asia-Pacific cultural sensitivity. Students' time is divided between the UH College of Business Administration campus, which is located close to the downtown area of Honolulu (Hawaii's capital city), and JAIMS, which is nestled in a peaceful waterfront suburb 20 minutes from downtown. Home to approximately 1,200 graduate and undergraduate students, the College offers a variety of degree, certificate, and executive programs. Established in 1972 by Fujitsu Ltd., JAIMS is a private, nonprofit postgraduate institute that also offers an academic program for non-U.S. citizens on Western management as well as various custom seminars.

Facilities

Both the College of Business Administration and JAIMS feature state-of-the-art computer labs and computerized classrooms with local area networks (LANs), large-screen computer video projectors, and multimedia computers with e-mail access. JAIMS houses the Business Education Technology Center. At the University of Hawaii, students have access to extensive Asia-Pacific resources and libraries.

Placement

While employment at the student's internship company is not the objective of the programs, in some cases graduates have been offered employment with their internship companies or through contacts established while in Asia. At the University of Hawaii, students have access to the Office of Career Services, which offers counseling, job skills workshops, job listings, employer interviews, resume editing, and job market and employer research resources. Students can also participate in recruiting events in the U.S. and Asia. At JAIMS, the Vice President for Academic Affairs and the JAIMS network of alumni around the world provide country-specific employment leads.

Admission

The programs begin in August and commence with graduation in Asia fifteen months later. Applicants must have a bachelor's degree from a regionally accredited U.S. college or university or its equivalent from a recognized foreign institution and a minimum grade point average of 3.0 or the equivalent of undergraduate and postbaccalaureate work. The minimum GMAT score is 500, but a score of 550 or above is recommended. Applicants whose native language is not English are required to submit official TOEFL scores. The GRE and IELTS may be substituted in countries where the GMAT and TOEFL are not offered. Preference is given to applicants with two or more years of work experience in supervisory or managerial positions.

Finances

The cost of JEMBA and CHEMBA is $29,000 for tuition, internship supervision, administrative fees, all textbooks and classroom materials, and the use of all libraries and computer resources. Costs for housing, meals, and travel are not included. Students are assisted in finding accommodations in Honolulu, Japan, and China. Various grants and scholarships are available.

Application Facts and Dates

Applications, including transcripts, GMAT records, and TOEFL scores, are accepted until July 1, although students who complete applications after March 1 may be at a disadvantage in consideration for financial aid and scholarships.

For information, contact:

JEMBA/CHEMBA Programs
University of Hawaii at Manoa
6660 Hawaii Kai Drive
Honolulu, Hawaii 96825-1192
Telephone: 808-395-2314
Fax: 808-396-7111 or 7112
E-mail: info@jaims.org
World Wide Web:
   http://www.jaims.org

University of Illinois at Urbana-Champaign

Illinois M.B.A.

Urbana, Illinois

THE ILLINOIS M.B.A.—THE DELIVERABLE IS SUCCESS THROUGH TEAMWORK

► *In this program, we focus on real-world business. The hands-on nature of things simply makes our students better prepared to contribute to the companies they work for after graduation.*

—Brian Wansink, Associate Professor of Marketing

Programs and Curricular Focus

The Illinois M.B.A. curriculum focuses on teamwork, integration of functional areas and course assignments, hands-on business experience, and quick feedback and response mechanisms.

For the first year of the program, students work in teams within four 7-week core course modules that guide them step-by-step through the processes of establishing or managing a business. Faculty members also work in teams and present particular business problems from their own functional perspectives—such as finance, accounting, and marketing. The faculty teams coordinate their assignments and case studies so student teams can integrate the different perspectives and provide comprehensive solutions. The assignments also require students to utilize the vast resources of the University, including the nation's third-largest academic library and a world-leading research center for supercomputer applications, virtual reality environments, and network software. The faculty and student teams remain in constant contact using First Class networking software, which allows students to receive quick responses to questions or raise issues about the curriculum.

In addition to the course modules, students participate in a weeklong Applying Business Perspectives seminar once every semester. Applying Business Perspectives seminars are in-depth computer simulations or case studies that require students to analyze and apply their functional knowledge, exercise leadership and motivational skills, and formulate effective solutions under tight time constraints. They must then present their results to a panel of judges selected from the world's leading firms.

During the second year of the Illinois M.B.A., each student focuses on a Professional Track that teaches skills specific to his or her chosen career. Students can select from eighteen subtracks, which include entrepreneurship and new venture creation or technology systems management, or design one of their own. Alternately, they can enroll in a Joint Degree Program with any of several other outstanding programs at the University; these programs include engineering, law, and medicine, among others. A capstone course during the second year pulls together all the lessons students have learned and provides them with an overview of contemporary business and its global future.

Students and the M.B.A. Experience

Computerworld magazine ranked the Illinois M.B.A. sixth in its September 1999 rating of the top twenty-five techno-M.B.A. programs. That ranking reflects the technological and entrepreneurial focus of many students in the program.

Forty percent of Illinois M.B.A. students have technological backgrounds, and more than 50 percent have expressed interest in starting their own company after graduation. The Illinois M.B.A. class of 2001 is 55 percent U.S. citizens and 45 percent international students; 33 percent are women. Twenty percent of the class are members of racial or ethnic minorities. The average student is 28 years old and brings nearly four years of work experience to the program. Of the 381 students in the program, 45 are pursuing joint degrees.

The Faculty

The Illinois M.B.A. faculty members are intimately involved and invested in the curriculum. For three years, faculty members worked closely with administrators and focus groups to develop the curriculum's structure and content. Throughout the semester, the faculty team members communicate extensively with students and among themselves to ensure that learning objectives and student needs are met.

The Business School Network

The University of Illinois is home to a world-renowned engineering program and the Beckman Institute for Advanced Science and Technology. The Illinois M.B.A. has built strategic partnerships with these groups by developing an Office for Strategic Business Initiatives (OSBI). Through the OSBI, students consult with researchers about the commercial applications of new technologies and software. Some of these "technology transfer" projects can even lead to key management positions in start-up companies based on the new technologies.

The OSBI also offers students opportunities to get involved with a project in a business incubation laboratory, participate in FAST-trac entrepreneurship training, or manage a venture capital fund. A project could involve helping a local business get off the ground, or it could mean developing licensing and marketing strategies for a new software product straight out of the National Center for Supercomputing Applications.

The College and Environs

Located within a 2- to 3-hour drive of Indianapolis, Chicago, and St. Louis, the University of Illinois and the twin cities of Urbana and Champaign form a thriving community rich in social, cultural, and recreational opportunities. Each year, the Krannert Center for the Performing Arts presents more than 350 plays, concerts, ballets, and operas. The University's Krannert Art Museum is second only to Chicago's Art Institute among Illinois public museums. The Division of Campus Recreation administers one of the most comprehensive recreational programs in the world. In

Illinois M.B.A. students relax between classes on the business campus of the University of Illinois.

results, verbal and written communication skills demonstrated in essays and interviews, TOEFL and TSE scores for nonnative speakers of English, demonstrated leadership qualities, professional work experience, analytical ability, and letters of recommendation. The average GMAT score for the class of 2001 was 619, and the average GPA was 3.4 on a 4.0 scale.

Applicants should hold a bachelor's degree from an accredited U.S. college or university or the equivalent from another country. Prior academic experience in business is not required. A minimum grade of B in at least one semester of calculus is helpful.

Finances

Tuition and fees for Illinois residents enrolling in fall 2000 are $11,840 for the academic year. Nonresident tuition and fees are $19,204. Students can expect to spend about $1500 for books, $8000 for room and board, and $2000 for personal expenses.

The Illinois M.B.A. offers a Student Management Leadership Grant program. The one-year renewable, grants are based on merit, not financial need. During their second year of study, grantees work 10 hours per week as assistants to the management of the program. The application for admittance to the Illinois M.B.A. is used in awarding grants.

addition to an array of intramural athletics, the division operates facilities for year-round basketball, tennis, squash, racquetball, and swimming.

Placement

Six staff members and several graduate assistants are fulfilling the Career Services Office's mission: to provide Illinois M.B.A. students with the tools and resources they need for their career development and provide employers with information on how to recruit on campus and identify Illinois M.B.A. students who meet their staffing needs. Arthur Andersen, Citibank, Eaton Corporation, Ernst & Young, Ford Motor Company, General Electric, Honeywell, Intel, KPMG, and Sun Microsystems are some of the major corporations recruiting Illinois M.B.A. students.

Among the most innovative services the office offers are its Web site and the

Career Focus program. The Web site features an online resumé book, an extensive listing of career fairs, and links to online career search services. Every fall, first-year M.B.A. students attend Career Focus, a day of workshops given by successful alumni on career development issues. The Career Services Office has also integrated career skills development into the communications portion of the Illinois M.B.A. curriculum. For example, a writing assignment offers the chance to write an interview response letter. A speaking assignment develops skills and themes that a student can ultimately use in an interview situation.

Admission

Admission to the Illinois M.B.A. is based on undergraduate grade point average over the last 60 credit hours, GMAT

Application Facts and Dates

The application deadlines are December 15, February 1, and April 1. Students are encouraged to apply on line or download an application from the Illinois M.B.A. Web site at the address listed below. To order an application by mail or for additional information, students can contact:

Illinois M.B.A. Admissions
410 David Kinley Hall
1407 West Gregory Drive
Urbana, Illinois 61801

Telephone: 217-244-7602
            800-MBA-UIUC (toll-free in the U.S. only)
Fax: 217-333-1156
E-mail: mba@uiuc.edu
World Wide Web: http://www.mba.uiuc.edu

The University of Iowa

Iowa City, Iowa

LEARNING AND WORKING TOGETHER

▶ *The Iowa M.B.A. program is designed for people who like to learn and work together. Often, assignments are completed by students working in teams, and group presentations are the rule rather than the exception. The program is small enough so that our students get to know our faculty and staff members and each other very well.*

The Pappajohn Building is a high-tech, state-of-the-art environment complete with Bloomberg financial markets technology, Dow Jones markets, LEXIS-NEXIS, and a real-time trading room. But it's also our students' home base; so, in addition to all the desirable learning tools, we have some of the comforts of home, such as study areas with upholstered chairs, meeting rooms for small groups of students working together, lockers, an ATM machine, parking under the building after 4:30 p.m. on weekdays and all weekend, and an in-house restaurant.

The unique combination of a top-notch M.B.A. program situated in a safe and cosmopolitan small city make The University of Iowa School of Management an excellent choice for anyone.

—Gary Fethke, Dean

Programs and Curricular Focus

The University of Iowa M.B.A. program provides students with a solid foundation for future growth and flexibility in business management. The curriculum is rigorous, but learning takes place in a collaborative environment that builds teamwork while encouraging independent problem solving.

Students tailor individual course portfolios to combine analytical skills, broad-based knowledge, and professional experiences into a package that will advance their personal career goals.

Concentrations are available in accounting, finance, management information systems, marketing, entrepreneurship, human resources, leadership and consulting, operations management, and product development and management. Students may also create their own concentration, incorporating courses from the University's other colleges, or pursue a dual-degree program in hospital and health administration, nursing, law, library and information science, or management information systems.

Students and the M.B.A. Experience

IMPACT, a weeklong orientation program for entering M.B.A. students, links students with one another and with faculty members even before course work begins. This col-laborative atmosphere is sustained throughout the program through team projects, student organization activities, alumni functions, corporate visits, and daily communication. Dedicated and diverse, Iowa M.B.A. students come from top undergraduate institutions worldwide and hold degrees and honors in disciplines ranging from English to engineering.

The average student is 27 years old and has three years of professional experience. Women comprise 24 percent of the student population, and members of minority groups make up 8 percent.

Fifty-four percent of students come from the Midwest, and 42 percent are international students.

❖ Global Focus

The University of Iowa M.B.A. program offers many opportunities for developing a global business perspective. A three-week program is offered in London and Paris during the winter break. Students complete one international elective course in this program. Corporate partners include Fortune 100 companies with multinational operations and middle-market businesses with extensive import/export activities. These companies provide internship and consulting opportunities and willingly share their vast knowledge of global markets and emerging economies.

The Iowa Institute for International Business (IIIB) fosters multicultural awareness and cooperation through ongoing student support. IIIB also assists students in arranging international internships and study-abroad opportunities.

Special Features

Information technology is dramatically altering the way business is conducted. Managers now have nearly instantaneous access to information about changing financial markets, customer demand, and competitive conditions in international and domestic markets. In addition to a state-of-the-art computer lab and trading room, Iowa M.B.A. students and faculty members benefit from the program's substantial investment in information technology: students have access to real-time information and benefit from the incorporation of new concepts and technology throughout the curriculum. Videoconferencing facilities provide communication with business leaders throughout the world.

The Faculty

Iowa M.B.A. faculty members are accomplished, dynamic, and dedicated to providing a comprehensive business education to students. Holding Ph.D.'s from some of the world's top educational institutions, all can apply practical experiences gained in such places as Tenneco, Inc.; Andersen Consulting; Citicorp; General Motors; and the Commodity Futures Trading Commission to the M.B.A. classroom.

Beyond their impressive credentials, Iowa M.B.A. faculty members are dedicated professionals who share a passion for teaching. They are enthusiastic about challenging students to excel, and they interact with students both inside and outside the classroom. This personal approach to management education is not often available to students in larger M.B.A. programs.

The Business School Network
Corporate Partnerships

The University of Iowa School of Management is fortunate to have excellent ties to and communication with the business com-

The Pappajohn Building is designed to provide a conducive learning environment.

munity—regionally, nationally, and globally. Prominent business leaders often visit campus to talk about issues facing their industries. Internship opportunities are plentiful, and many classes routinely involve students on consulting projects with the University's corporate partners, who span the globe and include companies representing every economic sector.

The College and Environs

Iowa City is a uniquely wonderful community. Here, students, faculty members, and townspeople work and play together harmoniously.

The University of Iowa is the very heart of Iowa City, both in fact and spirit. The oldest of Iowa's three state universities, it includes, in addition to the College of Business Administration, the Colleges of Dentistry, Education, Engineering, Law, Liberal Arts, Medicine, Nursing, and Pharmacy. There are approximately 28,000 students, of whom 6,000 are pursuing graduate study.

Chicago, Minneapolis, St. Louis, and Kansas City are almost equidistant from the Iowa campus, providing urban advantages when desired. The Iowa City community itself offers an impressive array of cultural and recreational diversions.

Facilities

The M.B.A. program is housed in the John Pappajohn Business Building, a beautiful, functional, and up-to-date setting that fosters interpersonal and technological interactions. The facility's classrooms, restaurant, and informal spaces encourage one-on-one communication, group discussion, and the impromptu exchange of ideas between students and faculty members. Completed in 1994, the John Pappajohn Building provides an ideal learning environment for M.B.A. study.

Technology Environment

In addition to the global information and videoconferencing capabilities of the Pappajohn Building, the facility houses the largest student computing facility on the University of Iowa campus. Three computing classrooms, available for M.B.A. student use, complement a laboratory of nearly 100 workstations. Technology in the computer laboratory, library, and classrooms provides direct links to the global community, ranging from real-time national and international stock market feeds and information databases to a full spectrum of electronic resources.

Placement

The M.B.A. career services staff provides everything from resources to referrals. Beginning early in a student's program, staff members help develop a resume, research companies, and explore career options. Through a far-reaching alumni network, brokering services, and videoconferencing capabilities, Iowa M.B.A. career services personnel work with students to find internships and employment opportunities in the students' chosen fields and geographic locations. Interviews are arranged at on-campus locations, employer offices, and national job fairs. The Career Resource Center, exclusively for M.B.A. student use, provides access to career development information and employer databases, plus computer, telephone, fax, and copier equipment, to facilitate the job search process.

Admission

Each applicant's entire portfolio is considered. The admissions committee reviews each file individually and in full, looking for candidates who are a good match with the Iowa program. Students are asked to submit a completed application form, transcripts of all undergraduate and graduate work, a resume, responses to essay ques-

tions, GMAT scores, three references, and an application fee. Work experience is a key factor. Admission is only available for the fall term (mid-August). April 15 is both the priority consideration date and the application deadline for international applicants. Applications received between April 15 and July 15 are reviewed on a space-available basis. Application reviews begin in January.

A minimum TOEFL score of 600 (paper-based) or 250 (computer-based) is required for all students for whom English is not the native language. International students must present proof of adequate funds to cover the full two years of study.

Finances

Tuition and fees for 2000–01 are $5866 for Iowa residents and $13,620 for nonresidents. Books and supplies cost approximately $1400 per year. Estimates provided by the Office of Student Financial Aid suggest that M.B.A. students budget approximately $920 per month for living expenses.

Merit-based scholarships and fellowships are available to M.B.A. students. All applicants are considered for these competitive awards. Awards are based on information found within the application portfolio (including GMAT scores, GPA, and work experience). Students are also encouraged to apply for need-based financial assistance through the University Office of Student Financial Aid. Second-year students are eligible for assistantships in the College of Business.

International Students

International students and issues are integrated into the Iowa M.B.A. program as critical elements of the learning process. Built-in global connections occur within the classroom when discussion takes place between international and domestic students under the direction of knowledgeable faculty members who weave global issues into the fabric of their courses.

Application Facts and Dates

Admission preference for the full-time program (fall entrance) is given to those applications completed by April 15. Electronic applications are available through the M.B.A. Web site.

Henry B. Tippie School of
   Management
The University of Iowa
108 John Pappajohn Business
   Building, Suite C140
Iowa City, Iowa 52242-1000
Telephone: 319-335-1039
             800-622-4692 (toll-free)
E-mail: iowamba@uiowa.edu
World Wide Web: http://www.biz.
   uiowa.edu/mba

University of Kansas

THE ROAD TO THE TWENTY-FIRST CENTURY

In today's business world, it is no longer enough to plan only for the short term, compete only against domestic firms, or accept today's technology as the final word. The realities of achieving success in business today are that we must learn to plan strategically for the long term as well as the short term, we must learn to compete globally as well as domestically, and we must continuously improve our product lines and our productivity by developing new technologies and more efficient methods of getting the job done. These truths of today will be even more true tomorrow and into the next century. At the University of Kansas, we teach our M.B.A. students critical and systems thinking, problem-solving skills, communications, leadership, teamwork, and the importance of lifelong learning—skills that will lead to success in the business world of tomorrow. If you are equal to the challenges ahead and would like to take your first step on the road to the twenty-first century in an environment of excellence, join our team today and learn the skills you'll need for tomorrow.

—Tom Sarowski, Dean

Programs and Curricular Focus

The new, improved full-time M.B.A. program retains the best of the traditional program—strong quantitative skills development; a solid base in marketing, finance, accounting, and human resources; and an outstanding spectrum of electives—with some striking innovations. Team building is stressed throughout the program, Immersion Weeks focus on critical new areas of business, and nine concentrations include finance, marketing, international business, information technology, and human resources management.

A top-notch faculty, an excellent placement record, actively supportive alumni, and the resources of a world-class university give the University of Kansas (KU) M.B.A. great value. This program is 60 credit hours long and takes two years to complete, full-time. Students are required to take an internship, study abroad, or participate in a similarly meaningful experience that complements first-year studies during the summer between the first and second years. Study-abroad opportunities include sites in Italy, France, England, Brazil, and Japan.

The part-time M.B.A. program offers the same faculty and academic excellence as the full-time program and can be completed in three years (48 credit hours). At least two years of meaningful work experience are required for admission. This program, taught at the Edwards Campus in Overland Park, Kansas (near Kansas City), features an enriched classroom environment. Students have an average of seven years of work experience.

Students and the M.B.A. Experience

KU's M.B.A. students represent a diverse cross section of the population. The current M.B.A. class consists of 34 percent women, 3 percent domestic members of minority groups, and 25 percent international students from seven countries. The average age of the students is 25 years, and the average length of full-time work experience is nearly two years.

❖ Global Focus

Each summer, many KU M.B.A. students study abroad in one of several programs. Students can choose to travel to Italy, France, England, Brazil, or Japan for this option. There is also an exchange program with ESC Clermont-Ferrand, France, which includes the exchange of both faculty members and students. International internships are also possible.

The Faculty

KU's 53 faculty members bring a mix of practical experience and theory to the classroom and provide a rich educational experience fostered by excellence in research. Members of the faculty publish nationally recognized textbooks, serve as editors of national publications, and perform consulting and research services for corporate entities. The faculty is diverse, consisting of 15 percent women and 15 percent members of minority groups, bringing additional perspectives and insights to the students.

The Business School Network

The KU School of Business draws extensively upon alumni and business professionals to serve as members of the Board of Advisors. These executives help to shape the future of the School and also volunteer to serve as mentors for the M.B.A. students, exposing them to the practical, real-time issues and management solutions being used in the corporate world today. These same executives help to identify internships for the students in their respective industries and are often a part of the students' networking and job search processes in their final year of M.B.A. study.

The College and Environs

The University of Kansas is a major educational and research institution with more than 27,000 students, including about 6,000 graduate students, and 1,900 faculty members. The School of Business is housed in Summerfield Hall, located in the heart of campus. The main campus occupies 1,000 acres of forested, rolling hills on and around Mount Oread in the city of Lawrence, a growing community of 68,000. Located only 35 miles west of Kansas City, historic Lawrence combines the atmosphere of a small college town with the cosmopolitan flavor of a major city. Shopping areas, restaurants, entertainment, and recreational facilities are easily accessible from campus.

Placement

The KU School of Business has its own Career Services Office where students can input resumes into an electronic database that is automatically screened for each employer's criteria. More than

A team of M.B.A. students works on a group assignment.

1,700 on-campus interviews with more than 200 companies were scheduled last year. Of the graduate students who completed their business degrees last year, 91 percent were placed within six weeks of graduation. The average starting salary for KU's M.B.A. graduates was $54,608.

Admission

Admission requirements include the equivalent of a four-year college degree in any major, completion of a semester of college algebra (or higher math), a nonrefundable $50 application fee, and scores from the Graduate Management Admission Test (GMAT). International students must also provide scores from the Test of English as a Foreign Language (TOEFL). The average GMAT score for students admitted to the program is 606. Ideally, students have two or more years of meaningful full-time work experience and strong academic credentials and show evidence of leadership, strong interpersonal skills, and potential for success in the business world.

Finances

Tuition and fees for Lawrence Campus courses for the 2000–01 academic year are $165.15 per credit hour plus a semester fee of $229 for in-state residents; $405.25 per credit hour plus a semester fee of $229 for out-of-state residents and international students. Tuition and fees for courses taken on Edwards Campus are $208.15 per credit hour, regardless of residency. Double- or single-occupancy rooms in residence halls cost approximately $3500–$4500 per academic year and include nineteen meals per week. Limited scholarship assistance, based on academic credentials, is available for both domestic and international students through the School of Business.

Application Facts and Dates

The application deadline is May 1 to begin the full-time M.B.A. program in Lawrence in August. The part-time M.B.A. program deadline is May 1 (for fall), October 1 (for spring), and March 1 (for summer).

School of Business
206 Summerfield Hall
University of Kansas
Lawrence, Kansas 66045-2003
Telephone: 785-864-4254
E-mail: dcollins@bschool.wpo.ukans.edu
World Wide Web: http://www.bschool.ukans.edu

University of Kentucky

Lexington, Kentucky

STRAIGHT TALK ABOUT THE M.B.A.

▶ *The M.B.A. program at the Carol Martin Gatton College of Business and Economics is widely recognized as offering a quality education at a relatively modest cost. A distinguished faculty, excellent learning environment, flexible curriculum, state-of-the-art computer facilities, and a superior library, plus a variety of internships and opportunities for study abroad, all add up to an M.B.A. degree that gives those seeking advancement and professional success that significant extra edge in today's highly competitive business environment. The curriculum is demanding. It challenges students to synthesize a large and diverse set of concepts and ideas, while gaining not only mastery and understanding of the technology needed for a business enterprise to succeed in a global economy but also a solid foundation in the ethical principles that must underlie any business operation. The program is deliberately selective and limited in size to ensure personal attention and guidance from the faculty as well as to facilitate networking and teamwork. In short, our M.B.A. graduates are well prepared to meet the present and future demands made of them by society and the world of business.*

—Richard W. Furst, Dean

Programs and Curricular Focus

The largest single gift in the history of the University of Kentucky (UK) has resulted in the renaming of the former College of Business and Economics after Carol Martin Gatton, a distinguished alumnus. Graduate programs offered include the Ph.D. in business administration, Ph.D. in economics, M.B.A., M.S. in accounting, and M.S. in economics. Joint-degree programs include B.S.in Eng./M.B.A. and M.B.A./J.D.

The M.B.A. program enrolls approximately 100 new students each year; the entering class size is deliberately limited to ensure personal contact with graduate faculty members and individualized attention. The program is designed to provide students with the education needed to prepare them for upper-level managerial responsibilities. Two 36-hour programs are offered: one is for those with an undergraduate degree in business who desire more specialized skills, the other is for students without an undergraduate degree in business but who are interested in acquiring a broad-based management training. A basic common core of seven courses provide an understanding of business enterprise, an understanding of quantitative methods and the applications of analysis to business decision making, development of leadership skills, the ability to solve complicated and realistic business

problems, and an understanding of managing a business enterprise in a global environment. For the business undergraduate, the remaining courses are electives that permit the development of skills in a particular area. Concentrations are offered in accounting and corporate finance; finance, real estate, and banking; international business; management information systems; and marketing and distribution. For the nonbusiness undergraduate, the remaining required courses provide an understanding of problems encountered in business enterprise as related to organizational behavior, production, marketing, and finance.

Students and the M.B.A. Experience

In 1999–2000, the College enrolled approximately 360 graduate students, of whom 239 were M.B.A. students. Of the 1999 M.B.A. class, women represented 27 percent, international students 7 percent, and members of minority groups 8 percent of the student body. Forty-four percent of the students were part-time and 20 percent had a nonbusiness undergraduate degree. The average age of students was 26. The amount of work experience varies from seasoned managers of many years to those without significant work experience in a managerial capacity. The program offers a judicious mix of teamwork and individual projects, case

study, and lectures, designed to improve analytic, technical, and communications skills. Students are selected on the basis of proven academic excellence and a commitment to succeed. A significant percentage of full-time M.B.A. students have internships.

❖ Global Focus

Students seeking an understanding of the global business environment find that the curriculum and the program supplies them with this opportunity. A core course on global business management provides the essential foundation, which can be supplemented by appropriate electives. The concentration in international business is available for those wishing to specialize. Study abroad is made possible by exchange agreements with premier institutions in Europe and Asia. There are a number of opportunities to interact with the many visiting faculty members and business experts from abroad who come to the college to share their expertise and culture with their U.S. counterparts. Facility in foreign language can be acquired or improved through the many courses offered at the University.

The Faculty

The College, headed by Dean Richard W. Furst and Associate Dean Michael G. Tearney, consists of three divisions; the School of Accountancy, with 18 faculty members; the School of Management, incorporating the areas of decision sciences and information systems, finance, management, and marketing, with a total of 40 faculty members under the direction of Dr. Donald Mullineau; and the Department of Economics, with 26 faculty members under the chairmanship of Dr. Glenn Blomquist. Faculty members have achieved both national and international recognition for excellence in teaching and research as well as for service to the commonwealth of Kentucky and the business community. Many of the faculty members are presently actively engaged in joint research projects with faculty members at institutions around the world including Austria, England, China, Indonesia, Kazakhstan, Sweden, and Croatia.

The Business School Network

Corporate Partnerships

The College's University of Kentucky Business Partnership Foundation consists of prominent individuals in the business and academic communities. The Board of Directors of the Foundation fulfills an important role in assessing the present and future needs of the business world and in advising the College on how to provide the education necessary to meet those needs in a manner consistent with the College's missions of excellence in teaching, research, and service. Local businesses provide scholarships and internships for M.B.A. students. Guest speakers from the business community visit the college on a regular basis throughout the year.

Prominent Alumni

There are more than 1,300 M.B.A. alumni in all fifty states and in twenty-two other countries. Prominent alumni of the College include the presidents and CEOs of numerous corporations including public companies listed on the NYSE. Inductees into the College's Hall of Fame include former State Governor Edward T. Breathitt; Carl F. Pollard, former Chairman and CEO of Columbia Healthcare, Inc.; James E. Rogers, Chairman, President, and CEO, PSI Holdings, Inc.; Warren W. Rosenthal; Chris Sullivan, CEO, Outback Steakhouse; Paul Chellgren, CEO, Ashland Oil, Inc.; and Carol Martin Gatton.

The College and Environs

The UK campus and the Gatton College of Business and Economics are close to the heart of downtown Lexington, a city with a population of 235,000, where many of the cultural and recreational amenities of a large city are combined with the charm and traditions of a small town. Famed for its horse farms, Lexington lies within a 500-mile radius of nearly three fourths of the manufacturing, employment, retail sales, and population of the United States. Established in 1865, the University of Kentucky has more than 24,000 students, of whom approximately 6,700 are graduate students. Founded in 1925 as the College of Commerce, the Carol Martin Gatton College of Business and Economics occupies a modern building with all the facilities needed to fulfill the mission of excellence in teaching, research, and service. The College is accredited by AACSB–The International Association for Management Education.

Technology Environment

As befits a Carnegie Foundation Research University of the first class, the University of Kentucky has excellent facilities. The $58-million William T. Young Library, which opened in spring 1998, contains more than 2.5 million volumes and receives more than 27,000 periodical and serial titles. The M. I. King Library houses several special and rare books collections. The Computing Center has several high-level systems supporting research and networking needs. Within the College are the electronic Business Information Center for state-of-the-art business database access and seven centers of research that serve as resources to the state, local, and international business community. At sites throughout the campus, computer workstations cater to the computing needs of all students.

Placement

The M.B.A. program is making a difference in graduates' incomes. The 1999–2000 graduates recorded a 97 percent increase in compensation over pre-M.B.A. salaries, with an average compensation of $55,735. Janie Thomas, MBA Director of Recruitment and Placement, provides many opportunities for students. Ms. Thomas recruits companies to interview in the MBA Center, co-coordinates the Business Career Fair with more than ninety participating companies, posts numerous position openings, and conducts seminars and one-on-one consultations for job searches. The students' determination and Ms. Thomas's leadership make a winning combination for the UK M.B.A. program.

Admission

Admission to the full-time program is for the fall semester only. Admission to the part-time program is possible in spring for students who already have an undergraduate degree in business. An undergraduate degree with a minimum GPA of 2.75 is required, together with the following course work: two principles of accounting courses (financial, managerial), two principles of economics courses (micro, macro), a course in statistics and probability, and an elementary calculus course. All prerequisite courses should be equivalent to at least 3 semester hours. Applicants must also submit a GMAT, and international applicants must also present a minimum TOEFL score of 550 overall and a minimum Test of Written English (TWE) score of 4.5. Academic background, GMAT score, personal recommendations, and the applicant's statement of purpose are all considered in the evaluation for admission. Demonstrated academic ability and potential for subsequent success in the business world are qualities that are looked for in applicants.

Finances

The College and Graduate School offer merit-based scholarships and fellowships. Approximately 20 percent of the fall 1999 entering class received some form of College-based aid, including scholarships for members of minority groups and disadvantaged students. Students of outstanding merit are nominated for Graduate School Fellowships. Eligible students may also obtain on-campus employment through the UK STEPS service and the UK work-study program.

The University of Kentucky operates on the semester system. For 1999–2000, in-state graduate tuition for a full-time student was $1798 per semester. Part-time students paid $188 per credit hour. Nonresident full-time graduate tuition was $5058 per semester. Part-time nonresident tuition was $550 per credit hour. The registration fee for full-time students was $168 per semester. Part-time students paid $6 per credit hour. A full-time nonresident student can expect to pay approximately $10,116 for tuition, fees, and books for an academic year.

On-campus housing rents range from $324 to $550 per month. A single student living frugally needs approximately $5800 in housing and living expenses for an academic year.

Application Facts and Dates

Admission to the College's graduate business programs is achieved by applying to both the Graduate School and the College. For fall admission to the M.B.A. program, the priority deadline for U.S. citizens is April 1. Domestic applications are considered until July 1 if space is available. The application deadline for international applicants is February 1. March 1 is the deadline for financial aid consideration. Successful applicants are generally notified within two weeks of receipt of all required documentation. For information, students should contact:

Ms. Janie Thomas
MBA Center
Gatton College of Business and
    Economics
University of Kentucky
Lexington, Kentucky 40506
Telephone: 859-257-4605
Fax: 859-323-9971
E-mail: jmthom5@pop.uky.edu

For application materials, students should contact:

Admissions
MBA Center
Gatton College of Business and
    Economics
University of Kentucky
Lexington, Kentucky 40506
Telephone: 859-257-1306
Fax: 859-323-9971
E-mail: kemper@pop.uky.edu
World Wide Web: http://gatton.uky.
    edu/

UofL The University of Louisville

College of Business and Public Administration

Louisville, Kentucky

THE M.B.A.: FUTURE TRENDS AND DIRECTIONS

▶ *Managers and leaders face unprecedented challenges in our rapidly changing world. The presence of the Internet is reshaping how organizations create value. Financial markets and distribution channels are becoming increasingly global. The digital revolution is transforming our economy and our world. Successful organizations are reshaping their business strategies and investing in information and communication technologies.*

At the University of Louisville College of Business and Public Administration, we are investing in the areas that will allow organizations to build their knowledge infrastructure. We are committed to helping our students develop the talent necessary to be successful in the New Economy: leadership, innovation, communication, adaptive-efficiency, and a comprehensive understanding of theory and practice.

Our faculty have current business experience, state-of-the-art research, and a student-centered approach and commitment toward teaching. They will help you discover your potential.

We believe that the University of Louisville offers you one of the best opportunities to study, learn, and experience the world of organizations whether they be large industrial firms, small or large entrepreneurial ventures, government, or not-for-profit organizations. Our value proposition is our commitment to your success. We look forward to working with you.

—Robert L. Taylor, Dean

Programs and Curricular Focus

The mission of the University of Louisville College of Business and Public Administration is to provide high-quality education and professional development in business, public administration, and urban policy that meets the special needs of a metropolitan constituency. Teaching, research, and service reflect innovation and responsiveness to a rapidly changing global environment. Undergraduate and graduate educations are complemented with continuing education and training programs, scholarly activity, student involvement, and community outreach. Faculty and staff members are committed to programs that reflect continuing intellectual growth, pragmatism, and the importance of human values.

Entrepreneurship is a particular focus of the business program. Faculty members work with select graduate students each year to help them actually launch a new venture. Students successfully completing New Venture Creation and Entrepreneurship I and II courses are assigned an experienced faculty mentor who assists them in taking a business plan to practical reality. Thus far, sixteen businesses have been created through this initiative in the past five years. For technology-based ideas, the Tele-

communications Research Center is used as an incubator where students and recent graduates receive ongoing technical and business support for a limited period after graduation. M.B.A. student teams compete annually in actual business plan competitions. Finally, a spirit of entrepreneurship pervades all of the curricula as a philosophy of thinking about business and careers.

Students may select either a two-year, lock step Integrative M.B.A. program with a focus on entrepreneurship or a flexible traditional M.B.A. program. The traditional M.B.A. offers a general management focus as well as concentrations in entrepreneurship, communications, health-care administration, and technology. The technology concentration is offered in cooperation with the Engineering School to students simultaneously enrolled in the Master of Engineering and M.B.A. programs.

A student's degree program is 36 semester credit hours, possibly more, depending upon undergraduate preparation. The M.B.A. program's 36-hour core curriculum consists of eight requisite 600-level courses and four approved electives. Serving as the academic common body of knowledge for the M.B.A. core requirements, a foundation core of 500-level courses provides those

students with less extensive undergraduate business backgrounds a means toward preparing for the M.B.A. core courses.

All required 600-level courses are offered in the fall and spring semesters, along with a variety of elective courses. A smaller selection of 600-level courses is offered during two summer sessions. The foundation core's 500-level course offerings are split between the fall and spring semesters and normally are not part of the summer course schedule.

In order to foster international expertise, the College of Business and Public Administration provides frequent opportunities for M.B.A. students to learn the international aspects of business administration, including cross-cultural perspectives. Such opportunities consist of courses, seminars, exchange programs, and independent study. M.B.A. students are strongly encouraged to take advantage of these opportunities. Many of the M.B.A. faculty members also teach in the college's M.B.A. programs in Athens, Hong Kong, and Singapore. This exposes our M.B.A. students to faculty with a truly global perspective.

Students and the M.B.A. Experience

The M.B.A. students at U of L bring a wide variety of work experiences and academic diversity to the program. With approximately two thirds of the students pursuing their graduate degrees on a part-time basis, classes benefit from a wealth of current and diverse real-world business experiences. In addition, the program is proud of its progress in attracting women and students of diverse ethnic and cultural backgrounds.

The M.B.A. program is primarily an evening program in which an individual can enroll as either a part-time or full-time student. During the fall and spring semesters, courses typically are offered Monday through Thursday, one evening per week, from 5:30 to 8:15 p.m. During the summer session, there are three successive sessions. The first is a three-week session with classes five evenings per week; the second and third are five-week sessions with classes three evenings per week. Although the majority of the program's student population enrolls on a part-time basis, courses are scheduled so that a student may pursue the program on a full-time basis of 9 hours per semester.

The M.B.A./J.D. program is offered jointly by the College of Business and Public Administration and the School of Law. The program combines the two-year M.B.A. program and the three-year Juris Doctor (J.D.) program into one four-year, full-time program. Upon successful completion of the program, the student is awarded both the M.B.A. and J.D. degrees. The M.D./M.B.A. program is offered jointly by the College of Business and Public Administration and the School of Medicine. The program combines the two-year M.B.A. with the four-year M.D. program into a five-year, full-time program. Requests for further information regarding these programs should be directed to the M.B.A. coordinator.

The Faculty

The College's faculty members offer exceptional teaching ability, applied business research, and individualized, high-quality interactions with students. Diversity, commitment, and professionalism characterize the faculty. Like the curriculum itself, the more than 70 faculty members reflect the changing nature of the workforce.

Ninety-five percent of the M.B.A. course work is taught by doctorally qualified faculty members who enrich the learning experience by providing a balance of theory and application. Faculty members enlist a wide variety of classroom approaches, including lectures, case studies, computer simulation and communication, group projects, and discussions. In addition, the development and demonstration of appropriate oral and written communication skills are an integral part of M.B.A. course objectives.

The Business School Network

Corporate Partnerships

While preparing individuals to add value to the community, the College of Business and Public Administration recognizes its role as an active partner in the development and growth of organizations in the region. The M.B.A. program is committed to working with the regional business community through applied research, consulting, and training. On a continual basis, M.B.A. students are offered special opportunities to meet and learn from some of the region's most dynamic and successful business leaders.

Prominent Alumni

The College notes among its alumni a number of the region's most distinguished business leaders, including Malcolm Chancey Jr., Chairman, Banc One Kentucky Corporation, Louisville; Dan Ulmer, former chair-

man of Citizen's Fidelity Bank (now PNC Bank), Louisville; David Jones, Chairman of the Board, Humana, Inc.; Gene Gardner, retired president of a major Louisville company and co-owner of the Louisville Riverbats AAA baseball organization; Charles McCarty, retired president, BATUS Industries; and James Patterson, fast-food executive, Long John Silver's, Chi Chi's, Wendy's, and Rally's.

The College and Environs

The University of Louisville is a metropolitan educational institution that celebrated its bicentennial in 1998. Consisting of thirteen academic units and spanning three campuses, the University became part of the Kentucky state system of higher education in 1970.

The College of Business and Public Administration is located on the 140-acre Belknap campus in the historic Old Louisville section of the city. Kentucky's largest urban center, Louisville offers some of the region's most diverse, enjoyable cultural surroundings and events. From the Kentucky Derby and its weeklong festival to the Kentucky Center for the Arts, the "River City" offers enough variety in cultural, recreational, and sports opportunities to rival cities three times its size.

Technology Environment

The College of Business and Public Administration provides an outstanding computer and technology environment. A computer classroom and lab containing more than fifty networked workstations supporting the latest technology is dedicated for use by business faculty members and students. In addition, the building houses the University's North Computing Center, which contains seventy additional workstations. Multimedia applications, electronic mail, interactive television, and LANs comprise an integral part of the M.B.A. curriculum.

Placement

The College works aggressively to build strong ties with regional organizations and on-campus recruiters in order to help students construct a network of professional contacts. Regional, national, and international companies visit regularly to recruit for full-time and internship positions.

Admission

Admission into the M.B.A. program is competitive. Entering M.B.A. candidates at the University of Louisville are in the top third of all entering M.B.A. candidates nationwide.

Applicants must submit a completed graduate application, along with a nonrefundable $25 application fee. In addition,

applicants must have sent to the University Admissions Office official transcripts, GMAT results, two letters of recommendation from individuals familiar with the applicant's academic performance, and a written personal statement outlining their rational for pursuing graduate study. International applicants are required to take the TOEFL if English is not their native language.

Finances

Estimated tuition and fees for full-time students in 2000–01 are $1883.50 per semester for Kentucky residents and $5352 for non-residents. For part-time students, courses cost approximately $206.50 per semester hour for Kentucky residents, while nonresidents pay $592 per semester hour. University fees are subject to approval of the Board of Trustees and may be changed without prior notice.

Although many graduate students live off campus, the University provides some graduate dormitory rooms and apartments. The Housing/Resident Administration maintains a referral file of off-campus rooms and apartments. Housing costs in Louisville are lower than in most other metropolitan areas.

A limited number of graduate research assistantships are available to full-time students. These grants require students to work up to 20 hours per week as research assistants to departmental faculty members and provide living stipends plus tuition. The University's Financial Aid Office and Student Employment Office also provide four types of assistance: scholarships, grants, educational loans, and part-time employment.

Application Facts and Dates

The College employs a rolling application deadline. For students wishing to begin course work in either the fall or spring semester, all application materials must be received at least 120 days prior to the semester's start. Those students planning to begin in the summer term must have all materials submitted at least eighty days before the start of course work in mid-May. For more information, applicants should address inquiries to:

M.B.A. Coordinator
Advising and Co-op Office
College of Business and Public
  Administration
University of Louisville
Louisville, Kentucky 40292
Telephone: 502-852-7439
E-mail: MBA@louisville.edu
World Wide Web: http://www.cbpa.
  louisville.edu

University of Maine

Orono, Maine

LEADERSHIP IN THE GLOBAL ECONOMY

The University of Maine (UM) Business School serves as the primary source of management education, research, and service in the state of Maine. Through the integration of research, teaching, and extensive interactions with the business community, the Maine Business School develops and communicates knowledge, prepares students for successful careers in a global economy, and contributes to the economic development of the region.

Maine's M.B.A. program affords the benefits of small classes and close interaction with the faculty and staff. Our diversity provides an optimal learning environment with students from a wide range of backgrounds and cultures. The combination of a committed teaching faculty and high-quality students has resulted in an outstanding M.B.A. program.

—Eric Brucker, Dean

Programs and Curricular Focus

The University of Maine M.B.A. program equips candidates with the concepts, analytical tools, and executive skills required for competent and responsible management. Built-in course and program flexibility enables the School to meet the needs of the individual student. Students have the opportunity to take up to 30 percent of their graduate course work in electives in order to meet their own career goals. Full-time students with an undergraduate degree in business administration can usually complete the 30-hour graduate program in one calendar year. Required courses include business, government, and society; behavioral analysis for administrative decisions; quantitative methods for business decisions; financial management; marketing management; management information systems; and management policy. Students are expected to be proficient in college algebra and the use of word processing and spreadsheet software. Students with no business course work can complete requirements in two years of full-time study. Under-graduate core courses include introduction to accounting, principles of management and organization, business finance, marketing, economics, and production and operations management.

Both the undergraduate and graduate programs in business administration are accredited by AACSB–The International Association for Management Education.

Students and the M.B.A. Experience

The current M.B.A. class is a heterogeneous group, with representatives from more than forty undergraduate colleges and universities and more than fifty different undergraduate majors. In 1999, eighteen countries were represented. More than 50 percent of the class have undergraduate preparation in fields other than business administration. The average age of entering students is 28. Women comprise 37 percent of the enrollment. Of the 9,000 University students, more than 2,000 are graduate students. Academic rigor, emphasis on teamwork, and esprit de corps among students and faculty are noted by many alumni as key components of their experience at UM.

The Faculty

Faculty members are actively engaged in scholarly work and public service activities, offering seminars and work-shops for business practitioners and providing consulting services both nationally and internationally, greatly enriching the classroom experience.

The Business School Network

Since 1965, more than 1,000 M.B.A. alumni have achieved positions of significant authority and responsibility in many organizations locally, nationally, and internationally. Many serve as mentors through the Maine Mentor Program.

The College and Environs

Students at the University of Maine benefit from the advantages of both rural and urban environments. Located just a 1- to 2-hour drive from Mount Katahdin, state parks, ski slopes, and the Maine coast, the University is a 4-hour drive on Interstate 95 from Boston. Bangor International Airport, located 8 miles from campus, provides service to many

Darlene Bay, Ph.D., Assistant Professor of Accounting. Accounting and business ethics.

Richard H. Borgman, Ph.D., Assistant Professor of Finance. Developing financial markets in Eastern Europe.

Eric Brucker, Ph.D., Professor of Business Administration and Dean.

Steven C. Colburn, Ph.D., Associate Professor of Accounting. Taxation.

Harold Z. Daniel, Ph.D., Assistant Professor of Marketing. Organizational buying behavior and strategic acquisition.

John K. Ford, D.B.A., Salgo Professor of Business Administration and Professor of Finance. Diversification of bond and stock portfolios.

Virginia R. Gibson, Ph.D., Associate Professor of Management Information Systems. Information systems for management decision support.

Carol B. Gilmore, Ph.D., Professor of Management and Interim Director of the M.B.A. Program. Collective bargaining.

Diana R. Lawson, Ph.D., Associate Professor of Marketing. International business and marketing strategy.

Ivan M. Manev, Ph.D., Assistant Professor of Management. Management of the multinational corporation.

Kim K. R. McKeage, Ph.D., Assistant Professor of Marketing. Retailing and consumer behavior.

Robert A. Strong, Ph.D., Professor of Finance. Asset allocation and purchasing power risk.

Peter Tarasewich, Ph.D., Assistant Professor of Management Information Systems. E-commerce and Web site design.

Gloria Vollmers, Ph.D., Associate Professor of Accounting. Accounting and business history.

Stephanie A. Welcomer, Ph.D., Associate Professor of Management. Social and cognitive networks.

major U.S. and international cities. The 1,100-acre campus is the site of a dynamic modern university, encompassing five colleges, various schools and academic programs, and a graduate school. The M.B.A. degree has been offered since 1965. In 1993, the $7-million Donald P. Corbett Business Building opened with several high-technology, seminar, and case classrooms. The Maine Center for the Arts provides cultural focus for the University campus, the communities of the region, and all Maine citizens. Musical, dance, and theatrical performances and lectures by distinguished speakers are presented in the 1,628-seat Hutchins Concert Hall. The center also includes the Hudson Museum and Palmer Gallery.

Facilities

The UM M.B.A. program exposes students to state-of-the-art systems for management decision support. Both mainframe and microcomputer facilities on the Orono campus are excellent. The central computing facility for the entire University of Maine System is located on the Orono campus. Public access microcomputer clusters are available in Fogler Library and the Student Union. The Fogler Library houses more than 900,000 volumes, subscribes to more than 6,700 journals, and is a tristate regional federal depository for publications of the U.S. government and a selective depository for Canadian government documents.

Technology Environment

The Business School supports labs and classrooms of networked Pentium-class microcomputers. Students have access to an extensive software library as well as the Internet and World Wide Web, the library, and the mainframe.

Placement

The University's Career Center provides a variety of services to assist students in obtaining positions following graduation. Services include individual career counseling, career information for exploring options, the mentor program, resume/vita critiques, job search workshops, mock interviews, job listings, employer information, assistance in identifying potential employers, and on-campus interviews.

Admission

All applicants must hold a four-year baccalaureate degree from a regionally accredited college or university. Consideration is given to an applicant's official transcript(s), GMAT scores, three letters of recommendation on forms provided in the application material, and potential for leadership in business. The mean GMAT score of entering students is 525. All applicants whose native language is not English must submit official TOEFL scores. The minimum score required is 550 (213 for the computer-based test). Although work experience is not required, the majority of students have three or more years of work experience. Students can apply for fall, spring, or summer admission.

Finances

In 1999–2000, tuition charges for one course per semester were $1686 for nonresidents and $594 for residents. The room and board (full meal plan included) cost was $2628 per semester. A comprehensive fee for 7 to 11 credit hours was $106.50 and for 1 to 6 credit hours, no charge. Other fees included a student activity fee of $17.50, a communications fee of $10, a recreation fee of $15, and a technology fee of $5 per credit hour. In addition, all international students and their dependents must purchase health insurance through the University unless they are sponsored by agencies providing comparable insurance coverage. Financial aid is extremely limited and highly competitive when available.

International Students

International students currently in the M.B.A. program represent eleven countries; campuswide, seventy countries are represented. Since 1980, 120 international students have graduated with an M.B.A. degree. The relatively small size of graduate classes permits students a one-on-one working relationship with faculty members. The International Programs Office assists with immigration matters and offers intercultural opportunities. The friendliness of fellow students makes the learning experience at UM positive. Classes with both full-time and part-time students add to the international student experience. Classmates are academic resources and constitute a network of professional contacts and allies for the future. For students who have completed the undergraduate core courses, the program can be completed within one calendar year.

Application Facts and Dates

It is recommended that all application material be received by February 15 for fall admission. Applications must be submitted no later than six weeks prior to the beginning of the semester. All official transcripts, test scores, letters of recommendation, and the $50 application fee must be on file prior to a review being made. Application fees cannot be waived. Application material should be sent directly to:

Graduate School
5782 Winslow Hall
University of Maine
Orono, Maine 04469-5782
Telephone: 207-581-1973
Fax: 207-581-3232
E-mail: mba@maine.edu
World Wide Web: http://www.umaine.edu/business/grad.html

University of Maryland, College Park

AN INCOMPARABLE EDUCATIONAL VALUE

The Robert H. Smith School of Business has put together a unique combination of resources that will provide you with an incomparable educational value. As you learn about our program, you should glean three primary elements that allow us to provide you with a great experience: quality, reasonable cost, and location.

Our implementation of a cutting-edge curriculum and the use of state-of-the-art information technologies is the keystone to the quality education that we provide. The Robert H. Smith School of Business is about half the cost of other top thirty M.B.A. programs, and our program is in a prime location that is just 35 minutes from both Baltimore and Washington, D.C.

Please visit us to learn why the Maryland M.B.A. deserves its place among the top 4 percent of all M.B.A. programs in the United States.

—Mark Wellman, Assistant Dean

Programs and Curricular Focus

The Robert H. Smith School of Business has put together an exceptional combination of resources that provides students with an incomparable educational value. Some of the many strengths of the Robert H. Smith School of Business are the top-quality and cutting-edge master's programs, a location that is minutes from Washington, D.C., financial aid for international students, and an M.B.A. that costs about half the amount of other top M.B.A. programs. Accredited by AACSB–The International Association for Management Education and a full member of the Graduate Management Admission Council, the Robert H. Smith School of Business is a leader in the field of graduate management education.

The Master of Business Administration (M.B.A.) program has a fully integrated experience-based curriculum designed to create the type of graduate that business has long demanded. The first half of the curriculum is spent gaining the fundamental skills and judgment necessary to succeed in a contemporary management team. Learning Modules (LMs) and course work ensure that new skills are applied in and out of the classroom.

LMs are intensive, experience-based courses that focus on specific topics, such as interaction with the federal government in Washington, D.C.; an international business simulation; and an exploration of ethics in the business environment. These courses provide the student with experi-ence in areas often ignored by other American M.B.A. programs.

The second year allows the student to specialize in a particular area of business and to participate in a Group Field Project. Group Field Projects assign teams of students to work as consultants to an American organization for a semester. The teams address specific concerns within the organization and make recommendations regarding those concerns to the management staff of the client organization. This program is required of all second-year, full-time students.

The Master of Science (M.S.) program requires a strong quantitative background. There are several areas of concentration available: information systems, operations research, statistics, logistics, transportation, and finance. The M.S. program can be completed in two to five semesters, depending on previously completed course work.

The doctoral (Ph.D.) program is designed to develop outstanding research scholars and teachers in the management-related disciplines. Specializations include accounting, finance, human resource management and labor relations, information systems, management science and statistics, management strategy and policy, marketing, organizational behav-ior, and transportation and logistics.

Students and the M.B.A. Experience

The student population of the M.B.A. program consists of about 430 full-time M.B.A. students, 45 M.S. students, and 100 Ph.D. students. Of the 1999 incoming class, 35 percent were international students and about 35 percent were women.

Special Features

The Robert H. Smith School of Business maintains formal and informal exchange arrangements with graduate business programs in seven countries around the world. Students can spend one semester of their second year at their exchange school.

The Faculty

There are 80 full-time faculty members assigned to M.B.A. programs, all of whom hold doctoral-level degrees. The following is a listing of chairpersons and their corresponding department areas of research.

Accounting: Dr. James Beddingfield, Chair.

Department research: Management accounting, accounting for regulated industries, government contract account-ing, capital budgeting, decision support systems, financial accounting, accounting information systems, tax, auditing, accounting ethics.

Finance: Dr. Lemma W. Senbet, Chair.

Department research: Corporate finance, financial institutions, investments, futures and options contracts, investment analysis, portfolio management, capital asset pricing theory, international finance, portfolio analysis, capital market theory, commercial banking, financial theory, agency theory.

Decision and Information Technologies: Arjand Assad, Chair.

Department research: End-user comput-ing, information systems analysis and design, knowledge-based systems, production management systems, database systems, network analysis, information technology in the workplace, software design and development, statistical quality control, multivariate process control, time-series analysis, vehicle routing and scheduling, large-scale systems modeling, network optimization, electronic commerce, virtual organizations, applied mathematical programming, decision support systems.

Management and Organization: Dr. Susan Taylor, Chair.

Department research: Performance appraisal and compensation design, management by objectives systems, executive leadership, strategy implementation, labor relations, goal setting, employee motivation, organizational staffing, teamwork, organizational life cycles, competitive strategy.

Marketing: Dr. Robert Krapful, Chair.

Department research: New product development, marketing strategy, international marketing, business-to-business marketing, consumer behavior, advertising.

Transportation, Business and Public Policy: Dr. Curtis Grimm, Chair.

Department research: Deregulation, international aviation, airline pricing and competition, carrier management, government policies toward business, international business regulation, global management strategies, international trade policies, international joint ventures, public utility pricing.

The College and Environs

The University of Maryland, College Park is the flagship institution of the University of Maryland System. The enrollment of approximately 34,000, of whom about 9,000 are graduate students, supports nearly 100 doctoral and master's programs. The University is a member of the prestigious fifty-eight-member Association of American Universities. The University of Maryland is further recognized as having more than a dozen programs rated among the ten best at public universities in the United States by the National Academy of Sciences and other prestigious organizations.

Nine miles from the White House, the Robert H. Smith School of Business is located on a 1,300-acre campus. This location affords students the benefits of a suburban setting while maintaining the cultural and employment opportunities of Washington, D.C., and Baltimore. In fact, the concert halls, museums, art galleries, and restaurants are a short 15-minute subway ride away in Washington, D.C.

Facilities

Classified as a Research I facility by the Carnegie Foundation (its highest ranking), the research facilities at the University of Maryland are among the best in the world. With the addition of National Archives II, the main repository of information for the government of the United States of America, Maryland offers access to one of the world's most complete collections of research material right in College Park. The University proper offers an outstanding library collection of about 2 million volumes, state-of-the-art laboratories, a network of campus research centers, and excellent microcomputing and mainframe computing facilities. Beyond the facilities at College Park, students have access, within minutes, to other world-class research facilities at sites such as the Library of Congress, the Smithsonian Institution, the Federal Reserve, and the National Libraries of Medicine and Agriculture, to name a few.

Admission

Application to the M.B.A. program is open to individuals holding a four-year bachelor's degree or its equivalent from an accredited college or university. Submission of a GMAT score is required. International students must submit a minimum score of 600 on the TOEFL, provide proof of adequate funds, and provide proof of immunizations.

Finances

Students are eligible for merit-based financial aid that is awarded as fellowships, which provide a waiver of all tuition plus a stipend for living expenses, and as graduate and teaching assistantships, which cover almost all tuition charges.

The low cost of the University of Maryland is a benefit to both domestic and international students. For the 2000–01 academic year, full-time tuition is $10,447 for in-state students and $15,525 for out-of-state students.

Living expenses in the Washington, D.C., area are comparable to those of other metropolitan areas in the United States. Students live both on and off campus, and the average cost for room and board is about $10,000 per academic year.

Application Facts and Dates

The decision to admit an applicant is based on a thorough evaluation of the candidate's managerial and leadership potential, ability to add perspective to the class, and evidence of academic excellence. Admission to the M.B.A. program is for fall only. Applicants should make inquiries to:

Director of M.B.A./M.S. Admission
2308 Van Munching Hall
University of Maryland
College Park, Maryland 20742
Telephone: 301-405-2278
Fax: 301-314-9862
E-mail: mba_info@rhsmith.umd.edu
World Wide Web: http://www.rhsmith.umd.edu

University of Massachusetts Amherst

Amherst, Massachusetts

DEVELOPING BUSINESS LEADERS FOR THE TWENTY-FIRST CENTURY

If you are looking for an M.B.A. experience that emphasizes small classes, teamwork, high academic and admission standards, international diversity, real-world assignments, and close contact with faculty members, I urge you to consider our program. It's the best of both worlds: a small-college atmosphere within a large university that is brimming with diverse academic and technology resources.

Our program cultivates strong relationships with the business community in our region. Isenberg School M.B.A. students participate in team assignments that apply their skills to those businesses. They also benefit from an increasingly active alumni network that regularly brings practitioners to campus and generates frequent opportunities for consulting assignments and employment after graduation.

Because our program is small, we are able to offer every student generous tuition subsidies. That makes us all the more selective, which ensures that our students are stimulating and focused. I urge you to compare our quality and cost to those of our competitors. You will find that we are one of today's best values in business education.

—Thomas O'Brien, Dean

Program and Curricular Focus

The objective of the Isenberg School of Management's M.B.A. program is to prepare professional managers for challenging business careers. The program offers two closely related types of courses: theoretical courses that concentrate on the basic models, concepts, and research in the underlying disciplines of behavioral science, economics, and quantitative analytical methods and practical courses that apply basic models to such business disciplines as accounting, management of human resources, finance, and marketing. The course of study also emphasizes techniques of corporate management, including policy analysis, strategic planning, and organization design and control. The full-time M.B.A. degree requires two years of study. The Isenberg School also offers a part-time Professional M.B.A. program for working managers and professionals. The M.B.A. degree requires a minimum of eighteen courses and 55 credit hours. Because of the heavy workload, the full-time program should not be taken at the same time as other courses of study or while working in a professional career.

The M.B.A. program emphasizes a core curriculum that trains students in the functional areas of business while exposing them to the analytic tools and methods used in decision making. In addition, students choose elective courses to enhance their individual interests. Core requirements provide an integrative base consisting of a solid background in the behavioral and quantitative fields, as well as thorough exposure to functional areas of business. Electives allow students to focus on specific fields such as accounting, finance, marketing, human resource management, and management information systems. Students are encouraged to consider courses offered by other on-campus schools or departments. Although the program requires no prior business education, students are expected to be proficient in math and to have previously completed a statistics and microeconomics course. In the final semester, a team-based practicum is required.

Students and the M.B.A. Experience

Fifty-five percent of students in the M.B.A. program are women; 35 percent are citizens of other countries and represent six continents. Students average five years of professional work experience in fields as varied as banking, finance, engineering, technology, nonprofits, and academia.

Entering students have an average GMAT score of 640 and an average undergraduate GPA of 3.3 in majors ranging from engineering and biology to the humanities, business, and math. The M.B.A. program welcomes students with unique backgrounds and interests that enhance group achievements.

To fully comprehend and utilize the new information provided by course work in the M.B.A. program, students participate in internships and co-ops during the summer between their first and second years. These work experiences are complemented by an intensive practicum during the final semester that thoroughly prepares M.B.A. graduates for their reentry into the business world.

The Faculty

The Isenberg School's 55 full-time faculty members have outstanding reputations in both teaching and research. Ninety-five percent of them hold the highest degrees in their fields. Three occupy endowed positions: the Flavin Family Chair in Entrepreneurial Studies, the John F. Smith Memorial Professor in Operations Management, and the Nirenberg Professor of Business Leadership.

The Isenberg School's faculty members' excellence in teaching is critical to its consistently high ratings in national surveys. The Princeton Review ranks the full-time M.B.A. program among the nation's top seventy. In research, Isenberg School faculty members have national reputations in financial risk analysis and alternative investments, financial and behavioral accounting, management science and operations management, and business leadership. The Isenberg School is home to two internationally prominent journals, the *Journal of Alternative Investments and Organization* and the *Interdisciplinary Journal of Organization, Theory, and Society*. At the Isenberg School, faculty members uphold another important tradition—accessibility. Their doors are always open to students.

The Business School Network

The Isenberg School M.B.A. program has an active and far-reaching network of alumni and business leaders whose involvement with the School includes the Business Advisory Council. The council advises the Dean on policies regarding relations with business, placement of M.B.A. students, and future directions for the School. In addition, the council provides opportunities for collaboration between representative corporate communities and the Isenberg School.

Specific initiatives include executive-in-residence programs and a professional development series. Both programs offer ample opportunities for students and members of the faculty and the business community to network. Alumni also participate as mentors, offering valuable advice and experience to M.B.A. students. In addition, the council assists in development of internship and co-op programs, faculty recruitment, and departmental support.

Prominent Alumni

Prominent alumni include George R. Ditomassi Jr., Executive Vice President, Global Innovations of Milton Bradley (Class of 1957); John P. Flavin, Chairman of the Board, Triangle Supply Company Inc. (Class of 1959); Ross Garber, Co-Founder, Vignette Corporation (Class of 1988); Richard A. Goldstein, Chairman and Chief Executive Officer, International Flavors and Fragrance (Class of 1963); Eugene M. Isenberg, Chairman and Chief Executive Officer, Nabors Industries (Class of 1950); Barbara Kipp, Partner, PricewaterhouseCoopers, LLP (Class of 1981); Jayne McMellen, Senior Vice President, State Street Bank (Class of 1962); Claudia Mott Wong, Retired Director of Small Capital Research, Prudential Securities (Class of 1980); Michael Mullen, Executive Director, Oppenheimer & Co. Inc. (Class of 1984); Michael G. Philip, Head, Global Equities Deutsche Bank (Class of 1982); and John F. Smith, Chairman and Chief Executive Officer of General Motors (Class of 1960).

The College and Environs

Situated in the heart of the beautiful Pioneer Valley, Amherst is a vibrant community that is rich in culture, history, education, and commerce. The University of Massachusetts, along with four major colleges—Amherst, Hampshire, Mount Holyoke, and Smith—constitute the Five College community, which is noted for its extensive educational resources and cooperation. The surrounding towns reflect the culturally rich and unique atmosphere of this collaboration. Just a few hours' drive from Boston and New York City and only 1 hour from Hartford, the area is infused with research and high-tech business opportunities, centers for art and entertainment, and assorted commercial and consumer enterprises. The Valley is truly a magnet for an extraordinary variety of people and opportunities.

Facilities

The Isenberg School of Management offers valuable resources outside the classroom. The School maintains its own reading room of business-related books and periodicals. The University's W. E. B. DuBois Library houses an outstanding collection of more than 2 million books, 13,000 journal and serial titles, extensive government document collections, and more than 150 online data sources, including LEXIS-NEXIS, Compustat, and Moody's Company Data. These resources, together with cooperative arrangements with other libraries, enable M.B.A. students to obtain virtually any book or periodical.

Technology Environment

The Isenberg School houses four computer laboratories, offering access to network software, high-speed Internet access, and a wide variety of software packages, including financial, statistical, modeling, and Web design software and the Microsoft Office suite of programs. These laboratories are connected to a UNIX mainframe. The School's computer facilities provide technical expertise and equipment resources that support M.B.A. students' sophisticated computing needs.

Placement

The M.B.A. Career Management Office offers individualized career advising and functions as the clearinghouse for M.B.A. recruiting, job postings, and alumni networking. M.B.A. students also utilize the Isenberg School Placement Office and Campus Career Network for additional recruiting opportunities. Alumni contacts and business partnerships are emphasized and developed throughout the two-year program. Graduates have been hired by PricewaterhouseCoopers; EDS; General Accounting Office; IBM; Lego Systems, Inc.; General Electric; Liberty Mutual Group; Pratt & Whitney; Teradyne Inc.; Spalding Sports Worldwide; Staples, Inc.; Madison Square Garden; and other prestigious companies.

Admission

Professionalism is an important measure for an Isenberg School applicant. Applicants have many different cultural and professional backgrounds and intensely competitive academic credentials. A bachelor's degree is required; however, no particular undergraduate major is favored. A strong grade point average is important. Applicants must take the GMAT, and a minimum TOEFL score of 600 is required of applicants whose native language is not English. In addition, applicants must submit a resume and two professional references, along with all transcripts, to the Office of Admissions at the Graduate School.

Finances

Full-time students pay tuition and fees of $5640 as Massachusetts residents and $13,212 as nonresidents. Living expenses, including books, supplies, and housing, are estimated at $8500 per year. The School offers research and teaching assistantships to approximately 90 percent of each class. Assistantships provide full tuition and fee waivers, along with $2622 per semester, to students in return for 10 hours of work each week. Several prestigious merit-based scholarships are also awarded. Need-based financial aid is provided through the financial aid office of the University.

International Students

The Isenberg School has a commitment to international business education. The fall 2000 class is 35 percent international students, and the curriculum integrates various international topics. A globally aware student body and faculty allow the M.B.A. program to face the real issues of the twenty-first-century business environment. In an effort to ease the transition for international students, the Foreign Students Office provides information and support, beginning at the moment of admission.

Application Facts and Dates

Applications for the full-time M.B.A. program are accepted for the fall semester only, with a deadline of March 1. The part-time Professional M.B.A. program offers admission for the fall, spring, and summer semesters, with respective application deadlines of July 1, December 1, and May 1. An online application is available at http://www.umass.edu/gradschool/applicants.html. To request a brochure and an application, students should contact:

Graduate Programs Office
209 Isenberg School of Management
University of Massachusetts
Amherst, Massachusetts 01003
Telephone: 413-545-5608
Fax: 413-545-3858
E-mail: gradprog@som.umass.edu
World Wide Web: http://www.som.umass.edu

University of Miami

> ### M.B.A. PROGRAMS AT THE UNIVERSITY OF MIAMI
>
> *The School of Business Administration is rapidly becoming a premier school for business education. Should you enroll as a student, you can look forward to classmates from all over the world whose diverse backgrounds and perspectives will enhance your learning. Your classes will be taught by our renowned faculty members, leading educators, and consultants to major corporations. Job placement is a priority at the University of Miami (UM). Our modern placement center provides personalized career development, on-campus interviews, career fairs, and forums. Join us . . . the business ideas and skills you'll acquire at UM will benefit you for a lifetime.*
>
> —Dr. Paul K. Sugrue, Dean

Programs and Curricular Focus

The School of Business Administration's M.B.A. program is accredited by AACSB–The International Association for Management Education. Meeting these accreditation standards is a measure of a school's excellence. The School has the distinction of having complete accreditation for its baccalaureate, master's, and accounting programs.

There are two program tracks offered. Track I is a one-year M.B.A. program for business undergraduates who have earned their degree within the past five years from a school accredited by AASCB–The International Association for Management Education. This track contains 36 credits, 24 of which are electives. Track II is a two-year track offered for all other students that includes 61 credits, 24 of which are also electives. The duration of the two-year program may be reduced to nineteen months by attending summer classes. Some required courses may be waived, depending on the individual's undergraduate background. Full-time students can choose to take three, four, or five courses per semester, all during the day or a mix of day and evening classes.

The curriculum is flexible and may be customized. Students may choose from twenty-six specializations: applied statistics, computer information systems, controllership, corporate finance, economics, finance, financial markets and banking, human resource management, international business, international finance, investments, leadership, legal implications, logistics, management, management information systems, management science, management

science applications, marketing, operations research, personal financial planning, political science, professional accounting, quality management, taxation, and telecommunications.

Students and the M.B.A. Experience

Located in a major hub of international trade and commerce, the School of Business Administration has been acclaimed for the global orientation and diversity of its faculty, student body, and curriculum. A third of the students are international, and more than a third are women. Approximately half of the students' undergraduate majors are from areas other than business. As of the fall 1999 semester, there were 527 students enrolled in the regular, full-time M.B.A. program. Entering students average 26 years of age, with three years of work experience.

Special Features

The School of Business Administration offers several programs. J.D./M.B.A. degrees can be earned, necessitating admission to both the law school and the M.B.A. program. The MIBS program earns the student an M.B.A. and a certificate in international business. This is a two-year program that features additional language training in Portuguese or Spanish and a four-month, University-arranged, paid corporate internship. Typically, students whose second language is English intern with a company in the United States; students whose first language is English are

generally placed overseas in the country where their second language is spoken. Prior work experience is necessary. A second master's degree in computer information systems, management science, or taxation may be earned with as few as 15 credits beyond the M.B.A. degree.

There is an active graduate business student association (GBSA) that organizes social and professional activities. Executives representing south Florida businesses act as guest speakers. Social events include beach parties, barbecues, and football tailgate parties. The Mentor Program provides personal interaction with experienced professionals.

The Faculty

Dean Paul Sugrue states, "Fine teaching is a necessary condition for the success of a faculty member at the School of Business Administration. It is proven by the ability to create and disseminate meaningful knowledge about the practice of business." Faculty members at the University of Miami's School of Business Administration are characterized by their strong commitment to the students. Their courses offer a blend of case studies and theory and emphasize practical application to the modern business world. They are recognized experts in their fields. All full-time, tenured faculty members hold a doctorate or the highest degree in their fields.

The Business School Network

Corporate Partnerships

The School of Business Administration maintains close ties to the Florida and international business communities. Miami is strategically located as a gateway between the United States, Latin America, and the Caribbean. Miami has emerged as a critical node in the global business network, and the strong feeling of excitement and growth in this area add significant value to the learning experience. Corporate affiliate–sponsored events are open to all graduate students. Students use these opportunities to meet and visit with top corporate executives in small-group and seminar settings. Through an annual membership commitment, participating corporations provide valuable support to the School.

The Mentor Program pairs University of Miami alumni and other professionals with graduate business students. These mentors are willing to assist with the personal and professional development of the M.B.A. students. Mentors serve as advisers, supporters, sponsors, tutors, and coaches. These relationships provide a link between academic theories and the realities of the business world. The program bolsters the students' sense of confidence by increasing their knowledge of the careers they are about to enter. It also creates a feeling of greater involvement with the community and provides students with a benchmark to strive for and, eventually, attain.

The College and Environs

Founded in 1925, the University of Miami is a private, independent, international research university. The first Master of Business Administration degree was offered in 1948. The University of Miami's School of Business Administration offers state-of-the-art facilities located on a lushly landscaped, 260-acre campus in Coral Gables, Florida, minutes from metropolitan Miami.

There are more than 13,500 degree-seeking students in approximately 110 undergraduate, ninety-five master's, fifty-five doctoral, and two professional areas of study. There are currently 1,865 full-time faculty members, whose ranks include Guggenheim Fellows, Fulbright Scholars, and National Science Foundation award recipients. Of this distinguished faculty, 97 percent hold doctorates or the highest degree in their fields.

Technology Environment

Computer facilities are located both in the School of Business Administration complex and at the University's Ungar Computer Center. A computer lab with seventy-five PCs is located in the business school complex. The Ungar Computer Center houses a DEC VAX cluster with two VAX 4000-600 systems and an IBM 9672-R42. In addition, the information resources department supports all data communications network requirements, including dial-up access facilities and an instructional support facility with three computer laboratories that house twenty-two terminals, thirty-six personal computers, and eleven Macintosh computers.

The combined University libraries, which can accommodate special research requests from students, contain more than 2.1 million volumes, 20,353 serial subscriptions, and 3.1 million microforms. More than 18,250 current periodical and serial publications are received. The Otto B. Richter Library is the heart of the library system and is also a Federal Government Documents Depository.

Placement

The Sanford L. Ziff Placement Center is dedicated to assisting students realize their career goals. After all, the most important reason to earn a graduate business degree is to prepare for a future in business. Offering a variety of services, from career counseling to resume preparation, the professional staff at the Ziff placement center assists and actively promotes graduate business students exclusively. During the 1998–99 academic year, the placement center arranged 125 corporate visits that yielded 1,000 interviews. The average starting salary for graduates was $51,300, with a high of $75,000.

Admission

The Graduate Admissions Committee welcomes applications from individuals whose undergraduate degrees are from accredited colleges or universities. Attendance at orientation prior to the beginning of the student's first term is mandatory. Students are admitted for programs starting in August and January.

A completed application file contains an application form, a nonrefundable $45 application fee, GMAT scores (less than five years old), and academic credentials, including an official transcript from each college or university attended (including summer school, part-time study, or postgraduate work—even for only one course). An additional final transcript showing the degree conferred and date of graduation should be sent after completion of any course work still in progress at the time of admission. Work experience is not required for admission. Recommendations are optional. Applicants from international institutions should provide statements by the officials of the institutions attended indicating the courses taken, grades earned, and classification of degree. If not in English, international credentials must be accompanied by certified translations. International applicants whose native language is not English and/or who did not earn an undergraduate degree from

an Englishspeaking institution must submit a TOEFL score with their application. The TOEFL should have been taken within two years prior to application for admission; a minimum score of 550 is required.

Finances

Tuition for 1999–2000 was $852 per credit hour. Living expenses were estimated at $10,600. There are a limited number of merit-based graduate assistantships. Typically, a graduate assistantship is for 60 percent to 75 percent of the student's tuition and includes a stipend of $1500 per semester. The student is assigned to a particular department and is expected to carry at least 12 credit hours and work 15 hours per week on assigned research or special projects. Early application is recommended for those requesting a graduate assistantship.

Students applying for need-based assistance must submit the Free Application for Federal Student Aid (FAFSA). Federal Perkins Loans, Federal Stafford Student Loans, and the Federal Work-Study Program are based upon the financial need of applicants and the availability of funds. Federal Stafford loans are available to students enrolled in 5 or more credit hours. The Unsubsidized Stafford Loan is a non-need-based federal loan program. The FAFSA must be completed and submitted to the processors by students requesting this loan, even if no need is demonstrated.

Application Facts and Dates

Decisions for admission are made on a rolling admission basis until the programs are closed. Because applications received early are evaluated first, applicants are urged to file a complete application as soon as possible. Applications should be received at least two months prior to the beginning of classes to provide sufficient time for processing. For questions regarding admission requirements or the status of an application, students should contact:

Graduate Business Programs
School of Business Administration
University of Miami
221 Jenkins Building
P.O. Box 248505
Coral Gables, Florida 33124-6524
Telephone: 305-284-4607
            800-531-7137 (toll-free,
            U.S. only)
Fax: 305-284-1878
E-mail: mba@miami.edu
World Wide Web: http://www.bus.
    miami.edu/grad

University of Michigan–Flint

Flint, Michigan

THE CHALLENGE OF THE UNIVERSITY OF MICHIGAN–FLINT M.B.A.

Accepting the challenge of the University of Michigan–Flint (UM–Flint) is an important decision. We seek bright, energetic men and women eager to accept the challenge of a modern program that encourages participants—students and faculty members—to think in new and creative ways. The UM–Flint M.B.A. challenges you to be an active learner. You will work and learn with diverse, highly qualified student and faculty colleagues who bring rich talents, backgrounds, and professional experiences to the program. The program will enhance your current knowledge and experience and provide many of the tools you will need for leadership positions. You will broaden your perspectives so you can approach problems not only from multiple function viewpoints, but from global and ethical perspectives as well.

I invite you to accept the challenge of our M.B.A. program. I am confident you will find it one of the most exciting and rewarding professional experiences of your life.

—Fred E. Williams, Dean

Programs and Curricular Focus

The University of Michigan–Flint School of Management is an upper-division professional school offering programs leading to the Master of Business Administration (M.B.A.) degree. The M.B.A. program (accredited by AACSB–The American Assembly for Collegiate Schools of Business) is designed for those individuals who have distinguished themselves in their previous college studies, show a high aptitude for management studies, and have, or soon may have, responsible positions in management.

The program is designed as a part-time 48-credit program that takes three years (thirty-three months) to complete. Classes meet in the evening, with students taking two courses in each fall and winter semester and one course in the spring session. The program is atypical of evening offerings, in that an entering group will stay together throughout. Students can profit not only from close relationships with faculty members, but also from extended associations with other students. The M.B.A. program is designed to educate individuals to think effectively about solutions for management problems. Its emphasis is on learning and applying the principles of problem solving, which leads to effective decision making. Accounting, organization, statistics, and

management studies highlight the first year, with analysis, economics, management, marketing, and operations studies hallmarks of the second year. Ethics, finance, management, strategy, and a focus elective are major components of the third year. Students can select additional course work in fields such as finance, management quality, and marketing and can reduce their course load to one class a semester or temporarily withdraw. UM–Flint requires that M.B.A. candidates complete all degree

requirements within seven years of the date of their first course.

Students and the M.B.A. Experience

More than 230 of UM–Flint's 6,171 students are presently in the M.B.A. program. The average graduate student is 29 years of age. Thirty-seven percent are women, and 15 percent are members of minority groups. The fall 1999 mean GPA was 3.2, and the mean GMAT was 528. Of those applying, 90 percent were accepted. Students in the program represent a variety of about twenty-five undergraduate degrees, including business, engineering, health care, and education. The average student has six years' work experience. The program prides itself on flexibility, its policy of keeping an entering group together, and promotion of close communication among students and faculty members.

Special Features

Entering students are part of a group called a cohort, which allows each student to quickly develop a strong professional network for personal and professional development that lasts beyond their time in the M.B.A. program. It also offers classes via

UM–Flint's Lansing program, at Lansing Catholic Central High School, for students who find that location more convenient. Classes are usually small, averaging 25 to 45 students, making the program's goal of close group support possible.

The Faculty

The 17 members of the School of Management's M.B.A. faculty are a diverse group who all hold doctoral degrees. Fields of specialization include marketing, accounting, quantitative methods, management, finance, and industrial/organizational psychology.

The Business School Network

The School of Management maintains close ties with many Michigan corporations. As part of its outreach program, the University has a Business Development Center that offers technical assistance, business plan assistance, and an Enterprise Community Database. There are also community development and service learning programs. Students are able to take advantage of the University of Michigan's ProNet program, a database that matches skills and availability of graduating students with corporations looking to fill positions.

The College and Environs

The UM–Flint campus is located on a 70-acre riverfront campus in an urban setting on the south bank of the Flint River. The campus, with skywalks connecting most major buildings, is a pleasing, comfortable environment that encourages academic success. There are major open spaces, including Wilson Park on the south edge. The Harding Mott University Center houses student activity offices, Clint's Cafe, and many areas in which students can study or relax. The University Pavilion is the focal point for food services and student services. The Recreation Center features a variety of

physical fitness areas and an indoor pool, whirlpool, and sauna. UM–Flint also operates WFUM-TV and WFUM-FM in the Mott Memorial Building. Flint's business district is adjacent to the campus, making students' access to the downtown area, Flint's College and Cultural Center, Mott Community College, Sloan Museum, the Flint Public Library, and additional city attractions easy.

Facilities

The Classroom Office Building is the setting for many general-purpose classrooms and faculty offices and is connected to the theater. An Adult Resource and Women's Center is maintained in the University Pavilion.

Students have full use of the Frances Wilson Thompson Library, which opened in 1994. Funded by donations from the Thompson family and others, it holds 147,000 volumes, 111,000 government documents, and 21,000 periodicals. CD-ROM players and a microfilm collection in excess of 500,000 items are also maintained. It also contains several special collections, including the Genesee County Historical Collection, and the Henry H. Crapo Room and the Coleman J. and Lois R. Ross Learning Resource Center.

Technology Environment

Microcomputer labs for students are located in both the Classroom Office Building and William R. Murchie Science Building. The labs and classrooms contain 156 computers with differing types of display and memory. Local area networks (LANs) provide additional storage. UNIX machines provide e-mail and other computerized services. Campus users can connect to the Internet through the MichNet Computer System.

Placement

UM–Flint's Cooperative Education and Career Center has a wide array of

programs for career exploration. The career advising staff provides up-to-date information on employment trends and salary statistics and offers vocational testing, resume preparation, and individual career counseling. Equally important to the school's M.B.A. program is the Adult Resource and Women's Center, which supports the older students returning to college after several years with help in course planning, financial aid, child care, study skills, career planning, and test-taking skills.

Admission

Suitability for a candidate for the M.B.A. program is based on a review of job experience, prior educational background, scores on the Graduate Management Admission Test (GMAT), and letters of recommendation. One year of college mathematics, including college algebra and either finite math or calculus, is required as are three letters of recommendation, one academic and two from employers. Applicants must have a bachelor's degree from an accredited college or university and submit official transcripts with a degree awarded and a resume showing job history.

Finances

Tuition for the 1999–2000 year, following the thirty-three-month program, was $2125.70 for 6 credit hours, which included a registration fee ($46.25), an activity fee ($10.75), and technical fee ($11.50). The first credit hour was $382.20 and each additional credit hour was $335. Financial aid is available in the form of grants and scholarships as well as various loans. The School is committed to not allowing the cost of a college education to stand between a student and a degree. Students should contact the Financial Aid Office (810-762-3444) for information on how it might be able to fill their needs.

Application Facts and Dates

Deadline for winter admission is November 1; for fall admission, July 1. Applications for both winter and fall admission are accepted for the Flint program, while only winter admission is available for the Lansing program. Applications received after the deadlines will be reviewed if class space is available. For more information, students should contact:

Janet McIntire, M.B.A.
Coordinator of M.B.A. Admissions
   and Student Services
School of Management
Flint, Michigan 48502-1950
Telephone: 810-762-3163
Fax: 810-762-3282
E-mail: jmcintir@flint.umich.edu

University of Minnesota

Carlson School of Management

Minneapolis, Minnesota

A PROFESSIONAL LEARNING COMMUNITY

As part of one of the world's leading research universities, the Carlson School of Management at the University of Minnesota contributes to a thriving intellectual environment. M.B.A. students are an integral part of what we term the School's "Professional Learning Community" of faculty members, students at all levels, alumni, and businesspeople working together to solve management challenges. Our integrated and flexible curriculum builds its strength off one of the United States' strongest and most involved business communities. The Carlson School, positioned at the point of intersection between theory and practice, provides an outstanding environment for the pursuit of academic excellence and for the solution of real-world problems.

—David S. Kidwell, Dean and Professor of Finance

Programs and Curricular Focus

In fall 1999, the Carlson M.B.A. debuted its new curriculum, reflective of what is going on in the business world on a global scale. It uses the strong foundation of past M.B.A. offerings while providing flexibility to meet individual needs.

It provides the integrated basics of business in which students learn relationships between business functions. First-semester courses include Financial Accounting, Statistics, Finance, Marketing, Operations, and Managerial Accounting. Students apply what they learn immediately via the Carlson Integrated Management Simulation. By running their own company, students practice and learn from their business decisions. In the second semester, students take strategy, choose a course in business economics, and begin taking electives. In the second year, students choose a course in organization management and continue taking electives.

The program keeps its strong emphasis on making business connections. The Executive Mentor Program in the first year gives students access to leaders of successful organizations. The Top Management Perspectives course in the second year brings business leaders into the classroom to share insights from their careers. Experiential options include consulting, making investment decisions for a $4-million fund, solving real e-business problems, moving a new product idea from start-up to the marketplace, and studying abroad.

Electives taken in the second semester of the first year prepare students for summer internships. Students can specialize in accounting, e-business, entrepreneurship, finance, health care, management information systems (MIS), marketing, operations, or strategy, or they can design their own concentration area.

Also available are a part-time M.B.A. program for working professionals, an Executive M.B.A. program, a J.D./M.B.A program, and an M.B.A./Master of Healthcare Administration (M.H.A.) joint-degree program.

Students and the M.B.A. Experience

The Carlson M.B.A. programs have approximately 270 full-time, 1,100 part-time, and 105 Executive M.B.A. students. Of the full-time students enrolled in the class of 2000, 31 percent were international, 26 percent were women, and 9 percent are members of minority groups. Twenty percent have undergraduate degrees in business, with the remaining students coming from diverse backgrounds. On average, students possess a 3.25 grade point average (on a 4.0 scale), a score of 645 on the GMAT, five years of work experience, and an age of 29 years. The diverse business industries and nonprofit sectors of the Twin Cities offer a living laboratory that fits everyone's learning needs.

Special Features

From the nation's first consulting field project to mentorship programs to study-abroad programs with top business schools, experiential programs ensure applicability of what is learned in the classroom. The New Product Design and Development course, the e-business practicum, and the Financial Markets Laboratory also provide for hands-on projects. Student-run programs through the M.B.A. Association include volunteer consulting for nonprofit companies, sponsored seminars, special interest clubs, social activities, and community services. A program for international students addresses cultural and language issues encountered in the classroom. The local chapter of the National Black M.B.A. Association provides networking opportunities for African-American students.

The Faculty

Faculty members who teach core courses meet regularly to talk about classroom progress. Their mission is to not only introduce M.B.A. students to the functional areas of business but also to the relationships among those areas. Faculty connections to the business community provide insider knowledge of what businesses need and, therefore, what students should learn to prepare for the future. M.B.A. faculty members are very involved with the students, from answering e-mails at odd hours to joining students at planned social events throughout the two years of the program. While the Carlson faculty maintains a high level of relevant business research to support the innovative nature of the program, an emphasis on quality teaching is an added focus.

The Business School Network

The Carlson School is aggressive in connecting with the business community—locally, nationally, and internationally. The School's Board of Overseers, made up of Fortune 500 and small- and medium-sized companies, reflects the diverse business community in Minneapolis and St. Paul. What distinguishes this community from other strong business communities is its cooperation and involvement with the School. Executives participate in the mentorship program, the Top Management Perspectives course, the

The University of Minnesota's Carlson School of Management is set against the backdrop of the downtown Minneapolis skyline.

classroom, the Financial Markets Laboratory, and curricular and program considerations.

The late Curt Carlson, entrepreneur and founder of Carlson Companies, donated $36 million to the School. A worldwide alumni network and the Alumni Advisory Board assist the School in many ways, and alumni donations enhance current programs, such as the Business Career Center's automated recruiting system, the Center for Entrepreneurial Studies, and international programs.

The College and Environs

Founded in 1919, the Carlson School is located near downtown Minneapolis and is 10 minutes from St. Paul. Students are close to the action yet enjoy a campus setting in tree-filled neighborhoods. The University of Minnesota is one of the most comprehensive universities in the country. There are 500 student organizations. Cultural and recreational facilities include the Recreation Center, the world-renowned Weisman Art Museum, and student theaters. *Fortune* ranked the Twin Cities in the top ten areas for U.S. businesses. From health care to high technology, students have access to almost all fields. With the world's largest shopping mall, Broadway road productions, lakes, professional sports, a variety

of restaurants, excellent schools, and affordable housing, the Twin Cities area is a desirable place to live.

Facilities

The new $45-million Carlson School building offers students an advanced management facility. The M.B.A. program integrates technology into every aspect of the curriculum and is recognized by *Computerworld* as one of the best "techno" M.B.A.'s available. The MIS program ranks third according to *U.S. News & World Report.* Classrooms have built-in Internet connections and are wired for advanced multimedia presentations and information technologies. There are five computer laboratories, the Financial Markets Laboratory, and videoconferencing capabilities.

Placement

The Business Career Center offers services and programs that help students in both determining a career path and finding the right employment opportunities, including resume critiques, mock interviews, career counseling, job-search workshops, national job fairs, and internship coordination. Twenty-four-hour access to job postings, interview schedules, and an alumni network are provided through an online database. More than

200 companies recruit Carlson students, and the School actively coordinates student visits to companies on the East and West Coasts.

Admission

Each year about 135 students enter the full-time Carlson M.B.A. program. Selection criteria measure demonstrated abilities as a student, manager, and leader; grade point average; scores on the GMAT; level and amount of work experience; personal statement; interpersonal and communication skills (an interview is recommended); and recommendation letters. Prerequisites include a bachelor's degree from an accredited U.S. college or university or the equivalent from another country, GMAT results, and completion of a calculus course with a grade of B or better.

Finances

Tuition for fall 2000 is $13,348 for Minnesota residents and $17,454 for nonresidents. Other expenses include $1500 for books, $1700 for fees and health insurance, and $6500 for living expenses per year. Scholarships are awarded based on academic merit. Also, private awards are available in the first and second years, requiring a special application. Graduate assistantships and loans are available.

Application Facts and Dates

Deadlines are January 1, March 1, and April 1 for domestic applicants and February 15 for international applicants. Decisions are mailed out six weeks after the deadline for domestic applicants and by April 15 for international applicants. The application can be downloaded or completed on the School's Web site (listed below) via Multi-App software or through Embark.com. For additional information:

2-210 M.B.A. Office—Admissions
Carlson School of Management
University of Minnesota
321 19th Avenue South
Minneapolis, Minnesota 55455
Telephone: 612-625-5555
            800-926-9431 (toll-free)
Fax: 612-626-7785
E-mail: mbaoffice@csom.umn.edu
World Wide Web: http://www.
    carlsonmba.csom.umn.edu

University of Mississippi

School of Business Administration

Oxford, Mississippi

BUSINESS AT THE NEXT LEVEL

Since 1946, when the first M.B.A. degree was awarded at the University of Mississippi, the M.B.A. Program has held a reputation for producing capable and qualified graduates. The program is known for its emphasis on practical knowledge and real-world experience while maintaining a high level of academic rigor. These traditional strengths now form the foundation for an entirely new M.B.A. program designed to give students the competitive edge in the global, cross-functional, and technologically intensive environment that will dominate the business world in the twenty-first century. Consider joining this exciting new program so that you can experience what is proudly referred to as "Business at the Next Level."

—W. Randy Boxx, Dean

Programs and Curricular Focus

The M.B.A. curriculum is designed to develop effective cross-functional decision-making skills in an environment that emphasizes practical applications and real-world experience.

The first year begins in July with an intensive orientation session that precedes the beginning of the fall semester. In this session, students develop essential skills in statistics, finance, computer usage, and communications. Students move through the fall and spring semesters as a cohort. Skills courses in both semesters develop advanced capabilities in math, statistics, communication, and computer applications. Three cross-functional courses are also taken in the fall semester: Mobilizing Technology in the Modern Business, the Business Environment, and Business Decision Making. Business Decision Making, which emphasizes the development of practical solutions to real business problems using cases and team projects, is continued in the spring semester. Two other core courses, Managing Operations Through the Life Cycle and the M.B.A. Project Course, are also taken in the spring.

Attendance in the second summer session is optional. Students who do attend take courses in their area of specialization and may be able to complete the program in December. Others complete the program in May. In the fall semester of the second year, all students take an integrative capstone course and courses in their area of specialization. Students who did not attend the summer session take specialization courses in the spring semester.

Students and the M.B.A. Experience

A diverse student body from all regions of the country, as well as many other countries, is an important resource of the program. Students with nonbusiness undergraduate degrees find the program to be well suited to their needs. The curriculum focuses on developing the analytical skills and breadth of judgment that are essential elements of effective decision making in any organization. A thorough understanding of the functional areas of business is built from the required courses. In addition, the program allows the flexibility to specialize in an area that serves the individual needs of the student. Instructional methods include lectures, cases, team projects, and group presentations. Some courses are team taught and most are cross-functional and highly integrative. The effective use of computer and information technology is emphasized throughout the program.

The Faculty

M.B.A. students benefit from close and personal contact with faculty members who come from leading universities across the nation and who have extensive research and consulting records. Many have several years of management experience as well. A number of the faculty members have international reputations in areas that define the cutting edge of business education and practice, such as economics, finance, management, marketing, MIS, and international business. These excellent teachers and researchers bring a wealth of academic and business experience into their classes, and they are accessible to and genuinely interested in all of their students.

The Business School Network

The School of Business Administration benefits in enormous measure from the loyalty and generosity of the Business Alumni Chapter and the Business Advisory Council. Both groups serve the School and its students by providing employment and internship opportunities, personal referrals and contacts, and opportunities for class projects. The Hearin Distinguished Lecture Series, the Otho Smith Fellows Program, and the Sam and Mary Carter Lecture Series bring prominent business leaders and scholars to campus on a regular basis to serve as guest lecturers in classes and to lead discussion forums with students. Business leaders from the local region are also frequent participants in classes, projects, and site visits.

The College and Environs

The University of Mississippi (Ole Miss) was founded in 1848 and its School of Business Administration opened its doors in 1917. The first Master of Business Administration (M.B.A.) degree was awarded in 1946. The M.B.A. program is accredited by the AACSB–The International Association for Management Education. Commonly ranked as one of the best places to live in the United States, Oxford is famous as the home of William Faulkner and, more recently, John Grisham. Nestled in the hills and forests of northern Mississippi, the University of Mississippi offers unsurpassed natural beauty and small-town Southern charm.

Facilities

The entirely new Business/Accountancy Building Complex, completed in the summer of 1998, defines a new level of business education, bringing students and faculty members together in an environ-

The new Business/Accountancy Building Complex features a student-oriented design and outstanding instructional facilities. Construction, completed in the summer of 1998, provides one of the most technologically advanced learning environments in the country.

ment that is designed to promote efficient learning and personal interaction. It incorporates the most advanced instructional technology available, including multimedia presentation facilities, distance learning classrooms, videoconferencing capabilities, and computer classrooms and labs. Other campus facilities, including the recently expanded library, offer students one of the best learning and living environments anywhere.

Technology Environment

The School of Business Administration has been on the cutting edge of information and instructional technology usage for many years. The new building complex described above contains more than 2,000 network connections, allowing students to attach to the LAN from anywhere in the building to communicate with faculty members and classmates, access online resources, and receive or submit assignments.

Placement

An aggressive and expanding program of placement and career services provides students with an extensive schedule of employment interviews throughout the academic year. Career planning seminars, resume workshops, mock interviews, and other services give students valuable experience in job search techniques. The use of online resources is encouraged. Semiannual career fairs attract many companies to campus. Professors actively

cultivate career opportunities with potential employers and help students develop career plans and objectives. The Business Advisory Council, composed of more than 50 top-level executives from prominent companies, serves as an important resource for internships, career opportunities, and personal contacts.

Admission

Admission is competitive and cohort size is limited. Applicants are evaluated based on their academic qualifications, GMAT score, work experience, and other personal attributes. Minimum requirements for admission in full standing include completion of an undergraduate program in an accredited U.S. college or its international equivalent with at least a 3.0 GPA on the last 60 semester hours of academic course work, an acceptable GMAT score, and two letters of recommendation. A TOEFL score of at least 600 is required for international applicants whose native language is not English. Work experience is helpful but not required. All students must have completed at least one semester of economics, statistics, and calculus prior to beginning the program. Familiarity with personal computers and standard business software applications is assumed, and all students are required to have a laptop computer. Admission may not be deferred. All students must begin the program in July.

Finances

The 1999–2000 tuition was $1527 per semester for Mississippi residents and

$3078 per semester for nonresidents. International students paid additional fees for insurance and other services. On-campus housing was approximately $930 per semester. Meal plans are available at additional cost. All costs vary over time. Off-campus housing is plentiful and reasonably priced. The John N. Palmer Assistantship and Fellowship Program provides financial aid and practical experience to students who have excelled in their undergraduate programs and who possess the academic and leadership skills to become successful business executives or entrepreneurs. Palmer Assistantships and Fellowships provide $1500 to $2000 per semester and a partial waiver of tuition charges.

Application Facts and Dates

The application deadline is April 15. However, application evaluations and admission decisions begin in February. Applications are considered in the order in which they are received complete with all required materials. For additional information, students should contact:

Dr. John Holleman
M.B.A. Program Director
School of Business Administration
253 Holman Hall
The University of Mississippi
University, Mississippi 38677
Telephone: 601-232-5483
Fax: 601-232-5821
E-mail: holleman@bus.olemiss.edu
World Wide Web: http://www.bus.
olemiss.edu

University of Missouri–Columbia

Columbia, Missouri

THE MISSOURI M.B.A.—DESIGNED TO MEET YOUR GOALS

Besides being challenging and contemporary, the Missouri M.B.A. program is flexible and friendly, with small class sizes and individualized attention from faculty and staff members. Our format allows you the flexibility to join the program at a time that better fits your schedule and the freedom to tailor your program of study to satisfy your personal interests and career goals. Missouri M.B.A. candidates are top caliber. Our admission standards are high and the curriculum is rigorous; you'll graduate with the knowledge, skills, and values necessary for success in the business world. Our M.B.A. program, with classes taught by the College's award-winning faculty, will provide the foundation you need to realize your professional goals.

—Bruce J. Walker, Dean

Programs and Curricular Focus

Flexibility and individuality are the hallmarks of the M.B.A. program at the University of Missouri (MU). The MU M.B.A. provides graduate professional management education to students from diverse backgrounds while allowing them to prepare for specific career paths. A student may enter the program at three times during the year. Foundation courses provide training in basic business functions; however, they may be waived for students having equivalent prior course work. Students may concentrate electives in the business areas of finance, marketing, and management, or they may individualize their programs with outside course work in areas as diverse as law, engineering, journalism, public relations, health-services management, or computer science. To complement the foundation and electives, the Missouri M.B.A. offers skill-enhancing experiences in communication, leadership, and teamwork. A professional perspective is infused through small group meetings with executives, summer internships, real-world case experiences, and professional development seminars designed specifically for M.B.A. students.

The Missouri M.B.A. program permits broad flexibility in the second year, enabling students to tailor programs of study to meet their specific needs and interests. Students complete a minimum of 34 and a maximum of 59 semester hours, assuming completion of prerequisite course work in business calculus, basic and intermediate statistics, and microeconomic theory, which must be accomplished prior to or concurrent with entering the program. A typical program is 46 semester hours. Joint-degree programs are also available for students wishing to pursue an M.B.A. degree simultaneously with a J.D., Master of Health Administration, or Master of Science in Industrial Engineering degree.

Students and the M.B.A. Experience

Admission to the Missouri M.B.A. program is selective; students admitted to the program are committed to and capable of academic and professional success. The program is kept relatively small, enrolling approximately 130 students a year. MU's M.B.A. students typically represent nearly thirty colleges in twenty states and fifteen countries; they hold undergraduate degrees in more than twenty different disciplines. Managerial experience is not a prerequisite for admission.

❖ Global Focus

Students can study abroad through MU's formal relationships with various international universities and selected exchange programs. MU M.B.A. students who are interested in international business can attend summer class in Asolo, Italy, as part of an International Business Studies Consortium. The College of Business recently offered its M.B.A. program at Nanjing University in the People's Republic of China and cooperates in several M.B.A. exchanges.

The MU M.B.A. network of alumni stretches to nations all around the globe.

Special Features

Beginning with the orientation, students have the opportunity to know their instructors and actively participate in and out of class. They might attend a reception at the home of a faculty member, have lunch with a visiting executive, help design a business plan for a small local business, or intern with a large company or maybe a start-up firm. Students gain real-world experience in team case project and consulting case courses, which require consultation with a local or regional business. By becoming a member of the student-led M.B.A. Association, a student has frequent social opportunities. MU M.B.A. students participate in service projects and frequently socialize with fellow M.B.A. students after an executive presentation. These opportunities promote personal involvement in the M.B.A. program and provide a personal touch difficult to find in larger, lock-step programs.

The Faculty

Effective teaching is a priority among College of Business faculty members, many of whom have won national and campus awards in recognition of their teaching. Innovative classroom techniques, computer technology, and effective class materials strengthen the learning process. In addition to the high quality of its classroom instruction, the College's faculty, which includes a large number of young, doctorally qualified instructors along with well-known senior professors, is recognized for its research productivity.

The Business School Network

Corporate Partnerships

Interaction between business leaders and M.B.A. students is facilitated through the College's Executive-in-Residence, Professor-for-a-Day, and M.B.A. Seminar programs. Held each year, M.B.A. Consulting Week invites business leaders to offer special seminars and presentations centered around a selected theme.

Prominent Alumni

The College's nearly 28,000 alumni contribute their expertise to organizations in every state and a multitude of other countries. *Business Week* magazine ranked MU as the number-one producer of corporate CEOs in both the state of Missouri and the Midwest, while *Fortune* ranked MU in the top fifteen nationally. The College has six advisory boards that bring CEOs, CFOs, and other top officials from Fortune 500 companies back to 'Mizzou' for regular visits and support.

The College and Environs

MU is the oldest state university west of the Mississippi River and the largest of the four campuses of the University of Missouri System. The University, which enrolls nearly 23,000 students, offers many cultural and sports events. Columbia is a warm, friendly, cosmopolitan, and safe college community with a population in excess of 75,000. Columbia's growing economy and low unemployment rate offer job opportunities for student family members. The community includes a large number of private apartment complexes oriented to both students and professionals that are conveniently located near campus. Sidewalk restaurants, pubs, coffeehouses, and the quaint downtown shopping district are within three blocks of MU and help make the community a very pleasant place to live.

Facilities

The MU libraries, including Ellis Library, house more than 2.6 million volumes, 5.3 million microforms, and nearly 23,000 serial titles. Friendly, professional staff members are available to answer questions, help solve research problems, and support numerous online and CD-ROM databases. MU has excellent recreational facilities as well as residence halls for men and women students. More than 300 unfurnished University apartments are available for married student families and single graduate students. Construction of Cornell Hall, the new home for MU's College of Business, is currently under way. The estimated completion date is late spring 2002; the building should be fully operational before the start of fall semester 2002. Cornell Hall will house state-of-the-art technology and classrooms.

Technology Environment

Middlebush Hall, which houses the College of Business, contains computer labs and classrooms with help desks staffed by user consultants. Networked PCs in Middlebush classrooms and computer labs provide access to the mainframe and the Internet as well as to a variety of up-to-date business software. Online database access available to students includes Academic Universe, Dow Jones News/Retrieval Service, ABI/Inform, Compact Disclosure SEC and Worldscope, and Compustat PC+. The College Research Center also provides computer support services, including COMPUSTAT, Census, CRSP, FDIC, and Citibank files.

Placement

The College's Career Services Office brings more than 200 recruiting firms to campus each year. Recent graduates have accepted employment throughout the United States, with annual starting salaries ranging from $35,500 to $100,000. Internships allow many students the opportunity to preview positions and companies prior to accepting employment. The Career Services Office also sponsors a career fair each fall and an internship fair each spring, coordinates and schedules on-campus interviews, maintains a job listing service for employers, and holds career development workshops and seminars.

Admission

Admission depends primarily upon the quality of the undergraduate work and the score received on the Graduate Management Admission Test (GMAT). The average entering grade point average is 3.3, and the average GMAT score is 622. The Test of English as a Foreign Language (TOEFL) is required of applicants whose native language is other than English and who do not have a degree from an institution in the United States.

Finances

In 1999–2000, Missouri residents and out-of-state graduate students paid educational fees of $167.80 and $504.80 per credit hour, respectively. Other miscellaneous fees of approximately $300 per semester are also assessed. Fees are subject to change without notice. M.B.A. assistantships are widely available to academically qualified students. These assistantships typically involve 10 hours of work per week at a rate of $2000 per semester and may be accompanied by a complete or partial waiver of tuition fees. Scholarships that may waive out-of-state tuition charges are also available to students with outstanding academic credentials. Scholarships, grants, and loans are also available through the MU Financial Aid Office. International students enrolled at MU can also apply for a Curator's Grant-in-Aid that allows them to remit educational fees at the in-state rate.

Application Facts and Dates

Students may enter the M.B.A. program in the fall semester (August), winter semester (January), or summer session (June). Application deadlines are August 1, December 1, and May 1, respectively, although earlier application is strongly encouraged. Admissions decisions are made on a rolling basis, usually within one month of receipt of all application materials. Exceptions to deadlines are possible if GMAT scores and transcripts are available. For more information, applicants should contact:

Ms. Barbara Schneider
Coordinator of Recruiting and
   Admissions
Graduate Studies in Business
College of Business
303D Middlebush Hall
University of Missouri
Columbia, Missouri 65211
Telephone: 573-882-2750
Fax: 573-882-0365
E-mail: grad@bpa.missouri.edu
World Wide Web: http://www.mba.
   missouri.edu

UNLV University of Nevada, Las Vegas

Las Vegas, Nevada

> ### EDUCATION FOR LIFE'S CAREER
>
> *At the University of Nevada, Las Vegas (UNLV), we have taken the position that the best education package we can offer to our students is a broad educational experience. Most professional managers are faced with a dynamic business environment that changes frequently. M.B.A. graduates from UNLV are prepared to accept and meet the business challenges that will come to them.*
>
> *We make every effort to challenge all students to magnify their talents in such a way that they will be ready to face the exciting challenges of a global economy.*
>
> —Dean, College of Business

Programs and Curricular Focus

The M.B.A. program at the College of Business at UNLV is designed for those who seek global career and leadership opportunities. Today's business leaders face challenges that are quite different from those of a generation ago. Faced with a global competitive business environment and supported by new information and communication technologies, organizational structures are changing. Success in the new marketplace requires teams of executives working across functions and across borders.

The innovative M.B.A. program at UNLV prepares students to succeed in today's business environment by providing them with the needed skills, knowledge, and tools to become visionary and creative leaders. The program, 33 credit hours of core and 15 credit hours of elective concentrations, focuses on ethics and critical thinking, business communications, the role of the firm and its goals and markets, firms' strategic planning and positioning, value chain management approach, international business culture, technology management, integration of curriculum, and teamwork. The faculty is committed to continuous quality improvement of the curriculum and teaching, to increased vertical and horizontal integration of course material, and to team teaching and team learning. To achieve the best outcome, the faculty embraces no one teaching method but rather employs a combination of methods best suited to the particular objectives of the course. Lectures, group discussions, seminars, case studies, computer simulations, and individual and group research projects are frequently used within courses and across the curriculum.

The College of Business at UNLV, including the M.B.A. program, is fully accredited by AACSB–The International Association for Management Education.

Students and the M.B.A. Experience

Since UNLV has taken the position that an M.B.A. candidate is best served with a broad general education, it follows that students from all academic majors are welcome in the program. The only prerequisites for students with a good academic record are that they come into the program with good computer, math, and English skills.

An M.B.A. education is much more meaningful if the student has had pertinent work experience. An M.B.A. is not an extension of undergraduate education but rather a degree allowing the student to become a scholar with specific career goals in mind.

The average age of students entering the program is 29 years, with five years of full-time work experience. The age range is 24 to 52 years. Women make up 30 percent of the student body, members of minority groups represent 10 percent, international students make up 12 percent of entering students, and 6 percent of the students already have advanced degrees.

Special Features

The highlights of the M.B.A. program include a holistic approach to business management that starts with the role of the firm, its goals and markets, its strategic planning and positioning, and value chain management; integrative course modules across the functional areas, including accounting and finance, as well as marketing and operations; major course modules with team teaching

using cross-departmental faculty and a greater emphasis on student teamwork; explicit emphasis on a framework for analysis of ethical issues and critical thinking; a greater emphasis on international studies through a specific course in international business and cross-cultural perspective, a greater internationalization of other courses, and international elective and concentration courses; an integrative Capstone Experience to integrate important issues in the M.B.A. core and to provide students with a live business team case; accommodating the needs of both full-time and part-time students by offering courses during nontraditional hours (early morning, late afternoon, and evening); maximizing students' learning and credit-hour load by offering courses in full- and half-semester (sixteen- and eight-week) models; and a dual concentration (18 hours of electives) that provides greater flexibility in tailoring programs of study to each student's needs and interests.

The Faculty

UNLV values outstanding classroom instruction and provides a rich learning environment that will motivate young scholars. All faculty members teaching in the M.B.A. program have doctoral degrees and are outstanding in their field of expertise. The faculty members have extensive experience in their chosen areas of instruction. The faculty includes professors with training and experience from many nations. Every M.B.A. candidate is assigned a faculty member to serve as his or her adviser and guide.

The Business School Network

Many of the faculty members consult with businesses in an attempt to find solutions to various problems confronting modern mangers. As a result, the faculty has established networks that are beneficial to students, faculty members, and the businesses. Many faculty members invite business leaders to visit and/or lecture in their classes. Many business executives provide support to the University and look at UNLV as their institution.

The College and Environs

While the University is relatively young, it has experienced rapid growth in recent years.

The student enrollment is about 21,000, with approximately 6,500 graduate students. Las Vegas is one of the fastest-growing cities in the United States and is the primary shopping and business district for more than 1.2 million people.

The University is located within the city, so students have easy access to all city services. The airport is less than 2 miles from the campus. The airport is one of the busiest in the United States, with easy connection to any location. Las Vegas is only a half-day automobile ride from Los Angeles or Phoenix.

Millions of international visitors come to Las Vegas, which indirectly provides opportunities for the students. There are many ethnic restaurants and grocery stores. Las Vegas is located on the edge of the desert, where the residents enjoy hot summers and mild winters. There are also large lakes and high mountains nearby, which provide students with the opportunity to appreciate the beauties of nature and to enjoy many forms of outdoor recreation.

Facilities

For the single student, there is excellent campus housing available. There are six dormitories, in which 2 students share each room. There are a few rooms available for single occupants, but this requires an additional fee. The dormitory room and board cost varies from $2700 to $3000 per semester. There are hundreds of apartments available near the University, with prices starting at $400 per month. There is a fine health facility on campus to provide emergency medical services. All students must purchase the Comprehensive Student Health Plan offered by UNLV.

For additional information on housing, students should contact the Office of Residential Life, 4760 Gym Road, Las Vegas, Nevada 89119 (telephone: 702-895-3489; fax: 702-895-4332).

Technology Environment

The College of Business has excellent computer facilities available for student use, including computer labs and electronic information centers. UNLV is one of the few universities in the world that has a Cray Supercomputer.

The College also sponsors research centers that make extensive use of modern facilities, such as the Center for Business and Economic Research and the Small Business Development Center.

Placement

The University has a very active student placement office on campus, offering numerous services to students. These include career workshops, resume preparation assistance, placement file services for current or future use, counseling, and information on job expectations and the employment outlook.

Admission

The College of Business at UNLV welcomes applications from college graduates in all fields. No specific undergraduate major is preferred. Applicants must hold a bachelor's degree from an accredited college or university. Applicants are evaluated based upon demonstrated academic ability as evidenced by a strong undergraduate record, a strong performance on the Graduate Management Admission Test (GMAT), maturity, motivation, leadership, communication skills, and interest in professional management. The requirements for admission include a grade point average (GPA) of 3.0 or higher on a 4.0 scale and a GMAT score of 550 or higher. The test score should be reflective of general, verbal, and quantitative aptitude, with each component above the 25th percentile. GMAT scores more than five years old are not accepted. Applicants with a GPA of less than 3.0 but not lower than 2.75 or a GMAT score not lower than 520 may be admitted as provisional students provided that (GPA x 200) + GMAT score is not less than 1,150.

International students must also have a minimum score of 550 on the Test of English as a Second Language.

Finances

UNLV is relatively inexpensive because it is a state-supported institution. The graduate resident tuition and registration fee was $100 per credit hour for fall 1999 to summer 2000; part-time nonresidents pay $196.50 per credit hour. Full-time nonresidents pay $3270 per semester. The graduate resident tuition and registration fee is $100 per credit hour for fall 2000 to summer 2001; part-time nonresidents pay $205 per credit hour. Full-time nonresidents pay $3173.50 plus $96.50 per credit hour per semester.

If a student chooses to live off campus, food and housing are relatively inexpensive compared to that of many other states.

Students may apply for graduate assistant positions. These positions are very competitive and are filled on the basis of student merit and University needs.

International Students

All international students are required to register with the Office of International Student Services (OISS). This office exists only to serve the students and to make their adjustment to campus life pleasant and productive. If necessary, an OISS representative can meet new students at the McCarran Airport upon arrival. For additional information regarding the OISS, students should call 702-895-3221.

There are more than 800 international students on campus representing more than fifty countries. Residence hall, alumni, and student organizations provide important support groups for international students interested in affiliating with social and business organizations.

For students who need to reinforce their language skills, the University provides education through the Center for English Language Studies. Beginning-, intermediate-, and advanced-level courses are offered.

Application Facts and Dates

Application deadlines are June 1 for the fall semester and November 15 for the spring semester. All international application materials must be completed and received by May 1 for the fall semester and October 1 for the spring semester. For additional information, students should contact the M.B.A. program:

University of Nevada, Las Vegas
Box 456031
4505 Maryland Parkway
Las Vegas, Nevada 89154-6031
Telephone: 702-895-3655
Fax: 702-895-4090
E-mail: cobmba@nevada.edu

University of Nevada, Reno

Reno, Nevada

A PIONEER IN BUSINESS PROGRAMS

The pioneering history of the College of Business Administration at the University of Nevada, Reno, mirrors that of the state of Nevada. Ours was one of the first universities in the United States to offer business and related programs, with courses taught as early as 1888. The present-day College of Business Administration was officially founded in 1956. Our Bachelor of Science and Master of Business Administration (M.B.A.) programs have been accredited by AACSB–The International Association for Management Education continuously since 1961, and we were among the first to receive separate accreditation for our accounting program. Our College is one of the most rapidly growing units of the University of Nevada, combining the excitement of testing new ideas with a commitment to achieving excellence in teaching.

—Mike Reed, Dean

Programs and Curricular Focus

The Master of Business Administration (M.B.A.) program is designed for people with a variety of backgrounds working in business and industry, government, or the nonprofit sector, particularly those who already hold management or executive positions. Students have flexibility in tailoring a program that meets their needs. The program offers a variety of industry or professional specializations, such as logistics and gaming, in addition to the traditional functional specializations, such as management and finance. All appropriate courses have international and computer components. The program is flexible to meet the needs of those presently in managerial and professional positions.

A typical class size is approximately 25 students. The program offers a mix of team-based assignments and individual projects. The style of instruction is also diverse and includes case study analysis, lecture, and seminar. Many students pursue independent study projects, and internships are available. The Logistics Management summer internship program has been particularly successful, with students being placed in major corporations throughout the United States.

The curriculum has been designed to promote understanding of the basic tools and techniques needed to manage effectively in a changing global marketplace. An M.B.A. from the University of Nevada, Reno, enables a manager or executive to perform a wide range of managerial functions, including managing human and material resources in a culturally diverse and rapidly changing technological world, making decisions based on complex accounting and financial information, using state-of-the-art information technology to support the operation and management of organizations, and marketing products and services with a clear understanding of the economic and socioeconomic trends of greatest importance. Graduates understand the implications of an increasingly global economy and the changing legal, ethical, cultural, and political environments of business and are able to develop business policies and strategies that are responsive to rapid change.

Students and the M.B.A. Experience

The College enrolls approximately 200 graduate students, of whom 150 are M.B.A. students. Approximately 30 percent of the students are full-time. The remaining 70 percent work full-time and attend classes in the evening. Women make up approximately 43 percent of the students in the program. Members of minority groups and international students represent 11 percent and 10 percent of the student body, respectively. The average age at admission is 29 years, with the range being 22 to 48. All students entering the program are required to have a minimum of two years of professional work experience. In a recent class, the average years of work experience was ten. The professional backgrounds of the students are quite diverse. Many have realized significant accomplishments and have already moved into managerial positions, while others have only recently begun their careers. Students bring their professional experience to the classroom. This creates a stimulating environment where academic theories are critically examined for their applicability to the real world.

The Faculty

The faculty of the College of Business Administration is an accomplished, dynamic group of professionals dedicated to providing the highest quality business education possible. The faculty members hold Ph.D.'s from some of the world's leading institutions and most have practical work experience in their fields. They are active in research and professional service and many have achieved national and international prominence in their fields. The M.B.A. faculty also has a high degree of international diversity. Its members are natives of many different countries, including Mauritius, England, Taiwan, Korea, Brazil, India, Iran, China, and Germany. An international faculty provides a global focus that is difficult to achieve in any other way.

The Business School Network

The College has excellent ties to the business community, both locally and nationally. The Dean's advisory board is an active, energetic group of senior executives and successful entrepreneurs who interact with the students and faculty in a variety of ways. The College also has several specialized organizations with which M.B.A. students can become involved. The Center for Logistics Management was established in 1988 to combine the resources of the business community and the University to focus on the field of logistics management. The center is aggressively utilizing this alliance by providing companies throughout the United States with a pool of graduates with specialized training in logistics, continuing education programs to train current employees, and ongoing research efforts to address the challenge ahead in one of today's fastest moving fields—logistics.

The Institute for the Study of Gambling and Commercial Gaming was formed in 1989 with the mission of broadening the base of knowledge and understanding of gaming and public policy in Nevada, the United States, and throughout the world. The institute has been actively involved in coordinating and sponsoring international conferences on gaming, publishing books and studies related to gaming and the commercial gaming industry, facilitating educational programs and courses dealing with various facets of gaming, and acting as an information gathering and dissemination center for current developments in gaming and public policy.

The Nevada Small Business Development Center (NSBDC) is a cooperative effort between the University and the United States Small Business Administration. Counselors provide services to existing and new small business enterprises throughout the state by helping them through all individual service areas, including assistance with business start-up, sources of capital, marketing, financial analysis, invention assessment, planning for growth, computer systems, and personnel issues.

The Bureau of Business and Economic Research (BBER), founded in 1956, is the applied research unit of the College of Business Administration. It provides a broad array of research services, publications, and consulting for private, local, state, and national business and governmental entities. The bureau operates on a statewide basis, matching the expertise of consultants, students, faculty experts, and databases with the needs of organizations outside the University.

The College and Environs

The University of Nevada, Reno, Nevada's land-grant institution, is the state's oldest university. It has an enrollment of approximately 12,100 students, of whom more than 25 percent are enrolled in graduate programs. The Reno area, at an altitude of 4,500 feet, has more than 290 days of sunshine a year. Warm, clear days are plentiful in spring, summer, and early fall. Late fall and winter are crisp, but mostly sunny. The city's valley location allows its residents and visitors to enjoy the scenic beauty of the high desert and the outdoor activities available in the spectacular Sierra Nevada Mountains and the incomparable Lake Tahoe, all less than an hour away. The city is also a short drive from more than a dozen prominent ski resorts, Yosemite National Park, the Pacific Crest Trail, San Francisco, and the Napa and Sonoma Valleys.

The area's 294,290 residents create an economy of diversity and entrepreneurial spirit. In addition to being a major recreational and gaming destination, Reno has become an important distribution center for many of the nation's top companies. The city enjoys extensive community support for the Reno Philharmonic, the Nevada Opera, the Reno Chamber Orchestra, and the Nevada Festival Ballet. In addition, the 56-year-old Reno Little Theater and the Nevada Repertoire Company offer traditional avant-garde entertainment year-round.

Facilities

The College of Business Administration is in the Nazir Ansari Business Building, a modern, six-story building. The building encourages students to interact in a relaxed, informal atmosphere in its student lounges and restaurant. Many of the classrooms have Internet connections, audio and video projection systems, and built-in podiums containing such equipment as electronic presenters, microcomputers, VCR/CD players, and connections for personal laptop computers.

Technology Environment

The College maintains several information technology laboratories available to M.B.A. students. These include the general purpose microcomputer lab, the Internet development lab, the networking and telecommunications lab, and the telecommuting lab. These networked facilities are all connected to the Internet, house approximately 100 microcomputers and other devices, and provide access to a wide variety of software applications and databases. The University library is highly automated and supports electronic access (from campus and through remote dial-up) to additional database resources and powerful bibliographic search tools.

Placement

The College's Office of Career Services works closely with students, the faculty, and the administration to integrate career assistance into the overall M.B.A. program, centralize career planning resources, and create a positive image for the program within the business community. The office currently maintains relationships with more than seventy major organizations who recruit regularly at the College. As a result of recent on-campus interviews, M.B.A. students have received job offers from organizations such as Electronic Data Systems, Ford Motor, Chrysler Corporation, Coca-Cola, Intel, Ernst and Young, DSC Logistics, American Micro Devices, Pepsi, Deloitte and Touche, and Kraft Foods.

Admission

Individuals holding baccalaureate degrees from accredited four-year institutions of higher education are encouraged to apply. Any academic background is acceptable, but students holding degrees in fields other than business may find the degree particularly beneficial. Fitness for graduate study in business is determined by previous higher education experience as determined by transcripts, results of the GMAT, letters of recommendation, and a personal statement of goals and objectives. International applicants are required to submit TOEFL results unless they received a degree from an institution where English is the language of instruction. The admissions committee also considers each applicant's personal and professional accomplishments as determined by a detailed resume. Applicants are required to have a minimum of two years of meaningful work experience at the time of admission. The committee seeks to admit men and women representing diverse geographic, racial, and religious groups.

Finances

Residents of the state of Nevada pay $109 per graduate credit in tuition and fees. Nonresidents and international students pay an additional $101 per credit for 1 to 6 credits or $3173.50 for 7 credits or more. All students pay a mandatory $57 per semester for health center fees. International students are required to pay a one-time registration fee of $75 and an annual fee for international student insurance of $219.

The College of Business Administration and the Graduate School award graduate assistantships (GAs) on a competitive basis. Students awarded a GA receive $9500 per ten-month academic year and $84.25 per credit toward their tuition and fees. Nonresident tuition is waived for students who receive a GA. In addition, all M.B.A. students are eligible for scholarships offered by the College and Graduate School.

Application Facts and Dates

Students are admitted into the M.B.A. program for both the fall and spring semesters. To be considered for the fall semester, all application materials must be received by February 1; for spring admission, application materials must be received by October 1. Applications received after the deadlines will be considered on a space-available basis.

For additional information, students should contact:

M.B.A. Program
College of Business Administration/024
University of Nevada, Reno
Reno, Nevada 89557
Telephone: 702-784-4912
Fax: 702-784-1773
E-mail: vkrentz@unr.edu
World Wide Web: http://www.unr.edu

University of New Haven

AN UPDATED M.B.A. FOR TODAY'S PROFESSIONAL

▶ *The working environment is changing, becoming more global and competitive. Information technology has revolutionized the way we do business. New service-based corporations and industries are forming, and established industries such as banking, health care, and energy are being reshaped. Professional success in today's world requires knowledge and skills in all of the basic business functional areas plus the ability to lead in a multicultural society, to build effective functionally integrated teams, and, most importantly, to successfully manage constant change. Because of these changes in the business environment and the increasingly robust economy, employers are intensifying their recruitment of M.B.A. graduates. The job market for new hires is expanding, and the possibilities for advancement abound. Now is the time to prepare for these new opportunities.*

Upon graduation, you will join more than 15,000 alumni from the University of New Haven (UNH) School of Business who work in businesses throughout the world.

—Linda R. Martin, Dean

Programs and Curricular Focus

The primary objective of the M.B.A. program at the University of New Haven is the development of leadership skills and a global perspective, which is required in today's complex business environment. Additional objectives include development of analytical skills and specialization training that produces effective performance in a range of organizations, from entrepreneurial to high technology and global. Many courses require cases, group projects, and in-class presentations. Since many students in the program are currently working in high-technology and multinational firms operating in Connecticut, class discussions reflect this rich mix.

The M.B.A. curriculum has three components that include a total of seventeen courses (51 credits). Students with prior studies in business might be able to reduce their requirements to as little as eleven courses (33 credits). Full-time students can complete their studies within twelve to twenty-two months. Part-time students typically take three to four years.

The first component is six courses covering core competencies. Although some students will need all six, those with a strong coverage of core undergraduate business studies may be able to waive most.

The second component consists of courses in seven required areas (commu-

nication, product creation, valuation, global issues, organizational change, business and society, and strategic vision).

The concluding component is four advanced electives. These may be used to explore a mix of interests or may be used to form a concentration from one of several areas (accounting, business policy and strategy, finance, health-care management, human resources, international business, marketing, public relations, sports industry, and technology management).

Students and the M.B.A. Experience

Nearly 500 students, many holding full-time jobs, are enrolled in the M.B.A. program at the University of New Haven. Most students are from the Northeastern United States, but the University has made a strong commitment to maintain a diverse student body. Women comprise 40 percent of the student population, and 10 percent are international students, representing approximately fifty countries.

Special Features

Trimester scheduling allows students to accelerate progress toward their degree, and, while a complete curriculum is available to full-time students, there are evening and weekend classes suitable for

working adults. Several courses are now offered on line as distance learning courses.

Students can enrich their personal and professional competences by selecting a concentration in a particular discipline, and some departments offer students the opportunity to obtain additional credit and practical experience by participation in an internship program.

The Faculty

The highly qualified faculty represents a combination of full-time academics who hold doctoral degrees in their specialties from a variety of prestigious institutions and part-time faculty members chosen from managers who have demonstrated a high degree of leadership and who have received national recognition for their applied research. Each brings practical insight and experience to the classroom.

Class size within the Graduate School is relatively small, averaging less than 25 students. Classes are kept small to allow for interaction and personal attention. The faculty members at UNH get to know students and act as sounding boards in discussions about business decisions and plans for personal and professional growth and development. UNH faculty members have international, national, and regional reputations in their fields through outstanding accomplishments in research and writing and as visiting lecturers.

The Business School Network

Most students in the M.B.A program hold full-time positions in regional businesses and nonprofit corporations; that experience allows the classroom to become a mechanism for extending students' learning into varied practical environments. Ongoing interaction with the business community also occurs through the Executive in Residence Program. Additional networking occurs through students' participation in the recently chartered chapter of Sigma Beta Delta, the National Honor Society in Business, Management, and Administration.

Each fall and spring, the Bartels' Fellowship Lecture Series brings a successful CEO or entrepreneur to campus to lecture and interact with faculty and students. Some Distinguished Bartels' Fellows have been Dr. David Ebsworth, President of Bayer Corporation; David Beckerman, President of Starter Corporation; Robert Beavers Jr., Senior Vice President of McDonald's Corporation; Francis Freidman, former CEO of GCI Group, Grey Advertising; Ronald G. Shaw, President and CEO of Pilot Pen; and William J. Weisz, former CEO of Motorola, Inc.

The College and Environs

The University's 73-acre campus is located in south-central Connecticut, on a hillside in West Haven that overlooks Long Island Sound and downtown New Haven. The area is semisuburban and is easily accessible by car, bus, train, or plane. The campus, located near the intersection of interstate highways 95 and 91, is 75 miles northeast of New York City and 135 miles southwest of Boston.

New Haven, just 10 minutes away from campus, is a city where arts and cultural activities flourish and coexist with science and business. Settled in the early 1600s and rich in history and heritage, the New Haven area is proud of its past, prouder of its present, and actively planning for its future. The city, considered by many as the "Gateway to New England," is a manufacturing center, a deep-water port, a major art center, and a college town with seven colleges and universities in the immediate area.

Facilities

The University of New Haven provides facilities for a full complement of student services, including career development and placement services; academic, vocational, and personal counseling; alumni relations; health services; housing; international student services; veterans' affairs; minority affairs; and services for

students with disabilities. In addition, there are athletic facilities and a campus store for the students' use and convenience.

Both on-campus and off-campus housing is available for graduate students.

Technology Environment

The UNH Center for Computing Services provides both administrative and academic computing support. Clusters of terminals and personal computers for student use are spread throughout the campus. A lab is located in the business building. Access to the Internet, graphics terminals, printing and plotting devices, laser printing, and a wide variety of data files and software and simulation packages are available.

Placement

The University of New Haven provides career development and placement services as well as academic, vocational, and personal counseling.

Admission

Admission decisions are based primarily on an applicant's undergraduate record. In support of their applications, students should submit scores from the Graduate Management Admission Test (GMAT).

Students for whom English is not their native language must present a TOEFL score of at least 500. International students must submit official, certified documents showing sufficient financial support from personal or sponsor's funds or a scholarship.

Finances

For the 1999–2000 academic year, the tuition rate was $1170 per 3-credit course. There are no other regular fees; however, there is a nonrefundable

application fee of $50 and an additional nonrefundable acceptance fee of $200 for international students not on scholarship. Students should calculate additional expenses for books, supplies, and housing.

Financial aid is available for domestic students in a variety of forms, including loans, grants-in-aid, work-study, fellowships, and assistantships. Financial aid is not available for international students.

International Students

Qualified international students are welcome in the M.B.A. program at the University of New Haven. Ten percent of the students currently enrolled are from approximately fifty countries outside the United States. To qualify, a prospective student must have completed an acceptable undergraduate degree program. All transcripts must be submitted in English.

The University has an Office of International Student Services that provides a full range of support services for international students.

To facilitate preparation for admission by international students, a branch of an internationally known English as a second language (ESL) school is located on campus.

Application Facts and Dates

For more information or applications, students should contact:

Joseph F. Spellman
Director of Graduate Admissions
University of New Haven
West Haven, Connecticut 06516-1999
Telephone: 203-932-7133
        800-DIAL-UNH Ext. 7133
        (toll-free)
E-mail: dharma@charger.newhaven.edu
World Wide Web: http://www.mba.newhaven.edu

The University of North Carolina at Greensboro

Greensboro, North Carolina

> ### LEADERSHIP IN A NEW ERA
>
> *At the Bryan School, our mission is to prepare students to perform successfully as business professionals in the global economy and to enhance the practice of managed organizations through high-quality teaching, research, and professional service. The fundamental knowledge and skills of business are enhanced through the global and information technology perspectives of our M.B.A. curriculum. Our graduates must understand global markets and be able to function in them. They must also be at the cutting edge of information technology.*
>
> *In the fall of 2000, we are adding Enterprise Resource Planning (ERP) to the Program. Our graduates will be experienced with the latest information technology being used by leading businesses in the world. As a member of the SAP University Alliance Program, the Bryan School has access to Enterprise Resource Planning software and training opportunities. The Bryan School's strength in Information Technology (IT) has grown along with our partnerships with area firms. Because of our long and mutually rewarding strategic partnerships, we are well positioned to introduce this new and innovative experience to our students.*
>
> —James K. Weeks, Dean

Programs and Curricular Focus

The Bryan M.B.A. prepares men and women for leadership roles in business and the community. It is designed to develop general managers who think and act strategically and who will lead in a global economy. Students are challenged throughout their experience to understand a broad, long-range perspective and to act decisively.

The program is designed for qualified students from all academic backgrounds and consists of 48 semester hours of course work—36 hours of required courses and 12 elective hours. Students may waive up to 12 hours of required coursework based on their undergraduate education. Through the required courses, students obtain a standard of understanding that all M.B.A.'s should possess. The elective courses provide a richer knowledge in different areas of management activity.

The heart of the program is a modular, flexible curriculum that enables students to take courses at their own pace and adjust their course load accordingly. The curriculum focuses on business strategy. The core curriculum is highly integrated and reflects concerns with today's pressing issues—information technology, global business operations, and the changing workforce and markets.

All M.B.A. classes are scheduled in the evening to meet the needs of students working full-time as well as to accommodate full-time students who are fulfilling assistantship and internship opportunities or who work part-time with regional firms. Classes are offered during fall and spring semesters as well as during two six-week summer sessions. Additionally, some distance education features are being incorporated to increase the convenience for working adults, without eliminating critical student-to-faculty and student-to-student contact.

The Bryan School of Business and Economics is the largest of The University of North Carolina at Greensboro's (UNCG) six professional schools. Its undergraduate and graduate programs are among the 25 percent of all business programs nationwide that are accredited by AACSB–The International Association for Management Education.

Enterprise Resource Planning is being incorporated as an integral component of the M.B.A. program. Two courses devoted to information technology are required in addition to the information technology (IT) topics included in the functional and strategy courses.

Several IT-related courses can be selected as a part of the M.B.A. program, including e-commerce, e-marketing, and internet economics. These courses, along with other courses offered by the Information Systems and Operations Management Department allows M.B.A.

students to craft an IT focus in the program by selecting IT courses as their electives.

In addition to the M.B.A., the Bryan School offers master's degrees in accounting, information technology, and applied economics. Many courses in these programs are available to M.B.A. students as electives.

Students and the M.B.A. Experience

A major benefit of the Bryan M.B.A. program is the interaction with fellow students. Ninety percent of the students work full-time and attend classes on a part-time basis. This provides many opportunities for students to meet and get to know other professionals with a wide variety of business backgrounds and adds greatly to their depth of understanding of business issues. Students work in teams with colleagues who bring an abundance of personal experience to the subject matter of each class.

Thirty-three percent of the students have undergraduate degrees in business; 32 percent have training in science and engineering. Sixteen percent have backgrounds in the humanities and social sciences. The typical student is 30 years old and has six years of work experience. Approximately one third of the students are women, and 13 percent are members of minority groups. Five percent of students enrolled in the program are international.

❖ Global Focus

The Bryan School's curriculum has a strong international component and is strengthened by core-level courses on global operations strategy as well as elective courses on aspects of international commerce. The Bryan M.B.A. program also offers exchange programs with several international business schools and opportunities to develop foreign language and management skills pertinent to individual regions.

The Bryan School's Center for Global Business Education and Research offers courses that allow students to experience business practices abroad. The courses include an intensive week-long trip to the area being studied. Courses have been developed for Berlin, Paris, Mexico City, and Morocco, with others in the planning stage.

The Faculty

The faculty of The University of North Carolina at Greensboro's (UNCG) Bryan School is committed to excellence in teaching. In a recent survey of students, the students rated the faculty as the most commendable feature of the M.B.A. program. Students recognize the commitment of the faculty to contributing to learning and appreciate the ease of access to the faculty.

National recruiting has brought together a staff of highly qualified academics whose teaching, scholarship, and work experience complement the M.B.A. program. Many have significant managerial and executive experience; several provide consulting services for individual clients and companies. A large number of faculty members are nationally and internationally recognized for their research accomplishments.

The Business School Network

Corporate Partnerships

The Business Advisory Board, a group of local and regional executives, fosters closer interaction between the School and the professional and business community. In addition to providing sound advice and counsel to the Dean and faculty, they play an integral part of the review process for curriculum and other program innovations.

In addition, relationships with local, national, and international corporations lead to field consulting projects and internships for students and to employment opportunities for graduates.

The College and Environs

The University of North Carolina at Greensboro has a total enrollment of 13,000, with 2,700 pursuing master's or doctorate-level work. The University has been highly regarded for more than a century for both its strong liberal arts tradition and its excellent professional

programs. Among the approximately 500 full-time faculty members are nationally known scholars whose research and creative work regularly contribute new knowledge to their fields.

The city of Greensboro is rich in culture and history, and is considered one of the most progressive cities in North Carolina. The current metropolitan population of the Piedmont Triad is 1.3 million, and Greensboro, with 280,000 residents, combines the resources and activities of a large metropolitan center with the amenities of a human-sized environment where one can get to know and care about one's neighbors.

Facilities

All M.B.A. classes are taught in the evening in the Bryan School of Business and Economics Building. The building's modern design accommodates the teaching and research needs of approximately 60 faculty members and 250 students.

Jackson Library, a modern nine-story structure, contains more than 2 million items, including government documents and microtext. The library subscribes to more than 6,100 newspapers, periodicals, and other serials. In addition, all M.B.A. students can utilize the inter-library loan system to access materials that are available in other libraries across the nation.

Technology Environment

Instructional and Research Computing provides comprehensive computing support and resources for campus users. The campus supports a highly distributed network supported by Novell file servers, network printers, SUN-based Solaris for UNIX support, and a large DEC VAX-cluster, including a VAX 6000-610. UNCG is an Internet node, including access to the N.C. Supercomputing Center. Microcomputer labs are readily available, including three in the Bryan Building.

Placement

Career counseling and placement services are provided through the University's

Career Services Center. A branch location of the office is located in the Bryan Building and is dedicated to serving business students.

Admission

Admission decisions are based on a combination of the undergraduate academic record, GMAT scores, an admission essay, relevant managerial experience, and recommendations. International student applicants whose native language is not English must also demonstrate English language proficiency. A minimum TOEFL score of 217 (computer-based) is required, along with proof of health and proof of adequate funds. Each application is reviewed on its own merits and is not compared with an applicant pool.

Finances

Full-time tuition for 1999–2000 for M.B.A. students is estimated at $1025 per semester for in-state students and $5252 per semester for out-of-state students. There are a limited number of assistantships and tuition waivers available. Competitively awarded Bryan Fellowships, with the opportunity to work with a faculty mentor, are also available.

Application Facts and Dates

Because of processing requirements, an admission for decision for the fall semester cannot be guaranteed unless all credentials are received before July 1; for spring semester, by November 1; and for summer session, by April 1. For international students, admissions application deadlines are May 1 for fall and October 1 for spring; admissions are coordinated through the International Student Office.

For further information, students should contact:

M.B.A. Program
P.O. Box 26165
The University of North Carolina at Greensboro
Greensboro, North Carolina 27402
Telephone: 336-334-5390
Fax: 336-334-4209
E-mail: mba@uncg.edu

University of Notre Dame

Notre Dame, Indiana

NEW M.B.A. INITIATIVES

The College of Business Administration prepares its students for a journey for which they can't buy a ticket— visiting new frontiers in technology and world markets, developing new and better products, anticipating creative marketing strategies to integrate into a changing world, looking at how we work as individuals and as a team, and devising systems to make the world better for us all. Our students graduate with the preparation they need to face this increasingly difficult but exciting journey that is filled with many possibilities.

—Carolyn Y. Woo, Dean

Programs and Curricular Focus

The University of Notre Dame's M.B.A. program is solidly based on the vision of its founders—to help develop the student's fullest potential and send him or her forth to make a difference in the world. This is accomplished by developing in the student the following portfolio of skills: critical thinking, teamwork, effective communication, a global business perspective, and the manager's ability to make practical and ethical business decisions. With more than eighty elective courses, fourteen concentration tracks, and two programs of study, the Notre Dame M.B.A. program provides students with a challenging and flexible educational experience.

The Two-Year program is designed for students with little or no academic background in business. In the first year of the program, students study the core business disciplines. The curriculum is tightly integrated so that students learn to analyze situations from the vantage point of each of the functional areas. The second year allows students to select the concentration track that furthers their interests and future prospects. Students are required to complete 63 credit hours of work over four semesters.

The One-Year program is designed for students who have an undergraduate degree in business. This program enables students to begin study in June and graduate the following May. Beginning with a ten-week summer semester, students attend intensive sessions in the core disciplines that are normally explored during the first year of the Two-Year program. After the summer semester, students move directly into the second year of the Two-Year program. They take a course in corporate strategy and elective courses in both international business and ethics while customizing the remainder

of their elective courses by choosing from one of the fourteen concentration tracks. Students must complete 44 credit hours of work over eleven months.

Students may also pursue a joint Master of Business Administration/Juris Doctor (M.B.A./J.D.) degree program that is offered jointly by the College of Business Administration and the Notre Dame Law School. Students can complete both degrees in a total of four years. Students must apply to each school separately.

Students and the M.B.A. Experience

Notre Dame attracts high-caliber students from more than 180 undergraduate institutions and nearly thirty countries. Approximately 30 percent of the student body is international students, 22 percent is from the Midwest, 19 percent is from the East, and 17 percent is from the West. The Two-Year students at Notre Dame represent a varied mix of undergraduate majors, including business, engineering, economics, math, science, and humanities. Notre Dame M.B.A. students range in age from 21 to 39 years, and they enter the program with more than four years of meaningful work experience. Nearly 30 percent of the students are women, and roughly 13 percent are members of minority groups.

❖ Global Focus

At Notre Dame, students can learn global perspectives firsthand and diversify their portfolio by studying in London, England; Santiago, Chile; or Monterrey, Mexico or through international internships.

At Notre Dame's London program, M.B.A. students learn from distinguished British professors who hail from prestigious institutions in the United Kingdom. Courses

are conducted at the technologically updated and renovated Notre Dame London Centre, which includes computer labs with instant Internet access. Students gain exposure to the European business environment through planned tours and professional networking opportunities.

Students who choose to study in Santiago begin with a two-week orientation during which they are immersed in the Spanish language and the cultural norms and traditions of South America. Courses are conducted in English at the Instituto Latino Americano de Doctrina y Estudios Sociales (ILADES) by eminent Chilean business faculty members. Chile serves as an ideal laboratory for learning about developing economies. Included in the program are visits to the Ministry of Finance and the stock exchange as well as tours of nearby copper mines and vineyards.

Notre Dame offers students the opportunity to learn about the economic and social infrastructure of Mexico through seminars at the Monterrey Institute of Technology. Students tour neighboring corporations and small businesses and meet face-to-face with top corporate executives.

In 1998, Notre Dame M.B.A. students launched a summer internship initiative in South Africa that combines service with valuable business experience. Through this outreach, students spend eight weeks in the townships of South Africa where they help small-business owners and entrepreneurs develop marketing and business plans.

Special Features

The Notre Dame M.B.A. experience begins with the orientation. During this orientation program, students engage in team-building exercises and attend two-week math and accounting review workshops as well as a Microsoft Excel workshop.

The Faculty

Notre Dame's faculty members are highly regarded, stand at the top of their fields, and are engaged in the business world. The professors have a passion for teaching and make an impact in their fields. The 4:1 student to faculty ratio ensures each student accessibility and personal attention.

The Business School Network

Notre Dame's alumni network is one of the most extensive in higher education, with more than 100,000 members in 240 alumni clubs worldwide. These clubs are actively involved in promoting the University and extending its learning community. Notre Dame also has active Asian Pacific, Black, and Hispanic alumni clubs.

Every year, Notre Dame attracts corporate executives who speak on campus through a variety of lecture series and classroom visits. Some of the most interesting networking discussions take place in small classroom settings where students work directly with corporate executives on classroom projects. For example, Corporate Strategy students connect with managers located in Germany using two-way videoconferencing, while students in Entrepreneurship work directly with local start-ups to develop a business plan for their product or service ideas. Because of the small class size, students have unique opportunities to meet with executives over breakfast, lunch, or at small receptions.

The College and Environs

Notre Dame was founded in 1842 by Rev. Edward Frederick Sorin and 6 brothers of the French religious community known as the Congregation of Holy Cross. The University's 1,250-acre campus is situated immediately north of the city of South Bend, Indiana. Its twin lakes and many wooded areas provide a setting of natural beauty for more than 100 University buildings. The total University enrollment is about 10,650 students, of whom approximately 8,014 are enrolled at the undergraduate level. The Law School, the graduate division of the College of Business Administration, and the Graduate School have a combined enrollment of 2,640 students.

With a population of approximately 250,000, South Bend has a familiar hometown feel yet is large and diverse enough to provide students with a myriad of cultural, shopping, and entertainment opportunities. The area is served by numerous city parks, golf courses, and county facilities that offer a variety of outdoor recreational activities. Medical and religious needs are adequately met by three hospitals and more than 220 churches and synagogues of all major denominations.

Facilities

Notre Dame's state-of-the-art College of Business Administration complex, opened in 1995, features a multimedia amphitheater, a computer lab, a two-level M.B.A. lounge, team rooms equipped with networked computers, and Media-on-Call classrooms with computer controls and a fiber-optic network that provides faculty members with access to satellite feeds from major international networks. The Doermer Center opened in the fall of 1999. This new placement facility is equipped with the latest videoconferencing technology.

Technology Environment

Notre Dame is a campus without boundaries. Whether in London or South Bend, every student is linked to the University's advanced computer network and has instant desktop access to the latest versions of leading business application software. The Thomas J. Mahaffey Jr. Business Information Center (BIC) provides students with easy online access to complete electronic business resources, such as Dow Jones News Retrieval Service, LEXIS-NEXIS, General BusinessFile ASAP, and Bridge real-time investment information. The College of Business Administration's Management Information Systems (MIS) laboratory enables students to develop software applications, test innovative hardware and software configurations, and explore entrepreneurial opportunities that are based on information technology applications.

Placement

The Doermer Family M.B.A. Career Development Center schedules interviews for full-time positions and summer internships with a variety of companies and organizations that recruit M.B.A.'s on campus each year. Placement professionals also receive and pass along numerous job postings for M.B.A.'s, many of which are received from supportive alumni. M.B.A. students also have contact with nearly 400 companies that come to campus each year to recruit undergraduate students, and, through participation in the National M.B.A. Consortium, students have the opportunity to interview with a large number of companies at the annual consortium in Chicago. International students are invited to take part in two international placement consortiums that are held annually in major cities, and students from minority groups are invited to attend professional development conferences that are sponsored by the National Black MBA Association and the National Society of Hispanic MBAs. Students may also take advantage of the center's career counseling, workshops, and career panels.

Admission

The University of Notre Dame M.B.A. program seeks highly qualified and well-rounded applicants. Typically, there are three characteristics of incoming students that have proven to be reliable gauges of success in the Notre Dame M.B.A. program: a demonstrated history and aptitude for academic success, at least two years of meaningful work experience, and leadership qualities that prove the student will be an active participant in the M.B.A. community. Because Notre Dame seeks well-rounded candidates, students are encouraged to apply even if their profile is atypical. The Graduate Management Admission Test (GMAT) is required for all

applicants to the M.B.A. program. Average GMAT scores and GPA are 639 and 3.2, respectively, for the class entering in fall 1999. The Test of English as a Foreign Language (TOEFL) is required for all applicants whose native language is not English.

Finances

Tuition for the 2000–01 academic year is $23,780. Tuition for the 2000 ten-week summer semester was $9510. Books and supplies average $1000 per year. Living expenses, including room, board, and personal expenses, total approximately $7500 per academic year for an average single student living on or off campus. Married students should expect to increase their living expenses by about $200 a month.

Fellowships are awarded primarily on merit and are open to all domestic and international applicants. All applicants are considered for fellowship awards if they mark the appropriate box on the application. Loans and campus employment opportunities are available to qualified students through the University's Financial Aid Office.

International Students

Because 30 percent of students enrolled in the Two-Year program are international, they have a notable influence on the program's learning environment. To ease their transition into the academic environment and enhance their educational success at Notre Dame, international students are required to attend a two-week language and culture workshop prior to orientation. The University's Office of International Student Affairs offers support, activities, and a newsletter specific to international students' concerns. Also, the M.B.A. Association's international student affairs committee attends to issues unique to international M.B.A. students and their families.

Application Facts and Dates

Admission decisions are made on a rolling basis. Applicants must submit all application materials on or before March 15, 2001, with a decision being mailed within four to five weeks after the application is completed. For additional information regarding the University of Notre Dame M.B.A. program, students should contact:

M.B.A. Admission
276 Mendoza College of Business
University of Notre Dame
Notre Dame, Indiana 46556-5646
Telephone: 219-631-8488
　　　　　800-631-8488 (toll-free
　　　　　　within the U.S.)
Fax: 219-631-8800
E-mail: mba.1@nd.edu
World Wide Web: http://www.nd.edu/~mba

The **Lauder** INSTITUTE

University of Pennsylvania

Joseph H. Lauder Institute of Management & International Studies

Philadelphia, Pennsylvania

> ### ONE WORLD, TWO DEGREES
>
> *Superb management skills merely open the door to a career as an international manager. To excel, individuals also need a solid grasp of the global environment of business and a finely tuned understanding of the culture, language, business practices, history, and politics of the regions in which they will work. The Joseph H. Lauder Institute of Management & International Studies provides this blend through a unique program that integrates two critical degrees: the M.B.A. and the M.A. in international studies. The Lauder Institute is a pioneer in integrating management education, international studies, and language and cross-cultural competencies.*
>
> —Dr. Stephen J. Kobrin, Director and William H. Wurster Professor of Multinational Management

Programs and Curricular Focus

The curriculum is an intensive, twenty-four-month program in conjunction with the Wharton School and the School of Arts and Sciences that integrates three essentials for the global manager. The first is a superior management education. The Wharton M.B.A. provides a foundation in the disciplines vital to the practice of professional development. The second essential is focused international studies. An integrated sequence of courses prepares Lauder students to understand the international political, economic, and social contexts in which their organizations will operate. The third is high-level language and cross-cultural courses. Mastery of a second language and detailed attention to regional, cultural, and managerial perspectives provide an essential base for future success.

All students complete the core management curriculum for the Wharton M.B.A. They also pursue a disciplinary concentration in any of Wharton's fields, such as strategic management, multinational management, marketing, finance, or operations management. Lauder students fulfill all of the requirements for the Wharton M.B.A. degree.

For the M.A. degree, students pursue an international studies course sequence in the social sciences and humanities with School of Arts & Sciences faculty members as well as courses in their regional and language specialization. Several courses, such as area history and international political economy, were designed particulaly for the Lauder program.

The advanced language and cultural perspectives program develops students' knowledge of another language and culture for use in professional settings. Students must attain superior proficiency in this second language to graduate. They live and study in the region of their specialization during the first summer's cultural immersion program abroad and typically arrange an Executive Internship in an international environment during their second summer. Students select from the following regional and language options: East Asia (Mandarin Chinese or Japanese), Europe (French, German, or Russian), Latin America (Portuguese or Spanish), or North America (English). Upon graduation, students are competent to function independently and conduct business in their selected language.

Students and the Program Experience

With a student body of approximately 100 students, the Lauder Institute is a small community of people devoted to international studies. All of the students enter the program with previous experience living, working, or studying outside their home countries. Eighty percent of the class has worked abroad for six months or more. All Lauder students are fluent in a second language, and 80 percent are fluent in a third language. Of the 50 students entering Lauder each May, 35 percent are women, 19 percent are members of minority groups, and 37 percent are international students from approximately thirteen countries.

❖ Global Focus

Lauder students do not just study a world region, they experience it. At least 20 percent of their time is spent abroad, where they are immersed in a region's language, economics, history, politics, law, religion, business, and culture.

Special Features

During their first summer abroad, students experience life and business in major cosmopolitan centers and regional areas. They gain in-depth appreciation for the country's history, society, politics, business, theater, art, and literature through the local language. Housing varies from country to country, ranging from university quarters to apartments to homes. Corporate visits, a highlight of the summer program, are conducted in the language of study and give students a firsthand look into the operations and cultures of international businesses. These visits to both multinational and indigenous companies provide opportunities for field projects associated with core courses in the M.B.A. program.

Executive Internships during the second summer provide the opportunity to work in a business setting rooted in another culture. Students take the lead in obtaining internships, with support from the Wharton School and the Lauder Institute. Over the years, Lauder students have held Executive Internships in 260 companies in thirty-eight countries. Students live and work in a country for twelve weeks, learning to apply their expertise in meaningful positions. Companies benefit from the advanced management and language skills the students bring. Often, internships lead to offers of permanent employment following graduation.

The Faculty

The Wharton School is ranked as the nation's premier school in management education and research. Today, the Wharton School comprises eleven departments and nineteen research centers. With a faculty of nearly 500 and a student body of more than 2,000, the Graduate Division of the University of Pennsylvania's School of Arts & Sciences is one of the world's leading graduate programs in the liberal arts. The school has thirty programs with some of the world's finest scholars on its faculty, contributing to the school's reputation for strong interdisciplinary research and instruction.

The Business School Network

Students benefit from a diverse, supportive, and dedicated community of classmates who enter the program from countries all over the world. Upon graduation, they join a still broader network of alumni in management positions around the globe. Lauder Institute graduates belong to a worldwide network of more than 750 alumni in more than forty countries. Lauder alumni offer one another valuable international experience and contacts, and frequently open doors to a wide array of opportunities.

Students enjoy exposure to senior executives of companies around the world through the Executive Lecture Series. Members of the Institute's Board of Governors, an impressive body of global corporate leaders, visit the campus each year and are dedicated to helping Lauder students become the global business leaders of the future.

The College and Environs

The University of Pennsylvania was founded in 1740 by Benjamin Franklin. The 260-acre Ivy League campus is located in University City, which contains several colleges, business and government offices, and one of the largest urban research parks in the nation. The University includes twelve leading graduate schools and serves more than 22,000 undergraduate, master's, and doctoral students.

Facilities

In addition to the vast resources of the Wharton School, the University of Pennsylvania, and the greater Philadelphia region, Lauder students enjoy many special benefits, including a modern building, simultaneous translation

facilities, satellite reception of world broadcasts, and the international camaraderie they find in the Lauder Lounge.

Placement

In addition to access to the Wharton Career Development and Placement Office, Lauder students benefit from a supportive and intimate network of alumni. Students remain in touch through personal friendships and ongoing support from the Institute, including newsletters, address lists, a regularly updated resume book, reunions, and alumni events in connection with summer immersion projects. Lauder graduates go out of their way to help one another, and they frequently speak of the bond they feel for fellow graduates. Lauder graduates have hired students for summer internships and full-time positions. As Edgar Bronfman Jr., President and CEO of Joseph E. Seagram & Sons, Inc., states, "Companies around the world recognize the value created in those who graduate from the Lauder Institute. There's no better business preparation, and graduates are positioned ideally for international management." Paul Fribourg, Chairman and CEO of Continental Grain Company, states, "Companies that want to build a worldwide business come here to hire. They know they'll find a concentrated group of very high-level people."

Admission

The Lauder Institute enrolls approximately 50 students into its M.B.A./M.A. program annually, all of whom have advanced knowledge of at least one nonnative language and are, by virtue of their experience and interests, strongly committed to international management careers. Admission to the Lauder Institute is highly competitive, and applicants are strongly encouraged to apply early. Applicants must complete both the regular Wharton M.B.A. application for admission and the Lauder Institute application. An international career focus, interest in enhancing their cross-cultural understanding, and exceptional leadership potential are the common denominators

for most successful applicants. Students are required to submit results of the Graduate Management Admission Test (GMAT), for which no minimum score is required. A TOEFL score is required of all applicants for whom English is not the native language, unless they have earned a degree from an English-speaking university. After the application materials have been submitted, candidates will be tested by telephone for oral proficiency in the language for which they have applied.

Finances

Over the course of the Institute's twenty-four-month program, in addition to the regular M.B.A. tuition, Lauder students pay an Institute fee of $17,000, which is subject to change. A limited number of scholarships and partial fellowships, need-based aid, and international student assistance is available to Lauder students.

Application Facts and Dates

The Lauder program begins in early May, and applications, which can be downloaded from the World Wide Web (address listed below), must be postmarked by the end of the first week of February. Both Wharton and Lauder use a rolling admission process and begin to evaluate applications and make admissions decisions in the middle of the previous November. Applicants receive a decision approximately eight weeks after Lauder and Wharton both receive a completed application.

For more information, students should contact:

Ms. Natacha Davis Keramidas
Associate Director for Admissions and
    Recruiting
The Lauder Institute
256 South 37th Street, 2nd Floor
Philadelphia, Pennsylvania 19104-
    6330
Telephone: 215-898-1215
Fax: 215-898-2067
E-mail: lauderinfo@wharton.upenn.
    edu
World Wide Web: http://lauder.
    wharton.upenn.edu

Wharton™ University of Pennsylvania

The Wharton School
University of Pennsylvania

The Wharton School

Philadelphia, Pennsylvania

AT THE FOREFRONT

A decade ago, long before E-commerce became the rage, Wharton researchers began digging into what one professor termed "full-contact, combat economics." Working with partners from AT&T, Merrill Lynch, MasterCard, Prudential Insurance, Unilever, and other major firms, Wharton faculty wrestled with the strategic implications of information technology and the economic value of information. The project led to the creation of one of the most popular electives in the school. In response to student interest, faculty developed a new major in Information: Strategy, Systems, and Economics (ISSE). Wharton continues to develop new majors in response to student interest, faculty insights, and marketplace demands. It is just one of the powerful ways that research from the most diverse and active group of business researchers in the world is translated into innovative programs in Wharton classrooms.

—Patrick T. Harter, Dean

Programs and Curricular Focus

Wharton's curriculum is designed to generate innovative ideas and creative thinking and to instill an excitement about learning. Students are challenged through their core courses, case studies, and leadership course work to formulate and solve problems.

The first year focuses on Wharton's business core, providing fundamental skill, knowledge, and perspectives. Traditional semesters are replaced by four tightly focused six-week quarters to expose students to the greatest number of subjects and to allow faculty to coordinate material across courses. Cohorts of 65 students, who take core courses together in the first year, form a strong social and academic group. Clusters of three cohorts form "a class within a class."

The second year allows students to choose electives from one of the largest selections of courses of any business school; this selection allows students to pursue one of seventeen majors or create joint majors and individualized programs. Students work individually and in 5-person learning teams to examine issues of self-awareness, teamwork, ethics, communication, effective negotiation, managing differences, managing careers, and power and authority.

The Joseph H. Lauder Institute of Management and International Studies offers a twenty-four-month joint-degree program to prepare future leaders to operate effectively and comfortably in a language and culture other than their own. This program leads to an M.B.A. from Wharton and an M.A. in international studies from the University's School of Arts and Sciences.

Wharton also offers joint-degree programs in the areas of communication, engineering, law, medical sciences, dental, veterinary, nursing, and social work.

The Wharton Executive M.B.A. program enables individuals with full-time job responsibilities in the private and public sectors to gain an M.B.A. degree without interrupting their careers. Experienced executives and highly promising managers nominated by their organizations enroll in the program. Classes meet all day Friday and Saturday on alternate weekends for two years.

Students and the M.B.A. Experience

Wharton students have outstanding records of professional achievement and bring a wide range of experience, insights, and interests to the classroom and to campus. Drawing on their experiences throughout the world, students offer diverse cultural viewpoints on business issues. They bring perspectives from undergraduate majors that range from English to engineering and work experience that extends from nonprofit management to marketing to corporate finance. Wharton M.B.A. students help shape the intellectual atmosphere of challenge and collaboration that is a central part of a Wharton education.

About 45 percent of incoming students have liberal arts and science degrees, and 20 percent have training in engineering. Almost all have had significant work experience in private, public, or nonprofit enterprises. Of an average class of 780 students entering Wharton each fall, 30 percent are women, 18 percent are members of minority groups, and 40 percent are foreign nationals from more than sixty countries.

❖ Global Focus

Wharton's curriculum has a strong international perspective, reinforced by a core course on global strategic management and a range of electives that provide insights into global business. In addition, the Wharton Global Immersion Program option offers four weeks of intense, hands-on experience and education abroad, following six weeks of classroom study. Recent groups have traveled to China, Europe, Latin America, and the ASEAN countries. Wharton also offers two international joint-degree programs, exchange programs with eleven leading international business schools, and opportunities to develop foreign language skills.

Special Features

A four-week preterm program ensures that students from diverse backgrounds begin the M.B.A. program on equal academic footing. The program includes an introduction to accounting, microeconomics, and statistics and optional courses in humanities and business history. The program ends with a two-day team-building retreat.

Beyond cohorts and learning teams, students pursue individual interests through more than 100 professional, social, and academic affairs clubs and task forces. Wharton also offers opportunities to work on service projects with area students and community organizations.

The Faculty

Wharton's 190 standing faculty members bring a diversity of perspectives, both theoretical and practical, to the classroom. They have earned worldwide recognition for excellence in both teaching and research. Their work has extended the frontiers of many fields—from conducting groundbreaking studies in international finance to developing one of the most widely used methods of marketing research to creating the first center for the study of entrepreneurship. Wharton professors have received numerous awards, including the Nobel Prize in Economic Sci-

ences and honors from the White House and the National Science Foundation.

The Business School Network

Corporate Partnerships

An advisory board of executives as well as corporate recruiters and alumni help shape the future development of the curriculum. In addition, more than 200 guest executive lecturers and speakers visit Wharton each year. In addition to contact with senior executives as guest lecturers in the classroom and in presentations and professional clubs, Wharton students have the opportunity to interact in a more intimate and informal context with business leaders through the Zweig Executive Dinner Series.

Prominent Alumni

Prominent alumni include the Hon. Walter H. Annenberg, a former ambassador and publisher; the Hon. William Brennan, a former chief justice; Charles S. Sanford Jr., Chairman, Bankers Trust; Reginald Jones, Chairman Emeritus, General Electric; Lewis Platt, Chairman and CEO, Hewlett-Packard; Yataro Kobayashi, Chairman and CEO, Fuji Xerox; Robert Crandall, former CEO, American Airlines; John Sculley, former CEO, Apple Computer; Jon Huntsman, Chairman and CEO, Huntsman Corporation; and Peter Lynch, former head of Fidelity Investment's Magellan Fund.

The College and Environs

The University of Pennsylvania was founded in 1740 by Benjamin Franklin. The 260-acre Ivy League campus is located in University City, which contains several colleges, business and government offices, and one of the largest urban research parks in the nation. The University includes twelve leading graduate schools and serves more than 22,000 undergraduate, master's, and doctoral students.

Facilities

In addition to a University library with nearly 4.5 million volumes, students use Wharton's Lippincott Library, which contains more than 232,000 volumes and 4,000 periodical titles specifically related to business, as well as copies of 5,000 corporate annual reports. Wharton's library computing center offers access to a variety of business, news, and information databases on optical disk and on line.

Technology Environment

From the prospective student to the alumnus, Wharton provides a network of electronic resources to support each individual's education, career, and personal development. During the admissions process, Wharton offers online opportunities to fill out applications, schedule interviews, find information, and chat with current and incoming students. For current M.B.A. students, the School's integrated intranet technology, SPIKE, provides a platform for communications, digital video streaming, class notes, course material, bidding for courses, library research, and discussion groups. Wharton also offers training courses, user documentation, and consulting services.

Placement

The Wharton Career Management Office coordinates more than thirty-five different programs for students, from identifying potential career areas and developing effective job search strategies to interviewing, negotiating, and evaluating offers. Programs include career management classes in the first year, alumni career panels, videotaped interview training, and seminars on negotiating offers.

Admission

Prerequisites for admission include completion of an undergraduate program in an ac-

credited U.S. college or its equivalent in another country, results of the Graduate Management Admission Test (GMAT) for which no minimum score is required, and completion of the Wharton application. A TOEFL score is required of all applicants for whom English is not the native language. Applicants are evaluated based on their personal qualities, academic background, and professional experience. Personal interviews are strongly encouraged but not required.

Finances

The 2000–01 educational budget for first-year students is $50,898. This cost includes tuition and fees, room and board, books and supplies, miscellaneous fees, and preterm expenses. Preterm fees apply only in the first year and vary, depending on the program components in which a student enrolls. The new Wharton Loan Program through PNC Bank now guarantees financial aid for Wharton M.B.A. students from anywhere in the world. The program allows students to borrow up to the cost of the total student budget, less any financial aid they receive.

International Students

There is a strong international student community at Wharton, with resources and programs to meet social, cultural, and professional interests. International students make up more than one third of the M.B.A. student body, and they represent more than sixty nationalities. Many of the campus club activities are generated by the cultural interests of M.B.A. students.

Application Facts and Dates

Although the final deadline for application is April 10, Wharton begins to evaluate applications and make admissions decisions in the middle of the previous November. Wharton uses a rolling admission process, evaluating applications in order of their receipt and completion. Applicants receive a decision approximately eight to twelve weeks after Wharton receives a completed application.

Ms. Rosemaria Martinelli
Director of M.B.A. Admissions
The Wharton School
University of Pennsylvania
3733 Spruce Street
Philadelphia, Pennsylvania 19104-6361
Telephone: 215-898-6183
Fax: 215-898-0120
E-mail: mba.admissions@wharton.upenn.edu
World Wide Web: http://www.wharton.upenn.edu/mba/

University of Pittsburgh

Programs and Curricular Focus

The Katz Graduate School of Business offers a unique eleven-month full-time M.B.A. program. The program begins each year in mid-July and is completed in mid-June. The program includes student participation in team-building exercises, learning organizations, capability assessments, and career evaluations. The curriculum provides a global management perspective in every phase of the program; emphasizes interrelationships across business functions; incorporates continuous quality improvement in theory and methods; focuses on teamwork, interpersonal skills, and the empowerment process; and applies leading-edge management theory to real-world problems and issues by emphasizing today's set of challenges.

Seven concentrations are offered, from accounting to strategic planning. Approximately fifty percent of the full-time M.B.A. program's credits are elective. In addition to traditional courses, students may also participate in project courses, internships, practicums, and independent studies.

The Katz School also offers an M.B.A. degree program that meets in the evenings and Saturdays to accommodate students who are employed full-time.

The Center for Executive Education offers a Master of Business Administration (E.M.B.A.) that is completed in two years. Classes are conducted on alternating Fridays and Saturdays.

Students and the M.B.A. Experience

Students in the Katz M.B.A. program bring to their studies an exciting variety of talents, backgrounds, and interests. On average, students have 4½ years of work experience in areas that include accounting, consulting, finance, information systems, manufacturing, and marketing and sales. About one third of the class generally have technical and engineering backgrounds. Students have worked in a wide variety of industries, from accounting to banking to manufacturing to health care. There is also a significant representation of students from abroad—representing approximately thirty countries—adding their experiences to the forum of ideas. A typical M.B.A. class generally includes students with degrees from as many as 150 undergraduate institutions. Undergraduate majors encompass the natural sciences and humanities, economics, business, engineering, the liberal arts and the performing arts, and virtually every other broad discipline. The varied perspectives of the students create a stimulating environment for interaction.

❖ Global Focus

The full-time M.B.A. class is divided into Management Learning Organizations (MLOs) with diverse memberships. These groups study together, prepare together, and form rotating teams as the basis for case discussions and group projects in many courses. This simulates what it is like to be in a real organization and helps students learn and practice trust building, communication, teamwork, conflict management, negotiation, and problem management skills.

Special Features

Full-time students ease into a rigorous academic schedule through the Transition Module. The Transition Module provides a series of workshops that integrate the basics of management while introducing the instructional environment at the Katz School. In addition, students have the opportunity to meet classmates during a series of social events, professional workshops, and classroom settings.

The Faculty

The faculty of the Katz School is internationally respected for its pioneering research and corporate consulting. The 70 full-time faculty members include recognized authorities in accounting, economics, finance, marketing, international business, behavioral science, quantitative methods, human resources management, operations management, management information systems, organizational studies, public and social policy, and strategic planning and policy. Corporations, governmental agencies, and not-for-profit groups commission research by the faculty members. The knowledge gained through faculty members' research and consulting becomes part of the experience of the M.B.A. student in the classroom.

The Business School Network
Corporate Partnerships

A city as important to the nation's economy as Pittsburgh is provides a wide range of opportunities for M.B.A. students. The Katz School takes advantage of these opportunities by offering an unparalleled series of activities that bring many of America's leading executives to the Katz School on a regular basis.

Through the American Assembly Dialogue, some of the country's highest-ranking executives gather on campus each spring to discuss the significant economic and social issues of the day in response to an agenda prepared by Pittsburgh M.B.A. students. The Katz School is the only school in the country to hold this annual event, which has been co-sponsored by the New York–based American Assembly since 1971.

The Executive Briefings series also fosters ties between students and business leaders. Two or three times each month, chief executives from major Pittsburgh and national corporations come to the Katz School to share their thoughts on those issues of most concern to them, then open the sessions to questions from students.

Through the Executives-in-Residence program, top executives are available on campus for one or two days, lecturing in classes and, just as importantly, mingling with students after class.

Prominent Alumni

The University of Pittsburgh counts among its alumni Donald R. Beall, Chairman and CEO, Rockwell International; Thomas E. Frank, President and CEO, Hickory Farms, Inc.; Robert H. Hood Jr., President, McDonnell Douglas Corporation; James J. Howard, Chairman and CEO, Northern States Power Company; Samuel A. McCullough, Chairman and CEO, Meridian Bancorp, Inc.; John M. Peterson, President and CEO (Retired), Erie Insurance Group; David M. Roderick, Chairman and CEO (Retired), USX Corporation; Charles Russell, President and CEO (Retired),

Visa International; John J. Shea, President and CEO, Speigel, Inc.; and Raymond W. Smith, Chairman and CEO, Bell Atlantic.

The College and Environs

Founded in 1787, the University of Pittsburgh is one of the oldest institutions of higher education in the United States. The Pittsburgh campus consists of ninety buildings on 132 acres. The campus includes the forty-two-story Cathedral of Learning, with its ornate Gothic architecture, which is the tallest school building in the Western world.

The city of Pittsburgh is the hub of the Eastern business wheel, equidistant from the major economic centers of New York and Chicago and only an hour's plane ride from other primary business points such as Philadelphia, Boston, Toronto, Montreal, Detroit, Atlanta, and Washington, D.C. Pittsburgh has a diverse economic base developed through both phases of its heralded renaissance, and it is a prominent transportation, technological, medical, commercial, and communications center as well as an international industrial leader. It is one of the country's largest corporate headquarters. Pittsburgh is an attractive city with a rich mixture of bustling industry and colorful neighborhoods. This combination of vital business and comfortable living is unusually compelling. Pittsburgh is consistently cited as one of the most livable cities in the United States.

Facilities

Mervis Hall, the home of the Katz Graduate School of Business, is sleek in appearance and represents the best in contemporary architecture and the forward-looking Pittsburgh corporate community. All M.B.A. classes are held here, which fosters a sense of unity among the M.B.A. students. The building's tiered classrooms and unique behavior science laboratory accommodate a variety of teaching modes, from case discussions and lectures to small-group exercises. Video cameras and playback systems as well as other contemporary audio and visual aids are a regular part of student learning.

Mervis Hall offers a computer and communications system that provides hands-on access to the Katz School's comprehensive internal and external data environment. The building incorporates state-of-the-art fiber optics that enable the school to have a complete communications system, including e-mail. The complex also includes a 9,000-square-foot library, interview rooms, a career library, and a videotape area. The facility also houses faculty and administrative offices,

student lounges, and offices for the School's research institutes.

Placement

The Career Services Center begins its work with each new M.B.A. class shortly after students arrive on campus. The initial step is individual counseling, which gives the student an opportunity to investigate career opportunities with the assistance of a placement officer. To enhance this phase of the placement process, the placement office sponsors lunchtime seminars in which middle- and upper-level managers from major companies meet with groups of students to speak informally about their jobs and careers. The Career Services Center schedules career seminars on topics such as writing effective resumes and cover letters, interviewing skills, and job search strategies. Students participate in mock interview sessions that are videotaped and analyzed by placement staff. The placement office maintains a comprehensive, up-to-date placement library with handbooks, business reviews, annual reports, and a database of contact persons for hundreds of companies and organizations. The placement office also compiles an M.B.A.-student resume directory, which is distributed to some 500 companies nationwide. Last year, more than 100 companies participated in on-campus interviewing, which began in November and continued through June.

Admission

The Katz School has developed an online inquiry and application system. Applicants may apply online and waive their application fee. All applicants are required to have earned an undergraduate degree or, for international applicants, the equivalent of a U.S. bachelor's degree. Applicants need not have had prior business course work to be eligible for admission. Applicants are required to have completed at least introductory college-level work in integral and differential calculus prior to enrollment in the M.B.A. program. All applicants are required to have taken the GMAT. The Test of English as a Foreign Language (TOEFL) is required if the applicant's native language is not English. The Admissions Committee reviews and evaluates each applicant's academic record, GMAT score, letters of recommendation, essays, professional work history, and other information presented by the candidate on the application. Deadline information can be obtained from the Katz School's Web site (listed below).

Finances

Tuition for 1999–2000 full-time Pennsylvania residents was $16,629 for the year of

study. Tuition for 1999–2000 full-time non-Pennsylvania residents was $28,326 for the year of study. Fees totaled $2418. Tuition for 1999–2000 for part-time/evening students was $481 per credit for Pennsylvania residents and $901 per credit for non-Pennsylvania residents. Fees for part-time students were $90 per term.

For full-time study, students should budget a minimum of $15,000 for the year—in addition to tuition and fees—for room, board, and miscellaneous expenses. This is a baseline estimate, since individual needs and preferences create a wide variance in actual living costs.

The primary source of financial assistance is tuition scholarships, which are awarded in various dollar amounts and applied against tuition charges. These scholarships are awarded primarily on the basis of academic merit, with financial need as a secondary consideration. Scholarship decisions are made and funds are typically distributed by early February, so early application is encouraged. Teaching fellowships and assistantships are not offered through the Katz School for students studying at the master's level. Because of the amount of course work students must undertake in the M.B.A. program, there is insufficient time to commit to a teaching fellowship.

International Students

Approximately 50 percent of the M.B.A. class are international students. The University of Pittsburgh's Office of International Services provides assistance with admissions and advising on personal, social, immigration, and financial matters.

Application Facts and Dates

Generally, applications are reviewed and decision notification is sent within a four- to six-week time frame from the date the application with all required documentation is received. Applicants requesting scholarship aid should submit their complete applications to the full-time M.B.A. program early. Deadline information can be obtained from the Katz School's Web site (listed below). Part-time/evening applicants should submit their completed applications one or two months prior to the preferred term of entry.

Office of Enrollment Management
276 Mervis Hall
Joseph M. Katz Graduate School of Business
University of Pittsburgh
Pittsburgh, Pennsylvania 15260
Telephone: 412-648-1700
Fax: 412-648-1659
E-mail: mba-admissions@katz.business.pitt.edu
World Wide Web: http://www.pitt.edu/

University of Reading

ISMA Centre

Reading, England

THE BUSINESS SCHOOL FOR FINANCIAL MARKETS

The value of any program of education and training in finance is the recognition it receives from the financial community at large. The market leaders who have given their support to ISMA Centre programs include Reuters, Bridge Telerate, Bloomberg, the London Stock Exchange, ISMA, and, of course, the member firms of ISMA themselves. Our graduates have been employed by more than 100 securities companies, including J. P. Morgan, Goldman Sachs, Dresdner Kleinwort Benson, C. S. First Boston, Warburg Dillon Read, Chase Manhattan, Barclays Capital, Nomura, and Merrill Lynch. If you are seeking a qualification in finance that includes an international dimension, then the ISMA Centre is the premier location in Europe for such programs.

—Professor Brian Scott-Quinn, Director, University of Reading ISMA Centre

Programs and Curricular Focus

The M.Sc. in international securities, investment, and banking is a postgraduate degree program that was established in 1994 and is an excellent route for students who seek a career in any area of the investment and securities industry, particularly front-office sales and trading roles. The M.Sc. in risk management, operations, and regulation focuses on two key nontrading areas of the investment and securities industry: identifying and controlling risk and the legal and regulatory infrastructure of financial markets. This program is designed for students with a first degree in law, for example, as well as those with a first degree in business.

These nine-month full-time programs are both academically and intellectually rigorous and are designed for those wishing to enter or those who are already in the international securities industry. They cover all financial markets and are equally suited to those who wish to work in U.S., European, Asian, or Australasian markets.

The unique INVEST dealing rooms have fifty Reuters 3000 dealing positions with live datafeeds, spreadsheet valuation models, computer-based derivative securities valuation, and portfolio management simulations. Students also have access to Bloomberg terminals in the purpose-built $5-million teaching facility.

The degree programs are divided into three terms of ten weeks each. The common first term provides a general introduction to the international securities industry, including industry training sessions, and develops the core concepts of corporate finance. Fixed income, equity, and derivative securities are then analyzed. The first term ends in early January with an examination on topics covered up to that time. The options in the second term then differ depending on the program chosen and include portfolio management, operations management, risk management, corporate control, financial regulation, and mergers and acquisitions.

Although these courses have many innovations in their content, delivery, and use of industry software, they have been designed to ensure that the topics covered also include the major areas required by many of the world's professional examination bodies, such as the Chartered Financial Analysts of America (CFA/AIMR). In addition, the Director of Professional Education has arranged for training to be provided to allow participants to undertake examinations such as the NYSE/NASDAQ Series examinations.

To supplement the existing programs, a twelve-month full-time master's degree in financial engineering and quantitative analysis has been developed. This program is designed for students with a first degree in engineering, mathematics, or physics, for example, as well as for those with a first degree in economics or econometrics. The Centre also awards Doctoral Scholarships in finance to suitably qualified candidates.

Students and the M.Sc. Experience

The ISMA Centre's programs are designed both for those who have recently graduated with a first degree in economics, accounting, or business and also for those with a first degree in other disciplines, such as computer studies, mathematics, physics, chemistry, or law. Students who have already had employment experience and have a good GMAT score are also welcome.

The master's degree provides individuals with the core competencies and skills required by firms operating in the international securities market.

Although 200 places are available each year, there are more than 800

The new purpose-built ISMA Centre building.

One of the dealing rooms at the ISMA Centre.

applicants. Because of this, the program can only accept those who are well qualified.

Students enter the program from more than fifty different countries. Many are from continental and Eastern Europe as well as the U.K., with more than 10 percent of applicants coming from the Americas. There are also students from the Middle East, Asia, and Australasia.

Special Features
The ISMA Centre is supported by the International Securities Market Association (ISMA), which serves as the market regulator and trade association of what has now become the largest capital market in the world after domestic government bond markets. The members of ISMA are the securities houses that trade international securities and meet the investment needs of their clients. There are currently about 700 member firms from fifty countries, clear evidence of the Association's international character.

ISMA, whose head office is in Zurich, Switzerland, has donated $5 million to the University for the construction of a purpose-built facility on campus exclusively for these programs and related international securities courses.

The Faculty
The ISMA Centre is part of the Business and Management Group in the Department of Economics, which was awarded an official research ranking of fourth out of 100 business and management units in British universities.

Every member of the full-time ISMA Centre teaching staff has a doctorate and is actively researching their specialist area of finance. They work alongside visiting professors who teach part-time on their specialist subject and have been involved professionally in the international securities industry as well as in financial research.

In addition to the academic staff members, the Centre enjoys weekly presentations from industry professionals from the City of London financial markets.

The Business School Network
Supported by ISMA, the Centre enjoys a privileged position in the provision of education and research in international securities, investment, and banking. Proximity to London allows representatives of the member firms working in the City of London to contribute their expertise and guidance to the program. As a partner of the Centre for the Study of Financial Innovation (CSFI), a London-based body financed by the securities industry, the ISMA Centre benefits from weekly presentations from city practitioners. The Centre is also one of the partners of Carnegie Mellon University in Pittsburgh in the Financial Analysis and Securities Trading (FAST) trading and investment simulation program.

The College and Environs
The University of Reading has more than a century of history. It was originally an extension college of Oxford University and received its Royal Charter in 1926. With student numbers exceeding 13,000, it is one of Britain's largest and most successful traditional universities, providing excellence in teaching and research.

The landscaped campus is situated on its own 300-acre site on the outskirts of Reading, which provides a central focus for academic, social, and recreational aspects of University life.

Reading is an outer commuter suburb of London located between Oxford and Windsor. London's Heathrow International Airport is conveniently nearby.

Facilities
The ISMA Centre is centrally situated on the University Campus and has its own high-specification facility comprising a 120-seat lecture theater, seminar rooms, catering facilities, resource and computer rooms, and unique INVEST dealing rooms with Bloomberg terminals and fifty Reuters 3000 dealing positions.

Students are also able to make use of the facilities elsewhere on campus, including the large University library, which offers CD-ROM databases and Internet services as well as the usual selection of books, periodicals, archives, and audiovisual materials.

The University of Reading has many residence halls, some with full en-suite facilities, which are conveniently situated on campus. Most sports, including American football, are supported by the University.

Placement
The Centre has excellent links with employers and selection firms and provides an assessment and career advisory service. Career opportunities are assisted by the distribution to employers of profiles of all the students in the program. The Centre's graduates benefit from recruitment visits from many of the international banks and securities houses based in the city.

Admission
Admission requirements are a minimum GPA of 3.3 or an upper second class honours degree or equivalent, two academic references, and an academic transcript. GMAT scores higher than 600 are preferred. There should be evidence of a high level of numeracy and English language fluency (minimum TOEFL score of 590 or minimum IELTS score of 7).

Those applying are expected to demonstrate an interest in a career in the fields of corporate finance, portfolio management, investment banking, securities, mergers and acquisitions, risk management, market regulation, and compliance or corporate treasury.

Finances
Full-time tuition for the M.Sc. program during the 2000–01 academic year is £9500 (approximately $14,000 U.S. dollars). The estimate of a year's living costs for 2000–01 is £5600 (approximately $8500 U.S. dollars).

Application Facts and Dates

For an explanatory brochure and application form, students should contact:

Samantha Heslop
University of Reading
ISMA Centre
Whiteknights
P.O. Box 242
Reading RG6 6BA
England
Telephone: 44-118-931-6675
Fax: 44-118-931-4741
E-mail: admin@ismacentre.reading.ac.uk
World Wide Web: http://www.ismacentre.reading.ac.uk

University of Rhode Island

HIGH-QUALITY EDUCATION WITH PERSONAL ATTENTION

It is with great pride that I present our M.B.A. programs to you. They are aimed toward individuals who have the passion and interest to succeed in their current or future positions. Our graduate programs draw on an outstanding faculty with the education and experience to challenge our students to achieve their objectives. In our programs, we do not take for granted the importance of bringing everyday business issues to the classroom for evaluation and solution as well as those issues that businesses will face in the future. The use of executives in residence, adjunct faculty members from the business community, and visiting professors from foreign institutions are an important part of the graduate education experience in our College. A dedicated faculty and staff focusing on the student differentiates us from other M.B.A. programs. I am proud to introduce you to our programs.

—Edward M. Mazze, Dean and the Alfred J. Verrecchia-Hasbro Inc. Leadership Chair in Business

Programs and Curricular Focus

The College of Business Administration at the University of Rhode Island (URI) offers three master's programs in business administration. The Kingston M.B.A. program integrates course work, career planning and development, and work experience within a one-calendar-year period. A group of up to 30 students begin the program in August and end over the summer with two required courses and an internship or two electives. It takes the traditional curriculum of eighteen courses and allocates these courses into "modules," each including a number of themes that are integrated throughout the program. Students work in teams on projects and presentations and are required to do an independent research project with assistance from a faculty mentor.

The Providence M.B.A. program is aimed at individuals who want to pursue a degree while maintaining their professional commitments. This program requires the completion of 54 credits, or eighteen courses. Waivers are available for students with previous business courses. These students generally take 36 credits to complete the program. Classes (with a maximum of 25 students) meet one night a week during the fall, spring, and summer sessions in Providence. Concentrations include accounting, finance, international business, management, management science and information systems, and marketing.

The Weekend Executive M.B.A. program meets every other Friday/Saturday for eighteen months at the W. Alton Jones campus in West Greenwich, Rhode Island. Classes start each August, with a class size of approximately 25 students. This program is designed around three modules, each with its own set of learning and behavioral objectives designed to have a direct impact on performance at work. The program includes the use of cases and projects that allow participants to use their work-related problems in their analyses, as well as a weeklong international trip.

Students and the M.B.A. Experience

The M.B.A. experience at URI combines case studies, lectures, simulations, team and individual projects, and presentations to develop the skills needed to excel in business. Executives in residence, adjunct faculty members from the business community, and visiting professors add an important dimension to the program. Students come from a diverse range of majors, industries, and job categories— making for a great learning and networking experience.

The fall 1999 entering class for the Kingston M.B.A. had average GMAT scores of 550 and an average undergraduate GPA of 3.2. Thirty-three percent are women, 33 percent are international, and 11 percent have an advanced degree. The average age is 26. The breakdown of undergraduate degrees is 17 percent in social science, 33 percent in business, 33 percent in engineering, 6 percent in economics, and 11 percent in math/science. The fall 1999 entering class for the Providence M.B.A. had average GMAT scores of 547 and an average undergraduate GPA of 3.0. Twenty-five percent are women and 18 percent have an advanced degree. The average age is 32. The breakdown of undergraduate degrees is 28 percent in social science, 29 percent in business, 20 percent in engineering, 5 percent in economics, and 18 percent in math/science. The fall 1999 entering class for the Executive M.B.A. had average GMAT scores of 554 and an average undergraduate GPA of 3.0. Seventeen percent are women and 17 percent have an advanced degree. The average age is 34. The breakdown of undergraduate degrees is 11 percent in social science, 22 percent in business, 39 percent in engineering, and 28 percent in math/science.

The Faculty

The College of Business Administration at URI consists of 55 faculty members. In addition to teaching, faculty members take part in a variety of research and consulting projects as well as participate in other professional and public service activities. Some are corporate board members, while most belong to professional organizations. Faculty members use a variety of teaching methods, including WebCT and e-mail courses. Class size is kept small for interaction amongst students and faculty members.

The Business School Network

The College of Business Administration is the headquarters for four internationally recognized institutes that specialize in academic and business research. The Institute for International Business supports the activities aimed at globalizing the curriculum by creating joint research projects and faculty and student exchanges with international universities in Russia and Germany. The Research Institute for Telecommunications and Information Marketing is a leader in the generation and dissemination of knowledge of telecommunications and information marketing. It does so through lectures by visiting executives, class projects, and research grants. The Research Center in Business and Economics brings together resources from various departments to assist business, nonprofit, and government agencies in formulating, conducting, and evaluating research projects. The center also conducts statewide consumer confidence surveys. The Pacific-Basin Capital Markets Research Center creates, maintains, and distributes capital market data for eleven nations in the Pacific Basin region. It provides an international forum for global communities of business and government to exchange ideas and information.

The College and Environs
URI was founded as a land-grant college in 1892. The University enrolls more than 10,300 undergraduate students and 3,000 graduate students. One of the seven colleges at URI, the College of Business Administration, which was 80 years old in 2000, offers the B.S., the M.B.A., the M.S. in accounting, and the Ph.D. in business administration. The Kingston M.B.A. takes place on the main campus in Kingston, Rhode Island—15 miles from scenic Newport and the Atlantic Ocean. It is only 30 miles south of the capital of Providence, where the Evening M.B.A. program is held. The W. Alton Jones Campus, home to the Executive M.B.A. program, lies on a 2,300-acre wooded site, furnished with the comforts of home, only minutes from a major highway.

Facilities
URI offers a wide variety of facilities on all campuses. The library collection of more than 1 million bound volumes and 1.5 million microforms is housed in the University Library in Kingston and Providence. Online public access is available to all students. The Dennis Callaghan Microcomputer Laboratory provides access to PC and PS/2 microcomputers and a broad range of software. The Decision Support Lab provides access to the University's extensive mainframe computer and superminicomputer facilities. Three Mac labs are also available for student use. E-mail addresses are given to each student upon arrival, with the ability for participants to access the Web through ISP addresses in various locations.

A large athletic complex with an indoor track, multipurpose courts, a swimming facility, a gymnastics training center, and two fitness rooms is available on the Kingston campus. Graduate housing, an international students' office, disability services, and special tutoring are also available.

Placement
URI helps students assess their goals, develop skills, and implement career objectives through the Career Services Department. Professional career advisers and planning specialists provide individual advising, noncredit workshops, on-campus interviews, and semester job fairs with leading global organizations. The staff members help students explore internships, job and career inquiries, resume and cover letter writing, job search methods, and research concerning potential employers. More than 90 percent of 1999 graduates were employed within three months after graduation, with a median starting salary of $55,000.

Admission
All candidates for admission are required to provide a completed application that consists of a statement of purpose, official scores from the Graduate Management Admission Test (GMAT), official transcripts from all universities attended, two letters of recommendation, and a $30 application fee for in-state residents ($45 for nonresidents). Applicants for whom English is not the native language are required to score 575 or above on the TOEFL.

Finances
Tuition for the 1999–2000 academic year for the entire Kingston One-Year program was $7300 for Rhode Island residents and $21,000 for nonresidents. Additional University fees were $1300 per semester. Tuition for the Providence M.B.A. program for Rhode Island residents was $197 per credit; it was $562 per credit for nonresidents. Fees were approximately $50 per semester. The Executive M.B.A. program, which includes tuition, room, meals, books, a notebook computer, and costs associated with the international trip, cost $35,000. Limited graduate assistantships are available for all full-time students. Students who work 10 hours per week receive half tuition plus a stipend; students who work 20 hours per week receive full tuition plus a stipend.

Application Facts and Dates
The application deadline for the Kingston One-Year M.B.A. and Executive M.B.A. programs is June 1 for U.S. citizens and April 15 for international students. Providence M.B.A. program applications are due July 15 for September admission and November 15 for January admission. For more information, applicants should contact:

Graduate Programs Office
College of Business Administration
210 Ballentine Hall, 7 Lippitt Road
University of Rhode Island
Kingston, Rhode Island 02881
Telephone: 401-874-5000
Fax: 401-874-7047
E-mail: hadz@uri.edu
World Wide Web: http://www.cba.uri.edu/Graduate/MBA.htm

University of Rochester

Rochester, New York

A SIMON SCHOOL EDUCATION—PREPARATION FOR A LIFETIME CAREER IN MANAGEMENT

▶ *The Simon School's integrated, cross-functional approach to management is enhanced by our small size and significant international composition. The school's small size promotes communication among faculty members and students that is very difficult to achieve in a large, departmentalized school. The international student body, combined with the School's emphasis on student teams, brings the global workplace to life for the Simon School student.*

—Charles I. Plosser, Dean

Programs and Curricular Focus

The Simon School's M.B.A. programs are designed to train individuals to solve management problems as team members in a study-team structure. The curriculum emphasizes learning the principles of economics and effective decision making through a mix of lecture, case study, and project courses. The degree program requires 67 hours (twenty quarter courses) and can be completed in six quarters of full-time study. Five core courses are required in the underlying disciplines of economics, applied statistics, accounting, and computers and information systems. One course must be taken in each of the functional areas of finance, marketing, operations management, and organization theory. A 3-credit course in business communications is required of all full-time students. Eleven elective courses are required, of which five or more may form a sequence of concentration, although a concentration is not required for graduation. The fourteen areas of concentration offered are corporate accounting, public accounting, accounting and information systems, business environment and public policy, computers and information systems, e-commerce, entrepreneurship, finance, health-care management, international management, marketing, operations management–manufacturing, operations management–services, and competitive and organizational strategy. Students may select an individualized double-concentration to customize their course of study in preparation for specific career objectives.

Students and the M.B.A. Experience

Each September approximately 170 students enter the Simon community as members of four cohorts (class teams). Another 60 students join their classmates in January as cohort number five. Each cohort takes all core classes together. September entrants complete the first-year core courses during the fall, winter, and spring quarters; the majority of January entrants complete core courses during the winter, spring, and summer quarters. Within each cohort, students are assigned to a study team of 4 or 5 members. Due to the large number of students from outside the United States (42 percent), the study-team structure at the Simon School takes on special significance. Each team always includes representatives from at least three countries.

Simon students enter the program with a wide range of educational, professional, and geographic backgrounds. In the class of 2001, 125 undergraduate institutions and forty-two countries are represented. Undergraduate majors include economics, humanities, social sciences, business and commerce, engineering, and math and science. Prior full-time work experience averages 5.7 years, and the average age is 29. Women comprise 14 percent of the class. Fifteen percent of Simon students are members of American minority groups.

❖ Global Focus

Of the leading business schools, the Simon School is one of the most geographically diverse. More than 40 percent of its students come from outside the United States. Approximately one third of its alumni reside and work outside of the United States, and about one third of its tenure-track faculty members have non-U.S. backgrounds. The Simon School emphasizes the high percentage of international students because the success of its hands-on approach to global management education depends in part on the cultural, geographic, and profes-

sional composition of the student management teams. The benefits of such a richly internationalized student and alumni population are obvious. A Simon School education combines rigorous training in the business disciplines and functions with cross-cultural training and lifelong professional contact with an international alumni network.

During the Broaden Your Horizons seminar series, students present lunch hour seminars about their various countries' cultures, economies, political environments, and business protocols. Exchange programs are offered with schools in eight countries, each approved by a faculty committee for compatibility with Simon M.B.A. program objectives. Interested students pursue study abroad during one quarter of their second year of study.

Special Features

The VISION program is the student-managed portion of the Simon School's M.B.A. program. Designed each year by a committee of second-year M.B.A. students, the VISION program consists of sixteen teaching modules that supplement and enhance the academic curriculum. Student managers use the human resources and expertise of corporate sponsors—in partnership with Simon administrators, faculty members, and other students—to present required (and some optional) modules covering such topics as project management, teamwork, negotiation skills, leadership training, and ethics. Past corporate partners have included AT&T, IBM, PepsiCo, Procter & Gamble Company, and Xerox Corporation, among others.

To ensure that Simon School graduates possess effective oral and written communication skills, they are required to complete a management-communication sequence comprising two courses, Presentation Skills and Business Writing and Editing.

The Faculty

The Simon School faculty is known internationally for leading scholarship in management education. There is a long tradition at Simon of coordinating teaching and research, as well as integrating knowledge from all of the functional areas into the curriculum. Faculty accessibility is a specific benefit of a Simon education. Teaching awards for the best teachers are presented annually by each M.B.A. class, and teaching is improved continuously through a formal faculty peer-review. Leading-edge research is intrinsic to teaching the basic scientific principles of management. Many research findings used by the Simon faculty in classroom study have served as foundations for corporate practices in use today. Simon faculty members serve as editors on six major academic journals, and six recent studies of research productivity rank them among the top five faculties in the United States.

The Business School Network

Corporate Partnerships

The Frederick Kalmbach Executive Seminar Series, jointly sponsored by the Simon School and the Graduate Business Club, features senior corporate executives who lecture annually on current issues in management. Each year a number of the series' speakers include members or professional associates of Simon's internationally prominent Executive Advisory Committee. Simon students participate in annual marketing-case competitions and consulting-case competitions and, through the VISION program described above, students interact directly with the employees of top international corporate partners. Students work directly with local worldwide corporations, such as Bausch & Lomb and Eastman Kodak Company, in project courses offered as part of the regular academic curriculum.

Prominent Alumni

The long list of successful Simon alumni includes Richard T. Bourns, Senior Vice President, Eastman Kodak Company; Paul A. Brands, Chief Executive Officer, American Management Systems; W. Scott Gould, Chief Financial Officer, United States Department of Commerce; Mark B. Grier, Executive Vice President, Financial Management, The Prudential Insurance Company of America; Charles R. Hughes, President, Hughes & Associates, Inc.; John C. MacDonald, Managing Director, Lehman Brothers; R. Kae Robertson, Partner, Ernst & Young; and Joseph T. Willett, Chief Operating Officer, Merrill Lynch Europe, Middle East and Africa (MLEMEA), Merrill Lynch & Co., Inc.

The College and Environs

The Simon School is part of the ivy-clad University of Rochester, an independent, leading research university offering graduate study in approximately fifty fields to about 2,700 of its 7,100 students. Situated near Lake Ontario, one of the Great Lakes, the metropolitan Rochester area (population 1 million) is home to many major international industries and entrepreneurial ventures, including Eastman Kodak Company, Bausch & Lomb, and Xerox Corporation's marketing group. Numerous cultural and recreational opportunities include the Rochester Philharmonic Orchestra and the University's own Eastman School of Music.

Facilities

Schlegel Hall, opened in 1991, is the Simon School's classroom and student services building. It contains case-style classrooms equipped with state-of-the-art technology and rear projection equipment, study rooms, a student lounge, and its own Computing Center. The center supports student-accessible IBM-compatible computers linked for data sharing and laser printing via local area networks and access to several external data sources, such as Bloomberg, Business News, and Dow Jones, as well as e-mail services on the Internet. A 38,000-square-foot addition is scheduled for completion in June 2001. On-campus graduate housing, both high-rise apartments and town houses, is available to Simon students. Off-campus housing is also available.

Placement

With an average placement rate of 97.3 percent for three years running, the Career Services Office is committed to Simon students' success. Through personalized career counseling, education, and the development of a targeted job search strategy, students are poised to secure meaningful internships and full-time opportunities in investment banking, finance, consulting, marketing, e-commerce, technology, operations, and start-up ventures. Aggressive corporate outreach and long-standing recruiting relationships account for 38 percent of full-time positions derived from on-campus interviews. In 1999, the mean total offer package for graduates was $94,500.

Admission

A Simon School Admissions Committee reads each application individually and evaluates recommendations, teamwork and communication skills, the nature and scope of prior work experience, the undergraduate academic record, GMAT scores, TOEFL scores as an indicator of English-language skills, evidence of leadership and maturity, and career focus. English language proficiency is critically important for successful interaction in the Simon School's geo-graphically diversified study-team structure. Potential contributions to Simon classmates and to the world's business community are carefully considered. All undergraduate majors are represented in the program.

Finances

In addition to the $75 application fee, tuition is $882 per credit hour, or $26,460 per year, for 2000–01. The cost of books and supplies averages $1300 a year, and living expenses (rent, food supplies, personal expenses, and health insurance) are estimated at less than $10,000 for the 2000–01 academic year. Both U.S. and international applicants are eligible for merit awards. The deadline for applying for merit-scholarship assistance is March 1 for September applicants and November 1 for January applicants.

International Students

There is an active program of support for international students in Rochester. The University of Rochester's International Student Affairs Office provides professional guidance to incoming international students. They are assisted by an independent, but University-affiliated, community volunteer group, the Rochester International Friendship Council, which locates host families for interested Simon students and helps students' spouses in language instruction and acculturation. Social outings and employment and cultural adjustment workshops are offered during late August orientation for all University international students. Instruction in English as a second language and orientation to U.S. culture are also available through the Simon English Language and U.S. Culture Program, offered each August.

Application Facts and Dates

Application deadlines are March 1 (for merit-scholarship consideration) and June 1 for September enrollment, November 1 for January enrollment. Students are notified of admissions decisions on a rolling basis. For additional information, students should contact:

Pamela Black-Colton
Assistant Dean for M.B.A. Admissions and Administration
William E. Simon Graduate School of Business Administration
University of Rochester
Rochester, New York 14627-0107
Telephone: 716-275-3533
Fax: 716-271-3907
E-mail: mbaadm@simon.rochester.edu
World Wide Web: http://www.simon.rochester.edu

University of St. Thomas

Graduate School of Business

Minneapolis and St. Paul, Minnesota

▶ **DECISION MAKING IN AN ETHICAL FRAMEWORK**

The Graduate School of Business at the University of St. Thomas has more than 3,000 students in nine graduate degree programs and is one of the five largest graduate schools of business in the U.S. Our programs are known for their excellence in teaching and their emphasis on an applications orientation.

Decision making under an ethical framework is a theme that runs throughout the M.B.A. programs' curricula. Class size is kept to 25 students or fewer to ensure appropriate interaction among students and the instructor. As a result, the classroom experience is dynamic and stimulating.

Through its excellence in teaching and service to the community and through the success of its alumni, the St. Thomas M.B.A. and other graduate business degree programs have gained the reputation of being among the best in the United States. We invite you to join us and help us add to that reputation.

—Theodore L . Fredrickson, Dean and McNeely Chair Professor

Programs and Curricular Focus

St. Thomas's Graduate School of Business offers a comprehensive array of educational resources encompassing nine degree programs and seventeen professional development centers and institutes. These are specifically designed to meet the needs of adult learners, with a strong theory-based and practitioner-oriented approach and curriculum. Students benefit from the enhanced knowledge that derives from immediately applying what they learn in the classroom to the challenges they experience in the workplace, with valuable real-world guidance and feedback from faculty members with extensive business and academic backgrounds.

The Evening M.B.A. program provides working professionals with a comprehensive business management education, beginning with a base of foundation and core courses tailored to students' individual needs. Students complete a minimum of four concentration courses, and the program culminates with one of four integrative capstone courses. Areas of concentration include accounting, environmental management, finance, financial services management, franchise management, health-care management, human resource management, information management, management, manufacturing systems, marketing, nonprofit management, real estate, risk and insurance management, sports and entertainment management, and venture management. Graduate-level certificates

are also available in some concentrations for students who choose not to earn a degree, but wish to gain expertise at an accelerated pace.

St. Thomas' newest program, the Day M.B.A., was launched in fall 1997. Designed for recent college graduates and career changers, it provides students with the business knowledge and skills they need to get their careers off to a strong start through an innovative curriculum with extensive experiential components.

Other master's programs offered by the Graduate School of Business include the Accounting M.B.A., a full-time, fifteen-month program for recent liberal arts and sciences graduates and those seeking a career change to the accounting profession; the Executive M.B.A., with an integrative focus for experienced managers; the Master of Business Communication, for professional communicators who wish to broaden their business knowledge and enhance their technical skills; the Master of International Management, for managers wishing to develop or extend a career in international business in the U.S. or abroad; the M.B.A. in Human Resource Management Program, for human resource professionals wishing to develop specific competencies; the M.B.A. in Medical Group Management Program, for health-care professionals and those wishing to develop a management career in that field; and the M.S. in Real Estate Appraisal Program, for real estate

appraisers who are involved in complex appraisal assignments.

Students and the M.B.A. Experience

St. Thomas's Graduate School of Business is the fourth-largest in the United States, with an enrollment of more than 3,000 students in its nine degree programs. Students come from a wide range of educational and professional backgrounds, with most from the region around the Twin Cities. The student body is composed of 55 percent men and 45 percent women; 5 percent are members of minority groups, and 4 percent are international students. Ages vary somewhat by program, ranging from the 20s to 40s and beyond. Postundergraduate work experience varies accordingly, and current students are employed at more than 2,000 companies. This diversity in the student body greatly enhances the educational experience through the different perspectives brought to team projects, classroom discussions, and other activities.

❖ Global Focus

International issues are addressed in the curricula of almost all the degree programs, and the Master of International Management program is specifically designed to provide the necessary business skills, foreign language proficiency, and cultural sensitivity needed to compete successfully in the global marketplace. In addition, students can take advantage of several study-abroad and exchange programs with affiliate schools in Europe, Asia, Canada, and South America.

The Faculty

St. Thomas's full-time and adjunct faculty members, many of whom are leaders in their industries, bring a wealth of business and academic experience to the classroom. This unique mixture of expertise results in leading-edge curricula and the real-world applied approach that makes a University of St. Thomas degree so valued in the business community. Students benefit from this expertise through the accessibility that results from small class sizes and the advisory or mentoring roles assumed by many faculty members.

The Business School Network

The Graduate School of Business is highly regarded in the business community and benefits from the support and involvement of leaders in multiple sectors of that community in a variety of ways. Many teach as adjunct faculty members, serve as guest lecturers, sponsor internships, or host students at their facilities. In addition, many serve on boards advising the school and its various degree programs and concentrations, thus ensuring a dialogue between the school and its corporate partners that results in curricula and programming that truly meet the demands of a competitive, rapidly changing marketplace. Several companies have sponsored endowed chairs in business ethics, family business, risk and insurance management, international management, management, and entrepreneurship. The Executive Fellows of the Graduate School of Business comprise distinguished retired CEOs and senior managers who remain active in both the business and academic communities, bringing their counsel and expertise to the school through a variety of special projects and initiatives. The Graduate School of Business also has thirteen professional development centers and institutes that have strong affiliations with many companies and professional organizations through advice and consulting services and sponsorship of custom and joint programming. St. Thomas's Small Business Institute, in affiliation with the Small Business Administration and the local business community, offers students opportunities to consult for growing small businesses. Finally, students have access, through various networking initiatives, to many of the more than 17,000 business alumni who have gone on to distinguished careers and leadership roles in thousands of companies.

The College and Environs

Founded in 1885, the University of St. Thomas is an independent, coeducational, comprehensive university with more than 10,000 students, half of whom are graduate students. The main campus is located in St. Paul, while the Minneapolis campus, built in 1991, is home to the Graduate School of Business. Classes are also held on the St. Paul campus and at five other convenient locations in and around the Twin Cities metropolitan area. Both the Minneapolis and St. Paul campuses are centrally located and easily accessible using public transportation.

Facilities

Students have access to more than 150 computing stations, which, in turn, provide access to the Internet, VAX network, e-mail system, electronic databases, and other library resources. Comprehensive library resources, with more than 300,000 volumes, are located on both the St. Paul and Minneapolis campuses, and the school also is a member of local seven-library consortium that provides computerized access to more than 1 million volumes. Distance learning facilities also exist on most campuses.

Placement

The University of St. Thomas Counseling and Career Services office is available to all students. Services range from self-assessment counseling to resume and interviewing skill workshops, complemented by a comprehensive library of directories and employment-related books and periodicals. This office also coordinates career fairs, recruitment visits by employers, resume referrals, and job listings. In addition, the Graduate School of Business has an extensive alumni network available for students to use as a resource and publishes listings of employment and internship opportunities available to students and alumni.

Admission

Admission requirements vary somewhat by degree program, especially with regard to previous work or managerial experience (many programs require at least two years of postundergraduate work experience) and requirements for a personal essay and letters of recommendation. In general, programs require GMAT scores above the 50th percentile, and TOEFL scores of at least 550 on the paper-based version or 213 on the computer-based version. The Executive M.B.A. program requires the Miller Analogies Test. The average undergraduate GPA of incoming students is 3.0, based upon receipt of official transcripts from applicants' schools.

Finances

Tuition for 2000–01 ranges from $463 to $560 per credit hour for all programs except the Executive M.B.A. program, which is $683 per credit hour. Book expenses vary by program and course. Financial aid is available through a variety of private, institutional, and federal programs, both need-based and non-need-based.

International Students

International students are welcomed at the University of St. Thomas, and the International Student Services Office has several programs to assist with counseling and support services, housing, visa services, and ESL courses, as well as many other special needs. Programs are available to help students become quickly acclimated to the school and the local community, and to make the most of their educational experience.

Application Facts and Dates

Applications are considered on a rolling basis; most programs adhere to a semester schedule, but cohort programs, such as the Accounting M.B.A., the Day M.B.A., the Executive M.B.A., and the M.B.A. in Medical Group Management Program, may have different start times. For specific information and application materials, students should contact:

Graduate School of Business
University of St. Thomas
1000 LaSalle Avenue, MPL251
Minneapolis, Minnesota 55403-2005
Telephone: 651-962-4200
          800-328-6819 Ext. 24200
          (toll-free)
Fax: 651-962-4260
E-mail: mba@stthomas.edu
WWW: http://www.stthomas.edu/
     gradbusiness

USD University of San Diego

San Diego, California

DEVELOPING GLOBAL BUSINESS LEADERS

The School of Business Administration at the University of San Diego (USD) is a dynamic institution with regional and global influence. Our mission statement sets the benchmark for our strategic thrusts: The School of Business is committed to improving global business practices through applied research and innovative, personalized education to develop socially responsible leaders. Faculty task forces interact with business leaders to continuously improve the M.B.A. and I.M.B.A. programs and to bring applied learning opportunities to our students. Students can participate in global learning experiences through USD programs in Mexico, Great Britain, France, Germany, and Hong Kong. USD is a community infused with values, where faculty members and students learn together.

—Dr. Curtis W. Cook, Dean

Programs and Curricular Focus

The Master of Business Administration (M.B.A.) and the International Master of Business Administration (I.M.B.A.) programs each encompass 48 units of academic study. Students may attend full-time or part-time, days or evenings. Students who work full-time can complete the degree on a part-time basis in the evening (usually within three years). Two summer sessions and a January intersession are also offered to provide the shortest completion time possible. A thesis is not required, and there are no comprehensive examinations. No specific undergraduate course prerequisites or fields of concentration are required. The students choose whether to focus their studies in such fields as finance, international business, management, marketing, new venture management, project management, real estate, electronic commerce, or supply management, or simply to obtain a broad-based general M.B.A. or I.M.B.A. degree. Students choose which elective courses to take, and in which semester, and whether to avail themselves of contact with local firms and well-placed alumni, whether to participate in internship programs here or abroad, or whether to experience international cultures through study-abroad opportunities.

The School of Business Administration also offers joint-degree programs in several areas. The joint programs include an M.B.A./J.D. and an I.M.B.A/J.D., which are offered in conjunction with the School of Law, and an M.B.A./M.S.N., which is offered in conjunction with the School of Nursing.

Students and the M.B.A. Experience

To meet the challenges of a new century, the student in the Master of Business Administration and International Master of Business Administration programs at the University of San Diego receives comprehensive training in theory and case analysis. This develops technical and financial skills, fosters global and strategic thinking, and provides a philosophy that stresses corporate responsibility and the interconnection of all the stakeholders of the business enterprise. These skills are reinforced through extensive team exercises and group projects in classes averaging just 25 students, and through interaction with businesses and business leaders locally, nationally, and internationally.

❖ Global Focus

The John Ahlers Center for International Business adds to the value of the USD graduate business school experience by providing students with a variety of international opportunities, including the International Executives in Residence Program, the International Speakers Series, international mentorship activities, and career advising for the international job search.

USD's International Business Programs (IBP) provides students with opportunities to gain international experience worldwide. Five-week and two-week graduate business study-abroad programs are offered in Europe, Latin America, and Asia. Currently, programs are administered in Barcelona, Munich, Buenos Aires, Hong Kong, and Monterrey, Mexico. IBP also sponsors a dual-degree program with the Instituto Tecnologico y de Estudios Superiores de Monterrey (ITESM) and semester-long exchanges with leading universities in France, Mexico, Argentina, and Italy. International internships and international student team consulting projects are also available. Through its various programs, IBP immerses participants in international business practice and sensitizes students to cultural differences that influence effective international interaction.

Special Features

The Master of Science in Executive Leadership (M.S.E.L.) is an innovative degree program that is jointly sponsored by the University of San Diego and the Ken Blanchard Companies. The M.S.E.L. program is designed for managers and leaders who have responsibility for managing people and are rising in their careers. It is the only program that features Ken Blanchard's highly acclaimed Situational Leadership II model. This model empowers individuals to identify needs and agree upon a leadership style solution to help companies achieve their organizational goals. The program is composed of 36 units of academic study that are delivered in an executive education format. The M.S.E.L. program is a cohort-based program where all students progress together through a series of twelve courses in slightly less than two years. For applications and more information, students should contact the Graduate Business Programs Office at 619-260-4828 or by e-mail at mirabile@acusd.edu.

The University of San Diego also offers two other Master of Science degrees. The Master of Science in Electronic Commerce (M.S.E.C.) is a highly focused 30-unit program designed for people who want, or have already begun, careers in electronic commerce. Since successful electronic commerce is a combination of business strategy and technology, the M.S.E.C. program includes both business and technology courses. The curriculum is designed to be flexible enough to provide a personalized educational experience that meets the needs of individual students, yet provides all students with a common core of knowledge in electronic commerce technologies, technology management, and strategies for electronic business.

The Master of Science in Global Leadership (M.S.G.L.) curriculum is designed for Navy officers and comprises 30 units. Each class is team-centered and organized into cohorts of approximately 25 students. There are three thematic areas to the program: leadership in the global environment, a comparative geopolitical tour of the major regions of the world, and business processes and techniques. For further information, students should contact the Graduate Business Programs Office at 619-260-2989 or by e-mail at portmartin@email.msn.com.

The Faculty

The University of San Diego School of Business Administration has been able to attract highly qualified faculty members with degrees from well-recognized universities around the world. Among the faculty members are 4 Fulbright scholars, more than a dozen certified in their professions, and more than 20 who have authored books in their fields. Almost all faculty members are doctorally qualified, or the equivalent, and remain current in their research and professional fields. Most faculty members are regularly invited to speak at conferences, seminars, and dinner meetings both in the U.S. and abroad and maintain regular contact with the business community. Faculty publications are frequent and recognized for their contribution to the business world as well as academia. The primary focus of members of the faculty remains educating students about the applicability of proven management theory.

The Business School Network

The University of San Diego Graduate School of Business enjoys a strong relationship with the corporate community. There are three advisory boards, the Accountancy Advisory Board, the Ahlers Center for International Business Board, and the Real Estate Finance Board. Each contributes its expertise and also advises on the planning and implementation of long-range programs.

A substantial number of graduate courses require practical projects working on current problems for local companies. The internship program places graduate students for three to six months with companies both in San Diego and overseas to work on major business projects. These projects and internships provide mutual benefit and positive interactions with the business community.

The School actively supports an Executives in Residence program in which corporate professionals work and teach at the University for a year. These business leaders bring the real and practical world into the classroom. Furthermore, other classes host guest speakers on current and relevant topics.

Finally, the Ahlers Center for International Business provides various programs that interrelate with the corporate community. The center hosts a Breakfast Briefing Series as well as half- and full-day seminars. The School actively nurtures this multidimensional relationship with the corporate community.

The College and Environs

The University of San Diego is an independent, Roman Catholic university founded in 1949. The 180-acre hilltop campus, known for its graceful Spanish Renaissance architecture, overlooks Missions Bay with breathtaking views of the Pacific Ocean and San Diego Bay. The campus is located in the nation's sixth-largest city and is ideally close to cultural, business, residential, and recreational areas of the city.

Facilities

The Helen K. and James C. Copley Library houses more than 360,000 books and bound periodicals and includes subscriptions to 2,200 journals and collections of reference works, government documents, pamphlets, newspapers in many languages, and rare books.

In addition to its own collection, Copley Library has network connections with most academic and large public libraries in North America and with major national bibliographic and informational databases available to USD students and faculty. Many databases are directly accessible to students from computer terminals in the library. SALLY, the online catalog of the campus libraries and Media Center, can be accessed by computer from home. More than 700 study spaces are available in group study areas, quiet carrels, and reading rooms.

Placement

Career Services promotes the professional development of graduate students and alumni. Providing targeted career advising to individuals and groups, the staff offers relevant resources and strategic services. Each semester, Career Services also conducts training workshops in popular topics, such as resume writing, interviewing, and networking skills. Career Services also provides a Resource Library that includes multimedia holdings that range from employer information to job and internship listings.

Career Services partners with the Alumni Career Network, faculty members, and graduate student organizations to sponsor annual events such as Career Night and Networking Forums. This office also coordinates on-campus interviewing and specialized career programs each semester. For more information, students should call 619-260-4654 or send an e-mail to careers@acusd.edu.

Admission

Matriculation into the M.B.A., I.M.B.A., and M.S.E.C. programs is possible in the fall semester, spring semester, or summer session. By utilizing a rolling admissions process, applications are evaluated individually as received, providing feedback to the applicant in a timely manner. Qualification for admission is based upon prior academic achievement, acceptable performance on the GMAT, three faculty appraisal forms or letters of recommendation, a current resume, and at least two years of full-time work experience. Additional requirements for international applicants include a minimum TOEFL score of 580 (237 on the computer-based exam) and a detailed evaluation of all international transcripts.

Finances

Tuition for the 2000–01 year is $675 per unit. The Office of Financial Aid provides information, counseling, and application processing for students who need assistance in meeting their educational and living expenses. Financial assistance consists of fellowships, scholarships, assistantships, employment (contact the Office of Human Resources or Student Employment Center), grants, and loans. Each type of aid has different application forms, requirements, and deadlines. For applications and more information, students should contact the Office of Financial Aid at 619-260-4514.

Application Facts and Dates

Admission is open for the fall and spring semesters and the summer session. The priority filing date for applications is May 1 for fall, November 15 for spring, and March 15 for summer.

For an application and more information, students should contact:

Office of Graduate Admissions
University of San Diego
5998 Alcala Park
San Diego, California 92110
Telephone: 619-260-4524
　　　　　800-248-4873 (toll-free)
E-mail: grads@acusd.edu

University of San Francisco

> ### POSITION YOURSELF AT THE CUTTING EDGE
>
> *Located on the edge of entrepreneurial and corporate opportunities in California's Silicon Valley and also on the edge of Pacific Rim cultures and markets, the McLaren School of Business prepares men and women of richly diverse backgrounds for leadership positions in the global business environment of the twenty-first century.*
>
> —Gary Williams, Dean

Programs and Curricular Focus

The McLaren M.B.A. program is fully accredited by AACSB–The International Association for Management Education and enjoys a reputation for excellence regionally, nationally, and internationally. The curriculum is designed to strengthen the analytical, practical, and interpersonal skills essential for success in the international marketplace.

Five integrative themes (communication skills, leadership dynamics, creative problem solving, global perspectives, and ethical action) are highlighted in each course to develop broadly experienced, visionary managers. Small classes (rarely larger than 25) ensure the individual attention necessary to develop first-rate communication skills and allow direct participation in cases and discussions focusing on current and future management and organizational issues.

The M.B.A. core curriculum comprises 33 units (thirteen courses). In addition, students choose 12 units (four courses) of electives and a capstone course for a total of 48 units. The core curriculum challenges students to diagnose and solve a wide variety of managerial problems. Through the use of case studies, guest speakers, computer simulations, and faculty-student interaction, course content closely mirrors real-world business experience.

The advanced elective courses enable the student to choose a study emphasis in one of six concentrations: e-business, finance, international business, management, marketing, and telecommunications.

Other programs include an Executive M.B.A. (E.M.B.A.) program for working professionals. Classes for the E.M.B.A. meet on alternating Fridays and Saturdays for twenty-one months. Applicants must have completed ten years of work experience, with at least five years of significant managerial experience.

Students and the M.B.A. Experience

USF's 2000 M.B.A. class of 248 included representatives from dozens of countries. The average age for the group was 28, with an average of five years' work experience. Corporations sponsoring employees for M.B.A. study included Andersen Consulting, Bank of America, Bechtel, Citibank, Clorox, Genentech, Hewlett Packard, Hitachi, Sun Microsystems, and many others.

Special Features

The Graduate Business Association (GBA) is a student organization committed to enhancing the quality of campus life for M.B.A. students. The GBA provides social and professional programs, faculty/course guides for students, and representation in the administration of the School.

The USF Consulting Group, open to all M.B.A. students, is a large club offering valuable consulting services to San Francisco–area businesses. The organization comprises five operational teams: Community Outreach, Database Management, Marketing, Quality Assurance, and Executive Board.

The *USF Business Journal* is published monthly by M.B.A. students. It features student-written articles about business topics and events, including information about M.B.A. activities and career opportunities as well as student/faculty profiles.

Many other organizations are eager to involve new student members. Several faculty-led international trips are scheduled each year on a for-credit basis.

The Faculty

All faculty members of the McLaren School of Business are committed above all to the personal and professional development of their students. More than 90 percent of the faculty members have earned doctorates at outstanding universities and are well-known as scholars and authors in their fields. They bring to the classroom an innovative enthusiasm for motivational education and up-to-date expertise in current business realities, gained in part through their consulting relationships with major corporations. In and out of the classroom, students find their professors deeply interested in their perspectives and in their progress in the program.

The Business School Network

The McLaren School of Business and its students benefit from the guidance of a distinguished domestic and international Advisory Council made up of outstanding business leaders. In addition, the network of alumni built up over the University's 143-year history gives M.B.A. students a rich resource for internships and career opportunities.

The College and Environs

The University of San Francisco, the city's largest private university, overlooks an urban area of incredible beauty, diversity, and opportunity. As America's gateway to the Pacific Rim, San Francisco is well-positioned to benefit from expanding trade with Asian and Latin American countries as well as the United States' traditional European partners.

This vibrant international trade center is also alive with the humanities, including theater, film, dance, musical performances, and fine art exhibitions.

Placement

The Career Services Center assists students in job placement and career planning. On-campus recruiting is conducted year-round and features such companies as Sprint, Wells Fargo, Eastman Kodak, and Andersen Consulting.

Admission

Admission to the McLaren M.B.A. program is available to individuals who fulfill the criteria listed in the Application for Admission, including records of undergraduate

preparation, acceptable GMAT scores, letters of recommendation, and a personal essay.

Finances

Tuition for the 2000–01 academic year is $746 per unit. (Students typically take 12 to 15 units per semester.) Average yearly expenses (books, room and board, transportation, and personal expenses) are approximately $13,000. A wide variety of financial aid programs are available, including McLaren Graduate Fellowships,

University Tuition Grants, and several student loan programs.

International Students

With students from more than fifty countries in recent years, the University of San Francisco is well prepared to meet the special needs of international students. English classes, housing advice, visa information, and other services are available. As an international trade center celebrating its ethnic diversity, San Francisco offers a welcoming

study and leisure environment for virtually all international students.

Application Facts and Dates

Students are admitted into the M.B.A. program for the fall, spring, and summer semesters. Admission decisions are made on a rolling basis. Applicants can expect a decision within four to five weeks of the date that their application is complete. For fall admission, the GMAT should be taken no later than May, with the application due by June 1. For spring admission, the GMAT should be taken no later than October, with the application due by November 10. For summer admission, the GMAT should be taken no later than February, with the application due by April 1.

Students' questions and requests for an application package are welcome. Applicants should contact:

McLaren School of Business
Graduate School of Management
University of San Francisco
2130 Fulton Street
San Francisco, California 94117-1080
Telephone: 415-422-6314
 415-422-6665 (for
  applications only)
Fax: 415-422-2502
E-mail: mbausf@usfca.edu
World Wide Web: http://www.usfca.edu/usf/mclaren

FACULTY LIST

Steven Alter, Professor of Information Systems and Decision Sciences; Ph.D., MIT, 1975.

Richard Babcock, Professor of Management; Ph.D., UCLA, 1970.

Jonathan Barsky, Associate Professor of Hospitality Management; Ph.D., Golden Gate, 1991.

Michael Becker, Professor of Organizational Psychology; Ph.D., Brigham Young, 1975.

Arthur Bell, Professor of Management; Ph.D., Harvard, 1973.

Rex Bennett, Professor of Marketing; Ph.D., North Carolina at Chapel Hill, 1972.

Keqian Bi, Professor of Finance; Ph.D., Florida, 1989.

Daniel L. Blakley, Professor of Applied Economics and Quantitative Methods; Ph.D., Duke, 1981.

Karl A. Boedecker, Professor of Marketing; Ph.D., Michigan State, 1974; J.D., San Francisco, 1982.

Stephen D. Calvert, Professor of Marketing; Ph.D., Cincinnati, 1979.

Mark V. Cannice, Assistant Professor of Finance; Ph.D., Indiana, 1997.

Rodger (Rongxin) Chen, Assistant Professor of Management; Ph.D., Texas at Dallas, 1996.

Thomas Costello, Associate Professor and Director of Hospitality Management; M.A., Saint Louis, 1972.

Barry W. Doyle, Professor of Finance; Ph.D., Oregon, 1984.

Alev M. Efendioglu, Professor of Management; Ph.D., LSU, 1978.

Shenzhao Fu, Associate Professor of Marketing; Ph.D., Indiana, 1989.

Leslie A. Goldgehn, Professor of Marketing; Ph.D., Northwestern, 1982.

Carol Graham, Assistant Professor of Accounting; Ph.D., Strathclyde (Scotland), 1995.

Oren Harari, Professor of Management; Ph.D., Berkeley, 1978.

Heather E. Hudson, Professor of Telecommunications Management and Policy and Director of Telecommunications Program; Ph.D., Stanford, 1974.

Stephen J. Huxley, Professor of Business Administration; Ph.D., California, San Diego, 1975.

Nicholas Imparato, Professor of Business Administration; Ph.D., Bowling Green State, 1970.

Kathleen Kane, Professor of Management; Ph.D., Claremont, 1990.

John Koeplin, S. J., Associate Professor of Accounting; Ph.D., North Texas, 1998.

Zhan Li, Associate Professor of Marketing; D.B.A., Boston University, 1994.

Byungha Lim, Assistant Professor of Management Information Systems; Ph.D., Iowa, 1996.

Paul Lorton, Professor of Information Systems; Ph.D., Stanford, 1973.

Robert N. Mefford, Professor of International Business and Operations Management; Ph.D., Berkeley, 1983.

Michael R. Middleton, Professor of Information Systems and Decision Sciences; Ph.D., Stanford, 1979.

Luis Murillo, Assistant Professor of Management; Ph.D., Berkeley, 1993.

L. W. Murray Jr., Professor of Finance; Ph.D., Clark, 1973.

Eugene Muscat, Professor of Management Information Systems and Associate Dean; Ed.D., USC, 1974.

Denis Neilson, Professor of Accounting and Associate Dean; Ph.D., Berkeley, 1974.

Joel Oberstone, Professor of Decision Sciences; Ph.D., USC, 1972.

Richard Puntillo, Professor of Finance; M.B.A., Berkeley, 1969.

Diane Roberts, Associate Professor of Accounting; Ph.D., California, Irvine, 1994.

Todd Sayre, Assistant Professor of Accounting; Ph.D., Arizona, 1995.

David G. Scalise, Professor of Business Law; J.D., San Francisco, 1973.

Edwin J. Shapiro, Professor of Quantitative Methods; Ph.D., Pittsburgh, 1962.

Dayle Smith, Professor of Management; Ph.D., USC, 1986.

Peggy Takahashi, Assistant Professor of International Management; Ph.D., Berkeley, 1998.

Manuel Tarrazo, Associate Professor of Finance; Ph.D., SUNY at Albany, 1992.

Nicholas Tay, Assistant Professor of Finance; Ph.D., Oklahoma, 1998.

Philip Taylor, Professor of Information Systems and Decision Sciences; Ph.D., Ohio State, 1975.

Heinz Weihrich, Professor of International Business and Management; Ph.D., UCLA, 1973.

David P. Weiner, Professor of Accounting; Ph.D., Michigan, 1972; CPA (New York).

Gary Williams, Professor of Management and Dean, McLaren School of Business; Ph.D., Stanford, 1966.

University of South Carolina

Columbia, South Carolina

GLOBALIZATION—MEETING BUSINESS NEEDS IN THE NEXT MILLENNIUM

▶ *The University of South Carolina's Darla Moore School of Business is an innovator in preparing students for careers in the global marketplace. We offer three distinct programs with opportunities for preparation that stress an international focus. Each program is based on a strong grounding in needed business skills supplemented by unique international experiences. Each program offers in-depth training, including one or more of the following: competency in one of eight languages, six-month in-country internships, a unique study-abroad program, and internationally oriented consulting opportunities. The School's innovative approaches to preparing students for the global marketplace have earned it international recognition. Such innovation is essential for business students who will be operating in a world of few boundaries and constant change.*

—*Rodney L. Roenfeldt, Interim Dean*

Programs and Curricular Focus

The School offers a Master of International Business Studies (M.I.B.S.) program, a Master of Business Administration (M.B.A.) program, and an International Master of Business Administration (I.M.B.A.) program.

The M.I.B.S. core curriculum spans all of the traditional disciplines in business administration, but with courses that are fully international in scope. Core courses are taught in four- to eight-week integrated modules, as well as some full-semester core and elective courses. Students start in the summer (June) or fall term, depending on undergraduate degree and foreign language proficiency. The M.I.B.S. program currently offers the following language tracks for U.S. nationals: Chinese, French, German, Italian, Japanese, Portuguese, and Spanish. Chinese and Japanese are three-year language tracks, and all others are two-year language tracks. All foreign national applicants are carefully screened for English language skills and enter the two-year foreign national (English) track. All M.I.B.S. students are required to learn a foreign language and to develop that language as well as cultural understanding through a six-month internship in a country where that language is spoken (foreign nationals intern in the United States).

The M.B.A. core curriculum of thirteen courses (39 hours) focuses on the fundamentals of business administration and starts in the fall of each year. In addition, five elective courses (15 hours) enable students to further develop their skills in a variety of areas or to specialize in a particular area of their choice. All eighteen of these courses are taught in four traditional sixteen-week semesters. M.B.A. students are encouraged to participate in an internship between the first and second years of the program. Study abroad as a part of the M.B.A. program is also encouraged. The combined 54-hour program prepares students from all educational backgrounds to assume managerial positions.

The International Master of Business Administration (I.M.B.A.) program, the School's most recent innovation in graduate business education, is a joint venture with Austria's most prestigious business school, the Wirtschaftsuniversität Wien (WU-Wien), more commonly known as the Vienna University of Economics and Business Administration. Through this partnership, the School is able to offer a fifteen-month, 48-credit-hour, all English language program of instruction leading to the I.M.B.A. degree. The I.M.B.A. core curriculum is a combination of the traditional M.B.A. and M.I.B.S. programs, with the first seven months of instruction in Vienna and the next eight months at USC. The curriculum includes twelve months of intensive business course work followed by a three-month project in management consulting. The instruction in Vienna is conducted by faculty from both WU-Wien and USC, while the instruction in

Columbia is conducted by USC faculty. The program starts at WU-Wien each May, with two terms of highly integrated business course modules. After completing this core curriculum in Vienna, the students come to USC for a semester of four electives and a capstone course on strategy and policy in a global enterprise. I.M.B.A. students then complete their curriculum with the field consulting project.

Students and the M.B.A. Experience

The students in USC's graduate business programs come from a wide variety of backgrounds, with qualifications varying from program to program. The total enrollment for all three programs for fall 1999 was 528 students. Women represent 38 percent of this student population, while minorities represent 5 percent. Foreign national students make up 28 percent of the student body; this adds greatly to the global perspective in business, as these students bring their experiences to the classroom. The typical entering student is 27 years old and has approximately three years of work experience.

The Faculty

The faculty of USC's Darla Moore School of Business has strong research interests that have won national and international visibility. Faculty members have nearly 100 articles and more than a dozen books published in a typical year and they stay on the cutting edge of the various academic disciplines represented in the School.

The Business School Network

The School's ties to the business community are strong, and these ties play several critical roles in the educational process. Relationships with local, national, and international corporations lead to field consulting projects for M.B.A. and I.M.B.A. students, to internships for M.I.B.S. students, and to employment opportunities for all graduates. The USC-Business Partnership Foundation is composed of business and

The H. William Close and Francis M. Hipp buildings comprise the Darla Moore School of Business's nine-story complex.

academic leaders who play an active leadership role for the School and are an integral part of the review process for curriculum and other program innovations.

The College and Environs

Founded in 1801, the University of South Carolina's main campus (and the Darla Moore School of Business) is located in downtown Columbia, the state's capital. The University has a total enrollment of more than 38,000 students, including USC's two other four-year campuses and five regional campuses. USC is a progressive, comprehensive institution committed to excellence in education and public service. On the Columbia campus, eleven colleges offer seventy-nine undergraduate degree programs. The commitment extends to the continued development and support of graduate education, and research is a priority. This commitment has led to growth in the variety and number of graduate programs available. Currently, USC enrolls more than 9,000 graduate students.

The city of Columbia is the seat of state government, is rich in culture and history, and is considered one of the most progressive cities in the Southeast. The current metropolitan population of 472,000 is expected to rise to 525,000 by the year 2010. The state's economy is flourishing, thanks to the tourism industry, international and domestic business, and industry giants. Government and industry are working together to provide excellent employment opportunities throughout the state.

South Carolinians appreciate the fine arts and are committed to the cultivation of the arts throughout the state. Columbia is the home of several outstanding museums and the nationally ranked Riverbanks Zoo. Diverse vacation spots are abundant throughout the state, including ocean resorts, historic cities, and the Blue Ridge Mountains.

Facilities

The Darla Moore School of Business is housed in the H. William Close and Francis M. Hipp buildings. The twin towers of the complex symbolize the working partnership between the School and the business community. Within the complex, the School is relatively self-sufficient with its business library, computer center, classrooms, and faculty offices. The library features a circulation collection that includes business and industrial directories and publications, with approximately 100 current subscriptions and back issues of selected magazines and newspapers and nearly 500 journals in microfilm format. Students also have access to the University's main library, which seats 2,500 users at one time and allows access to more than 7 million volumes, microfilm entries, manuscripts, and periodicals. The computer center has 150 interactive workstations accessing a large open-system network comprising multiple Novell and UNIX servers, with 650 clients and more than 32 billion characters of online storage. Through the campus network, users also have access to numerous software packages and mainframe processing.

Placement

Most placement services are coordinated by the School's Graduate Placement Office, which acts as a liaison between graduate students and prospective employers. In addition to on-campus interviewing opportunities, students benefit from the following available resources: a resume book, correspondence recruiting, placement referral network, career development seminars, and the M.I.B.S. alumni job bank.

Admission

Every applicant's complete file, including his or her academic record, resume, required essays, and GMAT scores, is evaluated through comparison with the current applicant pool for the appropriate program. Average GMAT scores and GPAs vary for the different programs, with M.I.B.S. being the most selective (a 1999 average GMAT score of 610 and an average GPA of 3.35). The School looks for reasons to admit students, not a reason to decline them.

Finances

Tuition for 2000–01 for all M.B.A. and M.I.B.S. students is estimated at $2007 per semester for in-state students and $4264 per semester for out-of-state students. There is a one-time, nonrefundable enrichment fee for the M.B.A. program of $2900 for in-state students and $4400 for out-of-state students. The M.I.B.S. program enrichment fee is estimated at $5000 in-state and $8800 out-of-state. Tuition and fees for the I.M.B.A. program are $25,000 total cost, with no enrichment fees.

A number of graduate assistantships and fellowships are available. Applications for these awards are considered in February, and the awards are based on merit, not need.

Application Facts and Dates

For best consideration, applications for all programs should be submitted by February 1. All applications for assistantships and fellowships must be received by February 1. Applications for all programs will be considered until the program is full or until approximately one month prior to the start of the program. For more information or an application package, students should contact:

Graduate Division, PGG98
The Darla Moore School of Business
University of South Carolina
Columbia, South Carolina 29208
Telephone: 803-777-4346
Fax: 803-777-0414

University of Southern California

Los Angeles, California

THE MARSHALL M.B.A.—A BUSINESS EDUCATION FOR THE REAL WORLD

The Marshall M.B.A. Program is characterized by a real-world focus and a heritage of innovation and change. Faculty and students explore business problems from a multidisciplinary perspective while emphasizing interpersonal skills designed to build global awareness, improve technological sophistication, and develop talents in leadership and entrepreneurial areas.

Working with one of the largest alumni networks of any business school in the world, we have an environment that fosters innovative ways of understanding and improving business today. Teams of students are assigned to tackle tough, real-world issues by applying theoretical concepts to real-time business problems in both profit and nonprofit settings. The Marshall M.B.A. provides a business education for the twenty-first century.

—Randolph W. Westerfield, Dean

Programs and Curricular Focus

The Marshall M.B.A. Program prepares men and women to become leaders at all levels of organizations in all sectors of the economy. Intellectual and practical in nature, the two-year M.B.A. program provides grounding in the functional business disciplines, hones analytic tools required to address management problems, and develops the interpersonal and communication skills necessary to lead. Along with the program's real-world focus, an emphasis on teamwork and the development of interpersonal skills are key elements of the Marshall M.B.A. Program.

In 2000, the Marshall School of Business sent its entire first-year class to study abroad in Chile, China, Indonesia, Japan, or Mexico through its Pacific Rim Education Program (PRIME). Committed to the study of global business, Marshall is the first major business school to require its students to travel abroad as part of the required core curriculum.

A new module of study for first-year students, Electronic Commerce, has been added to the core curriculum. The new course integrates changes taking place in all disciplines due to increasing technology. A team-taught module, it focuses on marketing, finance, communications, and operations.

Recognizing that an exemplary graduate management education must strike a balance between theory and practice, Marshall has developed a two-year curriculum that combines scholarship with practical experience. The newly redesigned first-year curriculum provides a carefully coordinated sequence of study that equips students with the fundamental tools and functional knowledge that every business leader must have. In contrast, the second year offers the opportunity to pursue electives in one or more areas of concentration. Based on the belief that each student has highly distinctive needs and goals, the Marshall Program provides tremendous latitude in allowing students to design a second-year course of study that best suits their particular interests.

In addition to the full-time M.B.A., the Marshall School offers a part-time M.B.A. (M.B.A.-PM), a one-year International M.B.A. (IBEAR M.B.A.), an Executive M.B.A. (E.M.B.A.), a Ph.D., and dual degree programs in dental surgery, East Asian studies, gerontology, industrial and systems engineering, Jewish communal service, law, medicine, nursing, planning, pharmacy, and real estate development.

Students and the M.B.A. Experience

The Marshall M.B.A. Program enrolls approximately 300 students each year. The average Marshall M.B.A. student is 28 years of age, with 4.5 years of work experience. International students comprise approximately 20 to 25 percent of the student population and represent more than twenty countries from around the world. Approximately 35 percent of the students are women. Every geographic region and major ethnic group of the United States is represented.

Special Features

At orientation, the entering class, second-year M.B.A. students, and core faculty and staff members engage in a series of intellectual and physical exercises aimed at demonstrating the power of teams to accomplish challenging tasks in high-quality ways. Sustained project teams, established at orientation, return to campus and become responsible for collaborative work in selected first-year classes. Throughout the year, these groups are evaluated and receive feedback not only on their completed projects but also on their teamwork skills.

The Faculty

There are nearly 180 faculty members in the Marshall School of Business, with expertise in such areas as international business, accounting, entrepreneurship, real estate, consulting, finance, human resources management, marketing, operations, information systems, business economics, and leadership. They are noted for their cutting-edge research, a constant drive to apply the business theories they develop to the real world, teaching excellence in the classroom, and an open-door policy toward students.

The Business School Network

The nearly 50,000 alumni of the Marshall School of Business form a renowned global network and have achieved remarkable success in the national and international business community. Dedicated alumni encourage their companies to recruit Marshall M.B.A. students and regularly return to campus to speak about careers, act as mentors, and provide consulting opportunities. In addition, alumni are actively involved with students in planning recruiting trips to major cities such as San Francisco and New York.

The College and Environs

Located on USC's main campus on 150 park-like acres south of downtown Los Angeles, the Marshall School is well positioned in a city where the diversity of manufacturing, financial, telecommunica-

tions, entertainment, and international trade activities rivals that of many countries. USC is committed to diversity and has one of the largest populations of international students of any private university in the United States. In addition, Los Angeles is a multicultural city that serves as America's gateway to the Pacific Rim.

Technology Environment

In fall 1999, Marshall opened the doors to Popovich Hall, one of the newest and most technologically sophisticated business school facilities in the nation. Popovich Hall features eight case-study rooms with audio and video teleconferencing capability, thirteen experiential learning classrooms with the capability to transmit lectures and presentations throughout the building, more than 1,100 data hookups in the building and outdoor courtyard, and more than 15 miles of fiber-optic and cable wiring.

Placement

The Career Resource Center is designed specifically to assist graduate-level stu-

dents with their career management process. It provides self-assessment, resume writing, interviewing, and salary negotiation workshops; career advising; mock interviews; alumni and corporate contact databases; job postings; and on-site visits by corporate recruiters. In addition, activities such as industry nights, corporate information sessions, alumni and corporate networking receptions, and company site visits offer students opportunities to meet and exchange information with prospective employers in a variety of settings.

Admission

The Admissions committee considers all qualified applicants who hold a bachelor's degree from an accredited undergraduate institution. The application is evaluated based upon prior academic performance, previous work experience, GMAT score, essay questions, letters of recommendation, and ability to demonstrate leadership and interpersonal skills. A TOEFL score is required for applicants who did not receive their bachelor's degree from an English-speaking institution. Interviews are held at the

discretion of the Admissions Committee or at GMAC-sponsored M.B.A. Forums.

Finances

Tuition and fees for the 2000–01 academic year are approximately $28,500. The Admissions Committee awards merit-based tuition fellowships to highly competitive applicants. Need-based loans are available to all eligible domestic applicants and to international applicants who have a cosigner who is a U.S. citizen.

International Students

USC has one of the largest populations of international students of any private university in the U.S., adding a unique perspective to classroom and teamwork experiences. International students represented 20 percent of the class of 1999, representing countries from Asia, Europe, Africa, and the Americas. The Office for International Students and Scholars provides orientation programs and continuing support services for international students. Trained counselors are available to advise international students on immigration regulations, academic progress, financial concerns, housing, and cross-cultural adjustment. Year-round social and cultural activities are also sponsored through this office.

Application Facts and Dates

Application deadlines begin in the fall, with a final deadline of April 1. Early application is encouraged. International applicants are encouraged to apply by February 7. For application materials and information, students should contact:

Marshall School of Business
M.B.A. Admissions
University of Southern California
Popovich Hall, Room 308
Los Angeles, California 90089-2633
Telephone: 213-740-7846
Fax: 213-749-8520
E-mail: marshallmba@bus.usc.edu
World Wide Web: http://www.
marshall.usc.edu

University of Southern California

Los Angeles, California

AN M.B.A. FOR THE PACIFIC CENTURY

▶ *USC's IBEAR M.B.A. Program is a unique undertaking in international management education. To successfully lead organizations today, one must know not only how to apply management skills in the international workplace but also how to cultivate and communicate with diverse peoples and create a globally informed vision of the opportunities that lie ahead. The IBEAR M.B.A. Program provides that knowledge base. Its practical, Pacific Rim–oriented international business curriculum, the teamwork that participants must demonstrate to complete real-world projects and consulting assignments, and the rich diversity of cultural and work experience that the participants themselves bring to discussions make the IBEAR M.B.A. Program the soundest of springboards for managers who want to lead business in the Pacific Century.*

—Randolph W. Westerfield, Dean

Programs and Curricular Focus

USC's IBEAR M.B.A. Program is the only one-year international M.B.A. program in North America that is accredited by AACSB–The International Association for Management Education. Designed for high-potential, midcareer managers, the program emphasizes business in and among Asia, North America, and South America.

Completing the equivalent of two years of course work in just one year requires intense dedication and focus but permits participants to minimize time away from the workplace and maximize their gains from the time invested.

Classes begin in mid-August with a three-week transition program in micro-computing and business communication, followed by four 11-week terms of M.B.A. classes. The curriculum consists

A team of IBEAR M.B.A. participants discusses travel plans to conduct overseas research for the International Business Consulting Project.

of nineteen integrated courses, including Management in a Global Economy, Global Marketing Strategies, International Financial Management, Global Strategic Planning, International Trade, The National and International Economy, and Global e-Commerce and Management Practices in the Pacific Rim. All courses emphasize international business issues.

The faculty members work closely to integrate course work across disciplines. They emphasize practical, team-based, project-based, and case-based learning.

Students and the M.B.A. Experience

The IBEAR M.B.A. Program is noted for the maturity of its participants and their diversity in terms of both culture and work experience. By working together every day for a year in the classroom and on many project teams, participants gain experiential understanding of cultural differences in business practices around the world.

Enrollment in each class is limited to 56 participants. They average 33 years of age and nine years of work experience. A minimum of five years of full-time work experience is required. Ages range from 26 to the mid-40s. The current class represents twenty countries. In its twenty years, IBEAR has served over 850 participants from forty-seven countries.

Special Features

A key feature of the program, the inclusion of international consulting

projects for major multinational firms, ensures each participant meaningful real-world experience in international business. From March to July, participants work in 4-member teams to complete a consulting project on an issue of pressing practical concern for a sponsor company, such as country-focused market entry, expansion strategy, regional business development strategy, offshore manufacturing feasibility, international sourcing, cross-border acquisitions, or the establishment of joint-venture operations. The IBEAR teams work closely with a project manager at their sponsor firm. Most of the projects require international travel.

Another special feature of the IBEAR M.B.A. Program is the transition program, which emphasizes computing, team-building, and presentation skills. There is also a team-development retreat and enrollment in the annual three-day Asia/Pacific Business Outlook Conference hosted at USC in March, sponsored by IBEAR and the U.S. Department of Commerce International Trade Administration. The conference is attended by 400 executives from U.S. and international firms, the Senior Commercial Officers of U.S. Embassies in the Asia/Pacific region, and experts from government, business, and academe who serve on the conference faculty.

The Faculty

IBEAR faculty members are selected from among the most respected of the 174 full-time faculty members in USC's Marshall School of Business. Both *Business Week* and *U.S. News & World Report* recently ranked USC's international business faculty and programs among the top twenty-five in the United States.

The Business School Network

IBEAR graduates join an influential, global network of more than 850 IBEAR alumni who hold senior positions in many of the most respected firms in the Pacific Rim and around the world. The bonds are strong in this extended IBEAR family. Alumni often return to campus to speak about their careers, serve as mentors, and

Popovitch Hall, the most advanced business school building in the U.S., houses all four Marshall School M.B.A. programs.

help facilitate links between USC and the business and academic communities abroad. They also encourage their companies to recruit IBEAR graduates. Alumni often contact IBEAR colleagues by phone or through the Internet for information, referrals, or to plan get-togethers around the globe. IBEAR maintains a database with current contact information on all of its alumni. IBEAR graduates also join a dynamic network of 50,000 business school alumni and 240,000 USC alumni.

IBEAR's network also includes many nonalumni friends in the business and public sectors around the world. USC has embarked on a strategic initiative to strengthen the University's international ties, especially with the countries in Asia and Latin America. IBEAR serves as a focal point for the promotion of teaching and research in international business. In addition to the M.B.A. Program, IBEAR provides a variety of nondegree executive education programs.

The College and Environs

Popovich Hall, one of the most techno-logically advanced M.B.A. school buildings in the United States, opened in summer 1999 and houses all four Marshall M.B.A. programs, including the IBEAR M.B.A. USC's parklike 150-acre main campus is just 2 miles south of Los Angeles' downtown business center. Founded in 1880, USC is the oldest and largest private university in the western United States. It offers degrees in 198 fields of study and eighteen professional schools. Its 28,000 students come from all fifty states and 105 countries. The University is strategically located in a city with a population of 7 million and a diversity of high-technology manufactur-ing, financial, telecommunications, and trade activities to rival many countries. As America's most important gateway to the Pacific Rim, Los Angeles provides an outstanding learning laboratory for managers interested in expanding their international horizons.

Technology Environment

IBEAR and the Marshall School of Business are committed to remaining at the forefront of technology. The tiered IBEAR case-study room is equipped with audio-video teleconferencing and data connections for each student. There are more than 1,100 data conections through-out the building, courtyard, and café. All IBEAR participants and faculty members are connected to the business school from their homes, which permits virtual group work and Internet communication worldwide. Assignments, data distribu-tion, substantive discussions, and program and social announcements are handled on the IBEAR bulletin board system. The business libraries offer electronic gateways to LEXIS-NEXIS and to a collection of more than 150 informational databases. Study carrels are wired into the network for laptop computer use. The Experiential Learning Center uses state-of-the-art video and multimedia equipment in five simulation rooms designed to improve presentation and negotiation skills.

Placement

The Career Resource Center provides personalized job search counseling and assistance to self-sponsored participants. Services include industry nights, network-ing opportunities, workshops, resume and interview preparation, and access to Marshall's alumni and business networks.

Admission

Applicants must have completed their undergraduate studies and have five or more years of full-time work and/or military experience. All applicants must submit official GMAT results. Interna-tional applicants must also submit official TOEFL scores.

Finances

The total cost of tuition and living expenses for the IBEAR M.B.A. is substantially less than that of most two-year M.B.A. programs at top 25 business schools. The advantage of IBEAR's one-year format is even greater when the opportunity cost of foregone income for a two-year program is considered. Total tuition and fees for the academic year are approximately $47,750 for 56 units (nineteen courses). Total living expenses for a single participant range from $1450 to $2000 per month, depending on choice of housing and transportation.

Scholarships of $10,000 to $25,000 are available to high-potential U.S. and international applicants.

International Students

IBEAR's objective is to build a diverse community of participants each year. Typically, the select class of 56 partici-pants represents over 15 countries. IBEAR provides financial assistance to high-potential foreign nationals on a merit basis. Diversity of cultural background and work experience within each class enhances the educational experience and strengthens the IBEAR network long after participants receive their degrees.

Application Facts and Dates

Admission decisions begin in October. IBEAR follows a rolling admission procedure and reviews applications as soon as all materials are received. For more information, students should contact:

Fujiko Terayama, Director of
    Admissions and Administration
IBEAR M.B.A. Program
Marshall School of Business
University of Southern California
Los Angeles, California 90089-0804
Telephone: 213-740-7140
Fax: 213-740-7559
E-mail: ibear@usc.edu
World Wide Web: http://www.ibear.
    com

The University of Tampa

> ## ACHIEVING YOUR PERSONAL BEST
>
> *There are many reasons to get your M.B.A. from The University of Tampa (UT), but three in particular stand out. We care about you as an individual, and when you enroll, you join a family, not just an institution or a Web site chatroom. We care about teaching, and our professors are both qualified and dedicated to helping you progress in the classroom. We care about technology and use it to enhance our teaching. The result is a school on the move taking the lead in business education.*
>
> *You can get a generic M.B.A. degree anywhere if all you want is a storefront certificate. But we believe there's more to it than that. Personal attention and teaching excellence are what set UT apart from the competition. Call, visit, or better yet, apply to The University of Tampa M.B.A. program. It will be one of the best decisions you ever make.*
>
> —Alan L. Weimer, M.B.A. Director

Programs and Curricular Focus

The accredited M.B.A. program consists of 39 hours of course work (for those applicants holding a bachelor's degree in business or related areas), 30 hours of which are required upper-level core courses. The remaining 9 elective hours may be used to investigate special areas of interest or, with an additional 3 hours, can be applied toward one of the following concentrations: accounting, finance, information systems management, international business, management, or marketing management. These concentrations provide the opportunity to combine an area of specialization with knowledge of the business world to enhance career options. This approach keeps the curriculum up to date so as to reflect the topics and skills essential to business success.

Students and the M.B.A. Experience

Approximately 80 percent of The University of Tampa's M.B.A. students work full-time in the Tampa Bay community (an area with a population of 2.2 million). The remaining 20 percent are full-time students. The average student is 31 years old and has seven years of working experience. Fourteen percent of the M.B.A. students are international. This mix enlivens the classroom and provides students with a wide variety of perceptions and backgrounds. The increasing contingent of

international students is typically full-time, and many serve as graduate assistants to faculty members.

❖ Global Focus

Today, virtually all professionals are involved in international business. An educational foundation infused with a global perspective has therefore become essential. In response to this challenge, The University of Tampa's M.B.A. faculty has thoroughly integrated its core curriculum with global business perspectives and has developed a separate concentration in international business. Students develop an appreciation for and an understanding of how to manage in today's international arena.

Special Features

Required M.B.A. courses help students develop an understanding of the operating systems in business enterprises and develop a broad strategic perspective. It is this perspective that is ultimately necessary to effect change and to lead an organization. Students learn to examine business processes from a cross-functional perspective, which in turn helps them avoid departmental narrowsightedness and make better top-level managerial decisions. Pre-M.B.A. courses (a lower-level core) are available for students requiring preparatory work prior to starting the upper-level core of M.B.A. courses.

The Faculty

All of the faculty members teaching in The University of Tampa's M.B.A. program have earned doctorates in their fields of expertise. Just as importantly, they were recruited to teach at The University of Tampa because of their teaching competence and real-world practical experience. Teaching excellence is the primary focus. A significant majority of every faculty member's performance evaluation is based upon excellence in teaching. Love of teaching is an essential characteristic of The University of Tampa faculty.

The Business School Network

Hundreds of community-based internships in practically every field enrich the historical partnership between the University and the business community and balance the concepts of learning by thinking and learning by doing. Further cementing the historical partnership, The University of Tampa faculty and staff members and students are involved in hundreds of community volunteer projects each year.

The College and Environs

Symbolically and geographically, The University of Tampa lies at the heart of the city of Tampa, one of the country's most exciting growth areas of the last decade. Tampa is Florida's west coast center for banking, commerce, government, law, manufacturing, and real estate. The campus, made up of thirty-seven buildings plus athletic facilities, open spaces, and park lands, covers 70 acres stretching along the banks of the Hillsborough River in the midst of Tampa's booming downtown.

Facilities

Although the College of Business considers the faculty and staff members and students its most valuable assets, other learning resources available include several unique elements. Through these, The University of Tampa's M.B.A. program offers innovative teaching and support not typically found in graduate programs. The Decision Support Center

The H. B. Plant Hall, formerly the Tampa Bay Hotel, circa 1891.

houses a range of software products, packages for financial and statistical analysis, international databases, and graphics presentation software. Computer labs, both Macintosh and IBM, are available. UT has three outstanding centers: the Center for Ethics, the Center for Quality, and the Center for Leadership. These centers assist students and business leaders in making ethical decisions, developing leadership and management skills, and applying total quality management concepts. An Applied Strategic Analysis project helps local businesses and provides students with the opportunity to study and apply what they learn through a consulting role. The Merl Kelce Library houses a number of research and study aids, including such user-friendly retrieval databases as ABI-INFORM, LEXIS-NEXIS, Disclosure, and the National Trade Data Bank.

Placement

The University provides a full range of career placement services, including testing, resume preparation, career opportunities, career days, interview opportunities, and industry trends.

Admission

Admission to UT's M.B.A. program is competitive and is based on a number of important factors, including a student's undergraduate grade point average, GMAT scores, and two letters of recommendation. Admission decisions cannot be made unless official copies of both transcripts and test scores are available in the Office of Graduate Admissions. Applications are processed on a rolling basis and admission can be effective in either the fall, spring, or summer session. Individual interviews are encouraged, but not required. Although a specific undergraduate major is not required, all students admitted to the M.B.A. program must have earned a four-year undergraduate degree.

Finances

Tuition for 2000–01 is $325 per credit hour. Tuition is payable at registration each semester. In addition, a $35 student services fee is required each term. The cost of books, supplies, health insurance, and personal expenses is additional.

Graduate assistantships are available each academic year. Assistantships provide tuition waivers for up to six classes per year plus a $3000 stipend. Recipients must be full-time students and work 20 hours per week for College of Business professors and administrators. Federal Stafford Student Loans are also available. The graduate and financial aid offices assist students with the preparation of necessary application forms. Graduate students who are not currently employed may apply for a noncredit internship with a local business.

International Students

All international applicants must submit a Test of English as a Foreign Language (TOEFL) score report with a minimum score of 550, transcripts from all previously attended colleges (printed in English), and financial certification with appropriate supporting documents.

Application Facts and Dates

Applicants wishing to be considered for admission should submit a completed application form to the Graduate Studies in Business Office. Completed applications include the $35 application fee, transcripts of all previous college work, the Graduate Management Admission Test (GMAT) score report, and two letters of recommendation from professionals (e.g., employers or professors) familiar with the applicant's academic potential. For further information, students should contact:

Graduate Studies in Business Office
The University of Tampa
Box O
401 West Kennedy Boulevard
Tampa, Florida 33606-1490
Telephone: 813-258-7409
Fax: 813-259-5403
E-mail: mba@alpha.utampa.edu
World Wide Web: http://www.utampa.edu

University of Tennessee

College of Business Administration

Knoxville, Tennessee

THE WHOLE IS GREATER THAN THE SUM OF THE PARTS: INTEGRATED LEARNING

The University of Tennessee M.B.A. program immerses students in an integrated environment like no other. Running their own businesses, working in teams, making decisions about problems as they arise, students learn business by doing business.

The result is an exciting new curriculum with an emphasis on applied learning, teamwork, integration across business functions, massive use of technology, and exposure to global issues.

The University of Tennessee is proud to be breaking the rules and setting new standards in graduate management education.

—C. Warren Neel, Dean

Programs and Curricular Focus

Students in the University of Tennessee, Knoxville (UTK), M.B.A. program learn how to learn, the most critical factor for success in a time as dynamic as ours. Tennessee M.B.A. students master the business fundamentals in a highly applied environment, work in teams to solve complex problems via conventional methods and new tools from information technology, and are prepared to enter a world of global competition fueled by information technology and led by an increasingly diverse workforce.

In the first year, the core curriculum immerses students in the most highly integrated and applied learning environment in existence. In a way it is "not like school at all," but is instead like working at a high level in a dynamic organization. In management teams of 6 peers, students run a hypothetical company. They learn how to assess what customers value, how to finance their operations, how to reengineer their processes, how to align personnel systems and operational processes, and how the business skills they are learning apply to companies they will be joining, creating, or working for in the future. The year ends with an intensive, integrated computer simulation game, The MarketPlace, which brings into sharp focus all of the skills and concepts students have learned throughout the year.

In the second year, students complete elective and concentration courses. In addition to such established concentrations as economics, finance, management, and marketing, the University of Tennes-

see offers innovative concentrations in entrepreneurism, global business, information technology, logistics and transportation, management science, and statistics. The goal of the second year is to round out the students' management education and to equip them with a specialty that will give them an edge in the job market.

Between the first and second years, students complete a summer internship. With the assistance of a career management specialist, students research careers, make contacts, and secure an internship for the summer. Tennessee M.B.A. students have consistently secured internships with some of the most renowned and progressive national and international companies.

UTK also offers two joint programs: the J.D./M.B.A. degree, which allows students to complete both degrees in one to two semesters less than each degree requires separately, and an M.S./M.B.A. degree in manufacturing management and engineering, which allows students to complete both degrees in two years, including one summer session.

Students and the M.B.A. Experience

Diversity defines the student profile of the UTK M.B.A. student. Tennessee M.B.A. students bring a wealth of experiences, both professional and personal, which enrich the learning environment. The average student has 4½ years of professional work experience; 93 percent have more than one year of

experience. Their professional experiences include the private, public, and nonprofit domain with a number of students also having been entrepreneurs.

About 37 percent have backgrounds in the arts and sciences, with 15 percent having engineering degrees. The average class size is 95; about 30 percent are women, 4 percent are members of minority groups, and 26 percent are foreign nationals who represent twelve countries.

❖ Global Focus

Throughout their M.B.A. careers, students apply what they learn to a global context. In the first year, they complete a major international project. In the second year, students can select a concentration in global business and get deep exposure to international management, finance, marketing, logistics, and related issues. In addition, the UTK M.B.A. program has partnerships with programs in France, China, and Chile, enabling students to travel abroad to study international business and international business education.

Special Features

During the summer, students utilize an interactive multimedia CD-ROM-based course to begin or strengthen their skills in spreadsheets, word processing, and database management.

There are also numerous student organizations that add great value to the students' M.B.A. education, and students are encouraged to join several. The Tennessee Organization of M.B.A.'s (TOMBA) is a must. Other organizations include New Ventures Now for aspiring entrepreneurs; the Global Business Club for students with international experience or aspirations; an investment club for students with their sights set on Wall Street; Corporate Connections, an organization that puts M.B.A. students in front of leaders of major businesses to describe the vitality and value of the UTK M.B.A. program and its students; Community Connections, an organization of M.B.A. students committed to public service; a marketing club; and numerous others.

The Faculty

Faculty members who teach in the M.B.A. program are selected for their outstanding teaching, research, and experience working with corporations. Many of the UTK M.B.A. faculty members are instructors in the executive education programs delivered through the Management Development Center. Working with corporate leaders, faculty members learn the kinds of skills and talents companies currently value and what they are likely to need in the future. They bring these concepts into the classroom to more accurately prepare M.B.A. students for the competitive world they will enter after graduation.

The Business School Network

Faculty, administration, and students are committed to maintaining active relationships with the local, national, and international business communities. M.B.A. administrators work closely with the chancellor of the University as well to maintain strong business and industry partnerships.

Corporate Partnerships

The UTK M.B.A. program is enriched by the close ties held with the College's Management Development Center, which trains approximately 1,000 corporate executives yearly, as well as the close ties held with the executive M.B.A. program, which enrolls close to 40 international executives each year. More than 30 guest executives visit UT annually as part of the Executive-in-Residence classes offered to M.B.A. students. The Dean maintains an Advisory Board consisting of executives from many national companies who meet with students and faculty once a year to assess the status and currency of the M.B.A. curriculum. In addition, a select group of M.B.A. students are chosen each year to serve on the Corporate Connections team, which serves as a means to market the M.B.A. program to the national business community.

The College and Environs

The University of Tennessee, Knoxville, a federal land-grant institution that began its tradition of service in 1794, is one of the nation's twenty largest universities, enrolling approximately 26,000 students, including 5,692 graduate students. The College of Business Administration is the second-largest college of the University, enrolling 3,900 students.

Knoxville lies within a metropolitan area of approximately 600,000 that houses major corporate headquarters and numerous industrial and commercial operations. Many cultural and entertainment activities are available year-round, and the nearby Great Smoky Mountains National Park offers year-round recreational opportunities. Knoxville is consistently rated as one of the top ten cities in the country in providing gracious amenities and a high quality of life.

Facilities

The University of Tennessee is the home of one of the finest library facilities in the nation. The Hodges Library has more than 2 million volumes and subscribes to 19,000 journals. In addition, the library has state-of-the-art electronic resources available for student research, communication, and information retrieval. M.B.A. classes are generally held in two classrooms specially reserved for the M.B.A. program. The University itself also has excellent cultural, recreational, fitness, and sports facilities.

Technology Environment

The chancellor of the University of Tennessee has challenged the school to become the "information university" for the state of Tennessee. Accordingly, the campus has an excellent information infrastructure for the M.B.A. program to use. Given the intense use of information technology in the M.B.A. program, each student is required to have his/her own laptop computer for document preparation, spreadsheet analysis, database design, computer graphics, and Internet and e-mail connections.

Placement

The UTK M.B.A. Program Placement Office coordinates with the campuswide Career Services Office for on-campus interviews and interviews via video teleconferencing. Additional services delivered exclusively to M.B.A. students include resume referrals for both intern and full-time searches, membership and participation in three University-business consortia, resume writing workshops, videotaped interviews, and three career management seminars aimed at developing students' skills in such areas as job/intern search strategies, salary negotiation techniques, and dressing for success.

Admission

Applications are accepted for fall semester only. The Admission Committee considers the applicant's academic record, with particular emphasis on the last two years of undergraduate work and any previous graduate studies; scores on the GMAT and TOEFL (if applicable); work experience and other activities that demonstrate leadership potential. Personal interviews are strongly recommended but not required.

Finances

The 2000–01 educational expense for first-year students is approximately $11,000 to $14,000, including $3606 annually for in-state tuition and $9674 annually for out-of-state tuition. (The total amount quoted includes M.B.A.-specific fees, books, supplies, room, board, and other miscellaneous costs.) Merit-based fellowships and assistantships are awarded by the College. Assistantships carry a full tuition waiver and a monthly stipend. Federal and state programs for student loans and grants and the Student Employment Service are administered by the Office of Financial Aid, 115 Student Services Building, 865-974-3131. The priority deadline is March 1.

International Students

There is a significant international student population at the University of Tennessee, Knoxville. (The M.B.A. program has 26 percent international students, with twelve nationalities represented.) The University's Center for International Education and the International House provide resources and programs to meet the cultural, social, and professional interests of the international students.

Application Facts and Dates

The M.B.A. program application deadline (fall entrance only) for domestic and international applicants is March 1. Admission decisions are made on a rolling basis. Applicants receive a decision approximately four to six weeks after the M.B.A. Program Office receives a completed application. For additional information, students should contact:

Donna L. Potts
M.B.A. Admissions Director
University of Tennessee
527 Stokely Management Center
Knoxville, Tennessee 37996-0552
Telephone: 865-974-5033
Fax: 865-974-3826
World Wide Web: http://mba.bus.utk.edu

The University of Texas at Arlington

College of Business Administration

Arlington, Texas

TRADITIONAL...ONLINE...COHORT-BASED

The M.B.A. curriculum aligns the expertise of our faculty with the educational outcomes that corporations seek. This enables students to keep pace with emerging technology and best practices. It also allows students to tailor their study programs to effectively address their unique educational needs and desired career outcomes. Our strategic location in the center of the dynamic Dallas/Fort Worth Metroplex provides enriched and seldom-matched educational and professional opportunities for both full-time and part-time students. As part of our $10-million renovation, classrooms in the College of Business Administration are equipped with cutting-edge instructional technologies that are second to none. Students completing the M.B.A. program develop the ability to function on teams and task forces, leverage global opportunities, formulate and execute leadership initiatives, apply new technologies to complex processes, and design integrated solutions for organizational challenges.

—Dan Himarios, Dean

Programs and Curricular Focus

Students from a wide variety of academic backgrounds choose the M.B.A. at the University of Texas at Arlington (UTA) because of its flexibility and academic rigor. Students now have three program options: a traditional M.B.A., a cohort-based M.B.A., and an Online M.B.A.

The traditional program allows students with limited academic business backgrounds to begin with up to 18 hours of core course work. Students who have had business classes within the past 10 years may waive core and deficiency courses (similar courses in which they earned a grade of B or better) and complete their advanced studies in as few as sixteen months. The College's innovative Saturday schedule and evening classes make the program convenient for working adults. Students may tailor their advanced programs, normally 36 hours in length, to include skill-building electives that are appropriate for their chosen functional area, level, and industry. Students with professional degrees may select electives in their professional areas such as engineering, science, or environmental studies. Students wishing to expand their career opportunities may complete reduced requirements for a dual (second) degree in business, engineering, architecture, nursing, social work, or urban affairs. The College also supports a dual degree with Thunderbird, The American Graduate School of International

Management, that allows students to earn an M.B.A. from UTA and a Master of International Management (M.I.M.). Students may take advantage of UTA's reasonable cost and excellent business curriculum and Thunderbird's specialized international studies.

The College also offers a cohort-based M.B.A. program, designed for working professionals who desire an educational experience equivalent to leading full-time programs. This program is currently offered on the UTA/Forth Worth Riverbend Campus.

The College is a participant in the University of Texas System M.B.A. Online Program. This innovative general management M.B.A. program is designed for students whose busy lifestyle, geographic isolation, or other restrictions prevent them from participating in a traditional in-residence program. The M.B.A. Online program is offered using the Internet and supplemental materials such as videotapes, audiotapes, and CD-ROM's.

The M.B.A. curriculum provides students with a competitive advantage through their expanded ability to effectively perform on challenging team, consulting, and leadership assignments that must deal with advanced technologies, organizational change, and emerging markets.

Students and the M.B.A. Experience

The student body in fall 1999 consisted of 462 students, with 170 pursuing their studies on a full-time basis. Approximately 90 percent of the students have industry experience, with the average being five years. Slightly less than half of the students have degrees outside of business, with engineering and science making up the largest group (20 percent). The student diversity makes the M.B.A. experience an innovative approach to learning about business teams in the global village. Thirty-four percent of the students are women, 24 percent come from forty-one different countries on every continent, and more than 15 percent are members of minority groups. Every year, students may participate in exchange programs in Australia, England, France, Germany, Korea, Mexico, or Norway, as well as participate in other study-abroad opportunities. These experiences allow students to perform at a broader level in the global village.

Special Features

Students may participate in a comprehensive careers program that begins with a careers class (BUS4 5338) that provides extensive individual assessment, analysis of career options, and guidance in networking with key people in possible future career fields. Once a career orientation is evaluated, the student is advised on recommended electives and encouraged to discuss options with advisers, key faculty members, and alumni. Students are then assisted in locating paid internships that will provide hands-on experiences in their chosen fields.

The Faculty

The College has 122 full-time equivalent faculty members, of whom 108 are full-time. More than 76 percent of full-time faculty members hold doctoral degrees from some of the most prestigious business schools in the U.S. Full-time faculty members are growing in both number and diversity; currently, they include 31 women and 19 members of minority groups. Faculty members are assigned to six departments.

> Accounting: John Beehler, Ph.D., Indiana.
> Economics: Daniel Himarios, Ph.D., Virginia Tech.
> Finance and Real Estate: Vincent Apilado, Ph.D., Michigan.
> Information Systems and Management Sciences: Sumit Sircar, D.B.A., Harvard.
> Management: Jerry Wofford, Ph.D., Baylor.
> Marketing: Carl McDaniel, D.B.A., Arizona State.

The Business School Network

The College of Business Administration has seven advisory councils and boards that serve as advocacy groups for the College, providing advice and support on such matters as curriculum, internship programs, facilities enhancements, career services for students, and staff and faculty recruitment. A special program developed by the founder of Banctec joins successful executives and entrepreneurs with faculty to assist in the development and conduct of specialized courses. The Small Business Institute also helps match the research needs of small businesses with M.B.A. students' interests and academic experience. Each year the college hosts "Business Week," featuring guest speakers from leading corporations. These councils, boards, and events provide personal contacts between the members of the College and the business community, which greatly assists in the shaping of the school's programs and the leaders of tomorrow.

The College and Environs

The Dallas/Fort Worth Metroplex is a large market and distribution center, a major convention site, a growing financial and cultural center, and the tenth-largest market in the U.S. Arlington, located midway between these larger cities, is a busy suburban city of 300,000 that contains many of the top entertainment sites in the state and boasts of one of the safest community environments among all major cities. The University, located on a peaceful 333-acre campus, has flourished for more than 100 years and has grown to become one of the top 100 universities based on enrollment in the U.S. The College of Business Administration, one of the largest in the nation with more than 4,900 graduate and undergraduate students, is housed in a modern facility that contains research centers, numerous computer labs, electronic classrooms, special libraries, and modern advising facilities.

Facilities

The College's student-centered environment is being enhanced by a $10-million building renovation. The updated facility features a comprehensive student service center that houses both advising and career services, a library extension with online library access, a copy center, a student study area, and offices for student organizations. In addition to upgraded computer labs, classrooms have been upgraded with state-of-the-art multimedia instruments, including ceiling-mounted monitors and data ports for students' laptop computers.

Technology Environment

In order to keep pace with rapidly changing technology, Enterprise Resource Planning (ERP) software is being implemented throughout the College. Currently, SAP/R3 software is being integrated into the business curriculum. Though students can conduct much of their library research through their PC and modem, the College houses ten laboratory facilities with more than 200 computers and related software libraries. Visual Basic, JAVA, Microsoft Office Suites, and the Netscape Web browser, as well as DOS, OS/2, and Windows operating systems, are available for use by students. Students also have access to several Microsoft products at a greatly reduced cost. All students have a VAX computer account and access to the Internet and are able to complete advising and registration via the Internet, using e-mail and CyberAdvising, the UTA-pioneered electronic advising system.

Placement

The Dallas/Fort Worth Metroplex provides a fertile lab for the exploration and pursuit of hundreds of career alternatives. The University annually hosts one of the largest "career day events" in Texas, which attracts top employers throughout the region. This event helps maintain one of the nation's largest student employment services, which offers 8,000-10,000 part-time jobs, co-ops, and internships. A core of career professionals participates in a comprehensive M.B.A. careers program and presents an array of seminars designed to enhance the candidate's circle of opportunities. Cooperative career fairs, extended electronic job listings, and an interactive resume data bank complement traditional on-campus interviews.

Admission

While managerial or supervisory experience is preferred, it is not required. Prerequisites for admission to this program include a bachelor's degree from an accredited university, a satisfactory GMAT score, past academic performance that demonstrates the potential for graduate work, three letters of recommendation that reflect an ability to perform at a high level, and a personal essay that persuasively outlines the student's academic goals, strengths, and weaknesses. An entering class of students will normally have an average GMAT score of 550 and an average GPA of 3.2.

Finances

Modest tuition rates and fees make this M.B.A. a great selection for students seeking the biggest "bang for the buck." The annual tuition and fees rate for the 2000–01 year for 30 semester hours of graduate course work is $4763 for in-state residents and $11,549 for out-of-state residents. The annual cost for textbooks and supplies is approximately $900. The annual costs (twelve months) for room, board, and incidentals may cost an additional $9000 (lower if shared living). A vehicle may be necessary to take full advantage of internships and work opportunities. Students are encouraged to participate in the M.B.A. loans program when necessary.

International Students

International students from every continent participate in the M.B.A. program. The University provides a Graduate English Skills Program that helps international students adjust to the culture and helps polish verbal skills that are vital to success in the M.B.A. classroom. International students should have a TOEFL score of at least 550.

Application Facts and Dates

Applications may be submitted for fall, spring, and summer semesters. Application deadlines are generally as follows: For U.S. students for fall semester the deadline is mid-June; for spring semester the deadline is mid-October; and for summer semester the deadline is mid-March. For international students, the deadline for fall semester is April 1; for spring semester the deadline is September 1; and for summer semester, the deadline is January 1.

Detailed information on application requirements and steps to take after acceptance are all explained on the University's World Wide Web home page, which is listed below. Application material may be downloaded from the Web or requested using the information listed below.

Graduate Business Programs
University of Texas at Arlington
UTA Box 19376
Arlington, Texas 76019-0376
Telephone: 817-272-3005
Fax: 817-272-5799
E-mail: admit@uta.edu
World Wide Web: http://www2.uta.edu/gradbiz

The University of Texas at Austin

Austin, Texas

A LIFE PLATFORM

Our program provides students with a life platform for obtaining their major personal and professional goals. In a narrow sense, it provides students with the concepts, insights, institutional knowledge, and analytical tools necessary to manage an organization in the rapidly changing political and economic environment. In a broad sense, through multiple formal and informal experiences, it provides students with self-knowledge of their talents and life goals that are the first step in leading others. Our program also provides connections with other students, faculty, alumni, and business leaders crucial for career success.

—Ramesh Rao, Associate Dean

Programs and Curricular Focus

The Texas M.B.A program is a two-year, 60-hour, full-time program. The seven-course (21-hour) core curriculum provides a broad, cross-functional perspective followed by thirteen electives. A student may choose to concentrate in an academic discipline, such as finance, marketing, or accounting, or follow a market-driven specialization, such as energy finance or information management. Specializations are offered within the following areas: accounting, finance, management, marketing, management science and information systems, and marketing/management science and information systems.

Texas offers one-semester exchange programs with nineteen international business schools (eleven of which are English-language programs) and joint-degree programs with seven international business schools. New programs are being developed continually. The Texas M.B.A. language track in Spanish is a one-year, three-course sequence specifically tailored for business students. In addition to enhanced language proficiency, students gain an understanding of Latin American economic structures, business practices, and protocols.

Students and the M.B.A. Experience

The student-selection equation is simple: quality inputs produce quality outputs. For that reason, the program's standards are highly competitive. The Texas M.B.A. program requires intelligent, experienced, and professional applicants. The most recent class hails from widely varying cultural, geographic, national, educational, and professional backgrounds. Talent and motivation are the only traits shared among all Texas

M.B.A. students. The average M.B.A. student has a GMAT score of 690, a GPA of 3.4, and five years of full-time work experience. The average age is 28. The class profile includes 24 percent women, 4 percent members of minority groups, and 30 percent international students. More than forty-five countries are represented in the international population. Each class is divided into a number of cohorts selected to create a diverse blend of academic, professional, and cultural backgrounds. The rigorous core curriculum fills most of the first year. In the core courses, students study accounting, statistics, information technology management, economics, finance, marketing, and operations. This survey of "the organization"—its many forms, influences, and surroundings—grounds every Texas M.B.A. student in a similarly excellent framework and provides a strong base for later, more focused course work.

Special Features

Today, many schools have small investment funds, but the M.B.A. Investment Fund, LLC remains the only private investment company to be managed by students. Formed in December 1994 with $1.6 million in capital, this investment company now manages nearly $11 million for 48 investors and has earned an average annualized return of 18.2 percent over the past five years. Twenty Texas M.B.A. students, competitively selected each year, identify and analyze investment opportunities, manage a diversified investment portfolio, and develop and manage client relationships. An advisory committee composed of finance faculty members and leading investment professionals guides the students throughout their fund management experience.

In its second year, the nation's first Energy Finance Program, a joint venture between the University of Texas at Austin and Enron, has enabled M.B.A. students to learn innovative ways in which commodities such as electricity and natural gas can be traded, much like equity stocks. Enron has pioneered and continues to lead risk management practices in the energy field, offering its customers innovative financing alternatives for long-term contracts related to domestic and international energy projects. The grant also funds scholarships for students exhibiting both academic excellence and leadership capabilities.

The International Entrepreneurial Challenge of the MOOT Corp® Program is a new venture competition in which graduate business students develop a detailed, growth-oriented business plan and then match their efforts against those of their peers from other top business schools. Originated by the Graduate School of Business (GSB) at the University of Texas at Austin, the program combines cutting-edge academic theories with the most effective business practices. It enables business school disciplines to be applied to actual entrepreneurial ventures in an integrated fashion.

The Center for Customer Insight (CCI) is a groundbreaking collaborative effort between the Business School and a group of corporate sponsors who are interested in providing a forum for both students and business executives to master the latest tools, techniques, and ideas for building profitable customer relationships. Andersen Consulting initiated the original concept for the Center for Customer Insight together with the University of Texas (UT) and joined the program as a CCI Founding Partner.

Teaming with Cisco Systems, e-commerce experts at the McCombs School of Business now produce one of the most comprehensive measurements of the U.S. Internet economy— the widely sited Internet Economy Indicators. In the Center for Research in Electronic Commerce, internationally known researchers Andrew Whinston and Anitesh Barua not only spearhead that endeavor, but run a living laboratory of e-commerce where M.B.A. students form and operate online companies. This electronic Digital Economy gives students firsthand experience with Internet commerce and serves as a powerful tool for researchers in this arena.

The Faculty

The faculty members (17 percent women, 16 percent international) are unusually committed to the development of their students on both personal and professional levels. This fact manifests itself in their extraordinary accessibility to business students. The faculty's close connections with the corporate world give its members a realistic, informed perspective on modern business, thus ensuring that the classroom remains as relevant as possible.

The Business School Network

Corporate Partnerships

Texas has outstanding relationships with such corporations as EDS, Enron, Andersen Consulting, Cisco Systems, and IBM. The corporate partners have joined with Texas to develop such lasting programs as the EDS Financial Technology and Trading Center, the Enron Energy Finance Program and Excellence Fund, the Center for Customer Insight with Andersen Consulting, the Internet Economic Indicators with Cisco Systems, and the laptop initiative with IBM. UT's proximity to Austin's entrepreneurial, high-tech community also lends a competitive advantage to the Texas M.B.A. program.

Prominent Alumni

Texas M.B.A. alumni are prominent leaders in many industries in the United States and abroad. They are dedicated and loyal supporters of the School who give generously of their time, experience, and counsel to current students and other alumni. Connections are maintained through the Graduate Business Network, the alumni organization that maintains an online alumni database of more than 15,000 graduate business alumni. Local chapters, annual reunions, and a variety of other programs support the Texas M.B.A. community.

The College and Environs

The program is uniquely defined by its environment. The University of Texas at Austin is the largest university in the United States and is internationally recognized as a premier research institution. The city of Austin has become a major leader in the development of technology and is a center of entrepreneurship.

Facilities

The McCombs School of Business encompasses a three-building complex on the main campus of the UT at Austin. The complex includes the Graduate School of Business,

the College of Business Administration (CBA), and the University Teaching Center. Executive-style classrooms are used for M.B.A. core curriculum instruction. Faculty offices are also housed within the CBA/GSB complex. The computer center supports more than 900 workstations in seven computer labs throughout the complex. The Millennium NT lab is equipped with 142 state-of-the-art workstations and 162 laptop ports accessible to all students, virtually around the clock.

Several new facilities opened this year in the business school complex. M.B.A. students now have access to thirteen private meeting rooms equipped with seating for five and network connectivity for smartboards, phones, conference-calling equipment, and ports. Also open to students is a technology-enabling reading room that seats 240 students. The room contains a variety of work areas, some dedicated to individual study and others for team study.

Technology Environment

All incoming graduate students are required to buy a specified corporate laptop computer, specially configured with a wealth of collaborative tools such as Microsoft Professional and Outlook 2000. This notebook program is intended to better prepare students for tomorrow's business needs.

Placement

Ford Career Center services include on-campus interview programs, individual career counseling, career panels, professional development seminars, and skill-building workshops. Also provided are resume referrals to prospective employers, publication of job announcements and resume books, salary information, assistance with company receptions, and the comprehensive Graduate Career Library. A new 10,000-square-foot corporate interviewing suite opened in February, 1998. A single, point-of-service reception foyer fronts the suite of forty-two interview rooms equipped with laptop ports and computers. More than 540 companies from across the nation and around the world come to the UT campus to interview, while several hundred more hire through the CareerWeb Jobline. This past year, 96 percent of Texas M.B.A. graduates had accepted employment offers three months after graduation.

Admission

The full-time M.B.A. program offers fall semester admission only. To be admitted to the program, applicants must submit letters of recommendation, official GMAT and TOEFL (for international students) scores, essay question responses, a current resume, and transcripts from all undergraduate insti-

tutions attended. Once a completed application is on file with the University, prospective students have the option to participate in an admission visit with an alumnus or with a member of the Texas Admission Committee in Austin. Students should see the Texas M.B.A. Web site below for one of four ways to apply. Supplementary admission requests may be required for specific specializations (e.g., energy finance and information management).

Finances

For Texas residents, the estimated cost of attendance for 2000–01 includes tuition of $3600 (first year, for 30 semester hours); fees, $4490 (including M.B.A., general University, and other fees); laptop computer, from $2000 to $3000; books and supplies, $1400 (per year); and living expenses, $11,386, for an estimated annual total of $23,376. For nonresidents, the estimated cost of attendance for 2000–01 includes tuition, $14,850 (first year, for 30 semester hours), fees, $4490 per year, for an estimated annual total of $34,626. For information about financial assistance opportunities and application deadlines for the Texas M.B.A., students should contact Ms. Mary Gielstra, Texas M.B.A. Financial Assistance Coordinator (telephone: 512-471-7607; fax: 512-471-4131; e-mail: mgielstra@mail.utexas.edu).

International Students

International students comprise 30 percent of the M.B.A. population and represent forty-five countries. Specific student groups that support international students' interests are the International M.B.A. Student Association, the Mexican Business Networking Association, and the Brazilian-American Business Group. Student groups sponsor International Nights each semester that highlight countries represented in the Texas M.B.A. program. The Ford Career Center has a dedicated career counselor on staff whose primary role is to service international students.

Application Facts and Dates

For more information, students should contact:

Dr. Carl Harris
Director of Admission, M.B.A.
    Program
McCombs School of Business
The University of Texas at Austin
P.O. Box 7999
Austin, Texas 76713-7999
Telephone: 512-471-7612
Fax: 512-471-4243 or 4131
E-mail: texasmba@bus.utexas.edu
World Wide Web: http://texasmba.bus.
    utexas.edu

The University of Texas at Dallas

► **MANAGEMENT EDUCATION—A HIGH PRIORITY**

There are many distinguishing features to the University of Texas at Dallas (UT Dallas). First, we have a very talented group of faculty members, many of whom have achieved national and international recognition, and we are recruiting the very best junior and senior faculty members. Second, we are located in a dynamic and growing area populated with many global and vibrant companies, offering the School a unique competitive advantage. We have an active industry Advisory Board, and we are committed to further strengthening our relationships with industry. Finally, we are part of a young but high-quality university that has identified management education as an area of high priority. All these features provide an environment in which we can deliver the highest quality education to our students.

—Hasan Pirkul, Dean

Programs and Curricular Focus

The School of Management strives to meet the challenges of a dynamic, technology-driven, global society. By partnering with the business community, the School delivers high-quality management education to a diverse group of students from all over the world. The programs address the complex needs of modern society build upon the development, understanding, distribution, and management of advanced technologies.

The University of Texas at Dallas School of Management offers the following graduate degrees: The Master of Business Administration (M.B.A.), the Master of Science in accountancy, the Master of Science in business administration (M.S.), and the Master of Arts in international management studies (M.I.M.S.).

The M.B.A. is the largest program, and it is offered in three different formats. The part-time M.B.A. program consists of evening classes designed to provide students with full-time jobs the opportunity to earn a graduate degree. The curriculum enables the student to specialize in finance, international management, management information systems, e-commerce, telecommunications, managerial economics, marketing, operations management, or organizations and strategy.

Two specialized, 48-hour M.B.A. degrees are offered in the School. The Cohort Program is a full-time arrangement with three semesters of course work offered primarily during the daytime. The Cohort M.B.A. focuses on developing "management skills for the information age." The

lock-step curriculum starts each fall and stresses ideas and concepts that provide tools for managing in the twenty-first century. Students range in age from 22 to 40 and have an average of four years of management experience.

Now in its eighth year, the Executive M.B.A. program (E.M.B.A.) focuses on "managing for change." The curriculum stresses the knowledge, skills, perspectives, and attitudes necessary to lead in the twenty-first century. The E.M.B.A. program is a lockstep, twenty-one-month program with classes on Friday and Saturday every other weekend. Participants in the program have at least 10 years of business experience.

Both the M.A. and M.S. programs are 36-hour degrees offered on a full-time or part-time basis. Classes are held primarily at night and allow specialization in accounting, decision sciences, finance and management economics, e-commerce, telecommunications, international management, marketing, and organizations and strategies.

Entrance to any master's program does not require a previous business degree.

Students and the M.B.A. Experience

Participants in the School of Management's graduate programs are primarily students with full-time jobs with a minimum of five years of managerial experience. Approximately 90 percent are pursuing degrees on a part-time basis while working locally at the many high-technol-

ogy corporations that surround the campus complex. They range in age from 28 to 50+. Almost half of the student body of the University is female. The minority population represents about 25 percent of the University's population. International students comprise 32.2 percent of the total student population.

There is a consistent international emphasis in the programs. It is driven by the faculty and the students. Programs include opportunities for field-based projects. Technology and its use is a primary focus of all graduate programs.

Special Features

There are two distance learning options at the School. The first is the self-paced Global M.B.A. Online. This program offers the same core courses and rates as UTD's traditional part-time M.B.A.. For this program all coursework is completed over the Internet. Students who take one or two classes per semester will complete the program in three to five years.

The second distance option is Global Leadership Executive Program which caters to executives with seven or more years of experience. The lock step, executive program combines online learning with group retreats and a international study tour. Students in the executive program can pursue the 48-credit-hour global leadership M.B.A. (G.L.E.M.B.A.) or a 36-credit-hour M.A. in International Management. Students complete the G.L.E.M.B.A. in forty months and the M.A. degree takes twenty-eight months to complete. Students already holding an M.B.A. may, under some circumstances, complete the M.A. in seventeen months. The global leadership track begins each January.

The School of Management also offers a special executive education program entitled Program/Project Management, designed primarily for certification of project managers. This certificate program can also lead to an M.S. or M.B.A. degree by taking additional hours. Offered once a month on a Thursday, Friday, and Saturday schedule, it is ideal for busy executives.

The School of Management has an alliance with The University of Texas Southwestern Medical School, which began offering a Master of Medical

Management designed for physicians and physician executives in 1998. The modular format runs every three months for 5½ days and can be noncredit or CME credit and/or academic credit. The program is taught jointly by School of Management faculty and UT Southwestern medical faculty.

The Faculty

The University of Texas at Dallas School of Management has strong, committed faculty members who teach all of the master's programs. All faculty members have extensive experience in master's education, consulting, and/or practical experience both domestically and internationally. Some are leading scholars. Many serve as editors of professional journals. Others have received awards for teaching excellence. At times, faculty members join together to team-teach selected courses. The faculty is supplemented in selected courses by outstanding UT Dallas faculty members from outside the School. All graduate courses are taught by faculty members with Ph.D.'s from universities across the nation, such as Stanford, Berkeley, Harvard, Carnegie Mellon, University of Minnesota, Rochester, and the University of Chicago. One highlight of the program is the addition of local corporate executives who supplement faculty teaching and who often provide case problems for student participation.

The Business School Network

The School of Management enjoys great support and counsel from the business community through its Advisory Council and President's Leadership Circle. Members of the council provide essential feedback for the various programs within the School. Business leaders are frequent speakers in the classroom, are included in all graduate retreats, and often work together with executive graduate students to resolve case problems. The School of Management, located in the north Dallas high-technology region, is fortunate to have Fortune 500 companies as employers of its students.

The College and Environs

Prior to becoming the University of Texas at Dallas in 1969, the University operated as the privately funded Southwest Center for Advanced Studies (SCAS). By act of the 61st Texas legislature, SCAS was transferred to the state of Texas. Graduate programs were expanded and enrollment for junior and senior undergraduate students began in September 1975. When the University opened its new campus buildings that year, the existing academic programs were organized into the Schools of Natural Sciences and Mathematics, Management, and Human Development. New programs were introduced through the Schools of Arts and Humanities, General Studies, and Social Sciences.

Facilities

UT Dallas is located between Richardson and Plano, two populous suburbs of almost 400,000 that are still growing rapidly. For the most part, the housing (apartments) available is less than 20 years old. For those who prefer to be on campus, the University has the Waterview Park Apartments, a series of low-rise, garden-style apartments run by a private company. These apartments have a long list of amenities, including kitchens, washer/dry-ers, alarm systems, and access to swimming and other recreational facilities.

Admission

Prerequisites for all graduate admissions include completion of an undergraduate calculus class and personal computer proficiency; spreadsheet proficiency is a must. Completion of a baccalaureate degree from an accredited institution is required; previous undergraduate work in business is not a requirement. Additional criteria for admission include the GMAT, completion of an application, and three recent letters of reference. A TOEFL score is required of all applicants for whom English is not the native language. Applicants are evaluated based on their personal qualities and academic background; GMAT scores are evaluated using the formula designated by the AACSB to evaluate admission criteria and professional experience. Personal interviews are not required. To download an application, applicants can send e-mail to grad-admission@utdallas.edu.

Finances

Resident tuition for 2000–01 is $1610.40 for full-time (9 hours) students and $628 for 3 hours for part-time students; nonresident tuition is $3545.40 for full-time (9 hours) students and $1273.80 for 3 hours for part-time students.

International Students

The School of Management at UT Dallas has a strong international graduate community. 32.2 percent of the graduate population is international, representing twenty nationalities. India, People's Republic of China, and Taiwan are the largest sources of international students.

Application Facts and Dates

The final deadline for fall admission is July 15 of each year; however, admission decisions are made in the order of application receipt and completion. Part-time students are admitted to the master's programs on a semester-by-semester basis. The deadline for spring admission is December 1; summer is May 1. The deadline for the Cohort M.B.A. and other specialized master's programs is July 15. For information, students should contact:

Mr. David Ritchey, Director of
  Advising Services
School of Management
University of Texas at Dallas
P.O. Box 830688, JO53
Richardson, Texas 75083-0688
Telephone: 972-883-2701
Fax: 972-883-6425
World Wide Web: http://www.utdallas.
  edu/dept/mgmt

The University of Texas at San Antonio

San Antonio, Texas

NOW GO EVEN FURTHER . . .

Business educators and practitioners have come to understand that building a personal business portfolio is a lifelong process. If you are ready to pursue a graduate business degree, the University of Texas at San Antonio (UTSA) has carefully developed a variety of high-quality programs. Choices range from the general M.B.A. and the M.B.A. with concentrations to a number of Master of Science (M.S.) and Master of Arts (M.A.) degrees in business-related disciplines. We also have a unique executive M.B.A. that focuses on personal leadership development and self-organizing systems for seasoned executives. Our modern campus and new business facility are equipped with the latest in teaching technologies, and our business faculty is dedicated to searching out and employing the most effective pedagogy. Our mission is to provide the graduate business program you need to further your personal business portfolio.

—James F. Gaertner, Dean

Programs and Curricular Focus

The College of Business is accredited by AACSB–The International Association for Management Education. A separate accreditation for the accounting programs, which was earned in 1997, further distinguishes the College among its peer institutions. Program integrity and quality is ensured by AACSB–The International Association for Management Education standards. In the association's latest review, the College was commended for its entrepreneurial spirit, vision, and responsiveness in building academic programs that match the needs of the business community, a state-of-the-art facility, and a faculty focused on real-world applications.

An alternative to the traditional programs includes weekend scheduling of M.B.A. courses for working professionals.

Advanced business degrees include:

- M.B.A., with concentration choices in business economics, employee relations, finance, health-care management, information systems, management accounting, management science, management of technology, marketing management, and taxation
- M.B.A. in international business
- Master of Taxation
- Master of Arts in economics

- Master of Science degrees in accounting, finance, information technology, and management of technology
- Executive M.B.A., which is exclusively for professionals with an average of ten years of full-time work experience who are seeking a program with an emphasis on leading in times of great change.

Students and the M.B.A. Experience

UTSA has a business graduate enrollment of more than 500. The students' average age is 28, with a 36 percent female enrollment. Approximately 65 percent attend graduate school part-time. Twenty-nine percent of the students are members of minority groups, and 6 percent are international students. Students recently admitted to the programs have an average GMAT of 540.

❖ Global Focus

Located in San Antonio, the College has enjoyed a strategic edge in offering opportunities to effectively integrate global business issues. A number of strong faculty and student exchange relationships have been developed with top institutions. The newest involves several universities from the People's Republic of China, and others include universities in Mexico and Canada. The College's central location in the Americas is particularly beneficial to the study of

NAFTA-related business issues. Both the College and University provide special program support through their International Programs Offices.

Special Features

A young and dynamic institution, UTSA has become one of the forty largest business schools in the nation since 1973 when it offered its first graduate course. The College's enrollment of about 4,200 has afforded it the latitude to offer fifteen graduate degree choices. Professional and faculty graduate advisers, as well as a placement coordinator, support College of Business graduate students. Program choices, combined with flexible scheduling plans, are available for virtually anyone who is seriously interested in pursuing a business graduate education. Programs have been developed to cater to the top-level executive looking for a challenging peer group experience, the mid-level manager returning for the tools necessary for promotion, and the more traditional full-time graduate student. A strong student organization, the MBA Association is only one of the many opportunities available for graduate students to enrich their academic experience.

The Faculty

UTSA has built an outstanding business faculty with Ph.D.'s from leading business schools nationwide. Forty-two percent of the faculty members are women or members of minority groups. Successful recruiting has created a broad and diverse faculty with a balanced approach to teaching, research, and service. The majority of business classes are taught by full-time professors, many of whom have practical business experience. Highly qualified professionals from the business community supplement the faculty in special topic categories.

The Business School Network

The College enjoys an extensive corporate community network. Faculty and students alike engage in professional organization affiliations and classroom projects, strengthening their ties to the

UTSA has one of the newest business school facilities in the nation.

business community. A 45-member Business Advisory Council of top-level executives from the local business community is committed to the College through recruiting, classroom interaction, financial support, and participation in the many social and academic activities. The Institute for Studies in Business partners faculty members and students with the business and community organizations seeking solutions to everyday business problems. The Center for Professional Excellence caters to both the individual executive and corporate leaders who are looking for custom programming in times of tremendous change.

The College and Environs

San Antonio, Texas, is the nation's eighth-largest city and is rich in history and culture. With 7 million visitors a year, it is the state's top tourist and convention site. The tourism, medical, and military industries, along with a growing communications and technology sector, make for a dynamic business community. The University, with an enrollment of approximately 18,600, is respected as an energetic, growing metropolitan university. With six new doctoral programs in the planning stages, including one in business, UTSA is rapidly moving toward classification as a doctoral-granting institution. It is the third-largest component of the University of Texas System and one of the state's fastest-growing public universities. The tri-campus operation includes a 600-acre campus located in northwest San Antonio and neighboring the famous Texas Hill

Country. The UTSA Downtown Campus and the Institute of Texan Cultures are located in the heart of San Antonio.

Facilities

The College moved into a new 205,000-square-foot, $30-million Business Building on the 600-acre UTSA campus in January 1997. UTSA students benefit from the growth of the University, and the Business Building is only one of many new academic buildings and facilities. Planning is underway for an additional 240,000-square-foot academic building with lecture halls, classrooms, and teaching laboratories. The Student Recreation and Wellness Center, which is scheduled to open in fall 2001, will include child-care facilities. Since 1994, UTSA has built five new buildings, including the first and second phase of a new Downtown Campus. The third phase began in October 1999.

Technology Environment

The University continues to make significant capital investments in equipment, creating new ways for students to retrieve information more quickly and easily and expanding its training, distance learning, and computer support programs. Initially, $4 million was dedicated to infuse the Business Building with the latest in teaching and learning technologies. Distance education and teleconference facilities, an advanced computer projects lab, two 30-station networked computer classrooms, wired study alcoves, and an additional 200-station general student computing facility are all part of the original technology available in the Business Building. Additional classrooms have been equipped with laptop computers.

Placement

In addition to the University Career Services Office, the College of Business provides direct access to a counselor. This M.B.A. counselor facilitates placement in permanent, part-time, or internship positions.

Admission

A bachelor's degree from an accredited institution is the basic requirement for admission to graduate study at UTSA. For admission to most graduate programs, applicants must meet University-wide graduate admission requirements and the following College of Business requirements: an approximate overall grade point average of at least 3.0 (on a 4.0 scale) in all work completed at the undergraduate level and an approximate composite score

of at least 500 (with no component less than the 20th percentile) on the GMAT. The GMAT results will only be accepted if the test has been taken no more than five years before the date of application. International students are also required to show proof of adequate funds, and proof of health/immunizations is recommended. International students whose native language is not English must submit TOEFL results with a minimum score of 500.

Finances

In fall 2000, full-time tuition (9 semester hours) and fees for residents are $1442. For nonresidents, they are $3377. Tuition and fee amounts are subject to change by Legislative action or by action of the Board of Regents of The University of Texas System. Changes in tuition and fees will be effective upon the date of enactment. Refer to each semester's Schedule of Classes for current tuition and fee amounts.

Financial aid is available in the form of fellowships, research assistantships, grants, scholarships, work-study, and loans. Financial aid is available to international students.

International Students

Services and facilities for international students include the international student office, international student center, international student housing, visa services, ESL courses, and counseling/support services.

Application Facts and Dates

For domestic applicants, applications and any required documents for the master's degree programs should be filed by July 1 for the fall semester, December 1 for the spring semester, and May 1 for the summer sessions. Deadlines for international students submitting applications for admission are April 1 for the fall semester, September 1 for the spring semester, and April 1 for the summer sessions.

Students should contact the office below for applications and instructions for completion:

Office of Graduate Studies
College of Business
The University of Texas at San
 Antonio
6900 North Loop 1604 West
San Antonio, Texas 78249
Telephone: 210-458-4330
Fax: 210-458-4332
E-mail: graduatestudies@utsa.edu
World Wide Web: http://www.utsa.edu/
 admgraduate

University of the Pacific

Stockton, California

EDUCATING INNOVATIVE LEADERS

The University of the Pacific M.B.A. program is committed to cultivating the leadership ability and innovative spirit of our students, in addition to training them in state-of-the-art technical business skills.

Our unique curriculum includes a heavy emphasis on experience in the workplace, which we achieve through class consulting projects, internships, and a mentor program that teams each full-time student with a senior business executive. Our small, highly interactive classes also encourage close working relationships between students and faculty, enabling faculty to challenge students to achieve their full potential.

Whether you are interested in the general management or the entrepreneurship track, the University of the Pacific M.B.A. is designed for students who want to make a difference.

—Mark Plovnick, Dean

Programs and Curricular Focus

The focus of the M.B.A. programs at the University of the Pacific is on training future business leaders to be competitive in the twenty-first century. The course work is challenging and provides a firm grounding in various academic disciplines yet goes beyond the traditional business school curriculum to emphasize critical leadership skills and a global perspective. The classes are small to encourage close student-faculty relationships.

There are two M.B.A. programs offered through the Eberhardt School of Business (ESB): the accelerated one-year, full-time program and the evening program, which can be completed on a full-time or part-time basis. The one-year M.B.A. is a unique, customized program that enables a limited number of students who have sufficient previous course work in business to complete the M.B.A. program in ten months. The team begins the program in early August, taking a three-week class entitled Leadership and Change that involves off-campus activities that can include outdoor adventure challenges, corporate visits, and other experiential assignments. The curriculum for the fall semester includes corporate finance, business and public policy, strategic marketing, and technology and innovation.

In January, the entire cohort travels overseas to take the Global Business Competition course. This includes classroom work, corporate visits, and cultural events. The entire experience provides students with the opportunity to actually live the culture and to attain the international perspective that is critical for M.B.A. degree holders today. Recent classes have been held in Seoul, Singapore, Kuala Lumpur, Santiago, Madrid, Barcelona, and Cork, Ireland. The spring semester includes Managing Productivity and Quality and Strategic Management, as well as the flexibility to choose a concentration with two elective courses. Students in the accelerated program are also matched with a senior manager from the business community who acts as a mentor and helps guide them through the M.B.A. program. Internships and consulting projects round out the workplace exposure emphasized by the M.B.A. program.

The evening program curriculum is divided into two phases totaling 54 semester units. Phase One includes eight courses covering basic business skills; these courses can be waived if similar courses have been successfully completed with a grade of B or better at the undergraduate or graduate level. Phase Two embodies the heart of the M.B.A. program, with two tracks—the general management M.B.A. and the entrepreneurship M.B.A. In each track, students take two courses that develop leadership and innovation skills, four courses that integrate the foundation course work into a managerial framework, and four elective courses that allow students to explore their areas of interest, such as finance, business law, marketing, or management information systems.

The University also offers a joint M.B.A./J.D. degree program with its McGeorge School of Law. This accelerated program allows students to complete both degrees in four years. The Master's International Program is offered in conjunction with the Peace Corps. This program allows individuals to complete their M.B.A. while also fulfilling a two-year Peace Corps service experience abroad.

Students and the M.B.A. Experience

The M.B.A. students at the University of the Pacific come from a wide variety of academic institutions, with diverse academic credentials. Geographically, a high percentage of students are from California, although there are students from throughout the United States and many other countries. Women comprise about 35 percent of the program's students, and approximately 20 percent of the students identify themselves as members of underrepresented groups. The average age of the students is 28, with 4.5 years of full-time work experience.

Special Features

The University of the Pacific M.B.A. program is unique in its overall emphasis on integrating the classroom experience with the business world and its focus on the personal as well as academic development of each student. The M.B.A. program offers an international study option each January for its students. The Global Business Competition course meets one week on campus and then travels overseas for a two-week period. The entrepreneurship M.B.A. program is a specialized course of study that complements the general management M.B.A. program and provides students with an intensified and rigorous exposure to the principles, tools, and ideas needed to succeed in entrepreneurial pursuits. Also available is the one-year M.B.A. program, which provides an unusual opportunity for a small group of students to experience an innovative fast-track M.B.A.

The Faculty

The Eberhardt School of Business is committed to teaching excellence. Teaching is the primary responsibility of the faculty. Research complements the teaching mission and enables faculty to offer instruction that is relevant and current, providing a high-

Michael Ballot, Professor; Ph.D., M.B.A.
Thomas Brierton, Associate Professor; J.D.
Donald W. Bryan, Associate Professor; Ph.D.
Lucien J. Dhooge, Assistant Professor; LL.M., J.D.
Cynthia F. Eakin, Assistant Professor; Ph.D.
Joel Herche, Associate Professor; Ph.D., M.B.A.
Ronald A. Hoverstad, Associate Professor; Ph.D.
Albert H. Huang, Assistant Professor; Ph.D., M.B.A.
John R. Knight, Associate Professor; Ph.D., M.B.A.
Georgine Kryda, Assistant Professor; Ph.D., M.B.A., M.I.M.
W. Anthony Kulisch, Associate Professor; D.B.A.
Unro Lee, Professor; Ph.D.
Jeffrey A. Miles, Assistant Professor; Ph.D., M.L.H.R., M.P.S.
Stefanie Naumann, Assistant Professor; Ph.D., M.L.H.R., M.P.S.
Newman Peery, Professor and M.B.A. Program Director; Ph.D., M.B.A.
Mark Plovnick, Professor and Dean; Ph.D.
Gerald V. Post, Professor; Ph.D.
Willard T. Price, Professor; Ph.D., M.P.W.A.
Robert Singh, Assistant Professor; Ph.D.
Ray Sylvester, Professor and Associate Dean; Ph.D., M.B.A.
Paul Tatsch, Associate Professor; Ph.D.
Eric Typpo, Assistant Professor; Ph.D.
Richard Vargo, Professor; Ph.D., M.B.A.
Cynthia Wagner, Associate Professor; Ph.D.
Suzanne B. Walghi, Assistant Professor; Ph.D., M.B.A.
Stephan W. Wheeler, Associate Professor; Ph.D.

quality learning experience for every student. While the faculty members have earned their academic credentials from the finest universities, most have significant experience in management or consulting; they integrate such experience into their course work.

The Business School Network
Corporate Partnerships
The University of the Pacific ESB has built strong relationships with the corporate community and strives to integrate the classroom experience with the business world in a variety of ways, including the Pacific Business Forum, which brings nationally and internationally recognized corporate or government leaders to campus several times a year to speak about current issues in the world today; the Westgate Center for Management Development, which provides management training for the regional business community; the Institute for Family Business, which assists family-owned businesses in finding and developing solutions to their unique business challenges; the Community Consulting Corps, which brings students together with managers of nonprofit organizations to work in a client-

consultant relationship to solve business problems; the Business Advisory Board, which includes 30 executives from local, regional, and national businesses who work closely with the dean and faculty at integrating the business school and the business world; the Mentorship Program, in which interested students in the full-time program are matched with an executive to help him or her make decisions regarding classes, careers, and the job search; and the Internship Program, which provides business exposure for students, either on an individual basis or as part of a consulting team.

The College and Environs
The University of the Pacific, with its red-brick buildings and ivy-covered walls, is now in its 150th year. California's first chartered university, the University of the Pacific was established in 1851, one year after California became a state. The main campus spreads more than 175 acres along the Calaveras River. Stockton is a short drive from San Francisco, Yosemite National Park, Lake Tahoe, the Napa and Sonoma wine country, Sierra skiing, and the state capitol in Sacramento. The University also has a dental school in San Francisco and a law school in Sacramento.

Technology Environment
The University has substantial academic computing resources available for students, with multiple laboratories distributed across the campus and a network linking the labs, personal computers, and the campus mainframe. The computer lab in the ESB has a Novell LAN with twenty-one 500-MHz Pentium-class computers. All graduate students are expected to take advantage of the University's electronic mail system and the Internet resources that are available.

Placement
The Career and Internship Office facilitates career decision making and job search assistance for all students on an individual basis and in small group sessions. It annually coordinates an on-campus recruiting program and a career fair, in addition to a variety of workshops and special programs. The office also maintains a Career Advisory Network, which links students to alumni of the University to help build their professional connections. In addition, the ESB Assistant Director for Career and Internship and ESB faculty and staff members work with alumni and corporations to secure internships and full-time positions for M.B.A. students.

Admission
Qualified candidates are admitted to the part-time evening program on a rolling basis for the fall semester, spring semester, and summer session. The accelerated one-year full-time program is limited to 25 students per class who are admitted and begin

in August as a cohort. Each candidate's file is evaluated on the basis of academic record, scores on the required Graduate Management Admission Test (GMAT), a personal essay, and three letters of recommendation. Although the entire "package" is considered for each applicant, the typical undergraduate GPA considered is 3.0 or higher. GMAT scores are generally 500 and above. A score of 550 or better on the TOEFL is required for all students for whom English is not the native language. In addition, international students must present proof of adequate funds to cover expenses for the entire M.B.A. program.

Finances
The annual expenses for an M.B.A. student at the University of the Pacific depend on a variety of factors. The 2000–01 tuition for the one-year program is $19,050. In the part-time program, costs are based on the number of courses a student takes (at $1905 per course in 2000–01). The cost of living in Stockton is relatively low, and students can find housing for about $400 to $550 per month. Room and board on campus are approximately $6000 per year, depending on the housing and meal plan options chosen. Full-time students must also pay a health services fee, which is approximately $250, and a University Center fee of $30. Financial assistance is available through scholarships, assistantships, and loans. Merit-based scholarships and teaching and research assistantships are available directly from the Eberhardt School of Business. These awards are generally determined by June 1, so students should submit applications by March 1 to be considered.

Application Facts and Dates
Application deadlines are June 1 for the fall semester, November 1 for the spring semester, and March 15 for the summer session. Since the one-year M.B.A. program is limited to 25 students per year, applicants to this program are advised to submit their applications by May 1 to guarantee consideration. M.B.A. admission decisions are made on a rolling basis, and applicants are notified immediately when decisions have been made. To ensure a quick response, application packages should be complete. For more information, contact:

Director of Student Recruitment
Eberhardt School of Business
Weber Hall, Suite 206
University of the Pacific
3601 Pacific Avenue
Stockton, California 95211
Telephone: 209-946-2629
       800-952-3179 (toll-free)
Fax: 209-946-2586
E-mail: mba@uop.edu
World Wide Web: http://www1.uop.edu/esb/docs/mba/index.htm

The University of Toledo

Toledo, Ohio

DEVELOPING BUSINESS LEADERS

At the University of Toledo (UT), we understand what it takes to succeed. After all, we have been educating and developing business leaders since 1933. Our rigorous M.B.A. curriculum skillfully integrates academic theory with real-world application. And like the business community we serve, we are committed to continuous improvement to keep our program in the forefront of business thought and practice. Our commitment to this philosophy is reflected in our faculty's superior records of accomplishment in mentoring, teaching, research, and consulting. The quality of our faculty, combined with our small class size, state-of-the-art facilities, and beautiful suburban setting, makes for a memorable and fulfilling learning experience that provides students with the needed skills and knowledge to succeed in an increasingly competitive environment.

—Dr. Thomas Sharkey, Interim Dean

Programs and Curricular Focus

The basic principles underlying managerial decision making are the main focus of the Master of Business Administration program. This program gives students a grasp of the techniques and the fundamentals of management as well as the breadth of knowledge necessary to prepare students for general management responsibility. Students can elect a broad (general) program or one with special emphasis on related areas in which they have particular interest. Specializations are offered in accounting, finance, human resource management, information systems, international business, management, marketing, and operations management. The joint J.D./M.B.A. program provides the opportunity for students to earn both a law degree and an M.B.A. in approximately three years.

The graduate curriculum may be built upon a bachelor's degree in business administration or any other baccalaureate degree. The length of the program varies depending on the nature of the undergraduate degree.

The Master of Business Administration degree is granted to students who satisfactorily complete a minimum of 30 semester hours of graduate course work in business administration, beyond a bachelor's in business administration, with a GPA of 3.0 or better. The required program for all students consists of basic core courses, advanced core courses, and specialization courses. Students who have an undergraduate degree in business administration are able to waive some or all of the basic core courses. No work experience is required for admission, although it adds significantly to the learning experience.

Students and the M.B.A. Experience

Variety best describes The University of Toledo. Students at UT come from around the United States and around the world and bring with them rich and varied backgrounds. The profile of an average student in the program in 1999–2000 was a 29-year-old with approximately five years of experience. Approximately 30 percent of the students in the program are full-time. Women account for more than a third of the students, while members of minority groups account for 23 percent. International students account for approximately 30 percent.

Special Features

In addition to traditional classwork, M.B.A. students can get hands-on experience through the Small Business Institute, the Institute for International Studies, and the award-winning UT Center for Family Business.

The Faculty

UT's faculty provides students with a dynamic and challenging learning environment. The faculty members in the College of Business Administration hold advanced degrees from a variety of distinguished institutions. Many are nationally and internationally recognized researchers whose articles have appeared in leading business and academic publications.

The Business School Network
Corporate Partnerships

The distinguished members of the College of Business Administration's Business Advisory Council (BAC) serve as a vital link to the corporate world. The BAC provides the College with valuable direction and advice, ensuring that a UT business education addresses current issues in today's business world. In addition, the College's Visiting Executives Program exposes students to executives from a variety of business backgrounds and helps to complement and build on students' classroom experiences. Business leaders in the program share their thoughts with students in designated classes on issues of concern to them and business in general. Several students are also selected to join the visiting executive and the dean of the College for either breakfast or lunch.

Prominent Alumni

The UT-M.B.A. Program provides individuals with the high-quality graduate business education necessary for success. The results speak for themselves. Many UT-M.B.A. graduates hold leadership positions in the business world. Among the school's prominent alumni are Ora Alleman, Executive Vice President, National City Bank; William Ammann, Vice President, Administration, Aeroquip-Vickers, Inc.; Michael Durik, Executive Vice President, The Limited Stores Inc.; Marvin Herb, CEO, Coca-Cola Bottling Company, Chicago; Julie Higgins, Executive Vice President, The Trust Company of Toledo; Donald Saunders, Vice Chairman, Toledo Edison; and Mark Tincher, Senior Portfolio Manager, Chase Manhattan Bank.

The College and Environs

Founded in 1872, The University of Toledo is Ohio's fourth-largest state-assisted university, with more than 23,000 students. Through its eight different colleges and schools, UT offers nearly 150 different academic majors. Located in a tree-lined subur-

Stranahan Hall, which won an award for its unique architectural design, is the home of the College of Business Administration at the University of Toledo.

ban area 6 miles from downtown Toledo, the more than 200-acre main campus combines classic architecture with beautifully landscaped grounds to make learning a truly enjoyable experience. As Ohio's fourth-largest city, Toledo also offers a host of business, industrial, social, and cultural opportunities. Toledo houses the headquarters of several Fortune 500 companies and features the Toledo Symphony, the Toledo Zoo, and the Toledo Museum of Art, one of the world's leading museums.

Facilities

The College of Business Administration's classrooms, computer labs, and faculty and administrative offices are located in Stranahan Hall. The main University library contains more than 1.5 million volumes and more than 1.4 million microform items. In addition, the library is a U.S. government documents depository and contains materials from the Census Bureau and the Department of Commerce. An online computer system allows students to access the catalog and serial records as well as databases, abstracts, and periodical indexes.

Technology Environment

UT is ranked fifty-first on the Yahoo! Internet Life list of America's 100 most wired universities, ahead of such schools as Michigan, Cornell, Penn State, Johns Hopkins, Princeton, Harvard, and Duke. In addition to the 115 networked Pentium PCs located in the four microcomputer labs in the College of Business Administration, there are approximately 400 more PCs located in various buildings across the campus. All machines on campus are networked, and students have access to

terminal software, the mainframe, VAX, and the campuswide network. This provides direct access to the library, among other locations, from any terminal on campus.

Placement

The University of Toledo's Office of Career Services offers M.B.A. students a broad support system throughout their program. Advising, workshops, and other programs are offered to enhance students' job-seeking skills and to help students make the contacts necessary to compete effectively for jobs in today's competitive job market. Assistance in assessing career goals and employment objectives is provided through individual counseling, workshops, seminars, and videotapes. The placement and career services offices also bring organizational representatives from both profit and nonprofit firms and health, education, and government agencies for on-campus interviews. In addition, students have access to computerized employment databases for job referrals in the tristate region and nationwide.

Admission

Admission is granted to individuals showing high promise of success in graduate business study. Applicants are considered for admission based on their undergraduate record; scores on the Graduate Management Admission Test (GMAT); managerial, professional, and leadership potential as exhibited by extracurricular activities, job experience, and community service; and a statement of purpose describing long-term goals and objectives. The GMAT score for students accepted into the

M.B.A. program has averaged between 500 and 525. The average undergraduate GPA is approximately 3.1.

Finances

Tuition and fees for full-time enrollment for 1999–2000 were approximately $6000 for Ohio residents and $12,000 for nonresidents. Graduate students live in off-campus housing.

The College of Business Administration offers graduate assistantships, tuition scholarships, and fellowships based primarily on achievement or merit. Most forms of assistance are awarded to students beginning their program in the fall.

Application Facts and Dates

Application deadlines for domestic and international students, respectively, are August 1 and May 1 for fall semester, November 15 and October 1 for spring semester, and April 15 and March 1 for summer semester. Admission decisions typically take one to two weeks once a student's admission file is complete. For more information, students should contact:

Dr. Bruce Kuhlman, Director of
  Graduate Studies
Office of Graduate Studies in Business
College of Business Administration
The University of Toledo
Toledo, Ohio 43606-3390
Telephone: 419-530-2775
Fax: 419-530-7260
E-mail: bruce.kuhlman@utoledo.edu
World Wide Web: http://www.utoledo.
  edu/MBA

Joseph L. Rotman School of Management
University of Toronto

University of Toronto

Joseph L. Rotman School of Management

Toronto, Ontario, Canada

SUCCEEDING IN THE NEW ECONOMY

Fierce global competition has created new challenges for business leaders and educators. At the Rotman School, we see this as an opportunity to stake out uncharted territories in business education. In an environment that views each individual as a uniquely valuable asset, we strive to develop integrative thinkers who can create global competitive advantage for themselves and their firms. We will prepare you to succeed in the New Economy with innovative, leading-edge training. Whether you decide to work for a multinational corporation, a small start-up, or start a firm of your own, the comprehensive, flexible University of Toronto M.B.A will give you the tools you need to compete and succeed in the new millennium.

—Roger L. Martin, Dean

Programs and Curricular Focus

Each year, the Joseph L. Rotman School of Management at the University of Toronto admits a select group of individuals from around the world into its M.B.A. program. Students are immersed in a demanding, innovative management curriculum, taught by some of the most distinguished business school faculty members in the country. The School is located in a world-class facility in the heart of Canada's financial capital and is accredited by the AACSB–the International Association for Management Education.

Top global firms actively recruit Toronto M.B.A. graduates, who are supported in their job search by a professional Career Development Centre. Seventy-four percent of graduating students hired in 1999 secured their jobs through the recruiting activities, programs, or resources of the School's Career Development Centre. The Toronto M.B.A. provides students with theoretical and practical understanding of the core business disciplines as well as the ability to think across the disciplines to solve complex real-world business problems in an integrated manner.

High-calibre classmates dramatically enhance the learning experience and provide a lifetime network of friends and contacts. Upon graduation, Rotman graduates join a vibrant extended worldwide alumni community of more than 16,000 graduates in eighty countries. Equipped with their internationally recognized degrees, Rotman graduates become leaders in all parts of the global economy.

In addition to the M.B.A. program, the Rotman School offers a variety of graduate programs in management designed to meet the needs of managers, professionals, and

scholars at various stages of their careers. Options include the Full-Time M.B.A. Program, which begins in September and takes twenty months to complete (2 eight-month academic periods or four semesters total) with a four-month summer break for internships and/or other work experience. The Part-Time M.B.A. Program, designed for working professionals and beginning in May, offers evening classes normally completed over nine terms that stretch over three years. The LL.B./M.B.A. Program, which begins in September, is a four-year joint-degree program offered by the Rotman School and the Faculty of Law. The distinctive Master of Management and Professional Accounting Program is a seven-term co-op program taken over twenty-seven months that is designed to educate students to become leaders in the accounting profession. Two of the terms are spent working in an accounting environment. The Executive M.B.A. Program, which begins in August, is a twenty-month program that is held on alternating Fridays and Saturdays. It is designed to enhance the leadership capabilities of senior managers.

Students and the M.B.A. Experience

Rotman School M.B.A. students are talented and high-achieving individuals with the potential to become exceptional managers and leaders in the global economy. They are selected for their high intellectual calibre as well as their ability to demonstrate that they have sought out interesting personal and professional challenges after completing their undergraduate education.

These are students who have worked in the real world for two or more years. The

range of previous professional experience is wide, with last year's class having an average of 3.98 years of work experience. Academic backgrounds run across all disciplines, from business to the arts, from engineering to the sciences. The most recent entering M.B.A. class has an average GMAT score of 672, placing them in the 93rd percentile of GMAT writers worldwide.

❖ Global Focus

The Toronto M.B.A. Program emphasizes international content throughout the curriculum. Students are continually exposed to a global perspective of management beginning in the first year. They are also engaged in several team projects for cross-cultural communications and skills development. A range of second-year elective courses focus specifically on international management. Students may also participate in graduate exchange programs with a number of top management schools around the world to add an even greater international dimension to the M.B.A. education. Students can elect to go abroad for one term in the second year of the program.

Special Features

The Toronto M.B.A. has been designed to provide students with the tools to adapt to constantly changing circumstances in business and in individual careers. Full-time M.B.A. students begin their studies with a mandatory four-day orientation session. It consists of an intense program of academic, social, and recreational activities designed to emphasize teamwork and class spirit. Students are also assigned to 6-member study groups that work together throughout the year. M.B.A. core courses are delivered in an integrated approach, with each course building on previous learning. Intensive focus is given to leadership and team-building skills and international business. In the second year, students are free to choose areas of specialization from a wide range of options, including more than forty-five elective courses offered each year—many of them innovative. The Rotman School was the first business school in the world to offer a course in derivatives and, in 1999, added courses in e-commerce and Internet marketing. Students are also free to take electives from the vast, rich course offerings of the University of Toronto.

The Faculty

Roger Martin, a prominent international management consultant, was named dean of the Rotman School in September 1998. Prior to joining Rotman, he was a director of the Massachusetts-based Monitor Company, which he joined in 1985. Martin has served as co-head of Monitor and was responsible for its day-to-day activities and more than 700 consultants worldwide. He was the founding chair of Monitor University, where he developed customized business education programs for leading corporations. In December 1999, Martin was named one of sixteen "unsung heroes and rising stars who have great impact on their colleagues, their industries, and the world around them" in *Fast Company* magazine's "Who's Fast 2000." This annual issue profiles "people whose energy, passion, and commitment make a real difference in the new economy."

Toronto M.B.A. students are taught by a management faculty that is recognized around the world for excellence in teaching and research. One indication of why this faculty is second to none in Canada is that 5 of the 7 Fellows of the prestigious Royal Society of Canada teaching at Canadian business schools are professors at the Joseph L. Rotman School of Management.

The Business School Network

Corporate Partnerships

The Toronto M.B.A. Program takes full advantage of its location in downtown Toronto by drawing on Canadian business leaders as classroom instructors and as speakers at special events. Group projects in the M.B.A. program frequently use local businesses as the focal point for their activities, and a wide variety of academic and research partnerships exist between the School and corporate Canada. The Dean's Advisory Council consists of some of Canada's top business leaders, who regularly meet to offer their advice and assistance to the School.

Prominent Alumni

The M.B.A. Program has produced more than 16,000 high-achieving graduates who occupy prominent leadership positions in business and other organizations around the world. They comprise part of the growing management alumni network of business contacts and friends, which includes graduates of the University of Toronto Bachelor of Commerce Program, Rotman M.B.A.s, LL.B./M.B.A.s, M.M.P.A.s, and graduates from Rotman's Ph.D. programs. Among Rotman's distinguished alumni are Joseph L. Rotman, Canadian entrepreneur and CEO of Clairvest Group; John Cassaday, President and CEO of Corus Entertainment; Leslie Dan, founder, Chair, and CEO of Novopharm Group of Companies; Michael Wilson, former Canadian Minister of Industry; Ira Gluskin, Gluskin Sheff & Associates.; F. Ross Johnson, former CEO, RJR

Nabisco; William Farlinger, Chair, Ontario Power Generation; and Ned Goodman, Chair and CEO, Dundee Bancorp, Inc.

The College and Environs

University of Toronto faculty members, students, and graduates enjoy an international reputation for excellence. Six of Canada's Nobel Prizes have been associated with the University. As Canada's largest university, with more than 50,000 students, the University of Toronto offers an unmatched diversity of opportunities. Students have access to some of the best thinkers in the world, first-rate sports and recreation facilities, and a rich and vibrant student community. They also enjoy full access to the Robarts Library, which is one of the top five research libraries in North America, ranked third (after Harvard and Stanford) in acquisitions.

Toronto, the heart of Canada's business community, was ranked by *Fortune* magazine in 1996 as the best international city in which to do business. It is also a terrific place to learn about business. With a metropolitan population of 4.5 million and with its safe clean streets, vibrant culture and entertainment, and diverse population from around the world, Toronto is the financial, commercial, and sporting centre of Canada. It has great restaurants and is a top North American centre for live theatre, music, film, and culture.

Facilities

The home of the Toronto M.B.A. Program is the Joseph L. Rotman School of Management, a spectacular, state-of-the-art teaching and research facility in the heart of Canada's financial capital. Opened in 1995, the facility houses all of the School's academic programs, centres and institutes, and the offices of professors. With its technologically advanced classrooms, attractive study spaces, a business library, and underground parking, the building is as comfortable as it is convenient. Throughout the year, the Rotman School enjoys a constant stream of visitors and guest speakers and is host to a wide variety of academic conferences and special events.

Placement

The Career Development Centre actively helps M.B.A. students prepare themselves for the job market and assists in the search and recruitment process. The service offers individual career counseling, resume clinics, mock interview sessions, a career resource library, a job listing service, and special information sessions on various career paths and industries. In addition, students receive training to polish their job search skills, such as resume writing and interviewing. Moreover, with an active on-campus recruiting program, students are able to interview with prospective employers from a wide range of industries in a variety of functional areas.

Admission

Competition for placement in the Rotman M.B.A. program is intense. For fall 1999, there were 1,085 applications for admission. Of the 217 students accepted, 130 enrolled. Candidates are evaluated on a total portfolio of previous performance, personal characteristics, and life experiences as well as professional and academic references. Candidates must have a recognized undergraduate degree with a minimum mid-B average in their final year (75 percent or a 3.0 GPA); GMAT scores above 550; a minimum of two years of full-time work experience preferred (five years for the part-time program); demonstrated evidence of leadership, initiative, and a superior capacity for high-level work productivity; three professional or academic reference letters; and an interview, when requested by the Admissions Office. Excellent command of written and spoken English is essential.

Finances

The two-year program tuition fee for domestic students entering the full-time M.B.A. program in September 2000 is CAN$32,800. International students pay CAN$41,000 for the two-year program. In addition to tuition, a full-time student spends approximately CAN$2500 per year on nonacademic incidental fees, books, and supplies. Lodging, food, and personal expenses are minimally estimated to be CAN$1000 per month or CAN$8000 per academic year. Tuition fees for 2001–01 are subject to final approval by the University's Governing Council.

Some financial assistance is available to qualified domestic applicants and on a very limited basis to international applicants. Scholarships and awards are generally made to the top 20 percent of the incoming class.

International Students

The Rotman School is a highly diverse, global community of men and women from many countries, cultures, and backgrounds. Approximately 30 percent of the students are non-Canadian citizens who come to Toronto from all over the world.

Application Facts and Dates

Applicants to the full-time program are admitted only in September of each year and must forward complete application credentials by one of the two application deadlines: January 15 or April 30. For more information, students should contact:

Toronto M.B.A. Program
Joseph L. Rotman School of
    Management
University of Toronto
105 St. George Street
Toronto, Ontario M5S 3E6, Canada
Telephone: 416-978-3499
Fax: 416-978-5812
E-mail: mbaprog@mgmt.utoronto.ca
World Wide Web: http://www.mgmt.utoronto.ca

University of Utah

▶ ## EDUCATION WITH IMPACT

What will you tell recruiters when you complete your graduate degree? Will you tell them about the courses you took on about your above-average GPA? The David Eccles School of Business has a different educational philosophy of emphasizing learning by application.

We kick off our program with a team-building community service project that partners student teams with corporate sponsors. Every student in our program is paired with a high-level corporate mentor who provides professional guidance and networking help for the student throughout the program. All students have the opportunity to compete in a new venture competition that provides start-up, seed funding. In addition, every graduate of our program has completed a significant business project for clients like Boeing, American Express, First Security Bank, and other firms, ranging from Internet start-ups to major international companies.

When David Eccles School of Business students meet with corporate recruiters, they talk about what they have accomplished and the results they have achieved. Education with impact—we mean it.

—Jack Brittain, Dean

Programs and Curricular Focus

Business leaders in the twenty-first century are faced with a unique set of challenges—challenges brought on by the globalization of markets, accelerating technological change, and the increasing diversity of the work force. The School's program is centered on developing the skills and knowledge individuals need to successfully create and lead organizations now and in the decades ahead.

The program begins with courses that teach the fundamental skills of teamwork, leadership, and effective communication. Group projects and oral presentations, integrated throughout the program, give students opportunities to strengthen interpersonal and oral communication skills. As students work through case analyses, they perfect their skills in problem identification, analysis, and decision making. The program culminates in an extensive field-study experience in which students actively participate in the decision processes of real companies in the real world. Students work directly with local and international companies, consulting on projects identified by participating businesses. They learn to work as a team while applying their classroom knowledge to the business world today.

Because the program places significant emphasis on effective communication and leadership skills, students are expected to

make contributions to the learning environment by daily participation in class discussions.

Students earn M.B.A. degrees through one of three programs of study. A traditional two-year day program serves students with nonbusiness undergraduate backgrounds. Students with bachelor's degrees in business from nationally accredited schools may be eligible for an accelerated one-year M.B.A. program. A three-year part-time evening program meets the unique needs of working professionals who wish to continue their full-time employment while pursuing an M.B.A. degree.

Optional study specializations include the International Business, Information Systems, and Product/Process Innovation. Joint programs of study available are the M.B.A./J.D. and the M.B.A./Master of Architecture.

The School offers the region's only Ph.D. program in Business Administration. Students may concentrate on research in accounting, finance, management (organizational behavior, strategy, operations), and marketing. Students work closely with faculty members on developing their research skills. Graduates are placed primarily in leading businesses or other professional schools.

Students and the M.B.A. Experience

Students who entered the program in 1999 represent twenty-six states and fourteen countries. Forty-two percent were women, 5 percent were members of ethnic minority groups, and 15 percent were international students. The 119 students who entered the two-year day and three-year evening programs have degrees in fifty-four different majors: 24 percent in behavioral sciences, 13 percent in business, 38 percent in science and engineering, and 25 percent in arts, humanities, education, and health. Ninety-four percent of day students and 100 percent of evening students have full-time work experience; day students have an average of just more than four years' experience, and evening students average eight years' experience.

❖ Global Focus

Students in the M.B.A. program have a rich proficiency in foreign language skills. Roughly 51 percent of students speak a second language, and 63 percent have experience abroad. Building on this unique strength, the program is designed to teach students to conduct business in a global environment. The School supports international field-study projects, internships, and study exchanges in which students expand their horizons and apply their language skills in a business environment.

The Faculty

The School's 77 faculty members have earned their degrees from some of the nation's most prestigious institutions including Wharton, Duke, Michigan, Harvard, and Berkeley. The faculty members' diverse research interests allow students to develop a broad background and acquire a spectrum of skills. The School's faculty members are considered top experts in their fields, in areas such as information systems, corporate finance, consumer behavior and research, international strategy, entrepreneurship, and human resources management.

The Business School Network
Corporate Partnerships

To further the School's mission of providing an experiential learning environment, the

The University of Utah is nestled at the foot of the majestic Wasatch Mountains.

David Eccles School of Business has established corporate partnerships throughout the community. Through a mentoring program, students are matched with mentors in their identified field of interest so they can gather important information about the real world of business. Students also gain real world knowledge through the Field Study Program, which places a team of students in a corporate environment to propose solutions to business problems. The Business at Breakfast presentation series provides a lively forum of exchange between community members, the faculty presenter, attending faculty members, and students. The Garn Distinguished Speaker Series attracts world-renowned speakers to address pertinent business issues and provides students with the opportunity to meet influential business people from within the community and from around the country. The National Advisory Board members guide the School on special projects and help secure resources for programs including diversity recruitment, scholarship development, and internships.

Prominent Alumni

Prominent alumni include David L. Gorham, retired Chief Financial Officer of *The New York Times;* J. Willard Marriott Jr., Chief Executive Officer of Marriott International; Dr. Steven R. Covey, Chairman and Founder of the Covey Leadership Center; Spencer F. Eccles, Chairman and Chief Executive Officer of First Security Corporation; Jake Garn, Vice Chairman of Huntsman Chemical Corporation and former U.S. Senator; and Jerry C. Atkin, President and Chief Executive Officer of Skywest Airlines.

The College and Environs

The University of Utah was founded in 1850. The 1,500-acre campus, located on the northeastern edge of Salt Lake City, reaches to the foothills of the majestic Wasatch Mountains. The University is a major research institution, with more than 1,500 projects in progress at any time. This level of research consistently ranks Utah among the country's top twenty-five public universities in attracting funding for research.

Salt Lake City, host of the 2002 Olympic Winter Games, is a city that blends subtle sophistication with the comfortable pace and friendliness of the West. Culture flourishes on the same scale as that of much larger cities. The Utah Symphony, Ballet West, and the Utah Opera Company are major attractions. NBA basketball, AAA baseball, and IHL hockey cater to sports enthusiasts. Rugged mountains, four distinct seasons, and ready access to outdoor recreation are enticing features of the University's location. Visitors and residents alike enjoy snow skiing at seven world-class ski resorts, all within 45 minutes of campus.

Facilities

In June 2000, the School opened the new C. Roland Christensen Center. This student-centered educational environment features discussion-method classrooms, a state-of-the-art computer technology center, student team discussion rooms, and a commons area designed to foster conversation and lively interaction.

Placement

Through the personalized attention of the M.B.A. Career Services Office, students are provided considerable assistance in securing positions in regional, national, and international companies.

M.B.A. students can utilize on-campus recruiting opportunities as well as career fairs, M.B.A. consortia events, and direct referrals to employers. In addition, M.B.A. Career Services offers job search workshops, self-assessment tools, special topics sessions (e.g. salary negotiation), and the SMART Start mentor program.

Admission

Students are admitted during just one admission cycle each academic year. The goal of admissions is to admit academically strong applicants who show the greatest potential for completing the program and succeeding in a career and whose backgrounds contribute to the academic excellence and the demographic, educational, and experiential diversity of each class.

The average GMAT score for those admitted in the 1999–2000 admission cycle was 602. The average undergraduate GPA was 3.4. International applicants are required to have a minimum TOEFL score of 600 (or 250 on the computer-based test) and a minimum TSE score of 45.

Applicants for the Ph.D. may take either the GRE (preferred) or the GMAT. The average GMAT score for those admitted in 1999 was 694.

Finances

In 2000-2001, annual tuition and fees for full-time (16 credits) study are $3,752 for residents and $10,954 for non-residents. Tuition and fees for part-time (8 credits) study are $2,271 and $6,457 for residents and nonresidents, respectively. Housing, food, insurance, and miscellaneous supplies and expenses are estimated to be $11,000 for twelve months.

The School of Business awards numerous privately funded scholarships to students based on need or academic merit. The School also supports several fellowships, which are awarded to individuals who enhance the ethnic, gender, or geographic diversity of the student body.

Application Facts and Dates

For the accelerated one-year M.B.A. program, January 15 and February 1 are the priority and final deadlines, respectively. March 15 and April 15 are the priority and final deadlines, respectively, for all other M.B.A. programs. For more information, students should contact:

Master's Programs Office
1645 East Campus Center Drive, Room 101
David Eccles School of Business
University of Utah
Salt Lake City, Utah 84112-9301
Telephone: 801-581-7785
Fax: 801-581-3666
E-mail: masters@business.utah.edu
World Wide Web: http://www.business.utah.edu/masters

Ph.D. Program Office
Telephone: 801-581-8625
Fax: 801-581-7214
E-mail: phdprogram@business.utah.edu
World Wide Web: http://www.business.utah.edu/phd

University of Washington

> ### NEW DIRECTIONS FOR THE M.B.A.
>
> *Students choose the University of Washington for the same reason I became Dean of the Business School in 1999. There are tremendous resources you can leverage here. An area ushering in the Information Age, with an international perspective and an entrepreneurial spirit, dominated by technology-related industry and new business ventures. A renowned research university with top-ranked programs and numerous interdisciplinary opportunities. A collegial atmosphere that nurtures relationship-building. An innovative approach to programs and processes with the focus on providing immediate value to students. Even without considering the astonishing natural beauty that draws many M.B.A. students to the University of Washington, wouldn't you rather receive your management education in one of the country's most dynamic business environments?*
>
> —Yash Gupta, Dean

Programs and Curricular Focus

The University of Washington M.B.A. program prepares graduates for success through study of both business fundamentals and the growing intersection between those fundamentals and new technologies in today's business environment. All programs begin only in the autumn quarter. The School offers a two-year, full-time program and a part-time, evening program that provide skills and training for people seeking career advancement or a change in career direction. The School also offers a two-year executive program for people with extensive top-management experience. Students can request information on the executive programs by e-mail (emba@u.washington.edu).

Both the full-time and part-time programs emphasize rigorous intellectual challenge, teamwork, leadership, international and entrepreneurial perspectives, the challenge of technology and e-business, and the application of classroom concepts to actual business problems. Students are expected to take a very active role in their education, giving life to the course materials.

The full-time program starts with an M.B.A. core that lasts roughly two and a half quarters. Material is presented in a sequence of three multidisciplinary, integrated courses taught by faculty teams representing all the major business disciplines. Students take core courses in sections of 50 students, which are further divided into study teams of 5 to 6 people. The structure of the core facilitates leadership, teamwork, and communication skills while helping students find innovative solutions from a broader array of

disciplines than normally provided in a more traditional academic structure. The core is followed by a set of "bridge" electives in the spring quarter. Students choose from specific business fields, where more specialized knowledge is helpful in internships and provides fundamental skills for second-year electives.

From start to finish, each full-time M.B.A. student works with a personal program counselor to develop a plan for academic studies, career contacts, and activities on and off campus that facilitate his or her objectives. The second year is a customized program of electives designed to gain desired expertise in one or more fields. In a typical year, students choose from nearly 100 electives in eleven business disciplines and may select up to four courses outside the Business School. Students can select special study options described in the Special Features section or may also earn concurrent master's degrees with the Schools of Law, Health Administration, Engineering, and International Studies.

The Evening M.B.A. program offers a similar academic experience but extends over eleven consecutive quarters, or nearly three years. Two nights each week for six quarters, students take a set of core courses in master's-level business fundamentals. In the last five quarters, evening students complete a program of electives chosen to advance their individual career objectives.

Students and the M.B.A. Experience

Each M.B.A. class includes people with unique strengths as well as impressive academic and professional qualifications. More than 30 percent of the students have undergraduate liberal arts degrees; 30 percent have science and technical backgrounds. Almost all entering M.B.A. students have at least two years of professional work experience. The program attracts students from forty-one states and twenty-three countries. Recent classes included 32 to 36 percent women, 15 to 18 percent members of minority groups, and 25 to 28 percent international students.

❖ Global Focus

The University of Washington is a recognized leader in global management education. All students take international management as part of the first-year core, and international business concepts are integrated throughout the curriculum. In addition to the many courses with international business components, the program offers a range of electives focused on global management issues. Students can also study abroad in twelve different exchange programs, pursue international internships, complete overseas study tours, and participate in weekly, on-campus, foreign language conversation sessions.

Special Features

In addition to their degree, M.B.A. students may earn a certificate in e-business, global business, or entrepreneurship. The internationally recognized Global Business Program (GBP), the Program in Entrepreneurship and Innovation (PEI), and the Program in e-Business all encourage students to explore new opportunities through course work, clubs, internships, speaker series, competitions, and special events on and off campus. Students have the opportunity to learn about economic development issues through the Business and Economic Development Program.

Nearly all M.B.A. students participate in club activities. Many first-year students join the Business Diagnostic Center, a student-run group that organizes consulting projects for teams of M.B.A. students. Many students participate in clubs focused on technology, consulting, investments, marketing, public speaking, community service, and socially responsible business practices.

The Faculty

The University of Washington M.B.A. philosophy emphasizes a partnership between students and faculty members. Professors at the University of Washington Business School have achieved recognition for both teaching and research. M.B.A.'s praise the faculty's active involvement in student learning and their integration of research and teaching. Professors take a personal interest in their students and, in return, they demand a high level of student effort and commitment.

The Business School Network

The M.B.A. program enjoys a strong relationship with the business community, spearheaded by Dean Yash Gupta. Proximity to cutting-edge industries and businesses in Seattle makes it easy for prominent business leaders and entrepreneurs to serve as guest speakers, visiting lecturers, and mentors. Faculty members invite executives into the classroom for perspectives on current issues; students also interact with executives through lecture series, consulting and business plan competitions, off-site business projects, and networking events. A large alumni network, accessible through the Alumni Sharing Knowledge program, provides information from a wide range of careers and geographical locales.

The College and Environs

The University of Washington is one of the nation's leading universities, achieving international recognition in both teaching and research. Since 1975, the University has ranked first among public institutions in the number of federal grants and contracts awarded to its faculty members. Its sixteen schools and colleges provide education to 34,000 students, who can choose from more than 100 academic disciplines and 5,000 courses. The University's prominence is assisted by its location in one of the fastest-growing regions of the country. The Puget Sound region is home to a large number of well-known companies, including Microsoft, Boeing, Nordstrom, Amazon.com, and Starbucks. Ranked as one of the country's most livable cities, Seattle also boasts world-renowned opera, ballet, and theater productions, an art museum, and an array of outdoor activities.

Facilities

The University of Washington library system is the twelfth largest in the nation and houses more than 5.4 million volumes. The Business School's Foster Library, located in the Seafirst Executive Center, holds a comprehensive collection of books, periodicals, reference materials, newspapers, pamphlets, CD-ROMs, videotapes, microfiche, and corporate annual reports. The library also offers a multitude of online search services and worldwide databases.

Technology Environment

Because of their strong relationships with the University of Washington Business School, companies such as Hewlett-Packard, Intel, and US West have awarded technology grants to enhance computer and other technology resources. These grants support computer labs, overnight laptop checkout services, mainframe computer facilities, research databases, laptop access ports in many locations throughout the School, and full Internet and University network access for students. The M.B.A. program requires all students to own a computer. In addition, use of computer and Web-based technologies is heavily incorporated into academic course work. Training courses for many different levels of expertise are offered for M.B.A. students who want to enhance their skill levels or learn new skills.

Placement

The Business Career Center (BCC) offers an array of services to M.B.A. students. The career process begins prior to starting the program through early meetings with a personal program counselor and ends with successful completion of an integrated two-year plan executed throughout the M.B.A. program. Whether students seek major career change or accelerated career advancement, the BCC offers programs and coaching in resume writing, interviewing, and salary negotiation. Students have access to the highly respected Mentor Program, M.B.A. career forums, and internship fairs. Special events, along with club-sponsored activities, give students outstanding opportunities to expand their network of corporate contacts. Students have the opportunity to explore career opportunities outside the U.S. with career staff members who specifically focus on international placement. National firms, including Intel, Hewlett-Packard, Andersen Consulting, Deloitte & Touche Consulting, Oracle, Amazon.com, Drugstore.com, and Nordstrom, participate in on-campus recruiting. Increasingly, small- and medium-sized firms and start-ups have joined the large firms in their search for University of Washington M.B.A. talent for internships and full-time employment.

Admission

To be eligible for admission, students must have completed a college-level calculus course and have a four-year undergraduate degree. To apply, candidates should submit the University of Washington M.B.A. application and take the Graduate Management Admission Test (GMAT). The TOEFL is required for non-U.S. citizens and permanent residents whose undergraduate course work was not conducted in English. In addition, interviews are strongly recommended.

Finances

The University of Washington is one of the best values in management education. Tuition for the 2000–01 academic year is $5745 for Washington State residents and $14,283 for nonresidents from the U.S. and international students. (Domestic nonresidents may petition for Washington residency in their second year of study.) All applicants are considered for a limited number of merit scholarships available to first-year students. Admitted students may apply for private scholarships, many of which are need-based, through an application form sent with the notice of admission. Financial aid through the Direct Loan program is available to U.S. citizens and permanent residents. Students seeking loans or applying for private scholarships administered by the School should submit the Free Application for Federal Student Aid (FAFSA) in a timely manner to the U.S. Department of Education, designating the University of Washington as a recipient school.

International Students

International students are drawn to the University of Washington by the beauty, diversity, dynamism, and relative safety of Seattle and the Pacific Northwest region. It is a supportive and interesting place, not only for students, but for their families as well. Students from outside the U.S. comprise roughly 25 percent of the entering M.B.A. class, representing as many as twenty-two countries. The University has a variety of active student groups and resources for international students. Language programs are available in the summer before the start of the M.B.A. program.

Application Facts and Dates

The University of Washington has a rolling admissions process with five filing dates. The first filing deadline for the full-time M.B.A. program is December 1. International students must submit their complete application packet no later than February 1. Domestic students must submit complete application packets by March 1. Evening M.B.A. applications are due by April 1. Interviews are recommended for the full-time M.B.A. program only. An interview should be arranged as early as possible, but no later than the filing deadline. For more information, applicants should contact:

M.B.A. Program Office
University of Washington
110 Mackenzie Hall
Box 353200
Seattle, Washington 98195-3200
Telephone: 206-543-4661
Fax: 206-616-7351
E-mail: mba@u.washington.edu
World Wide Web: http://depts.
    washington.edu/bschool

IVEY The University of Western Ontario

> ## INTEGRATED AND FOCUSED
>
> *The Ivey M.B.A. has long been regarded as one of the leading M.B.A. programs in the world. The Ivey program is highly integrated and focuses on the leadership skills and perspectives essential for success in a global marketplace. Our faculty members are dedicated to teaching and creating an intense and "real world" learning environment. As the second-largest producer of teaching cases in the world, Ivey utilizes a variety of interactive and experiential learning methods that capitalize on the rich base of experience in the class.*
>
> *Our general management focus and global perspective have led Ivey to be ranked repeatedly as the best business school in Canada by Canadian Business and among the top in the world by Financial Times, Business Week, The Economist Intelligence Unit, and Asian Business and Asia, Inc., among others*
> *—L. G. Tapp, Dean*

Programs and Curricular Focus

The M.B.A. program is two years in length. The first year is the same for all students, while the second year allows selection from an array of options.

The LL.B./M.B.A. program is a four-year limited-enrollment program offered jointly by the Business School and the Faculty of Law to train students for careers in which business and law overlap.

The executive M.B.A. and videoconferencing executive M.B.A. programs are for managers with exceptional potential and a minimum of eight years of work experience. The Ph.D. program provides advanced training in research and teaching and advanced substantive work in a specialized field.

Students and the M.B.A. Experience

The students in the M.B.A. program are distinguished by the diversity of their educational and professional backgrounds and their history of outstanding achievement. On average, they are 29 years of age, with five years of full-time work experience. They come from more than twenty countries worldwide. About 40 percent have substantial work or educational experience outside Canada, and about one third speak at least two languages.

❖ *Global Focus*

Ivey's programs help students to develop a global perspective—to work in a

business environment that increasingly transcends national boundaries. A multinational student body, faculty members with international experience as consultants and teachers, specialized international courses, and the integration of global issues in all core courses work to foster this perspective. The School also offers several special opportunities.

International exchanges are arranged with top business schools in Australia, Austria, Brazil, Denmark, France, Germany, Hong Kong, Italy, Japan, Korea, Mexico, the Netherlands, the Philippines, Singapore, Spain, Sweden, Switzerland, and other countries.

Each year, approximately 50 M.B.A. students travel to Eastern Europe and China to teach basic management skills to managers and entrepreneurs as part of the LEADER and China projects.

Ivey students have won case competitions in the United States and Hong Kong against teams from around the world.

In the second year, courses covering various international and entrepreneurial topics such as "Doing Business in Asia, Latin America, or Europe" and "Entrepreneurial Finance" are available.

Special Features

Learning at Ivey is highly interactive. Although there are some lectures, most of the classes rely heavily on case discussions, computer simulations, and role plays. Ivey is especially well known for its business cases. A case presents an actual business situation rather than

theories about business. Usually it describes a particular manager's problem that must be resolved. Students first analyze the case individually, trying to reach a decision, and then meet in a small study group to compare approaches. Finally, students meet with the entire class to discuss the case and its implications for management. During this time, students are also interacting frequently with executives and managers from various organizations. The whole process is designed to help students become effective decision makers. An essential part of Ivey's learning process is the study group. With organizational activity increasingly taking place in teams, this experience is critical for every effective manager.

In the first year, students are also exposed to an intensive workshop in managing diversity to help them understand the impact of greater diversity on management and how to harness that diversity to achieve better organizational performance.

The Faculty

Ivey's faculty members are renowned as excellent teachers. With degrees from esteemed universities, they welcome the challenge of creating a stimulating learning environment. As a result, they can be found as guest professors in universities around the world. And since their research centers on the practical problems of managers, they consult widely with diverse national and international businesses.

The Business School Network
Corporate Partnerships

The corporate community plays a significant role in the educational experience at Ivey. Class projects undertaken with corporations allow companies to show future managers how major institutions operate and implement key strategic changes. This interaction with executives and managers results in a strong integration of material in the first year of the program.

A board of advisers, consisting of key players in the Canadian business community, is also actively involved in maintaining the M.B.A. program's relevance in an increasingly demanding global environment.

A program of industry tours, seminars, and guest speakers features prominent business and government leaders, many of whom are Ivey Business School graduates.

Prominent Alumni

The Ivey experience does not end when the program is over. Students join a network of more than 11,000 men and women who have gone on to occupations in almost every place imaginable. Ivey has more than 1,000 presidents and chief executive officers in companies around the world.

The College and Environs

Since it was founded in 1878, the University of Western Ontario has established a tradition of excellence in teaching and research. One of Canada's oldest and largest universities, Ivey consists of seventeen faculties in the sciences, arts, social sciences, and professions, serving a body of more than 22,000. The University is particularly well known nationally and internationally for its professional schools, which include Business, Dentistry, Law, and Medicine.

London is called the Forest City in recognition of the many trees that line the streets and add beauty to its parks. With a population of 320,000, London is a university city as well as a center of services, light industry, and commerce.

The city is small enough to have a sense of community but sufficiently large and diverse to have many of the cultural, entertainment, and recreational amenities of a big city. Beyond the city, the beaches and parks of two of the Great Lakes are within an hour's drive. It is just 2 hours by car or train to both Toronto and Detroit.

Facilities

Students have access to all the University's libraries, including a specialized and well-stocked business library. The School operates its own computer facility and student laboratories with PCs that are accessible 24 hours a day. The National Centre for Management Research and

Development undertakes full-time research on major challenges facing management today.

Placement

The Career Management Department helps students plan their job search, write resumes, and develop interviewing skills. The office organizes on-campus visits by major corporations and helps both those corporations and students "make the match." Each fall, Career Management sends hundreds of employers resume books containing profiles of all second-year students. These companies may then invite students for an interview. The office also coordinates the activities of more than 400 organizations from across Canada and around the world that contact students for employment in a variety of fields.

The records show that Ivey graduates are highly valued in the job market—companies want the kinds of insights, perspectives, and skills that students develop in the program. Ivey graduates have achieved success in a wide range of careers. Many have become CEOs of major corporations. Other Ivey M.B.A. graduates are top civil servants, leading consultants, deans of other business schools, and entrepreneurs. Many decide to spend a few years in the corporate world and then start their own business.

Admission

Students must normally hold an undergraduate degree with high academic standing from an accredited university. The applicant's leadership skills, achievements, undergraduate grades, GMAT score, CAT TOEFL score (250 minimum), full-time work experience, and extracurricular involvement are all carefully considered. Ivey looks for applicants who have thoughtfully analyzed their personal and career goals and have demonstrated the potential to become leaders. Ivey is interested in individuals whose accomplishments indicate an ability to benefit from and contribute to the Business School. A few applicants without an undergraduate degree, who have at least seven years of challenging work experience, some university courses with high standing, and

other strong management qualities, may also gain admission. Ivey encourages applications from international students and members of minority groups.

Finances

The estimated tuition fee for all students is Can$20,000. The application fee is Can$100.

Costs for housing, medical insurance, food, transportation, and personal items range from Can$13,000 to Can$18,000 for single students and from Can$20,000 to Can$25,000 for a family of four. The cost of books and supplies ranges from Can$1500 to Can$2000 per year.

Well-qualified students are automatically considered for scholarships and awards.

International Students

With the globalization of trade, there is an increasing need for businesspeople to see beyond their own geographic boundaries. At Ivey, students will find outstanding people from diverse educational and cultural backgrounds working in an intense environment.

Students will discover the global economic, political, and technological factors that shape business activity in Canada and around the world. Students will also tap into the powerful network of Canadian business alumni.

Application Facts and Dates

Because the class fills early, students should submit an application as soon as possible. Files are evaluated on a rolling basis starting in November, and this process continues until April. The deadline for all applications is April 1. For more information, applicants should contact:

Larysa Gamula, Director, MBA
  Program Services
Ivey Business School
University of Western Ontario
London, Ontario N6A 3K7
Canada
Telephone: 519-661-3212
Fax: 519-661-3431
E-mail: mba@ivey.uwo.ca
World Wide Web: http://www.ivey.
  uwo.ca

University of Wisconsin–Madison

Madison, Wisconsin

A SPECIAL SCHOOL IN A SPECIAL CITY

The University of Wisconsin–Madison School of Business offers a unique package to graduate students—the resources of a large, top-notch public research institution; one of the finest business school facilities in the nation; faculty noted for outstanding teaching and research; and a superb track record in placing our graduates. Best of all, we are located in the heart of Madison, Wisconsin, long recognized as one of America's most livable cities.

—Andrew J. Policano, Dean

Programs and Curricular Focus

The M.B.A. program at the University of Wisconsin–Madison delivers a solid foundation in the core areas of business management in a flexible, tailored curriculum. Students select from more than a dozen functional majors designed to meet their career goals. A variety of highly regarded specialty programs, such as supply-chain management, arts administration, marketing research, and manufacturing and technology management, provide in-depth experience that few business schools can match. More than 100 elective courses are available each semester, including a wide range of Contemporary Topics seminars that keep students up to date on the latest business trends. For added flexibility, students may waive a portion of previously completed core curriculum courses to reduce the length of their program from four to three semesters.

The graduate business curriculum combines traditional lecture-style delivery with case analysis, project work, team interaction, and hands-on, practical experience in the business community. For example, applied security analysis students have the opportunity to manage a real money equity portfolio that is valued at $1.4 million or a $10-million fixed income portfolio. Entrepreneurship students research start-up companies and recommend how portions of the school's $900,000 venture capital fund should be invested.

Students and the M.B.A. Experience

Academic diversity marks graduate business students at Wisconsin. Approximately 40 percent of entering master's students come from nonbusiness backgrounds, including 25 percent from engineering, mathematics, and science, with the remainder

from social sciences, humanities, and fine arts. More than 100 undergraduate institutions from more than twenty-five different countries are represented.

In the fall 1999 entering class of 205 students, 35 percent were women, and 7 percent were from underrepresented groups. The class possessed an average of 4.5 years of work experience. Their average scores on the GMAT and TOEFL were 616 and 619, respectively, with an average GPA of 3.26.

Students are encouraged to go beyond the boundaries of the School of Business. The University of Wisconsin–Madison is a world-class center of research and learning. It provides an unparalleled opportunity to enrich a business student's knowledge and understanding in a variety of fields.

Special Features

The School of Business attempts to integrate an international perspective into all of its courses. In addition, it currently offers twelve semester-long study-abroad opportunities specifically designed to enhance students' understanding of the international business environment. Students may also choose to participate in shorter international experiences offered during the summer and spring breaks. In the past, such short courses have been offered in China, the Czech Republic, France, Hungary, Indonesia, Thailand, and the United Kingdom.

The Faculty

Close interaction between faculty members and students is a hallmark of the UW–Madison School of Business. More than 80 professors teach and conduct research. Many are leaders in their academic disciplines. In recent years, School of Business faculty members have been elected presidents of

a variety of prestigious professional organizations, including the American Accounting Association, the American Academy of Management, and the American Risk and Insurance Association. Business school faculty members have also been recognized for the caliber of their teaching, winning University and national teaching awards.

The Business School Network

Corporate Partnership

The University of Wisconsin–Madison School of Business is well known for responding to the business community's need for high-quality programs in emerging fields.

Invaluable input from businesses is provided to the School in a variety of ways: advisory boards, mentor programs, internships, and an extensive program to bring top executives into the classroom to share their experience with students.

Prominent Alumni

The School of Business has many nationally recognized business leaders among its more than 28,000 alumni, including Paul J. Collins, Vice Chairman, Citibank, N.A.; John P. Morgridge, Chairman of the Board, Cisco Systems, Inc.; and Arthur C. Nielsen Jr., former Chairman and CEO, A. C. Nielsen Company.

The College and Environs

The University of Wisconsin–Madison and the city of Madison provide a rich, multicultural experience. The city's population, including the growing suburbs, is approaching 350,000 and has a growing ethnic population. In addition, UW–Madison's 40,000-member student population is one of the most diverse in the nation. This diversity in ethnic heritages and nationalities of students, faculty, staff, and visiting scholars creates unique cultural and educational benefits to complement the strong academic base.

In 1998, Madison was voted best city in the country in which to live by *Money* magazine; Madison also received this honor from *Life* and *USA Today* in recent years. Situated along the shores of Lake Mendota, one of five lakes within the city's borders, Madison is considered one of the most picturesque college campuses

Grainger Hall, home of the UW–Madison School of Business, is one of the most visually appealing and technologically advanced business school facilities in the country.

in the country. It offers hilly terrain, scattered parks, and woodlands to augment the urban setting with a friendly neighborhood atmosphere. The capital city is also home to American Family Insurance, Oscar Mayer Foods, Rayovac Corporation, CUNA Credit Union, and several banks and research and technology parks.

UW–Madison is a university of Nobel Prize winners, recipients of the National Medal of Science, and members of the National Academies of Science, Engineering, and Education. It routinely ranks among the top five universities in the nation in terms of funded research.

Facilities

The UW–Madison School of Business is housed in Grainger Hall. The $40-million facility incorporates leading-edge instructional technology throughout its 260,000 square feet. It is one of the most visually appealing and technologically advanced business school facilities in the country.

The two lower levels of the building house thirty modern, spacious classrooms with the latest teaching technology, including an auditorium and two large lecture halls. The upper three levels contain continuing education facilities and offices for research and career services as well as for members of the faculty and administration. The library, one of thirty-one on the UW campus, offers electronic access to specialized databases across campus and around the world.

The School has several instructional computer labs, including a newly remodeled lab dedicated for graduate students, computer classrooms, its own research computer, and a building-wide network of computer outlets to allow students to use laptop computers in almost every corner of the building.

A state-of-the-art videoconferencing room allows School of Business faculty members and students to interact with employers, industry experts, and business leaders, in real time, anywhere in the world.

Grainger Hall was designed from the ground up to be "student friendly," offering student lockers, a graduate student lounge, mailboxes for students, and several other special features.

Placement

UW–Madison is known for the strength of its career development and placement assistance. In 1999–2000, nearly 300 employers interviewed on campus for graduate students seeking internships and full-time employment opportunities. In addition, more than 2,500 job listings are received and posted each year.

The staff of the Business Career Center (BCC) includes two advisers dedicated to providing assistance and resources to master's students.

The BCC offers a comprehensive array of services to help graduate students achieve their career goals. Utilizing resources available in the BCC and the Career Information Library, UW–Madison students learn about different career options/opportunities and develop essential search skills required to make informed choices throughout their professional careers.

In addition to the Career Focus Seminars offered each fall, the BCC sponsors a career fair, employer briefings, mock interviews, video teleconferencing/interviewing, and roundtable discussions, and a variety of workshops on career-related topics. These activities, coupled with individual career plans, employment strategies, and career counseling, help ensure UW students are able to find the positions they are looking for. In 1999, the average base salary was $62,899.

Admission

The School of Business seeks well-rounded students who possess a solid undergraduate education coupled with strong work experience. To this end, applicants should possess two years of full-time work experience, along with a strong undergraduate GPA.

In addition to academic credentials, test scores (GMAT and TOEFL), and work experience, personal achievements, motivation, leadership, communication skills (written and oral), international exposure, and recommendation letters are considered in the application process. Also, all international applicants are required to submit proof of financial resources along with the application for admission.

Interviews are recommended but not required. Applicants are encouraged to visit Grainger Hall to meet with an admissions representative, sit in on a class, speak with current students about their experiences, and see the school's state-of-the-art teaching, research, and computer facilities.

Finances

Tuition for the 1999–2000 school year was $6524 for Wisconsin residents, $11,728 for Minnesota residents (through reciprocity agreements), and $18,282 for nonresidents. Housing, books, and incidentals accounted for an additional $11,625. Applicants currently living outside the state of Wisconsin who attended a Wisconsin high school and whose parents continue to live in the state may be considered residents for tuition purposes.

More than one third of incoming students receive merit-based financial assistance in the form of scholarships and graduate assistantships. Fellowships for African-American, Hispanic American, and Native American students are available through the Consortium for Graduate Study in Management, the Wisconsin Investment Scholarship Program, and the Advanced Opportunity Fellowship. The deadline for merit-based financial assistance from the School of Business is February 15. Other University-wide fellowship opportunities may have earlier deadlines.

Application Facts and Dates

The application deadline is April 15 for September enrollment. The financial aid deadline is February 15.

For more information, to schedule a visit, or speak with an admissions representative, students should contact:

Graduate Programs Office
School of Business
3150 Grainger Hall
University of Wisconsin–Madison
975 University Avenue
Madison, Wisconsin 53706-1323
Telephone: 608-262-1555
          608-262-4000
Fax: 608-265-4192
E-mail: uwmadmba@bus.wisc.edu
World Wide Web: http://www.wisc.edu/bschool/

AT VANDERBILT
Vanderbilt University

> ### LEADERS FOR THE NEW ECONOMY
>
> *In the expanding global economy, M.B.A. students come to the Owen Graduate School for twenty months of rigorous study to prepare for a management career that will extend for thirty-five years or more. Our well-rounded, comprehensive curriculum prepares you to be a decisive, skilled problem solver. Owen M.B.A.'s employ cutting-edge functional knowledge to analyze the global, economic, political, and social climates; to lead change; and to take responsibility for their decisions. The atmosphere here is energized, and everyone knows they are part of something unique, something that will have a profound effect on their future.*
>
> —Joe Blackburn, Acting Dean

Programs and Curricular Focus

In the full-time program at Owen Graduate School of Management, students focus on the basics—"core" knowledge—in the first year, then tailor their selection of electives in the first and second years, choosing from one or more of Owen's functional concentrations, emphases, and even courses offered in other Vanderbilt schools.

Owen M.B.A.'s must complete 60 credit hours over four semesters. Students may choose to concentrate in accounting, finance, human resources and organizational management, marketing, operations, and telecommunications and electronic commerce. Students whose career plans require specialized or multidisciplinary study may ask a faculty adviser to help develop a customized concentration in general management. Owen's small classes and low student-faculty ratio promote effective learning in the classroom and help each student focus on topics of special interest and natural aptitude.

The course work requires regular contact with faculty members, research partners, and the business community—often through teams that mirror those used by today's successful businesses. Outside of the classroom, students further develop enhanced personal effectiveness and teamwork skills through group study and team projects.

Owen offers several dual-degree programs in conjunction with other schools on campus, and many individuals take advantage of the opportunity to obtain a dual degree. Current dual-degree programs include management/law (M.B.A./J.D.), management/engineering (M.B.A./M.E.), management/nursing (M.B.A./M.S.N.), management/Latin American studies (M.B.A./M.A.L.A.S.), and management/Doctor of Medicine (M.B.A./M.D.). Interested students must be admitted to each school separately.

Students and the M.B.A. Experience

The full-time M.B.A. class of 2001 had average GMAT scores of 632, an average GPA of 3.18, and average TOEFL scores of 619. Twenty-seven percent are women, 11 percent are members of U.S. minority groups, and 29 percent are international students (twenty-nine countries represented). They have an average of five years of work experience, and the average age is 28. Twenty-one percent of students are married. Eleven percent come from the mid-Atlantic region, 7 percent from the Midwest, 26 percent from the Northeast, 38 percent from the Southeast, 9 percent from the West, and 9 percent from the Southwest. Sixty-seven percent are from North America, 23 percent are from Asia/Pacific Islands, 5 percent are from Europe, 4 percent are from Latin America, and 1 percent are from Africa/Middle East. Undergraduate majors breakdown as follows: business, 30 percent; economics, 12 percent; engineering/technical, 18 percent; liberal arts, 11 percent; natural science, 8 percent; and social science, 21 percent.

Special Features

The Owen School faculty members perform collaborative research with industry partners through the School's research centers—the Financial Markets Research Center, the Center for Service Marketing, the Vanderbilt Center for Environmental Management Studies, and the E-Lab Research Program on Marketing in Computer-Mediated Environments.

Owen offers opportunities for M.B.A. students to participate in exchange programs with fifteen partner schools around the world. Most exchanges take place in the fall of the second year (third semester). Applications are due in the spring of the first year.

The Faculty

Owen's 65 faculty members bring research to life in the classroom. Students obtain cutting-edge knowledge of how theory and practice come together in business. The faculty members create an intense learning environment that is both demanding and fun. The spirit of respect and intellectual curiosity leads to many lifelong faculty-student friendships.

The Business School Network
Corporate Partnerships

Owen's quick climb into the top tier of business schools is in part the result of corporate contributions to research partnerships or other financial support provided by nearly 200 companies. In addition, companies provide many opportunities for students to work with them in a consulting role through the student-run Owen Consulting Services and in conjunction with professorial research interests.

Prominent Alumni

Owen alumni are a close network of individuals who demonstrate their commitment to the Owen community by volunteering to serve on committees that help the School in many of its activities. These activities include corporate relations/placement, recruiting/student relations, development, and alumni networking. Alumni know that the value of their M.B.A. degree continues to grow as Owen's reputation strengthens. Alumni assist in promoting the School and often cite that giving back is a reflection of the personal help they received from alumni and faculty and staff members at Owen.

The College and Environs

Vanderbilt University is located in Nashville, Tennessee. A major southern city and the Tennessee state capital, Nashville has a population of more than 1 million and lies within 600 miles of 50 percent of the population of the continental United States. A center for banking, finance, health care, publishing, automobile manufacturing, and insurance, Nashville is home base for many national and international corporations. Long known as "The Athens of the South," Nashville boasts a rich cultural life. Many museums and historic sites provide ample opportunities for leisure-time excursions or scholarly exploration. Nashville's mild weather, acres of green space, sense of history, and dynamic business climate create an ideal environment for learning and leisure.

Facilities

All support services for Owen students are located in Management Hall, a spacious, modern, multilevel building containing classrooms, seminar rooms, faculty and staff offices, lounges, a snack area, an auditorium, a dedicated computer lab, and a world-class library. Because Vanderbilt does not offer an undergraduate business major, Owen M.B.A.'s share these facilities only with other graduate business students.

Technology Environment

Owen at Vanderbilt established the first electronic commerce research center at a major business school. The School's broad curriculum and innovative research in telecommunications and electronic commerce (TEC) earned it recognition as a top ten M.B.A. program in these fields. The first electronic commerce class was taught at Owen in 1994. Today, Owen's TEC concentration and complementary e-commerce emphasis provide Vanderbilt M.B.A. students with more than twenty elective options. In addition to leading-edge research and groundbreaking course work, Owen students learn firsthand how new technology works through practically oriented classes, consulting projects with research center sponsors, and involvement with various student organizations.

Beginning with the fall 2000 entering class, the Owen School implements a pioneering wireless computer network that enables students and faculty and staff members to collaborate and communicate more efficiently. IBM Thinkpads with wireless capabilities are required for all first-year students as part of Owen's commitment to the practical use of new technologies. Owen at Vanderbilt has state-of-the-art facilities running new Dell Optiplex Pentium III PCs, which have 500-Mhz processors, 128 MB memory, CD-ROM, and 17-inch monitors. These machines run Microsoft Office 2000. Owen computers are networked for file-sharing, e-mail, and Internet access for faculty and staff members and students.

Placement

Owen's Career Planning and Placement Office teaches students to take an aggressive and personal approach to compete effectively for internships, for positions after graduation, and whenever considering a job change. During the first year of course work, students fine-tune their career goals by meeting one-on-one with a career-planning officer. During the second year, while students conduct a targeted job search, the Career Planning and Placement Office acts as an executive search firm, helping them evaluate the way in which their goals would fit with different job opportunities. About two thirds of Owen graduates secure offers directly through campus or consortia interviews; the remaining third have used Owen placement contacts and personal resources to pursue opportunities with companies that do not use campus services. The mean salary for the class of 1999 was $75,000.

Admission

Candidates for the Owen M.B.A. program must have a U.S. bachelor's degree or its equivalent from an accredited four-year college or university. In addition, candidates must have completed at least one semester of college-level differential and integral calculus and one semester of statistics and probability. The admission of candidates who have not taken calculus or statistics will be conditional upon the completion of a college-level course with a grade of B or better.

Finances

For 2000–01, tuition is $26,300, housing is $6650, meals are $2700, medical/dental is $400, student health insurance is $725, the activity and recreation fee is $250, transportation averages $1350, books and supplies average $1200, miscellaneous expenses average $1200, loan origination fees are $555, and the wireless laptop is $3098. This totals $44,428 for the year.

Permanent residents and U.S. citizens are eligible for a variety of loan programs. Students demonstrating need may qualify for federally funded work-study programs. All applicants are automatically considered for merit-based awards and scholarships.

Application Facts and Dates

A complete application includes the required interview, application forms, official test scores, official transcripts, recommendations, essays, and the application fee. To learn more about the M.B.A. program at Vanderbilt's Owen School, students should contact:

Owen Office of Admissions and
    Student Services
Owen Graduate School of
    Management
Vanderbilt University
401 21st Avenue, South
Nashville, Tennessee 37203
Telephone: 615-322-6469
        800-288-OWEN (6936,
        toll-free)
Fax: 615-343-1175
World Wide Web: http://mba.
    vanderbilt.edu

Villanova University

EDUCATING INDIVIDUALS TO PROSPER IN THE GLOBAL ECONOMY OF THE 21ST CENTURY

As technology races ahead and American businesses face the traumas created by the globalization of many markets, graduate programs must determine the type of educational experience that will be required to ensure that their students will have a competitive advantage as managers. The Villanova M.B.A. program provides a broad educational experience that enables its graduates to assume managerial responsibilities at all levels of business, government, and nonprofit organizations.

Just as important, however, Villanova adheres to its American, Catholic, and Augustinian tradition by emphasizing to students in its M.B.A. program the importance of creating strategies, making decisions, and executing plans within a framework of value judgments and ethical considerations.

Villanova's M.B.A. program is one of approximately 300 in the nation accredited by AACSB–The International Association for Management Education.

—Thomas F. Monahan, Ph.D., Dean

Programs and Curricular Focus

Villanova University's College of Commerce and Finance offers an M.B.A. program that targets working professionals who seek to improve their leadership and managerial skills. The intensive workday demands faced by the program's students necessitate that all course offerings be scheduled in the evenings and on Saturday mornings. In addition, many courses are now offered in an online format. The program is flexible, allowing students to progress at their own pace. The goals of the program include providing the student with knowledge, understanding, and synergistic appreciation of the disciplines involved in decision making; providing current and future leaders with the ability to identify problems, obtain relevant information, and evaluate alternative approaches, effectively employing technology to make and implement decisions; ensuring the development of ethical, responsible, and innovative leaders who understand their responsibility to promote the welfare of society; and increasing the capacity of managers to adapt to a rapidly changing domestic and global environment.

The M.B.A. course work is organized into three levels: basic core, advanced core, and elective. All basic core and advanced core courses are offered in a partial online format (50 percent online, 50 percent traditional classroom). A student initially takes courses at the basic core level. The number of required courses in the basic core varies from student to student, depending upon the area studied at the undergraduate level and the number of years since the undergraduate degree was earned. Qualifying exams are available for all basic core courses.

After satisfying the requirements of the basic core, the student starts the course work leading to the M.B.A. degree. Eleven courses beyond the basic core are required, including seven advanced core courses and four elective courses. Students may choose to develop expertise in an area by selecting a specialization (three elective courses) in e-business, finance, health-care management, international business, or marketing. For those who do not wish to specialize in one of these areas, they may tailor their M.B.A. degree by selecting those electives most appropriate for their career goals.

Villanova University also offers a joint J.D./M.B.A. program that enables students to work simultaneously in the College of Commerce and Finance and in the Villanova School of Law to obtain a joint degree.

The Villanova Executive M.B.A. program offers a new perspective on M.B.A. education through its thematic approach to corporate challenges and global business issues. This approach teaches executives how to apply key management and strategic-thinking skills to real-world scenarios, using a broad perspective of enterprise-wide knowledge. The curriculum is divided into five distinct modules, as well as an international seminar. Each module studies a business theme and integrates the appropriate business discipline (accounting, finance, marketing, management, and information systems) to that theme. Leadership and e-business strategy are taught from a variety of perspectives and are woven throughout the five-module program. This program is a dynamic educational experience designed to provide today's business leaders with enterprise-wide knowledge, systemic thinking skills, and the tools necessary to embrace change innovatively and strategically.

Students and the M.B.A. Experience

In order to uphold the quality of both the candidates and the program, the student population is maintained at approximately 650. Nearly 85 percent of applicants who are accepted by the college enroll. About 90 percent of the current student body are part-time students, with degrees from more than 100 different undergraduate schools. Their average age at admission is 27 years, with an average of five years of work experience in fields that include communications, banking, engineering, medicine, accounting, information systems, and law. Women comprise 36 percent of the student population. The undergraduate majors of the current M.B.A. candidates include business (58 percent), engineering (18 percent), science (11 percent), and liberal arts (13 percent).

❖ Global Focus

Villanova's M.B.A. program recognizes the importance of providing a curriculum that enables a student to learn how American business can best compete in the international arena. To that end, the program includes the study of issues relevant to international competition at both the basic core and advanced core levels. In addition, students must select one international course from a wide range of elective courses that focus on issues relating to competition in global environments. Courses are also available that include overseas travel. Recent destinations have included China and Russia.

Special Features

The unique features of Villanova's M.B.A. program include the option of taking all basic and advanced core courses in a partial online format (50 percent online, 50 percent traditional classroom); small classes—class size is limited in order to maintain a personalized learning environment; full-time faculty instructors—more than 95 percent of all M.B.A. classes are taught by full-time faculty members; technology integration in most courses; a superior student body; and a solid foundation—the program is built on the base of an undergraduate program that enjoys an excellent national reputation and has been in existence since 1922.

The Faculty

Throughout its history, Villanova University has earned a reputatoin as an institution that has made a strong commitment to the quality of teaching. Practical experience in business and government, in addition to a strong academic background, is characteristic of the faculty of the College of Commerce and Finance. More than 95 percent hold a Ph.D. or equivalent degree from more than forty different academic institutions. The faculty members' commitment to teaching excellence is documented by the fact that a sizeable percentage of the College of Commerce and Finance's 85 faculty members have been awarded the prestigious Lindback Award for Teaching Excellence. The faculty members are also deeply engaged in research activities and have published in many premier academic and professional journals.

The Business School Network

Corporate Partnerships

An advisory board of top executives and alumni help shape the future development of the curriculum and new programs. In addition, guest lecturers and speakers address the students each year, both on campus and in professionals organizations.

The College and Environs

Founded in 1842 under the leadership of the Order of St. Augustine, Villanova University has witnessed significant growth not only in its student population but also in its position in the academic community. This has been chronicled by a national survey showing Villanova as one of the nation's best comprehensive educational institutions.

Since 1900, the University has added to the original College of Liberal Arts and Sciences a College of Engineering (1905), a Science division for the College of Liberal Arts and Sciences (1915), the University College (1918), the College of Commerce and Finance (1922), the College of Nursing (1953), and the School of Law (1953). Today the student population is approximately 11,500, of which approximately 30 percent are engaged in graduate study.

Located on a tree-lined, 222-acre campus in the suburbs of Philadelphia, Villanova is close (by private or public transportation) to one of the oldest cities in the country—a city which offers the finest in ballet, theater, music, and art. It is also accessible (within a 2- or 3-hour drive) to New York City; Washington, D.C.; and Baltimore, Maryland.

Facilities

Bartley Hall, the home of the College of Commerce and Finance, is currently undergoing extensive renovations, which include a 50,000-square-foot addition. This new facility will house state-of-the-art classrooms, distance learning classrooms, a graduate student lounge, breakout rooms for student meetings and group study, and the Exchange, the College's cafeteria, complete with coffee bar and power and data connections for laptop computers.

The Falvey Memorial Library provides resources and facilities for study and research by graduate and undergraduate students, faculty members, and visiting scholars. The total seating capacity is more than 2,000 with a book capacity of more than 500,000 volumes. Annual reports for top corporations are readily available to M.B.A. candidates. The library also offers online access to a variety of databases. Students can access many databases and library resources from home and office using the Bartley Virtual Reading Room.

Technology Environment

Information technology is a key driver of the business curriculum and is integrated into most courses. The University was recently cited as one of the fifty most-wired universities in the country. The University's main computer center is located in Mendel Hall. Satellite computing centers are available in a number of other locations, including Bartley Hall, the home of the College of Commerce and Finance and the M.B.A. program. These centers are equipped with terminals, microcomputers, and reference materials and are staffed by professionals from University Information Technologies (UNIT). In addition, all classrooms in Bartley Hall are connected to the campus network and have Internet access. Many classrooms are set up for

student use of notebook computers with power and network ports, and all classrooms have multimedia capability. Power and network connections are available throughout the campus, including the Falvey Library, cafeterias, and student lounges. An increasing number of M.B.A. courses are being offered via distance learning. Villanova University is also an SAP University Alliance member.

Admission

Applicants must possess a baccalaureate degree from an accredited college or university. An applicant need not possess an undergraduate degree in business or have taken any business courses to be considered for admission. The applicant must submit documentation that includes a completed application, two essays, and two letters of recommendation along with a nonrefundable $40 application fee; official undergraduate and, if applicable, graduate transcripts for all institutions attended; and official test results from the Graduate Management Admission Test (GMAT). International applicants whose native language is not English are required to take the Test of English as a Foreign Language (TOEFL) and submit proof of adequate financial resources. Admission to the program is competitive. Applications are reviewed by an admissions committee comprised of faculty members.

Finances

Tuition and fees for the 2000–01 academic year are $530 per credit or $1590 per course. Information regarding financial assistance available to graduate students may be obtained from the University's financial assistance office. In addition, the M.B.A. program has a number of positions for graduate research assistants to work for faculty members engaged in research activities.

Application Facts and Dates

Students are admitted for enrollment in the fall and spring of each year. Applications should be submitted as far in advance as possible for the following deadlines: June 30 for the fall semester and November 15 for the spring semester. For additional information, students should contact:

Melinda B. German
Director, Graduate Studies in Business
Room 112-Bartley Hall
Villanova University
800 Lancaster Avenue
Villanova, Pennsylvania 19085-1699
Telephone: 610-519-4336
Fax: 610-519-6273
E-mail: mba@email.vill.edu
World Wide Web: http://www.mba.
  villanova.edu

Virginia Commonwealth University

Richmond, Virginia

RESPONDING TO THE CHANGING NEEDS OF BUSINESS

The Virginia Commonwealth University School of Business offers students high-quality instruction from internationally recognized professors, an urban location with connections to multinational corporations, and access to state-of-the-art business technologies. We are proud to boast full accreditation of all academic programs by AACSB–The International Association for Management Education. Focused course work on the international functions of management, finance, economics, marketing, and accounting, along with dynamic program offerings in enterprise-wide information systems, finance, global marketing management, real estate valuation, human resource management, risk management, and decision sciences, prepare graduates for increasingly global business interactions.

—Dr. Michael Sesnowitz, Dean

Programs and Curricular Focus

The Virginia Commonwealth University (VCU) School of Business offers graduate education in a variety of areas. The Master of Business Administration (M.B.A.) degree at VCU is intended to develop a knowledge of the functions and techniques of management, as well as an understanding of environmental and economic forces that influence administration and decision making. The curriculum is flexible and is designed for students with diverse undergraduate backgrounds. The program consists of eight foundation courses, eight required advanced courses, and either two electives for a general degree or four electives for a concentration. Concentration areas include decision sciences, economics, finance, information systems, marketing, human resource and industrial relations, real estate and urban land development, and risk management and insurance.

In addition, the School of Business offers degree programs leading to the Master of Accountancy, Master of Arts in economics, Master of Science in business, Master of Taxation, and Doctor of Philosophy (Ph.D.) in business. The Master of Arts degree in economics is designed to provide the necessary applied quantitative background for positions in the private and government sectors. Students pursuing the Master of Arts degree may also select a concentration in financial economics.

The Master of Science in business degree program requires students to select one area of concentration for more focused study. Each student completes at least four courses in general business foundation requirements, followed by at least ten courses from the chosen concentration area. Concentration areas include decision sciences, finance, global marketing management, human resource management and industrial relations, information systems, and real estate valuation.

The Master of Taxation program offers existing tax professions the opportunity to update and expand existing tax knowledge, as well as train students for entry into the field of taxation. The Master of Accountancy program offers students flexibility with specialization in auditing/financial reporting, accounting/information systems, and managerial and systems controllership. The Ph.D. program prepares individuals for faculty positions at colleges and universities that stress both research and teaching. The program provides students with in-depth research experience in dealing with theoretical and applied business topics. Ph.D. students select one major area of study and one minor area of study. Students can major in accounting, information systems, or organizational behavior.

Students and the M.B.A. Experience

Approximately 500 students are currently enrolled in the master's and doctoral programs of VCU's School of Business. Eighty percent of M.B.A. students are fully employed in the greater Richmond area and study on a part-time basis. To better serve these students, all foundation and required courses are offered in the evening, typically one night per week. Full-time students are also able to take some of their course work during the day or early evening hours. Course scheduling options, which guarantee course offerings each semester, are printed on a two-year basis, allowing students to plan their sequence of courses at least two years in advance. The typical part-time student completes the program within 3½ years. Full-time students with undergraduate degrees in business can complete the M.B.A. with concentration in as few as three semesters, with careful planning. The current class of M.B.A. students is 40 percent women and has an average of 6 years of work experience prior to enrolling in the program.

Special Features

Distinctive features of the graduate programs include, but are in no way limited to, a graduate curriculum in information systems that focuses on enterprise systems and provides students hands on experiences with state-of-the-art software systems such as SAP, J.D. Edwards, Oracle, PeopleSoft, SAS Enterprise Suite, and others. The curriculum in human resources management and industrial relations has no rival in the mid-Atlantic region. The global marketing management curriculum provides graduate students the unique opportunity to participate in exchange programs in France and Italy, as well as gain global experience via group projects completed via teleconferencing.

The Faculty

The School of Business has 102 full-time faculty members. Many faculty members have been recognized nationally for their teaching effectiveness, research contributions, and service to professional organizations. Faculty members participate in faculty development activities to stay abreast of their fields and many are active advisers to business entities in Richmond and elsewhere.

The Business School Network

The Business Council is a select group of more than 65 senior executive officers of national and international companies. Members of the Business Council serve as advisers on curricula and other school activities. Relationships developed through the Business Council serve as a pathway to business by providing more than 150 internship opportunities annually to students in School of Business programs.

The Alumni Council, the leadership group for the School's 14,000 alumni, provides advice and assistance for various School of Business activities throughout the year. The council has sponsored special events, educational series, and recruitment activities for School of Business students.

The College and Environs

Virginia Commonwealth University is located in Richmond, Virginia, the capital of the Commonwealth. VCU benefits from the rich cultural, industrial, and business offerings of the state, as well as its close proximity to the nation's capital, Washington, D.C. The Richmond metropolitan area has a growing economy with strong manufacturing, distribution, and medical centers that provide excellent employment opportunities. VCU was formed in 1968 by the merger of Richmond Professional Institute and the Medical College of Virginia. The School of Business was established in 1946 and began offering graduate degrees in 1962. VCU enrolls more than 22,000 undergraduate, graduate, and health professions students on its two campuses in Richmond.

Facilities

The School of Business is housed in the VCU Business Building, a facility that offers state-of-the-art technology classrooms, computer facilities, and team meeting rooms. University Library Services administers the James Branch Cabell and Tompkins-McCaw research libraries on both campuses and provides numerous electronic resources, federal and state documents, patents, and a wide variety of microform and media resources. The online catalog serves as the gateway to both print, nonprint, and electronic resources, including more than one million volumes. Electronic databases and a broad array of CD-ROMs that cover all disciplines constitute the backbone of electronic resources.

Technology Environment

The School of Business has fifteen electronic classrooms, each equipped with video-data projectors, computers with network and Internet connections, VCRs, and document cameras. Four computer classrooms and the walk-in lab have more than 180 state-of-the-art computers for use by business students. In addition, the department of information systems has three computer laboratories that serve upper-level information systems courses and its enterprise software initiatives. The department of economics uses its Experimental Economics Laboratory for research projects and student instruction in experimental economics. The accounting department's KPMG accounting lab is used to support upper-level accounting classes.

Placement

The Office of Graduate Studies in Business (GSIB) and VCU Career Center work cooperatively and collaboratively to provide students with current information regarding employment opportunities and career counseling activities. The GSIB annually sponsors a Graduate Business Placement Forum, which provides students and potential employers with the opportunity to meet in small information sessions and schedule individual appointments to discuss placement opportunities. The University Career Center maintains resumes and references of business students on a state-of-the-art database, allowing employers and students to access employment information individually via the World Wide Web.

Admission

Applicants to graduate programs in the VCU School of Business must submit an application for admission, two copies of official transcripts from each university or college previously attended, three letters of recommendation, a current resume, and a personal statement. Applicants to the Master of Accountancy, Master of Business Administration, Master of Science in business, Master of Taxation, and Doctor of Philosophy degree programs must submit current Graduate Management Admissions Test (GMAT) scores. Applicants for the Master of Arts in economics program must submit current Graduate Record Examination (GRE) scores.

Finances

All tuition and fee rates quoted below were approved for the 1999–2000 academic year. Tuition and fees for the 2000–01 year are anticipated to increase by 2.3 to 4.6 percent. In-state tuition and fees for full-time students have been set at $2556 per semester. Out-of-state tuition and fees for full-time students total $6513.50 per semester. In-state rates are set at $263.50 per credit hour for part-time students. Out-of-state rates have been set at $703.50 per credit hour for part-time students.

A limited number of master's assistantships are available through the Graduate Studies in Business office for full-time master's-level students with exemplary academic credentials. Endowed scholarships are also available through GSIB on an annual basis. Scholarships are generally offered in the spring for the following academic year.

Application Facts and Dates

Beginning for the spring 2000 semester, applications will be considered using a sequence of rounds. The timeline of each round provides students with a deadline to submit a complete application and a time frame by which a decision will be made and communicated to the applicant. Applications received in between rounds are processed no later than the notification date for the next scheduled round. Applications received after the last round are reviewed as quickly as possible and decisions are made as appropriate until the beginning of each semester. Priority for assistantship funding will be given to those applications received in the earliest admission round for the anticipated semester of entry. The deadline for spring application is November 1. The deadline for summer application is March 1. The deadlines for fall application are April 1 and June 1. For more information, students should contact:

Graduate Studies in Business
Virginia Commonwealth University
1015 Floyd Avenue, Room 4144
P.O. Box 844000
Richmond, Virginia 23284-4000
Telephone: 804-828-4622
Fax: 804-828-7174
E-mail: gsib@vcu.edu
World Wide Web: http://www.vcu.edu/busweb/gsib

Virginia Polytechnic Institute and State University

Pamplin College of Business

Blacksburg, Virginia

WHY THE PAMPLIN COLLEGE OF BUSINESS?

Besides being one of the Southeast's top business schools, we are Virginia's largest business school, accounting for 20 percent of all business degrees awarded from the state's fifteen public senior institutions. Our M.B.A. and other degree programs are all accredited by AACSB—The International Association for Management Education, which is the internationally recognized accrediting agency for graduate and undergraduate business programs.

We are committed to providing top-quality business education through outstanding teaching by full-time faculty members who are nationally recognized in theoretical and applied research. We are also committed to developing a global perspective in our students so that they may better understand the interdependence of nations in the world economy and how cultural differences can become the basis of strength. We are preparing our students for global business challenges with core courses that include the global context of business, international summer internships, and faculty-led study-abroad programs.

—Richard E. Sorensen, Dean

Programs and Curricular Focus

The Master of Business Administration degree at the Pamplin College of Business requires the completion of 48 semester credit hours. The program consists of a twofold educational process. First, through program prerequisites and a set of required courses, students gain proficiency in the basic disciplines of accounting, finance, management, management of information systems and information technology, marketing, and production/operations management. Students also acquire an understanding of the quantitative, economic, behavioral, and statistical tools required of a competent manager and a contributing team member.

Next, students are given an opportunity to strengthen their knowledge in a particular area through the careful selection of elective courses. They may concentrate in financial risk management, information and decision support systems, human resource management, leadership, finance, management, management science, marketing, and global business. They may also select a broader range of electives and not declare a formal concentration. Students are thus given flexibility to put together an M.B.A. program that is tailored to their individual professional goals.

The M.B.A. program prerequisites include proficiency with a computer operating system and office applications,

as well as knowledge of calculus and economics. Completing college-level courses in differential calculus and matrix algebra (usually two semesters) and economics (micro and macro) can meet the economics and calculus requirements. These requirements can be fulfilled by completing at least one college-level course in differential calculus and one college-level course each in microeconomics and macroeconomics. Students should also be familiar with matrix algebra.

The program provides a strong theoretical base, vital to the foundation of a future manager. A solid understanding of business functions and a sensitivity to the needs of organizational stakeholders enable managers to better understand and adapt to change. The classroom procedures offer students a blend of case study, lectures, role play, individual and group presentations, and simulation exercises.

Students and the M.B.A. Experience

The M.B.A. program has about 220 full-time students on campus. The students represent a diversity of ages, work experiences, undergraduate studies, nationalities, cultural backgrounds, and career interests. About one quarter of the students obtained their undergraduate degrees from out-of-state institutions, with approximately another quarter

having undergraduate degrees from universities outside the United States. The students come from about twenty-five countries. Business undergraduate majors comprise about 35 percent of the students; engineering or technical majors represent more than 30 percent. The average age of the entering students is 25. Students typically have more than two years of work experience. Men account for 65 percent of the students; women, 35 percent.

The College seeks to attract a cross-section of highly qualified individuals from different cultural and career backgrounds. Because diversity is a reality in today's workplace and in the global economy, students are encouraged to be open to and embrace differing views and interpretations of the world.

Special Features

The College also enrolls about 385 part-time students in its off-campus M.B.A. programs, offered in northern Virginia and other sites around the state.

The Northern Virginia M.B.A. Program has been fully accredited since 1971. The program offers professionals in the Washington, D.C., area an opportunity to earn an M.B.A. without interrupting their careers. Of the approximate 240 students enrolled in this program, more than 95 percent have full-time careers in engineering, computer applications, accounting, finance, human resources, and marketing.

The M.B.A. Program via ATM network provides courses that are received at sites through live videoconferencing—permitting students at various locations to interact with the instructor and with students in classrooms at other sites.

The Faculty

The College has about 125 full-time faculty members, many of whom are nationally recognized teachers and scholars with practical business experience. As a result of their dedication to advancing leading-edge business concepts, the faculty members have been involved with instituting nationally recognized research entities, such as the

Center for Study of Futures and Options Markets, Center for Wireless Telecommunications, Center for Relationship Development, and the Business/Technology Center.

The Business School Network

The Pamplin Advisory Council is a select group of 65 prominent business and government leaders from across the country who meet with College administrators to provide guidance on College programs, fund-raising, and ties with industry and government.

Alumni volunteers assist students in various capacities, including information interviews, networking referrals, referring resumes in their respective companies, and advising students seeking jobs within the alumni's specific geographic areas.

The alumni return to their alma mater to share their work experiences and to discuss factors for success that go beyond their technical knowledge.

Experienced recruiters conduct panel discussions and practice interviews for first-year students. M.B.A. students receive straightforward feedback on how they performed during the mock interviews, how they were perceived by recruiters, and what they can do to prepare for live interviews during their second year.

The College and Environs

Virginia Polytechnic Institute and State University, commonly known as Virginia Tech, was founded in 1872 as a land-grant college. Its recent history is one of rapid, well-planned growth. Virginia Tech is the largest university in the state in terms of full-time enrollment.

Virginia Tech, ranked in the nation's top fifty in terms of research expenditures, conducts a $121-million-a-year research program supporting more than 3,500 research projects. The Virginia Tech Corporate Research Center offers businesses the opportunity to establish close working relationships with the University.

Facilities

The Pamplin M.B.A. Program is housed in Pamplin Hall, a state-of-the-art academic facility. An atrium, combining large skylights with natural foliage, forms a creative yet relaxing environment for both students and faculty to interact.

Virginia Tech's Newman Library currently contains more than 1.7 million bound volumes, 5.2 million microforms, 5,000 videos and films, 6,700 cassettes and recordings, and more than 13,000

journals and periodicals. Access to the collection is provided through an online computer system, VTLS, which is an integrated system used by more than seventy-five other libraries around the world.

Technology Environment

The Pamplin College of Business is committed to providing its students with the best educational experience possible. Pamplin has three computer labs equipped with Pentium PCs. Students have unlimited access to the Internet. This virtual connection with the program allows students to download full-text articles from the library, register for classes, and download assignments. These and other time-saving activities allow students to focus on and devote more time to studies. Blacksburg and Virginia Tech are also the home of Blacksburg Electronic Village (BEV), the oldest and most connected Internet community in the world. With the growing importance of information and computer technologies, the program prepares students for a competitive and changing world.

Placement

The M.B.A. career service's mission is to help students identify and capitalize on their distinctive talents and focus on how their career objectives fit their personal and professional priorities. Individual counseling focuses on customizing the career planning and marketing process for each student. Two courses are offered to assist students: Career Marketing and Planning and the Job Search Strategy Seminar. Corporate briefings and alumni career events occur throughout the year.

Admission

Applicants to the Pamplin M.B.A. Program must take the Graduate Management Admission Test (GMAT) and have the official scores reported to Virginia Tech. In addition, each applicant is required to submit an application for admission, official transcripts of all past course work, two letters of recommendation, and a current resume.

Undergraduate grades (particularly those from the junior and senior years), GMAT scores, work experience, and letters of recommendation are all important, although each is only one measure of an individual's potential to pursue graduate study. Considered collectively, however, this information helps to determine which applicants are most likely to succeed in the program.

Finances

Estimated in-state tuition and fees for the 1999–2000 academic year were $4950. The out-of-state student rate was $7758. Estimated living expenses were $6700, and miscellaneous expenses were estimated at $1100 for both in-state and out-of-state students. Travel expenses are not included.

Merit-based financial aid is available for students with outstanding academic background, GMAT scores, work experience, leadership skills, and references. Financial aid is available for graduate students in the form of fellowships, instructional fee waivers, and graduate assistantships.

Need-based financial aid is based primarily on demonstrated financial need. In order to be considered, students must submit a Free Application for Federal Student Aid (FAFSA) for the appropriate year no later than February 15. The University will advise applicants of their financial aid awards by August 1.

International Students

Approximately twenty-five countries are represented in the M.B.A. program, and international students comprise about 25 percent of the program's student body. At the university level, there are thirty-five international student organizations and an international center, the Cranwell International Center, which is a focal point for cultural, social, and educational programs with a global focus. Films, dinners, lectures, parties, orientation programs, and community contacts are facilitated throughout the center.

Application Facts and Dates

Applications for admission are accepted at any time. Admission decisions are made within six to eight weeks after the application file is complete. Although most students enter the program in August, students may also enter in January (spring semester). Application materials should be received at least eight weeks before the beginning of the semester for which enrollment is requested. For more information, students should contact:

MBA Enrollment Services Coordinator
1044 Pamplin Hall (0209)
Virginia Polytechnic Institute and
    State University
Blacksburg, Virginia 24061
Telephone: 540-231-6152
Fax: 540-231-4487
E-mail: vtmba@vt.edu

Wake Forest University

Babcock Graduate School of Management

Winston-Salem, North Carolina

THE SCHOOL OF FIRST CHOICE

Exciting developments are taking place to make Babcock the 'school of first choice' for an increasing number of outstanding students. Babcock's recent strategic initiative—the 3/38 Plan (3 sections of 38 students)—provides the smallest first-year class sections of any major graduate business school in the nation. In the second year, you can tailor your studies for optimal learning with one of Babcock's career concentrations. Even after graduation, your education at Babcock will continue through new lifelong learning options.

The M.B.A. curriculum will give you a personalized and experiential learning experience, access to innovative technology in a modern facility, extensive team-based and cross-functional learning opportunities, a global management perspective, and the chance to acquire depth in your chosen career area.

Investment in the M.B.A. degree will be one of the most important decisions of your life. I invite you to visit and see firsthand why you should make the Babcock School your 'school of first choice.'

—Charlie Moyer, Dean

Programs and Curricular Focus

Babcock's curriculum stresses the integrated, global, and strategic nature of management. Students gain a broad managerial perspective, functional competence, and enhanced communication skills. Other hallmarks of the Babcock School are the state-of-the-art facilities, leading-edge technology, close interaction with faculty members, teamwork, emphasis on practical application, and dedication to lifelong learning.

Babcock's cross-functional first-year curriculum enables students to learn and apply knowledge across all management disciplines. Knowledge and problem-solving skills acquired in one class are applied to situations in another, and integrative exercises reinforce this approach. Also, knowledge builds as first-year students progress through three distinct modules: Business Foundations, Functional and Cross-Functional Applications, and Strategic Perspectives.

The first-year class, composed of 114 students, is divided into three sections of 38 students and study teams of 4 or 5 members with diverse academic and work-experience backgrounds. The first-year core courses include accounting, analysis and communications, financial management, international business management, international competitive policy, law and ethics, macroeconomics, management information systems, managerial economics, marketing management, operations management, organizational behavior, and quantitative methods.

Second-year students may choose to concentrate in one of the career concentrations in the areas of finance, marketing, operations, management consulting, entrepreneurship and family business, or information technology management. In addition, students can create their own concentration under the direction of a faculty member. Students have the opportunity to design an individualized curriculum to fit their specific career needs. An integral part of the second year is the management consulting practicum, which offers consulting projects that provide experiential learning.

The Babcock School offers three joint-degree programs: a J.D./M.B.A. degree program that takes four years to complete and M.D./M.B.A. and Ph.D./M.B.A. programs that take five years to complete.

Students and the M.B.A. Experience

Students benefit from the diverse backgrounds of their classmates. The average incoming student is 27 years old with four years of full-time work experience. Twenty-nine percent of the class are women, 24 percent is international, and minority students comprise 5 percent of the class. The entering class represents every region of the United States as well as eleven other countries. Babcock students have undergraduate degrees in business/accounting (33 percent), engineering/natural sciences (25 percent), economics (10 percent), social sciences (19 percent), and liberal arts/other degrees (13 percent).

❖ Global Focus

Multinational studies are interlaced throughout the curriculum. More than 80 percent of the faculty members have international experience.

Babcock offers three 2-week international study programs in China; Japan; and Oxford, England, and a semester abroad of study can be arranged in Europe or Latin America. In addition, an international summer internship is an option through Babcock's International Internship Program in Asia, Europe, and Latin America.

Special Features

A hallmark of the Babcock School is the personal attention students receive. The program is small enough for close relationships with other students and professors yet large enough for students to experience different cultures and academic and work backgrounds. The personalized approach is inherent in all aspects of the program, from faculty advisers for study groups to the career services staff making corporate calls on an individual student's behalf to the Mentor Program. The Babcock School's Mentor Program offers students a real-world perspective through one-on-one relationships with business professionals.

The Faculty

Babcock faculty members are excellent teacher-scholars and are experienced managers. They know how academic theory relates to conditions in practice. The faculty members take an interest in students' professional development and quickly come to know students as individuals.

Faculty members are actively engaged in research and publication for leading scholarly journals. Many develop cases, textbooks, and other classroom materials, supporting the schoolwide emphasis on teaching excellence. Faculty members also engage in consulting to stay abreast of current managerial practices.

The Business School Network

Babcock values its partnerships with corporate leaders, who support the School in many ways. Corporate leaders assist with career development by participating in the Mentor Program and the Career Symposium, a half-day event in which business leaders from various functional areas come to share their business experiences and advice. Prominent business leaders volunteer to speak to classes and clubs or to participate in one of two lecture series, sharing their views on the current business environment. The Babcock School's Board of Visitors is an advisory body of business leaders who provide strategic counsel to the School. Members are available to help students with career networking, and, along with other individuals and businesses, have generously provided scholarships for incoming students.

The College and Environs

Wake Forest University was founded in 1834 and is one of the oldest institutions of higher learning in North Carolina. The University is consistently ranked in Tier One of national colleges and universities. Total enrollment in the University is 6,015, with one third of these students enrolled in graduate or professional programs.

Wake Forest University is located in North Carolina's Piedmont Triad region, with a population that exceeds 1.2 million. Winston-Salem has a well-established reputation as the "city of the arts," with numerous museums, galleries, concerts, and organizations. Students also take advantage of Atlantic Coast Conference action, minor league baseball, and many philanthropic, club, and Student Government Association activities.

Technology Environment

Opened in 1993, the Worrell Professional Center for Law and Management is one of the most outstanding business school facilities in the United States. Babcock is committed to providing students with leading-edge technologies in information systems. As a result, the building is well equipped for studying, with each study room, study carrel, and most classrooms containing connections to link the students' ThinkPads to the computer network. Every student receives an IBM ThinkPad as part of tuition. Through the network, students can access the Professional Center Library, the Internet, and libraries and databases throughout

the world. Students have dial-in capability from home for activities such as checking e-mail or accessing the Intranet or professors' shared data files. Classrooms also include integrated computer and audiovisual equipment.

Placement

Babcock graduates are competitive in the marketplace. The Office of Career Services builds close working relationships with corporations, alumni, and other business professionals. Babcock students have access to top multinational companies through on-campus interviews and recruiting events in New York and Atlanta. Babcock also takes part in two international career conferences. The School's career planning assistance includes individual counseling, group seminars covering self-assessment and career management topics, videotaped practice job interviews with interview consultants, the Career Symposium, first- and second-year resume books, and a resume referral service. At the class of 2000's graduation, 90 percent of Babcock M.B.A. graduates had employment offers, and based on previous years, it is anticipated that between 98 and 99 percent will have offers by September 1, 2000. The median annual salary plus guaranteed bonus was $75,000.

Admission

Applicants must hold a bachelor's degree or its equivalent from an accredited college or university. Applicants are primarily evaluated on three criteria: academic record, GMAT scores, and work experience. Babcock's entering class has an average GPA of 3.2, an average GMAT score of 645, and an average of 4 years of work experience. Ninety-four percent of the incoming class has full-time postgraduate work experience. In addition, the admissions committee looks for evidence of leadership ability, teamwork skills, a strong sense of values, and unique talents, skills, or achievements. International students must submit a satisfactory score on the TOEFL and a certificate of finances, proving the availability of funds to cover two years of expenses. Interviews are strongly recommended for every applicant and are required for individuals lacking postgraduate work experience, with the exception of international applicants. There are no requisite courses for admission, but students need to have a working knowledge of statistics, accounting, and economics, plus sound spreadsheet skills.

Finances

The estimated student budget for the 2000–01 school year is $34,725, which

includes the following expenses: tuition, $22,100; books/supplies, $1500; room, $3600; board, $2000; utilities, $850; personal expenses, $2235; insurance (health and renter's), $675; transportation, $1640; and an SGA fee of $125. These expense estimates are based on a nine-month academic year for single students living off campus. There is limited on-campus housing for married couples and international students. Scholarship awards are made on the basis of merit and are awarded on a first-come, first served basis. Applicants who wish to be considered for merit-based scholarships should apply by March 1, and those who wish to be considered for the ten Babcock Scholars full-tuition scholarships must apply by February 15. Both U.S. citizens and international students are eligible for scholarships. The School also assists students with obtaining federally sponsored loans.

International Students

International students must arrive for the international student orientation program one week prior to general orientation. This program introduces international students to U.S. business and culture. Housing is available for international students in the Wake Forest International House on a space-available basis. The house is located within walking distance of the Babcock School.

Application Facts and Dates

Babcock makes admission decisions on a rolling basis, and decisions are made within one month of receipt of a completed application. The early admission deadline is December 1. Applications received after April 1 are considered on a space-available basis. Admission is for the fall semester only. For more information, students should contact the admissions office.

Admissions and Financial Aid
Babcock Graduate School of
    Management
Wake Forest University
P.O. Box 7659
Winston-Salem, North Carolina 27109
Telephone: 336-758-5422
         800-722-1622 (toll-free)
Fax: 336-758-5830
E-mail: admissions@mba.wfu.edu
World Wide Web: http://www.mba.
    wfu.edu

Walsh College of Accountancy and Business Administration

Troy, Michigan

EDUCATING TOMORROW'S BUSINESS LEADERS

A leader in business education for seventy-eight years, Walsh offers the traditional M.B.A. with a unique twist. Case studies and a focus on the entire business enterprise tailor this graduate program. Walsh also offers a Master of Science in Management (M.S.M.) program grounded in the practical approach. In addition to providing core management skills, the M.S.M. affords students a chance to develop specialized skills through four program concentrations. Program instructors are business practitioners as well as subject matter experts.

—Dr. Michael Wood, Dean

Programs and Curricular Focus

Rapidly advancing technology, the global marketplace, and changing organizational structures pose significant challenges for tomorrow's managers. Walsh College's M.B.A. and M.S.M. programs are designed to help managers meet these challenges and become true leaders in their fields.

More businesses, in particular those in the service industries, require or recommend graduate education for employee advancement. The M.B.A. and M.S.M. programs were developed with all managers and aspiring managers in mind.

The Walsh M.B.A. requires 36–51 semester credit hours. The core of the Walsh M.B.A. program includes eight courses that cover studies in accounting, economics, finance, management, and business strategy. In addition, four elective courses are taken from a variety of graduate degree offerings. Students can specialize by completing all four electives in the same business discipline. The M.S.M. requires 36 semester credit hours, with eight to nine core courses and an additional three courses in one area of concentration. The six concentrations are business operations, human resources, interactive marketing, international management, marketing, and interdisciplinary.

In addition to providing a high-quality education, Walsh demonstrates its commitment to the students through convenient class scheduling, with eleven- and fourteen-week evening courses and weekend classes currently offered at two locations in southeast Michigan; extended office hours for student services; tutoring; faculty mentoring; and state-of-the-art technology.

Interwoven throughout the curriculum is course work designed to help students develop competence in specific academic, information management, and technology competencies. Specific areas of competency include problem solving, systems thinking, information management, team development and performance, global perspectives, technology-accelerated communications, adaptation to and management of change, and entrepreneurial initiatives. With these abilities, Walsh graduates add productive value to the business world immediately.

Walsh College also offers Master of Science degrees in business information technology, finance, information management and communication, professional accountancy, and taxation.

Students and the M.B.A. Experience

Business professionals, professionals with a technical background, and even those with a liberal arts degree find that the M.B.A. and M.S.M. programs prepare them for the challenges of being a manager. Many of the students are engineers, automotive field employees, health-care professionals, business owners, or aspiring managers.

The Walsh M.B.A. provides a broad education in accounting, finance, and management while offering elective courses in a student's particular area of interest. Students attend an introductory seminar acquainting them with the M.B.A. program objectives and expectations. Technology is used to access information via the Internet and online databases, while students work individually and in teams. Decision making, critical thinking, systematic approach

development, complex problem solving, and communication skills are stressed in all courses. A new option, available to M.B.A. students, is a series of interactive marketing classes offered via the Internet.

The majority of the 274 students in the Walsh M.B.A. program and the 400 students in the M.S.M. program are working professionals, often with family responsibilities. The average graduate student is 33 years old. Fifty-three percent of the students are men, and 13 percent are members of minority groups. These individuals bring a broad range of experience to the classroom.

The Faculty

The faculty comprises business professionals holding master's and doctoral degrees and professional certifications. They include CPAs, attorneys, and marketing managers and analysts who bring "real-world" experience into the classroom and provide a network between students and business. Currently, there are 3 full-time and 30 part-time faculty members teaching in the management programs.

The Business School Network

Walsh College students are provided networking opportunities through internships, contact with faculty members and classmates holding professional positions, alumni activities, and student clubs, including the Student Government, Walsh College Accounting Club, and Finance/Economics Association. In addition, students are encouraged to join professional organizations with college chapters at Walsh, including the Association of Information Technology Professionals.

The College and Environs

Walsh College of Accountancy and Business Administration is a private upper-division institution with an enrollment of 3,120 students. The College offers bachelor's and master's degree programs in business administration and related fields. Walsh College was established on December 31, 1968, as a successor to Walsh Institute of Accountancy. The Institute was founded in 1922 by Mervyn B. Walsh, a prominent certified public accountant.

Facilities

Walsh College offers classes at four convenient locations in southeast Michigan, including Troy, Novi, Port Huron, and the University Center in Clinton Township. The M.B.A. and M.S.M. programs are offered at the Troy and Novi campuses.

The main campus in Troy, Michigan, is strategically placed to serve commuting students within the Detroit metropolitan area. Located on 20 acres, the College is approximately 17 miles north of downtown Detroit. The facilities are modern and exemplify a professional learning environment. No housing facilities are available on campus. Students attend classes during the day and evening and on Saturdays.

The Novi campus opened in 1993 and serves the residents of western Oakland and Wayne Counties. A new 35,000-square-foot, technology-enriched facility opened in 1998 on 11 acres. The new campus has fourteen classrooms, an all-electronic library, a computer lab, a conference center, and a bookstore. The Walsh M.B.A., the Master of Science in Finance, and the Master of Science in Management are offered at the Novi campus.

Technology Environment

Student labs are equipped with Pentiums that run Windows and Microsoft Office Professional. The library features an electronic card catalog, automated administration system, network-based CD-ROM, and Internet access.

Placement

Walsh College's Career Services Office assists current students and alumni in securing full-time, part-time, internship, or co-op positions either while attending the College or after graduation.

A wide range of services is offered, including workshops and programs such as on-campus recruiting in the spring and fall, job listings that are updated daily and posted at all four campuses, resume referrals, career days, and mock interview sessions. In addition, specific career development needs are addressed in individual appointments, providing assistance with resume preparation, job search techniques, interviewing skills, career planning, and career-related assessment. Finally, Career Services and the library have numerous resources, including more than 1,200 annual reports, industry-specific journals, online company databases, and corporate recruiting brochures.

Admission

Admission requirements for the M.B.A. program include an evaluation of undergraduate academic achievement, work experience, and GMAT score. In order to be prepared for the M.S.M. curriculum, students need two years of work experience and an academic background in accounting, economics, statistics, and microcomputers. The GMAT is not required for the M.S.M. program. Students needing preparation in specific areas of business study may complete prerequisite course work at Walsh.

Finances

Tuition for 1999–2000 was $283 per semester credit hour. A $75 nonrefundable registration fee was assessed each semester. The minimum registration deposit was $400. In addition, books for each course cost approximately $100.

Students interested in financial aid should complete and mail the Free Application for Federal Student Aid (FAFSA) to the Federal Processing Center before September 1. Graduate students who are Michigan residents and who demonstrate financial need through the information provided on the FAFSA may qualify for a Michigan Tuition Grant, which offers up to $2550 toward tuition costs, or a Federal Family

Education Loan (FFEL) with an annual maximum of $18,500.

Merit scholarships are available to new and continuing students based upon high academic achievement, as demonstrated by a grade point average of 3.5 or higher.

International Students

Six percent of the student population at Walsh College comprises international students representing thirty-two countries, with the majority coming from Canada and Europe. Students typically have family and friends living and working in southeast Michigan.

Application Facts and Dates

Students may begin their studies at the beginning of any academic semester. Applications for admission in a given semester are accepted until the beginning of that semester. However, students living overseas should make application to the College no later than six months before the start of classes. In addition, international applicants whose native language is not English must demonstrate a sufficient proficiency in English by attaining a score of 550 or better on the Test of English as a Foreign Language (TOEFL) or a score of 80 or better on the Michigan English Language Assessment Battery (MELAB). All classes at Walsh College are conducted entirely in English. Upon receipt of the application, Walsh College requests the official transcripts for the applicant to be sent from all other colleges previously attended. After evaluation, a letter is sent to the applicant regarding admission. For more information, students should contact:

Diane Zalapi, Director of Admissions
Walsh College
P.O. Box 7006
Troy, Michigan 48007-7006
Telephone: 248-689-8282
Fax: 248-689-0938
E-mail: mkt@walshcol.edu

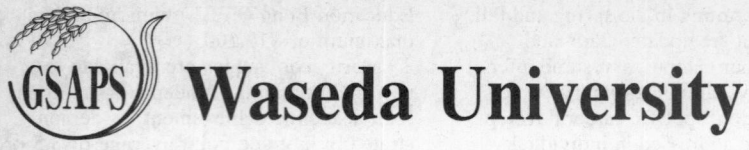

Waseda University

Tokyo, Japan

ASIA-PACIFIC FOCUS

In July 1997, Waseda University opened a new center called the Waseda Institute of Asia-Pacific Studies (WIAPS), which offers research and education programs and activities that focus on the Asia-Pacific region. The Graduate School of Asia-Pacific Studies (GSAPS), with a concentration in international relations and international management, cooperates with this new center in offering master's degree programs to educate professionals and executives in the public and private sectors to function as experts and researchers. GSAPS programs began in April 1998.

—Ken'ichi Goto, Dean, GSAPS

Program and Curricular Focus

Waseda University's M.B.A. program is a full-time intensive program intended to provide talented professionals with the necessary specialized international management skills to perform successfully in positions of responsibility in business administration in Asia-Pacific firms and organizations. The curriculum stresses not only knowledge-based techniques and methods in business and management but also infrastructure-related topics (such as business ethics, intercultural studies, comparative industry theory, environmental problems, ecology, negotiation, and methodologies, including system analysis, system design, and paradigm shifts). Students are required to complete a minimum of twelve months of study, 48 credits, and a thesis based upon a research project.

This program also offers internship and field study. Students are involved in a research project and are expected to accomplish a thesis related to the project. Also, students are offered opportunities to study a natural language intensively (Japanese, English, Mandarin, Korean, Thai, Pilipino, Malay, Indonesian, Vietnamese, or Spanish).

One of the characteristics of the graduate education program is the "Triangle Method," which consists of interaction among research, education, and society. The intention of WIAPS is to receive, then to research projects commissioned by governments, local authorities, and companies and to organize students to work on these projects. Students are educated through problem-solving and practice-oriented curricula. Multimedia education is also

emphasized. The language of instruction is English and Japanese, and the course is offered through four terms.

Students and the M.B.A. Experience

Students are required to have earned a B.A. degree (or the equivalent) following the completion of sixteen years of school education in a country other than Japan and have at least three years' working experience. The University welcomes applications from international students.

❖ Global Focus

In addition to the International Management Program, GSAPS offers the International Relations Program, which is tailored to meet the needs of global business leaders.

The Faculty

Half of all faculty members are executives of major corporations, specialists, and central and local government officials from both Japan and throughout the world. The University also invites visiting professors from prestigious business schools as guest speakers.

The Business School Network

Waseda University has a student and faculty member exchange agreement with more than 140 institutions of higher education all over the world. GSAPS uses this global network for maximizing results of international business education.

In addition, WIAPS's International Advisory Board (IAB), consisting of

GSAPS is located in Waseda University's Nishiwaseda Building.

distinguished members such as CEOs of leading Japanese companies, leaders of the global business world, and a former president, will provide valuable guidance and consultation for this program.

The College and Environs

In 1882, Shigenobu Okuma, one of the leading political figures of the Meiji Era, founded Tokyo College for Technical Studies (Tokyo-senmon-gakko) with the aim of upholding independence of learning, promoting the practical utilization of knowledge, and fostering good citizenship. In 1902, this institution became Waseda University.

Waseda University, located in the center of Tokyo, now consists of nine undergraduate schools, ten graduate schools, and various affiliated research institutions. It has about 1,500 full-time faculty members and about 50,000 students.

Waseda University is one of the most prestigious and most respected private universities in Japan in terms of its history, tradition, the number and achievements of its graduates, and the standard of its teaching and research.

Facilities

Central Library, which is located next to GSAPS's building, with a capacity of more than 4 million collections and a fully equipped audiovisual auditorium, offers an ideal environment for study and research. Waseda University also has an International Conference Center and a unique theater museum built in 1928 and devoted to the study of the history of drama.

Technology Environment

Waseda University provides full Internet access for every student, which includes an e-mail account and access to the NetNews and the World Wide Web.

To ensure that this environment can be used optimally, technical support is also given to students who are less familiar

Waseda University's Okuma Auditorium.

with computers. Students are also offered the chance to study artificial language (computer and Internet). The Media Network Center currently holds more than 2,000 PCs and 100 servers.

Waseda University's integrated network system enables students to reach a wide range of databases not only from international database providers but also from major newspapers.

Placement

The Career Development Office provides assistance to help graduating students in finding employment as well as individual counseling. It has on file information on almost 30,000 companies. It also publishes *Employment Guidance* and designs employment seminars that consider actual social and economic conditions as well as character of students based on rich data and long-time experience.

Admission

New students are admitted in either April or September. The Admissions Office is

considering accepting applicants based on either documentation screening, a language proficiency test (either Japanese or English), or an interview.

The academic calendar is as follows: spring term, April (new enrollment) to mid-July; summer session, late July to late August; fall term, early September (new enrollment) to late December; and winter term, early January to March.

For further details, students should contact the GSAPS Admissions Office mentioned below.

Finances

For the academic year 2000–01, the tuition fee is ¥1,300,000 plus a special program fee (first year only) of ¥400,000.

International Students

International students are encouraged to apply. Forty percent of the student body are international students who come from twelve countries, including China, Indonesia, Korea, and the U.S. The goal is for up to one half of all students to come from abroad. Students can take a degree in either Japanese or English (not all courses are given in English). The GSAPS Office helps students to adjust to life in Tokyo. It offers counseling on immigration regulations as well as academic, finance, and personal concerns.

Application Facts and Dates

Students should address all correspondence to:

Admissions Office
Graduate School of Asia-Pacific
   Studies
Waseda University
1-21-1 Nishi-waseda, Shinjuku-ku
Tokyo 169-0051, Japan
Telephone: 81-3-5286-3877
Fax: 81-3-5272-4533
E-mail: gsaps@list.waseda.ac.jp
World Wide Web: http://www.wiaps.
   waseda.ac.jp/gsaps/en/index.html

Washington University in St. Louis

▶ ### FLEXIBLE, EXPERIENTIAL, AND PERSONAL

We believe that the M.B.A. program at the Olin School of Business is unique in a number of ways. First, our program is, by design, quite small and very personal. Each year we enroll a class of about 150 unique and talented students who, upon their arrival, discover an environment that capitalizes on the benefits of size. These include personal attention, counseling, advising, and the opportunity for faculty members, staff members, and students to get to know one another very well. Another unique feature of our program is the flexible curriculum that recognizes that no 2 students' goals are identical and, therefore, no single curriculum can work best for everyone. You will enjoy maximum flexibility and choice in this program. Finally, we are proud of the many experiential learning opportunities that you will find at Olin—an ever-growing array of exciting hands-on programs that allow you to put into practice the things that you have learned along the way.

—Stuart I. Greenbaum, Dean, John M. Olin School of Business

Programs and Curricular Focus

The underlying theme of the Olin M.B.A. program is to maximize each student's learning by developing a unique program of study tailored to his or her own needs. Along with a comprehensive study of contemporary management fundamentals in areas such as accounting, economics, management, statistics, strategy, finance, marketing, and operations, each student designs a program that builds on existing knowledge, strengthens targeted areas, and broadens business experience and horizons. Once the fundamentals have been mastered, each student customizes his or her own program through the creative choice of electives, which comprise at least two thirds of the curriculum.

Experiential learning is an integral part of the Olin M.B.A. curriculum. Through six unique programs, students have the opportunity to apply what they learn in the classroom to real-world business situations. These might include managing an investment portfolio (the Investment Praxis), designing a business plan with an entrepreneur (the Hatchery), consulting with a major corporation (the Practicum) or a nonprofit organization (Taylor Community Consulting and Total Quality Schools), or examining global business practices (Global Management Studies).

The Olin M.B.A. curriculum requires two years and 60 credit hours of course work for completion, except in the case of dual-degree programs, which combine the M.B.A. program with degree study in areas such as law or East Asian studies. At least 40 credits are selected as electives. Because no single teaching method works best for all subjects, students at Olin learn through case analyses, lectures, discussions, computer simulations, tutorials, independent research, study groups, experiential learning, and computer modeling.

Students and the M.B.A. Experience

The full-time M.B.A. program enrolls approximately 150 new students each year. They have diverse undergraduate backgrounds, ranging from business and the humanities to engineering and the sciences. On average, an entering class arrives at Olin from more than thirty states and as many as twenty foreign countries. The typical student entering the Olin M.B.A. program is 27 years old, with nearly five years of work experience. Approximately 25 percent of the typical entering class are women, and 30 percent are international students.

All Olin M.B.A. students work in a team environment. This is especially true in the first semester of the program, when students work in their assigned team through the majority of the core curriculum. Working in teams enhances learning through diversity of thought, background, and experience.

The Faculty

Olin has approximately 20 tenured professors and an additional 35 tenure-track professors who are world-class scholars. Many serve on editorial boards, publish papers in top journals, and win various prizes and awards for their work. Equally important, Olin professors are known for their teaching excellence and availability for advising and counseling M.B.A. students one-to-one. They are instrumental in developing the curriculum and keeping it current with state-of-the-art business practices. In addition, Olin employs about 20 adjunct faculty members who are leaders in the business community and who bring to the classroom a passion for merging business theory with cutting-edge business practices.

The Business School Network

Corporate participation with the Olin M.B.A. program adds an enriching dimension to the M.B.A. experience, promotes a clearer understanding of corporate life, and exposes M.B.A. students to the realities of corporate decision making at the highest levels. It also helps M.B.A. students test and evaluate their personal career aspirations. Olin maintains a strong partnership with the corporate community through programs such as Lunch with a Pro, the Executive Speaker Series, the Techportal Series, and an online alumni connection. Business executives are also frequent visitors to Olin's M.B.A. classrooms as guest lecturers and panelists.

The College and Environs

Washington University has been an integral part of the St. Louis community since its founding in 1853 and today enjoys an international reputation for academic excellence. The learning experience at Washington University offers the supportive, comfortable atmosphere of a small college while also providing the resources and amenities of a major international university. The main campus, Hilltop, is situated in one of the most vibrant and attractive areas of St. Louis. Residential suburbs and Forest Park, the hub of St. Louis culture and

Simon Hall is the hub of student activity and contains spacious student lounges, classrooms, seminar rooms, faculty offices, a library, rooms for small-group study (wired for computer use), offices for student organizations and clubs, and a deli.

recreation, surround the University. St. Louis is a thriving metropolitan center with all the features of a large city, including art galleries, museums, theaters, amateur and professional spectator sports, and bustling ethnic neighborhoods and cuisine.

Facilities

The Olin M.B.A. program is housed in Simon Hall on the main Hilltop Campus of Washington University. Simon Hall features high-technology classrooms, spacious student lounges, faculty offices, seminar rooms, a library, a computer lab, wired group study rooms, and a deli.

Placement

The Weston Career Resources Center (WCRC) features a staff of full-time professionals dedicated to individually assisting students with their intern and permanent job searches. The WCRC also provides an array of valuable resources for M.B.A. students, including an extensive career resources library and databases of key placement contacts at major firms. On-campus recruiting, use of distance technology, company information

sessions, and corporate or industry receptions are other placement avenues supported by the WCRC. In addition, Olin's worldwide network of alumni is available for career assistance via a number of technologies maintained by the WCRC. The WCRC also has partnerships with student organizations to take the School's message on the road. This past year, road shows were implemented in San Francisco, Chicago, New York, and Boston, which are areas of particular interest to many of the M.B.A. students. These tremendously successful trips combined receptions, corporate visits, and interviewing, which resulted in outstanding placement connections for many students.

Admission

The Olin Admissions Committee reviews applications based on a series of five deadlines, with the earliest falling in mid-December. Qualified full-time M.B.A. students are admitted to start in the fall semester only. The committee reviews the full array of information requested in the application to determine a candidate's ability to perform in an intensely rigorous academic environment. The committee also seeks to identify students who will add significantly to the academic, cultural, and social character of the School. Prospective students must submit an Olin application (available as hard copy, online, or through M.B.A. Multi-App interactive software). The committee also requires a current GMAT score, results of the TOEFL exam (if applicable), official transcripts from each university previously attended, a work history form, essays, a resume, and two letters of recommendation. Each of these items is important to the admission committee and, therefore, an application cannot be reviewed until all documents have arrived.

Finances

The annual full-time M.B.A. tuition at Olin for the 2000–01 year is $27,000.

M.B.A. students should also expect to spend between $625 and $800 per month on room and board and an additional $1850 per year on books and supplies. Olin also recommends that students expect to pay an additional $3500 per year for miscellaneous expenses such as health insurance and travel. There are several financial aid options available to Olin M.B.A. students. Federal and University loan programs are need-based awards granted to U.S. students (or international students with U.S.-based cosigners). Merit-based fellowships and scholarships that recognize superior academic or professional accomplishment are available to all students. Applicants are automatically considered for merit-based awards once an admission application has been submitted and is complete. Merit-based awards can range from a partial scholarship to a full-tuition fellowship, such as the Wood Leadership Fellows program. A full-time financial aid officer is available to assist M.B.A. students in finding the necessary resources.

Application Facts and Dates

There are five separate deadlines for applying to the full-time M.B.A. program at Olin, with the first falling in mid-December and the fifth on May 1. Students who meet any of the deadlines receive their decision according to the schedule posted on the Olin M.B.A. Web site. All admission-related questions or requests can be directed to:

Pamela K. Wiese
Director of Admissions and Financial Aid
Olin School of Business
Washington University in St. Louis
Campus Box 1133
One Brookings Drive
St. Louis, Missouri 63130-4899
Telephone: 314-935-7301
Fax: 314-935-6309
E-mail: mba@olin.wustl.edu
World Wide Web: http://www.olin.wustl.edu/

WAYNE STATE UNIVERSITY — Wayne State University

Detroit, Michigan

THE WAYNE STATE M.B.A.—A PROGRAM FOR YOUR FUTURE

▶ *The M.B.A. program at Wayne State University is one of the oldest in the United States and, we believe, one of the finest. The School has assembled graduate faculty members who publish regularly in their discipline's most prestigious journals and who are dedicated to the highest teaching standards. The excellent academic credentials and impressive professional backgrounds of the students in the M.B.A. program serve not only to attract and retain our fine faculty but also to enrich the educational experience in the program through the insights they bring to the classroom.*

The faculty and staff members of the School of Business Administration have worked hard to make the graduate study of business an enjoyable and exciting experience for our M.B.A. students. Thank you for taking a closer look!

—Harvey Kahalas, Dean

Programs and Curricular Focus

The accelerated Master of Business Administration (M.B.A.) program at Wayne State University is designed to incorporate the fluid nature of business and industry in the twenty-first century. By emphasizing functional and conceptual knowledge, the comprehensive, high-impact M.B.A. program prepares individuals for successful careers in business, government, and other types of organizations. It is intended to prepare men and women for leadership and management positions in business, government, and other types of organizations. The core and elective requirements for the program consist of 36 semester hours of study (twelve courses). Applicants with a baccalaureate degree in business administration usually meet all of the program's foundation requirements. Applicants with baccalaureate degrees in fields other than business administration may have to complete certain foundation requirements in the following areas: accounting, economics, finance, management, management information systems, marketing, mathematics, production management, and statistics. Special accelerated foundation courses have been developed to help entering M.B.A. students to meet these requirements.

In addition to taking six core courses, the M.B.A. student may select from an extensive number of elective courses in accounting, business economics, finance, industrial relations, international business, management and organization behavior, management information systems, marketing, personnel/human resources management, quality management, and taxation. Graduate-level courses in other schools and colleges of the University may also be elected with special approval of the M.B.A. program director. Students interested in pursuing a J.D./M.B.A. should contact an adviser in the Office of Student Services.

The academic year is divided into two 15-week semesters and a split spring/summer semester; a full schedule of graduate courses is offered each term. Courses are taught in convenient suburban locations as well as on campus.

Students and the M.B.A. Experience

Wayne State M.B.A. students bring cross-cultural diversity and a broad range of employment experiences to the program. More than 93 percent of the students are employed full- or part-time, with an average of three years of work experience. Half of the M.B.A. students hold supervisory positions within their corporations.

The average student is 27 years old, with women making up 36 percent of the student base. International students comprise 5 percent of the M.B.A. population, bringing to the program valued input on business in their regions of the world.

Students in the Wayne State M.B.A. program find its strength to be the real-world experience their peers bring to classroom discussions and projects, combined with relevant business theory presented by the faculty. While 55 percent of current M.B.A. students hold undergraduate degrees in business, the remaining half are made up of engineering, liberal arts, fine arts, and science graduates.

The Faculty

Faculty members of Wayne State's School of Business Administration are recruited from the finest graduate programs both in America and abroad, and the excellent quality of both the graduate and undergraduate students has proven to be a powerful force in retaining this talented group. The business school faculty members publish more than 200 books, journal articles, and scholarly papers each year. They are regular contributors to the finest academic journals in the business disciplines.

In addition, the School is proud of the energetic group of business executives who teach as adjunct faculty members in the M.B.A. program. These experienced professional managers are consistently well-received by their graduate students.

The Business School Network

Corporate Partnerships

Among the strong partnerships that have been established between the School of Business Administration and prominent local and international corporations are relationships with ANR Pipeline Company, Comerica, EDS, Federal Mogul, Ford Motor Company, and Kmart Corporation.

Prominent Alumni

The School of Business Administration at Wayne State University counts among its alumni a number of notable business leaders, including Victor J. Fryling, President, CMS Energy Corporation, and Vice President, Consumers Power Company; Dennis O. Green, Chief Auditor, Citicorp and Citibank, N.A.; Eric Mittelstadt, President and CEO, GMFanuc Robotics Corporation; and Anne

Regling, Executive Vice President, Operations, Children's Hospital of Michigan.

The College and Environs

Tracing its origins to 1868, Wayne State occupies a 203-acre campus that is graced by open courtyards and malls and whose 94 buildings represent a blend of traditional and ultramodern architecture. The modern University campus is a distinctive element in Detroit's expansive cultural center, which includes the Fisher Theater, Detroit Institute of Arts, Historical Museum, Science Center, Public Library, and four University Theaters. Also near the campus are the Engineering Society of Detroit, the Detroit Medical Center, the Merrill Palmer Institute, and the General Motors World Headquarters. Detroit and southeastern Michigan provide extensive opportunities for study, research, cultural enjoyment, and employment.

Facilities

Wayne State, with three mainframe computers, operates one of the largest computing centers in the Detroit area. Links with MichNet provide users with access to the Internet (NSFNET), SprintNet, AutoNet, and Datapac networks. The University is also linked to the BITNET academic network. The total system is available 24 hours a day.

Currently, 300 terminals and 128 dial-up lines are available for student use. Students use terminals and microcomputers in the School's six microcomputer classrooms and laboratories as an integral part of many graduate courses.

Wayne State University is the host institution for Detroit Area Library Network (DALNET), made up of twelve local libraries. Through computer terminals in the libraries, users can access more than 7.8 million volumes, representing the majority of holdings in the area's educational institutions.

Placement

Working together with the School of Business Administration, the WSU Placement Office regularly places M.B.A. students in permanent positions locally, nationally, and internationally. The School of Business Administration annually offers a Career Day, providing students with an opportunity to meet recruiters from dozens of national and international manufacturing and service corporations; "How to Prepare for Your Business Career" is an annual conference for students interested in learning where to find the best jobs; and the M.B.A. Student Association publishes a resume book for annual corporate distribution. The University's Placement Reference Center offers information on major corporations, job searching, interviewing, and resume writing.

Admission

Admission to the Master of Business Administration program is open to students who have a baccalaureate degree in any discipline from a regionally accredited institution and who demonstrate high promise of success in the graduate study of business. A minimum 2.5 overall undergraduate honor point average (HPA) or 2.75 honor point average in the last half of the undergraduate program is required. In addition, a minimum GMAT score of 450 is required. No decision regarding a student's admission will be made without the GMAT results.

International students must have completed an appropriate four-year university-level program and, in addition to the above requirements, achieve a minimum score of 550 on the Test of English as a Foreign Language (TOEFL) or a score of at least 95 on the Michigan English Language Assessment Battery (MELAB).

Finances

The Office of Scholarships and Financial Aid provides students with information regarding sources of funds. Graduate research assistantships are offered through the School's academic departments. Stipends for 2000–01 average $10,875 for nine-month appointments. University graduate and professional scholarships are also available.

Tuition per semester in 2000–01 for Michigan residents is $350–$1226 (part-time) and $1401–$2100 (full-time). Non-Michigan residents pay $775–$2709 (part-time) and $3096–$4644 (full-time).

International Students

International students constitute 5 percent of the M.B.A. student body. The International Services Office offers assistance to all students with their new surroundings. The International Business Association also offers students an opportunity to know their fellow classmates and develop international networks through special events and business functions.

Application Facts and Dates

Application deadlines for graduate admission are August 1 for the fall term, December 1 for the winter term, and April 1 for the spring/summer term. International students must provide required materials four months prior to the beginning of the term. For more information, students should address inquiries to:

Office of Student Services
School of Business Administration
Wayne State University
Detroit, Michigan 48202
Telephone: 313-577-4510
            800-910-EARN (toll-free)
Fax: 313-577-5299
World Wide Web: http://www.busadm. wayne.edu

Webber College

Babson Park, Florida

DEVELOPING BUSINESS LEADERS FOR THE TWENTY-FIRST CENTURY

Webber College's M.B.A. program is designed to utilize in-class instruction, modern information technology, team projects, and practical consulting experience to prepare its graduates for global business competition. Our commitment at Webber is to advance the business careers of our partners—the students. We believe that human development is of critical importance and that growth is nurtured by interdependence. Students are encouraged to take advantage of our close-knit, friendly environment. Interactions between faculty members and students are not the exception but the rule.

The design and delivery of our curriculum emphasizes action rather than lecture. We make use of live cases, not just paper cases. The focus fosters team building, imagination, and innovation as students learn to apply conceptual theory to real-life situations. Leadership, entrepreneurship, ethics, communication, and global perspective are interwoven in our interdisciplinary curriculum.

—Dr. Nikos Orphanoudakis, Dean

Programs and Curricular Focus

The Webber College Graduate School of Business offers a unique nineteen-month, full-time program leading to a Master of Business Administration with an option in management or accounting. The degree consists of 36 credit hours, with courses offered one night a week over 6 ten-week periods. The College is accredited by the Southern Association of Colleges and Schools.

The Webber M.B.A. aims to assist students in enhancing their managerial skills through the delivery of techniques and best practices that integrate academic theory with contemporary applications. The program places a premium level of focus on developing students' critical-thinking skills so that they may more easily adapt to paradigm shifts within business.

The Webber College Graduate School of Business offers an M.B.A. program that focuses on the interdisciplinary nature of business practices. The program capitalizes on the faculty's ability to focus on proven traditional methods of teaching that integrate the various facets of effective business administration, while utilizing information technology to enhance problem-solving skills.

Through the practicum course(s), students undertake group-based consulting projects that give them the opportunity to test theoretical concepts in an applied setting.

Students and the MBA Experience

The Graduate School of Business is small in size, with approximately 35 graduate students. These small class sizes provide ample opportunity for students to exchange ideas with other students and interact closely with the faculty.

The students are distinguished by the diversity of their professional and ethnic backgrounds. The average age of the students in the M.B.A. program is 27, and approximately 90 percent of the class have had one year or more of professional, full-time employment experience. Students come from several states as well as several different countries. More than one third are women, and approximately 90 percent are employed full- or part-time.

The Faculty

The Webber College Graduate School of Business faculty members bring both professional and academic expertise to the classroom. The faculty members are distinguished in their fields and are dedicated to teaching.

The Webber College Graduate School of Business emphasizes strong faculty-student interaction, indicated by the small class size and the nature of the course work.

The Business School Network

Webber College has developed strong ties with the business community. Webber's proximity to Orlando is an asset for the M.B.A. program.

The Graduate School of Business is counseled by the Business Advisory Board. The board is composed of a group of business professionals who provide faculty members with advice on curricula and updated information on industry

needs and trends, as well as provide students with field experience opportunities.

In addition to the Business Advisory Board, the Graduate School is a member of several Chambers of Commerce in the area that, together with local businesses, provide the opportunity for students to apply and test theoretical concepts through consulting activities with the practicum.

The College and Environs

Webber College was founded in 1927 by Grace Knight and Roger W. Babson as a women's college, with the exclusive purpose of teaching women about business. It was the first school chartered under the educational and charitable laws of the state of Florida as a nonprofit organization. In September 1971, the first men were admitted to the College. The Graduate School of Business was established in September 1997 and granted its first degrees in February 1999.

Webber College is a small college with a total student body of approximately 450. The small size aids the students in getting to know the president as well as the faculty and staff members. It is located on a beautiful 110-acre campus along the shoreline of Lake Caloosa, approximately 45 minutes south of Orlando. The town of Babson Park, a small, rural residential community, is located in the heart of Florida's citrus county near a chain of freshwater lakes. Babson Park is conveniently located near many major recreational facilities and national tourist attractions in central Florida.

Facilities

The Roger Babson Learning Center, located in the central part of the campus, is a modern and comprehensive library facility that contains extensive collections of reference, research, and reserve materials keyed to business research. The center also offers access to several external data sources, such as EbscoHost, LEXIS-NEXIS Academic Universe, LIRN-Library, and several others.

The computer resource center is a data processing center and teaching facility whose microcomputers offer the latest modern technology for developing student excellence in business, communication, and creativity.

Placement

Webber College's career services professionals are available to advise and assist students in developing and attaining their career goals. Career management services available to M.B.A. students include an annual career day, a career expo, on-campus recruiting, an alumni database, career information and advising, a resume book, and seminars and interviews throughout the year by employment recruiters on campus.

While career services are available to all students, international students should be aware that job opportunities in the United States are limited by the type of visa they hold.

Admission

Men and women with baccalaureate degrees from regionally accredited

colleges or universities are eligible for consideration for admission. Admission to the Graduate School of Business is based on both quantitative and qualitative criteria. In addition to the application, the applicant must submit a resume, an essay, and a list of references. Academic qualifications are determined by evaluation of student performance at previous higher education institutions, and the GMAT may be required. In addition, international applicants are required to submit results from the TOEFL, unless they have obtained a degree from a college or university where English is the language of instruction.

Finances

The tuition for the 2000–01 academic year is $285 per credit hour. Book expenses vary by course.

On-campus housing is available to graduate students. Housing costs range from $665 to $730 per ten-week term. A meal plan is available for $530 per ten-week term.

Financial aid is available in the form of student loans for eligible students. In addition, many employers provide for, or subsidize, their employees' tuition expenses. For more information, students should contact the financial aid office (863-638-2929).

Application Facts and Dates

The standard academic year for the full-time M.B.A. program begins in late August and ends in late July. Options for other times of enrollment are also available. Applications are considered on a first-come, first-served basis. Applications may be obtained by mail or downloaded from the School's Web site. For additional information or questions regarding the Webber College Graduate School of Business, students should contact:

M.B.A. Coordinator
Graduate School of Business
Webber College
1201 North Scenic Highway
P.O. Box 96
Babson Park, Florida 33827-0096
Telephone: 863-638-2927
Fax: 863-638-2823
E-mail: mba@webber.edu
World Wide Web:
    http://www.webber.edu

Whitworth College

Whitworth Graduate School of International Management

Spokane, Washington

A SOLID FOUNDATION FOR GLOBAL OPPORTUNITIES

As we approach the ten-year anniversary for the Graduate School of International Management, we take great pride in the achievements of our hundreds of graduates who have accepted challenging positions in companies throughout the world. International business and global service organizations are expanding their operations dramatically and are regularly calling for our Master of International Management (M.I.M.) students. The M.I.M. degree provides students a business administration foundation with the advantages of proficiency in foreign language(s), international studies, and cross-cultural communication. M.I.M. graduates are able candidates for management positions in international marketing, strategic planning, export/import trade, project management, economic development, and Christian missions.

Using our second major federal grant in international business education, Whitworth's M.I.M. students are being linked electronically with classmates in European universities completing course projects as members of transoceanic teams. Ties with the Spokane Intercollegiate Research and Technology Institute (SIRTI) afford students the opportunity for paid internships in major technology commercialization initiatives. The curriculum has grown to include more studies in business law, E-commerce and technology management. Join with professionals from every continent who have chosen the Whitworth Graduate School of International Management.

—Dr. Dan C. Sanford, Director

Programs and Curricular Focus

The Whitworth Graduate School of International Management offers a course of study leading to the Master of International Management (M.I.M.) degree for recent college graduates and returning professionals. The M.I.M. curriculum is tailored to meet the needs of progressive organizations under the guidance of an advisory board of business and nonprofit organizational leaders.

Six elements of the curriculum make this program unique: a focus on cross-cultural competency, a foreign language component with business emphasis, instruction that stresses the role of Christian ethics and evaluates the value systems that may guide managers in decision making, internship and project opportunities that provide practical responses to business needs, team-based education that is both academic and experiential, and Internet enhancement of classroom learning. Most classes are taught in the evenings to attract active business professionals into the cohort.

Students may earn the 37-credit degree in fifteen consecutive months, or they may choose to take up to six years to complete the degree. Core classes are typically offered during the fall and spring terms, while internships, projects, and elective courses are usually completed during the summer and

second fall term. Students emphasizing non-profit or Christian service careers are guided by advisers in the choice of courses and research projects to best meet these goals. This degree is accredited by the Northwest Association of Schools and Colleges.

Students and the M.I.M. Experience

M.I.M. students bring business perspectives from richly diverse cultural and professional backgrounds. Countries represented include New Zealand, Japan, China, Taiwan, Korea, Kazakhstan, Russia, Pakistan, India, Kenya, Colombia, Mexico, Brazil, England, Nigeria, Ukraine, Austria, and the Netherlands. Students' professional backgrounds before entrance vary widely and include careers in the computer industry, banking, economic development, public utilities, urban planning, rural development, medicine, education, defense, and many other service industries. The median age of M.I.M. students is 32, with an average work experience of nine years. Approximately 40 percent of M.I.M. students are women, and 40 percent are international students. The diversity of backgrounds represented in each cohort group greatly enhances the learning process. Students frequently work together on multicultural teams, preparing projects and case studies. Graduates

from this program develop valuable skills in cross-cultural communications. A strong esprit de corps often develops among cohort groups, and some students finish the program with lifelong friendships formed.

Special Features

For students from disciplines that have not prepared students with the prerequisite course work, the M.I.M. program offers accelerated workshops in accounting, management, microeconomics and macroeconomics in late summer and early fall. Students may be admitted conditionally until prerequisite course work is completed. Later in the year, interested students may be introduced to Advisory Board members, who can serve as mentors, or attend workshops and special guest lectures by business leaders to assist with networking and career planning. Students are invited to join faculty members at trade council and Chamber of Commerce meetings. The Graduate School connects

FACULTY LIST

Faculty
John A. Falvey, Ph.D., Union (Ohio). International negotiations and dispute resolution, management for a global market, organizational behavior.
Susan Mabry, Ph.D., California, Irvine. Management technology.
Dan C. Sanford, Ph.D., Denver. Graduate School Director. East Asian studies, political environments.
Richard Schatz, Ph.D., Hawaii. International trade and finance, economic development.

Adjunct Faculty
Milton A. Cole, M.I.M., Thunderbird. Entrepreneurship and advanced applications in international management.
Bob Loomis, J.D., Gonzaga. International transactional law.
Marlene Niemeier, M.I.M., Whitworth. Ethical issues in international management.
Thomas Pitzer, M.S., Purdue. International marketing; survey of accounting, finance, and project appraisal.

Language Instructors
Chinese, Jianshe Liu. French, Michel Campbell. German, Christa Richardson. Japanese, Shoko Yano. Russian, Alexandra Lyssak. Spanish, Carmen Feliz. Language Coordinator, Karla Sammons.

Students meet the world at Whitworth.

with overseas study centers in Maastrict, Netherlands, and Seoul, Korea, where students may be hosted for one semester. Some classes offer students the opportunity to form teams electronically with students in foreign universities.

The Faculty

M.I.M. graduate faculty members are active in the field of international management studies and bring practical cross-cultural experience to the classroom. In addition to faculty members who hold direct appointments in the graduate school, instruction is also provided by regular adjunct professors carefully selected from the international business community. An excellent faculty member–student ratio permits many opportunities for the exchange of ideas outside of class hours and plenty of individual time with faculty members for advising.

The Business School Network

The Graduate School is strategically aligned with the Spokane Intercollegiate Research and Technology Institute (SIRTI). SIRTI unites higher education, government, and business and industry to help the region gain a competitive edge in the global economy. As part of this alliance, M.I.M. students may work with start-up high-tech businesses or conduct market studies for the commercialization of technology-based products. By participating in associations such as the International Trade Alliance, the Washington China Relations Council, and the Inland Northwest World Trade Council, students have hands-on learning about the dynamic world of international business.

The College and Environs

Whitworth College is a private liberal arts university affiliated with the Presbyterian (U.S.A.) Church. Whitworth's 200-acre campus is located 6 miles north of downtown Spokane in a beautiful setting of tall

pine trees and broad lawns. With an undergraduate class of 1,700 and 500 graduate students, total enrollment is approximately 2,200. M.I.M. courses are offered on the Whitworth campus and at SIRTI in downtown Spokane. Spokane, Washington, a metropolitan city with a population of 360,000, is a commercial and cultural center for more than a million people. Located in one of America's leading export states, Spokane is a major inland port for minerals, lumber, and agricultural products. Spokane has recently seen significant growth in the electronics and computer hardware and software industries. Spokane is located in the heart of the majestic Inland Northwest, just a 4-hour drive east of Seattle, Washington, and 5 hours south of Calgary, Alberta, Canada.

Technology Environment

Whitworth has four student computer labs available in its new library. The labs feature both IBM and Macintosh computers. All computers are networked and provide full access to the Internet. Residence halls are wired with network ports in every room, and remote access is available for off-campus students. The campus has an integrated library search capability through the Internet. Graduate classes may be designed around student chat rooms and online coaching by faculty.

Placement

A special department of the Graduate School offers assistance in internship placement and final project development. Internships and projects allow students to apply their management skills in ways that often lead directly to career opportunities in international business. Students present the results of their projects to a final faculty review panel. Select job postings and career opportunity announcements are available through e-mail, the M.I.M. student newsletter, and bulletin boards. There are occasional visits to the

campus by selected international business employers for the purpose of employment interviews. Students may request inclusion in the school's annual flyer featuring graduates who are seeking employment.

Admission

The M.I.M. program accepts applications from individuals with a bachelor's degree from an accredited college or university regardless of undergraduate field of study. Prerequisites include microeconomics, macroeconomics, principles of management, and principles of accounting (may be fulfilled through the special, accelerated workshops scheduled during late summer and early fall). The equivalent of one year of foreign language is desired. Students may study beginning foreign language in the fall term, but beginning-level classes do not apply toward the M.I.M. degree. Applicants should submit the M.I.M. application for admission, two recommendations (from professors or work supervisors), a one-page essay related to academic and career goals, a resume, official GRE or GMAT scores, official undergraduate transcripts, and a nonrefundable application fee. The Graduate School prefers applicants with at least five years of professional work experience. A minimum TOEFL score of 550 (213 on the computer-based test) is required of all applicants whose native language is not English. A minimum TWE (Test of Written English) score of 4.0 is desirable.

Finances

Tuition for the 2000–01 academic year is $365 per semester unit of credit. The estimated budget for nine months of full-time evening study at 20 credits is $16,585. This budget covers tuition, books, supplies, on-campus room and board, personal expenses (most graduate students live off-campus), transportation, medical insurance for international students, and loan fees for Stafford borrowers. Partial tuition scholarships are available through the Graduate School based on need and academic merit. M.I.M. merit scholarships are also available on a competitive basis to incoming students. The M.I.M. financial aid deadline is April 1.

Application Facts and Dates

The application deadline is March 1 for students who wish to be considered for financial aid in the fall semester. Although midyear entrance is allowed, students are strongly encouraged to begin their studies in September with their cohort peers.

Program Coordinator
Whitworth College
300 West Hawthorne Road, MS 2704
Spokane, Washington 99251-0001
Telephone: 509-777-3742
       800-929-6891 (toll-free)
Fax: 509-777-3723
E-mail: mim@whitworth.edu
World Wide Web: http://www.
   whitworth.edu/MIM/

Widener University

Chester, Pennsylvania

THE PHILOSOPHY BEHIND THE PROGRAM

The Graduate Program in Business Administration is designed to provide aspiring and practicing managers with the skills, social sensitivity, and interdisciplinary perspective needed to assume leadership roles in society. The core curriculum and electives deal equally with theoretical concepts and their practical applications. This results in a program that offers an integrated and comprehensive exposure to the knowledge believed to be of essential and lasting value to the business or institutional professional.

—Joseph A. DiAngelo Jr., Dean

Programs and Curricular Focus

Widener's School of Business Administration provides graduate and professional programs that are accredited by AACSB–The International Association for Management Education and focus on the self-paced graduate student and the special needs of the part-time student, so that Widener's commitment to taking the education of students personally is fulfilled. The program is designed to take full advantage of the working status of the majority of its students. Unlike the full-time student, the student/employee is immersed daily in the realities of organizational life. This concurrent relationship provides students with immediate opportunities to test and validate the relevancy of classroom learning. The blending of directed classroom study and daily work-related experience reinforces learning while supplementing it with the fuller understanding of how theoretical principles must be modified and adapted to fit particular environments.

The curriculum consists of a core program comprising key elements of economic and administrative theories that underlie managerial and entrepreneurial activity and advanced courses in functional areas. The core program includes course work in accounting; economic analysis; finance; marketing; operations of technology; quantitative methods and behavioral aspects of management; social, ethical, and global issues; and strategic management. Elective course work is available in accounting, economics, finance, human resources, international business, marketing, management information systems, and taxation.

Graduate transfer credit must be approved by the dean of the School of Business Administration and may be permitted subject to various restrictions.

The specific degree programs that are offered are the Master of Business Administration (M.B.A.); the Saturday M.B.A.; the M.B.A./CFP® track; the Master of Business Administration, Health and Medical Services Administration (M.B.A./HMSA); Master of Health Administration (M.H.A.); Master of Science in Accounting Information Systems (M.S.A.I.S.); Master of Science in Information Systems (M.S.I.S.); Master of Science in Juman Resource Management (M.S.H.R.M.); and Master of Science in taxation/CFP® track. Dual-degree programs offered are the J.D./M.B.A. in conjunction with the School of Law; M.E./M.B.A. with the School of Engineering; B.S./M.B.A. and B.S./M.S. through the School of Business Administration's undergraduate and graduate programs; Psy.D./M.B.A.(HMSA), Psy.D./M.H.A., Psy.D./M.B.A., and Psy.D./M.S.H.R. with Graduate Clinical Psychology; and M.D./M.H.A. and M.D./M.B.A.(HMSA) in conjunction with Jefferson Medical College of Thomas Jefferson University.

Widener also offers a Master of Public Administration degree program in the College of Arts and Sciences and, through the School of Law, LL.M. programs in corporate law and finance and health law. Widener is a university alliance member of SAP, allowing Widener to incorporate the latest technologies into the curriculum.

Students and the M.B.A. Experience

More than 600 students, mostly in their late twenties or early thirties, are currently enrolled in a Widener part-time evening graduate business program. Classes are conveniently held in the evening between 6:30 and 9:30 and are also available on Saturdays in a seminar format. Some students choose to take as many as three courses, which is considered a full-time program. While attending Widener, most are fully employed in a cross section of business environments, from small to large in size, encompassing manufacturing, the service industries, government, and nonprofit organizations.

❖ Global Focus

A senior executive from an international corporation has a two-year appointment as the School of Business Administration's Executive in Residence. The Executive in Residence maintains an office on campus and teaches courses. Students have the opportunity to meet with the Executive in Residence on a one-on-one basis during office hours.

Widener University is located on a 100-acre suburban campus. The eighty-five buildings include a mixture of modern and Victorian architecture.

Special Features

Learning by experience is incorporated into the programs in several ways. Some of the programs require clerkships, management and career development seminars, and residency experience. These are designed as vehicles to gain actual on-the-job learning and integration of academic theory with practice. Students are also invited to attend the banking and finance lecture series and the Nobel Laureate lecture series.

The Faculty

The unique blend of faculty talents combines state-of-the-art education with doctorally prepared as well as industry- and public administration–experienced professionals. The primary interest of each faculty member is teaching while simultaneously developing his or her own potential through ongoing research. Teaching style focuses not only on theory but also on the practical application of this material in the workplace. Widener is proud of its mandate as a teaching institution, featuring personal attention for each student at both the undergraduate and graduate level.

The Business School Network

Widener M.B.A. students are employed by such companies and organizations as Aetna U.S. Healthcare; A. I. DuPont Institute; ARCO; Arthur Andersen & Company; Bell Atlantic; Blue Cross/Blue Shield; Boeing; Campbell Soup; Chase Manhattan Bank; CIGNA; Coopers & Lybrand; Department of Defense; E. F. Hutton; General Electric; Honeywell; KPMG Peat Marwick; McNeil Lab; PECO; PFPC; PNC; RCA; QVC; SAP; SmithKline Beecham; SMS; Springfield School District; State of Delaware; Texaco; Upjohn; Vanguard; Xerox; and Zeneca.

The College and Environs

Widener University is recognized nationally and internationally as a distinguished private educational institution. An accredited university chartered in Pennsylvania and Delaware, Widener is today a three-campus university offering programs of study leading to associate, baccalaureate, master's, or doctoral degrees.

Founded in Wilmington, Delaware, in 1821, the University is composed of eight schools and colleges that offer liberal arts and sciences, professional, and preprofessional curricula. The University's schools include the College of Arts and Sciences, the School of Engineering, the School of Hospitality Management, the School of Human Service Professions, the School of Business Administration, the School of Nursing, the School of Law, and University College.

Facilities

Graduate business students may take advantage of the variety of facilities and services offered on both the main (Chester, Pennsylvania) campus and the Delaware Campus. Classes average fewer than 25 students each in Kapelski Learning Center or Academic Center North on the main campus and in Polishook Hall on the Delaware Campus.

Libraries are equipped with online computer indexing and personal computer labs for class or individual use.

Bookstores, accessible parking, and evening advisers are available on both campuses.

Placement

Graduate advisers are present each evening to help merge career goals with programs offered. To assist those who are relocating in the job market, there is a professionally staffed Career Advising and Placement Service (CAPS) on the main campus.

Admission

Admission to any of the graduate business programs involves completing the application and paying the nonrefundable application fee, submitting two letters of recommendation, and possessing a bachelor's degree. In addition, various programs require GMAT, GRE, or MAT scores, and the M.S. degree programs in taxation and accounting require the GMAT or documentation of CPA, CIA, or CMA certification. International students from non-English-speaking countries must take the Test of English as a Foreign Language (TOEFL).

Finances

For the 2000–01 academic year, students in the M.B.A. programs paid a tuition fee of $520 per credit. A limited number of graduate assistantships are available for full-time students (up to three courses per semester). Graduate assistants aid the faculty in research projects and work approximately 20 hours per week. Assistantships are awarded to students on campus. Assistantships are compensated by a stipend and tuition remission for up to three courses.

Application Facts and Dates

Applications must be received for fall semester entrance by July 1, spring semester by December 1, and for the summer semester by April 1. Applications from international students must be received two months prior to the dates given.

For more information, students should contact:

Graduate Programs
School of Business Administration
Widener University
One University Place
Chester, Pennsylvania 19013
Telephone: 610-499-4305
Fax: 610-499-4615
E-mail: gradbus.advise@widener.edu
World Wide Web: http://www.widener.edu

Wilfrid Laurier University

School of Business and Economics

Waterloo, Ontario, Canada

CHANGING THE FACE OF BUSINESS

The speed of innovation, competitiveness, and technical complexity in all business sectors has increased dramatically. A business education cannot guarantee success in this new world. Nothing can. But obtaining a solid grounding in the functional business disciplines and mixing this with case studies, simulations, and real business activities can make a big difference. At Laurier, we seek to develop leaders. The programs emphasize strategic thinking and problem solving. The Laurier experience encourages teamwork, enthusiasm, innovation, and competitiveness.

Laurier School of Business and Economics is a vibrant and dynamic school. The face of business is rapidly changing and we prepare our graduates for leadership positions to ensure that those changes become opportunities.

—A. Scott Carson, Ph.D., Dean

Programs and Curricular Focus

The Laurier M.B.A. programs stress the skills and abilities required to take effective action and to develop managers who know about management. Central to this philosophy is the belief that management must be problem solving and opportunity centered. While it is essential that managers know the theories and concepts of management, it is in handling the real challenges that businesses face that contributions are measured.

The learning environment at Laurier enables students to develop the skills needed to be effective decision makers. The presentation and defense of students' ideas, the exchange of ideas, and the critical evaluation by their peers form an important part of the classroom process.

Four M.B.A. programs are offered at Laurier: full-time on campus, part-time on campus, and two weekend-format programs in Toronto. They provide a broad overview of the major areas of business activities and consist of ten required half-credit courses, eight half-credit elective courses, and two research credits.

The core component of the full-time program is delivered in an integrated format. The program begins in mid-August and continues for twelve months.

The part-time program, offered through late afternoon and evening courses, normally consists of two courses per term for three terms per year. The program takes approximately three years and one term to complete.

The Toronto programs are offered Friday evenings and all day Saturdays on alternate weekends over a ten-term period. The academic cycle begins in early spring. A break is scheduled during the summer and from mid-December to January.

One of the Toronto programs developed in partnership with CMA Canada-Ontario is a combined M.B.A. and CMA designation. In this format, M.B.A. students can acquire both the degree and a certified management designation at the same time. This program was launched in April 2000.

Laurier's School of Business and Economics also offers an M.A. in business economics that prepares economists for a career in the private or public sector.

Students and the M.B.A. Experience

The Laurier M.B.A. program is one of the most innovative in Canada. Students offer a diverse range of academic and employment backgrounds. International students make up fifteen percent of the student body. Women comprise more than one third of the class. The average student age is 33, and all enter with successful track records in their work and technical backgrounds in their chosen fields.

❖ Global Focus

Students have the opportunity to be involved in projects that prepare them to manage in the complexities of the global marketplace. Optional International Study Tours offer an opportunity to combine field study with in-class components. Prior to the field-study component, students conduct background research into a country's economic, regulatory, and political environments. The experience culminates in a two-week international excursion to the region under investigation.

Special Features

Recognizing a need for innovation in business education programming, Laurier initiated Canada's first one-year M.B.A. program in 1986. The resulting integrative approach emulates the multidimensional nature of the business world. The part-time programs allow participants to enjoy the convenience of attending classes without disrupting work or family life.

The Faculty

Faculty members at Laurier are committed to the interplay between teaching and research. The combination of current research and innovative teaching provides Laurier Business and Economics students with an engaging, dynamic environment that stimulates learning. It also provides industry partners with valuable competitive intelligence.

Laurier has one of the largest business and economics faculties in Canada and, with the establishment of specialized chairs, Laurier offers tremendous breadth and depth in research and teaching expertise. More than 125 full- and part-time faculty members publish and consult worldwide, bringing industry experience and a global perspective to the classroom. This strongly positions students for future business endeavours and teaches them to capitalize on new, relevant, and late-breaking business trends.

The Business School Network

Strong ties have been developed between Laurier and the corporate community. Whether through research centres, an Integrated Case Exercise, a Speaker Series, the MBA Industry Dinner, or the

Dr. Hugh Munro, M.B.A. Director, in discussion with a group of students.

Laurier Business Leader of the Year Award, Laurier provides students with opportunities to connect and build relationships with local, national, and international business leaders.

Students take advantage of the University's connections and partnerships when choosing applied research projects. For example, the Applied Business Research initiative provides students with an opportunity to apply the techniques they have learned in the classroom to solve practical strategic management issues. Students work in teams on a live consulting project that matches their skills and interests to a corporate client. Staff support is provided to assign the teams to their projects.

The Laurier Institute offers customized management development programs, open-enrollment certificate courses, and case competitions. The Institute also provides case materials for academic purposes.

The College and Environs

Laurier has an ideal location in the hub of Canada's Technology Triangle, one of the most prosperous areas in the country, and just one hour west of metropolitan Toronto. Laurier's main campus is located in the city of Waterloo in the province of Ontario, Canada. The twin cities of Kitchener-Waterloo, with a combined population of approximately 300,000, are located 112 kilometers west of Toronto and 128 kilometers northwest of Niagara Falls. Residents of the region of Waterloo enjoy a rich cultural heritage, industry, and a high quality of life. Laurier's Toronto M.B.A. programs are presented at the Corporate Seminar Centre, 130 Adelaide Street West (at the corner of York and Adelaide), 34th floor.

Established in 1910 as Waterloo Lutheran Seminary, the institution later became known as Waterloo Lutheran University. In 1973, Wilfrid Laurier University became one of Ontario's provincially funded universities.

Technology Environment

First-class computing facilities are provided through a voluntary student-funded organization. All labs are equipped with Pentium computers and have Internet access. The School also provides notebook computers for overnight/weekend sign out. Through corporate assistance, an extensive upgrading of all classroom facilities within Laurier's School of Business and Economics has resulted in full multimedia capabilities.

Placement

Career Services provides assistance to all students both on an individual and group basis. The services are part of students' activities from their first term through graduation and beyond (with the Alumni Referral Service). A graduate student employment adviser works directly with the graduate students to provide one-on-one and group assistance. The adviser also helps market Laurier's M.B.A. graduates to prospective employers.

Throughout the academic year, Career Services workshops are offered on a regular basis on topics such as resume writing, job search techniques, networking, and informational interviewing. Programs and special events are scheduled throughout the academic year. These include an annual M.B.A. Fair and Employer Information Sessions. Each fall and winter semester, representatives from business, industry, government, and social services visit the campus to interview students for permanent employment available following graduation. Job postings, application deadlines, and interview dates are posted in Career Services. Many small and medium-sized companies as well as large corporations take advantage of the popular service.

Admission

Admission to the M.B.A. program is competitive and is based on the following criteria: a recognized undergraduate degree (or its equivalent), a minimum B average in the final year of study (73 percent, a 3.0 GPA, or second class honours); a minimum GMAT score of 550; full-time work experience (two years

or its equivalent); and three letters of reference (normally one academic and two professional). Applicants whose language of instruction during the undergraduate degree was not English must furnish evidence of proficiency in English. A minimum score of 213 on the computer-based TOEFL exam, or its equivalent, is required.

Finances

Tuition for the 1999–2000 academic year for Canadian full-time M.B.A. students was Can$8000 for the entire program; part-time students paid Can$1041 per term for each of the ten terms. International students paid Can$13,155 for the full-time program. Fees, books, case materials, and supplies were approximately Can$2560 per year for full-time students and Can$1500 per year for part-time students.

The total tuition for Laurier's Toronto M.B.A. program is currently Can$25,000, with an additional material and services fee that ranges between Can$4000 and Can$6000 for the total program. The total tuition for Laurier's Toronto M.B.A.-CMA program is currently Can$30,000, with an additional material and services fee that ranges between Can$6500 and Can$8500 for the total program. Fees are payable on an installment basis, three times per year.

Financial assistance is available to qualified applicants.

Application Facts and Dates

Applications for the full- and part-time on-campus programs are considered for the fall term only. Students are encouraged to submit a completed application early in the year in order to be considered for the first round of offers. The final date to apply is in early May. Applications for the Toronto-based programs should be received by mid-February for a spring start.

For further information, students should contact:

Marketing Assistant
School of Business and Economics
Wilfrid Laurier University
75 University Avenue, West
Waterloo, Ontario N2L 3C5
Canada
Telephone: 519-884-0710 Ext. 6220
Fax: 519-883-4044
E-mail: wlumba@wlu.ca
World Wide Web: http://www.wlu.ca/~wwwsbe

Willamette University

Salem, Oregon

A QUALITY LEARNING EXPERIENCE

The education and professional development of Atkinson students are the top priority of the Atkinson faculty and staff.

Our focus on teaching, integration, and the practical application of knowledge builds the perspective, experience, and decision-making skills needed for successful managerial careers, and our collegial atmosphere helps students develop the confidence and team skills of successful managers.

Our learning environment has already earned national recognition for the Atkinson School, and we remain firmly committed to providing a distinctive graduate management education—an education that offers the strategic benefits of professional growth, real-world experience, and confidence to meet the managerial challenges of today and tomorrow.

—Bryan M. Johnston, Dean

Programs and Curricular Focus

The Atkinson School M.B.A. for Business, Government, and Not-for-Profit Management prepares students for management careers in private and public organizations. The program enhances students' understanding of management decision making through an integrated curriculum, global perspective, and continual practical application of knowledge. The Atkinson School M.B.A. program is the only program in the U.S. accredited for both business administration (AACSB–The International Association for Management Education) and public affairs/administration (NASPAA).

The program is two academic years in length and is composed of ten core courses and ten elective courses. The balance of required and elective courses ensures a broad understanding of the functions of management and the flexibility to pursue individual career goals. Cocurricular seminars enhance teamwork, strategic career management, and communication skills.

The core curriculum is project based, experiential, cross-functional, and multisector in nature. Students learn the financial, marketing, human resources, accounting, economic, quantitative, organizational, international, and informational technology tools that support managerial decision making, and they apply what they learn through the distinctive PaCE Project, in which teams of students create and operate a real organization.

The elective curriculum provides the opportunity to pursue specific career interests in such areas as accounting, finance, general management, human resources, information technology, international management, marketing, organizational analysis, public management, and quantitative analysis/management science.

Teaching methods include case studies, team projects, consulting projects with organizations, group discussions, simulations, student presentations, internships, independent study/research, and lecture.

An accelerated, waiver-based M.B.A. program is available for qualified students. Willamette University also offers a four-year joint degree in law and management (J.D./M.B.A.).

Students and the M.B.A. Experience

The Atkinson student profile is characterized by a diversity of age and experience common in organizations. The average student is 26 years of age and has three years of work experience. Forty percent of the students are women, and 60 percent are men. Twenty-five percent are international students, and 8 percent are members of minority groups. Although generally from the Western United States, students come from twenty-two states and twenty-one countries. Most Atkinson students have undergraduate degrees in social science, liberal arts, or business. Most enter the program with experience in business, government, or not-for-profit organizations, but some enter directly after their undergraduate education.

The Atkinson School's size and exclusive focus on the master's level of study facilitates a high degree of interaction between faculty members and students. The learning environment is collegial and emphasizes teamwork and the practical application of knowledge. The program demands approximately 60 hours of academic work per week.

❖ Global Focus

The core curriculum integrates international issues of management, and the elective curriculum supports career interests in international management.

Special Features

Each year begins with Compass Week, a program of teamwork, strategic career management, academic review, and perspectives on important issues of management.

The core curriculum includes the Atkinson School PaCE Project, an extensive hands-on management project in which teams of students create a business, make a profit, close or sell the business, and then donate the profits to a local not-for-profit organization.

The Faculty

The Atkinson School faculty members are excellent teachers and nationally and internationally respected scholars. They are recipients of awards for outstanding teaching and research; leaders of professional and community organizations; authors of books, articles, software, and simulations; and consultants to business and government.

One hundred percent of the full-time faculty members have doctorates. Ninety-one percent have worked, consulted, or completed academic work internationally. Seventy-three percent have received awards for outstanding teaching/research. Eighteen percent are women.

Three endowed faculty chairs (business, public policy, and international management) provide additional resources

for faculty members to pursue teaching innovation and scholarly research.

The Business School Network

Corporate Partnerships

Interaction with leaders of business, government, and not-for-profit organizations is frequent and occurs through class projects, faculty/student consulting projects, internships, the visiting executive program, guest speakers, career services seminars, and site visits.

Prominent Alumni

The average alumnus is 39 years old and pursuing a career in small to large businesses, entrepreneurial ventures, government service, or not-for-profit organizations. Seventy percent of Atkinson alumni live and work in the Pacific Northwest. Thirty percent are located throughout the United States and internationally.

Information about titles and employers of Atkinson alumni is provided on the School's Web page and by request.

The College and Environs

Willamette University is an independent coeducational university with a total of 2,400 students enrolled in the College of Liberal Arts, College of Law, Atkinson Graduate School of Management, and the School of Education. The University was founded in 1842 and is recognized for excellence and innovation in academic and professional education. Willamette University is located in Salem, Oregon. Salem, the state capital of Oregon, is one of the most livable cities in the United States and provides easy access to the professional, cultural, and recreational resources of the Pacific Northwest.

Technology Environment

Atkinson students have 24-hour-a-day access to the computer laboratory, which provides Macintosh and IBM-compatible personal computers. A local network provides all standard word processing, spreadsheet, and graphics applications. The Internet provides access to worldwide information services and electronic mail. University library resources include books, periodicals, journals, and specialized computerized information databases, such as Academic Universe, Business Dateline, Business Index, EconLit, Wilson Business Abstracts, STAT-USA/ National Trade Data Bank, and Expanded Academic ASAP.

Placement

The Atkinson School works with employers to provide a complete program of services that connect students and alumni with employment opportunities. Career service programs help students develop strategic career management skills, improve job search skills, and obtain internships and employment. Services include workshops, internship programs, on-campus interviews, employment opportunity postings, national employment databases, individual counseling, mentoring programs, the Atkinson School Career Fair, and the Pacific Northwest M.B.A. Career Fair.

Admission

The Atkinson School welcomes applicants with diverse career objectives and experiences. Admission is based on academic ability and managerial potential. All applicants must submit an application for admission, the application fee, a personal statement of experience and professional goals, two letters of reference, official transcripts of all undergraduate and graduate course work, and official GMAT or GRE scores. International students for whom English is not the first language must also submit a TOEFL score of 550 or higher on the paper-based test or a score of 213 or higher on the computer-based test. International students must also provide documentation of funds sufficient to cover two years of educational and living expenses.

The average GMAT score is 550. The undergraduate GPA is 3.2. There are no specific prerequisite courses for admission, but students should have a solid understanding of mathematical principles and well-developed writing skills. Previous experience with economics, accounting, and personal computers (word processing and spreadsheet applications) is helpful.

Finances

Tuition for 2000–01 is $16,500. Books and supplies cost approximately $1200. Room and board expenses range from $4600 to $7050 per year, depending on personal choice of accommodations and lifestyle. Approximately 50 percent of full-time students receive merit-based scholarship assistance that ranges from 25 percent to 75 percent of tuition. Loans and work-study are available to eligible students.

Application Facts and Dates

Applications completed by March 31 receive priority consideration in admission and scholarship decisions. Applicants are notified when their application materials are received and are notified of the admission decision within three weeks after completion of the application process. For further information, students should contact:

Director of Admission
Atkinson Graduate School of
     Management
Willamette University
Salem, Oregon 97301
Telephone: 503-370-6167
Fax: 503-370-3011
E-mail: agsm-admission@willamette.
     edu
World Wide Web: http://www.
     willamette.edu/agsm/

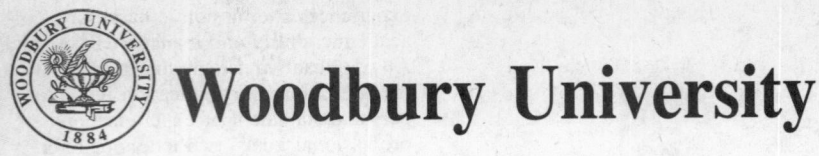

Woodbury University

School of Business and Management

Burbank, California

PREPARING BUSINESS LEADERS WITH ENTREPRENEURIAL SKILLS TO COPE WITH THE GLOBALIZATION OF BUSINESS

It has been said, "The world is like a drum; you strike it anywhere, and it resounds everywhere." This is certainly true in the world of business today. Political barriers are being erased in favor of commercial and economic flows that enhance global interaction, competition, and collaboration. The challenge for higher education is to provide our students with the entrepreneurial skills, vision, and creativity needed to lead business enterprises into the twenty-first century.

With its 117-year heritage in business education, Woodbury University has been preparing business leaders to cope with the realities of the present and to meet the challenges of the future. We are committed to preparing M.B.A. candidates with skills that support flexibility, critical thinking, and pragmatic problem solving.

—Richard King, Dean

Programs and Curricular Focus

The high quality of course work in Woodbury University's M.B.A. program is affirmed by the school's accreditation by the Association of Collegiate Business Schools and Programs (ACBSP). The courses in accounting, computer information systems, finance, international business, management, and marketing all emphasize teamwork and presentation skills. Designed primarily for those fully employed, classes are scheduled on weekends and evenings. More than 20 percent of the M.B.A. students are international and attend Woodbury's M.B.A. program full-time.

The M.B.A. curriculum has a comprehensive management core that provides

the basic foundation for understanding the various business disciplines and prepares the student for further study in general or specific interest areas. Areas of emphasis provide the opportunity for students to study more intensively according to their goals. Accounting covers major areas required for the CPA examination. Computer information systems includes systems design and development, communication networks, the Internet, and Web site development. Finance includes financial institutions, corporate finance, mergers and acquisitions, investment analysis, and capital markets. International business includes finance, economics, marketing, world business area studies, and comparative management. Management includes organizational behavior/human relations, policy studies, organizational theory, management systems, strategic planning, entrepreneurship, and strategy formulation. Marketing includes international marketing, advertising, contemporary marketing problems, and market research.

Woodbury courses are offered on the semester system. Candidates for the degree must complete 36 units or a total of twelve 3-unit courses. Students who hold undergraduate degrees in a discipline other than business may have to complete additional preparatory courses called the Common Professional Component, which may be waived through testing or work experience or taken as electives. Up to 6 units may be transferred from another accredited institution.

The program's flexibility allows for scheduling variations. A person in full-time employment typically takes two courses per term and can complete the degree in two years. Full-time students may complete the program within a year. There is no pressure, however, to conform to a particular schedule.

Students and the M.B.A. Experience

Professional men and women are drawn to the Woodbury M.B.A. program from a variety of industries in the United States and

abroad. Often sponsored by their home governments or multinational corporations, international students come to Woodbury's program from Brazil, China, Egypt, Indonesia, Chile, Nigeria, and Thailand as well as thirty other nations. Approximately 40 percent have undergraduate business degrees; the remaining 60 percent have done their undergraduate work in such fields as engineering, humanities, and the social sciences.

The Woodbury M.B.A. program does not lock candidates into one particular peer group. Instead, students get the opportunity to work with many different students as they explore each new subject area. In addition to strengthening the key business skill of team building, this structure allows an M.B.A. candidate to acquire the widest possible interaction with fellow students and professors. Class sizes are small, with an average of 18 students.

The Faculty

The Woodbury M.B.A. program augments its forward-looking orientation with faculty members who are leaders in their respective fields. A combination of full-time academics and seasoned professionals, Woodbury's M.B.A. professors have excellent academic credentials, which are complemented with current corporate executive and management experience. They come to Woodbury from the management ranks of major corporations and from entrepreneurial efforts in fields such as artificial intelligence and global management consulting, as well as from the most distinguished academic institutions, including Berkeley, Harvard, Stanford, and the Wharton School of Business.

The Business School Network

Corporate Partnerships

Ties between Woodbury's M.B.A. program and the southern California business community are strengthened by a large number of faculty members who are active participants in the day-to-day world of free enterprise. Teaching professionals come to Woodbury from such firms as The Walt Disney Company, Pacific Bell, and NASA.

Prominent Alumni

Woodbury graduates join a network of professionals who are business leaders in every part of the world—from a regional manager for a multinational oil company in Bangkok to an international banker from Mexico to an information systems director in Toronto. In Los Angeles, Woodbury alumni are found in the major accountancy firms and investment houses and in the entertainment industry, as well as in the fields of health care, information systems, and multimedia.

Alumni forums and a mentor program provide opportunities to solidify business relationships formed in the classroom.

The College and Environs

Situated in the hills of Burbank, the northernmost suburb of Los Angeles and media capital of the world, Woodbury offers students easy access to beaches, mountains, and deserts; it is within a 20-minute drive of downtown Los Angeles. Art, history, and science museums; professional sports events; and world-class entertainment are activities readily accessible to Woodbury students.

One of the largest cities in the United States, Los Angeles serves as a worldwide business and financial center. The University is linked to the international business, financial, design, and commercial communities, providing networking and career development opportunities for students who choose to take advantage of the wealth of business opportunities in southern California.

Facilities

Housed in a relaxing, cathedral-style building, Woodbury's Los Angeles Times Library provides a valuable resource for M.B.A. students to study either on campus or from wherever they may be with their personal computers. Multiple databases are available over the Internet via student passwords and offer access to more than 6,000 journals through online subscriptions, including LEXIS-NEXIS and Proquest Direct. The library houses a comprehensive collection of books, periodicals, CD-ROMs, and technical and year-end reports that are selected to meet the curricular needs of the students.

Woodbury also provides a modern online computer resource center that features sixty Windows PC and Macin-tosh computers with the latest in business and graphics software plus printers and scanners.

On-campus housing is available in two residence halls, which accommodate up to 189 students. Residential areas surrounding Woodbury also provide plenty of options for off-campus housing.

Placement

The Office of Career Services offers students individual, personal career counseling. In addition to annual career fairs and online job search facilities, the office coordinates mentor seminars, internships, job referrals, and career and resume development workshops.

Admission

M.B.A. candidates may begin study during any term. A bachelor's degree from an accredited institution and a minimum GPA of 2.5 are required for admission. Students with undergraduate degrees from institutions outside the United States may submit transcripts for individual consideration. The completed application should be submitted with a $35 fee ($50 for international students), transcripts from all colleges attended, TOEFL score (if applicable), and two letters of recommendation from professors or employers.

Finances

Tuition for the academic year 2000–01 is $595 per unit, making the tuition for the twelve-course M.B.A. program $21,420. Each semester, the University charges a services fee of $150 per semester plus the M.B.A. Association fee of $30. To approximate other costs, the University uses the California Student Aid Commission estimate of at least $9144 for two semesters for food, housing, transportation, books, and miscellaneous expenses.

Financial aid in the form of federal government subsidized and unsubsidized loans is available to U.S. citizens; international students may take out loans through private lending.

Application Facts and Dates

For applications, students may contact:

Master of Business Administration
Woodbury University
7500 Glenoaks Boulevard
Burbank, California 91510-7846
Telephone: 818-767-0888 Ext. 261
Fax: 818-767-0032
E-mail: mba@vaxb.woodbury.edu
World Wide Web: http://www.
woodbury.edu

Worcester Polytechnic Institute

THE MANAGEMENT OF TECHNOLOGY

An exciting opportunity in graduate management education is available at WPI, the nation's third-oldest private technological university. With our mission to educate students to contribute meaningfully to the management of organizations in a global, technical, and competitive environment, we prepare our graduates to address the key issues facing business today and in the future.

A New England location, small college environment, dedicated faculty, outstanding facilities, and superior record of graduates' successes make WPI one of the nation's most respected names in technology-based education.

—McRae C. Banks, Harry G. Stoddard Professor of Management and Department Head

Programs and Curricular Focus

Worcester Polytechnic Institute (WPI) offers a variety of graduate management programs focusing on the management of technology. WPI's Master of Business Administration (M.B.A.) program is a highly integrated, applications-oriented M.B.A. program. The WPI M.B.A. provides students with both the "big picture" perspective required of successful upper-level managers and the hands-on knowledge needed to meet the daily demands of the workplace. WPI's focus on the management of technology comes from the recognition that rapidly changing technology is driving the pace of business. WPI ensures that its students understand leading technology-based organizations, integrating technology into organizations, and creating new processes, products, and organizations based on technology. The program's strong emphasis on behavior skills prepares students to be leaders in any organization, and the global threads throughout the curriculum ensure that students understand the global imperative facing all businesses.

WPI's M.B.A. program features a 16-credit core of five cross-functional courses designed to give students a larger framework for understanding disciplinary material that is critical for managers in a globally competitive technological world. Core courses include interpersonal and leadership skills for technological managers, creating and implementing strategy for technological organizations, creating processes in technological organizations, business analysis for technological managers, and legal and ethical context of technological organizations. Each core course, with the exception of legal and ethical context

of technological organizations, has prerequisite requirements from within an 18-credit foundation. The purpose of the foundation is to ensure that students have a solid understanding of the basic functions carried out in organizations and of the environment in which they operate as well as an introduction to the tools used to analyze business problems. Foundation courses consist of the following nine 2-credit courses, each of which covers a major functional area of business: financial accounting, finance, organizational behavior, production/operations management, quantitative methods, principles of marketing, management information systems, economics of the firm, and domestic and global economic environment of business. Foundation-level courses are potentially waivable based on prior graduate or undergraduate course work.

The M.B.A. program also features a capstone Graduate Qualifying Project (GQP), which provides students with a hands-on, real-world opportunity to apply and enhance their classroom experience.

M.B.A. students are required to complete 12 credit hours of free elective course work, which may be taken within the Department of Management or within other academic departments at WPI. Elective concentration areas include e-commerce, management information systems, management of technology, production/operations management, technological innovation, technology marketing, and entrepreneurship. In addition, students have a 6-credit Option for Specialization, which requires 6 additional credits in a

particular functional area in combination with at least 6 credits of the free electives in the chosen area.

WPI also offers two highly specialized 30-credit Master of Science (M.S.) programs specifically designed for individuals seeking advanced academic training in a particular area. These include the M.S. in marketing and technological innovation and the M.S. in operations and information technology.

All graduate management degree programs provide internship, thesis, and independent study options. Part-time students typically complete the M.B.A. program in three to five years, dependent upon prior academic background, while full-time students may complete the M.B.A. program in as little as one year, dependent upon prior academic background. An M.S. degree program is typically completed in two to four years part-time or one year full-time.

Students and the M.B.A. Experience

Approximately 300 students are currently enrolled in WPI's graduate management programs. The majority are working professionals pursuing their degrees part-time in the evening. WPI students average eight years of prior full-time work experience when they commence their programs. Many students are practicing managers from the region's leading high-technology employers, creating a dynamic peer-to-peer educational experience as well as presenting outstanding networking opportunities. Students bring to class their experiences in the computer, electronics, biotechnology, machine tool, chemical, software, and defense industries, to name but a few, facilitating in-class discussions grounded in real-world experience.

Twenty-four countries are represented in WPI's Graduate Management Programs. Women comprise 28 percent of the student population. Students range in age from 21 to 56, with an average age of 33.

Special Features

Tailored to meet the challenges of working professionals, WPI offers full- and part-time graduate management study at its campuses in Worcester and Waltham, Massachusetts, as well as worldwide via its Advanced Distance Learning Network (ADLN).

Since 1979, WPI's Department of Management has been a leader in distance education. Courses are delivered worldwide to students on line or via individual videocassettes. Students then participate in the course via electronic means (Internet, e-mail, phone, or fax). The complete WPI M.B.A. may be earned via distance education.

The Faculty

The WPI management faculty is dedicated to academic excellence through scholarship and teaching. Faculty members approach the study of management from both theoretical and applications-oriented perspectives and use the classroom as a forum for exploring traditional management principles and practices and current management topics. Case studies, lectures, discussions, and computer simulations all contribute to a stimulating and challenging instructional program.

In addition to teaching, the Department of Management's faculty members are involved in a variety of sponsored research and consulting work. A sampling of current research includes quality control in information-handling processes, supply chain management, Latin American economic development, environmentally conscious manufacturing, management of biotechnology, strategy and new venture teams, and reengineering business education.

The Business School Network

Prominent Alumni

Numerous national and international business leaders are from the ranks of WPI alumni, including Steve Anderson, chief engineer, Neles-Jamesbury; Raymond Baker, vice president of manufacturing, Uvex Safety; Neil Buske, director of division engineering, Niagara Mohawk Power; Thomas Copp, president, Spectrum Wire; Leonard Devanna, president, Commonwealth Energy Enterprises; Robert Flaherty, first vice president for investments, Prudential Securities; Robert Foley, site operations manager, Texas Instruments; Charles Gordon, senior vice president, Swank; Ira Gregorman, vice president information systems, State Street Bank; Eric Gulliksen, vice president marketing, Koehler Manufacturing; David Holt, vice president of engineering, New England Electric; Michael Horgan, area operations manager, NYNEX; James Montagnino, North American operations manager, Data General; David Oberhauser, senior scientist, Polaroid; and David White, president, R. H. White Construction.

The College and Environs

WPI is set on an 80-acre hilltop campus situated in a residential section of Worcester, Massachusetts, a city of 170,000. Located in the heart of New England, Worcester is the second-largest city in the six-state region. WPI is located near many national and international businesses and industries and enjoys close working relationships with a number of major firms.

Worcester is well known for its many colleges and for such cultural centers as the Worcester Art Museum, which houses one of the finest collections in the country, and the world-renowned American Antiquarian Society, both of which are adjacent to WPI. Also nearby is the historic Higgins Armory Museum and the New England Science Center. Music is well represented by several excellent choruses, a symphony orchestra, and concerts performed by internationally recognized artists in the beautifully restored Mechanics Hall, one of the finest concert halls in the U.S. The city is home to several theater companies, and the 15,500-seat Worcester Centrum and the new Worcester Convention Center host a wide variety of entertainment events and meetings.

The city is within an easy drive of many historical sites, cultural centers, and recreational facilities. These include Boston's Freedom Trail, Old Sturbridge Village (a living museum depicting the 1830s rural village life), the beaches of Cape Cod and Maine, the ski slopes of New Hampshire and Vermont, the splendid country charm of the Berkshires, and several major metropolitan areas featuring world-class museums, concert halls, and professional sports teams.

Facilities

WPI's Computer Center (CCC) provides a full range of services and access to computer resources for the WPI community. Computer facilities are accessible from a wide variety of locations on campus, by modem, or from around the world via the Internet. The CCC workstation room houses twenty-four UNIX workstations. A PC file server drives laser printers in both the CCC and the Advanced Document Preparation (ADP) Lab and provides file service for several software packages, including PC-based desktop publishing and a scientific typesetting system. The microcomputer lab for the Department of Management, located in the Washburn Shops, currently includes thirteen high-end IBM-compatible microcomputers and is regularly updated to support state-of-the-art business software. In all, more than 350 personal computers are available for student use in general-access laboratories, computer classrooms, and specialized laboratories.

WPI's Gordon Library is home to more than 258,000 bound volumes and subscribes to more than 1,100 periodicals, supporting all graduate areas. The library provides online search services to hundreds of databases, interlibrary loan services, technical support, Internet access, CD-ROM databases, and a variety of other research support services.

Placement

The services of WPI's Career Development Center (CDC) are available to all WPI students and alumni. In a typical year, recruiters from more than 300 organizations, including large and small business firms, government, and civic and professional organizations, visit the campus. The CDC maintains a large reference library for WPI students and alumni. The CDC is also involved in on-campus recruiting, hot line job listings, resume referral, and corporate presentations.

Admission

Admission to WPI's graduate management programs is competitive. Admission is granted to applicants whose academic and professional records indicate the likelihood of success in a challenging academic program and whose career aspirations are in line with the focus of the specific degree program.

Applicants should have the analytic aptitude and academic preparation necessary to complete a technology-oriented management program. This includes a minimum of three semesters of college-level math or two semesters of college-level calculus. Applicants are also required to have an understanding of computer systems.

Current students have an average GMAT score of 575 and an average undergraduate CQPA of 3.1. The minimum TOEFL requirement is 550.

Finances

The estimated tuition and fees for full-time graduate students are $13,000 per academic year. Books and supplies average $900 per year. Local apartment rentals average $400 per month. The 2000–01 tuition rate is $703 per credit hour.

A limited number of fellowships are available for full-time students. Students should contact the Director of Graduate Management Programs for details.

Application Facts and Dates

Applicants are required to submit a formal application, a nonrefundable $50 application fee (waived for WPI alumni), official transcripts of all college work, three recommendations, a GMAT report (GRE may be substituted for M.S. applicants), and a TOEFL score if applicable. Applicants are accepted on a rolling admissions basis. Applicants should contact:

Norman D. Wilkinson
Director of Graduate Management
  Programs
Worcester Polytechnic Institute
100 Institute Road
Worcester, Massachusetts 01609

Telephone: 508-831-5218
Fax: 508-831-5720
E-mail: wpigmp@wpi.edu

Wright State University

Dayton, Ohio

STRIVING FOR EXCELLENCE

The College of Business and Administration at Wright State University is proud to be part of a major metropolitan university that cherishes and embraces its neighboring communities. Wright State University's mission includes a ". . . commitment to providing leadership addressing the educational, social, and cultural needs of the Greater Miami Valley and to promoting the economic and technological development of the region through a strong program of basic and applied research and professional service. Wright State desires to create an intellectually exciting community and encourages all students and faculty to strive for excellence." The College of Business and Administration, which is endowed with a rich tradition of academic excellence, is an integral part of this exciting endeavor and is committed to playing a critically important role in meeting the business and educational challenges in our region and beyond.

As the dean of the College of Business and Administration, I am proud to serve as the articulator and facilitator for many new and challenging initiatives as we embark on the twenty-first century. The faculty, students, and staff form a collaborative team that is involved in moving our college into the future. New initiatives focus on quality in education, leadership through teamwork, economic development, globalization, faculty and staff development, new program and new process developments, and developing networking relationships with businesses and other professional organizations.

—Rishi Kumar, Dean

Programs and Curricular Focus

The Wright State M.B.A. program provides a high-quality education that is both broad-based and professionally relevant. The program addresses the diverse needs of students through a three-stage curriculum. The first stage provides preparatory business course work for those individuals who lack such preparation or who need to update their background. The second stage gives the student a broad business base, utilizing quantitative tools and teamwork within the case method approach. Stage three allows students to pursue an area of study of particular interest to them.

Roughly 50 percent of the students entering the Wright State M.B.A. program do not have any undergraduate business courses, and others need to update or upgrade their knowledge. The first stage of the program consists of a series of survey courses. The courses provide the students with the necessary academic background to be successful in the program. The courses entail accountancy, business law, computer work, economics, finance, management, management science, marketing, mathematics, and statistics. The focus of the

courses is to relate material that the student will need to better understand and master the advanced M.B.A. course work. Students with a strong undergraduate background in business may not need to take any of these courses.

The second phase of the program, common to all students, entails advanced study of business, including an integration of the business disciplines. There is a significant case study and teamwork component in this stage of the course work. Cases from business in the areas of accountancy, finance, management, operations, and marketing are analyzed by individuals within their team of students and presented to the class. The students thus apply their knowledge of the discipline to real-world situations, while developing their communication skills. Approximately 50 percent of the courses, including economics, management science, and operations management, utilize quantitative methods. This helps students further develop their analytical skills.

The third stage of the students' study has a concentrated focus. Students can choose areas from business economics, finance, international business, logistics

management, management, management information systems, marketing, operations management, and project management. This stage of study is planned with a faculty adviser.

Students may choose to complete an additional degree while pursuing the M.B.A. degree. Degrees in social and applied economics and nursing are available.

Students and the M.B.A. Experience

The M.B.A. student body is one of the program's greatest strengths. The diversity of backgrounds enriches the educational experience of all. Upon admission to the program, almost 50 percent of the students have an undergraduate degree in business, another 20 percent studied engineering, around 10 percent were in mathematics and the sciences, and the remaining 20 percent studied the humanities, social science, economics, and other disciplines. More than 5 percent of the students have already earned another advanced degree. Although 57 percent of the students graduated from Midwestern colleges, almost 10 percent attended colleges in the South, another 10 percent in the West, and 5 percent in the Northeast. More than 20 percent of the students earned their degree from a non-U.S. institution.

Students bring with them a wealth of work experience, averaging about five years of full-time work experience from a wide array of industries and occupations. About 20 percent of admitted students have no full-time work experience. Women comprise about 40 percent of the student body. This diverse student body contributes to lively classroom discussion and enhances the analyzing of cases by student teams.

The Faculty

The 59 graduate faculty members of the College also have very diverse backgrounds. More than 90 percent (54) hold a doctoral degree in their area of teaching responsibilities. Sixty percent of the degrees were earned at Midwestern institutions, more than 15 percent from institutions in the West, more than 10 percent at schools in the South, and the remainder from universities in the Northeast or overseas. Almost 15 percent (8) are women. Although research is important, the emphasis is on the application of knowledge. A number of the faculty members have been employed outside of academia in full-time jobs and as consultants. They bring this wealth of experience to the classroom to bring theory to life.

The Business School Network
The College's Board of Advisors are respected leaders from the greater Dayton area. They come from manufacturing, banking, retailing, consulting, and nonprofit and governmental organizations. The board advises the College on a wide range of important issues, such as curricula and faculty development.

The College and Environs
Wright State University, founded in the mid-1960s, is located in suburban Dayton, Ohio. More than 16,000 students (more than 3,000 graduate students) from almost fifty different countries are pursuing studies in approximately 100 undergraduate majors and more than 30 graduate programs. The 557-acre campus has twenty-two major buildings, including a 10,632- to 13,000-seat multipurpose sports and entertainment complex, while also maintaining a 200-acre biological preserve.

The campus in Dayton is 75 minutes from Cincinnati and Columbus. Students can take advantage of cultural, entertainment, sports, and educational events in all three of these cities. The climate in southwestern Ohio allows one to enjoy all four seasons, with the average normal temperature ranging from 80°F in the summer to 20°F in the winter.

Placement
Wright State's placement activities are centralized in the Office of Career Services. This office assists undergraduate and graduate students from all degree programs in finding internship and co-op positions during their education and employment after graduation. Individual and group career counseling and planning are available. The office offers a job search course, resume preparation assistance, and resume referral (electronic and paper); it also arranges interviews and conducts successful career fairs. The office has available many publications that can assist students with their job search and career planning.

Admission
The College considers a number of factors in making admission decisions.

All applicants must hold a baccalaureate degree from a regionally accredited institution (individuals graduating from a non-U.S. institution must hold the equivalent of a four-year U.S. baccalaureate), submit official transcripts from all postsecondary institutions attended, have official scores on the Graduate Management Admission Test (GMAT) sent, and pay a $25 application fee. International students need to send official scores on the Test of English as a Foreign Language (TOEFL).

Students who have met all standards for admission to the program will be considered for admission on a regular basis and without conditions. Students with an admission index (AI) of 950 using the overall undergraduate grade point average (UGPA) or an AI of 1000 using the last half UGPA are eligible for regular admission but are not guaranteed this status. The AI is computed by multiplying the UGPA by 200 and adding the total GMAT score. Applicants who have completed graduate-level course work must have a 3.0 graduate GPA to be considered for regular admission. International applicants must meet the 550 minimum acceptable score on the TOEFL. Once these thresholds are met, the College's admission committee reviews the application materials and makes its recommendation to the School of Graduate Studies for a final determination.

Admission is granted for each quarter: fall, winter, spring, and summer. Approximately 660 students were admitted to the M.B.A. program during 1998 and 1999. The average UPGA was 3.0, and the average GMAT score was 510. The average age was 31, the average length of full-time work experience was five years (although about 20 percent had none), about 40 percent were women, approximately 10 percent were members of minority groups, and 27 percent were international. They held degrees in a wide array of disciplines, with 8 percent having previously earned another graduate degree.

Finances
For 1999–2000, the cost of 1 to 10½ credit hours was $175 per credit hour for Ohio residents and $302 for nonresidents. For 11 to 18 credit hours, it was $1856 per quarter for Ohio residents and $3232 per quarter for nonresidents. The international student fee was $52 per quarter. On-campus room and board (double occupancy) averaged $500 per month per person; off-campus room and board (double occupancy) averaged $450 per month per person. The approximate cost of books and supplies was estimated at $85 per course.

Graduate assistantships and fellowships are available to M.B.A. students, including first-year students, in addition to other traditional student loan programs. The Office of Financial Aid, E136 Student Union, administers the campus-based aid and student loan programs; there is an April 1 application deadline. The College administers the graduate fellowship program for full-time students. The fellowships are academically based and cover all tuition costs. The College administers the graduate assistantship (GA) program. GA applications are circulated to the departments for a decision approximately two months prior to the requested starting quarter. More than 40 GAs are employed by the College. A monthly (September through June) stipend of $400 (minimum) plus tuition waiver is paid in exchange for the student working an average of 20 hours per week for the College.

Application Facts and Dates
Admission application decisions are made up to the week before classes for a quarter. The School of Graduate Studies notifies students of the admission decision by mail within a week after the decision is made. To obtain information and application materials for the M.B.A. program, students should contact:

James Crawford
College of Business and
   Administration
110 Rike Hall
Wright State University
Dayton, Ohio 45435
Telephone: 937-775-2437
Fax: 937-775-3545
E-mail: james.crawford@wright.edu
World Wide Web: http://www.wright.
   edu/coba/mba/

Students should send all admission application materials to:

School of Graduate Studies
E344 Student Union
Wright State University
Dayton, Ohio 45435
Telephone: 937-775-2975

For information regarding international student admission, students should contact:

Office of International Student
   Programs
E190 Student Union
Wright State University
Dayton, Ohio 45435
Telephone: 937-775-5745
Fax: 937-775-5795

York University

Toronto, Ontario, Canada

PROGRAMS OFFERING THE BEST OF BOTH WORLDS

Established in 1966, York's Schulich School of Business is Canada's largest graduate school of management. We have built a strong reputation, both at home and abroad, for richly diverse, creative, real-world programs. Our students have the best of both worlds—innovation and tradition, both of which are kept in balance through a dynamic process of continuous improvement in programming and program delivery. In addition to becoming strong generalists, Schulich students have rich opportunities for multiple specializations and for the development of critical leadership, entrepreneurial, group, and negotiation skills. The School's combination of relevance, opportunity, and choice permits our graduates to build successful careers in the private, public, and nonprofit sectors.
—Dezsö J. Horváth, Dean

Programs and Curricular Focus

At the master's level, the Schulich School offers three degrees: the Master of Business Administration (M.B.A.), the Master of Public Administration (M.P.A.), and the International M.B.A. (I.M.B.A.). Entry to the M.B.A. and M.P.A. programs is in September or January. According to an applicant's educational background, the minimum length of these programs can vary from eight to sixteen months of full-time study. Part-time study is also possible. The I.M.B.A. is a full-time, six-semester program limited to 60 students entering in September. Schulich also offers a Ph.D. program.

Revised and restructured in the mid-1990s, York's M.B.A. degree prepares students to turn the challenges of a constantly changing business environment to advantage. Schulich's traditional strengths are a breadth and flexibility of programming, diversity of student body and faculty, a real-world focus, and its location at the centre of corporate Canada. To these have been added an increased emphasis on relevance, a more applied focus, the integration of international aspects of business across courses, a broader frame of reference for decision making that includes business issues such as ethics, e-business, and entrepreneurism, the development of a wide range of essential competencies such as communication and interpersonal skills, and increased specialization options.

Those in full-time studies are assigned to a cohort of 50 to 55 students with whom they take their first-year core courses. The average size of elective courses is 25. In all courses, much of the work is completed in smaller groups of 5 to 6 people.

In the first year of all master's-level programs, students become strong generalists after completing a core of required Foundations of Management courses. In the final second-year required course (the strategy field study), small groups of students complete a six-month detailed analysis of an actual organization. They present their findings and recommendations for improved performance to the organization's senior management. The course applies and integrates knowledge and skills acquired throughout the degree program.

The balance of the M.B.A.'s second year consists of elective courses selected from the School's more than 100 offerings from nineteen existing areas of specialization. These include management functions such as finance and marketing; industry sectors, including financial services, arts and cultural management, and real property; and special management topics such as international business, entrepreneurism, financial engineering, business and sustainability, e-business, public management, nonprofit management and leadership, and business ethics.

Students and the M.B.A. Experience

The Schulich student body is composed of Canadian and international students from a variety of educational and work-related backgrounds who are bright, dynamic, and culturally diverse. The average student is about 30 years of age. Of the total full-time and part-time master's-level complement of 1,250 students, 38 percent are women and 30 percent are international students. Their average work experience prior to admission is nearly 5½ years.

As a large, urban-centred institution, York University offers Schulich students the many benefits of its location in Toronto, one of the world's most cosmopolitan cities and the corporate and banking centre of Canada. In particular, this means students have access to expertise related to every kind of organization—large, small, domestic, global, family-owned, entrepreneurial, public, private, and nonprofit.

❖ Global Focus

Schulich has become a global business school, with a broad range of strategic alliances in more than forty-five countries around the world. International business issues are integrated into all Foundations of Management core courses. Schulich students gain first-hand international experience by spending a semester overseas at one of thirty of the world's leading management schools located in twenty countries in the Americas, Asia, Europe, and the Middle East. This academic partnership network is continually being expanded.

Special Features

Schulich offers an exceptional range of programming choices resulting in rich opportunities for individualized career planning. The School has pioneered master's-level niche programs in a number of specialized areas. In 1992, Schulich introduced Canada's first International M.B.A. program, in which students develop specialized region and country expertise, master a foreign language, and spend up to six months working and studying abroad.

The School also offers a growing number of joint and dual degrees. It was the first in Canada to offer a joint M.B.A./LL.B. degree. Schulich offers a joint M.B.A. degree with Laval University in Quebec and a dual degree with ESC Lyon in France. In fall 1999, it offers a new joint Master of Fine Arts (M.F.A.) and M.B.A. degree.

Schulich is committed to providing lifelong learning opportunities to practicing managers. It offers a unique M.B.A. Certificate in Advanced Management for graduates of recognized M.B.A. programs. The School's Division of Executive Development is the largest in Canada and is ideally situated in the heart of Toronto's financial district at King and Bay Streets in the Miles S. Nadal Management Centre.

The Faculty

Schulich has recruited its faculty internationally. There are currently 82 full-time faculty members. They have graduated from the world's top business schools, and applied and pure research are as fundamental to their mandate as educating tomorrow's corporate leaders. Teaching and research blend rigour and relevance in national and international contexts.

The Business School Network

The Schulich School has traditionally fostered strong ties to the business community in Canada and abroad. The Dean's Advisory Council, the International Advisory Council, and nine other advisory boards consisting of close to 200 distinguished CEOs, leading academics, and senior government representatives offer their advice and networks to support the strategic planning and implementation of Schulich programs.

Throughout the school year, prominent executives deliver talks and attend student-sponsored conferences. The School's York Consulting Group provides consulting services for small and medium-sized businesses and an action-learning opportunity for students. In addition, the Schulich Alumni Mentorship Program matches graduate-level students with alumni to help them find windows into their fields of interest.

The College and Environs

York University is the third-largest university in Canada, located in Toronto, Ontario—the country's industrial, commercial, and financial heartland.

York's main campus is situated on a 600-acre site at the northwest perimeter of the city. With a population of 40,000 students, York has all the necessary amenities and facilities typical of a large urban university campus. York is accessible by bus or car. The majority of business students commute, although many of the full-time students live in apartment-like housing on campus.

Technology Environment

All Schulich M.B.A. students are required to have access to their own computing equipment; they also have access to about forty multimedia Pentium machines and fifteen connection points for laptops in three labs within the School. Experienced staff members assist students during PC lab hours. Access to Lotus Notes e-mail, the Internet, and the Schulich School's computer network is provided through York's 1,200 dial-up lines or through private Internet Service Providers.

Placement

The Schulich Career Centre unit offers placement services geared specifically to the needs of its students. These services are part of students' activities from their first term through graduation and beyond. The services include a career week and career fair, on-campus company information sessions, on-campus recruiting, a Company and Career Information Library, an Immediate Opening Service, individual and group counselling, a graduate internship directory, a summer internship employment program, and instruction in self-assessment, resume writing, interviewing, and job search techniques. An effort is made to include in the job search process not only the large multinational companies but also the small to medium-size firms. Job opportunities are posted on the comprehensive resource and content-rich Career Centre Web site.

Admission

An applicant must possess an undergraduate degree from a recognized university and submit scores for the GMAT (Graduate Management Admission Test). Normally, an applicant will be accepted

only if he or she has achieved at least a B average or better in the last two full years (or equivalent) of academic work and achieved a set of acceptable scores on all three GMAT measurements. In addition, the applicant's work experience, demonstrated leadership qualities, communication skills, and apparent creativity and innovation are considered. In lieu of a degree, a nonbaccalaureate candidate must have at least eight years of high-quality management experience and must have demonstrated a strong upward progression in his or her career.

Finances

At the master's level, students pay fees each semester, according to whether they are enrolled on a full-time or part-time basis. The 2000–01 full-time tuition is approximately Can$5000 per semester for Canadian residents and approximately Can$10,000 per term for non-Canadian residents.

Application Facts and Dates

Application deadlines for regular M.B.A. or M.P.A. programs are April 1 for the fall term and July 15 for the winter term. The application deadlines for the M.B.A./LL.B. program (for September only) are November 1 (of the previous year) for the law application and April 1 (of the previous year) for the M.B.A. application. The application deadline for the I.M.B.A. (for September only) is May 1. Applications must be submitted to:

Division of Student Services
    and International Relations
Room 106, SSB
Schulich School of Business
York University
4700 Keele Street
Toronto, Ontario M3J 1P3
Canada
Telephone: 416-736-5060
Fax: 416-650-8174
E-mail: intladmissions@schulich.
    yorku.ca
World Wide Web: http://www.schulich.
    yorku.ca

Indexes

There are two indexes in this section. The first, **School Index,** is arranged alphabetically and gives page references for all colleges and universities in the guide. The second, **Areas of Concentration Index,** lists schools in alphabetical order under the specific areas of study available within the MBA program.

School Index

Areas of Concentration Index

In this index the page locations of the profiles are printed in regular type, announcements in italic type, and In-Depth Descriptions in bold type.

ACCOUNTING

ACTUARIAL SCIENCE

ENVIRONMENTAL ECONOMICS/ MANAGEMENT

EUROPEAN BUSINESS STUDIES

FACILITIES MANAGEMENT

FINANCE

FINANCIAL ECONOMICS

University of Southern Mississippi, College of Business Administration (MS) 264

University of the West of England, Bristol, Bristol Business School (United Kingdom) 531

University of Ulster at Jordanstown, Faculty of Business and Management (United Kingdom) 531

Virginia Polytechnic Institute and State University, Pamplin College of Business (VA) 429, **998**

Walsh College of Accountancy and Business Administration, Graduate Programs (MI) 254, **1002**

Walsh University, Program in Management (OH) 346

Weber State University, John B. Goddard School of Business and Economics (UT) 420

Widener University, School of Business Administration (PA) 375, **1014**

York University, Schulich School of Business (Canada) 475, **1026**

HEALTH CARE

Adelphi University, School of Business (NY) 295, **536**

Allentown College of St. Francis de Sales, Department of Business (PA) 356

Andrews University, School of Business (MI) 244

Anna Maria College, Program in Business Administration (MA) 229

Aquinas College, Graduate School of Management (MI) 245

Assumption College, Department of Business Studies (MA) 230, *230*

Aston University, Aston Business School (United Kingdom) 511

Auburn University, College of Business (AL) 83, **552**

Avila College, Department of Business and Economics (MO) 265

Baker College Center for Graduate Studies, Programs in Business (MI) 245, **556**

Baldwin-Wallace College, Division of Business Administration (OH) 335, *335,* **558**

Barry University, School of Business (FL) 149

Belmont University, Jack C. Massey Graduate School of Business (TN) 385

Benedictine University, Graduate Programs (IL) 176

Bernard M. Baruch College of the City University of New York, Zicklin School of Business (NY) 296, **566**

Boston University, School of Management (MA) 233, **572**

Bradley University, Foster College of Business Administration (IL) 177

Brandeis University, Heller Graduate School, Waltham (MA) 234, **578**

Brenau University, School of Business and Mass Communication (GA) 164

California Lutheran University, School of Business (CA) 100, *100*

California National University for Advanced Studies, College of Business Administration (CA) 100

California State University, Los Angeles, School of Business and Economics (CA) 105

Cambridge College, Program in Management (MA) 235

Cardinal Stritch University, College of Business and Management (WI) 438

Case Western Reserve University, Weatherhead School of Management (OH) 336, **586**

Charleston Southern University, Program in Business (SC) 380

Clark Atlanta University, School of Business Administration (GA) 165

Clark University, Graduate School of Management (MA) 235, **598**

College of Saint Elizabeth, Department of Business Administration/Economics (NJ) 283

Colorado Technical University, Program in Management (CO) 131

Dalhousie University, Faculty of Management (Canada) 461, **618**

Dallas Baptist University, Graduate School of Business (TX) 395

David Lipscomb University, Business Administration Program (TN) 386

Dominican University, Graduate School of Business (IL) 178, **622**

Duke University, Fuqua School of Business (NC) 324

Duquesne University, Graduate School of Business Administration (PA) 360, *360,* **628**

East Carolina University, School of Business (NC) 325, **630**

Eastern College, Graduate Business Programs (PA) 361, **632**

Eastern Washington University, College of Business Administration (WA) 431

Edith Cowan University, Faculty of Business and Public Management (Australia) 450

Emerson College, School of Communication, Management, and Public Policy (MA) 236, **638**

Escuela Superior de Administracion y Direccion de Empresas, Business School (Spain) 504

Fairfield University, School of Business (CT) 137, **648**

Fairleigh Dickinson University, Teaneck–Hackensack Campus, Samuel J. Silberman College of Business Administration (NJ) 284, **650**

Florida Atlantic University, College of Business (FL) 151

Francis Marion University, School of Business (SC) 381

Franklin University, Graduate School of Business (OH) 339

Fresno Pacific University, Graduate School (CA) 111

Gardner-Webb University, School of Business (NC) 326

The George Washington University, School of Business and Public Management (DC) 146, **666**

Georgia State University, J. Mack Robinson College of Business (GA) 168, **668**

Governors State University, College of Business and Public Administration (IL) 179

Grand Canyon University, College of Business (AZ) 92

Groupe ESC Toulouse, ESC Toulouse Graduate School of Management (France) 483

Howard University, School of Business (DC) 147

Idaho State University, College of Business (ID) 175

Imperial College, Management School (United Kingdom) 515

Indiana University–Purdue University Fort Wayne, School of Business and Management Sciences (IN) 196

Indiana University–Purdue University Indianapolis, School of Business (IN) 196

James Madison University, College of Business (VA) 424

Jones International University, Program in Business Communication, Englewood (CO) 132, **698**

Kansas Wesleyan University, Program in Business Administration (KS) 207

Kansas Wesleyan University, Program in Business Administration (KS) 207

Kutztown University of Pennsylvania, College of Business (PA) 363

Lake Erie College, Division of Management Studies (OH) 340

La Salle University, School of Business Administration (PA) 364

Lesley College, School of Management (MA) 238, **710**

Lewis University, College of Business (IL) 181

Louisiana State University and Agricultural and Mechanical College, E.J. Ourso College of Business Administration (LA) 215, *215*

Loyola College in Maryland, Sellinger School of Business and Management (MD) 224, **712**

Loyola University Chicago, Graduate School of Business (IL) 182, **716**

Lynn University, School of Business (FL) 154

Manchester Metropolitan University, Faculty of Management and Business, Department of Management (United Kingdom) 517

Marist College, School of Management (NY) 305

Marymount University, School of Business Administration (VA) 425

Maryville University of Saint Louis, The John E. Simon School of Business (MO) 268

McMaster University, Michael G. DeGroote School of Business (Canada) 464, **724**

Middle Tennessee State University, College of Business (TN) 387

Millsaps College, School of Management (MS) 262, **728**

Monmouth University, School of Business Administration (NJ) 285

Morehead State University, College of Business (KY) 212

National University, School of Business and Technology (CA) 115, **736**

New Hampshire College, Graduate School of Business (NH) 281, **738**

New School University, Robert J. Milano Graduate School of Management and Urban Policy (NY) 307, **740**

New York Institute of Technology, School of Management (NY) 308, **742**

Northern Arizona University, College of Business Administration (AZ) 93

Northwestern University, Kellogg Graduate School of Management (IL) 185

Nova Southeastern University, Wayne Huizenga Graduate School of Business and Entrepreneurship (FL) 154, **754**

Oakland University, School of Business Administration (MI) 250, *251*

Oklahoma City University, School of Management and Business Sciences (OK) 349

Old Dominion University, College of Business and Public Administration (VA) 426

Our Lady of the Lake University of San Antonio, School of Business and Public Administration (TX) 398

The Pennsylvania State University Great Valley Campus, Graduate Studies and Continuing Education (PA) 366

The Pennsylvania State University University Park Campus, The Mary Jean and Frank P. Smeal College of Business Administration (PA) 367, **762**

Pfeiffer University, Program in Business Administration (NC) 329

Philadelphia University, School of Business (PA) 368, **766**

Quinnipiac University, School of Business (CT) 137, **778**

Rensselaer at Hartford, Lally School of Management and Technology (CT) 138

Rider University, College of Business Administration (NJ) 287

Rivier College, Department of Business Administration (NH) 282

Robert Morris College, Program in Business Administration (PA) 369, **788**

Roosevelt University, Walter E. Heller College of Business Administration (IL) 187, **794**

Royal Melbourne Institute of Technology, Graduate School of Business (Australia) 453

INDUSTRIAL/LABOR RELATIONS

INDUSTRIAL ADMINISTRATION/ MANAGEMENT

University of Massachusetts Lowell, College of Management (MA) 243

University of Melbourne, Melbourne Business School (Australia) 454

University of Minnesota, Twin Cities Campus, Carlson School of Management (MN) 259, *260*, **926**

University of Mississippi, School of Business Administration (MS) 263, **928**

University of Newcastle, Graduate School of Business (Australia) 455

The University of North Carolina at Charlotte, College of Business Administration (NC) 331, *331*

University of Northumbria at Newcastle, Newcastle Business School (United Kingdom) 527

University of Oxford, Saïd Business School (United Kingdom) 528

University of Pennsylvania, Wharton School (PA) 373, **944**

University of Redlands, Alfred North Whitehead College for Lifelong Learning (CA) 126

University of St. Thomas, Graduate School of Business (MN) 260, **954**

University of South Australia, International Graduate School of Management (Australia) 456

University of Southern California, Marshall School of Business (CA) 128, *128*, **964**

The University of Tampa, College of Business (FL) 161, **966**

University of Technology, Sydney, Graduate School of Business (Australia) 457

The University of Texas at Arlington, College of Business Administration (TX) 411, **970**

The University of Texas at Austin, Graduate School of Business (TX) 412, **972**

The University of Texas at Dallas, School of Management (TX) 414, *414*, **974**

University of Ulster at Jordanstown, Faculty of Business and Management (United Kingdom) 531

University of Washington, School of Business Administration (WA) 434, **986**

The University of Western Australia, Graduate School of Management (Australia) 457

University of Wisconsin–Eau Claire, College of Business (WI) 441

University of Wisconsin–Madison, School of Business (WI) 442, **990**

Utah State University, College of Business (UT) 420

Virginia Polytechnic Institute and State University, Pamplin College of Business (VA) 429, **998**

Walsh College of Accountancy and Business Administration, Graduate Programs (MI) 254, **1002**

Waseda University, Graduate School of Asia-Pacific Studies (Japan) 493, **1004**

Western Illinois University, College of Business and Technology (IL) 192

Westminster College, The Bill and Vieve Gore School of Business (UT) 421

Willamette University, Geo. H. Atkinson Graduate School of Management (OR) 355, **1018**

York College of Pennsylvania, Department of Business Administration (PA) 377

York University, Schulich School of Business (Canada) 475, **1026**

INFORMATION SYSTEMS

Lancaster University, Management School (United Kingdom) 515

Mississippi State University, College of Business and Industry (MS) 263, **730**

Temple University, Fox School of Business and Management (PA) 372, *372*, **844**

University of Redlands, Alfred North Whitehead College for Lifelong Learning (CA) 126

INSURANCE

City University, Business School (United Kingdom) 512

College of Insurance, Program in Business Administration (NY) 298

Escuela Superior de Administracion y Direccion de Empresas, Business School (Spain) 504

Illinois State University, College of Business (IL) 180, **680**

National University of Ireland, Dublin, The Michael Smurfit Graduate School of Business (Ireland) 490

The Pennsylvania State University University Park Campus, The Mary Jean and Frank P. Smeal College of Business Administration (PA) 367, **762**

St. Cloud State University, G.R. Herberger College of Business (MN) 257

Salve Regina University, Graduate School (RI) 379, **812**

Sheffield Hallam University, Business School (United Kingdom) 520

Southern Methodist University, Edwin L. Cox School of Business (TX) 401, **830**

University of Georgia, Terry College of Business (GA) 172

University of Hartford, Barney School of Business and Public Administration (CT) 141

University of Illinois at Urbana–Champaign, College of Commerce and Business Administration (IL) 191, **906**

University of Mississippi, School of Business Administration (MS) 263, **928**

University of Nottingham, Business School (United Kingdom) 527

University of Pennsylvania, Wharton School (PA) 373, **944**

University of St. Thomas, Graduate School of Business (MN) 260, **954**

University of Technology, Sydney, Graduate School of Business (Australia) 457

University of Wisconsin–Madison, School of Business (WI) 442, **990**

INTERNATIONAL AND AREA BUSINESS STUDIES

American University in Cairo, School of Business, Economics and Communication (Egypt) 480

Ashridge, Ashridge Executive MBA Program (United Kingdom) 511

Bar-Ilan University, S. Daniel Abraham Center of Economics and Business, The Graduate School of Business (Israel) 491

Baylor University, Hankamer School of Business (TX) 395, **560**

Bocconi University, SDA Bocconi (Italy) 492

Cleveland State University, James J. Nance College of Business Administration (OH) 338, **602**

Copenhagen Business School, Faculty of Economics and Business Administration (Denmark) 480

Curtin University of Technology, Graduate School of Business (Australia) 449

Dominican University of California, School of Business and International Studies (CA) 110, **624**

Georgia Institute of Technology, Dupree College of Management (GA) 167

Instituto de Empresa, Business School (Spain) 505

Institut Superieur de Gestion, ISG International School of Business (France) 485

Lakeland College, Graduate Studies Division (WI) 439

Lakeland College, Graduate Studies Division (WI) 439

McGill University, Faculty of Management (Canada) 463, **722**

Monash University, Monash Mt. Eliza Business School MBA Programme (Australia) 451

Monterey Institute of International Studies, Fisher Graduate School of International Business (CA) 115, **732**

National University of Ireland, Dublin, The Michael Smurfit Graduate School of Business (Ireland) 490

Rollins College, Crummer Graduate School of Business (FL) 155, **792**

Rollins College, Crummer Graduate School of Business (FL) 155, **792**

Texas A&M University, Lowry Mays Graduate School of Business (TX) 404

University of Alberta, Faculty of Business (Canada) 467

The University of Arizona, Karl Eller Graduate School of Management (AZ) 94, **864**

University of California, Berkeley, Haas School of Business (CA) 122

University of Central Florida, College of Business Administration (FL) 158

University of Detroit Mercy, College of Business Administration (MI) 252

University of Edinburgh, Edinburgh University Management School (United Kingdom) 524, *524*, **898**

University of Florida, College of Business Administration (FL) 158, *159*, **900**

University of Michigan, School of Business Administration (MI) 252

University of Pennsylvania, Wharton School (PA) 373, **944**

University of Pittsburgh, Joseph M. Katz Graduate School of Business (PA) 373, **946**

University of Portland, Dr. Robert B. Pamplin, Jr. School of Business (OR) 355

University of Southern California, Marshall School of Business (CA) 128, *128*, **964**

University of Wales, Cardiff Business School (United Kingdom) 531

University of Washington, School of Business Administration (WA) 434, **986**

The University of Western Ontario, Ivey Business School (Canada) 474, *474*, **988**

University of Windsor, Faculty of Business Administration (Canada) 474

Wilkes University, College of Arts, Sciences and Professional Studies (PA) 376

Woodbury University, School of Business and Management (CA) 129, **1020**

York University, Schulich School of Business (Canada) 475, **1026**

INTERNATIONAL BANKING

American University in Cairo, School of Business, Economics and Communication (Egypt) 480

City University, School of Business and Management Professions (WA) 431, **590**

Dowling College, School of Business (NY) 300

Monterey Institute of International Studies, Fisher Graduate School of International Business (CA) 115, **732**

Rider University, College of Business Administration (NJ) 287

Sheffield Hallam University, Business School (United Kingdom) 520

Texas A&M International University, Graduate School of International Trade and Business Administration (TX) 404, **846**

Univeroiteit Nyenrode, Netherlands Business School (Netherlands) 497

The University of Arizona, Karl Eller Graduate School of Management (AZ) 94, **864**

University of Birmingham, Birmingham Business School (United Kingdom) 522

University of Brighton, Brighton Business School (United Kingdom) 522

University of Illinois at Urbana–Champaign, College of Commerce and Business Administration (IL) 191, **906**

INTERNATIONAL DEVELOPMENT MANAGEMENT

INTERNATIONAL ECONOMICS

INTERNATIONAL FINANCE

INTERNATIONAL MARKETING

INTERNATIONAL TRADE

JAPANESE BUSINESS STUDIES

MANAGEMENT

MANAGEMENT CONSULTING

MANAGEMENT INFORMATION SYSTEMS

University of California, Riverside, A. Gary Anderson Graduate School of Management (CA) 125, **880**

University of Chicago, Graduate School of Business (IL) 189, **884**

University of Detroit Mercy, College of Business Administration (MI) 252

University of Edinburgh, Edinburgh University Management School (United Kingdom) 524, *524,* **898**

University of Kansas, School of Business (KS) 209, **910**

University of Maryland, College Park, Robert H. Smith School of Business (MD) 227, **918**

University of Miami, School of Business Administration (FL) 159, **922**

University of Missouri–Columbia, College of Business (MO) 272, **930**

University of New Haven, School of Business (CT) 141, **936**

University of North Texas, College of Business Administration (TX) 411

University of Northumbria at Newcastle, Newcastle Business School (United Kingdom) 527

University of Oxford, Saïd Business School (United Kingdom) 528

University of South Carolina, The Darla Moore School of Business (SC) 382, *383,* **960**

The University of Texas at Arlington, College of Business Administration (TX) 411, **970**

The University of Texas at San Antonio, College of Business (TX) 415, **976**

The University of Western Ontario, Ivey Business School (Canada) 474, *474,* **988**

University of Windsor, Faculty of Business Administration (Canada) 474

Utah State University, College of Business (UT) 420

Virginia Polytechnic Institute and State University, Pamplin College of Business (VA) 429, **998**

Webster University, School of Business and Technology (MO) 274

Willamette University, Geo. H. Atkinson Graduate School of Management (OR) 355, **1018**

York University, Schulich School of Business (Canada) 475, **1026**

MANAGEMENT SYSTEMS ANALYSIS

Athabasca University, Centre for Innovative Management (Canada) 460, *460*

Ball State University, College of Business (IN) 193

Carnegie Mellon University, Graduate School of Industrial Administration (PA) 358, **584**

Copenhagen Business School, Faculty of Economics and Business Administration (Denmark) 480

Dalhousie University, Faculty of Management (Canada) 461, **618**

Deakin University, Faculty of Business and Law (Australia) 449

École Supérieure des Sciences Économiques et Commerciales, ESSEC Business School (France) 481

Graduate School of Business Administration Zurich, Business Programs (Switzerland) 507

Groupe ESC Toulouse, ESC Toulouse Graduate School of Management (France) 483

Houston Baptist University, College of Business and Economics (TX) 396

Murdoch University, School of Business (Australia) 452

National University of Ireland, Cork, Faculty of Commerce (Ireland) 489

Naval Postgraduate School, Department of Systems Management (CA) 116

Rensselaer Polytechnic Institute, Lally School of Management and Technology (NY) 311, **782**

Rivier College, Department of Business Administration (NH) 282

Seton Hall University, W. Paul Stillman School of Business (NJ) 290, **822**

Southern Illinois University Edwardsville, School of Business (IL) 188, *188,* **828**

State University of New York at Albany, School of Business (NY) 316

State University of New York Maritime College, Program in Transportation Management (NY) 321

Texas A&M University, Lowry Mays Graduate School of Business (TX) 404

The University of Arizona, Karl Eller Graduate School of Management (AZ) 94, **864**

University of Illinois at Chicago, College of Business Administration/MBA Programs (IL) 189

University of Illinois at Urbana–Champaign, College of Commerce and Business Administration (IL) 191, **906**

University of New South Wales, Australian Graduate School of Management (Australia) 455

The University of Texas at Arlington, College of Business Administration (TX) 411, **970**

Waseda University, Graduate School of Asia-Pacific Studies (Japan) 493, **1004**

MANAGERIAL ECONOMICS

Antioch Southern California/Santa Barbara, Program in Organizational Management (CA) 98

Ball State University, College of Business (IN) 193

Bangkok University, Graduate School (Thailand) 509

The Chinese University of Hong Kong, Faculty of Business Administration (China) 477

HEC School of Management, HEC MBA Program (France) 484

Institut Superieur de Gestion, ISG International School of Business (France) 485

Loyola University Chicago, Graduate School of Business (IL) 182, **716**

Murdoch University, School of Business (Australia) 452

National University of Ireland, Cork, Faculty of Commerce (Ireland) 489

Naval Postgraduate School, Department of Systems Management (CA) 116

New York Institute of Technology, School of Management (NY) 308, **742**

Northwestern University, Kellogg Graduate School of Management (IL) 185

Queensland University of Technology, Brisbane Graduate School of Business (Australia) 452

State University of New York Maritime College, Program in Transportation Management (NY) 321

University of California, Los Angeles, John E. Anderson Graduate School of Management (CA) 124, **878**

University of Chicago, Graduate School of Business (IL) 189, **884**

University of Illinois at Urbana–Champaign, College of Commerce and Business Administration (IL) 191, **906**

University of Mississippi, School of Business Administration (MS) 263, **928**

University of Puerto Rico, Río Piedras, Graduate School of Business Administration (PR) 447

The University of Texas at Dallas, School of Management (TX) 414, *414,* **974**

University of Washington, School of Business Administration (WA) 434, **986**

University of Western Sydney, Macarthur, Faculty of Business and Technology (Australia) 458

Utah State University, College of Business (UT) 420

Walsh University, Program in Management (OH) 346

Wayne State University, School of Business Administration (MI) 255, **1008**

Wichita State University, W. Frank Barton School of Business (KS) 210

MANPOWER ADMINISTRATION

Central Connecticut State University, School of Business (CT) 136

Naval Postgraduate School, Department of Systems Management (CA) 116

Southern Illinois University Edwardsville, School of Business (IL) 188, *188,* **828**

Swinburne University of Technology, Swinburne Graduate School of Management (Australia) 453

University of the West of England, Bristol, Bristol Business School (United Kingdom) 531

MANUFACTURING MANAGEMENT

Andrews University, School of Business (MI) 244

Ball State University, College of Business (IN) 193

Bond University, School of Business (Australia) 448

California Polytechnic State University, San Luis Obispo, College of Business (CA) 101

Clarkson University, School of Business (NY) 297, **596**

Georgia Institute of Technology, Dupree College of Management (GA) 167

Iowa State University of Science and Technology, College of Business (IA) 201, **692**

Kettering University, Graduate School (MI) 247

McGill University, Faculty of Management (Canada) 463, **722**

Murdoch University, School of Business (Australia) 452

National University of Ireland, Dublin, The Michael Smurfit Graduate School of Business (Ireland) 490

National University of Singapore, Graduate School of Business (Singapore) 501

New Hampshire College, Graduate School of Business (NH) 281, **738**

The Pennsylvania State University University Park Campus, The Mary Jean and Frank P. Smeal College of Business Administration (PA) 367, **762**

Purdue University, Krannert Graduate School of Management (IN) 198, **774**

Queensland University of Technology, Brisbane Graduate School of Business (Australia) 452

Rensselaer at Hartford, Lally School of Management and Technology (CT) 138

Rensselaer Polytechnic Institute, Lally School of Management and Technology (NY) 311, **782**

Rochester Institute of Technology, College of Business (NY) 313, **790**

State University of New York at Buffalo, School of Management (NY) 318, **834**

Texas A&M University, Lowry Mays Graduate School of Business (TX) 404

Universidad de las Américas–Puebla, School of Business Administration (Mexico) 495

The University of Alabama, The Manderson Graduate School of Business (AL) 87, **862**

University of Cape Town, Graduate School of Business (South Africa) 503

University of Notre Dame, Mendoza College of Business (IN) 199, **940**

University of Plymouth, Graduate Business School (United Kingdom) 528

University of Rochester, William E. Simon Graduate School of Business Administration (NY) 322, *323,* **952**

University of St. Thomas, Graduate School of Business (MN) 260, **954**

ORGANIZATIONAL BEHAVIOR/ DEVELOPMENT

ORGANIZATIONAL MANAGEMENT

PORT/MARITIME MANAGEMENT

PRODUCTION MANAGEMENT

PROFIT MANAGEMENT

PROJECT MANAGEMENT

Bocconi University, SDA Bocconi (Italy) 492
City University, School of Business and
Management Professions (WA) 431, **590**
Colorado Technical University, Program in
Management (CO) 131
Copenhagen Business School, Faculty of
Economics and Business Administration
(Denmark) 480
Cranfield University, Cranfield School of
Management (United Kingdom) 512, **616**
Curtin University of Technology, Graduate School
of Business (Australia) 449
The George Washington University, School of
Business and Public Management (DC) 146,
666
Groupe ESC Toulouse, ESC Toulouse Graduate
School of Management (France) 483
Henley Management College, Business Programs
(United Kingdom) 513
IEDC-Bled School of Management, School of
Business Administration (Slovenia) 502
Imperial College, Management School (United
Kingdom) 515
Jones International University, Program in
Business Communication, Englewood (CO)
132, **698**
Keller Graduate School of Management, Graduate
Program (IL) 181, **700**
Lancaster University, Management School (United
Kingdom) 515
Milwaukee School of Engineering, Engineering
Management Program (WI) 440
Murdoch University, School of Business
(Australia) 452
Naval Postgraduate School, Department of
Systems Management (CA) 116
Northern Kentucky University, College of
Business (KY) 213
Stevens Institute of Technology, Wesley J. Howe
School of Technology Management (NJ) 291
Tel Aviv University, Leon Recanati Graduate
School of Business Administration (Israel) 491
University of Calgary, Faculty of Management
(Canada) 468
University of Glasgow, University of Glasgow
Business School (United Kingdom) 525
University of Limerick, College of Business
(Ireland) 490
University of Melbourne, Melbourne Business
School (Australia) 454
University of San Diego, School of Business
Administration (CA) 127, **956**
University of Technology, Sydney, Graduate
School of Business (Australia) 457
University of the West of England, Bristol, Bristol
Business School (United Kingdom) 531
University of Wisconsin–Green Bay, Program in
Administrative Science (WI) 441
Walsh University, Program in Management (OH)
346
Western Carolina University, College of Business
(NC) 333
Western Illinois University, College of Business
and Technology (IL) 192
WHU Koblenz, Otto-Beisheim Graduate School of
Management (Germany) 488
Worcester Polytechnic Institute, Department of
Management (MA) 244, *244*, **1022**
Wright State University, College of Business and
Administration (OH) 346, **1024**

PUBLIC AND PRIVATE MANAGEMENT
Antioch Southern California/Santa Barbara,
Program in Organizational Management (CA)
98
Birmingham-Southern College, Program in Public
and Private Management (AL) 84
Boston University, School of Management (MA)
233, **572**

Brandeis University, Heller Graduate School,
Waltham (MA) 234, **578**
Cleveland State University, James J. Nance
College of Business Administration (OH) 338,
602
École Supérieure des Sciences Économiques et
Commerciales, ESSEC Business School
(France) 481
The George Washington University, School of
Business and Public Management (DC) 146,
666
HEC School of Management, HEC MBA Program
(France) 484
Lancaster University, Management School (United
Kingdom) 515
The University of North Carolina at Pembroke,
Graduate Studies (NC) 332
University of the Witwatersrand, Graduate School
of Business Administration (South Africa) 503
University of Wales, Cardiff Business School
(United Kingdom) 531

PUBLIC MANAGEMENT
Aston University, Aston Business School (United
Kingdom) 511
Bowie State University, Business Programs (MD)
222
Brandeis University, Heller Graduate School,
Waltham (MA) 234, **578**
Cleveland State University, James J. Nance
College of Business Administration (OH) 338,
602
Columbia University, Graduate School of Business
(NY) 299, **610**
Copenhagen Business School, Faculty of
Economics and Business Administration
(Denmark) 480
Cranfield University, Cranfield School of
Management (United Kingdom) 512, **616**
Deakin University, Faculty of Business and Law
(Australia) 449
Dowling College, School of Business (NY) 300
East Tennessee State University, College of
Business (TN) 386
École Supérieure des Sciences Économiques et
Commerciales, ESSEC Business School
(France) 481
Escuela Superior de Administracion y Direccion
de Empresas, Business School (Spain) 504
Gannon University, School of Business (PA) 361
The George Washington University, School of
Business and Public Management (DC) 146,
666
Governors State University, College of Business
and Public Administration (IL) 179
Groupe ESC Toulouse, ESC Toulouse Graduate
School of Management (France) 483
Hood College, Department of Economics and
Management (Interim) (MD) 223
IADE, Instituto Universitario de Administracion de
Empresas (Spain) 505
Imperial College, Management School (United
Kingdom) 515
Indiana University–Purdue University Fort Wayne,
School of Business and Management Sciences
(IN) 196
Lindenwood University, Department of Business
Administration (MO) 267
London School of Economics and Political
Science, The Graduate School (United
Kingdom) 516
Mississippi State University, College of Business
and Industry (MS) 263, **730**
Oklahoma City University, School of Management
and Business Sciences (OK) 349
Old Dominion University, College of Business and
Public Administration (VA) 426
Rockford College, Program in Business
Administration (IL) 186

Rockford College, Program in Business
Administration (IL) 186
Rockford College, Program in Business
Administration (IL) 186
St. Thomas University, Department of Business
Administration (FL) 156, **810**
Shenandoah University, Byrd School of Business
(VA) 427
Stanford University, Graduate School of Business
(CA) 121
Suffolk University, Frank Sawyer School of
Management (MA) 240, **840**
University of California, Davis, Graduate School
of Management (CA) 123, **874**
The University of Findlay, MBA Program (OH)
345
University of Hartford, Barney School of Business
and Public Administration (CT) 141
The University of North Carolina at Pembroke,
Graduate Studies (NC) 332
University of Nottingham, Business School
(United Kingdom) 527
University of Ottawa, Faculty of Administration
(Canada) 471
University of Pittsburgh, Joseph M. Katz Graduate
School of Business (PA) 373, **946**
University of South Australia, International
Graduate School of Management (Australia)
456
University of the District of Columbia, School of
Business and Public Administration (DC) 148
University of Wisconsin–Green Bay, Program in
Administrative Science (WI) 441
Willamette University, Geo. H. Atkinson Graduate
School of Management (OR) 355, **1018**
Yale University, Yale School of Management (CT)
142
York University, Schulich School of Business
(Canada) 475, **1026**

PUBLIC POLICY AND ADMINISTRATION
American University in Cairo, School of Business,
Economics and Communication (Egypt) 480
Aston University, Aston Business School (United
Kingdom) 511
Boise State University, College of Business and
Economics (ID) 174, **568**
Brandeis University, Heller Graduate School,
Waltham (MA) 234, **578**
Brigham Young University, Marriott School of
Management (UT) 418, **580**
Chaminade University of Honolulu, Program in
Business Administration (HI) 173
City University, School of Business and
Management Professions (WA) 431, **590**
Clemson University, College of Business and
Public Affairs (SC) 380, **600**
Concordia University Wisconsin, Division of
Graduate Studies (WI) 438, *439*
Copenhagen Business School, Faculty of
Economics and Business Administration
(Denmark) 480
Dalhousie University, Faculty of Management
(Canada) 461, **618**
De Montfort University, De Montfort University
School of Business (United Kingdom) 513
Eastern Washington University, College of
Business Administration (WA) 431
East Tennessee State University, College of
Business (TN) 386
École Supérieure des Sciences Économiques et
Commerciales, ESSEC Business School
(France) 481
Gannon University, School of Business (PA) 361
The George Washington University, School of
Business and Public Management (DC) 146,
666
IADE, Instituto Universitario de Administracion de
Empresas (Spain) 505

SUPPLY CHAIN MANAGEMENT

SYSTEM MANAGEMENT

TAXATION

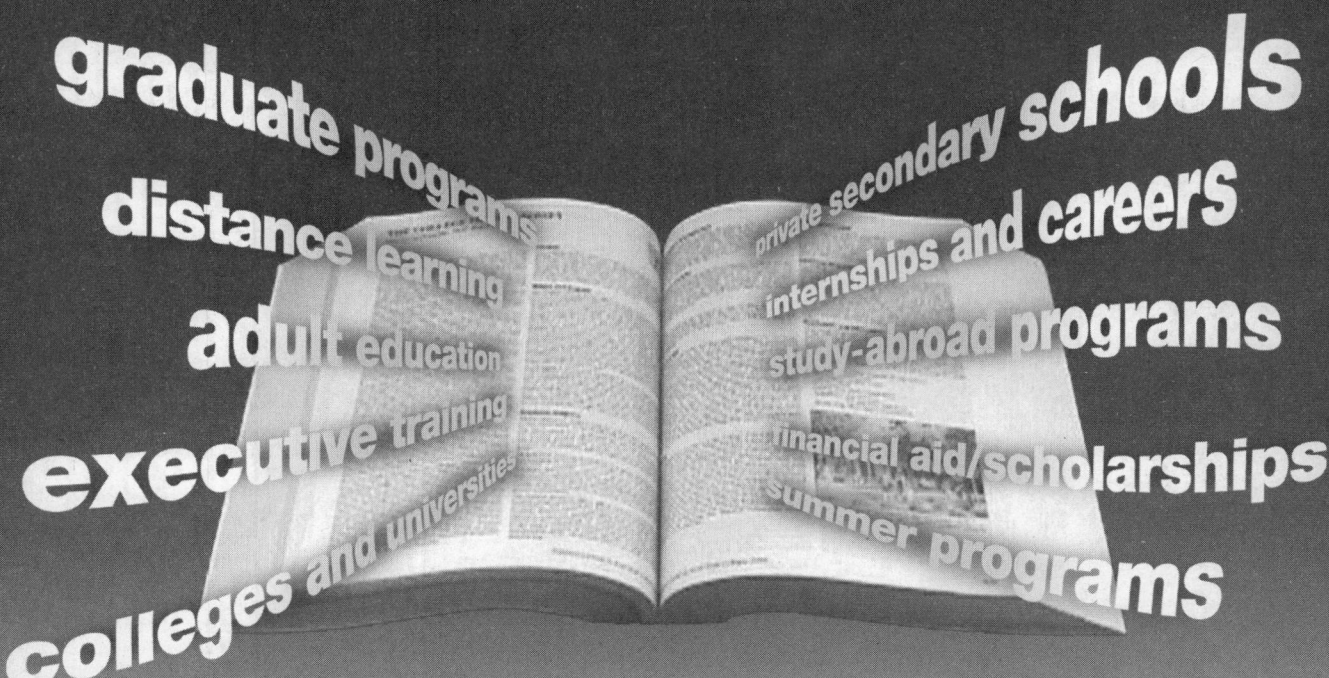